GEORGIA continued

GAU	Atlanta University, Atlanta.
GAuA	Augusta College, Augusta.
GColuC	Columbus College, Columbus.
GCuA	Andrews College, Cuthbert.
GDC	Columbia Theological Seminary, Decatur.
GDS	Agnes Scott College, Decatur.
GDecA*	Agnes Scott College, Decatur.
GDecCT*	Columbia Theological Seminary, Decatur.
GDoS	South Georgia College, Douglas.
GEU	Emory University, Atlanta.
GHi	Georgia Historical Society, Savannah.
GMM	Mercer University, Macon.
GMW	Wesleyan College, Macon.
GMiW	Woman's College of Georgia, Milledgeville.
GMilvC*	Woman's College of Georgia, Milledgeville.
GOgU	Oglethorpe University, Oglethorpe University.
GSDe*	University of Georgia, DeRenne Library.
GU	University of Georgia, Athens.
GU-De	— DeRenne Georgia Library.
GU-Ex	— Georgia State College of Business Administration Library, Atlanta.

HAWAII

HU	University of Hawaii, Honolulu.
HU-EWC	Center for Cultural and Technical Interchange between East and West, Honolulu.

ILLINOIS

I	Illinois State Library, Springfield.
IC	Chicago Public Library.
ICA	Art Institute of Chicago, Chicago.
ICF	Chicago Natural History Museum, Chicago.
ICF-A	— Edward E. Ayer Ornithological Library.
ICHi	Chicago Historical Society, Chicago.
ICIP	Institute for Psychoanalysis, Chicago.
ICJ	John Crerar Library, Chicago.
ICMILC*	Center for Research Libraries, Chicago.
ICMcC	McCormick Theological Seminary, Chicago.
ICN	Newberry Library, Chicago.
ICRL	Center for Research Libraries, Chicago.
ICU	University of Chicago, Chicago.
ICarbS	Southern Illinois University, Carbondale.
IEG	Garrett Theological Seminary, Evanston.
IEN	Northwestern University, Evanston.
IEdS	Southern Illinois University, Edwardsville.
IGK	Knox College, Galesburg.
IHi	Illinois State Historical Library, Springfield.
ILS	St. Procopius College, Lisle.
IMunS	Saint Mary of the Lake Seminary, Mundelein.
INS	Illinois State University, Normal.
IRA	Augustana College Library, Rock Island.
IRivfR	Rosary College, River Forest.
IU	University of Illinois, Urbana.
IU-M	— Medical Sciences Library, Chicago.
IU-U	— Chicago Undergraduate Division, Chicago.

IOWA

IaAS	Iowa State University of Science and Technology, Ames.
IaDL	Luther College, Decorah.
IaDuC	Loras College, Dubuque.
IaDuU	University of Dubuque, Dubuque.
IaDuU-S	— Theological Seminary Library.
IaDuW	Wartburg Theological Seminary, Dubuque.
IaU	University of Iowa, Iowa City.

IDAHO

IdB	Boise Public Library.
IdPI	Idaho State University, Pocatello.
IdPS*	Idaho State University, Pocatello.
IdU	University of Idaho, Moscow.

INDIANA

In	Indiana State Library, Indianapolis.
InAndC	Anderson College, Anderson.
InCollS*	St. Joseph's College, Rensselaer.
InGo	Goshen College Biblical Seminary Library, Goshen.
InHi	Indiana Historical Society, Indianapolis.
InIB	Butler University, Indianapolis.

INDIANA continued

InLP	Purdue University, Lafayette.
InNd	University of Notre Dame, Notre Dame.
InOlH*	St. Leonard College Library, Dayton, Ohio.
InRE	Earlham College, Richmond.
InRenS	St. Joseph's College, Rensselaer.
InStme	St. Meinrad's College & Seminary, St. Meinrad.
InU	Indiana University, Bloomington.

KANSAS

K	Kansas State Library, Topeka.
KAS	St. Benedict's College, Atchison.
KAStB*	St. Benedict's College, Atchison.
KHi	Kansas State Historical Society, Topeka.
KKcB	Central Baptist Theological Seminary, Kansas City.
KMK	Kansas State University, Manhattan.
KStMC*	St. Louis University, School of Divinity Library, St. Louis, Mo.
KU	University of Kansas, Lawrence.
KU-M	— Medical Center Library, Kansas City.
KWiU	Wichita State University, Wichita.

KENTUCKY

Ky-LE	Library Extension Division, Frankfort.
KyBgW	Western Kentucky State College, Bowling Green
KyHi	Kentucky Historical Society, Frankfort.
KyLo	Louisville Free Public Library.
KyLoS	Southern Baptist Theological Seminary, Louisville.
KyLoU	University of Louisville, Louisville.
KyLx	Lexington Public Library.
KyLxCB	Lexington Theological Seminary, Lexington. (Formerly College of the Bible)
KyLxT	Transylvania College, Lexington.
KyMoreT	Morehead State College, Morehead.
KyU	University of Kentucky, Lexington.
KyWA	Asbury College Library, Wilmore.
KyWAT	Asbury Theological Seminary, Wilmore.

LOUISIANA

L	Louisiana State Library, Baton Rouge.
L-M	Louisiana State Museum Library, New Orleans.
LCA	Not a library symbol.
LCS	Not a library symbol.
LHi	Louisiana History Society, New Orleans.
LNHT	Tulane University Library, New Orleans.
LNT-MA	Tulane University, Latin American Library, New Orleans.
LU	Louisiana State University, Baton Rouge.
LU-M	— Medical Center Library, New Orleans.
LU-NO	— Louisiana State University in New Orleans.

MASSACHUSETTS

M	Massachusetts State Library, Boston.
MA	Amherst College, Amherst.
MB	Boston Public Library.
MBAt	Boston Athenaeum, Boston.
MBBC*	Boston College, Chestnut Hill.
MBCo	Countway Library of Medicine. (Harvard-Boston Medical Libraries)
MBH	Massachusetts Horticultural Society, Boston.
MBHo*	Massachusetts Horticultural Society, Boston.
MBM*	Countway Library of Medicine (Harvard-Boston Medical Libraries).
MBMu	Museum of Fine Arts, Boston.
MBU	Boston University.
MBdAF	U.S. Air Force Cambridge Research Center, Bedford.
MBrZ	Zion Research Library, Brookline.
MBrigStJ*	St. John's Seminary, Brighton.
MBtS	St. John's Seminary Library, Brighton.
MCM	Massachusetts Institute of Technology, Cambridge.
MCR	Radcliffe College, Cambridge.
MCSA	Smithsonian Institution, Astrophysical Observatory, Cambridge.
MChB	Boston College, Chestnut Hill.
MH	Harvard University, Cambridge.
MH-A	— Arnold Arboretum.
MH-AH	— Andover-Harvard Theological Library.
MH-BA	— Graduate School of Business Administration Library.
MH-FA	— Fine Arts Library. (Formerly Fogg Art Museum)
MH-G	— Gray Herbarium Library.
MH-HY	— Harvard-Yenching Institute. (Chinese-Japanese Library)

MASSACHUSETTS continued

MH-L	— Law School Library.
MH-P	— Peabody Museum Library.
MH-PR	— Physics Research Library.
MHi	Massachusetts Historical Society, Boston.
MMeT	Tufts University, Medford.
MNF	Forbes Library, Northampton.
MNS	Smith College, Northampton.
MNoeS	Stonehill College Library, North Easton.
MNtcA	Andover Newton Theological School, Newton Center.
MSaE	Essex Institute, Salem.
MShM	Mount Holyoke College, South Hadley.
MU	University of Massachusetts, Amherst.
MWA	American Antiquarian Society, Worcester.
MWAC	Assumption College, Worcester.
MWC	Clark University, Worcester.
MWH	College of the Holy Cross, Worcester.
MWalB	Brandeis University, Waltham.
MWelC	Wellesley College, Wellesley.
MWhB	Marine Biological Laboratory, Woods Hole
MWiW	Williams College, Williamstown.
MWiW-C	— Chapin Library.

MARYLAND

MdAN	U.S. Naval Academy, Annapolis.
MdBE	Enoch Pratt Free Library, Baltimore.
MdBG	Goucher College, Baltimore.
MdBJ	Johns Hopkins University, Baltimore.
MdBJ-G	— John Work Garrett Library.
MdBP	Peabody Institute, Baltimore.
MdBWA	Walters Art Gallery, Baltimore.
MdU	University of Maryland, College Park.
MdW	Woodstock College, Woodstock.

MAINE

MeB	Bowdoin College, Brunswick.
MeBa	Bangor Public Library.
MeU	University of Maine, Orono.
MeWC	Colby College, Waterville.
MeWaC*	Colby College, Waterville.

MICHIGAN

Mi	Michigan State Library, Lansing.
MiAC	Alma College, Alma.
MiD	Detroit Public Library.
MiD-B	— Burton Historical Collection.
MiDA	Detroit Institute of Arts, Detroit.
MiDU	University of Detroit, Detroit.
MiDW	Wayne State University, Detroit.
MiEM	Michigan State University, East Lansing.
MiEalC*	Michigan State University, East Lansing.
MiGr	Grand Rapids Public Library.
MiH*	Michigan College of Mining and Technology, Houghton.
MiHM	Michigan College of Mining and Technology, Houghton.
MiU	University of Michigan, Ann Arbor.
MiU-C	— William L. Clements Library.

MINNESOTA

MnCS	St. John's University, Collegeville.
MnH*	Minnesota Historical Society, St. Paul.
MnHi	Minnesota Historical Society, St. Paul.
MnRM	Mayo Clinic and Foundation Library, Rochester.
MnSJ	James Jerome Hill Reference Library, St. Paul.
MnSSC	College of St. Catherine, St. Paul.
MnU	University of Minnesota, Minneapolis.

MISSOURI

MoHi	Missouri State Historical Society, Columbia
MoK	Kansas City Public Library.
MoKL	Linda Hall Library, Kansas City
MoKU	University of Missouri at Kansas City, Kansas City.
MoS	St. Louis Public Library.
MoSB	Missouri Botanical Garden, St. Louis.
MoSC*	Concordia Seminary Library, St. Louis.
MoSCS	Concordia Seminary Library, St. Louis.
MoSM	Mercantile Library Association, St. Louis.
MoSU	St. Louis University, St. Louis.
MoSU-D	— School of Divinity Library, St. Louis.
MoSW	Washington University, St. Louis.
MoU	University of Missouri, Columbia.

The National Union Catalog

Pre-1956 Imprints

A cumulative author list representing Library of Congress printed cards and titles reported by other American libraries. Compiled and edited with the cooperation of the Library of Congress and the National Union Catalog Subcommittee of the Resources Committee of the Resources and Technical Services Division, American Library Association

Volume 405

NANSEN, FRIDTJOF (C) - NATIONAL ASSOCIATION FOR MENTAL HEALTH (U.S.) (S)

Mansell 1975

Mansell Information/Publishing Limited
3 Bloomsbury Place, London WC1

The American Library Association
50 East Huron Street, Chicago, Illinois 60611

The paper on which this catalog has been printed is supplied by
P. F. Bingham Limited and has been specially manufactured by the
Guard Bridge Paper Company Limited of Fife, Scotland.
Based on requirements established by the late William J. Barrow
for a permanent/durable book paper it is laboratory certified
to meet or exceed the following values:

Substance 89 gsm
pH cold extract 9·4
Fold endurance (MIT ½kg. tension) 1200
Tear resistance (Elmendorf) 73 (or 67 × 3)
Opacity 90·3 %

Library of Congress Card Number : 67–30001
ISBN : 0 7201 0498 X

Printed by Balding & Mansell Limited, London and Wisbech, England
Bound by Bemrose & Sons Limited, Derby, England

American Library Association

Resources and Technical Services Division

Publisher's Note

Because of the large number of sources from which the information in the National Union Catalog has been collected over a long period of time an understanding of its scope and an acquaintance with its methods is necessary for the best use to be made of it. Users are therefore earnestly advised to make themselves familiar with the introductory matter in Volume 1. This fully defines the scope of the Catalog and sets out the basis on which the material reported to the National Union Catalog has been edited for publication in book form.

National Union Catalog Designation

Each main entry in the Catalog has been ascribed a unique identifying designation. This alphanumeric combination appears uniformly after the last line of the entry itself and consists of:

1 The letter N, signifying National Union Catalog.
2 The initial letter under which the entry is filed.
3 A number representing the position of the entry within the sequence under its initial letter.

This National Union Catalog designator is sufficient both to identify any main entry in the Catalog and to establish its position within the sequence of volumes. It is, however, recommended that when referring to titles by the National Union Catalog designation a checking element, such as the key word or initials of the title, be added.

Reported Locations

Alphabetic symbols which represent libraries in the United States and Canada follow the National Union Catalog designation. These groups of letters signify which libraries have reported holding copies of the work. The first library so represented usually is the one that provided the catalog information.

Printed on the end sheets of each volume is a list of most frequently used symbols, each followed by the full name of the library. *List of Symbols*, containing a comprehensive list of symbols used, is published as a separate volume with the Catalog. The Library of Congress has also issued *Symbols Used in the National Union Catalog of the Library of Congress*. In cases where a symbol is not identified in these lists the National Union Catalog Division of the Library of Congress will, on enquiry, attempt to identify the library concerned.

Other Developments

Under the terms of their agreement with the American Library Association, the publishers have undertaken to apply, as far as is practicable, new developments in library science and techniques which may have the effect of further enhancing the value of the Catalog. To this end, the publishers will be pleased to receive suggestions and enquiries relating to technical and production aspects of the Catalog and will be glad to consider proposals calculated to improve its utility and amenity. Mansell Information/Publishing Limited will be pleased also to advise libraries on possible applications of the methods and techniques developed for this and similar projects to their own requirements.

J.C.
London, *August 1968*

VOLUME 405

Nansen, Fridtjof. 1861–
Changes in oceanic and atmospheric temperatures and their relation to changes in the sun's activity.
(*In* U. S. Dept. of agriculture. Weather bureau. **Monthly weather review.** v. 46, p. 177–178. 31ᶜᵐ. Washington, 1918)
Author's abstract reprinted from Journal Washington academy of sciences, March 4, 1918, v. 8, p. 135–138.
Illustrated review, before the Washington academy of sciences, January 8, 1918, of the recent book: Helland-Hansen, Bjørn, & Nansen, Fridtjof. Temperatur-schwankungen des Nordatlantischen ozeans und in der atmosphäre ... Videnskapsselskapets skrifter, i mat.-naturv. kl, 1916, no. 9, Kristiania, 1917.
1. Temperature. 2. ₁Correlation, Meteorological₁ 3. Meteorology—Periodicity. ₍3. Periodicity in meteorology₎ 4. Sun-spots.

Agr 18–854

Library, U. S. Dept. of   Agriculture 1W37M   vol. 46

NN   0014954   DNAL OU

Nansen, Fridtjof, 1861–1930.
... Closing-nets for vertical hauls and for horizontal towing, by Fridtjof Nansen. Copenhague, A. F. Høst & fils, 1915.
8 p. illus. 25ᶜᵐ. (Publications de circonstance. no. 67)
At head of title: Conseil permanent international pour l'exploration de la mer.

1. Nets.   I. Title.

A 26—619

Stanford univ. Library
for Library of Congress   ₍a41b1₎

NN   0014955   CSt

Nansen, Fridtjof, 1861–1930.
Dagbok fra 1905. Med innledning av Jacob S. Worm-Müller. Oslo, Aschehoug, 1955.
lxvii, 184 p. ports, facsim. 23 cm.

1. Norway—Pol. & govt.—1814–1905.   I. Worm-Müller, Jacob Stenersen, 1884–

DL529.N3A3 1955   A 56–3504

Minnesota. Univ. Libr.
for Library of Congress   ₍8₎†

NN   0014956   MnU DLC CU MH NN OCl C WaU

V
919.81   Nansen, Fridtjof, 1861–1930.
N188pa   Dr. Fr. Nansens officielle rapport til etatsraad Gamél... Kjøbenhavn, Berlingske bogtrykkeri ved L.N.Kalcar, 1889.
31 p. 17ᶜᵐ.
Rare Book
Room   "Særskilt aftryk af 'Berlingske Tidende'."

1.Greenland, South - Descr. ₍2₎Norske Grønlandsekspedition, 1888–1889.

NN   0014957   CSt

Nansen, Fridtjof, 1861–
Dr. Nansen's north polar expedition.
n.p., n.pub., 1893.
p. 346–50   O.
Extract from the Geographical journal, 1893.
Bound in Arctic etc. v. 2.

NN   0014958   CaBViPA

Nansen, Fridtjof, 1861–1930.
Durch den Kaukasus zur Wolga. ₍Aus dem Norwegischen von Th. Geiger₎ Leipzig, F. A. Brockhaus, 1930.
183 p. plates, port., maps. 24 cm.

1. Caucasus—Descr. & trav.   I. Title.

DK511.C1N274   914.79   50–53913

WaU
NN   0014959   DLC CtY MB OrP NN PPGi OCl ICU CU IU

Nansen, Fridtjof, 1861–1930.
The earth's crust, its surface-forms, and isostatic adjustment, by Fridtjof Nansen ... Oslo, I kommisjon hos J. Dybwad, 1928.
121, ₍1₎ p. incl. illus., tables, diagrs. 22½ᶜᵐ.
Reprinted from "Avhandlinger utgitt av Det Norske videnskaps-akademi i Oslo. I. Mat-naturv. klasse 1927: no. 12."
Utgitt for Fridtjof Nansens fond.
"Literature": p. 117–121.

1. Earth-surface. 2. Isostasy. 3. ₍Geomorphology₎   I. Title.

G S 30–321

Library, U. S. Geological   Survey 503 N15

NN   0014960   DI-GS NIC NcU MH OU

Nansen, Fridtjof, 1861–   joint author.

Helland-Hansen, Bjørn, 1877–
... The eastern north Atlantic (with 19 figures in the text and 71 plates) ... Oslo, I kommisjon hos Cammermeyer, 1926.

Nansen, Fridtjof, 1861–1930.
... Die erforschung der unbekannten Innerarktis, karte der höhen, tiefen und strömungen im nordpolarbecken, von Fridtjof Nansen, mit erläuterndem text und 1 deckblatt zur karte nach Fridtjof Nansen zusammengestellt und ergänzt von Leonid Breitfuss. Gotha, J. Perthes, 1929.
cover-title, 8 p. fold. map. 28½ᶜᵐ.
At head of title: Aeroarctic. Internationale gesellschaft zur erforschung der Arktis mit luftfahrzeugen.
Map accompanied by guard sheet with routes outlined.
1. Arctic regions—Maps. 2. Arctic Ocean.   I. International society for the exploration of the Arctic regions by means of aircraft. II. Breitfuss, Lev L'vovich, 1864–   III. Title.

Library of Congress   G599.N3   30–16521

NN   0014962   DLC

E
99   NANSEN, Fridtjof, 1861–1930
E7 N158   Eskimålif, af Fridtjof Nansen. Illustrerad af Otto Sinding. Bemyndigad öfversättning af Ernst Lundquist. Stockholm, Hugo Gebers Förlag ₍1891₎
2 p.ℓ., 260 p. front., illus. (incl. music), plates 21 cm.
Head and tail pieces; initials.
Halfbound in late brown morocco, embossed brown cloth, spine lettered and stamped in gilt.
I. Lundquist,   Ernst, *1851-1938*, ed.

NN   0014963   MBCo

Nansen, Fridtjof, 1861–1930.
Eskimo life, by Fridtjof Nansen ... Tr. by William Archer. London, Longmans, Green, and co., 1893.
xvi, 350 p. front., illus., 15 pl. 23ᶜᵐ.

1. Eskimos—Greenland.   4—7811

Library of Congress   E99.E7N21

OC1W OCl NjP MB NN NdU WaU ICJ
NN   0014964   DLC MBCo MiU NIC CtY CLSU PPL PPFr

E99
.E7N21   Nansen, Fridtjof, 1861–1930.
1894   Eskimo life, by Fridtjof Nansen ... Translated by William Archer ... 2d ed. London and New York, Longmans, Green, and co., 1894.
xvi, 350 p. front., illus., 15 plates. 22ᶜᵐ.

1. Eskimos—Greenland.

NN   0014965   MB DN CoU CaBVaU OrPR

919.8   Nansen, Fridtjof, 1861–1930.
N188e5   Eskimoleben; aus dem norwegischen übersetzt von M.Langfeldt. Neue illustrierte ausgabe. Berlin, Globus verlag, g.m.b.h. [Vorwort 1891]
1891   vii,304p. front.(port.)illus.,plates. 22cm.

1.Eskimos - Greenland. I.Title. LC.

NN   0014966   CLSU PPG

E99
.E7N25   Nansen, Fridtjof, 1861–1930.
1903   Eskimoleben; aus dem Norwegischen übersetzt von M. Langfeldt. [Neue illustrierte Ausg.] Leipzig, Meyer, 1903.
viii, 304 p. illus. 22cm.

1. Eskimos—Greenland.   I. Langfeldt, Margarete, tr. II. Title.

NN   0014967   MB IU OrCS CaBVaU

Nansen, Fridtjof, 1861–1930.
... Eskimoleben; aus dem norwegischen übersetzt von M. Langfeldt. Illustrierte ausgabe. Berlin, Globus verlag, g. m. b. h. ₍1910₎
vii. 304 p. front. (port.) illus., plates. 22ᶜᵐ.

1. Eskimos—Greenland.   I Langfeldt, Margarete, tr. II. Title.

34–7751

Library of Congress   E99.E7N25   919.8

NN   0014968   DLC

Nansen, Fridtjof, 1861–1930.
Eskimoliv, af Fridtjof Nansen; med illustrationer af Otto Sinding. Kristiania, H. Aschehoug & co., 1891.
viii, 293 p., 1 l. incl. front., illus., 15 pl. 24ᶜᵐ.
Includes music.

1. Eskimos—Greenland.

Library of Congress   E99.E7N2   4—7810

NN   0014969   DLC

Nansen, Fridtjof, 1861–1930.
Eventyr-lyst; tale hollt som rektor ved St. Andrews Universitet 3.november 1926, av Fridtjof Nansen. Oslo, J.Dybwads forlag, 1926.
64 p. 20½ᶜᵐ.

1.Adventure and adventurers. I.Title.

NN   0014970   MiU FU NN

910.4   Nansen, Fridtjof, 1861–1930.
N15e   Eventyr-lyst. Ingen krig mere. To taler. Oslo, Dybwad, 1927.
100 p. port. 23cm.

1. Adventure and adventurers. I. Title.

NN   0014971   MnU

VOLUME 405

Nansen, Fridtjof, 1861–1930.

League of nations. *Secretary-general, 1919–1933 (Earl of Perth)*
... Exchange of Greek children and Bulgarian prisoners. Memorandum by the Secretary-general, adopted by the Council in Paris, February 22nd, 1921. ₍n. p., 1921₎

Nansen, Fridtjof, 1861–
La famine en Russie; conférence faite par le Dr Nansen au Trocadéro, le 17 février 1922... Compte rendu sténographique (publié in-extenso). Paris: ₍Comité français de secours aux enfants₎ 1922. 23 p. nar. 12°.

Cover-title.

1. Famines, Russia, 1922.
N. Y. P. L.   February 8, 1923.

NN   0014973   NN

₍Nansen, Fridtjof₎ 1861–1930.
... Famine in Russia ... ₍Geneva₎ 1922.
7 numb. l. 33ᶜᵐ.
Caption title.
At head of title: League of nations.
Official no.: C.173.M.92.1922.
Mimeographed.
Memorandum by Dr. Nansen. cf. leaf 1.
Notes from the Secretary-general of the League of nations and the minister of foreign affairs of Norway precede memorandum.

1. Russia—Econ. condit.—1918–   I. League of nations. II. Title.
                     A 46–5712
Woodrow Wilson memorial   library
for Library of Congress   ₍3₎

NN   0014974   NNUN-W

Nansen, Fridtjof, 1861–1930.
"Farthest north"; being the record of a voyage of exploration of the ship Fram, 1893–96, and of a fifteen months' sleigh journey by Dr. Nansen and Lieut. Johansen. With an appendix by Otto Sverdrup, captain of the Fram. London, Macmillan, 1897. 2v. (Macmillan's colonial library)

NN   0014975   CaBViPA CaBVa CaBViP CaBVaU

Nansen, Fridtjof, 1861–1930.
Farthest north; being the record of a voyage of exploration of the ship "Fram" 1893–96 and of a fifteen months' sleigh journey by Dr. Nansen and Lieut. Johansen, by Dr. Fridtjof Nansen. With an appendix by Otto Sverdrup ... About 120 full-page and numerous text-illustrations, 16 colored plates in facsimile from Dr. Nansen's own sketches, etched portrait, photogravures, and 4 maps ... New York, Harper & brothers, 1897.
2 v. fronts., illus., plates (part col.) ports., fold. maps. 24ᶜᵐ.
1. Arctic regions. 2. "Fram" expedition, 1st, 1893–1896. I. Sverdrup, Otto Neumann, 1854–1930. II. Title.
                     5–39019
Library of Congress   G700.1893.N2
——— Copy 2.
Copyright 1897: 10257.   10258

   PPAmSwM DAU TxU
PPRC1 WaWW CaBViPA CaBVaU OrStbM OrP OrCS MnHi
OU IU PHC PU PBm MiU OU OCl MH Nh NN WaU PPFr Wa
NN   0014976   DLC DN-O₄ DN KEmT OrStbM PSt NIC DAS

Nansen, Fridtjof, 1861–1930.
Farthest north; being the record of a voyage of exploration of the ship "Fram" 1893–96 and of a fifteen months' sleigh journey by Dr. Nansen and Lieut. Johansen, by Dr. Fridtjof Nansen. With an appendix by Otto Sverdrup ... about 120 full-page and numerous text-illustrations, 16 colored plates in facsimile from Dr. Nansen's own sketches, etched portrait, photogravures, and 4 maps ... New York, Harper & brothers, 1897.
2 v. fronts., illus., plates (part col.) ports., fold. maps. 24½ᶜᵐ.
New edition, with index.
1. Arctic regions. 2. "Fram" expedition, 1st, 1893–1896. I. Sverdrup, Otto Neumann, 1854–1930. II. Title.
Library of Congress   G700.1893.N22
                     5–39020

NN   PPA
   0014978   DLC NN IdU MtHi WaS MtBC OU ViU NjP

Nansen, Fridtjof, 1861–1930.
Fridtjof Nansen's "Farthest North"; being the record of a voyage of exploration of the ship Fram 1893–96 and of a fifteen months' sleigh journey by Dr. Nansen and Lieut Johansen with an appendix by Otto Sverdrup, captain of the Fram; about one hundred and twenty full page and numerous text illustrations, sixteen coloured plates in facsimile from Dr. Nansen's own sketches, etched portrait, photogravures and maps ... Westminster, A. Constable and company, 1897.
2 v. fronts., illus. (incl. plans) XVI col. pl., plates, ports., 4 fold. col. maps. 24½ᶜᵐ.

Author's autograph on fly-leaf of v.1.

1. Arctic regions. 2. "Fram" expedition, 1st, 1893–1896. I. Sverdrup, Otto Neumann, 1855–1930. II. Title: Farthest north.

   CU-I MeB OrCS CU-B MnHi IU OrHi KAS
NN   0014980   MiU WaSpG CaBVaU NN MdBP ICU NNC CoU

910.8
N188f
Nansen, Fridtjof, 1861–1930.
... Farthest north; being a record of a voyage of exploration of the ship "Fram" 1893–96, and of a fifteen months' sleigh journey by Dr. Nansen and Lieut. Johannsen, by Dr. Fridtjof Nansen; with an appendix by Otto Sverdrup ... London, George Newnes, 1898.
2 v. front., illus., plates, ports., map. 23cm.
1. Arctic regions. 2. "Fram" expedition, 1st, 1893–1896. I. Sverdrup, Otto Neumann. II. Title.

NN   0014981   FU CaOTP NBC CaBViPA CaBVa

Nansen, Fridtjof, 1861–
... Farthest north; being a record of a voyage of exploration of the ship "Fram" 1893–96, and of a fifteen months' sleigh journey by Dr. Nansen and Lieut. Johannsen, by Dr. Fridtjof Nansen; with an appendix by Otto Sverdrup ... ₍Popular ed.₎ New York and London, Harper & brothers, 1898.
vii, 679 p. front., illus., plates, ports., map. 22ᶜᵐ.

1. Arctic regions. 2. "Fram" expedition, 1893–1896.   I. Sverdrup, Otto Neumann, 1855–   II. Title.
Library of Congress   G700.1893.N24
                     4–16773
——— Copy 2.
919.8   ₍a27h2₎   G14

OrLgE
MiU WU CoU MB WaIC WaSp Or CaBViPA CaBVaU WaE IdPI
NN   0014982   DLC PRosC PP   ODW OCl PWcS PPD NcRS

Nansen, Dr. Fridtjof.
Farthest north.
Harper, 1899.   8°

NN   0014983   I OrU

315.8
N158fa
1897
Nansen, Fridtjof, 1861–1930.
Farthest North; being the record of a voyage of exploration of the ship "Fram" 1893–96 and of a fifteen months' sleigh journey by Dr. Nansen and Lieut. Johansen; with an appendix by Otto Sverdrup... New York, Harper, 190
v. illus. 25cm.

NN   0014984   OrU MWA

919.8
N15fa
1903
Nansen, Fridtjof, 1861–1930.
Farthest north; being the record of a voyage of exploration of the ship "Fram" 1893–96 and of a fifteen month's sleigh journey by Dr. Nansen and Lieut. Johansen, by Dr. Fridtjof Jansen. With an appendix by Otto Sverdrup ... About 120 full-page and numerous text-illustrations, 16 colored plates in facsimile from Dr. Nansen's own sketches, etched portrait, photogravures. New York, Harper & brother, 1903 ₍c1897₎
2 v. fronts., illus., plates (part col.) ports., fold. maps. 24cm.

NN   0014985   IU IaU MdBP

919.8
N15fa
1955
Nansen, Fridtjof, 1861–1930.
Farthest north; edited by Denys Thompson. London, Chatto and Windus ₍1955₎
v, 150p. maps. 19cm. (The Queen's classics)

An abridgement of the two-volume edition of 1897.

1. Arctic regions. 2. "Fram" Expedition, 1st, 1893–1896. I. Thompson, Denys, 1907–   ed. II. Title.

NN   0014986   IU ICarbS IEN

Nansen, Fridtjof, 1861–1930.
En ferd til Spitsbergen, av Fridtjof Nansen; billeder og karter av forfatteren. Kristiania, J. Dybwads forlag; ₍etc., etc.₎ 1920.
2 p. ℓ., 279, ₍2₎ p., 1 ℓ. front., illus. (incl. maps (1 double)) XXII pl. on 11 ℓ. diagrs. 24½ᶜᵐ.
"Denne bok skildrer en ferd til Bjørnøen og Spitsbergen i 1912."—Forord.

1. Spitzbergen—Descr. & trav. 2. Bear Island, Arctic Ocean.

NN   0014987   MiU NIC NN WaU

Nansen, Fridtjof, 1861–1930.
The first crossing of Greenland, by Fridtjof Nansen. Tr. from the Norwegian by Hubert Majendie Gepp ... With maps and numerous illustrations ... London and New York, Longmans, Green, and co., 1890.
2 v. fronts., illus. (incl. music) plates, ports., fold. maps. 23ᶜᵐ.
Introduction by J. Scott Keltie.

1. Greenland—Descr. & trav. 2. Arctic regions. I. Gepp, Hubert Majendie, tr. II. Title.
Library of Congress   G742.N18
                     5–24101

   ICJ MH MB ViU PPFr CaBVa Or
   NIC PPAN PPGi PPL OCU MiU OCl NNC MdBP NjP
NN   0014988   DLC DAS DN FTaSU DSI LU OKentU TNJ

G7₄2
.N18
1892
Nansen, Fridtjof, 1861–1930.
The first crossing of Greenland, by Fridtjof Nansen. Translated from the Norwegian by Majendie Gepp ... A new ed. abridged ... London and New York, Longmans, Green, and co., 1892.
2 p. l., vii–xii, 452 p. front., illus. (incl. ports.) fold. map. 20ᶜᵐ.

1. Greenland—Descr. & trav. 2. Arctic regions. I. Gepp, Hubert Majendie, tr. II. Title.

NN   0014990   MB OO I CtY CU PPRC1 PBm ICN MWA

919.8
N158pᵀg
1892
Nansen, Fridtjof, 1861–1930.
The first crossing of Greenland, by Fridtjof Nansen. Translated from the Norwegian by Hubert Majendie Gepp ... New ed. With numerous illustrations and map. London and New York, Longmans, Green, and co., 1895.
2p. l., vii–xii, 452p. front., illus. (incl. ports.) map. 19cm.
Translation of På ski over Grønland.
This abridged edition first published 1892.
1. Greenland – Descr. & trav. 2. Arctic regions. I. Gepp, Hubert Majendie, tr. II. Title.

NN   0014991   TxU OrP CaBVaU

NANSEN, FRIDTJOF, 1861–1930.
The first crossing of Greenland. Translated from the Norwegian by Hubert Majendie Gepp. New ed. London, New York, Longmans, Green, 1897. xii, 452 p. illus., map. 20cm.

1. Greenland—Descr. and trav.,   1800–1900.

NN   0014992   NN MeB CaOTP WaS CU FU OCl OU

VOLUME 405

Nansen, Fridtjof, 1861-1930.
The first crossing of Greenland, by Fridtjof
Nansen. Tr. from the Norwegian by Hubert
Majendie Gepp ... With maps and numerous illus-
trations ... London and New York, Longmans,
Green, and co., 1898.
xii, 446 p. illus. 19cm.
New impression.
1. Greenland--Descr. & trav. 2. Arctic
regions. I. Gepp, Hubert Majendie, tr. II.
Title.

NN 0014993   AU

Nansen, Fridtjof, 1861-
The first crossing of Greenland; tr.
from the Norwegian by Hubert Majendie
Gepp ... London, Longmans, Green & co.,
1902.
452 p. illus. maps.

NN 0014994   OCl

Nansen, Fridtjof.   919.8
The first crossing of Greenland; translated from the Norwegian by Hubert Majendie Gepp.   London: Longmans, Green,
and Co., 1906. xii, 452 p., 1 map. illus., port. 12°. (Silver
library.)

1. Greenland. 2. Arctic regions.   CENTRAL CIRCULATION.
translator.   3. Title. 4. Gepp, Hubert Majendie,
N.Y.P.L.   March 1. 1912.

NN 0014995   NN WaTC

919.8   Nansen, Fridtjof, 1861-1930.
N18f2   The first crossing of Greenland ... tr.
from the Norwegian by Hubert Majendie Gepp ...
Lond., N.Y. ɾetc.ɹ Longmans, 1910.
452p. front.(port.) illus. map. 19cm.
ɾThe Silver libraryɹ

1.Greenland. Descr.& trav. 2.Arctic
regions. I.Gepp,Hubert Marjendie, tr.
II.Title.

NN 0014996   N WaE CaBViP

919.8   Nansen, Fridtjof, 1861-1930.
N15f   The first crossing of Greenland. Tr.
1919   from the Norwegian by Hubert Majendie Gepp.
London, New York, Longmans, Green, and Co.,
1919.
xii, 452 p. illus., maps. 19 cm.

1. Greenland--Descr. & trav. 2. Arctic
regions. I. Gepp, Hubert Majendie, tr.
II. Title.

NN 0014997   LU OClW OCl

Nansen, Fridtjof, 1861-1930, ed.
...The first crossing of Greenland, by
Fridtjof Nansen. Tr.from the Norwegian by
Hubert Majandie Gepp... School ed.,ed.by J.
C.Allen. London, Longmans, Green and co.,
1923.
4 p.l.,148 p. front.(port.),illus. 19 cm.
Longman's class-books of English litera-
ture.

NN 0014998   DI-GS OrMonO

Nansen, Fridtjof, 1861-
... Før det blir for sent, av Fridtjof Nansen ... Kri-
stiania, J. Dybwad, 1915.
32 p. 22½ᶜᵐ.
At head of title: Norges forsvarsforening.
Title vignette.

1. Norway--Defenses. I. Norges forsvarsforening. II. Title.
                                                            21-2735
Library of Congress   UA750.N3

NN 0014999   DLC

Nansen, Fridtjof, 1861-1930.
Folkeforbundets første tiaar ...
see under title

Nansen, Fridtjof, 1861-
... Freiluftleben. Leipzig, F. A. Brockhaus, 1920.
215, ɾ1ɹ p. 19ᶜᵐ.
CONTENTS.--An den deutschen leser.--Auf schneeschuhen übers gebirge.--
Haraldsets jagdgeschichten.--Winter im gebirge.--Nach Island und Jan
Mayen.--Herbstjagd in den bergen.--Auf der auerhahnbalz.--Im bereich
Rondanes und der Sölenberge.

1. Outdoor life. I. Title.
Library of Congress   SK601.N35   23-465

NN 0015001   DLC CLU

Nansen, Fridtjof, 1861-1930
Ekd   Fra ghiacci e tenebre: la spedizione polare
893N1 norvegese, 1893-1896, narrata da Fridtjof Nansen,
seguita dalla relazione del capitano del Fram,
Otto Sverdrup. Versione italiana dall'originale
per opera di Cesare Norsa ... Roma,V.Enrico,
1897.
2v. front.(v.2),illus.,plates(part col.,part
double),fold.maps. 23cm.

NN 0015002   CtY

NANSEN, FRIDTJOF, 1861-1930.
Fram öfver polarhafvet; den norska polarfär-
den 1893-96 ... bemyndigad öfversättning från
Norskan under tillsyn af A.G. Nathorst. Stockholm, Albert Bonniers förlag, ɾ1897ɹ
2 v.

NN 0015003   Or

Nansen, Fridtjof, 1861-1930.
Fram over polhavet; den norske polarfaerd
1893-1896, af Fridtjof Nansen. Med et tillaeg
af Otto Sverdrup ... Kristiania, H.Aschehoug
& co., 1897.
2 v. fronts.,illus.,plates (part col.) ports.,maps
(part fold.) fold.diagr. 24ᶜᵐ.

1.Arctic regions. 2."Fram" expedition,1st,1893-1896.
I.Sverdrup,Otto Neumann,1855-

NcGU CSt CaBViPA WaS WaT
NN 0015004   MiU FU WaU OU MB N KU WHi MnHi NBuG

Nansen, Fridtjof, 1861-
Fridtjof Nansen's poolreis door hemzelf beschreven...
Amsterdam: L. J. Veenɾ, 1896ɹ 95 p. illus. (incl. ports.),
plan. 8°.
Repr.: Daily Chronicle, Nov. 2, 3, 4, 1896.

1. Arctic expeditions, 1893-1896.   2. Fram ɾshipɹ
N.Y.P.L.   November 21, 1927

NN 0015005   NN

Nansen, Fridtjof, 1861-
... Frilufts-liv; blade av dagboken. Kristiania, J. Dyb-
wad, 1916.
2 p. l., 233 p., 1 l. 20ᶜᵐ.
CONTENTS.--På ski over fjellet.--Haraldset'n.--Vinter i fjellet.--Til
Islann og Jan Mayen.--Høstjagt.--Tiurlek.--Ved Rondane og Sølen-fjell.

1. Outdoor life. I. Title.
Library of Congress   SK601.N3   17-6549

NN 0015006   DLC WU ICJ

796.5   Nansen, Fridtjof, 1861-1930.
N15f   Frilufts-liv; blade av dagboken. Kristi-
1923   ania, J. Dybwad, 1923.
2 p.l., 233p., 1l. 20cm.
Author's autograph presentation copy to
P. L. Mercanton.

NN 0015007   IU

Nansen, Fridtjof, 1861-1930, ed.
Für unsere kleinen russischen Brüder!
see under Bienz, Marguerite E., ed.

Nansen, Fridtjof, 1861-
Future North Polar exploration, 1898.
p. 293-305. illus. O.

NN 0015009   DAS

Nansen, Fridtjof, 1861-   No. 2 in *5810a.22
A geological sketch of Cape Flora and its neighbourhood. Illus.
(In Pompeckj. Jurassic fauna of Cape Flora. Pp. 1-32.
London, 1900.)

*D6215 — Geology. — Franz Josef Land.

NN 0015010   MB

Nansen, Fridtjof, 1861-
Gjennem Armenia, av Fridtjof Nansen. Oslo: J. Dybwads
forlag, 1927. 247 p. incl. plans, tables. front., maps, plates.
8°.
Plates printed on both sides.

1. Armenia--Descr. and trav., 1900-
N. Y. P. L.   July 9, 1928

NN 0015011   NN NIC

DS   Nansen, Fridtjof, 1861-1930.
165   Gjennem Armenia. Illustrert av Fridtjof
N34   Nansen. ɾOsloɹ Jacob Dybwad ɾ1941, c1927ɹ
1941   304 p. illus., maps (Fra Svalbard til
Kaukasus, 4)

NN 0015012   WaU

Nansen, Fridtjof, 1861-
Gjennem Kaukasus til Volga, av Fridtjof Nansen... Oslo:
J. Dybwads Forlag, 1929. 162 p. front., plates, ports. 2.
ed. 8°.
Plates printed on both sides.

472703A. I. Caucasus--Descr. and   trav.
N.Y.P.L.

NN 0015013   NN NIC MH FU

VOLUME 405

DK
511
C1
N27
1941

Nansen, Fridtjof, 1861-1930.
　　Gjennem Kaukasus til Volga. Illustrert
av Fridtjof Nansen. [Oslo] Jacob Dybwad
[1941, c1929]
　　155 p. illus., maps (Fra Svalbard til
Kaukasus, 5)

　　1. Caucasus - Description and travel.
I. Title. II. Series.

NN　　0015014　　WaU

DK
755
N15
1941

Nansen, Fridtjof, 1861-1930.
　　Gjennem Sibir. Illustrert av Fridtjof
Nansen. [Oslo: J. Dybwad, 1941, c1914]
　　335 p. illus., fold maps. (Fra Svalbard
til Kaukasus, 3)

NN　　0015015　　WaU

Nansen, Fridtjof, 1861-
　　Gjennem Sibirien, av Fridtjof Nansen.　Kristiania: J. Dybwad, 1914.　7 p.l., 386 p., front. (port.), 3 fold. col'd maps, 45 pl.
4°.

　　Plates printed on both sides.

1. Siberia.—Description and travel.　　1913. 2. Title.
N. Y. P. L.　　　　　　　　　　　　　October 27, 1915.

NN　　0015016　　NN ICN WU ICJ NdU

Nansen, Fridtjof, 1861-
　　...El hambre en Rusia; exposición del Dr. Nansen, repre-
sentante de Norvega, a la sesión del consejo de la Sociedad de las
naciones, el 17 de mayo de 1922.　[Genève: H. Vollet, 1922.]
12 p.　illus. (incl. map.)　8°.

　　Caption-title.
　　At head of title: Comite internacional de socorro a Rusia.

1. Famines—Russia, 1922. 2. Inter-　　　national Committee for Russian
Relief.
N. Y. P. L.　　　　　　　　　　　　　March 7, 1928.

NN　　0015017　　NN

Nansen, Fridtjof, 1861-
　　How can the north polar region be crossed?　N.p.n.pub.1893.
　　31p.pl(fold)map(fold)O.

　　Extract from the Geographical journal
Jan.1893.
　　Bound in Arctic etc. v.2.

NN　　0015018　　CaBViPA

Nansen, Fridtjof, 1861-
　　Hunting and adventure in the Arctic, by Fridtjof Nansen;
fully illustrated from drawings by the author. New York,
Duffield and company, 1925.
　　5 p. l., 3-462 p. front. (port.) illus. (incl. maps) plates. 23½ᶜᵐ. $4.00

　　1. Hunting—Arctic regions. 2. Arctic regions.　I. Title.
　　　　　　　　　　　　　　　　　25—7261
　　Library of Congress　　SK265.N3

MtU WaS OrCS CaBViPA OrU WaTC WaSp Or OrSaW OrU
NN MB
OEac OCl OOxM PPA PPFr NcC OClMN CaBViP CaBVaU
NN　　0015019　　DLC TxU CU OO LU CU-A NIC PP PPL MiU

Nansen, Fridtjof, 1861-1930.
　　In honor of Dr. Fridtjof Nansen
　　　　see under title

Nansen, Fridtjof, 1861-1930.
　　In Nacht und Eis; die Norwegische Polarexpedition, 1893-
1896, von Fridtjof Nansen, mit einem Beitrag von Kapitän
Sverdrup ... Autorisirte Ausgabe.　Erster-zweiter Band [und]
Supplement.　Leipzig, F. A. Brockhaus, 1897-1898.

　　3 v.　fronts. (v. 1-2) illus., plates (part col.) ports., fold. maps.　24ᶜᵐ.

　　Supplement has also added t.-p.: Wir Framleute, von Bernhard Nordahl;
Nansen und ich auf 86° 41', von Lieutenant Hjalmar Johansen.

OYesA NRU OClW PPGi MH NIC OU CU OKentU NN MU
NN　0015021　　ICJ WaS TNJ CaOTP NNC ViU WaU OCl IEdS

Nansen, Fridtjof
　　In Nacht und Eis; die Norwegische Polar-
Expedition, 1893-1896; mit einem Beitrag von
Kapitän Sverdrup... 6. Aufl... Leipzig, F. A.
Brockhaus, 1922-1927.
　　3 v. illus. plates (part col.) maps.

　　[Vol.3, Supplement [von Bernhard Nordahl und
Hjalmar Johansen] has added t.-p. with title:
Wir Framleute [von B. Nordahl]-Nansen und ich
auf 86° 14' [von H. Johansen] 2. Aufl.

NN　　0015022　　MiD

G 700
1893
.N 22

Nansen, Fridtjof, 1861-1930.
　　In Nacht und Eis.　Die norwegische Polarexpedition 1893-1896, von Fridtjof Nansen.
Ausgewählt von Fritz Gansberg ... Hamburg,
A. Janssen, 1911.
　　143 p.　8 illus. on 4 l.　19½cm.
　　(Added t.-p.: Wissenschaftliche Volksbücher
für Schule und Haus, hrsg. von F. Gansberg.
[bd. 12])

NN　　0015023　　MdBJ

Nansen, Fridtjof, 1861-1930.
　　In Nacht und Eis; die norwegische Polarexpedition, 1893-
1896.　Mit 33 Abbildungen auf Tafeln und im Text nach
Aufnahmen und Zeichnungen des Verfassers, sowie einer
vierfarbigen Übersichtskarte.　Neue Ausg. Wiesbaden, E.
Brockhaus, 1952.

　　341 p.　illus.　24 cm.　(Klassiker der Entdeckung)

　　Translation of Fram over Polhavet.
　　"Neue gekürzte Ausgabe ... bearbeitet von Erhard Rühle."

　　1. "Fram" Expedition. 1st, 1893-1896.　I. Title.

G700 1893.N225　　　　919.8　　　53-31886 ‡

NN　　0015024　　DLC

Nansen, Fridtjof, 1861-1930.
　　אין נאכם און אײז. דערציילם פון פ. מעסש. אידיש. י. קיפנים.
　　קיעוו. פארלאג "קולטורליגע." [Kiev] 1925.
　　62 p.　illus.　18 cm.　(No. 3 [פאַרלעראװיסנסשאַפטלעכע בילד׳ואַסמק)
　　Abridgment of Fram over Polhavet.

　　1. Arctic regions.　I. "Fram" Expedition. 1st, 1893-1896.　II.
Title.
　　　　　　　　　　　　Title transliterated: In nakht un ayz.

G700 1893.N29　　　　　　　56-52559 ‡

NN　　0015025　　DLC

Nansen, Fridtjof, 1861-
　　In northern mists; Arctic exploration in early times,
by Fridtjof Nansen ... tr. by Arthur G. Chater ... London, W. Heinemann, 1911.
　　2 v.　mounted col. fronts., illus.　26ᶜᵐ.
　　"List of the more important works referred to": vol. II, p. 384-396.

　　1. Discoveries (in geography)—Scandinavian. 2. Arctic regions. 3.
America—Disc. & explor.—Norse.　I. Chater, Arthur G., tr. II. Title.
　　　　　　　　　　　　　　　　　11—31644
　　Library of Congress　　G302.N23

PPRCl PPPD MiU ViU MtU WaSp CaBViP CaBVaU IdPI
NN　　0015026　　DLC KEmT WU WaU FU FTaSU OOxM PSC PBm

Nansen, Fridtjof, 1861-
　　In northern mists; Arctic exploration in early times,
by Fridtjof Nansen ... tr. by Arthur G. Chater ... with
frontispieces in color, and over one hundred and fifty
illustrations in black-and-white ... New York, Frederick
A. Stokes company, 1911.
　　2 v.　mounted col. fronts., illus.　26¾ᶜᵐ.　$8.00
　　"List of the more important works referred to": vol. II, p. 384-396.

　　1. Discoveries (in geography)—Scandinavian. 2. Arctic regions. 3.
America—Disc. & explor.—Norse.　I. Chater, Arthur G., tr. II. Title.
　　　　　　　　　　　　　　　　　12—313
　　Library of Congress　　G302.N24

Or CaBViPA CaBVa
OO MiU OClMN DN MB NN MB ICJ MeB OrU WaE WaT WaS
NN　　0015027　　DLC NcD MiU CoU NBuU TU OCl NIC NcU

Nansen, Fridtjof, 1861-

Pompecki, Josef Felix, 1867-
　　... The Jurassic fauna of Cape Flora, Franz Josef
Land, by J. F. Pompeckj. With a geological sketch of
Cape Flora and its neighborhood by Fridtjof Nansen.
[London, New York, Longmans, Green and co., 1900]

Nansen, Fritjof, [Mannkærleiki. Gefið
út að tilhlutun Bandalags kvenna. Reykjavík, Félagsprentsmiðjan, 1922.　12°.
pp. 22 + (2).　　　IcF91N188

NN　　0015029　　NIC

Nansen, Fridtjof, 1861-1930.
　　Methods for measuring direction and velocity of
currents in the sea.　With an appendix by
V.W. Ekman.　Copenhague, A. F. Höst & Fils,
1906.
　　42 p.　2 pl.　8°.　(Internat. Council for
the Study of the Sea Conseil Permanent Internat.
pour l'Explora. de la Mer.　Publ. de circonstance.
No. 34)

NN　　0015030　　NN

Nansen, Fridtjof, 1861-
　　Na-severni tocnu

NN　　0015031　　OCl

Nansen, Fridtjof, 1861-1930.
　　Nansens røst; artikler og taler.　Oslo, J. Dybwad, 1945
[1942]
　　3 v.　20 cm.
　　CONTENTS.—1. 1884-1896.—2. 1897-1915.—3. 1916-1930.

　　　　　　　　　　　　　　　　　A 48-2699*
　　Harvard Univ.　Library
　　for Library of Congress　　[1]

NN　　0015032　　MH FU WaU CtY CtY-M NcD KU

Nansen, Fridtjof, 1861-1930.
　　Nansens røst; artikler og taler av Fridtjof Nansen...　Oslo,
J. Dybwad, 1945.　3 v.　ports.　19cm.

　　CONTENTS.—1. 1884-1896.—2. 1897-1915.—3. 1916-1930.

407098-100B.　1. Essays, Norwegian.
N. Y. P. L.　　　　　　　　　　　　　December 23, 1947.

NN　　0015033　　NN ICU CaOTP MnU OCl NjP

Nansen, Fridtjof, 1861-
　　Nebelheim.　Entdeckung und Erforschung der nördlichen
Länder und Meere.　Leipzig: F. A. Brockhaus, 1911.　2 v.
illus., pl., port.　8°.

　　Bibliography, v. 2, p. 426-440.

1. Geography.—Discoveries.　　　　2. Voyages and travels.—History.
3. Arctic exploration.—History.　　　4. North, The.
N. Y. P. L.　　　　　　　　　　　　　December 29, 1911.

NN　　0015034　　NN TxU AkU LU CtY PPGi

VOLUME 405

Nanson, Fridtjof, 1861-
— New route to the north pole. 17 pp. (*Forum*, v. 11, 1891, p. 693.)

NN 0015035   MdBP

Nansen, Fridtjof, 1861-1930.
Nord i taakeheimen; utforskningen av jordens nordlige strøk i tidlige tider, av Fridtjof Nansen. Kristiania, J. Dybwad, 1911.

vii p., 1 l., ₍₄₎, 603 p. illus. (incl. maps) 27½ᶜᵐ.

Issued in 25 parts, 1910–1911.
"Literatur": p. ₍57₎–588.

1. Discoveries (in geography) 2. Arctic regions. 3. America—Disc. & explor.—Norse.

Library of Congress   G302.N2   10—12792

NN 0015036   DLC ICJ NdU

342.481   Nansen, Fridtjof, 1861-1930.
N158n   Norge og foreningen med Sverige. Kristiania, J. Dybwads forlag, 1905.
             88 p.

1. Norway - Politics and government.
2. Sweden - Politics and government.
3. Norway - Constitutional history. I. Title.

NN 0015037   WaU NNC MH InU NN FU MB

Nansen, Fridtjof, 1861-
The Norsemen in America...(London, Wm. Clowes & Sons, 1911).
Cover-title, p.(557)-580 illus. 24.9 cm.
From the Geographical Review, Dec. 1911.
L.S. from R. J. Brown to H. Vignaud inserted.

NN 0015038   MiU-C

Nansen, Fridtjof, 1861-
Northern waters; Captain Roald Amundsen's oceanographic observations in the Arctic seas in 1901. With a discussion of the origin of the bottom-waters of the northern seas. Christiania: J. Dybwad, 1906. 3 p.l., 145 p., 1 l., 11 pl. illus. 4°. (Videnskabs-Selskabet i Christiania. Skrifter. I. Mathematisk-naturvidenskabelig Klasse. 1906. no. 3.)

1. Oceanography, Arctic seas.
N. Y. P. L.   November 20, 1911.

NN 0015039   NN DAS MH-Z CaOTP MiU

Nansen, Fridtjof, 1861-   Scan 1692.6.5
La Norvège et l'union avec la Suède; traduit par Gabriel Rouy. Paris, F. Juven, [1905].
pp. viii, 98 +.

NN 0015040   MH

Nansen, Fridtjof, 1861-
Norway and the union with Sweden, by Fridtjof Nansen. London, Macmillan and co., limited; New York, The Macmillan company, 1905.
vi p. 1 l., 96 p. 19ᶜᵐ.
                                    JN7445.1905.N2
—— Supplementary chapter to Dr. Fridtjof Nansen's Norway and the union with Sweden. London, Macmillan and co., limited; New York, The Macmillan company, 1905.
cover-title, ₍97₎–155, ₍1₎ p. 19½ᶜᵐ.
1. Norway—Pol. & govt.—1814–1905. 2. Sweden—Pol. & govt.—1814–1905. 3. Norway—Constitutional history.

Library of Congress   JN7445.1905.N21   5—30262

MiU NcD NIC PPT NN DN NjP PHC
NN 0015041   DLC PV PP MB WaS NdU WaT CoU OCl OU

JN
7445   Nansen, Fridtjof, 1861-1930
.1905   Norwegen und die Union mit Schweden.
N26   Leipzig, Brockhaus, 1905.
          iv, 71p. 22cm.

Bibliographical footnotes

1. Norway - Pol. & govt. - 1814-1905.
2. Sweden - Pol. & Govt. - 1814-1905.
3. Norway - Constitutional history.
I. Title.

NN 0015042   TNJ MH OU

Nansen, Fridtjof, 1861-1930, ed.
The Norwegian North polar expedition, 1893–1896; scientific results, ed. by Fridtjof Nansen ... Pub. by the Fridtjof Nansen fund for the advancement of science. London, New York ₍etc.₎, Longmans, Green and co.; Christiania, J. Dybwad, 1900–06.

6 v. illus., plates, charts, diagrs. 30 x 23 cm.
The volumes consist of memoirs paged separately and numbered consecutively as published, without regard to the systematic arrangement.

Franz Josef land, by A. G. Narhorst.—IV. An account of the birds, by R. Collett and F. Nansen.—V. *Crustacea*, by G. O. Sars. 1900.
vol. II. VI. Astronomical observations arranged and reduced under the supervision of H. Geelmuyden.—VII. Terrestrial magnetism, by A. S. Steen.—VIII. Results of the pendulum observations and some remarks on the constitution of the earth's crust, by O. E. Schiøtz. 1901.
vol. III. IX. The oceanography of the North polar basin, by F. Nansen.—X. On hydrometers and the surface tension of liquids, by F. Nansen. 1902.
vol. IV. XI. *Diatomaceæ* from the ice-floes and plankton of the Arctic ocean, by H. H. Gran.—XII. The lower Silurian at Khabarova, by Johan Kiær.—XIII. The bathymetrical features of the North Polar seas, with a discussion of the continental shelves and previous oscillations of the shore-line, by F. Nansen. 1904.
vol. V. XIV. On the bottom deposits of the North Polar sea, by O. B. Bøggild. With appendix I: Analyses of the bottom deposits, by O. Heidenreich and C. J. J. Fox. Appendix II: *Thalamophora* of the bottom deposits and the mud from the ice surface, by Hans Kiær.—XV. On deadwater: being a description of the so-called phenomenon often hindering the headway and navigation of ships in Norwegian fjords, and elsewhere, and an experimental investigation of its causes, etc., by V. W. Ekman. With a preface by V. Bjerknes.—XVI. *Protozoa* on the ice-floes of the North Polar sea, by F. Nansen. 1906.
vol. VI. XVII. Meteorology, by H. Mohn. 1905.
1. Scientific expeditions. 2. Arctic regions. 3. "Fram" expedition, 1st, 1893–96. I. Fridtjof Nansens fond til videnskabens fremme. II. Title.

Library of Congress   Q115.N89   1—11165

MdBP Nh
WaU PBm OClWHi OrCS CaBVaU DAS DN PPAN PPAmP
NN 0015045   DLC MeB NcD CU OCl MiU OU OO CLSU ICJ

Nansen, Fridtjof, 1861-
The oceanographic problems of the still unknown Arctic regions. N.Y., 1928
1-14p. 8°

(Reprint Amer. Geog. Soc., Prob. of Polar Res., Spec. Publ. No. 7)

NN 0015046   MWA

Nansen, Fridtjof, 1861-1930.
... The oceanography of the North polar basin, by Fridtjof Nansen ... ₍London, New York, Longmans, Green, and co.; etc., etc.,₎ 1902.

3 p. l. xi, 427 p. incl. tables. XXXIII pl. (incl. diagrs., charts) 29½ x 23ᶜᵐ. (The Norwegian North polar expedition, 1893–1896. Scientific results, ed. by Fridtjof Nansen. vol. III ₍no. IX₎)

1. Arctic regions. 2. Arctic ocean.
                                                      A 21—896
Chicago. Univ. Library   Q115.N8 vol. 3
for Library of Congress   ₍a41c1₎

NN 0015047   ICU MB PPAN

Nansen, Fridtjof, 1861-
... On hydrometers and the surface tension of liquids, by Fridtjof Nansen. ₍London, New York, Longmans, Green, and co.; etc., etc.,₎ 1902₎

87, ₍1₎ p. illus. 29½ x 23ᶜᵐ. (The Norwegian North polar expedition, 1893–1896. Scientific results, ed. by Fridtjof Nansen. vol. III ₍no. X₎)
Half-title.

1. Hydrometer. 2. Capillarity.
                                                      A 21—899
Title from Univ. of Chicago   Q115.N8 vol. 3 Printed by L. C.

NN 0015048   ICU MB

V
559.8   Nansen, Fridtjof, 1861-1930.
N188o   On North polar problems. By Dr.Fridtjof Nansen.
          ₍London, Royal geographical society, 1907₎

          p.₍469₎-487,585-601. maps (1 fold.) diagrs.
Rare Book   23ᶜᵐ.
  Room   Caption title.
          "From 'The Geographical journal' for November and December, 1907."

1.North pole. 2.Glaciers - Arctic regions.
I.Title: North polar problems.

NN 0015049   CSt

V
551.36   Nansen, Fridtjof, 1861-1930.
N188o   ...Oscillations of shore-lines. By Prof. Dr. Fridtjof Nansen... ₍London and Beccles, Printed by W.Clowes and sons,limited, 1905₎
          cover-title, ₍604₎-616,₍1₎ p. fold.
Rare Book   profile. 24½ᶜᵐ.
  Room   Seal of Royal geographical society at head of title.
          "From 'The Geographical journal' for December, 1905."

1. Shore-lines.   2.Coasts - Norway. I.Title.

NN 0015050   CSt

919.8   NANSEN, Fridtjof, 1861-1930.
N15o   ... Over Grønland og Polhavet. Minne-utgave... Oslo, H. Aschehoug & co. (W. Nygaard) 1930-32 (v.1, 1932)

          3v. illus., plates, ports., maps (part fold.) 25cm.

          "Revidert utgave ved Bjørn Helland-Hansen."
          Contents.- 1. På ski over Grønland. Eskimoliv.- 2.-3. Fram over Polhavet.

1. Greenland. Description and travel.
2. Eskimos. Greenland. 3. Fram (Ship)
4. Arctic regions. I. Helland-Hansen, Bjørn, 1877- . II. Title.

NN 0015052   MnU

919.8   Nansen, Fridtjof, 1861-1930.
N15ol   Over Grønland og polhavet. ₍Rev. utg. ved Bjørn Helland-Hansen₎ Oslo, Aschehoug, 1942.
          v.

          Contents.- v.1. På ski over Grønland. Eskimoliv.-

NN 0015053   WaU

Nansen, Fridtjof, 1861-
... På ski over Grønland; omarbeidet utgave. Oslo, H. Aschehoug & co., 1928.

3 p. l., 170 p. front., illus. (incl. ports.) map. 20ᶜᵐ.

"I foreliggende bok har forfatteren søkt å gi, i en sammentrengt form, selve fortellingen om den første ferd over Grønland."—Pref.

1. Greenland—Descr. & trav. 2. Arctic regions. I. Title.

Library of Congress   G742.N17 1928   29—4067

NN 0015054   DLC

Nansen, Fridtjof, 1861-
På ski over Grønland... Oslo: H. Aschehoug & Co., 1928.
170 p. front. (port.), illus., map. rev. ed. 12°.

1. Arctic expeditions, 1888. 2. Green-land—Descr. and trav., 1800-1900.
3. Title.
N. Y. P. L.   May 9, 1929

NN 0015055   NN

VOLUME 405

Nansen, Fridtjof, 1861–1930.
... Paa ski over Grønland, en skildring af den Norske Grønlands-ekspedition 1888–89; med illustrationer af A. Bloch, Th. Holmboe, Eiv. Nielsen og E. Werenskiold samt 4 farvelagte karter. Kristiania, H. Aschehoug & co., 1890.

xii p., 1 l., 704 p. incl. front., illus., plates, ports. port., fold. maps. 23ᶜᵐ.

"Skiløbningen, dens historie og udvikling": p. ₍72₎–127.

1. Greenland—Descr. & trav. 2. Arctic regions. 3. Skis and skirunning. ı. Norske Grønlands-ekspedition, 1888–1889. ıı. Title.

Library of Congress　　　　G742.N17

13—19254

NN　0015056　　DLC WaU NdU WaS CtY

919.8
N15pS
Nansen, Fridtjof, 1861–1930.
På skidor genom Grönland; en skildring af den Norska Grönlands-expeditionen 1888–89. Med illustrationer af A. Bloch, Th. Holmboe, E. Nielsen och E. Werenskiold samt 4 förglagda kartor. Bemyndigad svensk öfversättning af O. W. Alund. Stockholm, Bonnier ₍1890₎
671 p. illus., plates, ports., fold. maps.

1. Greenland - Description and travel. 2. Arctic regions. 3. Skis and skiing. I. Norske Grønlands -ekspedition, 1888–1889. II. Title.

NN　0015057　　WaU

Nansen, Fridtjof, 1861–
Pimeassa ja pakkasessa; suomennos. Helsinki, Kustannososakeyhtio kirja ₍1923₎ ꟼ
₍68 p.₎ port. pl.

(Matkoja ja seikkailuja ... no. 4)

NN　0015058　　OCl

Nansen, Fridtjof, 1861–1930.

League of nations.
... Plan d'établissement des réfugiés arméniens. Exposé général et documents principaux. ₍Genève, Imp. Kundig, 1927₎

Nansen Fridtjof, 1861–1930.
Pohjan pimeillä perillä. Norjalainen naposeuturethi 1893–1896. Otto Sverdrupin kirjoittamalla lisäyksellä. (Finish) tr. by T. Pakkala. Hels, 1897.
2 vols. O.

NN　0015060　　WaS

NANSEN, Fridtjof, *1861–*
La première traversée du Grönland. 1886. Illus. Portrs. Map.

(Tour du monde. Vol. 61, pp. 129–208. Paris, 1891.)
Abrégé d'après l'édition norvégienne, par Charles Rabot.

NN　0015061　　MB

Nansen, Fridtjof, 1861–
... *Protozoa* on the ice-floes of the North polar sea, by Fridtjof Nansen ... ₍London, New York, Longmans, Green, and co.; etc., etc., 1906₎

22 p. viii pl. 30 x 23ᶜᵐ. (The Norwegian North polar expedition, 1893–1896. Scientific results, ed. by Fridtjof Nansen. vol. v ₍no. xvɪɪ₎)

Half-title.
Each plate preceded by leaf with descriptive letterpress.

1. Protozoa—Arctic regions.

A 21–905

Title from Univ. of Chicago　Q115.N8 vol. 5　Printed by L. C.

NN　0015062　　ICU MB

Nansen, Fridtjof, 1861–1930.

International labor office, *Geneva.*
... Rapport du dr. Fridtjof Nansen, président de la commission chargée d'étudier la question du placement des réfugiés arméniens. ₍Genève? 1925₎

Nansen, Fridtjof, 1861–1930.
... Rapport sur le rapatriement des prisonniers de guerre, par le dr. Nansen, haut commissaire de la Société. ₍Report on the repatriation of prisoners of war by Dr. Nansen, high commissioner of the League ₍of nations₎₎ ₍n. p., 1921₎

6, 6 numb. l. 32½ᶜᵐ.

At head of title: A. 86. 1921.
Autographed from type-written copy; leaves numbered in duplicate; French and English.

1. Repatriation. ı. League of nations.
(L. of N. author file Brv; topic file C: Prisoners of war, Repatriation)

Library of Congress　　　JX5141.N3

CA 22–609 Unrev'd

NN　0015064　　DLC

Nansen, Fridtjof, 1861–
FOR OTHER EDITIONS
SEE MAIN ENTRY
Conference of government representatives to consider proposals for the settlement of refugees in overseas countries, *Geneva*, 1927.
... Réfugiés arméniens et russes. ₍Genève₎ Imp. Kundig, 1927.

D638
.R9A6
1922b
Nansen, Fridtjof, 1861–1930.

League of Nations. *High Commissioner for Refugees (1921–1930)*
Réfugiés russes. Discours du dʳ Fridtjof Nansen, Haut commissaire de la Société des Nations, à la séance de la Cinquième commission de l'Assemblée le 15 septembre 1922, en supplément de son rapport (A. 84. 1922) Russian refugees. Speech delivered by Fridtjof Nansen, High Commissioner of the League of Nations, to the Fifth Committee of the Assembly on September 15th, 1922, in amplification of his report (A. 84. 1922). ₍Genève, 1922₎

Nansen, Fridtjof, 1831–

League of nations.
... Réfugiés russes, arméniens, assyriens, assyro-chaldéens et turcs. Rapport à la dixième Assemblée. ₍Genève₎ Imp. Granchamp, 1929.

Nansen, Fridtjof, 1861–1930.

League of nations.
... Réfugiés russes et arméniens. Rapport à la huitième session ordinaire de l'Assemblée. ₍Genève₎ Imp. Kundig, 1927.

Nansen, Fridtjof, 1861–1930.
... Repatriation of prisoners of war. Report presented by Dr. Nansen, and adopted by the Council of the League of nations, meeting in London, on 16th June 1920. ₍n. p., 1920₎

5 numb. l., 1 l. 33ᶜᵐ.

Caption title.
League of nations' official no.: 20/41/33.
Mimeographed.
Previously issued as League document 20/4/108.
Issued also in French.

1. European war, 1914–1918—Prisoners and prisons. 2. Repatriation. ı. League of nations.

A 47–2891

Woodrow Wilson memorial　　library
for Library of Congress　　₍2₎

NN　0015069　　NNUN-W

Nansen, Fridtjof, 1861–1930.
... Repatriation of prisoners of war. Report by Dr. Nansen. ₍Geneva, 1921₎

4 numb. l. 33ᶜᵐ.

League of nations official no.: C.188.M.115.1921.
Mimeographed.
Issued also in French.

1. European war, 1914–1918—Prisoners and prisons. 2. Repatriation. ı. League of nations.

A 47–2887

Woodrow Wilson memorial　　library
for Library of Congress　　₍2₎

NN　0015070　　NNUN-W

Nansen, Fridtjof, 1861–1930.

International labor office, *Geneva.*
... Report by Dr. Fridtjof Nansen, president of the commission appointed to study the question of the settlement of Armenian refugees. ₍Geneva? 1925₎

Nansen, Fridtjof, 1861–1930.
Report... of an Enquiry by a committee of experts

League of nations.
... Scheme for the settlement of Armenian refugees. General survey and principal documents. ₍Geneva, Imp. Kundig, 1927₎

Nansen, Fridtjof, 1861–1930.

League of nations.
... Report on the work of the High commission for refugees presented by Dr. Fridtjof Nansen to the fourth Assembly. ₍Genève, Imp. Jent. s. a., 1923₎

Nansen, Fridtjof, 1861–
Rusland og freden, av Fridtjof Nansen... ₍Kristiania: J. Dybwads forlag, 1923. xi, 151 p. illus. (incl. ports.) 2. ed. 8°.

1. Economic history—Russia.
N. Y. P. L.

August 6, 1926

NN　0015074　　NN FU MH WaS

Nansen, Fridtjof, 1861–
Russia & peace, by Dr. Fridtjof Nansen. London, G. Allen & Unwin ltd. ₍1923₎

162 p., 1 l. 19ᶜᵐ.

"In this book the endeavour has been made to render ... a brief account of the existing social, and especially economic, conditions in this vast and unhappy country, in the light of my impressions and those of my collaborators during the years that we have worked there."—Pref.

1. Russia—Econ. condit. 2. Russia—Soc. condit. ı. Title.

Library of Congress　　　HC335.N26

24—2642

NN　0015075　　OCl OClW MiU PPL NjP NN
　　　　DLC DNW PPT CaBVaU WaU KEmT CtY NIC

Nansen, Fridtjof, 1861–
Russia & peace, by Dr. Fridtjof Nansen. New York, The Macmillan company, 1924.

162 p., 1 l. 19¼ᶜᵐ.

"In this book the endeavour has been made to render ... a brief account of the existing social, and especially economic, conditions in this vast and unhappy country, in the light of my impressions and those of my collaborators during the years that we have worked there."—Pref.

1. Russia—Economic conditions. 2. Russia—Social conditions. ı. Title.

A 24–790

Title from N. Y. State　　Libr.　Printed by L. C.

NN　0015076　　PU PPFr MB NN
　　　　N TxU DAU WaS OrU NjN NcD PP OU OCl

Nansen, Fridtjof, 1861–1930.

League of nations.
... Russian and Armenian refugees. Report to the eighth ordinary session of the Assembly. ₍Geneva₎ Imp. Kundig, 1927.

Nansen, Fridtjof, 1861–1930.

League of nations.
... Russian, Armenian, Assyrian, Assyro-Chaldean, and Turkish refugees. Report to the tenth Assembly. ₍Geneva, Imp. Kundig, 1929.

VOLUME 405

Nansen, Fridtjof, 1861–1930.
... Russian refugees. Acceptance by Dr. Nansen of the post of High commissioner. ⌊Geneva⌋ 1921.
1 l. 33ᶜᵐ.
Caption title.
At head of title: ... League of nations.
Official no.: C.337.M.239.1921.
Mimeographed.
Issued also in French.

1. League of nations. High commissioner for refugees (1921–1930)
A 47–2911

Woodrow Wilson memorial   library
for Library of Congress   ⌊2⌋

NN   0015079   NNUN–W

Nansen, Fridtjof, 1861–1930.
League of nations.
... Russian refugees; general report on the work accomplished up to March 15th, 1922, by Dr. Fridtjof Nansen, high commissioner of the League of nations. ⌊Lausanne, Printed for the "League of nations" by Imprimeries réunies s. a., 1922⌋

Nansen, Fridtjof, 1861–1930.
League of nations.
... Russian refugees. Report by Dr. Nansen. ⌊Geneva⌋ 1923.

N1582
Nansen, Fridtjof, 1861–1930.
Russland und der friede. Leipzig, F. A. Brockhaus, 1923.
188 p. illus., ports.

1. Russia – Econ. condit. 2. Reconstruction (1914–1939) – Russia.

NN   0015082   NNC IU IEN MH ICarbS CSt–H

DK265
.N965
Nansen, Fridtjof, 1861–1930.
Russland und die welt, von Fridtjof Nansen, Gerhart Hauptmann, Maxim Gorki. Berlin, Verlag für politik und wirtschaft ⌊1922⌋

Nansen, Fridtjof, 1861–
...Science and the purpose of life... London: Watts & Co., 1912. 16 p. 12°. (Pamphlets for the million. no. 9.)
"Issued for the Rationalist Press Assoc., Ltd."

1. Rationalism.
N Y P L

NN   0015084   NN

Nansen, Fridtjof, 1861–
... Siberien ein zukunftsland. Leipzig, F. A. Brockhaus, 1914.
x, 383 p. front., plates, ports., fold. maps. 23½ᶜᵐ.

1. Siberia—Descr. & trav. I. Title.

Library of Congress   DK755.N2
17–3468

NN   0015085   DLC NcD OC1 IU

Nansen, Fridtjof, 1861–
... Sibirien, ein zukunftsland. 2. aufl. Leipzig, F. A. Brockhaus, 1916.
x, 383 p. front., plates, ports., fold. maps. 23½ᶜᵐ.

1. Siberia—Descr. & trav. I. Title.
21–17689

Library of Congress   DK755.N2 1916

NN   0015086   DLC CaBVaU MoU CU IU GASC

DK 755
.N214
NANSEN, FRIDTJOF, 1861–1930
Sibirien, ein Zukunftsland. 3. Aufl. Leipzig, F.A. Brockhaus, 1919.
383 p. illus.

1. Siberia--Descr. I. Title.

NN   0015087   InU

Nansen, Fridtjof, 1861–   957 R500
142286 ... Sibirien, ein Zukunftsland. Vierte Auflage. Leipzig, F. A. Brockhaus, 1922.
viii, 383 p. front., plates, ports., 3 fold. maps. 23½ᶜᵐ.
At head of title: Fridtjof Nansen.

NN   0015088   ICJ TNJ MiU

Nansen, Fridtjof, 1861–
Some oceanographical results of the expedition with the "Michael Sars" headed by Dr. J. Hjort in the summer of 1900. Preliminary report by Fridtjof Nansen. Christiania: A. W. Brøgger, 1901. p. ⌊129–⌋161. charts (part col'd). 8°.
Title from cover.
Repr.: Nyt Magazin for Naturvidenskab, Bind 39, Heft 2.

1. Ocean.—Expeditions, 1900.   2. Ocean.—Exploration.
N. Y. P. L.   August 23, 1922.

NN   0015089   NN CtY PPAmP MH

Nansen, Fridtjof, 1861–1930.
... Speech by Dr. Nansen. ⌊Geneva, 1927⌋
2 p. 33 cm.
Caption title.
At head of title: ... League of nations. Extract from the minutes of the twentieth meeting of the eighth ordinary session of the Assembly (September 26th, 1927)
Official no.: C.L.150.1927.IV.Annex.
An "annex" accompanying a circular letter (official no.: CL.150.-1927.IV) sent out by the League of nations to its members.
Issued also in French.
An appeal for support of the settlement scheme for Armenian refugees.
1. European war, 1914–1918—Refugees. 2. Armenians.   I. League of nations.
A 47–4032

Woodrow Wilson   Memorial Library
for Library of Congress   ⌊a47c1⌋

NN   0015090   NNUN–W

Nansen, Fridtjof, 1861–
... Spitzbergen, mit 180 zeichnungen, karten und diagrammen vom verfasser. Leipzig, F. A. Brockhaus, 1921.
327, ⌊1⌋ p. front., illus., plates, ports., maps (1 double) diagrs. 23½ cm.
"Dieses buch schildert eine fahrt nach der Bäreninsel und nach Spitzbergen im jahre 1912."

1. Spitzbergen—Descr. & trav. 2. Bear Island, Arctic Ocean.
G780.N6   23—7041

NN   0015091   DLC IU ICJ

Nansen, Fridtjof, 1861–1930.
... Spitzbergen; mit 180 zeichnungen, karten und diagrammen vom verfasser. 2. aufl. Leipzig, F.A. Brockhaus, 1922.
327 p. front., illus., maps. 23 cm.
1. Spitsbergen.

NN   0015092   CU

NANSEN, Fridtjof, 1861–
Spitzbergen waters. Oceanographic observations during the cruise of the "Veslemoy" to Spitzbergen in 1912. Christiania, J. Dybwad, 1915.
pp.⌊5⌋–132.

NN   0015093   MH–Z

Nansen, Fridtjof, 1861–
Sporting days in wild Norway, pages from my diary, by Dr. Fridtjof Nansen. With an introduction by W. Branch Johnson, illustrated by the author. London, T. Butterworth, ltd. ⌊1925⌋
270 p. incl. front. illus. (incl. map) 21ᶜᵐ.

1. Sports—Norway. I. Johnson, W. Branch. II. Title.
Library of Congress   SK209.N3   25–14064

NN   0015094   DLC TNJ CU CtY NN Or

---

x Fram over polhaver. Russ

Microfilm Nansen, Fridtjof, 1861–1930.
21729 ... Среди льда и ночи. Переводъ съ норвежскаго В. Семе-
G нова. Съ приложеніемъ біографическаго очерка жизни Нансена, составленнаго по соч. Бреггера и Рольфсена. С. Петербургъ, Изд. П. П. Сойкина ⌊1897⌋
212 p. illus. 21 cm. (Полезная библіотека)
"Нашъ очеркъ не составляетъ ... дословнаго перевода ... 'Fram over polhaver' ... Это только извлеченіе, составленное ... возможно ближе къ подлиннику."

1. Arctic regions. I. "Fram" Expedition. 1st, 1893–1896. II. Title.
Title transliterated: Sredi l'da i nochi.
LC copy replaced by microfilm.   53–52672

NN   0015095   DLC

Nansen, Fridtjof, 1861–
The strandflat and isostasy. By Fridtjof Nansen. (With 170 illustrations and maps in the text) ... Utgit for Fridtjof Nansens fond. Kristiania, I kommission hos J. Dybwad, 1922.
viii, 313 p. illus. 27½ᶜᵐ. (In Videnskapsselskapets i Kristiania. Skrifter. I. Matematisk-naturvidenskabelig klasse, 1921, no. 11)
"Literature": p. 307–313.

1. Isostasy. I. Fridtjof Nansens fond til videnskabens fremme. II. Title.
[AS283.O56]   A 29–433
Title from John Crerar   Libr. Printed by L. C.

NN   0015096   ICJ CtY CSt MiU NN MH

Nansen (Fridtjof) [1861–]. The structure and combination of the histological elements of the central nervous system. pp. 29–214, 1 l., 11 pl. 8°. [*Bergens*, 1887.]
Cutting from: Bergens Mus. Aarsber. 1886, Bergen, 1887.

NN   0015097   DNLM OC1W PPWI

Film
1022
no. 4
NANSEN, Fridtjof, 1861–
The structure and combination of the histological elements of the central nervous system. ⌊Bergen, 1887⌋
p. ⌊29⌋–214. illus.
Film copy.
Reprinted from Bergens museums aarsberetning, 1886.
Bibliography: p. ⌊172⌋–193.

NN   0015098   DNLM

Nansen, Fridtjof. Svalbard. *Extr. fr.* Norsk geografisk tidsskrift. Bd. I, 1926, pp. 1–30.   IcB51N188
Principally directed against G. Holm's article of 1925. See *Catal.* II, 106.

NN   0015099   NIC

VOLUME 405

Nansen, Fridtjof, 1861-1930, joint author.

Helland-Hansen, Bjørn, 1877-
Temperatur-schwankungen des nordatlantischen ozeans und in der atmosphäre; einleitende studien über die ursachen der klimatologischen schwankungen. von Bjørn Helland-Hansen und Fridtjof Nansen. Mit 48 tafeln und 97 figuren im text ... Kristiania, In kommission bei J. Dybwad, 1917.

Nansen, Fridtjof, 1861-1930, joint author.

Helland-Hansen, Bjørn, 1877-
... Temperature variations in the north Atlantic ocean and in the atmosphere. introductory studies on the cause of climatological variations (with forty-eight plates), by Bjørn Helland-Hansen and Fridtjof Nansen ... City of Washington, Smithsonian institution, 1920.

Nansen, Fridtjof, 1861-
Through Siberia, the land of the future, by Fridtjof Nansen ... Tr. by Arthur G. Chater ... London, W. Heinemann, 1914.
xvi, 447, ₁1₎ p., 1 l. front., plates, ports., 3 fold. maps, diagrs. 25½ᶜᵐ.

1. Siberia—Descr. & trav.   i. Chater, Arthur G., tr.   ii. Title.

14—30976

Library of Congress   DK755.N3

OOxM OU PPA ICJ KEmT PP PU ScU MU WaS IdU
NN 0015102   DLC DAS CSt-H NjP KyLoU CU AU PBm OC1

Nansen, Fridtjof, 1861-
Through Siberia, the land of the future, by Fridtjof Nansen ... tr. by Arthur G. Chater ... New York, Frederick A. Stokes company; London, W. Heinemann, 1914.
xvi, 477, ₁1₎ p., 1 l. incl. front. plates, ports., fold. maps, diagrs. 25½ᶜᵐ.
$5.00
Printed in Great Britain.

1. Siberia—Descr. & trav.   i. Chater, Arthur G., tr.   ii. Title.

15—10968

Library of Congress   DK755.N3 1914 a

MiU Or WaT
NN CaBVaU LU OrCS OrU NcU IEN NBuU MtBuM NIC OrPS
NN 0015103   DLC DN DI-GS NjNbS PHC PPL PU PP OO MB

Nansen, Fridtjof, 1861-1930.
... Through the Caucasus to the Volga; translated by G. C. Wheeler ... New York, W. W. Norton & company, inc. ₁1931₎
255 p. front., plates, ports. 21½ᶜᵐ.
"First published in Norwegian under the title 'Gjennem Kaukasus til Volga', 1929."
"Printed in Great Britain."

1. Caucasus—Descr. & trav.   i. Wheeler, Gerald Clair William Camden, tr.   ii. Title.

31—26733

Library of Congress   DK511.C1N27

₍5-5₎   914.79

PP PHC PPA PU WaE CaBViP WaT WaSp WaS OrU CaBVa
NN 0015104   DLC FTaSU MH NIC NjN OC1 MB IU NN CU

Nansen, Fridtjof, 1861-
...Unter Robben und Eisbären; meine ersten Erlebnisse im Eismeer... Leipzig: F. A. Brockhaus, 1926. x, 369 p. incl. tables. front. (port.). illus. (incl. plans). 8°.

231161A. 1. Sport—Arctic regions.   2. Seals and seal fisheries—Arctic regions. 3. Bear, Polar. 4. Arctic regions—Descr. and trav.
N. Y. P. L.   April 19, 1926

NN 0015105   NN

Nansen, Fridtjob, 1861-1930.
... V noci in ledu; priredil Fran Albrecht. Ljubljana, Zalozila tiskovna zadruga, 1928.
106, ₍1₎ p. plates, map.

NN 0015106   OC1

910.9   Nansen, Fridtjof, 1861-1930.
N188Yr   Vers le pôle, traduit et abrégé par Charles Rabot. 100 illustrations, d'après les photographies et les dessins de l'explorateur. Paris, Ernest Flammarion, éditeur, n.d.
₁vii₎ –viii, 466p. fronts. (port.) illus. 23cm. (Édition illustrée.)

1. North pole. 2. Arctic regions. 3. Scientific expeditions. x. ref. Polar expeditions.

NN 0015107   LNHT

NANSEN, FRIDTJOF, 1861-1930.
...Vers le pôle; traduit et abrégé par Charles Rabot... Paris: E. Flammarion₍, 1897₎. viii, 424 p. incl. front. (port.) illus. (incl. facsim., maps.) 22½cm.

600127A. 1. Arctic expeditions, 1893-1896. 2. "Fram" ₍ship₎. I. Rabot, Charles, 1856-   , ed.

NN 0015108   NN MeB

Nansen, Fridtjof, 1861-1930.
Во мракѣ ночи и во льдахъ; путешествіе Норвежской экспедиціи на кораблѣ "Фрамъ" къ Сѣверному полюсу. Полный переводъ со шведскаго М. Вечеслова, подъ ред. Н. Березина. С.-Петербургъ ₍Изд. О. Н. Поповой₎ 1897.
2 v. illus., ports., fold. maps (1 in pocket) 24 cm.
Vol. 2 translated from the English.
Translation of Fram over polhaver.

1. Arctic regions.   i. "Fram" Expedition. 1st, 1893-1896. ii. Title.
Title transliterated: Vo mrakîe nochi i vo l'dakh.

G700 1893.N28   53-52673 rev

NN 0015109   DLC

S21g   Nansen, Fridtjof, 1861-1930.
162   The waters of the north-eastern North Atlantic. Investigations made during the cruise of the Frithjof, of the Norwegian royal navy, in July 1910 ... Leipzig,1913.
2p.l.,₍139p.incl.illus.(incl.diagrs.) tables. 17 charts on 12 fold.pl.(part.col.) 23½cm.
(Hydrographisches Supplement (2.Ser. ₍no.3₎) zu Bd.IV der Internationalen Revue der gesamten Hydrobiologie und Hydrographie)
"Literature": p.135-139.

NN 0015110   CtY CaBVaU DAS

Nansen, Fridtjof, 1861-1930.

Mohn, H₍enrik₎ 1835-
Wissenschaftliche ergebnisse von Dr. F. Nansens durchquerung von Grönland 1888. Von Prof. H. Mohn ... und Dr. Fridtjof Nansen. Mit sechs tafeln und zehn figuren im text ... Gotha, J. Perthes, 1892.

Nansen, Fridtjof, 1861-1930
see also **Nansen memorial fund.**

Nansen, Hans Leierdahl, 1764-1821
Bemærkninger over det, den svenske Rigsdags Constitutions-Committees Betænkning i anledning af Hans Kgl. Majestæts naadige proposition til en rigssact, som bilag tilføiede dictamen af Hr.Axel Gabr.Silverstolpe, indleverede til Norges ordentlige Storthing d.6te Sept., 1815. Christiania, Trykt hos Jacob Lehmann, 1815
44 p.

NN 0015113   MH

Nansen, Liv.

See

Høyer, Liv (Nansen),1893-

D   Nansen, Odd, 1901-
805   Day after day. Translated from the
.G3   Norwegian by Katherine John. London, Putnam
N352   ₍1949₎
1949   600 p. illus. 22cm.

Translation of "Fra dag til dag."
Published in the U.S.A. as "From day to day."

1. World War, 1939-1945 - Prisoners and prisons, German. 2. World War, 1939-1945 - Personal narratives, Norwegian.   I. John, Katherine (Gower) tr. II.   Title.

NN 0015115   GU PU WaU

Nansen, Odd, 1901-
Fra dag til dag, med illustrasjoner av forfatteren. Oslo, Dreyer ₍1947, ᵉ1946₎
3 v. illus., ports. 25 cm.

1. World War, 1939-1945 — Prisoners and prisons, German. 2. World War, 1939-1945—Personal narratives, Norwegian.   i. Title.

D805.G3N35   47—29584*

NN 0015116   DLC WaU OrP

Nansen, Odd, 1901-
From day to day; tr. by Katherine John. New York, G. P. Putnam's Sons ₍1949₎
xiii, 485 p. illus., ports. 23 cm.
"This diary ... has ... been much reduced in the English version."

1. World War, 1939-1945 — Prisoners and prisons, German. 2. World War, 1939-1945—Personal narratives, Norwegian.   i. John, Katherine (Gower) tr. ii. Title.

D805.G3N352   940.547243   49-7431*

PPFr WaT PPFC
Or OrP OrU WaS WaTC Mi NNC PP PPT PHC PPL WaS
PSt AAP OU CaBVa CaBVaU IdU OrCS KMK MtBC MtU
NN 0015117   DLC ICU KU MB TxU ViU MH NIC NcU MU

Nansen, Odd, 1901-
I ellevte time; en appell til Europarådet om det tyske flyktningeproblem. Oslo, Dreyer ₍1951₎
89 p. 20 cm.

1. Refugees, German.   i. Title.

HN449.N25   51-30948 ‡

NN 0015118   DLC MnU IU NN

Nansen, Odd, 1901-
Koncentrationslägren i Hitler-riket, av Odd Nansen och Tim Greve. ₍Översättning från författarnas norska manuskript av Ulla Weibust₎ Stockholm, Bonnier ₍1951, ᵉ1950₎
59 p. 18 cm. (Studentföreningen Verdandis småskrifter, nr 510. Politik och sociala problem)

1. Concentration camps—Germany.   i. Title.
AC50.U73 nr. 510

————— Copy 2.   DD256.5.N3   52-19808 ‡

NN 0015119   DLC MiU

VOLUME 405

Nansen, Odd, 1901–
　...Nestekjærlighetens front...　Oslo, Dreyer, 1947.　18 p.
20cm.

　1. United nations.

NN　0015120　NN

D805
.G5N354　Nansen, Odd, 1901–
1949
　　Von Tag zu Tag, ein Tagebuch. ₍Aus dem
　Norwegischen übertragen von Ingeborg Goebel₎
　Hamburg, H. Dulk ₍1949₎
　363 p.　21cm.
　Translation of Fra dag tildag.

　　1. World War, 1939–1945—Prisoners and prisons,
　German. 2. World War, 1939–1945—Personal narra-
　tives, Norwegian. I. Goebel, Ingeborg, tr.　II.
　Title.

NN　0015121　ViU

PT8175　Nansen, Peter, 1861–1918.
.N2　　Samlede skrifter. ₍København₎ Gyldendalske
1908　Boghandel, Nordisk Forlag, 1908–09.
　　3 v.
　　Contents.—v.1. Julies dagbog. Maria. Guds
　fred.—v.2. Et hjem. Fra rusaaret. Judiths
　aegteskab.—v.3. Noveller. Skitser. Drama-
　tiske smaating.

NN　0015122　ICU CU IU NcU CtY

Nansen, Peter, 1861–1918.
　... Samlede skrifter. Anden udgave ... Kjøbenhavn og
　Kristiania, Gyldendal, 1917.
　　3 v. 2 mounted ports.　19ᶜᵐ.
　　"Denne 2. udgave ... fremtræder som et uforandret optryk af 1.
　udgave fra 1908–09."—v. 1, p. ₍5₎
　Bibliographical note at end of each volume.
　　CONTENTS.—1. bind. Julies dagbog. Maria. Guds fred.—2. bind.
　Et hjem. Fra rusaaret. Judiths ægteskab.—3. bind. Noveller. Skitser.
　Dramatiske smaating.

A 32–2789

Title from Univ. of Mich.　　　Printed by L. C.

NN　0015123　MiU

PT8175
.N2　Nansen, Peter, 1861–1918.
1920　　Samlede skrifter. 3. udg. Kjøbenhavn,
　Gyldendal, 1920.
　　3 v. 2 mounted ports.　19cm.

　　CONTENTS.—1. bind. Julies dagbog. Maria.
　Guds fred.—2. bind. Et hjem. Fra rusaaret.
　Judiths aegteskab.—3. bind. Noveller.
　Skitser. Dramatiske smaating.

NN　0015124　ViU MH

Nansen, Péter, 1861–1918.
　　A Menthe testvérek. Maria, a szerelem
　könyve; fordította Varságh János.　Budapest,
　Franklin-Társulat [194–?]
　164 p.
　Hungarian.

NN　0015125　OCl

Nansen, Peter, 1861–*1918.*
　... Æventyr om smaa og store. Kjøbenhavn, H. Kop-
　pel, 1917.
　155 p., 1 l.　17½ᶜᵐ.　kr. 3.50
　"Oplag: 2700 ekspl."
　CONTENTS.—Tut.—Postkatten.—Skrivebordstæppet.—En gammel konge,
　en stor digter og en lille pige.—Nationalsangen.—Den vingeløse engel.

　1. Fairy tales.　1. Title.

Library of Congress　　　PT8175.N2A7 1917
18–13838

NN　0015126　DLC

Nansen, Peter, 1861–1918.
　...Æventyr om Smaa og Store.　Kjøbenhavn: H. Koppel,
1917.　155 p., 1 l.　16°.
　On cover: Fjerde Tusinde.

　1. Fiction (Danish). 2. Title.
N. Y. P. L.

NN　0015127　NN

Nansen, Peter, *1861–1918.*　1896, Berlin.
　Aus dem ersten Universitätsjahre.

NN　0015128　NjP

PT8175　Nansen, Peter, 1861–1918.
N2A6　　Ausgewählte Werke. ₍Autorisierte Übertra-
1919　gung von Mathilde Mann₎　Berlin, S.Fischer,
　1919.
　　3 v. port.　19cm.
　　Each vol. has also special t.p.
　　Vol.2 lacks ed. statement.
　　Contents.—1.Bd.Jugend und Liebe; ausge-
　wählte Novellen. 8.–11. Tausend.—2.Bd.Thea-
　ter. 5.–7.Tausend.—3.Bd.Die Romane des Her-
　zens. 5.–7. Tausend.

　　I.Mann, Mathilde (Scheven), 1859–

NN　0015129　CSt PPG RPB InU

Nansen, Peter, 1861–
　... Brødrene Menthe; trykt som manuskript. Kjøben-
　havn, Fr. Bagges kgl. hofbogtrykkeri, 1915.
　188 p. front. (port.) 24ᶜᵐ.　kr. 20

　1. Title.

Library of Congress　　　PT8175.N2B7 1915
17–5400

NN　0015130　DLC

PT8175　Nansen, Peter, 1861–1918.
N2B7　　Brødrene Menthe. 2. opl. Kjøbenhavn, Gyldendal, 1916.
1916　199 p.

NN　0015131　CU

Nansen, Peter, 1861–
　　Brødrene Menthe.　Kjøbenhavn: Gyldendalske Boghandel,
1916.　199 p.　3. ed.　12°.
　Author's name at head of title.

　1. Fiction (Danish). 2. Title.
N. Y. P. L.　　　February 15, 1917.

NN　0015132　NN

PT
8175　Nansen, Peter, 1861–1918.
N2　　Brødrene Menthe. 4. opl. Kjøbenhavn og
B7　Kristiania, Gyldendal, 1916 ₍c1915₎
1916　199 p.

NN　0015133　WaU

Nansen, Peter, 1861–
　　Die Brüder Menthe. Roman von Peter Nansen. (Neue
Rundschau. Berlin, 1916. 8°. Jahrg. 27, p. 881–900,
1033–1054, 1183–1212.)

　1. Fiction (Danish). 2. Title.
N. Y. P. L.　　　November 5, 1921.

NN　0015134　NN CSt

Nansen, Peter, *1861–1918*
　Die feuerprobe; kleine erzählungen.　Berlin, S. Fischer,
1899.
　3 p. l., 158 p.　12°.
　Original in Danish.
　CONTENTS.—Die feuerprobe.—Das erleuchtete fenster.—Die cavaliere der
jungen witwe.—Frau Beate.—Des bürgermeisters winterüberzieher.—Aus
dem lazarett.—Der stimulant.—In den hellen nächten.
1–19008—M 4

NN　0015135　DLC

Nansen, Peter, 1861–1918.
　Fra Rusaaret; Breve til og fra Stud. jur. Emil Holm, ved Peter
Nansen.　Kjøbenhavn: I. H. Schubothes Boghandels Forlag,
1892.　183 p.　12°.

605786A. 1. Fiction, Danish. I. Title.
N. Y. P. L.　　　September 12, 1932

NN　0015136　NN

PT　Nansen, Peter, 1861–1918.
8175　　Eine glückliche Ehe.　Berlin, S. Fischer,
N2　₍n.d.₎
G5　149 p.　18cm.

NN　0015137　CU–I

Nansen, Peter, 1861–
　Eine glückliche ehe.　Berlin, S. Fischer,
1894.
　3 p. l., 168 p.　19 cm.
　Tr. from the Danish by M. Mann.

NN　0015138　CtY

Nansen, Peter, *1861–*
　Eine glückliche ehe. 2. aufl. Berlin, S. Fischer, 1896.
　2 p. l., 168 p.　12°.
　Tr. from the Danish by M. Mann.

　1. Mann, Frau Mathilde (Scheven) tr.
1–G–2542

NN　0015139　DLC

PT8175　Nansen, Peter, 1861–1918.
N2G8　　Eine glückliche ehe, von Peter Nansen.
　Fünfte auflage (neuntes und zehntes tausend)
　Berlin, S. Fischer, 1905.
　　2p. ₀. ₍5₎–172p.　19cm.

NN　0015140　NBuG

PT
8175
N2　Nansen, Peter, 1861–1918.
Z5　　Eine glückliche Ehe, und andere
G52　Novellen. Leipzig, H. Fikent [1922?]
1922　245 p.

NN　0015141　WLacU

839.813
N188g　Nansen, Peter, 1861–1918.
　　Gottesfriede. 4. Aufl.　Berlin,
　S. Fischer, 1902.
　231p. 19cm.

NN　0015142　IEN

VOLUME 405

Nansen, Peter, 1861-1918.
    ... Guds fred. 2.opl. Kjøbenhavn, P. G.
Philipsens forlag, 1895.
    2 p.l., 199 p. 18¼ᶜᵐ.
    "Fjerde tusend."

NN   0015143   ViU KyU

Nansen, Peter.
    Guds Fred. Kjøbenhavn, Gyldendal, 1902.
    2 p.l., 199 p.   12°.
    3. ed.

NN   0015144   NN

Nansen, Peter, 1861-1918.
    ...Hendes Elskede; Noveller.   København: H. Koppel,
1918.   157 p., 1 l.   12°.
    At head of title: Peter Nansen.
    Contents: Hendes Elskede. Døden. Sorg. Trofasthed. De gamle fine og
de nye.

1. Fiction (Danish). 2. Title.
N. Y. P. L.   February 18, 1920.

NN   0015145   NN

Nansen, Peter, 1861-1918.
    Herman Bangs vandreaar
       see under   Bang, Herman Joachim, 1857-1912

Nansen, Peter. 1861-
    Der Hochzeitsabend.   Lustspiel in einem Aufzug.   Einzig autori-
sierte Übersetzung aus dem Dänischen von Ernst Brausewetter.
— Leipzig. Reclam. [1914.] 21 pp. [Universal-Bibliothek. 5629.]
14 cm., in 8s.

No. 7 in 4896.50.568

K1356 — T.r. — S.r.c. — Brausewetter, Ernst, tr. 1863-.

NN   0015147   MB

Nansen, Peter, 1861-1918.
    ...Judiths Ægteskab.   Kjøbenhavn: Gyldendalske Bog-
handels Forlag, 1898.   193 p.   18½cm.

652413A. 1. Drama, Danish.   I. Title.
N. Y. P. L.   August 18, 1933

NN   0015148   NN

Nansen, Peter, 1861-
    Judiths ehe; ein roman in gesprächen.   Berlin, S.
Fischer, 1899.
    3 p. l., 188 p.   12°.
    Original in Danish.
                     1-19809—M 4

NN   0015149   DLC

839.813
N188juXG   Nansen, Peter, 1861-1918.
    Judiths Ehe.   Berlin, Fischer, 1906.
    191p.   19cm.

NN   0015150   IEN

Nansen, Peter, /861-
    Jugend und Liebe; ausgewählte Novellen.   Berlin: S.
Fischer; 19—?].   328 p.   port.   12°.
    Contents: Eine glückliche Ehe.   Aus dem ersten Universitätsjahre. Die Feuer-
probe.   Das erleuchtete Fenster.   Das Bürgermeisters Winterüberzieher.   Der
Simulant.   Aus dem Tagebuch eines Verliebten.   Ein Weihnachtsmärchen.   Der
Weihnachtsbaum.   Fräulein Mimi.   Eine Ballunterhaltung.

NN   0015151   NN

Nansen, Peter, 1861-1918.
    Jugend und Liebe; ausgewählte Novellen, von Peter Nansen.
Berlin: S. Fischer, 1909.   328 p.   front. (port.)   12°.
    "Autorisierte Übertragung von Mathilde Mann."
    Contents: Vorwort von Herman Bang.   Eine glückliche Ehe.   Aus dem ersten
Universitätsjahre.   Die Feuerprobe.   Das erleuchtete Fenster.   Des Bürgermeisters
Winterüberzieher.   Der Simulant.   Aus dem Tagebuch eines Verliebten.   Ein Weih-
nachtsmärchen.   Der Weihnachtsbaum.   Fräulein Mimi.   Eine Ballunterhaltung.

1. Fiction (German).—Translations   from Danish. 2. Mann, Mathilde,
1859-   , translator. 3. Title.
N. Y. P. L.   January 16, 1923.

NN   0015152   NN

Nansen, Peter, 1861-1918
    Jugend und Liebe; ausgewählte Novellen.
Berlin, S. Fischer, 1917.

    328 p.   front. (port.)   18cm.

NN   0015153   OKentU

Nansen, Peter, 1861-1918.
    Julia naploja; forditotta Feher Margit.
Budapest, Kultus kiadasa, n.d.
    ₍220 p.₎

NN   0015154   OCl

NANSEN, Peter.
    Julies dagbog.
    1893.

NN   0015155   WaU

Nansen, Peter, 1861-1918.
    ... Julies dagbog. 2.opl. Kjøbenhavn, P. G.
Philipsens forlag, 1894.
    278 p.   18½ᶜᵐ.
    First published in the Copenhagen daily "Politikken".

NN   0015156   ViU

Nansen, Peter, 1861-1918.
    ...Julies Dagbog...   Kjøbenhavn: Gyldendalske Bog-
handels Forlag, 1900.   278 p.   3. ed.   12°.

555316A. 1. Fiction, Danish.   I. Title.
N. Y. P. L.   December 31, 1931

NN   0015157   NN

Nansen, Peter, 1861-1918.
    Julies tagebuch; roman. Berlin, S. Fischer, 1895.

    2 p. l., 235, ₍1₎ p.   19ᶜᵐ.

    I. Title.
                     1-19810
    Library of Congress   PT8175.N2J93 1895

NN   0015158   DLC

Nansen, Peter, 1861-1908.
    Julies Tagebuch.   Berlin: S. Fischer ₍19—?₎   175 p.   12°.

1. Title.
N. Y. P. L.   November 21, 1935

NN   0015159   NN

Nansen, Peter, 1861-1908.
    Julies tagebuch; roman ...   4.aufl.
...   Berlin, S.Fischer, 1908.

    253p.   19cm.

    Originally written in Danish under
title "Julies dagbog" and first published in the Copenhagen daily "Politikken."

NN   0015160   CLSU PPG

PT
8175   Nansen, Peter, 1861-1918.
N2J8   Julies Tagebuch; Roman von Peter Nansen.
1910   Berlin, G. Fischer Verlag ₍1910₎
      175p.   17 1/2 cm.   (Fischers Bibliothek
    zeitgenössischer Romane. 2. Jahrg., 8. Bd.)

      Originally published in Danish as "Julies
dagbok" and first published in the Copenhagen
daily "Politikken."

NN   0015161   NcGU TNJ

PT 8175   NANSEN,PETER,1861-1918
.N2 J9   Julies Tagebuch; Roman.   Berlin, S. Fischer
    ₍1921₎
      175 p.   (Fischers Bibliothek zeitgenössi-
scher Romane)

NN   0015162   InU

Nansen, Peter, 1861-1918.
    Julijin dnevnik; roman jedne djevojke.   Danski napisao Petar
Nansen.   Zagreb: Kr. zemaljska tiskara, 1918.   151 p.   12°.
    (Zabavna biblioteka. Kolo 9, knjiga 103.)

    Translated by N. Vavra.

1. Fiction, Danish. 2. Vavra, Nina,   translator. 3. Title.
N. Y. P. L.   January 29, 1927

NN   0015163   NN OCl

NANSEN,Peter,1862-1918.
    Korte Veje;Scener og Smaahistorier.   Kjøben-
havn,Forlagt af I.H.Schubothes Boghandel,1890.

    18 x 9 cm.

NN   0015164   MH

Nansen, Peter, 1861-1918.
    ...Kurrer paa Traaden; Telefon-Samtale...   ₍København₎
F. Bagges Kgl. Hof-Bogtrykkeri, 1908.₎   39 p.   21cm.
    One of 150 copies printed.
    "Julen 1908, trykt som Manuskript for Venner."

659152A. 1. Monologues, Danish.   I. Title.
N. Y. P. L.   September 11, 1933

NN   0015165   NN

Nansen, Peter, 1861-1918.
    Lægekongressens heroer; tolv billeder: ₍Pasteur, Lister, Vir-
chow, Bert, Esmarch, Key, Crudeli, Chauveau, Donders, Paget,
l'anum, Lange₎ af Dr. Bonifacius ₍pseud.₎   Kjøbenhavn, "Nuti-
dens" forlag, 1884.   86 p.   port.   22cm.

NN   0015166   NN DNLM

Nansen, Peter, 1861-
    ... Livets lyst. København, H. Koppel, 1917.
    206 p., 1 l.   19½ᶜᵐ.   kr. 4.25
    CONTENTS.—Moderens brev.—Brevet, der ikke blev aabnet.—Født af en
kvinde.—En bridge-aften.

1. Title.
                          18-11344
    Library of Congress   PT8175.N2L5 1917

NN   0015167   DLC NN

VOLUME 405

Nansen, Peter, *1861–*
Love's trilogy. Julie's diary, Marie, God's peace. From the Danish of Peter Nansen by Julia Le Gallienne. Boston, J. W. Luce and company, 1907.
4 p. l., 377 p. 19ᶜᵐ.

I. Title. II. Title: Julie's diary. III. Title: Marie. IV. Title: God's peace.

A 15–676

Title from Univ. of   Oregon. Printed by L. C.

NN 0015168   OrU ViU NIC MB OU

Nansen, Peter, 1861–1918.
PT8175 Love's trilogy; Julie's diary, Marie ₍and₎
N2A25 God's peace. From the Danish...by Julia Le Gallienne. Boston, J.W. Luce, 1908.
377 p. 20ᶜᵐ.

NN 0015169   CSt OrU

Nansen, Peter, *1861–*
Maria; ein buch der liebe. Berlin, S. Fischer, 1895.
2 p. l., 166 p. 12°.
Originally written in Danish under title: Maria, en bog om kjærlighed.

1–19311–M 4

NN 0015170   DLC

Nansen, Peter, 1861–1918.
Maria; ein Buch der Liebe, von Peter Nansen.   Berlin: S. Fischer, 1915.   165 p.   19cm.

134584B. 1. Fiction, Danish.   I. Title.
N. Y. P. L.
February 2, 1943

NN 0015171   NN

Nansen, Peter, 1861–1918
Maria; ein Buch der Liebe. Berlin, Fischer, 1920

NN 0015172   MH

Nansen, Peter, 1861–
Maria. En Bog om Kærlighed. Kjøbenhavn, Gyldendal, 1902.
2 p.l., 160 p. 12°.
5. ed.

NN 0015173   NN

Nansen, Peter, 1861–1918.
Marie; roman traduit du danois par Gaudard de Vinci. Dessins de Pierre Bonnard. Paris, Éditions de la Revue blanche, 1898.
243 p. illus. 19 cm.

I. Bonnard, Pierre, 1867–1947, illus. II. Title.
NC248.B58N3 Rosenwald Coll.   67–123135

NN 0015174   DLC ICN MB NN

Nansen, Peter, 1861–1918.
Marie: a book of love, by Peter Nansen; translated by Julia Le Gallienne. Boston, J. W. Luce and company, 1924.
3 p. l., ix–xvi p., 1 l., 83 p. 21½ᶜᵐ.

I. Le Gallienne, Mrs. Julia (Norregard) tr. II. Title.

Library of Congress   PZ3.N158Ma   25–8785

NN 0015175   DLC OU PHC MB

Nansen, Peter, 1861–1918, ed.
Nordische novellen. Neumünster i. H., Nordische verlags-anstalt, 1910.
167 p.

Contents:–Jakob Knudsen: Ein wiedersehn.–Martin Andersen-Nexö: Anne-Maries reise nach Kopenhagen.–Otto Rung: Kapellmeister Stroganoff.

NN 0015176   NNC

Nansen, Peter, 1861–1918.
... Portrætter. Kjøbenhavn, H. Koppel, 1918.
173 p., 1 l. 19½ cm.
"Disse portrætter er blevne til gennem en halv snes aar ... de er fremkomne—i dagblade og tidsskrifter, oftest ved død, undertiden ved fest."–Fortale.
CONTENTS.—Frederik VIII.—Herman Bang.—Bjørnstjerne Bjørnson.—Holger Drachmann.—Edv. Blaumüller.—Henrik Ibsen.—Prins Hans.—Georg Brandes.—"Politiken" i dens ungdom.—Hørup.

1. Denmark—Biog. 2. Bjørnson, Bjørnstjerne, 1832–1910.
3. Ibsen, Henrik, 1828–1906.   I. Title.

CT1272.N3   19—16530

NN 0015177   DLC MB

Nansen, Peter, 1861–1918.
...Portrætter... Kjøbenhavn: H. Koppel, 1918.   173 p., 1 l.   2. ed.   12°.
Contents: Frederik VIII. Herman Bang. Bjørnstjerne Bjørnson. Holger Drachmann. Edv. Blaumüller. Henrik Ibsen. Prins Hans. Georg Brandes. "Politiken" i dens Ungdom. Hørup.

1. Frederik VIII, king of Denmark, 1843–1912. 2. Bang, Herman Joachim, 1857–1912. 3. Bjørnson, Bjørnsterne, 1832–1910. 4. Drachmann, Holger Henrik Herboldt, 1846–1908. 5. Blaumüller, Edv. 6. Ibsen, Henrik, 1828–1906. 7. Hans, prince of Georg Morris Cohen, 1842– .   8. Brandes, 1841– .   9. Hørup, Viggo Lauritz Bentheim, 1841–
N. Y. P. L.

NN 0015178   NN NIC

Nansen, Peter, 1861–1918
Die Romane des Herzens; eine Liebestrilogie. Berlin, S. Fischer, 1916.
410p. 18cm.

NN 0015179   OKentU

Nansen, Peter, *1861–1918*
Die Romane des Herzens; eine Liebestrilogie.   Berlin: S. Fischer, 1921.   411 p.   12°.
Contents: Julies Tagebuch. Maria. Gottesfriede.

NN 0015180   NN

Nansen, Peter, *1861–*
Szent Bekesseg, regeny; forditotta Telekes Bela. Budapest, Athenaeum, 1921.
₍159 p.₎

NN 0015181   OC1

Nansen, Peter, 1861–1918.
Drama Theater, von Peter Nansen.   Berlin, S.
PT2627 Fischer, 1912.
E7274
247p. 17½cm.
Contents: Judiths ehe.–Eine glückliche ehe.–Kameraden.–Ein hochzeitsabend.–Die gestörte verbindung.

I. Title: Judiths ehe. II. Title: Eine glückliche ehe. III. Title: Kameraden. IV. Title: Ein hochzeitsabend. V. Title: Die gestörte verbindung. VI. Title.

NN 0015182   NBuG OKentU IEN MH

832 Nansen, Peter, 1861–1918.
Theater... Berlin, S. Fischer, 1912.
247 p. 18cm.
Contents: Judiths ehe. Eine glückliche ehe. Kameraden. Ein hochzeitsabend. Die gestörte verbindung.
Microcard copy on 2 cards. Louisville, Ky., Falls City Microcards, 1964.

NN 0015183   OrU

PT Nansen, Peter, 1861–1918.
8175 Theater. ₍2. Auflage₎ Berlin, S. Fischer,
N2 1912.
T45 247p. 18cm.
1912 German translations of original Danish.

NN 0015184   CtU

PT Nansen, Peter, 1861–1918
8175 Theater. Berlin, S. Fischer, 1919 ₍c1912₎
N2 247p. 19cm. (His Ausgewählte Werke, 2. Bd.)
T5

NN 0015185   WU

Nansen, Peter, 1861–1918, ed. and tr.
Verdens storbyer
see under *title*.

Nansen, Peter, *1861–*   G832-N
Theater. Berlin: S. Fischer, 1922.   247 p.   12°.
Contents: Judiths Ehe. Eine glückliche Ehe. Kameraden. Ein Hochzeitsabend. Die gestörte Verbindung.

I. Titles.
N. Y. P. L.   June 14, 1930

NN 0015187   NN

Nansen, Peter, 1861–1918.
Wanderjahre
see under Bang, Herman Joachim, 1857–1912.

Nansen Gödö Denki Kabushiki Kaisha
see
Namsön Chŏn'gi Chusik Hoesa.

Nansen international office for refugees.
... Appeal ₍Geneva, 1934?₎
2 numb. l. 33ᶜᵐ.
Caption title.
At head of title: ... Office international Nansen pour les réfugiés, sous l'autorité de la Société des nations. Nansen international office for refugees, under the authority of the League of nations.
Mimeographed.
Appeal by the Nansen office for help in providing clothing for refugees.

1. Refugees. 2. Russia—Hist.—Revolution, 1917–1921—Refugees.
A 47–2386

Woodrow Wilson memorial   library
for Library of Congress   ₍1₎

NN 0015190   NNUN-W

Nansen International Office for Refugees.
Budget for the year 1932–
Geneva.
pts. 33 cm.
Issued with the following official nos. :
1932 : A.4(c) 1931.x.
1933 : A.4(c) 1932.x.
1934 : A.4(c) (1) 1933.x.
1935 : A.4(c) 1934.x.
1936 : A.4(c) 1935.x.
1937 : A.4(c) 1936.x.
1938 : A.4(c) 1937.x.
1. League of Nations—Finance.
A 49–7106*

Woodrow Wilson   Memorial Library
for Library of Congress   ₍2₎

NN 0015191   NNUN-W

VOLUME 405

Nansen International Office for Refugees.
Communiqué. ₁Geneva, 1932₁
3 l. 33 cm.
Caption title.
"P.4.1932."
"Advances granted to refugee organisations by the governing body at its sixth session, October 28th, 1932": leaf 3.

1. Refugees₁ Political₁   I. League of Nations.
A 50–78

Woodrow Wilson   Memorial Library
for Library of Congress   ₍2₎

NN   0015192   NNUN-W

Nansen international office for refugees.
... Communiqué. ₁n. p., 1933₁
2 numb. l. 33ᶜᵐ.
Caption title.
At head of title: ... Office international Nansen pour les réfugiés, sous l'autorité de la Société des nations.
Mimeographed.
Concerns the work of the administrative council of the Nansen office at the end of its seventh session.

1. Refugees. 2. Russia—Hist.—Revolution, 1917–1921—Refugees.
A 47–2385

Woodrow Wilson memorial   library
for Library of Congress   ₍1₎

NN   0015193   NNUN-W

Nansen international office for refugees.
₁Letter, dated May 4, 1931, from the chairman of the governing body, on the organization and plans of the Nansen international office for refugees₁ Geneva, 1931.
3 numb. l. 33ᶜᵐ.
On leaf 1 : League of nations.
Official no. : C.300.M.141.1931.
Mimeographed.
Transmitting an appeal for the formation of the Nansen memorial fund.
Issued also in French.

1. Nansen memorial fund.   I. League of nations.
A 47–2566

Woodrow Wilson memorial   library
for Library of Congress   ₍2₎

NN   0015194   NNUN-W

Nansen international office for refugees.
... Memorandum submitted by the Nansen international office for refugees concerning the affiliation of its staff to the pensions and sickness insurance funds of the League of nations. Geneva, 1931.
6 p. incl. tables. 33ᶜᵐ.
Caption title.
Official no. : A.58.1931.

1. League of nations—Officials and employees. 2. Nansen international office for refugees—Officials and employees. 3. League of nations. Staff pensions fund. 4. League of nations. Staff provident fund.
A 47–3843

Woodrow Wilson memorial   library
for Library of Congress   ₍2₎

NN   0015195   NNUN-W

Nansen International Office for Refugees.
Nansen International Office for Refugees.
Resignation of M. Max Huber, President of the Governing Body
see under   League of Nations. Assembly. General Committee.

Nansen international office for refugees.
... Position of Russian women in the Far East. Geneva, 1934.
5 p. 33 cm.
Caption title.
At head of title : League of nations ... Advisory commission for the protection and welfare of children and young people.
Official no. : C.T.F.E.630. (C.P.E.474)
Mimeographed.
Concerns mainly condition in Shanghai.
Submitted to the Advisory commission, by the Representation in China of the Nansen international office for refugees.

1. Prostitution—Shanghai. 2. Woman—Employment—Shanghai. 3. Russia—Hist.—Revolution, 1917–1921—Refugees. I. League of nations. Advisory commission for the protection and welfare of children and young people.
A 47–4808

Woodrow Wilson memorial   library
for Library of Congress   ₍2₎

NN   0015197   NNUN-W

Nansen International Office for Refugees.
₁Refugees. Geneva, 1932.
₁1₁ 4 l. 33 cm.
On 1st leaf : League of Nations. Information Section.

1. Refugees.   I. League of Nations. Secretariat. Information Section.
A 50–2844

Woodrow Wilson   Memorial Library
for Library of Congress   ₍1₎

NN   0015198   NNUN-W

Nansen International Office for Refugees.

JX1975   **Inter-Governmental Advisory Commission for Refugees.**
.A2   Report. Sept. 1930–Mar. 1935. ₁Geneva₁
1933.
C.226.
M.136

Nansen international office for refugees.
... Report by M. Michael Hansson, former president of the governing body of the Nansen international office for refugees, on the activities of the office from July 1st to December 31st, 1938. ₑGeneva₁ 1939.

2p.   33cm.   (A.19.1939.XII)

At head of title₁ ... League of nations.
Series of League of nations publications.
XII. B. International bureaux. 1939. XII. B. 2.

NN   0015200   NBuG

Nansen International Office for Refugees.
Report of the Governing Body. Apr. 1931–Dec. 1938.
Geneva.
9 v. 33 cm.
Report year irregular.
Report for Apr. 1931/June 1932 issued as Series of League of Nations publications: XIII. Refugees. 1932.XIII.1. Reports for July 1933–Dec. 1938 issued as Series of League of Nations publications: XII.B. International bureaux. 1934.XII.B.2; 1935.XII.B.1; 1936.XII.B.3; 1937.XII.B.3; 1938.XII.B.2; 1939.XII.B.2.
Issued with the following official numbers :
Apr.–June 1931 : A.27.1931.
Apr. 1931–June 1932 : A.24.1932.

July 1932–June 1933 : A.19.1933.
July 1933–June 1934 : A.12.1934.
July 1934–June 1935 : A.22.1935.XII.
July 1935–June 1936 : A.23.1936.XII.
July 1936–June 1937 : A.21.1937.XII.
July 1937–June 1938 : A.21.1938.XII.
July–Dec. 1938 : A.19.1939.XII.
L. C. set incomplete ; Apr.–June 1931 and July 1932–June 1933 wanting.

1. European War, 1914–1918—Refugees. 2. Refugees, Political. (Series: League of Nations. Publications: XII.B. Refugees. 1932. XIII.1. Series : League of Nations. Publications : XII.B. International bureaux. 1934.XII.B.2 ₁etc.₁)

JX1975.A25   33–8517 rev 3*
—— Copy 2.   JX1975.A2

NN   0015202   DLC CSt-H ICJ OO MiU OU PBm IdU OrU

Nansen International Office for Refugees.
Report on the liquidation of the Office, submitted to the Council of the League of Nations by Judge Hansson, president of the Governing Body ... in accordance with the decision of the seventeenth Assembly of the League of Nations, adopted by the Council on May 25th, 1937 (ninety-seventh session) June 14, 1937. Geneva, 1937.
19 p. 33 cm.
Caption title.
At head of title : League of Nations.
Official no. : A.11.1937.XII (C.226.1937.XII)

1. ₁Refugees₁   I. Hansson, Michael, 1875–1944.
A 49–5026*

Woodrow Wilson   Memorial Library
for Library of Congress   ₍2₎

NN   0015203   NNUN-W

Nansen International Office for Refugees.
Report to the Governing Body on the accounts of the year 1933–
Geneva.
nos. 33 cm.
Title varies: 1938–39. Audited accounts for the financial year ...
Issued with the following official numbers :
1933 : A.3(d) 1934.x.
1934 : A.3(a) 1935.x.
1935 : A.3(a) 1936.x.
1936 : A.3(d) 1937.x.
1937 : A.3(c) 1938.x.
1938 : A.3(c) 1939.x.
1. League of Nations—Finance.

A 49–7093*

Woodrow Wilson   Memorial Library
for Library of Congress   ₍2₎

NN   0015204   NNUN-W

Nansen international office for refugees.
... Some refugee problems. ₁n. p., 1933₁
6 numb. l. 33ᶜᵐ.
Caption title.
At head of title : ... Nansen international office for refugees under the authority of the League of nations.
Mimeographed.
CONTENTS.—Refugee camp at Beyrouth destroyed by fire.—The plight of the Russian refugee flood victims in Manchuria.—Transfer of Armenian refugees to the Armenian (Erivan) republic.—Nansen memorial fund.

1. Refugees. 2. Armenians. 3. Nansen memorial fund. 4. Russia—Hist.—Revolution, 1917–1921—Refugees.
A 47–2410

Woodrow Wilson memorial   library
for Library of Congress   ₍2₎

NN   0015205   NNUN-W

Nansen international office for refugees.
... Special report submitted to the seventeenth Assembly of the League of nations by M. Michael Hansson, acting president of the Governing body. ₁Geneva₁ 1936.
11 p. 33ᶜᵐ.
At head of title : ⟨Communicated to the Assembly, the Council and the members of the League.⟩ Official no.: A. 27. 1936. XII. Geneva, September 7th, 1936. Nansen international office for refugees, under the auspices of League of nations.
Series of League of nations publications. XII. B. International bureaux. 1936. XII. B. 7.

1. European war, 1914–1918—Refugees. 2. Refugees, Political. I. Hansson, Michael, 1875–   II. League of nations.
(L. of N. author file BIV ; topic file C : Refugees)
37–6689

Library of Congress   D637.N3 1936
                             ₍3₎   940.3159

NN   0015206   DLC CaBViP IdU OrU GU PBm

Nansen international office for refugees
see also League of nations. High commissioner for refugees (1921–1930) ; League of nations. High commissioner for refugees (1939–1946)

Nansen lodge no. 43
see   International Scandinavian Workmen's Association. Lodge no. 43, Madison, Wis.

Nansen memorial fund, an appeal by ... Aristide Briand ... Viscount Cecil of Chelwood ... Julius Curtius ₁and others₁ ... ₁Geneva, 1931₁
₁4₁ p. 33ᶜᵐ.
"Appeal for a memorial fund for the completion of the humanitarian work of Dr. Fridtjof Nansen."
Distributed to members of the League of nations with League document C.300.M.141.1931.
Issued also in French.

1. Nansen memorial fund.   I. Briand, Aristide, 1862–1932. II. Cecil, Edgar Algernon Robert Gascoyne-Cecil, viscount, 1864–
A 47–2274

Woodrow Wilson memorial   library
for Library of Congress   ₍2₎

NN   0015209   NNUN-W

Nansenfondet
see
Fridtjof Nansens fond til videnskabens fremme.

Nansenkontoret for flyktninger
see
Nansen international office for refugees.

Nansens fond til videnskabens fremme
see
Fridtjof Nansens fond til videnskabens fremme.

VOLUME 405

Nansen's Nordpolarfahrt, 1893-1896.
(Newspaper clippings.) (1896.)
2 sheets.

1. Nansen, Fridtjof, 1861-1930.

NN 0015213 DAS

Nansenskolen, Lillehammer
  see Lillehammer, Norway. Nansenskolen.

Nanshi Chōsakai. Nampō Bunko.
(Nanshi Chōsakai shozoku Nampō Bunko shozō tosho mokuroku)
南支調査會所屬南方文庫所藏圖書目錄 ﹝東京﹞
昭和19 i.e. 1944﹞
  5 v. (10, 1236 p. on double leaves) 25 cm.

  1. Asia—Bibliography—Catalogs. 2. Oceanica—Bibliography—Catalogs. I. Title. II. Title: Nampō Bunko shozō tosho mokuroku.
Z3009.N34   72-807152

NN 0015215 DLC

Nanshi hōmen shihō jimu shisatsu hōkokusho.
南支方面司法事務視察報告書 ﹝臺北﹞ 臺灣總
督府外事部 ﹝昭和19 i.e. 1944﹞
  2, 218 p. 25 cm. (臺灣總督府外事部調查 第136. 政治部門 第7)
  Prepared by 齋藤省一郎 等
  法院組織法: p. 25-37.
  1. Justice, Administration of—China. I. Saitō, Shōichirō, 1889- II. Formosa (Government-General of Taiwan, 1895-1945). Gaijibu. III. China. Laws, statutes, etc. Fa yüan tsu chih fa. Japanese. 1944. IV. Series: Formosa (Government-General of Taiwan). Gaijibu. Taiwan Sōtokufu Gaijibu chōsa, dai 136.
                                       72-805107

NN 0015216 DLC

(Nanshi keizai sōsho)
南支經濟叢書 福大公司企畫課編 ﹝臺北 福大公司 昭和14- i.e. 1939-
  v. 22 cm.
  Cover title.
  On cover of v. 2: 長野政東責任編輯

  1. China—Economic conditions—1912-1949—Collected works. I. Nagano, Masaki, ed. II. Fukudai Kōshi. Kikakuka.
HC427.8.N35   74-815969

NN 0015217 DLC

(Nanshi Nan'yō bōeki sankō hyō)
南支南洋貿易參考表 ﹝臺北﹞ 臺灣總督府殖產局商
工課 ﹝昭和10 i.e. 1935﹞
  2, 369 p. 22 cm.

  1. East (Far East)—Commerce. 2. Asia, Southeastern—Commerce. I. Formosa (Government-General of Taiwan, 1895-1945). Shokusankyoku. Shōkōka.
HF3761.N35   74-817767

NN 0015218 DLC

Nanshin Nihon Sha.
(Dai Nan'yō no kuniguni)
大南洋の國々 南進日本社編 ﹝大阪 昭和16
i.e. 1941﹞
  124, 81, 4, 101 p. maps. 19 cm.
  大南洋產業資源精圖附錄
  Bibliography: p. 3-4 (3d group)
  1. Asia, Southeastern—Economic conditions. 2. Asia, Southeastern—Economic conditions—Maps—Indexes. I. Nanshin Nihon Sha. Dai Nan'yō sangyō shigen seizu. II. Title.
HC412.N2587 1941   74-815347

NN 0015219 DLC

Nanshin Nihon Sha. Dai Nan'yō sangyō shigen seizu.

HC412
.N2587
1941
Orien
Japan
Nanshin Nihon Sha.
(Dai Nan'yō no kuniguni)
大南洋の國々 南進日本社編 ﹝大阪 昭和16
i.e. 1941﹞

Nanshin Seinenkai.
(Dai Nan'yō o hiraku)
大南洋を拓く 南進青年會編 ﹝早川居冲編輯
東京﹞ 拓南社 ﹝昭和17 i.e. 1942﹞
  2, 10, 282 p. illus. 19 cm.
  Subtitle on cover: 南進青年の手引
  Bibliography: p. ﹝245﹞-282.
  1. Japan—Emigration and immigration. 2. Japanese in southeastern Asia. 3. Asia, Southeastern—Economic conditions. I. Hayakawa, Orioki, ed. II. Title.
JV8721.Z9N33 1942   73-822977

NN 0015221 DLC

Nansich-Hamburger, Abraham ben Solomon
  see
Nanzig, Abraham, 18th cent.

Nansimum Co., Va.
  see Nansemond Co., Va.

NANSIUS, Franciscus.
Ad Nonni Paraphrasin Evangelii Iohannis
Graece & Latine editam curae secundae.
Lugduni Batavorum, ex officina Plantiniana,
1593.

  pp. (16), 56, (7).

  1. Bible. N. T. John. Greek. Paraphrases. (1589) Nonnus Panopolitanus. (Graeca paraphrasis sancti Evangelii secundum Ioannem) I. Nonnus Panopolitanus.

NN 0015224 MH

Nanson, E J
Methods of election. [Melbourne, Mason,
Firth & M'Cutcheon, 1882]
  44 p. 8°. (Royal Society of Victoria)
  Title fr. cover.

NN 0015225 NN MH

Nanson, E J
Proportional representation. [Melbourne,
Mason, Firth & McCutcheon, 1880?]
  19 p. 8°.
  Read before the Royal Society of Victoria,
July 8, 1880.
  In: SEH. p.v. 3.

NN 0015226 NN

Nanson, H. J.
Rhodesia, Southern. Census office.
  ... Report of the director of census regarding the census taken on the 4th May, 1926 ... Salisbury, Rhodesia, Printed by the government printer, 1927.

NN 0015228 MdBP

Nanson, William
Carlisle cullery tenure. 9 pp.
﹝Archaeol. Journ. v. 40, 1883, p. 55.﹞

Nanson, William, joint ed.

Ferguson, Richard Saul, 1837-1900, ed.
  Some municipal records of the city of Carlisle, viz., the Elizabethan constitutions, orders, provisions, articles, and rules from the Dormont book, and the rules and orders of the eight trading guilds, prefaced by chapters on the corporation charters and guilds, illustrated by extracts from the Courtleet rolls and from the Minutes of the corporation and guilds. Ed. by R. S. Ferguson ... and W. Nanson ... Carlisle, C. Thurnam & sons, 1887.

W
4
P23
1940
Nansot, Alfred, 1915-
  Les accidents mortels consécutifs à la ponction lombaire. Rennes, Impr. commerciale de l'Ouest-Éclair, 1940.
  29 p., 1 l. (Paris. Université. Faculté de médecine. Thèse. 1940. no. 312)

NN 0015230 DNLM CtY

Nansot (P.-E.) * Des quarantaines. 30 pp. 4°.
Paris. 1859. No. 161. v. 534.

NN 0015231 DNLM

Nansouty, Max Charles Emmanuel Champion de, 1854-1913.
  ... Actualités scientifiques. L'air liquide. — L'artillerie para-grêle. — La conquête de l'espace. — Télégraphie intersidérale. — Le ver à soie mécanique. — Les ponts géants. — Les gants électriques. — etc., etc. Paris, F. Juven. [1901].
  [4], 301, [2] p. illus. 20cm.
  At head of title: Max de Nansouty.

NN 0015232 ICJ MB

Nansouty, Max Charles Emmanuel Champion de, 1854-
  ... Aérostation, aviation, par Max de Nansouty ... ouvrage illustré de 582 figures dans le texte. Paris, Boivin & cie, 1911.
  2 p. l., 758 p., 1 l. illus., diagrs. 30cm. (In Figuier, Louis. Les merveilles de la science. ﹝Nouv. éd.﹞ Paris, 1911. t. iv) fr. 15

  1. Aeronautics.
Library of Congress   TL547.N3   11-25031

NN 0015233 DLC DAS KMK MiU NN CoD MB

Nansouty, Max Charles Emmanuel Champion de, 1854-
  ... L'Année industrielle
  see under ... L'Année industrielle.

Nansouty, Max Charles Emmanuel Champion de, 1854-
  Le chemin de fer glissant de Girard et Barre. Avec figures dans le texte. Paris, Tignol, 1890.
  38 p., 1 l., 1 pl. 12°. (Bibliothèque des actualités industrielles, No. 34)

NN 0015235 NN

HD
9710
N3
Nansouty, Max Charles Emmanuel Champion de, 1854-
  Chemins de fer automobiles. Paris, Boivin ﹝191-?﹞
  395 p. illus.

  AUTOMOBILES
  Chemins de fer automobiles

NN 0015236 KMK

VOLUME 405

Nansouty, Max Charles Emmanuel Champion
de, 1854–
Le ciment armé, le verre armé et la
fabrication mécanique des bouteilles. Dessins
de L. Fillol et A. Collombar. Paris,
Schleicher Frères, [190–?]
36 p. illus. 12°.

NN 0015237 NN

QC
521
N3
Nansouty, Max Charles Emmanuel Champion de,
1854–
Electricité. Paris, Boivin, ᶜ1911.
748 p. illus.

NN 0015238 KMK

TA2
.G3
Nansouty, Max Charles Emmanuel Champion de,
1854–1913, ed.
Le Génie civil; revue technique générale des industries fran-
çaises et étrangères. t. 1–
1 nov. 1880–
Paris.

Nansouty, Max Charles Emmanuel Champion de, 1854–
Les laboratoires de chi-
nie. 8°. [n. p., n. d.]
Cutting from : La Génie civil, 1892, ii. 145–148, 2 pl.
Ser. also, de Pietra Santa (Prosper) & de Nan-
souty (Max). La crémation. 8°. Paris, 1881.

NN 0015240 DNLM

Nansouty, Max Charles Emmanuel Champion de,   L625.09 R200
1854–
116690 .... La locomotive et les chemins de fer, par Max de Nansouty. Ouvrage illustré de 330 figures dans le texte. Paris,
Boivin & cⁱᵉ, [1912].
[4], 388 p. illus. (incl. diagrs.) 29½ᶜᵐ. (Les merveilles de la science, [t. v,
Chemins de fer-automobiles].)

NN 0015241 ICJ

Nansouty, Max Charles Emmanuel de, 1854–
Le machinisme dans la vie quotidienne, par Max de
Nansouty. 28 planches en hors texte. Paris, P. Roger et
cⁱᵉ, 1909.
300 p. plates. 20½ᶜᵐ. (On cover: Collection de "la vie quotidienne")

1. Machinery. 2. Machinery in industry. 3. Technology. 4. Industrial
arts.
10–6507
Library of Congress   T47.N3

NN 0015242 DLC CU ICJ

TJ
755
N3
Nansouty, Max Charles Emmanuel Champion de,
1854–
Moteurs; à explosion–à eau–à air–à vent.
Paris, Boivin, ᶜ1911.
748 p. illus.

MOTORS
Moteurs

NN 0015243 KMK

TJ
145
N3
Nansouty, Max Charles Emmanuel Champion de,
1854–
Outillage mécanique. Paris, Boivin [191–?]
367 p. illus.

MECHANICAL ENGINEERING
Outillage mécanique

NN 0015244 KMK

Nansouty, Max Charles Emmanuel Champion de,
1854–1913.
Faraud, Louis.
Plus lourd que l'air. Étude sur la navigation aérienne, par
m. L. Faraud ... Précédée d'une analyse par m. Max de
Nansouty ... Paris, Imprimerie Chaix, 1888.

NANSOUTY, Max Charles Emmanuel Champion de, 1854–
Les poissons voyageurs; saumons, truites,
aloses anguilles, par Max de Nansouty. Dessins
de L. Fillot. Paris, Librarie C. Reinwald,
Schleicher frères, Editeurs.
19 p. illus. 19 1/2 cm.

NN 0015246 MH

Nansouty, Max Charles Emmanuel Champion de, 1854–
Quelques fruits; châtaignes, prunes e.
pruneaux, marrons d'Inde. Dessins de L. Fillol. Paris.
[18–?] 8°. pp. [2], 34. Illustr.

NN 0015247 MH-A

NANSOUTY, Max Charles Emmanuel Champion de, 1854–   39
La télégraphie optique. Illus.
(Science et guerre. Pp. 1–48. Paris, 1888.)

NN 0015248 MB

Nansouty, Max Charles Emmanuel Champion de,   624.0944 E34
1854–
103818 .... La tour Eiffel de 300 mètres à l'Exposition universelle de
1889, historique et description, par Max de Nansouty, ...
Avec un portrait de M. Eiffel, 24 figures, dont 8 hors texte, et 2
planches. Paris, B. Tignol, [1889].
xviii, [2], 116 p. fold. front., illus. (incl. diagrs.), 9 pl. (1 fold.) 19ᶜᵐ. (Bibliothèque des actualités industrielles. Nº 25.)

NN 0015249 ICJ PPL ViU MB

Nansouty, Max Charles Emmanuel Champion de, 1854–
...La Tour Eiffel de 300 mètres à l'Exposition universelle de
1889, historique et description, par Max de Nansouty... Paris:
B. Tignol, 1889?). xviii, 138 p. incl. front. illus. (incl. port.),
plates. 2. ed. 12°. (Bibliothèque des actualités industrielles. no. 25.)

503083A. 1. Eiffel tower. 2. Ser.
N. Y. P. L.   November 18, 1930

NN 0015250 NN NNC

PN
2091
S8
N3
Nansouty, Max Charles Emmanuel de, 1854–1913
Les trucs du théâtre, du cirque et de la
foire, par Max de Nansouty. Paris, Librairie
A. Colin, 1909.
159p. illus. 21cm. ("La Petite biblio-
thèque." Sér. C: science récréative)

1. Theaters – Stage-setting and scenery
2. Circus 3. Fairs I. Title

NN 0015251 WU NN NNC MH NjP CU

T2
.V6
Nansouty, Max Charles Emmanuel Champion de, 1854–
La Vie scientifique, sous la direction de Max de Nan-
souty; revue universelle des inventions nouvelles et
sciences pratiques ...
Paris, F. Juven & cie. 1896–

Nansouty, Max de
see Nansouty, Max Charles Emmanuel
Champion de, 1854–

Nant (A.) * Sur les tumeurs blanches des articu-
lations. 21 pp. 4°. Paris, 1817, No. 202, v.
127.

NN 0015254 DNLM

Nant, Candide de
see Candide, frere, name in religion of
Henri Causse, 1874–

"Nant, Ellis o'r", bardic name
see Pierce, Ellis, "Ellis o'r Nant", d. 1912.

Nanta, André.   L616.15 R202
.... Étude des lympho et des myélo-dermies (manifestations
109114 cutanées des états leucémiques et aleucémiques). Paris, C.
Bougault; [etc., etc.], 1912.
201, [4] p. 25½ᶜᵐ.
At head of title: Docteur A. Nanta, ...
Also published as Thèse – Univ. de Toulouse.
"Bibliographie," p. [181]–201.

NN 0015257 ICJ NIC ICRL CtY OO

Nanta, Henri.
... La situation de l'établissement congré-
ganiste au point de vue pénal en droit français...
Alger, 1913.
25 cm.
Thèse – Univ. d'Alger.
Bibliographie, p. [118]–114.

NN 0015258 CtY NjP

SB191
.R5D8
Nanta, J.
Dumont, René, 1904–
... La culture du riz dans le delta du Tonkin; étude et pro-
positions d'amélioration des techniques traditionnelles de
riziculture tropicale. Préface de m. Yves Henry ... Paris,
Société d'éditions géographiques, maritimes et coloniales,
1935.

Nantahala and Tuckasege land and mineral company.
Preliminary report on the lands of the Nantahala &
Tuckasege land and mineral association. By David
Christy ... Cincinnati, Wrightson and company, print-
ers, 1856.
24 p. 23ᶜᵐ.
With this is bound its Second preliminary report. 1858.

1. Mines and mineral resources—North Carolina. 2. Mines and mineral
resources—Tennessee. 3. Agriculture—North Carolina. I. Christy,
David, b. 1802.
G S 15–919
Library, U. S. Geological   Survey 403(231) N2

NN 0015260 DI-GS PPAN OClWHi

Nantahala and Tuckasege land and mineral company.
Second preliminary report of the Nantahala & Tuckasege land and mineral company, for 1858. Cincinnati,
Wrightson & company, printers, 1858.
24, 44 p. illus. 23ᶜᵐ.
With appendix: The southern highlands, as adapted to pasturage and
grape culture. By David Christy. Cincinnati, 1858.

1. Mines and mineral resources—North Carolina. 2. Viticulture—North
Carolina. I. Christy, David, b. 1802.
CA 7–3371 Unrev'd
Library of Congress   TN380.N2

PPAN NcU
NN 0015261 DLC DI-GS NcU TxU PHi OOxM OClWHi

... Nantahala folio, North Carolina-Tennessee
see under [Keith, Arthur] 1864–1944.

VOLUME 405

Nantasket Beach, Mass. National conference on
Americanization in industries, 1919.

see

National conference on Americanization in industries, Nantasket Beach, Mass., 1919.

Nantasket views; wreckage of the great storm, November
27th, 1898. Thirty views, covering coast from Pemberton to
Cohasset. Dorchester, Mass., B. W. Putnam, *1899.
1 p. l., 30 mounted phot. 18½ x 27ᶜᵐ.

1. Nantasket beach, Mass.—Descr.—Views.

Library of Congress   F74.N15N2

99-970 Revised

NN   0015264   DLC

Nante, Professor
      see   Glassbrenner, Adolf, 1810-1876.

Nante auf der Berlin-Potsdamer-eisenbahn
      see under   [Lenz, Ludwig] 1813-1896.

Nante in Potsdam und im lustlager bei Nedlitz
      see under   [Lenz, Ludwig] 1813-1896.

848
N19a   Nantel, Adolphe, 1886-
          ... À la hache. Montréal, Éditions A.Lé-
          vesque, 1932.
          3 p. l., [9]-232 p., 2 l. 19ᶜᵐ. (On cover: L'âme
          canadienne)
          On cover: Deuxième tirage.

NN   0015268   MiU CaQMM NjP CaBVaU

Nantel, Adolphe, 1886-
      Au pays des bûcherons. Illus. de Louis
      Gagnon. Montréal, Éditions de l'A.C.F.[1932]
      186 p.   24 cm. (Albums canadiens)

NN   0015269   CaBVaU

Nantel, Adolphe (1886-
      Au pays des bûcherons; illustrations de
      Louis Gagnon.
      188p. Mont.,Edns.A.C.F.,[1937].
      (Albums canadiens.)

NOTE: His "A la hache" republished for young people

NN   0015270   CaOTU

Nantel, Adolphe, 1886-
      A saga of Lac Clair. An episode in the life of a Laurentian
woodman, from the book "A la Hache," by Adolphe Nantel; translated from the French by B. K. Sandwell.   Montreal, Privately
printed, 1937.   5 p. l., 13-21 p., 1 l. incl. col. front.   25cm.
      "Two hundred and fifty copies...were printed for Charles Corbett Ronalds."
      "Greetings," signed and dated: C. C. Ronalds, Christmas, 1937, prelim. l. 3-4°.

54R0314. 1. Forest fires—Canada,   1924. I. Sandwell, Bernard Keble,
1876-   , tr. II. Title.

NN   0015271   NN

Nantel, Adolphe, 1886-
      ... La terre du huitième; roman. Montréal, Éditions de
l'Arbre [*1942]
      2 p. l., [7]-190 p., 1 l. 19½ᵐ.

I. Title.

                                          A 43-768

Harvard univ. Library
for Library of Congress   [2]

NN   0015272   MH CaBVaU WaS CaOTU MB OOxM PPT

[Nantel, Antonin] 1839-1929, comp.
      Les fleurs de la poésie canadienne...   Montréal, C. O.
Beauchemin & Valois, 1869.   134 p.   17cm.
      Compiled by Ant. Nantel.

298579B. 1. Poetry, Canadian-   French—Collections. I. Title.
N. Y. P. L.   May 11, 1945

NN   0015273   NN CaBVaU RPB RWoU

Nantel, Antonin, 1839-1929, comp.
      Les fleurs de la poésie canadienne. 2d. éd.,
      augm. et précédée d'une préface, par m. l'abbé
      A. Nantel...   Montréal, C.O. Beauchemin &
      fils, 1896.
      2 p. l., x, 255 p.   22 cm.
      Contains brief bibliographical notices of the
      poets represented.

NN   0015274   RPB CaOTU

Nantel, Antonin, 1839-   comp.
      Les fleurs de la poésie canadienne. 4. éd., augm. et
      précédée d'une préface, par A. Nantel. Montréal, Li-
      brairie Beauchemin, limitée, 1911.
      2 p. l., x, 255 p.   22½ᶜᵐ.
      Contains brief biographical notices of the poets represented.

      1. French-Canadian poetry (Selections) 2. Poets, French-Canadian.
      I. Title.
                                          13-7872
Library of Congress   PQ3910.N2

NN   0015275   DLC NcD NN

---

fColl
NA62f   Nantel, Antonin, 1839-   comp.
1924   Les fleurs de la poésie canadienne. 5. éd.,
          augm. et précédée d'une préface, par m. l'abbé
          A. Nantel ...   Montréal, Librairie Beauchemin,
          1924.
          205 p.   22 cm.

          Contains brief biographical notices of the
          poets represented.

NN   0015276   RPB

NANTEL, ANTONIN, 1839-1929.
      Le lexique de la langue algonquine par M. l'abbé Cuoq.
2pp. Clipping from La Minerve, Montréal, Aug. 1, 1887.

NN   0015277   ICN

[NANTEL, ANTONIN]
      Lexique de la langue Iroquoise. Par M. l'abbé Cuoq,
prêtre de St-Sulpice. Étude bibliographique...
Exc. from Les Annales Térésiennes. Dec., 1882,
pp.108-114. Pilling 956.

NN   0015278   ICN

PE1129
.F7N3   Nantel, Antonin, 1839-1929
1909   Nouveau cours de langue anglaise selon
          la méthode d'Ollendorff a l'usage des écoles,
          académies, pensionnats et collèges. Cette
          éd. rev. par T. J. Brennan. Montreal,
          Beauchemin [1909?]
          vii, 263 p.   19cm.

          1. English language—Composition and exercises.
          2. English language—Text-books for foreigners—
          French. I. Bren-   nan, T. J., ed.

NN   0015279   ViU

Nantel, Antonin, 1839-1929.
      ...Pages historiques et littéraires.   Montréal: Arbour
et Dupont, 1928.   431 p.   front. (port.)   12°.

441096A. 1. Essays, Canadian-French.   2. Sainte-Thérèse, Quebec—Biog.
3. Schools, Parochial—Roman Catholic   —Canada—Sainte Thérèse. 4. Quebec
(province)—Biog.
N. Y. P. L.   November 13, 1929

NN   0015280   NN MH CtY MiU CaBVaU

Nantel, Guillaume Alphonse, 1852-1909.
      La colonisation du nord-ouest de la province de Québec. Con-
férence de l'honorable G.-A. Nantel, le 7 mai 1895, devant la Société de colonisation de Montréal.   Montréal: E. Senécal & fils,
1895.   59 p.   8°.

444459A. 1. Land settlement—Canada   —Quebec. 2. Quebec (province)—
Descr. and trav., 1800-1900.
N. Y. P. L.   November 6, 1929

NN   0015281   NN MH CaBViP

Nantel, Guillaume Alphonse, 1852-1909.
      Discours sur l'instruction publique prononcé
au Cercle Ville-Marie, le 5 Juin 1893. Québec,
1893.
      34 p.   22 cm.

NN   0015282   MH

Nantel, Guillaume Alphonse, 1852-1909.
      ...La métropole de demain; avenir de Montréal.   Montréal:
Typ. Adjutor Menard, 1910.   xvii, 186 p.   front. (port.)   8°.
      Edited by Arthur Beauchesne.

275000A. 1. Municipal govern-   France—Paris. 2. Municipal government—Canada—Montreal. 3. Cities-   Plans—Canada—Montreal. 4. Beau-
chesne, Arthur, 1876-   , ed.
N. Y. P. L.   February 15, 1927

NN   0015283   NN MnU CaBVaU MH

[Nantel, Guillaume Alphonse,] 1852-1909
      Notre Nord-Ouest provincial. Étude sur la vallée de l'Otta-
wa; accompagnée de cartes géographiques...   Montréal: E.
Senécal & fils, 1887.   99 p., front. (fold. map.)   8°.

1. Quebec (Province). 2. Title.
N. Y. P. L.   November 27, 1915.

NN   0015284   NN CaOTU LNHT MiU MnHi MH CaNSWA

Nantel, J   de.
      ... La veuve consolée par Jésus; préface de M. le
chanoine Poulin. Avignon, Aubanel frères [*1918]
      3 p. l., ix-xv, 74, [4] p. 14ᵐ.   fr. 0.50

I. Title.

Library of Congress   BV4900.N3   18-21258

NN   0015285   DLC

VOLUME 405

Nantel, Maréchal.
...Autour d'une décision judiciaire sur la langue française en
Canada.   Montréal, Les Éditions des Dix, 1941.   25 p.
23½cm.

1. Canada—Languages. I. Les   Dix, Montreal.
N. Y. P. L.   June 21, 1944

NN   0015286   NN CaOTU

Nantembō
    see
Nakahara, Tōshū, 1839-1925.

Nantembō Tōshū
    see
Nakahara, Tōshū, 1839-1925.

Nantermoz (Auguste) [1877-   ]. *Contribution à l'étude du traitement de l'atrophie
tabétique des nerfs optiques. Des dangers de la
médication iodurée. 47 pp. 8°. *Lyon*, 1898,
No. 153.

NN   0015289   DNLM

Nanterre, Marc.
    Jacques Robillot ... Préf. de Victor Demange. Illus. de
J. Morette. Metz, Le Républicain lorrain, 1950.
    183 p. illus., ports. 24 cm.
    "Extraits de lettres et d'œuvres inédites. Le chant de Ryno
(par J. Robillot)": p. 155-183.

1. Robillot, Jacques.
                                                 A 52-2370
New York. Public Libr.
for Library of Congress   ₍₁₎

NN   0015290   NN

                France
**Nanterre, Centre de propagande et de vulgarisation
    de la clôture électrique**
    see   Centre de propagande et de vulgarisation
de la clôture électrique, Nanterre.

Nanterre, France. Télémécanique électrique
    see Télémécanique électrique.

Nantes, Anne de.
    ...Essai sur le féminisme. Préface du R. P. Y. de La Brière
... Avignon: Aubanel fils ainé, 1926. 113 p. 12°.

Bibliographical footnotes.

388290A. 1. Woman—   Emancipation—France.
N. Y. P. L.   December 13, 1928

NN   0015293   NN DCU

Nantes, Antoine de, pseud.
    see Najac, Émile de, 1828-1889.

Nantes, Antoine François de, comte, 1756-1936.
    see Francois de Nantes, Antoine, comte,
1756-1836.

Nantes, Bernardo de
    see
Bernard *de Nantes, Capuchin, fl.* 1709.

Nantes, Henry, appellant.
    Before the Most Noble and Right Honourable
the Lords commissioners of appeals in prize
causes. The Birmingham, William Benton
Foster, master. Henry Nantes, of London,
merchant, claimant of the several goods specified
in the shedule annexed to his claim, on behalf of
American subjects ... appellant, against Charles
Hamilton, commander of the private ship of war,
Oporto, respondent. On an appeal from the High
court of admiralty of England. Second appeal.
Appellant's case.   [London? 1796?]
    2 p., 1 l.   42.5 cm.
    Caption-title.

NN   0015297   CSmH

Nantes, Henry, appellant.
    Before the most noble and right honorable the
Lords Commissioners in prize causes... Further
case on behalf of the respondent.
        see under Hamilton, Charles, respondent.

Nantes, Louise Françoise, mlle de
        see Bourbon-Condé, Louise Françoise,
duchesse de, 1673-1743.

Nantes, Oliva Sabuco de
        see Sabuco de Nantes, Oliva, b. 1562.

Asia
DS689   **Nantes, Pantaleon**
.L8N35   Kasaysayan at talā ng bayan ng Lukban,
        Quezon, sinulat ni Pantaleon Nantes.
        ₍Manila, Benipayo Press, c1952₎
        xv, 237 p. illus.

        1. Lucban, Philippines – History.
        I. Title.

NN   0015301   HU

Nantes Barrera, Oliva Sabuco de
        see Sabuco de Nantes, Oliva, b. 1562.

DC   **Nantes.**
141   A l'Assemblée nationale. ₍Paris,
F87+   Desenne, 1791₎
v.219   28 p. 22cm.

        Protesting against the elections made
        in August.
            Signed by hand: Minée, Mosneron, Mame?

        1. Loire-Inférieure, France (Dept.)
        Assemblée électorale. 2. France. Assemblée
        nationale   législative, 1791-
        1792--Elec   tions

NN   0015303   NIC

Nantes.
    Amélioration du service d'eau de la ville de Nantes.
Rapport. Nantes, Impr. de P. Pledran, 1890.
    4 p. l., ₍7₎-110 p. fold. map, 4 fold. plans. 22½ᶜᵐ.
    Signed: L'ingénieur en chef des ponts-et-chaussées, E. Lefort.

    1. Nantes—Water-supply.   I. Lefort, E.
                                                 22-25919
    Library of Congress   TD272.N3A5 1890

NN   0015304   DLC

Nantes.
    Arrêté des officiers municipaux de la
ville de Nantes. Du 4 novembre 1788.
Nantes, A.J. Malassis, 1788.
    22 p.   20cm.
    Appended to Journal de correspondance
de Paris à Nantes, v.1.

    1. France. Tiers-état.

NN   0015305   MnU

₍NANTES.
    Arrêté des officiers municipaux de la
ville de Nantes, du 4 novembre 1788; suivi de
la Requête du tiers-état [by Jacques-Edmé-
Léger Cottin], et de l'Arrêté du 6 du même
mois. n. p. [1788.] 38 p.   DFDT p.v.26, no.13
See Part 1, Pamphlets, no. 1147.

NN   0015306   NN

Nantes.
    ... Budget pour l'exercice 18
₍Nantes, 18
    v. 34ᵐᵐ.
At head of title, 18   : Ville de Nantes.
On cover, 18   : République Française. Ville de Nantes.
pour l'exercice 18   Nantes, 18   Budget

    1. Budget—Nantes.
                                                 11-8896
    Library of Congress   HJ9047.N32

NN   0015307   DLC

Nantes.
    Catalogue de la collection Minéralogique,
Géognostique et Minéralurgique ...
        see under Dubuisson, François René André.

Nantes. [Communication by the commune of
Nantes of the names and signatures of its municipal
officers.]
    33Xₓₓ p. ₂ (address on back). Dated 18 floréal an 7 [17
May 1799]. Signed by eleven civic officials, headed by *Sagot,
président,* and by *Louis Dufou,* commonry of the Directoire
exécutif. Bearing the seal of the commune. Addressed to
the administrators of the municipality of Valenciennes.

NN   0015309   NIC

Nantes.
    Copie du procès-verbal des députés de
la Commune de Nantes, à la séance de
l'ordre du Tiers-état, tenue à l'hôtel-
de-ville de Rennes, le 25 décembre 1788,
& déposée le même jour en l'étude de me.
Jolivet ... ₍Nantes? 1789?₎
    4 p.   20cm.
    Appended to Journal de correspondance
de Paris à Nantes, v.1.

    1. Nantes. Politics and government.

NN   0015310   MnU

Nantes.
    Discours prononcé a l'hôtel de la bourse...
        see under Omnes-Omnibus, pseud.

Nantes.
    Essai di bibliographie sommaire mantaise...
        see under La Nicolliere-Teijeiro,
Stephan de, 1824-1900.

VOLUME 405

Nantes.
Extrait du registre des délibérations de la ville et comté de Nantes
see Lallié, Alfred François, 1832-
Les moyades de Nantes. 1879.

Nantes.
Extrait du registre des délibérations de la ville et comté de Nantes
see Phelippes de Coatgouredes de Tranjolly, François Anne Louis.
Noyades, fusilliades, ou réponse au rapport...

Nantes.
Inventaire sommaire des archives communales anterieures á 1790...
see under Archives de la ville de Nantes.

Nantes.
—— Placets adressés au roi et à la reine;
Requête ⟨by Jacques-Edme-Léger Cottin⟩ aux officiers municipaux de la ville de Nantes, et Arrêté du 6 novembre 1788. n. p. ⟨1788⟩ 20 p.
DFDT n.v.26, no.8

I. Leger Cottin, Jacques Edme.

NN 0015316 NN

DC
141
Nantes
Placets adressés au roi et à la reine.
Requête ⟨by Jacques Edme Léger Cottin⟩ aux officiers municipaux de la ville de Nantes, et Arrêté du 6 novembre 1788.
⟨n.p., 1788⟩
1 card. 7½ x 12½ cm. (Hayden, French revolutionary pamphlets, 1819)

Microcard copy.
Collation of the original: 20 p.

NN 0015317 MiEM

NANTES.
Police générale de la ville, fauxbourgs banlieue et comte de Nantes. Nantes, 1721.

NN 0015318 MH-L

NANTES.
Privileges accordez par les ducs de Bretagne et nos rois tres-chrestiens, aux maires, échevins bourgeois & habitans de la ville & faux-bourgs de Nantes, verifiés en parlement & en la chambre des comptes de Bretagne. Nantes, N. Verger, 1730.

12°.

NN 0015319 MH-L

Nantes.
Privilèges accordés par les ducs de Bretagne et les rois de France ... 1883
see under La Nicollière-Teijiero, Stéphane de, 1824-1900, ed.

France
N=26
M74
1609
Nantes.
Privileges, franchises, libertez, et exemptions des officiers, ouuriers & monnoyers de la monoye de Nantes, leurs concedes & octroyez par les ducs de Bretaigne & roys de France, verifiez de temps en temps par arrests de la cour de Parlement dudict pays. Nantes, Par Pierre Doriou, 1609.
53 ⟨i. e. 58⟩ numb. ₤. 21½cm.

Numerous errors in foliation.
Royal coat of arms on title-page.

NN 0015321 CtY-L

Nantes.
Rapports sur le fonctionnement des divers services municipaux en 19

⟨Nantes, 19 8°.

1. Municipal government, France: Nantes.
N.Y.P.L.   January 16, 1923.

NN 0015322 NN

Nantes.
Relation du voyage des cent trente-deux Nantais, envoyés à Paris. 1794, 1823
see under title

Nantes.
Requête aux officiers municipaux de la ville de Nantes, et arrêté du 6 novembre 1788. ⟨Nantes? 1788⟩

16 p. 20cm.

Appended to Journal de correspondance de Paris à Nantes, v.1.

1. France. Tiers-état.

NN 0015324 MnU

Nantes.
Usages locaux et arrêtés municipaux de Nantes par L. de la Borie. Nantes: L. de la Borie, 1910. 3 p.l., ix-xiii p., 1 l., 172 p. 12°.

1. Municipal charters etc., France: Nantes, 1910. 2. La Borie, L. de, editor.
N.Y.P.L.   July 14, 1911.

NN 0015325 NN

Nantes. Archives communales
see Archives de la ville de Nantes.

NANTES. Bibliothèque municipale.
Catalogue de l'Exposition du centenaire de 1848 en France, en Europe, et dans l'Union française, organisée par la Bibliothèque municipale de Nantes, dans le patio du Musée des beaux-arts, 8 au 31 mars 1948. [Nantes, 1948] 62 f. 31cm.

1. France—Hist. — Revolution of 1848—Bibl.   t. 1948.

NN 0015327 NN

Nantes. Bibliothèque municipale.
Catalogue méthodique de la Bibliothèque publique de la ville de Nantes, par Émile Péhant... v. 1-   Nantes: Guéraud et cie. ⟨etc.⟩ 1859-   v. 24cm.

Vol. 7 by Pierre Morin.
"Tiré à 504 exemplaires... 50 sur papier de Holland (numérotés)," v. 1-3; umbered 50, 38 and 5, respectively.
Bookplate of the Marquis de Granges de Surgères in v. 1-6.
Autograph letters inserted in v. 1-6.
CONTENTS.—v. 1. Sciences religieuses, philosophiques et sociales.—v. 2. Sciences naturelles, exactes et occultes. Arts.—v. 3. Belles-lettres.—v. 4-5. Histoire.—v. 6. Histoire (suite). Polygraphie. Nouvelles acquisitions.—v. 7. Supplément.

1. Bibliography—Catalogues—   Libraries, Public—France—Nantes.
I. Morin, Pierre, 1825-1895.   II. Péhant, Émile, 1813-1876.
N.Y.P.L.   September 17, 1940

NN 0015328 NN NNC MH

Nantes. Bibliothèque municipale.
... Collection Dugast-Matifeux. Catalogue des manuscrits ... Nantes, Impr. F. Salières, 1901-03.
2 v. port. 25cm.
At head of title: Bibliothèque publique de la ville de Nantes.
"Tiré à 300 exemplaires."
Caption title, v. 1: Documents pour servir à l'histoire de la Vendée rassemblés et mis en ordre par Charles Dugast-Matifeux et Benjamin Fillon.
CONTENTS.— t. 1. Documents révolutionnaires, par J. Rousse et M. Giraud-Mangin.— t. 2, 1. ptie. Documents antérieurs à la révolution, par R. Blanchard. 2. ptie. Documents divers, par J. Rousse et M. Giraud-Mangin.
1. Manuscripts. France—Catalogs. 2. France—Hist.—Revolution—Bibl. 3. Manuscripts, French—Catalogs. 4. Vendée—Hist.—Bibl. I. Dugast-Matifeux, Charles, 1812-   II. Fillon, Benjamin, 1819-1881. 1894. III. Rousse, Joseph, 1838-   IV. Giraud-Mangin, Marcel, 1872-   v. Blanchard, René, 1846-
Library of Congress   Z6621.N194   7-21190 Revised

NN 0015329 DLC MH CtY

Nantes. *Bureau diocésain*
see
Brittany. *États. Commission diocésaine. Nantes.*

Nantes. Bureau Municipal d'Hygiène.
... Bulletin annuel. [no.]
Nantes, 19
8°.
1. Hygiene (Public) France: Nantes.

NN 0015331 NN DL

French Rev.
DC
141
F87+
v.158
Nantes. Chambre de Commerce.
A Messieurs composant la Chambre des Députés des départemens. ⟨Paris, Le Normant, 1818⟩
4 p. 27cm.

Signed: Le Président, F. Collet ⟨et al.⟩

1. Customs administration—France—Nantes.
2. Bonded warehouses & goods—Nantes.

NN 0015332 NIC

Nantes—*Chambre de commerce.* Cacaos. [Nantes.] 1878.
8°. pp. 4. (Paris—Exposition universelle de 1878. Exposition des ports de commerce.)

NN 0015333 MH-A

Nantes. Chambre de commerce.
Compte rendu des travaux...

Nantes,   4°.

Title varies: 18 -1900, Rapport sur la situation commerciale et industrielle; 1901-1911, Exposé des travaux de commerce; 1912-1913, 1919-   , Compte rendu des travaux...

1. Economic hist.—France—Nantes.
N.Y.P.L.   November 17, 1930

Reports for 1914-1918 issued together with title: La Chambre de commerce pendant la guerre.
1901-   in two parts, each with separate t.-p. and paging. Part 2 has title: Rapport.. sur la situation commerciale et industrielle (1919-   , Renseignements sur la situation commerciale et industrielle... Documents statistiques concernant le port de Nantes et la Loire maritime).

NN 0015335 NN

Nantes. Chambre de Commerce.
Étude sur la traite des noirs avant 1790 au point de vue du commerce nantais
see under Augeard, Eugène.

Nantes   Chambre de Commerce.
Franco-British exhibition, London, 1908. The port of Nantes. Account published by the Chamber of Commerce. Nantes: M. Schwob Co., 1908. 2 p.l., (1)5-11 double p., 2 diagr., 1 pl.
8°.
In: TLH p. v. 17, no. 11.

1. Commerce, France : Nantes.   2. Exhibitions, London, 1908.
N.Y.P.L.   December 11, 1912.

NN 0015337 NN MH

VOLUME 405

Kress Room
Nantes. Chambre de commerce.
Mémoire ... contre les demandes d'établissements d'entrepôts de douanes à Paris et dans d'autres villes de l'intérieur du Royaume. Nantes, V.Mangin, 1819.
2 p.l., ₃₃-38 p. 19.5 cm.

Signed: L.Levesque aîné, président; A.Bonamy, L.Bureau ₄and others₎

1.Customs administration - France.

NN 0015338 MH-BA

Nantes. Chambre des comptes
see
Brittany. Chambre des comptes
France. Chambre des comptes (Nantes)

Nantes. Chambre royale
see France. Chambre royale (Nantes)
[in supplement]

DC 141 F87+ v.296
Nantes. Citizens.
Eclaircissemens demandés au Parlement de Paris sur son arrêt du 6 mars, par les jeunes gens de Nantes. Nantes, Impr. patriotique, 1789.
42 p. 22cm.

1. Liberty of the press--France. I France. Parlement (Paris) II. Title.

NN 0015341 NIC NN

Slavery F 1923 S22
Nantes. Citizens.
Pétition des citoyens commerçans, colons, agriculteurs, manufacturiers, & autres de la ville de Nantes. Lettre des commissairts ₄sic₎ de la Société d'agriculture, des arts & du commerce de ladite ville, aux commissaires de l'Assemblée coloniale de la partie françoise de Saint-Domingue; et réponse des commissaires de Saint-Domingue. ₄Paris, Impr. de L. Potier de Lille, 1792?₎
16,11 p. 21cm.

No. 7 in a vol. lettered: Saint-Domingue, 1788-1800.

NN 0015342 NIC

Nantes. Citizens
Les habitans de la commune de Nantes au Corps législatif. [P, an 7]
3 p.
At head of title: Corps législatif. Conseil des Anciens

NN 0015344 MH

Nantes. Commission diocésaine
see
Brittany. États. Commission diocésaine. Nantes.

W 2 GF7.1 L8C7r
NANTES. Conseil de salubrité
Rapport général sur les travaux.
Nantes, 18
v.
Vol. for 1827 bound in pam. vol. 1788.
Continued by the same title issued by the Conseil central de salubrité of the department of Loire-Inférieure.
1. Public health - France

NN 0015346 DNLM

Nantes. Conseil de santé des hospices.
Formulaire des hôpitaux de Nantes ...
see under title

French Rev. DC 141 F87+ v.520
Nantes. Corps administratifs.
Adresse des Corps administratifs de la ville de Nantes ₄2 mai 1793. Paris, Impr. nat., 1793₎
6 p. 18cm.

On the rebellion in Brittany.
Reprinted in archives Parlementaires, v. 64, p. 7.

NN 0015348 NIC

W qN191c 1909
NANTES. École de plein exercice de médecine et de pharmacie
Centenaire de l'Ecole de médecine et de l'internat en médecine des hôpitaux de Nantes. Souvenir du 3 juillet 1909. Nantes, Dugas, 1909.
116 p. illus., ports.

NN 0015349 DNLM

W1 NA128S
Nantes. Ecole de plein exercice de médecine et de pharmacie.
Séance de rentrée de l'Ecole de plein exercice de médecine et de pharmacie et de l'Ecole des sciences et des lettres.
1875-
Nantes.
v.
Continues the Séance de rentrée ... of the Ecole préparatoire de médecine et de pharmacie, Nantes.
At head of title: Académie de Rennes. Enseignement supérieur à Nantes.
I. Académie de Rennes. Enseignement supérieur à Nantes.

II. Nantes. Ecole supérieure des sciences et des lettres. III. Title

NN 0015351 DNLM

Nantes. École municipale de rééducation professionnelle pour les mutilés t réformés de la guerre.
... L'école municipale de rééducation professionnelle pour les mutilés et réformés de la guerre, 1916-1918; notice illustrée. Nantes, Imprimerie armoricaine, 1918.
2 p. l., ₍7₎-64 p. plates, diagr. 21½ᶜᵐ.
At head of title: République Française. Ministère de l'intérieur. Ville de Nantes.

1. Disabled—Rehabilitation, etc.—France.
18–23655
Library of Congress UB365.F9N3

NN 0015352 DLC NN MB DNLM OO ICJ

W1 NA128S
Nantes. Ecole préparatoire de médecine et de pharmacie.
Séance de rentrée de l'Ecole préparatoire de médecine et de pharmacie et de l'Ecole des sciences et des lettres.
Nantes, 18 -1875.
v.
Title varies slightly.
At head of title: Académie de Rennes. Enseignement supérieur à Nantes.
Continued by the Séance de rentrée ... of the Ecole de plein exercice de médecine et de pharmacie, Nantes.
I. Académie de Rennes. Enseignement supérieur à Nantes.

II. Nantes. Ecole supérieure des sciences et des lettres. III. Title

NN 0015354 DNLM

Nantes. Ecole supérieure des sciences et des lettres
Séance de rentrée de l'Ecole de plein exercice de médecine et de pharmacie
see under Nantes. Ecole de plein exercice de médecine et de pharmacie.

Nantes. Exposition des beaux-arts, 1886.
Catalogue des objets exposés. Nantes Impr. du commerce, 1886.
141 p. front. 18 cm.
1. Nantes-Antiq. 2. Art objects in Nantes.

NN 0015356 NjP

W4 N19
Nantes. Faculté de médecine et de pharmacie. Bibliothèque.
Liste des thèses. Nantes, [195-?]-
v.
Continued by Liste des thèses issued by the Bibliothèque of the Université de Nantes.
1. Dissertations, Academic - bibl. I. Title: Liste des thèses, Faculté de médecine et de pharmacie de Nantes

NN 0015357 DNLM

Nantes. Faculté de Théologie
see Nantes. Université. Faculté de Théologie.

WX 2 GF7 N1H8r
NANTES. Hospice général
Rapport sur le service médical du quartier d'aliénés. Nantes, 18
v.
1884-90? reports by Alcée Biaute.
I. Biaute. Alcée, 1849-1913.

NN 0015359 DNLM

Nantes. Institut Pasteur de la Loire-Inférieure. L610.7461 r
.... Bulletin du Laboratoire de bactériologie. .... Nantes, 78146 [1901]-1907.
Library has 1900/01-1905/06. plates, diagrs. 25½ᶜᵐ.
At head of title: Institut Pasteur de la Loire-Inférieure.
Dr. Rappin, director.
1901/02 wanting.

NN 0015360 ICJ ICRL DNLM

Nantes. Maire.
...Compte administratif.
₍Nantes,   sq. f°.
1. Municipal finance—France—Nantes.
N. Y. P. L.   January 13, 1928

NN 0015361 NN

Nantes. Maire.
...Exposé fait par le maire sur l'oeuvre accompli... 18
₍Nantes, 18   8°.
Quadrennial.
Title varies slightly.
1. Municipal government—France— Nantes.
N. Y. P. L.   February 7, 1929

NN 0015362 NN

352.044 N15g
Nantes. Maire.
Guerre 1914-1919. La municipalité et son oeuvre; rapport présenté au Conseil municipal ... Nantes, 1920.
426p.

NN 0015363 IU

VOLUME 405

1784 Nantes. Merchants.
fNa   Mémoire des négociants de Nantes,
contre l'admission des étrangers dans
nos colonies. ₍Nantes, Imprimerie de
Brun, l'aîné, 1784₎

19 p.   38cm.

Caption title.
1. France. Colonies. Commerce. 2.
France. Commerce. West Indies. 3. West
Indies. Commerce. France. I. Title.

NN   0015364   MnU

DELL
COLLECTION
1774 Nantes. Merchants.
fNa   Observations des négocians de Nantes,
sur un écrit qui a pour titre, Mémoire
en réponse a celui du commerce de France,
imprimé au Port-au-Prince, sur la fin de
1773. ₍Nantes, Imprimerie de va. Brun,
1774₎

22 p.   41cm.

Caption title.
Text of the   Mémoire and of the
Observations in   parallel columns.
1. France. Com-   merce. West Indies.
West Indies. Commerce. France.

3. Mémoire en réponse à celui de
commerce de France. I. Title.

NN   0015366   MnU

Nantes. Musée archéologique.   571.07461 Q300
.... . Catalogue du Musée archéologique de Nantes. Troisième
156668 édition. Par M. P. de Lisle du Dreneuc, ... avec la collabora-
tion de MM. P. Soullard ... et l'abbé G. Durville, ... Nantes,
Impr. moderne Joubin & Beuchet frères, 1903.
viii, 376 p. 23ᵐᵐ.
At head of title: Département de la Loire-Inférieure.
"Publications sur le Musée archéologique de Nantes," p. [iv].

NN   0015367   ICJ

Nantes. Musée archéologique.   L571.07461 M900
Catalogve dv Mvsée départemental d'archéologie de Nantes et
154728 de la Loire-Inférieure. Deuxième édition. Par Fᵈ Parenteav.
Nantes, Impr. V. Forest et É. Grimaud, 1869.
[4], iv, 140 p. illus., xii pl. 274ᵐᵐ.

NN   0015368   ICJ DSI

NANTES - Musée de peinture et de sculpture.

See NANTES - Musée des beaux-arts.

Nantes. Musée des beaux-arts.
... Catalogue, par Marcel Nicolle ... Avec la collaboration de Émile Dacier ... Nantes, Au Musée des beaux-
arts, 1913.
2 p. l., ₍viii₎-xlvi, 670 p., 1 l. 16ᵐᵐ.
At head of title: Ville de Nantes.   Musée municipal des beaux-arts.
"Bibliographie": p. ₍xxxii₎-xliv.

1. Art—Nantes—Catalogs.   I. Nicolle, Marcel. II. Dacier, Émile,
1876-   17-851
Library of Congress   N2143.A6 1913

NN   0015370   DLC NN PPPM

NANTES - Musée des beaux-arts.
Catalogue des tableaux et statues du Musée
de Nantes. Nantes,Ve C.Mellinet,1854.

NN   0015371   MH-FA

Nantes.____ Musée des beaux-arts.   4079a.12
= Catalogue des tableaux et statues du Musée de Nantes. 7e édition
Nantes. Mellinet. 1859. 310, (15) pp. 12°.

NN   0015372   MB

Nantes. Musée des beaux-arts.
Catalogue et guide, par Luc Benoist, conservateur du
Musée. Nantes, 1953.
254 p. 19 cm.

1. Paintings—Nantes—Catalogs. 2. Sculpture—Nantes—Catalogs.
I. Benoist, Luc, 1898-
N2143.A6 1953   54-41753 ‡

NN   0015373   DLC CdU CU CtY MH

Nantes. Musée des beaux-arts
Chefs d'oeuvre des collections nantaises; ₍exposition₎
mai 1954. Nantes, 1954.

34 p.

NN   0015374   MH-FA

NANTES - Musée des beaux-arts.
Collection Clarke de Feltre. Nantes,Ve
C.Mellinet,1854.

pp.34+.
At head of title:Musée de peinture & de
sculpture de Nantes.

NN   0015375   MH-FA

Nantes. Musée des beaux-arts.
E. Phélippes-Beaulieux, H.-W. Deville, R. Pinard; catalogue de l'oeuvre complet de chaque graveur. ₍Nantes, Éditions du Musée des beaux-arts, 1955.
47 p. illus. 19 cm.

1. Engravings, French—Catalogs.   I. Phélippes-Beaulieux, E.,
1829-1874. II. Deville, H.-W., 1871-1968. III. Pinard, René, 1885-1968.
IV. Title.
NE647.N3   68-129781

NN   0015376   DLC CtY MH

Nantes. Musée des beaux-arts.
Guide à travers les salles, par Luc Benoist, conservateur
du Musée. Nantes, 1953.
32 p. 18 cm.

1. Paintings—Nantes. 2. Sculpture—Nantes.   I. Benoist, Luc,
1898-
N2143.A7   54-41752 ‡

NN   0015377   DLC

Nantes. Musée des beaux arts.
Histoire et description du Musée de Nantes
see under Merson, Olivier, 1822-1902.

Nantes. Musée des beaux-arts.
Notice historique sur le Musée de Peinture
de Nantes ...
see under Saint-Georges, Henri de.

Nantes. Musée des beaux-arts
Retrospective Pierre Roy, 1880-1950; préface de
J.Lanoë. Catalogue par L.Benoist. Nantes, 1953.

20 p. plates

NN   0015380   MH-FA

0180 Nantes. Musée Dobrée.
.669   ...Autographes; inventaire des lettres,
chartes et pièces manuscrites. Nantes,
Grimaud, 1901.
6,146,26 p. 19 ᶜᵐ.

1.Autographs—Collections.

NN   0015381   NjP

Nantes. Musée Dobrée.
Catalogue des estampes. Nantes: Vié ₍1904₎. 2 p.l., xv,
257 p., 1 l. 12°.
At head of title: Musée Th. Dobrée.
Introduction, by Gustave Bourcard.
Autograph presentation copy from G. Bourcard to F. Weitenkampf.

1. Engravings.—Collections.   France: Musée Dobrée. 2. Bourcard, Gustave, 1846-   April 22, 1916.
N. Y. P. L.

NN   0015382   NN

Nantes. Musée Dobrée.   708.461 ɪ
.... . Catalogue général des collections, par P. de Lisle du
156665 Dreneuc, ... Nantes, Impr. moderne Joubin & Beuchet frères,
1906.
[4], xxi, [2], 1019 p. plates, 1 port. 204ᵐᵐ.
At head of title: Musée Th. Dobrée.
"Publications relatives au Musée Th. Dobrée," p. [2] at beginning.

NN   0015383   ICJ

Nantes. Musée Dobrée.
Musée T. Dobrée. Notice par Pitre de
Lisle du Dréneuc ... ₍Nantes, Grimaud,
1898₎
39 p. illus. (port.) 23 cm.
"Extrait de l'ouvrage Nantes et la Loire-
inférieure, publié ... en 1898."
I. Lisle du Dréneuc, Pitre de.

NN   0015384   NjP

Nantes. Musée Dobrée. *Bibliothèque.*
Catalogue de la bibliothèque du Musée Thomas Dobrée ...
sous la direction de M. P. De Lisle Du Dréneuc, conservateur.
Nantes, au Musée Thomas Dobrée, 1903-04.
2 v. fronts. (v. 2, port.) illus., facsims. 23ᵐᵐ.
No more published.
CONTENTS.—t. 1. Manuscrits par l'abbé G. Durville. 1904.—t. 2. Imprimés (1ʳᵉ partie ₍impressions des quinzième seizième siècles₎) par
M. Louis Polain. 1903.
1. Incunabula—Bibl.—Catalogs. 2. Manuscripts. France—Catalogs.
3. Bibliography—Rare books.   I. Lisle du Dréneuc, Pitre de. II. Polain, Louis, 1866-   III. Durville, Georges, 1853-
Library of Congress   Z027.N22   5-8721 Revised

NN   0015385   DLC MdBWA ICJ NN CtY

Nantes. Musée Dobrée. *Bibliothèque.*   017.44 ɴ15
.... . Catalogue sommaire de la bibliothèque, par P. de Lisle du
67000 Dreneuc. Nantes, Impr. moderne Joubin & Beuchet frères, 1905.
[4], 207, [2] p. 21ᵐᵐ.
At head of title: Musée Th. Dobrée.
—— .... . Supplément au Catalogue sommaire de la bibliothèque .... Nantes, 1908.
40 p. 18ᵐᵐ.

NN   0015386   ICJ ICN

Nantes. Musée Thomas Dobrée
see
Nantes. Musée Dobrée.

Nantes. Musées départementaux de Loire-Atlan-
tique. Musée Dobrée
see
Nantes. Musée Dobrée.

VOLUME 405

Nantes. *Musées des arts décoratifs.*
... Faïences et poteries rustiques. Paris, C. Massin et c⁰ᵉ
₁1929₎   ❦
15, ₁1₎ p. illus., 40 pl. (part col.) 32¼ᶜᵐ. (L'Art populaire français,
collection publiée sous la direction de Joseph Gauthier)

1. Pottery.   I. Title.

S 34-292

Library, Smithsonian   Institution

NN 0015389   DSI OC

Nantes. *Ordinances, etc.*
Arrests, ordonnances, reglemens et deliberations, expediées
sur les principales affaires de la ville & communauté de
Nantes ...
Nantes, 17
v. 19ᶜᵐ.

44–50884

Library of Congress   JS5075.N34A3

NN 0015390   DLC MH

Nantes. Saint-Pierre (Cathedral)

Géricault, Jean Louis André Théodore, 1791–1824.
Théodore Géricault; correspondance officielle relative au tableau qui lui avait été commandé pour Nantes, communiquée
par m. le baron de Girardot.
(*In* Archives de l'art français ... Paris, 1862. 21¼ᶜᵐ. 2. sér., t. 2,
p. 72–80)

W 2   **NANTES.** Service municipal d'hygiène
GF7.2   Bulletin annuel.
N1S4
Nantes, 19
v.
1. Public health - France - Nantes
2. Vital statistics - France - Nantes

NN 0015392   DNLM

W 2   **NANTES.** Service municipal d' hygiène
GF7.2   Rapport annuel. 1951-
N1S4   Nantes.
v.
Continues Nantes. Service municipal
d' hygiène. Bulletin annuel.
1. Public health - France - Nantes
2. Vital statistics - France - Nantes

NN 0015393   DNLM

Nantes. Société académique
see   Société académique de Nantes et du
département de la Loire-Inférieure.

Nantes. Société archéologique
see   Société archeologique et historique de
Nantes et de Loire Atlantique.

Nantes. Société d'agriculture, des arts et
du commerce
see   Société d'agriculture des arts et
du commerce de Nantes.

Nantes. Société de geographie commerciale
see   Société de geographie commerciale
de Nantes.

Nantes.   Société des bibliophiles bretons et
de l'histoire de Bretagne
see
Société des bibliophiles bretons et de l'histoire de Bretagne, *Nantes.*

Nantes. Société des horticulteurs
see   Société des horticulteurs de Nantes.

Nantes. Société des sciences naturelles de l'Ouest
de la France
see   Société des Sciences Naturelles de
L'Ouest de la France, Nantes.

Nantes. Société industrielle.
see   Société Industrielle de Nantes.

Nantes. Société nantaise d'horticulture
see   Société nantaise d'horticulture.

.5A   **NANTES. UNIVERSITÉ. Faculté de Théologie.**
6468   Epistola S. Facultatis Theologiae Nan-
no.27   netensis ad Eminentissimum Cardinalem Noal-
lium. ₁Nantes, 1717₎
₁2₎ℓ. 26cm.
"Traduction de la precedente lettre ...
au sujet de la Constitution Unigenitus":
ℓ.₁2₎

NN 0015403   ICN

Nantes. (Diocese).
Catechisme du diocèse de Nantes ...
see under   Catholic Church. Catechisms.
French.

5A   **NANTES (Diocese)**
6468   Copie de la lettre des peres de l'Ora-
no.23   toire de Nantes, à Monseigneur le Cardinal
de Noailles. ₁Nantes? 1717₎
₁1₎ℓ. 26cm.
Concerning the Papal bull Unigenitus.

NN 0015405   ICN

Nantes (Diocèse)
Documents pour servir à l'histoire du diocèse de
Nantes
see under   Cahour ₁Abel₎ editor.

Nantes (Diocese)
Protestation de 105 curés de la Bretagne, contre la
nouvelle organisation civile du clergé, adressée à
l'Assemblée nationale. np, nd.

32 p.
Dated: avril 1790

NN 0015407   MH

NANTES (DIOCÈSE).
Statuts et réglements du diocèse de Nantes,
publiés par M.gr de Guérines, évêque de Nantes,
à la retraite ecclésiastique, le 29 août 1837.
Nantes, C. Mellinet, 1837.

20 cm.

NN 0015408   MH

Nantes (Diocèse) Siège présidial
see   Catholic Church in France.
Siège présidial de Nantes.

... **Nantes.** Paris, Hachette, 1930.
64 p. illus., 8 pl., fold. map. 17½ᶜᵐ. (Les guides bleus illustrés)

1. Nantes—Descr.—Guide-books.
Library of Congress   DC801.N2N2   31–1616
Copyright A—Foreign   9100

NN 0015410   DLC

Nante's darstellungen scheinbarer zauberei
see under   ₁Lenz, Ludwig₎ 1813–1896.

Nantes en dix-neuf cent ...
see under   Lepère, Auguste, 1849–1918.

Nantes et la Loire-Inférieure
see under   Chevalier, Pierre Michel
Francois, called Pitre-Chevalier, 1812–1864.

Nante's Tod
see under   ₁Arnim, Harry, graf von₎
1824–1881.

Nante's Weinachtswanderung und Neujahrsgruss
see under   ₁Lenz, Ludwig₎ 1813–1896.

Nantet, Jacques, 1910-
Bataille pour la faiblesse. ₁Paris₎ Gallimard ₁1948₎
236 p. 19 cm. (Les Essais, 29)
Bibliographical footnotes.

1. Liberty. 2. Property. 3. Nationalism and nationality.
I. Title.
HM271.N3   323.4   49–27142*

NN 0015416   DLC NRU IU

VOLUME 405

Nantet, Jacques, *1910 –*
... Les sanctions dans le Pacte de la S. d. n. Historique et conditions d'application. Paris, Les Éditions Domat-Montchrestien, 1936.

3 p. l., ₍9₎–240, ₍2₎ p. 25½ᶜᵐ.

"Annexe. Pacte de la Société des nations": p. ₍227₎–288.
"Bibliographie": p. ₍224₎–226.

1. Sanctions (International law) 2. League of nations. Covenant. Article 16. i. Title.

Library of Congress   JX1975.6.N3   39–1798

NN   0015417   DLC IU CtY NN

Nantet, Jacques, 1910–
Soyons neutres. Lyon, IAC ₍1950₎
62 p. 20 cm.

1. European federation. 2. Europe—Politics, 1945–   i. Title.
D844.N27   A 51–5442
New York. Public Libr.
for Library of Congress   ₍3₎†

NN   0015418   NN DLC

Nantouil, Amaury de la Barre de, baron

see

La Barre de Nanteuil, Amaury de, baron.

Nanteuil, Auguste de La Barre de
see   La Barre de Nanteuil, Auguste comte de.

PQ1823   Nanteuil, Célestin, 1813–1873, illus.
.L4
Rare bk.   Molière, Jean Baptiste Poquelin, 1622–1673.
Coll.   ... Œuvres choisies de Molière. Éd. épurée, illustrée de 20 grands dessins de Célestin-Nanteuil, gravés par mm. Brevière et Trichon. Paris, P. C. Lehuby ₍1846₎

Nanteuil, *Claire Julie (Pascales) de, 1843*
... Alain le baleinier. Ouvrage illustré de 51 vignettes dessinées par A. Paris. Paris, Hachette et cie., 1896.
2 p. l., 278 p., 1 l. illus., plates. 24½ᶜᵐ.

1. Whaling.   i. Paris, A., illus.   ii. Title.
A 18–1591
Title from Harvard Univ.   Printed by L. C.

NN   0015422   MH

NANTEUIL, CLAIRE JULIE (PASCALES) DE, 1843–
...Alexandre Vorzof; ouvrage illustré de 80 vignettes dessinées par Myrbach. Paris: Librairie Hachette et cie., 1894. 302 p. incl. plates. illus. 8°.

At head of title: **Mme. P. de Nanteuil.**

567391A. 1. Fiction, French. I. Myrbach, illustrator. II. Title.

NN   0015423   NN MB

Nanteuil, Claire Julie (Pascales) de, 1843-
Captain; translated by Laura Ensor ... L., 1890.

386 p. 8vo.

NN   0015424   PPL ViW

Nanteuil, Claire Julie (Pascales) de, 1843-
Capitaine ... 2d ed. Paris, 1868.

NN   0015425   PSC

Nanteuil, Claire Julie (Pascales) de, 1843-
L'epave mystérieuse ... 2d ed. Paris, 1891.
298 p.

NN   0015426   PSC

Nanteuil, Claire Julie (Pascales) de, 1843-
En esclavage, ouvrage illustré ... Paris, 1891.

NN   0015427   PPL

Nanteuil, Claire Julie (Pascales) de, 1843-
En esclavage, par Mme. de Nanteuil. [Paris] Hachette [1925] 319 p. illus. (Bibliothèque bleue.)

1. Algeria – Fiction. (TITLE)

NN   0015428   NN

Nanteuil, Claire Julie (Pascales) de, 1843-
... En esclavage. Illustrations de A. de Parys.   Paris, Librairie Hachette [1925]
3 p. l., [5]-319, [1] p.   incl. front., illus. 18 cm.   (On cover: Bibliothèque rose illustrée).

NN   0015429   CtY

Nanteuil, Claire Julie *(Pascales) de, 1843-*   66g2.26
L'héritier des Vaubert. Ouvrage illustré de 80 vignettes dessinées par Alfred Paris.
= Paris. Hachette & cie. 1895. (3), 330, (1) pp. Illus. Plates. 8°.
The scene is laid in France and on board French vessels, early in the Nineteenth Century.

E3364 — T.r. — France. Hist. Fict.

NN   0015430   MB PPL

Nanteuil, Claire Julie (Pascales) de, 1843-
... Nella schiavitù. Illustrato da 60 incisioni in legno di Myrbach ... Milano, Verri ₍189-?₎

2 p. l., 293 p., 1 l. illus., plates. 25cm.

At head of title: P. de Nanteuil.

Translation of En esclavage.

NN   0015431   NCH

PH 3875   Nanteuil, Denis Clerselier de, b. 1650.
.N25 C2   Le campagnard dupé, comedie en vers irregu-
1671 P   liers. Par D. C. de Nantéüil ... Hannover, W. Schwendiman, 1671.
2 p.l., [4]-64 p. 19cm.

Photostat copy (negative)
Page 64 incorrectly bound between first and second prelim. leaf.
Leaves folded in Japanese style.

NN   0015432   MdBJ

N6j85   Nanteuil, E   de
898N   La paume et le lawn-tennis, par E. de Nanteuil, G. de Saint-Clair [et] Delahaye. Paris, Hachette, 1898.
422p. illus., ports., diagrs., tables. 20cm. (Bibliothèque du sport)

1. Tennis.

NN   0015433   CtY NN

Nanteuil, Gaugiran de
see
Gaugiran-Nanteuil, P   Charles, 1778–ca. 1830.

PQ1542   Nanteuil, Geneviève.
.A2N3
Tristan.
Tristan et Iseut; adaptation de Geneviève Nanteuil, 10 illustrations en couleurs de Jean Gradassi. Paris, Éditions du Panthéon, 1952.

Hfr   Nanteuil, Georges
na100   ... Monsieur Jean, comédie en un acte. Paris, P.-V.Stock, 1907.
44p. 19cm.
"Représentée pou la première fois au théâtre du Grand-Guignol, le 20 janvier 1907."

NN   0015436   CtY NN

Nanteuil, H   de.
Collection de monnaies grecques ₍par₎ H. de Nanteuil ... Paris, J. Florange ₍etc.₎ 1925.
xiv, 343 p., 1 l. and portfolio of ix pl. 26½ᶜᵐ.

1. Coins, Greek.

NN   0015437   MiU NjP NN MH

Nanteuil, Jacques.
L'épopée missionnaire de Théophane Vénard. Paris, Bloud & Gay ₍1950₎
119 p. 19 cm.

1. Vénard, Jean Théophane, 1829–1861. 2. Catholic Church—Missions. 3. Missions—China.

BX4705.V43N3   52–15007

NN   0015438   DLC CtY

Nanteuil, Jacques.
Le fanal exhaussé; cinquante ans d'activité littéraire. Préf. de Henri Pourrat. Niort, Cahiers de l'Ouest ₍1955₎
278 p. 19 cm.
Bibliography: p. ₍4₎

CONTENTS.—L'avenue bordée de cyprès.—Interludes.—Essais et méditations.—Poitou, mon Poitou.—Pages d'histoire et de critique.

1. French literature—20th cent.—Addresses, essays, lectures. i. Title.
A 56–852
Illinois. Univ. Library
for Library of Congress   ₍3₎

NN   0015439   IU OrU NN CU CtY

Nanteuil, Jacques.
... Ferdinand Brunetière, par Jacques Nanteuil. Paris, Bloud et Gay ₍1933₎
159 p. incl. front. (port.) 19ᶜᵐ. (Les maîtres d'une génération)
Printed in Belgium.
"Bibliographie": p. 157–158.

1. *Brunetière, Ferdinand, 1849–1906.
Library of Congress   PQ67.B8N3   35–10186
₍2₎   928.4

NN   0015440   DLC CtY NN CU MU LU OO MiU OCl NcD

VOLUME 405

BR115
.C5M27

Nanteuil, Jacques.
 ₍Marrou, Henri Irénée₎
 ... Fondements d'une culture chrétienne; supplément: Paul Archambault, René Aigrain ₍et₎ Jacques Nanteuil. ₍Paris₎ Bloud & Gay ₍1934₎

Nanteuil, Jacques.
 Le généralissime de vingt ans, Henri de La Rochejaquelein
  see his   Henri de la Rochejaquelein...

Nanteuil, Jacques.
 Ginès de Passamont, gentilhomme de grand chemin; roman ₍par₎ Gaston Giraudias (Jacques Nanteuil) Niort, Éditions Saint-Denis ₍1943₎
 282 p. 19 cm.

 ɪ. Title.
 PQ2674.A54G5   79–209975

NN   0015443   DLC

Nanteuil, Jacques.
 Henri de la Rochejaquelein, le généralissime de vingt ans. Paris, A. Bonne ₍1952₎
 281 p. 19 cm.   (La Grande et la petite histoire)

 1. La Rochejaquelein, Henri du Vergier, comte de, d. 1794. 2. Vendean War, 1793–1800. ɪ. Title: Le généralissime de vingt ans.
 DC218.N35   923.244   53–36994 ‡

NN   0015444   DLC NIC NN

Nanteuil, Jacques.
 ...L'inquiétude religieuse et les poètes d'aujourd'hui; essais sur Jules Laforgue, Albert Samain, Charles Guérin, Francis Jammes. Paris: Bloud & Gay, 1925. 203 p. 12°.

205636A. 1. Laforgue, Jules, 1860–1858–1900. 3. Guérin, Charles, 1873–5. Christianity—Tendencies, 20th cent. N. Y. P. L.
1887. 2. Samain, Albert Victor, 1907. 4. Jammes, Francis, 1868–
October 22, 1925

NN   0015445   NN MiU WaU InU ICU

Nanteuil, Jacques.
 Sainte Radegonde, princesse barbare et reine de France, par Jacques Nanteuil. ₍Paris₎ Bloud & Gay, 1938.
 188, ₍2₎ p., 1 l. 18½°.
 "Bibliographie": ₍2₎ p. at end.

 1. Radegonde, Saint, d. 587.
                  40–2816
 Library of Congress   BX4700.R3N3
         ₍2₎   922.244

NN   0015446   DLC ICN CtY

Nanteuil, Jacques.
 Le Val de Sèvre du pays de Mélusine au marais Poitevin. Niort, Éditions Saint-Denis ₍1949₎
 75 p. illus., map. 19 cm.

 1. Sèvre-Niortaise Valley—Descr. & trav. ɪ. Title.
 DC611.S513N3   914.462   A 50–7201
 New York. Public Libr.
 for Library of Congress   ₍3₎†

NN   0015447   NN DLC

Nanteuil, Jacques, joint author.
Lamandé, André, 1886–
 ... La vie de René Caillié, vainqueur de Tombouctou ... Paris, Plon ₍1928₎

Nanteuil, P   Charles Gaugiran–,
               see
Gaugiran-Nanteuil, P   Charles, 1778–ca. 1830.

Nanteuil, Mme. P   de
     see   Nanteuil, Claire Julie (Pascales) de, 1843–

Nanteiul, Robert, 1623–1679.
 ... Catalogue de l'oeuvre gravé de Robert Nanteuil...
  see under   Petitjean, Ch.

Nanteuil, Robert, 1623–1678.
 Catalogue of an exhibition of engraved portraits by Robert Nanteuil
  see under   Keppel, Frederick, & Co.

Nanteuil, Robert, *1623–1678.*
 Line engravings.   Lent by Lessing J. Rosenwald. Philadelphia, 1929.
 16 p.

NN   0015453   PPDrop

Nanteuil, Robert, 1623–1678, engr.
Marolles, Michel de, 1600–1681.
 Les memoires de Michel de Marolles, abbé de Villeloin. Divisez en trois parties, contenant ce qu'il a vû de plus remarquable en sa vie, depuis l'année 1600. Ses entretiens auec quelques-vns des plus sçauants hommes de son temps. Et les genealogies de quelques familles alliées dans la sienne, auec vne brieue description de la tres-illustre maison de Mantoüe & de Neuers ... Paris, Antoine de Sommaville, 1656–57.

Nanteuil, Robert, 1623–1678, engr.
Loret, Jean, 1595–1665.
 La mvze historiqve; ov Recveil des lettres en vers, contenant les nouuelles du temps. Écrites a son altesse mademoizelle de Longueuille. Par le sⁱ Loret ... A Paris, Chez Charles Chenavlt, imprimeur ordinaire du roy, au bout du Pont S. Michel, à l'entrée de la ruë de la Huchette. M.DC.LVIII–₍LX₎

Nanteuil, Robert, 1623–1678.
 A notable collection of the works of the peintre-graveur Robert Nanteuil
  see under   Knoedler (M.) and Company, inc.

Nanteuil, Robert, 1623–1678, illus.
Gaultier, Denis, d. 1672.
 La rhétorique des dieux et autres pièces de luth de Denis Gaultier. par André Tessier ... Paris, E. Droz, 1932–33.

Nanteuil, Robert de, *baron.*
 ... Les portraits d'Elvire, le masque arraché, la vraie figure de l'amie de Lamartine; avec une lettre-préface de m. René Doumic ... Trois planches et un tableau généalogique hors texte. Paris, Les Presses universitaires de France, 1931 ₍i. e. 1934₎
 2 p. l., ₍vii₎–viii, 226 p., 1 l. front. (port.) fold. facsims., fold geneal. tab. 19ᶜᵐ.
 At head of title: Bⁿ de Nanteuil.
 "Achevé d'imprimer en 1934."
 "Il a été tiré de cet ouvrage ... 200 exemplaires sur papier d'alfa, numérotés de 11 à 210. No. 57."
 1. Charles, Julie Françoise (Bouchaud des Hérettes) 1784–1817. 2. Lamartine, Alphonse Marie Louis de, 1790–1869. ɪ. Title.
                       42–34342
 Library of Congress   PQ2326.N35

NN   0015458   DLC CU IaU GU WU IU

Nantglyn, Bardd
   see   Davies, Robert, 1769?–1835.

Nanthou, François Félix Hyacinthe Muguet de
   see   Muguet de Nanthou, François Félix Hyacinthe, 1760–1808.

Map
G
7010
1806
N3
Nantiat, Jasper
 The Russian dominions in Europe drawn from the latest maps, printed by the Academy of Sciences, St. Petersburg; revised and corrected, with the post roads and new governments from the Russian Atlas of 1806. London, W. Faden, 1808.
 col. map 108 x 92 cm.

 Scale approx. 50 miles to the inch.

 1. Russia—Maps.

NN   0015461   NIC

Nanticoke, *Pa.*
 Controller's annual statement ...
 ₍Nanticoke, 19
 v. tables. 19ᶜᵐ.

 1. Finance—Nanticoke, Pa.
                 ca 36–1996 Unrev'd
 Library of Congress   HJ9013.N124
         ₍2₎   352.10074832

NN   0015462   DLC

Nanticoke, Pa., residential and business register, 1919– including the towns and villages of Alden Station, Askam, Avondale, Chauncey, Christopher, Conerete City, Dundee, Glen Lyon, Hunlock Creek, Korn Krest, Mocanaqua, Newport Center, Sheatown, Sugar Notch, Warrior Run, and West Nanticoke ... ₍1st– issue₎ ₍Nanticoke₎ H. C. Morris
 v. 23ᶜᵐ.

 1. Nanticoke, Pa.—Direct. 2. Luzerne Co., Pa.—Direct.
                 20–3863
 Library of Congress   F159.N2N19

NN   0015463   DLC

Nanticoke Indians. *Treaties, 1757.*
New York *(Colony) Treaties, etc.,* 1757.
 Proceedings and treaty with the Shawanese, Nanticokes, and Mohickander Indians, living at Otsiningo, on one of the west branches of the Susquehanna river. Negotiated at Fort-Johnson, in the county of Albany, in the province of New-York; by the Honourable Sir William Johnson, bart. &c. Published by order of His Excellency the Right Honourable John, earl of Loudoun ... New-York: Printed and sold by J. Parker and W. Weyman, at the New printing-office in Beaver-street, MDCCLVII.

VOLUME 405

Nantier, Étienne.
Mains mûres. Paris, P. Seghers ₁1952₎
34 p. 18 cm. (Poésie 52, 157)

ɪ. Title.

A 53-447

Illinois. Univ. Library
for Library of Congress   ₁ɪ₎

NN 0015465   IU NN NNC

Nantier, Étienne.
Sillons. Paris, P. Seghers ₁1954₎
53 p. 19 cm.
Poems:

ɪ. Title.

A 55-2974

Illinois. Univ. Library₎
for Library of Congress   ₁ɪ₎

NN 0015466   IU NN

Nantigny, Louis Chasot de
see
Chasot de Nantigny, Louis, 1692-1755.

Nantilus, Captain, pseud.
SEE
Eldridge, Clement

Nantiporto, notaio del
see Pontani, Gaspare, ca. 1449-ca. 1524.

Nantke, Hans, 1899–
Ueber thallamuserkrankung.
Inaug. diss. Bonn , 1926.
Bibl.

NN 0015470   ICRL CtY

HB3711 Nantke, Rudolf, 1907–
.N15   Eine untersuchung über den zwangs-
sparprozess im konjunkturzyklus..
Düren-Rl., Dissertations-druckerei, 1934.
128 p. 21 ᶜᵐ.

Inaug.-diss. – Frankfurt am Main.
Lebenslauf.
"Literaturverzeichnis": 2 p. at end.

NN 0015471   NjP CtY MiU

Nantlais, *bardic name*
see **Williams, William Nantlais, 1874–**

南島雜話 永井龍一編纂 鹿児島 白塔社 昭和8
₁1933₎
2 v. (double leaves) illus. 24 cm.
Mimeographed.
Vol. 2 has cover title: 南島雜話補遺篇

1. Ryukyu Islands—Soc. life & cust.   ɪ. Nagai, Ryūichi, ed.
Title romanized: Nantō satsuwa.

J 65-1630

Harvard Univ. Chinese.   Japanese Library 4150.851
for Library of Congress   ₁ɪ₎

NN 0015473   MH-HY

Nanton, Robert, 1563-1635.
see
Naunton, Sir Robert, 1563-1635.

Nantua, Simon de, pseud.
Histoire d'Albert
see Toepffer, Rodolphe, 1799-1846.

Nantuas, Judah Loeb ben Joseph Rophe
see **Judah Loeb ben Joseph Rophe.**

₁**Nantucket**₎ *pseud.*
The spectre ship of Salem; a tale of a naval apparition
of the seventeenth century ... Salem, Mass., 1907.
xxii p. 25½ᶜᵐ.
Pref. signed: P. K. Foley.
"Seventy-six copies printed for George Francis Dow."
"The prose sketch ... was first₎ published in Blackwood's magazine (Edinburgh) for March, 1830, over the pseudonym 'Nantucket' ... Whittier's
poetic rendering of the legend, with prefatory note ₍p. xvii–xxii of the
present edition₎ was published in 'American anecdotes' (Boston, 1830,
vol. ɪɪ, pages 40–44)"

ɪ. Whittier, John Greenleaf, 1807–1892. ɪɪ. Foley, Patrick Kevin, ed.

Library of Congress   8-4260

NN 0015477   DLC MWA RPB

Nantucket, Mass.
Nantucket illustrated
see Nantucket, illustrated.

NANTUCKET, Mass.
Report [of the] town and county of Nantucket.
[Nantucket]   v.   23cm.

Annual.

NN 0015479   NN

Nantucket, Mass.
Statement of the receipts and expenditures
of the town...
see under Nantucket, Mass. Finance
Committee.

Nantucket, *Mass.*
Vital records of Nantucket, Massachusetts, to the year
1850 ...   Boston, Mass., The New England historic genealogical society at the charge of the Eddy town-
record fund, 1925–
v. 23½ᶜᵐ. ₍New England historic genealogical society. Vital records of the towns of Massachusetts₎
Alphabetical indexes to the manuscript records of the town, supplemented
by information from church registers, cemetery inscriptions, and other
sources.

ɪ. Registers of births, etc.—Nantucket, Mass. ɪ. Title.

Library of Congress   F72.N2N126   25-27172

NN ICN
NN 0015481   DLC NIC MtHi WaSp MeB MWA MB CaBVaU

Nantucket, Mass. Advertising Committee.   2389.138
Nantucket Island, Massachusetts. An ideal health and vacation re-
sort.
= [Nantucket. 1907.] (15) pp. Illus. Folded map. 8°.
The title is on the cover.

G6566 — Nantucket, Mass. Descr. Guide-books.

NN 0015482   MB MWA

Nantucket, Mass. Atheneum
see Nantucket Atheneum.

Nantucket, Mass. Charles G. Coffin
mansion
see
Charles G. Coffin mansion, Nantucket, Mass.

Nantucket, Mass. Citizens.   No. 21 in **G.323.3
MEMORIAL of the inhabitants of Nantucket, praying an increase of duty
on imported tallow.
Washington. Gales & S. 1824. 5 pp. 8°.

NN 0015485   MB

Nantucket, Mass. Citizens.
Petition of the inhabitants of the island &
town of Nantucket, in the state of Massachusetts.
11th February, 1803. Referred to the Committee
of commerce and manufacturers. 16th February,
1803. Report made, considered and agreed.
7th November, 1803. Referred to a committee
of the whole House, on Monday next.
[Washington? 1803]
8 p.   21 cm.   [Binder's title: Reports
&c. I sess. 8 Cong.]

NN 0015486   CtY

Nantucket, *Mass. Committee on education and free
schools.*
An address to the inhabitants of Nantucket, on education and free schools. Providence, Knowles, Vose & company, 1838.
24 p. 22ᶜᵐ.
Signed: Cyrus Peirce, James Mitchell, Henry F. Edes, Wm. Mitchell,
Wm. Coffin.
"By request of the secretary of the Board of education, the undersigned were appointed a committee to address you on the subject of education and free schools." *cf.* p. ₍3₎

1. Education.

E 10-181

Library. U. S. Bur. of   Education LA305.N2A3

NN 0015487   DHEW

Nantucket, Mass. Finance Committee.
Statement of the receipts and expenditures of the town and
county of Nantucket.
Nantucket,   8°.
Annual.
Report year ends February 1st.

1. Municipal finance—U. S.—Mass.   —Nantucket. 2. Finance—U. S.—
Mass.—Nantucket County.
N. Y. P. L.   October 15, 1934

NN 0015488   NN

NANTUCKET, Mass.— First Congregational Church.
The confession of faith and covenant.
Boston, 1850.

NN 0015489   MH

[Nantucket, Mass. Loan exhibition committee]
Loan exhibition of heirlooms...
see under title

Nantucket, Mass. Maria Mitchell Association
see
Nantucket Maria Mitchell Association.

VOLUME 405

NANTUCKET, Mass. Pleyel society.

See PLEYEL SOCIETY, Nantucket.

Nantucket, Mass.   School committee.
Report...1842/43 46/47 72/73
82/83 87/88 1932.
Nantucket, 1843- (1933)
6 v.

NN 0015493   DHEW

Nantucket agricultural society.
Transactions for 1856,...Nantucket, 1857-1900.

NN 0015494   Nh

Nantucket "Argument settlers"
see under [Turner, Harry Baker]
1877-

Z881   NANTUCKET   ATHENEUM. LIBRARY.
.N15C   Catalogue ... with its rules and regulations.
1883   Nantucket, Hussey & Robinson, 1883.
iv, 143 p.

NN 0015496   ICU

027.4   Nantucket *Atheneum. Library*
N158   Catalogue.   Comp. by Mrs. Richard F. Bond.
Chelsea, Mass., C.H. Pike, 1900.
121p. 25cm.

J. Catalogs, Library. I. Bond, Mrs.
Richard F.

NN 0015497   OrU

The Nantucket directory ...
Boston, Mass., Union publishing co.
v. 24ᵐ.

1. Nantucket, Mass.—Direct.

Library of Congress   F72.N2A18   19-16556

NN 0015498   DLC

Nantucket Harbor.   1848.

NN 0015499   NWM

Nantucket Historical Association.
Bulletin. v. 1-
Nantucket, 1896-
v. in   illus., maps. 24 cm. irregular.

F72.N2N2   60-24958

NN 0015500   DLC PHC Nh MWelC MB NN MiD

Nantucket historical association.
Centennial catalogue of the Nantucket historical association.
Published by the Society.   Nantucket (Mass.) Inquirer and
mirror press, 1895.
27 p. 24ᵐ.

I. Title   40-16147

Library of Congress   F72.N2N236
                        (2)   974.49

NN 0015501   DLC ICU MWA

Nantucket historical association.
Constitution and by-laws of the Nantucket historical
association, incorporated July 9, 1894.   Nantucket, Mass.
(Inquirer and mirror print) 1894.
19, (1) p. 15½ᵐ.

                                24-7453

Library of Congress   F72.N2N21

NN 0015502   DLC MWA PHi Nh

F72   Nantucket Historical Association.
N2H68
Historic Nantucket. v. 1-
July 1953-
Nantucket, Mass., Nantucket Historical Association.

Nantucket historical association.

Shurrocks, Alfred F.
Indian artifacts collected on Nantucket, Massachusetts, and
presented to the Nantucket historical association by Alfred F.
and Alice Albertson Shurrocks. (Nantucket Island, Mass.,
The Inquirer and mirror press, ᶜ1940)

Nantucket historical association.
[Papers]   Nantucket, 1898.
v. 1-2   O.

NN 0015505   RPB

Nantucket Historical Association.
Nantucket newspapers.   1902.

NN 0015506   MNBedf

Nantucket historical association.

Macy, William Francis, 1867-
Nantucket's Oldest house (1686) "The Jethro Coffin house",
"The Horseshoe house", written and compiled for the Nantucket historical association by William F. Macy ... Nantucket, The Inquirer and mirror press, 1929.

Nantucket Historical Association.
Proceedings. 1st-   annual meeting; 1895-
Nantucket, Mass.
v. in   illus. 24 cm.
INDEXES:
Vols. 51-55, 1945-49. 1 v.

1. Nantucket, Mass.—Hist.—Societies.

F72.N2N16   974.497   7-40922 rev*

NN 0015508   DLC MWA KyU ICN PHi PHC Nh MB

Nantucket Historical Association.
Quakerism on Nantucket., 1955

see under

Dell, Burnhan North.

Nantucket historical association.

Worth, Henry Barnard.
... Quakerism on Nantucket since 1800, by Henry Barnard
Worth. (Nantucket, Mass.) Nantucket historical association,
1896.

Nantucket Historical Association.
Ye old mill, 1746, Nantucket, Mass.
see under Macy, William Francis, 1867-

Nantucket, illustrated. Copyright ... by A. Wittemann ...
New York, The Albertype co., ᶜ1888.
1 p. l., 15 pl. 12 x 17ᵐ.

1. Nantucket, Mass.—Descr.—Views. I. Wittemann, Adolph, 1845-
1938.
                                1-12201 Revised
Library of Congress   F72.N2N3

NN 0015512   DLC MWA

NANTUCKET in the ocean.   n.p., [1889?]

NN 0015513   MH

Nantucket Inquirer
see Nantucket Inquirer and mirror.

Nantucket inquirer and mirror.
[Nantucket,Mass.]
54cm.

Began publication June 23, 1821.
Frequency varies.
Title varies: June 23, 1821-1865, Nantucket
inquirer.

NN 0015515   CtY

Nantucket Inquirer *and mirror.*
Inquirer Office, Nantucket, Dec. 29,
'56. Dear Sir:- By the list of papers
which you will receive at the State
House, you will please notice that the
Nantucket Inquirer is published tri-
weekly, and weekly ... Legislatively
yours, John Morissey, editor of Nantucket Inquirer. [Nantucket? 1856]

broadside, 12½ x 10cm.

NN 0015516   MHi

Nantucket Maria Mitchell Association.
Annual report. 1st-
1902/03-
(n. p.)
v. in   illus. 15-24 cm.
Report year ends Jan. 31.
Title varies : 1902/03-   Report.

Q11.N15   15-21929 rev*

NN 0015517   DLC PHC NN ICRL ICJ AzU MB TU CtNlC

VOLUME 405

Nantucket Maria Mitchell association.
... Bulletin. no. 1– ; May 1923–
[Nantucket? Mass., 1923–
v. 19ᵐ.
At head of title: The Nantucket Maria Mitchell association.

CA 33–799 Unrev'd

Library of Congress   Q11.N147

NN 0015518   DLC CU

Nantucket Maria Mitchell association.
The Nantucket Maria Mitchell association. Founded 1902,
incorporated July 18, 1903. [Philadelphia, Ferris & Leach,
printers, 1909?]
11, [1] p. illus. 20½ᵐ.
Portrait on t.-p.

1. Mitchell, Maria, 1818–1889.
                                          40–2086
Library of Congress   QB36.M7N3
——— Copy 2.   [2]   925.2

NN 0015519   DLC MWA

Nantucket Maria Mitchell association.

Albertson, Alice Owen.
Nantucket wild flowers, by Alice O. Albertson ... illus-
trated by Anne Hinchman ... New York and London,
G. P. Putnam's sons, 1921.

Nantucket Maria Mitchell association.
Publications. v. 1–4. 1906–1943.

NN 0015521   CU TxDaM PU ICJ

Nantucket Maria Mitchell Association. Report
see its Annual report.

Nantucket receipts. Ninety receipts collected chiefly
from Nantucket sources. Boston, Robert brothers. 1874.
40 p. 17ᵐ.

Compiled by Susan Harris Coleman Hosmer.

1. Cooking, American—Nantucket.
                                          8–23707†
Library of Congress   TX715.N193

NN 0015523   DLC

Nantucket receipts; one hundred receipts collected from Nantucket housewives. [Nantucket, 1915] 40 p. 19cm.

"The little booklet called 'Nantucket receipts' was first published in 1874 ... The
'receipts' were originally arranged by Mrs. Susan C. Hosmer ... for the benefit of the
Nantucket Atheneum. Afterwards Mrs. Hosmer turned the collection over to Miss
Caroline L. Tallant, of Boston, who added to the number of receipts and had it printed
... under the title 'Nantucket receipts'... This [is the] second edition."— *Explanatory
foreword.*

1. Cookery, American. I. Title.
N. Y. P. L.
                                          May 26, 1943

NN 0015524   NN

NANTUCKET, Siasconset and Gay Head, Massachusetts. Scenes,
historical notes and poems collected to preserve the memories
of happy vacations spent there. [Compiled by] Alice Mac Kinnon
Holt. Mount Vernon, N.Y., 1911. 6 l., 36 f. 28cm.

Scrapbook of postcards, poems, etc.

787850A. 1. Nantucket, Mass. I. Holt, Alice Mac Kinnon.

NN 0015525   NN

Nantucket Sorosis, Nantucket.   5589.229
Constitution.
= [Nantucket. 1893.] [4] pp. 12°.

G3391 — Women's clubs.

NN 0015526   MB

NANTUCKET SURF-SIDE COMPANY.   No. 9 in *Map 20.
Map of Surf-Side, the property of the Nantucket Surf-Side company.
Boston, 1873. Size, 16⅛ x 33¾ inches. Scale, 400 feet to 1 inch.
Submap. — Map of Nantucket island.

NN 0015527   MB

Nantucket weekly magazine. v. 1, no. 1–
June 28, 1817–
[Nantucket, Mass., A. G. Tannatt]
v. 30 cm.
Ceased publication with Jan. 3, 1818 issue. Cf. R. A. Douglas-
Lithgow. Nantucket, a history. 1914. p. 30.

I. Tannatt, Abraham G., pub.

AP2.N135   58–53652

NN 0015528   DLC

Nantucket's first tea; an old-time romance.   [Nantucket,
Mass.: Inquirer and Mirror press, 1907]   24 p.   illus.   13 x
8cm.

For discussion of authorship, see Freehafer, E. G. A Nantucket ghost walks again.
New York, 1940.

——— ——— [1926]   10 l.
Newspaper clippings and letter, inserted.

I. Collyer, Robert, 1823–1912   *supposed author.*
1. Fiction, American. I. Title.
N. Y. P. L.   *Card revised*
                                      June 3, 1941

NN 0015529   NN

Nantungchow, China
see   Nan-t'ung, China.

Nantungchow Christian Hospital
see   Nan-t'ung, China. Nantungchow
Christian Hospital.

Nantwich (The) brine and medicinal baths;
particulars of their curative properties and of
brine treatment. 32, 12 pp., 1 l. 12°. *Nantwich. 1883.*

NN 0015532   DNLM

Nanty, Daniel Georges François, 1914–
T113   ... Folliculinothérapie des symptomes psychi-
P21   ques de la ménopause ... Paris, 1939.
1939   Thèse – Univ. de Paris.

NN 0015533   CtY

NANTZ, F[rederic] C[oleman]
An actor's vindication of his profession
in reply to a sermon preached by John McCrea
Mar. 19th, 1837. at King's Lynn. Lynn, [Eng]
W. Whittingham, [1837].

pp.18,

NN 0015534   MH

Nanu, Adina.
Gh. Tattarescu. [Ed. 1.   București] Editura de Stat pentru
literatură și artă [1955]. 35 p. 30 illus. 20cm. (Maeștrii
artei romîneşti)

Picture captions in Rumanian, Russian, English, French and German.
Summaries in Russian, English, French and German.

1. Tattarescu, Gheorghe, 1818–1894.

NN 0015535   NN InU DSI OC1 KU

Nanu (Constantin-G.) *Purpura chronique, à
grandes ecchymoses. 113 pp. 8°. *Paris, 1900,*
No. 326.

NN 0015536   DNLM

Nanu, D. Al.
...Le poète Eminescou et la poésie lyrique française.
Paris: J. Gamber, 1930.   152 p.   front.   8°.

497960A. 1. Eminescu, Mihail,   1850–1889. 2. French literature—Foreign influence of.
N. Y. P. L.   November 25, 1930

NN 0015537   NN InU

Nanu (G.) [1860–]. *Sur les ostéomes sous-
périostiques de la mâchoire inférieure. 50 pp.,
1 l. 4°. *Paris. 1884. No. 145.*

NN 0015538   DLC ICRL

Nanu, Helene Alexander, 1874–
Zur psychologie der zahlauffassung ... Würzburg,
C. J. Becker's universitäts-buchdruckerei, 1904.
2 p. l., 56 p., 1 l. incl. tables. 2 fold. pl. 22ᵐ.
Inaug.-diss.—Würzburg.
Vita.

6–8899

NN 0015539   DLC ICRL

Nanu (Jean-Georges) [1862–]. *Notes sur
le choléra de 1892 observé à l'Hôpital Necker.
139 no. 4°. *Paris, 1893. No. 85.*

NN 0015540   DNLM

NANU, O.
Des nullités du contrat de mariage.
Paris, 1914.

Thèse —- Univ. de Paris.

NN 0015541   MH-L

Nanu, Stefan, 1863–
Hda51   Der Wortschatz des Istrischen ... Leipzig,
1   1895.
N15   Pamphlet
         Inaug.-Diss. - Leipzig.
         Lebenslauf.
         "Litteratur": p.[49]-51

NN 0015542   CtY ICRL MH NjP

Nanu, Zaïra
Considérations sur la conduite à tenir
dans la présentation du front. Paris,
Librairie Lipschutz, 1934.
                                      83
Thèse.

NN 0015543   DNLM CtY NNC

VOLUME 405

Nānubhāi Bhāidās Ābuvālā

see

Abuvala, Nanubhai Bhaidas, 1894-

Nanuet, N. Y. Baptist church.
...The centennial jubilee of the Nanuet Baptist Church, Nanuet, Rockland county, New York, including the history of the church, which embodies the early history of the Baptist denomination in Rockland county, and the foundation of its Baptist churches ... Jersey City: A. J. Doan. 1898. 16 p. 8°.

Cover-title.
At head of title: 1798. 1898.

1. Nanuet, N. Y.—Churches   (Baptist).
N. Y. P. L.   August 22, 1922.

NN 0015545   NN

Nanuet, N. Y. Church of St. Anthony.
Catholic devotional prayers and hymns for congregational use. Nanuet, N. Y. ₍1955₎
95 p. illus. 22 cm.

1. Catholic Church—Prayer-books and devotions—English.
I. Title.
BX2110.N3   264.1   55-58680 †

NN 0015546   DLC

Nanuet, N. Y. St. Anthony's Church
see
Nanuet, N. Y. Church of St. Anthony.

WO   Nanula, Antonio, 1780-1846.
N193L   Lettera... al chiarissimo Ab. Alessandro
1839   Casano... Palermo, 1839.
    188 p. 20 cm.

"Estratta dal Giornale letterario, n. CCI."
Includes bibliographical references.

1. Surgery, Operative. I. Title.

NN 0015548   WU-M DNLM

Nanula, Antonio, 1780-1846.
Il testamento del Cav. Antonio Nanula, eseguito da Gaetano Navarro e Francescantonio Scafati. Napoli: Coster, 1846.
105, iv. p. front. 8°.

1. Wills—Italy, 1846. 2. Navarro,   Gaetano. 3. Scafati, Francescantonio.
N. Y. P. L.   June 21, 1928.

NN 0015549   NN

Nanvutty, P
see Nanavutty, Piloo.

Nany-Arssy
see
Boujassy, Jeanne

Nanyang brothers, inc., *New York*.
Rules for playing mah jong. New York, Nanyang brothers, inc. ₍*1923₎
₍15₎ p. illus. 15½ᵐ.

1. Mah jong.
Library of Congress   GV1299.M3N45   24-1894

NN 0015552   DLC

Nanyang Siang Pau, *Singapore*
see
Nan-yang shang pao, *Singapore*.

₍Nanylon.₎
The outlook for the world. ₍n. p., 1917.₎ 15 p. 16°.

Caption-title.
Signed: Nanylon.

1. European war, 1914– . 2. Title.
N. Y. P. L.   July 12, 1918.

NN 0015554   NN

Nanylon.
The present war, ₍by₎ Nanylon. n. p. ₍1915?₎ 11 p. 16°.

Cover-title.

1. European war, 1914– .—Address- es, sermons, etc. 2. Title.
N. Y. P. L.   September 29, 1916.

NN 0015555   NN

Nan'yō Bōeki Chōsakai.
(Nan'yō no hōko)
南洋之寶庫 ₍南洋貿易調査會編 東京 萬卷
堂 大正3 i. e. 1914₎
2, 5, 265 p. 19 cm.

1. Asia, Southeastern. 2. Islands of the Pacific. I. Title.
DS504.5.N34   73-817448

NN 0015556   DLC

DS504   Nan'yō Dantai Rengōkai.
.5   (Dai Nan'yō nenkan)
.D3   大南洋年鑑 第 -9 回 昭和 -18 ₍19 -48. 東京₎
Orien   南洋團體聯合會
Japan

南洋華僑卜金融機關 附南洋事情小觀 ₍東京₎ 東
亞印刷株式會社印行 大正6 ₍1917₎
2, 66 p. 23 cm.
Cover title.

1. Asia, Southeastern—Economic conditions. 2. Banks and banking—Asia, Southeastern. 3. Japanese in Southeastern Asia.
Title romanized: Nan'yō Kakyō to kin'yū kikan.
HC412.N259   73-815014

NN 0015558   DLC

Nan'yō Keizai Kenkyūjo, Tokyo.
(Bisumāku Shotō menseki jinkō hyō)
ビスマーク諸島面積人口表 ₍東京₎ 南洋経済
研究所 昭和19₍1944₎
₍6₎, 11 p. 21 cm. (Its 南洋資料 第365號)
Cover title.
Prepared by 篠田久万太.
Bibliography: 3d prelim. page.
1. Bismarck Archipelago—Population. I. Shinoda, Kumata. II. Title. III. Series: Nan'yō Keizai Kenkyūjo, Tokyo. Nan'yō shiryō, dai 365-gō.
HC411.A1N3 no. 365   72-802942
₍HB3694.B55₎

NN 0015559   DLC

Nan'yō Keizai Kenkyūjo, Tokyo.
₍Boruneo menseki jinkō hyō₎
ボルネオ面積人口表 ₍東京₎ 南洋經濟研究所
昭和18₍1943₎
₍5₎, 5 p. map. 21 cm. (Its 南洋資料 第232號)
Cover title.
Prepared by 篠田九萬太.
Bibliography: 4th prelim. page.
1. Borneo—Population. I. Shinoda, Kumata. II. Title. III. Series: Nan'yō Keizai Kenkyūjo, Tokyo. Nan'yō shiryō, dai 232-gō.
HC411.A1N3 no. 232   72-803683
₍HB3648.B67₎

NN 0015560   DLC

HC411   Nan'yō Keizai Kenkyūjo, Tokyo.
.A1N3
no. 83   Orita, Kazuji.
Orien   (Boruneo Suisan Kabushiki Kaisha sōgyō keiei no
Japan   kushin)
    ボルネオ水産株式會社創業經營の苦心 ₍東京₎
    南洋經濟研究所 昭和17₍1942₎

HC411   Nan'yō Keizai Kenkyūjo, Tokyo.
.A1N3
no. 5   Enomoto, Eishichi.
Orien   (Dabao kaitaku no kaiko to tembō)
Japan   ダヴァオ開拓の回顧と展望 ₍東京₎ 南洋經濟
    研究所 昭和16₍1941₎

Nan'yō Keizai Kenkyūjo, Tokyo.
(Firippin no menseki jinkō hyō)
フィリッピン面積人口表 ₍東京₎ 南洋経済研
究所 昭和17₍1942 i. e. 1943₎
4, ₍22₎ p. map. 21 cm. (Its 南洋資料 第183號)
Cover title.
Prepared by 篠田九萬太.
Bibliography: p. ₍22₎
1. Philippine Islands—Population. I. Shinoda, Kumata. II. Title. III. Series: Nan'yō Keizai Kenkyūjo, Tokyo. Nan'yō shiryō, dai 183-gō.
HC411.A1N3 no. 183   72-803127
₍HB3649₎

NN 0015563   DLC

Nan'yō Keizai Kenkyūjo, Tokyo.
(Fukkoku no Tōa shinshutsu narabini Indoshina keiryaku shi nempyō)
佛國の東亞進出並に印度支那經略史年表 ₍東
京₎ 南洋經濟研究所 昭和17₍1942 i. e. 1943₎
59, ₍1₎ p. 21 cm. (Its 南洋資料 第142號)
Cover title.
編纂擔任者 井出德夫.
Bibliography: ₍60₎
1. Indochina, French—History—Chronology. 2. French in French Indochina. I. Ide, Tokuo. II. Title. III. Series: Nan'yō Keizai Kenkyūjo, Tokyo. Nan'yō shiryō, dai 142-gō.
HC411.A1N3 no. 142   72-802962
₍DS542₎

NN 0015565   DLC

Nan'yō Keizai Kenkyūjo, Tokyo.
(Garumisukangawa o sakanoborite)
ガルミスカン川を溯りて ₍東京₎ 南洋経済研
究所 昭和18₍1943 i. e. 1944₎
2, 22 p. 21 cm. (Its 南洋資料 第327號)
Cover title.

1. Reclamation of land—Pelew Islands. 2. Japanese in the Pelew Islands—History. 3. Japan—Emigration and immigration. I. Title. II. Series: Nan'yō Keizai Kenkyūjo, Tokyo. Nan'yō shiryō, dai 327-gō.
HC411.A1N3 no. 327   74-815712
₍HD1741.M64₎

NN 0015566   DLC

VOLUME 405

Nan'yō Keizai Kenkyūjo, Tokyo.
(Gōshū chimei sakuin)
濠洲地名索引　〔撰任者　吉氷清　東京〕　南洋
經濟研究所　昭和17〔1942 i.e. 1943〕
6, 116 p. 21 cm.
Cover title.

1. Australia—Gazetteers.   I. Yoshihi, Kiyoshi, 1907-   II.
Title.   III. Series: Nan'yō Keizai Kenkyūjo, Tokyo. Nan'yō shiryo, dai
179-gō.
HC411.A1N3 no. 179   72-802908
[DU90]

NN   0015567   DLC

Nan'yō Keizai Kenkyūjo, Tokyo.
(Gōshū kōsan tōkei hyō)
濠洲鑛産統計表　〔編纂撰任者　重信鑀裁　東
京〕　南洋經濟研究所　昭和17〔1942 i.e. 1944〕
26 p. 21 cm. (Its 南洋資料　第132號)
Cover title.

1. Mines and mineral resources—Australia—Statistics.   I.
Shigenobu, Jōsai.   II. Title.   III. Series: Nan'yō Keizai Kenkyūjo, To-
kyo. Nan'yō shiryo, dai 132-gō.
HC411.A1N3 no. 132   72-803130
[HD9506.A72]

NN   0015568   DLC

Nan'yō Keizai Kenkyūjo, Tokyo.
(Hirippin rekishi nempyō)
比律賓歷史年表　〔東京〕　南洋經濟研究所　昭
和18〔1943 i.e. 1944〕
2, 36 p. 21 cm. (Its 南洋資料　第314號)
Cover title.
Bibliography: p. 2 (1st group)

1. Philippine Islands—History—Chronology.   I. Title.   II. Se-
ries: Nan'yō Keizai Kenkyūjo, Tokyo. Nan'yō shiryo, dai 314-gō.
HC411.A1N3 no. 314   72-803671
[DS667]

NN   0015569   DLC

Nan'yō Keizai Kenkyūjo, Tokyo.
(Indo chimei sakuin)
印度地名索引—不含セイロン島及印度洋諸島—
北緯自8°00′至37°00′　東經自61°30′至97°00′〔撰
任者・吉氷清　東京〕　南洋經濟研究所　昭和18
〔1943〕
4, 38 p. 21 cm. (Its 南洋資料　第224號)
Cover title.
1. India—Gazetteers.   I. Yoshihi, Kiyoshi, 1907-   II. Title.
II. Series: Nan'yō Keizai Kenkyūjo, Tokyo. Nan'yō shiryo, dai 224-gō.
HC411.A1N3 no. 224   72-803670
[DS405]

NN   0015570   DLC

Nan'yō Keizai Kenkyūjo, Tokyo.
(Indo ni okeru Ei-Futsu kōsō shi gaiyō)
印度に於ける英佛抗爭史概要　〔東京〕　南洋經
濟研究所　昭和17〔1942〕
26 p. 21 cm. (Its 南洋資料　第81號)
Cover title.
Prepared by 黒木彬
Bibliography: p. 26.

72-803090

NN   0015571   DLC

Nan'yō Keizai Kenkyūjo, Tokyo.
(Indo rekishi nempyō)
印度歷史年表　〔編纂撰任者・黒木彬　東京〕
南洋經濟研究所　昭和18-　〔1943-〕
v.〔 21 cm. (Its 南洋資料　第353　號)
Cover title.

1. India—History—Chronology.   I. Kuroki, Akira.   II. Title.
III. Series: Nan'yō Keizai Kenkyūjo, Tokyo. Nan'yō shiryo, dai 353-gō
〔etc.〕
HC411.A1N3 no. 353, etc.   72-803680
[DS433]

NN   0015572   DLC

Nan'yō Keizai Kenkyūjo, Tokyo.
(Indo shi gaiyō)
印度史概要　〔蓄述撰當者　黒木彬　東京〕　南
洋經濟研究所　昭和17〔1942 i.e. 1943〕
3 v. 21 cm.
Cover title.
Bibliography: p. 42-43 of v. 3.
CONTENTS: 上　太古より英歐兒帝國造一中　歐羅巴諸國の印度經
略—下　印度民族運動

1. India—History.   I. Kuroki, Akira.   II. Title.   III. Series: Nan'-
yō Keizai Kenkyūjo, Tokyo. Nan'yō shiryō, dai 175-gō.
HC411.A1N3 no. 175-177   72-802862
[DS436.A1]

NN   0015573   DLC

Nan'yō Keizai Kenkyūjo, Tokyo.
(Indoyō shotō chimei sakuin)
印度洋諸島地名索引　自東徑20°00′至同約110°
00′　自北緯30°00′至南緯53°30′〔撰任者　吉氷
清　東京〕　南洋經濟研究所　昭和18〔1943〕
iii, 26 p. 21 cm. (Its 南洋資料　第256號)
Cover title.

1. Islands of the Indian Ocean—Gazetteers.   I. Yoshihi, Kiyoshi,
1907-   II. Title.   III. Series: Nan'yō Keizai Kenkyūjo, Tokyo.
Nan'yō shiryo, dai 256-gō.
HC411.A1N3 no. 256   72-804045
[DT468]

NN   0015574   DLC

Nan'yō Keizai Kenkyūjo, Tokyo.
(Jawa menseki jinkō hyō)
ジャワ面積人口表　〔東京〕　南洋經濟研究所
昭和18〔1943〕
〔4〕, 8 p. map. 22 cm. (Its 南洋資料　第227號)
Cover title.
Bibliography: 4th prelim. page.
Prepared by 篠田九萬太

1. Java—Population.   I. Shinoda, Kumata.   II. Title.   III. Se-
ries: Nan'yō Keizai Kenkyūjo, Tokyo. Nan'yō shiryo, dai 227-gō.
HC411.A1N3 no. 227   72-802947
[HB3648.J3]

NN   0015575   DLC

HC411
.A1N3
no. 174,
etc.
Orien
Japan

Nan'yō Keizai Kenkyūjo, Tokyo.

Konishi, Tatehiko.
(Konishi Kaigun Taisa nampō ronsaku)
小西海軍大佐南方論策　〔小西千比古著　東京〕
南洋經濟研究所　昭和17-　〔1942-

Nan'yō Keizai Kenkyūjo, Tokyo.
(Kyū Ran'in ni okeru omo naru dochakujin shuzoku)
旧蘭印に於ける主なる土着人種族　〔東京〕　南
洋經濟研究所　昭和17〔1942〕
12 p. 21 cm. (Its 南洋資料　第75號)
Cover title.

1. Ethnology—Indonesia.   I. Title.   II. Series: Nan'yō Keizai
Kenkyūjo, Tokyo. Nan'yō shiryo, dai 75-gō.
HC411.A1N3 no. 75   72-803250
[GN635.D9]

NN   0015577   DLC

Nan'yō Keizai Kenkyūjo, Tokyo.
(Kyū Ran'in tōchi no kompon hōshin to iwayuru jichishū
ni tsuite)
舊蘭印統治の根本方針といはゆる自治州に就い
て　〔東京〕　南洋經濟研究所　昭和17〔1942〕
3 p. 21 cm. (Its 南洋資料　第76號)
Cover title.

1. Local government—Indonesia.   I. Title.   II. Series: Nan'yō
Keizai Kenkyūjo, Tokyo. Nan'yō shiryo, dai 76-gō.
HC411.A1N3 no. 76   72-805626
[JS7192]

NN   0015578   DLC

Nan'yō Keizai Kenkyūjo, Tokyo.
(Madagasukarutō chimei sakuin)
マダガスカル島地名索引—コモール(コモロ)諸
島ヲ含ム—〔撰任者　吉氷清　東京〕　南洋經濟研
究所　昭和18〔1943〕
22 p. 21 cm. (Its 南洋資料　第193號)
Cover title.

1. Madagascar—Gazetteers.   I. Yoshihi, Kiyoshi, 1907-
II. Title.   III. Series: Nan'yō Keizai Kenkyūjo, Tokyo. Nan'yō shiryo.
dai 193-gō.
HC411.A1N3 no. 193   72-802907
[DT469.M24]

NN   0015579   DLC

HC411
.A1N3
no. 45
Orien
Japan

Gotō, Kōji, 1890-
(Mindanaotō no suiryoku denki ni kansuru kōsatsu)
ミンダナオ島の水力電氣に關する考察　〔東京〕
南洋經濟研究所　昭和17〔1942〕

Nan'yō Keizai Kenkyūjo, Tokyo.
(Mōrishasu shōnenkan)
モーリシヤス小年鑑　〔撰當者　池田雄藏　東
京〕　南洋經濟研究所　昭和17〔1942〕
11 p. 21 cm. (Its 南洋資料　第137號)
Cover title.

1. Mauritius.   I. Ikeda, Yūzō, 1905-   II. Title.   III. Series:
Nan'yō Keizai Kenkyūjo, Tokyo. Nan'yō shiryo, dai 137-gō.
HC411.A1N3 no. 137   72-803336
[DT469.M4]

NN   0015581   DLC

Nan'yō Keizai Kenkyūjo, Tokyo.
(Naichi ni okeru Beizai yōto mokuroku)
内地に於ける米材用途目錄　〔編纂撰任者　仲
田浩藏　東京〕　南洋經濟研究所　昭和18〔1943〕
28 p. 21 cm. (Its 南洋資料　第209號)
Cover title.

1. Timber—America.   I. Nakada, Kōzō.   II. Title.   III. Series:
Nan'yō Keizai Kenkyūjo, Tokyo. Nan'yō shiryo, dai 209-gō.
HC411.A1N3 no. 209   72-803033
[SD434]

NN   0015582   DLC

Nan'yō Keizai Kenkyūjo, Tokyo.
Naichisan mokuzai yoto mokuroku
内地産木材用途目錄　〔撰任者　仲田浩藏　東
京〕　南洋經濟研究所　昭和18〔1943〕
2 v. 22 cm. Its 南洋資料　第207-208號
Cover title.
CONTENTS: 其一. 計葉樹之部—其二. 濶葉樹之部

1. Timber—Japan. 2. Forest products—Japan.   I. Nakada, Kozo.
II. Title.   III. Series: Nan'yō Keizai Kenkyūjo, Tokyo. Nan'yō shiryo,
dai 207-208-gō.
HC411.A1N3 no. 207-208   72-803145
[SD541]

NN   0015583   DLC

Nan'yō Keizai Kenkyūjo, Tokyo.
(Naichisan take oyobi shuro yōto mokuroku)
内地産竹及棕櫚用途目錄　〔東京〕　南洋經濟研
究所　昭和18〔1943〕
10 p. 22 cm. (Its 南洋資料　第223號)
Cover title.

1. Bamboo—Varieties.   I. Title.   II. Series: Nan'yō Keizai Ken-
kyūjo, Tokyo. Nan'yō shiryo, dai 223-gō.
HC411.A1N3 no. 223   72-803338
[SB317.B2]

NN   0015584   DLC

VOLUME 405

Nan'yō Keizai Kenkyūjo, Tokyo.
(Nampō chiiki menseki jinkō gaihyō)
南方地域面積人口概表　〔東京〕　南洋經濟研究
所　昭和17〔1942 i.e. 1943〕
　2, 2, 7 p.　21 cm.　(Its 南洋資料　第181號)
　Cover title.
　Prepared by 篠田九万太.
　Bibliography: p. 1-2 (2d group)
　1. Asia—Population.　2. Oceanica—Population.　I. Shinoda,
Kumata.　II. Title.　III. Series: Nan'yō Keizai Kenkyūjo, Tokyo. Nan'
yō shiryō, dai 181-gō.
HC411.A1N3　no. 181　　　　　　　　72-803154
[HB3635]

NN　0015585　DLC

Nan'yō Keizai Kenkyūjo, Tokyo.
(Nampō chimei jiten mokuroku)
南方地名辭典目錄　〔東京〕　南洋經濟研究所
昭和18〔1943〕
　3 p.　22 cm.　(Its 南洋資料　第238號)
　Cover title.
　1. Names, Geographical—Bibliography.　2. Geography—Dictionaries—Bibliography.　I. Title.　II. Series: Nan'yō Keizai Kenkyūjo,
Tokyo. Nan'yō shiryō, dai 238-gō.
HC411.A1N3　no. 238　　　　　　　　72-803423
[Z6004.D5]

NN　0015586　DLC

Nan'yō Keizai Kenkyūjo, Tokyo.
南方軍政建設の方針　東京　南洋經濟研究所出
版部　昭和17〔1942〕
　11 p.　21 cm.　(Its 南洋資料　第46號)
　1. World War, 1939-1945—Asia, Southeastern.　I. Title.　(Series: Nan'yō Keizai Kenkyūjo, Tokyo. Nan'yō shiryō, dai 46-gō)
Title romanized: Nampō gunsei kensetsu no hōshin.
HC411.A1N3　no. 46　　　　　　　　J 66-535

NN　0015587　DLC

Nan'yō Keizai Kenkyūjo, Tokyo.
〔Nampō jumoku meishō taishō hyō〕
南方樹木名稱對照表　〔東京〕　南洋經濟研究所
昭和18〔1943 i.e. 1944〕
　〔4〕, 26 p.　21 cm.　(Its 南洋資料　第233號)
　Cover title.
　Bibliography: 4th prelim. page.
　1. Trees—Nomenclature (Popular)　I. Title.　II. Series: Nan'yō
Keizai Kenkyūjo, Tokyo. Nan'yō shiryō, dai 233-gō.
HC411.A1N3　no. 233　　　　　　　　72-803934
[QK477]

NN　0015588　DLC

HC411
.A1N3
no. 27
Orien
Japan
Nan'yō Keizai Kenkyūjo, Tokyo.
Kōrinkai.
(Nampō ringyō hōjin kigyōsha shirabe)
南方林業邦人企業者調　〔東京〕　南洋經濟研究
所　昭和17〔1942〕

Nan'yō Keizai Kenkyūjo, Tokyo.
(Nampō ringyō kankei kigyōsha shirabe)
南方林業關係企業者調　〔東京〕　南洋經濟研究
所　昭和17〔1942 i.e. 1943〕
　2, 73 p.　21 cm.　(Its 南洋資料　第141號)
　Cover title.
　1. Forest products—Japan—Directories.　2. Forest products—Asia,
Southeastern—Directories.　I. Title.　II. Series: Nan'yō Keizai
Kenkyūjo, Tokyo. Nan'yō shiryō, dai 141-gō.
HC411.A1N3　no. 141　　　　　　　　72-804345
[HD9766.A82]

NN　0015590　DLC

Nan'yō Keizai Kenkyūjo, Tokyo.
(Nampōken yūyō jumoku meishō hyō)
南方圈有用樹木名稱表—南ボルネオ—〔編者
仲田浩藏　東京〕　南洋經濟研究所　昭和19
〔1944〕
　188 p.　21 cm.　(Its 南洋資料　第368號)
　Cover title.
　1. Trees—Borneo.　2. Trees—Nomenclature (Popular)　I. Nakada, Kōzō.　II. Title.　III. Series: Nan'yō Keizai Kenkyūjo, Tokyo. Nan'
yō shiryō, dai 368-gō.
HC411.A1N3　no. 368　　　　　　　　72-803408
[QK490.B65]

NN　0015591　DLC

Nan'yō Keizai Kenkyūjo, Tokyo.
(Nampōken yūyō shokubutsu meishō hyō)
南方圈有用植物名稱表—モルツケン地方—〔編
者・仲田浩藏　東京〕　南洋經濟研究所　昭和19
〔1944〕
　216 p.　21 cm.　(Its 南洋資料　第393號)
　Cover title.
　1. Plant names. Popular—Indonesia—Moluccas.　I. Nakada, Kōzō.
II. Title.　III. Series: Nan'yō Keizai Kenkyūjo, Tokyo. Nan'yō shiryō,
dai 393-gō.
HC411.A1N3　no. 393　　　　　　　　72-803856
[QK13]

NN　0015592　DLC

Nan'yō Keizai Kenkyūjo, Tokyo.
(Nan'yō Guntō kankei zasshi kiji mokuroku. Dai 24-rui)
南洋群島關係雜誌記事目錄　第二四類　農業畜
產に關するもの　〔東京〕　南洋經濟研究所　昭和
19-　〔1944-
　v.　21 cm.　(Its 南洋資料　第410-　號)
　Cover title.
　1. Agriculture—Micronesia—Bibliography.　I. Title.　II. Series:
Nan'yō Keizai Kenkyūjo, Tokyo. Nan'yō shiryō, dai 410-gō 〔etc.〕
HC411.A1N3　no. 410, etc.　　　　　73-816991
[Z5075.M65]

NN　0015593　DLC

Nan'yō Keizai Kenkyūjo, Tokyo.
(Nan'yō Guntō suiro zu shi mokuroku)
南洋群島水路圖誌目錄　〔東京〕　南洋經濟研究
所　昭和19〔1944〕
　3, 8 p.　21 cm.　(Its 南洋資料　第425號)
　Cover title.
　1. Oceanica—Maps—Bibliography—Catalogs.　2. Nautical charts—
Bibliography—Catalogs.　I. Title.　II. Series: Nan'yō Keizai Kenkyūjo, Tokyo. Nan'yō shiryō, dai 425-gō.
HC411.A1N3　no. 425　　　　　　　　72-803405
[Z6027.O35]

NN　0015594　DLC

Nan'yō Keizai Kenkyūjo, Tokyo.
(Nan'yō kankei tosho mokuroku)
南洋關係圖書目錄　〔東京〕　南洋經濟研究所
昭和16〔1941〕
　50 p.　21 cm.　(Its 南洋資料　第1號)
　Cover title.
　1. Asia, Southeastern—Bibliography.　I. Title.　II. Series: Nan'-
yō Keizai Kenkyūjo, Tokyo. Nan'yō shiryō, dai 1-gō.
HC411.A1N3　no. 1　　　　　　　　　72-803309
[Z3221]

NN　0015595　DLC

Nan'yō Keizai Kenkyūjo, Tokyo.
(Nan'yō kankei tosho mokuroku)
南洋關係圖書目錄　（目錄票第六一ヨリ第一五
〇迄）　〔東京〕　南洋經濟研究所　昭和18〔1943〕
　2, 8 p.　21 cm.　(Its 南洋資料　第211號其ノ2)
　Cover title.
　1. Asia—Bibliography—Catalogs.　2. Oceanica—Bibliography—Catalogs.　I. Title.　II. Series: Nan'yō Keizai Kenkyūjo, Tokyo. Nan'yō
shiryō, dai 211-gō, sono 2.
HC411.A1N3　no. 211, sono 2　　　　72-803308
[Z3009]

NN　0015596　DLC

Nan'yō Keizai Kenkyūjo, Tokyo.
南洋經濟研究所所藏圖書目錄　東京　昭和15
〔1940〕
　3, 126, 80 p.　22 cm.

———— 追加　東京　昭和15-　〔1940-
　v.　22 cm.
　Harvard has suppl. v. 1-2, bound with main vol.
　1. Asia, Southeastern—Econ. condit.—Bibl.
Title romanized: Nanyō Keizai Kenkyūjo
shozō tosho mokuroku.
Harvard Univ.　Chinese-　Japanese Library　4375
for Library of Congress　〔4〕
J 65-2473

NN　0015597　MH-HY

HC411
.A1N3
no. 33
Orien
Japan
Nan'yō Keizai Kenkyūjo, Tokyo.
(Nan'yō mokuzai shigen gaiyō)
南洋木材資源概要　〔東京〕　南洋經濟研究所　昭和
17〔1942〕

Nan'yō Keizai Kenkyūjo, Tokyo.
南洋資料
東京　南洋經濟研究所出版部
　no.　21 cm.
　Published 1941-44. Cf. 学術雜誌總合目錄 1959.
　1. Asia, Southeastern—Econ. condit.—Collections.　I. Title.
Title romanized: Nan'yō shiryō.
HC411.A1N3　　　　　　　　　　　　J 66-331

NN　0015599　DLC

Nan'yō Keizai Kenkyūjo, Tokyo.
(Nan'yōchō rekidai chōkan meibo oyobi ryakureki)
南洋廳歷代長官名簿及略歷　〔東京〕　南洋經濟
研究所　昭和18〔1943 i.e. 1944〕
　3 p.　21 cm.　(Its 南洋資料　第312號)
　Cover title.
　1. Japan. Nan'yōchō—Registers.　I. Title.　II. Series: Nan'yō
Keizai Kenkyūjo, Tokyo. Nan'yō shiryō, dai 312-gō.
HC411.A1N3　no. 312　　　　　　　　72-804061
[JQ1621.A2]

NN　0015600　DLC

HC411
.A1N3
no. 6
Orien
Japan
Nan'yō Keizai Kenkyūjo, Tokyo.
Japan. Nan'yōchō. Naimubu. Kikakuka.
(Naurutō jijō)
ナウル島事情　〔東京〕　南洋經濟研究所　昭和
16〔1941〕

Nan'yō Keizai Kenkyūjo, Tokyo.
〔Nihon nampō hatten shi nempyō〕
日本南方發展史年表　〔撰當者　木田道太郎
東京〕　南洋經濟研究所　昭和18〔1943 i.e. 1944〕
　104 p.　21 cm.　(Its 南洋資料　第342號)
　Cover title.
　Bibliography: p. 103-104.
　1. Japan—Relations (general) with Southeastern Asia—Chronology.
2. Asia, Southeastern—Relations (general) with Japan—Chronology.
I. Kida, Michitarō.　II. Title.　III. Series: Nan'yō Keizai Kenkyūjo,
Tokyo. Nan'yō shiryō, dai 342-gō.
HC411.A1N3　no. 342　　　　　　　　72-805966
[DS489.59.J3]

NN　0015602　DLC

Nan'yō Keizai Kenkyūjo, Tokyo.
〔Nyū Ginia chimei shūsei〕
ニウギニア地名集成　南洋經濟研究所編　東京
丸善　〔昭和18 i.e. 1943〕
　2, 2, 156 p.　map(on lining paper)　18 cm.
　1. Names, Geographical—Indonesia—Irian Barat.　I. Title.
DU744.N26　　　　　　　　　　　　72-804579

NN　0015603　DLC

VOLUME 405

Nan'yō Keizai Kenkyūjo, Tokyo.
[Nyū Ginia chimei shūsei. Selections]
西部ニウギニア河川誌 [東京] 南洋經濟研究
所 昭和18[1943 i.e. 1944]
31 p. 21 cm.
Cover title.
ニウギニア地名集成...中から西部ニウギニア...の河川關係記事を抜出
し地理的順序に排列したもの
1. Rivers—Indonesia—Irian Barat.   I. Title. II. Series: Nan'yō
Keizai Kenkyūjo, Tokyo. Nan'yō shiryō, dai 304-gō.
Title romanized: Seibu Nyū Ginia kasenshi.
HC411.A1N3 no. 304
[GB1348.I7]   72-805444

NN   0015604   DLC

HC411
.A1N3
no. 140
Orien
Japan
Nan'yō Keizai Kenkyūjo, Tokyo.
(Nyū Ginia kaitaku kenkyū kondan kiroku)
ニウギニア開拓研究懇談記錄 [東京] 南洋經濟研
究所 昭和17[1942 i.e. 1943]

Nan'yō Keizai Kenkyūjo, Tokyo.
(Nyū Ginia kankei tosho mokuroku)
ニウギニア關係圖書目錄 [東京] 南洋經濟研
究所 昭和19[1944]
23 p. 21 cm.
Cover title.

1. New Guinea—Bibliography. 2. Indonesia—Bibliography. I.
Title. II. Series: Nan'yō Keizai Kenkyūjo, Tokyo. Nan'yō shiryō, dai
390-gō.
HC411.A1N3 no. 390
[Z4811]   72-803337

NN   0015606   DLC

Nan'yō Keizai Kenkyūjo, Tokyo.
(Nyū Ginia menseki jinkō hyō)
ニウギニア面積人口表 [編纂擔當者 篠田九
馬太 東京] 南洋經濟研究所 昭和18[1943 i.e.
1944]
6, 48 p. map. 21 cm. (Its 南洋資料 第350號)
Cover title.
Bibliography: p. 48.
1. New Guinea—Population. I. Shinoda, Kumata. II. Title. III.
Series: Nan'yō Keizai Kenkyūjo, Tokyo. Nan'yō shiryō, dai 350-gō.
HC411.A1N3 no. 350
[HB3648.N4]   72-803153

NN   0015607   DLC

Nan'yō Keizai Kenkyūjo, Tokyo.
(Nyū Ginia sonrakushi)
ニウギニア村落誌—東經一四一度以西—東京
南洋經濟研究所 昭和19— [1944-
v. maps. 21 cm. (南洋資料 第464 號)
Cover title.
CONTENTS: 其の1. 北岸西部

1. Names, Geographical—Indonesia—Irian Barat. I. Title. II.
Series: Nan'yō Keizai Kenkyūjo, Tokyo. Nan'yō shiryō, dai 464-gō [etc.]
HC411.A1N3 no. 464, etc.
[DS744]   72-807860

NN   0015608   DLC

Nan'yō Keizai Kenkyūjo, Tokyo.
(Nyū Karedonia chimei shūsei)
ニウカレドニア地名集成 南洋經濟研究所編
東京 丸善 [昭和19 i.e. 1944]
iii, 98 p. map (on lining paper) 18 cm. (Its 南洋資料 第214號)
Prepared by 三吉朋十
Bibliography: p.
1. Names, Geographical—New Caledonia. I. Miyoshi, Tomokazu,
1882-   II. Title.   III. Series: Nan'yō Keizai Kenkyūjo, Tokyo.
Nan'yō shiryō, dai 214-gō.
HC411.A1N3 no. 214
[DU720]   72-803752

NN   0015609   DLC

HC411
A1N3
no. 63
Orien
Japan
Nan'yō Keizai Kenkyūjo, Tokyo.
Takagi, Saburō.
(Nyū Karedonia saikin jijō)
ニウカレドニア最近事情 [東京] 南洋經濟研
究所 昭和17[1942]

Nan'yō Keizai Kenkyūjo, Tokyo.
(Nyū Karedonia yōran)
ニウカレドニア要覽 [東京] 南洋經濟研究所
昭和17[1942]
1. 70 p. 21 cm. (Its 南洋資料 第54號)
Cover title.
植村鷹千代之を擔任して...編輯したるものなり
Bibliography: p. 70.
1. New Caledonia. I. Uemura. Takachiyo. II. Title. III. Series: Nan'yō Keizai Kenkyūjo, Tokyo. Nan'yō shiryō, dai 54-gō.
HC411.A1N3 no. 54
[DU720]   72-803818

NN   0015611   DLC

HC411
.A1N3
no. 9
Orien
Japan
Nan'yō Keizai Kenkyūjo, Tokyo.
(Ōma no kenkyū)
黄麻の研究 附・佛領印度支那に於ける黄麻 [東
京] 南洋經濟研究所 昭和17[1942]

Nan'yō Keizai Kenkyūjo, Tokyo.
(Oranda no Tōindo sakushu shi)
和蘭の東印度搾取史 [東京] 南洋經濟研究所
昭和17[1942]
1, 38 p. 21 cm. (Its 南洋資料 第66號)
Cover title.
本史作成は所員越村長次の擔當せし[もの]
Bibliography: p. 38.
1. Nederlandsche Oost-Indische Compagnie. I. Koshimura, Chōji.
II. Title. III. Series: Nan'yō Keizai Kenkyūjo, Tokyo. Nan'yō shiryō,
dai 66-gō.
HC411.A1N3 no. 66
[HF483.E6]   72-803711

NN   0015613   DLC

HC411
.A1N3
no. 259
Orien
Japan
Nan'yō Keizai Kenkyūjo, Tokyo.
Parao Asahimura Kensetsu Zadankai, Tokyo, 1943.
(Parao Asahimura Kensetsu Zadankai kiroku)
パラオ朝日村建設座談會記錄 [東京] 南洋經
濟研究所 昭和18[1943]

Nan'yō Keizai Kenkyūjo, Tokyo.
(Ran'in ni okeru ramī no saibai)
蘭印に於けるラミーの栽培 [東京] 南洋經濟
研究所 昭和17[1942]
2, 9 p. 21 cm. (Its 南洋資料 第14號)
Cover title.

1. Ramie. 2. Fiber plants—Indonesia. I. Title. II. Series:
Nan'yō Keizai Kenkyūjo, Tokyo. Nan'yō shiryō, dai 14-gō.
HC411.A1N3 no. 14
SB259]   72-803751

NN   0015615   DLC

HC411
.A1N3
no. 293
Orien
Japan
Nan'yō Keizai Kenkyūjo, Tokyo.
Sugiura, Yōichi, 1891-
(Ranryō jidai Serebesu rinsei gaiyō)
蘭領時代セレベス林政概要 [東京] 南洋經濟
研究所 昭和18[1943]

Nan'yō Keizai Kenkyūjo, Tokyo.
(Seirontō chimei sakuin)
セイロン島地名索引 III [北緯5°53′より9°51′迄
東經79°42′より81°55′迄] [東京] 南洋經濟研究
所 昭和17[1942 i.e. 1943]
1, 2, 1, 25 p. 21 cm. (Its 南洋資料 第111號)
Cover title.
水路部發行海圖第2903號を基本とした
1. Ceylon—Gazetteers. I. Title. II. Series: Nan'yō Keizai
Kenkyūjo, Tokyo. Nan'yō shiryō, dai 111-gō.
HC411.A1N3 no. 111
[DS488.9]   72-803407

NN   0015617   DLC

HC411
.A1N3
no. 301
Orien
Japan
Nan'yō Keizai Kenkyūjo, Tokyo.
Katō, Masaaki.
[Seirontō Tamiru imin to sono minzoku seisaku]
セイロン島タミール移民と其の民族政策 [東
京] 南洋經濟研究所 昭和18[1943]

Nan'yō Keizai Kenkyūjo, Tokyo.
(Sekai seien tōkei hyō)
世界製鹽統計表 [東京] 南洋經濟研究所 昭
和17[1942]
9 p. 21 cm. (Its 南洋資料 第143號)
Cover title.

1. Salt industry and trade—Statistics. I. Title. II. Series:
Nan'yō Keizai Kenkyūjo, Tokyo. Nan'yō shiryō, dai 143-gō.
HC411.A1N3 no. 143
[HD9213.A2]   72-802927

NN   0015619   DLC

Nan'yō Keizai Kenkyūjo, Tokyo.
(Serebesu menseki jinkō hyō)
セレベス面積人口表 [東京] 南洋經濟研究所
昭和18[1943]
5, 32 p. map. 21 cm. (Its 南洋資料 第237號)
Cover title.
Prepared by 篠田九萬太
Bibliography: p. 32.
1. Celebes—Population. I. Shinoda, Kumata. II. Title. III. Se-
ries: Nan'yō Keizai Kenkyūjo, Tokyo. Nan'yō shiryō, dai 237-gō.
HC411.A1N3 no. 237
[HB3648.C44]   72-802946

NN   0015620   DLC

Nan'yō Keizai Kenkyūjo, Tokyo.
(Soromon Shotō chimei shūsei)
ソロモン諸島地名集成 南洋經濟研究所編 東
京 丸善 [昭和18 i.e. 1943]
iv, 116 p. map (on lining paper) 18 cm. (Its 南洋資料 第213號)
Prepared by 三吉朋十
Bibliography: p. iii-iv.
1. Names, Geographical—Solomon Islands. I. Miyoshi, Tomokazu, 1882-   II. Title. III. Series: Nan'yō Keizai Kenkyūjo, Tokyo. Nan'yō shiryō, dai 213-gō.
HC411.A1N3 no. 213
[DU850]   72-803562

NN   0015621   DLC

Nan'yō Keizai Kenkyūjo, Tokyo.
(Sumatora menseki jinkō hyō)
スマトラ面積人口表 [東京] 南洋經濟研究所
昭和18[1943]
6, 23 p. map. 21 cm. (Its 南洋資料 第229號)
Cover title.
Bibliography: p. 6 (1st group)
Prepared by 篠田九萬太
1. Sumatra—Population. I. Shinoda, Kumata. II. Title. III.
Series: Nan'yō Keizai Kenkyūjo, Tokyo. Nan'yō shiryō, dai 229-gō.
HC411.A1N3 no. 229
[HB3648.S85]   72-802958

NN   0015622   DLC

Nan'yō Keizai Kenkyūjo, Tokyo.
(Tahichitō yōran)
タヒチ島要覽 [編纂擔任者 植村鷹千代 東
京] 南洋經濟研究所 昭和17[1942]
1, 26 p. illus. 22 cm. Its 南洋資料 第129號
Cover title.
Bibliography: p. 26.
1. Tahiti. I. Uemura, Takachiyo. II. Title. III. Series: Nanyō Keizai Kenkyūjo, Tokyo. Nan'yō shiryō, dai 129-gō.
HC411.A1N3 no. 129
DU870]   72-802831

NN   0015623   DLC

VOLUME 405

HC411
.A1N3
no. 152
Orien
Japan

Nan'yō Keizai Kenkyūjo, Tokyo.

Suikōsha ni okeru Ko Matsuoka Shizuo Shi Tsuitō
Zadankai, Tokyo, 1942.

(Taiheiyō minzokugaku no kaisō Kaigun Taisa Matsuoka
Shizuo)

太平洋民族學の開削海軍大佐松岡靜雄 〔東京〕
南洋經濟研究所 昭和18〔1943〕

Nan'yō Keizai Kenkyūjo, Tokyo.
(Taiheiyō shotō dendō jigyō no gaiyō)
太平洋諸島傳道事業の概要 〔東京〕 南洋經濟
研究所 昭和17〔1942〕
2 v. 21 cm. (Its 南洋資料 第84–85號)
Cover title.
三吉朋十をして...執筆せしめた〕

1. Missions—Islands of the Pacific. I. Miyoshi, Tomokazu,
1882– II. Title. III. Series: Nan'yō Keizai Kenkyūjo, Tokyo.
Nan'yō shiryō, dai 84–85-gō.
HC411.A1N3 no. 84–85　　　　72-802945
[BV3670]

NN　0015625　　DLC

Nan'yō Keizai Kenkyūjo, Tokyo.
(Taiheiyō shotō menseki jinkō hyō)
太平洋諸島面積人口表 〔東京〕 南洋經濟研究
所 昭和18〔1943〕
11 p. 21 cm. (Its 南洋資料 第226號)
Cover title.
Prepared by 篠田九萬太

1. Islands of the Pacific—Population. I. Shinoda, Kumata. II.
Title. III. Series: Nan'yō Keizai Kenkyūjo, Tokyo. Nan'yō shiryō, dai
226-gō.
HC411.A1N3 no. 226　　　　72-802979
[HB3693]

NN　0015626　　DLC

Nan'yō Keizai Kenkyūjo, Tokyo.
(Tannin shigen to shite no kōjurin)
タンニン資源としての紅樹林 〔仲田浩藏編纂
東京〕 南洋經濟研究所 昭和18〔1943〕
2. 57 p. illus. 21 cm. (Its 南洋資料 第199號)
Cover title.

1. Mangrove. I. Nakada, Kōzō. II. Title. III. Series: Nan'yō
Keizai Kenkyūjo, Tokyo. Nan'yō shiryō, dai 199-gō.
HC411.A1N3 no. 199　　　　72-803046
[SB313]

NN　0015627　　DLC

Nan'yō Keizai Kenkyūjo, Tokyo.
(Tasumania nendaiki)
タスマニア年代記 〔編纂擔當者・重信鎰裁 東
京〕 南洋經濟研究所 昭和17〔1942〕
2. 16 p. 21 cm. (Its 南洋資料 第109號)
Cover title.
Bibliography: p. 1–2 (1st group)

1. Tasmania—History—Chronology. I. Shigenobu, Jōsai. II.
Title. III. Series: Nan'yō Keizai Kenkyūjo, Tokyo. Nan'yō shiryō, dai
109-gō.
HC411.A1N3 no. 109　　　　72-802905
[DU470]

NN　0015628　　DLC

Nan'yō Keizai Kenkyūjo, Tokyo.
(Tōbu Nyū Ginia kitagawa kasenshi)
東部ニウギニア北側河川誌 〔編纂擔當者・前野
貞 東京〕 南洋經濟研究所 昭和18〔1943 i. e.
1944〕
2. 9 p. 21 cm. (Its 南洋資料 第357號)
Cover title.
Includes bibliographies.

1. Rivers—New Guinea (Ter.) I. Maeno, Tadashi, ed. II. Title.
III. Series: Nan'yō Keizai Kenkyūjo, Tokyo. Nan'yō shiryō, dai 357-gō.
HC411.A1N3 no. 357　　　　72-805437
[GB1393.N4]

NN　0015629　　DLC

HC411
.A1N3
no. 41
Orien
Japan

Nan'yō Keizai Kenkyūjo, Tokyo.

(Tōindo zairyū Nihonjin kongo no seikatsu taido ni
tsuite)
東印度在留日本人今後の生活態度に就いて 〔東京〕
南洋經濟研究所 昭和17〔1942〕

Nan'yō Keizai Kenkyūjo, Tokyo.

Japan. Nan'yōchō. Naimubu. Kikakuka.

(Tonga Shotō jijō)
トンガ諸島事情 〔東京〕 南洋經濟研究所 昭
和17〔1942〕

HC411
.A1N3
no. 258,
etc.
Orien

Nan'yō Keizai Kenkyūjo, Tokyo.

(Uchi Nan'yō o kizukishi hitobito)
内南洋を築きし人々 〔東京〕 南洋經濟研究所
昭和18–〔1943–

HC411
.A1N3
no. 297,
etc.
Orien

Nan'yō Keizai Kenkyūjo, Tokyo. Nan'yō shiryō, dai 297-gō.

Kokubu, Shōzō.

(Biruma to Indo no hikaku)
ビルマと印度の比較 〔國分正三・小西千代太對
談 東京〕 南洋經濟研究所 昭和18–〔1943–

HC411
.A1N3
no. 322
Orien
Japan

Nan'yō Keizai Kenkyūjo, Tokyo. Nan'yō shiryō, dai 322-gō.

Asano, Akira, 1901–

(Jawa no shin bunka shoken)
ジャワの新文化所見 淺野晃述 〔東京〕 南洋
經濟研究所 昭和18〔1943 i. e. 1944〕

HC411
.A1N3
no. 337
Orien
Japan

Nan'yō Keizai Kenkyūjo, Tokyo. Nan'yō shiryō, dai
337-gō.

Schoonheyt, Louis Johan Alexander.
(Nyū Ginia no Oranda ryūkeichi Tanā Merā)
ニウギニアの和蘭流刑地タナー・メラー 〔スホ
ーンヘイト醫師述 越村長次譯 東京〕 南洋經濟
研究所 昭和18〔1943 i. e. 1944〕

Nan'yō Keizai Kondankai, *Tokyo and Osaka, 1939.*
南洋經濟懇談會報告書 東京 南洋協會 昭和
15〔1940〕
3. 354 p. group ports. 26 cm.
Cover title.
南洋協會主催の下に...昭和14年9月14日より4日間東京
に於いて、同月20日より2日間大阪に於いて開催された...南
洋經濟懇談會の報告書
1. Asia, Southeastern—Econ. condit.—Congresses. I. Nan'yō
Kyōkai.
　　　　　Title romanized: Nan'yō Keizai Kondankai hōkokusho.
HC412.N26 1939　　　　J66–273

NN　0015636　　DLC

Nan'yō Kenkyūkai.
(Nan'yō Kenkyūkai shozō tosho mokuroku)
南洋研究會所藏圖書目録 和漢文之部 〔東京〕
昭和11〔1936〕
133 p. (on double leaves) 24 cm.
Cover title.

1. Oceanica—Bibliography—Catalogs. 2. Asia, Southeastern—Bibliography—Catalogs. I. Title.
Z955.T762 1936　　　　72-803829

NN　0015637　　DLC

Nan'yō Kōgyō Chōsa Kumiai.
(Ranryō Tō-Indo shisatsu hōkoku)
蘭領東印度視察報告 〔コロール〕 南洋廳 〔大
正13 (1924) 序〕
1, 8, 362 p. maps. 22 cm.
Cover title.
本編ハ南洋興業調査組合ノ提出セル視察報告書ノ一部
ナリ〕
Errata slip inserted.

1. Indonesia. I. Japan. Nan'yōchō. II. Title.
DS615.N3 1924　　　　73-819913

NN　0015638　　DLC

Nan'yō Kōhatsu Kabushiki Kaisha.
(Nan'yō Kōhatsu Kabushiki Kaisha nijisshūnen)
南洋興發株式會社二十週年 〔東京 昭和16
i. e. 1941〕
1 v. (unpaged, chiefly illus.) 26 cm.

1. Nan'yō Kōhatsu Kabushiki Kaisha.
HD9505.S68N35　　　　73-817635

NN　0015639　　DLC

Nan'yō Kyōkai.
Bulletin.
Tokyo.
v. 22 cm. monthly.

1. East (Far East)
DS501.N3　　　　950.062　　48-38987 rev*‡

NN　0015640　　DLC

Nan'yō Kyōkai.
Bulletin. Éd. française.
〔Tokyo〕
v. in 21 cm. monthly.
Issued also in English.

DS501.N32　　　　915　　48-38988 rev*‡

NN　0015641　　DLC

Nan'yō Kyōkai.
大南洋圏 南洋協會編 東京 中央公論社 昭
和16〔1941〕
4, 458 p. illus., maps, tables. 20 cm.

1. Asia, Southeastern. I. Title.
　　　　　Title romanized: Dai Nan'yō ken.
DS503.5.N3　　　　J 60–2953
Hoover Institution
for Library of Congress　　〔3〕†

NN　0015642　　CSt-H DLC

Nan'yō Kyōkai.
南洋案内 南洋協會編 〔東京 1942〕
2. 2. 16, 771 p. illus., maps. 19 cm.

1. Asia, Southeastern. I. Title.
　　　　　Title romanized: Nan'yō annai.
DS504.5.N35　　　　72-823988

NN　0015643　　DLC

HC412
.N26
1939
Orien
Japan

Nan'yō Kyōkai.

Nan'yō Keizai Kondankai, *Tokyo and Osaka, 1939.*
南洋經濟懇談會報告書 東京 南洋協會 昭和
15〔1940〕

VOLUME 405

Nan'yō Kyōkai.
南洋鑛產資源　南洋協會編　東京　生活社　昭和 17 ₍1942₎
4, 10, 679 p. fold. maps (1 in pocket) tables. 22 cm.

1. Mines and mineral resources—Asia, Southeastern. 2. Mines and mineral resources—Oceanica. I. Title.
Title romanized: Nan'yō kōsan shigen.
TN99.N3　　　　　　　　　　　　　　　　　J 60-3099
Hoover Institution

NN　0015645　　CSt-H DLC

___

Nan'yō Kyōkai.
(Nan'yō Kyōkai nijūnenshi)
南洋協會二十年史　₍東京　昭和 10 i.e. 1935₎
2, 8, 378, 25 p. plates. 23 cm.

HF331.J3N34　　　　　　　　　　　　　72-802317

NN　0015646　　DLC

___

Nan'yō Kyōkai.
蘭印經濟概觀　南洋協會編纂　東京　昭和 15 ₍1940₎
7, 166 p. 2 fold. maps, tables. 23 cm.
Errata slip inserted.
Bibliography: p. 166.

1. Indonesia—Econ. condit.　I. Title.
Title romanized: Ran'in keizai gaikan.
HC447.N3　　　　　　　　　　　　　J 61-4403
Harvard Univ. Chinese-　　Japanese Library 4375.2
for Library of Congress　　₍3₎

NN　0015647　　MH-HY DLC

___

Law　　Nan'yō Kyōkai.

(Ranryō Tō-Indo tochi hō)
蘭領東印度土地法　改訂增補　東京　南洋協會　₍大正 13 i.e. 1924₎

___

Nan'yō Kyōkai
South seas; studied economically, culturally, etc. Tokyo, The South sea association, 1940.
1 p. l., iv, 177, ₍1₎ p. illus. (maps) plates, port. 22ᶜᵐ.
Colophon mounted on p. ₍178₎
"Second edition."--p. ₍178₎

1. Oceanica. 2. Indo-China.　I. Title.　　41-14979
Library of Congress　　DU22.S03 1940

NN　0015649　　DLC NIC WU

___

Nan'yō Kyōkai.
(Tō-Indo rōdō seisaku shi)
東インド勞働政策史　南洋協會編　₍東京　昭和 18 i.e. 1943₎
2, 4, 174 p. 22 cm.
Based on A. D. A. de Kat Angelino's Staatkundig beleid.
Includes bibliographical references.
1. Labor laws and legislation—Indonesia—History. 2. Labor policy—Indonesia—History. 3. Netherlands—Colonies—Administration.　I. Kat Angelino, Arnold Dirk Adriaan de, 1890 or 1-Staatkundig beleid. II. Title.
　　　　　　　　　　　　　　　　　74-817821

NN　0015650　　DLC

___

Law　　Nan'yō Kyōkai.

Straits Settlements.　Laws, statutes, etc.
₍Trade marks ordinance, 1938. Japanese₎
海峽植民地商標登錄法施行細則條令　東京　南洋協會　昭和 14 ₍1939₎

___

SH307　Nan'yō Kyōkai.　Taiwan Shibu.
S7N35
Orien　(Nan'yō suisan shigen)
Japan　南洋水產資源　₍臺北　南洋協會臺灣支部編發行　昭和 4 i.e. 1929₎

___

HC665　Nan'yō Kyōkai.　Taiwan Shibu.
.K6
Orien　Koide, Mitsuji, 1880-
Japan
(Nyū Jirando yōgyō gaikyō)
新西蘭羊業概況　₍小出滿二著　臺北　南洋協會臺灣支部　₍大正 9 i.e. 1920₎

___

SB269　Nan'yō Kyōkai.　Taiwan Shibu.
.H22
Orien　Haga, Kuwagorō.
Japan
(Sekai kōhi taikan)
世界珈琲大觀　₍芳賀鍬五郎著　臺北　南洋協會臺灣支部　₍大正 12 i.e. 1923₎

___

S471　Nan'yō Kyōkai.　Taiwan Shibu.
.M272
T386　Ohara, Issaku.
Orien
Japan　(Tawao chihō ni okeru kaikon jigyō)
タワオ地方に於ける開墾事業　₍小原一策著　臺北　南洋協會臺灣支部　₍大正 9 i.e. 1920₎

___

(Nan'yō-mokuzai shigen gaiyō)
南洋木材資源概要　₍東京₎　南洋經濟研究所．昭和 17 ₍1942₎
139 p. illus. 21 cm.　(南洋資料　第33號)
Cover title.
「南洋の木材資源」は昭和十四年一月「研究資料」第二年第一輯に特輯された記事である

1. Timber—Asia, Southeastern.　I. Nan'yō Keizai Kenkyūjo, Tokyo. II. Nan'yō Keizai Kenkyūjo, Tokyo. Nankyō resources. III. Series: Nan'yō Keizai Kenkyūjo, Tokyo. Nan'yō shiryō, dai 33-gō.
HC411.A1N3 no. 33　　　　　　　　72-803044
[SD527.S65]

NN　0015656　　DLC

___

DS563　Nan'yō nenkan.
.5
.Y83　(Yūhō Tai-koku no genkyō)
Orien　友邦泰國の現況　泰國要說　₍編者・臺灣總督府外事部　臺北₎　南方資料館　₍昭和 17 i.e. 1942₎
Japan

___

DS592　Nan'yō oyobi Nihonjin Sha.　Hensanbu.
.M36
Orien　(Marai ni okeru hōjin katsudō no genkyō)
Japan　馬來に於ける邦人活動の現況　₍南洋及日本人社編纂部編纂₎　新嘉坡　南洋及日本人社　₍1917₎

___

HC412　Nan'yō Saibai Kyōkai.
.H49
Orien　(Higashikuni no Miya goten ni okeru Nan'yō jigyō kōen shū)
Japan　東久邇宮御殿に於ける南洋事業講演集　₍東京　南洋栽培協會　昭和 5 i.e. 1930₎

___

Nan'yō Saibai Kyōkai.
南洋の栽培事業　Cyclopedia of tropical agriculture.
南洋栽培協會編纂　東京　昭和 10 ₍1935₎
8, 20, 1123 p. illus., maps, tables. 23 cm.
In Japanese.

1. Tropical plants. 2. Agriculture—Asia, Southeastern.　I. Title. II. Title: Cyclopedia of tropical agriculture.
Title romanized: Nan'yō no saibai jigyō.
　　　　　　　　　　　　　　　　　J 60-3079
Hoover Institution
for Library of Congress　　₍3₎

NN　0015660　　CSt-H

___

(Nan'yō suisan shigen)
南洋水產資源　₍臺北　南洋協會臺灣支部編發行　昭和 4 i.e. 1929₎
4 v. illus. 23 cm.
CONTENTS: 第1卷　南洋之水產　農林省編　南洋の水產　臺灣總督府編　南支那之水產業　臺灣總督府編第一卷—第2卷　江蘇省浙江省水產業　臺灣總督府編　南支那水產業　農林省編　南支那比律賓近海に於ける漁業試驗　臺灣總督府編　新嘉坡に於ける漁業狀況　永�卷　南支那水產業　臺灣總督府編　漁業資料・索引—第4卷　印度支那の水產業　向井寉資　南洋の經濟調查　鹿兒島縣水產試驗場編　香港・廣東拉に東京灣漁業調査報告　琉球市廳編　英領馬來に於ける水產物取引狀況　南洋協會新嘉坡商品陳列所編　南洋に於ける水產業調査書　拓務省拓務局編　新嘉坡に於ける邦人水產業　華南銀行編　南洋鮪漁業調査試驗報告　三重縣水產試驗場　水產業と海外發展　前根壽一著　太平洲沿海に於ける貝類漁業調査　臺灣總督府水產試驗場編

1. Fisheries—Asia, Southeastern.　I. Nan'yō Kyōkai. Taiwan Shibu.
SH307.S7N35　　　　　　　　　　72-805631

NN　0015663　　DLC

___

(Nan'yō to Kakyō)
南洋ト華僑　₍東京？　1939？₎
16. 406 p. 23 cm.
L.C. copy imperfect: cover wanting; title from caption.

1. Chinese in southeastern Asia.
DS509.5.C5N3　　　　　　　　　　72-799167

NN　0015664　　DLC

___

Pamph.　NANZ, Carl Friedrich
v. 461　Die Besessenen im Neuen Testamente. Ein exegetischer Versuch mit Ruecksicht auf Dr. Strauss Leben Jesu. Reutlingen, Johann Conrad Maecken, 1840.
ii 42p. 21cm.

NN　0015665　　MH-AH MH NIC

___

Nanz, Carl Friedrich.
Christliche kindsleichenreden ... Reutlingen, Macken, 1839-40.
3 v in 1.

NN　0015666　　PPLT

___

Nanz, Carl Friederich.
Emanuel Swedenborg, der Nordische sener ... 2d ausg. Ravenburg, Gradmann und Knapp, 1841.
66 p.

NN　0015667　　PBa

___

Nanz, Carl Friederich.
Emanuel Swedenborg ... 2d ausg. Schwab, Hall, F. F. Haspel'schen buch., 1851.
66 p.

NN　0015668　　PBa

___

Nanz, Edith M
Soldiering for Christ in Chile; the story of the Soldiers' and gospel mission of South America ... by Edith Nanz ... Introduction by William M. Strong. Grand Rapids, Mich., Zondervan publishing house ₍1942₎
2 p.l., 7-93 p. 19ᶜᵐ.

1. Missions—Chile. 2. Soldiers' and gospel mission of South America. I. Title.
Library of Congress　　BV2853.C5N3　　43-11762
　　　　　　　　　　　₍3₎　　₍265₎　278.3

NN　0015669　　DLC

VOLUME 405

UB790　Nanz, Hans.
.N2　　Befehlsberechtigung und gehorsamspflicht im schweizer.
militärstrafrecht mit berücksichtigung des deutschen mili-
tärstrafgesetzbuches ...　Männedorf, Buchdr. E. Meyer,
1916.
177 p.　21ᶜᵐ.
Inaug.-diss.—Zürich.
"Literatur-angabe": p. ₍171₎-175.

1. Military law—Switzerland.　2. Military discipline.

NN　0015670　ICU ICRL

MANN
QK　　Nanz, Ralph Simpson, 1889-
541　　　The Bryales of Ithaca and vicinity. ₍Ithaca,
N19　　N. Y.₎ 1923.
76 l.　2 fold. tables.　28 cm.

"Submitted in partial fulfillment of the
requirements for a minor in the Dept. of Botany."

1. Mosses - New York (State)　I. Title.

NN　0015671　NIC

QE999　Nanz, Robert Hamilton, 1923-
　　　　Composition and abundance of fine-grained
(G1)　Precambrian sediments of the southern Canadian
Shield.　1952.
188 l.

Thesis—Univ. of Chicago.

1. Geology, Stratigraphic—Precambrian.
2. Geology—Canadian Shield.

NN　0015672　ICU

Nanz, Robert Hamilton, 1923-
　　Composition and abundance of fine-grained Pre-Cambrian sediments of the southern Canadian shield.　Chicago, 1952.　xiv,
188 l.　illus., maps.

Film reproduction.　Positive.
Diss.—Chicago.
Bibliography, leaves 181-188.

1. Sedimentation and deposition—　　U.S.—Middle West.　2. Sedimentation and deposition—Canada.　3. Ge-　　ology, Stratigraphic, Pre Cambrian
—U.S.—Middle West.　4. Geology,　　Stratigraphic, Pre-Cambrian—Canada.
t. 1952.

NN　0015673　NN

Nanzan Daigaku, Nagoya, Japan.
Collectanea Universitatis Catholicae Nanzan.
see under title

Nanzan University, Nagoya, Japan
see
Nanzan Daigaku, Nagoya, Japan.

W　　NANZANDO'S medical dictionary.　Editorial
13　　Board: T. Ogawa ₍and others₎ 1st ed.
N193　　Tokyo, 1954.
1954　　　iii, 1353 p.　illus.
1. Medicine - Dict. - English-Japanese
2. Medicine - Dict. - Japanese-English
I. Ogawa, T　　　ed.

NN　0015676　DNLM

Nanzando's medical dictionary.　Editorial
board: T. Ogawa [and others] 2.ed。
Tokyo, Nanzando, 1954。　111,1353 p.
illus.　25cm。

Added t.-p. in Japanese; entries are in
Japanese, followed by the equivalent word
or phrase in English, German, and French;
definition or explanation is in Japanese.
1. Medicine—Dictionaries, Japanese.
2. Medicine—Dictionaries, Polyglot.
I。Ogawa. Teizo.

NN　0015677　NN

(Nanzatsuboku Kaidaimo kan shitetsu rosen chōsa
hōkoku)
南雜木一快大茂間私鐵路線調査報告　₍奉天₎　南滿
洲鐵道株式會社奉天調査室　昭和18₍1943₎
112 l.　illus.　25 cm.　₍交通調査資料 甲第2號₎
Cover title.
At head of title: 極秘 (rubber stamped)
本報告ノ取扱メハ滿鐵調査局二於テ爲シタルモノ

1. Railroads—Liaoning, China (Province)　I. Minami Manshū
Tetsudō Kabushiki Kaisha. Chōsakyoku.　II. Minami Manshū Tetsudō
Kabushiki Kaisha. Hōten Chōsashitsu.　III. Series: Kōtsū chōsa shiryō.
Kō dai 2-gō.

TF102.L52M36　　　　　　　　73-817700

NN　0015679　DLC

₍Nanzig, Abraham₎ 18th cent., supposed author.
₍London, 1789₎ עולם חדש. ונקרא עולם הפוך. לונדן,
7 l.　21 cm.

1. Judaism—England.　I. Title.
Title transliterated: 'Olam ḥadash.
BM292.N3　　　　　　　　58-54037

NN　0015680　DLC

---

de Nanzio (Ferdinando).　Intorno al concepi-　1802-1873.
mento ed alla figliatura di una mula. Memoria.　1 p. l., 17 pp., 2 pl.　roy. 8°.　Napoli, stamp.
e cartiere del Fibreno, 1846.
Repr. from: Atti d. vii. adunanza d. sc. ital. in Napoli.

NN　0015681　DNLM

Nanzio, Ferdinando de, 1802-1873.　L599.725 Looz
Intorno al concepimento ed alla figliatura di una mula.　Memoria
del prof. cav. Ferdinando de Nanzio, ...　Con 2 tavole in rame.
Terza edizione con giunte: Napoli, Stamperia e cartiere del
Fibreno, 1850.
29, [2] p.　II pl.　29¼ x 22½ᶜᵐ.

NN　0015682　ICJ

---

de Nanzio (Ferdinando) [1802-73].　Sul tito
contagioso de' bovi o peste bos-ungarica ingene-
ratosi il 1837 nelle Puglie; memoria.　58 pp. 8°.
Napoli, A. Della Croce, 1863.
Repr. from: Le utili conoscenze.

NN　0015683　DNLM

I
636.0834　Nanzio, Ferninando de, 1802-1873.
N158t　　　Trattato teorico-pratico della ferratura
... Napoli ₍Tipografia del Vecchio₎ 1843.
2 p. ℓ., vi, ₍1₎-155 ₍1₎p.　fold. plates.

1. Horseshoeing　I. For. auth. cd.　II. Title
III. Vet.med. cds.

NN　0015684　WaPS

Nanziposto, notaro del
see　Pontani, Gaspare, ca. 1449-ca. 1524.

Nao, Genjō.
法律と宗教との關係　名尾玄乘編　東京　明治
35 (1902) 序₎
3, 2, 555, 2 p.　23 cm.
Caption title.

1. Religion and law.　I. Title.
Title romanised: Hōritsu to shūkyō to no kankei.
J 60-3080 rev
Hoover Institution
for Library of Congress　　　₍r62b2₎

NN　0015686　CSt-H

JS7366
.9
.I 4T33　₍Taihoku-shū ribanshi₎
Orien　臺北州理蕃誌　₍舊宜蘭聽　臺北　臺北州警務部
Japan　大正12-13 i.e. 1923-24; v. 1, 1924₎

Nao, Shigeyuki.

Nno falta nem sobeja nada a minha mulher:
comedia en un acto, imitação do hespanhol...
Lisboa, 1874.
40 p.　12°.
In: NQM p. v. 9, no. 1.

NN　0015688　NN

NÃO falta nem sobeja nada a minha mulher; comedia em um acto, imitação do hespanhol, por E. A. de
Villar Coelho.　Lisboa, 1874.　40 p.　17cm.

Microfiche (neg.)　1 sheet.　11 x 15cm.　(NYPL FSN 13, 548)

1. Drama, Spanish--Trans-　　lations into Portuguese.
I. Villar Coelho, Eduardo　　Augusto de, tr.

NN　0015689　NN

La nao Santa Maria...
see　Spain.　Comisión arqueológica
ejecutiva.

Nno volto a Lisboa! ... Scena comica.
[Lisbon? 188-?]
(1) 4-8 p.　16°.
In: NQM p. v. 97, no. 16.
Title-page wanting.

NN　0015691　NN

Naoetsu-machi, Japan.
₍Naoetsu chōshi₎
直江津町史　₍編纂者・直江津町　直江津町（新
潟縣）　直江津町役場　昭和29 i.e. 1954₎
2, 3, 17, 946 p.　illus.　22 cm.

1. Naoetsu, Japan—History.　I. Title.
DS897.N347A47　　　　　　73-816607

NN　0015692　DLC

875.1　Naogeorgus, Thomas, 1511-1563.
N15a　　Agricvltvrae sacrae libri quinque, Thoma Naogeorgo Straubingensi autore. Hoc scripto, lector,
non solum omnibus numeris absoluti theologi ex-
pressam imaginem es habiturus, uerūetiam quibus
instructum doctrinis, ac moribus imbutum, ad om-
nem sanctissimi huius muneris exercitationem esse
oporteat, plenissimé cognosces.　Basileæ ₍1550₎
4 p.l., 167p.　16½cm.
The date 1550 appears on p.167.
Signatures: α⁴(last verso blank) A-K⁸, L⁴(last
verso blank)
Initials.

NN　0015693　IU NcD

Naogeorgus, Thomas, 1511-1563.
Een christelijcke tragedia. Die coopman ofte
dat oordeel geheeten. Daerinne die hoovet-stu-
cken ofte gront-leeringhen van twee religien,
die Romische papistische, ende die Gereformeerde
euangelische: niet uyt partydighe vernuft ofte
affectie sonder na waerheytende getuychnis der
Heyligden Schrift, duytlijck ende claer teghens
een ander worden voor ooghen ghestelt. Met
eene anghehenckte sluyt-reden, ende corte ver-
maninghe, tot Christlijcken eenicheyt ende reformation. Aen de Provinciale Staten van stadt
Groeningen ende Ommelanden. Voormaels in exilio

Continued in next column

VOLUME 405

Continued from preceding column

ghestellet,ende al nu van nieus vveder re-
videret door eenen vvtgevveken liefhebber des
vader-landes. Tot Groeningen, Gedruckt by Hans
Sas, Anno 1613.
[366] p. 14^{cm}.

Translation by D.van Amsweer of the Latin play Mercator seu judicium by T.Naogeorgus.

I.Amsweer,Doede van,1546-1631, tr. II.Title. III.
Title: Die coopman.

NN 0015695   MiU

Case
Y   NAOGEORGUS, THOMAS, fl.1511-1563.
682   De dissidiis compendia libri II. Adiuncta
.N 151   est etiam Satyra, ante annos aliquot scripta, in
         Ioannem del'la Casa...Sodomiae patronum. Basi-
         leae,1559.
            123,[5]p. 17cm.
            In verse.
            Appended ([5]p.): Catalogvs librorvm, avreum
         Babylonis calicem referentium. In catalogvm av-
         thorvm, et librorum, quos Paulus IIII Papa, pro
         haereticis & damnatis passim proscribi noluit
         (signed R.G.) In catalogvm Pavli IIII, quo ortho-
         doxae religionis   authores omnes pro -
         scribit (signed   B.M.)
            Unidentified   armorial bookplate.

NN 0015696   ICN NNH PU NjP

Naogeorgus, Thomas, fl. 1511-1563.

Bolte, Johannes, 1858-   *ed.*
   Drei schauspiele vom sterbenden menschen: 1. Das Münchner spiel von 1510. 2. Macropedius, Hecastus, 1539. 3. Naogeorgus, Mercator, 1540. Herausgegeben von Johannes Bolte.
Leipzig, K. W. Hiersemann, 1927.

---

*G.3975
.8   Naogeorgus, Thomas, 1511-1563.
         Hamanvs tragoedia nova svmpta e Bibliis, re-
      prehendens calumnias & tyrannidem potentum, &
      hortans ad uitae probitatem & metum Dei. [Lip-
      siae, M. Blum] Anno M. D. XLIII [1543] mense A-
      prili.
         [127] p. 15cm.
         Printer's device on t. p.
         Colophon: Lipsiae. Ex officina typographica
      honesti viri Michaelis Blum. Anno, & Virginis
      partu, 1.5.43. m   Aprili.

      I. Title: Hama   nus.

NN 0015698   MB PU

---

*GC5
N1592   Naogeorgus, Thomas, 1511-1563.
551h   Hieremias. Tragoedia nova, ex propheta
         Hieremia svmpta, hisce temporibus ualde
         accommoda, cum luculenta praefatione. Thoma
         Naogeorgo straubingensi autore ...
         Basileae. [1551].
            [216]p. 16cm.
            Dedication dated: Datum Basileae 4 iulij.
         M. D. LI.
            Errata: p.[19]. In this copy the three
         errata for Mlv (p.[182]) have been corrected.

NN 0015699   MH DFo PU

Naogeorgus, Thomas, 1511-1578.
   In catalogum haereticorum nuper Rome editum,
Thomae Naogeorgi Satyra. Adiectis etiam alijs,
eiusdem argumenti. [n.p.] Anno 1559.
   39 p. 16 cm.
   No. 3 in bound volume of 16th century tracts.

NN 0015700   MH-AH

Naogeorgus, Thomas, 1511-1563.
Rare Book   In primam D. Ioannis Epistolam annotationes,
Room   quae uice prolixi, commentarij esse possunt.
MLzB35   Thoma Naogeorgo Straubingensi autore. [n.p.]
544n   Anno 1544.
            150numb.l.,1l. 15cm.
            Signatures: A-T^8 (T7 blank)

NN 0015701   CtY ICN

Rare
PA   Naogeorgus, Thomas, 1511-1563.
8138   Incendia, sev Pyrgopolinices tragoedia
A18   recens nata, nephanda qvorvndam Papistici
no.6   gregis exponens facinora. Thoma Naogeorgo
         ... authore. Vitebergae, Apvd Georgivm
         Rhav, 1541.
            49 l. 16cm.

            Autograph on t. p.: Leonardvs Sperl, 1547.
            No. 6 in vol. lettered: Acolastus, Christus
         redivivus, Ovis Perdita, Studentes, Reuchlin
         2 Com., Incendia.

NN 0015702   NIC NNC MH PU DFo IU

Naogeorgus, Thomas, 1511-1563.
   Der kauffman / oder Das gericht. Ein geistliche tragoedi,
darinnen der vnderschid apostolischer vnd grob papistischer
lehr vnd trosts im schweren geistlichen kampff dess gewissens
nutzlich / den einfältigen zu vnderricht fürgestellt vnd abge-
bildet wirdt. Vor etlichen jaren in latein beschriben / durch
Thomam Naogeorgun, sonst Kirchmeyr genant / von Straubingen. An jetzo aber in teutsche reymen gebracht / durch
m. Jacobvm Rvlichvm Augustanum. Getruckt im jahr
M.D.XCV.
   10 p. l., 256, [14] p. 1 illus. 15cm.
   Colophon: Getruckt inn der keiserlichen reichstatt Lindaw am Bo-
densee / bey Johann Lud-   wig Brem. Im jahr 1595.
   Title vignette (coat of   arms)
   I. Rulich, Jacob, 1559-   1612, tr. II. Title.

Library of Congress   PA8555.N3M45 1595   36-2276

NN 0015703   DLC CtY

---

*G.3577
.5   [Naogeorgus, Thomas] 1511-1563.
         Le marchant converti. Tragedie excellente.
      En laquelle la vraye & fausse religion ... sont
      au vif representees ... [Lyon] Par Gabriel Car-
      tier, 1582.
         [188] p. 12cm.
         Title vignette.
         "Ioan Crespin aux fideles de Flandres ... ":
      p.[3-4]

      I. Crespin, Jean, d. 1572, tr. II. Title.

NN 0015704   MB

Bd.w.   [Naogeorgus, Thomas] 1511-1563.
11333   [Mercator]
            A-H^8, I^2. (A1 [title-page] and all after I2
         lacking; I1-2 bound after A7) 8vo. 13.5x8.6cm.
            First edition 1540.
            "Epistola Dedicatoria" to Heinrich der Fromme,
         Duke of Saxony, by Thomas Naogeorgus, sig.A2r-
         A5v.
            Bookplate of William North, Baron Grey of
         Rolleston, 1703; North family library-Harmsworth
         copy.

            Bound with P. Frarinus, An oration, 1566, and
         other works.

NN 0015706   DFo

Naogeorgus, Thomas, 1511-1563.   *B.4225.1.269/270
   Mercator (1540). [Von] Thomas Naogeorgus [pseud.]
   (*In* Bolte, Johannes, editor. Drei Schauspiele vom sterbenden
Menschen. Pp. 161-319. Leipzig. 1927.).

   Drvas — T.r. Morality. — Moralities.

NN 0015707   MB

Naogeorgus, Thomas, 1511-1563.
   Das Päpstisch Reych. Ist ein Buch ... Darin der Babst mit
seinen geldern, leben, glauben, Gottsdienst, ceremonien vnd
Cerimonien ... beschrieben ... Durch Thomam Kirchmair. [n. p.]
1555.   168 l.   19cm. (4°.)

   See: Grässe, IV, 23.
   In verse.
   Translator's dedication signed: Burcardus Waldis.
   Presumably printed in Germany.
   First published in Latin in 1553.

NN 0015708   NN ICU

Naogeorgus, Thomas, 1511-1563.
   Pammachius. Eyn kurtzweilig tragoedi darinn
auss warhafftigen hystorien furgebildet, wie die
Bäpst und Bischoffe, das predig und hirten ampt
verlassen...Beschriben im latein zu Wittemberg
durch Thomas Kirchmeyern von Straubingen und
jüngst verteütschet. [1539] 201p.

   Source of information: Maltzahn. Deutscher
bücherschatz, p.180.

NN 0015709   OClWHi

Naogeorgus, Thomas, 1511-1563.
   ... Thomas Naogeorgvs Pammachivs. Hrsg. von Johannes
Bolte und Erich Schmidt. Berlin, Weidmann, 1891.

   xxvi p., 1 l., 151 p. 19^{cm}. (Lateinische litteraturdenkmäler des xv.
und xvi. jahrhunderts. 3)
   Reprint of original edition, including t.-p.: Vitebergae, typis Ioannis
Luft, 1538.
   Bibliography: p. vii-xxvi.

   I. Bolte, Johannes, 1858-   ed. II. Schmidt, Erich, 1853-1913, joint
ed. III. Title.

Library of Congress   PA3115.L3 hft. 3   2—261

NN 0015710   DLC PPT OU MB TxU ICU MdBP PHC NIC

Naogeorgus, Thomas, 1511-1563.

Stubbs, Philip, *fl.* 1581-1593.
   Phillip Stubbes's Anatomy of the abuses in England in Shakspere's youth, A. D. 1583 ... Ed. by Frederick J. Furnivall.
London, Pub. for the New Shakspere society, by N. Trübner &
co., 1877-9-82.

Rare Book   Naogeorgus, Thomas, 1511-1563.
Room   The popish kingdome, or reigne of Anti-
Gr8   christ, written in Latine verse by Thomas
36g   Naogeorgus, and englyshed by Barnabe Googe
           ... Imprinted at London by Henrie Denham,
           for Richarde Watkins.Anno.1570.
              5p.l.,88numb.l.,4l. 1 illus.(coat of
           arms) 19cm.
              Signatures: [A]^2B-Y^4(B4 blank)Aa-Bb^4[Cc]^4.
              Imperfect: some side-notes bled.

NN 0015712   CtY DFo MWiW-C CSmH

Humanities
Library
Microfilm
AC   Naogeorgus, Thomas, 1511-1563.
4   The popish kingdome, or reigne of Antichrist, written in
E5   Latine verse by Thomas Naogeorgus, and Englyshed by Barnabe
Reel   Googe ... Imprinted at London by Henrie Denham, for Richarde
no.   VVatkins ... 1570.
346   University microfilms no. 14940 (case 58, carton 346)
              Short-title catalogue no. 15011.

              I. Catholic church. I. Googe, Barnabe, 1540-1594, tr.
           II. Title.

NN 0015713   MiU WaPS

Naogeorgus, Thomas, 1511-1563.
   Popular and popish superstitions and customs
on Saints-days and Holy-days in Germany and
other Papist lands A.D. 1553, being the fourth
booke of "The Popish Kingdome; or, Reigne of
Antichrist, written in Latine verse by Thomas
Naogeorgus (or Kirchmaier),and Englyshed by
Barnabe Googe... Anno 1570." (In: New
Shakspere Society. Series 6. Nos. 4 & 6.:
Stubbes (P.) Anatomy...   London, 1877-1882.
Pt. 1. Sec. 2. Appendix. p. 321-376)

NN 0015714   NN

---

*GC5
N1592   Naogeorgus, Thomas, 1511-1563.
553p   Regnum papisticum. Opvs lectv ivcvndum
         omnibus ueritatem amantibus: in quo papa cum
         suis membris, uita, fide, cultu, ritibus,
         atq[ue] caeremonijs, quanti fieri potuit, uere
         & breuiter describuntur, distinctum in libros
         quatuor. Thoma Naogeorgo autore. Adiecta sunt &
         alia quaedam huius argumenti, lectu non indigna.
         [Basel?] 1553. Mense iunio.
            171,[2]p. 15.5cm.
            Pages 110,116 & 152 misnumbered 119,16 & 158.

Continued in next column

VOLUME 405

Continued from preceding column

Errata: [2]p. at end.
With this is bound his Sylvvla carminvm
aliqvot ... 1553 and his Sylva carminvm in
nostri temporis ... [1553]

NN 0015716   MH NcU TxU NjP ICN PPL IU DFo CtY ViU

Naogeorgus, Thomas, 1511-1563.
Regnum Papisticum; Nunc postremò recognitum & auctum.
Opvs ... in quo Papa cum suis membris, uita, fide, cultu, ritibus
atꝗ cæremonijs .. describuntur .. Thoma Naogeorgo autore.
Adiecta sunt & alia quaedam huius argumenti .. ᵣBasileæ, Ex
Officina Ioannis Oporini₎ 1559. 243 ᵢi. e. 359₎ p., 16 l. 16cm.
(8°.)

Brunet, IV, 6.   Grässe, IV, 23.
With colophon.

Numbers 273-288 repeated in paging. p. 359 wrongly numbered 243.
In verse.
First published 1553.
The additional poems include: In Ioannem Del'la Casa...Satyra, De Dissidiis
Componendis, In Catalogvm Hæreticorvm Nuper Romæ editum, Satyra, and Sylvvla
Carminvm (with special t.-p.)

1. Catholic church, Roman, Anti-   2. Poetry, German, Neo-Latin.
3. Satire, German, Neo-Latin.   Card revised
N. Y. P. L.   April 15, 1942

NN NNH
0015718   NN TxU MnU CU MH ICN TxU IU NNUT CU-W

Naogeorgus, Thomas, 1511-1563.
Reprint of The Popish Kingdome, or reigne of Antichrist,
written in Latin verse by Thomas Naogeorgus and Englyshed
By Barnabe Googe, 1570. Ed. with brief memoir of his life
by Charles Hope ... London, Imprinted at the Chiswick press,
by C. Whittingham & co., for the editor, and sold by W.
Satchell & co., 1880.
xviii p., reprint (5 p. l., 80 numb. l.), ᵣ81₎-74 p. 22½ᵐ.
With reproduction of original t.-p.: The Popish Kingdome, or reigne of
Antichrist, written in Latine verse by Thomas Naogeorgus, and englyshed
by Barnabe Googe ... ᵣImprinted at London by Henrie Denham, for
Richarde VVatkins Anno. 1570. (Within ornamental border)
I. Googe, Barnabe, 1540-1594, tr. II. Hope, Robert Charles, 1885-   ed.
18—6977
Library of Congress   PR2279.G4P6

NN 0015719   DLC OrU NIC FU CtY NcD MdBP PU-F

Naogeorgus, Thomas, 1511-1563.
Rvbricæ sive svmmæ capitvlorvm ivris
canonici. Lugduni, 1570.

NN 0015720   MH-L

Naogeorgus, Thomas, 1511-1563.
Rvbricae, sive svmmae capitvlorvm
ivris canonici, Thomae Naogeorgi ...
opera in lucem editae. Adiunctus
quoque est in calce, praecipuorum
locorum, qui in decretis tractantur,
index. Lvgdvni, apvd Gvlielmvm,
1574.
286 p. 12cm.
Title vignette (device of printer₎

NN 0015721   MH-L

Naogeorgus, Thomas, 1511-1563?
Rvbricae sive Svmmæ capitvlorvm iuris canonici, Thomæ
Naogeorgi Straubingensis opera in lucem editæ. Adiunctus
quoque est in calce, præcipuorum locorum, qui in decretis tractantur, index. Lvgdvni, apvd Gvlielmvm Rovillivm, 1578.
286 p. 12ᵐ.
Publisher's device on t.-p.

1. Canon law—Dictionaries.   I. Title.
35-34708

NN 0015722   DLC MH-L

Law

Naogeorgus, Thomas, 1511-1591.
Rvbricae, sive svmmae capitvlorvm ivris canonici, Thomae Noageorgi...opera in lucem e-
ditae. Adiunctus quoque est in calce, praecipuorum locorum, qui in decretis tractantur,
index. Lvgdvni, apvd Gvlielmvm Rovillivm,
1588.
286 p. 12 cm.
Bound with Lancellotti, G.P.,1511-1591. In-
stitvtiones. Lvgdvni, 1587.

1. Canon Law.   I. Title.

NN 0015723   DLC

Spec.
BX 1935 Naogeorgus, Thomas, 1511-1563.
L 34   Rvbricae sive Svmmae capitvlorvm ivris
1606   canonici, Thomae Noageorgi ᵣsic₎ Straubingensis opera in lucem editae. Adiunctus quoque
est in calce, praecipuorum lccorum, qui in
decretis tractantur, index. Lvgdvni, Apud
Haered. Guill. Rouillij, 1606.
286 p. 13 cm.
Publisher's device on t. p.
Bound with Lancellotti, G. P. Institvt-
iones ivris canonici. Lvgdvni, 1606.

Stratford   Lee Morton collection.

NN 0015724   MoSW

Naogeorgus, Thomas, 1511-1563.
Satyrarum libri qvinqve priores: Thoma
Naogeorgo Straubingensi autore. His sunt
adiuncti, De animi tranquillitate duo libelli:
unus Plutarchi, latinus ab eodē factus: alter
Senecę: cum annotationib. in utrumq ...
Basileae, Per Ioannem Operinum [1555]
14.5 cm.
Colophon: Basileae, Ex officina Ioannis
Oporini, anno salutis humanæ M.D.LV. mense
Iulio.

NN 0015725   CtY PPL

Bd.w.   ᵣNaogeorgus, Thomas₎ 1511-1563, ed.
PA   Sylua carminum in nostri temporis corruptelas,
8555   praesertim religionis, sanè quàm salsa & festiua,
N3   ex diuersis hinc inde autoribus collecta ᵣBasle?
R4   1553?₎
1553
Copy 2   127 ᵣ1₎ p. a-h⁸. 8vo.
Cage

NN 0015726   DFo CtY RPB MH TxU IEN

---

*GC5   [Naogeorgus, Thomas, 1511-1563, comp.]
N1592   Sylvvla carminvm aliqvot à diuersis, pijs &
553p   eruditis uiris conscriptorum: quib. uariæ de
religione sententiæ & controuersiæ breuissimè
explicantur ...
[Basel?] 1553.
16p. 15.5cm.
Bound with his Regnum papisticum, 1553.

NN 0015727   MH TxU NjP CtY PPL DFo

Naogeorgus, Thomas, 1511-1563.
Tragoedia Alia Nova Mercator Sev Ivdicivm, In Qva In Con-
spectū ponuntur Apostolica & Papistica doctrina, quantum utraꝗ;
in conscientiæ certamine ualeat & efficiat, & quis utriusꝗ; futurus
sit exitus. Thoma Naogeorgo...autore... ᵣIngolstadii?
Alexander Weissenhorn? 15₎40. 76 l. 15cm. (8°.)

Grässe, IV, 23.
In verse.
With autograph of H. A. Werumeus.

58734. 1. Drama, German, Neo-   Latin. I. Title: Mercator Sev
Ivdicivm.   Card revised
N. Y. P. L.   October 24, 1949

NN 0015728   NN DFo

---

*GC5   [Naogeorgus, Thomas, 1511-1563]
N1592   [Tragoedia nova Pammachius, autore Thoma
5411   Naogeorgo straubingensi. Cum praefatione
luculenta.]
[Excusum Vitebergæ, typis Ioannis Luft. Anno
M.D.XXXVIII.tertio idus maij.]
[162]p. 15cm.
Signatures: A⁶,B-I⁸,K⁴,L⁸ (L8 blank).
Imperfect: A1-A6 (t.-p. & dedication) wanting;
title supplied from type facsimile in the 1891
edition.
Bound with his   Incendia, 1541.

NN 0015729   MH CtY DFo NNC PU FU

Naogeorgus, Thomas, 1511-1563.
Tragoedia Nova Pammachius, autore Thoma Naogeorgo...
Cvm Præfatione Lvcvlenta.   Augustæ, Per Alexandrum Vueis-
senhorn, 1539. 82 l. 15cm. (8°.)

Grässe, IV, 23.
Last leaf (blank?) wanting.
In verse.
With autograph of H. A. Werumeus.

58687. 1. Drama. German, Neo-   Latin. I. Title: Pammachius.
Card revised

NN 0015730   NN IU

Naogeorgus, Thomas, 1511-1563. Tragoedia nova
Pammachius.
Berger, Arnold Erich, 1862-   ed.
Die schaubühne im dienste der reformation ... von Arnold
E. Berger. Leipzig, P. Reclam jun., 1935-

NN 0015732   NjP

Naogeorgus, Thomas, 1511-1563.
Vom bapstum; ein newe seer schöne
tragedia... aus dem latin verdeudscht
durch Justum Menium...   Wittemberg,
1539.
[271] p. 15 cm.
I. Menius, Justus, 1499-1558, tr.

NN 0015732   NjP

Naogeorgus, Thomas, 1511-1563.
Vom Bapstumb. ᵣEine newe seer schone Tragedia
Thomae Naogeorgi ᵣsonst Kirchmeyer genant₎ aus
dem Latin verdeudscht durch Justum Meni.
(In Das Drama der Reformationszeit. Hrsg. von
Dr. R. Froning. n.d. p.ᵣ183₎-382. ᵣDeutsche
National-Litteratur, v. 22₎)
Microcard edition.

NN 0015733   ICRL

Naogra andeliga wisor
        see under   [Rudman, Andrew] 1668-1708.

Naohiko Masaki
        see Masaki, Naohiko, 1862-1942.

LA   Naoi, John Yutaka, 1906-
1312   The Japanese educational reformation after
N3   World War II. Washington, D. C.,The Catholic
1955a   University of America Press,1955.
14p. 24cm.

Abstract of thesis - Catholic University of
America.

1. Education - Japan - 1945-   I. Title.

NN 0015736   MU MB NjR NN DS

Naoi, Takeo, 1897-
朝鮮戦乱の真実 直井武夫著 東京 民主日本
協会 昭和 28 ᵣ1953₎
187 p. 17 cm. (民主日本文庫 5)

1. Korean War, 1950-1953. I. Title. (Series: Minshu Nihon
bunko, 5)
Title romanised: Chōsen senran no shinjitsu.

DS918.N3   J 69-1 ‡

NN 0015737   DLC CLU-O

DK41   Naoi, Takeo, 1897-
.N525   Soren
Orien   Nihon Gaisei Gakkai.
Japan   ソ連 ᵣ直井武夫等著₎ 日本外政学会出版局編
集 東京 日本外政学会 昭和30 ᵣ1955₎

VOLUME 405

Naoi ngearra-chluichi
see under   [Foley, Richard] ed. & tr.

Naom Columcille; the life of St. Columcille, in Irish and English, by a Redemptorist father.   Dublin: M. H. Gill & son, ltd., 1907.   121 p.   18½cm.
Irish and English on opposite pages.

495937. 1. Columba, Saint, 521-597.   2. Gaelic language, Irish—Texts and translations. I. A Redemptorist   father.   *Card revised*
N. Y. P. L.   *March 19, 1942*

NN   0015740   NN

Naoki, Sanjūgo, pseud.
(Genkurō Yoshitsune)
源九郎義經   直木三十五著   東京   四季社
﹝昭和26-27 i. e. 1951-52﹞
2 v.   19 cm.

1. Minamoto, Yoshitsune, 1159-1189—Fiction.   I. Title.

PL857.A58G4   72-805243

NN   0015741   DLC

Naoki, Sanjūgo, pseud.
關ヶ原   直木三十五著   東京   春陽堂   昭和7
﹝1932﹞
358 p.   illus.   16 cm.   (日本小説文庫 3)

I. Title.
Title romanized: Sekigahara.
J 64-1308

Harvard Univ.   Chinese-   Japanese Library   5063
for Library of Congress   ﹝1﹞

NN   0015742   MH-HY

---

*7267.50
Naokoło świata. [Illustrowany miesięcznik pod redakcja Stanisława Lama.]   Nos. 1-17.   1924. 25.
— Warszawa. Gebethner & Wolff.   [1924, 25.]   1 v.   Illus. Portraits.   24.5 cm., in 8s.

N1427 — Poland. Lang. Works in Pol. ... — Poland. Periodicals. — Periodicals.
Polish. — Lam, Stanisław, ed.

NN   0015743   MB MiD NN

Naomani, Shibli
see
Shibli Numani, Muhammad, 1857-1914.

Naomh O'Huidhrin, Giolla na
see   O'Huidhrin, gilla na naomh, d. 1420.

Naomi, Aunt, pseud.
see
Landa, Gertrude.

Naomi, the Hindoo widow.
[London:The Religious tract society,ca. 1850.]
8p.   illus.   10cm.
Caption title.
No. 4 in a half blue mor. vol. numbered: 666.

NN   0015747   PPRF

Naomi; eller, Jerusalems sidste dage, af Mrs. J. B. Webb
see under   [Peploe, Annie (Molyneux)) "Mrs. J. B. Peploe"] 1805-1880.

Naomi or The last days of Jerusalem
see under   [Peploe, Annie (Molyneux)] 1805-1880.

F262
.R2N2
1890
Naomi Wise, or, The Wrongs of a beautiful girl.   Enacted in Randolph County, North Carolina, about the year 1800.   ﹝Pinnacle, N. C.﹞, W. C. Phillips, Printer, 189-?﹞
27 p.   17½cm.
Caption title.
Printed paper covers.

1. Randolph Co., N. C.—Hist. 2. Salem, N. C.—
Hist. 3. Wise, Naomi. 4. Lewis, Jonathan, fl.
1800.

NN   0016003   ViU NcU

NK2003
.P5
The Naomi Wood collection.

Philadelphia.   Woodford Mansion.
The Naomi Wood collection, "an illustration of household gear during Colonial years."   Woodford Mansion, Fairmount Park, Philadelphia, Pa.   ﹝Philadelphia﹞ 1947.

Naomi's home.   A true story.   Boston, D. Lothrop & co.; Dover, N.H., G. T. Day & co., 1872.
2 p.l., ﹝7﹞-58p. incl.front., illus., plates. 15cm.   ﹝Little folks series﹞

NN   0016005   IU

Naón, Eduardo M   *ed. and tr.*
... Ley de bancarrotas de los Estados Unidos de América. B﹝ueno﹞s Aires, Impr. de J. Tragant ﹝pref. 1918﹞
2 p. l., ﹝vii﹞-xv, 287 p.   24ᶜᵐ.

1. Bankruptcy—U. S. 2. Forms (Law)—U. S.   I. U. S. Laws,
statutes, etc.
43-26623

NN   0016006   DLC

Naón, Eduardo M.
Ministerio público comparado, su organización y funcionamiento, por el Dr. Eduardo M. Naón ...   París, Casa editorial franco-ibero-americana ﹝1929?﹞
2 p. l., ﹝7﹞-274 p., 2 l.   18 x 14ᶜᵐ.

1. Justice, Administration of.   I. Title.

Library of Congress   JF701.N3   30-15669

NN   0016007   DLC NcD

NAÓN, Pedro J.
Eglantinas.   ﹝Buenos Aires? Revista nacional﹞ 1901.

NN   0016008   MH

Naón, Rómulo Sebastian, 1875-1941, ed.
Apuntes de derecho comercial marítimo
see under   Obarrio, Manuel.

Naón, Rómulo Sebastian, 1875–
... Argentine constitutional ideas.   Address delivered before the American bar association at the annual meeting held in Washington, D. C., on October 22, 1914, by the Honorable Rómulo S. Naón, ambassador from Argentina to the United States ...   Washington ﹝Govt. print. off.﹞ 1914.
19 p.   23ᶜᵐ.   (﹝U. S.﹞ 63d Cong. 2d sess. Senate. Doc. 618)
Presented by Mr. Fletcher. Ordered printed October 24, 1914.

1. Argentine Republic—Constitutional law.   I. Title.

Library of Congress   JL2018.N3   14-30896 Revised

NN   0016010   DLC OrU PPT PU-L PHi MiU OO

F
1415
.N13
Naón, Rómulo Sebastian, 1875–
La defensa de los intereses pan-americanos es garantía de la independencia nacional; reportaje al doctor Rómulo S. Naón, publicado en "Crítica" de 12 de julio de 1940.   [Buenos Aires? 1940]
20 p.   16 cm.

NN   0016011   DPU

Naón, Rómulo Sebastian, 1875–
...Deslinde de facultades nacionales y provinciales...   Buenos Aires, A. Monkes, 1896.
5 p.l., ﹝17﹞-287 p.   23cm.

At head of title: Universidad de la capital. Facultad de derecho y ciencias sociales.
Tesis-Universidad de Buenos Aires.

NN   0016012   NcD

Naón, Rómulo Sebastian, 1875–
... Deslinde de facultades nacionales y provinciales ...   Buenos Aires, Impr. de A. Monkes, 1898.
6 p.l., [17]-287 p.   26 cm.
Thesis - Buenos Aires.
Two leaves preceding dedication page cut out.
Contains author's presentation inscription.

NN   0016013   CtY

Naón, Rómulo Sebastian, 1875–
Discurso pronunciado por el ministro de justicia é instrucción pública, Dr. Rómulo S. Naón, en el acto inaugural de los cursos de la Universidad nacional de Córdoba el 23 marzo de 1909.   Buenos Aires, Talleres gráficos de la Penitenciaria nacional, 1909.
2 p. l., ﹝7﹞-24 p.   20½ᶜᵐ.

1. Córdoba, Argentine Republic. Universidad nacional.   I. Title.
E 15-556 Revised

Library, U. S. Bur. of   Education   LE21.C8N2

NN   0016014   DHEW MB

Naón, Rómulo Sebastian, 1875–
Discursos pronunciados por el ministro de justicia é instrucción pública, dr. Rómulo S. Naón, al inaugurar los nuevos edificios de la Escuela práctica de medicina (capital federal), Colegio nacional de Santiago del Estero y Escuela normal mixta de Azul.   Buenos Aires, Talleres gráficos de la Penitenciaría nacional, 1908.
2 p. l., ﹝7﹞-89 p.   21ᶜᵐ.

1. Education—Argentine republic. 2. Education—Addresses, ﹝essays,﹞
lectures, ﹝etc.﹞
E 15-557 Revised

U. S. Off. of educ.   Library   LA548.7.N2
for Library of Congress   ﹝r41b2﹞

NN   0016015   DHEW

VOLUME 405

Naón, Rómulo Sebastian, 1875–
… The European war and Pan Americanism, by Rómulo S. Naón … New York, American association for international conciliation, Interamerican division, 1919.
19 p. 19½cm. (International conciliation. Interamerican division bulletin, no. 20)
"Reprinted … from the Columbia university quarterly, of New York, issue of April, 1919."
"Written for the quarterly, February 1, 1919; simultaneous publication in La Nación of Buenos Ayres. English version, by Peter H. Goldsmith."—Columbia univ. quarterly, vol. XXI, April 1919, no. 2, p. ⌈85⌉
1. European war, 1914– 2. American republics. I. Goldsmith, Peter H., tr. II. Title.
19–14981
Library of Congress JX1907.A85 no. 20

NN 0016016 DLC WaS MiU ViU

Naón, Rómulo Sebastian, 1875–
… La guerra europea y el panamericanismo, por Rómulo S. Naón … Nueva York, Asociación americana para la conciliación internacional, 1919.
19 p. 19½cm. (Conciliación internacional. Boletín 21 de la División interamericana)
"Original español del cual se hizo la versión inglesa publicada en The Columbia university quarterly de Nueva York, número correspondiente al segundo trimestre del año corriente."
Published also in La Nación, Buenos Aires.
1. European war, 1914– 2. American republics.
19–14982
Library of Congress JX1907.A85

NN 0016017 DLC MiU OU

Naón, Rómulo Sebastian, 1875-
Inviolabilidad de la propiedad minera; demanda presentada ante la Suprema Corte de Justicia de la nación por inconstitucionalidad del decreto del gobierno de Salta de 31 de mayo de 1928. ⌈Estudio del Dr. Rómulo S. Naón⌉ Buenos Aires, Editorial Muro, 1928.
281 p. fold. maps.

NN 0016018 NNC CtY NNC-L

Naón, Rómulo Sebastian, 1875–
… Los ministros (su carácter y función constitucional) … Buenos Aires, Impr. de Coni hermanos, 1905.
77 p. 18½cm.
"Memoria presentada para optar á la cátedra de derecho constitucional y aprobada por la Facultad de derecho y ciencias sociales de la Universidad de Buenos Aires."
1. Cabinet officers—Argentine Republic. 2. Ministerial responsibility.
14-7221 Revised
Library of Congress JL2042.N3

NN 0016019 DLC CtY

Naón, Rómulo Sebastian, 1875–
… The rights of neutrals. Address on the rights of neutrals in the light of the new problems presented by the present European war, before the governing board of the Pan American union at Washington, December 8, 1914, by Hon. Rómulo S. Naón, ambassador from Argentina … Washington, Govt. print. off., 1915.
5 p. 23cm. (⌈U. S.⌉ 63d Cong., 3d sess. Senate. Doc. 801)
Presented by Mr. Chilton. Ordered printed February 2, 1915.
1. Neutrality. 2. European war, 1914– I. Title.
15-26106 Revised
Library of Congress JX5371.N2

NN 0016020 DLC MiU OO NN

Naón, Rómulo Sebastian, 1875–
Some Argentine constitutional ideas. An address delivered at the University of Virginia, Founder's day, April 13, 1917, by the Honorable Romulo S. Naon … ⌈Charlottesville? Va., 1917⌉
cover-title, 16 p. 23½cm.
"Reprinted from the Alumni bulletin for April, 1917."
1. Argentine Republic—Constitutional law.
19—12366
Library of Congress JL2015.1917.N3

NN 0016021 DLC

Naón, Rómulo Sebastian, 1875–
… El triunfo del verdadero panamericanismo y sus relaciones con la paz universal, por Rómulo S. Naón … New York, Asociación americana para la conciliación internacional, División panamericana, 1915.
16 p. 19½cm. (Conciliación internacional. Boletín especial ⌈de la División panamericana. no. 4⌉)
"Discurso pronunciado el día del fundador en el Instituto Carnegie Pittsburgh, Estados Unidos de Norte America, abril 29 de 1915."
1. American republics. 2. Peace.
16-18939 Revised
Library of Congress JX1907.A85 no. 4

NN 0016022 DLC

Naor, Binyamin.
אל הקבוצה. ⌈הוצאת⌉ איחוד הקבוצות והקיבוצים.
⌈Tel-Aviv, 1953/54⌉
23 p. illus. 18 cm.
1. Collective settlements—Israel. I. Title.
Title transliterated: El ha-kevutsah.
HX765.P3N3 59–55072 ‡

NN 0016023 DLC

Naor, Menahem.
The Bible and the Land
see his ha-Mikra veha- Arets.

Naor, Menahem.
Hebrew language and grammar; a practical textbook, by Menahem Naor, PH. D. 2. ed., rev. throughout. Jerusalem, R. Mass, 1942.
98 p.; 94 p. 21½ cm.
Added t.-p.: עברית, השפה ודקדוקה. ספר־למוד ללומדים בעזרת־מורה או בלעדיה מאת ד"ר מנחם נאור. מהדורה ב' מתוקנת.
"Key" (8 p.) inserted.
1. Hebrew language—Grammar. 2. Hebrew language—Chrestomathies and readers.
PJ4567.N28 1942 492.48242 44—15701

NN 0016025 DLC NNUT

Naor, Menahem.
Hebrew language and grammar; a practical textbook by Menahem Naor... 3d rev. ed. Jerusalem, R. Mass, 1944.
98,⌈94⌉,8p. 22cm.

NN 0016026 NNU-W NcD

PJ 5012 N19 1947
Naor, Menahem.
Hebrew, language and grammar; a practical textbook. 4th rev. ed. Jerusalem, R. Mass, 1947.
98; 94 p. 22cm.
Added t.p., in Hebrew.
"Key" (8 p.) inserted in pocket.
1. Hebrew language--Grammar. 2. Hebrew language--Chrestomathies and readers.

NN 0016027 NIC

Naor, Menahem
Hebrew language and grammar; a practical textbook. 5th rev.ed. Jerusalem, R.Mass, 1949
98, 94 p.
Added t.p.in Hebrew
Text in Hebrew and English
Key (8 p.) inserted

NN 0016028 MH NN

PJ 4567 .N19
NAOR, MENAHAN
Hebrew language and grammar; a practical textbook. 7th rev. ed. Jerusalem, R. Mass, 1950.
98+8+94 p.
Includes Reader, with Hebrew t.-p.
1. Hebrew language--Grammar. 2. Hebrew language--Readers.

NN 0016029 InU TxU OCH

Naor, Menahem.
Hebrew language and grammar; a practical textbook, by Menahem Naor, PH. D. 8th ed. Jerusalem, R. Mass, 1953.
98 p.; 94 p. 21½cm.
Added t.-p.: עברית, השפה ודקדוקה. ספר־למוד ללומדים בעזרת־מורה או בלעדיה מאת ד"ר מנחם נאור. מהדורה ב' מתוקנת.
"Key" (8 p.) inserted.
First published under title: A practical textbook of the Hebrew language.

NN 0016030 IU ViRUT MB

Naor, Menahem.
עיקרי הדקדוק העברי, תורת־הנקוד—תורת־הצורות—תרגילים. מהדורה ד., בשנויים ובתקונים. חיפה, בית־הספר הריאלי העברי, תש"ה ⌈1944/45⌉
118 p. 21 cm.
1. Hebrew language—Grammar. I. Haifa. Beth Sefer Reali Ivri.
Title transliterated: 'Ikare ha-dikduk ha-'ivri.
PJ4567.N268 55—48625

NN 0016031 DLC

Naor, Menahem.
עיקרי הדקדוק העברי; תורת־הנקוד, תורת־הצורות, תרגילים. מהדורה ה. מתוקנת. היפה, בית־הספר הריאלי העברי, תש"ז.
⌈Haifa, 1946/47⌉
118 p. 23 cm.
1. Hebrew language—Grammar.
Title transliterated: 'Ikare ha-dikduk ha-'ivri.
PJ4567.N27 52–59395

NN 0016032 DLC

Naor, Menahem.
המקרא והארץ, באור גיאוגרפי לתנ"ך. תל־אביב, הסתדרות המורים העברים בישראל, תשי"ב-
⌈Tel-Aviv, 1952-
v. 24 cm. (אוצר המורה)
Added t. p.: The Bible and the Land, a geographical commentary on the Old Testament, with an atlas to the Bible.
Bibliography: v. 1, p. ⌈194⌉ v. 2, p. (חלק) 12-13 (1st group)
CONTENTS.— חלק א. תורה. ב. נביאים ראשונים.
1. Bible. O. T.—Geography. 2. Palestine—Historical geography. (Series: Otsar ha-moreh) *Title transliterated:* ha-Mikra veha-Arets.
BS630.N3 54–55688

NN 0016033 DLC

BJ5 N159n
Naor, Menahem
Neues Lehrbuch der hebräischen Sprache; für Unterricht und Selbststudium. Jerusalem, Divan Book and Art shop, 1935.
x, 95, 112 p. illus. 24 cm.
Reader and glossary (Hebrew text) with Hebrew t.p.: 112 p.
1. Hebrew language - Grammar. I. Title.

NN 0016034 CtY-D

VOLUME 405

Naor, Menahem.
... A practical textbook of the Hebrew language, for teaching and self-instruction. Jerusalem, Divan book and art shop, 1933.

viii, 100, 127, [1] p. 24½ᵐ.

Reader and glossary (Hebrew text) with Hebrew t.-p.: 127 p.

1. Hebrew language—Grammar.

A 40-1697

Newberry library
for Library of Congress   .9.

NN   0016035   ICN MB IaU ICU

Naora, Nobuo, 1902–
S26b   Human artifacts excavated at Dōkantin, Korea.
782   [Tokyo, Dai Ichiji Mammō Gakujutsu Kenkyū Dan]
6(3   1939 [i.e. 1940]
12p. illus. 26cm. (Scientific Expedition to Manchoukuo, 1st., 1933. Report, sect. 6, pt. 3, [no. 2])
English title preceded by title in Japanese.
Japanese text with resumé (p.11-12) in English.
1. Korea - Antiq. 2. Stone age - Korea. I.Ser.

NN   0016036   CtY

Naora, Nobuo, 1902–
Q115   [Manshu Teikoku Kitsurin-shō Kokyaton
.M27   dalikkai ...]
sect. 2,   Tokunaga, Shigeyasu, 1874-1940.
pt. 1   滿洲帝國吉林省顧鄉屯第一回發掘物研究報文
Orien   Report of diggings at Ho-chia-kou, Ku-hsiang-tung, Kirin, Manchoukou. 德永重康直良信夫著 東京 第一次滿蒙學術調査研究團] 1934.

Naora, Nobuo, 1902–
Q115   [Manshu Teikoku Kitsurin-shō Kokyaton
.M27   hakkutsu ...]
sect. 6,   Tokunaga, Shigeyasu, 1874-1940.
pt. 2   滿洲帝國吉林省顧鄉屯發掘ノ古生人類遺品
Orien   Palaeolithic artifacts excavated at Ho-chia-kou in Ku-hsiang-tung, Manchoukuo. 德永重康直良信夫著 東京 第一次滿蒙學術調査研究團] 1936.

Naora, Nobuo, 1902–
[Nihon honyū dōbutsu shi]
日本哺乳動物史 直良信夫著 [丹波市町(奈良縣)] 養德社 [昭和19 i.e. 1944]
2, 4, 265 p. illus. 22 cm.

1. Mammals—Japan.   I. Title.
QL729.J3N36   72-807253

NN   0016039   DLC

Naora, Nobuo, 1902–
日本舊石器時代の研究 直良信夫著 東京 寧樂書房 昭和29 [1954]
2, 298 p. illus., maps. 26 cm. (早稻田大学考古学研究室報告 第2冊)
Added cover title: Old stone age in Japan.
Bibliography: p. 294-298.
1. Stone age—Japan.   I. Title.   (Series: Waseda Daigaku, Tokyo. Kōkogaku Kenkyūshitsu. Waseda Daigaku Kōkogaku Kenkyūshitsu hōkoku, dai 2-satsu)
Title romanized: Nihon kyū sekki jidai no kenkyū.
J 66-1160
Princeton Univ. Gest   Oriental Library
for Library of Congress   [2]

NN   0016040   NjP-G NNU

Naora, Nobuo, 1902–
Old stone age in Japan.
see his Nihon kyū sekki jidai no kenkyū.

Naoroji, Dadabhai, 1825-1917.
British rule in India. Lond., 1898
3p. 8°

NN   0016042   MWA MH

NAOROJI, Dadabhai, 1825–
[Collection of pamphlets on affairs in India.]
London, etc., 1898, etc.

NN   0016043   MH

Naoroji, Dadabhai, 1825–
The Commerce of India. (From Journ. Soc. of Arts, Feb. 17, 1871) [London]
24 p. 8°. [In v. 451, College Pamphlets]

NN   0016044   CtY

Naoroji, Dadabhai, 1825–
... Condition of India. Correspondence with the secretary of state for India, by Dadabhai Naoroji. Bombay, Printed by N. R. Ránina, 1881.
1 p. l. 2, 79 p. 21ᶜᵐ.
At head of title: Private.
1. India—Econ. condit. 2. Gt. Brit.—Colonies—India.
4-34370†
Library of Congress   HC435.N2

NN   0016045   DLC

Naoroji, Dadabhai, 1825–
Debate on the address in reply to the Queen's speech. Amendment praying for re-adjustment of the financial relations between the United Kingdom and British India. Speech delivered by Mr. Dadabhai Naoroji, M. P., in the House of commons, February 12th, 1895. [London] British committee of the Indian national congress [1895?]
cover-title, 8 p. 21½ᶜᵐ.
Caption title: Indian expenditure.
1. Finance—India.
8-13526
Library of Congress   HJ1310.N17

NN   0016046   DLC NN MiU

Naoroji, Dadabhai, 1825–
Essays, speeches, addresses and writings, (on Indian politics,) of the Hon'ble Dadabhai Naoroji ... (with life and portrait,) ed. by Chunilal Lallubhai Parekh ... Bombay, Caxton printing works, 1887.
2 p. l., 3, ii, [3], 8, 584, v p. front. (port.) 21½ᶜᵐ.
1. India—Pol. & govt.—1765–   I. Parekh, Chunilal Lallubhai.
11-3043
Library of Congress   DS479.N2

NN   0016047   DLC CU IU MiU

GN
320   Naoroji, Dadabhai, 1825-1917.
.N19   The European and Asiatic races. Observations on the paper read by John Crawfurd ... before the Ethnological society, on February 14th, 1866 ... London, Trübner and co., 1866.
32 p.
"Read before the Ethnological society, March 27th, 1866."
With this is bound Crawford, John. The plurality of the races of man. 1867.

NN   0016048   MiU

Naoroji, Dadabhai, 1825-1917.
The financial administration of India. [London]
23 p. 8°.. [In v. 451, College Pamphlets]

NN   0016049   CtY

Naoroji, Dadabhai, 1825-1917.
Indian budget debate. Motion for full parliamentary inquiry. Speech ... in the House of Commons, 14th August, 1894. [London] Brit. Commit. Ind. Nat. Cong., 1894.
16 p. 8°.

NN   0016050   NN MH

Naoroji, Dadabhai, 1825-1917.
Indian exchanges and bimetallism. By Dadabhai Naoroji ... London, Foulger & co. [1886]
21, [1] p. 21 cm. [Pamphlets on India, v.6]
1. Bimetallism.

NN   0016051   CU CtY

Naoroji, Dadabhai, 1825-1917.
YA 11335   Indian national Congress, 9th annual session, presidential address... Dec., 27, 1893.
London, n.d.
43p

NN   0016052   DLC

Naoroji, Dadabhai, 1825-1917.
The manners and customs of the Parsees; a paper read before the Liverpool philomathic society 13th March 1861. 25p. Liverpool, Printed by D. Marples, 1861.

NN   0016053   OCl

Naoroji, Dadabhai, 1825-1917.
The manners and customs of the Parsees. A paper read before the Liverpool Philomathic society, 13th March, 1861. By Dadabhai Naoroji ... London, Printed by S. Straker & sons, 1864.
25 p. 21ᶜᵐ. [With his The Parsee religion ... London? 1861?]
1. Parsees. 2. Cultus, Parsee.   I. Title.
44-36242
Library of Congress   BL1570.N3

NN   0016054   DLC MdBP MiD

Naoroji, Dadabhai, 1825-1917.
On the duties of local Indian associations in connection with the London association. By Dadabhai Naoroji. London, Printed by W. Clowes & sons, 1868.
16 p. 21½ᶜᵐ. [With East India association, London. Journal. London, 1868. v.2]
1. India.
18-5917
Library of Congress   DS401.E3 vol. 2

NN   0016055   DLC CtY

Naoroji, Dadabhai, 1825-1917.
The Parsee religion, by Dadabhai Naoroji, esq. ... Read before the Liverpool Literary and philosophical society, March 18th, 1861 ... [London? 1861?]
32 p. 21ᶜᵐ.
Caption title.
With this is bound the author's The manners and customs of the Parsees ... London, 1864.
1. Zoroastrianism. 2. Parsees.   I. Title.
44-36241
Library of Congress   BL1570.N3

NN   0016056   DLC

VOLUME 405

308
Z
Box 695 Naoroji, Dadabhai, 1825-1917.
The Parsee religion ... London, Pearson, 1862.
cover-title, 31 p.

"From the Proceedings of the Liverpool literary and philosophical society."

1. Zoroastrianism. 2. Parsees.

NN   0016057   NNC

Naoroji, Dadabhai, 1825-1917.
Poverty and un-British rule in India, by Dadabhai Naoroji. London, S. Sonnenschein & co., lim., 1901.
xiv p., 1 l., 675 p. 22ᵐ.

CONTENTS.—The poverty of India.—The condition of India.—Sir M. E. Grant Duff's views about India.—Speeches in the House of commons.—Royal commission on the administration of expenditure in India.—A selection from addresses.

1. India—Econ. condit. 2. Gt. Brit.—Colonies—India. I. Title.

Library of Congress   HC435.N22

2-3481

MoU NIC MiU OCl MH NN ICJ MB
NN   0016058   DLC CaBVaU WaS NcD FMU NcU TxU CtY

Naoroji, Dadabhai, 1825-
Poverty of India. By Dadabhai Naoroji. London, Printed by V. Brooks, Day and son, 1878.
1 p. l., ii, 83 p. incl. tables. 21ᶜᵐ.

"Extracts from papers read before the Bombay branch of the East India association, in February, April and July, 1876."

1. India—Econ. condit. 2. Gt. Brit.—Colonies—India.

3-26138 Additions

Library of Congress   HC435.N23

NN   0016059   DLC MU CtY WaU

Naoroji, Dadabhai, 1825-
Poverty of India. Papers and statistics, by **Dadabhai** Naoroji. London, W. Foulger & co., 1888.
vii, 227 p. incl. tables. 21½ᶜᵐ.

"Papers read before the Bombay branch of the East India association, in 1876."—Slip inserted before t.-p.

1. India—Econ. condit. 2. Gt. Brit.—Colonies—India. 3. India. I. **Title.**

13-16109

Library of Congress   HC435.N24

NN   0016060   DLC

Naoroji, Dadabhai, 1825-1917.
Revised memorandum on the most important reforms needed by India. n.p. [188-?]
8 p. sm. 8°.

NN   0016061   MB

Naoroji, Dadabhai, 1825-1917.
The rights of labour. London, F. W. Evans, [1904]
11 p. 8°.
Rev. ed.
Repr.: "Westminster Review", July, 1890.

NN   0016062   NN

[Naoroji, Dadabhai,] 1825-1917.
Royal Commission on the Administration of the Expenditure in India. 1895. [no.] 1,   [London: A. Bonner, 1895-97.]
1 v.   8°.

Letters addressed to Lord Welby, chairman of the commission, signed: Dadabhai Naoroji.

1. India—Govt., 1895. 2. Finance—   India, 1895.   3. Title.
N. Y. P. L.   November 20, 1929

NN   0016063   NN MH

Naoroji, Dadabhai, 1825-1917.
Sir M. E. Grant Duff's views about India. By Dadabhai Naoroji.   London, 1887.
35 p.   24 cm.   [Pamphlets on India. v. 6]
Reprinted from the Contemporary review, Aug. and Nov. 1887.
1. Grant Duff, Sir Mountstuart Elphinstone, 1829-1906.

NN   0016064   CU

Naoroji, Dadabhai, 1825-1917.
Speeches and writings. 1st ed.   Madras, G. A. Natesan [189-]
208 p. port. 19 cm.

1. India. For. rel. Gt. Brit. Addresses, essays, lectures.

NN   0016065   IEN

DS
479.1
N19As   Naoroji, Dadabhai, 1825-1917.
Speeches and writings of Dadabhai Naoroji. 1st ed. Madras, G.A. Natesan [1906?]
vi, 656, xii, 208 p. port. 18 cm.

NN   0016066   NRU CaBVaU MH

DS
479
.N2   Naoroji, Dadabhai, 1825-1917.
Speeches and writings. 1st ed. Madras, G. A. Natesan [1918?]; label: Supplied by Alavi Book Depot, Bombay;
656, 208 p. 18 cm.

1. India - Pol. & govt. - 1765-1947.

NN   0016067   WU IU

DS
479
N26   Naoroji, Dadabhai, 1825-1917.
Speeches and writings of Dadabhai Naoroji.
2d ed. Madras, G. A. Natesan [n.d.]
686 p., 216 p.

INDIA--POL. & GOVT.-- 1765-1947

NN   0016068   KMK ICU NcD MiU WaU MoU

DS
479
N3
1920   Naoroji, Dadabhai, 1825-1917.
Speeches and writings. 2d ed. Madras, G.A. Natesan [1920?]
vi, 686, 207 p. 18 cm.

1. India - Pol. & govt. - 1765-1947.

NN   0016069   CU-S

Naoroji, Dadabhai, 1825-
The state and government of India under its native rulers. Lond., 1853
49 p.   8°

(Reprint, 1899, from India Reform. No. IX)

NN   0016070   MWA

Naoroji, Dadabhai, 1825-1917.
Statement submitted to the Indian Currency Committee of 1898. Lond., 1898
16 p.   8°

NN   0016071   MWA NN

Naoroji, Dadabhai, 1825-1917.
The Wants and Means of India. A paper at meeting of E. India. Assoc.   1870.
12 p.   8°.   [In v. 452, College Pamphlets]

NN   0016072   CtY

Naoroji, Dadabhai, 1825-1917
see also
Dadabhai Naoroji Memorial Prize Fund.

Naoroji Kanga, Sorabji
see   Kanga, Sorabji Naoroji.

Naouit, Edit.
Nitoquert, by Edit Naouit. Pittsburgh, Pa., F. R. Palmer, 1914.
2 p. l., 84 p. front. (port.) 23½ᶜᵐ. $1.60
"Edition strictly limited to five-hundred copies of which this is number 18."
Drama in blank verse.

I. Title.

15-1043

Library of Congress   PS3527.A26N5 1914

NN   0016075   DLC

LD
3907
.G7
1968
.N26
also
Film
T7670   Naoum, Adil G., 1937-
On the groups of inertia of smooth manifolds.
44 p.
Thesis (Ph.D.) - N.Y.U., Graduate School.

1. Dissertations, Academic - N.Y.U. - 1968. I. Title.

NN   0016076   NNU

NAOUM, Demetrius F.   1881-
Der abschluss von völkerrechtlichen verträgen insbesondere nach griechischem staatsrecht. (art. 32 der griechischen staatsverfassung). Athen, 1905.

70-(2) p.
Inaug.-diss. --- Leipzig.
"Literaturverzeichniss": p. [66]-70.

NN   0016077   MH-L NjP ICRL CtY

PA5610
.N25K8
1924   Naoum, Nina
Κυπαρίσσια. Ἀθῆναι, 1924.
68 p.   20 cm.

NN   0016078   OCU

VOLUME 405

Naoúm, Phokion P 1875–
Explosivstoffe und Zündwaren, von Dr. phil. Ph. Naoum ... (Unter Benutzung des von H. Kast bearbeiteten entsprechenden Abschnittes der vorhergehenden Auflage dieses Werkes)

(*In* Chemisch-technische Untersuchungsmethoden. Achte Auflage. **Berlin,** 1932. 24ᶜᵐ. 3. Bd., p. ₁1159₁–1338. illus., diagrs.)

Includes bibliographical notes.

NN 0016079 ICJ

Naoúm, Phokion P 1875–
Nitroglycerin und nitroglycerinsprengstoffe (dynamite) mit besonderer berücksichtigung der dem nitroglycerin verwandten und homologen salpetersäureester, von dr. phil. Phokion Naoúm ... Berlin, J. Springer, 1924.
xi, 416 p. illus. 23½ᶜᵐ.

1. Nitroglycerin.
Library of Congress   TP285.N3   25–6062

NN 0016080 DLC MiU NN

Naoúm, Phokion P 1875–
... Nitroglycerine and nitroglycerine explosives, by Phokion Naoúm ... authorized English translation with notes and additions by E. M. Symmes ... Baltimore, The Williams & Wilkins company, 1928.
xi, 469 p. illus., plates. 23½ᶜᵐ. (The world wide chemical translation series; ed. by E. E. Reid, no. 1)

1. Nitroglycerin.   I. Symmes, Ernest Montgomery, tr.
Library of Congress   TP285.N35   28–18626

ODW OU MiHM ICJ MB
NN 0016081 DLC CU CtY NcD NcRS PSt PWcS PPF OCl

Naoúm, Phokion P 1875–
Schiess- und sprengstoffe, von dr. Ph. Naoum ... Mit 12 abbildungen und zahlreichen tabellen. Dresden und Leipzig, T. Steinkopff, 1927.
xi, 212 p. illus. 22ᶜᵐ. (*Added t.-p.:* Technische fortschrittsberichte ... hrsg. von B. Rassow ... bd. xvi)
Chapter xi, "Flüssigluft-sprengstoffe," by K. F. Meyer.
Advertising matter: p. 200–212.

1. Explosives.   I. Title.
Library of Congress   TP270.N3   28–9662

NN 0016082 DLC CU NN ICJ

Naoúm, Phokion P., 1875–
Ueber umlagerungen der stereoisomeren dibenzalbernsteinsäuren und a-benzal-y-diphenylitaconsäuren Leipzig, 1899.
Inaug. diss.

QD341
.A2N2

NN 0016083 DLC PU CtY

Naoum Nazo, Albert, 1910–
... Contribution à l'étude historique du bouton de Bagdad ... Paris, Jouve, 1935.
46 p. 24 cm. (Paris. Université. Faculté de médecine. **Thèse.** 1935. no. 525)

1. ₁Leishmaniasis, Cutaneous₁   I. ₁Series₁
                                              Med 48–261
U. S. Army Medical Libr.   [W4P23 1935]
for Library of Congress   ₁1₁

NN 0016084 DNLM

¶
4
A86   NAOUMIDĒS, Spyridōn Dēmētriou
1949   Περὶ τῆς ὑποτροπῆς τῆς νεφρολιθιάσεως.
             Ἀθῆναι, 1949.
             142 p.
             Title transliterated: Peri tēs hypotropēs tēs nephrolithiaseōs.
             Thesis – Athens.
             1. Kidneys – Calculi

NN 0016085 DNLM

Naoumovitch, Svetislav, 1897–
... De l'association de la paralysie générale et de la folie maniaco-dépressive; contribution à l'étude de la nature et de la génèse des états délirants dans la paralysie générale progressive ... Bordeaux, 1929.
Thèse – Univ. de Bordeaux.
"Bibliographie": p. [113]–120.

NN 0016086 CtY

Ναούρι, L. *Les pneumatocèles par ostéome du sinus frontal [Lyon] 100p. 8ᵒ. Bourg, 1936.

NN 0016087 DNLM

Nap, Christophorus Meijer
    see Meijer Nap, Christophorus.

Nap, Cy. pseud.
    see
Olin, Allen H.

Nap, E J
De koekbakkerij, door E. J. Nap en B. Muller. Doetinchem, C. Misset ₁1948₁
88 p. illus. 23 cm.

1. Cake.   I. Muller, B., writer on bakeries.   II. Title.
TX771.N3   49–23590*

NN 0016090 DLC

Nap, Jacobus Matthijs, 1873–
Concessies voor publieke ondernemingen ... Groningen, 1898.
23 cm.
Proefschrift – Groningen.

NN 0016091 CtY

Nap, Jacobus Matthijs, 1873–
Dateering en rechtskarakter der z. g. Lex Julia municipalis. Amsterdam, J. Müller, 1910.
52 p. 25 cm. (Verhandelingen der Koninklijke Akademie van Wetenschappen te Amsterdam. Afdeeling Letterkunde. Nieuwe reeks, deel 11, no. 4)

1. Lex Julia municipalis. 2. Heraclean tablets.   I. Series: Akademie van Wetenschappen, Amsterdam. Afdeeling voor de Taal-, Geschiedkundige en Wijsgeerige Wetenschappen. Verhandelingen, nieuwe reeks, deel 11, no. 4.
AS244.A52 n. r., deel 11, no. 4   A 48–1626 rev*

Cleveland. Public Libr.
for Library of Congress   ₁r48c2₁†

NN 0016092 OCl CtY DLC

Nap, Jacobus Matthijs, 1873–
Die Römische republik um das j. 225 v. Chr., ihre damalige politik, gesetze und legenden, von J. M. Nap ... Leiden, A. W. Sijthoff, 1935.
xvi, 457 p. 25 cm.

1. Rome—Pol. & govt.—s. c. 265–30. 2. Rome—Legal antiquities. 3. Legends—Rome.
DG246.N3   937.04   36–14507 rev

NN 0016093 DLC NcU OU MiU LU ICU NcD OCU CaBVaU

Nap, N   A   comp.
De financieele verhouding en de werkloosheidsfinanciering; verzameling voorschriften van een toelichting voorzien door N. A. Nap ... 's-Gravenhage, Vereeniging van nederlandsche gemeenten ₁1943₁
2 p. l., 71 p. 22½ cm.
Includes directives issued by Departement van binnenlandsche zaken and other ministries.

1. Insurance, Unemployment — Netherlands. 2. Taxation — Netherlands—Law. 3. Local finance—Netherlands.   I. Netherlands (Territory under German occupation, 1940–1945) Departement van binnenlandsche zaken. II. Title.
HD7096.N3N3   A F 47–1578 rev
Harvard univ. Library
for Library of Congress   ₁r47c1₁†

NN 0016094 MH DLC IU

Nap, Rudolf Sicco Tjaden
    see
Modderman, Rudolf Sicco Tjaden, 1904–

Nap and his friends in their glory...
    see under [Rowlandson, Thomas] 1756–1827.

Nap aprân li; métod Lobak. [n. p., 1946] 40 p. illus.
Cover title. FISHER COLLECTION.

1. Creole dialects – Haiti – Readers.

NN 0016097 NN

Napa, Cal. Asylum for insane
    see California. State Hospital, Napa.

F868   Napa, Calif. Chamber of Commerce.
N2N19   Beautiful Napa, a pictorial journey. [Napa, Calif., 191–?]
           [24] p. illus., maps. 22x30cm.

NN 0016099 CU-B

F869   Napa, Calif. Chamber of Commerce.
N16N17   Napa – Napa County, California. Napa, Calif. [1951]
           [12] p. (incl. cover) illus. 23cm.
           Cover title.

1. Napa, Calif. – Description. 2. Napa Co., Calif. – Description and travel.

NN 0016100 CU-B

Napa, Calif. Charters, 1874.
    Charter and ordinances of the city of Napa, Napa county, California. Napa city, Reporter publishing house. 1874.
    84 p. 21 cm. Original front paper cover.
    Front cover reads: A compendium of the local laws applicable to Napa county, with the charter and ordinances of the city of Napa ... 1874. Errata slip tipped in on p. [81]

NN 0016101 CSmH

VOLUME 405

232z   Napa, Calif. Charters. 1892.
N195c   Charter for the city of Napa, prepared and proposed by the
1892   Board of Fifteen Freeholders, elected December 31st, 1892.
Law   [Napa, 1893?]
Library   7 p.

Caption title.

1. Napa, Calif. Board of Freeholders.

NN 0016102   CU

Napa, Calif. Free Public Library
   see Goodman Library, Napa, Calif.
   [supplement]

Napa, Calif. Goodman Library
   see Goodman Library, Napa, Calif.
   [supplement]

Napa, Calif. Ordinances, etc.
   Municipal code: general ordinances of the
City. Adopted July 19, 1954, by Ordinance no.
1131. Published by order of the City Council.
[Napa?] Original printing by Nemes Printing
Co., 1955-
   2 v. (loose-leaf) 28 cm.

   At head of title: City of Napa, California.
   Codification by John F. Dunlap.
   Contents.- v. 1. Municipal code: general
ordinances of the City.- v. 2. Changes in the
Municipal code.

NN 0016105   CLU-L

S   Napa, Calif. Ordinances, etc.
C88   Ordinances. no.
N160o   [Napa]
   1 v. (loose-leaf) 39 cm.

   Cover title.

NN 0016106   CLU-L

F869   Napa, Calif. St. John's Church.
N16N3   A history of the Catholic Church and a business directory of the
City of Napa. [Napa] 1942.
   37 p. 20cm.

   Cover title.

   1. Napa, Calif. St. John's Church. 2. Church history - California - Catholic Church. 3. Napa, Calif. - Direct. I. Title.

NN 0016107   CU-B

Napa, Calif. State Asylum for the Insane
   see California. State Hospital, Napa.

Napa, Calif. State Hospital
   see California. State Hospital, Napa.

Napa (*Attack transport*)
   Napalogue. [Berkeley? Calif.] 1946]
   107 p. illus., ports., map (on lining papers) 28 cm.
   Cover title.

   1. World War, 1939-1945—Naval operations, American. 2. World
War, 1939-1945—Pacific Ocean. I. Title.

   D774.N3A3   940.545   49-54078*

NN 0016110   DLC ICN MB TxU NN PP

A Napa Christchild, and, Benicia's letters
   see under [Gunnison, Charles Andrew]
   1861-1897.

Napa city and county portfolio and directory; photographic reproductions of picturesque Napa County
   views, showing some of its mountains, valleys and
   dales, its orchards, vineyards and fruits, its homes,
   churches and schools, stores, factories, etc. Napa, Cal.,
   H. A. Darms [*1908]
   3 p. l., 3-126 p. front., illus. 28½ x 36cm.

   1. Napa, Cal. — Descr. — Views. 2. Napa Co., Cal. — Descr. & trav. —
Views. 3. Napa, Cal.—Direct. I. Darms, H. A., pub.

   Library of Congress   F869.N19N19   8-23136

NN 0016112   DLC CU-A NjP

The Napa Classic. Published monthly during the
   college year. 1888-1890. Napa, California,
   by Junior Class of Napa College, 1888-1890.
   22 nos. in 1 volume. 8 vo. Bound in
   3/4 black· roan   black cloth boards.

NN 0016113   CSmH

Napa college, Napa, Calif.
   Year book ... 1872/73, 1873/74, 1887/88,
   1893/94. Napa, 1873-1894.
   4 v. in 1. plates. 22 cm.
   Title varies: 1870-73, Catalogue of Napa
collegiate institute: 1893-94 Year book of Napa
college.
   Incorporated in 1870 as Napa collegiate institute;
re-incorporated in 1886 as Napa college.

NN 0016114   CU CSmH

Napa collegiate institute, Napa, Calif.
   see Napa College, Napa, Calif.

Napa co., *Calif.*
   Comparative statement, receipts and expenditures ...
[Napa? 19
   v. tables. 35½cm.
   Mimeographed.

   1. Finance—Napa co., Calif. I. Title.

   35-34992
   Library of Congress   HJ9012.C2N23   352.10979419

NN 0016116   DLC

Napa co., *Calif.*
   The Great register of the county of Napa,
state of California. Being a list of uncan-
celled names existing on the Great register ...
October 4th, 1880.   Napa city, California:
Napa county reporter book, news, and general
job printing establishment. 1880.

   cover-title, 27, [2] p. 42 1|2 cm.

   1. Napa co., Calif.--Registers.

NN 0016117   CSmH

Napa Co., Calif.
   History of Napa and Lake Counties, California
      see under title

Napa County, Cal.
   Land register. Oakland,--
   92p. 8°

NN 0016119   MWA

Napa Co., Calif.
   ⌐Valuable information about N. Co. Napa,
1885.
   16p. 8°

NN 0016120   MWA

336.395   Napa County, Calif. Auditor-Controller.
N195f   Final budget

   [n.p.]
   v. tables. 23x26cm. annual.

   Report year ends June 30.

   1.Budget - Napa County, Calif.

NN 0016121   CLSU

F868   Napa Co., Calif. Board of Supervisors.
N2868   Napa County California. [Napa, Printed by Francis &
Francis, 191-]
   [24] p. illus. 18cm.

   1. Napa Co., Calif. - Descr. & trav. 2. Agriculture - California - Napa Co. 3. Fruit- culture - California - Napa Co.

NN 0016122   CU-B

4HC-   Napa Co. Calif. Board of Supervisors.
74   The resources of Napa County, California
illustrated and described. Napa, Pub. by
authority of the Board of Supervisors, 1887.
   34 p.

NN 0016123   DLC-P4

L903   Napa Co., Calif. Office of Superintendent of
C23N3   Schools.
Educ.   Official directory.
Library
   [Napa]
   v.

   Title varies:
      List of teachers and clerks of districts.
      Directory.
      School directory.

NN 0016124   CU

F868   Napa County Agricultural Association.
N2N35   Premium list, rules and regulations of the annual Napa
County Fair.

   [Napa, Calif.] 19
   v.   illus. 19cm.

   1. Agricultural exhibitions - California - Napa Co. I.
Napa County Fair. II. Title.

NN 0016125   CU-B

VOLUME 405

The Napa County Reporter.
Napa City: Cal., published every Saturday
by Montgomery & Cox, 1857.
1 nos., vol. 1, no. 48 mutilated, rebacked
with crepeline. Lg. fol.

NN 0016126 CSmH

Napa Quicksilver Mining Company.
Report of the directors to the stockholders of the Napa
Quicksilver Mining Co... With by-laws of the company.
April 15th, 1873. ₍New York, 1873.₎ 37 p. 8°.

Clipping inserted, with notice of the company's bankruptcy, Oct. 1873.

1. Mercury.—Mines and mining,   U. S.: California.
N. Y. P. L.   May 20, 1924.

NN 0016127 NN

Beinecke
Library
Folio   The Napa register. v.1-
AN5   Aug.10, 1863-
N19   Napa City, Calif.
N19   61cm. weekly.

Title varies: 1863, Napa Valley register.
Ceased publication with issue of Dec. 7,
1921.

NN 0016128 CtY

Napa Soda Springs, the famous mountain resort of
the Pacific coast
see under ₍Anderson, Winslow₎

F862   Napa Stock Farm, Calif.
.23   Catalogue of the Napa Stock Farm, thoroughbred yearlings,
N2   property of Mr. Adolph B. Spreckels (San Francisco) to be sold
         by public auction.

         San Francisco, New York City ₍18
         v. in   23cm.

         Title varies slightly.

NN 0016130 CU-B

Napa Valley register
see The Napa register.

Napad bandytow; czyli, Tym razem
jeszcze mu uszlo na sucho; krotochwila
w jednej odslonie. Poznan, n.d.
₍14 p.₎

(Teatr Ludowy, nr. 5)

NN 0016132 OCl

Napakiak, Native Village of
see Native Village of Napakiak.

Napal, Dionisio R   1887-1940.
... Comentario evangélico para los domingos y fiestas del año
eclesiástico. Buenos Aires, Editorial Stella maris, 1937.
631. ₍1₎ p. 19ᶜᵐ.

1. Bible. N. T. Epistles and Gospels, Liturgical—Commentaries.
2. Bible—Commentaries—N. T. Epistles and Gospels, Liturgical. I.
Title.
                                        37-39017
Library of Congress   BX2005.N3
                       ₍2₎   264.026

NN 0016134 DLC IU DPU NcU

F 2847   NAPAL, DIONISIO R   1887-1940.
.P57 N19   El comodoro Martín Rivadavia. Buenos Aires,
         Talleres Gráficos Argentinos, 1925.
         76 p. ports.

1. Rivadavia y Villagrán, Víctor José Martín, 1852-
2. Argentine Republic—Hist.—Naval. I. Title.

NN 0016135 InU

Napal, Dionisio R   1887- 1940.
Filiberto de Oliveira Cézar, por Dionisio R. Napal. ₍Buenos
Aires₎, 1935.
30 p., 1 l. ports., coat of arms. 18½ᶜᵐ.

1. Oliveira Cézar, Filiberto de, 1856-1910.

                                        36-4108
Library of Congress   F2846.O46
————— Copy 2.   ₍2₎   928.6

NN 0016136 DLC CLU MB NN

Napal, Dionisio R   *comp.*
Hacia el mar (antología argentina) Prólogo, selección
y notas de Dionisio R. Napal. Buenos Aires, Agencia general
de librerías y publicaciones, 1927.
446 p., 1 l. 19ᶜᵐ.

1. Argentine literature (Selections: Extracts, etc.) 2. Argentine Republic—History, Naval. I. Title.
                                        28-20413
Library of Congress   PQ7735.N3

NN 0016137 DLC MB OU CLSU ViU

Napal, Dionisio R   1887-1940.
... El imperio soviético. 7. ed. (de 28,000
ejemplares) Buenos Aires, Editorial Stella
maris ₍1933₎
285, ₍1₎ p. 19 cm.

NN 0016138 NcD

Napal, Dionisio R   1887-1940.
... El imperio soviético. 8. ed. (de 5.000 ejemplares).
B₍uenos₎ Aires, Editorial Stella maris ₍1933₎
315, ₍1₎ p. incl. col. front. (port.) 19ᶜᵐ.

1. Russia—Pol. & govt.—1917-   2. Russia—Econ. condit.—1918-
3. Communism—Russia. I. Title.
                                        33—33317
Library of Congress   DK266.N25 1933
                       ₍a43c1₎   947.084

NN 0016139 DLC CU ICJ NN MB OCl WaS

Napal, Dionisio R   1887-1940.
... El imperio soviético. 9. ed. (de 7.000 ejemplares).
B₍uenos₎ Aires, Editorial Stella maris ₍1934₎
303, ₍1₎ p. 19ᶜᵐ.
"Bibliografía": p. 289-290.

1. Russia—Pol. & govt.—1917-   2. Russia—Econ. condit.—1918-
3. Communism—Russia. I. Title.
                                        34-33231
Library of Congress   DK266.N25 1934
                       ₍2₎   947.084

NN 0016140 DLC NcD NcU

Napal, Dionisio R   1887-1940
... O imperio soviético; tradução de A. B. Martins Aranha.
S. Paulo ₍Empreza graphica da Revista dos tribunaes₎ 1934.
xvi, 226 p., 1 l. 18½ᶜᵐ.
"Parecéres da imprensa argentina sobre 'El imperio soviético'":
p. ₍v₎-xvi.
"Bibliographia": p. ₍217₎-218.

1. Russia—Pol. & govt.—1917-   2. Russia—Econ. condit.—1918-
3. Communism—Russia. I. Martins Aranha, Antonio B., tr. II. Title.

Library of Congress   DK266.N256   41-24605
                       ₍2₎   947.084

NN 0016141 DLC OU

Napal, Dionisio R   1887-1940.
... Junto al surco. Buenos Aires, Agencia general de librería y publicaciones, 1926.
316, ₍2₎ p. 19ᶜᵐ.
CONTENTS.—El comodoro Martín Rivadavia.—Función patriótica y
social de la conscripción obligatoria.—Mi visión de Pío x.—Roque Sáenz
Peña.—Elcira M. Belloni.—Ser o no ser.—Oratoria.—Inauguración del
"Barrio Nicolás Mihanovich".—Justicia social.—S. s. Pío xi.—El evange-
llo y la paz.—Un apóstol moderno ₍don Bosco₎

I. Title.

Library of Congress   AC75.N3   32-12785
                       ₍2₎   081

NN 0016142 DLC

Napal, Dionisio R   1887-1940.
...Visiones y recuerdos del camino, a bordo de la fragata
Presidente Sarmiento (1925-1926)... Buenos Aires: Agencia
gral. de librería y publicaciones₍, 1927₎. 271 p. 2. ed. 12°.

1. Voyages and travel, 1900-
N. Y. P. L.   February 29, 1928

NN 0016143 NN

Napal, Dionisio R   1887-1940.
... Visiones y recuerdos del camino, a bordo de la fragata
Presidente Sarmiento (1925-1926) 3. ed. (3. y 4. millar)
B₍uenos₎ Aires, Editorial Stella maris ₍1932₎
3 p. l., 9-287, ₍1₎ p. 18½ᶜᵐ.

1. Voyages and travels. I. Title.

Library of Congress   G470.N3 1932   33-37613
                       ₍2₎   910.4

NN 0016144 DLC

Napal, Dionisio R   1887-1940.
... Visiones y recuerdos del camino, a bordo de la fragata
Pte. Sarmiento (1925-1926) 4. ed. (6. millares) B₍uenos₎
Aires, Editorial Stella maris ₍1934₎
3 p. l., ₍9₎-270, 1 l. 19ᶜᵐ.

1. Voyages and travels. I. Titles.
                                        35-30255
Library of Congress   G470.N3 1934   910.4

NN 0016145 DLC NcU

Napal, el escritor, el orador, el apóstol. Buenos Aires, Editorial Stella maris ₍1941₎
2 p. l., 7-248, ₍2₎ p. col. front. (port.) 22ᶜᵐ.

1. Napal, Dionisio R., 1887-1940.
                                        42-23832
Library of Congress   BX4705.N23N3
                       ₍2₎   922.282

NN 0016146 DLC NcU NN PU PPT MB NNC

VOLUME 405

Napalkov, S   N
Орошение земель в центрально-чернозёмных областях.
Москва, Знание, 1952.

23 p. 22 cm. (Всесоюзное общество по распространению политических и научных знаний. Серия 3, № 8)

1. Chernozem soils. 2. Irrigation—Russia. I. Title. (Series:
Vsesofuznoe obshchestvo po rasprostranenifu politicheskikh i nauchnykh znanil. Serifa 3, 1952, no. 8)
                              Title transliterated: Oroshenie zemel' v
                              tsentral'no-chernozemnykh oblastfakh.

S241.V83 no. 8   53–30889

NN   0016147   DLC

Napalogue
see under   Napa (Attack transport)

NAPANEE, Ont. Ordinances.
By-laws of the corporation of the village
of Napanee, in the county of Lennox, [and
Addington] for the years 1855 to 1861, inclusive. Napanee, "Standard" cheap job office,
1861.

pp. 34.

NN   0016149   MH

NAPANEE, Ont. St. Patrick's church.
Catholic home guide./ Napanee, Ont., Napanee
Express, 1909.

pp.20.
Advertisements on the recto of each leaf.

NN   0016150   MH

F   The Napanee standard.
1059   The Napanee standard, 1862-3 [and 1866;
L5   extracts] Compiled and edited by Walter S.
L56   Herrington. Napanee, Ont., Published by
v.12-13 the Society, 1926-28.
         2 v. 25cm. (Lennox and Addington
         Historical Society. Papers and records,
         v. 12-13)

         1. Canada--Pol. & govt.--1841-1867. 2.
         U. S.--Hist.--Civil War--Foreign public
         opinion. 3.   Fenians. I. Herrington, Walter St   evens, 1860-
         ed.

NN   0016151   NIC

NAPANOCH, N.Y.   Eastern New York reformatory

See NEW YORK (State) Reformatory, Napanoch.

Napanoch, N.Y.   Institution for Defective Delinquents.
See
New York (State) Institution for Defective Delinquents,
Napanoch.

Napanoch, N.Y. Reformatory.
                      see
New York (State) Reformatory, Napanoch.

V   Naparsimasonut Ikiortiksat. Nalakamit Nakor-
499.37   samidlo Noungmionie. Nakitigkat kaladlit
N195   Nunane, 1856.
Bendet   [20] p. 13x10½cm.
Room   A fragment of dried alga, evidently intended
         as an illustration, is mounted on p.[6]
         "Lægebog, der handler om levnetsmidler til
         syge, sting og angmaset."- *cf.* C.G.F.Pfaff, Bibliographia groenlandica, 1890, p.188.
         First medical book printed in Greenland.
         Contents.- Nerisagsanik naparsimasunut.- Kapartunik.- Angmasunik

         1.Eskimo langua   ge - Texts.

NN   0016155   CSt

Napatico.
         vol. 1-
         enero
Nueva York, National Paper and Type Company,
1920-
         v. illus., ports. 28cm. monthly?

         "Publicado de vez en cuando por la National
Paper & Type Company y para circular exclusivamente entre los miembros de la 'Familia National'".

NN   0016156   NNC

Napea, Oloff, pseud.
         see Badcock, John, fl. 1816-1830.

NAPEIR, John.

See NAPIER, John, 1550- 1617.

         ... De Napelsche beroerte
         see under [Giraffi, Alessandro]

330.9415 Naper, James Lenox   William, 1791-1868.
P19   Observations in answer to Mr. G. Poulett
         Scrope's question of "How is Ireland to be
         governed?" addressed to him by J.L.W.Naper...
         Dublin, James McGlashan, 1846.
         16p. 21½cm.   (In [Pamphlets: state of Ireland. 1845-1847])

         1. Landlord and tenant--Ireland. 2. Land
         tenure--Ireland. I. Scrope, George Julius
         Duncombe Poulett. How is Ireland to be governed.

NN   0016160   LU

Naper, James Lenox William, 1791-1868.
         Observations on the elective franchise
and fixity of tenure as connected with
agricultural improvement. Addressed to the
landlords, landholders, and tenantry of
Ireland ... Dublin, W.Curry, jun. and
company [etc., etc.] 1843.
         29 p. 21.5 cm.

         Bound with his Remarks on the relations
of landlord and tenant in Ireland, 1843.

NN   0016161   MH-BA

Naper, James Lenox William, 1791-1868.
         Remarks on the relations of landlord and
tenant in Ireland. With suggestions for their
improvement, addressed to the Earl of Devon ...
Dublin, W.Curry, jun. and company, 1843.
         24 p. 21.5 cm.

         "For private circulation."
         With this are bound his Observations on the
elective franchise, 1843; Suggestions for the
more scientific and general employment of
agricultural   labourers, 1844.

NN   0016162   MH-BA

Naper, James Lenox William, 1791-1868.
         Suggestions for the more scientific and
general employment of agricultural labourers,
together with a plan which would enable the
landlords of Ireland to afford them suitable
houses and gardens, with applotments, [!]
at a fair rent, being observations on chapter X.
of Dr. Kane's "Industrial resources of Ireland."
... Dublin, W.Curry, jun. and company [etc.,
etc.] 1844.
         24 p. 21.5 cm.

         Bound with his Remarks on the relations
of landlord and tenant in Ireland, 1843.

         1.Labor - Ireland. 2.Landlord and tenant -
Ireland. I.Kane, Sir Robert John, 1809-1890.
The industrial resources of Ireland, 1844.

NN   0016164   MH-BA NN

Naper, Joy H   Naper,   contestant.
         ... Joy H. Naper, contestant, v. J. D.
Skinner, respondent. Transcript on appeal.
Williams & Carpenter, att'ys for respondent.
Geo. G. Blanchard, att'y for contestant.
Sacramento, H. A. Weaver & co.'s law printing
office [1874.]
         cover-title,71 p. 26cm.
         At head of title: No.   in the Supreme
court of the state of California.

NN   0016165   CU-B

Naper, Thorvald, 1872-
         Kragerø håndverkerforening gjennem 75 år, 1879-1954.
[Kragerø, 1954]
         44 p. illus. 24 cm.

         1. Kragerø håndverkerforening.

HD2346.N62K7   56-34793

NN   0016166   DLC

Nap'erskiĭ, K   E
         see
Napiersky, Karl Eduard, 1799-1864.

NAPERVILLE, Ill.
Souvenir of the Naperville home coming.
May 29th to June 1st, 1917.
see under title

[Naperville, Ill. Centennial historical committee]
Naperville centennial. [Aurora, Ill., Printed by the Strathmore co., °1931]
         76 p. illus. (incl. ports., facsims.) 23ᶜᵐ.

         On cover: Naperville centennial, 1831–1931; June fifth and sixth, 1931.
The story of Naperville presented by the Centennial historical committee. *cf.* Foreword.
         "Copyright ... [by] Fort Payne chapter—Daughters of the American
revolution, Naperville, Illinois."

         1. Naperville, Ill.—Hist. I. Daughters of the American revolution.
Illinois. Fort Payne chapter, Naperville. II. Title.   31-17292
Library of Congress   F549.N3N3
——— Copy 2.
Copyright A 40160   [2]   977.324

NN   0016169   DLC ICJ

Naperville, Ill. Council.
         Proceedings of the Council and statement of receipts and
disbursements ...
[Naperville, 19
         v. in   23ᶜᵐ. irregular.
         Some of the volumes include ordinances.

         1. Naperville, Ill.—Pol. & govt. I. Naperville, Ill. Ordinances, etc.

JS13.N134 c   46-44989

NN   0016170   DLC

VOLUME 405

Naperville, Ill. Edward Sanatorium
   see   Edward Sanatorium, Naperville, Ill.

Naperville, Ill. Evangelical Theological Seminary,
   This institution was incorporated in 1873 as Union Biblical Institute. It was housed in buildings of North-Western College (later called North Central College). In 1910 the name was changed to Evangelical Theological Seminary and since 1911 it has occupied its own buildings.

Naperville, Ill. Evangelical theological seminary.
Catalogue...
Naperville, Ill.

BV4070
.E82

NN 0016173   DLC ICN MH-AH

BX7255 NAPERVILLE, ILL. FIRST CONGREGATIONAL CHURCH.
f.N2A1A3 Records of the church at DuPage i.e. Naper-
Rare bk ville, July 13, 1833-Mar.2, 1893. Naperville
210 l. 32 x 40 cm.
Photocopy (Negative); two pages on each leaf.
In portfolio.
This church, established as Presbyterian in 1833, became Congregational in 1834.

1. Manuscripts, English--Facsimiles.

NN 0016174   ICU

Naperville, Ill. Midwest institute of international relations. 1937.

   see

Midwest institute of international relations, Naperville, Ill., 1937.

Naperville, Ill. North Central College.
   This Institution has its origin in 1861 as the Plainfield College of the Evangelical Association of North America, Plainfiled, Ill. In 1864 the name was changed to North Westner College. In 1870 the college was moved to Naperville, Ill. In 1926 the name of the college was changed to North Central College.

NN 0016176   MH

Naperville, Ill. North Central College.
   Alumni news
      see under Alumni news of North-Western college.

Naperville, Ill. Northwestern College.   *4499-249
Bulletin. [Quarterly.] Vol. 14 (no. 1). April, 1924.
= Naperville, Ill. [1924.] v. 19 cm.
Additional unbound parts. as received, may be found in covers on the same shelf-number. They are not noted on this card until bound.
Each bulletin is catalogued separately.

NN 0016178   MB

Naperville, Ill. Northwestern college.
   Catalogue of North-western college and Union biblical institute.
   Naperville, The College
   v. plates. 20½ᶜᵐ.

1. Naperville, Ill. Union biblical institute.

CA 11-848 Unrev'd

Library of Congress   LD4011.N7

NN 0016179   DLC ICJ MB ICN

Naperville, Ill. North-western college.
   ... The inauguration, Edward Everett Rall, ph. d., as president of North-western college ... Naperville, Ill., 1917.
   40 p. illus., port. 23¼ᶜᵐ. (Bulletin. vol. vii, no. 3, October, 1917)
   Contents.—Program of exercises.—Inauguration ode.—Account of inauguration (from the College chronicle)—Representatives of colleges in attendance.—Address, Samuel P. Capen.—Address of installation, Samuel P. Spreng.—Inaugural address, Edward Everett Rall.—Extracts from first annual report of President Rall.

1. Rall, Edward Everett.

E 18-292

Library, U. S. Bur. of   Education LD4011.N8A2

NN 0016180   DHEW

Naperville, Ill. North-western college.
Life at North-western college. Naperville Ill., The College, 1919.
28 p. illus. 23½ cm. (North-western college bulletin, vol. 8, no.2, July, 1919)

NN 0016181   DHEW

JS13   Naperville, Ill. Ordinances, etc.
.N134 c
Naperville, Ill. Council.
   Proceedings of the Council and statement of receipts and disbursements ...
   Naperville, 19

Naperville, Ill. Ordinances, etc.
   Revised ordinances, city of Naperville. Adopted April 19, 1926. Naperville, 1926
   2 p. l., 153 p. incl. tables, forms. 24ᶜᵐ.

I. Title.

Library of Congress   JS1159.N3A5 1926
                       (2)   352.077324

37-6997

NN 0016183   DLC IU

Naperville, Ill. Union biblical institute

   see

Naperville, Ill. Evangelical theological seminary.

Naperville centennial
   see under [Naperville, Ill. Centennial historical committee]

M   Nápěvy ku písním obsaženým v "Poutní knize
2142   Velehradské". Všechna práva vyhražena
C9   nakladateli. V Brně, 1885.
N19   18 p. 19cm.

For 1-4 voices, largely unacc.

1. Hymns, Czech. I. Title: Poutní knize Velehradské.

NN 0016186   NIC

Napey, Hipolite.
   The Harrisburg business directory. 1842
      see under Polk's greater Harrisburg city directory.

Naphan, Edmund A   joint author.
   Understanding the irrigated soils

   see under

McCormick, John A

Naphegyi, Gabor, 1824-1884.
   The album of language. Illustrated by the Lord's prayer in one hundred languages, with historical descriptions of the principal languages, interlinear translation and pronunciation of each prayer, a dissertation on the languages of the world and tables exhibiting all known languages, dead and living. By G. Naphegyi ... Philadelphia, J. B. Lippincott & co., 1869.
   4 p. l., 11-323, (1) p. col. front., col. illus. 38½ x 31ᶜᵐ.
   Added t.-p., illustrated in colors; colored initials.
   1. Language and languages. 1. Lord's prayer. Polyglot. 11. Title.

Library of Congress   P351.N2   11-11023

PPL MiU OC1 PP MB MdBP
NN 0016189   DLC OKentU CU OC NjNbS MdBP PPLT PU

Naphegyi, Gábor, 1824-1884.
   Among the Arabs. A narrative of adventures in Algeria. By G. Naphegyi ... Philadelphia, J. B. Lippincott & co., 1868.
   252 p. incl. front. (port.) 19ᶜᵐ.

1. Algeria—Descr. & trav.

5-9818

Library of Congress   DT279.N19

WU
NN 0016190   DLC NcD IEN ViU PPAN OCH PPL PU MdBP

Naphegyi, Gábor, 1824-1884.
   Among the Arabs. A narrative of adventures in Algeria. By G. Naphegyi ... Philadelphia, J. B. Lippincott & co., 1869.
   252 p. incl. front. (port.) 19ᶜᵐ.

1. Algeria—Descr. & trav. 1. Title.

40-37715

Library of Congress   DT279.N19 1869

NN 0016191   DLC

Naphegyi, Gábor, 1824-1884.
   Ghardaia; or, Ninety days among the B'ni Mozab: adventures in the oasis of the desert of Sahara. By G. Naphegyi ... New York, G. P. Putnam & sons; London, S. Low, son & Marston, 1871.
   1 p. l., 348 p. front. 19ᶜᵐ.
   Added t.-p., illustrated.

1. Mzab—Descr. & trav. 1. Title. 11. Title: Ninety days among the B'ni Mozab.

Library of Congress   DT333.N19   5-11003

PPDrop
NN 0016192   DLC IEN C NcD CtY PPL PU-Mu OC1 MB

Naphegyi, Gábor, 1824-1884.
   The grand review of the dead. Written for the occasion of the decorating of the soldier's graves, May 30th, 1869, by G. Naphegyi ... New York, The author, 1869.
   1 p. l., (5)-23 p. 23ᶜᵐ.

1. U. S.—Hist.—Civil war—Poetry. 2. Memorial day.

Library of Congress   E647.N19   12-22180

NN 0016193   DLC GU RPB OC1WHi NcD PHi

VOLUME 405

2
2730

Naphegyi, Gábor, 1824–1884.
    History of Hungary, and sketches of Kossuth,
Bem, Dembinsky, and Görgey.
New York, 1849.

NN   0016194   DLC

Naphegyi, Gábor, 1824–1884.
    Hungary: from her rise to the present time, under the
guidance of Lewis Kossuth, in the years 1848 and 1849. Together with the original portraits of Hungary's valiant chiefs
and leaders in the last revolution. By Doctor Gabor Naphegyi ... New York, Published by the author, 1849.
    32 p. 4 port. 24½ᵐ.

    1. Hungary—Hist.—Uprising of 1848-1849.
                                                                3—8514
    Library of Congress   DB935.N19

NN   0016195   DLC ViU OClWHi MB

Naphegyi, Gábor, 1824–1884.
    Lord's prayer in sixty languages
        see under   Lord's prayer. Polyglot.

Naphen, Henry Francis, 1847–
    Chinese-exclusion bill. Speech ... Friday,
April 4, 1902. Washington, 1902.
    15 p.
            :YA5000
            J17

NN   0016197   DLC

Naphen, Henry Francis, 1847–   4229a.78
Colonial imperialism . . . Speech in the House of Representatives,
    . . . May 17, 1900.
= Washington. 1900. 20 pp. 8°.

F7889 — Territorial expansion. United States. — United States. Colo.

NN   0016198   MB

Naphen, Henry Francis, 1847–
    Trusts ... Speech of Hon. Henry F. Naphen, of Massa-
chusetts, in the House ... May 31, 1900. Washington ₍Govt.
print. off.₎ 1900.
    8 p. 24ᵐ.

    1. Trusts, Industrial—U. S.—Speeches in Congress.
                                                    1-4496 rev.
    Library of Congress   HD2795.N3

NN   0016199   DLC MB ICRL

Napheys, George Henry, 1842–1876.
    The body and its ailments: a handbook of familiar di-
rections for care and medical aid in the more usual complaints and injuries ... By George H. Napheys ... Philadelphia, H. C. Watts & co., 1876.
    iii, ix–xxiii, 25–438 p. col. front., illus. 19½ᵐ.

    1. Medicine, Popular.
                                                    7—10382
    Library of Congress   RC81.N25

NN   0016200   DLC PPJ PU ICJ

Napheys, George Henry, 1842–1876.
    Counsels on the nature and hygiene of the
masculine function
        see his   The transmission of life.

Napheys, George Henry, 1842–1876, ed.

Half-yearly compendium of medical science: a synopsis
of the American and foreign literature of medicine, surgery and the collateral sciences. for six months ...
pt. 1–   Jan. 1868–
Philadelphia, S. W. Butler ₍etc.₎ 1868–

Napheys, George Henry, 1842–1876.
    Handbook of popular medicine, embracing the anatomy
and physiology of the human body ... etc. With over 300
choice dietetic and remedial recipes ... By George H.
Napheys ... Rev. to the latest date. Philadelphia, H. C.
Watts co., 1878.
    1 p. L, xv, 1 L, iv–xxiii, 25–438 p. front. (port.) illus. 19½ᵐ.
    Published in 1876 under title: The body and its ailments.

    1. Medicine, Popular.
                                                    7–10238†
    Library of Congress   RC81.N255

NN   0016203   DLC OCl OClW-H PV

Napheys, George Henry, 1842–1876.   616.024 N600
                                          124173
    Handbook of popular medicine, embracing the anatomy and
physiology of the human body; illustrations of home gymnastics;
instructions for nursing the sick; the domestic treatment of the
ordinary diseases and accidents of children and adults; plan for
a family health record, etc. With over 300 choice dietetic and
remedial recipes, and more than 100 engravings on wood. Especially adapted for general and family instruction and reference.
By George H. Napheys, ... Revised to the latest date. Philadelphia, H. C. Watts Co.; St. Louis, N. D. Thompson & Co.;
₍etc., etc.₎, 1879.
    [2], xv, iii, ix–xi, 12–408 p. front., (port.), 105 illus. 19½ᶜᵐ.

NN   0016204   ICJ

Napheys, George H., 1842–76.
    —— Handbook of popular medicine, embrac-
ing the anatomy and physiology of the human
body; illustrations of home gymnastics; instructions for nursing the sick; the domestic
treatment of the ordinary diseases and accidents
of children and adults; plan for a family health
record, etc. With over 300 choice dietetic and
remedial recipes, and more than 100 engravings
on wood. Especially adapted for general and
family instruction and reference. xv, xxiii,
24–408 pp., port. 12°. *Philadelphia, H. C.
Watts Co.* 1882.

NN   0016205   DNLM PPC PV

Napheys, George Henry, 1842–1876.
    Handbook of popular medicine, embracing the
anatomy and physiology of the human body;
illustrations of home gymnastics _ with over
300 choice dietetic and remedial recipes _
especially adapted for general and family
instruction and reference _ rev. to the latest
date. Philadelphia, D. McKay, 1887.
    1p.ℓ.,xvp.,1ℓ.,ix–xxiii,25–408p. illus.
19 1/2cm.

NN   0016206   CtY-M OCl

WBC   NAPHEYS, George Henry, 1842-1876.
N195m   Modern medical therapeutics.
           ₍1st₎–   ed.   Philadelphia, Brinton
           ₍etc.₎ 1870–
                   v.
               1st–2d, 4th eds. have title: Modern
           therapeutics. 9th ed. combined with the
           author's Modern surgical therapeutics,
           Therapeutics of gynecology and obstetrics,
           and Therapeutics of diseases of children,
           under title: Modern therapeutics, medical

           and surgical.
               4th–8th eds. edited by D. G. Brinton.

               I. Brinton, Daniel Garrison, 1837-
           1899, ed. II. Napheys, George Henry,
           1842-1876. Modern therapeutics

NN   0016208   DNLM

Napheys, George Henry, 1842–1876.
    Modern medical therapeutics: a compendium of recent
formulæ, and specific therapeutical directions. By Geo.
H. Napheys ... 3d ed., rev. and improved. Philadelphia,
S. W. Butler, 1871.
    vii, 9–496 p. 19½ᵐ.

    1. Therapeutics. 2. Medicine—Formulae, receipts, prescriptions.
                                                    7—8790
    Library of Congress   RM101.N19 1871

NN   0016209   DLC MBCo PPHa NjP PPC ICJ Nh

WB
300   Napheys, George Henry, 1842–1876.
N195   Modern therapeutics: a compendium of recent
1876   formulae, approved treatment, and specific
           methods in medicine and surgery... 4th ed.
           rewritten, and enl. Philadelphia, Brinton,
           1877 ₍cl876₎
               xv, 17–609 p. tables. 24 cm.

               1. Therapeutics – 19th century. I. Title.

NN   0016210   NcU-H

Napheys, George Henry, 1842–1876.
    Modern medical therapeutics: a compendium of recent
formulæ and specific therapeutical directions, from the
practice of eminent contemporary physicians, American
and foreign. By George H. Napheys ... 5th ed., enl. and
rev. Philadelphia, D. G. Brinton, 1878.
    1 p. L, v–xv, 17–598 p. 24ᵐ.
    Edited by D. G. Brinton.

    1. Therapeutics. 2. Medicine—Formulae, receipts, prescriptions.
    I. Brinton, Daniel Garrison, 1837–1899, ed.

    Library of Congress   RM101.N19 1878   7–8784

NN   0016211   DLC ICRL DNLM OClW-H OO MiU ViU ICJ

Napheys, George Henry, 1842–1876.
    Modern medical therapeutics: a compendium of recent
formulæ and specific therapeutical directions, from the
practice of eminent contemporary physicians, American
and foreign. By George H. Napheys ... 6th ed., enl. and
rev. Philadelphia, D. G. Brinton, 1879.
    xvi, 17–607 p. 24ᵐ.
    Edited by D. G. Brinton.

    1. Therapeutics. 2. Medicine—Formulae, receipts, prescriptions.
    I. Brinton, Daniel Garrison, 1837–1899, ed.

    Library of Congress   RM101.N19 1879   7–8785

NN   0016212   DLC MiU OCl MH MB PPC

Napheys, George Henry, 1842–1876.
    Modern medical therapeutics: a compendium of recent
formulæ and specific therapeutical directions, from the
practice of eminent contemporary physicians, American
and foreign. By George H. Napheys ... 7th ed., enl. and
rev. Philadelphia, D. G. Brinton, 1880.
    xv, 17–604 p. 24ᵐ.
    Edited by D. G. Brinton.

    1. Therapeutics. 2. Medicine—Formulae, receipts, prescriptions.
    I. Brinton, Daniel Garrison, 1837–1899, ed.

    Library of Congress   RM101.N19 1880   7–8786

NN   0016213   DLC OCl ICRL CtY AAP RPB OrU-M

Napheys, George Henry, 1842–1876.
    Modern medical therapeutics ... 7th ed.
enl. & rev. Phila., Briton, 1881.
    604 p.

NN   0016214   PPPH

VOLUME 405

Napheys, George Henry, 1842–1876.
Modern medical therapeutics: a compendium of recent formulæ and specific therapeutical directions, from the practice of eminent contemporary physicians, American and foreign. By George H. Napheys ... Ed. by Joseph F. Edwards, M. D., and D. G. Brinton, M. D. 8th ed., enl. and rev. Philadelphia, D. G. Brinton, 1885.
xv, 17–629 p. 24ᶜᵐ.

1. Therapeutics. 2. Medicine — Formulae, receipts, prescriptions. ι. Edwards, Joseph F., 1853–   ed. ιι. Brinton, Daniel Garrison, 1837–1899, ed.

Library of Congress   RM101.N19 1885   7–8787

NN   0016215   DLC ICRL PPHa PPC ICJ

Napheys, George Henry, 1842–1876.
Modern surgical therapeutics: a compendium of current formulæ, approved dressings and specific methods for the treatment of surgical diseases and injuries. By George H. Napheys ... Rev. to the most recent date. Philadelphia, D. G. Brinton, 1878.
xv, 17–587 p. 24ᶜᵐ.

1. Therapeutics, Surgical.
                                                   7–2962
Library of Congress   RD51.N247

PU PP
NN   0016216   DLC DNLM MB OC1 PPC OC1W-H OO ICJ

Napheys, George Henry, 1842–1876.
Modern surgical therapeutics: a compendium of current formulæ, approved dressings and specific methods for the treatment of surgical diseases and injuries. By George H. Napheys ... 6th ed., rev. to the most recent date. Philadelphia, D. G. Brinton, 1879.
xvi, 17–605 p. 24ᶜᵐ.

1. Therapeutics, Surgical.
                                                   7–2963
Library of Congress   RD51.N249

NN   0016217   DLC DNLM MiU OC1 PPC

Napheys, George Henry, 1842–1876.
Modern surgical therapeutics: a compendium of current formulæ, approved dressings and specific methods for the treatment of surgical diseases and injuries. By George H. Napheys ... 7th ed., rev. to the most recent date. Philadelphia, D. G. Brinton, 1881.
xvi, 17–612 p. 24 cm. (*Half-title:* The Modern therapeutic series. ιι)

1. Therapeutics, Surgical.

RD51.N25   7—2964

NN   0016218   DLC WaU PPJ PPC CtY-M KMK DNLM

NAPHEYS, George Henry, 1842–1876.
Modern surgical therapeutics; a compendium of current formulae approved dressings and specifi methods for the treatment of surgical diseases and injuries. 7th edition. Philadelphia, Brinton. 1882.

xvi, 612 pp.   22 cm.

NN   0016219   MBCo

Napheys, George Henry, 1842–1876.
Modern therapeutics: a compendium of recent formulæ and specific therapeutical directions. By Geo. H. Napheys ... Philadelphia, S. W. Butler, 1870.
309 p. 17¼ᶜᵐ.

1. Therapeutics. 2. Medicine—Formulae, receipts, prescriptions.
                                                   7–8165
Library of Congress   RM101.N19 1870

NN   0016220   DLC DNLM PPF ICJ MiU PPC

Napheys, George Henry, 1842–1876.   615.5 N100
Modern therapeutics: a compendium of recent formulæ and specific therapeutical directions. By Geo. H. Napheys, ... Second edition — revised and improved. Philadelphia, S. W. Butler, 1871.
vii, 412 p. 19ᶜᵐ.

NN   0016221   ICJ PPC ICRL DNLM KyU N MB

Napheys, George Henry, 1842–1876.
Modern therapeutics: a compendium of recent formulæ, approved treatment, and specific methods in medicine and surgery, with an appendix on hypodermic medication, inhalation, aeration, and other remedial agents and therapeutic methods, of recent introduction. By George H. Napheys ... 4th ed., re-written and enl. Philadelphia, D. G. Brinton, 1877.
xv, ₍17₎–609 p. 24ᶜᵐ.
"Editor's preface" signed: D. G. B₍rinton₎
1. Therapeutics. 2. Medicine—Formulae, receipts, prescriptions. ι. Brinton, Daniel Garrison, 1837–1899, ed.
                                                   7—8788
Library of Congress   RM101.N19 1877

PU-Med ICJ
NN   0016222   DLC ICRL Nh PPHa PPC OU OC1W OC1W-H

Napheys, George Henry, 1842–1876.
Napheys' Modern therapeutics, medical and *surgical* including the diseases of women and children, a compendium of recent formulæ and therapeutical directions from the practice of eminent contemporary physicians, American and foreign. 9th ed., rev. and enl. ... By Allen J. Smith ... and J. Aubrey Davis ... Philadelphia, P. Blakiston, son & co., 1892–93.
2 v. 24½ᶜᵐ.
CONTENTS.—v. 1. General medicine, and diseases of children.—v. 2. General surgery, gynecology and obstetrics.
1. Therapeutics. 2. Therapeutics, Surgical.   ι. Smith, Allen John, 1863–   ed. ιι. Davis, J. Aubrey, ed.
                                                   7—8783
Library of Congress   RM101.N19 1892

NN   0016223   DLC ICJ DNLM NIC OU MiU OC1W-H PPHa

Napheys, George Henry, 1842–1876.
Brinton, Daniel Garrison, 1837–1899.
Personal beauty: how to cultivate and preserve it in accordance with the laws of health. By D. G. Brinton ... and Geo. H. Napheys ... Springfield, Mass., W. J. Holland, 1870.

Napheys, George Henry, 1842–1876.
The physical life of woman: advice to the maiden, wife, and mother, by George H. Napheys. London, C. Miller ₍n.d.₎
₍8₎ 320 p. 20 cm.

Preliminary leaves misprinted.

1. Woman—Health and hygiene. I. Title.

NN   0016225   NcGU

RG121   Napheys, George Henry, 1842–1876.
.N2
1869   The physical life of woman: advice to the maiden, wife, and mother. By Geo. H. Napheys ... Philadelphia, G. Maclean, 1869.
           252 p.   19ᶜᵐ.
           Autographed by author.

           1. Woman—Health and hygiene.

NN   0016226   ViU CtY PHi

613.88 Napheys, George Henry, 1842–1876.
N16p   The physical life of woman: advice to the mai-
1870   den, wife, and mother. By Geo. H. Napheys ... Fiftieth thousand, enlarged and revised.   Philadelphia, New York ₍etc.₎ G. Maclean; Cincinnati & Chicago, E. Hannaford & co., 1870.
          1 p.l., 322p.   19cm.

          "Notes" (bibliographical): p.305-312.

          1. Woman--Health and hygiene. I. Title.

NN   0016227   IU PU OO MWA WaU

3A   NAPHEYS, GEORGE HENRY, 1842–1876.
6531   The physical life of woman: advice to the maiden, wife, and mother. Enl. and rev. Philadelphia, G. Maclean; Cincinnati, E. Hannaford & co., 1871.
            12,₍2₎,322p.   19cm.

NN   0016228   ICN OrU

Napheys, George Henry, 1842–1876.   618.1 M900
The physical life of woman: advice to the maiden, wife, and mother. By Geo. H. Napheys, ... Ninetieth thousand, enlarged and revised. Philadelphia, New York, G. Maclean, ₍etc., etc.₎, 1872.
₍2₎, 322 p. 19ᶜᵐ.

NN   0016229   ICJ NcD-MC NRCR ICRL DNLM

Napheys, George Henry, 1842–1876.
The physical life of woman: advice to the maiden, wife, and mother. By George H. Napheys ... New stereotype ed., entirely rewritten, enl., and rev. Philadelphia, J. F. Fergus & co.; Cincinnati, E. Hannaford & co.; ₍etc., etc.₎ 1873.
ix, 11–14, ₍17₎–426 p. front. (port.) 19ᶜᵐ.

1. Woman—Health and hygiene.

                                                   16-25699
Library of Congress   RG121.N2

NN   0016230   DLC PPC MiU ICRL

Napheys, George Henry, 1842–1876.
The physical life of woman: advice to the maiden, wife and mother. To which is added Parturition without pain, by M.L. Holbrook. [4th Canadian ed.] Toronto, Maclear, 1875.

308, 82 p. illus. 19 cm.

NN   0016231   CaBVaU

Napheys, George Henry, 1842–1876.   618.1 N300
The physical life of woman: advice to the maiden, wife, and mother. By George H. Napheys, ... New stereotype edition, entirely rewritten, enlarged and revised. Philadelphia, H. C. Watts & Co.; Boston, G. M. Smith & Co., ₍etc., etc.₎, 1876.
ix, 11–426 p. front. (port.) 18½ᶜᵐ.

NN   0016232   ICJ ICRL

Napheys, George Henry, 1842–1876.
The physical life of woman: advice to the maiden, wife and mother. New ed., with the final corrections of the author and a biographical sketch. Philadelphia, H.C. Watts; St. Louis, N.D. Thompson, 1878.
x,xv₍11₎–426p. front.port. 19cm.

1.Sex manuals. 2.Women.

NN   0016233   NcD-MC OO

Napheys, George Henry, 1842–1876.   618.1 N001
The physical life of woman: advice to the maiden, wife, and mother. By Geo. H. Napheys, ... Enlarged and revised. Walthamstow, F. Mayhew, 1879.
320 p. 19ᶜᵐ.
"Notes," p. 305-312.

NN   0016234   ICJ

VOLUME 405

396
N195p.3   Napheys, George Henry, 1842-1876.
            The physical life of woman: maiden, wife and
            mother. New [i.e. 3d] ed. with the final cor-
            rections of the author and a biographical
            sketch. Chicago, W.M. Wood, 1880.
            xv,426p. port. 19cm.

            1. Woman. Health and hygiene. I. Title.

NN   0016235   IEN PPC

RG121   Napheys, George Henry, 1842-1876.
N3   The physical life of woman: advice to the
1880   maiden, wife, and mother, by Geo.H.Napheys.
            To which is added Paturition without pain, by
            M.L.Holbrook. [3d ed.] Toronto, Rose Pub.
            Co.[1880]
            382p. 19cm.

            1. Woman - Health and hygiene. I. Holbrook,
            Martin Luther, 1831-1902. Paturition without
            pain. I. Title. II. Title: Paturition without
            pain.

NN   0016236   IaU CaBVaU

Napheys, George Henry, 1842-1876.

    The physical life of woman: advice to the
maiden, wife, and mother. New ed. Philadelphia,
Watts, 1882.

    426 p.

NN   0016237   OrU-M NcD

NAPHEYS, GEORGE HENRY, 1842-1876.
    The physical life of woman: advice to the maiden, wife
and mother. By George H. Napheys... New edition. With
the final corrections of the author, and a biographical
sketch. Philadelphia: H. C. Watts & co., 1884. x, xv,
11-426 p. 19cm.

    484588. 1. Woman—Health and hygiene.

NN   0016238   NN NBuG PPL

Napheys, George Henry, 1842-1876.
    The physical life of woman: advice to the
maiden, wife and mother. New ed., with the
final corrections of the author. Philadelphia,
D. McKay, 1887.
    426p.

NN   0016239   ICRL ICJ

613.88   Napheys, George Henry, 1842-1876.
N16p   The physical life of woman: advice to the maid-
1888   en, wife and mother. New ed. With the final
            corrections of the author, and a biographical
            sketch. Philadelphia, D. McKay, 1888.
            x, xv, 11-426p. 19cm.

            1. Woman--Health and hygiene. I. Title.

NN   0016240   IU CtY MHi

RG   Napheys, George Henry, 1842-1876.
121   The physical life of woman; advice to the
N2   maiden, wife and mother. New [i.e. third] ed.
1889   with the final corrections of the author and
            a biographical sketch. Philadelphia, David
            McKay, 1889.
            xv [1], 11-426p. 19cm.

            1. Woman - Health and hygiene.

NN   0016241   IMunS

WP   NAPHEYS, George Henry, 1842-1876
N195p   The physical life of woman; advice
1890   to the maiden, wife and mother. New
            stereotype ed. with the final corrections
            of the author. New York, Hartranft
            [c1890]
            436 p.
            Imprint from label mounted on title
            page.
            Title

NN   0016242   DNLM OO

RG   Napheys, George Henry, 1842-1876.
121   The physical life of woman; advice to the
N161p   maiden, wife and mother. To which is added,
1927   Parturition without pain, by M. L. Holbrook.
            Chicago, M.A. Donohue [1927]
            366 p.

            1. Woman - Health and hygiene. I. Holbrook,
            Martin Luther, 1831-1902. Parturition without
            pain. II. Title.

NN   0016243   CLU

Napheys, George Henry, 1842-1876, ed.

    The Physician's annual for 1872. A complete calendar
for the city and country practitioner: comprising a
monthly calendar; hospital calendar of the principal
cities of the United States ... Ed. by S. W. Butler,
M. D., and Geo. H. Napheys, M. D. Philadelphia, S. W.
Butler, 1872.

Napheys, George Henry, 1842-1876.
    Das physische leben des weibes: rathschläge für die
jungfrau, gattin und mutter. Von Geo. H. Napheys ...
Philadelphia, New-York [etc.] G. Maclean; Cincinnati und
Chicago, E. Hannaford u. co., 1871.
    1 p. l., v-vi, ix-xiii, 15-352 p. 19ᶜᵐ.

    1. Woman—Health and hygiene.

Library of Congress   RG121.N23   8-928†

NN   0016245   DLC DNLM PPG

Napheys, George H[enry] 1842-1876.
    The prevention and cure of disease:
a practical treatise on the nursing and
home treatment of the sick ... By Geo.
H. Napheys ... Springfield [Mass.] W. J.
Holland & co., [c1871]

NN   0016246   OO

Napheys, George Henry, 1842-1876.
    The prevention and cure of disease: a practical trea-
tise on the nursing and home treatment of the sick ... By
Geo. H. Napheys ... Springfield [Mass.] W. J. Holland
& co., 1872.
    1 p. l., 9-1110 p. front., plates. 25½ᶜᵐ.

    1. Medicine, Popular.

Library of Congress   RC81.N26   7-10381†

NN   0016247   DLC OO

Napheys, George H[enry] 1842-1876.
    The prevention and cure of disease: a practical treatise
on the nursing and home treatment of the sick ... By
Geo. H. Napheys ... Springfield [Mass.] W. J. Holland &
co., 1872.
    1 p. l., 9-1151 p. front., plates. 25½ᶜᵐ.

    1. Medicine, Popular. 2. Hygiene.

Library of Congress   RC81.N27   7-9779†

NN   0016248   DLC

Napheys, George Henry, 1842-1876.
    Prevention and cure of disease ... Spring-
field, Holland, 1875.
    1151 p.

NN   0016249   PPC

Napheys, George Henry, 1842-1876.
    The prevention and cure of disease:
A practical treatise on nursing and
home treatment of the sick. Holland,
Springfield, 1876.
    1151 p.

NN   0016250   OC1W-H NjP

Napheys, George Henry, 1842-1876.
    The prevention and cure of disease:
A practical treatise on nursing and
home treatment of the sick. Holland,
Springfield, 1877.
    1151 p.

NN   0016251   OC1W-H

HQ   NAPHEYS, George Henry, 1842-1876
N195t   The transmission of life. Counsels on
            the nature and hygiene of the masculine
            function. By George H. Napheys.
            1st- ed. Philadelphia, J. G. Fergus
            [etc.] 1871-
            v.

NN   0016252   DNLM PPAN NcGU PU

Napheys, George Henry, 1842-1876.
    The transmission of life. Counsels on the nature and
hygiene of the masculine function. By George H. Napheys ... 2d ed. Philadelphia, J. G. Fergus & co., 1871.
    229 p. 18½ᶜᵐ.
    Bibliographies at end of each chapter.

    1. Hygiene, Sexual. I. Title.
                                                        8—1914
Library of Congress   RC881.N215

NN   0016253   DLC NcD OO PPHa

Napheys, George Henry, 1842-1876.
    The transmission of
life. Counsels on the nature and hygiene
of the masculine function. By George
H. Napheys ... Sixth ed. enl. and rev.
Philadelphia, J. G. Fergus & co., 1871.
    346 p. illus.

NN   0016254   OFH

Napheys, George Henry, 1842-1876.
    [Transmissions of life ... 7. ed. Phila.,
Fergus, 1871.
    346 p.

NN   0016255   PPC

RC881   Napheys, George Henry, 1842-1876.
N215   The transmission of life. Counsels on the
1871   nature and hygiene of the masculine function.
            By George H. Napheys ... Ninth edition.
            Enlarged and revised. Philadelphia, J. G.
            Fergus & co., 1871 .

            ivp.,2ℓ.,vp.,7-346,v-xxxip. 19cm.

            1. Hygiene, Sexual. I. Title.

NN   0016256   NBuG DNLM ICJ

VOLUME 405

NAPHEYS, GEORGE HENRY, 1842-1876.
The transmission of life. Counsels on the nature and hygiene of the masculine function. By George H. Napheys ... Thirteenth edition, enlarged and revised. Philadelphia: J. G. Fergus & co. [etc., etc.] 1872. v, 7-346, v-xxxi p. 19cm.

720241A. 1. Hygiene, Sexual.

NN   0016257   NN

RC881
.N22
1873
Napheys, George Henry, 1842-1876.
The transmission of life. Counsels on the nature and hygiene of the masculine function. 14th ed., enl. and rev.   Atlanta, Wm. Flint & Co., 1873 [c1871].
iv, v, 7-346, v-xxxi p. 19 cm.

"Testimonials": v-xxxi p. at end.

1. Hygiene, Sexual. I. Title.

NN   0016258   T

Napheys, George Henry, 1842-1876.
The transmission of life ... 15th ed. Phila., J. G. Fergus & co., 1873.
346 p.

NN   0016259   PPC PPPSW

Napheys, George Henry, 1842-1876.
The transmission of life. Counsels on the nature hygiene of the masculine function. 21st ed. rev. enl. Philadelphia, J. G. Fergus, 1875.
346, 31 p.

NN   0016260   MiU

RL881
.N21t
1877
Napheys, George Henry, 1842-1876.
The transmission of life. Counsels on the nature and hygiene of the masculine function. 14th ed., enlarged and rev. Philadelphia, H.C. Watts, 1877.
xv, 362p. front. 20cm.

1. Hygiene, Sexual. I. Title. II. Napheys, George Henry, 1842-1876. Counsels on the nature and hygiene of the masculine function.

NN   0016261   IEG

Napheys, George Henry, 1842-1876.
The transmission of life. Counsels on the nature and hygiene of the masculine function. By George H. Napheys ... New ed. With the final corrections and additions of the author, and with a biographical sketch. Philadelphia, H. C. Watts co., 1878.
8 p., 1 l., xv, 9-362 p. incl. front. (port.) 19½ᶜᵐ.

1. Hygiene, Sexual.   I. Title.

Library of Congress   RC881.N22   8—1885

NN   0016262   DLC MH

Napheys, George Henry, 1842-1876.
The transmission of life. Counsels on the nature and hygiene of the masculine function. By George H. Napheys ... New ed. With the final corrections and additions of the author, and with a biographical sketch. Philadelphia, H. C. Watts co., 1880 [1878].
8 p., 1 l., xv, 9-362 p. incl. front. (port.) 19½ᶜᵐ.

NN   0016263   IU TxU CoU OO PPC

Napheys, George Henry, 1842-1876.
The transmission of life. Counsels on the nature and hygiene of the masculine function. New ed. With the final corrections and additions of the author, and with a biographical sketch. Philadelphia, H.C.Watts co., 1882.

NN   0016264   MH

612.61
N19
Napheys, George Henry, 1842-1876.
The transmission of life. Counsels on the nature and hygiene of the masculine function. New ed., with the final corrections and additions of the author, and with a biographical sketch. Phil., H.C.Watts co., 1883 [°'78]
362p. 19cm.

1. Hygiene. Sexual. I. Title.

NN   0016265   N

Napheys, George Henry, 1842-1876.
The transmission of life; counsels on the nature and hygiene of the masculine function, by George H. Napheys ... New edition, with the final corrections and additions of the author, and with a biographical sketch. Philadelphia, H. C. Watts & Co., 1884.
8 p., 1 l., xv, 9-362 p. 19ᶜᵐ.
Bibliography at end of some chapters.

NN   0016266   ICJ ViU

Napheys, George Henry, 1842-1876.
The transmission of life. Counsels on the nature and hygiene of the masculine function. With ... corrections and additions of the author, and with a biographical sketch. Philadelphia, D. McKay, 1887.
v. 7-8, 1 l., xv, 9-362, v-xxxi p. 12°.
New ed.

NN   0016267   NN

Napheys, George Henry, 1842-1876.
The transmission of life. Counsels on the nature and hygiene of the masculine function. By George H. Napheys ... Philadelphia, J. G. Fergus & co., 1889.
New ed.

NN   0016268   OFH PPL

Napheys, George Henry, 1842-1876.
The transmission of life. Counsels on the nature and hygiene of the masculine function. By George H. Napheys ... New edition. With the final corrections and additions of the author, and with a biographical sketch. Philadelphia, D. McKay, 1894.
iv, v, 7-362, v-xxxi p.   19 cm.

NN   0016269   ViU

Napheys, George Henry, 1842-1876.
The transmission of life. Counsels on the nature and hygiene of the masculine function. By George H. Napheys ... New edition. With the final corrections and additions of the author, and with a biographical sketch. Philadelphia, D. McKay, 1898.
iv, v, 7-362, v-xxxi p. 19ᶜᵐ.
"Testimonials": v-xxxi p. at end.

1. Hygiene, Sexual.   I. Title.

                                                32-34201
Library of Congress   RC881.N22 1898   612.61

NN   0016270   DLC NN

Naphin, Francis J
Legal rules applicable to wages, hours of labor, overtime pay and employment records, being a digest of the Wages and hours law, the Walsh-Healey act and related laws of thirteen states. By Francis J. Naphin. San Diego, Calif., 1944.
1 p. l., 94 numb. l. 28 x 21½ᶜᵐ.
Reproduced from type-written copy.

1. Labor laws and legislation—U. S.   I. Title. II. Title: Wages and hours law. III. Title: Walsh-Healey act.
                                                45-16441
Library of Congress   HD7834.N25
                           [n2]   331

NN   0016271   DLC

Naphtali, David.
Oh! You Indians; a reply to Oh! You English. Allahabad, Kitabistan [1944]
136 p. 19 cm.

1. Karaka, Dosoo Framjee, 1911-   Oh! You English. 2. India—
Soc. life & cust.   I. Title.

DS421.5.N3   915.4   48-35738*

NN   0016272   DLC MiU CtY

Naphtali, Fritz, 1888-
Abbau und Aufbau; Rückblick auf das Wirtschaftsjahr 1925. Frankfurt am Main, Frankfurter Societäts-Druckerei G.m.b.H., 1926.
48 p.   diagrs.   22 cm.

NN   0016273   MH

Naphtali, Fritz, 1888-
Im Zeichen des Währungselends; das Wirtschaftsjahr 1922 und seine Lehren. Von Fritz Naphtali.   Frankfurt a. M.: Frankfurter Societäts-Druckerei, G.m.b.H. [1923.]   92 p.   8°.

1. Money, Germany, 1922. 2. Fi-   nance, Germany, 1922. 3. Banks
and banking, Germany, 1922.
N. Y. P. L.   May 8, 1924.

NN   0016274   NN CSt-H MH CtY

Naphtali, Fritz, 1888-
Im zeichen des währungselends, von Fritz Naphtali. 2. verm. aufl. Frankfurt am Main, Frankfurter societäts-druckerei g. m. b. H., Abt. buchverlag, 1923.
103 p.   diagr. 21½ᶜᵐ.

1. Currency question—Germany. 2. Germany—Econ. condit.—1918-
I. Title.
                                                28-5355
Library of Congress   HG999.N3 1923

NN   0016275   DLC NjP

Naphtali, Fritz, 1888-
Kapitalkontrolle. Jena, E. Diederichs, 1919.
23 p.   21 cm.   (Deutsche Gemeinwirtschaft, 8)

NN   0016276   MH

330.1
N16k
Naphtali, Fritz, 1888-
Konjunktur, arbeiterklasse und sozialistische wirtschaftspolitik ...   Berlin, J. H. W. Dietz nachf., 1928.
32p.   (On cover: Schriften der Freien sozialistischen hochschule)
On cover: Reichsausschuss für sozialistische bildungsarbeit.
"Vortrag, gehalten am 25. februar 1928 in der Freien sozialistischen hochschule, Berlin."
Author's autograph presentation copy.
1. Business cycles. 2. Labor and laboring classes. 3. Ger-   many--Economic policy.

NN   0016277   IU MH

VOLUME 405

Naphtali, Fritz, 1888–
משק מלחמתי. ‪[הוצאת‬ משרד ראש הממשלה, שרותי המודיעין.
‪[Tel-Aviv?,‬ 1949/50‪]‬
24 p. 17 cm. (מדיה המדינה‪]‬)

1. Israel—Econ. condit.   *Title transliterated: Meshek milḥamti.*

HC497.P2N285   57–50808 ‡

NN   0016278   DLC MH

Naphtali, Fritz, 1888–
Waehrungsgesundung und Wirtschaftssanierung; Rückblick
auf das Wirtschaftsjahr 1924, von Fritz Naphtali. Frankfurt
am Main: Frankfurter Societäts-Druckerei, G.m.b.H., 1925.
84 p. incl. diagrs., tables. 8°.
Repr.: Frankfurter Zeitung.

1. Economic history—Germany.
N. Y. P. L.   December 22, 1926

NN   0016279   NN

Naphtali, Fritz, 1888–
Wertschwankungen und Bilanz, von Fritz Naphtali. Frankfurt am Main: Frankfurter Societäts-Druckerei, G.m.b.H., 1921.
24 p.   8°.
Bibliography, p. 3–4.

1. Prices and money, Germany, 1921.   2. Exchange (Foreign), Germany, 1921. 3. Finance, Germany,   many, 1921.
N. Y. P. L.   December 22, 1923.

NN   0016280   NN CU

Naphtali, Fritz, 1888–   joint author.
Kahn, Ernst, 1884–
Wie liest man den handelsteil einer tageszeitung? Von
Ernst Kahn und Fritz Naphtali. 110. tausend, neue bearbei-
tung. Frankfurt am Main, Frankfurter societäts-druckerei
g. m. b. h., 1930.

Naphtali, Fritz, 1888–
Wie liest man den wirtschaftsteil einer tageszeitung? Neu
herausgegeben von Otto Hoffmann. Frankfurt a. M., So-
cietäts-verlag ‪[1936]‬

Naphtali, Fritz, 1888–   *ed.*
Wirtschaftsdemokratie, ihr wesen, weg und ziel, herausgegeben im auftrage des Allgemeinen deutschen gewerkschaftsbundes von Fritz Naphtali. 3., unveränderte aufl. 8. bis 10.
tausend. Berlin, Verlagsgesellschaft des Allgemeinen deutschen gewerkschaftsbundes gmbh, 1928.
192 p. 23ᶜᵐ.

1. Socialism. 2. Industry. 3. Capitalism. 4. Germany—Econ. condit.—1918–   I. Allgemeiner Deutscher gewerkschaftsbund. II. Title.
                                                        37–8645
Library of Congress   HX276.N3 1928 b
                                         ‪[3]‬   335

NN   0016283   DLC NN MH NcD CaBVaU

HD
3611
.N35
1929
Naphtali, Fritz, 1888–
Wirtschaftsdemokratie, ihr Wesen, Weg
und Ziel, hrsg. im Auftrage des Allgemeinen
deutschen Gewerkschaftsbundes. 4. unveränderte Aufl. Berlin, Verlagsgesellschaft des
Allgemeinen deutschen Gewerkschaftsbundes,
1929.
   192 p.
   1. Socialism. 2. Industry. 3. Capitalism
4. Germany - Econ. condit. - 1918-1933.
I. Allgemeiner deutscher Gewerkschaftsbund.

NN   0016284   DAU MH ICU

Naphtali, Fritz, 1888–   *ed.*
Wirtschaftsdemokratie, ihr Wesen, Weg und Ziel, hrsg.
im Auftrage des Allgemeinen deutschen Gewerkschaftsbundes. 5., erweiterte Aufl. Berlin, Verlagsgesellschaft des
Allgemeinen deutschen Gewerkschaftsbundes, 1931.
221 p. 23 cm.

1. Socialism. 2. Industry. 3. Capitalism. 4. Germany—Econ.
condit.—1918–   I. Allgemeiner Deutscher Gewerkschaftsbund.
II. Title.

HD3611.N35 1931   338.91   53–48888 †

NN   0016285   DLC

Naphtali, Fritz, 1888–
Wirtschaftskrise und Arbeitslosigkeit, volkstümlich darge-
stellt von Fritz Naphtali; nach einem Vortrag, gehalten in der
Freien Sozialist. Hochschule in Berlin am 8 November 1930.
Berlin: J. H. Dietz Nachf., G.m.b.H., 1930. 32 p. 12°.

635480A. 1. Labor, Unemployed.   2. Crises and panics, 1929–1930.
N. Y. P. L.   June 6, 1933

NN   0016286   NN MH

Naphtali, Fritz, 1888–
Wirtschaftspolitik und Sozialpolitik, von Fritz Naphtali.
(In: Sozialpolitische Studien; Festgabe. Berlin, 1929. 8°.
p. 95‪[–111].‬)

478068A. 1. Economics—Theory.   2. Legislation, Social.
N. Y. P. L.   June 20, 1930

NN   0016287   NN

BM506
.B33Z8
1926
Hebr
Naphtali, Ḥayyim Jacob, ed.
Zuenz, Aryeh Loeb, 1773 (ca.)–1833.
... מעיני החכמה על מס' בבא מציעא ... הכינו ... ארי' ליב
ציננ ... נדפס כעת מחדש במעלם תיקונים ע"י ... חיים יעקב
נפתלי וע"י ... אברהם בנימין זילברברג ... בילגורייא. בדפוס
נ. קראנענבערג. תרפ"ו.
‪[Bilgoraj, Skład w druk. N. Kronenberga, 1926]‬

NN   0016288

Naphtali, Leonard Mathias, 1927–
The adsorption of hydrogen and carbon dioxide on a
nickel-kieselguhr catalyst. Ann Arbor, University Micro-
films ‪[1954]‬
(‪[University Microfilms, Ann Arbor, Mich.]‬ Publication no. 8390)
Microfilm copy of typescript. Positive.
Collation of the original: xiii, 155 l. illus., diagrs., tables.
Thesis—University of Michigan.
Abstracted in Dissertation abstracts, v. 14 (1954) no. 8, p. 1188–
1189.
Bibliography: leaves 151–155.

1. Adsorption. 2. Hydrogen. 3. Carbon dioxide. 4. Catalysis.
5. Nickel.   I. Title.
Microfilm AC–1   no. 8390   Mic A 55–3076
Michigan. Univ. Libr.
for Library of Congress   ‪[1]†‬

NN   0016289   MiU DLC

QD341
.H9N3
Naphtali, Max, 1874–
I. Beitraege zur Friedel-Crafts'schen reaction.
II. Ueber orthophenetidin und seine derivate.
Berlin, 1899.
50p.
Inaug. diss. Heidelberg.

NN   0016290   DLC PPC PU

Naphtali, Max.
Chemie, technologie und analyse der naphthensäuren, von
dr. M. Naphtali ... Mit 48 tabellen. Stuttgart, Wissenschaftliche verlagsgesellschaft m. b. h., 1927.
5 p. l., 9–144 p. 25ᶜᵐ. (*Added t.-p.:* Monographien aus dem gebiete
der fett-chemie, hrsg. von prof. dr. K. H. Bauer ... bd. VIII)

1. Naphthenic acids.   I. Title.
Library of Congress   QD341.A2N25
                                                        28–13653

NN   0016291   DLC CtY PPAtR NjR PPEFH ICJ NN

Naphtali, Max.
Die kohle und ihre wandlungen, von dr. Max Naphtali ...
Berlin, Ullstein ‪[*1928]‬
136, ‪[1]‬ p., 1 l. illus., diagrs. 17¼ᶜᵐ. (*Half-title:* Wege zum wissen.
‪[95]‬)

1. Coal. 2. Coal-tar products.   I. Title.
Library of Congress   ᵀᴺ801.N3   29–7761

NN   0016292   DLC CU

Naphtali, Max, joint ed.
Technische entwicklung auf dem gebiete der kohlenwasserstoff-
öle und fette ... An hand der internationalen patentlite-
ratur bearbeitet von prof. dr. Fritz Croner u. dipl.-chem. dr.
Max Naphtali ... Berlin, M. Krayn, 1928–

Naphtali ben Isaac, *ha-Kohen,* 1649–1719.
בית רחל ושער הלל יה. פאר ושבח מנהגים ותיקונים. אמשטר-
ד. בבית ובדפוס המשותפים הירן לוי רופא והתנו קאשמן
‪[Amsterdam, 1761]‬ ‪תקכ"א‬
16 l. 18 cm.

1. Cabala. 2. Jews. Liturgy and ritual. Occasional prayers. I.
Title.   *Title transliterated:* Bet Raḥel ve-sha'ar halel Yah.
                                                        A 54–6848
New York. Public Libr.
for Library of Congress   ‪[1]‬

NN   0016294   NN

Naphtali ben Isaac, *ha-Kohen,* 1649–1719.
שער ההכנה וצוואות נפלאות. ‪[n. p., n. d.]‬
20 l. 19 cm.

1. Wills, Ethical.   I. Jews. Liturgy and ritual. Readings. II.
Title.   *Title transliterated:* Sha'ar ha-hakhanah.
[BM675.R4N   ]   A 56–1297
New York. Public Libr.
for Library of Congress   ‪[2]‬

NN   0016295   NN

Naphtali ben Isaac, *ha-Kohen,* 1649–1719.
שער ההכנה. קושמאנדינה. בדפוס המחוקק יונת.
‪[Constantinople, 1734]‬
36, 12 l. 17 cm.

1. Wills, Ethical.   I. Jews. Liturgy and ritual. Readings. II.
Title.   *Title transliterated:* Sha'ar ha-hakhanah.
BM675.R4N3 1734   56–48527

NN   0016296   DLC

Naphtali ben Isaac, *ha-Kohen,* 1649–1719.
שער ההכנה. עם הצוואה. לבוב. בדפוס אהרן במהור"ר חיים
דוד. ‪[Lemberg, 1794]‬
40, ‪[2]‬ l. 18 cm.
"הלכות הרב ישעיה": leaves ‪[41]–[42]‬

1. Wills, Ethical.   I. Jews. Liturgy and ritual. Readings.
II. Horowitz, Isaiah, 1555 (ca.)–1630. III. Title.
                    Title transliterated: Sha'ar ha-hakhanah.
[BM675.R4N   ]   A 56–1305
New York. Public Libr.
for Library of Congress   ‪[3]‬

NN   0016297   NN

Naphtali ben Isaac, *ha-Kohen,* 1649–1719.
שער ההכנה וצוואות נפלאות.
Zolkiew, Bei S. Meyerhoffer, 1848.
34 (i. e. 33) l. 19 cm.

1. Wills, Ethical.   I. Jews. Liturgy and ritual. Readings. II.
Title.   *Title transliterated:* Sha'ar ha-hakhanah.
[BM675.R4N   ]   A 56–1306
New York. Public Libr.
for Library of Congress   ‪[3]‬

NN   0016298   NN

VOLUME 405

Naphtali ben Isaac, ha-Kohen, 1649–1719.
שער ההכנה וצוואות נפלאות. קראקא, בדפוס ב. גיצהאלס.
Kraków, 1935. תרצ״ה.
52 p. 21 cm.

1. Wills, Ethical. I. Jews. Liturgy and ritual. Readings. II.
Title. *Title transliterated:* Sha'ar ha-hakhanah.
BM675.R4N3 1935 56–48538

NN 0016299 DLC

Naphtali ben Isaac, ha-Kohen, 1649–1719.
שער נפתלי. בקשות. ברין, בבית ובדפוס פראנץ יאזעף נייאמאן,
Brünn ₁1757₎ בשיר״ת.
37 l. 22 cm.

1. Jews. Liturgy and ritual. Seliḥot. II. Title.
Title transliterated: Sha'ar Naftali.
BM675.S4N3 54–55643

NN 0016300 DLC

Naphtali ben Isaac, ha-Kohen, 1649–1719.
שער נפתלי. בקשות. מינסק, תק״ע.
₁Minsk, 1810₎
103 l. 17 cm.

1. Jews. Liturgy and ritual. Seliḥot. II. Title.
Title transliterated: Sha'ar Naftali.
[BM675.S4] A 54–252
New York Public Libr.
for Library of Congress ₁2₎

NN 0016301 NN

Naphtali ben Isaac, ha-Kohen, 1649–1719.
צוואה מהרב נפתלי כ״ץ. ראדין. בדפוס י. מ. לנר. תרע״א.
Радин, 1911.
26 p. 20 cm.

1. Wills, Ethical. *Title transliterated:* Tsava'ah.
BJ1286.W6N32 52–52462

NN 0016302 DLC

Naphtali ben Isaac, ha-Kohen, 1649–1719.
הצוואה מהרב נפתלי הכהן. מונקאטש, ש. ז. כהנא,
Munkács ₁1904₎ תרס״ד.
16 l. 19 cm.

1. Ethics, Jewish. *Title transliterated:* ha-Tsava'ah meha-rav Naftali ha-Kohen.
A50–8050
New York Public Libr.
for Library of Congress ₁3₎

NN 0016303 NN

Naphtali ben Isaac, ha-Kohen, 1649–1719.
צוואת רבי נפתלי. הוספנו כאן בתחלתו תולדות הגאון
המחבר. ירושלם. המוסד להוצאת ספרי מוסר והסידות. תשט״ו
₁1954/55₎
82 p. 16 cm.

1. Wills, Ethical. *Title transliterated:* Tsava'at Rabi Naftali.
[BJ1286.W6N] HE 65–1053
Hebrew Union College. Library
for Library of Congress ₁2₎

NN 0016304 OCH

Naphtali ben Isaac, ha-Kohen, 1649–1719.
צוואת הגאון נפתלי הכהן. פיורדא. בדפוס איצק בן ליב
ב״ב ₁תקמ״ז.
₁Fürth, 1786/87₎
1 v. (unpaged) 18 cm.

1. Wills, Ethical. *Title transliterated:* Tsava'ot.
BJ1286.W6N3 52–51626

NN 0016305 DLC CLU

Naphtali ben Isaac, ha-Kohen, 1649–1719.
צוואות נפתלי הכהן, ליֹשר האדם לעבודת בוראו. הובא
לבית הדפוס ע״י בנימין מק״ק מעליץ. פיורדא, איצק בן
ליב. ₁Fürth, 1776₎
29 l. 15 cm.

1. Ethics, Jewish. *Title transliterated:* Tsava'ot Naftali ha-Kohen.
A 50–8051
New York Public Libr.
for Library of Congress ₁4₎

NN 0016306 NN

Naphtali ben Isaac, ha-Kohen, 1649–1719.
צוואות נפתלי הכהן. ותמציתו בלשון אשכנ. ווילנא,
מ. מן, תקס״ג. ₁Vilna, 1803₎
24 l. 18 cm.

1. Ethics, Jewish. *Title transliterated:* Tsava'ot Naftali ha-Kohen.
A 50–8048
New York Public Libr.
for Library of Congress ₁3₎

NN 0016307 NN

Naphtali ben Isaac, ha-Kohen, 1649–1719.
צוואות נפתלי הכהן. ווארשא, תד״ר.
W Warszawie, Drukarni W. J. Lebensohna, 1844.
17 l. 19 cm.
With synopsis in Judeo-German.

1. Ethics, Jewish. *Title transliterated:* Tsava'ot Naftali ha-Kohen.
A 50–8049
New York Public Libr.
for Library of Congress ₁3₎

NN 0016308 NN

Naphtali ben Phinehas Zeeb ha-Levi
see
Levy, Naphtali

Naphtali ha-Levi, of London
see
Levy, Naphtali

Naphtali Herz ben Abraham, of Bychów Stary.
FOR OTHER EDITIONS
SEE MAIN ENTRY
PJ4603 Mussafia, Benjamin, 1606 (ca.)–1675. (Zekher rav)
.M8 זכר רב. עם ביאור אשכנזי ₁מאת נפתלי הערץ במהור״ר אברהם₎
1835 וספר מעם זקנים ₁חיברתי, דוד בלא״א יהודא ליב הלוי דק״ק דובנא₎
Hebr אוסמהרא. ע״י א. קלאהרפין. תקצ״ה.
B₁ Ocrpora, 1835.

Naphtali Hirz Treves
see Treves, Naphtali Hirz, *16th cent.*

Naphtali; or, a true and short deduction of the wrestlings of the church of Scotland, etc.
see under Steuart, Sir James, 1635–1715.

Naphtali, or, The wrestlings of the Church of Scotland for the kingdom of Christ
see under ₁Steuart, Sir James₎ 1635–1715.

...**Naphtolrot** oder Türkischrot? Beiträge zur Frage der Farbechtheit roter Inlettstoffe. Mit einem Anhang über "Das Federdichthalten der Inletts." Eine Ergänzungsschrift zum Band II der "Deutschen Textil-Bücherei": Willy Otto, "Textilveredlung" (Bleicherei, Färberei und Druckerei). Hannover: S. Hein & Co.₁ 1925.₎ 35, 13 p. 12°. (Deutsche Textil-Bücherei. Bd. 2a.)

Repr. in part from "Manufakturist," 1924–1925.

1. Dyes and dyeing, Cotton. 2. Cotton fabrics and fibre. 3. Otto, Willy: Textilveredelung. 4. Ser.
N. Y. P. L. April 29, 1927

NN 0016315 NN

WA N195a 1890 **NAPIAS, Henri,** 1842–
L'assistance publique dans le département de Sambre-et-Loire.
Paris, Lecrosnier et Babé, 1890.
vii, 88 p.

NN 0016316 DNLM

WA N195e 1882 **NAPIAS, Henri,** 1842–
L'étude et les progrès de l'hygiène en France de 1878 à 1882, par H. Napias ₁et₎ A. J. Martin. Paris, Masson, 1882.
xi, 546 p. illus.
At head of title: Société de médecine publique et d'hygiène professionnelle.
I. Martin, André Justin

NN 0016317 DNLM NN PPC

NAPIAS, HENRI, 1842–
... L'ÉTUDE ET LES PROGRÈS DE L'HYGIÈNE EN FRANCE DE 1878 À 1882. PAR M. H. NAPIAS ... [ET] A. J. MARTIN ... 2. ÉD. PARIS, 1883.
AT HEAD OF TITLE: SOCIETE DE MÉDECINE PUBLIQUE ET D'HYGIÈNE PROFESSIONNELLE.

NN 0016318 MdBJ

Napias, Henri, 1842– 012.61 50
Exposé des titres et travaux scientifiques du docteur Henri Napias, ... Paris, L. Battaille et cie, 1896.
47 p. 24cm.

NN 0016319 ICJ

Napias (Henri) [1842–1901]. L'hygiène scolaire en France; le bâtiment scolaire; le mobilier; hygiène de la vue; durée des classes; le ménage; colonies de vacances; maladies contagieuses à l'école; inspection médicale, pp. 29–58, 8°. Wien, 1887.
Forms pt. 3, 12. Hft. of VI. Internat. Cong. f. Hyg. u. Demog. zu Wien.

NN 0016320 DNLM

VOLUME 405

WA
N195m
1882

NAPIAS, Henri, 1842-1901.
Manuel d'hygiène industrielle,
comprenant la législation française et
étrangère ... Paris, Masson, 1882.
viii, 580 p. illus.

NN   0016321   DNLM PBL

Napias, Henri, 1842-1901.
—— Rapport et projet de règlement pour l'application de la loi du 12 juin 1-93. 50 pp. 8°. *Melun, Imp. administrative, 1-93.*

NN   0016322   DNLM

Napias, Henri, 1842-1901.
——. Réglementation des crèches publiques et privées. Rapport présenté par ... 28 pp. 8°. [*Melun, 1896.*]

NN   0016323   DNLM

Napias (Louise). *Action de la bactéride charbonneuse sur les hydrates de carbone. 27 pp., 21. 8°. *Seraux, 1900, No. 1. École de pharmacie de Paris.*

NN   0016324   DNLM

WAA
N195q
1881

NAPIAS, Maxime
La question des odeurs de Paris;
législation et procédure des établissements dangereux, insalubres, ou incom-
modes. Paris, Rousseau, 1881.
112 p.

NN   0016325   DNLM

Napier, *pseud.*
The essays of Napier [pseud.], originally published in the Jeffersonian and Virginia Times.
Norfolk: Printed by T. G. Broughton ..... 1833.
12 p.   23½ cm.
Essays signed: Napier.
A series of Essays, under the signature of 'Locke'
supposedly Abel Parker Upshur ... which assuming the
Resolutions of '98 as the foundation, clearly demonstrated Nullification to be the original mode of state-
interposition against the unconstitutional legislation of
the General Government. The following numbers as con-
clusively exhibit the preference of Nullification to
Secession as a State remedy ... both series are from the
pen of a distinguished citizen of Eastern Virginia ...
Verso of t.-p.
Nullification.
1844. supposed autho   I. Upshur, Abel Parker. 1790-
                                     r. II. Title.

NN   0016326   ViU ViW MH

Napier, Alexander, M.D., tr.
Guttmann, Paul, 1834-1893.
A handbook of physical diagnosis, comprising the throat,
thorax, and abdomen, by Dr. Paul Guttmann ... Tr. from
the 3d German ed. by Alex. Napier ... New York, W. Wood
& company, 1880.

Napier, Alexander, M.D.
Seven cases of myxoedema treated by thyroid
feeding... n. p., n. pub., n. d.
cover-title: 19 p.

Reprinted from the Glasgow medical journal for
August, 1894.

NN   0016328   MiDW-M

Napier, *Mrs.* Alexander
see
Napier, Robina.

Napier, Alexander, 1814-1887, tr.
Michaelis, Adolf Theodor Friedrich, 1835-1910.
The Holkham bust of Thucydides, a study in Greek
iconography, by Adolf Michaelis ... Tr. from the German by Alexander Napier ... Cambridge, Printed for
private circulation at the University press, 1878.

Napier, Alexander, 1814-1887, ed.
Boswell, James, 1740-1795.
The life of Samuel Johnson, LL. D. Together with The jour-
nal of a tour to the Hebrides, by James Boswell, esq. New
editions with notes and appendices by Alexander Napier ...
London, G. Bell and sons, 1884.

Napier, Alexander, 1814-1887, ed.
Barrow, Isaac, 1630-1677.
The theological works of Isaac Barrow ... Edited for the
syndics of the University press by the Rev. Alexander Napier
... Cambridge [Eng.] The University press, 1859.

Napier (A[lexander] D[isney Leith]). Fibrin-
ous polypoid uterine tumour; and puerperal
albuminuria. 26 pp. 12°. *Edinburgh, Oliver &
Boyd, 1884.*

NN   0016333   DNLM

Napier, Alexander Disney Leith.
The menopause and its disorders (with chapters on menstruation) by A.D.Leith Napier ...
London, The Scientific press,limited, 1897.
xv,307 p.   illus.,VI pl.   25½ cm.
"General bibliography" at the beginning of most
chapters; "References to authorities quoted" at end of
each chapter.

1.Menstruation—Cessation.

NN   0016334   MiU DLC PPC

Napier, Alexander Disney Leith
—— Notes on the treatment of uterine pro-
lapse, with an account of a new modified method of anterior colporrhaphy. 12 pp. 8°. *Edinburgh, Oliver & Boyd, 1887.*

NN   0016335   DNLM

Napier, Alexander Disney Leith,
—— The thermometer in obstetrics and gyn-
aecology. 30 pp., 1 ch. 8°. *London, H. K.
Lewis, 1890.*

NN   0016336   DNLM

Napier, Ann, *pseud.*
see
Naumann, *Mrs.* Nancie, 1905-

Napier (Antoine-Georges) [1876-   ]. *Traitement des tumeurs malignes inopérables ou
récidivantes par les sels de quinine (méthode
de Jaboulay). 71 pp. 8°. *Paris, 1901, No. 564.*

NN   0016338   DNLM

E
5
.N 155

NAPIER, ARCHIBALD NAPIER, 1st baron, 1576-1645.
Memoirs of Archibald, first lord Napier
written by himself. Published from the original
manuscript, in the possession of the present Lord
Napier. Edinburgh,1793.
100p.

NN   0016339   ICN NjP

Napier, Arthur Sampson, 1853-1916.
Ein altenglisches Leben des heiligen Chad.
[Halle, 1888]
[131]-156 p.   21 cm.
Caption title.
Reprinted from Anglia. Bd. 10.

NN   0016340   CtY NcD

Napier, Arthur Sampson, 1853-1916.
Collation der altenglischen Gedichte im
Vercellibuch. [Berlin, 1889]
66-73 p.   21 cm.
Caption title.
Sonder-Abdruck: Zeitschrift für deutsches
Alterthum und deutsche Litteratur. Bd. 33.

NN   0016341   CtY NcD

Napier, Arthur Sampson, 1853-1916.
Contributions to Old English lexicography.
By Prof. A.S. Napier. n.p., n.d.
71 p.   O.   (In, Collected monographs. v.188)
Another copy in v.233.

NN   0016342   NcD

Napier, Arthur Sampson, 1853-1916.
Contributions to old English lexicography. By Arthur S.
Napier... Hertford: Printed by S. Austin & sons, ltd., 1906.
94 p.   22cm.
"Reprinted from the Philological society's Transactions, 1906."
"List of manuscripts quoted from," p. 2-3; "List of books referred to," p. 3-4.

C. P. G. SCOTT COLLECTION
Purchased for J. S. Billings Mem. Coll.
—Dictionaries, English.
889881A.   1. Anglo-Saxon language   June 15, 1937
N. Y. P. L.

NN   0016343   NN NcD

Napier, Arthur Sampson, 1853-1916.
Contributions to Old English lexicography. [London, K. Paul, Trench, Trübner,
1906]
265-358 p.   22cm. (Transactions of the
Philological Society, 1906, no.10)

Caption title.

1. Anglo-Saxon language - Dictionaries -
English. 2. English language - Middle English
(1100-1500) - Dictionaries. I. Philological
Society, London. Transactions. II. Title: Old
English lexicography.

NN   0016344   OCU NcU

ar W
9640

Napier, Arthur Sampson, 1853-1916.
Contributions to Old English literature.
[Oxford, Clarendon Press, 1901]
[355]-381 p.   fold. plates. 22cm.

Reprinted from An English miscellany,
presented to Dr. Furnivall in honour of his
seventy-fifth birthday. Oxford, Clarendon
Press, 1901.
Contents.—An Old English homily on the
observance of Sunday.—The Franks casket.

NN   0016345   NIC

VOLUME 405

Napier, Arthur Sampson, 1853–1916, *ed.*
... The Crawford collection of early charters and documents now in the Bodleian library; ed. by A. S. Napier ... and W. H. Stevenson. Oxford, Clarendon press, 1895.
xl, 167, ₍1₎ p. 22 x 20 cm. (Anecdota oxoniensia. ₍Mediaeval and modern series. pt. vii₎)

1. Gt. Brit.—Charters, grants, privileges.   i. Stevenson, William Henry, 1858–1924, joint ed.
AC9.A6 4th ser., pt. 7   12–37028

NN 0016346   DLC NN LU MU NBuU PBm OU OC1W MiU WU

Napier, Arthur Sampson, 1853–1916, *joint ed.*
An **English** miscellany; presented to Dr. Furnivall in honour of his seventy-fifth birthday. Oxford, Clarendon press, 1901.

Napier, Arthur Sampson, 1853–1916, ed.
A fragment of the Ancren riwle
see under Ancren riwle.

*PD
2007 **Napier, Arthur Sampson,** 1853–1916.
F8N1   The Franks casket, by Arthur S. Napier ... Oxford [H. Hart] 1900.
       22 p. 6 pl.

       "Reprinted from the Furnivall celebration volume."

       1. Inscriptions, Runic.   I. Title.

NN 0016349   CLU

Napier, Arthur Sampson, 1853–1916, *ed.*
History of the holy rood-tree, a twelfth century version of the cross legend, with Notes on the orthography of the Ormulum (with a facsimile) and a Middle English Compassio Mariae. By Arthur S. Napier ... London. Pub. for the Early English text society, by K. Paul, Trench, Trübner & co., limited, 1894.
llx, 86 p. fold. facsim. 23¼ᶜᵐ. (On cover: Early English text society. ₍Original series₎ 103)
Bibliography: p. x–xi.
1. Cross and crosses—Legends. 2. Ormulum.   i. Oxford. University. Bodleian library. Mss. (343) ii. Title. iii. Compassio Mariae.
Library of Congress   PR1119.A2 no. 103   12–17048

       KEmT PSt PU ODW OU OCU ViU MdBP NjP
NN 0016350   DLC NN MiU MB CaBVaU OrU WaWW NcD NNC

Napier, Arthur Sampson, 1853–1916.
A hitherto unnoticed Middle English manuscript of the seven sages. [Reprinted from the Publications of the Modern Language Assoc. of America. Vol. XIV, no. 4]
c.p. O. (In, Collected monographs. v. 201)

NN 0016351   NcD MWA

Napier, Arthur Sampson, 1853–1916, **ed.**

Jacob and Joseph.
Iacob and Iosep; a middle English poem of the thirteenth century, ed. by Arthur S. Napier ... Oxford, Clarendon press, 1916.

Napier, Arthur Sampson, 1853–1916.
Notes on the orthography of the Ormulum. Oxford, University press, 1893.
4 p. facsim.

NN 0016353   OC1W CtY InU

Napier, Arthur Sampson, 1853–1916, *ed.*
Old English glosses, chiefly unpublished; ed. by Arthur S. Napier ... Oxford, Clarendon press, 1900.
xxxix, ₍1₎, 302 p. 23½ x 19¼ᶜᵐ.
Issued also as "Anecdota oxoniensia. ₍iv₎ Mediaeval and modern series. pt. xi."

1. Anglo-Saxon language—Glossaries, vocabularies, etc.   i. Title.
Library of Congress   PE274.A5N2   1—25086

       OO MiU OCU NIC MB WaU NjP ViU NcD RPB MoU PU OU
NN 0016354   DLC WaWW CaBVaU OrU CtY TU PPL PP PU

Napier, Arthur Sampson, 1853–1916, ed.

Chrodegang, *Saint, bp. of Metz, d.* 766.
The Old English version of the enlarged rule of Chrodegang together with the Latin original. An Old English version of the Capitula of Theodulf together with the Latin original. An interlinear Old English rendering of the Epitome of Benedict of Aniane. By Arthur S. Napier ... London, Pub. for the Early English text society by K. Paul, Trench, Trübner & co., ltd. ₍etc.₎, 1916.

Napier, Arthur Sampson, 1853–1916.
An Old English vision of Leofric, Earl of Mercia. By A.S. Napier. [Reprinted from the Philological Society's Transactions, 1908] Hertford, Stephen Austin & Sons, 1908.
288 p. O. (In, Collected monographs, v. 239)

NN 0016356   NcD

ar W
9530 Napier, Arthur Sampson, 1853–1916.
       Über die Werke des altenglischen Erzbischofs Wulfstan.   Weimar, Hof-Buchdruckerei, 1882.
       71 p. 23cm.

       Diss.--Göttingen.

       1. Wulfstan, Saint, 1012?–1095.

NN 0016357   NIC NcD NjP RPB CtY PBm MiU ICN MH

Napier, Arthur Sampson, 1853–1916, ed.

Wulfstan II, *abp. of York, d.* 1023.
Wulfstan; sammlung der ihm zugeschriebenen homilien nebst untersuchungen über ihre echtheit, hrsg. von Arthur Napier. 1. abt.: Text und varianten. Berlin, Weidmann, 1883.

Napier, B.   Williamson-

       see

Williamson-Napier, B.

Napier, Bunyan Davie.
From faith to faith; essays on Old Testament literature. ₍1st ed.₎ New York, Harper ₍1955₎
223 p. 22 cm.

1. Bible. O. T.—Criticism, interpretation, etc.   i. Title.
BS1171.N35   221.7   55–8525 ‡

       PPT FU ScClcU KyWAT KyU FMU KyLxT
       OCU IU PHC NRCR OrP PBL MH–AH WaT PPLT ScU AU
       OC1Tem PSC PPWe NcD MB PPDrop PPEB OOxM ODW IU
NN 0016360   DLC FTaSU UU NIC IdPI OrCS OrPR OO

Napier, Carl H 1897–
International calendar manual ... 2500 calendars, 1 A. D. to 2500 A. D. Jefferson City, Mo., Mid-State Print. Co., 1951.
64 p. 23 cm.
Includes bibliography.

1. Calendar, Perpetual.   i. Title.
CE92.N3   529.3   51–33901 ‡

NN 0016361   DLC MoS

Napier, Catherine.
The lay of the palace ... London, J. Ollivier, 1852.
19 p. 12°.

NN 0016362   NN CtY

Napier, *Sir* **Charles,** 1786–1860.
An account of the war in Portugal between Don Pedro and Don Miguel. By Admiral Charles Napier. London, T. & W. Boone, 1836.
2 v. 19¼ᵐ.

1. Portugal—Hist.—Miguel i, 1828–1834.
                              4-34498†* Cancel
Library of Congress   DP657.N2

NN 0016363   DLC InU MdBP PPL PP DN

NAPIER, *Sir* Charles, 1786–1860.
Guerra da successão em Portugal. Pelo almirante Carlos Napier, conde do Cabo de São Vicente. Londres: 1836. Traduzida em Portuguéz por Manoel Joaquim Pedro Codina. Liaboa, Typographia commercial, 1841.

       2 vol.   Port 707.32.

NN 0016364   MH

Napier, *Sir* **Charles,** 1786–1860.
The history of the Baltic campaign of 1854. From documents and other materials furnished by Vice-Admiral Sir C. Napier ... Edited by G. Butler Earp ... London, R. Bentley, 1857.
xlvi p., 1 l., 622 p. 23ᵐ.
Errata slip inserted.

1. Crimean war, 1853–1856. 2. Baltic sea. 3. Gt. Brit.—History, Naval—19th cent.   i. Earp, George Butler, ed. ii. Title: Baltic campaign of 1854.
Library of Congress   DK214.N35   43–44749

       DNW DN
NN 0016365   DLC ICN MdBP NN MBAt MH PPL NcD CU KU

Napier, *Sir* **Charles,** 1786–1860.
The navy: its past and present state. In a series of letters, by Rear-admiral Sir Charles Napier ... Ed. by Major-general Sir William Napier ... London, J. & D. A. Darling, 1851.
2 p. l., viii, 259 p. 22ᶜᵐ.

1. Gt. Brit.—Navy—Hist.   i. Napier, Sir William Francis Patrick, 1785–1860, ed. ii. Title.
                              13–6399
Library of Congress   VA454.N19

       CaBViP
NN 0016366   DLC NcD CtY NN MBAt MdAN NcD DN

[Napier, Sir Charles, 1786–1860]
The navy; letter to the Duke of Wellington upon the actual crisis of the country in respect to the state of the navy. [London, Printed by A. Spottiswoode, 1838]

       44 p. 21 cm.
       "Not published."

NN 0016367   MH

VOLUME 405

Napier, *Sir* **Charles,** 1786–1860.
Our foreign policy towards Spain and Portugal. By Captain Napier, R. N. London, Ridgway, 1838.
18 p. 20½ᶜᵐ.

1. Spain—Hist.—Carlist war, 1833–1840. 2. Gt. Brit.—For. rel.—Spain.
3. Spain—For. rel.—Gt. Brit. 4. Gt. Brit.—For. rel.—Portugal. 5. Portugal—For. rel.—Gt. Brit. 6. Portugal—Hist.—Miguel I, 1828–1834. I. Title.
16–23857

Library of Congress   DP219.2.N3

NN   0016368   DLC

DA70
.A1
vol. 83   **Napier,** *Sir* **Charles,** 1786–1860.
Gt. Brit. *Admiralty.*
Russian war, 1854, Baltic and Black sea; official correspond-
ence, edited by D. Bonner-Smith ... and Captain A. C. Dewar
... ₍London₎ Printed for the Navy records society, 1943.

Napier, *Sir* **Charles,** 1786–1860.
The war in Syria. By Commodore Sir Charles Napier ... London, J. W. Parker, 1842.
2 v. 19ᶜᵐ.

1. Egypt—Hist.—Mohammed Ali, 1805–1849. 2. Syria—Hist. 3. Turkey—Hist.—1829–1878.
5–9545

Library of Congress   DT104.N19

NN   0016370   DLC DNW CSt CtY MdAN PPL DGU MdBP MH

Napier, Charles Frederic, 1876–

U. S. *Federal trade commission.*
Preliminary report of the Federal trade commission on
investment and profit in soft-coal mining ... Washington, Govt. print. off., 1922.

NAPIER, *Sir* CHARLES JAMES, 1782–1853.
Answer to major Jacob's letter. [Portsea, S.
Horsey, 1851] 16 p. 20cm.

Microfiche (neg.) 1 sheet. 11 x 15cm. (NYPL FSN 12,054)
Caption title.
Signed: C. J. Napier.
Includes J. Jacob's reply.
1. Army, British, in India.   I. Jacob, John, 1812-1858.

NN   0016372   NN

Napier, *Sir* **Charles James,** 1782–1853.
The colonies: treating of their value generally—of the
Ionian Islands in particular ... Strictures on the admin-
istration of Sir Frederick Adam ... By Colonel Charles
James Napier, c. b. London, T. & W. Boone, 1833.
x, ₍xiii₎-xv, ₍1₎, 608 p. 18 pl. (incl. front., maps, plans) 22½ᶜᵐ.

1. Ionian Islands. 2. Adam, Sir Frederick, 1784–1853. 3. Gt. Brit.—Colonies—Administration.
8–18162†

Library of Congress   DF901.I65N3

NN   0016373   DLC MH-BA

Napier, *Sir* **Charles James,** 1782–1853.
Colonization; particularly in Southern Australia: with
some remarks on small farms and over population. By
Colonel Charles James Napier ... London, T. & W.
Boone, 1835.
xxxii, 268 p. 22ᶜᵐ.

1. South Australia—Emig. & immig. 2. South Australia—Econ. condit.
10–14083†

Library of Congress   JV9227.A4 1835

    CtY NN ICJ NjP
NN   0016374   DLC MH-BA MdBP DN NIC MH PPL PU OCU

Napier, *Sir* **Charles James,** 1782–1853.
Defects, civil and military, of the Indian government.
By Lieutenant-General Sir Charles James Napier ...
Ed. by Sir W. F. P. Napier ... 2d ed. London, C. Wes-
terton, 1853.
xii, 437, ₍1₎ p. 22ᶜᵐ.
First edition published London, 1853.
"Supplementary chapter. By the editor": p. ₍357₎–437.

1. India—Pol. & govt.—1765–   2. India—History, Military. 3. India—Hist.—British occupation, 1765–   I. Napier, Sir William Francis
Patrick, 1785–1860, ed. II. Title.

Library of Congress   DS446.5.N3   S—11948

NN   0016375   DLC NcD MH CU WaU KMK NN

Napier, Maj.-Gen. *Sir* **Charles James,** 1782–1853.
—— Defects, civil and military, of the Indian
government. Ed. by Lieut.-Gen. Sir W. F.
P. Napier. 3 ed. London, 1854. 8°.   8454

NN   0016376   MdBP

DS446
.5
.N3
1857   **Napier,** *Sir* **Charles James,** 1782–1853.

Defects, civil and military, of the Indian
government. 4th ed. Edited and with an
introductory pref. written for this edition,
by Sir W. F. P. Napier. London, C. Westerton,
1857.
xii, 437 p. 22cm.
"Supplementary chapter. By the editor": p. 357–437.

1. India—Pol. & govt.—1765–1947. 2. India—
History, Military. 3. India—Hist.—British
occupation, 1765–1947. I. Napier, Sir William
Francis Patrick, 1785–1860, ed.

NN   0016377   ViU

NAPIER, *Sir* CHARLES JAMES, 1782–1853.
An essay on the present state of Ireland, showing
the chief cause of, and the remedy for, the existing
distresses in that country. Dedicated to the Irish
absentee landed proprietors, as proving that, although
their absence is injurious to Ireland, it is not the
primary cause of the sufferings endured by the Irish
people. London, Ridgway, 1839. 70 p. 21cm.
Film reproduction. Negative.
1. Ireland—Hist., 1800–   1850.

NN   0016378   NN NNC

---

624   **Napier,** *Sir* **Charles James,** 1782–1853.
N197   Farewell address to the officers of the army.
re   ₍n.p., 1850?₎
230–242 p. ₍With the author's Remarks on
military law. 1837₎

NN   0016379   CU

NAPIER, *Sir* CHARLES JAMES, 1782–1853.
A letter on the defence of England, by corps of
volunteers and militia. Addressed to the members of
Parliament. London, E. Moxon, 1852. 28 p. 21cm.

Microfiche (neg.) 1 sheet. 11 x 15cm. (NYPL FSN 12,050)

1. Militia—Gt. Br., 1852.   2. Defense—Gt. Br., 1852.
i.m.e. Subs. for copy in   VWZH p.v. 1.

NN   0016380   NN MH CLU PPL

Napier, *Sir* **Charles James,** 1782–1853
Letter to Sir Henry Bunbury, describing
the difficulties of the campaign in Sind.
1845.
₍10₎p.

Manuscript, with typewritten copy.

NN   0016381   OCl

Napier, ₍**Charles James**₎ 1782–1853.
A letter to ... Sir J. Hobhouse ... on the baggage of the
Indian army. *London : E. Moxon,* 1849. ₍1₎, 5–65 pp. 8°.

NN   0016382   NN PPL

Napier, Charles James, 1782–1853.
A letter to Sir J. Hobhouse on the baggage of
the Indian army ... 4th ed. London, 1849.
67 p. 22.5 cm.

NN   0016383   CtY

Napier, *Sir* **Charles James,** 1782–1853.
A letter to the Right Hon. Sir J. Hobhouse ...
on the baggage of the Indian army ... 5th ed.
London, Republished by M. Walbrook, 1880.
67 p. 21 cm. [Binder's title: British India,
v. 7]

NN   0016384   CtY

Napier, *Sir* **Charles James,** 1782–1853, *ed.*
Lights and shades of military life. Ed. by Major-General Sir Charles Napier ... London, H. Colburn, 1840.
₍2₎ v. 20½ᶜᵐ.

Translation by Frederic Shoberl of Alfred de Vigny's Servitude et grandeur militaires (v. 1) and of Elzéar Blaze's La vie militaire sous le premier empire (v. 2)

1. France—Army—Military life. I. Vigny, Alfred Victor, comte de,
1797–1863. Servitude et grandeur militaires. II. Blaze, Elzéar Jean Louis
Joseph, 1786–1848. La vie militaire sous le premier empire. III. Shoberl,
Frederic, 1775–1853, tr. IV. Title.
14–21382 Revised

Library of Congress   U768.N3

NN   0016385   DLC CtY PPL CaBVaU

Napier, Sir Charles James, 1782–1853, ed.
Lights and shades of military life. Ed. by
Major-General Sir Charles Napier... London, H.
Colburn, 1850.
xii, 428p. 23cm. 2d ed.

NN   0016386   PPiU MdBP MiU PPL

Napier, Sir Charles James, 1782–1853.
... Papers relating to the resignation of ...
Chas. J. Napier, G.C.B., commander-in-chief
in India
see under title

Napier, *Sir* **Charles James,** 1782–1853.
Records of the Indian command of General Sir Charles
James Napier, g. c. b., comprising all his general orders,
remarks on courts martial, etc. etc., with an appendix,
containing reports of speeches, copies of letters, and
notices of his public proceedings, extracted from contemporaneous prints. Comp. by John Mawson ... Calcutta, R. C. Lepage and company, 1851.
1 p. l., 4, xiv p., 1 l., 244, lix p. front. (port.) 22½ᶜᵐ.
Filled chiefly with the records of more than 200 court-martial trials which
passed under Sir Charles Napier's supervision. cf. Pref.
1. Courts-martial and courts of inquiry—India. I. Mawson, John,
comp. II. Gt. Brit. Army. Courts-martial.
22–6216

Library of Congress   DS477.67.N3

NN   0016388   DLC

Napier, *Sir* **Charles James,** 1782–1853.
Remarks on military law and the punishment of flog-
ging. By Major-General Charles J. Napier ... London,
T. and W. Boone, 1837.
iv, xii, 276 p. 21½ᶜᵐ.

1. Military law—Gt. Brit. 2. Corporal punishment.
15–19533

Library of Congress   UB625 1837

NN   0016389   DLC CtY-L MdBP NIC PP

VOLUME 405

Napier, *Sir* Charles James, 1782–1853.
William the Conqueror. A historical romance. By Gen. Sir Charles Napier ... Posthumous work. Lieut.-Gen. Sir William Napier, K. C. B., editor. London, New York, G. Routledge & co., 1858.
xi, 465 p. 18ᶜᵐ.

1. William, the Conqueror, king of England, 1027?–1087—Fiction. I. Napier, Sir William Francis Patrick, 1785–1860, ed.

Library of Congress   PZ3.N162W   7–23116†

NN 0016390   DLC CtY PPL MB NjP

Napier, Charles Ottley Groom.
See
Groom Napier, Charles Ottley, b. 1839.

---

*Napier, Claude, 1869–   **joint tr.**
Victorin, Harald, 1889–   FOR OTHER EDITIONS SEE MAIN ENTRY
The Eaglet, by Captain Harald Victorin. London, L. Dickson, limited, 1933.

---

*Napier, Claude, 1869–   joint tr.
Åkerman, Johan, 1896–
Economic progress and economic crises, by Johan Åkerman, PH. D. Translated by Elizabeth Sprigge and Claude Napier. London, Macmillan and co., limited, 1932.

Napier, Claude, 1869–   joint tr.
Geijer, Erik Gustaf, 1783–1847.
... Erik Gustaf Geijer: Impressions of England, 1809–1810; compiled from his letters and diaries. With an introduction by Anton Blanck. translated by Elizabeth Sprigge and Claude Napier ... London, J. Cape ₁1932₁

---

*Napier, Claude, 1869–   joint tr.
Böök, Fredrik, 1883–
An eyewitness in Germany, by Fredrik Böök; translated from the Swedish by Elizabeth Sprigge and Claude Napier. London, L. Dickson, limited ₁1933₁

D415   Napier, Claude, 1869–   tr.   FOR OTHER EDITIONS SEE MAIN ENTRY
.P62
1938a   Posse, Amelie, 1884–
... Further. London, G. Routledge & sons, ltd. ₁1938₁

Napier, Claude, joint tr.
Hagberg, Knut Hjalmar, 1900–
Kings, Churchills and statesmen; a foreigner's view, by Knut Hagberg; translated from the Swedish by Elizabeth Sprigge & Claude Napier. London, John Lane; New York, Dodd, Mead and company ₁1929₁

Napier, Claude, 1869–   joint tr.
Edqvist, Dagmar.
The marriage of Ebba Garland, by Dagmar Edqvist; translated from the Swedish by Elizabeth Sprigge & Claude Napier. London, L. Dickson, limited, 1933.

Napier, Claude, 1869–   joint tr.
Haslund-Christensen, Henning, 1896–   FOR OTHER EDITIONS SEE MAIN ENTRY
Men and gods in Mongolia (Zayagan) by Henning Haslund ... translated from the Swedish by Elizabeth Sprigge and Claude Napier; with 57 illustrations and a map. New York, E. P. Dutton & co., inc. ₁*1935₁

---

*Napier, Claude, 1869–   joint tr.
Gudmundsson, Kristmann, 1902–   FOR OTHER EDITIONS SEE MAIN ENTRY
... Morning of life; translated from the Norwegian by Elizabeth Sprigge and Claude Napier. Garden City, N. Y. Doubleday, Doran & company, inc., 1936.

Napier, Claude, 1869–   tr.
Gustaf-Janson, Gösta.   FOR OTHER EDITIONS SEE MAIN ENTRY
The old man's coming, by Gustaf Janson. London, L. Dickson & Thompson, ltd. ₁1936₁

CT174   Napier, Claude, 1869–   joint tr.
.H33
Hagberg, Knut Hjalmar, 1900–
Personalities and powers, by Knut Hagberg. Translated from the Swedish by Elizabeth Sprigge & Claude Napier. London, John Lane ₁1930₁

DS793   Napier, Claude, 1869–   joint tr.
.G6H43
Hedin, Sven Anders, 1865–
Riddles of the Gobi desert, by Sven Hedin; with 24 illustrations; translated from the Swedish by Elizabeth Sprigge and Claude Napier. New York, E. P. Dutton & company, 1933.

Napier, Claude, joint tr.
1869–
Hoel, Sigurd, 1890–
Sinners in summertime, a novel by Sigurd Hoel, translated from the Norwegian by Elizabeth Sprigge and Claude Napier. New York, Coward-McCann, inc., 1930.

PZ3   Napier, Claude, 1869–   joint tr.
.P4415
St   Petersen, Nis, 1897–1943.
... The street of the sandalmakers; a tale of Rome in the time of Marcus Aurelius; translated from the Danish by Elizabeth Sprigge and Claude Napier. New York, The Macmillan company, 1933.

Napier, Claude, 1869–   joint tr.
Haslund-Christensen, Henning.
Tents in Mongolia (Yabonah) adventures and experiences among the nomads of Central Asia, by Henning Haslund; translated from the Swedish by Elizabeth Sprigge and Claude Napier; with 6. .lates and a map. New York, E. P. Dutton & co., inc. ₁*1934₁

Napier, Claude, 1869–   tr.
Bergman, Hjalmar Fredrik Elgerus, 1883–1931.
... Thy rod and thy staff, translated from the Swedish by Claude Napier. London ₁etc.₁ J. Cape ₁1937₁

Napier, Claude, 1869–   tr.   FOR OTHER EDITIONS SEE MAIN ENTRY
Wøller, Johan, 1878–
... Zest for life; recollections of a philosophic traveller; translated from the Danish by Claude Napier. New York, A. A. Knopf, 1937.

F869   Napier, Claude E
K6N3   Knights Ferry, gateway to Mother Lode. ₁1st ed. Oakdale, Calif., Printed by Oakdale Leader, c1949₁
75 p. illus. 22cm.

NN 0016409   CU–B

Napier (D.) & son, ltd.
Instruction book for Napier 12-cylinder aero engine. 1928.

NN 0016410   WaS

Napier, D., & son, ltd.
... Instruction book for Napier 12-cylinder aero engine, series XI. type (known as the "lion" in the Royal air force) ... Acton, London, D. Napier & son. lᵗᵈ. ₁1930?₁
231 p. incl. illus., plates (part fold.) fold. pl. 18½ᶜᵐ.
At head of title: Second edition (revised)
Most of the plates numbered as leaves.

1. Aeroplanes—Motors.

Library of Congress   TL703.N3A3 1930   33–14188
₍2₎   [621.4387] 629.13435

NN 0016411   DLC

Napier (D.) & son, ltd.
Napier aero engines. 1926.

NN 0016412   WaS

Napier, D., & son ltd.
... Napier aero engines ... Moteurs d'aviation Napier ... Motores de aviación modelo Napier ... London, D. Napier & son lᵗᵈ. ₁1928?₁
1 p. l., 2–31 p. 36 pl. 26 x 32½ᶜᵐ.
At head of title: Third edition.
Colored plate mounted on cover.
Most of the plates accompanied by guard sheet with descriptive letterpress.
French, English and Spanish in parallel columns.

1. Aeroplanes. 2. Aeroplanes—Motors. I. Title.

                                32–34710
Library of Congress   TL670.N3   629.13334085

NN 0016413   DLC WaS

D629.183   Napier, D., & son, ltd.
N162   Napier aero engines. London ₁1930?₁
13 p. illus.

1. Aeroplanes – Motors.

NN 0016414   NNC

---

qTL703.N3   Napier (D.) & Son, ltd.
N197so   Some famous air achievements. Quelques fameux exploits de l'air. London ₁1929?₁
28p. plates. 30cm.

Exploits of aeroplanes using Napier engines.
Text in English and French.
DLC: 4 TL 331

1.Aeroplanes. Motors 2.Aeroplane racing I.Title

NN 0016415   CoD WaS DLC–P4 DLC

VOLUME 405

Napier, David Dehane.
David Napier, engineer, 1790–1869 ₍and₎ an autobiographical sketch, with notes ₍by David Bell₎ Glasgow, J. Maclehose, 1912.
135 p. illus. 26 cm.

1. Napier, David, 1790–1869.

VM140.N3N3   62–57454 ‡

NN 0016416   DLC CU DSI NN AU ICJ OrCS CaBVaU

Napier (Duncan). Neurotonics (the art of strengthening the nerves). A new view of health and disease in relation to the nervous system, the influence of mental emotions upon the body and the origin of chronic diseases, with numerous cases and instructions for cure. 32. ed. 96 pp. 8°. London, *Houlston & Stoneman*, 1854.

NN 0016417   DNLM

---

*QP91
N2
1951
Napier, Edward Anthony, 1928–
A study of the effect of dilute hydrochloric acid on the separation of the iron from hemoglobin; a thesis submitted to the Faculty of the Graduate School of Arts and Sciences of the University of Buffalo in partial fulfillment of the requirements for the degree of Master of Arts. Buffalo, 1951.
3p.ℓ.,69 numb.ℓ.   28cm. (Buffalo. University. Masters' theses)
Typewritten   copy (carbon)

NN 0016418   NBuG

Napier, E₍dward Delaval Hungerford Elers₎ 1808–1870.
Excursions along the shores of the Mediterranean. By Lᵗ.-Colonel E. Napier ... London, H. Colburn, 1842.
2 v. fronts. 20ᶜᵐ.

1. Mediterranean Sea—Descr. & trav.   4-21438

Library of Congress   D974.N21

NN 0016419   DLC MdBP MB

Napier, Edward Delaval Hungerford Elers, 1808–1870.
Excursions in Southern Africa, including a history of the Cape Colony, an account of the native tribes, etc., by Lt.-Colonel E. Elers Napier ... London, W. Shoberl, 1849.
2 v. fronts. illus., ports., facsim. 19ᶜᵐ.
Portions of this work originally appeared in the "New monthly magazine". *cf.* Introd.

1. Cape of Good Hope—Hist. 2. Africa, South—Hist.—Kafir wars, 1811–1868. I. Title.
                                5—16923
Library of Congress   DT835.N2

NN 0016420   DLC CtY NN MB NIC NjP PPL

Napier, Edward Delaval Hungerford Elers, 1808–1870.
Excursions in Southern Africa, including a history of the Cape Colony, an account of the native tribes, etc., by Lt.-Colonel E. Elers Napier ... London, W. Shoberl, 1850.
2 v. fronts., illus., ports., facsim. 20ᶜᵐ.

NN 0016421   MB MdBP OCU CtY MBU MH IEN

Napier, Edward Delaval Hungerford Elers, 1808–1870.
The life and correspondence of Admiral Sir Charles Napier, κ. c. b., from personal recollections, letters, and official documents. By Major-General Elers Napier ... London, Hurst and Blackett, 1862.
2 v. fronts. (v. 1, port.) maps. 22ᶜᵐ.

1. Napier, Sir Charles, 1786—1860.

Library of Congress   DA88.1.N2N2
                                5—954

CaBViP
NN 0016422   DLC PU OoxM ViU MdBP ICN NcD CtY MiU

Napier, Edward Delaval Hungerford Elers, 1808–1870.
The linesman; or, Service in the guards and the line during England's long peace and little wars. By Colonel Elers Napier ... London, G. W. Hyde, 1856.
3 v. 18½ᵐᵐ.

1. Gt. Brit.—Army—Military life.   I. Title.
                                44–46352
Library of Congress   PZ3.N1621Li

NN 0016423   DLC ICU DNW

Napier, Edward Delaval Hungerford Elers, 1808–1870.
Memoir of the Elers family, and an account of their connexion with the Hungerfords of Black Bourton Place, Oxfordshire. By Lieut.-General E. Hungerford D. Elers Napier ... London, Printed by Taylor and co., 1870.
23 p. 22½ᵐᵐ.

1. Elers family.   I. Title.
                                17–30476
Library of Congress   CS439.E38

NN 0016424   DLC NN

DT844
.6
.N2
₍**Napier, Edward Delaval Hungerford Elers**₎ 1808–1870.
Past and future emigration; or, The book of the Cape. Ed. by the author of "Five years in Kafirland." London, T. C. Newby, 1849.
₍3₎, vii, 379 p. front. (fold. map) 21ᶜᵐ.

1. Cape of Good Hope—Hist. 2. British in Cape of Good Hope.

NN 0016425   ICU RPB WU

Napier, Edward Delaval Hungerford Elers, 1808–1870.
Reminiscences of Syria and fragments of a journal and letters from the Holy Land. London, T. C. Newby, 1843.
2 v. 21 cm.

1. Syria—Descr. & trav. 2. Palestine—Descr. & trav. 3. Syria—Hist. 4. Turkey—Hist.—1829–1878.
                                48–32551*
DS98.A2N3

NN 0016426   DLC TxU CtY MB MdBP OCH DSI

Napier, Edward Delaval Hungerford Eleres, 1808–1870.
Reminiscences of Syria and the Holy Land. L, Parry, Blenkarn, 1847
2 v.

NN 0016427   MH

Uzn36
I3
840n
Napier, Edward Delaval Hungerford Elers, 1808–1870.
Scenes and sports in foreign lands ...
London, H. Colburn, 1840.
2v. fronts.,plates. 21cm.

NN 0016428   CtY OC1 ICN MdBP PPL WU

GV
1101
N3
HRC
Napier, Edward Delaval Hungerford Elers, 1808–1870.
Wild sports in Europe, Asia, and Africa. Illus. by drawings taken from nature. By Lt.-Colonel E. Napier. In two volumes. London, H. Colburn, 1844.
2v. plates. 20cm.

Inscribed: J.E.R. Oldfield October 1910.

1. Voyages and travels. I. Title.

NN 0016429   TxU NNC MB CtY IU

WC
14568
Napier, Edward Delaval Hungerford Elers, 1808–1870.
Wild sports in Europe, Asia, and Africa. Philadelphia, E. Ferrett, 1846.
224p.   [E. Ferrett & Co.'s Cabinet series of entertaining books. no. 1]

NN 0016430   CtY InU MH NBuG

Napier, Elers
See
Napier, Edward Delaval Hungerford Elers, 1808–1870.

649.1
C115e8
Napier, Elizabeth.
The nursery governess, by Elizabeth Napier, published after her death by her husband, Charles James Napier. London, T. and W. Boone, 1834.
75 p. [with: Cadogan, William. An essay on nursing and the management of children. 1805]

1. Children - Care and hygiene. I. Title.

NN 0016432   WaU

Napier, Mrs. Elizabeth Miriam Squire (Sprigge)
see
Sprigge, Elizabeth, 1900–

₍**Napier, Elma**₎ 1892–
... Duet in discord. London, A. Barker, ltd. ₍1936₎
4 p. l., 3–279 p. 19½ᶜᵐ.
Author's pseud., Elizabeth Garner, at head of title.

I. Title.   37–3278
Library of Congress   PZ3.N16224Du

NN 0016434   DLC

₍**Napier, Elma**₎ 1892–
Duet in discord, by Elizabeth Garner ₍pseud.₎ New York, A. A. Knopf, 1937.
5 p. l., 3–230 p., 1 l. 21ᶜᵐ.
"First American edition."

I. Title.   37–12273
Library of Congress   PZ3.N16224Du 2

NN 0016435   DLC IdU OU CLU NN PPL

Napier, Elma, 1892–
Nothing so blue, by Elma Napier ...   Kensington₍, London₎: At the Cayme Press,1927. 186 p., 1 l.   8°.
Reprinted in part from the Manchester Guardian.
Mark of the Cayme Press on last leaf.
Contents: Les iles sous le vent. Indo-Chine. Queensland. Backwards and forwards.

362701A. 1. Australasia—Descr.   and trav. 2. Title.
N.Y.P.L.   July 6, 1928

NN 0016436   NN NcD

Napier, Elma, 1892–
Winter is in July. London, Cape ₍1949₎
239 p. 21 cm.
Continuation of the author's autobiography Youth is a blunder.

I. Title.
PR6027.A59Z53   828.91   50–21025

NN 0016437   DLC OrCS

VOLUME 405

Napier, Elma, 1892–
Youth is a blunder, by Elma Napier... London, J. Cape ₁1948₎ 224 p. 21cm.

NN 0016438 NN

Napier, Ernest Saxon, 1891–
The German credit problem, a plea for simple and effective control, by E. Saxon Napier. London, London general press ₁1931₎
43 p. 21½ᶜᵐ.

1. Credit. 2. Finance—Germany. ₍2. Germany—Finance₎ ɪ. **Title.**
Agr 32–535
Library, U. S. Dept. of Agriculture 284N16

NN 0016439 DNAL NN

Napier, Eva Maria Louisa (Macdonald) *lady,* 1846–
Can man put asunder? By Lady Napier of Magdala ... London, J. Murray, 1911.
vi, 305 p. 19½ᶜᵐ.

ɪ. Title.

12–22961
Library of Congress PZ3.N1623C

NN 0016440 DLC NN

Napier, Francis, d. 1875.
Notes of a voyage from New South Wales to the north coast of Australia, from the journal of the late Francis Napier. ₍Glasgow? pref. 1876.₎ 96 p. front. (port.), illus., maps, plates. 12°.

Introduction by James Robert Napier.
Notes by Mr. W. Keddie, p. ₍89–₎96.

4458A. 1. Australia.—Explorations. 1867. 2. Natural history, Australia.
3. Keddie, William.
N. Y. P. L. June 14, 1921.

NN 0016441 NN ICN MH

Napier, Francis H.
see Napier, Francis John Hamilton Scott, b. 1850.

Napier, Francis John Hamilton Scott, 1850–
Grenada...
see under Bacon, Edward Denny.

Napier, Francis John Hamilton Scott, 1850–
ed.
Napier, Mark, 1798–1879.
"The Lanox of Auld." An epistolary review of "The Lennox, by William Fraser," by Mark Napier. Edinburgh, D. Douglas, 1880.

4HE **Napier, Francis John Hamilton Scott,**
576 1850–
Saint Vincent; with notes and publishers' prices, by Francis H. Napier and E. D. Bacon. London, S. Gibbons, 1895.
107 p.
(The Stanley Gibbons philatelic handbooks, no. 4)

NN 0016445 DLC-P4 MB OCl CaBVaU

NAPIER, Francis John Hamilton Scott, 1850– .
South Australia. [Handbook of its postal issues.] With notes and publishers' prices.
London, 1894. (7), 135 pp. Plates. [The Stanley Gibbons philatelic handbooks.] 8°.
By Francis H. Napier and Gordon Smith.

NN 0016446 MB OCl

Napier, Francis John Hamilton Scott, 1850–
joint author.
Bacon, Edward Denny.
... The stamps of Barbados, with a history and description of the star-watermarked papers of Messrs. Perkins, Bacon & co. By E. D. Bacon and F. H. Napier. Three sheets of autotype illustrations of stamps, three facsimile reproductions of the star watermarks, an appendix containing copies of original correspondence, etc., and a reference list with the publishers' prices. London, S. Gibbons, limited, 1896.

Microfilm **Napier, Francis Napier,** baron, 1819–1898.
BV-15
Missions: their temporal utility, rate of progress, and spiritual foundation, stated in the addresses of Lord Napier, Canon Lightfoot, and Bishop Kelly, at the annual meeting of the Society for the Propagation of the Gospel, on the 29th April, 1873. London, Macmillan, 1873.

Napier, Francis Napier, baron, 1819–1898.
Notes on modern painting at Naples, by Lord Napier. London, J. W. Parker and son, 1855.
xx, 165, ₍1₎ 17ᶜᵐ.

1. Painting—Naples—Hist. 2. Painters, Italian—Naples. ɪ. Title.
15–12983
Library of Congress ND621.N2N2

NN 0016449 DLC NcU PPL

SPECIAL COLLECTIONS
SELIGMAN
16592 **Napier, Francis Napier,** baron, 1819–1898.
St49 Opening address delivered at the sixteenth annual Congress of the National Association for the Promotion of Social Science, held at Plymouth and Devonport, September, 1872 by Lord Napier and Ettrick ... London ₍Head, Hole & Co.₎ 1872.
29 p. 23 cm.

No. 7 of a volume of pamphlets with main entry Stewart, Charles. Statement as to the mode of erection and tenure of cottages for laborers. Edin- burgh, 1859.

NN 0016450 NNC

Microfilm **Napier, Francis Napier,** baron, 1819–1898.
BV-15
The Value of missions in India, estimated by laymen who have seen them. ₍London, Society for the Propagation of the Gospel in Foreign Parts, 1872?₎

Napier, Francis Patrick
see Napier, Sir William Francis Patrick, 1785–1860.

Napier, Frank.
Curtains for stage settings; a practical guide to their use with the necessary adjuncts, by Frank Napier ... London, F. Muller, ltd. ₍1937₎
x, 146 p. illus. 19 cm.

1. Theaters—Stage-setting and scenery. 2. Drapery. ɪ. Title.
PN2091.S8N27 792 38–3135

NN 0016453 DLC OrU IU PSt OrU GU CaBVaU

Napier, Frank.
Curtains for stage settings; a practical guide to their use with the necessary adjuncts, by Frank Napier ... London, F. Muller, ltd. ₍1949₎
x, 146 p. illus. 19 cm.
"Second edition."

NN 0016454 OrPS LU INS FU TxU OrU

Napier, Frank.
Noises off; a handbook of sound effects, by Frank Napier ... with a foreword by Tyrone Guthrie. London, F. Muller ltd. ₍1936₎
x, 117 p. illus. 19ᶜᵐ.

1. Theaters—Stage-setting and scenery. ɪ. Title.
Library of Congress PN2091.S8N3 37–6716
₍2₎ 792

MtBC CaBVa
NN 0016455 DLC CaBVaU PSt KU NBuU PBm NN MtU

Napier, Frank.
Noises off; a handbook of sound effects, by Frank Napier ... with a foreword by Tyrone Guthrie. London, F. Muller ltd. ₍1945₎
x, 117 p. illus. 19 cm.
"Second edition."

NN 0016456 NSyU TU

Napier, Frank.
Noises off; a handbook of sound effects, by Frank Napier ... with a foreword by Tyrone Guthrie. London, F. Muller ltd. ₍1948₎
x, 117 p. illus. 19 cm.
"Third edition."

NN 0016457 LU NNC GU MiU NcGU NN

Napier, Geoffrey
see
Glemser, Bernard, 1908–

NAPIER, G[eorge] C[ampbell].
Collection of journals and reports received from Capt. G. C. Napier, on special duty in Persia, 1874. London, printed by G.E.Eyre and W. Spottiswoode for Her Majesty's stationery office, 1876.

1.8°. Map.
At head of title-page:- Strictly confidential.

NN 0016459 MH

PR 10
L9 T4 **Napier, George Glen.**
1889 The homes and haunts of Alfred Lord Tennyson, by George G. Napier, 1889.

NN 0016460 CaBVaU

Ex
3955 **Napier, George Glen.**
.831
The homes and haunts of Alfred lord Tennyson. Glasgow, J. Maclehose & sons, 1892.
xvi, 204 p. front., illus. (incl. facsims.) plates, map. 23½ᶜᵐ.

Contains book-plate of Henry Van Dyke.

1. Tennyson, Alfred Tennyson, 1st baron- Homes and haunts.

OCl NFQC TxFTC
NN 0016461 NjP ODW NcD IEdS CtY FMU MdBP MB

VOLUME 405

PR5584 **Napier, George Glen.**
.A1N2   The homes and haunts of Alfred, Lord Tennyson, poet laureate. By George G. Napier, M. A. New York, Macmillan and co., 1892.
    xvi, 204 p. front., illus. (incl. facsims.) plates, ports., map. 23½ᶜᵐ.

    1. Tennyson, Alfred Tennyson, 1st baron, 1809–1892. 2. England—Descr. & trav. 3. Literary landmarks—England.

NN   0016462   ICU CaBVaU OrPR

Napier, George Glen.
    The homes and haunts of Sir Walter Scott, bart., by George G. Napier ... Glasgow, J. MacLehose & sons, 1897.
    xiv, 216 p. front., illus., pl., port., map. 24ᶜᵐ.
    "Five hundred and fifty copies of this book have been printed for sale on Japanese vellum paper."

    Subject entries: Scott, Sir Walter, bart., 1771–1832.
                                   2–12166

    CaBVaU
NN   0016463   DLC PPL IdU TU RPB WU FU MB ScU

Ga
E645   **Napier, George Moultrie,** 1863–1932.
N198a   Address of Geo. M. Napier on the occasion of the dedication of Confederate Monument, Lafayette, Georgia, April 27, 1909. ₍Monroe, Ga., Tribune Print., 1909?₎
    ₍14₎ p. 24cm.

    Monument erected by the Daughters of the Confederacy to the memory of the Confederate soldiers of Walker County, Ga.

NN   0016464   GU

Ga
LB2826   **Napier, George Moultrie,** 1863–1932.
G4N3   The improvement of our schools. ₍Atlanta₎ Published by the Georgia Campaign Committee, 1911.
    12 p. 23cm.

    1. Education - Georgia - Finance. I. Title.

NN   0016465   GU

Napier, George Moultrie, 1863–1932.
    Should the constitution of this state be so amended as to allow municipal corporations to exempt new factories from taxation for a term of years? Paper before the Georgia Bar Association, 1898.

NN   0016466   PU-L

S401
U6A257 **Napier, George S**
no.227   Report to the Government of Israel on fishing methods. Rome, 1954.
    14 p. table. 28 cm. (Report no. 227)
    "T.A. - 287/S/11 Proj. ISR/9"

    1. Fisheries - Israel. (Series: Food and Agriculture Organization of the United Nations. Expanded technical assistance program. FAO report no. 227)

NN   0016467   DI

Napier, George Samuel Frederick, 1862–
    The stamps of the first issue of Brazil. London, Séfi, Pemberton, 1923.
    121 p. illus. 40 plates (in pocket) 27 cm.
    "Limited edition of 200 copies ... No. 22."

    1. Postage-stamps—Brazil.   I. Title.

    HE6185.B7N2   59–58829

NN   0016468   DLC DSI

Napier, Sir George Thomas, 1784–1855.
    The early military life of General Sir George T. Napier, K.C.B., written by himself, edited by his son, Gen. W.C.E. Napier. 2d ed. London, J. Murray, 1886.
    xiii, 253 p. port. 20 cm.

NN   0016469   NcD

Napier, *Sir* George Thomas, 1784–1855.
    Passages in the early military life of General Sir George T. Napier, K. C. B., written by himself, edited by his son, General W. C. E. Napier ... London, J. Murray, 1884.
    xi, ₍1₎, 295, ₍1₎ p. front. (port.) 21ᶜᵐ.

    I. Napier, William Craig Emilius, 1818–1903, ed.   42–11512

    Library of Congress   DA68.22.N26A3

    MdBP NcD CU IaU OCl
NN   0016470   DLC CSt ViU CtY PPL MiU DNW MH InU

Napier, Geraldine
    see
Glemser, Bernard, 1908–

Lilly
PR 5102   ₍NAPIER, HAMPDEN₎
.N 16 O 7   The songs, duets, &c. in The oracle, or, The interrupted sacrifice, a grand opera in two acts, as performed for the first time in this country at the Theatre-Royal English Opera House, on Monday, August 7, 1826 ... London, The Proprietor ₍1826₎
    27 p. 21 cm.

    First edition.
    Bound in   quarter red morocco.

NN   0016472   InU

Napier, Henry Alfred, 1797–1871.
    Historical notices of the parishes of Swyncombe and Ewelme in the county of Oxford. By the Hon. and Rev. Henry Alfred Napier ... Oxford, Printed for the author, by J. Wright, 1858.
    xxi, 454 p. illus., 37 pl. (part col.) 2 plans, geneal. tables (part fold.) 31½ᶜᵐ.

    1. Swyncombe, Eng.—Hist. 2. Ewelme, Eng.—Hist.
                                  3—15700

    Library of Congress   DA690.S99N19

NN   0016473   DLC Vi CtY NcD CU MdBP

Napier, *Hon.* Henry Dundas, 1864–
    The experiences of a military attaché in the Balkans, by Lt.-Col. the Honble. H. D. Napier, C. M. G. London, Drane's ₍1924₎
    293 p. incl. facsim. front., pl., ports., fold. map. 25ᶜᵐ.

    1. European war, 1914–1918—Balkan Peninsula. 2. Balkan Peninsula—Politics.   I. Title.
                                   26–2062

    Library of Congress   D560.N3

    CtY NcD KU MiU NN GU TU
NN   0016474   DLC DNW FTaSU NB MH CtY MBU NNC MnU

Napier, *Hon.* Henry Dundas, 1864–
    Field-Marshal Lord Napier of Magdala, G. C. B., G. C. S. I., a memoir by his son, Lieut.-Colonel Hon. H. D. Napier ... London, E. Arnold & co., 1927.
    xl, 348 p. front. (port.) plates, maps, plan. 22½ᶜᵐ.

    1. Napier, Robert Cornelis Napier, 1st baron, 1810–1890. 2. Gt. Brit.—History, Military—19th cent.
                                  28–7767

    Library of Congress   DA68.32.N3N3

    MB NN
NN   0016475   DLC CtY NcD CaOTP NcU NSyU MiU NjP

Napier, Henry Edward, 1789–1853.
    Florentine history, from the earliest authentic records to the accession of Ferdinand the Third, grand duke of Tuscany. By Henry Edward Napier ... London, E. Moxon, 1846–47.
    6 v. plates, maps, plan. 18ᶜᵐ.

    1. Tuscany—Hist.
                                    4–30778

    Library of Congress   DG736.N19

    MB ViU OU
    WaU OOxM OCl OCl OClW MdBP NIC PHC PP OCU NjP NN
NN   0016476   DLC PV NIC DN CtY WaS WaSpG OKentU

Napier, Henry Edward, 1789–1853.
Napier, *Lady* Sarah (Lennox) Bunbury, 1745–1826.
    The life and letters of Lady Sarah Lennox, 1745–1826, daughter of Charles, 2nd duke of Richmond, and successively the wife of Sir Thomas Charles Bunbury, bart., and of the Hon : George Napier; also a short political sketch of the years 1760 to 1763, by Henry Fox, 1st lord Holland; ed. by the Countess of Ilchester and Lord Stavordale ... London, J. Murray, 1901.

Napier, Henry Edward, 1789–1853.   2544.145.1
    Memoir of Lady Sarah ₍Lennox₎'s early life.
    (In Napier, Lady Sarah Lennox. Life and letters. Vol. 1, pp. 83-96. New York, 1901.)

NN   0016478   MB

Napier, Henry Edward, 1789–1853.
    New England blockaded in 1814; the journal of Henry Edward Napier, lieutenant in H. M. S. Nymphe, edited by Walter Muir Whitehill. Salem, Peabody museum, 1939.
    xxi, 88 p., 1 l. 7 pl., 2 charts (1 fold.) 26ᶜᵐ.
    "Printed for the Peabody museum ... by the Southworth-Anthoensen press, Portland, Maine. The edition consists of sixty copies on Laverstoke rag paper, numbered from 1 to 60, and twelve hundred copies on Sterling antique paper." This copy not numbered.
    1. U. S.—Hist.—War of 1812—Naval operations. 2. U. S.—Hist.—War of 1812—Personal narratives. 3. Nymphe (Frigate)   I. Whitehill, Walter Muir, 1905–   ed.   II. Title.

    Library of Congress   E360.N29   40–4267
    ———— Copy 2.
    Copyright A 137533   ₍8₎   973.5255

    WaSpG WaS KMK MeB MB GU WHi MShM
NN   0016479   DLC MsSM ICN LU PPAmP OCl WaU MH CSmH

Napier, J   M.
    Agriculture for school and farm. vol. 1–   South Carolina ed. by J. M. Napier, W. H. Barton, W. P. Stewart ... ₍Columbia, S. C.₎ 1915–
    v. illus. 23ᶜᵐ.

    1. Agriculture.   I. Barton, Wade Hampton, 1867–   joint author. II. Stewart, William Pliny, 1874–   joint author.

    Library of Congress   S495.N15   16–2265

NN   0016480   DLC

VOLUME 405

Pam.
Coll.
2117
Napier, J   M
Society Hill and some of its contributions
to state and nation. Paper read before the
Darlington County Historical Society, May 8,
1947 ... ₍Darlington, S. C., 1947?₎
17 p. 28 cm.

Imperfect copy: p. 17 wanting.
Reproduced from typewritten copy.

1. Society Hill, S. C. 2. Darlington
county, S. C.

NN 0016482   NcD

HX948
N36
Napier, J   P   , 1913-
A survey of the Japan communist party.
Tokyo, Japan, Nippon Times ₍1952₎
66p. 21cm.

1. Communism. Japan

NBC NN MiU MH MiD InU
NN 0016483   IaU OrU AAP NNC PV KU TxU WaU ICU NIC

Napier, James, 1810–1884.
The ancient workers and artificers in metal, from references
in the Old Testament, and other ancient writings. By James
Napier ... London, Simpkin, Marshall, and co.; ₍etc., etc.₎
1856.
viii, 176 p. 17½ᵐ.

1. Metallurgy—Hist. 2. Bible—Metallurgy. ɪ. Title.
41–42104
Library of Congress   TN616.N3

NN 0016484   DLC CtY CU NIC

Napier, James, 1810–1884.
Chemistry applied to dyeing. By James Napier ... Philadelphia, H. C. Baird, 1853.
xv, ₍25₎–429 p. illus. 19½ᵐ.

Glasgow edition (R. Griffin & company) has title: A manual of the art
of dyeing.

1. Dyes and dyeing—Chemistry.
42–41601
Library of Congress   TP897.N2 1853 a

NN 0016485   DLC IU PPWI PPL MiU MH NN ICRL

398.341
N162f
1879
Napier, James, 1810–1884.
Folk lore: or, superstitious beliefs in
the West of Scotland within this century.
Showing the probable relation of the modern
festivals of Christmas, May Day, St. John's
Day, and Halloween, to the ancient sun and
fire worship. Paisley, Alex Gardner,
1879.
142p. 20cm.

1. Folk-lore. Scotland. 2. Holidays.
3. Superstition. I. Title.

NN 0016486   KU

Napier, James, 1810–1884
Folk; or, Superstitious beliefs in the
west of Scotland within this century, with an
appendix shewing the probable relation of the
modern festivals of Christmas, May day, St. John's
day, and Halloween to ancient sun and fire worship. vii,(1),190p. Paisley, A. Gardner, 1879.

OCU PU CU OKentU NRU OC1 MH NN ICJ MiU ICU NjP
NN 0016487   OC1 WaU ICN DLC MdBP WaS NcD CtY NIC

Napier, James, 1810–1884.   623.09261 N16
⁴⁰⁰⁶⁸ Life of Robert Napier of West Shandon, chevalier of the Legion
of Honour; knight commander of the Order of the Dannebrog;
president of the Mechanical Engineers. By James Napier, F.R.S.E.
... . Edinburgh and London, W. Blackwood and Sons, 1904.
xiv, 267 p. 31 pl., 7 ports. incl. front., 1 plan. 23ᶜᵐ.

NN 0016488   ICJ IdU OrCS CtY CU MiDW NcD MiD

667.2
N162m
Napier, James, 1810–1884.
A manual of dyeing receipts for general
use, with numerous samples of dyed cloth
and silk. 2d ed., rev. and enl. London,
R. Griffin, 1858.
88p. illus.

1. Dyes and dyeing. I. Title.

NN 0016489   PP NN RPB

Napier, James, 1810–1884.   667.2
N500
A manual of dyeing and dyeing receipts, comprising a system
of elementary chemistry, as applied to dyeing, with receipts
for the general reader for dyeing any colour on cotton, silk, and
wool, with coloured pattern of cloth of each fabric, by James
Napier ... Third edition. London, C. Griffin and Co., 1875.
xxviii, 420 p. incl. illus. (incl. mounted col. samples) tables. 22ᵐ.

"Glossary of technical terms used in the dye-house, with the chemical names":
p. ₍413₎–416.

NN 0016490   ICJ ICRL NIC ICU TU NcRS PPPCPh

Napier, James, 1810–1884.
A manual of electro-metallurgy: including the applications
of the art to manufacturing processes. By James Napier ...
London, J. J. Griffin & co. and Glasgow, R. Griffin & co., 1851.
xii, 142 p. illus., diagrs. 19ᵐ. (Added t.-p.: Encyclopedia metropolitana: or, System of universal knowledge ... 2d ed. rev. 2d division.
Applied sciences)

1. Electroplating.
TS670.N3 1851   47–33369

NN 0016491   DLC

Napier, James, 1810–1884.
A manual of electro-metallurgy: including the
applications of the art to manufacturing processes. By James Napier ... 2d ed., rev. and
enl. Illustrated by engravings. London, John
Joseph Griffin and co; and Glasgow, Richard
Griffin & co. 1852.
xii, 152 p. illus. 19cm. (Added t.-p.: Encyclopaedia metropolitana: or, System of universal knowledge ...
on a methodical plan projected by Samuel Taylor Coleridge.
2d ed. rev. 2d division. Applied sciences ₍14₎)
1. Electrometallurgy. I. Ser.

NN 0016492   ViU PPF NN NWM Wa

Napier, James, 1810–1884.
A manual of electro-metallurgy; including
the applications of the art to manufacturing
processes. From the second London ed., rev.
& enl. Philadelphia, H.C. Baird, 1853.
356 p.

NN 0016493   NBuU NN OU PPL PPWI IU NcU

Napier, James, 1810–1884.
Manual of electro-metallurgy, with
the applications of the art to
manufacturing processes. ed. 2.
London, 1857.

NN 0016494   ODW

NAPIER, JAMES, 1810–1884.
A manual of electro-metallurgy: including the applications of the art to manufacturing processes. By James
Napier... Fourth edition, revised and enlarged. Illustrated
by engravings. London [etc.] R.Griffin and Co., 1860.
vi, 166 p. incl. tables. illus. 19cm.

1. Electrometallurgy, 1860.

NN 0016495   NN MH MiD CU

Napier, James, 1810–1884.   537.85 M700
⁴³⁷¹ A manual of electro-metallurgy : including the application of the
art to manufacturing processes. Fourth American, from the
fourth London edition, revised and enlarged. vi,[2],489–639 p.
il. O. Philadelphia: H. C. Baird, pref. 1867.
Reprinted from Byrne, Oliver. The practical metal worker's assistant. 1864.

NN 0016496   ICJ OrU PPF

671
N15m
1868
Napier, James, 1810–1884.
A manual of electro-metallurgy: including the
application of the art to manufacturing processes. By James Napier ... 4th American, from the
4th London ed., rev. and enl. ... Philadelphia,
H. C. Baird, 1868.
vi p., 1 l., 489-639p. illus. 24cm.
"Reprinted from ... Byrne's Practical metal worker's assistant."- Publisher's note.
"Works published on electro-metallurgy": p.508.

1. Electroplating.

NN 0016497   IU NjP CtY ICJ CSt PPF

NAPIER, JAMES, 1810–1884.
A manual of electro-metallurgy: including the applications of the art to manufacturing processes. By James
Napier... Fifth edition, revised and enlarged. With illustrations. London: C.Griffin and Co., 1876.   xiii, 216 p.
incl. tables. illus. 18½cm.

NN 0016498   NN CtY NjP PPF MiU NNC WvED

Napier, James, 1810–1884.
A manual of the art of dyeing. By James Napier ...
Glasgow, R. Griffin & company; ₍etc., etc.₎ 1853.
xvi. 405 p. illus. 20ᵐ.

1. Dyes and dyeing. ɪ. Title.
17–29404
Library of Congress   TP897.N2

NN 0016499   DLC

Napier, James, 1810–1884.
Manufacturing arts in ancient times, with special reference to Bible history. By James Napier ... London,
Hamilton, Adams, & co.; ₍etc., etc.₎ 1874.
v p., 1 l., 367 p. 20ᵐ.

1. Bible—Antiq. 2. Industrial arts—Hist.
17–10927
Library of Congress   T16.N18

NN 0016500   DLC PPFr OC1 MWA OU ICJ DNLM MdBP LU

Napier, James, 1810–1884.
Manufacturing arts in ancient times, with special reference to Bible history. By James Napier ... Paisley,
A. Gardner, 1879.
iv, ₍iii₎–v p., 1 l., 367 p. 20ᵐ.

1. Bible—Antiq. 2. Industrial arts—Hist.
5–4704
Library of Congress   T16.N2

NN 0016501   DLC N ScU PP OC1 CaBVaU WaS

VOLUME 405

DA890
.G5N3
Napier, James, 1810-1884.
   Notes and reminiscences relating to
Partick.   Glasgow, Hugh Hopkins, 1873.
   2 p. ℓ., ix ₍1₎ 270 p. front.,plates,maps
(1 fold.) coat of arms. 21 cm.

   Partick was a former burgh of Lanark
County, Scotland; now a part of Glasgow.

   1. Glasgow--Hist. 2. Partick, Scot.--Hist.
I. Title.

NN   0016502   T MH

Napier, James, 1810-1884.
   The practical metal-worker's assistant...
      see under Byrne, Oliver, ed.

Napier, James, 1810-1884.
   A system of chemistry applied to dyeing. By James
Napier, F. C. S. A new and thoroughly rev. ed., completely
brought up to the present state of the science, including
the chemistry of coal tar colors. By A. A. Fesquet ...
With an appendix on dyeing and calico printing as shown
in the Universal exposition, Paris, 1867 ... Philadelphia,
H. C. Baird, 1869.
   xvi, ₍17₎-422 p. incl. tables. diagrs. 24ᵐ.

   1. Dyes and dyeing.   I. Fesquet, A. A., ed.
                                        8--28457

   Library of Congress   TP897.N21

NN   0016504   DLC NcRS MdBP NRCR OC1 ICJ ICRL

M815.4   Napier, J ames C.
N16d   Discussion of national questions, by Hon. J.
          C. Napier... Decided views on financial matters
          and operation of Dingley law. The Spanish-
          American war and its results... Nashville, Tenn.
          National Baptist publishing board, 1898.

          21p. port. 22cm.

NN   0016505   DHU

Napier, James Joseph, 1907-
   The law of valuation (Northern Ireland and Irish free state)
by James J. Napier ... and Herbert A. McVeigh ... Belfast,
T. H. Jordan, 1935.
   3 p. l., vi, 176 p. 21¾ᵐ.

   1. Assessment—Northern Ireland. 2. Assessment—Irish free state. 3.
Taxation—Northern Ireland—Law. 4. Taxation—Irish free state—Law.
I. McVeigh, Herbert Andrew, 1908-   joint author. II. Title.
                                            36-21266
   Library of Congress   HJ3464.I 7N3
                                ₍2₎   336.29

NN   0016506   DLC CtY MH-L

Napier, James Murdoch.
   Inspection of European mints. Report by James M. Napier,
engineer appointed by the lords commissioners of Her Britannic
Majesty's Treasury.   London: W. Clowes & Sons, 1870.   33 p.
8°.

1. Mints. 2. Great Britain. Treasury.
N. Y. P. L.   May 11, 1927

NN   0016507   NN

Napier, James Patton.
   Common stocks as investments for life insurance
companies. Phil, 1931.
   90 p.

NN   0016508   PU

Napier, James Robert, 1821-1879.
   On a formula expressing a more uniform method of voting
at joint-stock companies' meetings than that of the act 19 and 20
Victoria, cap. 47.   By James R. Napier ... ₍Glasgow? 1858₎
   2 p. fold. pl. 22ᵐ.

   Caption title.
   From the Transactions of the Philosophical society of Glasgow, February, 1858.

   1. Corporation law—Gt. Brit.
                                            7-26680
   Library of Congress   HD2743.N2

NN   0016509   DLC

VM751
.N19
Napier, James Robert, 1821-1879.
   On sections of least resistance for ships of
limited breadth and limited draft of water. By
James Robert Napier. Read before the Glasgow
philosophical society, Dec. 17, 1862.
[Glasgow, 1862]

NN   0016510   DLC

Napier, James Robert, 1821-1879.
   ... On ships' lights. By Mr. James R. Napier, F. R. S.
Read before the institution, 28th October, 1868 ... Glasgow, Printed by W. Munro, 1868.
   cover-title, 11 p. 3 pl. (2 fold., 1 col.) 22ᵐ.

   At head of title: Institution of engineers in Scotland ...
   "Reprinted from the Transactions of the institution by permission of
the council."

   1. Ships' lights.
                                            18-4221
   Library of Congress   VM815.N18

NN   0016511   DLC

Napier, James Robert, 1821-1879.
   On the most profitable speed for a fully laden cargo
steamer for a given voyage. By Mr. James R. Napier.
Read before the Philosophical society of Glasgow, November 29, 1865. ₍Glasgow, Bell and Bain, printers, 1865₎
   6 p. 21½ᵐ.
   Caption title.

   1. Navigation. 2. Steamboats.
                                            16-19364
   Library of Congress   VK545.N3

NN   0016512   DLC

Napier, James Robert, 1821-1879.
   ... Papers by Mr. James R. Napier ... Read before the
Institution ₍of engineers in Scotland₎ 23rd December, 1868.
And 17th February, 1869. Reprinted from the Transactions
of the institution by permission of the council. Glasgow,
Printed by W. Munro, 1869.
   cover-title, 7, 4, 5 p. illus, fold. pl. 22 cm.

   CONTENTS.—Remarks on Mr. Hoey's paper "On water distribution
and the regulation of the supply."—On Boussard and Bariquand's
"moderateur parabolique," and Morton's "governor."—On Wollaston's
pressure gage.
   1. Water—Distribution. 2. Governors (Steam-engine) 3. Ventila-
tion.
      TA7.N21   5-36698

NN   0016513   DLC

Napier, James R₍obert₎ 1821-1879.
   Papers on the Balancing of a steam saw, Memoir of the
late David Elder, esq., and on a Rule for calculating the
displacement of ships. By Jas. R. Napier. (Reprinted
from the Transactions of the Institution by permission
of the council.) Glasgow, Printed by W. Munro, 1866.
   8, 14, 5 p. illus, diagrs. 21½ᵐ.

   1. Mechanical engineering—Addresses, essays, lectures. 2. Elder, David,
·1785-1866.
                                            6-24304†
   Library of Congress   TJ7.N19

NN   0016514   DLC

Napier, James Robert, 1821-1879.
   ... Remarks on the 3rd, 13th, and 14th articles of the
Admiralty regulations for preventing collisions at sea.
By Jas. R. Napier ... Received and read 27th November,
1867. ₍Glasgow, 1867₎
   6 p. fold. col. pl. 22ᵐ.
   From the Transactions of the Institution of engineers in Scotland.

   1. Collisions at sea—Prevention.
                                        CA 17-2245 Unrev'd
   Library of Congress   VK373.N2

NN   0016515   DLC

Napier, James Robert, 1821-1879, joint author.

Watts, Isaac, d. 1876.
   Shipbuilding, theoretical and practical. Illustrated by a
series of engravings, from drawings furnished by some of the
most eminent British shipbuilders. By Isaac Watts ... W. J.
M. Rankine ... Frederick K. Barnes ... James Robert Napier
... Corresponding and general editor, W. J. Macquorn Rankine ... London ₍etc.₎, W. Mackenzie, 1866.

Napier, John, 1550-1617.
   Arcanvm svppvtationis arithmeticae: quo doctrina & praxis sinvvm ac triangvlorvm mirè abbre-
uiatur. Opvs ovriosis omnibvs, geometris praesertim,& astronomis vtilissimvm. Inventore,nobilis-
simo barone Merchistonio ... Lvgdvni, apud I.
A. Hvgvetan, & M. A. Ravaud, M. DC. LVIII.
   4 p.ℓ.,56 p.; ₍9₎₁ p.; 62 p., 1 ℓ. diagrs. 21½ᶜᵐ.
   Title vignette (printer's device)
   All after the 4 prelim. leaves is identical with the U.
of M.copy of the author's "Logarithmorvm canonis descriptio ... Lvgdvni, apud Barth.Vincentium, M.DC.XX." in every
detail except the location of the "Extraict du priuilege
du roy" (leaf at end) and the date (31.mars 1620) given

in the colophon beneath it.
   ₍Part 2₎ has special t.-p.: Seqvitvr tabvla canonis
logarithmorvm seu arithmeticarvm svppvtationvm. S'en-
suit l'indice du canon des logarithms ... Lvgdvni,
apud Barthol.Vincentivm ₍1620₎
   ₍Part 3₎ lacks p.₍1₎-4,including special t.-p.:
Mirifici logarithmorvm canonis constrvctio; et eorvm
ad natvrales ipsorum nvmeros habitudines; vna cvm appendice,de alia eâque praestantiore logarithmorum specie condenda. Quibus accessere propositiones ad trian-
gvla sphaerica faciliv₍s₎ calculo resolvenda: vnA cvm

annotationibus aliquot doctissimi d.Henrici Briggii in
eas,e memoratam appendicem. Authore & inuentore Ioanne
Nepero,barone Merchistonii,&c. ... Lvgdvni, apud Bar-
tholomaeum Vicentium, M. DC. XX.

   1.Logaritims. 2.Trigonometry. I.Briggs,Henry,1561-
1630. II.Title.

NN   0016519   MiU

Napier, John, 1550-1617.
   The bloody almanack ... 1643
      see under Booker, John, 1603-1667.

Napier, John, 1550-1617.
   The bloudy almanack ... 1647
      see under Walker, Henry, called the
Ironmonger, supposed author.

Napier, John, 1550-1617, supposed author.
   The bloudy almanack. 1651
      see under title

VOLUME 405

Napier, John, 1550–1617.
The construction of the wonderful canon of logarithms by John Napier, baron of Merchiston translated from Latin into English with notes and a catalogue of the various editions of Napier's works, by William Rae Macdonald, F. F. A. Edinburgh and London, W. Blackwood and sons, 1889.

4 p. l., ₍xii₎–xix, 169 p. 27 x 21ᶜᵐ.
"A catalogue of the works of John Napier of Merchiston, to which are added a note of some early logarithmic tables and other works of interest, compiled by William Rae Macdonald": p. ₍101₎–169.
1. Logarithms. 2. Trigonometry. 3. Napier, John, 1550–1617 – Bibl.
I. Macdorald, William Rae, 1843–

8–11763

Library of Congress   QA33.N46

OCU MiU OO NN MH
NN 0016523   DLC MiEM InU TU CtY NcD MeB CU PBm

Napier, John, 1550–1617.
De arte logistica Joannis Naperi Merchistonii baronis libri qui supersunt. Edinburgi, 1839.

7 p. l., ₍iii₎–xciv p., 2 l., ₍3₎–162 p. front. (port.) illus. (facsima.) pl. 27 x 21½ cm. ₍Maitland club. Publications. no. 47₎
Title vignette.
Half-title preceding text: The Baron of Merchiston his booke of arithmeticke and algebra. For Mr. Henrie Briggs, professor of geometrie at Oxforde.
Edited by Mark Napier.
Published also as no. 62 of the Bannatyne club publications.
1. Mathematics—Early works to 1800. 2. Arithmetic—Before 1846. 3. Algebra. I. Napier, Mark, 1798–1879, ed. II. Title.

DA750.M3 no. 47   18—14262

AAP
NN 0016524   DLC NcD NIC MH WU CLU CaBVaU InU ICJ

Napier, John, 1550–1617.
De arte logistica Joannis Naperi Merchistonii baronis libri qui supersunt. Edinburgi ₍Printed by Ballantyne and Hughes₎ 1839.

4 p. l., ₍iii₎–xciv p., 2 l., ₍3₎–162 p. front. (port.) illus. (facsims.) pl. 29 x 23ᶜᵐ.
Title vignette.
Half-title preceding text: The Baron of Merchiston his booke of arithmeticke and algebra. For Mr. Henrie Briggs, professor of geometrie at Oxforde.
Edited by Mark Napier.
Only L copies printed in this form.—Ms. note on flyleaf, signed M. Napier.
Published also as no. 47, and Bannatyne club publications, no. 62.
1. Mathematics — Early works to 1800. 2. Arithmetic — Before 1846. 3. Algebra. I. Napier, Mark, 1798–1879, ed. II. Title.

22–1522

Library of Congress   QA33.N3

OCU
NN 0016525   DLC PU ICN NN IU OCl CU RPB NjP MB

Napier, John, 1550–1617.   510.83 6
A description of the admirable table of logarithmes: with a dec- 103840 laration of the most plentifvl, easy, and ſpeedy vſe thereof in both kindes of trigonometrie, as alſo in all mathematicall calculations. Invented and pvblished in Latin by that Honorable L₍ord₎ Iohn Nepair, Baron of Marchifton, and tranflated into Englifh by the late learned and famous mathematician Edward Wright. With an addition of an instrumentall table to finde the part proportionall, inuented by the tranflator, and defcribed in the end of the booke by Henry Brigs, ... All peruſed and approued by the author, & publiſhed ſince the death of the tranflator. London, Printed by N. Okes, 1616.

₍22₎, 89, ₍90₎, 8 p. 1 fold. diagr. 14¼ᶜᵐ.

NN 0016527   ICU ICJ PPL MWiW-C CU

Napier, John, 1550–1617.
A Description Of The Admirable Table Of Logarithmes: With A Declaration of the most Plentifull, Easie, and Speedy vse thereof in both kinds of Trigonometrie, as also in all Mathematicall Calculations. Inuented and published in Latine by that Honourable Lord Iohn Nepair, Baron of Marchifton, and translated into English by the late learned and famous Mathematician, Edward Wright. With an addition of the Instrumentall Table to finde the part Proportionall, intended by the Translator, and described in the end of the Booke by Henrie Brigs... All perused

and approued by the Authour... London, Printed for Simon Waterson, 1618.   2 p.l., 16 p., 12 l., 89(1) p., 45 l., 8 p.   pl. 15cm. (12°.)

STC 18352.
Preliminary leaf 1 and 1. 1–2 following on p. 16 blank. For full description, cf. A catalogue of the works of John Napier compiled by William Rae Macdonald, p. 144–147.   (In: Napier, John. The construction of the wonderful canon of logarithms. Edinburgh, 1889.)
"An Appendix... shewing the practise of the Calculation of Triangles," 16 p. following t.-p.

249488B. 1. Logarithms. 2. Loga-   rithms—Tables. I. Briggs, Henry, 1561–1630. II. Wright, Edward,   1558?–1615, tr.
N. Y. P. L.   December 13, 1943

NN 0016529   NN DFo InU CtY MiU PU CSmH RPB NjP

Napier, John, 1550–1617.
A Description of the admirable table of logarithmes: with a declaration of the most plentifull, easie, and sppedy vse there-of in both kinds of trigonometry, as also in all mathematicall calculations. Inuented and published in Latine by that Honourable Lord Iohn Nepair, Baron of Marchiston, and translated into English by the late learned and famous mathematician, Edward Wright. With an addition of the Instrumental table to finde

the part Proportionall, intended by the translator and described in the end of the booke by Henrie Brigs, geometry-reader at Gresham-house in London. All perused and approued by the authour, and published since the death of the translator for the ease of the student.   London, Printed for Simon Waterson, 1618.
16p.   23cm.

Photocopy.

1. Logarithms - Early works to 1800.
I. Wright, Edward, 1558?-1615, tr. II. Title.

NN 0016532   NBuC

Napier, John, 1550–1617.
Een duydelicke verclaringhe vande gantsche Openbaringhe Joannis des Apostels. T'samen ghestelt in twee tractaten: Het eene ondersoeckt ende bewijst de ware verclaringhe der selver. Ende het ander, appliceert ofte voeght, ende eygentse paraphrastischer ende historischer wijse totten text. Wtghegeven by Johan Napier, Heere van Marchistoun, de Jonghe. Nu nieuwelicx obergeset wt d'Engelsche in onse Nederlandsche sprake, door M. Panneel... Middelburgh: Symon Moulert, 1600. 5 p.l., 64 p., 2 l., 237(1) p., 5 l., 1 fold. table. 12° in fours.

Black letter.

T.-p. and 2 following leaves missing. Work begins on recto of 4. leaf: Den Seer Wtnemenden Hooghen ende Machtighen Prince Jacobo de seste Coninck der Schotten ghenade ende vrede, etc.
Title from W. R. MacDonald's Catalogue of... Napier's works, in: J. Napier. The construction of the wonderful canon of logarithms. Edinburgh, 1889. 8°. First Dutch from first English edition.

1. Bible.—New Testament: Revela-   tion. Commentary. 2. Panneel, Michiel, translator. 3. Title.
N. Y. P. L.   October 27, 1914.

NN 0016534   NN

Napier, John, 1550–1617.
Eerste deel vande nievwe telkonst, inhovdende verscheyde manieren van rekenen, waer door seer licht konnen volbracht worden de geometrische ende arithmetische questien. Eerst ghevonden van Ioanne Nepero ... ende uyt het latijn overgheset door Adrianvm Vlack. Waer achter bygevoegt zijn eenige seer lichte manieren van rekenen tot den coophandel dienstigh, leerende alle ghemeene rekeninghen sonder ghebrokens af veerdighen. Mitsgaders nieuwe tafels van interesten, noyt voor desen int licht ghegeven. Door Ezechiel de Decker ... Noch is hier achter byghevoeght de Thiende van Symon Stevin ...

Ter Govde, By Pieter Rammaseyn, 1626.
6 p.l., 308, ₍128₎, 27 p. illus.(diagrs.) tables. 22ᶜᵐ.
Head and tail pieces.
Errors in binding: p.149-150 and 151-152, and p.153-154 and 155-156 reversed.
"Ezechiel de Decker Van coopmans rekeninghen ... ": p.₍149₎-308.
"De thiende. Leerende door onghehoorde lichticheyt alle rekeninghen onder den menschen noodigh vallende,

afveerdighen door heele ghetallen, sonder ghebrokenen. Door Simon Stevin" (27 p. at end) has special t.-p.

1. Calculating-machines. 2. Arithmetic—Before 1846. I. Vlacq, Adriaan, tr. II. Decker, Ezechiel de, fl. 1626-1659. Van coopmans rekeningen. III. Stevin, Simon, 1548-1620. De thiende leerende door onghehoorde lichticheyt. Translation of Rabdologia.

NN 0016537   MiU RPB

Napier, John, 1550–1617.
Illustr. Neperi Scoti Canonis mirifici trigonometrici ... In principio ad dena quaeque secunda, sub finem ad quindena, vicena aut tricena, ex B. Vrsino diductus: et tam ad novam trigonometriae logarithmicae praxin, quàm ad faciliorem & pleniorem Tabb. Rvdolphi astronomicarum vsum compendiosiss. seorsim sic editus à Iacobo Bartschio ... Sagani Silesiorvm, e typographeio Ducali, 1630-31.

₍307₎ p. tables. 15¼ᶜᵐ.
Signatures: A-D⁶, E-O⁸, B-L⁶, M-T⁸, X-Z⁶.
Issued in 3 parts; subtitles vary slightly.

CONTENTS.—Pars I. Canon manvalis logarith- & antilogarithmorvm semicircvli.—Pars II. Canon manvalis differentialium seu mesologarithmorum qvadrantis.—Particvla III. Trichil-hexacosias antilogarithmorum scrvpvlosiorvm.
Pages ₍193₎-307₎ (signatures P-Z) comprise the following works of Jakob Bartsch: Tabvla canonica secundorum mobilivm prosthaphaeretica ... 1631 (signature P), Ioan. Keppleri ... Logarithmorum logisticorum heptacosias quintuplicatae ... 1631 (signatures Q-T), and Tabvlae; sive, Canon manvalis sinvvm logarithmicvs ... 1630 (signatures X-Z)

1. Logarithms. I. Bartsch, Jakob, 1600-1633, ed. II. Ursinus, Benjamin, 1550-1617. III. Rudolff, Christoph, b. ca. 1550. IV. Title: Canonis mirifici trigonometrici.

NN 0016540   MiU

Napier, John, 1550–1617.
Logarithmorum canonis descriptio; seu Arithmeticarum supputationum mirabilis abbreviatio. Eiusque usus in utraque trigonometria ut etiam in omni logistica mathematica, amplissimi, facillimi & expeditissimi explicatio, Authore ac inventore Ioanne Nepero ... [Printer's mark] Lugduni, Apud. Barth. Vincentium ₍1619₎-20.
2 v. in 1., tables. diagrs. 21 cm.

NN 0016541   RPB

QA33 Napier, John, 1550–1617.
.N18   Logarithmorum canonis descriptio; sev, Arithmeticarvm svppvtationvm mirabilis abbreviatio. Eiusque vsus invtraque trigonometria vt etiam in omni logistica mathematica, amplissimi, facillimi & expeditissimi explicatio. Authore ac inuentore Ioanne Nepero ... Lvgdvni, apud B. Vincentium, 1620.
2 v. in 1. diagrs. 20ᶜᵐ.
Title in red and black within double line border.
Vol. 2 "Tabula" has special t.-p.

1. Logarithms. 2. Trigonometry.

NN 0016542   ICU NN CU MiU MH MB WU NN CtY-M DN-Ob

Napier, John, 1550–1617.
A mathematicall manuel
see under Dansie, John.

Napier, John, 1550–1617.
Mirifici logarithmorum canonis descriptio, ejusque usus, in utraque trigonometria; ut etiam in omni logistica mathematica, amplissimi, facillimi, & expeditissimi explicatio. Authore ac inventore, Ioanne Nepero, barone Merchistonii &c. Scoto. Edinbvrgi, Ex officinâ A. Hart, 1614.
4 p. l., 57, ₍9₎ p. diagrs. 19 x 14ᶜᵐ.
Title within ornamental border.

1. Logarithms. 2. Trigonometry.

4-5707

Library of Congress   QA33.N44

NN PPL CtY MiU PBL InU NNC CtNowaB
NN 0016544   DLC NIC ICU TxU MWiW-C RPB CSmH MB

STC Napier, John, 1550–1617.
18350   Mirifici logarithmorum canonis descriptio ... Edinburgi, excudebat Andreas Hart, 1619.

Pt.1: ₍A₎², A-H⁴, I¹, a-1⁴, m¹. Pt.2: A-H⁴, I². (Pt.1 ₍A₎1, blank, lacking. Pt.2: gatherings C-G lacking; gatherings H-I misbound after pt.1 c4.) 4to. diagrams
Contains "Admonitio" on pt.1, sig. m1v.
Each part has a separate title-page. Part 1, sig. A1r. reads: Mirifici logarithmorum canonis descriptio ... Edinburgi, ex officinâ Andreae

Continued in next column

VOLUME 405

Continued from preceding column

Hart, 1614. This part was also published separately and is entered in the STC as 18349a.
Part 2, sig. A1r. reads: Mirifici logarithmorum canonis constructio ... vnà cum Appendice ... Edinburgi, excudebat Andreas Hart, 1619. This part was published after the author's death by his son, Robert Napier.
Napier, The construction ... and A catalogue (1889) pp. 137-141.
Cashel Cathedral   library copy.

NN   0016546   DFo

QA33   Napier, John, 1550-1617.
.N18   Mirifici logarithmorvm canonis constrvctio; et corvm ad natvrales ipsorum numeros habitudines; vna cvm appendice, de alia eâque præstantiore logarithmorum specie condenda. Quibus accessere propositiones ad triangula sphærica faciliore calculo resolvenda: unà cum annotationibus aliquot doctissimi d. Henrici Briggii in eas, & memoratam appendicem. Authore & inuentore Ioanne Nepero ... Lvgdvni, apud B. Vincentium, 1620.
62, [1] p. diagrs. 20cm. [With his Logarithmorvm canonis descriptio. Lvgdvni, 1620]
Title within double line border.
1. Logarithms. 2. Trigonometry.

NN   0016547   ICU MH MB NN NjP WU CU MCM

Napier, John, 1550-1617.
Mirifici logarithmorvm canonis constrvctio; et corvm ad natvrales ipsorum numeros habitudines; vna cvm appendice, de alia eâque præstantiore logarithmorum specie condenda, quibus accessere propositiones ad triangula sphaerica faciliore calculo resolvenda: vnà cum annotationibus aliquot doctissimi D. Henrici Brigii in eas, & memoratam appendicem. Authore & inuentore Ioanne Nepero, barone Merchistonii ... Lvgdvni, apud B. Vincentium, 1620. [Paris, Librairie scientifique A. Hermann, 1895]
62 p., 1 l. diagrs. 24cm.
A facsimile reprint of the second of the Lyons editions described in the Napier tercentenary memorial volume.
Reprodduction of t.p. on inside of back cover: Catalogvs librorvm officinae Elzeviriae ... Lvgdvni Batavorvm, ex officinâ Elzeviriana, 1628.
1. Logarithms. 2. Trigonometry. I. Briggs, Henry, 1561-1630.

NN   0016549   MiU CU

Napier, John, 1550-1617.
Napier tercentenary memorial volume
see under Knott, Cargill Gilston, 1856-1922.

Napier, John, 1550-1617.
Napiers narration
see under title

Case
C   NAPIER, JOHN, 1550-1617.
4799   Ovvertvre de tovs les secrets de l'Apo-
.612   calypse, ov Revelation de s. Iean. En deux traités... Mise en françois par Georges Thomson... Edition 2., amplifiée d'annotations & de quatre harmonies sur l'Apocalypse par le translateur... La Rochelle,N.De La Croix,1605.
[24₃],446(i.e.406),[36₂]p. fold.tab. 18½cm.
Title within ornamental border.
Error in paging: no.401-440 omitted.

NN   0016552   ICN

FR8   Napier, John, 1550-1617.
N19f   Ovvertvre de tovs les secrets de l'Apocalypse ov Revelation de S.Iean ... Par Iean Napeir (c.à.d. Nompareil) sieur de Merchiston: reueuë par lui-mesme. Et mise en françois par Georges Thomson ... Edition troisieme amplifiee d'annotations, & de quatre harmonies sur l'Apocalypse par le translateur ... A La Rochelle,Par Noel de la Croix,1607.
10p.l.,406,[22]p.,3l.,31p. fold.tab. 18cm.
"Qvatre harmonies svr le Revelation de S.Iean ... par G.T.E. 1607", 3l.,31p.at end, has special title-page.

NN   0016553   NNUT

Napier, John, 1550-1617.
Ovvertvre des secrets de l'Apocalypse, ov Revelation de S. Iean. En deux traités: l'vn recherchant & prouuant la vraye interpretation d'icelle: l'autre appliquant au texte ceste interpretation paraphrastiquement & historiquement. Par Iean Napeir ... et mise en françois par Georges Thomson ... Edition seconde, amplifiée d'annotations, & de quatre harmonies sur l'Apocalypse, par le translateur ... La Rochelle, Par les heritiers de H. Haultin, 1603.
16 p.l., 318 p., 15 l.; 4 p.l., 24 p. 2 fold tables. 17.5 cm.

NN   0016554   CtY-M

STC   Napier, John, 1550-1617.
18354   A plaine discouery of the whole Reuelation of Saint Iohn: set downe in two treatises: the one searching and prouing the true interpretation thereof: the other applying the same paraphrastically and historically to the text. Set foorth by Iohn Napeir l. of Marchistoun younger. Wherevnto are annexed certaine oracles of Sibylla, agreeing with the Reuelation and other places of Scripture.
Edinbvrgh,Printed by Robert Walde-graue,printer to the Kings   Majestie.1593.   Cum

priuilegio regali.
7p.l.,269,[11]p. illus.(coat of arms). 19cm.
Title within made-up woodcut border.
Pages 26,107,229 & 258 misnumbered 62,10,239 & 358.
"Faults escaped": recto of 7th prelim. leaf.
Another copy. 19cm.
In this copy   p.107 is correctly numbered.

         WaPS DCU CtY NjPT DFo CU
NN   0016556   MH NN MWiW-C CtY-M MH-AH CSmH MiU

Case
C   NAPIER, JOHN, 1550-1617.
4799   A plaine discoverie of the whole Revelation of
.611   Saint Iohn: set down in two treatises: the one searching and proving the true interpretation thereof: the other applying the same paraphrastically and historicallie to the text... Wherevnto are annexed certaine oracles of Sibylla, agreeing with the Revelation. Newlie imprinted and corrected. [Edinburgh,R.Waldegrave]for T.Norton [London]1594.
[14],269,[11]p. illus.(coat of arms) 19cm.
Head-pieces, initials.
Includes text.
STC 18355.
Bound by J.   Leighton.
Bookplate: Wil-   liam Stirling.

NN   0016557   ICN CSmH MnU MiU CSmH NNUT

AC   Napier, John, 1550-1617.
4   A plaine discoverie of the whole Revelation of Saint Iohn:
E5   set down in two treatises ... by Iohn Napeir ... Wherevnto
Reel   are annexed certaine oracles of Sibylla, agreeing with the
no.   Revelation and other places of Scripture. Newlie imprinted
324   and corrected. [Edinburgh, R. Walde-graue] Printed for Iohn Norton ... 1594.
University microfilms no. 15020 (case 54, carton 324)
Short-title catalogue no. 18355.
1. Bible. N.T. Revelation - Commentaries. 2. Bible. N.T. Revelation - Prophecies.

NN   0016558   MiU WaPS

Napier, John, 1550-1617.
A plaine discovery, of the vvhole Revelation of S. Iohn: set downe in two treatises: the one searching and proving the true interpretation thereof: the other applying the same paraphrasticallie and historicallie to the text. Set foorth by Iohn Napier l. of Marchiston. And now revised, corrected and inlarged by him. With a resolvtion of certaine doubts, mooved by some well affected brethren. Wherevnto are annexed, certaine oracles of Sibylla, agreeing with the Revelation and   other places of Scripture.

London,Printed [by A.Hart in Edinburgh] for Iohn Norton.1611.   Cum privilegio regiae maiestatis.
4p.l.,375p. 18.5cm.
Printer's mark (McK.378) on p.91,366 & 375.
Pages 56,199 & 323 misnumbered 65,19 & 333.
STC 18356a.

       NN NNC NNUT DFo NNG
NN   0016560   MH OkU MHi MH-AH MWiW-C IaU CU MH CtY

Napier, John, 1550-1617.
A plaine discovery of the whole Revelation of Sᵗ. John: set down in two treatises: the one searching and proving the true interpretation thereof: the other applying the same paraphrastically and historically to the text. By John Napier ... With a resolution of certain doubts, moved by some well affected brethren. Wherevnto are annexed certain oracles of Sibylla, agreeing with the Revelation, and other places of Scripture. And also an epistle which was omitted in the last edition. The 5th ed.: cor. and amended. Edinbvrgh, Printed for A. Wilson, 1645.
6 p. l., 244, 32, 31-38 p. 19½cm.
1. Bible. N.T. Reve-   lation—Commentaries. 2. Bible-
Commentaires—N. T.   Revelation. I. Title.
                                        40-23190
Library of Congress   BS2825.A2N3

NN   0016561   DLC IEN CtY DFo CLU-C InU NNUT MWA

Napier, John, 1550-1617.
Rabdologiæ, Sev Nvmerationis Per Virgulas Libri Dvo: Cum Appendice de expeditissimo Mvltiplicationis Promptvario. Quibus accessit & Arithmeticæ Localis Liber vnvs. Authore & Inventore Ioanne Nepero, Barone Merchistonii, &c. Scoto. [Printer's mark] Edinbvrgi, excudebat Andreas Hart, 1617.
6 p. l., 154 p. incl. tables, diagrs. 4 fold. diagr. 15cm.
Signatures: ¶⁶, A-F¹², G⁵.
Contemporary white vellum binding.
1. Calculating-machines. 2. Mathematics — Early works to 1800.
I. Title.
                                        28-13367
Library of Congress   QA75.N27

       ICU ICJ PPAmP NN MB IU
NN   0016562   DLC CtNowaB PBL DFo MH MWiW-C WU

Napier, John, 1550-1617.
Rabdologiæ sev Nvmerationis per virgulas libri duo: cum appendice de expeditissimo mvltiplicationis promptvario. Quibus accessit & arithmeticæ localis liber unus. Authore & inventore Ioanne Nepero, barone Merchistonij, &c. Scoto. Lvgdvni [Batavorvm] Typis P. Rammasenij, 1626. 6 p.l., 139 p., 2 l. diagrs., tables. 14½ x 8½cm. (12°.)
Last two leaves blank.

For authority for imprint, cf. A catalogue of the works of John Napier compiled by William Rae Macdonald. p. 132-133. (In: Napier, John. The construction of the wonderful canon of logarithms. Edinburgh, 1889.)
First published in Edinburgh, 1617 (q. v.).
Imperfect: t.-p. mutilated, last leaf wanting.

1. Napier's bones. 2. Multiplica-   tion. I. Title.   Card revised
N. Y. P. L.   January 31, 1939

NN   0016564   NN

QA33   NAPIER,JOHN,1550-1617.
.N21   Rabdologiæ sev nvmerationis per virgulas libri duo: cum appendice de expeditissimo mvltiplicationis promptvario. Quibus accessit & arithmeticæ localis liber vnus. Authore & inventore Ioanne Nepero... Lvgd.Bata vorvm,typis P.Rammasenij,1628.
[12],139 p. fold.tables,diagrs.(part fold.) 13cm.
1.Mathematics--Early works to 1800. 2.Calculating machines.

NN   0016565   ICU

VOLUME 405

Napier, John, 1550–1617.
... Rabdologiae, sev Numerationis per virgulas libro duo:authore & inventore Joanne Nepero, barone Merchistonii &c. Scoto. Edinburgi, Excudebat Andreas Hart, 1617. [Chicago, 1927.]
cover-tit. [10], 154 p. incl. tables, diagrs. 3 fold. pl. 17cm.
Photostat copy; original in library of Felt and Tarrant Mfg. Co., Chicago.

510.84 28
101390

NN   0016566   ICJ

Napier, John, 1550–1617.
Rabdology, or Calculation by means of virguloe. Two books with an appendix on the short way for multiplication. To which is added one book on local arithmetic, by the author and inventor, Napier, baron of Merchiston, etc., Scotland. Edinburg, Edited by A. Hart, 1617. [Chicago, 1926.]
[1], 154 leaves incl. tables, diagrs. 28cm.
Translated from the Latin by J. Lestrohan.
Typewritten carbon copy.

L510.84 27
106243

NN   0016567   ICJ

Napier, John, 1550–1617.
Raddologia, ouero Arimmetica virgolare in due libri diuisa; con appresso vn' espeditissimo prontvario della molteplicatione, & poi vn libro di Arimmetica locale ... Auttore, & inuentore il baron Giovanni Nepero, tradottore dalla latina nella toscana lingua il cavalier Marco Locatello; accresciute dal medesimo alcune considerationi giouueuoli. Verona, appresso A. Tamo, 1623.
8 p. l., 269, [1] p. incl. fold. pl., tables (2 fold.) diagrs. (3 fold.) 16½cm.
Device of Angelo Tamo on verso of last leaf.
1. Calculating-machines. 2. Mathematics—Early works to 1800.
I. Locatello, Marco, tr. II. Title.

Library of Congress   QA75.N314

44–50857

NN   0016568   DLC NNC CtY NjP ICU CU MiU

Napier, John, 1550–1617.
Rhabdologia neperiana. Das ist / Newe / vnd sehr leichte art durch etliche stäbichen allerhand zahlen ohne mühe / vnd hergegen gar gewiss / zu multipliciren vnd zu dividiren, auch die regulam detri, vnd beyderley ins gemein vbliche radices zu extrahirn: ohne allen brauch des sonsten vb- vnnd nützlichen ein mahl eins / alss in dem man sich leichtlich verstossen kan / erstlich erfunden durch einen vornehmen schottländischen freyherrn herrn Johannem Neperum, herrn zu Merchiston. ¿c. Anjtzo aber auffs kürtzeste / alss jmmer müglich gewesen / nach vorhergehenden gnugsamen probstücken ins deutsche vbergesetzt / durch M. Benjaminem Ursinum. churf. brandenburgischen mathematicum ... Berlin, Gedrukt im Grawen kloster / durch George Rungen / im jahre Christi 1623.
[24] p. 4 pl. 19½cm.
The first book only; contains the method of calculating by rods.
1. Calculating-machines. 2. Mathematics—Early works to 1800.
I. Ursinus, Benjamin, 1550–1617, tr. II. Title.

QA75.N3

24–14810

NN   0016570   DLC

Napier, Sir John,   1550–1617.   No. 3 in *3939.52
Zehntausend Logarithmi, der absolut- oder ledigen Zahlen von I. biss auff 10000. Nach Herrn Johannis Neperi Baronis Merchstenij Art vnd Invention, welche Heinricus Briggius illustrirt, vnnd Adrianus Vlacq augirt, gerichtet. Nürnberg/In Verlegung Wolffgang Endters. M.DC.XXXVII. [103] pp. Tables. 18½ cm., in 4s.

N9793 — Vlacq, Adrian, ed., fl. 1650. — Logarithms. — Briggs, Henry, ed., 1561–1630.

NN   0016571   MB MiU

Napier, John McGuire, 1887–
Agriculture for school and farm. vol. I–   South Carolina ed. by J. M. Napier, W. H. Barton, W. P. Stewart ... [Columbia, S. C.] 1915–
[v. illus. 23cm.

1. Agriculture.   I. Barton, Wade Hampton, 1867–   joint author.   II. Stewart, William Pliny, 1874–   joint author.

Library of Congress   S495.N15

16–2265

NN   0016572   DLC

Napier, John Mellis, 1882–   FOR OTHER EDITIONS SEE MAIN ENTRY

FOR OTHER EDITIONS SEE MAIN ENTRY

Australia. *Royal commission on monetary and banking systems.*
... Report of the Royal commission appointed to inquire into the monetary and banking systems at present in operation in Australia, and to report whether any, and if so what, alterations are desirable in the interests of the people of Australia as a whole, and the manner in which any such alterations should be effected. Canberra, L. F. Johnson, commonwealth government printer [1937]

Napier, John T., tr.

Teaching of the twelve apostles.
The Teaching of the twelve apostles.
(*In* The ante-Nicene fathers ... Buffalo, 1885–97. 26cm. vol. VII (1886) p. [369]–383)

Napier, Sir Joseph, 1804–1882.
Appendix to Napier's Digest of the civil bill and manor court acts, containing the recent statute, with notes and additional decisions.   Dublin, Hodges and Smith, 1836.
176–270 p.   19 cm.   (With Ryan, Richard. A digest of the Irish church temporalities act. 1833)

NN   0016575   PV

Napier, Sir Joseph, bart., 1804–1882.
Argument of Joseph Napier ... House of lords. Viscount Dungannon, appellant, v. Smith, respondent. [Dublin? 1845?]
48 p.   24cm.
Caption title.
Mr. Napier's reply: p. 30–44.
"Papers on legal education": p.[45]–48.
No. 4 of a volume lettered: Pamphlets; law, &c.

NN   0016576   MiU-L

[Napier, Sir Joseph] 1804–1882.
A brief memoir of William John Napier, by his father / ... Printed for his private friends. [London, C. A. Mackintosh, printer] 1876.
66 p. front. (port.) 18½cm.

1. Napier, William John, 1837–1874.   I. Title.

Library of Congress   CT788.N3N3

21–11425

NN   0016577   DLC

Napier, Joseph, 1804–1882.
Church temporalities (Ireland)... L., Seeleys, 1854.
44 p.

NN   0016578   CtY

Napier, Sir Joseph, 1804–1882.
The college and the university.   Communicated to the governing body of the college, and to the Senate of the university by the Right Hon. Sir Joseph Napier ... Dublin, University press, 1871.
32 p.   21cm.
No. 12 of a collection of pamphlets lettered : University education, Ireland, v. 1.

2–14783

NN   0016579   DLC DHEW

Napier, Sir Joseph, 1804–1882.
Edmund Burke: a lecture ... delivered before the Dublin young men's Christian association in connection with the United Church of England and Ireland, in the Metropolitan hall, May the 28th, 1862. [Dublin, 1862]
111p.

824
N16e

NN   0016580   IU

Napier, *Sir* Joseph, 1804–1882.
The education question. Thoughts on the present crisis. By the Right Hon. Joseph Napier. 3d ed. Dublin, Hodges, Smith & co., 1860.
6, [3]–45 p.   20½ cm.

1. Church and education [in] Gt. Brit.   I. Title.

E 15–1630

Library, U. S. Bur. of   Education LC116.G7N2 1860

NN   0016581   DHEW CtY

Napier, Sir Joseph, 1804–1882.
England or Rome, which shall govern Ireland? A reply to the letter of Lord Monteagle. By Joseph Napier... Dublin, W. Curry and co. [etc., etc.] 1851.
68 p.   21cm.
[Pamphlets. State of Ireland. no. 13]

1. Church and state in Ireland. 2. Monteagle, Thomas Spring-Rice, 1st baron, 1790–1866. Letter ... on the subject of the Ecclesiastical titles act.

BR796
.P23
no.13

NN   0016582   ICU

Napier, Sir Joseph, 1804–1882.
England or Rome, which shall govern Ireland? A reply to the letter of Lord Monteagle. 2d ed. Dublin, William Curry and Co., 1851.
68 p.
Bound with 1575.

NN   0016583   TxDaM

Napier, Joseph, 1804–1882.
Irish King's Bench and Exchequer see under Alcock, John C.

Napier, Sir Joseph, 1804–1882.
Labour and knowledge; labour and rest. Two lectures. Dublin, W. Curry, 1859.
56p. 20cm.

BJ
1498
N28

1. Work 2. Knowledge 3. Leisure
I. Title II. Title: Labour and rest

NN   0016585   WU

Napier, Joseph   1804–
Landlord and tenant bills. Reply to the letter of the Earl of Donoughmore on the landlord and tenant bills. Dublin, Grierson, 1853.
20 p.

NN   0016586   OO

VOLUME 405

Napier, *Sir* Joseph, 1804–1882.
　　The lectures, essays, and letters of the Right Hon. Sir Joseph Napier, bart. ... with an introduction by his daughter. Forming a supplement to "The life." Dublin, Hodges, Figgis, and co.; London and New York, Longmans, Green, and co., 1888.
　　5 p. l., 495, ₁1₎ p. front. (port.) pl. 22½ᵐ.

　　　　　　　　　　　　　　　　　　　　　2–1016
　　Library of Congress　　　　　ACS.N18

NN　0016587　　DLC MdBP MH TxU

Napier, Sir Joseph, 1804–1882.
　　Lectures on Butler's Analogy of religion, to the constitution and course of nature. Delivered before the members of the Dublin Young men's Christian association in connection with the United church of England and Ireland, by the Right Hon. Joseph Napier ... Dublin: Hodges, Smith & co., 1864.　vii, 325 p.　19½cm.

　117859B. 1. Butler, Joseph, bp. of　　　Durham, 1692–1752. Analogy of
　religion.
　N. Y. P. L.　　　　　　　　　　　　　　　　July 10, 1941

NN　0016588　　NN ViU

Napier, Sir Joseph, 1804–1882.
　　The life and letters of the Right Honble Sir Joseph Napier ...
　　　　see under　Ewald, Alexander Charles, 1842–1891.

Napier, *Sir* Joseph. 1804–83. Literature
and art. 26 pp. ₍*Dublin afternoon lectures*, 2 s. p. 1.₎—

NN　0016590　　MdBP

Napier, Sir Joseph, 1804–1882.
　　The miracles; Butler's argument on miracles, explained and defended: with observations on Hume, Baden Powell and J.S. Mill. To which is added a critical dissertation by H.L. Mansel. Dublin, Hodges, 1863.
　　53 p.
　　Microfilm (negative) of original in the British Museum. 1 reel.
　　1. Butler, Joseph, Bp. of Durham, 1692–1752.
　　2. Miracles.　I.　　　　　Mansel, Henry Longueville, 1820–1871.　　II. T.

NN　0016591　　NjP

Napier, Sir Joseph, bart., 1804–1882.
　　[Second report] Copy of the separate report made to Her Majesty by the Right Honourable Sir Joseph Napier, bart.
　　　　see under　Gt. Brit.　English and Irish Law and Chancery Commission.

330.9415
N199s
　　Napier, Sir Joseph, 1804–1882.
LIMITED　Speech of the attorney general for Ireland,
CIRCULATION （The Right Hon. Joseph Napier, M.P.) on introducing the new code for regulating the relation of landlord and tenant in Ireland. In the House of Commons, Monday, November 22, 1852. Extracted from Hansard's Parliamentary Debates. [London, Woodfall and Kinder, 1852?]
　　26 p.　21cm.

　　Unbound. In quires.

　　1. Land - Ireland.　2. Land tenure - Ireland.
　3. Property - Ireland.　I. Hansard's Parliamentary Debates Extract.　II. Title: Regulation of landlord and tenant in Ireland.　III. Title.

NN　0016594　　FU

941.58　Napier, Sir Joseph, 1804–1882.
C692　　William Bedell: a lecture delivered
v.4　　before the Dublin Young men's Christian
no.8　association in connexion with the United church of England and Ireland in the Metropolitan hall, March the 13th, 1863 ...　[Dublin, 1864]
　　35p.

　　[Collins pamphlets. v.4, no.8]

NN　0016595　　IU

Napier, Lionel Everard, 1888–
　　... Anæmia in pregnancy in Calcutta; an analysis of hæmatological and other data from 529 pregnant women, by L. Everard Napier ... and M. I. Neal Edwards ... Calcutta, Pub. under the authority of and for the Indian research fund association by Thacker, Spink & co., ltd. ₍1941₎
　　iv, 135 p. incl. tables, diagrs. 24½ᵐ. (Indian medical research memoirs ... no. 33. December, 1941)
　　"An inquiry under the Indian research fund association. From the School of tropical medicine, Calcutta."
　　"References": p. 98–99.
　　1. Pregnancy.　2. Anemia.　3. Blood.　I. Neal Edwards, Margaret Isabel, joint author.　II. Indian research fund association.　III. Calcutta. School of tropical medicine　　　and hygiene.　IV. Title.

　Princeton univ. Library　　　　　　　　　A 45–705
　for Library of Congress　　　　　.5,

NN　0016596　　NjP

Napier, Lionel Everard, 1888–
　　Hæmatological technique, by L. Everard Napier ... and C. R. Das Gupta ...　3d ed., rev. by C. R. Das Gupta ... Calcutta, Dhur, 1945.
　　viii, 128, ₍4₎ p. illus. (part col.) 25 cm.

　　1. Blood—Examination.　I. Das Gupta, C. R., joint author.

　　　　　　　　　　　　　　　　　　Med 48–464
　U. S. Army Medical Libr.　　　　[WB335N199h 1945]
　for Library of Congress　　　　　₍1₎

NN　0016597　　DNLM

Napier, Lionel Everard, 1888–
　　Kala azar; a handbook for students and practitioners, by L. Everard Napier and Ernest Muir. London, Milford, Oxford University Press, 1923.
　　vi₍2₎160p. illus.(1 fold.)10 plates(incl. front.& maps,part col.,1 fold.) 23cm.

　　1.Leishmaniasis, Visceral.　I.Muir, Ernest, joint author.　　II.Title.

NN　0016598　　NcD-MC NN PPC

WC　　NAPIER, Lionel Everard, 1888–
715　　Kala-azar, a handbook for students
N199k　and practitioners. 2d ed. London,
1927　Oxford Univ. Press, 1927.
　　viii, 203 p. illus.
　　1. Leishmaniasis - Visceral

NN　0016599　　DNLM CU MH PPC KMK

W　　Napier, Lionel Everard, 1888–
1　　Memorandum on anaemia in pregnancy in
IN2754　India, by L. Everard Napier and M. I.
no.7　Neal Edwards. Including Haematological technique, by L. Everard Napier and C. R. Das Gupta. Calcutta, Thacker, Spink, 1942.
　　174 p. illus. (part col.) (Indian Research Fund Association. Special report no. 7)

NN　0016600　　DNLM

Napier, Lionel Everard, 1888–
　　The principles and practice of tropical medicine, by L. Everard Napier ... Calcutta, Thacker, Spink & co., ltd.; London, W. Thacker & co., 1943–
　　v. col. front., illus. (incl. maps) plates (part col.) diagrs. 25ᵐ.
　　"References" at end of most of the chapters.

　　1. Tropics—Diseases and hygiene.
　　　　　　　　　　　　　　　　　　　46–17329
　Library of Congress　　　RC961.N3
　　　　　　　　　　　₍3₎　　　　　　　　616.09

NN　0016601　　DLC MtU DNLM

Napier, Lionel Everard, 1888–
　　The principles and practice of tropical medicine, by L. Everard Napier ... New York, The Macmillan company, 1946.
　　xvi p., 1 l., 917 p. double col. front., illus. (incl. maps, diagrs.) plates (part col.) 25½ᵐ.
　　"References" at end of most of the chapters.

　　1. Tropics—Diseases and hygiene.
　U. S. Surg-gen. off. Libr.　　　　　S G 46–204
　for Library of Congress　　RC961.N32
　　　　　　　　　　　₍7₎†　　　　　　　616.09

　　　CoU ICJ TxU ViU PU DLC
NN　0016602　　DNLM CaBVaU CaBViP OrU-M DNLM NcD PSt

AP4　　Napier, Macvey, 1776–1847, ed.
.E3
　　The Edinburgh review, or critical journal. v. 1–250 (no. 1–510) ; Oct. 1802–Oct. 1929. Edinburgh, A. and C. Black; ₍etc., etc., 1803–90; London ₍etc.₎ Longmans, Green, and co.; New York, Leonard Scott publication company, 1891–1929.

Napier, Macvey, 1776–1847.
　　Hypocrisy unveiled, and calumny detected: in a review of Blackwood's magazine ... 4th ed. With app. Edinburgh, Printed for F. Pillans, 1818.
　　cover-title, ₍3₎–55 p. 4 p.

　　"Wrongly ascribed to James Grahame, advocate." Halkett and Laing.

NN　0016604　　MiU

Napier, Macvey, 1776–1847.
　　Lord Bacon and Sir Walter Raleigh. By the late Macvey Napier ... Cambridge ₍Eng.₎ Macmillan and co., 1853.
　　2 p. l., ii, 273 p. 19ᵐ.
　　Essay on Lord Bacon reprinted from the Transactions of the Royal society of Edinburgh, 1818; essay on Sir Walter Raleigh, from the Edinburgh review, 1840.

　　1. Bacon, Francis, viscount St. Albans, 1561–1626.　2. Raleigh, Sir Walter, 1552?–1618.

　　　　　　　　　　　　　　　　　　11–10804
　Library of Congress　　　B1197.N3

NN　0016605　　DLC CtY NcD MdBP NIC NcU

Napier, Macvey, 1776–1847.
　　Memoir of Sir John Leslie. By Macvey Napier ...
　　₍*In* Leslie, Sir John. Treatises on various subjects of natural and chemical philosophy. Edinburgh, 1838. 20ᵐ. p. ₍1₎–46₎
　　Written for the seventh edition of the Encyclopædia britannica.

　　1. Leslie, Sir John, 1766–1832.

　　　　　　　　　　　　　　　　　　6–36275†
　Library of Congress　　　QC3.L64
　　——— Copy 2, separate.　　Library of Congress QC16.L6N2

NN　0016606　　DLC

Napier, Macvey, 1776–1847.
　　Remarks illustrative of the scope and influence of the philosophical writings of Lord Bacon.

　Q41　　Royal society of Edinburgh. Transactions. Edinburgh, 1818. 28ᵐ.
　.E2　　v. 8, p. 373–425.
　(vol. 8)　　　　　　　　　　　　　　　CA 5–445 Unrev

NN　0016607　　DLC NN

VOLUME 405

Napier, Macvey, 1776–1847.
Selection from the correspondence of the late Macvey Napier, esq.; edited by his son, Macvey Napier. London, Macmillan and co., 1879.
xvi, 555 p. 22ᶜᵐ.

ɪ. Napier, Macvey, 1807 or 8–1893, ed.

U. S. Dept. of state. Libr.   S D 19–135 Revised
for Library of Congress   [PR1346.N   ]

PBm PPL PHC MdBP OC1 OC1W CaBVaU
NN   0016608   DS NcRS NbU TU NcU NcD CtY MH CSmH

Napier, Macvey, 1776–1847.
... Selections from the correspondence of the late Macvey Napier, esq.; ed. by his son, Macvey Napier. London, Harrison and sons, printers, 1877.
xvi, 536 p. 23½ᶜᵐ.
At head of title: Printed for private circulation only.

ɪ. Napier, Macvey, 1807 or 8–1893, ed.

Library of Congress   PR1346.N3   15–19148

NN   0016609   DLC IaU

Napier, Macvey, 1776–1847.

Leslie, *Sir John,* 1766–1832.
Treatises on various subjects of natural and chemical philosophy. By Sir John Leslie ... With a biographical memoir. Republished from the Encyclopædia britannica. Edinburgh, A. and C. Black, 1838.

Napier, Margaret.
The hundredth applicant, a play in one act, by Margaret Napier. London, Rich & Cowan, ltd. [1934]
21 p., 1 l. 18½ᶜᵐ.

ɪ. Title.
                                    CA 34–501 Unrev'd
Library of Congress   PR6027.A6H8 1934
Copyright D pub. 25506   822.91

NN   0016611   DLC NN

Napier, Margaret.
Songs of the dead, by Margaret Napier; with an introduction by Edward Garnett. London, John Lane; New York, John Lane company, 1920.
50 p. 22½ᶜᵐ.

ɪ. *Garnett, Edward, 1868–   ɪɪ. Title.

Library of Congress   PR6027.A6S6 1920   20–17909

NN   0016612   DLC CSt NcD WU NN

Napier, Margaret.
Wayside war; a play in one act, by Margaret Napier. (In: Hampden, J., playwright, editor. Four modern plays. London [1931?]. 16°. p. 71–100.)

632938A. 1. Drama, English.   ɪ. Title.
N. Y. P. L.   April 22, 1933

NN   0016613   NN

NAPIER, MARGARET.
Wayside war; a play in one act, by Margaret Napier. (In: Hampden, J., ed.   Fifteen modern plays. London [1934] 19cm.   p. 265–294.)

755071A. 1. Drama, English. 2. Great Britain—Hist.— James II, 1685–1688—Drama. ɪ. Title.

NN   0016614   NN

Napier, Mrs. Mark
       see Sprigge, Elizabeth, 1900–

14825   **Napier, Mark,** 1798–1879.
.669   The case for the crown in re the Wigtown martyrs proved to be myths versus Wodrow and Lord Macaulay, Patrick the Pedler and Principal Tulloch. Edinburgh, Edmonston, 1863.
          8,142 p. 22½ᶜᵐ.
          With this is bound History vindicated in the case of the Wigtown martyrs, by the Rev. Archibald Stewart. 1869.

NN   0016616   NjP PPL

Napier, Mark, 1798–1879, reporter.

Scotland. *Court of teinds.*
Cases decided in the Court of teinds, from May 1821, to June 1831. Reported by Patrick Shaw, Alexander Dunlop, Mark Napier, and J. M. Bell ... Edinburgh, W. Blackwood; London, T. Cadell [etc.] 1831.

Napier, Mark, 1798–1879.
Commentaries on the law of prescription in Scotland. By Mark Napier ... Edinburgh, T. & T. Clark; London, Benning & co. [etc.] 1854.
vii, [v]–944 p. 22ᶜᵐ.
"The four first chapters ... were published so long ago as 1839."— Advertisement.

1. Prescription (Law)—Scotland.   ɪ. Title.
                                          33–35060
NN   0016618   DLC MH–L CtY IU

Napier, Mark, 1798–1879, ed.

Napier, John, 1550–1617.
De arte logistica Joannis Naperi Merchistonii baronis libri qui supersunt. Edinburgi [Printed by Ballantyne and Hughes] 1839.

Napier, Mark, 1798–1879.

Millar, John Hepburn, 1864–1929.
A handbook of prescription according to the law of Scotland, by J. H. Millar ... Edinburgh, W. Green and sons, 1893.

          Napier, Mark, 1798–1879, ed.
DA750
.B2
no. 93   **Spottiswood, John,** *abp. of St. Andrews,* 1565–1639.
          History of the Church of Scotland, beginning the year of our Lord 203, and continued to the end of the reign of King James vɪ. By the Right Rev. John Spottiswoode ... With biographical sketch and notes by the Right Rev. M. Russell ... Edinburgh, Printed for the Spottiswoode society, 1847–51.

Napier, Mark, 1798–1879.
History of the partition of the Lennox. By Mark Napier ... Edinburgh, W. Blackwood and sons; [etc., etc.] 1835.
xvi, 256 p. illus. 23ᶜᵐ.
Title vignette.

1. Lennox, Earldom of.

Library of Congress   DA758.3.L6N2   6–36772

NN   0016622   DLC CaOTP NcD DeU ScU FU OC1 MB CaBVaU

Div.S.   **Napier, Mark,** 1798–1879.
274.1
S849ZN   History rescued in answer to "History vindicated" being a recapitulation of the "case for the crown" and the reviewers reviewed in re the Wigtown martyrs. Edinburgh, Edmonston and Douglas, 1870.
          cclxxiii, 142 p. illus. 23ᶜᵐ.
          Includes reprint of the author's: The case for the crown in re the Wigtown martyrs proved to be myths versus Wodrow and Lord Macaulay, Patrick the Pedler   and Principal Tulloch. Edinburgh, 1863.

          1. Stewart, Archibald, minister at Glasserton. History vindicated in the case of the Wigtown martyrs. 2. Covenanters. ɪ. Title. ɪɪ. Title: The case for the crown in re the Wigtown martyrs proved to be myths.

NN   0016624   NcD MH ICN PPL CBBD CaBVaU

Napier, Mark, 1798–1879.
"The Lanox of Auld." An epistolary review of "The Lennox, by William Fraser," by Mark Napier. Edinburgh, D. Douglas, 1880.
2 p. l., xii, 153 p. illus. (incl. coats of arms) plates, geneal. tab. 29ᶜᵐ.
"Note" signed: Francis Napier.

1. Fraser, William, 1816–1898. The Lennox. 2. Lennox family. 3. Lennox, Earldom of.   ɪ. Napier, Francis John Hamilton Scott, 1850–   ed. ɪɪ. Title.
                                          17–23083
Library of Congress   DA758.3.L6N3

NN   0016625   DLC OC1WHi NN

DA   **Napier, Mark,** 1798–1879.
803   The life and times of Montrose; illustrated
.7   from original manuscripts, including family
A3   papers now first published from the Montrose
N21   charter-chest and other private repositories. Edinburgh, Oliver & Boyd, 1840.
          xx, 537 p. illus. 19cm.

          1. Montrose, James Graham, 1st marquis of, 1612–1650.

NN   0016626   NIC NjR IU PU NN CtY ScU MiDB MdBP MH

Napier, Mark, 1798–1879.
Memoirs of John Napier of Merchiston, his lineage, life, and times, with a history of the invention of logarithms. By Mark Napier, esq. Edinburgh, W. Blackwood; [etc., etc.] 1834.
xvi, 534 p. illus., plates, 4 port. (incl. front.) facsims. (1 fold.) 28½ x 22½ᶜᵐ.

1. Napier, John, 1550–1617. 2. Logarithms—Hist.

Library of Congress   QA29.N2N2   5—12354

          MiU
NN   0016627   DLC MdBP PBm OkU NcD OU TxU PPL CtY

VOLUME 405

Napier, Mark, 1798–1879.
Memoirs of the Marquis of Montrose. By Mark Napier ... Edinburgh, T. G. Stevenson; ₍etc., etc.₎ 1856.
2 v. fronts., illus., ports., facsims. 22ᶜᵐ.
Paged continuously.

1. Montrose, James Graham, 1st marquis of, 1612–1650.
3—26022

Library of Congress　　　DA803.7.A3N3

CtY PPL OCl
NN　0016628　　　DLC CSt NjPT CU-A CU-S NcU MdBP NcD

Napier, Mark, 1798–1879.
Memorials and letters illustrative of the life and times of John Graham of Claverhouse, viscount Dundee. By Mark Napier ... Edinburgh, T. G. Stevenson; ₍etc., etc.₎ 1859–62.
3 v. fronts., plates, ports., facsims. 23½ᶜᵐ.
Title vignette, mounted: armorial shield of Dundee.

1. Dundee, John Graham of Claverhouse, 1st viscount, 1648–1689.
2. Scotland—Hist.—Stuarts, to the union, 1371–1707.
1—2089

Library of Congress　　　DA804.1.D9N2

ICN NN WaS ScU
NN　0016629　　　DLC CtY TxU ILfC MnU Vi MdBP OCl MiU

₍**Napier, Mark**₎ 1798–1879, *ed.*
Memorials of Montrose and his times ... Edinburgh, Printed for the Maitland club, 1848–50.
2 v. fronts., ports., facsims. 27 x 22ᶜᵐ. ₍Maitland club. Publications. no. 66₎
Title vignette (coat of arms)
Edited by Mr. Napier; preface signed: Mark Napier.

1. Montrose, James Graham, 1st marquis of, 1612–1650.
18–14281

Library of Congress　　　DA750.M3 no. 66

NN　0016630　　　DLC MH MdBP OU MsU PU MiU OCl

Napier, Mark, 1798–1879.
Montrose and Covenanters, their characters and conduct, illustrated from private letters and other original documents hitherto unpublished, embracing the times of Charles the First, from the rise of the troubles in Scotland, to the death of Montrose. By Mark Napier ... London, J. Duncan, 1838.
2 v. 22ᶜᵐ.

1. Montrose, James Graham, 1st marquis of, 1612–1650. 2. Covenanters. 3. Scotland—Hist.—Stuarts, to the union, 1371–1707.
3—28431

Library of Congress　　　DA803.7.A3N2

ICarbS ViU
MiU OCl MdBP MB NjP NNUT MnU WaU PU PPL NcU NNC
NN　0016631　　　DLC CtY MH-AH NcU CtY-D NjNbS OClW NN

Napier, Milton F　　1900–
The legislative process and how it works; a word picture of how laws are made in the General Assembly of Missouri and in the Congress of the United States. Includes a glossary of legislative and constitutional words, terms, and phrases for the layman, student, teacher, and lawmaker. The ten commandments of good citizenship. Missouriana. ₍St. Louis? ᶜ1950₎
36 p. illus. 23 cm.
Cover title.

1. Legislation—U. S. 2. Legislation—Missouri.　ɪ. Title.

JK1064.N35　　　328.778　　　51–2787

NN　0016632　　　DLC

Napier, Nina.
How B.C. joined Canada, by Nina Napier ... N.p., n.pub., n.d.
Cover-title, unpaged, 31x14cm.

Galley-proofs.

NN　0016633　　　CaBViPA

Napier, Nina.
John Masefield. ₍In Archives of the Letters club of the University of British Columbia. v. 1. January to April, 1920₎
31 p.

NN　0016634　　　CaBVaU

Napier, Nina.
Joseph Conrad, by Edna Marwick ... ₍In the Archives of the Letters club of the University of British Columbia, v. 2, October to November, 1920₎
p. 1–35

NN　0016635　　　CaBVaU

Napier, Nina.
Library levity. Seattle, Printed by F. McCaffrey at his Dogwood Press, 1946.
₍38₎ p. illus. 21 cm.
Poems.

1. Libraries—Poetry.　ɪ. Title.
A 48–5700*

Missouri. Univ. Libr.
for Library of Congress　₍2₎

CaBVaU CaBVa CaBViP CaBViPA
NN　0016636　　　MoU MiD TU LU Mi WaT WaSp WaS Wa Or

Napier, Norman.
... Time on love's dial, by Norman Napier ... ₍London, A. L. Carruthers, 1921₎
cover-title, 38 p. incl. illus. 22ᶜᵐ. (Christian novels. no. 872)
Advertising matter interspersed.

ɪ. Title.
26–24682

Library of Congress　　　PZ3.N1624Ti

NN　0016637　　　DLC

Napier, Patrick Chapman.

G3934
.B54
1953　**Waldsmith, Arnold J**　1907–
W3　　City map of Boca Raton, Florida, 1953. Dania, Fla., P. C. Napier ₍1952₎

Napier, Patrick Chapman.
City map of Deerfield Beach, Broward County, Florida. Dania, Fla., 1952.
map 29 x 44 cm. on sheet 45 x 57 cm. fold. to 23 x 10 cm.
Scale ca. 1 : 13,000.
Signed: A. Waldsmith.
Includes street index.

1. Deerfield Beach, Fla.—Maps.　ɪ. Waldsmith, Arnold J., 1907–
G3934.D45 1952.N3　　　Map 53–61

NN　0016639　　　DLC NNC PSt NN INS

₍**Napier, Rachel Moore (Baker)**₎
₍Bibliography of the works of Ray Stannard Baker. n. p., 194–₎
1 v. (unpaged) 29 cm.

1. Baker, Ray Stannard, 1870–1946—Bibl.

Z8068.49.N4　　　48–40071*‡

NN　0016640　　　DLC

Napier, Rachel (Baker)　ᴹᵒᵒʳᵉ　　comp.
Ray Stannard Baker, "David Grayson"; a bibliography... Amherst, Mass., 1943.
125 numb. ℓ.

1. Baker, Ray Stannard, 1870––Bibl.

NN　0016641　　　NjP

Napier, Richard.　　　Ind 8o8.34.5
Remarks on Lieut.-Colonel Outram's work, entitled " The Conquest of Sinde, a Commentary." London, J. Ridgway, 1847.
pp. viii, 138.

Outram, Sir James

NN　0016642　　　MH

Napier, Rob Ross, 1878–1952.
The surging battle line .... ₍poem. Victoria, B.C.? n.d.₎
fold. broadside (27 x 24 cm.) illus.
Title taken from first line of the poem.

NN　0016643　　　CaBViPA

Napier, Rob Ross, 1878–1952.
Ipres, April 22–28, 1915 ₍by₎ R. Ross Napier. ₍Victoria, B.C.? n.d.₎
broadside (15 x 10 cm.)
Poem.

NN　0016644　　　CaBViPA

Napier, Robert, d. 1766.
₍**Moreau, Jacob Nicolas,** 1717–1804, *comp.*₎
Mémoire contenant le précis des faits, avec leurs pièces justificatives, pour servir de réponse aux Observations envoyées par les ministres d'Angleterre, dans les cours de l'Europe. Paris, De l'Imprimerie royale, 1756.

Napier, Robert, d. 1766.　　FOR OTHER EDITIONS SEE MAIN ENTRY
₍**Moreau, Jacob Nicolas,** 1717–1804.₎
A memorial, containing a summary view of facts, with their authorities, in answer to the Observations sent by the English ministry to the courts of Europe. Translated from the French. Philadelphia: Printed, by James Chattin, 1757.

Napier, Robert, d. 1766.
Reasons humbly offered to prove that the letter printed at the end of the French memorial of justification is a French forgery, and falsely ascribed to His R----l H------ss ... London, Printed for M. Collyer, 1756.

VOLUME 405

Napier, Robert, 1791–1876.
Catalogue of the works of art forming the collection of Robert Napier ... Mainly comp. by J. C. Robinson ... London, Priv. print., 1865.

x, 326 p. 25½ᶜᵐ.

Head-pieces.

1. Art—Private collections. I. Robinson, Sir John Charles, 1824–1913, comp.

Library of Congress   N5245.N3   15–14360

NN   0016648   DLC DI-GS OC1MA MdBP PPPMA NN

Napier⟨ Robert⟩ & sons, Glasgow.
Machinery of the British & North American Royal mail steam ship "Arabia" and of the West India Royal mail steam ship "La Plata." Constructed by Messrs R. Napier & sons. London ⟨etc.⟩ W. Mackenzie ₁1855?₁ x p. plates. 39cm.

358297B.   1. Marine engines.
N.Y.P.L.   January 8, 1952

NN   0016649   NN CtY

Napier, Robert Cornelius Napier, 1st baron, 1810–1890.
Letters of Field-Marshall Lord Napier of Magdala concerning Abyssinia, Egypt, India, South Africa, etc., edited by Lt.-Col. the Hon. H. D. Napier ... Norwich, Jarrold & sons, ltd.; London, Simpkin Marshall ₁1936₁

viii, 161 p., 1 l. front., plates, ports., facsims. 22½cm.

Errata slip   inserted before p. 179.

NN   0016650   NcD MB ICN CU NN CtY

Napier, Robert D., 1821–1885.
On the velocity of steam and other gases, and the true principles of the discharge of fluids... By R. D. Napier. London: E. & F. N. Spon, 1866. 61 p. incl. diagr., tables. - 8°.

391541A.   1. Gases—Flow.
N.Y.P.L.   October 7, 1929

NN   0016651   NN

Napier, Robert Hellier, 1884–1918.
Robert Hellier Napier in Nyasaland; being his letters to his home circle, edited by the Rev. Alexander Hetherwick ... Edinburgh and London, W. Blackwood and sons, 1925.

iv p., 2 l., 158 p., 1 l. plates, ports. 18½ᶜᵐ.

Map on lining-paper.

1. Missions—Nyasaland. I. Hetherwick, Alexander, 1860–   ed.

Library of Congress   BV3625.N8N3   26–10267

NN   0016652   DLC CtY NN

Napier, Robert W.
John Thomson of Duddingston, landscape painter; his life and work, with some remarks on the practice, purpose and philosophy of art, by Robert W. Napier ... Edinburgh, London, Oliver and Boyd, 1919.

xxii, 567, ₁1₁ p. front. (port.) plates. 27½ᶜᵐ.

Bibliography: p. 535–538.

1. Thomson, John, 1778–1840.

Library of Congress   ND497.T65N3   20–6277

NN   0016653   DLC MB NN OC1 NNC CtY WU MiU ILfC

Napier, Robina, "Mrs. Alexander Napier," ed.
Piozzi, *Mrs.* Hester Lynch (Salusbury) Thrale, 1741–1821.
Johnsoniana. Anecdotes of the late Samuel Johnson, LL. D., by Mrs. Piozzi, Richard Cumberland, Bishop Percy and others, together with the Diary of Dr. Campbell and extracts from that of Madame d'Arblay. Newly collected and edited by Robina Napier. London and New York, G. Bell & sons, 1892.   FOR OTHER EDITIONS
           SEE MAIN ENTRY

Napier, Robina, "Mrs. Alexander Napier," ed.
Johnson, Samuel, 1709–1784.
Johnson's Lives of the poets. Edited, with notes, by Mrs. Alexander Napier. And an introduction by J. W. Hales ... London, G. Bell and sons, 1890.

Napier, Robina, tr.

DK26
.M726
1881

Moltke, Helmuth Karl Bernhard, *Graf* von, 1800–1891.
Letters from Russia, tr. by Robina Napier. New ed. London, C. K. Paul, 1881.

Napier, Robina, "Mrs. Alexander Napier."
Boswell, James, 1740–1795.
The life of Samuel Johnson, LL. D. Together with The journal of a tour to the Hebrides, by James Boswell, esq. New editions with notes and appendices by Alexander Napier ... London, G. Bell and sons, 1884.

Napier, Robina, tr.

DB80
.8
.M52
1881a

Metternich-Winneburg, Clemens Lothar Wenzel, *fürst von,* 1773–1859.
... Memoirs of Prince Metternich, 1773–₁1835₁ Edited by Prince Richard Metternich. The papers classified and arranged by M. A. de Klinkowström. Translated by Mrs. Alexander Napier. In four parts ... New York, Harper & brothers, 1881.

Napier, Robina, ed.
A noble boke off cookry ffor a prynce houssolde
    see under title

Napier, Rodger.
Murder by jury, a layman's inquiry, by Rodger Napier ... London, Faber & Faber limited ₁1931₁

48 p. 20ᵐᵐ. (*Half-title:* Criterion miscellany, no. 32)

1. Jury—Gt. Brit. 2. Justice, Administration of—Gt. Brit. I. Title.

           34–31610

Library of Congress   ₁3₁   340.4

NN   0016660   DLC IEN NcU LU NN CaBVaU

Napier, Rosamond
    see Lawrence, Rosamond (Napier) *lady,* 1878–

Napier, Ruth, 1923–
Lost heritage. London, Hammond, Hammond ₁1955₁

256 p. 19 cm.

I. Title.

PZ4.N212Lo   56–30508 ‡

NN   0016662   DLC

Napier, Ruth, 1923–
The way back, a novel. London, Hammond, Hammond ₁1952₁

191 p. 19 cm.

I. Title.

PZ4.N212Way   52–65924 rev ‡

NN   0016663   DLC

Napier, *Lady* Sarah (Lennox) Bunbury, 1745–1826.
The life and letters of Lady Sarah Lennox, 1745–1826, daughter of Charles, 2nd duke of Richmond, and successively the wife of Sir Thomas Charles Bunbury, bart., and of the Hon: George Napier; also a short political sketch of the years 1760 to 1763, by Henry Fox, 1st lord Holland; ed. by the Countess of Ilchester and Lord Stavordale ... London, J. Murray, 1901.

2 v. fronts., plates, ports. 23 cm.

CONTENTS.—I. Introduction. Lord Holland's memoir. Mr. Henry Napier's memoir. Letters of Lady Sarah Lennox.—II. Letters of Lady Sarah Lennox (cont'd.) Appendices: A. J'ai vu. (Written by Lady Susan O'Brien in 1820) B. Changes between 1760 and 1818. (By Lady Susan O'Brien) C. The Ilchester oak. (Extract from 'Seventy years of Irish life,' by W. R. Le Fanu) D. Colonel and Lady Sarah Napier's children. E. Lord Edward Fitzgerald. 1798. (Extract from Elizabeth, 3d lady Holland's journal) F. Lord Edward Fitzgerald's death. (Extract from a paper written by Miss Emily Napier) G. Death of Charles James Fox. (Extract from Mrs. C. J. Fox's journal) H. Letter from Mrs. George Napier to her step-mother, Mrs. Craig. 1812. I. Part of a letter from Mrs. George Napier to Mrs. Craig. J. Conversations between the Duke and Duchess of Gloucester and Lady Susan O'Brien during a visit at Melbury. (Extract from Lady Susan O'Brien's journal)

I. Holland, Henry Fox, 1st baron, 1705–1774. II. Ilchester, Mary Eleanor Anne (Dawson) countess of, ed. III. Ilchester, Giles Stephen Holland Fox-Strangways, 6th earl of, 1874– joint ed. IV. Napier, Henry Edward, 1789–1853.

DA506.N2A2   2–1251

           NcGU NcD MeB CSt OrU CaBVaU
NN   0016666   DLC DeU MB PPA OU OC1 MiU TxU MH PPL

DA
506
N2A2
1901a

Napier, *Lady* Sarah (Lennox) Bunbury, 1745–1826.
The life and letters of Lady Sarah Lennox, 1745–1826, daughter of Charles, 2nd duke of Richmond, and successively the wife of Sir Thomas Charles Bunbury, bart., and of the Hon: George Napier; also a short political sketch of the years 1760 to 1763, by Henry Fox, 1st lord Holland; ed. by the Countess of Ilchester and Lord Stavordale. New York, Scribner, 1901.
2 v. fronts., plates, ports. 23cm.

NN   0016667   MU

DA506
N2A2
1902

Napier, *Lady* Sarah (Lennox) Bunbury, 1745–1826.
The life and letters of Lady Sarah Lennox, 1745–1826, daughter of Charles, 2nd duke of Richmond, and successively the wife of Sir Thomas Charles Bunbury, bart., and of the Hon: George Napier; also a short political sketch of the years 1760–1763, by Henry Fox, 1st Lord Holland; ed. by the Countess of Ilchester and Lord Stavordale. 2d ed. London, J. Murray, 1902.
654 p. fronts., plates, ports. 23cm.

NN   0016668   GU

Napier, *Lady* Sarah (Lennox) Bunbury, 1745–1826.
The life and letters of Lady Sarah Lennox, 1745–1826, daughter of Charles, 2nd duke of Richmond, and successively the wife of Sir Thomas Charles Bunbury, bart., and of the Hon: George Napier; also, a short political sketch of the years 1760 to 1763, by Henry Fox, 1st lord Holland. Edited by the Countess of Ilchester and Lord Stavordale ... London, J. Murray; New York, C. Scribner s sons, 1902.
xxiv, 654 p. front., plates, ports. 23 cm.

First published (in 2 volumes) in 1901.
"Captain Henry Napier's memoir of Lady Sarah's early life": p₁ ₁83₁–96.

          PP RPB TU
NN   0016669   Vi WaU KyU NN CtY OEac OC1 OO ViU MH

VOLUME 405

Napier, Lady Sarah (Lennox) Bunbury, 1745-1826.
The life and letters of Lady Sarah Lennox, 1745-1826, daughter of Charles, 2nd Duke of Richmond, and successively the wife of Sir Thomas Charles Bunbury, Bart., and of the Hon. George Napier; also a short political sketch of the years 1760-to 1763 by Henry Fox, 1st Lord Holland. Edited by the Countess of Ilchester and Lord Stavordale. ₍One vol. ed.₎ New York, Scribner, 1902.
654p. plates, ports. 23cm.

NN   0016670   IaU NIC OCU WaWW WaT OrCS

Napier, Lady Sarah (Lennox) Bunbury, 1745-1826.
The life and letters of Lady Sarah Lennox, 1745-1826, daughter of Charles, 2nd duke of Richmond, and successively the wife of Sir Thomas Charles Napier, bart., and of the Hon: George Napier; also a short political sketch of the years 1760 to 1763, by Henry Fox, 1st lord Holland; ed. by the Countess of Ilchester and Lord Stavordale ... London, J. Murray, 1904.
654 p. fronts., plates, ports. 23 cm.

NN   0016671   IEdS CSmH

NAPIER, SYDNEY ELLIOTT. 1870- . ed.
The book of the Anzac memorial. New South Wales. Sydney, Beacon press. 1934. 93 p. illus. (part col.) 29cm.

1. Military parks, cemeteries and monuments--Australia--Sydney.

NN   0016672   NN

Napier, Sydney Elliott, 1870-
The genesis and growth of solicitors' associations in New South Wales, together with a brief history of the Incorporated law institute of New South Wales, written by S. Elliott Napier and E. Newton Daly ... Sydney, The Law book co. of Australasia ltd.; ₍etc., etc.₎ 1937.
1 p. l., 29 p. front. (port.) pl. 24½ᶜᵐ.

1. Lawyers—New South Wales. 2. Law—Societies. 3. Incorporated law institute of New South Wales. I. Daly, Edwin Newton, 1874- joint author. II. Title.

38-13997

NN   0016673   DLC CtY

Napier, Sydney Elliott, 1870-
The magic carpet, and other essays and adventures, by S. Elliott Napier... Sydney: Angus & Robertson, Ltd., 1932. 237 p. 19cm.

Reprinted in part from various periodicals.
CONTENTS.—The magic carpet.—On throwing eggs.—"Words, words, words!"—Getting home on William.—Cricket and the poets.—The art of forgetting.—Friendship with books.—Verbal phosphates.—Trifles light as air.—Thoughts on thinking.—The loveliest lyric in the language.—The game of chess.—The bridge.—Pure cussedness.—The first Armistice day.—Conceit and other "vices."—The lighter side of the law.—The Victorians.—The gentle art of public eating.—Trafalgar times.—A strange experience.—Touching the apple.—The humours of the catalogue.—On starting and stopping.—The cricket of prose.—Joan rediviva.—Science, fiction, and the eternal mystery.

6½3532A. 1. Essays, Australian. I. Title.
N.Y.P.L. September 11, 1933

NN   0016674   NN MH TxU

Napier, Sydney Elliott, 1870-
Men and cities; being the journeyings of a journalist, by S. Elliott Napier. Sydney and London, Angus & Robertson, limited, 1938.
6 p. l., ₍3₎-200 p., 1 l. front., plates. 22ᶜᵐ.

1. Voyages and travels. I. Title.
40-1991

Library of Congress   G463.N3
    ₍2₎   910.4

NN   0016675   DLC CtY

Napier, Sydney Elliott, 1870-
On the Barrier Reef; notes from a no-ologist's pocket-book ₍by₎ S. Elliott Napier. Sydney, Angus & Robertson limited, 1928.
7 p. l., ₍3₎-173, ₍1₎ p. front., plates, 2 maps. 22ᶜᵐ.

1. Great Barrier Reef, Australia. 2. Natural history—Great Barrier Reef, Australia.

Library of Congress   QH197.N3   28-26715

NN   0016676   DLC CLSU TxU CU PP OCl

Napier, Sydney Elliott, 1870-
On the Barrier Reef; notes from a no-ologist's pocket-book ₍by₎ S. Elliott Napier. Sydney, Angus & Robertson limited, 1929.
193p. illus.

University of Texas bookplate: A.L. Tremewen, Australian Collection.

NN   0016677   TxU

S29
934n
Napier, Sydney Elliott, 1870-
On the barrier reef; notes from a no-ologist's pocket-book. 6th ed. Sydney, Angus & Robertson,1934.
xii,201p. illus. 19cm.

NN   0016678   CtY MH

Napier, Sydney Elliott, 1870-
Potted biographies, by S. Elliott Napier... Sydney, Dymocks book arcade ₍1930₎ 46 p. 18cm.

Poems.

NN   0016679   NN CLU TxU CaBVaU

821.99
N212u
Napier, Sydney Elliott, 1870-
Underneath the bough: a book of verses. Sydney, W.C.Penfold. ₍1937₎
159p. 19cm.

NN   0016680   NcU

Napier, Sydney Elliott, 1870-
Walks abroad; being the record of the experiences of two Australians in the wilds of the United Kingdom, by S. Elliott Napier... Australia: Angus & Robertson, Ltd., 1929. 328 p. front., plates. 12°.

499041A. 1. Great Britain—Descr. and trav., 1914- . I. Title.
N.Y.P.L.   November 25, 1930

NN   0016681   NN

DA620
N3
1933
Napier, Sydney Elliott, 1870-
Walks abroad; two Australians in the wilds of England, Scotland, and Ireland. 3d ed. rev. Australia, Angus, 1933.
290p. front.,plates. 19cm.

1. Gt. Brit. - Description and travel.

NN   0016682   IaU TxU

4K
Gr.
Brit.
331
Napier Thomas Bateman, 1854-1933
A concise practice of the Queen's Bench and Chancery Divisions and of the Court of Appeal, based on the rules of 1883. With an appendix of questions on the practice intended for the use of students. London, Stevens, 1884.
321 p.

NN   0016683   DLC-P4

Napier, Thomas Bateman, 1854-
A digest of the leading points in the subject of criminal law necessary to be known for bar and university law examinations. Done into questions and answers. By T. Bateman Napier ... and Richard M. Stephenson ... London, W. Maxwell & Son ₍etc.₎ 1888.
1 l., viii, 120 p. 22 cm.

NN   0016684   CtY

Napier, Thomas Bateman, 1854-   *3629.22
The history of joint stock and limited liability companies. (In A century of law reform. Pp. 379-415. London, 1901.)

E2579 — Corporation law.

NN   0016685   MB RP

Napier, Thomas Bateman, 1854-
A modern digest of the law necessary to be known for the final examination of the Incorporated Law Society...London, 1887.

NN   0016686   PPB

Napier, Thomas Bateman, 1854-
The new land taxes and their practical application, being an examination and explanation from a legal point of view of the land clauses of the Finance (1909-10) act, 1910 ⟨10 Edw. 7, ch. 8⟩ By T. B. Napier. London, Stevens and sons, limited, 1910.
lxxiv p., 1 l., 286 p. 25½ᶜᵐ.

1. Land—Taxation—Gt. Brit. I. Gt. Brit. Laws, statutes, etc., 1901-1910 (Edward VII)
10-24779

Library of Congress   HJ4337.N3

NN   0016687   DLC ICJ MB

Napier, Thomas Bateman, 1854-
The new land taxes and their practical application, being an examination and explanation from a legal point of view of the land clauses of the Finance (1909-10) act, 1910 ⟨10 Edw. 7, ch. 8⟩ and the Revenue act, 1911 ⟨1 Geo. 5, c. 2⟩ by T. B. Napier ... 2d ed. London, Stevens and sons, limited, 1912.
2 p. l., clii, 660 p. 25ᶜᵐ.

1. Land—Taxation—Gt. Brit. I. Gt. Brit. Laws, statutes, etc., 1901-1910 (Edward VII) II. Gt. Brit. Laws, statutes, etc., 1910- (George V)
13-5395

NN   0016688   DLC ICJ NjP OU PU-L NIC

NAPIER, T₍homas₎ Bateman, 1854-1933 and Stephenson, Richard M₍osey₎.
A Practical Guide to the Bar. London, 1888.

viii+100 p.

NN   0016689   MH-L

Napier, Thomas Bateman, 1854-1933.
A practical guide to the bar. By T. Bateman Napier ... and Richard M. Stephenson ... 2d ed. By Richard M. Stephenson. London, H. Cox, 1904.
viii, 128 p. 19ᶜᵐ.

"Appendix ... of principal text books": p. ₍127₎-128.

1. Lawyers—Gt. Brit. 2. Inns of court, London. I. Stephenson, Richard Mosey, joint author.
43-40034

NN   0016690   DLC ViU-L CtY

VOLUME 405

Napier, Thomas G.
  The multiple review speller, book one-two.
for the first-eighth grades, by Thomas G.
Napier ... Austin, Tex., W. S. Benson & co.,
publishers, (c.1924)
  2 v. illus. 19 cm.

  Blank pages at end of each volume for
"Individual spelling demons."
  Contents.-Book one. First, second, third,
fourth, and fifth grades.- Book two. Sixth
seventh and eighth grades.

NN   0016691   DHEW

Napier, Thomas G., joint author.
Douglas, Oscar Berry.
  Progress in spelling ... by O. B. Douglas ... Mary Shipp
Sanders ... T. G. Napier ... and L. H. Hubbard ... Austin,
Tex., W. S. Benson & co. (c1931)

Napier, Thomas Hewell.
  Trends in the curricula for training teachers, by Thomas
Hewell Napier ... Nashville, Tenn., George Peabody college
for teachers, 1926.
  139 p. 23ᶜᵐ. (George Peabody college for teachers. **Contributions**
to education. no. 27)
  Thesis (PH. D.)—George Peabody college for teachers, 1926.
  Without thesis note.
  Bibliography: p. (137)–139.

  1. Teachers, Training of—U. S.   I. Title.

  Library of Congress   LB1715.N3 1926   27-9531

NN   DHEW
     0016693   DLC OrU PWcS PU OCU OU MiU ViU OCl

Napier, W. E. L.
  With the trench mortars in France, by Capt. W. E. L. Napier
... (Auckland: Alpe Bros. & Co., 1923.) 110 p. plans,
plates, ports. 12°.

  Cover-title: With the N. Z. trench mortars in France.

156131A. 1. Mortars (Ordnance).   2. Trench warfare. 3. European
war, 1914-1918—Regimental hist.—   New Zealand
N.Y.P.L.   January 21, 1925

NN   0016694   NN

Ga
F291
N213s   Napier, W   T   W
          A speech on the Stay Law and state of the
        country. Delivered by request in the Re-
        presentative Hall, on the evening of Feb.
        1st, 1866. Macon, Ga., J.W. Burke, 1867.
          15 p. 22cm.

          Cover title.

          1. Moratorium. 2. Stay Law. 3. Recon-
        struction - Ga.   I. Title.

NN   0016695   GU GU-De

Napier, Sir Walter John, 1857- FOR OTHER EDITIONS
Braddell, Roland St. John.   SEE MAIN ENTRY
  The law of the Straits settlements; a commentary ⟨2d
ed.⟩ by Roland Braddell ... Singapore (etc.) Kelly and
Walsh, limited, 1931-32.

Napier, Sir Walter John, 1857-
  Nationality in the succession states of Austria-Hungary. By
Sir Walter Napier ...
  (In Grotius society, London. Problems of peace and war. London,
1933. 22ᶜᵐ. v. 18, p. 1-16)

  1. (Nationalism and) nationality. 2. Minorities—Europe.

Carnegie endow. int. peace.   Library   A 33-1788
for Library of Congress   JX31.G7 vol. 18

NN   0016697   NNCE PPT DLC WaU-L DCE

Napier, Sir Walter John, 1857-
  Staatenlosigkeit; being a report on the condition
of statelessness in which the subjects of the former
Austro-Hungarian empire are left under the peace
settlement
        see under   International Federation of
League of Nations Societies. Special Committee
on Staatenlosigkeit.

Napier, Sir Walter John, 1857-   ed.

Straits Settlements law reports. Published under the direction of the Committee of the Singapore bar with the approval of the judges of the Supreme court. 1893-   Vol.
1–   Singapore, Printed and pub. for the Committee of
the Singapore bar by Kelly and Walsh, limited (etc., 1893?–

Napier, William.
  Correspondence between the Hon. William Napier, on
behalf of the English shareholders of the Grand trunk
railroad company, and the Honble. Wm. Cayley, (inspector general) with an introductory memorandum on
the subject of the Grand trunk railroad of Canada. Toronto, Printed by S. Derbishire & G. Desbarats, 1856.
  44 p. 24½ᶜᵐ.

  1. Grand trunk railway.   I. Cayley, William, joint author. II. Canada.
Inspector general.

                                        A 21-1094
  Title from Bureau of   Railway Economics. Printed by L. C.

NN   0016700   DBRE ICU CaNSWA CaOTU

Napier, William of London?
        see   Napier, William, fl. 1851-1865.

Napier, William, 1740?-1812, pub.
  A selection of original Scots songs in three
parts, the harmony by Haydn
        see under Haydn, Joseph, 1732-1809,
comp. and arr.

Napier, William, 1740?-1812, pub.
  A selection of the most favourite Scots-songs
chiefly pastoral
        see under title

[NAPIER,William] fl.1851-1865.
  London sewage;a letter to John Thwaites,esq.
London,E.Stanford,1864.

  21 cm. pp.23.
  Signed:William Napier,W.Hope.

NN   0016704   MH

Napier, William, fl. 1851-1865.
  ... Report and papers of suggestions on the proposed
gathering grounds for the supply of the metropolis from the
soft-water springs of the Surrey sands; addressed to the
General board of health, by the Honble. William Napier.
Presented to both houses of Parliament by command of Her
Majesty. London, Printed by W. Clowes & sons, for H. M.
Stationery office, 1851.
  74 p., 1 l. 22 cm. (Technological pamphlets. v. 13, no. 3)
  At head of title: General Board of health.
  1. London—Water-supply.   I. Great Britain. General board of
health.

  T7.T25   5-30815

NN   0016705   DLC DNLM NN

Kress   Napier, William, fl. 1851-1865.
Room   Suggestions for the supply of the metropo-
        lis from the soft water springs of the Surrey
        Sands, addressed to the General board of
        health ... London, Smith, Elder, and co.,
        1851.
          x, 113 p.incl. tables. 22 cm.

          1.London - Water-supply.

NN   0016706   MH-BA

Napier, William Craig Emilius, 1818-1903.   5958.14
  Military reconnaissance. Originally compiled for the use of the
students of the Staff College.
  (In Jarry, Jean. Outpost duty ... Pp. 59-144. London. 1869.)
  List of French authors consulted. p. 62.

1.3800 — Scouts and scouting. Military.

NN   0016707   MB

Napier, William Craig Emilius, 1818-1903, ed.

Napier, Sir George Thomas, 1784-1855.
  Passages in the early military life of General Sir George T.
Napier, K. C. B., written by himself, edited by his son, General
W. C. E. Napier ... London, J. Murray, 1884.

Napier, William Craig Emilius, 1818-1903.   5958.14
  The principles of road-making. Originally extracted (for the use of
the Staff College) from a pamphlet by Major John Pitt Kennedy,
upon "Road-making in the hills;" "The aide mémoire to the military sciences;" and other works.
  (In Jarry, Jean. Outpost duty ... Pp. 145-175. Illus. Plans.
London. 1869.)

N1954 — Roads. Construction and repair.

NN   0016709   MB

Napier, William Ewart, 1881-1952, ed.

The Chess weekly. v. 1-4; June 6, 1908-Mar. 12, 1910. Brooklyn, N. Y. (The Chess weekly (inc.) 1908)-10.

Napier, William Ewart, 1881-1952
  Napier's Amenities and background of chess-
play
        see under title

946.06 **Napier, Sir William Francis Patrick, 1785-**
N213b   **1860**
          Battles of the Peninsular war. London,
        H. Frowde [n. d.]
          254 p. illus., map. (Herbert Strang's
        library)

          1. Peninsular war, 1807-1814. I. Title.

NN   0016712   CaQML

Napier, Sir William Francis Patrick, 1785-1860.
  Colonel Napier's justification of his third volume;
forming a sequel to his Reply to various opponents, and
containing some new and curious facts relative to the
battle of Albuera ... London, T. & W. Boone, 1833.
  35 p. 22½ᶜᵐ.

  1. Napier, Sir William Francis Patrick, 1785-1860. History of the war
in the Peninsula. 2. Albuera, Battle of, 1811.

                                        12-16508
  Library of Congress   DC231.N242

NN   0016713   DLC NN NcD FTaSU

VOLUME 405

DA
68.12   Napier,Sir William Francis Patrick,1785-1860.
.N2   Comments upon a memorandum of the Duke of
N2   Wellington and other documents censuring Lieut.-
        General Charles James Napier,with a defence of
        Sir C.Napier's government of Scinde,by Captain
        Rathborne. London, C.Westerton, 1854.
            97 p.   22 cm.

            1.Napier,Sir Charles James,1782-1853.
        2.Punjab--Hist. 3.Sind,India--Hist. I.Welling-
        ton,Arthur Wellesley,1st duke of,1769-1852.
        II.Rathborne,M.R.

NN   0016714   MiU

Spec.
Coll.   Napier, *Sir* William Francis Patrick, 1785-
1845   1860.
.N3   The conquest of Scinde, with some introduct-
        ory passages in the life of Major-General Sir
        Charles James Napier. By Major-General W. F. P.
        Napier. London, T. & W. Boone, 1845.
            2 v. 23 cm.

            Red cloth.

NN   0016715   DGU

Napier, *Sir* **William Francis Patrick,** 1785-1860.
    The conquest of Scinde, with some introductory pas-
sages in the life of Major-General Sir Charles James
Napier ... By Major-General W. F. P. Napier ... 2d
ed. London, T. & W. Boone, 1845.
    2 p. l., 531, [1] p. 2 fold. maps, 3 fold. plans. 22cm.

    1. Sind, India. 2. Napier, Sir Charles James, 1782-1853.

    Library of Congress   DS477.N22   5—2059

        NjP
NN   0016716   DLC MdBP MiU CSt ICU IU CU WaU ViU PU

Napier, William Francis Patrick, 1785-1860.
    Counter-remarks to Mr. Dudley Montagu
Perceval's remarks upon ... Napier's ... History
of the Peninsular War ... London, T. & W.
Boone, 1835.
    40 p.   nar.8°.

NN   0016717   NN NBuG

Napier, Sir William Francis Patrick, 1785-
Napier, *Sir* **Charles James,** 1782-1853. 1860, ed.
    Defects, civil and military, of the Indian government.
By Lieutenant-General Sir Charles James Napier ...
Ed. by Sir W. F. P. Napier ... 2d ed. London, C. Wes-
terton, 1853.

Napier, *Sir* **William Francis Patrick,** 1785-1860.
    English battles and sieges in the Peninsula. Extracted
from his "Peninsula war," by Lieut.-Gen. Sir William
Napier ... London, Chapman and Hall, 1852.
    vii, 549 p. front. (port.) 19½cm.

    1. Peninsular war, 1807-1814.

    Library of Congress   DC231.N23   4—11164

NN   0016719   DLC

                                              1860.
946.06 Napier, Sir William Francis Patrick, 1785-
N16p   English battles and sieges in the
1854   Peninsula and south of France. Extract-
        ed from his "History of the war in the
        Peninsula". London, 1854.
            549p. front.(port)

NN   0016720   IU

Napier, *Sir* William Francis Patrick, 1785-1860.
    English battles and sieges in the Peninsula. Extracted
from his 'Peninsula war.' By Lieut.-Gen. Sir William
Napier ... London, J. Murray, 1855.
    vii, 469 p. front. (port.) 19cm.

    1. Peninsular war, 1807-1814.
                                              4-11165

                    DC231.N232

NN   0016721   DLC CaOTU CtY NjP NcU

946.06 **Napier, Sir William Francis Patrick, 1785-1860.**
N162e   **English battles and sieges in the Peninsula.**
1866   **By Lieut.-Gen. Sir William Napier ... Extract-**
        ed from his 'Peninsular war.' New ed. Lon-
        don, J. Murray, 1866.
            vii, 469p. front.(port.) 19cm.

            1. Peninsular War, 1807-1814. I. Title.

NN   0016722   TxU

Napier, Sir William Francis Patrick, 1785-1860.
    English battles and sieges in the Peninsula...
Extracted from his 'Peninsular war'. New ed.
London, J. Murray, 1877.
    vii, 469 p. front. (port.) 19 cm.

NN   0016723   NcD

Napier, Sir William Francis Patrick, 1785-1860.   355.0942 L200
    English battles and sieges in the Peninsula. By Lieut.-Gen. Sir
112417 William Napier, ... With portrait. Popular edition. London,
    J. Murray, 1906.
        vii, 469, [1] p. front. (port.) 20½cm.

NN   0016724   ICJ

DC
231   Napier, Sir William Francis Patrick,
.N232   1785-1860.
1910   English battles and sieges in the
        Peninsula. By Lieut.-Gen. Sir William
        Napier. London, J. Murray, 1910.
            vii, 469p. front. (port.) 19cm.

            1. Peninsular war, 1807-1814.

NN   0016725   KU

Napier, Sir William Francis Patrick, 1785-1860.
    Extracts from Napier's Peninsular war.
Burt, Thomas Seymour, 1805-1890.
    Memoranda of some events connected with my life at
Addiscombe college, Croydon; Brompton barracks, Chatham; Cawnpore, India; San Sebastian, Spain; and Ku-
rachee, Scinde. By T. Seymour Burt ... Dorking, Printed by R. J. Clark, 1886.

Napier, *Sir* **William Francis Patrick,** 1785-1860.
    General Sir Charles Napier, and the Directors of the East
India company. [Signed W. Napier, *i. e.,* Sir William
Francis Patrick Napier, General.] London: C. Wester-
ton, 1857. 45 pp. 8°.

    In: *C p. v. 1061.

NN   0016727   NN

Napier, *Sir* **William Francis Patrick,** 1785-1860.
    History of General Sir Charles Napier's administra-
tion of Scinde, and campaign in the Cutchee Hills. By
Lieut.-Gen. Sir William Napier ... London, Chapman
and Hall, 1851.
    ix, [1], 415 p. 12 pl. (incl. front.) 2 fold. maps, plan. 22cm.

    1. Sind, India. 2. Napier, Sir Charles James, 1782-1853.

    Library of Congress   DS477.N4   5—2058

        OC1 NcD CU WaU
NN   0016728   DLC MdBP NNC MoU InU MiU PPL CLSU

Napier, Sir William Francis Patrick, 1785-1860.
    History of general Sir Charles Napier's adminis-
tration of Scinde, and campaign in the Cutchee hills.
By lieut. gen. Sir William Napier. With maps and
illustrations. London, C. Westerton, 1854.
    (10), 415 p.   8°.

NN   0016729   MB

Napier, *Sir* **William Francis Patrick,** 1785-1860.
    The history of General Sir Charles Napier's administra-
tion of Scinde, and campaign in the Cutchee Hills. 3d ed.
London, C. Westerton, 1858.
    ix, 415 p. plates, maps (part fold.) 22 cm.

    1. Sind, India--Hist. 2. Napier, Sir Charles James, 1782-1853.

                    DS477.N4   1858   50-50945

NN   0016730   DLC DN

Napier, *Sir* **William Francis Patrick,** 1785-1860.
    The history of General Sir Charles Napier's conquest of
Scinde. By Lieut.-Gen. Sir W. F. P. Napier ... 2d ed. London, C. Westerton, 1857.
    2 p. l., 361, [1] p. fold. maps, fold. plans. 23cm.
    L. C. copy imperfect : 1 map wanting.

    1. Sind, India--Hist. 2. Napier, Sir Charles James, 1782-1853.
                                              46-28484
    Library of Congress   DS477.N43   1857

NN   0016731   DLC ICN MH

Napier, *Sir* **William Francis Patrick,** 1785-1860.
    History of the war in the Peninsula, by Major-General
Sir W. F. P. Napier, K. C. B. (Abridged.) London [etc.]
T. Nelson and sons [n. d.]
    296 p. 2 col. pl. (incl. front.) 19½cm.
    "The intention of this reprint has been to assemble in one volume those
portions of the History which chronicle the more famous feats of British
arms ... A connected story of the peninsular campaigns."—Preface.

    1. Peninsular war, 1807-1814.
                                              A 11-170
    Title from New Haven   Libr. Printed by L. C.

NN   0016732   CtNh NcU CtY MB

Napier, *Sir* **William Francis Patrick,** 1785-1860.
    History of the war in the peninsula, and in the south
of France, from the year 1807 to the year 1814. By
Major-General Sir W. F. P. Napier ... London, G. Routledge [n.d.]
    [3 v.] maps. 19cm.

NN   0016733   OrPR OCX

Napier, Sir William Francis Patrick, 1785-1860.
    History of the War in the Peninsula and in
the south of France, from the year 1807 to the
year 1814. London, T. & W. Boone, 1828-1840.
    6 v.

    Vol. 1 published by John Murray.

NN   0016734   DAU NWM PU ICN PPT MB IaU ICU

Napier, William Francis Patrick, 1785-1860.
    History of the war in the Peninsula and in
the south of France, from the year 1807 to the
year 1814. London, J. Murray, 1828-40.
    6 v. maps. 23 cm.

    Imprint varies: v.2-6, London, T. & W. Boone.

    ScU
NN   0016735   OrPR KU ViLxW Wa CaBVa IaU PPT MiU

VOLUME 405

946.06 Napier, Sir William Francis Patrick, 1785-1860.
N213h History of the war in the peninsula and in
1840 the south of France, from the year 1807 to
the year 1814. 2d ed.... London, T. & W.
Boone, 1832-1840.
6v. maps 23cm.

NN 0016736 NcU

Napier, Sir William Francis Patrick, 1785-1860
History of the war in the peninsula, and in
the south of France, from the year 1807 to the
year 1814. 3d ed. ... London, T. & W. Boone,
1834-1840.
6v. plans,maps.

NN 0016737 ScU

Napier, Sir William Francis Patrick, 1785-1860.
History of the war in the peninsula, and in the
south of France, from the year 1807 to the
year 1814. By W.F.P. Napier. 3d ed.
London, T. and W. Boone, 1835-46. 6v., maps.

Vol.4, 2d ed.; v.5-6, no edition number.

NN 0016738 OClW MH

Napier, Sir William Francis Patrick, 1785-
1860.
WD History of the war in the Peninsula and in
7100 the south of France, from the year 1807 to
the year 1814. Oxford, D. Christy, 1836.
504 p.

NN 0016739 CtY NIC NcD

Napier, Sir William Francis Patrick, 1785-1860.
History of the war in the peninsula. Oxford,
Ohio, D. Christy, 1838.
v. (American periodical series: 1800-1850.
737)

Microfilm edition.
Positive copy.
Film includes v.1 (1807-1812) only.
Filmed with: Historical family library devoted
to republication of standard history. v.1, no.1-25.
Gibbon,

Edward. The decline and fall of the Roman
Empire. Oxford, Ohio, 1838-1841.

NN 0016741 ICRL OC1WHi IU

946.06 Napier, Sir William Francis Patrick, 1785-1860.
qN21a History of the war in the peninsula and in
the south of France, from the year 1807 to the
year 1814 ... With a biography of the author,
by the American editor. Oxford, Ohio, D.
Christy, 1838-1842.
2v. in 1. 28cm.

Imprint varies.

1.Peninsular war,1807-1814.

NN 0016742 N DeU NN OC1WHi GA

Napier, Sir [William] F[rancis] P[atrick].
History of the war in the Peninsula, and in the south of
France, from the year 1807 to the year 1814. Brussels: Meline,
Cans and Co., 1839. 3 v. 4. ed. 8°.

NN 0016743 NN NBuU N PHi ViLxW MH MdBP ViW

946.06 Napier, Sir William Francis Patrick, 1785-1860.
N162h History of the war in the Peninsula and in
1839 the south of France, from the year 1807 to the
year 1814. By W.F.P. Napier ... The 4th ed. ..
Paris, Printed for C. Hingray, 1839-40.
3v. in 4. maps, plans. 22cm.

NN 0016744 TxU

Napier, Sir William Francis Patrick, 1785-1860.
History of the war in the peninsula and
in the south of France, 1807-14. 1842. 5 v.

NN 0016745 DN CtY NcA-S OClW OOxM OCX NcU

Napier, Sir William Francis Patrick, 1785-1860.
History of the war in the Peninsula and in the south of
France, from the year 1807 to the year 1814. By W. F. P.
Napier ... from the 4th ed. ... Philadelphia, Carey and
Hart, 1842.
4 v. plans, maps. 24cm.

1. Peninsular war, 1807-1814.

25-5056

Library of Congress DC231.N2 1842

DN MB NjP ICN ViU PPA OKentU NBuC T NcU
NN 0016746 DLC NNC IdRR DeU PKsL PBm MeB MdBP

Napier, Sir William Francis Patrick, 1785-1860.
History of the war in the Peninsula,
and in the south of France; from the
year 1807 to the year 1814. New York,
Redfield, 1844.
2 v. in 1.

NN 0016747 OClW

Napier, Sir William Francis Patrick, 1785-1860.
History of the war in the Peninsula, and in the
south of France, from the year 1807 to the year
1814, by W. F. P. Napier... New York, J. S. Redfield, Clinton Hall, 1847.
792, [ix]-xxiv p. 28cm.

NN 0016748 MsU ViU Nh OC1 OO MH

DC231 Napier, Sir William Francis Patrick, 1785-1860.
N2 History of the war in the Peninsula and in the south of France
1850 from the year 1807 to the year 1814. London, New York, F.
Warne [pref.1850]
6 v. maps, plans.

First English ed. published, 1828-40.

NN 0016749 CU

Napier, Sir William Francis Patrick, 1785-1860.
2 History of the war in the peninsula and in the
2114 south of France, from 1807 to 1814.
New York, [1850?]

NN 0016750 DLC OClW

Napier, Sir William Francis Patrick, 1785-1860.
History of the war in the peninsula, and in the south
of France, from the year 1807 to the year 1814. By
Major-General Sir W. F. P. Napier ... New ed. ... London, T. and W. Boone, 1851.
6 v. maps. 19cm.

1. Peninsular war, 1807-1814.

4-11163

Library of Congress DC231.N22

NN 0016751 DLC NjP NcU PPLas ViU MH MB

Napier, Sir William Francis Patrick, 1785-
1860.
History of the war in the Peninsula and
in the south of France, from the year 1807
to the year 1814. New York, Redfield,
1853.
792p.

NN 0016752 ICarbS NN PV

946.06 Napier, Sir William Francis Patrick, 1785-1860.
N162 History of the war in the Peninsula, and in
1855 the south of France, from the year 1807 to the
year 1814. New York, Redfield, 1855.
xxiv,[9]-792p. 28cm.

NN 0016753 OrU ViU

Napier, Sir William Francis Patrick, 1785-1860.
History of the war in the Peninsula and in the south of
France, from the year 1807 to the year 1814. By Major-
General Sir W. F. P. Napier ... New ed., rev. by the
author ... London, T. and W. Boone, 1856.
5 v. maps, plans. 19cm (v. 3: 20½cm)

1. Peninsular war, 1807-1814.

12-19810

Library of Congress DC231.N223

NN 0016754 DLC ViU PU PHC TxU PV OC1JC MH

Napier, Sir William Francis Patrick, 1785-1860.
History of the war in the peninsula, and in the south
of France, from the year 1807 to the year 1814. By
Major-General Sir W. F. P. Napier ... New ed. ... New
York, A. C. Armstrong [1856?]
5 v. maps. 21cm.

NN 0016755 MtU

946.06 Napier, Sir William Francis Patrick,
N162h 1785-1860.
1860 History of the war in the Peninsula
and in the south of France, from the
year 1807 to the year 1814. New ed.,
rev. by the author. London, Boone,
1860.
6v. maps. 20cm.

NN 0016756 KU

DC231 Napier, Sir William Francis Patrick, 1785-
.N226 1860.
History of the war in the peninsula and in
the south of France, from A.D. 1807 to A.D.
1814, by Major-General Sir W.F.P. Napier ...
In five volumes with portraits and plans.
New York, W.J. Widdleton, 1862.
5 v. fronts.(ports.) maps, plans. 21 cm.

NN 0016757 T MdBP MH

Napier, Sir William Francis Patrick, 1785-1860.
History of the war in the Peninsula and in the
south of France from the year 1807 to the year
1814, by Major-General Sir W. F. P. Napier...
[With fifty-five maps and plans...] N. Y.,
W. J. Widdleton, 1863.
6 v. front. (port.) maps, plans.

First English ed. published, 1828-40.
v.6,Plates. Phila., Carey & Hart [1842]

NN 0016758 MiD OC1WHi PP MB

VOLUME 405

946.06
N162h
Napier, Sir William Francis Patrick, 1785-
1860.
History of the war in the Peninsula and
in the south of France, from A.D. 1807-
A.D. 1814. New York, W. J. Widdleton,
1864.
5 v. maps, ports. 21cm.

NN   0016759   MiDW CtY NjP

Napier, Sir William Francis Patrick, 1785-1860.
History of the war in the peninsula and in
the south of France, 1809-14.
N.Y.,1868.
5 v.   12°

NN   0016760   I

946.06
N213h
1851
Napier, Sir William Francis Patrick, 1785 1860
History of the war in the Peninsula and in the south of
France, from the year 1807 to the year 1814 New. rev
ed.   London, Barthes & Lowell, 1876
6v. maps, plans
This edition first published 1851. London, T. & W. Boone

NN   0016761   FTaSU

946.06
N162h
1876
Napier, Sir William Francis Patrick, 1785-1860.
History of the war in the Peninsula and in
the south of France, from the year 1807 to the
year 1814. By W.F.P. Napier ... London, New
York, G. Routledge and sons [1876-82]
3v. maps, plans. 18½cm.
Vol. 3 has sub-title.
CONTENTS.--[v.1] 1807-1810.--[v.2] 1810-1812.-
[v.3] 1812-1814.

NN   0016762   TxU CU MiU OU

942.06
N162h
1882
Napier, Sir William Francis Patrick, 1785-1860.
History of the war in the Peninsula and in the
south of France from the year 1807 to the year
1814, by Major-General Sir W.F.P. Napier ...
New ed., rev. ... London, Barthès & Lowell,
1882.
6v. maps, plans. 20½cm.

First English ed. published, 1828-40.

NN   0016763   TxU

Napier, Sir William Francis Patrick, 1785-1860.
History of the war in the Peninsula and in
the south of France, from A. D. 1807 to A. D.
1814, by Major-General Sir W. F. P. Napier ...
New edition. New York, Armstrong, 1882.
5 v. fronts. (ports.) maps. 21cm.

On cover: Standard edition.
1. Peninsular war, 1807-1814.

NN   0016764   NNC ICRL DNW

Napier, *Sir* **William Francis Patrick, 1785-1860.**
History of the war in the Peninsula and in the south of
France from the year 1807 to the year 1814, by Major-General
Sir W. F. P. Napier ... With fifty-five maps and plans ...
London and New York, F. Warne and co. 1886.
6 v. front. (port.) maps, plans. 20½cm.
First English edition published, 1828-40.

NN   0016765   NcGU

Napier, Sir William Francis Patrick, 1785-1860.
History of the war in the Peninsula and in the
south of France from A. D. 1807 to A. D. 1814,
by Major-General Sir W. F. P. Napier ... with
portraits and plans ... New ed. New York,
Worthington co., 1890.
5 v. tables. 20 cm.

On spine: Peninsular war.
Portraits and plans wanting in this edition.
Vol. 1 mutilated: part of p. 307-308 torn off.
1. Peninsular war. 1807-1814.

NN   0016766   Vi IdU RPB OCU MH OC1

NAPIER,Sir W[illiam] F[rancis] P[atrick],1785-
1860.
History of the war in the peninsula and in
the south of France from the year 1807 to the
year 1814. London, and New York, F. Warne
and Co., 1892.

6 vol. Maps.
"Chandos classics , 134-139."

NN   0016767   MH

Napier, *Sir* William Francis Patrick, 1785-1860.
History of the war in the Peninsula and in the south
of France from the year 1807 to the year 1814, by Major-
General Sir W. F. P. Napier ... With fifty-five maps and
plans ... London and New York, F. Warne and co. [190-?]
6 v. front. (port.) maps, plans. 20½cm.
First English ed. published, 1828-40.

1. Peninsular war, 1807-1814.

Library of Congress   DC231.N227   4-22832/2

NN   0016768   DLC PBa NN WaS WaT

Napier, *Sir* William Francis Patrick, 1785-1860.
History of the war in the peninsula and in the south of
France, from the year 1807 to the year 1814, by Major-General
Sir W. F. P. Napier ... London and New York, F. Warne
and co. [190-?]
6 v. maps, plans. 19½cm. (*On cover:* Chandos classics)

1. Peninsular war, 1807-1814.

Library of Congress   DC231.N225   4-18011
                            [a37b1]   -946.06

NN   0016769   DLC

Napier, Sir William Francis Patrick, 1785-
History of the war in the Peninsula
and in the south of France, from the
year 1807 to the year 1814. Kansas
City,Hudson-Kimberly,1904.   3v.plans,
maps.

NN   0016770   OrU CaBVa

DC
231
.N2
1921
Napier, Sir William Francis Patrick, 1785-1860.
History of the war in the Peninsula and in
the south of France from the year 1807 to the
year 1814. With fifty-five maps and plans.
London, New York, F. Warne [1921?]
6v. maps, plans. 20cm. (Chandos classics)

1. Peninsula War, 1807-1814. I. Series.

NN   0016771   OrU

946.06
N213PD
Napier, Sir William Francis Patrick, 1785-
1860
A letter to General Lord Viscount Beresford, being an answer to his Lordship's
assumed refutation of Colonel Napier's justification of his third volume ... London, T.
& W. Boone, 1834.
37 p. 23 cm. [With Beresford, W. C. B.
Refutation of Colonel Napier's justification
of his third volume. London, 1834.]
1. Beresford, William Carr Beresford, viscount
1768-1854. Refutation of Colonel Napier's
justification of   his third volume.

NN   0016772   NcD NN NBuG

Napier, Sir William Francis Patrick, 1785-1860.
Letter to J. Prettyman on Sind occupational
forces and prospects for the country, based on
his brother's advices. 1846.
[7]p.

Manuscript, with typewritten copy.

NN   0016773   OC1

Napier, *Sir* William Francis Patrick, 1785-1860.
The life and opinions of General Sir Charles James Napier,
G. C. B., by Lieut.-Gen. Sir W. Napier ... London, J. Murray,
1857.
4 v. fronts. (ports.) map. 20cm.

1. Napier, Sir Charles James, 1782-1853.
                                          5—953
Library of Congress   DA68.12.N2N2

                MdBP NSyU IU GU FTaSU PPFr ILfC
NN   0016774   DLC NcU ViU MB NcD CtY KMK MiU OC1

DA68
.12
.N22
Napier, Sir William Francis Patrick, 1785-1860.
Life of General Sir William Napier... Ed.by H.A.
Bruce... London,J.Murray,1864.
2 v. 21cm.

1.Napier,Sir William Francis Patrick,1785-1860.

                MH M MBAt PPULC MiU NcD
NN   0016775   ICU NRU ViU NB CU CtY NN IU ViU ICN

DC
232
.5
N21
Napier, Sir William Francis Patrick, 1785-
1860.
[Maps and plans drawn for the History
of the war in the Peninsula and in the south
of France, from the year 1807 to the year
1814. Philadelphia, Carey & Hart, 184-?]
55 plates. 23cm.

1. Peninsular war, 1807-1814--Maps.
I. Napier, Sir William Francis Patrick,
1785-1860. History of the war in the
Peninsula.

NN   0016776   NIC

Napier, Sir **William Francis Patrick, 1785-1860.**
A narrative of the Peninsular campaign 1807-1814, its battles
and sieges; abridged from "The history of the war in the Peninsula," by Lieut.-General Sir W. F. P. Napier ... By William T.
Dobson ... London: Bickers & Son, 1889. vi, 408 p. front.,
map, plates. 8°.

144282A. 1. Peninsular war.   2. Dobson, William T., editor.
N. Y. P. L.   November 28, 1924

NN   0016777   NN OC1 PPL CU

Napier, Sir William Francis Patrick, 1785-
1860, ed.

Napier, *Sir* Charles, 1786-1860.
The navy: its past and present state. In a series of
letters, by Rear-admiral Sir Charles Napier ... Ed. by
Major-general Sir William Napier ... London, J. & D. A.
Darling, 1851.

VOLUME 405

Napier, William Francis Patrick, 1785-1860.
The new poor law; an essay. Dublin, S. J.
Machen, 1841.
8 p. 22cm.

"From the Citizen, or Dublin monthly magazine, for August, 1841."

1. Poor laws - Ireland.

NN 0016779   NNC

Napier, William Francis Patrick, 1785-1860.
Observations on the corn law, addressed to
Lord Ashley, because his persevering efforts
to protect the factory children give him a
just title to the respect of all persons who
acknowledge the value of justice and benevolence in national policy. London, T. & W.
Boone, 1841.
16 p. 21cm.

NN 0016780   NNC MH-BA PU NjP

Napier, William Francis Patrick, 1785-1860.
A reply to Lord Strangford's "Observations"
on ... Colonel Napier's "History of the war in
the Peninsula".   London, T. & W. Boone, 1835.
14 p.   8°.
2. ed.

NN 0016781   NN NBuG

Rare
DC
231
N21R4
Napier, Sir William Francis Patrick, 1785-1860.
A reply to various opponents; particularly
to "Strictures on Colonel Napier's History of
the war in the peninsula." Together with
observations illustrating Sir John Moore's
campaigns. London, T. & W. Boone, 1832.
57 p. 23cm.

1. Peninsular War, 1807-1814. 2. Strictures on Colonel Napier's History of the war
in the penins   ula. 3. Moore, Sir
John, 1761-   1809.

NN 0016782   NIC

946.06
N213PD
Napier, Sir William Francis Patrick, 1785-1860.
A reply to various opponents: particularly
to "Strictures on Colonel Napier's History
of the war in the Peninsula." Together with
observations illustrating Sir John Moore's
campaigns ... The 2d ed. London, T. & W.
Boone, 1833.
57, [1] p. 23 cm. [With Beresford, W.
C. B. Refutation of Colonel Napier's justification of his third volume. London, 1834]

NN 0016783   NcD CtY NBuG NN

Napier, Sir William Francis Patrick,
1785-1860.
Six letters, in vindication of the
British army, exposing the calumnies of
the Liverpool financial reform association ...
2d ed. London, E.Moxon, 1849.
29, [1] p. 20.5 cm.

NN 0016784   MH-BA

Napier, Sir William Francis Patrick, 1785-1860,
ed.

Napier, *Sir* Charles James, 1782-1853.
William the Conqueror. A historical romance. By Gen.
Sir Charles Napier ... Posthumous work. Lieut.-Gen. Sir
William Napier, K. C. B., editor. London, New York, G. Routledge & co., 1858.

Napier, William John, 1837-1874.
A brief memoir of William John Napier, by his
father
see under [Napier, Sir Joseph] 1804-1882.

Pam.
Coll.
20413
Napier, William Joseph, 1857-1925.
Land law reform: a historic and legal
justification of a land tax ... Auckland, N. Z.,
Printed at the Star Office, 1890.
16 p. 22 cm.

1. Land. Taxation. New Zealand I. Title

NN 0016787   NcD

Napier, William Marianus
see
Napper, William Marianus, 1619-1693.

NAPIER MILES,Mrs.E.
Poems written in sun and shade. London,etc.,
Burns Oates & Washbourne Ltd.,1921.
pp.(8),464.

NN 0016789   MH

Napier of Magdala, Field Marshall Lord
see Napier, Robert Cornelius Napier,
1st baron, 1810-1890.

Napier of Magdala, Lady.
see
Napier, Eva Maria Louisa (Macdonald) Lady, 1846-

Napier, N. Z. Harbour Board.
Statement of accounts with reports and statistics.
Napier.
v. 25-34 cm. annual.
Report year ends Sept. 30.
Title varies slightly.

1. Napier, N. Z.—Harbor.

HE560.N3A3   387.1   50-38069

NN 0016792   DLC

Napier, N. Z. Hawkes Bay Art Gallery and Museum
see Hawkes Bay Art Gallery and Museum, *Napier, N. Z.*

Napier & son, ltd.
see Napier, D., & son, ltd.

Napier tercentenary exhibition
see
Edinburgh. Napier tercentenary exhibition.

Napiereźa-Kowalski, Władysław
Chemia nieorganiczna. Lippstadt, Wydawn.
Jutra Pracy, 1947.
164 p. illus.

NN 0016796   MiD

QD305
.A8N21
Napiéralski, Bernard.
Ueber einige secundaere diamine der fettreihe.
Zur kenntniss einer neuen isochinolinsynthese.
Zuerich, 1893.
61p.
Inaug. diss. Basel.

NN 0016797   DLC CtY PU

Napiéralski (Erasme). * Du chloral aux points
de vue clinique, physiologique et thérapeutique.
56 pp. 4°. *Paris*, 1870, No. 215.

NN 0016798   DNLM

Napieralski (Thadéo-Félix) [1875-   ]. *Le
vertige voltaïque dans les lésions de l'appareil
auditif. 56 pp., 1. 8°. *Paris*, 1901, No. 475.

NN 0016799   DNLM CU

Napier's amenities and background of chess-play.
Unit 1-3. Brooklyn, N. Y., 1934-35. 3 no.
in 1 v. illus. 22cm.

Unit 1 also called vol. 1.
Edited by W. E. Napier.

Bequest of Gustavus A. Pfeiffer

1. Chess—Per. and soc. publ. I. Napier, William
Ewart, ed. II. Napier,   William Ewart.

NN 0016800   NN MiD MH OCl

NAPIERS | Narration: | Or, | An Epitome | Of | His Booke On The |
Revelation. | Wherein are divers Misteries disclosed, | touching the
foure Beasts, seven Vials, seven Trumpets, | seven Thunders, and seven
Angels, as also a discovery of | Antichrist: together with very probable
conjectures | touching the time of his destruction, and | the end of the
World. | A Subject very seasonable for these last Times. | . . . (3 lines ;
ornaments)
London, | Printed by R. O. and G. D. for Giles Calvert. 1641.| 18.4x14.3 cm.
(1,20)p.

NN 0016801   NNUT-Mc MWiW-C CtY MnU CSmH

Napierski, *pseud.*
see
Lange, Antoni, 1861-1929.

Napierski, Stefan, *pseud.*
see
Eiger, Stefan Marek, 1899-

Napiersky, August Wilhelm, 1823-1885.
Das passageninstrument des Mitauischen
observatoriums. Mitau,1869.

NN 0016804   NjP

[Napiersky, August Wilhelm] 1823-1885.
Die Polhöhe von Mitau. Mitau. J. F. Stefgenhagen, 1873.
18 p. 28cm. in 32cm.

Volume of pamphlets.

NN 0016805   NNC

VOLUME 405

Napiersky, Herbert. Die Amsel schweigt.

PT2621
.U53S3 **Kuhn, Eva.**
Die schöne Lau; ein Märchenspiel, frei nach Mörike.
Leipzig, A. Strauch ₁19—₎

Napiersky, Herbert
In dieser klaren Sternennacht. Stimmensatz.
Hamburg, Hanseatische Verlagsanstalt, c. 1943

Parts.

(Klingender Feierabend - Heft 11.)
Publisher's plate no.: 1311

NN   0016807   NN TxU IaU MB PP

Napiersky, Herbert, *ed.*
Liebliche Weihnacht, Wunder des Leuchtens; neue Lieder
zu Weihnachtszeit in Instrumentalsätzen. ₁Instrumental-
Ausg. Partitur₎ Köln am Rhein, P. J. Tonger ₁19—₎ Pl.
no. P. J. T. 8538.
score (24 p., p. 24 advertisement) 33 cm.
Christmas songs by modern German composers for voice or unison
chorus, string orchestra and woodwinds.
1. Sacred songs (Medium voice) with instr. ensemble. 2. Christmas
music. I. Title.
M2103.N3L5   52-65410

NN   0016808   DLC NN MH

Napiersky, Herbert
Tal und Hügel sind verschneit. Stimmensatz.
Hamburg, Hanseatische Verlagsanstalt, ₍c. 1943₎

Parts.

(Klindjender Ferreabend - Heft 11, Nr. 3.)
Publisher's plate no.: 1311 d¹.

NN   0016809   NN TxU IaU MB PP

Napiersky, Herbert
Wir zünden an den ᴸichterkranz. Stimmensatz.
Hamburg, Hanseatische Verlagsanstalt, ₍c. 1943₎

Parts.

(Klingender Feierabend - Heft 11.)
Publisher's Plate no.: 1311 q.

NN   0016810   NN TxU IaU MB PP

Napiersky, Jakob Gottlieb Leonhard,   1819-1894,
editor.
Bodeckers Chronik livländischer und rigas-
cher Ereignisse, 1593-1638
see under   Bodecker, J.

DK651   NAPIERSKY,JAKOB GOTTLIEB LEONHARD,1819-1894,ed.
.R5N2   Die Erbebücher der Stadt Riga, 1384-1579.
Hrsg. von der Gesellschaft für Geschichte und
Alterthumskunde der Ostseeprovinzen Russlands.
Riga, N. Kymmel, 1888.
83+515 p.

NN   0016812   InU MH

Napiersky, Jakob Gottlieb Leonhard, 1819-
1894, ed.
Die libri redituum der Stadt Riga
see under   Riga.

HQ1018   NAPIERSKY,JAKOB GOTTLIEB   LEONHARD,1819-1894
.G5N2   Die morgengabe des rigischen rechts... Dorpat,
1842.
₁1₎,71,₁1₎p.   20cm.
Inaug.-diss.--Dorpat.

1.Marriage. 2.Gifts.

NN   0016814   ICU

Napiersky, Jakob Gottlieb Leonhard, 1819-1894, *ed.*
Die quellen des Rigischen stadtrechts bis zum jahr 1673.—
Herausgegeben von J. G. L. Napiersky ... Mit zwei schrift-
proben. Riga, J. Deubner, 1876.
cxxxiv, 348 p. 2 fold. pl. (facsims.) 23ᶜᵐ.
Contains: Das älteste für Reval aufgezeichnete Rigische stadtrecht
(ca. 1227-1238.—Das Rigische recht für Hapsal, 1279; Das Hapsalsche
stadtrecht, 1294.—Das Hamburgisch-Rigische recht, 1270.—Die umgear-
beiteten Rigischen statuten.—Die Rigischen civiloquia oder burspraken,
1376-ca. 1650.—Ordnungen des Rigischen rathes, 16.-17. jahrh.—Sena-
tusconsulta, 1295-1673.
1. Law—Riga—Sources. 2. Law—Baltic provinces. I. Riga. Laws,
statutes, etc. II. Reval. Laws, statutes, etc. III. Hapsal, Estonia.
Laws, statutes, etc. IV. Title.
32-24722

NN   0016815   DLC MH NN NNC-L

Napiersky, Karl Eduard, 1799-1864, ed.
Actenstuecke zur Geschichte der Noldeschen Händel in Kurland zu Anfang des siebzehnten Jahrhunderts; gesammelt und mitgetheilt von Dr C. E. Napiersky.   Riga: E. Frantzen, 1839.
xxxvi, 238 p.   ports.   f°.   (Monumenta Livoniae antiquae.
Bd. 2.)
Bibliographical footnotes.

242005A.   1. Courland—Hist., 16th-   17th cent.—Sources. 2. Ser.
N. Y. P. L.   December 30, 1926

NN   0016816   NN

Napiersky, Karl Eduard, 1799-1864, joint
author.
Recke, Johann Friedrich von, 1764-1846.
Allgemeines schriftsteller- und gelehrten-lexikon der pro-
vinzen Livland, Esthland und Kurland. Bearbeitet von Johann Friedrich v. Recke ... und Karl Eduard Napiersky ...
Mitau, J. F. Steffenhagen und sohn, 1827-32.

Napiersky, Karl Eduard, 1799-1864, ed.

Teutonic knights.

Auszug aus der Chronik des Ordens vom deutschen
hause zu St. Marien in Jerusalem, soweit solche auf Livland bezug nimmt, mit einer einleitung, abweichenden
lesarten, anmerkungen und einigen worterklärungen.
(*In* Scriptores rerum livonicarum ... Riga und Leipzig, 1853, '48. 26ᵐᵐ.
1. bd. (1853) p. ₁829₎-906, ₁2₎)

Napiersky, Karl Eduard, 1799-1864, ed.

Eucaedius, Augustinus.

Avlaevm Dvnaidvm, continens seriem ac svccessiones
archiepiscoporvm rigensivm in Livonia, scriptvm ad
rverendissimvm ₁₎ ac illvstrissimvm principem ac dominvm dominvm Sigismvndvm Avgvstvm ... a Avgvstino
Evcaedio ... Witebergae, 1564.
(*In* Scriptores rerum livonicarum ... Riga und Leipzig, 1853, '48. 26ᵐᵐ.
2. bd. (1848) p. ₁393₎-426)

NAPIERSKY, KARL EDUARD, 1799-1864.
Beiträge zur Geschichte der Kirchen und Prediger in
Livland. Mitau, Druck und Verlag von W.F.Häcker,
1843-52.   4 v. in 2 24cm.

Electrostatic reproduction, The New York public library.
Continued by Keussler, August Wilhelm von, 1810-1887. Dr. Napiersky's
Beiträge zur Geschichte der Kirchen und Prediger in Livland fortgesetzt.

CONTENTS.—Heft 1. Livländische Kirchen- und Prediger-Matrikel.—
Heft 2. Lebensnachrichten von den livländischen Predigern, mit litter-
ärischen Nachweisen, T.1. A-G.—Heft 3-4. Lebensnachrichten von den
livländischen Predigern, mit literärischen Nachweisen, T.2-3. H-Z.
1. Esthonia—Biog. 2. Latvia—Biog. 3. Evangelical Lutheran church—
Livonia. 4. Evangelical Lutheran church--Clergy. I. Keussler, August
Wilhelm von, 1810-1887. Dr.   Napiersky's. IV. Beiträge zur
Geschichte der Kirchen und   Prediger fortgesetzt. II. Title.

NN   0016821   NN

Napiersky, Karl Eduard, 1799-1864.
Dr. Napiersky's Beiträge zur Geschichte der
Kirchen und Prediger in Livland fortgesetzt
see under   Keussler, August Wilhelm
von, 1810-1887.

NAPIERSKY, Karl Eduard, 1799-1864.
Bericht an die K. Akademie der Wissenschaften über das Werk Necrolivonica, oder Alterthümer Liv-Esth- und Curlands von Dr. Kruse (Fr.)
St. Petersburg, n.d.

NN   0016823   MH

₁Napiersky, Karl Eduard,₎ 1799-1864, ed.
Das Buch der Aeltermänner grosser Gilde in Riga. Drei
Abtheilungen, von 1540 bis 1566, 1568 bis 1573, und 1590 bis
1611. ₁Riga: E. Frantzen, 1844.₎ 286 p. 8°. (Monu-
menta Livoniae antiquae. Bd. 4.)
"Vorrede" signed: Dr. C. E. Napiersky.
Bibliographical footnotes.

242007A.   1. Gilds—Russia—Riga.   2. Title. 3. Ser.
N. Y. P. L.   January 7, 1927

NN   0016824   NN

Napiersky, Karl Eduard, 1799-1864, ed.
Chronica der prouintz Lyfflandt ...
see under   Russow, Balthasar, ca. 1540-
1601.

Bonaparte
Collection NAPIERSKY, KARL EDUARD, 1793-1864.
No.13521   Chronologischer conspect der lettischen literatur von 1587 bis 1830, mit theilweiser benutzung
v.3   von dr. K.G.Sonntag's handschriftlich hinterlasse-
nen "Notzen zur lettischen literatur von 1700 bis
1825"   Mitau,J.F.Steffenhagen,1831.
281p. 18½cm.   (in Lettisch-literärische
gesellschaft. Magazin 1831. bd.3, 2.-3.stück)
----- Erste fortsetzung die jahre 1831 bis 1843
umfassend, nebst nachträgen zu den früheren
Riga,Müller,1844.
161p. 18½cm.   (in Lettisch-literärische
gesellschaft. Maga-   zin 1844. bd.7, 3.stück)

v.3
Bonaparte ----- Zweite fortsetzung die jahre 1844 bis 1855
Collection umfassend, nebst nachträgen zu den früheren.
No.13523 Mitau,J.F.Steffenhagen und sohn,1858.
131p. 18½cm.   (in Lettisch-literärische
v.12   gesellschaft. Magazin 1858. bd.12. 1.stück)
— ----- Dritte fortzetzung die jahre 1856 bis 1868
v.14   umfassend, bearbeitet von Aug. Döbner.   Mitau,
J.F.Steffenhagen,1869.
80p. 18½cm.   (in Lettisch-literärische
gesellschaft. Magazin 1869. bd.14, 3.
stük)

NN   0016827   ICN NN PU

Napiersky, Karl Eduard, 1799-1864, ed.
...Ergänzung des von Dr. Liborius Bergmann
herausgegebenen Fragments einer Urkunde der
ältesten livländischen Geschichte in Versen
see under   Livländische reimchronik.

[NAPIERSKY, Karl Eduard von] 1799-1864.
Die feldzüge der Russen in Livland und der
Livländer in Russland um das jahr 1480. n.p.,
[1847].

pp. (60).

NN   0016829   MH

VOLUME 405

4Z
850
Napiersky, Karl Eduard, 1799-1864.
Fortgesetzte Abhandlung von livländischen Geschichtschreibern; ein literar-historischer und bibliographischer Versuch. Der kurl. Gesellschaft für Literatur und Kunst vorgelegt im März 1823. Mitau, J. F. Steffenhagen, 1824. 176 p.

NN   0016830   DLC-P4 NN

DK65
.A45
Napiersky, Karl Eduard, 1799-1864, ed.

Russia. *Arkheograficheskaía komissiia.*
Грамоты, касающіяся до сношеній Сѣверо-Западной Россіи съ Ригою и ганзейскими городами въ XII, XIII и XIV вѣкѣ. Найдены въ рижскомъ архивѣ К. Э. Напіерскимъ и изданы Археографическою комиссіею. Санктпетербургъ, Въ Тип. Имп. Академіи наукъ, 1857.

[Napiersky, Karl Eduard] 1799-1864, ed.
Index corporis historico-diplomatici Livoniae, Esthoniae, Curoniae; oder: Kurzer auszug aus derjenigen urkundensammlung welche für die geschichte und das alte staatsrecht Liv-, Ehst- und Kurland's, mit unterstützung Sr. Majestät des hochseligen kaisers Alexander I von Russland, und auf verwilligung Sr. Majestät des königs Friedrich Wilhelm III. von Preussen, aus dem geheimen, ehemaligen Deutsch-ordens-archive zu Königsberg von den ritterschaften Liv-, Ehst- und Kurland's zusammengebracht worden ist, und wie solche, mit einigen stücken aus inländischen archiven vermehrt, bei einer

edlen ritterschaft des herzogthums Livland aufbewahrt wird. Auf veranstaltung und kosten der verbundenen ritterschaften Liv-, Ehst- und Kurland's hrsg. ... 1198-1631. Riga und Dorpat, E. Frantzen, 1833-35.
2 v. in 1. 36½ᶜᵐ.

CONTENTS. — 1. th. Vom jahre 1198 bis zum jahre 1449. — 2. th. Vom jahre 1450 bis zum jahre 1631, mit einigen anhängen.

1. Teutonic knights — Hist. — Sources.   2. Baltic provinces — Hist.—Sources.   I. Title.

Library of Congress   DK511.B3N2

5—7163

NN   0016833   DLC PU NN KU NNC

[Napiersky, Karl Eduard] 1799-1864, ed.
Kurze Uebersicht der älteren Geschichte der Stadt Riga, von 1200 bis 1581. Versuch einer gründlichern Behandlung derselben; nebst einem Anhange von Urkunden. (In: Monumenta Livoniae antiquae. Riga, 1844. Bd. 4, p. [xv]-ccclxv. 8°.)

"Vorrede" signed: Dr. C. E. Napiersky.
Bibliographical footnotes.

242007A. 1. Riga—Hist. 2. Title.   3. Ser.
N. Y. P. L.   January 7, 1927

NN   0016834   NN

Napiersky, Karl Eduard, 1799-1864, ed.

Livländische reimchronik.
Ditleb's von Alnpeke Livländische reimchronik, enthaltend Der riterlichen meister vnd bruder zu Nieflant geschicht; nach dem Bergmannschen drucke mit den ergänzungen und den abweichenden lesearten der Heidelberger handschrift neu bearb. und hrsg.
(*In* Scriptores rerum livonicarum ... Riga und Leipzig, 1853, '48. 26ᶜᵐ. 1. bd. (1853) p. [489]-827).

Napiersky, Karl Eduard, 1799-1864, ed.

Horner, Thomas, *15th cent.*
Livoniae historia in compendium ex annalibus contracta a Thoma Hornero Egrano. Item, De sacrificiis et idolatria veterum Livonum et Borussorum libellus Iohannis Menecii. Witebergae, ex officina Iohannis Lufft, 1562.
(*In* Scriptores rerum livonicarum ... Riga und Leipzig, 1853, '48. 26ᶜᵐ. 2. bd. (1848) p. [371]-392)

Napiersky, Karl Eduard, 1799-1864, ed.

Fabricius, Dionysius, *17th cent.*
Dionysii Fabricii ... Livonicae historiae compendiosa series. In quatuor digesta partes ab anno millesimo centesimo quinquagesimo octavo usque ad annum MDCX. Curante Gustavo Bergmann P. R. Ed. 2. auctior et emendatior. Stanno Ruiensi, CIƆIƆCCXCV.
(*In* Scriptores rerum livonicarum ... Riga und Leipzig, 1853, '48. 2. bd. (1848) p. [427]-510)

DK511
.L3S4
bd. 1
Napiersky, Karl Eduard, 1799-1864, ed.

Henricus *Lettus, 13th cent.*
Origines Livoniae sacrae et civilis, sev Chronicon livonicvm vetvs, continens res gestas trivm primorvm episcoporvm: qvibvs devictae a Saxonibvs, et ad sacra christianorvm tradvctae Livonibvs absolvitvr historia: a pio qvodam sacerdote, qvi ipse tantis rebvs interfvit, conscripta, et ad annvm Christi nati CIƆIƆCCXXVI. dedvcta. E codice ms. recensvit, scriptorvm cvm aetate, tvm locis vicinorvm testimoniis illvstravit, Silvamqve docvmentorvm et triplicem indicem

adiecit Ioan. Daniel Grvber ... Francofvrti et Lipsiae, anno MDCCXL.
(*In* Scriptores rerum livonicarum ... Riga und Leipzig, 1853, '48. 26 cm. 1. bd. (1853) p. [i]-xii, [1]-488)

DK3
.A133
Napiersky, Karl Eduard, 1799-1864, ed.

Russia. *Arkheograficheskaía komissiia.*
Russisch-livländische Urkunden. Gesammelt von K. E. Napiersky. St. Petersburg, Buchdr. der Kaiserlichen Akademie der Wissenschaften, 1868.

DK511
.L3S4
2 bd.
Napiersky, Karl Eduard, 1799-1864, ed.

Hermelin, Olof Nilsson Skragge, 1658-1709†
Svmmi polyhistoris Olavi Hermelini ... De origine Livonorvm disqvisitio, qvam propter raritatem ac praestantiam ad flagrantissima mvltorvm desideria pvblicae lvci restitvit M. Georgivs Caspari ... Lipsiae, apvd haeredes I. Grossii, MDCCXVII.
(*In* Scriptores rerum livonicarum ... Riga und Leipzig, 1853, '48. 26 cm. 2. bd. (1848) p. [543]-566)

Napiersky, Karl Eduard, 1799-1864, ed.

Menius, Fridericus, *d.* 1659.
Friderici Menii ... Syntagma de origine Livonorum. Dorpati, 1632.
(*In* Scriptores rerum livonicarum ... Riga und Leipzig, 1853, '48. 26ᶜᵐ. 2. bd. (1848) p. [511]-542)

Napiersky, K[arl] E[duard], 1799 - 1864.
Zweite Fortsetzung des chronologischen Conspect's der lettischen Literatur, die Jahre 1844 bis 1855 umfassend, nebst Nachträgen zu den früheren, bearbeitet von C. E. Napiersky. Mitau: J. F. Steffenhagen vnd Sohn. 1858. 1 p.l., 131 p. 12°.

1. Lettish literature.—Bibliography,   1844-55.
N. Y. P. L.   N. Y. PUBLIC LIBRARY April 27, 1911.

NN   0016843   NN

NAPIERSKY, Leonhard.
Die morgengabe des rigischen rechts. Dorpat, 1842.

pp. 71.
Diss. --- Dorpat.

NN   0016844   MH-L DLC-P4

Napiersky, Stefan, *pseud.*
see
Eiger, Stefan Marek, 1899–

[Napini, Bartolommeo]
Hd42.575b Rime pedantesche di celebre autor calabrese. Sopra varj morali, critici, e dillettevoli argomenti secondo il gusto del presente secolo; opera data in luce da Aristarco Scanabue [pseud.] che serva di utile intrattenimento per ogni onesta, e civil conversazione ... Londra, Paoli Sei, 1780.
3 v. in 1. 16cm.
Made up of the sheets of the Guastalla edition of 1759, with new t.-p. and with the first leaf of each preface reprinted in order to attribute

it to Aristarco Scanabue, pseudonym used by Baretti in Frusta letteraria, instead of to Don Polipodio Calabro - cf. Melzi,G. Dizionario di opere anonime e pseudonime di scrittori italiani, t.2, Milano,1852.
The t.-ps. of parts 2 and 3 are the same as that of part 1, with the numeral "I" changed in ink to read "II" and "III" respectively.

NN   0016847   CtY ICU

[Napini, Bartolommeo]
Hd42.575 Sonetti pedanteschi di Don Polipodio Calabro [pseud.] podagogo, e pastoro; por la prima volta da un fedelissimo ms. raccolti, e pubblicati da mastro Erenio Calepodigero. Centuria prima [-terza]. Guastalla, Giacomo Benj.Kross,1769-70.
3 v. in 1. 15½ cm.
The same sheets were reissued in 1780, with title: Rime pedantesche di celebre autor calabrese. Sopra varj morali, critici, e dillettevoli argomenti secondo il gusto del

presente secolo; opera data in luce da Aristarco Scanabue [pseudonym used by Baretti in Frusta letteraria]

NN   0016849   CtY MH

Napione (Carolus Antonius). Memoria sul lincurio. 14 pp., 1 l. 4°. Roma, A. Fulgoni, 1795.

NN   0016850   DNLM

QT
N214m
1912
NAPIONE, Ettore.
Il motore umano, come è costrutto, come funziona, quanto può rendere. Torino, Casa editrice "Praxis" [1912] 359 p.

NN   0016851   DNLM

Napione, Giovanni Francesco Galeani, conte di Cocconato Passerano.
see
Galleani Napione, Giovanni Francesco, conte di Cocconato Passerano, 1748-1830.

Napione, Teresio.
...Studi sulla fortuna di Chateaubriand nella letteratura e nell'arte italiana; contributo alla storia del nostro romanticismo. Torino: G. B. Paravia & c., 1928. vii, 179 p. plates, port. 4°.
At head of title: Teresio Napione, Fr. Leone delle Scuole cristiane.
Bibliographical footnotes.

1. Chateaubriand, François Auguste   René, vicomte de, 1768-1848.
2. Romanticism in literature, Italian.   3. Romanticism in art.
N. Y. P. L.   June 14, 1929

NN   0016853   NN MH OrU

Napione di Cocconato, Gian Francesco Galeani,Conte
see
Galleani Napione, Giovanni Francesco, conte di Cocconato Passerano, 1748-1830

VOLUME 405

Napisanie o pravej vere.
   De auctore expositionis verae fidei S.
Constantino Cyrillo adscriptae ...
      see under Kos, Stanislaus, S.S.

Napjus, Eelco, 1728-1803.
   Geschiedkundige kronijk en beschrijving van
de stad Sneek, door E. Napjus ... 2. verm. en
verb. druk.   Sneek, Smallenburg, 1826.
   xxii, 162 p.   23 cm.

NN 0016856   NNC MH

Napjus, Eelco, 1728-1803.
   Historisch chronyk, of, Beschryvinge van Oud en
Nieuw Sneek ... door Eelco Napjus ... Sneek,
Olingius, 1772.
   156 p. 19 cm.

   Second edition has title: Geschiedkundige kronijk en beschrijving van de stad Sneek.

NN 0016857   NNC MH

Napjus, Jan Wendelinus, 1891
   [Alardus Auletius, 1545-1606] Ned. tschr.
geneesk., 1925, 69: pt. 2, 2559-63.

NN 0016858   DNLM

RG591 Napjus, Jan Wendelinus, 1891-
.N2   Over de wijze van ontstaan van de mola hydati-
       dosa... Groningen, M. de Waal, 1917.
          [7], 83 p. 23½ cm.

       Proefschrift—Groningen.

       1. Mole, Hydatid.

NN 0016859   ICU DNLM MiU

Napkelet. 1.-   kötet; 1923 jan.-
   Budapest, Magyar Irodalmi Társaság.
      v. in   21-25 cm.
   Frequency varies.
   Editors: 1923-37, C. Tormay.—1937-   M. Kalláy.

   1. Hungarian literature—Period.   I. Magyar Irodalmi Társaság.
II. Tormay, Cécile, 1876-1937, ed. III. Kalláy, Miklós, 1887-   ed.

PH3001.N3   57-55672

NN 0016860   DLC MH NNC NN OClW

053.9
N162

   Napkelet; heti közlöny.
      évf. 1-
             1857-
   Pest, Emich Gusztáv, 1857-
      v. illus., ports. 29cm. weekly.

   Within évf. issues numbered sz. 1-52.
   Vol. 1 has subtitle: budapesti képes ujság.
   Annual t.-p. has also subtitle: A hasznos is-
meretek, társaslet, irodalom, művészet és divat
erdekében, hölgyek és férfiak szamara egyarant.
   Imprint varies: évf. 1-2, 1857-58, Müller Emil.
   Editor: Vahot   Imre.

NN 0016861   NNC

AE
31
N214
1927

   A Napkelet lexikona. Budapest, Magyar
Irodalmi Társaság, 1927.
   2 v. illus. (part col.), ports.

   1. Encyclopedias and dictionaries,
Hungarian I. Magyar Irodalmi Társaság,
Budapest

NN 0016862   DNLM

HJ9362
.T66

   Napky, M., joint author.

   Tosco, Manuel.
      Ingresos del gobierno local, 1924-25/1951-52, preparado
por M. Tosco y M. Napky. Tegucigalpa, Banco Central de
Honduras, 1953.

NAPLES, Étienne.
   De la stipulation pour autrui et de la
gestion d'affaires, notamment dans leurs rapports avec l'assurance sur la vie au profit d'un
tiers. Bordeaux, 1897.

   Thèse --- Bordeaux.

NN 0016864   MH-L

Naples, Marie Caroline Ferdinande Louise de, duchesse de
   Berry
         See
Berry, Marie Caroline Ferdinande Louise de Naples, duchesse de,
   1798-1870.

Naples.
   A Carlo Troya il municipio di Napoli, 20
settembre 1901.   Napoli, F. di Gennaro e
A. Morano, 1901.
   22 p.   l.8°.
   "Carlo Troya. Discorso del professore
Michelangelo Schipa", p. [9]-22.

NN 0016866   MH

Naples.
   Annuario. Notiziario delle autorità, amministrazioni ed
instituzioni napoletane.
   Napoli.
      v. 27 cm.
   Issues for   "a cura dell'Ufficio statistica del comune."

   1. Naples—Registers.   I. Naples. Divisione statistica.

JS31.N352   49-43004*‡

NN 0016867   DLC

HJ9051
.N3B2

   Naples.
      ... Bilancio di previsione dell'entrata e della
spesa per l'esercizio finanziario ... 1924-
   Napoli, 1924-
      1 v.   tables (part fold.) 34 cm.
   At head of title, 1924-   : Comune di
Napoli ...

NN 0016868   DLC

Naples.
   Bollettino del comune di Napoli
      see
Napoli; rivista municipale.

Naples

—. Bollettino medico demografico del comune
di Napoli. No. 5 (Feb. 5), 1881. fol. [Napoli,
1881.]

NN 0016870   DNLM

Naples.
   Carlo Poerio. Edizione a cura e spese del
municipio di Napoli.   Napoli, F. Giannini, 1867.
   l.8°.
   "Errata" slip inserted at end.

NN 0016871   MH

Naples.
   Winckelmann, Johann Joachim, 1717-1768.
   Ercolano e Pompei. Piccola antologia Winckelmania-
a a cura del comune di Napoli nel III. Congresso
archeologico internazionale. [Napoli, Tip. Giannini]
1912.

Naples.
   Haec est illa Neapolis. A cura del comune di Napoli
MCMXIII. [Napoli, F. Giannini & figli, 1913]
   vii, [1], 94 p., 1 l. plates, ports. 23°°.
   Title within ornamental border.
   CONTENTS.—Napoli nel canto dei poeti.—Ricordi dell' Università di
Napoli: Dalla Storia dello studio di Napoli di G. Origlia. L'Università
di Napoli prima del '60, di L. Settembrini. F. de Sanctis e la sua se-
conda scuola, di F. Torraca.
   1. Naples—Descr. 2. Art—Naples. 3. Naples. Università. 4. Sanc-
tis, Francesco de, 1818-1883. I. Origlia Paolino, Giovanni Giuseppe.
II. Settembrini, Luigi, 1813-1876. III. Torraca, Francesco, 1853-1938.
IV. Title.
                                        14-7601 Revised
   Library of Congress   DG844.A5 1913

NN 0016873   DLC NN

4HF Naples.
661   Il mercato bestiame dal Medio
     evo al 1934, XIII E. F. Napoli,
     F. Giannini, 1935.
        79 p.

NN 0016874   DLC-P4

Naples .
   Napoli nella storia e nella vita. A cura del comune.   Napoli:
[F. Giannini & figli,] 1916.   xli, 146 p. facsim., illus. (incl.
ports.), plan, plates. f°.
   "Il comune di Napoli questi scritti, dettati dall'amore delle patrie memorie,
raccolse e ordinò, perchè di Giuseppe de Blasiis, patriota, scrittore, insegnante, rima-
nesse vivo l'esempio e il ricordo."
   Contents: Introduzione. Commemorazione del de Blasiis nel Consiglio Comunale di Napoli. Dalle opere di Giuseppe de Blasiis. Lettere e documenti riguardanti
le relazioni tra il de Blasiis e il comune di Napoli. Bibliografia.

   1. Naples (city).—History.   2. Blasiis, Giuseppe de,
1832-1914.   1832-1914.
N. Y. P. L.   October 21, 1922.

NN 0016875   NN CSt

Naples.
   Relazione sul progetto di convenzione tra il
comune di Napoli e la Società dei tramvai
napoletani. 1908.
   66 p.

NN 0016876   PP

Naples.
   Relazione sulle opere di risanamento, ampliamento
e fognatura della città di Napoli...
   Napoli, 1

TD80
.N3A3

NN 0016877   DLC

VOLUME 405

Naples.
 Riscatto del debito vitalizio del comune di
Napoli; a proposta e relazione dell' Assessore A.
Germicca. 1908.
 41 p.

NN   0016878   PP

Naples.
 ₍Correra, Luigi₎
 Saggi della tipografia napoletana nel sec. xv; catalogo
di xl fotografie riprodotte a cvra del mvnicipio di Napoli
ed esposte alla Mostra internazionale di Torino del MCMXI
... Napoli, F. Perrella e c., 1911.

Naples.
 Stato civile delle dodici sezioni della città di Napoli e
suoi villaggi dall'anno 1809 all'anno 1865. Formato sui
registri depositati nello Archivio di Stato di Napoli. Napoli, Officina tip. di R. Rinaldi e G. Sellitto, 1879.
  1 v. (unpaged) 30 cm.
  Introd. signed : Camillo Minieri Riccio.

  1. Naples—Statistics, Vital.   I. Minieri-Riccio, Camillo, 1813–
1882. II. Naples. Archivio di Stato. III. Title.

  HB3600.N36A5   72–223975

NN   0016880   DLC

Naples. Studi e proposto per la esecuzione del
progetto definitivo della fognatura generale
della città di Napoli. cl, 208 pp., 12 pl., 2 maps.
fol. *Napoli, F. Giannini ° figli, 1888.*

NN   0016881   DNLM

Naples. Accademia degli aspiranti naturalisti
    see   Accademia degli aspiranti naturalisti.

Naples.   Accademia delle scienze
    see
Accademia delle scienze, Naples.

Naples. Accademia delle scienze fisiche e
                                  matematiche
    see
Accademia delle scienze fisiche e matematiche,
                                  Naples.

Naples.   Accademia di archeologia,lettere e
                                  belle arti.
    see
Accademia di archeologia, lettere e belle arti,
                                  Naples.

N6014
.N26

Naples. Accademia di belle arti e liceo artistico.
 Mostra celebrativa del bicentenario, 1752–1952. Galleria
dell'Accademia, ottobre–novembre, 1954. ₍Introd. al Catalogo: Costanza Lorenzetti. Catalogo curato da W. Nespoli,
M. Napoli, F. Caiazzo. Napoli, 1954₎
  67 p. 145 plates. 22 cm.

  1. Art, Italian—Exhibitions.   I. Title.

                                      A 56–4376

Harvard Univ. Library
for Library of Congress   ₍8₎

NN   0016886   MH DLC MiU

780.7   Naples. Accademia di musica.
N16𝑒   Leggi e stabilimenti della nobile Accademia
        di musica delle signore dame, e de'signori
        cavalieri nella città di Napoli esistente
        con real permesso de'7. maggio 1778.
        Napoli, F. Raimondi, 1789.
        64p. 20cm.

NN   0016887   IU

Naples. Accademia di scienze morali e politiche
        see
Accademia nazionale di scienze morali e politiche, *Naples.*

Naples.   Accademia ercolanese di archeologia
        see
Accademia ercolanese di archeologia, Naples.

Naples. Accademia internazionale letteraria,
        scientifica ed artistica
        see   Accademia internazionale letteraria,
scientifica ed artistica, Naples.

Naples,   Accademia medico chirurgica.
        see
Accademia medico-chirurgica, Naples.

Naples. Accademia militare
        see
Naples. Scuola militare.

Naples. Accademia degli aspiranti naturalisti
    see   Accademia degli aspiranti naturalisti.

Naples. Accademia pontaniana
        see
Accademia pontaniana, *Naples.*

Naples. Accademia pontaniana di scienze morali e politiche
        see
Accademia nazionale di scienze morali e politiche, *Naples.*

Naples. Archivio Angioino
        see
Naples. Archivio di stato.Registri angioini.

Music
D780
AN16
        Naples. Archivio dell'Oratorio dei Filippini.
        Città di Napoli. Parma, Officina grafica
        Fresching, 1918.
        xiv, 108 p. illus., facsim. 31cm. (Cata-
        logo generale)

        At head of title: Associazione dei musicologi
        italiani.
        Bound with Naples. Conservatorio di musica
        "San Pietro a Majella." Bibliotheca. Città
        di Napoli. 1934.

NN   0016896   NNC

CD1606
1953
        Naples. Archivio di Stato.
         Archivi privati; inventario sommario. ₍Introd. di R.
        Filangieri₎ Roma, 1953–54.
          2 v. 25 cm. (Ministero dell'interno. Pubblicazioni degli archivi
        di Stato, 11, 14)

          1. Archives—Italy—Naples.   (Series: Italy. Ministero dell'in-
        terno. Pubblicazioni degli archivi di Stato, 11, 14)
                                              A 57–231
        Harvard Univ. Library
        for Library of Congress   ₍8₎

NN   0016897   MH DLC CtY ICN PU NN IaU OU ICU MiU MU

Naples. Archivio di Stato.
 Cholera on board U.S. Man-of-War Delaware,
1835, at Naples
        see under title

Naples. Archivio di Stato.
 Codice diplomatico amalfitano, a cura di Riccardo Filangieri di Candida. Napoli, Stab. tip. S. Morano, 1917–51.
  2 v. facsim. 25 cm.
  Vol. 2 has imprint : Trani, Vecchi.
  CONTENTS.—v. 1. Le pergamene di Amalfi esistenti nel R. Archivio
di Stato di Napoli (dall'anno 907 al 1200)—v. 2. Le pergamene di
Amalfi già nell'Archivio di Stato di Napoli (1201–1822) Appendice
(860–1291)
  1. Amalfi—Hist.—Sources.   I. Filangieri di Candida Gonzaga,
Riccardo, conte, 1882–   II. Title.

  DG975.A43N3   67–33333

        ICN InU NNC NN MH
NN   0016899   DLC ViU CLU CtY OCU IU MH-L DDO WU

Naples. Archivio di Stato.
 Indice dei processi civili, notati
nella Pandetta scrivano cristina,
dell'Uffizio di giustizia. Napoli,
Officina tipografica di R. Rinaldi e
G. Sellitto, 1882.
4K   29 p.
11557

NN   0016900   DLC-P4

Naples. Archivio di Stato.
 Indice dei processi, notati nella
Pandetta detta miscellanea dell'Uffizio
di giustizia. Napoli, Officina tipografica di R. Rinaldi e G. Sellitto, 1882.
4K   57 p.
11558

NN   0016901   DLC-P4

Naples. Archivio di Stato.
 Inventario cronologico-sistematico dei registri angioini
conservati nell'Archivo di Stato in Napoli. Napoli, Tip.
di R. Rinaldi e G. Sellitto, 1894.
  lxxxvii, 542 p. 28 cm.
  Preface signed by the editor, Bartolommeo Capasso.
  Includes bibliographical references.

  1. Naples (Kingdom)—History—Sources—Bibliography. 2. Naples
(Kingdom). Regia Cancelleria.   I. Capasso, Bartolommeo, 1815–
1900. II. Title.

  CD1606 1894   73–252169

NN   0016902   DLC MU NN

HE840
.N3C5
        Naples. Archivio di Stato.

        Cisternino, Riccardo, *ed.*
         La marina mercantile napoletana dal xvi al xix sec.; capi-
        tani in alto mare (cronache) ₍di₎ Riccardo Cisternino ₍e₎
        Giuseppe Porcaro. Napoli, F. Fiorentino, 1954.

VOLUME 405

DG848.46
.N3
   Naples. Archivio di stato.
      Mostra del risorgimento italiano
   nelle provincie meridionali; catalogo
   compilato dal sopraintendente Eugenio
   Casanova. Napoli, Stab. tip. S.
   Morano, 1911.
      xvi, 197 p. illus., facsims. 19 cm.

      1. Italy, Southern--History.
   2. Naples (Kingdom)--History--Sources.
   3. Italy--History--1789-1870--Sources.
   I. Casanova, Eugenio, 1869-1951, comp.
   II. Title

NN 0016904   NRU NN

JS5852
.A3C8
   Naples. Archivio di Stato.

   Cutolo, Alessandro, 1899-
      I privilegi dei sovrani angioini alla città di Napoli.
   Napoli, A cura del Comune, 1929.

DG848
.11
.N38
   Naples. Archivio di Stato.

   Naples (Kingdom) Regia Cancelleria.
      Regesto della Cancelleria aragonese di Napoli, a cura di
   Jole Mazzoleni. Volume unico. Napoli, L'Arte tipografica, 1951.

   Naples. Archivio di stato.
      Regesto delle pergamene di Castelcapuano
   (a. 1268-1789)
      see under   Mazzoleni, Jole.

   Naples. Archivio di stato.
      Regii neapolitani archivi monumenta edita ac illustrata.
   Neapoli, ex Regia typographia, 1845-61.
      6 v. 28 x 22½ᵐ.
      Edited by Antonio Spinelli, Antonio de Aprea, Michele Baffi, Giuseppe
   Genovesi, Gennaro Seguino, Angelo Granito and Carlo Guacci.
   Vol. 2 numbered vol. 1. pt. 2.
      CONTENTS.--v. 1. 703-947.--v. ¡2¿ 948-980.--v. 3. 981-1000.--v. 4. 1001-
   1048.--v. 4. 1049-1114.--v. 6. 1115-1130.

      1. Naples (Kingdom)--Hist.--Sources.   I. Spinelli, Antonio, ed.

   DG847.1.A4   3-30632 rev 2

NN 0016908   DLC NN MoU DDO NIC TNJ DeU CtY PU

   Naples. Archivio di stato.
      Repertorio delle pergamene della università
   e della città di Aversa dal luglio 1215 al 30 aprile,
   1549
      see under   Aversa, Italy. Università.

   Naples. Archivio di Stato.
      Repertorio delle pergamene della università o comune di
   Gaeta (1187-1704). Napoli, Tip. di R. Rinaldi e G. Sellitto, 1884.
      viii, 335 p. 24 cm.
      "Autografi de' sovrani, vicerè e grandi uffiziali del regno": p. 295-
   323.

      1. Gaeta, Italy--History--Sources.   I. Title.

   DG975.G13N36   72-216895

NN 0016910   DLC NN CU OU

   Naples. Archivio di stato.

   Minieri-Riccio, Camillo, 1813-1882, ed.
      Saggio di codice diplomatico formato sulle antiche scrit-
   ture dell'Archivio di stato di Napoli, per Camillo Minieri Riccio ... Napoli, Officina tip. di R. Rinaldi e G. Sellitto ¡etc.¿ 1878-80.

   Naples .   Archivio di stato.
      La "Statistica" del regno di Napoli del 1811
      see under   Cassese, Leopoldo, ed.

HB3600
.N36A5
   Naples. Archivio di Stato.

   Naples.
      Stato civile delle dodici sezioni della città di Napoli e
   suoi villaggi dall'anno 1809 all'anno 1865. Formato sui
   registri depositati nello Archivio di Stato di Napoli. Napoli, Officina tip. di R. Rinaldi e G. Sellitto, 1879.

   Naples. Archivio di stato.
      Syllabus membranarum ad Regiae siclae archivum pertinen-
   tium ... Neapoli, ex Regia typographia, 1824-45.
      3 v. in 2. 29 x 23ᵐ.
      CONTENTS.--I. Quo membranae ... ab anno 1266. ad annum 1285., seu
   ... Caroli I. ... regno scriptae, continentur, perpetuisque adnotationibus
   illustrantur opera et studio A. A. Scotti, 1824.--II. A Caroli II. ad
   Roberti regnum. Pars prima, in qua membranae a prid. id. Ian.
   MCCLXXXV. ad XI. kal. Ian. MCCC. scriptae continentur. Opera et studio
   Antonii de Aprea, 1832. Pars secunda, in qua membranae a kal. Ian.
   MCCC. ad XI. kal. Ian. MCCCIX. scriptae continentur. Opera et studio
   Antoni de Aprea. 1845.
      1. Archives--Italy--Naples. 2. Naples (Kingdom)--Hist.--Sources--
   Bibl. I. Scotti, Angelo Antonio, ed. II. Aprea, Antonio de, ed. III.
   Title.

   CD1606 1824   7-3413 rev 2

NN 0016914   DLC NIC IU WaU CtY MdBP PU

   Naples. Archivio di Stato. Cancelleria angioina.
      Della dominazione angioina
      see under   Minieri-Riccio, Camillo,
   1813-1882.

   Naples. Archivio di stato. Carte farnesiane.

   Pérez Bustamante, Ciriaco.
      El cronista Antonio de Herrera y la historia de Alejandro
   Farnesio, por C. Pérez Bustamante ... Santiago, Tip. de "El
   Eco franciscano", 1934.

DH185
.C3
   Naples. Archivio di stato. Carte farnesiane.

   Cauchie, Alfred, 1860-1922, ed.
      ... Inventaire des Archives Farnésiennes de Naples au point
   de vue de l'histoire des Pays-Bas catholiques, pub. par Alfred
   Cauchie ... et Léon van der Essen ... Bruxelles, Kiessling et cⁱᵉ,
   1911.

   Naples. Archivio di stato. Fascicoli angioini.
      Bruchstücke mittelalterlicher enqueten
      see under   Sthamer, Eduard Heinrich,
   1883-

   Naples. Archivio di stato. Registri angioini.

   Boüard, Alain de, 1882-   ed.
      Documents en français des archives angevines de Naples
   (règne de Charles Iᵉʳ); transcrits par P. Durrieu et A. de
   Boüard, publiés par A. de Boüard ... Paris, E. de Boccard,
   1933.

DG12
.B85
vol. 17
   Naples. Archivio di stato. Registri angioini.

   Jamison, Evelyn Mary, 1877-
      Documents from the Angevin registers of Naples:
   Charles I.
      (In British School at Rome. Papers. London. 27 cm. v. 17
   (new ser., v. 4, 1949) p. ¡87¿-180¿)

1552
.669
.6625
   Naples. Archivio di stato. Registri angioini
      Inventario cronologico-sistematico dei
   Registri angioini conservati nell'Archivio
   di stato in Napoli. Napoli, Rinaldi, 1894
      lxxxvii,542 p. 28 cm

      Pref. signed: Bartolommeo Capasso

      1. ANJOU, HOUSE OF 2. ARCHIVES - NAPLES
   (KINGDOM) I. Capasso. Bartolomeo, 1815-1900
   II.T

NN 0016921   NjP NNC ICU ICN CU

   Naples. Archivio di stato. Registri angioini.
      Nuovi volumi di registri angioini ora formati
   con quaderni e fogli che già esistevano dimenticati
   e confusi nell'Archivio di Stato di Napoli
      see under   Capasso, Bartolommeo, 1815-
   1900.

   Naples. *Archivio municipale.*
      Catalogo ragionato dei libri, registri e scritture esistenti
   nella sezione antica, o prima serie, dell'Archivio municipale
   di Napoli (1387-1806) Napoli, Stab. tip. del cav. F. Giannini, 1876-1920.
      3 v. in 4. 27 cm.
      Part 1-2 compiled by Bartolommeo Capasso; pt. 3 by Raffaele
   Parisi.
      CONTENTS.--pt. 1. Città in generale ed in relazione colla suprema
   autorità dello Stato e col resto del Regno.--pt. 2. Tribunale degli eletti
   o di S. Lorenzo e sue dipendenze.--pt. 3. Tribunali e deputazioni ordi-
   narie e straordinarie. 2 v.
      1. Archives--Naples. 2. Naples (Kingdom)--Hist.--Sources.
   I. Capasso, Bartolommeo, 1815-1900, comp. II. Parisi, Raffaele, comp.
   III. Title.

   CD1606 1876   55-45627

NN 0016923   DLC NN CtY

4K
9277
   Naples Arte della Seta
      Statuti dell'arte della seta a
   Napoli, e legislazione della Colonia
   di S. Leucio. Appendice al volume
   "L'arte della seta a Napoli e la Colonia
   di S. Leucio". Napoli, 1933.
      145 p.

      (Consiglio provinciale dell'economia
   corporativa di Napoli. Monografie
   economiche)

NN 0016924   DLC-P4

   Naples. Associazione italiana di diritto marittimo
      see   Associazione italiana di diritto marittimo

   Naples. Avvocatura erariale
      Indice delle quistioni di dritto
   trattate dalla R. Avvocatura erariale
   di Napoli nelle allegazioni difensive
   messe a stampa nell'anno 18
   Napoli, G. Salvati, 18 -
      v. 25½cm.

NN 0016926   MH-L

   Naples. Azienda autonoma di soggiorno, cura e turismo
      see
   Azienda autonoma di soggiorno, cura e turismo, *Naples*.

   Naples. Banco di Napoli
      see   Banco di Napoli.

   Naples. Banco di SS. Giacomo e Vittoria
      see   Banco di SS. Giacomo e Vittoria,
   Naples.

VOLUME 405

Naples. Basilica del Carmine Maggiore.
Basilica del Carmine Maggiore, Napoli. Per
l'inaugurazione dei lavori di ricostruzione e di
restauro della basilica, 29 gennaio 1955. Napoli, Tipomeccanica, 1955.
31 [1] p. illus. 24 cm

NN   0016930   ODaU-M

Naples. R. Biblioteca borbonica
see
Naples. Biblioteca nazionale.

Naples. R. Biblioteca Brancacciana.
... Catalogo topografico-descrittivo dei manoscritti
della R. Biblioteca Brancacciana di Napoli
Napoli, L. Lubrano [1918-
1918/19-   illus. 28ᶜᵐ. [With Bollettino del bibliofilo. Napoli. v. 1-
At head of title: Alfonso Miola.
Issued in parts with each number of the Bollettino, and paged continu-
ously.
In the present copy these parts are collected at end of v. 1-   of
Bollettino.
1. Manuscripts. Italy—Catalogs.   i. Miola, Alfonso, 1844-
Library of Congress   Z1007.B69   21-21641

NN   0016932   DLC NNC CtY ICU MH

Naples. R. Biblioteca Brancacciana.
Notizie storiche, bibliografiche e statistiche
sulla Biblioteca Brancacciana di Napoli nel
MDCCCXCVIII.   Roma, Società editrice Dante
Alighieri, 1900.
cover-title, 1 p.l., [5]-8 p.   25 cm.

NN   0016933   CtY

Naples. Biblioteca dei Girolamini
see
Naples. Biblioteca del monumento nazionale dei
Girolamini.

Naples. Biblioteca del monumento nazionale dei Girolamini.
I codici manoscritti della Biblioteca oratoriana di Napoli; illustrati da Enrico Mandarini ...   Opera premiata
dalla R. Accademia di archeologia, lettere e belle arti di
Napoli.   Napoli [etc.] A. & S. Festa, 1897.
xix, 401, [2] p. illus., facsim. 34ᶜᵐ.
Label mounted on cover: Napoli, Libreria antica e moderna Riccardo
Marghieri di Gius ...
1. Manuscripts. Italy—Catalogs.   i. Mandarini, Enrico.   ii Title
Library of Congress   Z6621.N25   2-586

NN   0016935   DLC NNC NjP CtY NIC

Naples. Biblioteca del monumento nazionale dei
Girolamini.
L'Oratorio dei Filippini e la scuola musicale
di Napoli ...
see under   Pannain, Guido, 1891-

Naples. Biblioteca nazionale.
L'arte della miniatura nel secolo XIV
see under   De arte illuminandi.

Naples. Bibliotea nazionale.
Aulo Giano Parrasio; studio biografico-critico.
Da codici e documenti inediti ···
see under   Lo Parco, Francesco, 1872-

Z 809   NAPLES--Biblioteca nazionale
.N21   Le biblioteche della Campania et della
Calabria. Elenco e consistenza. A cura della
Soprintendenza bibliografica di Napoli.   Napoli,
1950.
94 p.   (I quaderni della Biblioteca
nazionale di Napoli. Serie 3, no.3)
Introduzione signed: Guerriera Guerrieri,
Soprintendente bibliografica.
1. Libraries--Italy. I. Guerrieri, Guerriera,
ed. II. ts

NN   0016939   InU FTaSU MH

Naples (*City*) Biblioteca nazionale.
Catalogo dei codici arabi della Biblioteca nazionale di
Napoli; per Lupo Buonazia. [Firenze, Successori Le
Monnier, 1880]
1 p. l., [200]-241 p. 23½ᶜᵐ.
Separate from Cataloghi dei codici orientali di alcune biblioteche d'Italia,
stampati a spese del Ministero della pubblica istruzione. Firenze, 1878-86,
fasc. ii, p. 200-241.
Subject entries: 1. Manuscripts, Arabic—Catalogs.   2. Manuscripts.
Italy—Catalogs.
8-16176
Library of Congress, no.   Z6621.N21A8.

NN   0016940   DLC

Naples. Biblioteca nazionale.
Catalogus bibliothecae latinae veteris et classicae
manuscriptae, quae in Regio neapolitano museo borbonico adservatur, descriptus a Cataldo Iannellio. Neapoli, ex Regia typographia, 1827.
xii, 302 p. 28½ᶜᵐ.
1. Manuscripts. Italy—Catalogs. 2. Manuscripts, Latin—Catalogs.
i. Jannelli, Cataldo.
Library of Congress   Z6621.N21L3   7-15248

NN   0016941   DLC PPL ICU NjP

FILM   Naples. Biblioteca nazionale.
15538   Catalogues bibliothecae latinae veteris et class-
Z   icae manuscriptae, quae in Regio neapolitano museo
borbonico adservatur, descriptus a Cataldo Iannellio.
Neapoli, ex Regia typographia, 1827.
xii, 302 p. On film (negative)
Microfilm. Original in Biblioteca nazionale,
Naples.
1. Manuscripts. Italy--Catalogs. 2. Manuscripts,
Latin--Catalogs. I. Jannelli, Cataldo, 1781-1841.

NN   0016942   CU

Naples. Biblioteca nazionale.
Codices graeci mss. Regiae bibliotecae Borbonicae descripti atque illustrati...   Neapoli, Ex
Regia typographia, 1824-1832.
2 v.

NN   0016943   DDO

Naples. Biblioteca nazionale.
Codices graeci mss. Regiae bibliothecae borbonicae descripti atque illustrati a Salvatore Cyrillo ...   Neapoli,
Regia typographia, 1826-32.
2 v.   29ᶜᵐ.
1. Manuscripts. Italy—Catalogs. 2. Manuscripts, Greek—Catalogs.
i. Cirillo, Salvatore.
Library of Congress   Z6621.N21G7   7-15249

NN   0016944   DLC MH

Naples. Biblioteca nazionale.
Codices graeci mss. Regiae bibliothecae
Borbonicae descripti atque illustrati a
Salvatore Cyrillo ... Neapoli, Regia
typographia, 1826-32.
Microfilm copy, made in 1961 of the
original in Vatican. Biblioteca vaticana.
Positive.
Negative in Vatican. Biblioteca vaticana.
Collation of the original as determined
from the film: 2 v.
1. Manuscripts. Italy--Catalogs. 2.
Manuscripts, Greek--Catalogs. I. Cirillo,
Salvatore. (Series: [Manuscripta, micro-
films of rare and out-of-print books.
List 25, no.15])

NN   0016946   MoSU

Naples. Biblioteca nazionale.
Codices mss. operum S. Thomae de Aquino, et
S. Bon... venturae in Regia Neapolitana Biblioteca
see under   [Miola, Alfonso], 1844-

Naples. Biblioteca nazionale.
Codicum saeculo xv impressorum qui in Regia biblioteca
borbonica adservantur catalogus ordine alphabetico digestus
notisque bibliographicis illustratus labore, et industria F.
Francisci de Licteriis ...   Neapoli, ex Regia typographia 1828-
33.
3 v. 44ᶜᵐ.
CONTENTS.—t. 1. A-K.—t. 2. L-Q.—t. 3. R-Z.
Z240.N21

—— Supplementum ad catalogum Codicum saeculo xv impressorum qui in Regia biblioteca borbonica adservantur
ordine alphabetico digestum ... labore et industria F. Francisci
de Licteriis ...   Neapoli, ex Regia typographia, 1841.
1 p. l., 276 p. 44ᶜᵐ.
1. Incunabula—Bibl.—Catalogs.   i. Lettieri, Francesco.   ii. Title.
6-13782 Revised
Library of Congress   Z240.N21 Suppl.

NN   0016949   DLC IU ICU NN

Naples. Biblioteca nazionale.
Cocozza, Giovanni, 1859-
... Di un nuovo giornale di contabilità finanziaria e
patrimoniale per le biblioteche italiane fondato su' principii dell' equivalenza ... Napoli, Tip. di F. Sangiovanni,
1904.

Naples. Biblioteca nazionale.   L017.45 N16
Indice delle pubblicazioni periodiche possedute dalle biblioteche
di Napoli/ [6],109 p. Q. Napoli 1899.
Compiled under the direction of the Biblioteca universitaria and the Biblioteca
nazionale of Naples.

NN   0016951   ICJ

VOLUME 405

Naples. Bibliotheca Nazionale.
Mercurii Monachi pernecessaria de pulsibus
doctrina ex ms. cod
see under   Mercurius Monachus.

Naples. Biblioteca nazionale.
Mostra bibliografica agostiniana

see under

Naples. Mostra bibliografica agostiniana, 1954.

Naples. Biblioteca nazionale.
Mostra bibliografica del 1848 napoletano.
Napoli, 1948.

47 p. illus. (I quaderni della Biblioteca
nazionale di Napoli, ser.3, n.2)

NN 0016954   MH

Naples. Biblioteca nazionale.
Mostra bibliografica per la storia della Chiesa in Campania e in Calabria; Anno Santo 1950. A cura di Guerriera Guerrieri, soprintendente bibliografica. Napoli, 1950?

71 p. illus. 25 cm.

Bibliography: p. 63-68.

1. Calabria — Church history — Bibl. 2. Campania — Church history—Bibl. I. Guerrieri, Guerriera, ed. II. Title.

Z7778.I 8N3   016.2745   51-31758

NN 0016955   DLC CtY MiD DDO NN

Naples. Biblioteca nazionale.
... Mostra di autografi e carteggi di Giacomo
Leopardi. [Napoli] 1937.
35 p. facsims. 20 cm.
At head of title: R. Biblioteca nazionale
"Vittorio Emanuele III" - Napoli.
1. Leopardi, Giacomo, conte, 1798-1837.
2. Leopardi, Giacomo, conte, 1798-1837 -
Bibliography.

NN 0016956   NNC DLC-P4

---

*ML141
.N36V43   Naples. Biblioteca Nazionale.
1951   Nel cinquantesimo anniversario della
morte di Giuseppe Verdi. Mostra [e]
catalogo. Napoli, 1951.
64 p. port. 21 cm. (I Quaderni
della Biblioteca Nazionale di Napoli.
Ser. 3, n. 4)

1. Verdi, Giuseppe— Bibl. 2. Verdi,
Giuseppe—Catalogs. 3. Verdi, Giuseppe,
1813-1901—Anniversaries, etc.
1951. 4. Music—Exhibitions.

NN 0016957   MB MH

Naples. Biblioteca nazionale.
Notizia della Biblioteca nazionale di Napoli. [Napoli,
Pe' tipi del Fibreno, 1872]

95 p. 24cm.

Signed: Il prefetto della Biblioteca, Vito Fornari.
"Published for the Vienna exposition of 1873."
"Appendice prima. Manoscritti": p. [39]-69. "Appendice seconda. Libri
a stampa": p. [71]-95.

1. Manuscripts. Italy—Catalogs. 2. Incunabula—Bibl.—Catalogs. 3.
Vienna. Weltausstellung, 1873—Italy. I. Fornari, Vito, 1821-1910. II.
Title.

Library of Congress   Z810.N21   12—19241

NN 0016958   DLC

Naples.   Biblioteca nazionale.
Notizia della Biblioteca nazionale di Napoli.
Napoli, Detken & Rocholl, 1874.
119 p.

At head of title: Vito Fornari.
Published for the Vienna exposition of 1873.
"Appendice prima. Manoscritti": p. [39]-83.
"Appendice seconda. Libri a stampa": p. [85]-
119.

NN 0016959   IU NN InU CU

Naples. Biblioteca nazionale.
Notizie di manoscritti neolatini
see under   Miola, Alfonso, 1844-

Naples. Biblioteca nazionale.
Notizie storiche, bibliografiche e statistiche
sulla Biblioteca nazionale di Napoli nel
MDCCCXCVIII. Roma, Società editrice Dante
Alighieri, 1900.

cover-title, 19 p. 25½cm.

Includes lists of "Manoscritti più antiche" and "Incunabuli e libri rari" (p.10-11)
"Bibliografia": p.14-19.

NN 0016961   MiU CtY

Naples. Biblioteca nazionale.
I papiri ercolanesi. Napoli, Grannini, 1954.

1 v. (Its Quaderni, ser.3, no.5)

NN 0016962   MH NcD NjP

Naples. Biblioteca nazionale.
Quaderni.
serie 1, no. 1
serie 2, no.
serie 3, no. 1-

Napoli, Industria tipografica artistica,
1938-
v. illus., facsims. 21-25cm.

NN 0016963   NNC CtY

Naples. Biblioteca nazionale.
Raccolta de' pue belli...dipinti, musaici ed
altri monumenti rinvenuti negli scavi reali di
Ercolano, di Pompei e di Stabia... Napoli, 1857.

NN 0016964   PPL

Naples. Biblioteca nazionale.

[Correra, Luigi]
Saggi della tipografia napoletana nel sec. xv; catalogo
di xl fotografie riprodotte a cvra del mvnicipio di Napoli
ed esposte alla Mostra internazionale di Torino del MCMXI
... Napoli, F. Perrella e c., 1911.

Naples. Biblioteca nazionale.
Le scritture in volgare
see under   Miola, Alfonso, 1844-

Naples. Biblioteca nazionale
see also Naples. Museo nazionale di S. Martino. *Biblioteca.*

Naples. Biblioteca Nazionale. Mss (IE35)
Introduzione alla lingua portoghese
see under title

Naples. Biblioteca nazionale.
Mss.(III.B.27)
Δημωδη ποιηματα άγνωστου συγγραφεως
(κατα τον κωδικα III.B.27 της Βιβλιοθηκη
της Νεαπολεως) Άθηναι, 1955. 28 p.
facsim. 26cm. (Athens. Panepistēmion.
Spoudastērion byzantinēs kai neohellēnikēs

philologias.[Dēmosieumata.9])

At head of title: Γεωργιου θ. Ζωρα.
Title transliterated: Dēmōdē poiēmata
agnōstou syngrapheōs.

1. Poetry,   Byzantine—Collections. I. Series.   II. Zoras, Giorgio,
ed.

NN 0016970   NN

Naples. Biblioteca nazionale. Mss. (VI.E.40)
[6 anonymous l'Homme armé Masses]

15th-century ms. in choir-book format.
Microfilm of the original in the Biblioteca Nazionale,
Naples. 1 reel.

NN 0016971   NjP

Naples. Biblioteca nazionale. Mss. (VI.G.11)
[Missel de Rouen, notation à petits carrés liés sur 4
lignes noires. 12th cent.]

237 [i.e. 474] p.
Microfilm (positive)

NN 0016972   MH-I

Naples. Biblioteca nazionale. Mss. (VI.G.34)
[Sacred vocal music. 12th cent.]

139 [i.e. 278] p.
Microfilm (positive)

NN 0016973   MH-I

Naples. Biblioteca nazionale. Mss.
(XII. E. 4)

Govi, Gilberto, 1826-1889.
Intorno alla data di un discorso inedito pronunciato da Federico Cesi fondatore dell' Accademia de' Lincei e da esso intitolato: Del natural desiderio di sapere et institutione de Lincei per adempimento di esso. Ricerche del socio G. Govi lette nella seduta del 4 aprile 1880.
(*In* Atti della R. Accademia dei Lincei. Memorie della Classe di scienze morali, storiche e filologiche. Roma, 1880. 29½cm. ser. 3, vol. v, p. 244-261)

Naples. Biblioteca nazionale. Mss. (xii. E. 27)
De arte illuminandi.
An anonymous fourteenth-century treatise, De arte illuminandi, the technique of manuscript illumination; translated from the Latin of Naples ms. xii. E. 27 by Daniel Varney Thompson, jr. ... and George Heard Hamilton. New Haven, Yale university press; London, H. Milford, Oxford university press, 1933.

Naples. Biblioteca nazionale. Mss. no. XIII. B.26.
... Fablo Giordano's relation of Capri
see under   Giordano, Fabio, ca. 1540-
ca. 1590.

VOLUME 405

Naples. Biblioteca nazionale. Mss. no.
    XIII. B. 26.
₍Douglas, Norman₎
    ₍Materials for a description of Capri. London and
Napoli, 1904–15₎

PR2061   NAPLES. BIBLIOTECA NAZIONALE. Mss. (XIII.B.29)
.M48A17   Un ignoto ricettario medico inglese del XIV
1940   secolo trovato nella Biblioteca nazionale di
Napoli. Testo originale, trascrizione a fronte,
introduzione, note e glossario a cura di
Tarquinio Vallese. Napoli, A. G. D. A. ₍1940₎
    66 p. 19 facsims.
    Text (p.18–55) with facsimile of manuscript
and transcription on opposite pages.

    1. Medicine, Medieval.

NN   0016978   ICU

B3581   Naples. Biblioteca nazionale. Mss.
.O7   (XIII. B. 53)
1869 a   Vico, Giovanni Battista, 1668–1744.
    Cinque orazioni latine inedite di Giovan Battista Vico, pub-
blicate da un cod. ms. della Biblioteca nazionale per cura del
bibliotecario Antonio Galasso. Con un discorso preliminare.
Napoli, D. Morano ₍etc.₎ 1869.

Naples. Biblioteca universitaria
    see
Naples. Università. *Biblioteca.*

Naples. Botanical garden
    see
Naples. Università. *Orto botanico.*

Naples. Camera di commercio ed arti
    see Naples (Province) Camera di **commercio ed arti.**

Naples. Camera di commercio ed industria
    see
Naples (Province) Camera di **commercio ed industria.**

Naples. Camera di commercio, industria e **agricoltura**
    see Naples (Province) Camera di **commercio, industria**
e agricoltura.

---

375   Naples. Casa de' Miracoli.
:215s   Statuto della Real Casa di Educazione delle
RARE BOOK   donzelle ben nate eretta nel soppresso Monist-
COLLECTION tero de' Miracoli nella Città di Napoli.
    [Ornament] Napoli, Dalla Tipografia di Angelo
Trani, 1818.
    79 p. 1 table (fold.) 21cm.

    Head and tail pieces. Catchwords.
    Dedication signed: Napoli 28 Luglio 1818.
L'Umilissimo e Fedelissimo Suddito Il Presidente della Real Casa de' Miracoli, Duca

de' Sangro.
    Note inserted: Liegatura alle Armi di
Ferdinando II. Re delle due Sicilie 1818.
Copia di presentazione.
    Bookplate of Oliver Henry Perkmis.
    Bound in red leather, heavily stamped;

gilt border, spine and all edges. Royal coat
of arms in gilt on both boards.

NN   0016987   FU

W 1   NAPLES. Casa di salute Fleurent.
NA138L   Bollettino.
    Napoli [1875?]-1909.
        v. illus.
    Part of title on microfilm.
    No more published?
    Title: Bollettino della Casa di
salute Fleurent, Napoli

NN   0016988   DNLM

Naples. Centro de studi per la Magna Grecia
    see   Centro di studi per la Magna
    Grecia, Naples.

Naples. Centro mediterraneo della moda e dell'artigianato
    see
Centro mediterraneo della moda e dell'artigianato, *Naples.*

LC1047   Naples. Centro studi per il Mezzogiorno.
.I8R8   Russo, Giuseppe, 1905–
    ... Scuola, istruzione tecnica e sviluppo industriale del
mezzogiorno. Napoli, Istituto meridionale editoriale, 1949.

Naples. Certosa di San Martino.
    Monuments artistiques et religieux de la
Chartreuse de S. Martin à Naples
    see under title

Naples. Certosa di San Martino
    see also
Naples. Museo nazionale di S. Martino.

Naples. Chambre de commerce française
    see   Chambre de commerce française,
Naples.

Law   Naples. Charters.
    Privilegia fidelissimae civitatis Neapolis.
[Napoli,1536].
    16 l.   27 cm.
    Bound with Naples.Charters. Privilegij et
capituli con altre gratie concesse a la fidelissima cita de Napoli. [Napoli,1543].
    Colophon: Stampato in Napoli per Ioanne
Sultzbach Alemano,appresso alla gran Corte
de la Vicaria...M.D.XXXVI.
    Title in red and black within ornamental

civitatis...1536.
woodcut border;initials.
On verso of t.p.: In gene//rali par//la-
mento nea//poli cele//bra//to.
Publisher's device on verso of last leaf.

    1.Naples-Charters,grants,privileges. I.Nap-
les(Kingdom)Laws,statutes,etc. II. Title.

NN   0016996   DLC

Italy   Naples. Charters.
N16   Privilegi, capitvli, e gratie, concesse al
18   fedelissimo popvlo napolitano, & alla sua piazza.
1624   Con le sue annotationi di nuouo aggionte. Et il
discorso intorno all'officio di decurioni; hoggi
detti capitanij d'ottine, seu piazze populari,
di nuouo ampliato, & aumentato. Opera composta
per Francesco Imperato ... Napoli, per Gio.
Domenico Roncaglilo, 1624.
    96,[3]p. 20cm.

NN   0016997   CtY-L

Law   Naples. Charters.
    Privilegii et capitoli,con altre gratie
concesse alla fideliss. città di Napoli,&
Regno per li... ri di casa de Aragona,con-
firmati et di nuouo concessi per la maestà
cesarea dell'imperator Carlo Qvnto,et re Filippo nostro signore,con tutte le altre gratie concesse per tutto questo presente anno
MDLXXXVII Con nuoue additioni,et la tauola
delle cose notabili. In Venetia,per Pietro
Dusinelli,ad instantia di Nicolò de Bottis,
1588.

    1 p.l.,[8],183 l.   31 cm.
    Title vignette(coat of arms of Naples);
head pieces;initials.
    Side notes.

    1.Naples-Charters,grants,privileges. I.Na-
ples(Kingdom)Laws,statutes,etc. II.Title.

NN   0016999   DLC CtY IU MH MH-BA

Law   Naples Charters.
    Privilegii et capitoli con altre gratie
concesse alla fidelissima città di Napoli,&
regno per li...Rì di casa de Aragona. Confir-
fimati, et di nuovo concessi per...imperator
Carle V.et re Filippo nostro signore. Con
tutte le altre gratie concesse per tutto
questo presente anno MDLXXXVII. Con nuove addizioni,&la tavola delle cose notabili. E di
nuovo ristampati con le nuove gratie,e privilegii conceduti e confirmati dalla Sacra

cesarea e cattolica maesta di Carle VI.im-
peratore. Sino all'anno 1720. Tomus I₍-II].
Milano,1719-20[v.1,1720].
    2 v.   34 cm.
    Vol.2 has title: Privilegj e capitoli con
altre grazie concedute alla...citta,e regno
di Napoli delli...re'Filippo II,Filippo III,
Filippo IV, e Carle II.
    1.Naples-Charters,grants,privileges.I.Nap-
les (Kingdom) Laws,statutes,etc. II.Title.

NN   0017001   DLC IU

Law   Naples, Charters.
    Priuilegij et capituli con altre gratie
conces//se a la fidelissima cita de Napoli:
& regno prt li....ri de casa de Aragona con-
fir//mati,& de nouo concessi per la maesta
caesarea. [Napoli, 1543].
    1 p.l.,[2],192 l.   27 cm.
    Colophon: ₍T₎Stampato in...Napoli per Gio-
uanne sulezbach alemano...nel anno mille et
cinquecento et quaranta tre...
    Title within ornamental woodcut border;i-
nitials.

    Bound with Privilegia fidelissimae civi-
tatis Neapolis. Napoli, 1536.

    1.Naples-Charters,grants,privileges. I.Nap-
les(Kingdom)Laws,statutes,etc. II.Title.

NN   0017003   DLC MH-L WaU CtY

Naples. Circolo cattolico per gl'interessi di
    Napoli
        see   Circolo cattolico per gl'interessi di
    Napoli.

VOLUME 405

Naples. Circolo degli aspiranti naturalisti

see

Societa di naturalisti in Napoli.

Naples. Circolo giuridico
        see   Circolo giuridico di Napoli.

Naples. Circolo numismaticó
        see   Circolo numismaticó napoletano,
        Naples.

Naples. Circolo scacchistico
        see   Circolo scacchistico napoletano.

Naples. Clinica tisiologica
        see
        Naples. Università. *Istituto sanatoriale "Principi di
        Piemonte."*

Naples.   Collegio asiatico
        see
Naples. Istituto orientale.

Naples. Collegio de' nobili
        see   Collegio de' nobili, Naples.

Naples. Collegio degli ingegneri ed architetti
        see   Collegio degli ingegneri ed architetti,
        Naples.

W 6   NAPLES. Collegio degli Speziali.
P3   Parere dell'almo Collegio de Spetiali di Napoli sopra l'Opobal-
v. 2487   samo mandatoli dalli signori consoli del Collegio de' Spetiali di
no. 7   Roma. Con un picciolo Trattato dell'opobalsamo orientale di
           Giuseppe Donzelli ... Napoli, Francesco Savio, 1640.
           [8] p. 22 cm.

           1. Donzelli, Giuseppe, 1596-1670 2. Rome (City) Collegio
           degli Speziali I. Title

NN 0017013   DNLM

Naples. Collegio dei cinesi
        see
Naples. Istituto orientale.

Naples. Collegio di musica.   8051.3
    Atti sovrani risguar'nti il riordinamento del Real collegio di
    musica di Napoli.
    Napoli. Stamperia reale. 1856. xvi, 58, (12) pp. Tables. 27
    cm., in 4s.

L7467 — Naples, City, Italy. F.a. Music.

NN 0017015   MB

Naples. Collegio di musica.
    Statuto e regolamento del Real Collegio di musica di Napoli.
    Napoli: G. de Angelis, 1873.   48 p.   8°.

1. Music—Conservatories—Italy—   Naples.   July 2, 1925
N. Y. P. L.

NN 0017016   NN

Naples. Collegio militare
        see
Naples. Scuola militare.

---

510   Naples. Collegium neapolitanum Societatis Jesu.
I29   Institutiones geometricae, et arithmeticae
          propositae studiosis mathematicae in
          Collegio neapolitano Societatis Jesu.
          Neapoli, Ex Typographia F.Mosca, MDCCXI
          [i.e.1711]
          161,[2] p. front.,diagrs.(part fold.)
          15cm.

          1.Mathematics - Early works to 1800.
          2.Geometry - Early works to 1800. LC

NN 0017018   CLSU

Naples. Comitato cittadino per l'anno giubilare
        see
        Comitato cittadino per l'anno giubilare, *Naples.*

Naples. Commissione municipale per la conservazione
    dei monumenti.
    L'abside dell' antica basilica di S. Giorgio Mag-
    giore in Napoli. Napoli, 1881.
    40 p.

NN 0017020   MH

Naples. Commissione municipale per la con-
    servazione dei monumenti.
    ...Scoperte di antichità in Napoli dal 1876
    a tutto il 1897...
        see under   Colonna, Fernando.

---

f NA9204   Naple   Commissione per lo studio del
N3A2   piano regolatore generale.
City &   Relazione illustrativa del nuovo piano regolatore redatta
Regional   dall'avv. Nicola Galdo.   Napoli, 1955-58.
Planning   5 v. in 3. illus., plates(part mtd., part col.) plans(part col.)
Library   tables. 33cm.

           At head of title: Comune di Napoli. Ufficio tecnico. Com-
           missione per lo studio del piano regolatore generale.

           1. Cities and towns - Planning - Naples. 2. Naples (City) -
           Civic improvement. I. Galdo, Nicola.

NN 0017022   CU NNC

Naples. Congresso degli scienziati italiani.

see

Congresso degli scienziati italiani. 7th, Naples,
                                        1845.

Naples. Congresso di medicina e igiene coloniale. *5th,*
    1934
        see
Congresso di medicina e igiene coloniale.

Naples. Congresso di medicina legale e delle assicura-
    zioni e di antropologia criminale
        see
Congresso di medicina legale e delle assicurazioni e di an-
    tropologia criminale, *Naples, 1940.*

Naples. Congresso di studi coloniali. *2d,* 1934
        see
Congresso di studi coloniali, 2d Naples, 1934.

Naples. Congresso giuridico nazionale. *4th,* 1897
        see Congresso giuridico nazionale. *4th, Naples, 1897.*

Naples. Congresso internazionale marittimo,
                                        1871.
        see
Congresso internazionale marittimo, Naples, 1871.

Naples. Congresso nazionale per la pubblica
    moralita, 4th,. 1914.
        see   Congresso nazionale per la pubblica
    moralita.

Naples. Conservatorio di musica.
    [Collection of manuscript scores of sacred and
    secular vocal music from the Naples Conservatory
    of music
        see under title

Naples. Conservatorio di musica.
    Mostra donizettiana. Catalogo del R. Conservatorio di musica
    di Napoli.   Bergamo: Istituto italiano d'arti grafiche, 1897.
    39 p. incl. facsim. 23cm.

                                        JUILLIARD FOUNDATION FUND.
    1. Donizetti, Gaetano, 1797-1848—
    —Italy—Naples.   Bibl. 2. Music—Exhibitions
    N. Y. P. L.   August 31, 1933

NN 0017031   NN CtY

VOLUME 405

Naples. Conservatorio di musica. Premio-Bellini.
Florimo, Francesco, 1800–1888, ed.
   Album Bellini. Premio-Bellini; introduzione, programma, cronaca dell' inaugurazione del monumento, appendice, rendiconto, a cura di Francesco Florimo. Napoli, Pei tipi Nicotra, 1887.

Naples. Conservatorio di musica "San Pietro a Majella."
   Annuario.
   Napoli.
      v. illus. 25 cm.

   MT5.N2C85   A. 61-1096
   Oregon. Univ. Libr.
   for Library of Congress   ⟨8⟩†

NN   0017033   OrU DLC

Naples. Conservatorio di musica "San Pietro a Majella."
   Bollettino. anno 1–
   nov. 1937–
   Napoli.
      v. in   illus., ports., music. 20 cm. 4 no. a year.

   MT5.N2C83   780.72945   50–41687

NN   0017034   DLC

Naples. Conservatorio di musica, "San Pietro a Majella".
   Catalogo delle opere musicali ... Citta di Napoli
      see under   Associazione dei musicologi italiani.

Film
M
19
   Naples. Conservatorio di musica "San Pietro a Majella".
   [Collection of manuscript scores of keyboard music. n.p., n.d.]

   Pagination of manuscripts: p. 70–100.
   Contents.- Ciaccona.- Balletto.- Ballo della battaglia.- Corrente.- Corrente.- Toccata.- Toccata.- Recercar.- Recercar.- Pastorale.

      1. Piano music - To 1800.

NN   0017036   CLU

Naples. Conservatorio di musica "San Pietro a Majella."
   Concerto sinfonico ... Programma.
   ⟨Napoli, 19
      v. 18½–21ᶜᵐ.
   Title varies slightly.

      1. Concerts—Programs. 2. Orchestral music—Analysis, appreciation.
                                              46–36658
   Library of Congress   MT125.N28   Brief cataloging

NN   0017037   DLC

Naples. Conservatorio di musica "San Pietro a Majella."
   Mostra autografi musicali della scuola napoletana; settembre-ottobre 1936. Napoli, Confederazione fascista dei professionisti e degli artisti, Unione provinciale ⟨1936⟩
      iv, 58 p. ports., facsims. (music) 20 cm.
   At head of title: Anno xiv, celebrazioni della campania.

      1. Music—Manuscripts—Exhibitions. 2. Music—Manuscripts—Italy—Naples. 3. Manuscripts—Italy—Catalogs. 4. Manuscripts, Italian—Catalogs. I. Title.

   ML141.N3C6   62–28183

NN   0017038   DLC NN CU ICU IaU MH

FILM
A954
M
   Naples. Conservatorio di musica "San Pietro a Majella." Biblioteca. MSS.
   (33.5.16)
   [Cantate ed arie.   16--]
   150 ℓ. On film (negative)

   Microfilm copy of the manuscript.
   Title supplied by U.C. Music Library.
   For voice and continuo.   Italian words.
   Includes cantatas and arias by A. Stradella, P.S. Agostini, and other.

   I. Stradella, Alessandro, 1655-1682./Works, vocal. Selctions. II. Agostini, Pietro Simone, ca. 1650-ca. 1690./ Works, vocal. Selections.

NN   0017040   CU

FILM
MS
M786.802
N161
   Naples. Conservatorio di musica "San Pietro a Majella"–-Mss. (61.4.11)
   ⟨A collection of 34 intraas, canzonas, pastorales, frammentos, versos, pezzos, ricercars and chansons by Galluccio, Erc. Pasquini, P. Vandelem, Sansone, Trabaco, G. B. Converso, C. Merulo, Gaetano and anonymous composers. In keyboard score⟩ ca. 1600.
   score (64 ℓ.)

   Pages numbered as leaves. Leaves 20, 25ᵛ

   and 28–31ʳ blank?
   Inventory: Gasparini, Naples conservatory catalogue, 1934, 549.
   Microfilm (negative) of Ms. Naples, Conservatorio di musica, 1968. 1 reel. 35mm.

NN   0017042   IU

Naples. R. Conservatorio di musica "San Pietro a Majella."
   Museo storico musicale.
   ... Il Museo storico musicale di "S. Pietro a Majella." (Con 155 fotografie fuori testo). Napoli, F. Giannini & figli, 1930.
      3 p. l., ⟨9⟩–158 p. plates, ports., facsim. (music) 25ᶜᵐ.
   At head of title: Ettore Santagata.
   Illustration mounted on cover.
   "I sei conservatori di Napoli": p. ⟨9⟩–13.

      1. Musical instruments—Catalogs. 2. Musicians—Portraits—Catalogs. 3. Musicians—Autographs. 4. Naples—Conservatories of music.   I. Santagata, Ettore, comp.
                                              41–40856
   Library of Congress   ML136.N15C6
                              ⟨2⟩   781.9

NN   0017043   DLC CU IU NcD NN ViU

Naples. Consiglio comunale.
   Atti...Consiglio comunale. 1908–

NN   0017044   PP

Naples. Consiglio Comunale.
   Bilancio di previsione dell'entrata e della spesa per l'esercizio finanziario 1909.

NN   0017045   PP

Naples. Consiglio notarile.
   Rivista di legislazione fiscale e giurisprudenza notarile; tasse—imposte—riscossione—notariato. Rivista delle riviste ...
      v. ⟨1⟩–   1906–
   Napoli, Stabilimento tipografico cav. N. Jovene e c. ⟨etc.⟩ 1906–

Naples. Convegno dei tecnici e degli industriali del Mezzogiorno e delle isole. *1st, 1949*
   see Convegno dei tecnici e degli industriali del Mezzogiorno e delle isole. *1st, Naples, 1949.*

Naples. Convegno di genetica, *1952*
      see
   Convegno di genetica, *Naples, 1952.*

Naples. Convegno nazionale interuniversitario di studi politico-sociali, 1940
      see
   Convegno nazionale interuniversitario di studi politico-sociali, *Naples, 1940.*

Naples. Deputazione napoletana di storia patrie
      see
   Deputazione napoletana di storia patria, Naples.

JS81
.N352
   Naples. Divisione statistica.
   Naples.
      Annuario. Notiziario delle autorità, amministrazioni ed instituzioni napoletane.
      Napoli.

Naples. *Divisione statistica.*
   ... Annuario statistico ...
   Napoli, 19
      v. maps, diagrs. 31ᶜᵐ.
      At head of title, 19   : Ufficio di statistica del comune di Napoli;
   19   : Divisione statistica del comune di Napoli.

      1. Naples—Stat.
   Library of Congress   HA1879.N3A32   45–53312

NN   0017052   NN IEN DLC

Naples. Divisione statistica.
   Pubblicazioni dell' ufficio statistico della città di Napoli. Nos. 43, 46, 47, 49–52 bis, 1879; Nos. 1–5, 46, 47, 1880. imp. fol. [Napoli, 1879–80.]
   Continued as the following.

NN   0017053   DNLM

Naples. Divisione statistica.
   Relazione sul v. censimento generale della popolazione e sul 1. censimento industriale ⟨1911⟩. Napoli: F. Giannini & figli, 1912.
   35, 83 p., 19 diagr., 2 maps. f°.

      1. Naples (Italy).—Census, 1911.
   N. Y. P. L.   March 24, 1916.

NN   0017054   NN

NAPLES. Divisione statistica.
   ...Il VII censimento della popolazione in Napoli; saggi sul movimento demografico partenopeo. Napoli: F. Giannini & figli [1934?] 327 p. incl. tables. 27½cm.

      At head of title: Ufficio di statistica del comune di Napoli diretto dal dott. Paolo Conca...

   814931A. 1. Naples—Census, 1931.

NN   0017055   NN

VOLUME 405

Naples. Duomo.
Metropolitanae ecclesiae Neapolitanae provisiones consistoriales a saeculo xv ad xix ex authenticis documentis in lucem editae
see under Calenzio, Generoso, ed.

Naples. Ente autonomo del porto di Napoli
see
Ente autonomo del porto di Napoli.

Naples. Ente autonomo del Teatro di San Carlo
see Ente autonomo del Teatro di San Carlo, *Naples.*

Kress
Room
Naples. Esposizione, 1842.
Elenco di saggi de' prodotti della industria napolitana presentati nella solenne mostra del dì 30 maggio 1842 ... Napoli, Dalla tipografia Elantina, 1842.
103 p. 26.5 cm.

Added engraved title page.

1.Industrial arts - Sicily. 2.Sicily - Industries. I.Title. II.R.Istituto d'incoraggiamento di Napoli.

NN 0017059 MH-BA

Naples. Esposizione nazionale d'igiene, 1900.
Bologna alla esposizione nazionale d'igiene in Napoli...
see under title

709.6711
N215a
Naples. Exposition d'art colonial, 1934.
Arts du Cameroun à l'Exposition d'art de Naples, 1934. [Paris, Agence économiques des colonies autonomes et des territoires africains sous mandat, 1934?]
23p. illus., 24 plates. 22cm.

1. Art. Exhibitions. 2. Art. Cameroons. I. Title.

NN 0017061 IEN

Naples. Exposition internationale de l'industrie maritime, 1870.
Règlement pour l'Exposition internationale de l'industrie maritime à Naples en 1870. Naples, Empr. [!] des frères Testa, 1870.
25, [2] p. 21½cm.

1. Naval art and science—Exhibitions.

18–17273

Library of Congress VM6.N2

NN 0017062 DLC

Naples. Fondazione politecnica del mezzogiorno
see
Fondazione politecnica del mezzogiorno, *Naples.*

Naples. Gabinetto letterario
see Gabinetto letterario, *Naples.*

Naples. Grande archivio del regno
see Naples. Archivio di stato.

Naples. Gruppo universitario "Mussolini"
see
Gruppo universitario fascista "Mussolini," *Naples.*

Naples. International congress of agricultural credit
see
International congress of agricultural credit. *1st, Naples,* 1938.

Naples. International Congress of Philosophy. *5th, 1924*
see International Congress of Philosophy, 5th, Naples, 1924.

Naples. Internationaler agrarkredit-kongress.
see
International congress of agricultural credit, 1st, Naples, 1938.

Naples. Institut français
see
Grenoble. Université. Institut français de Naples

W 1
NA1405
NAPLES. Istituto antirabbico.
Rendiconto delle vaccinazioni anti rabbiche.
1896–98—
Napoli.
v.
Issued 1904 as Le vaccinazion' antirabiche.
Editors: 1896–98, 1901- A. Calabrese (with A. Russo, 1901-)— 1898-1900, D. Pace and L. d'Amato.

1. Rabies - Immunity I. Calabrese, Alfonso, ed. II. Pace, Domenico, ed. Title

NN 0017072 DNLM

Naples. Istituto d'incoraggiamento.
see
Istituto d'incoraggiamento di Napoli.

Naples. Istituto di belle arti.
Statuto organico dell' Istituto di belle arti. [Naples, 1861]
35 p. 29cm.

NN 0017074 NN

Naples. Istituto di finanza della R. Università
see Naples. Università. *Istituto de finanza.*

Naples. Istituto di scienze e lettere "Santa Chiara"
see
Naples. Istituto superiore di scienze e lettere "Santa Chiara."

Naples. Istituto di tisiologia "Principe di Piemonte"
see
Naples. Università. *Istituto sanatoriale "Principi di Piemonte."*

Naples. Istituto italiano per gli studi storici
see Istituto italiano per gli studi storici, *Naples.*

W 1
NA141G
NAPLES. Istituto medico-cerusico-farmaceutico.
Giornale. v. 1, quaderno 1; genn. 1846. Napoli.
120 p. illus.
No more published?

NN 0017079 DNLM

Naples. Istituto nazionale dei motori.
... Prove sui gasogeni costruiti in Italia per autoveicoli. Napoli, Fondazione politecnica del mezzogiorno, 1940.
2 p. l., 167, [1] p. illus., fold. tables, diagrs. 25ᶜᵐ.
At head of title: Consiglio nazionale delle ricerche. Istituto nazionale dei motori, diretto dal prof. ing. P. Ferretti.

1. Gas-producers. 2. Motor fuels. I. Fondazione politecnica del mezzogiorno, Naples.
45–26595
Library of Congress TL229.G3N3
[2] 629.25144

NN 0017080 DLC MiU NNE TxHR

Naples. Istituto omeopatico.
Prolusioni al corso di materia medica
see under Migliore, Carlo.

Naples. Istituto orientale.
Annali dell' Istituto superiore orientale.
Roma, 19
v. plates, facsims. 25ᶜᵐ.
Publication began in 1929. *cf.* Union list of serials.
Some articles in Italian, some in French, some in German.
Editor: 19 Costanzo di Marzo.

1. Oriental philology—Societies. I. Marzo, Costanzo di, ed.
45–32693
Library of Congress PJ6.N32
[2] 490.6245

NN 0017082 DLC MiU NcD OC1

490.6
N162a
Naples. Istituto orientale.
Annali. v.1-10, n.1/2, 1929-dic. 1937/mar. 1938; nuova serie, v.1- 1940-
Napoli.
v. plates, facsims. 25cm.

Articles in Italian, French, English or German.

1. Oriental philology - Societies.

CLU IU
NN 0017083 TxU MiU DAU CSt-H InU CU MH CSt

VOLUME 405

Naples. Istituto orientale.
Annuario.
Napoli.

v. 25 cm.

Issues for   published by the institute under a variant
name: Istituto universitario orientale.

DS1.N333   53-33357

NN 0017084   DLC

Naples. Istituto orientale.

WC
13008   La cerimonia del "venticinquennale".
[Napoli, 1952]
79p. illus.

At head of title: Istituto Universitario
Orientale, Napoli.

NN 0017085   CtY

Naples. Istituto Orientale.
Documenti e titoli sul privato fondatore
dell'attuale R. Istituto (antico "Collegio
dei cinesi" in Napoli) Matteo Ripa. Sulle
missioni in Cina nel secolo XVIII e sulla
costituzione e consistenza patrimoniale della
antica fondazione, per Gherardo de Vincentiis.
Napoli, G. Salvati [etc.] 1904.
/v. 30cm.
"Edizione in estratto di soli cento
esemplari numerati." This copy not numbered.
1. Ripa, Matteo, 1682-1746. 2. Missions in
China. I. Vincentiis, Gherardo de.

NN 0017086   MnU

DT374   Naples .   Istituto orientale.
N3   Elementi per la toponomastica etiopica, [a cura degli studenti
A. Bombaci [et al.] Napoli, Stab. industrie editoriali meridionali, 1937.
312 p. map.

At head of title: R. Istituto superiore orientale di Napoli.

I. Ethiopia - Gazetteers. I. Bombaci, Alessio, 1914-
I. Title.

NN 0017087   CU DLC-P4

Naples. Istituto orientale.
Memorie. Napoli, Tipografia Melfi & Joele, 1904.
190 p. 25 cm.

"Fascicolo 1. Anni scolastici 1900-'901 a 1903-'904."
No more published? Cf. Union list of serials.

DS41.N35   50-53255

NN 0017088   DLC ICU

Naples. Istituto orientale.
... Regio istituto orientale di Napoli. Statuto approvato con
regio decreto 9 dicembre 1926, n. [2425, Estratto dal Bollettino ufficiale n. 13 del 29 marzo 1927—anno v. Roma, Provveditorato generale dello stato, Libreria, 1927.

100 p. incl. tables. 23cm.

At head of title: Ministero della pubblica istruzione. Direzione generale istruzione superiore.
In lower left corner of t.-p.: 374

I. Italy. Direzione generale per l'istruzione superiore.

                                                34-508
Library of Congress   PJ69.N3A5 1926   490.71145

NN 0017089   DLC

NAPLES. ISTITUTO ORIENTALE.
Fd12   Scritti dedicati alla memoria di Francesco
N162   Gallina. Roma, 1943.
II.2   vii, 350 p. 13 plates. (Pubblicazioni
dell'Istituto Universitario Orientale di
Napoli. Annali, n.s., v. 2)
Bibliographical foot-notes.

1. Gallina, Francesco, 1861-1942.
2. Ethiopia. 3. Education - Libya.

NN 0017090   CtY ICU

AS222   NAPLES. ISTITUTO ORIENTALE.
.N452   Scritti in onore di Francesco Beguinot per il
n.s.   suo settantesimo compleanno. [Napoli, 1949.
v.3   xii, 497 p. illus., plates, facsims. (part
(Or)   fold.) plans. (Istituto Universitario Orientale
di Napoli. Annali, n.s., v.3)
"Scritti del Prof. Francesco Beguinot": p. [ix]-
xii. Bibliographical footnotes.

1. Beguinot, Francesco, 1879-   2. Semitic
philology—Col-   lections. 3. Africa,
North.

NN 0017091   ICU

AS222   NAPLES. ISTITUTO ORIENTALE.
.N452   Scritti in onore di Luigi Bonelli. Roma,
n.s., v.1 Edizioni Universitarie, 1940.
313 p. plates, facsims. (Pubblicazioni dell'
Istituto universitario orientale di Napoli.
Annali. Nuova ser., v.1)
Bibliographical foot-notes.

1. Bonelli, Luigi, 1865-   2. Turkish
philology—Col- lections. 3. Oriental
philology—Col- lections

NN 0017092   ICU

Naples. Istituto orientale.
PG3892
.O55
Onats'kyĭ, Ĭevhen, 1894-
... Vocabolario ucraino italiano. Roma, 1941.

Naples. Istituto orientale.
... Un trentennio di vita brasiliana nella
corrispondenza diplomatica napoletana
see under   [Luigi, Giuseppe de']

Naples. Istituto orientale. Seminario di
slavistica.

Pubblicazioni del Seminario di Slavistica,
series 1, no. 1-   Napoli, Raffaele
Pironti e Figli, 1950-

v.

NN 0017095   CaBVaU

Naples. Istituto sieroterapico italiano
see Istituto sieroterapico italiano.

Naples. Istituto superiore di ingegneria
see **Naples.** Università. *Facoltà di ingegneria.*

Naples. Istituto superiore di scienze e lettere "Santa
Chiara."
Annali.
Napoli, R. Monastero S. Chiara.

v. illus. 25 cm.

AS222.N772   54-1620

NN 0017098   DLC

Naples. Istituto superiore di scienze economiche e commer-
ciali.
... Annuario ...
Napoli,

v. diagrs. 27½cm.

At head of title: R. Istituto superiore di scienze economiche e commerciali di Napoli.

                                                34-30806
Library of Congress   HF1152.N25
[a2]   650.7114573

NN 0017099   DLC IU NN MnU OU PPT

Naples. Istituto superiore navale
see
Naples. Istituto universitario navale.

Naples. Istituto superiore orientale
see
Naples. Istituto orientale.

Naples. Istituto universitario navale.
Annali, pubblicati a cura del corpo accademico.
Napoli, 19

v. illus., plates, maps, tables, diagrs. 25½cm.

Publication began in 1932. cf. Union list of serials.
Vols.   issued under an earlier name of the institute: Istituto
superiore navale.

1. Naval art and science—Societies, etc.
                                                45-34531
Library of Congress   V589.N313
[2]   359.071145

NN 0017102   DLC FTaSU ICRL N NN

Naples. Istituto *universitario navale.*
VK555
.S58
Simeon, Giuseppe.
... Corso di navigazione, svolto dal prof. Giuseppe Simeon.
Napoli, G. U. F. "Mussolini," Sezione editoriale, 1938.

Naples. Istituto *universitario navale.*

Italy. *Laws, statutes, etc., 1900-*   (*Victor Emmanuel III*)
... Regolamenti didattico ed amministrativo del R. Istituto
superiore navale di Napoli "Vice ammiraglio Pasquale Leonardi Cattolica" (RR. decreti 15 ottobre 1925, n. 2040 e 3
dicembre 1925, n. 2359) Roma, Provveditorato generale dello
stato, Libreria, 1926.

H137   **Naples.** Istituto universitario navale.
.S7   Studi economici. anno 1-

apr. 1941-

[Napoli, etc.]

VOLUME 405

Naples. Istituto universitario navale. *Osservatorio marittimo italiano.*
    Rendiconti. v. 1–   1921/22–
    ₍Napoli₎
    v. illus. 24 cm.

    1. Oceanography—Italy—Societies, etc. 2. Shipping—Italy—Societies, etc. 3. Ship-building—Italy—Societies, etc. 4. Aids to navigation—Italy—Societies, etc.

VK588.N3   64–50705

NN 0017106   DLC

Naples. Istituto universitario orientale
    see
Naples. Istituto orientale.

945.7
N162n   **Naples. Liceo Antonio Genovesi.**
1889   Nei dintorni di Napoli; passeggiate compiute
Stark dagli alunni del R. Liceo Antonio Genovesi nell'
Lib'y anno scolastico 1888–89. Napoli, A. Morano,
    1889.
    xi, 71p. 17½cm.

    Edited by Vincenzo Campanile.

    1. Naples. I. Campanile, Vincenzo, ed.
II. Title.

NN 0017108   TxU

Naples. Liceo ginnasio Vittorio Emanuele II.
    Annuario. Anno scolastico 1929–30.

NN 0017109   ICU

DG842   **Naples. Magistrato municipale**
N3
      Manuale del forestiero in Napoli.
Small Napoli, Borel E Bompard, 1845.
Books   6 p.l., iv, 384 p. fold. map. 13 cm.

    1. Naples—Description—Guidebooks. I.
Title.

NN 0017110   RPB

332.33 **Naples. Monte di manso.**
N162   Capitoli, e regole del regal Monte di manso,
1793   fondato dal marchese di Villa. 4.ed., in cui
    si sono a diversi capitoli aggiunte alcune
    note, necessarie per la maggior intelligenza
    del governo di detto monte. Napoli, G. de
    Bonis, 1793.
    120p. 23cm.

NN 0017111   IU

WC   **Naples. Monte di Manso.**
10494   Capitoli e regole del regal Monte di
    Manso, fondato dal Marchese di Villa.
    5.ed., in cui si sono a diversi capitoli,
    aggiunte alcune note, necessarie per la maggior
    intelligenza del governo di detto Monte. In
    Napoli, S. Troise, 1802.

NN 0017112   CtY

332.33 **Naples. Monte grande de maritaggi.**
N16c   Capitoli del Monte grande de maritaggi.
    Napoli, P. Palumbo, 1746.
    55, ₍6₎, xxxiii p. plates. 31cm.

    "Aggiunta di conclusioni del Monte grande
de'maritaggi": xxxiii p. at end.

    1. Pawnbroking—Naples. 2. Marriage—Italy.

NN 0017113   IU

Naples. Mostra bibliografica agostiniana, *1954.*
    Mostra bibliografica agostiniana, 27 novembre 1954.
Napoli, Industria tipografica artistica, 1954.
    85 p. plates, facsims. 25 cm. (I Quaderni della Biblioteca nazionale di Napoli, ser. 3, n. 6)
    "Premessa" signed: Guerriera Guerrieri.
    CONTENTS.—Opere di S. Agostino.—Opere su S. Agostino.—Tradizioni bibliografiche agostiniane a Napoli.—Pubblicazioni varie esposte a complemento della mostra.—Elenco degli scritti di S. Agostino.

    1. Augustinus, Aurelius, Saint, Bp. of Hippo—Bibl. I. Guerrieri, Guerriera.

                              A 55–7397

Catholic Univ. of   America. Library
for Library of Congress   ₍2₎

NN 0017114   DCU CtY-D MH

Naples. Mostra bibliografica del Mezzogiorno e della Sicilia,
    1929.
    ..., Mostra bibliografica dell' Italia meridionale e della Sicilia. ₍Napoli, 1929₎
    1 p. l., ₍v₎–xi, 86 p. pl., facsims. 24½cm.
    Plates printed on both sides.
    At head of title: I. Congresso mondiale delle biblioteche e di bibliografia.
    "A spese del municipio."
    Edited by Gaetano Burgada and Antonio Boselli.
    "Comitato ordinatore della Mostra bibliografica del Mezzogiorno e della Sicilia": leaf laid in.
    1. Italy — Bibl. 2. Sicily — Bibl. 3 Manuscripts. Italy. 4. Bibliography—Rare books. I. Burgada, Gaetano, 1873– II. Boselli, Antonio, conte, 1879– III. World congress of libraries and bibliography, 1st, Rome and Venice, 1929. ₍IV₎ Title.

    Library of Congress   Z2341.N21   32–12450
                             ₍3₎   015.45

NN 0017115   DLC

GT877 **Naples. Mostra d'oltremare e del lavoro italiano nel mondo.**
.I 8C5
    Cipriani, Lidio, 1894–
    ... Abitazioni indigene dell' Africa orientale italiana. Napoli, Edizioni della Mostra d'oltremare ₍1940₎

GN799 **Naples. Mostra d'oltremare e del lavoro italiano nel mondo.**
.P4G7
    Graziosi, Paolo, 1907–
    ... L'arte rupestre della Libia ... Napoli, Edizioni della Mostra d'oltremare, in vendita presso la Casa editrice Le Monnier, Firenze ₍1942₎

QH195 **Naples. Mostra d oltremare e del lavoro italiano nel mondo.**
.S3S3
    Scortecci, Giuseppe.
    ... Biologia sahariana. Napoli, Edizioni della Mostra d'oltremare ₍1940₎

Naples. Mostra d'oltremare e del lavoro italiano nel mondo.
    Le comunicazioni in A. O. I. Fac-simile della impostazione editoriale della parte della "guida catalogo," riservata al settore della produzione. Napoli, F. Raimondi, [194–]

    unnumbered.

NN 0017119   NjP

D163   **Naples. Mostra d'oltremare e del lavoro italiano nel mondo.**
.5
.I 8M6 **Monti, Gennaro Maria,** 1896–
    ... L'Italia e le crociate in Terra Santa. Napoli, Edizioni della Mostra d'oltremare ₍1940₎

ML350 **Naples. Mostra d'oltremare e del lavoro italiano nel mondo.**
.B35
    Barblan, Guglielmo.
    ... Musiche e strumenti musicali dell' Africa orientale italiana. Napoli, Edizioni della Triennale d'oltremare, 1941.

Naples. Mostra d'oltremare e del lavoro italiano nel mondo.
    Le rassegne filateliche della Mostra d'oltremare. Ente autonomo Mostra d'oltremare e del lavoro italiano nel mondo, Napoli. ₍Napoli, 1933?₎
    27 p. illus. 24 cm.

    1. Postage-stamps—Exhibitions. I. Title.

HE6191.N3   59–53848

NN 0017122   DLC

N6918 **Naples. Mostra d'oltremare e del lavoro italiano nel mondo.**
.O 7
    Ortona, Ugo, 1889–
    ... Le terre d'oltremare e l'arte italiana contemporanea. Napoli, Edizioni della Mostra d'oltremare ₍1941₎

ND614 **Naples. Mostra d'oltremare e del lavoro italiano nel mondo.**
.O 7
    Ortolani, Sergio, 1896–
    ... Le terre d'oltremare e l'arte italiana dal quattrocento all'ottocento. Napoli, Edizioni della Mostra d'oltremare ₍1940₎

Naples. Mostra d'oltremare e del lavoro italiano nel mondo
    see also **Naples. Palazzo delle esposizioni della Mostra d'oltremare.**

Naples. Mostra d'oltremare e del lavoro italiano nel mondo,
    1940.
    La mostra d'arte retrospettiva alla Triennale d'oltremare. Catalogo. Napoli, Edizioni della Mostra d'oltremare ₍1941₎
    51 p., 1 l., 53–57 p., 1 l. XLVI pl. 22½ cm.
    Text by various writers.

    1. Art, Italian—Exhibitions. I. Title.

N6914.N3   49–30930 rev

NN 0017126   DLC

Naples. Mostra d'oltremare e del lavoro italiano nel mondo,
    1940.
    I. Mostra triennale delle terre italiane d'oltremare, Napoli, Campi Flegrei, 9 maggio–15 ottobre, 1940–XVIII. Documentario. ₍Napoli, 1940₎
    308 p. incl. illus., ports. plates (part col.) 37½ cm.
    In six parts, each preceded by illustrated half-title not included in paging.
    Advertising matter included in paging.

T773 1940.A5   606   45–42820 rev

NN 0017127   DLC IEN NN InLPU

VOLUME 405

Naples. Mostra d'oltremare e del lavoro italiano
nel mondo, 1952.
Atti. 1952–
see under   Congresso di Studi Etnografici
Italiani.

**Naples. Mostra d'oltremare e del lavoro italiano nel mondo,
1952.**
Fontainebleau e la maniera italiana. ₁Mostra₎ Napoli,
Mostra d'oltremare e del lavoro italiano nel mondo, 26
luglio–12 ottobre 1952. ₁Catalogo a cura di Ferdinando
Bologna e Raffaello Causa. Firenze, Sansoni ₁1952₎
xi, 101 p. 108 plates. 22 cm.

Bibliography: p. ₁71₎–91.

1. Art—Exhibitions.   I. Bologna, Ferdinando.   II. Title.

Harvard Univ. Library   A 56–6400
for Library of Congress

NN 0017129	OC1MA NNC KU ICU DSI MWelC OC1SA CLCM MH MiDA OO MdBWA CU MiU NjP NN NcD

Paterno
T
773
.M3
1952

Naples. Mostra d'Oltremare e del Lavoro Italian
nel Mondo, 1952.
1ᵃ mostra triennale del lavoro italiano nel
mondo, Napoli, giugno–ottobre 1952. ₍Napoli,
1952₎
278 p. illus. (part col.) maps, ports. 34cm.

Front cover lacking.

1. Exhibitions.   2. Italy – Industries.
I. Title.

NN 0017130   NNC DI NN

DT31
.G65

Naples. Mostra d'oltremare e del lavoro italiano
nel mondo, 1952
Giornata eurafricana, Naples, 1953.
Giornata eurafricana, Napoli 10 ottobre 1953; ₁atti₎
Presidente: Francesco Saverio Caroselli. Napoli, R. Pi-
ronti ₁1954₎

TT500
.C76
1954

Naples. Mostra d'oltremare e del lavoro italiano
nel mondo, 1954.
**Congresso internazionale della moda, del tessile e dell'ab-
bigliamento, *Naples, 1954.***
Congresso internazionale della moda, del tessile e dell'ab-
bigliamento sotto l'alto patronato del Ministero dell'industria e commercio, Palazzo dei congressi della Mostra d'oltremare, 2–4 settembre 1954. ₁Atti₎ Napoli, R. Pironti ₁1955₎

Art
Library
J735
I8
954N

Naples. Mostra del Ritratto Storico
Napoletano.
Catalogo; a cura di G. Doria e F.
Bologna. Pref. di Amedeo Maiuri. Napoli,
Ente Provinciale per il Turismo ₍e₎
Azienda Autonoma di cura Soggiorno e
Turismo [1954?]
xx, 129 p. 48 plates (part col.) 23 cm.

Exhibition held at the Palazzo Reale,
ottobre – novembre 1954.

NN 0017133   CtY NNC OC1MA MH DeU

Naples. Mostra della pittura napoletana dei
secoli XVII–XVIII–XIX
see under   Naples (Province) Ente
provinciale per il turismo.

NAPLES.   Mostra della scultura lignea nella Campania, 1950.
Sculture lignee nella Campania. Catalogo della mostra a cura di
Ferdinando Bologna e Raffaello Causa. Prefazione di Bruno Molajoli.
Napoli, Palazzo reale, 1950.   [Napoli, 1950] 217 p.   100 pl.   24cm.

1. Wood carving—Exhibitions—Italy—Naples. 2. Wood carving, Italian
—Campania. I. Bologna,   Ferdinando, ed. II. Causa,
Raffaello, ed.

NN 0017135   NN MH OC1MA

**Naples. Mostra della scultura nel presepe napoletano del
Settecento, 1950.**
La scultura nel presepe napoletano del Settecento; catalogo della mostra, a cura di Bruno Molajoli, Napoli, 1950.
21, ₍57₎ p. illus. 25 cm.

"La mostra ... è stata organizzata per iniziativa del Comitato cittadino per l'anno giubilare."
Bibliography: p. ₍66₎

1. Crib in Christian art and tradition.   2. Sculpture—Naples.
I. Molajoli, Bruno, 1905–   ed.   II. Title.

N8180.N3 1950   62–45482

NN 0017136   DLC OC1MA

Naples. Mostra di medicina aeronautica, 1953.
Mostra di medicina aeronautica

see under

Congresso di medicina aeronautica. 5th, Naples,
1953.

DG848
.4
N35

Naples.   Mostra di riccordi storici
del risorgimento del Mezzogiorno d'Italia.
Catalogo.   Napoli, a cura del Comitato
della Mostra, 1912.
334, lvii p.   illus., ports., facsims.

NN 0017138   CU MH CLU NN

Naples. Mostra di Stampe e "Guazzi"
Napoletani dell '800.
Catalogo a cura di Augusto Cesareo.
Napoli. Palazzo Reale.   Settembre-
Ottobre 1953.   Napoli, Ente Provin-
ciale per il Turismo ₍1953₎
52, ₍3₎ p. plates.   22 cm.

Bibliography: p. ₍53₎

1. Water-colors.   2. Cesareo,
Augusto.

NN 0017139   CtW

Naples. Mostra nazionale d'arte ispirata alla Montagna.
Matese 1952; 3 agosto–3 settembre 1952. Naples,
Editrice Rinascita Artistica, 1952
2 v.
At head of title: Manifestazioni nazionali d'arte
"Matese 1952"
Contents: 1. Catalogo. 2. Illustrazione.

NN 0017140   MH-FA

Naples. Mostra triennale delle terre italiane d'oltremare
see
Naples. Mostra d'oltremare e del lavoro italiano nel
mondo.

Naples. Museo borbonico
see
Naples. Museo nazionale.

Naples. Museo civico Gaetano Filangieri.
Catalogo del Museo civico Gaetano Filangieri, principe di
Satriano. v. 1–   Napoli: Tipografia dell' Accademia reale
delle scienze, 1888–   v.   20½cm.

"Il palazzo Como, memorie storiche," by Bartolommeo Capasso, v. 1, p. ix–lvii.
"Descrizione artistica delle antiche facciate del palazzo Como," by Edoardo Cerillo,
v. 1, p. lix–lxxiii.

1. Art—Collections—Italy—Naples.
1815–1900.   II. Cerillo, Edoardo.   I. Capasso, Bartolommeo,
N. Y. P. L.   November 25, 1932

NN 0017143   NN NjP MB

Naples. Museo commerciale e coloniale.
Hermès; bollettino ufficiale del Museo commerciale e coloniale di Napoli
see under title

Naples. Museo della Floridiana
see
Naples. Museo "Duca di Martina."

Naples. Museo di Capodimonte.
Catalogo illustrativo del Real museo di Capodimonte.
see under   Alberti, Alberto, lawyer.

Naples. Museo Duca di Martina.
... Il Museo "Duca di Martina" nella villa
"La Floridiana" di Napoli ...
see under   Romano, Tersa Elena.

Naples. Museo e gallerie naizonali di Capodimonte
see also
Naples. Museo nazionale.

ND2575
.W5
1943

Naples. Museo nazionale.   FOR OTHER EDITIONS
                           SEE MAIN ENTRY
Wiegand, Theodor, 1864–1936.
Antike fresken, zehn farbige wiedergaben, mit einer ein-
leitung von Theodor Wiegand. München, R. Piper & co. ₁1943₎

Naples. Museo nazionale.
The antiquities of Herculaneum
see under   Accademia ercolanese di
archeologia.

Naples. Museo nazionale.
... The archaeological collections. 2d ed., with 161 illustra-
tions and one plan. Naples, Richter & c., editors ₍n. d.₎
48 p. plates, fold. plan. 19½ᵐ.
At head of title: National museum of Naples.
Illustration on t.-p.; mounted illus. on cover.

1. Art, Ancient.

33–36753

Library of Congress   N2730.A53   708.5

NN 0017151   DLC KU CU PPiPT CU ICU MH ViU PPPM

VOLUME 405

'08.5   Naples. Museo nazionale.
N16a   The archaeological collections. New ed.
         rev. by G. Consoli Fiego. Naples, S. A.
         Richter, 1914.
            49p., 162 illus., folded plans.

            1.Classical antiquities.

NN   0017152   MiDA

708.5   Naples. Museo nazionale.
N16ar   The archaeological collections.   Naples,
         Richter ₍192–₎
            115p. illus., fold.plan. 20cm.

            1. Art, Ancient.

NN   0017153   IU NRU

         Naples. Museo nazionale -
            The archaeological collections. 3.rev.ed. ...
         Naples,Richter& c.,₍1938₎
            66p.₍70₎pl.1 fold.map. 20cm.

NN   0017154   OClMA MH-FA

N2730   NAPLES. MUSEO NAZIONALE.
.A4   ... The archaeological collections. New ed.
1938   rev. by G. Consoli Fiego ... Naples, S. A. Rich-
(C1)   tor ₍1938?₎
            49, ₍1₎ p. plates, plans.
            At head of title: National museum of Naples.

            1. Art, Ancient.

NN   0017155   ICU

         Naples. Museo nazionale.
            The archaeological collections. New ed.
         rev. by G. Consoli Fiego, with 162 illustra-
         tions and one map. Naples, Richter & C.,
         publishers ₍1950?₎
            49p. plates, fold. plan. 20cm.

            At head of title: National Museum of
         Naples.
            Illustration on t.-p.; mounted illus. on
         cover.
            I. Art, Ancient

NN   0017156   MtU

N   Naples. Museo nazionale.
2730   L'arte al Museo nazionale di Napoli.
A6   Descrizione dei principali monumenti,
         con 102 tavole illustrative di quadri,
         sculture, numismatica, oggetti antichi,
         ecc. Napoli, Società editrice Partenopea
         [n.d.]
            71 p. 102 plates.

            1. Art - Naples. I. Title.

NN   0017157   CLU

N 2730   Naples. Museo nazionale.
A415   Auszug aus
1950   dem Führer verfasst von D. Bassi [et al.]
         hrsg. von A. Ruesch. Neapel, Richter,
         ₍1950?₎at
            358 p. illus.
            1. Art - Naples - Catalogs. I. Ruesch,
         Arnold, 1862-   ed.
            At head of title:Das Nationalmuseum in
         Neapel.

NN   0017158   CaBVaU

      Naples. Museo nazionale.
         Cabinet des objets precieux
            see under   Finati, Giovanni Battista.

      Naples. Museo nazionale.
         Catalogo del Museo nazionale di Napoli. Collezione
      Santangelo ... Napoli, Stab. tip. in S.ᵃ Teresa, 1866–67.
         2 v. 37½ x 27ᶜᵐ. ₍With Naples. Museo nazionale. Catalogo ...
      Medagliere. Napoli, 1870–71₎
         CONTENTS.—₍v. 1₎ Monete greche.—₍v. 2₎ Monete del medio evo.

         1. Numismatics.   i. Fiorelli, Giuseppe, 1823–1895, ed.

         Library of Congress   CJ43.N3   15–10390

NN   0017160   DLC OCU CtY PLatS

fN2730   Naples(City) Museo nazionale.
A45   Catalogo del Museo nazionale di Napoli.   Napoli, Tip.
          italiana nel Liceo V. Emanuele, 1866–69 [v.3, 1866]
             4 v. in 1. 38cm.

             Vols. 2 and 3 published by the Stab. tip. in Sᵃ Teresa.
          Prefaces signed: Fiorelli.

             Contents. - 1. Raccolta epigrafica: Iscrizioni greche ed
          italiche. - 2. Raccolta epigrafica: Iscrizioni latine. - 3. Raccolta
          pornografica. - 4. Armi antiche.

NN   0017161   CU CtY

Gt11   Naples. Museo nazionale.
004   Catalogo del Museo nazionale di Napoli:
          armi antiche. Napoli, Tipografia italiana,
          1869.
             2p.l.,23p. 38cm.
             Preface signed: Fiorelli.

             1. Arms and armor, Greek. 2. Arms and
          armor, Roman. I. Fiorelli, Giuseppe, 1823-
          1895.

NN   0017162   CtY MH

      Naples. Museo nazionale.
         Catalogo del Museo nazionale di Napoli; medagliere ...
      Napoli, Stab. tip. in S.ᵗᵃ Teresa, 1870–
         v. in   37½ x 27ᶜᵐ.
      Imprint varies.
      Prefatory remarks signed : Fiorelli.

         1. Numismatics.   i. Fiorelli, Giuseppe, 1823–1895, ed.

         Library of Congress   CJ43.N3   15–10589

NN   0017163   DLC PLatS DCU-H CtY OCU

      Naples. Museo nazionale.
         Catalogo del Museo nazionale di Napoli. Raccolta epigrafica
      ... Napoli, Tip. italiana nel Liceo V. Emanuele, 1867–68.
         2 v. in   39½ᶜᵐ.
      Preface signed : Fiorelli.
         CONTENTS.—I. Inscrizioni greche ed italiche.—II. Inscrizioni latine.

         i. Fiorelli, Giuseppe, 1823–1895, ed.

                                                          15–6867
         Library of Congress   CN25.N3A5   1868

NN   0017164   DLC CtY OCU ViU

      Naples. Museo nazionale.
         Catalogo del Museo nazionale di Napoli. Raccolta por-
      nografica. Napoli, Stab. tip. in S.ᵃ Teresa, 1866.
         2 p. l., 17 p. 38½ᶜᵐ.
      Pref. signed: Fiorelli.
         CONTENTS.—I. Monumenti greci ed etruschi.—II. Monumenti romani.

         1. Pompeii — Antiq. 2. Herculaneum — Antiq. 3. Phallicism. 4. Art,
      Greco-Roman.   i. Fiorelli, Giuseppe, 1823–1895, ed.

                                                          15–10145
         Library of Congress   N2730.A15 1866

NN   0017165   DLC CtY

739   NAPLES. Museo Nazionale.
N162c   Catalogo delle oreficerie del Museo Nazionale
          di Napoli. Roma, La Libreria dello Stato,
          1941.
             2p.l.,5-193p.,1l. 29cm.

             Prefatory material signed Amedeo Maiuri,
          Laura Breglia.

             1. Goldsmithing - Naples - Catalogs. 2. Art
          - Naples - Catalogs. I. Breglia, Laura. II.
          Maiuri, Amedeo, 1886-

          ICU PBm MiDA MH DDO WU
NN   0017166   TxU NNC CtY CU NcD NNU MoU MdBWA

      Naples. Museo nazionale.
         Catalogo sistematico descritivo delle fotogra-
      fie dei monumenti pompeiani
         see under   Corte, Matteo della, 1875-

Jg3   Naples. Museo nazionale.
53   Catalogue complet des petits bronzes du
          Musée national de Naples, suivant la nouvelle
          numération d'après le dernier classement.
          Par Domenico Monaco ... 2.éd., rev. et cor.
          Naples,₍Imp.de l'Indicateur général du
          commerce₎1885.
             2p.l.,39p. 19cm.
             "La collection des petits bronzes ...
          renferme à peu-près treize mille objets
          provenant des fouilles de Pompéi et
          d'Herculanum."

NN   0017168   CtY

      Naples. Museo Nazionale.
         Catalogue des statues en marbre existantes
      au Musée Bourbon à Naples.   Naples, L'Impri-
      merie d'Angelo Trani, 1820.
         54 p.   21 cm.

NN   0017169   PPPM CtY

      Naples. Museo nazionale.
         Catalogue du cabinet des objets précieux, appartenans á la
      riche collection du Musée Bourbon á Naples.   ₍Naples: Types
      de Dominicis, 1820.₎ 159(1) p.   16°.

      1. Art (Ancient).—Collections, Italy :   Naples.
      N. Y. P. L.   September 22. 1914

NN   0017170   NN

      Naples, Museo nazionale.
         Collection of the most remarkable monuments
      of the National museum. Published by Francis
      Garguilo.   Naples [n.d.]
         2 v.

NN   0017171   PPL

      NAPLES. Museo Nazionale.
         Collection of the most remarkable monuments
      of the National Museum, published by Raphael
      Gargiulo, comptroller. 3d ed. Naples, 1863.

         30 cm. Plates.

NN   0017172   MH-FA

      Naples. Museo nazionale.
         Collection of the most remarkable monuments of
      the National museum; published by Raphael Gargiulo.
      3d ed. Naples, Gargiulo, 1865.
         4 p.

NN   0017173   PP

VOLUME 405

Naples. Museo nazionale.
Collection of the most remarkable
monuments of the National museum; published by Raphael Gargiulo.
Naples, 1868.
4v. in 2, 120 pl. F.

NN 0017174   PP PU-Mu PPD PP-W MB

Naples. Museo nazionale.
Collection of the most remarkable monuments of the
National museum, by Raphaël Gargiulo ... 1st ed.
now pub. Naples, 1870.
4 v. in 2. 240 pl. (partly fold.) 31cm.

i. Gargiulo, Raffaele, ed.

1–3432
Library of Congress   N2730.A6

NN 0017175   DLC PPCCH OrU NcU OU PSC MH NN

708.5   Naples. Museo nazionale.
qN215C   Collection of the most remarkable monuments of the National museum: pub. by Raphaël Gargiulo ... 1st ed. now pub.
Naples, 1872.
4 v. in 1, 240 pl. (part fold.) 31ᵐ.

NN 0017176   NcD

Naples. Museo nazionale.
Collection of the most remarkable
monuments of the National museum; pub. by
Raphael Gargiulo... Naples, 1873.
4v. in 1, 240 pls., 31cm.

NN 0017177   MdBWA PPPM

Naples. Museo nazionale.
A complete hand book to the National Museum in Naples accord-
ing to its new arrangement, with plans of the building, a historical
sketch of the museum, and an appendix relative to Pompeii and
Herculaneum; translated from the original work of Domenico
Monaco ... by H. M. Tiknor (sic) ... Second edition.   Naples
(Printed by V. Morano) 1879. xii, 289 p.   2 plans. 19cm.

Binder's title: National Museum in Naples.
Lettered on cover: Hôtel de Russie, Naples.

793994A. 1. Art—Collections—   Italy—Naples. I. Monaco, Domenico.
II. Ticknor, H. M., tr.
N.Y.P.L.   October 9, 1936

NN 0017178   NN PU MeWC

Naples. Museo nazionale.
A complete handbook to the National museum in
Naples, according to the new arrangement ...
The original work by Domenico Monaco ... the
English ed. by E. Neville Rolfe ... 3d ed.
London, 1883.
19 cm.
Also published with title: One day in the
Naples museum ...

NN 0017179   CtY MB CU

Naples. Museo nazionale.
A complete handbook to the National museum
in Naples according to the new arrangement...
the original work by Domenico Monaco... English
editor, E. Neville-Rolfe... 10th ed. Naples,
Santa Maria a Lanzati a Foria, 1905.
136 p. 18 cm.

NN 0017180   MH-FA

708.5   Naples. Museo Nazionale.
N16M6   Complete handbook to the Naples Museum
according to the new arrangement. With
plans and historical sketch of the
building, and an appendix relative to
Pompeii and Herculaneum, by Domenico
Monaco; English editor E. Neville Rolfe.
4th ed. London, Printed by W. Clowes,
1886.
xii, 235p. plans.

I.Monaco,   Domenico, 1838-

NN 0017181   MH MiDA

N2730   Naples. Museo nazionale.
.A4   A complete handbook to the Naples museum, according to
1888   the new arrangement. With plans and historical sketch of
the building, and an appendix relative to Pompeii and Herculaneum. By Domenico Monaco ... English editor, E.
Neville Rolfe ... 5th ed. Naples (E. Pietrocola) 1888.
xii, (3), 252 p. 2 plans. 17½ᶜᵐ.
"List of authors quoted": p. (vi)

NN 0017182   ICU RPB PP

Naples. Museo nazionale.
A complete handbook to the Naples museum according to
the new arrangement, with plans and historical sketch of the
building, and an appendix relative to Pompeii and Herculaneum. By Domenico Monaco ... English editor: E. Neville
Rolfe ... 6th ed. Naples (Stab. tip. E. Pietrocola) 1893.
xii, 274 p. 2 plans. 18¼ᶜᵐ.
"List of authors quoted": p. (vi)

1. Art—Naples—Catalogs. I. Monaco, Domenico, 1838-   comp.
II. Neville-Rolfe, Eustace, 1845-1908, ed. and tr.

33–25555
Library of Congress   N2730.A4 1893   708.5

NN 0017183   DLC CtY NN

N2730   Naples. Museo nazionale.
.A4   A complete handbook to the Naples museum, according to
1897   the new arrangement. With plans and historical sketch of the
(Art) building. The original work by Domenico Monaco ... English editor: E. Neville Rolfe ... 7th ed. Naples (Stab. tip.
Lanciano e Pinto) 1897.
xii, 228 p. 2 plans. 18¼ᶜᵐ.

1. Art—Naples—Catalogs.

NN 0017184   ICU

Naples. Museo nazionale.
A complete handbook to the Naples Museum according to the
new arrangement, with plans and historical sketch of the building;
the original work by Domenico Monaco ... English editor: E.
Neville Rolfe ... Seventh edition.   Naples (Stab. tip. Lanciano
e Pinto) 1898. xii, 228 p. plans. 18cm.

288597. 1. Art—Collections—Italy—   Naples. I. Monaco, Domenico.
II. Neville-Rolfe, Eustace, 1845-   1908, editor.   Revised
N.Y.P.L.   May 22, 1934

NN 0017185   NN CtY

708.5   Naples. Museo Nazionale.
N16M6c   A complete handbook to the Naples
Museum according to the new arrangement, with plans and historical sketch
of the building. The original work
by Domenico Monaco. English editor:
E. Neville Rolfe. 8th ed. Naples,
1899.
xii, 226p. plans.

I.Monaco,   Domenico, 1838-

NN 0017186   MiDA

Naples. Museo nazionale.
A complete handbook to the Naples museum
according to the new arrangement with plans
and historical sketch of the building. The
original work by Domenico Monaco. English
editor: E. Neville-Rolfe, 9th ed. Naples,
Gradini Sannicandro, 1900.
226 p.

NN 0017187   DDO

N2730   Naples. Museo nazionale.
A4   A complete handbook to the Naples museum
1901   according to the new arrangement, with plans
and historical sketch of the building. The
original work by Domenico Monaco ... English
editor: E. Neville-Rolfe ... 10th ed. Naples,
Santa Maria a Lanzati a Foria, 1901.
xii, 136p. 2 plans. 18 cm.

1. Art—Naples—Catalogs. I. Monaco, Domenico
1838-   comp. II.   Neville-Rolfe, Eustace
1845-1908, ed.   and tr.

NN 0017188   RPB

Naples. Museo nazionale.
Ruggiero, Ettore de, 1841-
Conferenze archeologiche tenute nel Museo nazionale
di Napoli, da Ettore de Ruggiero. Prima serie ... Con
tre tavole litografiche. Roma, Regia tipografia, 1873.

Naples. Museo nazionale.
Dissertationis isagogicae ad Herculanensium
voluminum explanationem pars I
see under title

Naples. Museo nazionale.
Dissertazione esegetica
see under Carelli, Francesco, 1750-1832.

Naples. Museo nazionale.
... Estratto della
Guida, compilata da D. Bassi, E. Gabrici,
L. Mariani ... (etc.) per cura di A. Ruesch ...
Napoli, Richter & c. (1908?)
291 p.   27 pl. on 24 l., fold. plan. 17 cm.
Plates printed on both sides.
1. Art – Catalogs. I. Bassi, Domenico,
1859-   II. Ruesch, A., ed.

NN 0017192   OCU

Naples. Museo nazionale.
Estratto della guida, comp. da D. Bassi
(et al.) per cura di A. Ruesch. Approvato
dal Ministero della pubblica istruzione.
Napoli, Richter (1911?)
291, 47 p. fold. plan. 18ᶜᵐ.
"La presente guida è un nuovo compendio dell'
opera dettagliata: 'Guida illustrata del Museo
Nazionale di Napoli ...'"
1. Art—Naples—Catalogs. I. Ruesch, Arnold,
1882-   II. Italy. Ministero dell' educazione
nazionale.

NN 0017193   ViU CtY CaOTP

Naples—Museo nazionale.
... Estratto della Guida compilata da D. Bassi,
E.Gabrici, L.Mariani, O.Marucchi, G.Patroni,
G.de Petra, A.Sogliano, per cura di A.Ruesch.
Approvato dal Ministero della pubblica istru-
zione. Napoli, Richter & co. (1926)
2p.l.(7)-291p. 47p.of plates,fold.plan.
17cm.

NN 0017194   MoU MH

VOLUME 405

N
2730
A4
1911

Naples. Museo nazionale.
Excerpt of the guide by D. Bassi, E.
Gabrici, L. Mariani, O. Marucchi, G. Patroni,
G. de Petra, A. Sogliano. Edited by A.
Ruesch. Approved by the Ministry of Educa-
tion. Naples, Richter & co. [1911?]

272 p. illus., fold. plan. 18 cm.
(pbk.)
"This guide book is a new, abridged edition
of the detailed volume, 'Guida illustrata
del Museo Naziona   le de Napoli, approvata

dal Ministero della Pubblica Istruzione,
compilata da D. Bassi, E. Gabrici, L. Mariani [etc] ... per cura di A. Ruesch.'"--
Prefatory note.

1. Art--Naples--Catalogs. (I. Ruesch, Arnold, 1882-   II. Italy. Ministero dell'
educazione nazionale. III. Title.   dao

NN 0017196   IEdS CLU TU

Avery
A
2730
1633

Naples. Museo nazionale.
Excerpt of the guide by D. Bassi [and others]
edited by A. Ruesch. Approved by the Ministry
of Education. Naples, Richter [192-?]
272 p., 47 p. of illus., fold plans. 18cm.

At head of title: Naples, National Museum.

NN 0017197   NNC DDO NN

708.5
N16e

Naples. Museo nazionale.
Extrait du guide,
compile par D.Bassi [et al] par les soins de A.
Ruesch. Approuvé par le Ministère de l'instruc-
tion publique. Naples, Richter & cie. [1911?]
287 p. 47 p. of illus., fold. plan.
At head of title:Musee national de Naples
"Avertissement" 11 p. bound in front.

I. Ruessch, Arnold, 1882-   ed.

NN 0017198   MiDA

Naples. Museo nazionale.
... Galleria de' vasi ...
see Jorio, Andrea de, 1769-1851.
Real museo borbonico. Galleria de vasi.

N2730
A4

Naples. Museo nazionale.
Guida del Museo nazionale di Napoli e suoi
principali monumenti illustrati. Napoli,
Stabilimento tipografico [1900?]

62p. 111 plates 26cm.

1.Art-Naples-Catalogs.

NN 0017200   NBuG

Naples.   Museo nazionale.
Guida del Real museo borbonico, per F. A. Napoli, 1840.   58 p.
22cm.

1. No subject. I. A., F.
N.Y.P.L.   February 7, 1946

NN 0017201   NN MB

J465
N162G
1908

Naples. Museo nazionale.
Guida illustrata del Museo nazionale di Napoli, appro-
vata dal Ministero della pubblica istruzione; comp. da
D. Bassi, E. Gábrici, L. Mariani, O. Marucchi, G. Patroni,
G. de Petra, A. Sogliano, per cura di A. Ruesch. Napoli,
Richter & co., 1908-11.

2 v. illus. 17ᵐ.
Volume 2 has title: Pinacoteca; catalogo di
Aldo de Rinaldis.
1. Art--Naples--Catalogs. I.² Ruesch, A.

NN 0017202   CtY NjP MH

Naples. Museo nazionale.
Guida illustrata del Museo nazionale di Napoli, approvata
dal Ministero della pubblica istruzione; comp. da D. Bassi,
E. Gábrici, L. Mariani, O. Marucchi, G. Patroni, G. de Petra,
A. Sogliano, per cura di A. Ruesch. Napoli, Richter & co.
[1909?]

500 p. illus. 17ᵐ.

1. Art--Naples--Catalogs. I. Ruesch, Arnold, 1882-1929. II. Italy.
Ministero dell' educazione nazionale.
9--19784

Library of Congress   N2730.A4 1909

NN 0017203   DLC IU MB PBm PU

N
2730
.A23
1911

Naples. Museo nazionale.
Guida illustrata,approvata dal Ministero
della pubblica istruzione. [Napoli, Richter,
1911]
2 v. illus. 23 cm.
Contains bibliographical references.
CONTENTS.--pte.1. Antichità; guida compilata
da D.Bassi [et al.] per cura di A.Ruesch. 2.ed.
--pte.2. Pinacoteca. Catalogo di Aldo de Rinaldis.
I. Bassi,Dominico,1859-   II.Ruesch,Arnold,
1882-1929. III.Rinaldis,Aldo de,1882-1949.

NN 0017204   MiU MH

708.5
N16M6g

Naples. Museo Nazionale.
Guida nuovissima delle antichità
del Museo Nazionale di Napoli, con
appendice su Pompei ... Autore:
Domenico Monaco 16e ed. Napoli,
Richter [n.d.]
86p.

1.Italy - Antiquities. I.Monaco,
Domenico,   1838-

NN 0017205   MiDA MH

Naples. Museo nazionale
Guida per la gallerie dei quadri del Museo reale Borbonico, compilata da G.P. Napoli, 1831.

103 p.

I. P., G.

NN 0017206   MH-FA

Naples. Museo nazionale.
Guide des antiques du Musée national de Naples
suivant la nouvelle nomenclature assignée aux
objets d'après le dernier classement. Avec
plans du Musée et des notices sur Pompei et
Herculanum par Domenico Monaco ... 11. ed.
Naples,D. Monaco, 1908.
xii [4], [3]--166 p. plan. 19 cm.
1. Art - Naples - Catalogues. 2. Italy -
Antiq. I. Monaco, Domenico, 1838-

NN 0017207   CU

Naples. Museo nazionale.
Guide des petits bronzes du Musée national
de Naples. 1882.

NN 0017208   MH

N
.A234
186-

Naples. Museo nazionale.
Guide du Musée national de Naples,avec éclaircissements et illustrations des principaux monuments. Naples, Impr.S.Pietro [186-?]
68 p. 111 plates. 26 cm.

NN 0017209   MiU

Naples. Museo nazionale.
Guide du Musée national de Naples. Avec
éclaircissements et illustrations des principaux
monuments. Naples [1880?]
26 cm.

NN 0017210   CtY

Naples. Museo nazionale.
Guide du musée royal Bourbon, par F. A.
Naples, 1840. 88 pp. 8°.

NN 0017211   MB

NAPLES (city). MUSEO NAZIONALE.
Guide du Musée royal Bourbon par F. A. Naples, 1841.
96 p. 20½cm.

1. Art--Collections--Italy--Naples. I. A., F.

NN 0017212   NN

708.5
N16gu

[Naples. Museo nazionale]
Guide du Musée royal Bourbon. Nouv. éd. rev.
et augm. _ Naples, Imprimerie du Vésuve, 1841.
264p.

1. Art--Naples. I. Title.

NN 0017213   IU

NAPLES (city). MUSEO NAZIONALE.
Guide général du Musée national de Naples suivant le nouvel arrangement, par Dominique Monaco... Naples: Imprimerie de V. Morano, 1874. xvi, 280 p. 19½cm.

1. Art--Collections--Italy--Naples. I. Monaco, Domenico.

NN 0017214   NN

Naples. Museo nazionale.
Guide général du Musée national de Naples, suivant la nouvelle numération d'après le dernier classement; avec plan du
musée et une description historique sur Pompéi et Herculanum.
Par Domenico Monaco ... soigneusement revu par Édouard
Montagne ... 4. éd. Naples [Imp. de l'indicateur général du
commerce] 1884.
xvi, 272 p. plans. 17½ᵐᵐ.

1. Art--Naples--Catalogs. I. Monaco, Domenico, 1838-
II. Montagne, Édouard, ed.
33--18311

Library of Congress   N2730.A3 1884 a   708.5

NN 0017215   DLC

VOLUME 405

Naples. Museo nazionale.
Guide général du Musée national de Naples, suivant le nouvel arrangement avec plan du musée par Domenico Monaco ... 2. éd., rev. et augm. Naples ¡Impr. de V. Morano¡ 1875.
xii, 294 p. fold. plan. 18ᶜᵐ.
¡Hazlitt tracts, v. 35, no. 3¡

1. Art—Naples—Catalogs. I. Monaco, Domenico, 1838-

23-3979

Library of Congress   AC911.H3 vol. 35, no. 3

NN   0017216   DLC

708.5 Naples. Museo nazionale.
N16g3   Guide général du Musée national de
         Naples, suivant le nouvel arrangement
         avec plan du musée par Domenico Monaco.
         3.éd.   Naples, 1878.
         307p. plans.

NN   0017217   IU

Naples. Museo nazionale.
Guide général du Musée national de Naples.
1890.

NN   0017218   MH-FA

Naples. Museo nazionale.
Guide général du Musée national de Naples.
1897.

NN   0017219   MH

708.5 Naples. Museo nazionale.
N16g   Guide général du Musée national de Naples,
1900   suivant la nouvelle numération d'après le
       dernier classement; avec plan du musée et des
       notices sur Pompéi et Herculanum. Par Domenico
       Monaco. 8.éd. Naples ¡Impr. A. Lanciano &
       G. Pinto¡ 1900.
       xvi, 276p. plans. 18cm.

1. Art—Naples—Catalogs. I. Monaco, Domenico,
1838-

NN   0017220   IU

Naples. Museo nazionale.
Guide illustré du Musée national de Naples,
approuvé par le Ministère de l'instruction
publique; auteurs: G. de Petra ... A. Sogliano...
G. Patroni [et al.] ... Naples, Richter & co.
[1897?]
224 p.   illus. (incl. ports.) fold. plan.
16.5 cm.
"Le présent guide, sauf pour la partie qui
concerne la Pinacothèque, est un abrégé de
l'ouvrage détaillé: 'Guida illustrata del Museo
nazionale di Napoli'."

NN   0017221   CtY

Naples. Museo nazionale.
Guide illustré du Musée national de Naples,
approuvé par le Ministère de l'instruction
publique. Auteurs: G. de Petra [et al.]
Naples, Richter [190-?]
224 p. illus., plan. 17 cm.

NN   0017222   NNC

N   Naples. Museo nazionale.
2730   A guide in the National Museum of
.A42x   Naples, and its principal monumentes.
1874   Naples, Printed at S. Pietro A Maiella
        [1874?]
        64 p. 111 plates. 27 cm.

1. Art—Naples—Catalogs. I. Title

NN   0017223   OKentU NN NNC MH

N 2730   NAPLES—Museo nazionale.
.A42   A guide in the National Museum of Naples
         and its principal monuments. Naples ¡19--?¡
         64 p. 111 plates.

1. Art—Naples—Catalogs. 2. Naples—Museo
nazionale. Art cds.

NN   0017224   InU

Naples. Museo nazionale.
... Guide pour la galerie des peintures anciennes, par
la chanoine de Jorio. 2. éd. rev., cor. et augm. Naples,
de l'Imprimerie française, 1830.
viii, ¡9¡-94, ¡2¡ p. 22ᶜᵐ.
At head of title: Musée royal Bourbon.
With Jorio, Andrea de. Guida di Pompei ... 1836.

I. Jorio, Andrea de, 1769-1851.

NN   0017225   MiU

Naples. Museo nazionale.
Guide pour le Musée royal Bourbon, contenant les peintures anciennes.—Les monumens égyptiens.—Les sculptures en marbre, les sarcophages, les ornemens d'architecture, les bas-reliefs et les mosaïques.—Les statues en
bronze,—et la collection épigraphique; par François
Verde ... Jean Pagano ... et par Charles Bonucci ... Tr.
par C. J. J. Naples, Impr. du Fibrène, 1831.
xiv p., 1 l., 235 p., 2 l. 21ᶜᵐ. ¡With Palmerini, Niccolò. Opere d'intaglio
del cav. Raffaello Morghen. Firenze, 1824¡
1. Art objects—Naples—Catalogs. I. J., C. J., tr. II. C. J. J., tr.
III. Verde, Francesco. IV. Pagano, Giovanni. V. Bonucci, Carlo, 1799-1870.
19-4501
Library of Congress   NE662.M6P3

NN   0017226   DLC

Naples. Museo nazionale.
Guide pour le Musée royal Bourbon ... par François Verde ... Jean Pagano ... et par Charles
Bonucci ... Traduit par C. J. J. Naples, L'imprimerie et cartière du Fibrène, 1831-32.
2 v. in 1. 21½ cm.

Vol. 2 by François Verde and Jean Pagano.
Vol. ¡1¡: xiv p., 1 l., 235 p., 2 l.; v. 2¡
ix p., 1 l., 194 p.
1. Art - Naples - Catalogs. I. Verde, Francesco
II. Pagano, Giovanni. III. Bonucci, Carlo, 1799-187,
IV. J., C. J.,   tr.

NN   0017227   NNC

Naples. Museo nazionale.
Handbook of the antiquities in the National museum at
Naples, according to the new arrangement, with historical
sketch of the building and an appendix relative to Pom-
peii and Herculaneum. The original work by Domenico
Monaco ... English editor: E. Neville-Rolfe ... 11th ed.
Naples ¡Stab. tip. Lanciano e Veraldi¡ 1906.
xii, 138 p. 18ᶜᵐ.

1. Art—Naples—Catalogs. 2. Italy—Antiq.   I. Monaco, Domenico,
comp. II. Neville-Rolfe, Eustace, 1845-1908, ed. and tr.

15-7071
Library of Congress   N2730.N3

NN   0017228   DLC MH

708.5   Naples. Museo nazionale.
M74h   Handbook of the antiquities in the
        national museum at Naples according to
        the new arrangement, with historical
        sketch of the building & an appendix
        relative to Pompeii & Herculaneum...
        English ed. E. Neville-Rolfe. Ed. 12.
        Naples, 1906.
        142p.

NN   0017229   IU MB

Mu708.5   NAPLES. Museo nazionale.
N 158.9.EN   Handbook of the antiquities in the Nation-
          al museum at Naples according to the new ar-
          rangement with three plans and historical
          sketch of the building... The original work
          by Domenico Monaco... English editor: E.Nev-
          ille-Rolfe... 13th ed. Naples,Santa Ma-
          ria ai Lanzati a Foria,1907.
          viii,¡4¡,147p. plans. 19½cm.

NN   0017230   PU NN CU PPDI

N2730   Naples. Museo Nazionale.
.N3   Handbook of the antiquities in the Naples
1908   Museum, according to the new arrangement, with
         three plans and historical sketch of the
         building and an appendix relative to Pompeii
         and Herculaneum. The original work by Domenico
         Monaco. English editor: E. Neville-Rolfe.
         14th ed. Naples ¡Stab. Tip. Lanciano e
         Veraldi¡ 1908.
         viii, 148 p. plans.   19cm.
         1. Art—Naples—   Catalogs. 2.Italy—Antiq.
         I.Monaco, Domenico,   comp. II. Neville-Rolfe,
         Eustace, 1845-1908,   ed. and tr

NN   0017231   ViU

Naples. Museo nazionale.
Herculanensium voluminum que supersunt
see under   Accademia di archeologia,
lettere e belle arti, Naples.

Naples. Museo nazionale.
Illustrated guide to the National museum in Naples.
Naples¡ n.d.¡

NN   0017233   NjP NBuG

Naples. Museo nazionale.
Illustrated guide to the National museum in Naples, sanc-
tioned by the Ministry of education, editors, G. de Petra ... A.
Sogliano ... G. Patroni ... Naples, Richter & co. ¡1897?¡
226 p. illus. (incl. ports.) fold. plan. 16½ᶜᵐ.
"This guide book is, with the exception of those pages describing the
Picture gallery, an excerpt from the encyclopaedic 'Guida illustrata del
Museo nazionale di Napoli'."

1. Art—Naples—Catalogs.   I. Petra, Gullio de, 1841-
II. Italy. Ministero dell' educazione nazionale.
S 39-12 Revised
Smithsonian inst. Library
for Library of Congress   [N2730.A   ]

NN   0017234   DSI IdU TU PPiPT CtY TU

Naples. Museo nazionale.
Illustrated guide to the National museum in Naples, sanctioned by the Ministry of education; editors: G. de Petra ...
A. Sogliano ... G. Patroni ¡etc.¡ ... Naples, Richter & co.
¡1909?¡
226 p. illus., fold. plan. 16½ᶜᵐ.
"This guide book is, with the exception of those pages describing the
picture gallery, an excerpt from the ... 'Guida illustrata del Museo nazionale di Napoli, approvata dal Ministero della pubblica istruzione, compilata da D. Bassi, E. Gabrici, L. Mariani ¡etc.¡ ... per cura di A.
Ruesch'."—Prefatory note.
1. Art—Naples—Catalogs. I. Ruesch, Arnold, 1882- II. Italy.
Ministero dell' educazione nazionale.
40-451
Library of Congress   N2730.A4 1909 a
¡2¡

NN   0017235   DLC CU OrU MdBJ ViU MB KU

VOLUME 405

Naples. Museo nazionale.
    Illustrated handbook to the National museum in Naples, according to the new arrangement... Naples, 1911.
    Ed. by Domenico Monaco.

NN   0017236   MH-FA NjP

708.5
N162   NAPLES. Museo nazionale.
    Illustrated handbook to the National museum in Naples, according to the new arrangement... The original work by Domenico Monaco... English editor: E. Neville-Rolfe... 16th ed.   Naples [Stab. tip. Lanciano e Veraldi] 1913.

    8 p.l., 212 p.   illus. (incl. facsim.) 17cm.

    Lettered on cover: 17th edition.
    1. Art in   Naples. Catalogs. I. Neville-Rolfe,   Eustace, 1845-1908, ed. and tr. II. Monaco, Domenico, b.1838.

NN   0017237   MnU

N2730
A4
1914   Naples. Museo Nazionale.
    Illustrated handbook to the National Museum in Naples, according to the new arrangement. With plates. The original work by Domenico Monaco. English editor: E. Neville-Rolfe. 17th ed. Naples, 1914.
    xiii, 206 p. illus., plans. 18 cm.

    1. Art--Naples--Catalogs. I. Monaco, Domenico, 1838-   comp. II. Neville-Rolfe, Eustace, 1845-1908, ed. and tr.

NN   0017238   PPiPT MH-FA

CJ215   Naples. Museo nazionale.
.N2   Index nummorum veterum qui in Museo R.borbonico adservantur. [Roma,185-?]
    39 p. 25ᶜᵐ.

    From Annali di numismatica,t.2.

    1.Coins,Ancient.

NN   0017239   ICU

LimCat
40
71-3   Naples. Museo Nazionale.
    Inscriptiones veteres quae in Regio Museo Borbonico, adservantur inscriptionum Latinarum. Classes prima sacrae. Neapolic, Regio Typographia, 1857.
    140p. facsims. 37cm.

    1. Inscriptions, Latin. I. Title.

NN   0017240   PSt

N 2730
A8   Naples. Museo nazionale.
    Masterpieces of art in the National Museum in Naples: the bronze and marble sculptures; the antiquities of Pompeii and Herculaneum. Florence, G. Fattorusso [c1925]
    32 p. illus. 25 cm.   (The Medici art series, no. 7A)

    Running title: Wonders of Italy.

    1. Art - Naples - Catalogs I. Title. II. Title: Wonders of Italy.

NN   0017241   OU OO NNC MiDA PPPM

Naples. Museo nazionale.
    Masterpieces of art in the national museum in Naples; first part, the bronze and marble sculptures, the antiquities of Pompeii and Herculaneum ... Florence,Fattorusso[c1926].
    Front.illus.plates,0.   (The Medici art series)

NN   0017242   CaBViP OrU

N2730
A6
1929   Naples. Museo nazionale.
    Masterpieces of art in the National museum in Naples: the bronze and marble sculptures, the antiquities of Pompeii and Herculaneum. With 205 illustrations. Florence, G. Fattorusso [c1929]

    33 p. incl. front., illus. 24cm. (Half-title: The Medici art series. no. 7A)

    Title vignette.
    Stamp of Pro   f. U. Marcellini on half-title.

NN   0017243   CSmH DDO

Naples. Museo nazionale.
    ... Medaglie moderne, catalogo di Aldo de Rinaldis ... Napoli, R. Ricciardi, 1913-
    v. 19½ᶜᵐ.

    At head of title: Museo nazionale di Napoli.
    Vol. 1 has also special t.-p.
    Bibliography: v. 1, p. [viii].

    CONTENTS.—I. Medaglie dei secoli XV e XVI.

    1. Medals—Italy. 2. Medalists.   I. Rinaldis, Aldo de, 1882-   ed.

    CJ6192.N3   47-38332

NN   0017244   DLC

CN528   NAPLES. MUSEO NAZIONALE.
.5   Memoria Bartolommeo Borghesi sopra un'iscrizione del console L. Burbuleio Optato Ligariano,
.N21   serbata nel Museo reale. Napoli, Dai torchi del Tramater, 1838.
    77 p.
    At head of title: Reale Accademia ercolanese.
    Contains Latin inscriptions with commentaries about officials of the Roman Empire.
    1. Inscriptions, Latin. 2. Rome--Antiq.
    I. Borghesi, Bartolomeo conte, 1781-1860.

NN   0017245   ICU

Naples.   Museo Nazionale.
    Meisterwerke der Kunst im National-Museum zu Neapel; Bronzen und Marmor Skulpturen, Altertuemer aus Herculanum und Pompeji... Florenz, Fattorusso [c1927]

    33 p. (chiefly illus.) (Medici-Kunstbuecher, 7A)

NN   0017246   MH-FA

N2730   NAPLES. MUSEO NAZIONALE.
.A4   Les monuments du Musée national de Naples;
1879   gravés sur cuivre par les meilleurs artistes italiens. Text par Domenico Monaco. Naples, Impr. de V. Morano, 1879.
    28 p., 160 plates.

    1. Art--Naples--Catalogs. 2. Italy--Antiq. I. Monaco, Domenico, 1838-

NN   0017247   CU

F708.5   Naples. Museo nazionale.
N21m   Les monuments du Musée national de Naples gravés sur cuivre par les meilleurs artistes italiens Texte par Domenico Monaco.   Naples, Imprimerie de l'indicateur général du commerce, 1882.
    28 p. plates (part. fold.) 30 cm.

    1. Art - Naples - Catalogs. 2. Italy - Antiq. 3. Pompeii. 4.   Herculaneum. I. Monaco, Domenico, 1838-   comp.

NN   0017248   NN NcU

708.5
qN215M   Naples. Museo nazionale.
    Les monuments du Musée national de Naples; cent soixante planches, gravées sur cuivre par les meilleurs artistes italiens, reproduisant quatre cent quatre objets des diverses branches de l'art et de l'archéologie. Texte par Domenico Monaco. Naples [Impr. E. Pietrocola] 1890.
    33 p. 160 plates. 30 cm.
    On spine: Musée national de Naples.

NN   0017249   NcD

Naples. Museo nazionale.
    Les monuments du Musée national de Naples; cent soixante-huit planches, gravées sur cuivre par les meilleurs artistes italiens, reproduisant quatre cent soixante-quinze objets des diverses branches de l'art et de l'archéologie. Texte précédé par des notices sur Pompéi et Herculanum par Domenico Monaco ... Naples [Impr. E. Pietrocola, 1890.
    4 p. l., 1v, 35 p. 168 pl. (1 fold.) 29½".

    1. Art—Naples—Catalogs. 2. Italy—Antiq. 3. Pompeii. 4. Herculaneum. I. Monaco, Domenico, 1838- comp.

    Library of Congress   N2730.A4 1890
                                    20—22659

NN   0017250   DLC

Naples. Museo nazionale.
    Monuments principaux du Musée national de Naples. Naples, [1865?]

    39 p.   110 engr. plates   28 cm.

NN   0017251   PPPM

N6921   Naples. Museo nazionale
R5M3   Musée Royal Bourbon, par Michel B. Naples,
(SA)   Fernandes, 1837.
    210 p. 18 cm.

    Catalogue.
    Bound with Marcheselli, C. F. Pitture delle chiese di Rimino...1837.

    I. B   , Michel.

NN   0017252   NjP

Naples. Museo nazionale.
    Le Musée royal-Bourbon, décrit par le Chev. J. B. Finati ... 1. éd. française. Naples, Imprimerie Virgilio, 1843.
    88, [2], [5]-260 p., 1 l., [5]-84 p. fold. pl. 19".

    1. Art—Naples—Catalogs.   I. Finati, Giovanni Battista, comp.

    Library of Congress   N2730.A35 1843
                                  15—12300

NN   0017253   DLC MH

N2730   Naples. Museo nazionale.
.F28
Rare Bk   **Famin, Stanislas Marie César,** 1799-1853.
Coll   Musée royal de Naples, peintures, bronzes et statues érotiques du cabinet secret, avec leur explication par M. C. F., contenant 60 gravures coloriées.   Paris, A. Ledoux, 1836.

Naples. Museo nazionale.
    Museo Napoli.   [n.p., n.d.]
    35 pl. 41 cm.
    Binder's title.
    In case.
    Plates tipped in and printed on both sides.
    "Short notes on the history of the Naples museum", in Italian, English, French, and German, tipped in before plates.
    1. Art - Naples. 2. Sculpture - Naples. I. Title.

NN   0017255   CU

VOLUME 405

Naples. Museo nazionale.
Museo Borbonico. n.p. [18-]

2 v. plates.
Consists of plates only.

NN 0017256 MH

NK4640
.C617
fasc. 29,
etc.
Naples. Museo nazionale.
Rocco, Anna.
Museo nazionale di Napoli. Roma, Libreria dello Stato, 1953-

Naples. Museo nazionale.
... Il Museo nazionale di Napoli; oreficeria - toreutica - gliptica - vitriaria - ceramica ... see under Pesce, Gennaro.

Naples. Museo nazionale.
Le mystagogue; guide général du Musée royal Bourbon ... Par le chevalier Bernard Quaranta ... Naples, Impr. du Fibreno, 1844.
xv, [1], 307 p. 21¼ᵐ.

1. Art—Naples—Catalogs. 2. Italy—Antiq. 1796-1867. I. Quaranta, Bernardo,
9-13893†

Library of Congress N2730.A4 1844

NN 0017259 DLC NN

Naples. Museo nazionale.
Le mystagogue; guide général du Musée royal Bourbon ... Par le chevalier Bernard Quaranta ... Naples, Impr. de N. Fabricatore, 1846.
xiv p., 1 l., 272 p. 22¼ᵐ.

1. Art—Naples—Catalogs. 2. Italy—Antiq. 1796-1867. I. Quaranta, Bernardo,
9-13896†

Library of Congress N2730.A4 1846

NN 0017260 DLC DSI NjP MH

Naples. Museo nazionale.
Napoli, Museo nazionale. [n. p., n. d.]
cover-title, 36 pl. on 18 l. 13 x 17½ᵐ.

1. Sculpture—Naples. 2. Paintings—Naples.
43-37552

Library of Congress N2730.A63

NN 0017261 DLC

Naples Museo nazionale.
Napoli, Museo nazionale. 40 tavole. [Naples, 19—] 1 p.l., 40 pl. on 20 l. 20½ x 26cm.

Descriptive letterpress in Italian, French and English.

944162A. 1. Art—Collections— Italy—Naples.
N. Y. P. L. July 8, 1938

NN 0017262 NN

Naplos (*City*) *Museo nazionale.*
... Das Nationalmuseum zu Neapel; eingehende [!] archeologische beschreibung mit 162 illustrierten tafeln, wozunter [!] 6 die neuesten ausgrabungen (Haus der Vetii befreffend [!]) von Cav. L. Conforti ... Neapel, J. Chiurazzi & fils [etc., 1901]
2 p. l., 50 p., 1 l. 164 pl. 34½ x 27ᵐ.

At head of title: Übertragung aus dem franz. texte von Prof. P. E. Lorenz.
Title in red and black.
8-11205

NN 0017263 DLC

708.5
N16M6n
Naples. Museo Nazionale.
A new catalogue of the pictures at the National Museum in Naples, by Domenico Monaco ... Naples, 1881.
64p.

I. Monaco, Domenico, 1838-

NN 0017264 MiDA

Naples. Museo nazionale.
A new general hand-book to the National museum in Naples according to its latest arrangement, with an appendix relative to Pompeii and a vade mecum to the Certosa di S. Martino, by Achilles Migliozzi, curator at the museum. Translated by V. J. Naples: Printed by cav. G. de Angelis and son, 1876. viii, 430 p. 18½cm.

982184A. 1. No subject. I. Mi- gliozzi, Achilles. II. J., V.
N. Y. P. L. August 16, 1939

NN 0017265 NN

Naples. Museo nazionale.
Nouveau guide du Musée royal bourbon see under Aloe, Stanislao d' .

708.5
N16m
Naples. Museo nazionale.
Nuova guida generale del Museo nazionale di Napoli secondo i più recenti riordinamenti corredata di un'appendice riguardante Pompei e la certosa di S. Martino co'suoi monumenti artistici e religiosi ... Napoli, G. de Angelis e figlio, 1876.
445p.

1. Naples. Museo nazionale. 2. Art--Naples.

NN 0017267 IU

Naples. Museo nazionale.
Nuova guida generale del Museo nazionale di Napoli, secondo i più recenti riordinamenti, corredata di un' appendice riguardante Pompei e l'Eruzione che la distrusse di Achille Migliozzi ... 3. ed. Napoli, 1882.
208 p. 18 cm.

1.Art - Naples - Catalogs. I. Migliozzi, Achille.

NN 0017268 NNC MH

Naples (city). Museo nazionale.
Nuove guide generali dei musei nazionali di Napoli e di S. Martino, disposte secondo le ultime classificazioni e numerazioni per Antonio Muro... Prima edizione... Napoli: A. Bellisario e. c., 1887. 183, 35 p. 17½-cm.

Cover-title; each part has special t.-p.

287618-19. I. Art—Collections— Italy—Naples. I. Muro,
Antonio. II. *Naples Museo* *nazionale di S. Martino.*
May 22, 1934

NN 0017269 NN

Naples. Museo nazionale.
... Officina de' papiri, descritta dal canonico Andrea de Jorio ... Napoli, Dalla Stamperia francese, 1825.
87, [5] p. III pl. (incl. facsim.) 22ᶜᵐ.

At head of title: Real Museo borbonico.

1.Manuscripts (Papyri) I. Jorio, Andrea de, 1769-1851.

NN 0017270 MiU RPB NjP ICU

Naples. Museo nazionale.
One day in the Naples museum, according to the new arrangement, with plans and historical sketch of the building by Domenico Monaco. English editor: E. Neville Rolfe. 2d ed. Naples, 1889.

NN 0017271 MH

Naples. Museo nazionale.
One day in the Naples museum, according to the new arrangement, with plans and historical sketch of the building. The original work by Domenico Monaco, curator ... English editor: E. Neville-Rolfe ... 4th ed. Naples [Stab. tip. Lanciano e Pinto] 1892.
xii, 168 p. 2 plans. 18½ᵐ.

NN 0017272 CtY

Naples. Museo nazionale.
One day in the Naples museum, according to the new arrangement, with plans and historical sketch of the building. The original work by Domenico Monaco, curator ... English editor: E. Neville-Rolfe ... 5th ed. Naples [Stab. tip. Lanciano e Pinto] 1893.
xii, 171 p. 2 plans. 18.5 cm.
"List of authors quoted": p. [vi]
Also published with title: A complete handbook to the National museum in Naples ...
1. Art - Naples - Catalogs. I. Monaco,

Domenico, comp. II. Neville-Rolfe, Eustace, 1845-1908.

NN 0017274 CtY OO

Naples. Museo nazionale.
One day in the Naples museum, according to the new arrangement, with plans and historical sketch of the building. The original work by Domenico Monaco, curator ... English editor: E. Neville-Rolfe ... 6th ed. Naples [Stab. tip. Lanciano e Pinto] 1895.
xii, 171 p. 2 plans. 18½ᵐ.
"List of authors quoted": p. [VI]

1. Art—Naples—Catalogs. I. Monaco, Domenico, comp. II. Neville-Rolfe, Eustace, 1845-1908. III. Title.
15-2353

Library of Congress N2730.A4 1895

NN 0017275 DLC NcU

NK7352
.S5
folio
Naples. Museo nazionale.
Siviero, Rodolfo.
Gli ori e le ambre del Museo nazionale di Napoli. [Firenze] Sansoni [1954]

Naples. Museo nazionale.
Famin, Stanislas Marie César, 1799-1853.
Peintures, bronzes et statues-érotiques, formant la collection du cabinet secret du Musée royal de Naples, avec leur explication; par C. Famin ... Paris, Typ. Everat, 1832.

VOLUME 405

Naples. Museo nazionale.

Piccoli bronzi...da Carlo Ceci...
Napoli, S. Piscopo, 1854.

[21]p. incl. pls., 36 x 49.5cm.

NN 0017278   MdBWA CtY MH PU ViU

Naples. Museo nazionale.
Piccoli bronzi del Real museo borbonico distinti per
categorie in dieci tavole, descritte e disegnate da Carlo
Ceci ... 2. ed. riv. e di molto accresciuta. Napoli, Stamp.
Piscopo [1858]

cover-title, [12] p. x (i. e. 12) col. pl. 52 x 37ᶜᵐ.

1. Bronzes—Catalogs.   i. Ceci, Carlo.

Library of Congress   NK7907.C4   12—14905

NN 0017279   DLC NN NjP TxU CLSU PP PPD MiD

NAPLES.   MUSEO NAZIONALE.
...The picture gallery. Topographical guide. Naples:
Richter & c. [1929?]   19 p. front., 70 [1. on 36 1.
19cm.

At head of title: National museum, Naples.

NN 0017280   NN

N
2730   Naples. Museo nazionale.
.A3   Pinacoteca del Museo nazionale di Napoli;
          catalogo. Napoli, Richter, 1911.
          568 p., 69 p. of illus.
          Compiler's name at head of title: Aldo
          de Rinaldis.

          I. Rinaldis, Aldo de, 1882-   II. Title.

NN 0017281   MiU PBm

N
2730   Naples. Museo nazionale.
Alp   Pinacoteca del Museo nazionale di Napoli.
1928   Catalogo di Aldo de Rinaldis. Nuova ed.
          Napoli, Richter, 1928.
          xxiv, 479p. illus. 18cm.

          1. Art - Naples - Catalogs.   I. Rinaldis,
          Aldo de, 1882-

NN 0017282   NRU NN CLCM

Naples. Museo nazionale.
... La Pinacoteca del Museo nazionale di
Napoli ... *Roma* [1932]
          see under Quintaville, Armando, 1894-

Naples. Museo Nazionale.
N2730   Pitture del Museo Reale Neapolitano in
P76   Portici, le quali dall'anno 1738, fin ora
f   furono trovate nell'antico Erculano, e
          Pompei, e i loro contorni colle spiega-
          zioni incise d'appresso l'originale da
          Giovanni Baltassare Probst, intragliatore
          in rame. [n.p.] C.F.Bürghen, 1795.
          36 p., 98 plates(some on double leaves)
          37cm.
          1.Paintings - Italy. I.Probst, Giovanni
          Baltassare.   II.Title.

NN 0017284   CSt

Naples. Museo nazionale.
Pitture murali e mosaici
see under   Elia, Olga.

N2730   Naples. Museo nazionale
.M69   Principal monuments in the National
          Museum of Naples. Naples, Printed by F.
          Ferrante [ca.1863]
          37p. 111plates(part fold.) 26cm.

          1. Art - Naples - Catalogs.

NN 0017286   PSt

Naples. Museo nazionale.
The principal objects of art in the National Museum of
Naples, engraved by the best Italian artists; text by Domenico
Monaco... Naples [V. Morano], 1877. 20 p., 168 pl. 4°.

100113A. 1. Art.—Collections,   Italy: Naples: Museo Nazionale.
2. Monaco, Domenico.
N. Y. P. L.   October 25, 1923.

NN 0017287   NN

N2730   Naples. Museo nazionale.
.M7   The principal objets [!] of art in the National museum of
          Naples, engraved on copper-plates by the best Italian artists;
          text by Domenico Monaco, curator ... Naples [D. Monaco]
          1880.
          34 p. 160 pl. (part fold.) 29ᶜᵐ.

NN 0017288   NN PSt

Naples. Museo nazionale.
The principal objets [!] of art in the National museum
of Naples, engraved on copper-plates by the best Italian
artists; text by Domenico Monaco, curator ... Naples
[D. Monaco] 1881.
34 p. 160 pl. (part fold.) 29ᶜᵐ.

1. Art—Naples—Catalogs.   i. Monaco, Domenico. ii. Title.

                                       2-11704 Revised
Library of Congress   N2730.M7

NN 0017289   DLC WaS CtY NIC OCU

---

naples. Museo nazionale.   *4072.96
Raccolta de monumenti più interessanti del Re. Museo Borbonico e
di varie collezioni private. Publicati da Raffaele Gargiulo, im-
= piegato nel detto Re. Museo.
   Napoli. 1825. (140) plates. Engraved title-page. 23½ × 29 cm.
   Works of art from Pompeii, Herculaneum, and Stabia.
   Inserted are two views and a plan of Pompeii.

K9890 — Pompeii, Italy. Antiq. — Herculaneum, Italy. Antiq. — Stabia, Italy.
Antiq. — Antiquities. — Gargiulo, Raffaele, ed.

NN 0017290   MB CtY MH PPAFA

Art
Library   Naples. Museo Nazionale.
NB115   Raccolta de monumenti più interessanti del R.[1]
.N37   Museo Borbonico e di varie collezioni private.
          Publicati da Raffaele Gargiulo... Naples, 1842.
          160 pl. (1 fold.) [12] p. in ms. 29 cm.
          Engraved t.-p.
          160 engraved, unnumbered plates.
          Name of Museum changed in 1861 to Museo Nazio-
          nale.
          Contents written by hand on hand ruled paper
          bound in at end.

NN 0017291   NcU

Naples. Museo nazionale.
J567   Raccolta de' più belli ed interessanti dipinti, musaici
+8361b   ed altri monumenti rinvenuti negli scavi reali di Erco-
          lano, di Pompei e di Stabia, che ammiransi nel Museo
          reale borbonico. Napoli, 1854.

          1 p. l., 160 pl. (1 fold.) incl. plan. 29½ᶜᵐ.

          Engraved t.-p. with ornamental border.
          "Disegnati dal regio disegnatore Gius. Abbate."
          Manuscript index.

NN 0017292   CtY PPPM MiD

Naples. Museo nazionale.
Raccolta de' più belli ed interessanti dipinti, musaici
ed altri monumenti rinvenuti negli scavi reali di Ercolano, di Pompei e di Stabia, che ammiransi nel Museo
reale borbonico. Napoli, 1859.

1 p. l., 150 pl. (1 fold.) incl. plan. 29½ᶜᵐ.

Engraved t.-p. with ornamental border.
"Disegnati dal regio disegnatore Gius. Abbate."
Manuscript index.

1. Paintings—Naples. 2. Sculpture—Naples. 3. Herculaneum. 4. Pompeii. 5. Stabiae. i. Abbate, Giuseppe.
                                          9-15577 Revised
Library of Congress   N2730.A5 1859
        —— Copy 2.   Incomplete; 55 plates only.

NN 0017293   DLC ViU NjP

Naples. Museo nazionale.
Raccolta de più belli ed interessant dipinti,
musaici ed altri monumenti rinvenuti negli
scavi di Ercolano, di Pompei, e di Stabi. Napoli,
Paderni, 1861.
150 p.

NN 0017294   PU

Naples. Museo nazionale.
Raccolta de più belli ed interessanti dipinti, musaici ed
altri monumenti rinvenuti negli scavi di Ercolano, di
Pompei, e di Stabia, che ammiransi nel Museo nazionale
... Napoli, 1865.

3 p. l., 151 pl. (1 fold.) incl. plan) 30½ᶜᵐ.

Engr. t.-p. within ornamental border.
"Per cura di Pompeo Paderni."
Index in Italian and French.

1. Paintings—Naples. 2. Sculpture—Naples. 3. Herculaneum. 4. Pompeii. 5. Stabiae. i. Paderni, Pompeo.

                                          21-8469
Library of Congress   N2730.A5 1865

NN 0017295   DLC

Naples. Museo nazionale.
Raccolta de' più belli ed interessanti dipinti ... di Ercolano, Pompei,
e di Stabia ... Napoli, 1867.

NN 0017296   NjN

Naples. Museo nazionale.
Raccolta de più belli ed interessant dipinti,
musaici ed altri monumenti tinvenuti negli scavi
di Ercolano, di Pompei, e di Stabi. Napoli,
Pompeo Paderni, 1870.
151 p.

NN 0017297   PU

Naples. Museo nazionale.
Raccolta de più belli ed interessanti dipinti, musaici ed altri
monumenti rinvenuti negli scavi di Ercolano, di Pompei, e
di Stabia, che ammiransi nel Museo nazionale ... Napoli,
1871.

1 p. l., 153 pl. (1 fold.; incl. plan) 28ᶜᵐ.

Engraved title, within ornamental border.
"Per cura di Pompeo Paderni."
Index in [English] and French.

NN 0017298   ViU MH

VOLUME 405

Naples. Museo nazionale.
Raccolta de' più belli ed interessante
dipinti, musaici ed altri monumenti rinvenuti
negli scavi di Ercolano, di Pompei e di Stabia.
Napoli, per cura di Tarallo e Paderni, 1871.

NN 0017299   MH MiD NN PP NjP MdBWA MiD

---

ar X   Naples. Museo nazionale.
5172   Raccolta de più belli ed interessanti dipinti, musaici ed
          altri monumenti rinvenuti negli scavi di Ercolano, di
          Pompei, e di Stabia, che ammiransi nel Museo nazionale
          ... Napoli, 1874.
            1 l. 165 plates. 30cm.
            Engr. title, within ornamental border.
            "Per cura di Pompeo Paderni."
            Index in Italian and French.

NN 0017300   NIC MB

---

*N2730   Naples.   Museo nazionale.
A5   Raccolta de più belli ed interessanti dipinti,
1879   musaici ed altri monumenti rinvenuti negli scavi
          di Ercolano, di Pompei, e di Stabia, che
          ammiransi nel Museo nazionale ... Napoli,
          Per cura di Tarallo e Paderni, 1879.
            1p.8.,165 plates(1 fold.)₄4₃p. 29½cm.
            Engraved title, within ornamental border.
            Index in French and English.

          1. Paintings,   2. Sculpture.
          Naples.   3. Her-   4. Pompeii.
          5. Stabiae. I.   culaneum. I.
                            Title.

NN 0017301   NBuG

N2730   Naples.   Museo nazionale.
A577   Raccolta delle più interessanti dipinture e de' più belli musaici
1830   rinvenuti negli scavi di Ercolano, di Pompei, e di Stabia che ammi-
         ransi nel Museo reale barbonico.   Napoli, 183[0?]
           1 l., 118 plates,

          1. Art - Naples. 2. Herculaneum. 3. Pompeii. 4. Stabiae.

NN 0017302   CU CtY

Naples. Museo nazionale.
  Raccolta delle più interessanti dipinture e de più belli musaici
rinvenuti negli scavi di Ercolano, di Pompei, e di Stabia che ammiransi nel Museo reale borbonico. Napoli, 1843. 1 l., 120 pl.
29½cm.

597720A. 1. Italy—Archaeology.
N. Y. P. L.   August 19, 1932

NN 0017303   NN NjP CU

708.5
Nap   Naples. Museo Nazionale.   Le raccolte
M972   archeologiche. | II. Edizione a cura di G.
         Consoli Fiego. Napoli, S. A. Richter & c.
         [n.d]

           51 p. text. 67 p. of pl. 20 cm.
           At head of title:Museo nazionale di Napoli.

         I. Archaeological collection, Museo Nazionale,
         Naples, Italy.   II. Consoli Fiego, Giuseppe.
         1889?-1938.

NN 0017304   CLCM

Naples. Museo nazionale.
  Le raccolte archeologiche.   Napoli,
Richter & c., [1925]
  111 p. illus., fold. plan. 20 cm.
  At head of title: Museo nazionale di Napoli.

NN 0017305   RPB

Classical   Naples. Museo Nazionale.
Club   Le raccolte archeologiche. 2. ed. Napoli,
J465   S. A. Richter [1937]
N162G   51 p. illus., fold. plan. 20 cm.
1937
Rm.19
              1. Art, Ancient.

NN 0017306   CtY

Naples. Museo nazionale.
  Real museo borbonico ... Napoli, Stamperia reale,
1824–57.
  16 v. fronts., plates (part col., part fold.) plans (part fold.) 28ᶜᵐ.
  Preface signed: Cav. Antonio Niccolini.
  The descriptive letterpress by A. Niccolini, G. Bechi, and others.
  Each volume includes "Relazione degli scavi di Pompei" by G. Bechi and
others.
  "Elenco degli autori moderni, che trattarono delle città di Pompei e di
Ercolano ...": v. 1, p. [1]–11.

    1. Art—Naples. 2. Paintings. 3. Sculpture. 4. Italy—Antiq. 5. Pom-
peii.   I. Niccolini, Antonio.

                                              9—13895
  Library of Congress   N2730.A8

        NcD PP NjN MiU MH IaU
NN 0017307   DLC MdBP CSt IEN CtY TxU OU OClMA PU

Naples. Museo nazionale.
  Recollections of Naples
        see under Wrench, Frederick.

708.5   Naples. Museo nazionale.
qN21re   Recueil des monumens les plus intéressans
         du Musée national, publiés par le professeur
         François Gargiulo. Nouvelle ed. ... Naples,
         Detken & Rocholl [n.d.]
           4 v. in 1. plates. 32 cm.

           Chiefly plates.
           Imprint taken from label mounted over
         original.

           1. Sculpture.   ..nples. Catalogs. 2.
         Sculpture, Repro-   ..uctions of. 3. Art
         objects, Naples.

NN 0017309   N PP

Naples. Museo nazionale.
  Recueil des monumens les plus intéressans du Musée Royal-
Bourbon et de plusieurs autres collections particulières; publié
par Raphael Gargiulo. Seconde édition, augmentée de nouvelles
planches. Naples, 1845. 2 v. pl. 4°.

  1. Art.—Collections: Italy: Naples.   2. Gargiulo, Raffaelle, editor.
N. Y. P. L.   August 6, 1913.

NN 0017310   NN

N2730   Naples. Museo nazionale.
.A65   Recueil des monumens les plus inté-
1851   ressans de Musée Royal Bourbon, et de
         plusieurs autres collections parti-
         culières, publiés par Raffaele Gargiu-
         lo. 3.éd. Naples, 1851.
           v. plates(part.fold.) 30x24cm.

           I.Gargiulo, Raffaele, ed.

NN 0017311   NNU

Naples. Museo nazionale.
  Le raccolte archeologiche.   Napoli,
Richter & c., [1925]
  111 p. illus., fold. plan. 20 cm.
  At head of title: Museo nazionale di Napoli.

Naples. Museo nazionale.
  Recueil des monumens les plus intéressans
de Musée Royal Bourbon ... pub. par Raffaele
Gargiulo. 3. ed. Naples, 1856.

NN 0017312   NjP

Naples. Museo nazionale.
  Recueil des monumens les plus intéressans du
Musée national. 3e éd. 1862.

NN 0017313   MH

Naples. Museo nazionale.
  Recueil des monumens les plus intéressans du Musée national,
et de plusieurs autres collections particulières, publiés par
Raffaele Gargiulo ... 3. éd. Naples, 186₃3?₁
  4 v. in 1. 240 pl. (part fold.) 30 x 24ᶜᵐ.
  Engraved t.-p.
  Two hundred forty engravings (part fold.) numbered 1–60, in each
of the four volumes; preface (4 p.) in vol. I, and index (i. e. table of
contents) in each volume.
  Caption of last leaf, vol. IV, reads: "Index du quatrième volume contenant sculptures ... du Museo royal Bourbon". Hence date of publication is probably earlier than 1863, the name of the museum having
been changed in 1861 to Museo nazionale.
  An earlier edition, with Italian t.-p., was issued in 1825.
    I. Gargiulo, Raffaele, ed.

  Library of Congress   N2730.A65   2–7092

NN 0017314   DLC CtY

Naples. Museo nazionale.   *4072.147
  Recueil des monuments les plus intéressans du Musée national et
de plusieurs autres collections particulières. 4e édition. Vol.
3, 4.
  Naples. 1867. 120 plates. L. 8°.
  Contents. — 3. Pierres fines gravées, objets en or et en argent, peintures
murales et mosaïques du Musée de Naples. 4. Sculptures en terre-cuite,
et vases peints italo-grecs du Musée de Naples.

F8471—Museo nazionale, Naples.—Fine arts. Colls.—Italy. Antiq.—Antiquities.

NN 0017315   MB NN MH

N2730 Naples. Museo nazionale.
f.A4   Recueil des monumens les plus intéressans du Musée na-
1874   tional, publiés par Raffaele Gargiulo ... Nouv. éd. Naples,
       1874.
         [1], [12] p. 168 pl. (part fold.) 31ᶜᵐ.

           1. Sculpture—Naples—Catalogs. 2. Sculpture, Reproductions of. 3. Art ob-
         jects—Naples.

NN 0017316   ICU CtY PP

N2730   Naples. Museo nazionale.
f.A2   Recueil des monuments les plus intéressants
1876   du Musée national de Naples, publiés par le Prof.
         François [!] Gargiulo. Nouv.éd. Naples [1876?]
           [24] p. 170 pl. 31cm.

           Abridged ed., comprising 170 of the 240
         plates of the original ed., with title in English:
         Collection of the most remarkable monuments of
         the National Museum, published by Raphaël
         Gargiulo. 4 v. Naples, 1872.

NN 0017317   OCU

Naples .   Museo nazionale.
  Il Regal Museo Borbonico descritto da Giovambatista Finati
... Dedicato a sua Maestà Ferdinando I ... Tomo 1
              Napoli: G. de Bonis, 1817–   front. (plan.)   v.
17cm.

  CONTENTS.—Tomo 1. Delle statue.

————— ————— Seconda edizione corretta ed accresciuta. Tomo 1,
            Napoli: G. de Bonis, 1819.   v. in   17cm.

————— ————— Terza edizione migliorata ed accresciuta. Tomo 1
            Napoli: Dalla Stamperia Reale, 1827   v.   19cm.

  1. No subject. I. Finati, Giovam-   batista.   Card revised
N. Y. P. L.   October 23, 1942

NN 0017319   NN NjP CtY MBAt

VOLUME 405

N2730 NAPLES. Museo nazionale.
.A4   Il Regal museo borbonico, descritto da Giovam-
1819 batista Finati ... Napoli, Stamperia reale, 1819-
      23.
        3 v.

    1. Art—Naples—Catalogs.

NN 0017320   ICU

Naples. Museo nazionale.
    Il Regal museo borbonico, descritto dal Cav.
Giovambatista Finati ... 2. ed.,, migliorata ed
accresciuta. Napoli, Dalla Stamperia reale,
1842.
    xii, [2], 5-334 p., 1 l. fold. plan. 19.5 cm.
    Mss. notes by Ashbel Smith.
    1. Smith, Ashbel, 1805-1886 – Association
copy.

NN 0017321   TxU NNC

N2730 Naples. Museo nazionale.
.A35   Il regal museo borbonico, descritto dal cav.
       Giovambatista Finati...
       Napoli, 1846.

NN 0017322   DLC

Naples. Museo nazionale.
    Souvenirs du Musée national
        see under Martorana, Pietro, 1819-

Naples. Museo nazionale
    Specimens from the Naples museum; one hundred
and sixty plates, engraved on copper by the
best Italian artists, illus. four hundred and
four objects from every branch of art and
archaeology by Domenico Monaco, with descriptive
letterpress, carefully rev. and amplified from
the best authorities, by E. Neville Rolfe.
Lond., William Clowes, 1884.
    23 p. 160 plates.
    I.Neville-Rolfe, Eustace. II. Monaco, Domenico

NN 0017324   MiD CU ICRL MA PP CU

708.5 Naples. Museo nazionale.
N 162 S   Specimens from the Naples Museum. One hundred
       and sixty plates engraved on copper by the best
       Italian artists, illustrating four hundred and
       sixty objects from every branch of art and archae-
       ology, by Domenico Monaco, curator of the Naples
       Museum. With descriptive letterpress, carefully
       rev. and amplified from the best authorities, by
       E. Neville-Rolfe. Naples, 1889.
         29 p. 160 plates. 30m.

NN 0017325   OO MiD NjNbS NRU MH

Naples. Museo nazionale.
    Specimens from the Naples Museum. One hundred and
sixty-five plates engraved on copper by the best Italian
artists, illustrating five-hundred objects from every branch
of art and archæology, by Domenico Monaco, curator of the
Naples Museum. With descriptive letterpress, carefully
rev. and amplified [1] from the best authorities, and an historical and descriptive sketch of Pompeii and Herculaneum,
by E. Neville Rolfe, Esq. Naples [189-?]
    v, 33 p. plates. 30 cm.
    1. Art—Naples. I. Monaco, Domenico, b. 1838. II. Neville-Rolfe,
Eustace, 1845-1908.
    N2730.A67   48-34027*

NN 0017326   DLC OCISA

N   Naples. Museo Nazionale.
2730   Specimens from the Naples Museum. One
A67   hundred and sixty-five plates engraved on
      copper by the best Italian artists, il-
      lustrating five-hundred objects from every
      branch of art and archaeology, by Domenico
      Monaco, curator of the Naples Museum. With
      descriptive letterpress, carefully rev. and
      amplified [1] from the best authorities,
      and an historical and descriptive sketch
      of Pompeii and Herculaneum, by E. Neville
      Rolfe, Esq.   Naples, 1895.

      v,33p. 165pl. 30cm.

    1.Art – Naples. I.Monaco, Domenico, b. 1838. II.Neville-
Rolfe, Eustace,   1845-1908.

NN 0017328   CLSU ICU MB NBuG PU

Avery
A
2730   Naples. Museo nazionale.
N1641   Specimens from the Naples Museum. One
       hundred and sixty-five plates engraved on
       copper by the best Italian artists, illus-
       trating five-hundred objects from every
       branch of art and archaeology. With descrip-
       tive letterpress, carefully revised and am-
       plified from the best authorities, and an
       historical and descriptive sketch of Pompeii
       and Herculaneum by E. Neville Rolfe. Naples,
       1895.
         v, 33 p. 165 plates (part fold.) 30cm.
         "New edition."

NN 0017329   NNC CU-S

Naples. Museo nazionale.
708.5   Specimens from the Naples Museum. One hundred
qN215S and sixty-eight plates engraved on copper by the
       best Italian artists, illustrating four hundred
       and sixty-six objects from every branch of art
       and archaeology, by Domenico Monaco, curator of
       the Naples Museum. With descriptive letterpress,
       carefully rev. and amplified from the best
       authorities by E. Neville Rolfe, Esq. Naples,
       1889. 31 p. plates. 29 cm.

    1. Art. Naples. 2. Classical antiquities.
I. Monaco, Domenico, b. 1838. II. Neville-Rolfe,
Eustace, 1845-   1908.

NN 0017331   NcD NN CtY FMU NBuG NRU PP OU PBL

Naples. Museo nazionale.
Finati, Eduardo.
    Sulla tazza istoriata di sardonica orientale che serbasi nel
real Museo Borbonico osservazioni di Eduardo Finati.
[Naples] Dalla tipografia di Antonio Cons, 1859.

Naples. Museo nazionale.
    Les tableaux de Musée de Naples
        see under Lenormant, François, 1837-1883.

Naples. Museo nazionale.
    ... Le terracotte figurate del Museo nazionale di Napoli; con
14 tavole e 150 illustrazioni nel testo. Firenze, Vallecchi [1926]
    xxxiii, 216 p. illus., xiv pl. 30m. (Collezione meridionale ... Se-
rie iii: Il Mezzogiorno artistico. [1])
    At head of title: ... Alda Levi.

    1. Terra-cottas—Naples—Catalogs. 2. Terra-cottas, Greco-Roman.
i. Levi, Alda.
                                                32-13410
Library of Congress   NB145.N3
                       [2]   738

          ODO MB CSt NN NjP MiU
NN 0017334   DLC PU-Mu NBuU InU MdBWA PPAmP PP PBm

Naples. Museo nazionale.
    ... Terracotten aus dem Museo nazionale zu
Neapel
        see under Heydemann, Heinrich, 1842-
1889.

Naples. Museo nazionale.
    Die vasensammlungen des Museo nazionale
zu Neapel
        see under Heydemann, Heinrich, 1842-
1889.

759.5 Naples. Museo nazionale di S. Martino.
N215mo   Mostra di bozzetti napoletani del '600 e
       '700. Napoli, Museo di S. Martino maggio -
       agosto 1947. Napoli, Museo di S. Martino,
       1947.
         69p. 32plates. 17cm.

    At head of title: Soprintendenza alle gal-
lerie della campania.

    1.Paintings – Naples. 2.Paintings – Exhibi-
tions. 3.Paint-   ings, Italian.

NN 0017337   NcU OC1MA NjP

Naples. Museo nazionale di S. Martino.
    Nuove guide generali dei musei nazionali di
Napoli e di S. Martino ...
        see under Naples. Museo nazionale.

Naples. Museo nazionale di S. Martino.
    ... Rassegna mensile di disegni delle raccolte
del Museo di S. Martino, 1953. [Naples]
Soprintendenza alle gallerie della Campania, 1953.
    [ii] [67] p. 15 illus. on 8 pl. 14.5 cm.
    At head of title: Soprintendenza alle gallerie
della Campania.
    Text signed: Raffaello Causa.

NN 0017339   OC1MA

Naples. Museo nazionale di San Martino
    Le sale Marcello Orilia. A cura della
Soprintendenza alle gallerie. Napoli, 1955
    11 p. plates

NN 0017340   MH-FA

709.45 Naples. Museo nazionale di S. Martino.
N162m   III mostra di restauri. Museo di S.
       Martino, 20 Dicembre 1953-20 Marzo 1954.
       [Napoli, 1953]
         Cover title, 23p., 28 illus

    Includes bibliography.

    1.Art – Italian. 2.Paintings – Conserva-
tion and restoration. 3.Sculpture – Conservation and restoration. I.Causa,Raffaello, com[

NN 0017341   MiDA MH PPPM OC1MA

Naples. Museo nazionale di S. Martino. *Biblioteca.*
    La biblioteca del Museo nazionale nella certosa di S.
Martino in Napoli ed i suoi manoscritti, esposti e catalo-
gati da Carlo Padiglione. Napoli, F. Giannini, 1876.
    xcii, [7], 806, [2] p. 20m.

    1. Manuscripts, Italian—Catalogs. 2. Manuscripts. Italy—Catalogs.
i. Padiglione, Carlo, 1827-
                                                4-23188
Library of Congress   Z6621.N26

NN 0017342   DLC NjP ICU CU-S

VOLUME 405

Naples. Museo nazionale di S. Martino. *Biblioteca*
see also Naples. Biblioteca nazionale.

Naples. Museo nazionale e pinacoteca
see Naples. Museo nazionale.

Naples. National Museum
see
Naples. Museo nazionale.

ML120 NAPLES. ORATORIO DEI FILIPPINI.
f.I8   Città di Napoli. Archivio dell'Oratorio dei
A85   Filippini. «Compilatore delle schede Salvatore
v.10   di Giacomo» Parma, Freschng, 1918.
          xiv, 98 p. illus., port., music. (Associa-
          zione dei musicologi italiani. Catalogo genera-
          le delle opere musicali)

          I. Giacomo, Salvatore di, 1862-1934, ed.

NN 0017346   ICU

Law
      Naples. Ordinances, etc.
        Regolamento del mercato agricolo generale
      approvato con provvedimento 18 Aprile 1929 n.
      39, dalla G.P.A. il 14-5-1929 n. 15257-2 e
      modificato con atto dei 28 Maggio detto anno
      n. 9, reso esecutivo il 24-6-1929 n.20874-2.
      Napoli, F.Giannini & Figli, 1929.
        47,[1] p. 27 cm.

        1.Law-Naples. I.Title.

NN 0017347   DLC

4X   Naples. Ordinances, etc.
It   Regolamento di igiene e di polizia
1613   sanitaria e provvedimenti diversi
         relativi all'igiene e sanità pubblica
         per la Città di Napoli. Napoli, R.
         Tip. F. Giannini, 1928.
           135 p.

NN 0017348   DLC-P4

4RA   Naples. Ordinances, etc.
326   Regolamento di igiene e di polizia
         sanitaria e provvedimenti diversi
         relativi all'Igiene e sanità pubblica
         per la Città di Napoli. Napoli, R.
         Stab. tip. F. Giannini, 1938.
           135 p.

NN 0017349   DLC-P4

Naples. Ordinances, etc.
    Regolamento edilizio pel comune di Napoli. Approvato con
R. decreto del 14 aprile 1892.   Napoli: R. Stabilimento Tipografico Francesco Giannini & figli, 1910. 46 p. pap. 8°.

    Title from cover.

1. Building construction.—Juris-   prudence, Italy: Naples: 1892.
N. Y. P. L.   January 3, 1912.

NN 0017350   NN

Naples. Orto botanico
see
Naples. Università. *Orto botanico.*

Naples. Ospedale "Cardinale Ascalesi."
    Statistica generale sanitaria.
Napoli.
        v. 25 cm.

        RA989.I 9N28   55-24659 ‡

NN 0017352   DLC

Naples. Ospedale clinico.
    Relazione all' illmo sig. ministro dei lavori
pubblici ...
        see under Travaglini, Federico.

W 1   NAPLES. Ospedale dei pellegrini.
NA145L   Annali clinici. v. 1-3; 1871-73.
          Napoli.
            3 v. in 2.
            Title: Annali clinici dello Ospedale
          dei pellegrini di Napoli

NN 0017354   DNLM

Naples. Ospedale del Pio Monte della
    Misericordia.
        Relazione delle cure termo-minerali dei
Gorgitelio praticate in Napoli da fanciulli infermi recoverati nell' ..., durante la state del
1884. 58 pp., 3 l. 8°. Napoli, L. De Bonis,
1884.

NN 0017355   DNLM

W 1   NAPLES. Ospedale della pace.
NA146   Annali clinica.
          anno 1-   1878-
          Napoli.
            v. illus.

NN 0017356   DNLM DLC

W 1   NAPLES. Ospedale incurabili.
NA146R   Annali clinici. anno 1-9, genn./mar.
          1835-ott./dic. 1843; nuova ser., anno
          1-8, 1876-83; ser. 3, anno 1, genn./febbr.
          ott./dic. 1887. Napoli.
            18 v. in 14. illus.

            Title: Gli Annali clinici dell'Ospedale
          degl'incurabili in Napoli

NN 0017357   DNLM

Naples. Ospedale incurabili.
    Annali clinici dello Ospedale incurabili, nuova serie. Di-
rettori dott¹. M. Semmola e T. Livio de Sanctis ... redattori
e collaboratori tutt' i medici e chirurgi dell' Ospedale ...
anno 1-   Napoli, 1876-
        v.   plates (part fold.) diagrs. (part fold.) 23½cm. bimonthly.
    Vol. 1 has title: Annali clinici ... Direttori dott¹. M. Semmola e T.
Livio de Sanctis ... redattori annuali prof¹. Diodato Borrelli, de Bonis,
Frusci e d'Ambrosio, collaboratori tutt' i medici e chirurgi dell'Ospedale ...

    1. Medicine, Clinical—Hospital reports. 2. Medicine—Period.
Semmola, Mariano, 1831-1896. II. Sanctis, Tito Livio de. III. Title.

Library of Congress   RC31.N25O7   8-14163

NN 0017358   DLC DNLM ICJ

Naples. Ospedale incurabili.
    Regolamento per la proscrizione e summi-
nistrazione de' farmachi agl' infermi nell' ...
34 pp. 8°. Napoli, G. Migliaccio, 1852. [P. v.,
1130.]

NN 0017359   DNLM

Naples. Ospedale incurabili.
    Reparto delle le-
sioni violente, diretto dai prof¹¹ A. De Giaco-
no e M. Barba. Resoconto clinico-statistico
del biennio 1894-5. Redatto dagli assistenti D¹¹
M. Carbonaro, P. Manisera, F. Paturzo ed A.
Santoro; con una relazione sui casi di lesioni violente curati dal 1° settembre 1891 al 31 dicembre 1893. 264 pp. roy. 8°. Napoli, A. Trani,
898.

NN 0017360   DNLM

Naples. Ospedale internazionale. (Villa Bentinck)
    Rapporti del comitato.
Napoli.
        8°.

NN 0017361   DNLM

Naples.   Ospedale internazionale (Villa Bentinck)
            Statuto e regolamento. 3. ed. 8 pp.
        16°. Napoli, F. Giannini & figli, 1888.

NN 0017362   DNLM

Naples. Ospedale S. Eligio.
    Statistica dell'ospedale S. Eligio
        see under Romanelli, Luigi.

Naples. Osservatorio Astronomico di Capodi-
    monte.
QB8   Annuario. 1846-
N3   Napoli, Stamperia dell'Iride.
                    tables. 18cm.

        1. Ephemerides.

NN 0017364   DLC CtY

Naples. Osservatorio astronomico di Capodimonte.
    Calendario.
Napoli.
        v. 19 cm.

        1. Astronomy—Observations.

        QB4.N18   58-51526

NN 0017365   DLC DAS DN-Ob ICJ

Naples. Osservatorio astronomico di Capodimonte.
    ... Catalogo astrografico 1900.0, zona di Cata-
nia, fra + 46° e + 55° ... Napoli, 1928-
                    31cm.

                DLC:QB

    Contents.--

    v.2-6. Declinazione da + 47° a + 49°, ascensione
retta da 12ʰ a 18ʰ, comprendente 36 lastre il cui
centro ha la declinazione 48°.

    v. 5³-4. Declinazione da + 50° a + 52°, ascensione
retta da 6ʰ a 12ʰ, comprendente 30 lastre il cui
centro ha la declinazione 51°,--

    v. 6³-4. Declinazione da + 51° a + 53°, ascensione
retta da 6ʰ a 12ʰ, comprendente 30 lastre il cui
centro ha la declinazione + 52°.

    1.Astrographic catalog and chart.

NN 0017368   NNC CU DLC

VOLUME 405

Naples. R. Osservatorio astronomico di
  Capodimonte.
  ... Cenno storico sull'attivita dell'istituto
  nel primo secolo di vita. Napoli, Tipografia
  R. Contessa & fratelli, 1929.
    cover-title, 24 p.   26½ cm.
    At head of title: R. Osservatorio astrono-
  mico di Capodimonte.
    "Elenco delle pubblicazioni del R. Osserva-
  torio astronomico di Capodimonte, Napoli":
  p. 14-20.

NN 0017369   DN-Ob DSI DAS

M82.2/457
N215cl   Naples. Osservatorio astronomico di Cap-
         odimonte.
           Il clima di Napoli, 1821-1887. Memoria di
         Vincenzo Canino. Roma, Stabilimento Bon-
         tempelli, 1889.
           36 p. diagrs., tables. 33 cm.

           Estratto dagli Annali dell'Ufficio Cent-
         rale de Meteorologia e Geodinamica, pt.1,
         v.9,1887.

NN 0017370   DAS

Naples. Osservatorio astronomico di Capodimonte.
  Comentarj astronomici della specola reale di Napoli. Di
  Carlo Brioschi, direttore della medesima ... Vol. I. Napoli,
  Tip. nella Pietà de' Turchini, 1824-26.
    viii, 152, 207 p. v fold. pl. (incl. plans) 30 x 23½ᶜᵐ.
    Issued in two parts.
    No more published?

    1. Astronomy—Observations.   I. Brioschi, Carlo, 1782?-1833.
    II. Title.
                                                    9—2656
    Library of Congress   QB4.N2

NN 0017371   DLC CtY

Naples. Osservatorio astronomico di Capodimonte.
  Contributi astronomici.
  Pavia ₍etc.₎, Tip. M. Ponzio ₍etc.₎, 19
    v. illus. 25 cm.
    Began publication in 1933. Cf. Union list of serials.

    1. Astronomy—Collected works.

    QB1.N33A2   60-24286

    DSI OC1W PSC OU
NN 0017372   DLC CtW IaU CU PU-Math TxU AzU IEN

Naples. Osservatorio astronomico di Capodimonte.   N164
  ... Contributi geofisici ... Napoli, 1914-
    Library has no. 1-13. tables. 25ᶜᵐ.
    At head of title: R. Osservatorio astronomico di Capodimonte.

NN 0017373   ICJ DN-Ob

QC830   Naples. Osservatorio astronomico di Capodimonte.
N5   Determinazioni assolute della componente oriz-
          zontale della forza magnetica terrestre.
        18
        ₍Naples?₎
            v. 30 cm. annual.

            1. Magnetism, Terrestrial - Observations. I.
          Title.

NN 0017374   OU

QC830   Naples. Osservatorio astronomico di Capodimonte.
.N33   Determinazioni assolute della componente ori-
          zontale della forza magnetica terrestre negli an-
          ni 1904-1909.
          Naples,1912-
          1 v.
          cover-title

NN 0017375   DLC

QC830   Naples. Osservatorio astronomico di Capodimonte.
.N33   Determinazioni assolute della inclinazione mag-
          netica. 18
          ₍Naples₎
            v. 26-30 cm. annual.

            1. Magnetism, Terrestrial - Observations.
          I. Title.

NN 0017376   OU

QC830   Naples. Osservatorio astronomico di Capodimonte.
.N35   Determinazioni assolute dell' inclinazione...
          durante l'anno 1904-06-1911-
          Naples, 1907-12
          4 v.
          cover-title

NN 0017377   DLC

Observatory   Naples. Osservatorio Astronomico di Capodi-
QB4   monte.
N33   Elenco delle pubblicazioni del personale
              dell'Osservatorio. 1824/1913-
              Napoli.
                    25cm.

              Title varies slightly.

NN 0017378   DLC RPB DN-Ob DAS

Naples. Osservatorio Astronomico di Capodimonte.
  Memorie astronomiche. no. 1-
  1915-

NN 0017379   AzU CU RPB DLC DN-Ob

Naples. Osservatorio Astronomico di Capodimonte.
  [Miscellaneous publications]   [Naples?
  1905?-
    pams. 26 cm.

NN 0017380   OCU

Naples. Osservatorio astronomico di Capodimonte.
  Nuova determinazione della latitudine geografica del Reale Osservatorio di Capodimonte
         see under   Angelitti, Filippo, 1856-

520.6   Naples. Osservatorio astronomico di Capodimonte
N162o   Osservazioni. v.1-
Physics   Pavia, M. Ponzio, 1950-
Lib'y   v. illus. 24cm.

          Chiefly reprints.

          1. Astronomy - Collected works.

NN 0017382   TxU MiU

QB82
N3
        Naples. Osservatorio astronomico di Capodimonte.
          Rapporto sull' attività.
        Napoli.
          v. 19 cm.

        QB82.N3   58-53923 rev ‡

NN 0017383   DLC DN-Ob

Naples. Osservatorio astronomico di Capodimonte.
  Riassunti decadici e mensili delle osser. meteoriche. 1899
  n.p. 1900
  8°

NN 0017384   DLC

Naples . Osservatorio astronomico di Capodimonte.
  Valori medj decadici e mensili e riassunto
annuale delle osservazioni meteoriche fatte...
nell'anno 1900. Napoli, 1901.
  9 p. 26 cm.

  Napoli, Rendiconto,   1901.

NN 0017385   DN-Ob

QC851   Naples. Osservatorio astronomico di Capodimonte.
N5   Variazioni della declinazione magnetica osser-
          vate nella R. Specola di Capodimonte.
        18
        ₍Naples?₎
            v. 26-30 cm. annual.

            1. Magnetism, Terrestrial - Diurnal variations.
          I. Title.

NN 0017386   OU

QE527
.N3   Naples. Osservatorio vesuviano.
        Annali.

      Napoli,
        v. illus., plates, maps, diagrs. 25ᵐ.
        Published in four series: 1859-70; new ser., 1873; ser. 3, 1924-26;
      ser. 4, 1927-32? cf. Union list of serials.
        Ser. 3, "a cura del Comitato vulcanologico della R. Università di
      Napoli"; ser. 4, "a cura di A. Malladra."

        1. Vesuvius.   I. Malladra, Alessandro, 1868-   II. Naples. Uni-
      versità. Comitato vulcanologico.
                                                          45-29040
        Library of Congress   QE527.N3
                                        ₍2₎   551.21072

NN 0017387   DLC ICJ DSI NN ICRL RPB

Naples. Osservatorio Vesuviano.
  Relazioni delle Commissioni. (Per l'Osservatorio
Vesuviano parere. Relazione della Commissione in-
caricata di proporre il rimedio piu opportuno per
eliminare i danni derivanti all' Osservatorio
Vesuviano dalla ferrovia elettrica.)
       Clipping of (24) p. 27cm.
Napoli, Regia Universite, Annuario (?). 1903-04,
p. 177-210.

NN 0017388   DN-Ob

Naples. Palazzo delle esposizioni della mostra d'oltremare
  Seconda Rassegna delle arti figurative nel Mezzogiorno
Palazzo delle arti della mostra d'oltremare, sede della
rassegna delle arti figurative, Napoli, agosto-settembre
1954. np [1954?]
  67 p. illus.

NN 0017389   MH-FA

VOLUME 405

Naples. Palazzo reale.
　Catalogo

　　see under

Naples. Mostra del Ritratto Storico Napoletano.

Naples. Palazzo reale.
　Mostra dell'antica maiolica abruzzese,
catalogo. Napoli, Palazzo reale, 1955.
　　55 p.　88 pl. (8 col. incl. col. front.)
24.5 cm.
　　Bibliography: p. 23-24, p. 32.
　　Catalog compiled by Gian Carlo Polidori.
　　Contents: La Maiolica di Castelli d'Abruzzo
by G.C. Polidori; La ceramica a Napoli e
l'influsso abruzzese by Elena Romano.

NN　0017391　OC1MA

Naples. Palazzo reale.
　Sculture lignee nella Campania
　　see under　Naples. Mostra della scultura
lignea nella Campania, 1950.

Naples. Pinacoteca del Museo nazionale
see
Naples. Museo nazionale.

Naples. *Prefettura*
　　see
Naples (*Province*) Prefettura.

Naples. Pretura
　　see Italy. Pretura (Naples)

Naples. Real ... Reale ... Regi ... Regia ... Regio ...

　An institution with a name beginning with any of these adjectives
is listed in this catalog under the name of the city followed by the
name of the institution, omitting the initial adjective, e. g., Naples.
Università, not Regia Università.

Naples. Reggia
　　see
Naples. Palazzo reale.

Naples. Regio istituto universitario navale
　　see
Naples. Istituto universitario navale.

---

fZ　NAPLES. S. ANGELO A NILO (Church) Biblioteca.
79　　Bibliothecæ S. Angeli ad Nidum [!] ab in-
.N 16　clyta Brancatiorum familia constructæ, et ab
aliis deinceps auctæ catalogus, in quo singuli
singularum artium, & scientiarum libri, qui in
quavis fere lingua exstant, auctorumque cogno-
mina ordine alphabetico recensentur.　Neapoli,
Abbat, 1750.
　331, 8p.　35½cm.

Continued in next column

Continued from preceding column

　Originally given to the church of S. Angelo
a Nilo, this col-　lection later became the
basis of the R.　Biblioteca Brancacciana.

NN　0017399　ICN

Naples. San Gennaro (*Cathedral*)
　　see
Naples. Duomo.

Naples. San Martino (*Carthusian monastery*)
　　see
Naples. Certosa di San Martino.

Naples. San Severino (*Abbey*)
　Hymnarius severinianus. Das hymnar der abtei S. Severin
in Neapel. Nach den codices Vaticanus 7172 und Parisinus
1092. Herausgegeben von Guido Maria Dreves, s. j. Leipzig, O. R. Reisland, 1893.
　　2 p. l., p. [5]-143. facsim. 22½ cm. (*Added t.-p.:* Analecta hymnica
medii aevi. xiva)
　　1. Catholic church—Hymns. 2. Hymns, Latin.　I. Vatican.
Biblioteca vaticana. Mss. (Vat. lat. 7172)　II. Paris. Bibliothèque
nationale. Mss. (Lat. 1092)　III. Catholic church. Liturgy and ritual.
Hymnary.　IV. Dreves, Guido Maria, 1854-1909, ed.　V. Title.
　　[BV468.A6　vol. 14a]　　　　　　A C 34—96

Illinois. Univ. Library
for Library of Congress　　[a53d½]

NN　0017402　IU NNUT KAS MB NN NcD

Microfiche
BV
468
.A6
v.14a　Naples. San Severino (*Abbey*)
　Hymnarius severinianus. Das hymnar der abtei S. Severin
in Neapel. Nach den codices Vaticanus 7172 und Parisinus
1092. Herausgegeben von Guido Maria Dreves, s. j. Leipzig,
O. R. Reisland, 1893.
　　2 p. l., p. [5]-143.　　　　(Analecta hymnica
medii aevi. xiva)
　　Microfiche. Washington, D. C. Microcard
Editions. 3 sheets.
　　1. Catholic Church—Hymns. 2. Hymns, Latin.　I. Vatican. Biblioteca vaticana. Mss. (Vat. lat. 7172)　II. Paris. Bibliothèque nationale.
Mss. (Lat. 1092)　　　　III. Catholic Church. Liturgy and
ritual. Hymnary.　　　IV. Dreves, Guido Maria, 1854-1909.
ed. v. Title.　　　VI. Series.

NN　0017403　INS OO

Micro
3
Analecta　Naples. San Severino (Abbey)
v.14a　Hymnarius severinianus. Das Hymnar der
Abtei S. Severin in Neapel. Nach den codices
Vaticanus 7172 und Parisinus 1092. Herausgege-
ben von Guido Maria Dreves, S.J. Leipzig,
O.R. Reisland, 1893.
　　4 cards. 7.5x12.5cm. (Analecta hymnica
medii aevi, 14a)
　　Micro-transparency (negative). Washington,
D.C., Microcard Editions, 1962)
　　Collation of the original: 143p.
　　1. Catholic chur　　ch - Hymns. 2. Hymns,
Latin.

NN　0017404　PSt

Naples. Santa casa dello Spirito Santo.
　Regole, et instrvttioni della Santa casa dello
Spirito Santo di Napoli, concluse dalli signori
gouernatori di quella nell' anno 1664, diuise in
quattro parti, cioè, chiesa, conseruatorio, casa,
e banco ... [Napoli, 1664]
　　8 p.l., 53, [2] p.　31 cm.
　　Contains bookplates of the marchese of Salsa
and the earl of Dudley.
　　1. Church finance - Accounting.

NN　0017405　CU

Naples.　　SS. Apostoli Pietro e Paolo
　(Greek church)
　Delle istorie della chiesa greca [de' SS.
Apostoli Pietro e Paolo] in Napoli esistente
　　see under　[Meola, Gian Vincenzio]

Naples. Scuola Benedettina di Mosaico.
　La inaugurazione e la esposizione de'saggi di
lavoro della Scuola Benedettina di Mosaico nel
monumento sacro de'Santi Severino e Sossio in
Napoli, 16 Giugno, 1889
　　see under title

Naples. Scuola d'applicazione per gli ingegneri
　see Naples. Università. *Facoltà di ingegneria.*

Naples. Scuola d'ingegneria
　see Naples. Università. *Facoltà di ingegneria.*

Naples. Scuola di applicazione di ponti e strade
　see Naples. Università. *Facoltà di ingegneria.*

Naples. Scuola industriale Alessandro Volta.
　... Regio decreto d'istituzione, regolamento e programmi d'insegnamento. Napoli, R. Tip. comm. F. Giannini
& figli, 1888.
　　125 p.　22ᶜᵐ

　I. Italy. Laws, statutes, etc.

　　　　　　　　　　E 15-1631

Library, U. S. Bur. of　　Education T173.N2A3

NN　0017411　DHEW

Naples.　　Scuola media di studii commerciali ed attuariali.
　Cinque anni di vita della R. Scuola media di studii commerciali ed attuariali di Napoli. Napoli, Tip. A. & S.
Festa, 1911.
　　158 p., 1 l. 26ᶜᵐ.
　　"Biblioteca, catalogo per autori": p. [113]-146.

　1. Business education—Naples.

　　　　　　　　　　E 11-1570

Library, U. S. Bur. of　　Education HF1152.N2S4

NN　0017412　DHEW ICJ

Naples. Scuola militare.
　Annuario.
　[Napoli,
　　v. illus., plates, ports., facsims. 25½ᶜᵐ.

　　　　　　　　　　　45-41175

Library of Congress　　U589.N3R5

　　　　　[2]　　　　　　355.071

NN　0017413　DLC

Naples. Scuola superiore politecnica
　see Naples. Università. *Facoltà di ingegneria.*

BA695　Naples,　　　　　Seminario.
C363s　Plausus Seminarii Archiepiscopalis Neapoli-
tani. In adventu Eminentiss. Principis D.
Josephi S. R. E. Card. De Aguirre Protectoris
Regni Siciliæ Post reparatam valetudinem. ...
Neap. Ex Officina Sociorum Parrino, &
Mutij 1695. Superiorum licentia.
　74 p. 15cm. 12º
　Address to José Sáenz de Aguirre (p. 5-30)

Continued in next column

VOLUME 405

Continued from preceding column

signed: Constantius Criscolus Semin. Alumnus.
Pages 31-74 contain commendatory poetry in
Latin and Greek by various authors.
In this copy there is a blank leaf at end.

Bound in contemporary calf with: Synopsis
Collectionis Maximæ Conciliorum Omnium
Hispaniæ, Et Novi Orbis. Rome, 1695.
Palau(2)284305.

NN   0017417   RPBJC

Naples. Seminario.
   Regole del Seminario napoletano
      see under   Naples (Archdiocese)
   Archbishop, 1734-1754 (Giuseppe Spinelli)

x946.05 Naples   . Seminario.
C19Wc   Rev. Seminarii archiep. neapolitani Pro repa-
    rata Caroli II. Hispaniarum regis valetudine
    soteria eminentiss. ac rever. dom. d. Jacobi
    S. R. E. cardin. Cantelmi, archiep. neapol.
    jussu concepta.   Neapoli, In nova Typographia
    Dominici Antonii Parrino juxta Divæ Claræ, è
    regione domus professæ Societatis Jesu, 1697.
    [10], 3-84, [3]p. 22cm. [With Componimenti
    recitati nell'Accademia [napoletana] a'dì IV. di
    novembre, anno M.DC.XCVI ragunata nel real pala-
    gio in Napoli per la ricuperata salute di Carlo
    II. re di Spagna.   Napoli, 1697]
       Title vignette;   tail-pieces.

NN   0017419   IU

Naples.   Servicii del gaz.
   Riscatto ed assunzione diretta dei servizii del
gas. 1909.
   67 p.

NN   0017420   PP

Naples.   Servizio delle tramvie.
   Riscatto ed assunzione diretta del servizio
delle tramvie urbane. 1909.
   94 p.

NN   0017421   PP

HA1379   Naples .   Sezione statistica.
.N3   Bollettino statistico mensile ... (Anno XXIX,
    1903) [Napoli, 1903]
    1 v.   tables, fold. diagrs.   27 cm.

NN   0017422   DLC

Naples.   Sindaco.
   Al consiglio comunale. Relazione del sindaco
sul problema delle case popolari ed economiche
(seduta del consiglio del 4 agosto 1909)
   18 p.

NN   0017423   PP

Naples. Società africana d'Italia
      see
Società africana d'Italia, Naples.

Naples. Società americana d'Italia
      see
Società americana d'Italia, Naples.

Naples. Società di naturalisti.
      see
Società di naturalisti in Napoli.

Naples. Società Luigi Camoens
      see   Società Luigi Camoens, Naples.

Naples. Società meridionale di elettricità
      see
Società meridionale di elettricità.

Naples. Società napoletana di storia patria
      see   Deputazione napoletana di storia
patria. Naples.

Naples. Società nazionale emancipatrice di mutuo
   soccorso del sacerdozio italiano
      see   Società nazionale emancipatrice e di
mutuo soccorso del Sacerdozio italiano, Naples.

Naples. Società orticola napoletana. *See* Società
   orticola napoletana.

Naples. Società pontaniana
      see
Accademia pontaniana, *Naples.*

Naples. Società reale Borbonica
      see
Accademia delle scienze, Naples.

Naples. Società reale di Napoli. Accademia
   delle scienze fisiche e matematiche
      see   Accademia delle scienze fisiche e
matematiche, Naples.

Naples. Società reale di Napoli. Accademia di
   scienze morali e politiche
      see   Accademia nazionale di scienze
morali e politiche, Naples.

Naples. *Soprintendenza alle antichità*
   see **Italy.** *Soprintendenza alle antichità. Naples.*

Naples. *Soprintendenza bibliografica per la Campania e la
   Calabria*
      see
Italy. *Soprintendenza bibliografica per la Campania e la
   Calabria.*

Naples. Specola reale
      see
Naples. Osservatorio astronomico di Capodimonte.

Naples. Stabilimento degl'incurabile e luoghi
   riuniti.
   Statuti per lo Reale Stabilimento... Napoli, 1839.
   247 p.,4 tab. 8°

NN   0017439   DNLM

Naples. Stamperia reale
      see   Naples (Kingdom) Stamperia reale.

Naples. Stazione sperimentale per l'industria delle pelli e
   materie concianti.
      ...Tannini sintetici.   Napoli: R. Stazione sperimentale per
   l'industria delle pelli, 1924?]   140 p.   8°

      At head of title: Dr. Vittorio Casaburi.
      Errata slip inserted.

504693A. 1. Tannins, Synthetic.
N. Y. P. L.   January 13, 1931

NN   0017441   NN

Naples. Stazione sperimentale per l'industria delle
   pelli e delle materie concianti
      see *also*
Turin. Stazione sperimentale per l'industria delle e
   delle materie concianti.

Naples. Stazione Zoologica.
   Arbeiten aus dem bakteriologischen
Laboratorium der zoologischen Station zu Neapel
      see under   Kruse, Walter, 1864-   ed.

Naples. Stazione Zoologica.
   I Cefalopodi viventi nel Golfo di Napoli
      see under   Jatta, Giuseppe.

Naples. Stazione zoologica.
   Erster jahresbericht der Zoologischen station in Neapel. Leipzig, W. Engelmann, 1876.
   iv, 92 p. 23ᵐᵐ.
   Continued in the Mittheilungen.

   1. Zoology—Societies, etc.
                                                    16-18150

   Library of Congress   QL1.N136

NN   0017445   DLC MH

VOLUME 405

QL
133
N162

Naples. Stazione zoologica.
Fauna und flora des Golfes von Neapel und der angrenzenden Meeres-Abschnitte. Hrsg. von der Zoologischen Station zu Neapel. Leipzig, W. Engelmann, 1880-
38 v. in   illus., plates (part col.)   21-33 cm.

Publisher varies.
Vols. 35-38 have title: Fauna e flora del Golfo di Napoli.
Vols. 9, 14, 15 bound together as 1 volume. Vols. 10, 12, 13 bound together as 1 volume.
Contents.- 1. Ctenophorae. Die Ctenophoren, von C. Chun.-

- 2. Fierasfer. Le specie del genere Fierasfer nel Golfo di Napoli e regioni limitrofe, von C. Emery.- 3. Pantopoda. Die Pantopoden, von A. Dohrn.- 4. Corallina. Die Corallinenalgen von Graf zu Solms-Laubach.- 5. Die Chaetognathen. I chetognathi, anatomia e sistematica con aggiunte embriologiche, von B. Grassi.- 6. Caprelliden, von P. Mayer.- 7. Die Cystoseiren. Le cystoseirae, von R. Valiante.- 8. Bangiaceen, von G. Berthold.- 9. 1. Theil. Die Actinien. Le attinie, von A. Andres.- 10. Doliolum. Die Arten der Gattung Doliolum, von B. Uljanin.- 11. Die Polycladen

(Seeplanarien) von A. Lang.- 12. Cryptonemi ceen, von G. Berthold.- 13. Die Koloniebildenden Radiolarien (Sphaerozoëen), von K. Brandt.- 14. Polygordius. Le genre polygordius, von J. Fraipont.- 15. Die Gorgoniden, von G. v. Koch.- 16. Capitelliden, von H. Eisig.- 17. Caprelliden: Nachtrag, von P. Mayer.- 18. Die Enteopneusten, von J. W. Spengel.- 19. Pelagische Copepoden (Systematik und Faunistik) [und] Atlas, von W. Giesbrecht 2 v.- 20. Gammarini, von A. della Valle.- 21. Ostracoden, von G. W. Müller.- 22. Nemertinen, von O. Bürger.- 23. Cefalopodi,

von G. Jatta.- 24. Die Seesterne des Mittelmeeres, von H. Ludwig.- 25. Asterocheriden, von W. Giesbrecht.- 26. Rhodomelaceen, von P. Falkenberg.- 27. Mytiliden, von T. List.- 28. Ichthyotomus sanguinarius, von H. Eisig.- 29. Rhizocephala, von G. Smith.- 30. Phoronis, par M. de Selys-Longchamps.- 31. Protodrilius, von U. Pierantoni.- 32. Tricladen, von J. Wilhelmi.- 33. 1. Teil. Stomatopoden, von W. Giesbrecht.- 34. 1.- Teil. Echiuriden, von F. Baltzer.- 35. 1, 1.-2. Band- Die Cephalopoden, von A. Naef.   v.- 36. Die

- Syngnathiden, von M. Rauther.- 37. Acantharia, von W. Schewiakoff [und] Atlas. 2 v.- 38. Uova, larve e stadi giovanili di Teleostei, di Salvatore Lo Bianco. 3 v. in 2.

1. Marine fauna - Naples, Bay of. I. Title. II. Title: Fauna e flora del Golfo di Napoli. (Author/title anals) (Subject anals)

NN   0017450   ICJ NjP AAP CSt PU-Z
CU-S OrCS CaBVaU CU PPAN OU PPWI MnU

Naples. Stazione zoologica.
Das 25jährige Jubiläum der Zoologischen Station zu Neapel, am 14. April 1897 [Leipzig, Druck von Breitkopf & Härtel, 1897.]
44 p. 24ᶜᵐ.

590.7361
P700
159790

NN   0017451   ICJ

Naples. Stazione zoologica.
Guida per l'acquario della Stazione zoologica di Napole. Napoli, Delken & Rocholl, 1880.
vii, [1], 69 p. 20ᶜᵐ.

Written by Richard Schmidtlein.
Preface by C. A. Dohrn.

1. Schmidtlein, Richard.

A 18-1917

Title from Harvard Univ.   Printed by L. C.

NN   0017452   MH

Naples. Stazione zoologica.
Guida per l'acquario della Stazione zoologica di Napoli. 4a ed., con 175 figure intercalate nel testo. Modena, Società tipografica, antica Tipografiei Soliani, 1898.
103 p. illus. 23ᵐᵐ.

A 18-1918

Title from Harvard Univ.   Printed by L. C.

NN   0017453   MH

Naples. Stazione zoologica.
Guida per l'acquario della Stazione zoologica di Napoli. 5a ed., con 175 figure intercalate nel testo. Napoli, Tip. A. Trani, 1905.
107 p. illus. 24½ᶜᵐ.

A 18-1919

Title from Harvard Univ.   Printed by L. C.

NN   0017454   MH

Naples. Stazione zoologica.
Guide pour l'aquarium de la Station zoologique de Naples. 4ᵉ éd., avec 167 illustrations. Naples, Impr. A. Trani, 1898.
104 p. illus. 24ᶜᵐ.

A 18-1920

Title from Harvard Univ.   Printed by L. C.

NN   0017455   MH

Adelmann
QL
69
A1M33

Naples. Stazione zoologica.
Guide to the aquarium of the Zoological Station at Naples.   Naples, H. Detken [189-?]
64 p. 23cm.

No. 1 in a vol. lettered: Marine laboratories.

1. Aquariums.

NN   0017456   NIC

Naples. Stazione zoologica.
Guide to the aquarium of the Zoölogical station at Naples. 3d ed., with 167 illustrations. Leipzig, Printed by Breitkopf & Härtel, 1892.
93 p. illus.   23 cm.
Cover title: Aquarium neapolitanum.

NN   0017457   CSt NjP

Naples. Stazione zoologica.
Guide to the aquarium of the Zoological station at Naples. 4th ed., with 175 illustrations. Leipzig, Breitkopf & Härtel, 1896.
101 p. illus. 23ᵐᵐ.

A 18-1921

Harvard univ. Library
for Library of Congress   [a39b1]

NN   0017458   MH CtY ViU NIC FMU

574.92074
N16g
1902

Naples. Stazione Zoologica.
Guide to the aquarium of the Zoological Station at Naples. 5th ed.   Naples, printed by A. Trani, 1902.
101p. illus. 24cm.

1. Aquariums. 2. Marine biology--Naples.

NN   0017459   IU CSt CtY NjP

QL
69
N25
A3
1906

Naples. Stazione zoologica.
Guide to the aquarium. 6th ed., with 175 illus.   Naples, A. Trani, 1906.
101 p. illus. 24cm.

1. Aquariums.   I. Title.

NN   0017460   NIC CtY PBa MB

Naples. Stazione zoologica.
Guide to the aquarium of the Zoological station at Naples. 7th ed. with 175 illustrations. Naples, F. Giannini & sons, 1910.
102 p. illus. 23 cm.
On cover: Aquarium neapolitanum.

NN   0017461   CU

QL
69
N25
A3
1925

Naples. Stazione zoologica.
Guide to the aquarium of the zoological station at Naples. 9th. ed. with illus. Napoli, F. Giannini, 1925.
123 p. illus. 25cm.

1. Aquariums.   I. Title.

NN   0017462   NIC CU MH PLF

Adelmann
QL
69
A1M33

Naples. Stazione zoologica.
Hauptgrundzüge des Contractes zwischen Dr. Anton Dohrn und der Stadt Neapel betreffend die Errichtung der Zoologischen Station. [Leipzig, Breitkopf und Härtel, 187-?]
8 p. 23cm.

No. 4 in a vol. lettered: Marine laboratories.

1. Dohrn, Anton, 1840-1909. II. Naples.

NN   0017463   NIC

Naples. Stazione zoologica.
Leitfaden für das Aquarium der Zoologische Station zu Neapel. Leipzig, 1880.

[5], 82 p.   8°.

NN   0017464   MH-Z

Naples, Italy. Stazione zoologica.
Leitfaden für das Aquarium. 2ᵉ ed. Leipz., 1884.

1 pam. 8°.

NN   0017465   MH-Z

Naples. Stazione zoologica.
Leitfaden für das Aquarium der Zoologischen station zu Neapel. 4. aufl., mit 175 illustrationen. Leipzig, Druck von Breitkopf & Härtel, 1894.
102 p. illus.   23.5 cm.
--- Atlas. [1. aufl. ?]   Neapel, Zoologische station, 1883.
cover-title, 1 p.l., 47 pl.   24 cm.
1. Marine fauna.

NN   0017466   CU

Naples. Stazione zoologica.
Leitfaden für das aquarium der zoologischen Station zu Neapel.   Naples, 1899.
8°.
5th ed.

NN   0017467   MH-Z

VOLUME 405

Naples. Stazione zoologica.
Leitfaden für das aquarium der Zoologischen station zu Neapel. 6ᵃ. aufl., mit 175 illustrationen. Neapel, Druck von A. Trani, 1905.
102 p. illus. 23½ᵐ.

1. Marine fauna.
A 18-1592 Revised

Title from Harvard   Univ. Printed by L. C.

NN 0017468   MH

Naples. Stazione zoologica.   590.7361 ᴵ
Mittheilungen aus der Zoologischen Station zu Neapel. Zugleich ein Repertorium für Mittelmeerkunde. Erster–22. Band, ...
Berlin, R. Friedländer & Sohn, 1879–1921.
22 vol. illus., plates (part col.), maps, tables. 23–25ᵐ.
Succeeded by its Pubblicazioni.
Author index to vol. 1–10, 1879–1893, in vol. 10; to vol. 11–20, 1893–1913, in vol. 20.
Vol. 1–5: Leipzig, W. Engelmann.
Vol. 12, no. 4, wanting.

NN 0017469   ICJ MnU NIC NjP DNLM NjP PU–BZ NcD

---

ar W
50362
Naples. Stazione zoologica.
Preis-Verzeichnis der mikroskopischen Präparate welche durch die Zoologische Station zu Neapel zu beziehen sind. ₍Neapel, 1881₎
16 p. 24cm.

"Vorbemerkung" signed by A. Dohrn.

I. Dohrn, Anton, 1840-1909. II. Title.

NN 0017470   NIC

Naples. Stazione zoologica.
Pubblicazioni. v. 1–
Milano, U. Hoepli, 1916–
v. illus., plates (part col.) diagrs. 24 cm.
Preceded by Mittheilungen aus der Zoologischen station zu Neapel. Contributions in Italian, French, English, and German.
Beginning with 1918 the contributions on physiology and biological chemistry are in a separate series with subtitle: Ricerche di fisiologia e di chimica biologica.

1. Zoology—Societies, etc.

QL1.N138   22—83

DNLM TU UU
ICJ TxU NcD NIC PPAN OrPR GEU NhD IU CaBVaU MH NcU
NN 0017471   DLC FTaSU ViU OkS CU–S MtU RPB CStbS

Naples. Stazione zoologica.
Pubblicazioni. Ricerche di fisiologia e di chimica biologica. v. 1,
Milano, U. Hoepli, 1919–
v. illus. 24ᵐ.
Contributions in Italian, French, English, and German.
The contributions on physiology and biological chemistry were formerly included in the Pubblicazioni della Stazione zoologica.

1. Physiology—Societies, etc. 2. Biological chemistry—Societies, etc.

Library of Congress   QL1.N139   CA 21–514 Unrev'd

NN 0017472   DLC ICJ NIC MtU OrCS CaBVaU ICJ

Naples. Stazione zoologica.
Relazioni tenute al Convegno su gli agenti mutageni
see under   Convegno su gli agenti mutageni Stazione zoologica, Naples, 1949.

Naples. Stazione zoologica.
Relazioni tenute al Convegno sulla struttura submicroscopica del protoplasma
see under   Convegno sulla struttura submicroscopica del protoplasma, Naples, 1951.

Naples. Stazione zoologica.
XXV anniversario della fondazione della stazione zoologica di Napoli
see under   Dohrn, Anton, 1840-1909.

Naples. Stazione zoologica.

Zoologischer jahresbericht ...
Hrsg. von der Zoologischen station zu Neapel
Leipzig, 18

Naples. Stazione zoologica.
Zum Tage des fünfundzwanzigjährigen Bestehen₍ [der Zoologischen Station zu Neapel] 14.April 1897.

NN 0017477   MH PPAN

Naples. Stazione zoologica. *Biblioteca.*
Die bibliothek der Zoologischen station zu Neapel. Verzeichniss der daselbst bis zum ende des jahres 1873 vorhandenen bücher. Leipzig, W. Engelmann, 1874.
iv, 91 p. 23ᵐ.
Compiled by Anton Dohrn.

1. Zoology—Bibl. ɪ. Dohrn, Anton i. e. Felix Anton, 1840–1909.

Library of Congress   Z7999.N21   G—2197

NN 0017478   DLC

Naples. Stazione zoologica. *Biblioteca.*
Zweiter nachtrag zum bibliothekskatalog der Zoologischen station zu Neapel. Leipzig, W. Engelmann, 1879.
cover-title, 51, ₍1₎ p. 24ᵐ.
Compiled by Anton Dohrn.

1. Zoology—Bibl. ɪ. Dohrn, Anton, 1840–

Library of Congress   Z7999.N21   1-G-2197a

NN 0017479   DLC CtY

Naples. Stazione zoologica. Biblioteca.
3ᵗᵉʳ Nachtrag ...   Leipzig, 1881.
cover-title, 41, [1] p.   24.5 cm.
With bibliography.

NN 0017480   CtY

NAPLES. *Supremo magistrato di salute.*
Rapporto sul cholera-morbus.
Napoli : Cataneo. 1831. 20 pp. 8°

NN 0017481   MB

WCG
N215p
1845
NAPLES. Supremo magistrato di salute. Commissione medica.
La peste orientale relativamente al sistema delle quarantene, memoria scritta dal Cav. Giuseppe Carbonaro. Napoli, Cataneo, 1845.
65 p.
I. Carbonaro, Giuseppe

NN 0017482   DNLM

WCB
qN215i
1854
NAPLES.   Supremo magistrato di salute. Facoltà medica
Intorno al colera di Napoli dell'anno 1854; relazione della Facoltà medica al Soprindente generale et al Supremo magistrato di salute. Relatore, Salvatore de Renzi. Napoli, Nobile, 1854.
335 p.
The first of two parts; no more published?
I. Renzi, Salvatore de, 1800-1872

NN 0017483   DNLM CtY

Naples .Supremo magistrato di salute. Facoltà medica.
Istruzioni al pubblico sul contagio della tisichezza, scritte per sovrano comando dalla Facolţa medica del Supremo magistrato di sanità di Napoli. In Napoli, Presso G.Migliaggio, 1782.
64 p. 19 ᶜᵐ.

1.Tuberculosis in Italy.

NN 0017484   NjP

Naples .   Teatro San Carlo.
Cento anni di vita del teatro San Carlo, 1848-1948
see under   Filippis, Felice de,   ed.

Naples. Teatro San Carlo.
Exhibition of a most beautiful model representing the interior of the celebrate and largest of modern theatres, that of San Carlo, at Naples... London, Brown, 1819.
8 p. 18 cm.

NN 0017486   CSmH

Naples. Teatro   San Carlo
Il Teatro di S.Carlo. [Napoli, A cura dell'Ente Autonomo del Teatro 1951]
239 p. illus., plates
At head of title: Citta di Napoli

NN 0017487   MH NN

Naples. *Ufficio d'igiene e di sanità pubblica.*
... La mortalità per tubercolosi in Napoli, pel dott. cav. Raffaele Serafino. Estratto dal giornale il Benessere. Nuova serie. Anno x—luglio 1903—fasc. 13.ᵉ Napoli, Tip. Melfi & Joele, 1903.
6 p. 24ᵐ.
At head of title: Ufficio d'igiene e di sanità pubblica della città di Napoli.
Signed: Dottor Raffaele Serafino dell' Ufficio d'igiene del municipio di Napoli.

1. Tuberculosis—Naples. ɪ. Serafino, Raffaele.

9-34741†

Library of Congress   RC316.I 8N3

NN 0017488   DLC

Naples. *Ufficio di statistica*
see
Naples. *Divisione statistica.*

VOLUME 405

Naples. Università.
Annuario della Regia università degli studj di Napoli.

Napoli, 18

v. 24–27ᶜᵐ.

Library of Congress   LF3541.C5   CA 7—2274 Unrev'd

NN   0017490   DLC NN ICJ

Law   **Naples. Università.**

... **Appunti** delle lezioni di diritto civile; ipoteche secondo le lezioni del corso ufficiale. Napoli, G. U. F. "Mussolini," Sezione editoriale, 1940.

Law   Naples. Università.

... **Appunti** di diritto civile i contratti. Napoli, G. U. F. "Mussolini," Sezione editoriale, 1940.

Law   Naples. Università.

... **Appunti** di diritto romano; il processo privato secondo le lezioni del corso ufficiale. Napoli, G. U. F. "Mussolini," Sezione editoriale, 1940.

Naples. Università.
Un biennio di rettorato 1905–1907; relazione del prof. Carlo Fadda. Napoli, Tip. della Regia università, Cimmaruta & Tessitore, 1907.

151 p. fold. plan, tab. 26½ᶜᵐ.

I. Fadda, Carlo, 1853–

8–29065

Library of Congress   LF3541.B3 1907

NN   0017494   DLC

NAPLES. Università.
Calendario scolastico della R.Università' degli studi di Napoli coll'albo de' professori della medesima e colle istruzioni, per gli aspiranti ai gradi accademici ed agli attestati di abilità'. Napoli, nella Stamperia reale, 1815.

pp.40.

NN   0017495   MH

Naples. Università.
Centenario della Cattedra di zoologia nella R. Università di Napoli, 1806–1906. Napoli, Stab. tip. della R. Università, 1906.

58 p. 31ᶜᵐ.

Cover-title has date, 1907.

Agr 9–98

Library, U. S. Dept. of   Agriculture 411N16

NN   0017496   DNAL PPAN

H458   Naples. Università.
020   Commemorazione di Francesco de Sanctis nel primo centenario della nascita, a cura della R.Università di Napoli. Napoli[F.Giannini & figli]1917.

viii,95p.,front.(port.) 29cm.

No.678.

Contents.-Introduzione. - Discorso del rettore magnifico prof.Alberto Marghieri. - Discorso commemorativo, letto dal prof. Francesco Torraca. - Tre lezioni e un discorso

di Francesco de Sanctis: Giulietta e Romeo, lezioni del 1847. La rappresentazione del brutto nella Divina commedia, lezione del 1855. La "Vita solitaria" del Leopardi, lezione del 1876   Il discorso per la istituzione del Circolo filologico di Napoli, (1876).

NN   0017498   CtY CU MH WU

Law   Naples. Università.

... **Compendio** di diritto romano, i diritti reali. Napoli, Sezione editoriale del G. U. F. "Mussolini," 1940.

Naples. Università.
Corso di paleografia e di diplomatica. Interpretazione dei documenti e tesario anno accademico 1945–46. Napoli, Humus [1946]

28 p. 26 cm.
At head of title: R.Universita di Napoli.

NN   0017500   MH

QM551   Naples. Università.
.D5   Diamare, Vincenzo, 1872–
... Corso ufficiale di istologia, fisiologia generale, ed embriologia; lezioni raccolte da Lucio Cutolo e Vittorio Fabrizio ... 2. ed. Napoli, G. U. F. "Mussolini," Sezione editoriale, 1941–

Naples. Università.

Ruggiero, Roberto de, 1875–
... Introduzione alle scienze giuridiche e istituzioni di diritto civile; corso ufficiale del prof. Roberto de Ruggiero ... Unica pubblicazione autorizzata. Napoli, L. Alvano, 1911–

Law   Naples. Università.

Baratta, Vincenzo.
... Lezioni di diritto privato comparato. Napoli, G. U. F. "Mussolini," Sezione editoriale, 1939.

RA425   Naples, Università.
.M39   ₁Mazzeo, Mario₁
... Lezioni di igiene, secondo il corso ufficiale. Napoli, G. U. F. "Mussolini," Sezione editoriale, 1940–

RE321   Naples. Università.
.L6
Lo Cascio, Girolamo, 1894–
... Lezioni sul tracoma, tenute dal prof. G. Lo Cascio, raccolte e pubblicate dal dott. Antonino de Crecchio. Napoli, G. U. F. "Mussolini," Sezione editoriale, 1940.

Naples. Università.
Notizie intorno alla origine, formazione e stato presente della R. Università di Napoli per l'Esposizione nazionale di Torino nel 1884, rettore Luigi Capuano. Napoli, Tip. dell' Accademia reale delle scienze, 1884.

268 p. plans (partly fold.) tables (partly fold.) 23½ᶜᵐ.

Bibliographies interspersed.
"Movimento scientifico ed opere pubblicate dai professori di questo periodo": p. 150–257.

1. Naples. Università—Hist.   I. Capuano, Luigi.

E 10–285

Library, U. S. Bur. of   Education LF3543.A3

NN   0017506   DHEW IU

Naples. Università.
Raccolta di leggi e regolamenti sulla istruzione superiore, pubblicata per cura della r. Università di Napoli. Napoli, Stab. tip A. Trani, 1878.

189 p. 23½ᶜᵐ.

1. Educational law and legislation—Italy.   I. Italy. Laws, statutes, etc. II. Title.

33–18200

NN   0017507   DLC

Naples. Università.
... Regia università di Napoli. Statuto approvato con ordinanza ministeriale del 25 ottobre 1924. Estratto dal Bollettino ufficiale I. n. 51 del 16 dicembre 1924. Roma, Libreria dello stato, 1925.

42 p. 23ᶜᵐ.

At head of title : Ministero della pubblica istruzione. Direzione generale istruzione superiore.
In lower left corner of t.-p. : 313

I. Italy. Direzione generale per l'istruzione superiore.

34–21090

Library of Congress   LF3541.A7 1924   378.45

NN   0017508   DLC

Naples. Università.
... Regia università di Napoli. Statuto approvato con regio decreto 14 ottobre 1926, n. 2090. Estratto dal Bollettino ufficiale I, n. 1 del 4 gennaio 1927-anno v. Roma, Provveditorato generale dello stato, Libreria, 1927.

50 p. 22½ᶜᵐ.

At head of title : Ministero della pubblica istruzione. Direzione generale istruzione superiore.

I. Italy. Direzione generale per l'istruzione superiore.

34–21091

Library of Congress   LF3541.A7 1926   378.45

NN   0017509   DLC

Naples. Università.
Schema del corso di storia del diritto romano
see under   Milone, Filippo.

Naples. Università.
Settimo centenario della R. Università di Napoli, 1224–1924. ₁Napoli, 1924?₁

198 p. illus. 23 cm.

I. Title.

LF3559.5.A66   72–204203

NN   0017511   DLC WU IEN IU CtY MiU

Naples. Università.
Sunto del corso di diritto internazionale dettato nella r. università di Napoli
see under   Milone, F[ilippo]

VOLUME 405

Naples. Università.
L'Università di Napoli incendiata dai tedeschi, 12 settembre 1943. Napoli, G. Macchiaroli, 1944.
2 p. l., 7–53 p., 5 l. plates. 20½ᵐ.

1. World war, 1939–1945—Destruction and pillage—Italy.

LF3552.A4 1944   378.45   47–15150

NN 0017513   DLC MH CtY IEN NIC

Naples. Università. Biblioteca.
Indice delle pubblicazioni periodiche possedute dalle biblioteche di Napoli
see under Naples. Biblioteca nazionale.

Naples. Università. Biblioteca.
Relazione sulla biblioteca universitaria di Napoli, presentata dal Commissario regio ... alla giunta di Vigilanza.   Napoli, Tip. della R. Università,

23cm.

NN 0017515   MnU

Naples. Università. Biblioteca degli istituti giuridici.
Bollettino
anno

Naples.
v.

Includes bibliographies.

NN 0017516   NNC-L

WO
qN215r
1910
NAPLES. Università. Clinica chirurgica (1st)
Rendiconto scientifico-clinico di un quinquennio (1905-1909) Napoli, Morano, 1910.
xxxiii, 626 p. illus.

NN 0017517   DNLM ICRL CtY

W 1
AC872
n. 3
1953
NAPLES. Università. Clinica delle malattie del sistema nervoso
Memorie scientifiche dedicate a Vito Maria Buscaino nel xxv anno del suo insegnamento. ₁Napoli, 1953₁
viii, 544 p. illus., port. (Quaderni di Acta neurologica, 3)
1. Buscaino, Vito Maria, 1887-
2. Nervous system - Collected works
Title   Series: Acta neurologica.
Quaderni, 3

NN 0017518   DNLM

Naples. Università. Clinica medica.
Prospetto che contiene i risultamenti ottenuti nella Clinica medica della Regia Università de'studi di Napoli
see under Antonucci, Giuseppe.

W
19
qN215
NAPLES. Università. Clinica medica generale e terapia medica
₁Collection of publications₁

The library has a collection of miscellaneous publications of this organization kept as received. These publications are not listed nor bound separately.

NN 0017520   DNLM

W 1
NA159
NAPLES. Università. Clinica oculistica.
Lavori. v. 1-5; 1887-88 — 1897-98. Napoli.
5 v. illus., port.
Issues for 1887-88?—1889-90 called: Lavori eseguiti negli anni scolastici.
No more published?

NN 0017521   DNLM ICRL

Naples. Università. Clinica Odontoiatrica.
Atti. ₁v.1₁-12; 1946-1957. Napoli, 1946-1957.
10v. in 5. illus. annual.
Title varies: v.1-7, Atti della Società Napoletana di Stomatologia; v.8-11, Atti della Clinica Odontoiatrica e della Società Napoletana di Stomatologia.
Superseded by Archivio stomatologico.

NN 0017522   ICRL

WU
24
N215d
1953
NAPLES. Università. Clinica odontoiatrica.
Un decennio di attività, 1942-1952. Napoli, Pironti ₁1953₁
35 p. illus.

NN 0017523   DNLM

W
1
NA161
Naples. Università. Clinica Otorino-laringologica
Atti.

Napoli ₁19
v. illus.

Some articles have summaries in Italian, French, German and English.

1. Otorhinolaryngology - Periodicals

NN 0017524   DNLM

W 1
AR595
₁.33-36
₁1922-25
NAPLES. Università. Clinica otorino-laringologica.
Pubblicazioni. v. 1-10; 1922-25. Napoli.
10 v. illus.
Issued as supplements to Archivio italiano di otologia, rinologia e laringologia and bound with v. 33-36, 1922-25, of that publication.
1. Otorhinolaryngology - Collected works I. Archivio italiano di otologia,

rinologia e laringologia. Supplemento

NN 0017526   DNLM

W 1
NA162
NAPLES. Università. Clinica pediatrica
Pubblicazioni. 1938-39 — 1940-41. Napoli.
2 v. illus.
Collected reprints.
No more published ?
1. Pediatrics - period.

NN 0017527   DNLM

Naples. Università. Clinica tisiologica
see
Naples. Università. Istituto sanatoriale "Principi di Piemonte."

Naples. Università. Comitato vulcanologico.
see
QE527
.N3   Naples. Osservatorio vesuviano.
Annali.

Napoli,

QA37
.C22
1941
Naples. Università. Facoltà di agraria.

Cancellara, Eduardo.
... Lezioni di matematica ₁del₁ prof. ing. Eduardo Cancellara. 2. ed., perfezionata e arricchita di numerosi esercizi. Napoli, GUF Mussolini, Sezione editoriale, 1941-42.

Naples. Università. Facoltà di agraria di Portici
see Portici. Istituto superiore agrario.

HB7
.S7
Naples. Università. Facoltà di economia e commercio.

Studi economici. anno 1-

apr. 1941-,

₁Napoli, etc.₁

Naples. Università. Facoltà di economia e commercio. Istituto di finanza.
see Naples. Università. Istituto di finanza.

Naples. Università. Facoltà di filosofia e lettere
see Naples. Università. Facoltà di lettere e filosofia.

Naples. Università. Facoltà di giurisprudenza
see Naples. Università. Facoltà giuridica.

Naples. Università. Facoltà di ingegneria.
Annuario.
Napoli.

v. in   24-26 cm.
Publication suspended for the years 1915/16-1917/18, inclusive.   -19
Issued under earlier names of the faculty:
R. Scuola superiore politecnica di Napoli.—19   R. Scuola di ingegneria di Napoli.

T173.N34   52-18334

NN 0017536   DLC

Naples. Università. Facoltà di ingegneria.
Catalogo della biblioteca. Napoli, Tip. dell' Accademia reale delle scienze, 1887.
84 p. 28 cm.
At head of title: R.ª Scuola d'applicazione per gl'ingegneri in Napoli.
Pref. signed: Guido Grassi.

1. Engineering—Bibl.—Catalogs. 2. Technology—Bibl.—Catalogs.
I. Grassi, Guido Giovanni, 1851-

Z5854.N21   10-6897 rev 2*

NN 0017537   DLC

VOLUME 405

Naples. Facolta di ingegneria.
Pubblicazione deliberata dal Consiglio direttivo in occasione della Esposizione nazionale di Torino. Anno 1898. 124 p. il. F. Napoli [1898].
"Pubblicazioni dell'attuale personale insegnante," p. 106-121.

NN 0017538   ICJ

Naples. Università. *Facoltà di ingegneria.*
Pubblicazioni. 1.– ser. (n. 1– dic. 1932–
[Napoli]
v. in illus. 31-36 cm. annual.
Issued under earlier names of the faculty: 1932, R. Scuola di ingegneria di Napoli.—1933-34, R. Istituto superiore di ingegneria di Napoli.

1. Engineering—Collected works.

TA4.N3   620.6245   52-18335

NN 0017539   DLC NNE IU

Naples. Università. *Facoltà di ingegneria.*
R. Scuola superiore politecnica di Napoli. Nella ricorrenza del primo centenario MDCCCXI-MCMXI. Napoli, Stab. tip. cav. N. Jovene, 1911.
198 p. illus. 31 cm.
Pub. by the faculty under its earlier name: R. Scuola superiore politecnica di Napoli.
"Regolamenti": p. [163]-176.
"Pubblicazioni del personale insegnante": p. [177]-198.

1. Technical education—Italy.

T173.N38 1911   12-12131 rev 2

NN 0017540   DLC

Naples. Università. *Facoltà di ingegneria.*
Statuto approvato con Ordinanza ministeriale del 25 ottobre 1924. Roma, Libreria dello Stato, 1925.
22 p. 23 cm.
Pub. by the faculty under its earlier name: Regia Scuola d'ingegneria di Napoli.
In lower left corner of t. p.: 190.
"Estratto dal Bolletino ufficiale I, n. 50 del 9 dicembre 1924."

1. Technical education—Italy.

T173.N31 1924   49-52404*

NN 0017541   DLC

Naples. Università. *Facoltà di ingegneria.*
Statuto approvato con Regio decreto 14 ottobre 1926, n. 2199. Roma, Provveditorato generale dello Stato, Libreria, 1927.
21 p. 23 cm.
Pub. by the faculty under its earlier name: Regia Scuola d'ingegneria di Napoli.
In lower left corner of t. p.: 544.
"Estratto dal Bollettino ufficiale I, n. 3 del 18 gennaio 1927-anno V."

T173.N31 1926   607.4573   34-20814 rev*

NN 0017542   DLC

Naples. Università. *Facoltà di lettere e filosofia.*
Annali.
[Napoli]
v. 27 cm.

AS222.N782   55-36668 ‡

NN 0017543   DLC CtY

Naples. Università. Facoltà di lettere e filosofia.
Architetti e scultori del Quattrocento.
Appunti a cura di Antonio Videtta. Anno 1953-54
see under Mariani, Valerio, 1899-

Naples. Università. *Facoltà di lettere e filosofia. Istituto di archeologia e di antichità pompeiane*
see **Naples.** Università. *Istituto di archeologia e di antichità pompeiane.*

Naples. Università. *Facoltà di lettere e filosofia. Istituto di storia dell'arte*
see
Naples. Università. *Istituto di storia dell'arte.*

Naples. Università. *Facoltà di medicina e chirurgia. Clinica tisiologica*
see
Naples. Università. *Istituto sanatoriale "Principi di Piemonte."*

Naples. Università. *Facoltà di medicina e chirurgia. Istituto di tisiologia "Principe di Piemonte"*
see
Naples. Università. *Istituto sanatoriale "Principi di Piemonte."*

Naples. Università. *Facoltà di medicina e chirurgia. Scuola di perfezionamento in ostetricia e ginecologia*
see
Naples. Università. *Scuola di perfezionamento in ostetricia e ginecologia.*

Naples. Università. *Facoltà di scienze agrarie, Portici*
see Portici. Istituto superiore agrario.

Naples. Università. *Facoltà di scienze matematiche, fisiche e naturali. Museo zoologico*
see
Naples. Università. *Museo zoologico.*

Naples. Università. Facolta di scienze naturali.
Cinquantesimo anniversario dell'insegnamento di Arcangelo Scacchi. Napoli, Tip.della R.Università, 1891.
23 cm. Front.and table.

NN 0017552   MH

Naples. Università. *Facoltà di scienze naturali. Museo zoologico*
see
Naples. Università. *Museo zoologico.*

FL6
N215p
Naples. Università. Facoltà giuridica.
Pubblicazioni. 1-   Napoli, E.Jovene, 1943-
v.   24 cm.

1.Law - Collections.

NN 0017554   MiU-L CtY TxDaM

Naples. Università. Facoltà giuridica.
Relazione della Commissione incaricata dell' esame del "Progetto preliminare d'un nuovo Codice penale".
see under Italy. Commissione incaricata dell'esame del "Progetto preliminare d'un nuovo Codice penale."

Naples. Università. Gabinetto di anatomia comparata.
Anatomia comparata. Catalogo sistematico del Gabinetto nella Regia università degli studi di Napoli. Napoli, Stamperia del Fibreno, 1868.
4 p.l.,105,[1] p.,1 l. col.fold.plan. 22cm.
Introduction signed: Paolo Panceri.

1.Anatomy,Comparative--Catalogs and collections.
I.Panceri,Paolo.

NN 0017556   MiU

QL
814
N215c
1868
Naples. Università. Gabinetto di anatomia comparata.
Anatomia comparata. Catalogo sistematico ... Napoli, Fibreno, 1868.
105 p. col. illus.
QL
814
N215c
1868
Suppl
--- --- Supplemento ... Napoli, Fibreno, 1872-
v.

NN 0017557   DNLM

Naples. Università. Istituto di anatomia chirurgica e medicina operatoria.
... Chirurgia ipofisaria...
see under Angeli, Aurelio.

Naples. Università. Istituto di anatomia e fisiologia comparate.
Lavori eseguiti.
Vol.5 (1938).
Collected reprints.

NN 0017559   MH-Z

DE1
.M6
Naples. Università. Istituto di archeologia e di antichità pompeiane.
Μουσεῖον; rivista di scienze classiche. anno 1-4; 15. gen. 1923-20. apr. 1928. Napoli, Rondinella e Loffredo, 1923-28.

Naples. Università. *Istituto di costruzioni idrauliche ed impianti speciali idraulici*
see **Naples.** Università. *Istituto di idraulica e costruzioni idrauliche.*

NAPLES.   Università. Istituto di filosofia teoretica.
Pubblicazioni.
Napoli, Libreria scientifica editrice.

1. Philosophy.

NN 0017562   NN

VOLUME 405

HB7
.S7
     Naples. Università. Instituto di finanza.

Studi economici. anno 1–

     apr. 1941–

     ₁Napoli, etc.₎

Naples. Università. Istituto di fisica terrestre.

     Valori ovarii diurni delle precipi-
tazioni registrate all'Istituto ...
1909-16 inclusive.
     Naples. 1917. 47 p. 33 cm.

NN   0017564   DAS

Naples. Università. Istituto di Genetica.
Convegno di genetica

see under

Convegno di genetica, Naples, 1952.

Naples. Università. Istituto di geologia applicata.
Memorie e note. v. 1–   1947/48–
Napoli.
     v. illus., maps. 25 cm.

     1. Geology—Italy—Collected works.
QE1.N17
           rev   G S 49–215
                   MARC-S

NN   0017566   DLC CtY IU MH-Z ICRL

Naples .Istituto di idraulica e costruzioni idrauliche.

     ₁Pubblicazioni₎
₁n.₎ 1

₁Napoli, 193   25½ – 31½cm.
     nos.   charts, diagrs., illus., tables.
     Irregular.

     1. Engineering, Hydraulic—Per.   and soc. publ.
N.Y.P.L.   November 27, 1941

     On t.-p.: n. 1–   R. Università di Napoli. Istituto di costruzioni idrauliche ed
impianti speciali idraulici.
     Occasional issues include a bibliography.

     CONTENTS.
n. 1. IPPOLITO, GIROLAMO. La moderna tecnica della filtrazione di acque potabili e l'im-
     pianto di Corongiu. ₁1934?₎

n. 3. NEBBIA, GUIDO. Sul tracciamento dei profili di correnti liquide permanenti gra-
     dualmente varie. ₁1936?₎
n. 4. NEBBIA, GUIDO. Rappresentazioni grafiche adimensionali delle quantità di moto
     in correnti liquide libere. ₁1936?₎

n. 5. PISTILLI, GIUSEPPE. La clorazione delle acque ed i recenti progressi nei procedi-
     menti di potabilizzazione. ₁1936?₎
n. 6. NEBBIA, GUIDO. Venturimetri per canali a sezioni di forma generica. ₁1936?₎
n. 7. NEBBIA, GUIDO. Venturimetri per canali a sezioni di tipo monomio; considera-
     zioni analitiche sui coefficienti di efflusso. ₁1937?₎
n. 8. IPPOLITO, GIROLAMO. Il laboratorio di costruzioni idrauliche nella Facoltà di inge-
     gneria della R. Università di Napoli. ₁1937?₎
n. 9. NEBBIA, GUIDO. Correnti liquide permanenti e venturimetri per canali. ₁1937?₎

n. 10. IPPOLITO, GIROLAMO. Risorse idrauliche dell' Etiopia. ₁1937?₎
n. 11. AVOLIO DE MARTINO, GASTONE. Esame critico comparativo dei sistemi più in uso
     per la depurazione delle acque di fogna. ₁1938₎
n. 12. IPPOLITO, GIROLAMO. L'impianto di epurazione delle acque di fogna di potenza.
     ₁1938₎
n. 13. NEBBIA, GUIDO. Sulla risoluzione di una equazione caratteristica di alcune cor-
     renti fluide. ₁1938₎
n. 14. NEBBIA, GUIDO. Le linee delle quantità di moto totali in correnti liquide per-
     manenti gradualmente varie. ₁1938₎

Continued in next column

Continued from preceding column

49. Opere di sfioro del serbatoio di Bau-Muggeris [di] G. A. de Martino.
     [1948]
50. Di un tipo di opera di presa da torrenti [di] G. A. de Martino. [1949]
51. Un problema di foronomia alla luce della teoria del potenziale [di] M.
     Viparelli. [1948?]

52. L'alimentation d'eau potable et la décharge des égouts dans les
     territoires parcours par de longs cours d'eau et dépourvues d'autres
     ressources hydriques [par] Girolamo Ippolito.   [1949]
53. Un exemple d'alimentation d'eau potable dans les territoires aride
     avec des populations éparses [par] Giuseppe Pistilli. [1949]
54. L'ozono nella purificazione delle acque [di] Giuseppe Pistilli.   1949.

55. Contributo al calcolo delle portate di piena col metodo dell'invaso per
     reti di fognatura serventi aree minori di 30 ha [di] Guido de Martino.
     1950.
56. Dell'onda generata da una corrente veloce in alta lenta.   [1950]
57. Studio del moto vario in una condotta forzata [di] Giuseppe Pistilli.
     [1947?]

NN   0017574   NN

W 1
NA163
     NAPLES. Università. Istituto di medicina
del lavoro.
     [Pubblicazioni]

     Napoli [1938?]–
         v. illus.
     Collected reprints.
     1. Industrial medicine - period.

NN   0017575   DNLM

NAPLES.   Università. Istituto di paleografia
     e diplomatica.
     [Pubblicazioni]
     Napoli, L'Arte tipografica Napoli.

     1. Paleography, Italian.

NN   0017576   NN

Naples. Università. Istituto di patologia generale.
     ...Pubblicazioni 1931/1932–
     [Napoli? 1932–]
         v. plates, diagrs.   24 1/2 cm.
     Consists of reprints.

NN   0017577   DSI

RB1
.N3
     Naples. Università. Istituto di patologia generale
     ... Ricerche. 1929/30–   [Napoli,
     1930–]
         1 v.   8°.   S.   unb.

NN   0017578   DLC DSI

W 1
NA163H
     NAPLES. Università. Istituto di patologia
     speciale chirurgica e propedeutica
     clinica.
         Pubblicazioni scientifiche. 1938-39—
     1940-41. Napoli.
         2 v. illus.
     Collected reprints.
     No more published?
     1. Surgery - period.

NN   0017579   DNLM

NAPLES.   Università. Istituto di scienza delle
     costruzioni.
     [Pubblicazioni] n. 101-date.
     Napoli [1957]-date.   no.   illus., diagrs.,
     tables, maps.   22-32cm.

     Irregular.
     English, French or Italian.
     1. Building--Theory.

NN   0017580   NN

NAPLES.   Università. Istituto di storia dell'
     architettura.
     [Pubblicazioni]
     Napoli, Edizioni scientifiche italiane.

NN   0017581   NN

NAPLES.   Università. Istituto di storia
     dell'arte.
     Saggi e ricerche.
     Napoli, Libreria scientifica editrice.

NN   0017582   NN

NAPLES.   Università. Istituto di storia economica
     e sociale.
     Biblioteca degli Annali.
     Milano, Giuffré.

NN   0017583   NN

QL
1
N21
     Naples. Università. Istituto e Museo di
     Zoologia.
     Annuario. v. 1–   1949–
     Naples.
         v. illus. 25 cm.

     Supersedes Annuario del Museo
Zoologico dell' Università di Napoli.

     1. Zoology - Italy.

NN   0017584   NIC NcU DNAL OU PPAN

Naples. Università. *Istituto ed orto botanico*
     see
Naples. Università. *Orto botanico.*

QP
71
P57
     Naples. Università. Istituto fisiologico.
     Rendiconto dell'Istituto fisiologico della
     R. Università di Napoli dall'epoca della sua
     fondazione fino al principio dell'anno sco-
     lastico 1863-64 per cura del direttore D.ʳ
     Giuseppe Albini e dei coadjutori dottori F.
     Vizioli e F. Fede.   Napoli, T. Cottrau,
     1863.
         35 p. pl. 24cm.

     No. 17 in vol. lettered: Physiological
pamphlets.

NN   0017586   NIC

Naples. Università. Istituto navale
     see   Naples. Istituto universitario navale.

Naples. Università. Istituto orientale
     see
Naples. Istituto orientale.

Naples.Università.Istituto sanatoriale "Principe di
     Piemonte."
     Archivio di tisiologia. v. 1–
     gen./feb. 1946–
     Napoli.

VOLUME 405

W 1
NA141P
Naples. Universita. Istituto sanatoriale
"Principe di Piemonte".
Bollettino dell'Istituto sanatoriale
"Principi di Piemonte" dell'I. N. P. S.,
Clinica tisiologica della R. Università
di Napoli. anno 1-2; mar. 1944-dic. 1945.
Napoli.
2 v.
No more published?
1. Tuberculosis - period. I. Naples.
Università. Clinica tisiologica. Title:

Bollettino dell'Istituto sanatoriale
"Principi di Piemonte" dell'I. N. P. S.,
Clinica tisiologica della R. Università
di Napoli

NN 0017591 DNLM

Law
Naples. Università. Istituto sanatoriale
"Principi di Piemonte."
Il Diritto sanitario moderno. anno 1-
1953-
Parma ₁Tip. riunite Donati₎

W 1
NA141S
Naples. Universita. Istituto sanatoriale
"Principi di Piemonte"
Lavori scientifici, Istituto sanatoriale
"Principi di Piemonte" dell'I. N. P. S.,
Clinica tisiologica della R. Università
di Napoli.
1937/39-
Napoli,
v. illus.
Collected reprints.
1. Tuberculosis - period. I. Naples.

Università. Clinica tisiologica. Title.

NN 0017594 DNLM

Naples. Università. Istituto psichiatrico e
neuropatologico.
... Le capsule surrenali nella paralisi
progressiva
see under Angelico, Giuseppe.

Naples. Università. Istituto superiore navale
see Naples. Istituto universitario
navale.

Naples. Università. Istituto zoologico.
.... Fauna degli Astroni ... Napoli R. stabilimento tipografico F. Giannini & figli, 1915-28.
2 v. in 1. illus.(incl.maps) 14 pl.(part col.,
fold.) 30cm. (Annuario del Museo zoologico
della R. Università di Napoli (nuova serie)
Supplemento)

On cover: Ricerche dell' Istituto zoologico
della R. Università di Napoli.
Vol.2 has imprint: Napoli, Officina cromo-
tipografica "Aldine".
Includes bibliographies.
Contents.- fasc.I. 1. Monticelli, F.S. Il
cratere di "Astroni" nella Campania. 2. Mar-
colongo, I. Gastrotrichi. 3. Pierantoni, U.
Oligocheti. 4. Caro li, E. Collembola I. Su di

un nuovo genere di meelidae. 5. Iroso, I.
Rotiferi. 6. Savi, L. I ciliati aspirotrichi.
7. Della Valle, P. Tardigreda-fasc.II.
8. Cillis, O.M. de. I nematodi. 9. Torelli, B.
La Notiphila chamaeleon Becker e la sua larva
rinvenuta. 10. Arcangeli, A. Primo contributo
alla fauna degli isopodi degli Astroni. 11.
Zirpolo, G. Sulla presenza del Lophopus cristal-
linus Pallas. 12. Caroli, A. Le specie di
Corisa.

NN 0017598 CU DSI NcU ICJ CtY

Naples. Università. Laboratorio di entomologia
agraria
see Portici. Istituto superiore agrario.
Laboratorio di entomologia agraria.

Naples. Università. *Laboratorio di fisiologia umana "F. Bottazzi."*
Principii di fisiologia umana. Napoli, Idelson ₁1950-
v. diagrs. 24 cm.

1. Physiology. I. Title.

A 53-1205

Temple Univ. Library
for Library of Congress   QP34.N37
₁3₎

NN 0017600 PPT DNLM

Naples. Università. Laboratorio di zoologia
generale e agraria
see Portici. Istituto superiore agrario.
Laboratorio di zoologia generale e agraria.

W 1
NA164
NAPLES. Università. Museo zoologico
Annuario. v. 1-6, 1861-66; nuova ser.,
v. 1-8, no. 2, 24 ag. 1901-1948. Napoli.
14 v. in illus.

Superseded by the Annuario of the
Istituto e museo di zoologia, Università
di Napoli.
Title: Annuario del Museo zoologico
della R. Università di Napoli

NN 0017602 DNLM DLC DSI NcU OU ICJ

QK
73
.N2
A3
Naples. Università. Orto botanico.
Ad Catalogum plantarum Horti Regii Neapolitani
anno 1813 editum. Appendix prima. Neapoli, Ex
Typographia Amuliana, 1815.
vi,76 p. 20 cm.
Preface signed: Michael Tenore.
Bound with its Catalogo delle piante del
Regal Giardino botanico di Napoli. ₁Napoli?₎
1807.
I.Tenore,Michele, 1781-1861.

NN 0017603 MiU

Naples. Università. *Orto botanico.*
Bullettino.

Napoli,
v. illus., plates. 24½ᵐ.
Publication began in 1899. *cf.* Union list of serials.

1. Botany—Societies, etc. 2. Botany—Italy.

45-33675

Library of Congress   QK1.N3
                                    580.6245

NN 0017604 DLC IU MiU ICJ

Naples. Università. *Orto botanico.*
Catalogo delle piante che si coltivano nel R. Orto botanico
di Napoli, corredato della pianta del medesimo, e di annotazioni. Napoli, Tip. dell'Aquila di V. Puzziello, 1845.
xii, 104 p. fold. plan. 30 cm.
Preface signed: M. Tenore.

I. Tenore, Michele, 1781-1861.

QK73.N2A3   5-38656 rev*

NN 0017605 DLC MH-A

QK
73
.N2
A3
Naples. Università. Orto botanico.
Catalogo delle piante del Regal Giardino
botanico di Napoli. ₁Napoli?₎ Stamperia reale,
1807.
28 p. 20 cm.
Preface signed: Michele Tenore.
Bound with its Ad catalogum plantarum Horti
Regii Neapolitani anno 1813 editum. Appendix
prima. Neapoli, 1815.

I.Tenore,Michele, 1781-1861.

NN 0017606 MiU

Naples. Università. *Osservatorio vesuviano*
see
Naples. Osservatorio vesuviano.

Naples. Università. *Scuola d'applicazione per gli ingegneri*
see Naples. Università. *Facoltà di ingegneria.*

QP251
.M6
Naples. Università. Scuola di perfezionamento
in ostetricia e ginecologia.
Moracci, Espedito.
... Fisiologia della riproduzione. Napoli, G. U. F. "Mus-
solini," Sezione editoriale, 1939.

Naples. Università. *Scuola di specializzazione in ostetricia e ginecologia*
see
Naples. Università. *Scuola di perfezionamento in ostetricia
e ginecologia.*

NAPLES. Università. Seminario di storia
medioevale e moderna.
[Pubblicazioni]
Napoli, F. Fiorentino.

NN 0017611 NN

Naples. Zoologische Station
see Naples. Stazione zoologica.

207
N16r
Naples (Archdiocese)--Archbishop, 1734-1754 (Giuseppe Spinelli)
Regole del Seminario napoletano compilate, e
pubblicate per ordine dell'eminentiss. e rever.
sig. cardinale Giuseppe Spinelli arcivescovo. Con
una raccolta di preghiere ad uso de'seminaristi.
In Napoli, Dalla Stamp. di D. Roselli, 1744.
232p.
Title vignette.

1. Naples. Seminario. I. Spinelli, Giuseppe,
cardinal, 1694-1763

NN 0017613 IU

Naples (Archdiocese) Archbishop, 17 -1782
(Serafino Filangieri)
Deux mandements et trois affiches de
Serafino Filangieri
see under Filangieri, Serafino, Abp.
of Naples, b. 1713.

VOLUME 405

Law
Naples(Archdiocese) Curia.
Decisiones cvriae archiepiscopalis neapolitanae, in qvibvs praxis rervm civilivm criminalium, & ecclesiasticarum in eadem curia tractatarum dilucide continetur. Pars prima [- ter-
tia]...Nunc secundo in lucem editum...Avthore
Io. Aloysio Riccio...Accessere dvo indices...
Neapoli, ex typographia Dominici de Ferdinando
Maccarani, 1622.
3 v. in 1. 30 cm.
1.Canon law. I.Riccio, Giovanni Luigi, Bp.,
d.1643. II.Title.

NN   0017615   DLC

BQV
480
N31
C5
Naples (Archdiocese) Curia.
Decisionvm cvriae archiepiscCopal]is
neopolitanae in qvibvs praxis rervm civilivm,
criminalium, & ecclesiasticorum in eadem
curia tractatarum dilucide continetur. [Pars
prima?] [...secunda] [...tertia]. Avthore Io.
Aloysio Riccio. Coloniae Allobrogvm, apvd
Philippvm Albert, 1628.
3 v.

Pars prima? is evidently a second printing
and lacks designation as "Pars prima."

Pars secunda has date 1620, and pars
tertia "apud Iacobum Castellanum" is dated
1625.

I. Riccio, Giovanni Luigi, Bp. d. 1643.

NN   0017617   CU-L

Naples (Archdiocese) Seminario
see Naples. Seminario.

Naples (Archdiocese) Synod.
Acta et decreta Synodi Neapolitanae.
Neapoli, impensis Anelli Sanuiti, 1568.
Microfilm copy, made in 1960 of the
original in Vatican. Biblioteca vaticana.
Positive.
Negative in Vatican. Biblioteca vaticana.
Collation of the original as determined
from the film: [18], 214, [1] p.
1. Councils and Synods. Diocesan. (Series:
[Manuscripta,   microfilms of rare and
out-of-print   books. List 18, no.
23])

NN   0017619   MoSU

Naples (Archdiocese) Synod.
Constitutiones et decreta diocesanae synodi neapol. ... Romae, 1627.

NN   0017620   CLL

Naples (Archdiocese) Synod, 1694.
Synodus dioecesana ab eminentiss. et
reverendiss. dom. D. Jacobo ... celebrata ...
anno 1694. Romae, Ex typographia Rev.
Camerae Apostolicae, 1694.
326 p.   23 cm.
1. Councils and synods, Diocesan. 2. Ecclesiastical law-Italy. I. Title.

NN   0017621   MBtS

BV
480
N21
1882
Naples (Archdiocese) Synod, 1882.
Prima synodus dioecesana ab ill.mo Gulielmo
San felicio O.S.B. archiepiscopo et patritio
Neapolitano celebrata diebus IV. V. VI. VII.
Iunii MDCCCLXXXII. Neapoli, ex Typographia
Archiepiscopali. 1882.

1, 200, 63 p. front., 26 cm.

I. Sanfelice d'Acquavella, Guglielmo, Cardinal,
1834-1897.

NN   0017622   DCU

Naples (Commune)
see Naples.

BQV
479
N3
1576
A2
Robbins
coll.
Naples (Ecclesiastical Province) Synod, 1576.
Constitvtiones et decreta provincialis synodi
neapolitanae, svb...Mario Carrafa Archiepiscopo
neapolitano, anno Domini M.D.LXXVI. Neapoli,
ex Officina Saluiana, 1580.
[6], [108], [36] p.

1. Councils and synods, Provincial - Naples.
I.Carafa, Mario, Abp. of Naples, d. 1576.

NN   0017624   CU-L MBtS

Naples (Ecclesiastical Province) Synod, 1699.
Concilium provinciale Neapolitanum ab eminentiss.
ac reverendiss. dom. D. Jacobo Cardinali Cantelmo...
celebratum anno 1699. n. p., n. d.
298 p. 23 cm.

NN   0017625   MBtS

Naples (*Kingdom*)
see also
Sicily.

Naples (Kingdom)
Almanacco reale del regno delle due. Sicilie
see under Almanacco reale del regno
delle due Sicilie.

4DG
561
Naples (Kingdom)
Capitulation militaire avec S.M. le
roi des Deux-Siciles. [   ]
1828.
69 p.

NN   0017628   DLC-P4

NAPLES, (Kingdom)
Documenti ufficiali della corrispondenza del
governo di S.M.Siciliana con quello di S.M.
Britannica risguardante i due macchinisti del
Cagliari, Watt e Park. Napoli, tipografia del
Giornale ufficiale, 1858.

[4°. pp.50.

NN   0017629   MH

Naples (Kingdom) Copye des briefs van den Spainschen viceroy van
Napels aen de Turckschen keyser Mahometh de III
...waer in hy den selven soect op te hissen tegen de republijcke van Venetien, ende te ruden
tot de conqueste van Candien. Wt de Italiaensch
sprake verduytscht. n.p., 1617. 2 l. 4°.

NN   0017630   NN

945N16
N164
Naples (Kingdom)
Etichetta della Real Corte delle due Sicilie.
Napoli, A. Trani, 1808.
122 p

1. Naples (Kingdom) - Court and courtiers.
2. Etiquette - Naples (Kingdom)

NN   0017631   NNC

NAPLES (KINGDOM).
Gaète. Documents officiels. Paris, E.Dentu,
1861.

NN   0017632   MH

Naples (*Kingdom*)
Giornale costituzionale del regno delle Due Sicilie.

[Napoli, 18
v. 51½ᵐ. daily (Irregular)
Supersedes Naples (Kingdom) Monitore delle Due Sicilie.
Caption title, 18   -Mar. 24, 1848, Giornale del regno delle Due
Title varies: Sicilie.
Mar. 27, 1848-   Giornale costituzionale del regno
delle Due Sicilie.
1. Naples (Kingdom)—Pol. & govt.
45-45904

Library of Congress   J7.I 5N3

NN   0017633   DLC

Naples (*Kingdom*)
Istruzioni generali di sanitá del regno di Napoli, pubblicate nell' anno 1751, attualmente in vigore per ordine
di S. M. Napoli, A. Trani, 1813.
104 p. 27ᶜᵐ.

1. Naples (Kingdom)—Sanit. affairs. I. Title.
21-5817

Library of Congress   RA275.N3

NN   0017634   DLC

NAPLES, (Kingdom).
Manifesto del governo delle Due Sicilie.
[Napoli, 1821.]

1.8°. pp. (2), 9.

NN   0017635   MH

Naples (Kingdom)
Notizie estratte da' registri pubblici sullo
stato, e l' amministrazione della finanza dei
dominii continentali del Regno delle due
Sicilie dal 1. gennaio 1831 a tutto decembre
1847. [Napoli, 1849]
11 p.   28 cm.

1.Finance, Public. Naples (Kingdom) I.Title.

NN   0017636   MnU

VOLUME 405

Naples (Kingdom)
  Ruoli de' generali ed uffiziali attivi e sedentanei del reale esercito e dell' armata di mare di Sua Maestà il re del regno delle Due Sicilie per l' anno 1850.   Napoli: Dalla Reale Tipografia Militare, 1851.   1 p.l., 2, 7-248 p.   half lea.   8°.

1. Navy, Italy, 1850.
N. Y. P. L.   September 11, 1913.

NN   0017637   NN

Naples (*Kingdom*)
  Ragguaglio de' pesi e delle misure di capacità e monete estere delle principali piazze di commercio secondo la loro resa in Napoli.   Napoli, Dalla tipografia del Ministero e real segreteria di stato della polizia generale, 1826.
  31 p.   23ᵐ.

1. Weights and measures—Tables, etc.   2. Money—Tables, etc.
                                          CA 9-4689 Unrev'd
Library of Congress   HF5715.I 8N2

NN   0017638   DLC

Naples (Kingdom)
  Revue des erreurs et des mensonges publiés par m.Gladstone dans ses Deux lettres adressées au comte d'Aberdeen sur les procès politiques dans le royaume des Deux-Siciles ... Traduction.   Paris, A.Vaton, 1851.
  2 p.l.,72 p.   21½ᶜᵐ.
  A translation from the Italian of the Neapolitan government's reply to W.E.Gladstone's Two letters to the Earl of Aberdeen on the state prosecutions of the Neapolitan government. Mr.Gladstone's answer,An examination of the official reply of the Neapolitan government,will be found in his Gleanings of past years,v.4.

  No.4 in ₍Guizot collection of pamphlets. v.13 (Binder's title: Mélanges de politique extérieure. 1846-1854)

  1.Gladstone,William Ewart,1809-1898. Two letters to the Earl of Aberdeen.

NN   0017640   MiU

Naples (*Kingdom*) *Amministrazione generale delle regie poste e dei procacci.*
  Stato generale delle regie poste e del servizio del procaccio in Sicilia organizzato l'anno 1839.   Palermo, L. Dato, 1839.
  132, ₍2₎ p. map, tab. 21ᶜᵐ.

1. Postal service—Sicily.
                                          1-19862
Library of Congress   HE7016.S5N2

NN   0017641   DLC

Naples (Kingdom) *Camera della summaria.*
  DCCXXVII.Arresta Regiae camerae svmmariae neapolitanae¦,qvae vvlgo Decreta generalia, & exemplaria nuncupantur. Collecta à D.D. Donato Antonio de Marinis ... Venetiis, apud Nicolaum Pezzana, M.DC.XCVI.
  122,₍9₎ p.   33½ᶜᵐ. ₍With Marinis,Donato Antonio de. Svmma,et observationes ad singvlas decisiones Regiae camerae svmmariae regni Neapolis ... 1696₎
  Publisher's device on t.-p.

NN   0017642   MiU-L

Naples (Kingdom) *Camera della summaria.*

Marinis, Donato Antonio ᵈᵉ, 1599?-1666.
  D. Donati Antonii de Marinis Opera iuridica in quinque tomos distributa; cum additionibus Leonardi Rodoerii, Caroli Antonii de Luca, Caroli de Alexio, Francisci Reverterii, & Camilli de Curte.   Necnon nuperrimis Felicis Cappelli animadversionibus. ₍Venetiis, apud Nicolaum Pezzana, 1758₎

Naples (Kingdom) *Camera della sumaria.*
  Ritus regiae camerae summariae regni Neapolis
      see under   Gaeta, Goffredo, di, d. 1463.

Naples (Kingdom) Consigli d'intendenza ne' dominii al di la del Faro.
  Discorsi pronunciati dagl'intendenti delle provincie dei reali dominii al di la del Faro nell'apertura de'Consigli provinciali del 1851. Palermo, Stab. tip. dell'Armonia, 1851.

NN   0017645   MH

Naples (*Kingdom*) *Consiglio di Capuana*
  see
Naples (*Kingdom*) *Sacro regio consiglio.*

Naples (*Kingdom*) *Consiglio di santa Chiara*
  see
Naples (*Kingdom*) *Sacro regio consiglio.*

Naples (Kingdom) Consiglio di stato
      see   Naples (Kingdom) Sacro regio consiglio.

Naples (Kingdom) Consiglio rotale.
  Decisiones consigli rotalis romani
      see under   Catholic Church. Rota Romana.

Naples (Kingdom) Constitution. 1812.
  Atto parlamentario stipulato li ₍sic₎ 7 novembre 1812 dal protonotaro del regno di Sicilia.   Palermo: Scuola tip. "Boccone del povero," 1912. xxxviii, 232 p. front., ports.   4°. (Documenti per servire alla storia di Sicilia. ser. 2, v. 8.)
  Includes "Atti di dissensi e proteste fatti...nel corso del Parlamento generale straordinario del 1812."

1. Sicily—Hist., 1812. 2. Constitu-   tions—Sicily, 1812. 3. Two
Sicilies (kingdom). Parlamento.   4. Ser.
N. Y. P. L.   September 10, 1926

NN   0017650   NN

Naples (Kingdom) Constitution. 1812
  Gt. Brit. *Foreign office.*
  Correspondence respecting the affairs of Naples and Sicily. 1848-1849 ... London, Printed by Harrison and son ₍1849?₎

NAPLES (Kingdom)   Constitution. 1815.
  Costituzione politica del regno di Napoli dell'anno 1815, sotto Gioacchino Murat. Collazionata e correta da Angelo Lanzellotti. Napoli, 1820.

  pp. 55.

NN   0017652   MH

Naples (Kingdom) Constitution. 1820.
  Costituzione politica del Regno delle Due Sicilie. Edizione fatta per ordine e sotto la direzione del Parlamento. Napoli, presso Gennaro Matarazzo, 1821.
  111 p. (incl. cover) 21 cm.
  1. Constitutional law - Naples (Kingdom)
I. Title.

NN   0017653   DLC MH NIC

Naples (Kingdom) Constitution. 1820.
  Costituzione politica del regno delle Due Sicilie. Ed. fatta per ordine e sotto la direzione del parlamento del 1820. [With: Ragguaglio di tutte le principali discussioni relative agli atti legislativi del parlamento del 1820, and Progetto di organizzazione della guardia nazionale, compilato dal deputato Borrelli] Napoli, 1848.

NN   0017654   MH

Naples (Kingdom) Constitution. 1848.   BWD p.v.20
  La costituzione politica del regno seguita da tutte le leggi elettorali per la nomina dei deputati, da quelle sulla Guardia Nazionale e da vari altri decreti sul regime costituzionale. Operetta dedicata a tutti i rappresentanti del popolo.   Napoli: G. Nobile, 1849.   84 p.   12°.

1. Constitutions, Two Sicilies.   2. Statutes, Two Sicilies.
N. Y. P. L.   January 5, 1914.

NN   0017655   NN

NAPLES (Kingdom)   Constitution.
  Costituzione politica della monarchia proclamata e sanzionata, 10 Feb., 1848. Napoli, dalla Stamperia reale, 1848.

  pp. 18.

NN   0017656   MH MB

NAPLES. (Kingdom)   Constitution. 1848.
  Costituzione politica della monarchia proclamata e sanzionata da Sua Maestà il re, etc. Napoli, 1848.

NN   0017657   MH

Naples (Kingdom)   Constitution. 1848.   2729.26
  Ferdinando II. per la gracia di Dio re del Regno delle Due Sicilie, di Gerusalemme ec., duca di Parma, Piacenza, Castro, ec. ec., gran principe ereditario di Toscana, ec. ec.
= Napoli. 1848. 16 pp. 12°.
  The title is on the cover.
  Contains the proclamation of the constitution of February 11, 1848.

  G8471 — Ferdinand II., King of the two Sicilies. 1810-1859.

NN   0017658   MB MH

Naples (Kingdom) Corte suprema di giustizia.
  Atto di accusa contro di Francesco Nicola de Mattheis, Raffaele d'Alessandro [and others]
      see under   Mattheis, Francesco Nicola de.

VOLUME 405

Naples (Kingdom) Corte suprema di guistizia.

Naples (*Kingdom*) *Laws, statutes, etc.*
Comentario sul Codice per lo regno delle Due Sicilie e propriamente sulla parte quarta. Leggi della procedura ne' giudizj penali, messe in rapporto colle disposizioni delle altre parti del Codice istesso, e corredate ne' rispettivi articoli delle aggiunzioni, cangiamenti, modifiche e dilucidazioni cui sono andate soggette: mercè una raccolta di leggi, decreti, rescritti, regolamenti, atti ministeriali e decisioni della Corte suprema di giustizia dal 1809 a tutto ;dicembre 1838; ... Opera di Orazio Giaccari ... Avellino, Da' tipi di de Feo, e Guadagno, 1838–39.

Naples (Kingdom) Corte Suprema di Giustizia.
Pel principe d. Ettore Pignatelli nella causa della graduatoria Monteleone
see under Monteleone, Maria Carmela Caracciolo, duchessa di, defendant.

Naples (Kingdom) Corte Suprema di Giustizia.
Ragionamento pel credito dotale della duchessa di Monteleone, d. Maria Carmela Caracciolo
see under Monteleone, Maria Carmela Caracciolo, duchessa di, defendant.

Naples (Kingdom) Corte suprema di giustizia.
Pubblico ministero
see Naples (Kingdom) Pubblico ministero presso la Corte suprema di giustizia.

LAW   Naples (Kingdom) Courts.

Naples (*Kingdom*) *Laws, statutes, etc.*
Comento sulle leggi civili del regno delle Due Sicilie, ove si espongono i principj delle stesse leggi; le variazioni tra l'antica e moderna legislazione; un cenno sulla concordanza coi codici esteri; il confronto colle leggi romane e col dritto patrio; la giurisprudenza fornita delle comuni teorie dei giureconsulti ricevute nel foro; la estesa menzione dei decreti, rescritti, ministeriali ed arresti e decisioni delle corti giudicatrici, applicati a ciascuno articolo, di Annibale Giordano ... Napoli, Stamperia del Fibreno, 1848–64.

Naples (Kingdom) Courts.
Decisioni delle gran corti civili in materia di diritto. Napoli, 1827–31[33].

4°. 5 v.

Same. 2ª ed. Napoli, 1840–43.

4°. v.1–2,5–7.

NN 0017665   MH-L

Naples (Kingdom) Courts.
Decisioni delle Gran corti civili in materia di diritto,pubblicate da Michele Agresti ... Napoli, Dalla Stamperia francese, 1827–40.
9 v. 26cm.
Vols.5–9: Dalla Stamperia e cartiera del fibreno.

NN 0017666   MiU-L

Naples (*Kingdom*) *Courts.*
Decisioni delle gran corti civili in materia di diritto, pubblicate da Michele Agresti. Napoli, Stamperia e cartiera del Fibreno, 1830–44 ;v.1, 1841;
9 v. in 10. 27 cm.
Vols. 1–3, 5–8: 2. ed.
Includes several essays by M. Agresti.

Continued in next column

Continued from preceding column

1. Law reports, digests, etc.—Naples (Kingdom) Michele, 1775–1855, ed. II. Title.   I. Agresti,

51–49984

NN 0017667   DLC

Law
Naples (Kingdom) Courts.
Novissimae decisiones civiles,criminales,& canonicae:tam regii tribvnalis avdientiae prouinciarum capitinatae,Apuleae,et comitatus Mollisij regni Neapolis,quam causarum delegatarum:avthore Io.Maria Novario...Opus quidem vtilissimum et valde practicabile,omni doctrina refertum,et maximopere desideratum:singulis in foro laicali,& ecclesiastico versantibus per necessarium. Accessere duo indices,vnus scilicet argumentorum,alter vero rerum notabilium.[Napoli], ex Tvpographia Petri Chouёr,

1637.
[16],301, [48] p. 31 cm.
Title vignette;head and tail pieces;initials. In double columns.

1.Law reports,digests,etc.-Naples(Kingdom).
I.Novario,Giovanni Maria,17th cent. II.Title.

NN 0017669   DLC

Law
Naples(Kingdom) Courts.
Theatrum et examen omnium decisionum regni Neapolitani,in quo universae praedefinitiones dialecto,& arguto,eruditoque schemate legalibus principiis enodatius examinantur,feraciusque probantur,magna ex parte accurae conciliantur:quinimo unicuique definitioni pro ipsius illustratione,nonnullae facti species insitae sunt,in queis aliae dissertantur finitiones: inde est,quod amplius bis centum,& mille practicabiles articuli,qui in Senatu Neapolitano decisi fuere,affatim comprobantur. Auctore

omnium decisionum...
Matthaeo Surrentino Cavensi.Opus et erudito judici,et patrono pro attexedo scripto,pro clientibus defensandis suis ac Tyronibus senatus apprime necessarium. Neapoli,in Nova Typographia Michaelis Aloysii Mutio,1699.
4 p.l.,556,[66] p. 36 cm.
Title vignette;head and tail pieces;initials.
1.Law reports,digests,etc.-Naples(Kingdom).
I.Sorrentino,Matteo,fl.17th cent. II.Title.

NN 0017671   DLC

Naples (Kingdom) Curia
see
Naples (Kingdom) Regia cancelleria.

Naples (Kingdom) Deputati per la sanità.
Consulta de medici per preservarsi da mali correnti nella città di Napoli
see under title

NAPLES (KINGDOM) Direttore generale di ponti e strade.
Esposizione del sistema generale delle strade de' Dominij al di qua del Faro. Detteda da Sua Maestá al Direttore generale di ponti e strade. Napoli, Reale tipografia della guerra, 1839.

pp.64.

NN 0017674   MH

Naples (Kingdom) Fonderie royale
see Naples (Kingdom) Stamperia reale.

Naples (Kingdom) Giunta provvisoria di governo.
Manifesto della Giunta provvisoria di governo al parlamento nazionale. [Napoli] presso il Trani [1820]
2, 52 p. 1.8°.
Signed: Cav. Melchiorre Delfico, Ten. Gen. Parisi, Davide Winspeare [and others]

NN 0017676   MH

Naples (Kingdom) Governo costituzionale.
Manifesto del governo delle Due Sicilie.
[Napoli, 1821]
9 p. f°.

NN 0017677   MH

Naples (Kingdom) Gran corte criminale.
Decisione della GranCorte Criminale di Napoli a carico degl' imputati dei fatti chᵉebbero luogo nel giorno 15 maggio 1848 in Napoli.
[Napoli,1848]. 16 p. 8°.

NN 0017678   NN

Naples (Kingdom) Gran corte criminale e speciale.
Atto di accusa del P.M. con le successive decisioni della Gran corte criminale e speciale di Napoli nella causa degli avvenimenti politici del 5 settembre 1848
see under Naples (Kingdom) Pubblico ministero presso la Gran corte criminale e speciale di Napoli.

Naples (Kingdom) Gran corte criminale e speciale.
Conclusioni pronunziate innanzi alla Gran corte speciale di Napoli nella causa degli avvenimenti politici del 15 maggio 1848 ne' giorni 18, 20, 21 settembre 1852, dal consigliere della suprema corte di giustizia, procuratore generale del re, Filippo Angelillo.   Napoli, Stamp. e cartiere del Fibreno, 1852.
1.8°.
Decision of the court in the trial of those responsible for the revolution of the 15th of May in the Kingdom of Naples.

NN 0017680   MH

Naples (Kingdom) Gran corte criminale e speciale di Basilicata
see Basilicata. Gran corte criminale.

4K   Naples (Kingdom) Gran corte de conti.
It   Giornale delle decisioni della Gran
1490 corte de conti e di altri provvedimenti relativi all'applicazione de'principj di pubblica amministrazione. Napoli, Tip. di A. Trani, 1818–19.
5 v. in 1

NN 0017682   DLC-P4

Naples (Kingdom) Gran corte de conti.
Legge,decreti,e regolamenti per la organizzaione ed attribuzioni della Gran corte de'conti in Sicilia. Palermo,nella R.Stamperia,1818.

24°.

NN 0017683   MH

Naples (*Kingdom*) *Gran corte della vicaria, Tribunale della* see **Naples** (*Kingdom*) *Tribunale della gran corte della vicaria.*

VOLUME 405

945.08
D357
Naples (Kingdom) Gran corte speciale.
Decisione della Gran Corte Speciale de Napoli nella causa della setta l'Unità Italiana, pubblicata alla udienza del 1° febbraio 1851. Napoli, Stamperia del Fibreno, 1851.
183 p.

1. Unità Italiana. 2. Italy - Hist. - 1849-1870 - Sources

NN 0017685 NNC CtY

4K-
993
Naples (<u>Kingdom</u>) <u>Gran corte speciale.</u>
Decisione della Gran corte speciale di Napoli nella causa degli avvenimenti politici del 15 maggio 1848. Napoli, Stamperia e cartiere del Fibreno, 1852.
215 p.

NN 0017686 DLC-P4

Naples (*Kingdom*) *Grande archivio del regno*
see Naples. Archivio di stato.

Naples (Kingdom) Laws, statutes, etc.
Antiche consuetudini delle città di Sicilia
see under La Mantia, Vito, 1822-1904.

Naples (Kingdom) Laws, statutes, etc.
Atti governativi
see under Ettore, Giuseppe d', ed.

JN5289
A3
Case B
Naples (Kingdom) Laws, statutes, etc.
Capitula constitut[iones] vtriusque Siciliae. [Neapoli, apud Ioannem Pavlvm, 1551]
5 pt. in 1 v. 30cm.

Binder's title.
Parts [1,3,4] have special title-pages with title vignette, coat of arms of Kingdom of Naples. Pts.[2] and [5] have caption titles only.
Printer's device at end of pts.[1] and [5].
Contents.- [pt.1] Sicily. Laws,statutes, etc. Capitvla regni Siciliae, cvm glosis Do. Neapol[i]tani, Sebastiani Neapolitani, Do. Lucae

de Penna, & Do. Nicolai de Neapoli, nouiter correcta, ac diligenti castigatione emendata. (Caption title: Constitvtiones Regni Siciliae, per excellentissimvm v.i.d. Do. Andream de Yseernia) (11 p.[?],378 [i.e.376] p.)- [pt.2] Naples (Kingdom) Laws, statutes, etc. Constitvtiones & statuta illustrissimi domini Regis Caroli Hieursalem, & Siciliae Regis, pro exequendo subscripto statuto.

(3-94 [i.e.84] p.)- [pt.3.] Sicily. Curia regis. Ritvs magnae cvriae, vicariae Regni Neapolis, Hactenvs inordinate posin, demum ad ordinem redacti per v.i.d. Do. Caesarem de Perrinÿs, nunc uerò diligenmssimè correcti ac emendati. (30 p.)- [pt.4] Naples (Kingdom) Laws, statutes, etc. Pragmaticae Regni, novae, et antiqvae, cum pragmaticis inuietissimi Caroli Quinti, imperatoris. De novo additis.

(72,[2] p.)- [pt.5] Naples (Kingdom) Laws, statutes, etc. Repertorivm constitutionum ac capitulorum Regni & glosarum Do. And. de Yseernia v.i.doc. (64 [i.e.67] p.).

I. Sicily. Laws, statutes, etc.
II. *Andrea d'Isernia, 1220(ca.) - 1316*

NN 0017693 CU

Naples (Kingdom) Laws, statutes, etc.

Sicily. *Laws, statutes, etc.*
Capitula regni Siciliæ, quæ ad hodiernum diem lata sunt, edita cura ejusdem regni deputatorum Herculis Michaelis Brancifortii, Buteræ principis ... [et al.] Panormi, excudebat A. Felicella, 1741-43.

Naples (Kingdom) Laws, statutes, etc.
Capitvla regni vna cvm apparatv, ac vtilissimis, et necessariis prioribvs, et novis supplectionibus, insignis ac excellentissimi vtriusq[iuris doctoris domini Ioannis Antoni de Nigris ... et lectura domini Sebastiani de Neapoli, Nicolai de Neapoli, Bartolomei de Capua, & Lvce de Penna ... [Campanie, apud Io. Dominicum Nibium] 1561.
290 numb. l. 30 cm.
Signatures: A-Z⁶, AA-ZZ⁶, AAA⁶, BBB⁸.

Imperfect: folios 15-16 (sig. C3-4) lacking; folios 39-40 (sig. G3-4) duplicated.
De Nigris' coat of arms on title-page; printer's mark at end: initials.
Errors in foliation: 12, 287 incorrectly numbered 11, 278 respectively.
"Repertorium" with separate title-page preceding main work: 42 numb. l.
Bound in a vellum leaf from an antiphonary.

NN 0017696 CtY

Naples (Kingdom) Laws, statutes, etc.

Lindenbrog, Friedrich, 1573-1648, ed.
Codex legvm antiqvarvm, in qvo continentvr: Leges Wisigothorvm. Edictvm Theodorici regis. Lex Bvrgvndionvm. Lex Salica. Lex Alamannorvm. Lex Baivvariorvm. Decretvm Tassilonis dvcis. Lex Ripvariorvm. Lex Saxonvm. Angliorvm et Werinorvm. Frisionvm. Longobardorvm. Constitviones siculæ sive neapolitanæ. Capitvlare Karoli M. et Hlvdowici impp. &c. Quibus accedunt Formulæ solennes priscæ publicorum privatorumque negotiorum, nunc primum editæ: et glossarivm ... Ex bibliotheca Frid. LindenbrogI. J. c. Francofvrti, apud Ioannem & Andream Marnios & consortes, cIↄIↄCXIII.

NN 0017699 DLC MH

Naples (*Kingdom*) *Laws, statutes, etc.*
Codice delle leggi del regno di Napoli, di Alessio de Sariis ... Napoli, V. Orsini, 1792-97.
12 v. in 6. 24 x 19½ᶜᵐ.
CONTENTS.—v. 1. Della ragion ecclesiastica e sue pertinenze.—v. 2. Del diritto pubblico: de trattati di pace e di commercio esteriore colle potenze straniere.—v. 3. Dell' alto dominio del principe nel creare i magistrati, e le leggi.—v. 4. Delle regalie, de' ministri di azienda, e del real patrimonio.—v. 5. De fiscali, dell' amministrazione delle università, e della pubblica annona.—v. 6. De' baroni, e de' feudi, e della ragion feudale.—v. 7. Della ragion militare.—v. 8. Del' pubblico commercio interiore per terra e per mare, e della pubblica sanità.—v. 9. Degli officj pubblici, e degli officiale.—v. 10. Delle scienze, e dell' arti.—v. 11. Dell'ordine de' giudizj, e delle azioni.—v. 12. De' delitti privati, e pubblici, e delle pene.

—— Epitome; o sia Indice generale de la Storia e del Codice delle leggi del regno di Napoli, di Alessio de Sariis, Con ordine alfabetico. Napoli, V. Orsini, 1797.
296 p. 24 x 19½ᶜᵐ.

I. Sariis, Alessio de, ed. II. Sariis, Alessio de. Dell' istoria del regno di Napoli. III. Naples (Kingdom) Treaties, etc.

47-35232

NN 0017699 DLC MH

Kress
Room
Naples (Kingdom). Laws, statutes, etc.
... Bando da parte della prefata Regal Maestà e della Regia Camera della Sommaria: Mosso il pietoso, e clementissimo animo della Maestà del Re nostro signore, intento sempre al sollievo, ed alla felicità de'suoi fedelissimi popoli, dalle reiterate suppliche di molte popolazioni tanto del ripartimento di tagliacozzo, che degli altri ripartimenti degli Abruzzi, perchè abolisse il sistema della fida delle pecore rimaste, o sia doganelle ... Napoli, Nella stamperia de'Fratelli Marotta, 1797.

broadside 48 x 36.5 cm. (folded to 15 x 11 cm)

Dated at end: 18. gennaro 1797.
Bound with (Camilli, Francesco Saverio) Memoria sui danni apportati allo stato e al fisco dalla fida delle pecore rimaste, 1795.

1.Sheep - Naples (Kingdom)

NN 0017701 MH-BA

Naples (Kingdom) Laws, statutes, etc.
Bando delli carcerati per tvtto il regno [Napoli, 1559]
[4] p. 24 cm.

NN 0017702 ICN

Naples (Kingdom) Laws, statutes, etc.
Bulletino delle leggi del regno di Napoli
see its Collezione delle leggi e de' decreti reali del regno delle Due Sicilie

---

Naples (Kingdom) Laws, statutes, etc.
Codice di commercio annotato
see under France. Laws, statutes, etc.

Naples (Kingdom) Laws, statutes, etc.
Codice di commercio dell'impero francese adottato nel regno di Napoli per ordine di S.M. Ed. originale, e sola uffiziale. Napoli, Nella stamperia Simoniauo, 1809.
viii, 184 p. 19.5 cm.

NN 0017705 MH-BA NcD-L

Naples (Kingdom) Laws, statutes, etc.
Codice di procedura civile, annotato ... .
see under France. Laws, statutes, etc.

Naples (Kingdom) Laws, statutes, etc.
Codice diplomatico del regno di Carlo I
see under Giudice, Giuseppe, ed.

Naples (Kingdom) Laws, statutes, etc.
Codice diplomatico dei rei aragonesi
see under La Mantia, Francesco Giuseppe, d. 1930, ed.

Naples (Kingdom) Laws, statutes, etc.
Codice ecclesiastico Sicolo ... Con note ed illustrazioni. Palermo, 1846-51.
4 v.

NN 0017709 PU

Naples (Kingdom) Laws, statutes, etc.
Codice Ferdinando o codice marittimo compilato per ordine di Ferdinando IV. Napoli, 1781.
4 v.
1. Maritime law - Naples (Kingdom)
I. Title.

NN 0017710 CU-L

4K
It.
1667
Naples. (Kingdom) Laws, statutes, etc.
Codice per lo regno delle due Sicilie. 1. ed. originale ed uffiziale. Napoli, Dalla Real tip. del Ministero di Stato della Cancelleria generale, 1819-
v. 3, 5

NN 0017711 DLC-P4

VOLUME 405

4K
It
152B

Naples (Kingdom) Laws, statutes, etc.
Codice per lo regno delle Due
Sicilie. 2. ed. uffiziale. Napoli,
Dalla real tip. del Ministero di
Stato della Cancelleria Generale,
1819 -
     v. 2-5

Contents.--v. 1.
--v. 2. Leggi penali.--v. 3-4.
della procedura ne'giudizj civili.

--v. 5. Leggi di eccezione per gli
affari di commercio.

NN   0017713   DLC-P4

349.45
N162

Naples (Kingdom) Laws, statutes, etc.
Codice per lo regno delle Due Sicilie.
Napoli, Dalla Stamperia Reale, 1819-27 [pt.1,
1827]
     5 v. in l.   21 cm.
     Pts. 2, 4 have imprint: Napoli, Presso A.
Trani; pt.5. has imprint: Napoli, Dalla Real
Tipografia del Ministero di Stato della
Cancelleria Generale.
     Contents.--pt.1. Leggi civili. 6. ed. uffi-
ziale.-[pt.2]   Leggi penali.-

Codice per lo regno...

pt.3. Leggi della procedura ne'guidizj civili.
3. ed. uffiziale.-[pt.4] Leggi della procedura
ne'guidizj penali.-pt.5. Leggi di eccezione
per gli affari di commercio. 2. ed. uffiziale.

     I.Sicily. Laws, statutes, etc. II.Title.

NN   0017715   MnU

Law

Naples (Kingdom) Laws, statutes, etc. Codice
per lo Regno delle Due Sicilie. 1825.

France. Laws, statutes, etc.
     Le leggi della procedura civile, opera di G. L. S. Carré;
nella quale opera l'autore ha fuso la sua analisi ragionata,
il suo trattato e le sua quistioni sulla procedura. Novella-
mente volgarizzata ed accresciuta della nuova procedura civile del Regno delle Due Sicilie, dagli avvocati F. Carrillo
e P. Liberatore. Napoli, Da' torchi del Tramater, si vende
nella libreria di B. Borel, 1825-

Naples (Kingdom) Laws, statutes, etc.
     Codice per lo regno delle Due Sicilie ... 7. ed. uffiziale. Na-
poli, Stamperia reale, 1829-
     v. 21½ᶜᵐ.

     I. Title.

                                        32-22418

NN   0017717   DLC

4K
Sicily
4

Naples (Kingdom) Laws, statutes, etc.
Codice per lo regno delle Due
Sicilie. Parte prima, Leggi civili,
col confronto delle leggi romane e
del dritto mediosicolo; annotato di
tutti i corrispondenti reali decreti,
rescritti, regolamenti ed atti ministeriali pubblicati finora, colla
indicazione degli articoli delle diverse parti del codice, di altre leggi, statuti e regolamenti che vi han
concessione, e colla corrispondenza

degli articoli del Codice civile
francese. Palermo, Presso Pedone e
Muratori, 1832-33.
     4 v.

NN   0017719   DLC-P4

4K
It
1670
v. 3

Naples (Kingdom) Laws, statutes, etc.
Codice per lo regno delle Due
Sicilie. 6. ed. uffiziale. Napoli,
Dalla Stamperia reale, 1834-
     v. 3

NN   0017720   DLC-P4

Naples (Kingdom) Laws, statutes, etc.
     Codice per lo regno delle Due Sicilie ... 12. ed. uffiziale.
Napoli, Dalla Stamperia reale, 1842-
     v. 21½ᶜᵐ.
     CONTENTS.—1. pte. Leggi civili.

     I. Sicily. Laws, statutes, etc. II. Title.

                                        30-32795

NN   0017721   DLC

NAPLES (KINGDOM) - Laws,statutes,etc.
Codice per lo regno delle Due Sicilie.
Napoli,Stab.tip.di D.Capasso,1848.

5 pt.

NN   0017722   MH

K
25
N16c
1848

Naples (Kingdom). Laws, statutes, etc.
Codice per lo Regno delle Due Sicilie.
Napoli, Capasso. 1848-49 [v.1, 1849]
     5 v. in l.

     Contents.- pt.1 Leggi civili.- pt.2. Leggi
penali.- pt.3. Leggi della procedura ne' giudiz-
civili.- pt.4. Leggi della procedura ne' giudiz
penali.- pt.5. Leggi di eccezione per gli affar
di commercio.

     I. Title.

NN   0017723   CLU

IAPLES (KINGDOM) - Laws,statutes,etc.
Codice per lo regno delle Due Sicilie. Corre-
iato di un rinvio in fine di ciascun articolo,
etc. Compilato dall'avvocato Luigi Dentice e c.
Napoli,Stab.tip.di Domenico Capasso,1849.

5 pt.   Ital 535.48.5

Supplemento. Napoli,D.Capasso,1850.

NN   0017724   MH

Naples (Kingdom) Laws, statutes, etc.
     Codice per lo regno delle Due Sicilie col supplemento delle
leggi, decreti ed altri atti sovrani in materia di diritto privato
e pubblico, coordinati al Codice medesimo per cura di una
commessione di real ordine istituita. Napoli, Stamperia reale,
1850.
     2 v. in 3. 16½ᶜᵐ.
     On half-title of v. [1]: Codice ... parte prima. Leggi civili.
     The "Supplimento" (bound in 2 vols.; paged continuously) has title:
Supplimento al Codice, ossia Collezione di leggi, decreti ed altri atti
sovrani di massima in materia di diritto privato e pubblico, messa in
relazione col Codice medesimo per cura di una commessione di real
ordine istituita. Diritto privato.
     I. Title.
                                        32-22417

NN   0017725   DLC

Law

Naples (Kingdom) Laws, statutes, etc. Codice
per lo Regno delle Due Sicilie.

Moreno, Vincenzo, ed.
     Digesto del diritto civile nuovissimo, ordinato ed annotato
da Vincenzio Moreno [Francesco Vaselli e Cesare Marini]
Con volgarizzamenti novelli di Luigi Lo Gatto. Napoli,
A. Perrotti, 1851-54.

Naples (Kingdom) Laws, statutes, etc.
     Codice per lo Regno delle Due Sicilie, messo in confronto
con i codici vigenti in Francia e le leggi romane ed annotato
per una esatta correlazione degli articoli tra loro; i varî atti
sovrani e ministeriali che ne hanno spiegate, ampliate, modi-
ficate o abrogate le disposizioni; le principali massime di
giurisprudenza dettate dalla Corte suprema di giustizia in
Napoli ... aggiungendo ... tutte le diverse altre leggi, decreti
... che formano il complemento del medesimo codice, o che
con esso hanno stretta attenenza, dall'avv. Giuseppe d'Ettore.
2. ed. migliorata ed accresciuta. Napoli, Stab. tip. del Servi
Tullio, 1859-

     v. 24 cm.
     CONTENTS.—v. 1. pt. 1. Leggi civili.
pt. 3. Leggi della procedura ne' giudizii civili.
pt. 5. Leggi di eccezione per gli affari di commercio.

     I. Ettore, Giuseppe d', ed.

                                        51-45252

NN   0017728   DLC

Naples (Kingdom) Laws, statutes, etc.
Collezione degli editti determinazioni decriti e
leggi di S. M.
     see its Collezione delle leggi e de' decreti
reali del regno delle Due Sicilie

LB2671
N3
1806

Naples (Kingdom) Laws, statutes, etc.
Collezione delle leggi, de'decreti e di altri
atti riguardante la pubblica istruzione promul-
gati nei già reame di Napoli dall'anno 1806 in
poi ... Napoli, Stamperia e cartiere del Fibreno, 1861-63.
     3 v. 24cm.

     Contents.- v.1. Dal 1806 al 1820.-v.2. Dal 1821
al 1848.-v.3. Dal 1849 al 1861.

     1.Educational law and legislation - Naples (King-
dom)

M223739-41, v.1-3

                                        1 Doc.

NN   0017730   CU MH

NAPLES (Kingdom)   Laws,Statutes,etc.
Collezione delle leggi,decreti,reali rescritti
e ministeriali sull' amministrazione civile del
regno delle Due Sicilie.   Caserta,Tipografia
della intendenza,1833.
     4o.

NN   0017731   MH-L

Naples (Kingdom) Laws, statutes, etc.
     Collezione delle leggi e de' decreti reali del regno delle Due
Sicilie ... anno [1806,-
Napoli, Dalla Stamperia reale [etc., 1806?-
     v.   tables (part fold.) forms (part fold.) 19-22ᶜᵐ.
     In 1 vol. each year 1806, 1815, 18   ; in 2 vols. each year (semestre
I-II) 1807-1814, 1816-18
     1806 covers period Feb. 15 to Dec. 31; 1815 covers period May to De-
cember.
     Supplements for 1816, 1824, 1826, 1831 issued in separate volumes.
     Title varies: 1806, Collezione degli editti, determinazioni, decreti e
leggi di S. M.
     1807, sem. I-1814, sem. II. Bullettino delle leggi del regno di Napoli.
1815, sem. I-1816, sem. I. Collezione delle leggi e decreti reali del
regno di Napoli.

     1816, sem. II; 1817, sem. II. Collezione delle leggi e decreti reali del
regno delle Due Sicilie.
     1817, sem. I. 1818, sem. I-   Collezione delle leggi e de'
decreti [etc.]

     I. Title. II. Title: Due Sicilie, Collezione delle leggi ... del regno
delle.
                                        33-6388

NN   0017733   DLC NjP CU ViU MiU NN

VOLUME 405

Naples (Kingdom) Laws,statutes,etc.
Collezione delle leggi e de' decreti reali del regno delle Due
Sicilie. Anno 1806–1860, settembre 6.   Napoli: Stamperia reale₁,
1806?₁–60. 93 v. 19½–21½ cm.
Semiannual.
Title varies: 1806, Collezione degli editti determinazioni, decreti, e leggi di S. M.;
1807–1814, Bullettino delle leggi del regno di Napoli; 1815 – June, 1816, Collezione
delle leggi e decreti reali del regno di Napoli, July, 1816–1860, Collezione delle leggi e
de' decreti reali del regno delle Due Sicilie. (Varies slightly.)
Publisher varies: 1806–1809, Stamperia simoniana; 1810–1811, Stamperia francese; 1812–1813, Fonderia reale e Stamperia del Min. della segreteria di stato (varies

slightly); 1814–1817, and July, 1821–1860, Stamperia reale; 1818, Reale tipografia della
Cancelleria generale; 1819 – June, 1820, Real tipografia del Min. di stato della cancelleria
generale; July, 1820 – June, 1821, Real tipografia del Min. di stato degli affari interni.

1. No subject.   I. Naples (kingdom).   Statutes.   *Revised*
N. Y. P. L.   November 23, 1932

  NN 0017735   NN MiU

Naples (Kingdom)' Laws, statutes, etc.
Collezione delle leggi e de' decreti (Indexes)
Indice generale-alfabetico della collezione
delle leggi e dei decreti per il regno delle Due
Sicilie, distinto per materie con ordine cronologico lavoro eseguito da domenicantonio vacca.
2d ed., dall'anno 1806 a tutto il 1840.   Napoli,
Stabilimento tipografico all'insegna dell'ancora,
1841.
    iv p., 1 l., 950 p.   21.5 cm.
    This set is continued by "Raccolta ufficiale
delle leggi e dei decreti del regno d'Italia"
which is in the University library.

  NN 0017736   CtY

Naples (Kingdom). Laws, statutes, etc.
Collezione delle leggi e de' decreti emanti
nelle Provincie Continentali dell' Italia
Meridionale druante il periodo della dittatura
da' 7 settembre a' 6 novembre 1860.   Napoli,
1860.

  NN 0017737   MH-L

Naples (Kingdom). Laws, statutes, etc.
Collezione delle leggi e de' decreti
emanti nelle Provincie Continentali dell'
Italia Meridionale durante il periodo della
luogotenenza, da' 7 novembre 1860 a' 30 aprile
1861 [al 31 ottobre 1861]. Napoli, 1861–62.

    2 v.

  NN 0017738   MH-L

Naples (Kingdom) Laws, statutes, etc.
Collezione delle leggi e decreti reali del
regno delle Due Sicilie. 15 febbrajo 1806–30
aprile 1861.   Napoli, Dalla tipografia nazionale,
[1806]–1861.
    83 v. illus. tables (fold.) 20–22 cm.
    Title varies: 1806, Collezione degli editti,
determinazioni, decreti, e leggi di S. M.; 1807,
Bullettino delle leggi; 1808–1815 pt. I, Bullettino
delle leggi del regno di Napoli; 1815 pt. I–
1816, Collezione delle leggi e decreti reali del
regno di Napoli; 1860 pt. II, Collezione delle
leggi e de'decreti emanati nelle provincie con—

tinentali dell'Italia meridionale durante il periodo
della dittatura; 1860 pt. III–1861, Collezione
delle leggi e de'decreti emanati nelle ...
luogotenenza.
    1816, 1824, and 1831 have supplements.

  NN 0017740   CtY

Naples (*Kingdom*) *Laws, statutes, etc.*
Collezione di reali rescritti, leggi decreti e regolamenti, istruzioni, ministeriali e sovrane risoluzioni in materia civile, penale,
ecclesiastica, commerciale ed amministrativa ... 1806/17–
Napoli, Stabilimento tipografico di F. Azzolino ₁etc.₁ 1844–
    v. in   21½ᵐ.
    Annual, 1841–
    Title varies slightly.
    Printer varies.
    Francesco Dias, editor.
    INDEXES:
      1806–40, 2 v. in 1, lettered : ₁v.₁ 12.
    I. Dias, Francesco, ed.

                                          47–34738

  NN 0017741   DLC MH-L

Naples (Kingdom) Laws, statutes, etc.
Comentari sulla prima parte del Codice per
lo regno delle Due Sicilie, relativa alle leggi
civili
            see under Magliano, Francesco.

Naples (*Kingdom*) *Laws, statutes, etc.*
Comentario sul Codice per lo regno delle Due Sicilie e propriamente sulla parte quarta. Leggi della procedura ne' giudizj
penali, messe in rapporto colle disposizioni delle altre parti del
Codice istesso, e corredate ne' rispettivi articoli delle aggiunzioni, cangiamenti, modifiche e dilucidazioni cui sono andate
soggette: mercè una raccolta di leggi, decreti, rescritti, regolamenti, atti ministeriali e decisioni della Corte suprema di
giustizia dal 1809 a tutto ₁dicembre 1838₁ ... Opera di Orazio
Giaccari ... Avellino, Da' tipi de Feo, e Guadagno, 1838–39.
    3 v. 204ᵐ.
    1. Criminal procedure—Naples (Kingdom)   I. Giaccari, Orazio, ed.
    II. Naples (Kingdom) Corte suprema di giustizia. III. Title.

                                          37–39007

  NN 0017743   DLC

Law   Naples (Kingdom) Laws, statutes, etc.

France. *Laws, statutes, etc.*
Comentario sulle leggi della procedura civile di C. ₁i. e.
G.₁ L. T. ₁i. e. J.₁ Carré. 3. ed. francese, accresciuta nel
belgio del confronto con le opere di Pigeau ₁et al.₁ 1. ed.
italiana. Arricchita della conferenza degli articoli del
codice francese con quelli del Codice pel regno delle Due
Sicilie, delle disposizioni legislative emanate posteriormente
alle leggi di procedura ne' giudizi civili, e della giurisprudenza della Suprema corte di giustizia napoletana, dall'avvocato Luigi Lo Gatto. Napoli, Dallo stab. dell'Antologia
legale di Capasso, 1853–56.

Naples (*Kingdom*) *Laws, statutes, etc.*
Comento sulle leggi civili del regno delle Due Sicilie, ove si
espongono i principj delle stesse leggi; le variazioni tra l'antica
e moderna legislazione; un cenno sulla concordanza coi codici
esteri; il confronto colle leggi romane e col dritto patrio; la
giurisprudenza fornita dalle comuni teorie dei giureconsulti
ricevute nel foro; la estesa menzione dei decreti, rescritti, ministeriali ed arresti e decisioni delle corti giudicatrici, applicati a
ciascuno articolo, di Annibale Giordano ... Napoli, Stamperia
del Fibreno, 1848–64.
    10 v. front. (port.) fold. tab., diagrs. 26ᵐ.
    Vol. 10 has imprint: Napoli, Stabilimento tipografico degli scienziati,
letterati ed artisti.
    1. Civil law—Naples   (Kingdom)   I. Giordano, Anni-
bale, ed. II. Naples (King-   dom) Courts.
                                          47–33514

  NN 0017745   DLC

Law   Naples (Kingdom) Laws, statutes, etc.
Aversa, Italy. Laws, statutes, etc. Commentaria
ad consvetvdines...1605.

Law
Naples (Kingdom) Laws, statutes, etc.
Commentarii in capitvla regni neapolitani
...Ioannis Antonii de Nigris...Hac postrema
editione a multis erroribus repurgati. Sebastiani ac Nicolai de Neapoli, Bartholomaei de
Capua,& Lucae de Penna additamenta,quaedam ad
eadem capitula exarata,eiusdem auctoris cura
& diligentia suo quoquo loco inserta. Cum indice rerum memorabilium locupletissimo. Venetiis,apud Ioannem Variscum,& Socios,1582.
    255,[34] l. 30 cm.

Continued from preceding column

Title vignette(publisher's device);initials.
In double columns.

    1.Law-Naples(Kingdom). I.Nigris,Giovanni
Antonio de, 1502-1570. II.Sebastiano di Napoli,d.1362. III.Nicolo di Napoli. IV.Capua,
Bartolommeo de,fl.1300. V.Luca da Penna,ca.
1320 - ca 1390. VI.Title.

  NN 0017748   DLC

Law
Naples (Kingdom) Laws,statutes,etc.
Commentarii in capitvla Re gni Neapolitani...
Ioannis Antonii de Nigris...Hac postrema editio-
ne a multis erroribus repurgati. Sebastiani ac
Nicolai de Neapoli, Bartholomaei de Capua, &
Lucae de Penna additamenta quaedam ad eadem
capitula exarata...Cum indice rerum memorabi-
lium locupletissimo. Venetiis, apud haeredes
Johannis Varisci, 1594.
    245, [35] l. 30 cm.
    1.Law-Naples(Kingdom). I.Nigris, Giovanni
Antonio de, 1502-1570. II.Title.

  NN 0017749   DLC

Naples (Kingdom) Laws, statutes, etc.
Concordata inter Benedictum XIV ... et
Carolum Borbonium Siciliarum regem
            see under Ceraso , Contradino.

Naples (Kingdom) Laws, statutes, etc.
Constitvtiones Regni Neapolitani cvm glossis.
Constitvtiones Regni Neapolitani cum glossis...
Sebastiani Neapodani, Marini de Caramanico,
Bartholomei de Capua, & Luce de Penna, cu
additionibus & apostillis D. Nicolai Superantij...
MDXXXVII. [Colophon, Lugduni cuse a ...
Joanne Crespin, al's du Quarre. Anno a partu
virgineo, 1537. Mese Martio]
    9 p.l., 2-148 numb. l. 18 cm.
    Signatures: A⁸a–s⁸t4.
    Title in red and black, with vignette.

  NN 0017751   CtY-L

NAPLES, (Kingdom) Laws, statutes, etc.
Constitvtiones regni vtriusqve Siciliae,
glossis ordinariis, commentariisque Andreae de
Isernia, ac Bartholomaei Capuani,etc. illustratae. Omnia à Gabriele Sarayna, elaborata, auct₁
atque emendata. Lugduni, sumptibus Joannis
Andreae de Bottis, 1559.

f°. pp. (52), 532 (127)
With manuscript marginal notes.

  NN 0017752   MH

D0861   NAPLES (Kingdom) Laws, statutes, etc.
.2   Constitvtiones Regni vtrivsqve Siciliae,
.W21   glossis ordinariis, commentariisque excellentis.
Rare Bk I.V.D. Domini Andreae de Isernia, ac D. Bar-
         tholomaei Capuani, atque nonnullorum cũm vete-
         rum, tũm recentiorum I.C. lucubrationibus illus-
         tratae. Quibus accesserunt capitula eiusdem
         Regni, ritus Magnae Curiae Vicariae, plurimorum
         Iurisperitorum interpretationibud nunc primũm
         exornatae. Omnia à D. Gabriele Sarayna I.C.
         Veronensi summo studio elaborata, aucta, atque

         emendata. Additio etiam memorabilium rerum
         Indice copiosissimo ab eodem D. Gabriele nunc
         primũm in lucem emisso. ₁Paris? priuilege 1559₁
         ₁44, 460 ₁62₁ p.
         Title vignette.
         Copy imperfect: t.p. repaired, lacks imprint.
         I. Sicily. Laws, statutes, etc. II. Ysernia,
         Andreas de. III. Capua, Bartolommeo de, fl.
         1300. IV.   Saraina, Gabriello.
         fl. 1560-1590.

  NN 0017754   ICU

Continued in next column

VOLUME 405

Naples (Kingdom) Laws, statutes, etc.
  Compilations.
  Constitvtiones Regni vtrivsqve Siciliae,
glossis ordinariis, commentariisque ...
Andreae de Isernia, ac d. Bartholomaei de
Capua, atque nonnullorum cùm veterum, tum
recentiorum i.c lucubrationibus illustratae. Quibus accesserunt capitvla eiusdem
regni, ritvs Magnae curiae vicariae ...
Omnia à d. Gabriele Sarayna ... summo
studio elaborata, aucta, atque emendata ...

  Lvgdvni, apud haeredes Iacobi Iuntae,
1560.
    26 p.l., 532, ₍127₎ p. 31½cm.
    Title vignette (coat of arms)

NN   0017756   MH-L

Naples (*Kingdom*) *Laws, statutes, etc.*
  Constitvtiones Regni vtrivsqve Siciliæ; glossis ordinariis,
commentarifsque excellentiss. i. v. d. Domini Andreæ de
Isernia, ac D. Bartholomæi Capuani, atque nonnullorum cùm
veterum, tùm recentiorum i. c. lucubrationibus illustratæ.
Quibus accesserunt capitvla eiusdem regni, ritvs Magnæ
Curiæ vicariæ, plurimorum iurisperitorum interpretationibus nunc primùm exornatæ. Omnia à D. Gabriele Sarayna
i. c. Veronensi summo studio elaborata, aucta, atque emendata. Addito etiam memorabilium rerum indice copiosissimo

  ab eodem D. Gabriele nunc primùm in lucem emisso.
Lvgdvni, Apud hæredes I. Iunctae, 1568.
    460 p. 32 cm.

    I. Andrea d'Isernia, 1220 (ca.)–1316. II. Bartolomeo da Capua,
1248–1328. III. Saraina, Gabriello, fl. 1560–1590. IV. Title.
                                                   65-58572

NN   0017758   DLC MiU-L CtY

Naples (*Kingdom*) *Laws, statutes, etc.*
  Constitvtiones Regni vtrivsqve Siciliæ, glossis ordinarijs,
commentarijsque excellentiss. i. v. d. Domini Andreæ de
Yzernia, ac D. Bartholomęi Capuani, atque nonnullorum cùm
ueterum, tum recentiorum i. c. lucubrationibus illustratæ: et
maximè studio, & opera prestantissimi iurisconsulti D.
Gabrielis Saraynę Veronensis auctæ, atque locupletatæ,
Quibus accesserunt capitvla eiusdem regni, ritvs Magnæ
curiæ, vicariæ, & pragmaticæ, tam antiquæ, quàm nouæ, ac
etiam nouissimæ, per S. C. M. editae: plurimorum iurisperi-

torum doctissimis, necnon acutissimis interpretationibus
exornatæ. Nunc postremò post omnes omnium aliorum editiones, summa cum diligentia excussæ, atq₃ ad primam suam
integritatem in vsum studiosorum redactæ. Addito etiam ab
eodem Domino Gabriele, tam rerum, quàm vocabulorum
indice copiosissimo. Venetiis, 1580.
    26 p. l., 532, ₍127₎ p. 31½ cm.
    Title vignette.
    I. Sicily. Laws, statutes, etc. II. Andrea d'Isernia, 1220 (ca.)–1316.
III. Bartolomeo da Capua, 1248–1328. IV. Saraina, Gabriello, fl. 1560–
1590. V. Title.
                                                   22—9154

NN   0017760   DLC NbU CU CtY

Film   Naples (Kingdom) Laws,statutes,etc.
1014   Constitvtiones Regni vtrivsqve Siciliae,glossis
        ordinarijs,commentarijsque excellentiss.i.v.d.Do-
        mini Andrgae de Yzernia,ac d.Bartholomaei Capuani,
        atque nonnullorum cùm ueterum,tum recentiorum i.c.
        lucubrationibus illustratae: et maximè studio,&
        opera prestantissimi iurisconsulti d.Gabrielis
        Saraynę Veronensis auctae,atque locupletatae. Qui-
        bus accesserunt capitvla eiusdem regni,ritvs Mag-
        nae curiae,vicariae,& pragmaticae,tam antiquae,
        quàm nouae,ac etiam nouissimae,per S.C.M.editae:
        plurimorum iurispen-   ritorum doctissimis necnon

        acutissimis interpretationibus exornatae. Nunc
        postremò post omnes omnium aliorum editiones,
        summa cum diligentia excussae,atq₃ ad primam
        suam integritatem in vsum studiosorum redactae.
        Addito etiam ab eodem Domino Gabriele,tam rerum,
        quàm vocabulorum indice copiosissimo. Vcnetiis,
        1580.
          26 p. l.,532 ₍127₎ p. 32 cm.
          Title vignette.

        Continued in next column

Continued from preceding column

  Microfilm (negative) of original at Library
of Congress. Washington,D.C., U.S. Library of
Congress,Photoduplication Service, 1966.

    I.Sicily. Laws,statutes,etc. II.Ysernia,
Andreas de. III.Capua,Bartolommeo de,fl.1300.
IV.Saraina,Gabriello,fl.1560.

NN   0017763   NSyU

Law
  Naples (*Kingdom*) *Laws,statutes,etc.*
    Constitvtiones regvm regni vtrivsqve Sici-
liae mandante Friderico II.imperatore per Petrvm de Vinea...novissima hac editione svmma
cvra recognitae,et innvmeris prope,qvibvs antea scatebant,erroribvs,omnino pvrgatae ad fidem antiqvissimi palatini codicis cvm graeca
earvmdem versione e regione latini textvs ad-
posita qvibvs nvnc primvm accedvnt assisiae
regvm regni Siciliae et fragmentvm qvod svper-
est regesti eivsdem imperatoris ann.1239.&
1240. Neapoli,ex Regia Typographia,1786.

          tiones regvm...1786.
    xxiv,459 p. 37 cm.
    Title in red and black.
    Latin and Greek in parallel columns.

    1.Law-Naples(Kingdom). I.Pier delle Vigne,
1190?-1249. II.Title.

NN   0017765   DLC MdBP MH

JN5287   Naples (Kingdom) Laws, statutes, etc.
A3   Constitvtiones Regvm Regni vtrivsqve Siciliae,
1786   mandante Friderico II, Imperatore per Petrvm de
Case   Vinea capvanvm praetorio praefectvm, et
B   cancellarivm concinnatae, novissima hac
          editione svmma cvra recognitae, et innvmeris
          prope, qvibvs antea scatebant, erroribvs,
          omnino pvrgatae. Ad fidem antiqvissimi Palatini
          codicis cvm graeca earvmdem versione e regione
          latini textvs adposita quibvs nvnc primvm
          accedvnt assisiae Regvm Regni Siciliae et
          fragmentvm qvod svperest regesti eivsdem
          imperatoris, ann. 1239. & 1240.   Neapoli,
          ex Regia typographia. MDCCLXXXVI.
          4 p.ℓ., v-xxiv,   159 p. 41cm.

          Title vignette.
          Signatures: a-o⁴,d²,A-Z⁴,Aa-Zz⁴, Aaa-Lll⁴,
      Mmm².
          Contents. - Constitvtiones Regni Siciliae. -
          Assisiae Regvm Regni Siciliae. - Regestvm im-
          peratoris Frederici II. annor. 1239, & 1240. -
          In constitvtionvm Regni Siciliae codicem variae
          lectiones.

NN   0017767   CU NNC IU

JN   Naples (Kingdom) Laws,statutes,etc.
5286   Constitvtiones Regvm,Regni vtrivsqve Siciliae
A5   mandante Friderico II.Imperator per Petrvm de
         Vinea concinnatae,novissima hac editione svmma
         cvra recognitae,et innvmeris prope,qvibvs antea
         scatebant,erroribvs,omnino pvrgatae ad fidem
         antiqvissimi palatini codicis,cvm Graeca earvrden
         versione e regione Latini textvs adposita qvibvs
         nvnc primvm accedvnt assisiae Regvm Regni Siciliae
         et fragmentvm qvod svperest regesti eivsdem
         imperatoris ann.1239.& 1240. Neapoli, Ex Regia
         Typographia,1786.
           459 p.
           Photocopy.

NN   0017768   NSyU

Naples (*Kingdom*) *Laws, statutes, etc.*
  Constitutionum regni Siciliarum libri III. cum commentariis
veterum jurisconsultorum. Accedit nunc primum Dominici
Alfeni Varii j. c. Commentarius ad Friderici II ... constitu-
tionem De rebus non alienandis ecclesiis. Editio absolutissima.
Neapoli, sumptibus Antonii Cervonii, 1773.
    xl, 560 p. 38½ᵐ.
    Major part of annotations contributed by Andreas de Isernia.

    I. Sicily. Laws, statutes, etc. II. Andrea d'Isernia, 1220 (ca.)–1316.
III. Vario, Domenico Alfeno, 1729–ca. 1794.
                                                   47–36283

NN   0017769   DLC CU PU NSyU NN

---

*K   Naples (Kingdom) Laws, statutes, etc.
25   Constitutionum regni Siciliarum libri III. cum
N16c   commentariis veterum jurisconsultorum. Accedit
1773   nunc primum Dominici Alfeni Varii j. c. comment
        arius ad Friderici II. ... constitutionem de
        rebus non alienandis ecclesiis.   Neapoli,
        sumptibus Antonii Cervonii, 1773.
          2 v.

          Major part of annotations contributed by
        Andreas de Isernia.
          Vol. 2 has title: Capitula regni utriusque

        Siciliae, ritus magnae curiae vicariae et
        pragmaticae, doctissimis Andreae de Isernia,
        Bartholomaei de Capua, & aliorum illustrium
        jurisconsultorum commentariis illustrata ...

          I. Sicily. Laws, statutes. II. Andrea
        d'Isernia, 1220 (ca.)-1316. III. Vario,
        Domenico Alfeno, 1729-ca.1794. IV. Title.
        V. Title: Capitul   a regni utriusque Siciliae.

NN   0017771   CLU PPB CU

Law
  Naples(*Kingdom*) *Laws,statutes,etc.*
    Consve/tvdines Neapoli/tanae cvm glosa
Napodani. Nvnc primvm avthore Camillo Salerno additionibvs ill.ivrisconsvltorvm qvos ver-
sa pagina indicabis,necnon et svis avctae
correctae & multifariam illustratae. Neapoli,
apud Ioannem de Boy,1567.
    ₍20₎,296,₍2₎ p. 30 cm.
    Title vignette(coat of arms);head and tail
pieces;initials.
    1.Law-Naples(Kingdom). I.Salernus,Camillus.
II.Title.

NN   0017772   DLC NN

K   Naples (Kingdom) Laws, statutes, etc.
5488   Consuetudines Neapolitanae cum glosa Napodani.
N3   Nunc primum authore Camillo Salerno additionibus
1567   ill. iurisconsultorum ... necon et suis auctae,
Cage   correctae & multifariam illustrate ... Neapoli,
        Apud Ioannem de Boy, 1567.

          ₍40₎ 396 ₍4₎ p. +⁴, a², ₍2d₃a⁶, b⁸, A², B⁴,
        C-F⁶, G⁴, ₍2d₃G-K⁶, L⁸, M-2I⁶, 2K⁸. Fo.

NN   0017773   DFo NN

4K   Naples (*Kingdom*) Laws, statutes, etc.
1199   Consuetudines neapolitanae, cum
        glossa Napodani, primum a Camillo
        Salerno suis, &c quamplurium ill.
        JCC. in frequenti epistola descrip-
        torum additionibus auctae ... denique
        a Carolo de Rosa ... [et al.] cum
        indice locupletissimo, materiarum,
        titulorum ac consuetudinum & para-
        graphorum, nec non glossarum. Nea-
        poli, A. Cervonii, 1775.
          2 v.

NN   0017774   DLC-P4 MH

Naples (Kingdom) Laws, statutes, etc.
  Consvetvdines Neapolitane cvm glosis excel-
lentissimi Do. Neapolitani Neapolitani. Vna cum decisionibus sacri regii consilii, regie camere svmarie, ac magne curie vi-
carie: necnon excellentum V.I.D. Do. Antonii
de Alexandro, Do. Mattei de Afflicto, & aliorum. Consilia insuper Do. Diomedis Mariconde,
Do. Mattei de Afflicto, & Do. Antonini de
Vivaia: cum additionibus iuris cõmunis, ac.
V.I.D. Do. Scipionis Ianuarii Neap. ...

  Neapoli, Apud Ioannem Paulum Suganappum in
platea Armeriorum, 1546.
    28 p. l., 117, ₍1₎ l. 32cm.

    Title vignette (coat of arms)
    Text in parallel columns.

NN   0017776   NNC

VOLUME 405

Naples (*Kingdom*) *Laws, statutes, etc.*
Consvetvdines neapolitanae, vna cvm novis additioni-
bvs Felicis de Rubeis, Vincentij de Franchis, Iacobi
Anelli de Bottis, regiorum consiliariorum Regni neapoli-
tani, atque Thomæ Nauclerij ... Additiones vero DD.
Vincentii, et Jacobi Anelli de Bottis, sunt præter eas
aliàs Neapoli impressas ... Venetiis, apud Petrum Dusi-
nellum, sumptibus Nicolai de Bottis, 1588.
22 p. l., 12, 396 p., 24 numb. l. 29ᶜᵐ.
Title vignette.
I. Rubeis, Felix de, bp., d. 1568. II. Franchi, Vincenzo de', 1530?-1601.
III. Botti, Jacopo Anello de', fl. 1580. IV. Nauclerus, Thomas, fl. 1580. V.
Title.
21-20494

NN 0017777   DLC CU MH

Law
Naples (Kingdom) Laws, statutes, etc.
Salerno. *Ordinances, etc.*
Le consuetudini inedite di Salerno. Studio
storico-giuridico(con documenti inediti)per
Giovanni Abignente, professore pareggiato di
storia....Roma, Tipografia Vaticana, 1888.

Law
Naples (Kingdom) Laws, statutes, etc.
Patrizi, Stefano, *d.* 1797.
...Consultationes sacri, et regii juris.
Neapoli, ex Typographia Francisci Morelli,
1770.

DG
403
C76
v.159
Naples (Kingdom). Laws, statutes, etc.
Copia del decreto que el excelentissimo Señor Conde de Oñate
y Villamediana Virrey, Lugartheniente, y Capitan General de este
reyno, a mandado hazer sobre el repartimiento de las imposiciones,
que an quedado despues de las gracias concedidas por el serenissimo
señor D. Ivan de Avstria. Napoles, Egidio Longo [1648]
[7] p. [Consilia/statuti collection, v.159]

1. Taxation - Naples (Kingdom). I. Oñate y Villamediana,
Iñigo Vélez de Guevara Tasis, conde de, 1597-1658. I. Title.
III. Series.

NN 0017780   CLU

Naples (Kingdom) Laws, statutes, etc.
Corso completo di dritto amministrativo
see under   Dias, Francesco.

Naples (Kingdom) Laws, statutes, etc.
Del real ordine militare di S.Giorgio della
riunione. Legge istitutiva...e decreto che
abolisce l'ordine delle Due Sicilie. Napoli,
1855.
4°. 4 pl.   Ital 3820.20

NN 0017782   MH

4K
950
Naples (Kingdom) Laws, statutes, etc.
Dell'enfiteusi, comento al tit. IX
L. III della I. parte del codice per
lo Regno delle due Sicilie, scritto
dall'avv. Salv. Jannelli. Palermo,
Stamperia di F. Lao, 1845.
439 p.
I Jannelli, Salvatore, ed.

NN 0017783   DLC-P4

Naples (Kingdom) Laws, statutes, etc.
Alianelli, Niccola.
Delle antiche consuetudini e leggi marittime delle provincie napolitane; notizie e monumenti pubblicati per cura
di Niccola Alianelli. Napoli, Fratelli de Angelis, 1871.

Law
Naples (Kingdom). Laws, statutes, etc.
Lombardi, Luigi, fl. 1883-1885.
Delle origini e delle vicende degli usi civici nelle provincie
napolitane, studio storico-legale. Con 3 appendici: Della
Sila di Calabria; Il Tavoliere di Puglia; Leggi, decreti e
istruzioni relative ai demanii com., feud., eccl., alla Sila e al
Tavoliere. 2. ed. ampliata e migliorata. Napoli, E. An-
fossi, 1885.

Naples (Kingdom) Laws, statutes, etc.
Entwurf eines straf-gesetzbuchs für die
Schweizer-regimenter im dienste Seiner Aller-
christlichsten Majestät
see   Naples (Kingdom) Ministerio della
guerra.

Law
Naples (Kingdom) Laws, statutes, etc.
Priaroggia, Giovanni Ambrosio, *b.*1644.
...Fasciculus florum ultimarum voluntatum
theorice, et practice ad usum publicorum no-
tariorum congestus locupletissimo indice re-
rum memorie dignarum adnexo. Panormi, ex
Typographia Joannis-Baptistae Aiccardo, 1707.

V589
.55
Naples (Kingdom) Laws, statutes, etc.
...Ferdinando II. per la grazia di Dio re del'
regno delle due Sicilie. ...
[Caserta, 1843]

NN 0017788   DLC

Naples (Kingdom) Laws, statutes, etc.
Formolario ossia istruzioni teorico-pratiche
sulla legge della navigazione di commercio dei
25 febbraio 1826 per lo Regno delle Due Sicilie...
see under   Arancio, Francesco.

Law
Naples (Kingdom) Laws, statutes, etc.
Thomae Grammatici...in constitvtionibvs, ca-
pitvlis, et pragmaticis regni Neap. et ritibvs
Magnae curiae vicariae additiones, & apostil-
lae, quas tum ipse lucubrarat, tum ex aliquot
ueterum, & modernorum iurisconsultorum uigiliis
uiuens congesserat. Accesserunt etiam aliquae
utillimae, et pulchrae questiones...Bartholo-
maei de Capua, et amplissimus totius uoluminis
index. Nvnc primvm in lvcem aeditae. Venetiis,
1562.
1 p.l.,[3],173,[17] l.   32 cm.

Colophon:...apud Ioannem Variscum, expensis
Baptistae de Christophoro Bibliopolae Parthe-
nopei...
Title vignette(printer's device);initials.
In double columns.
1.Law-Naples(Kingdom). I.Grammatico, Tommaso,1473-1556. II.Capua, Bartolommeo de, fl.
1300. III.Naples(Kingdom) Tribunale della
gran corte della vicaria. IV.Title.

NN 0017791   DLC ICU

Beinecke
Library
P70
Af27
+556
Naples (Kingdom) Laws, statutes, etc.
Matthæi de Afflictis ... In vtrivsqve
Siciliae, Neapolisqve sanctiones, et con-
stitvtiones, novissima praelectio. Inter-
iecta sunt Io. Anto. Batij erudita adno-
tamenta. Lvgdvni,1556.
302,222numb.l.,47l.   33cm.
Signatures: a-oo⁸pp⁶A-DD⁸EE⁶AAA-FFF⁸
(FFF₈ [blank?] wanting)

NN 0017792   CtY

Law
Naples(Kingdom) Laws,statutes,etc.
Matthaei de Afflictis...in vtrivsqve Siciliae,Neapolisq.sanctiones,et constitvtiones
novissima praelectio. Prima pars super primum
[secvnda pars super secundum & tertium]librum.
Interiecta sunt Ioannis Antonij Batij,et aliorum erudita adnotamenta. Venetiis,1562.
2 v. 33 cm.
Title vignette;initials.
1.Law-Naples(Kingdom). I.Afflito,Matteo d',
1443(ca)-1523. II.Title.

NN 0017793   DLC MH-L

Law
Naples (Kingdom) Laws,statutes,etc.
Matthaei de Afflictis...in vtrivsq.Siciliae,
Neapolisq.sanctiones,& constitutions nouissima praelectio. Interiecta svnt Ioan.Antonii
Batii,& aliorum erudita annotamenta. Hac postrema editione a mvltis quibus scatebat erroribus,repurgata. Prima commentarii pars in primvm[secvnda commentarii pars in secvndvm &
tertium]earundem constitutionum librum.Summis,
atque indice locupletissimo illustra.ta. Venetiis,apud Ioannem Variscum & Socios,1580.

2 v. in 1 37 cm.
Title vignette;head and tail pieces;ini-
tials.
1.Law-Naples(Kingdom) Laws,statutes,etc.
I.Afflito,Matteo d',1443(ca)-1523. II.Title.

NN 0017795   DLC OU

Law
Naples (Kingdom) Laws,statutes,etc.
Matthaei de Afflictis...in vtrivsq.Siciliae,
Neapolisq. sanctiones,& constitutions nouis-
sima praelectio.Interiecta svnt Ioan.Antonii
Batii,& aliorum erudita annotamenta. Hac post-
rema editione a mvltis quibus scatebat erro-
ribus,repurgata.Prima commentarii pars in pri-
mvm[secvnda commentarii pars in secvndvm &
tertium]earundem constitutionum librum. Sum-
mis,atque indice locupletissimo illustrata.
Venetiis,apud Ioan.Variscum,& Paganinum de
Paganinis,1588.
Library of Congress

2 v. in 1. 38 cm.
Title vignette(publisher's device);head
pieces;initials.
In double columns.
1.Law-Naples(Kingdom). I.Afflito,Matteo d',
1443(ca)-1523. II. Title: ...in vtrivsq.Sici-
liae,Neapolisq.sanctiones & constitutions.

NN 0017797   DLC

x262.9
C28t
Naples (Kingdom)--Laws, statutes, etc.
Istruzioni, che si danno alle università
del regno per la formazione de'catasti.
eNapoli, S. Porsile, regio stampatore, 1741,
xxxi, xii, e7,p. 29cm.
Bound with Catholic Church. Treaties, etc.,
1740-1759 (Benedict XIV) Trattato di accomodamento tra S. Sede, e la corte di Napoli.
eNapoli, 1741,
Two broadsides dated Aug.14 and 23, 1741
dealing with the "Catasti" for universities of
the kingdom of Naples prefixed.

NN 0017798   IU

VOLUME 405

Naples (Kingdom) Laws, statutes, etc.
Legge concernente l'abolizione della tratta
de' negri. Napoli, Stamperia reale, 1839.

31 p. 28 cm.

French and Italian texts in parallel columns.

Acquiescence of the Kingdom of Naples to
British-French agreements concerning the
slave-trade.
1.Slave-trade.   I.Title.

NN   0017799   MnU

HE587   Naples (Kingdom) Laws, statutes, etc.
N15A5   Legge di navigazione di commercio de' 25 di
          febbrajo 1826.
          Napoli, 1826.

NN   0017800   DLC

Naples (Kingdom) Laws, statutes, etc.
Legge organica dell'ordine giudiziario pe'
reali dominj oltre il Faro.   Napoli, Dalla real
tip. del Ministero di stato della cancelleria
generale, 1819.
(2) 47,(2)p. sm. 4°.

NN   0017801   MH

NAPLES (KINGDOM) - Laws,statutes,etc.
Legge organica dell'ordine giudiziario e
tariffa delle spese giudiziarie nelle materie
civili e criminali pel regno delle Due Sicilie.
[Napoli],D.Capasso,1849.

NN   0017802   MH

Naples (*Kingdom*) *Laws, statutes, etc.*
Le leggi civili per lo regno delle Due Sicilie, ravvicinate
nelle loro disposizioni e con quelle contenute nelle altre parti
del Codice ed esposte con le discussioni e col dritto contro-
verso, dall'avvocato Giuseppe Miraglia. 2. ed. Napoli, Stab.
tip. all'insegna dell'ancora, 1846-52.

2 v. 27 cm.

1. Civil law—Naples (Kingdom)   I. Miraglia, Giuseppe, 1816-
1900, ed.
                                            48-38407*

NN   0017803   DLC MH-L

Naples (Kingdom) Laws, statutes, etc.
Leggi preservati stabilite
see under title

Naples (Kingdom) Laws, statutes, etc.
La legislazione angioina
see under Trifone, Romualdo, 1897-

Naples (*Kingdom*) *Laws, statutes, etc.*
Legislazione positiva degli archivii del regno, contenente la
Legge organica dei 12 novembre 1818 e gli annessi regolamenti,
insieme con tutti i consecutivi reali decreti, rescritti e mini-
steriali riguardanti gli archivii, raccolte dal marchese Angelo
Granito ... soprantendente generale degli archivii del regno.
Preceduta da un discorso del medesimo intorno agli archivii.
Napoli, Tip. di F. Raimondi, 1855.
6 p.l., 490 p. fold. plan. 24 cm.
"Atti riguardanti lo stabilimento del Grande archivio del regno nel
già Napoletano del ss. Severino e Sossio": p. [121,-151.
1. Naples. Archivio di stato. 2. Archives—Naples (Kingdom)
I. Granito, Angelo, marchese di Castellabate, 1782-1861, ed.

CD1605.A5   1855   47-41492

NN   0017806   DLC NN MH

Naples (Kingdom) Laws, statutes, etc

Legislazione positiva del regno delle Due
Sicilie dal 1806 a tutto il 1840 esposta meto-
dicamente in tanti parziali trattate per quanti
sono i diversi rami della pubblica amministrazione,comprendovi tutte le leggi...classifica-
ti secondo il piano del cavaliere de Tòmasis.
Napoli,1841-45.

9 vols.
Same. Dal 1841 a tutto il 1845. Napoli,
1845.

NN   0017807   MH-L

Naples (*Kingdom*) *Laws, statutes, etc.*
Lois de la procédure criminelle et lois pénales du royaume
des Deux-Siciles, tr. par M. Victor Foucher ... précédées d'un
Aperçu sur l'organisation et la compétence de l'ordre judiciaire
de ce royaume, par le même. Rennes, Chez Blin; [etc., etc.]
1836.

xl, 476 p. 21ᶜᵐ. (*Half-title:* Collection des lois civiles et criminelles
des états modernes. 4. livr.)

I. Foucher, Victor, 1802-1866, tr. II. Title.

7—1392

NN   0017808   DLC NN MH

Naples (Kingdom) Laws, statutes, etc.

Byzantine empire. *Laws, statutes, etc.*
A manual of later Roman law, the Ecloga ad Procheiron
mutata founded upon the Ecloga of Leo III and Constantine v
of Isauria, and on the Procheiros nomos of Basil I, of Macedonia, including the Rhodian maritime law edited in 1166
A. D., rendered into English by Edwin Hanson Freshfield, M. A.
Cambridge, Printed at the University press, 1927.

Naples (Kingdom) Laws, statutes, etc.
Manuale di dritto civile, ossia Comentario sul
codice civile contenente la spiegazione isolata di
ciascun articolo...
see under Boileux, Jacques Marie, 1803-
1872.

Naples (*Kingdom*) *Laws, statutes, etc.*
Manuale militare o sia collezione di leggi e regolamenti
per le truppe di S. M. il re delle Due Sicilie, redatte dal
c. F. L. Napoli, A. Garruccio, 1812.

4 v. forms. 21 cm.
CONTENTS.—t. 1. Parte giudiziaria.—t. 2. Disciplina de' corpi.—
t. 3-4. Parte amministrativa.

1. Military law—Naples (Kingdom)   I. L., F. II. F. L. III. Title.
                                            50-54529

NN   0017811   DLC

Naples (Kingdom) Laws, statutes, etc.

Brilla, Vincenzo.
Nomothecivm parthenopœvm, sive Ivris neapolitani prompt-
varivm, in qvo perpetuo commentario ad Consuetudines ciui-
tatis Neapolis adhibito, omnes ferè quæstiones ad eandem rem
pertinentes enodantur, & illustrantur, cvm ... consuetudinario
textu. Avthore Vincentio Brilla ... Neapoli, ex typographia
Francisci Molli, 1679.

Naples(Kingdom) Laws, statutes, etc.
Nuova collezione delle prammatiche del regno di
Napoli. Napoli, 1803-08.
15 v.

NN   0017813   MH-L

Law   Naples (*Kingdom*) **Laws,statutes,etc.**
Andreae Provenzalis...observationes, et
glosemmata as consvetvdines neapolitanas, et
Napodani, ac coeterorum, qui in interpretan-
dis consvetvdinibus floruerunt, loca lustran-
da, quae hactenus latuerunt in tenebris,opvs
tam dicentibus, quam petentibus ius apprime
necessarium, diu expetitum, et nunc noviter
excussum. Posthvmvm dvplici indice, argvmen-
torvm altero, altero rerum notabilium exor-
natum, & auctum. Neapoli, typis Iacobi Gaffa-

ri, expensis Io: Dominici Bove, 1646.
6 p.l., 291, [36] p. 32 cm.
Title in red and black; head pieces; initials.

1.Law-Naples (Kingdom). √I.Provenzale, Andrea, d. 1646. II.Title.

NN   0017815   DLC

UA
748   Naples (Kingdom) Laws,statutes,etc.
.N23   Ordinanza del re delle Sicilie che servir
A4   de e d'istruzione,e di regolamento a'cadetti,
        sottobrigadieri,brigadieri,ed uffiziali del
        Battaglione Real Ferdinando formato per alto
        real comando. In Napoli, Nella Regia stam-
        peria, 1772.
        [8],235,[5],xxiii p. 21 cm.
        Signed at end: Antonio del Rio.
        Armorial bookplates: Ex libris Marchionis
        Salsae; anonymous,with motto: Comme je fus
        [Viscount Dudley and Ward?]
        1.Naples (Kingdom) Escrito. Battaglione
Real Ferdin-   ando. I.Ferdinando I,
King of the   Two Sicilies,1751-1825
II.Rio,An-   tonio del.

NN   0017816   MiU

Naples (Kingdom) Laws, statutes,etc.
Ordinanza della amministrazione militare
del regno delle due Sicilie. Napoli, dalla reale
tipog. della guerra, 1824.
xviii, 379 p. fol.

NN   0017817   DNLM

DG
403   Naples (Kingdom). Laws, statutes, etc.
C76   Ordinanza di sua maestà pel governo, il
v.272   servizio e la disciplina delle reali truppe
        nelle piazze. Napoli, Dalla Reale Tipografia
        della Guerra, 1831.
        383,xlvii p. [Consilia/statuti collection,
        v. 272]

        1. Military law - Naples (Kingdom).
        I. Title. II. Series.

NN   0017818   CLU

Naples (Kingdom) Laws, statutes, etc.
Ordinanza di sua maestà pel servizio delle
piazze de' suoi reali dominj. Napoli, Nella
stamperia reale, 1788.
Microfilm copy, made in 1967, of the original in Vatican. Biblioteca vaticana. Positive.
Negative film in Vatican. Biblioteca
vaticana.

Collation of the original, as determined
from the film: xx, 286 p. forms.

I. Title. (Series: [Manuscripta, microfilms of rare and out-of-print books. List
69, no. 10])

NN   0017820   MoSU

VOLUME 405

355.45
Itl44
Naples(Kingdom) Laws, statutes, etc.
Ordinanza di sua maestà per gli esercizj e
le evoluzioni delle truppe di fanteria. Napoli,
Dalla reale tipografia militare, 1846-1852.
3 v. fold maps, plans, diagrs., music.

1. Italy. Esercito. Fanteria. 2. Italy -
History - 1815-1870. 3. Italy - Politics and
government - 1815-1870.

NN 0017821 NNC

Law

Naples (Kingdom) Laws,statutes,etc.
Ordinanza di Sua Maesta per l'esercizio,
e per le manovre delle sue truppe di fanteria. Napoli,nella Stamperia Reale,1788.
160p.(incl.cover) 2 fold. 22 cm.
Title vignette(coat of arms of Naples).
Side-notes.
Plates drawn by Gius.Guerra.
1.Military law-Naples(Kingdom). I.Title.

NN 0017822 DLC

4K Naples (Kingdom) Laws, statutes, etc.
9929 Ordinanza di Sua Maestà sulla
giurisdizion militare, e sopra
delitti, e le pene della gente di
guerra. Napoli, Stamperia regale,
1789.
271, 63 p

NN 0017823 DLC-P4 CLL

Naples (*Kingdom*) *Laws, statutes, etc.*
Ordinanze generali della real Marina del regno delle Due
Sicilie ... Napoli, Dalla stamperia della Reale accademia
di marina, 1818.
3 v. tables (part fold.) 28½ cm.
Each vol. has title vignette and head-piece.
CONTENTS.—v. 1-2. Servizio di terra. Dal titolo I. al XVIII. ed
ultimo.—v. 3. Servizio di mare.

1. Naples (Kingdom) Marina.
VB629.N3A5 1818 7-11809

NN 0017824 DLC

Naples (*Kingdom*) *Laws, statutes, etc.*
Ordinanze generali della real marina del regno delle Due
Sicilie del 1818. 2. ed. ... Napoli, Reale tipografia mili-
tare, 1856.
3 v. tables (partly fold.) 23cm.
CONTENTS.—v. 1-2. Servizio di terra. Dal titolo I. al XVIII. ed ultimo.—
v. 3. Servizio di mare.
— Modelli che accompagnano ... le Ordinanze generali della real marina del regno delle Due Sicilie. Napoli,
Reale tipografia militare, 1856
151, (1) p. 29cm.
CONTENTS.—Modelli che accompagnano il titolo IV. del vol. I. pte. I.—
Modelli che accompagnano il titolo VI.-VII. del vol. I. pte. I.—Modelli che
accompagnano il titolo XIV. del vol. II. pte. I.—Tariffe della real marina
del regno delle Due Sicilie.
1. Naval law—Naples (Kingdom) 2. Tariff—Naples (Kingdom)
Library of Congress VB629.N3 1856
7-11810-1

NN 0017825 DLC

DG Naples(Kingdom). Laws, statutes, etc.
403 Ordini, et instruttioni generali, e particolari, da osseruarsi
C76 tanto per li delegati, quanto per li gouernatori, da deputarsi per
v.138 il buon gouerno delli arrendamenti, delle gabelle, delle nuoue
imposizioni, e delli officij tolti, e non tolti, quali si danno in-
solutum, & pro soluto delli consignatarij d'essi. Date, & ordinate
per l'Illustrissimo, & eccellentissimo signore conte d'Ognatte, e
di Villamediana, vicerè, luogotenente, e capitan generale in
questo regno, col voto, e parere del Regio Collateral Consiglio.
Napoli, Egidio Longo [1649]
[21] p. [Consilia/statuti collection, v.138]
1. Taxation - Naples (Kingdom). I. Oñate y Villamediana,
Iñigo Vélez de Guevara Tasis, conde de, 1597-1658. II. Title.
III. Series.

NN 0017826 CLU

DG Naples (Kingdom). Laws, statutes, etc.
403 Philippvs dei gratia rex, &c. Napoli, R.
C76 Mollo, 1648.
v.148 [3] p. [Consilia/statuti collection, v. 148]

Begins: D. Giovanne d'Avstria Gran Prior di
Castiglia, e di Leone, Governatore Generale di
tvtte l'armi maritime de S. M....

1. Taxation - Naples (Kingdom). I. Series.

NN 0017827 CLU

Law

Naples (Kingdom) Laws,statutes,etc.
Placita principvm sev constitvtiones regni
Neapolitani cvm glossis. Constitvtiones regni
Neapolitani cum glossis dominorum Sebastiani
Neapodani, Marini de Caramanico, Bartholomaei
de Capua, & Lucae de Penna, cum additionibus
& apostilis Nicolai Superantij...cum notulis
suis insertis, atq castigatione ipsa quam nobis exhibuit Neapolis, necnon duplici index
legum et rubricarum de nouo addito. [Lugduni],
1533.
8 p.l., 107, [1] l. 25 cm.

Colophon: Lugduni cuse a...Dionysio de Har-
sy.
On verso of last leaf printer's device of
Simon Vincent.

1.Law-Naples(Kingdom). I.Title.

NN 0017829 DLC NNC

Naples (Kingdom) Laws, statutes, etc.
... Placita principvm sev constitvtiones regni
neapolitani cvm glossis ... dominorum Sebastiani
Neapodani, Marini de Caramanico, Bartholomaei
de Capu, & Lucae de Penna ... [Lyons,
Dionysius de Harsy] 1534.
8 p.l., 107 numb. l., 1 l. 25.5 cm.
Signatures: ✚4, *4, a-z4, A-D4.
Title-page printed in red and black, with wood-
cut in center and woodcut border showing the
portraits of famous Neapolitan jurists; initials.
Colophon date: 1533.

Andrea d'Isernia's name though omitted from
the title of this edition was the foremost glossator
of these laws.
Device of Simon Vincentius on verso of last
leaf.
On verso of title-page is the permission given
to Antoine Vincent, publisher and bookseller at
Lyons to have the book printed and prohibiting
other printers from reprinting it within four
years. His request had been for six years.

NN 0017831 CtY

349.457 Naples (Kingdom)—Laws, statutes, etc.
N16c Placita principvm sev, Constitvtiones Regni
1534 Neapolitani cvm glossis. Constitvtiones Regni
Neapolitani cum glossis Sebastiani Neapoldani,
Marini de Caramanico, Bartholomæi de Capua, &
Lucæ de Penna, cum additionibus & apostellis
Nicolai Superantij, cum notulis suis locis
insertis, atq castigatione ipsa quam nobis
exhibuit Neapolis. Lugduni, Cuse a D. de
Harsy 1534.

Microfilm copy (negative) made in 1961 of
the original in the British Museum.
Collation of the original, as determined
from the film: 107l.
Most of the glosses are by Andrea d'Isernia.
The colophon is dated, 1533.

I. Andrea d'Isernia, 1220(ca.)-1316. II. Title.

NN 0017833 IU

Law Naples (Kingdom) Laws, statutes, etc.

Zerbi, Rocco.
La polizia amministrativa municipale del Regno delle
Due Sicilie. Napoli, Tip. dell'Urania, 1846.

Naples (Kingdom) Laws, statutes, etc.
Polizia ecclesiastica del regno delle Due
Sicilie
see under Giliberti, Vito.

Naples (Kingdom) Laws, statute, etc.
... Pragmatica circa il ius prohibendi del tobacco. Napoli, nella regia stampa di Egidio Longo,1650:
[3] p.

NN 0017836 MH

Naples (*Kingdom*) *Laws, statutes, etc.*
Pragmaticæ, edicta, decreta, interdicta, regiæqve sanctiones
Regni neapolitani quæ olim viri consvltissimi collegervnt
svisqve titvlis tribvervnt Prosper Caravita ... Fabivs de Anna
... Alexander Rovitvs ... et al, Dominicvs Alfenvs Varivs
I. c. recensvit; omissaque a veteribus collectoribus ex auctoritate
veterum codicum restituit. Quaeue lata essent ab anno
cIↃIↃCCXVIII, ad hunc diem collegit, suisque titulis tribuit; aliis,
quae ab iis excederent, proprias rubricas posuit: eorumque ad
oram paginae epitomas, seu summaria adiecit: foedera addidit:
titulos omnes ad litterarum seriem disposuit: indices omnium

Pragmaticæ, edicta, decreta, interdicta, regiæqve sanctiones
Regni neapolitani quæ olim viri consvltissimi collegervnt
svisqve titvlis tribvervnt Prosper Caravita ... Fabivs de Anna
... Alexander Rovitvs ... et al, Dominicvs Alfenvs Varivs
I. c. recensvit; omissaque a veteribus collectoribus ex auctoritate
veterum codicum restituit. Quaeue lata essent ab anno
cIↃIↃCCXVIII, ad hunc diem collegit, suisque titulis tribuit; aliis,
quae ab iis excederent, proprias rubricas posuit: eorumque ad
oram paginae epitomas, seu summaria adiecit: foedera addidit:
titulos omnes ad litterarum seriem disposuit: indices omnium

legum, et rerum, ac verborum auxit ... Neapoli, svmptibvs
Antonii Cervonii, 1772.
4 v. 37½cm.

I. Vario, Domenico Alfeno, b. ca. 1725, ed. II. Caravita, Prospero, fl.
1550. III. Anna, Fabio de, 1555-1605. IV. Rovito, Alessandro.

45-32440

NN 0017838 DLC PU CLU

Law

Naples (Kingdom) Laws,statutes,etc.
Pragmaticae, edicta, decreta, regiae Q. sanctiones regni Neapolitani, nedum ab...Sci-
pione Rovito, tunc primario causarũ patreno...
editae, vervm etiam omnes aliae, quae prius
desiderabantur, et quae vsque adhuc fuerunt
promulgatae cum praetermiss. vsque ad diem
XXIJ Iunij MDCXXXIII. Per...Alexandrvm Rovi-
tvm...otio inopino congestae, & sub rubricis
collocatae. Accessit rvbetvm legale totivs
regni, seu index omnium paenarum a constitu-

tionibus, capitulis, et pragmaticis regni in-
flictarum. Cvm qvatvor argvmentis, rubricarum,
pragmaticarum tam secundum initia, quam ex
temporis serie, & rerum satis abundantibus vsque affatim. Neapoli, ex Typographia Aegidij
Longhi, 1623.
40 p.l., 816 p. 34 cm.
Added t.p. : "Rvbetvm legale totivs regni"
1.Law-Naples(Kingdom). I.Rovito, Scipione.
1556-1636. II.Title. III.Title:Rvbetvm legale.

NN 0017840 DLC

Naples (Kingdom) Laws, statutes, etc.
... Pragmaticae recentes Caroli Siciliae
regis Romanorvmqve imperator ... [Neapoli,
per Antonium de Frizis Corinalden., 1524]
2 p.l., cxxvii numb. l., [14] p. 28 cm.
Signatures: a-d6, e8, A-Q6, AA8.
Title and coat of arms of Spain within ornamental border, the lower edge of which consists
of two woodcuts; the left shows Italia driving
out the Gallic cock, the right the king of France
(Charles VIII) who had conquered Naples in 1435.
At head of title: Carolvs V.

Imperfect: 30 leaves (sig. A-E6) lacking.
Numerous errors in foliation, partly due to
the fact that foliation stops with folio xxx and
continues on what should be folio 66, but is
numbered xxxv. In a note on folio xxx verso the
reader is asked to correct the numbering in
manuscript.
This edition is apparently not listed in any
bibliography.

NN 0017842 CtY

VOLUME 405

Law
Naples (Kingdom) Laws, statutes, etc.
   Pragmaticarvm Regni Neapolis commentaria, a
diuersis sparsim hactenus excusa; nvper opera
solertia, et indvstria Scipionis Roviti. Nedum
in hoc vnum volumen, iuxta suas quasq; rubricas
congesta, sed eius additionibus satis concinne
illustrata: quibus accesserunt desideratissimae
ipsiusmet lucubrationes ad aliquot selectas
pragmaticas, quas septima pagina indicabit.Nunc
primum summa cum diligentia impressae...Vene-
tiis, sumptibus Andree Peregrini, & Ioan. Leonardi Cepollari, 1590.

   ticarvm Regni Neapolis...1590. (Card 2)
21 p.l., 170 l. 31 cm.

   1.Law-Naples(Kingdom). I.Rovito, Scipione,
1556-1636. II.Title.

NN 0017844   DLC

Naples (Kingdom) Laws, statutes, etc.
   Pragmatice regni nove et antiqve itervm
emendate additis mvltis qve in aliis privs
impressis deerant vt legentibvs patebit
m. d. xxxiii. [1533]
   29 fol. 4°

NN 0017845   MH-L

Naples (Kingdom). Laws, statutes, etc.
   Pragmatice regni nove et antiqve, cvm pragmaticis in-
victissimi Caroli Qvinti Imperatoris de novo additis. Neapoli, Apud I. P. Suggannappum, 1545.
   28 l. 32 cm.

   1. Law—Naples (Kingdom)   I. Title.

                                          73-200459

NN 0017846   DLC

Naples (Kingdom) Laws, statutes, etc.

   ... [Prammatica] hauendo sua maestà per
li bisogni, che vi sono di assistere alla
difesa di questo regno à fan che goda vna
continua, e buona pace, hauuto necessità
di pensare à qualche impositione, e sia
men graue à poueri, e con la quale possi
euitare di mettere qualche altra comanda,
con sua Real Cedula di 5 d'agosto 1639 che
si debbia all'esempio delli regni di Spagna
introdurre in questo nõ mõ fidele, è pronto

al seruitio della sua real corona l'impositione della carta sigillata ... [Napoli,
Egidio Longo, 1640]
   [8] p. 30cm.

   No title page; title taken from first
lines of text.

NN 0017848   MH-L

ITA/NAP Naples (Kingdom) Laws,statutes,etc.
202   [Prammatici e banni del regno di Napoli.
PRA   Naples, E. Longo, 1631-37]
   1 v. 30cm.

   Various pagings.
   The first item in this volume was printed by
G.T. di Stefano.

NN 0017849   MH-L

Law
       Naples (Kingdom) Laws, statutes, etc.

   Siciliani, Ferdinando.
      Pratica teorica penale del foro militare col complesso della
   legislazione imperante. Napoli, Tip. di P. Tuso, 1852-53.

Naples (Kingdom) Laws, statutes, etc.
   Privilegia fidelissimae civitatis Neapolis
      see under Naples. Charters.

Law   Naples (Kingdom) Laws, statutes, etc.

   Naples. Charters. Privilegii et capitoli con
altre gratie...

Law   Naples (Kingdom) Laws, statutes, etc.

   Naples. Charters. Priuilegij et capituli...
1543.

Naples (Kingdom) Laws, statutes, etc.
   Proclami e sanzioni della repubblica napoletana
      see under Colletta, Carlo, ed.

Naples (*Kingdom*) *Laws, statutes, etc.*
   Progetto di decreto per l'ordinamento della pubblica istruzione seguito da un rapporto ragionato per Vincenzo Coco.
Napoli, Tip. degli eredi Migliaccio, 1848.
   xxiii, 140 p. 21 cm. (Opere di Vincenzo Coco, v. 1)

   1. Educational law and legislation—Naples (Kingdom)
   I. Cuoco, Vincenzo, 1770-1823. II. Title.

                                          66-42971

NN 0017855   DLC CaBVaU

Naples(Kingdom) Laws, statutes, etc.
   [La penultimo a
assolutamente ne nostri Dominij sotto la
pena de dover essere i Liberi Muratori
puniti come perturbatori della pubblica
tranquillità, e come rei di violati dritti
della nostra sovranità: Naples, Porfile,
1751. [4] p. 29cm. (Spain. Reales ordenes.
4:73]

NN 0017856   CU-B

Naples (Kingdom) Laws, statutes, etc.
   Prospetto delle modificazioni fatte alle tariffe della real
marina del 1.° ottobre 1818 con posteriori reali decreti, e rescritti
di massima emanati a tutto il 30. settembre 1840.   Napoli: Dalla
Reale Tipografia della Guerra, 1840.   169 f.   half lea.   4°.

   Interleaved

   1. Navy, Two Sicilies.
   N. Y. P. L.   January 7, 1915.

NN 0017857   NN

Naples (*Kingdom*) *Laws, statutes, etc.*
   Prospetto delle modificazioni fatte alle Ordinanze generali della real marina. Napoli, Reale tipografia militare,
1858.
   137 p., 1 l. tables. 29ᵐᵐ.

   "Prospetto delle modificazioni fatte alle tariffe della real marina del 1.°
ottobre 1818 con posteriori reali decreti e rescritti di massima emanati a
tutto il 30 settembre 1840": p. [85]-137.

   1. Naval law—Naples (Kingdom)   2. Tariff—Naples (Kingdom)

   Library of Congress   VB629.N3 1858   7-11812

NN 0017858   DLC

Naples (Kingdom) Laws, statutes, etc.

Byzantine empire. *Laws, statutes, etc.*
   A provincial manual of later Roman law: the Calabrian
Procheiron on servitudes & bye-laws incidental to the tenure
of real property, rendered into English by Edwin Hanson
Freshfield, LL. D. Cambridge. Printed at the University press,
1931.

Naples (Kingdom) Laws, statutes, etc.
   Il puro gius feodale napoletano
      see under Ammirati, Filippo.

Naples (Kingdom) Laws, statutes, etc.
   Raccolta delle consuetudini siciliane
      see under Siciliano Villanueva, Luigi.

DG868   Naples (Kingdom) Laws, statutes, etc.
.44   Raccolta di atti e decreti del governo
A2   dal 7 maggio 1849-[luglio 1850] in poi.
      Palermo, Stamperia A. Gagliani, 1849-50.
      4 v. in 2.

   1. Sicily - Hist. - 1815-1870 - Sources.
   I. Title.

NN 0017862   CU

Law
   Naples (Kingdom) Laws, statutes, etc.
      Regni Sicilie constitutiones per...Andream
de Isernia et alios doctores cõñatae, et appo-
stillare: et appostillis congruenter suis locis
nouiter postatiam impressionem positis: vna cũ
repertorio dicti Andree ac etiam ritibus magne
cure vicarie nouiter summa cum diligentia im-
presse. [Naples], 1533.
      8, [4], 175, xxviiii, 12, 32, 34 l. 30 cm.
   Colophon:...sumptibus Bernardi de Cantis et
Joannis Pauli de Suganappis.
      I.Andrea d'Isernia,1220(ca.)-1316. II.Title.

NN 0017863   DLC MH-L CtY

WA   NAPLES (Kingdom) Laws, statutes, etc.
N215r   Regolamenti sanitarii per lo regno
1820   delle Due Sicilie sanzionati da Sua Maestà
      in consequenza della legge de' 20 ottobre
      1819 ... Napoli, Orsino, 1820.
      189 p. illus.

NN 0017864   DNLM MH

Naples(Kingdom) Laws,statutes,etc.
   Regolamento per guarentire le provincie del regno dalla diffusione del cholera asiatico,
qualora vi penetrasse. 18 pp. 4°. Napoli, dai
tipi di Cataneo, 1819.

NN 0017865   DNLM

Naples (Kingdom) Laws, statutes, etc.
   Repertorio amministrativo... 5. ed. Napoli, 1851-
59.
   6 v.

NN 0017866   NjP

Law   Naples (Kingdom) Laws, statutes, etc.

   Mattei, Saverio, 1742-1795.
      Saggio di risoluzioni di diritto publico
   ecclesiastico del regno di Napoli. In Siena,
   nella Stamperia di Luigi, e Benedetto Bindi,
   1776.

Naples (Kingdom) Laws, statutes, etc.

Molfetta. Italy. Ordinances, etc.
   Gli statuti dei secoli XV e XVI intorno al
governo municipale della citta di Molfetta
ora per la prima volta pubblicati per cura di
Luigi Volpicella. Napoli, 1875.

VOLUME 405

Naples (Kingdom) Laws, statutes, etc.
Statuti dell' arte della seta a Napoli, e legislazione della colonia di S. Laucio
see under   Naples.   Arte della Seta.

Law

Naples (Kingdom) Laws, statutes, etc.
Catanzaro. Arte della Seta.
Statuti dell'Arte della Seta in Catanzaro preceduti da una relazione fatta all Camera di Commercio ed Arti sulla origine progresso e decadenza dell'Arte della Seta in Catanzaro dal suo segretario Filippo Marincola s. Floro ...Catanzaro,Tipografia Municipale,1880.

NAPLES (KINGDOM) - Laws,statutes,etc.
Statuto penale militare per lo regno delle Due Sicilie. Statuti penali per l'armata di mare,etc. Napoli,D.Capasso,1843.

Table.

NN   0017871   MH

Naples (*Kingdom*) *Laws, statutes, etc.*
Su le procedure di spropriazione forzata degl'immobili e diritti reali immobiliari e di graduazione tra creditori, e su li giudizi incidentali per tali procedure, secondo la Legge de' 29 dicembre 1828. Comento teorico practico di Fortunato Cafaro. 3. ed. riv. ed accresciuta delle notizie di tutti gli atti legislativi e della giurisprudenza su la materia; non che di un comento su le riforme alle leggi ipotecarie contenute nella Legge de' 15 febbraio 1843. Napoli, Stamperia dell'Iride, 1844.
180, 115 p.   26 cm.
1. Eminent domain—Naples (Kingdom)   I. Cafaro, Fortunato, ed.

55-50315

NN   0017872   DLC

4K   Naples (Kingdom) Laws, statutes, etc.
Italy   Supplimento alle 5 parti del Codice
1657   per lo Regno delle due Sicilie; ossia,
Elenco ragionato delle leggi, decreti, rescritti e ministeriali che ne hanno modificato o dilucidate le disposizioni a tutto il 1842, compilato dal dottor P. A. Ridola. 2. ed., migliorata ed accresciuta. Napoli, S. Starita, 1843.
119 p.

Bound with Oliva, Carlo. Trattato della competenza de'giudici di circondario in materia civile. Messina, 1844.

-- --- Continuazione. Anni 1843 -1844. Napoli, S. Starita, 1845.
14 p.

NN   0017874   DLC-P4

HJ6239
.N5   Naples (Kingdom) Laws, statutes, etc.
1818   [Tariffe] [Napoli? 1818
Office   iii[i], 93 p. incl. tables   27½x22cm.
Title-page wanting.
Decree signed and dated: Portici, 20 aprile 1818 ... Ferdinando. Il segretario di stato ministro delle finanze ... De'Medici. Il segretario di stato ministro cancelliere ... marchese Tommasi.
[Full notes & contents on pub. cat. card]
1. Tariff—Naples   (Kingdom)—Law.   I. Title.

NN   0017875   DLC

Naples (*Kingdom*) Laws, statutes, etc.
Tariffe d'importazione, di esportazione, de'dazj di consumo, e delle tare pubblicate col Real decreto del 30 novembre 1824. Coll'aggiunta di tutte le modifiche e spiegazioni successive. Dirette e pubblicate dal Ministero e real segreteria di stato delle finanze. Napoli, Stamperia fabricatore, 1844.
xvii, 134 p.   39½ᶜᵐ.

1. Tariff—Naples (Kingdom)—Law.   I. Naples (Kingdom) Ministero delle finanze.

26-23435

Library of Congress   HJ6239.N5 1824

NN   0017876   DLC

Naples(Kingdom) Laws,statute,etc.
Tavole pel Progetto di ordinanza di Sua Maesta il re del regno delle Due Sicilie per l'esercizio e manovre di artiglieria. [Napoli Napoli Reale litografia militare, 1844.   116 pl.   24 x 31cm.

278093B.   1. Army, Italian—Naples.
N.Y.P.L.

January 4, 1943

NN   0017877   NN

Naples (Kingdom) Legación. Spain.
Fiestas ...
see under title

MICROFILM
FH
M55

Naples (Kingdom) Legation. U. S.
Notes from the Legation of the Kingdom of the Two Sicilies to the Dept. of State, 1826-1860. Washington, National Archives, 1943.
reels. (National Archives. Microfilm publications. Microcopy no. M55)

Microfilm copy. Positive.
Contains notes, with their enclosures, addressed to the Dept. of State by ministers and other representatives from the Kingdom of the Two Sicilies to the United States.

NN   0017879   NNC

Naples (*Kingdom*) *Magna curia vicaria*
see **Naples** (*Kingdom*) *Tribunale della gran corte della vicaria.*

Naples (Kingdom) Marina.
Per la intendenza generale della Real Marina contro la Compagnia Raffaele Rubattini e socii di Genova; discorso sulla legittimità della preda del piroscafo sardo, il Cagliari ad uso della Commissione delle prede e naufragi sedente in Napoli.   Napoli, Reale tipografia militare, 1857.
vii, 210, 71 p. fold.map.   38cm.

"Appendice contenente i documenti, dei quali fa uso l'Intendenza Generale della Real Marina ..." 71 p. at end.

1. Compagnia Raffaele Rubattini e socii, Genoa.   II. Cagliari (Ship)

NN   0017881   CU

Naples (*Kingdom*) *Ministero degli affari esteri.*
Documenti relativi alle proposizioni di riconciliazione del re Ferdinando II colla Sicilia. [Palermo, Tip. di F. Lao, 1849]
cover-title, 3-8 p. 26ᶜᵐ.

1. Naples (Kingdom)—For. rel.—France. 2. France—For. rel.—Naples (Kingdom) 3. Sicily—Hist.

Library of Congress   DG848.56.S5

5-9598

NN   0017882   DLC

Naples (*Kingdom*) *Ministero degli affari interni.*
Annali civili del regno delle Due Sicilie.
Napoli, Tip. del Real ministero degli affari interni, 1833-
v. in   plates (partly fold.) fold. maps, fold. plans, tables (partly fold.) fold. diagr. 28½ᶜᵐ.
Each vol. is issued in two parts, each part covering a period of two months.
Each part contains "Osservazioni meteorologiche," gennaio 1833- Bibliographies interspersed.

1. Naples (Kingdom)—Econ. condit. 2. Meteorology—Naples (Kingdom)

Library of Congress   DG840.A3   7-28556

NN   0017883   DLC PU MH NjP ICRL

NAPLES (KINGDOM)   Ministero degli affari interni.
Rapporto al parlamento nazionale. [Napoli, 1820].

31.8 cm. pp.(2),52.
Half-title serves as title.
Signed p.23: Ministro degli affari interni, Giuseppe Zurlo.

NN   0017884   MH

---

q330.9457 Naples(Kingdom) Ministero degli af-
N162r   fari interni.
Rapporto sullo stato del regno d i Napoli per gli anni 1810, e 1811 presentato al re nel suo consiglio di stato dal Ministro dell'interno. Napoli [1812]
93, 69p.

Signed: Il Ministro dell'interno, Giuseppe Zurlo.

"Indice de'diritti e prestazioni che i comuni del regno di Napoli hanno dedotto di esigersi dagli ex-baroni, e de'quali ha giudicato la commissione feudale": 69p.

NN   0017886   IU

Naples (Kingdom) Ministero degli affari interni.
La "Statistica" del regno di Napoli del 1811
see under Cassese, Leopoldo, ed.

Naples (Kingdom) Ministero della giustizia.
Atti e documenti del processo di maestà per gli avvenimenti del 15 maggio 1848 in Napoli con una consultazione di magistrati e pubblicisti italiani sopra le quistioni legali e costituzionali della causa (giudizio di accusa) Torino, F. de Lorenzo, 1851.
17.5 cm.
"Introduzione" signed: Giuseppe Massari.
"Atto di accusa nella causa degli avvenimenti politici del 15 maggio 1848" p. 1-31: "Documenti ai quali si accenna nell'atto di accusa", p. [33]-53.

"Atto di accusa" signed: Filippo Angelillo.
I. Angelillo, Filippo.

NN   0017889   CtY

Naples (Kingdom) Ministero della giustizia.
Atto di accusa nella causa degli avvenimenti politici del 15 maggio 1848. Napoli, Stamperia del Fibreno, 1851.
52 p.   27.5 cm.
Signed: Filippo Angelillo.
"Elenco de' documenti": p. [33]-52.
I. Angelillo, Filippo.

NN   0017890   CtY

VOLUME 405

DG
848.44
N162r

Naples (Kingdom). Ministero della polizia
  generale.
    Rapporto del Ministro della polizia generale,
sulla congiura ordita nell'anno 1807, contro
l'armata francese nel Regno di Napoli, e contro
la persona, e gli stati di S. M. Giuseppe
Napoleone. [Naples, 1807]
    74 p. illus.

    1. Naples (Kingdom) - Hist. - Sources.
I. Title.

NN   0017891   CLU

Naples (Kingdom) Ministero delle finanze.
    Collezione degli stati discussi per l'anno
1847, preceduti da una memoria sullo stato
finanziero de'reali domini a di quà del faro
ne'principj dell'anno 1848.   Napoli, dallo
Stab. tip. di N. Fabricatore, 1848.
    f°.
    Imperfect: p. [107]-108 mutilated; part of
text wanting.

NN   0017892   MH

Naples (Kingdom) Ministero delle finanze.
    Rapporto al parlamento nazionale su i debiti e
crediti dello stato al primo luglio 1820, presentato dal ministro delle finanze nel giorno 9 dicembre 1820. [Napoli, 1820]
    [2], 32,[12]p.

NN   0017893   MH

Naples (Kingdom) Ministero delle finanze.
Naples (*Kingdom*) *Laws, statutes, etc.*
    Tariffe d'importazione, di esportazione, de' dazj di
consumo, e delle tare pubblicate col Real decreto del 30
novembre 1824. Coll'aggiunta di tutte le modifiche e
spiegazioni successive. Dirette e pubblicate dal Ministero e real segreteria di stato delle finanze. Napoli,
Stamperia fabricatore, 1844.

NAPLES (Kingdom) Ministero delle giustizia.
               Quadro sta-
tistico generale sull' amministrazione della
giustizia penale ne' reali domini di qua del
faro per l'anno 1833 rassegnato a Sua Maestà il
re dal ministro [Niccola Parisio]. Napoli,
dalla stamperia reale, 1836.

4°.
At head of title: Ministero di grazia e giustizia.

NN   0017895   MH

Naples (*Kingdom*) *Navy*
  see Naples (*Kingdom*) *Marina.*

Naples (Kingdom) Parlamento.
    ...Atti del Parlamento delle Due Sicilie 1820-1821. Editi
sotto la direzione di Annibale Alberti, raccolti e illustrati da Egildo
Gentile, con premessa di Michelangelo Schipa... Bologna: N.
Zanichelli, 1926. 2 v. 4°. (Reale accad. nazionale dei
Lincei, Rome. Atti delle assemblee costituzionali dal Medio Evo
al 1831. Ser. 2 «Parlamenti dell'eta moderna». Sezione 3¹⁻².)

1. No subject. 2. Alberti, Annibale,   editor. 3. Gentile, Egildo, com-
compiler. 4. Schipa, Michelangelo,   1854- . 5. Ser.
N. Y. P. L.   March 30, 1927

NN   0017897   NN

Q945D
At84N

Naples (Kingdom) Parlamento.
    Atti del parlamento delle due Sicilie
1820-1821. Editi sotto la direzione di
Annibale Alberti, raccolti e illustrati da
Egildo Gentile con premessa di Michelangelo
Schipa.   Bologna, N.Zanichelli,1926-1941.
    6v. in 7. 29cm.   (Atti delle assem-
blee costituzionali italiane dal medio evo
al 1831. Ser.2:Parlamenti dell'età moderna.
Div.3: Parlamento delle due Sicilie)

NN   0017898   PU MH NN ICN NNC CtY NIC

Naples (Kingdom) Ministero della guerra.
    Entwurf eines straf-gesetzbuchs für die
Schweizer-regimenter im dienste Seiner Aller-
christlichsten Majestät.   Naples, 1832.
    87+ p. 4°.
    Title-page and text in German and French.

NN   0017899   MH

F
3596
.614

NAPLES (Kingdom) Parlamento.
    Atti relativi all' intervento di S.M. il re
delle due Sicilie nel Congresso di Leybach ac-
compagnati da tutti i documenti correlativi, e
disposti in guisa da dilucidare la storia del
nuovo reggimento costituzionale del regno. 1.
ed. uffiziale.   Napoli, Nella Stamperia del
parlamento nazionale, 1821.
    100p. 22cm.

NN   0017900   ICN

Naples (Kingdom) Parlamento.
    [Broadside consisting of addresses from the
parliament to Ferdinando I.,etc., 1820-28.]
n.p., n.d.

NN   0017901   MH

Naples (Kingdom) Parlamento.
    Diario del Parlamento nazionale delle Due
Sicilie negli anni 1820 e 1821 ... Edizione fatta
per cura di Carlo Colletta. Napoli, 1864.
    28 cm.   (Colletta, C., ed. Raccolta di
documenti che servono ad illustrare i tre ultimi
periodi rivoluzionari ... [1863-66] parte 2.)
    I. Colletta, Carlo,   *ed.*

NN   0017902   CtY

Naples (Kingdom) Parlamento.
    Parlamenti generali del regno di Sicilia
        see under   Mongitore, Antonino, 1663-
1743.

Naples (Kingdom) Parlamento.
    Parlamento siciliano
        see under   Genuardi, Luigi, 1882-

Naples (Kingdom) Parlamento.
    Ragguaglio di tutte le principali discussioni
relative agli atti legislativi del Parlamento
del 1820, disposte secondo l'ordine delle tor-
nate parlamentarie dalla prima all'ultima adunanza, seguito dal conto del Tesoriere del
Parlamento suddetto relativo agli esiti
occorsi nella prima, e seconda legislatura.
[Napoli, Da' Torchi del Tramater, 1848]
    302, xxxxii, 12 p.

    "Costituzione   politica del regno dell
Due Sicilie":   xxxxii p.

NN   0017905   NNC MH

Naples (Kingdom) Parlamento. Camera dei
  deputati.
    Tornate della Camera de' deputati del
Parlamento napoletano nella sessione 1848-1849,
con tutti i progetti di legge in essa presentati,
per Carlo Colletta.   Napoli, 1866.
    28 cm.   (Colletta, C., ed. Raccolta
di documenti che servono ad illustrare i tre
ultimi periodi rivoluzionari ... [1863-66]
parte 3)
    I. Colletta, Carlo.   *ed.*

NN   0017906   CtY MH

Naples (Kingdom) Procuratore generale del re
  presso la Gran corte criminale e speciale
  di Basilicata.
    Atto di accusa del procuratore generale del
re presso la gran corte criminale e speciale di
Basilicata
        see under   Basilicata. Gran corte
criminale.

Naples (Kingdom) Procuratore generale del re
  presso la Gran corte speciale di Napoli.
    Conclusioni pronunziate ... nella causa
della setta l'Unita Italiana
        see under   Angelillo, Filippo.

4K
10224

Naples (Kingdom) Pubblico ministero presso la
  Corte suprema di giustizia.
    Conclusioni del Pubblico ministero
presso la Corte suprema di giustizia
nella causa della successione al fu
marchese di Ducenta trattata a camere
riunite nel di 14 giugno 1826.
[18   ]
    104 p.

    Bound with Civitella, Diego. Delle
consuetudini di Napoli...Napoli, 1785.

NN   0017909   DLC-P4

Naples (Kingdom) Pubblico ministero presso la Gran
  corte criminale e speciale di Napoli.
    Atto di accusa del P.M. con le successive
decisioni della Gran corte criminale e speciale di
Napoli nella causa degli avvenimenti politici del
5 settembre 1848.   Napoli, Stamperia del Fibreno,
1851.
    77 p., 1 l. 27.5 cm.
    Atto di accusa signed: Filippo Angelillo.
I. Angelillo, Filippo. II. Naples (Kingdom) Gran
corte criminale e speciale. III. Title.

NN   0017910   CtY NN

Naples (Kingdom) Pubblico ministero presso la Gran
  corte criminale e speciale di Napoli.
    Requisitorie ed atti di accusa del Pubblico
ministero presso la G. corte criminale e speciale
di Napoli con le correlative decisioni della
G.C. medesma e della Suprema corte di giustizia
nella causa degli avvenimenti politici del 15 maggio
1848.   Napoli, Stamperia del Fibreno, 1851.
    23.5 cm.
    "Atto di accusa", p. [87]-115; Elenco dei
documenti ai quali si accena nell'Atto di accusa",
p. [116]-135.

    "Atto di accusa" signed: Filippo Angelillo.
I. Angelillo, Filippo.

NN   0017912   CtY

Naples (*Kingdom*) *Real marina*
  see Naples (*Kingdom*) *Marina.*

Naples (*Kingdom*) *Regia Camera della summaria*
  see
  Naples (*Kingdom*) *Camera della summaria.*

VOLUME 405

Naples (*Kingdom*) *Regia Camera summaria neapolitana*
see
Naples (*Kingdom*) *Camera della summaria.*

Naples (*Kingdom*) *Regia cancelleria.*
Gli atti perduti della Cancelleria angioina, transuntati da Carlo de Lellis, pubblicati dal R. Istituto storico italiano per il medio evo ... Roma, Nella sede dell' Istituto, 1939–
   v. 26½ᵐ. (Added t.-p.: Istituto storico italiano per il medio evo. Regesta chartarum Italiae ... ₍v. 25
"Pubblicati sotto la direzione di Riccardo Filangieri."
Part I, v. 1–   "a cura di Bianca Mazzoleni."
CONTENTS.—pte. 1. Il regno di Carlo I.
   1. Naples (Kingdom)—Hist.—Sources. I. Lellis, Carlo de, d. ca. 1660. II. Istituto storico italiano, Rome. III. Filangieri di Candida Gonzaga, Riccardo, conte, 1882– ed. IV. Mazzoleni, Bianca, ed. V. Title.
Newberry library
for Library of Congress   [CD1402.R5 vol.25]
  ₍3₎   (945)
A 42–4440

NN 0017916   ICN IU CLU NIC

Naples (Kingdom) Regia cancellería.
  Le Codice aragonese
    see under Naples (Kingdom) Sovereigns, etc. 1458–1494. (Ferdinando I)

Naples (Kingdom) Regia Cancelleria.
Regesto della Cancelleria aragonese di Napoli, a cura di Jole Mazzoleni. Volume unico. Napoli, L'Arte tipografica, 1951.
   xxii, 341 p. 26 cm. (Ministero dell'interno. Pubblicazioni degli archivi di Stato, 7)
At head of title: Archivio di Stato di Napoli.
"Justitiae" (p. ₍185₎–297) in Latin.
CONTENTS: Privilegiorum I–VII (nell'Archivio di Stato) — Justitiae (frammento nell'Archivio di Stato).
   1. Naples (Kingdom)—History—Sources. I. Mazzoleni, Jole, ed. II. Naples. Archivio di Stato. III. Title. IV. Series: Italy. Ministero dell'interno. Pubblicazioni degli archivi di Stato, 7.

DG848.11.N38   74–264232

NN 0017918   DLC CtY NIC PU MH NN NNC DDO ICN IU NjP

DG   Naples (Kingdom) Regio cancelleria.
841   I registri della Cancelleria angioina, rico-
.A16   struiti da Riccardo Filangieri con la collabora-
T3   zione degli archivisti napoletani. Napoli,
v.1– Presso l'Accademia, 1949–
       v. 25 cm. (Accademia Pontaniana,
     Naples. Testi e documenti di storia napoletana.
     v. 1–

       1. Naples (Kingdom) – Hist. – Sources. I.
     Filangieri di Candida Gonzaga, Riccardo, conte,
     1882– ed.

NN 0017919   DCU

Naples (*Kingdom*) *Regia Cancelleria.*
I registri della Cancelleria angioina, ricostruiti da Riccardo Filangieri con la collaborazione degli archivisti napoletani. Napoli, L'Accademia, 1950–
   v. facsim. 25 cm. (Testi e documenti di storia napoletana pubblicati dall'Accademia pontaniana, v. 1–
Vol. 1–3, 5–6, 9–13 edited by Riccardo Filangieri; v. 4, 7, 14– by Jole Mazzoleni; v. 8 by Jolanda Donsì Gentile.
Includes bibliographical references.
   1. Naples—Hist.—Sources. I. Filangieri di Candida Gonzaga, Riccardo, conte, 1882– ed. II. Title. (Series: Accademia pontaniana, Naples. Testi e documenti di storia napoletana, v. 1–)

DG841.A64 vol. 1, etc.   63–30258

              ICN
NN 0017920   DLC NNC PU NN NcD MH NcU ICU DDO NIC

DB   **Naples (Kindom) Regia Cancelleria.**
841   I registri della Cancelleria
N3   angioina, ricostruiti da Riccardo
     Filangieri con la collaborazione
     degli archivisti napoletani. Napoli,
     L'Accademia, 1951–
       v. facsim. 25cm. (Accademia
     pontaniana, Naples. / Testi e
     documenti di storia napoletana, v.
     1–)
       Holdings on author card only.
     Vol. 1–3, 5–6, 9–13 edited by
     Riccardo Filangieri; v. 4, 7, 14– by
     Jole Mazzoleni; v. 8 by Jolanda
     Donsì Gentile.

NN 0017921   MU MiU

Naples (*Kingdom*) *Sacro real consiglio*
see
Naples (*Kingdom*) *Sacro regio consiglio.*

JN5289 **Naples (Kingdom) Sacro regio consiglio.**
f.A5   Avreæ decisiones ... Nicolai Antonii Gizza-
1656   relli, in qvibvs illvstriores, tam contractvvm
Rare   & vltimarum voluntatum casus, quam arduæ crimi-
Book nales, consuetudinariæ, ac feudales controue-
     siæ, maxima dicendi claritate... In dvos libros
     distribvtae. ... Additionibvs eximiorum iure
     consultorum ... His accesserunt responsum singu-
     lare Francisci Mele & nouissimè additiones ad
     nonnullas decisiones Andreæ Persici. Neapoli,
     Apud C. Gauallum, 1656.
       2 v. in 1.
       1. Law reports,
     Naples (Kingdom'   digests, etc.––

NN 0017923   ICU

Law

   Naples (Kingdom) Sacro regio consiglio.
     Avreae, et analyticæ additiones ad decisio-
    nes Sac. regni neap. consilii Antonii Capycii.
    Avctore Io. Iacobo Masvllo...Nunc primum excus-
    sae. Neapoli, apud Constantinum Vitalem, 1604.
    29 p.l., 366, [1] p. 19 cm.

      1.Law reports, digests, etc.-Naples(Kingdom).
    I.Capece, Antonio, d.1547. II.Masullo, Giovan-
    ni Giacomo, d.1613. III.Title.

NN 0017924   DLC

Naples (Kingdom) Sacro regio consiglio.
   Decisiones ...
   For the editions of 1586, 1610, 1616, 1626, 1675, edited by Vincenzo de Franchi see under Franchi, Vincenzo de, 1530?–1601.

Law

   Naples (Kingdom) Sacro regio consiglio.
     Decisiones sacri consilii neapolitani, a
    Matthaeo de Afflictis...summa diligentia, pariq;
    iudicio collectae, nunc denuo maiore. quam ha-
    ctenus vnquam, cura studioq; emendatae. Qvibvs
    nunc primum accesserunt Thomas Grammatici...
    nouae, et hactenus nunquam conspectae annota-
    tiones, et toti operi plurimum lucis, et stu-
    diosorum rationibus non parum commoditatis al-
    laturae. Lvgdvni, apud haeredes Iacobi Iun-
    tae, 1552.

      821, [136] p. 19 cm.
    "Index verborvm, rervm, ac sententiarvm" has
    special t.p.

      1.Law reports, digests,etc.-Naples(Kingdom).
    I.Afflito, Matteo d'.1443(ca.)-1523. II.Gram-
    matico, Tommaso, 1473-1556. III.Title.

NN 0017927   DLC MH-L IaU

Naples (Kingdom) Sacro regio consiglio.
   Decisiones ... d. Antonium Capycium
   ... aeditae ... Quibus in hac nostra
   2.ed. Vota, quae deerant, & quatuor
   decisiones, nusquam alias impressas
   addidimus ... Venetiis, apvd Ivntas,
   1555.
    24, 171 numb. l. 32cm.
   Printer's device on t.-p. and last leaf.

NN 0017928   MH-L

Naples (Kingdom) Sacro regio consiglio
   Decisiones Neapolitanae d. Matthaei
   de Afflictis ... Nũc demũ in Gallia
   excusum, sed velut ex itegro reparatũ
   exit ... opera praesertim Remundi
   Fraguier ... ₍Lugduni, Dionysii de
   Harsy₎ 1533.
    ₍41₎, 242 numb. l. 25cm.
   Colophon: Lugduni in calcographia
   Dionysii de Harsy typographi soler-

Continued in next column

Continued from preceding column

   tissimi mense Decembₗi. 1532.
   "Tabellas novae decisionvm" (41
   unnumb. l. at beginning) has separate
   t.-p. dated 1534.
   Device of Simon Vincentius on verso
   of 41st prelim. leaf and leaf 242.
   Badly wormed throughout.

NN 0017930   MH-L NBuG

Naples (*Kingdom*) *Sacro regio consiglio.*
   Decisiones Neapolitanae D. Matthaei de Afflictis; re et fama nobile, re et fama nobile et nvnqvam satis æstimatũ opus votorũ decisionumq; insigniũ causarũ Sacri Cõsilij Neapolitani, quas Matthæus ab Afflictis Parthenopæus vnus è senatoribuˢ collegit, nũc demũ in Gallia excusum, sed velut ex itegro reparatũ exit, sũmarijs, sed velut ex itegro reparatũ exit, sũmarijs, titulis, additionibus & indice illustratum opera præsertim Remundi Fraguier. ₍Lugduni₎ S. Vĩcẽt.; ₍in calcographia D. de Harsy₎ 1533–34.
    2 v. in 1. 25 cm.

          Vol. 2 has title: Tabellae novae Decisionvm D. Matthaei ab Afflictis.

      1. Law reports, digests, etc.–Naples (Kingdom)   I. Afflitto, Matteo d', 1443 (ca.)–1523. II. Fraguier, Remundus, fl. 1531, ed. III. Title.

              67–39727

NN 0017932   DLC

Law

   Naples (Kingdom) Sacro regio consiglio.
     Decisiones Neapolitanae d.Matthaei de Af-
    flictis. Re et fama nobile et nvnqvam satis
    aestimatũ opus votorũ decisionq̃e insigniũ
    causarũ Sₐcri cõsilij neapolitani,quas incõ-
    parabilis doctrinae...Matthaeus ab Afflictis
    Parthenopaeus vnus è senatoribus collegit,nũc
    demũ in Gallia excusum,sed velut ex integro
    reparatũ exit,sũmarijs,titulis,additionibus &
    indice illustratum opera,praesertim Remundi
    Fraguier...[Lugduni],1537.
    172,[31] l. illus. 26 cm.

      Colophon:Lugduni sumptu honesti viri Anto-
    nij Uincentij in Calcographia Mathie bonhome
    Typographi solertissimi,mense Julio,1537.
    Title in red and black;initials.
    In double columns.

      1.Law reports,digests,etc.-Naples(Kingdom).
    I.Afflito,Matteo d',1443(ca)-1523.II.Title.

NN 0017934   DLC MiU NN

Naples (Kingdom) Sacro regio consiglio.
   Decisiones novae Sacri regii concilii neapolitani, nunc editae per excellentissimum uirum
   iuris utriusq; doctorem dominvm Antonivm Capycivm
   regium consiliarium ad omnes fermè quotidianos
   casus enucleandos causidicis omnibus nedum utiles,
   sed perquàm necessariae. Cum indice accuratis-
   simo, copiosissimiq; Venetiis [apud Haeredes
   Lucaeantonij Iuntae] 1541.
   26 p.l., 161 numb. l. 30 cm.

    Errors in paging.

NN 0017935   NNC

Law

   Naples (Kingdom) Sacro regio consiglio.
     Decisiones novae Sacri regii consilii nea-
    politani, Antonij Capycij...non minus neces-
    sariae, quam vtiles ijs, qui cum in priuatis,
    tum in publicis forensibusq; causis versantur.
    In quibus castigandis & ornandis tantum olei
    operaeq; a quodam in vtriusq; iuris facultate
    insigni professore nunc primum impensum est,
    vt ad communem omnium vtilitatem nihil prae-
    terea desyderari possit. Accessit syllabus
    mire fidelis rerum sententiarumque in totum
    corpus, a Sygismvndo Hadria, vna cum omnium

    dictionum indice, nunc primum ad frontem ope-
    ris adjecto. Lvgdvni, apud Paulus Miralietum,
    sub insigni d.Pauli, 1547.
    [110], 687 p. 18 cm.
    At end: Lugduni,Mathias Bonhomme,excudebat.
    Title vignette; initials.
    In double columns.

      1.Law reports,digests,etc.-Naples(Kingdom).
    I.Capece, Antonio, d.1545. II.Title.

NN 0017937   DLC CLL

VOLUME 405

Law

Naples (Kingdom) Sacro regio consiglio.
   Decisiones novae Sacri regii consilii neapolitani,Antonij Capycij...non minus necessariae,quam vtiles ijs,qui cum in priuatis,
tum in publicis forensibusq;causis versantur.
In quibus castigandis & ornandis tantum olei
operaeq;a quodam in vtriusq;iuris facultate
insigni professore nunc primum impensum est,
vt ad communem omnium vtilitatem ni//hil
praeterae desyderari possit. Accessit syllabus mire fidelis rerum sententiarumque in

   "Index...a Ioanne Baptista Zillleto...edi-
tus" has added t.p.
   Title vignette(printer's device).
   In double columns.

   1.Law reports,digests,etc.-Naples(Kingdom).
I.Grammatico,Tommaso,1473-1556. II.Ziletti,
Giovanni Battista,fl.1559. III.Title.

NN   0017939   DLC PPB

xfK349.457
N32   Naples (Kingdom) Sacro regio consilio.
   Celeberrimi...Thomae Grammatici...Decisiones
novissimae, quas ipse unus ex Regijs Consiliarijs, ex causis potissimum per eum in Sacro
Regio Neapolitano Concilio relatis, summa cura,
summoq; iudicio selegit. Nunc primum ad communem omnium legum studiosorum utilitatem,
in lucem prodeunt. Quibus accedunt Consilia quaedam pulcherrima, & Questiones perq; utiles,
eiusdem authoris. Cum indice locupletissimo.
Venetiis, Apud Iuntas, 1547.
   [36], 183l.   32cm.

   Colophon: Finis Decisionum, Quaestionum, &
Consiliorum, Thomae Grammatici... Quae omnia
nuper Venetijs in officina haeredum Lucae
Antonij Iuntae...impressa fuere. Anno dñi.
MDXLVII. Mense Maij.

   1. Law reports, digests, etc. - Naples
(Kingdom) I. Grammatico, Tommaso, 1473-1556,
ed.

NN   0017941   IaU

Law

Naples (Kingdom) Sacro regio consiglio.
   Decisiones Sacri consilii neapolitani,a
Matthaeo de Afflictis...summa diligentia,
pariq;iudicio collectae,nunc demuo maiore,
quam hactenus unquã,cura studioq;emendatae.
Qvibvs nunc primum accesserunt Thomae Grammatici,...nouae,et hactenus nunquam conspec-
tae annotationes,et toti operi plurium lucis,
et studiosorum rationibus non parum commodi-
tatis allaturae. Venetiis,apud Dominicum Li-
lium, 1557.
   359,one blanc,[58] l.,last two blanc.

   "Index...a Ioanne Baptista Zillleto...edi-
tus" has added t.p.
   Title vignette(printer's device).
   In double columns.

   1.Law reports,digests,etc.-Naples(Kingdom).
I.Grammatico,Tommaso,1473-1556. II.Ziletti,
Giovanni Battista,fl.1559. III.Title.

NN   0017943   DLC MnU I

Law

Naples (Kingdom) Sacro regio consiglio.
   Decisiones s.regii consilii neapolitani
per...Antonivm Capycivm...ediate,ad omnes
ferme quotidianos casus enucleandos,causi-
dicis omnibus nedum vtiles,sed perquam necessariae. Vota praetereà quae daerant,&
quatuor decisiones nusquàm aliàs impressas,
in hac postrema editione addidimus omnia nũc
denub diligentissimè ab omnibus mendis recognita. Adiecto indice rerum ac uerborum
copiosissimo,maxime ampliato proũt signo

Continued in next column

Continued from preceding column

hoc * reperitur. Venetiis,apud Dominicum Li-
lium,155?
   [43], 255 l.   16 cm.
   Title vignette(printer's device);initials.
   In double columns.

   1.Law reports,digests,etc.-Naples(Kingdom).
I.Capece,Antonio,d.1547. II.Title.

NN   0017945   DLC

Naples (Kingdom) Sacro regio consiglio.
   Decisiones sacri regii consilii
Neapolitani, ab...eiusdem sacri con-
silij regijs consiliarijs collectae,
Matthaeo de Afflictis, Antonio Capycio,
Thoma Grammatico... Nunc demum hac
postrema editione diligentius recog-
nitae...
   Lvgdvni, svmptibvs haered. Lvcae
Antonii Ivnctae, 1566.
   4 p.l., 958 p. and index, fol.

NN   0017946   DCU

Law

Naples (Kingdom) Sacro regio consiglio.
   Decisiones Sacri regii consilii Neapolitani per d.Thomam Grãmaticum Neapolitanum,...
ex causis per eum in sacro regio neapolitano
consilio relatis summa cura,summoque indice
selectae. His accessere,consilia qvaedam
pulcherrima,et quaestiones perquam vtiles
eiusdem auctoris. Ad haec,index rerum,& verborum locupletissimus. Qvae omnia regenti
hac,nostra editione diligentissime expolita
sunt,accuratissimeq;elaborata. Venetiis, a-
pud Ioannem Mariã Bonellum, 1569.

   [172] p.,one leaf blanc,677,[1] p. 16 cm.
   Title vignette;initials.
   In double columns.

   1.Law reports,digests,etc.-Naples(Kingdom).
I.Grammatico,Tommaso,1473-1556. II.Title.

NN   0017948   DLC

Rare
K   Naples (Kingdom) Sacro regio consiglio.
   [Decisiones Sacri Regii Consilii Neapo-
N19   litani ab ... eiusdem Sacri Consilii regijs
1572   consiliarijs collectae, Matthaeo de Afflic-
   tis, Antonio Capycio, Thoma Grammatico ...
   Venetiis, Apud Hieronymum Scottum, 1572]
   2 v. ([190], 1375 p.) 22cm.

   Imperfect copy: title pages wanting.
Title from L. C. catalog and from caption
title of vol. 2.

NN   0017949   NIC PU

Spec.
KBG   Naples (Kingdom) Sacro regio consiglio.
T6   Decisiones Sacri Regii Consilii Neapolitani, per D. Thomam Grammaticvm ... ex cavsis
   tam per pisvm, quàm per alios Dn. Consiliarios
D544   in eodem sacro Consilio relatis, summa cura,
   singularique iudicio collectae: & per eundem
   in publicam iurisconsultorum vtilitatem, iam-
   pridem euulgatae. Nvnc avtem vltra omnes
   svperiores editiones diligentissimè reuisa,
   atque emendatissimè recusa. Vna cvm indice

rervm et verborvm locupletissimo, ad calcem
operis reiecto. Francofvrti ad Moenvm [N.
Bassaei] 1573.
   295 p. 34.2 cm.
   Bound with Toulouse (Archdiocese) Decisiones capellae Tholosanae ... Francofurti,
1575.

   Signatures: A-Z⁶, a⁶, b⁴.
   Title vignette (device of N. Bassaeus)
   Initials; tail-pieces.
   Running title: Decisiones Neapolitanae
Thomae Grammatici.

NN   0017952   CtU

Naples (Kingdom) Sacro regio consiglio.
   Decisiones Sacri Regii Consilii Neapolitani,
Vincentio de Franchis ... Auctore ... Venetiis,
1580.

J. Franchi, Vincenzo de, 1530?-1601.

NN   0017953   PU

Naples (*Kingdom*)   *Sacro regio consiglio.*
   Decisiones Sacri regii consilii neapolitani ab excellent. viris,
i. c. clarissimis, eivsdem Sacri consilij regijs consiliarijs collectæ,
Matthæo de Afflictis, Antonio Capycio, Thoma Grammatico, Io.
Thom. Minadoi. Cuius Minadoi Decisiones antea non excusas,
nunc recèns adiecimus: infinitisq; mendis omnia purgauimus:
adiecto sub finem rerum & verborum indice locupletissimo.
Lvgdvni, sumptibus Philippi Tinghi, Florentini, 1581.
   4 p. l., 863, [87] p.   35ᵐ.
   1. Law reports, digests, etc.—Naples (Kingdom)   I. Afflitto, Matteo
d'. 1443(ca)-1523.   II. Capece, Antonio, d. 1545.   III. Grammatico, Tommaso, 1473-1556.   IV. Minadoi, Giovanni Tommaso, 1505-1556.

                                20–16138 rev

NN   0017954   DLC IEG

Law

Naples (Kingdom) Sacro regio consiglio.
   Decisiones S.regii consilii neapolitani,
per...Antonivm Capycivm...editae:ad omnes
ferme quotidiana casus enucleandos causidicis omnibus nedum vtiles,sed perquam necessariae. Vota praeterea quae deerant,& quatuor
decisiones nusquam alias impressas,in hac
postrema additione addidimus.Omnia nunc demuo
diligentissima recognita,adiecto indice rerum ac verborum copiosissimo. Venetiis, apud
Io.Baptistam Hugolinum,1583.
   [130],774 p.   16 cm.

   Title vignette(printer's device);initials.

   1.Law reports,digests,etc.-Naples(Kingdom).
I.Capece,Antonio,d.1545. II.Title.

NN   0017956   DLC

Naples (*Kingdom*)   *Sacro regio consiglio.*
   Decisiones Sacri regii consilii neapolitani, per d. Thomam
Grammaticvm ... ex causis per eum in Sacro regio neapolitano
consilio relatis summa cura, summoq̃ iudicio selectæ. His accessere, consilia qvædam pulcherrima, & quæstiones perquam
vtiles eiusdem auctoris. Ad hæc, index rerum, & verborum
locupletissimus. Quæ omnia recenti hac nostra editione diligentissimè expolita sunt, accuratissimeq̃; elaborata. Venetiis,
apud Ioan. Baptistam à Porta, 1583.
   95 p. l., 780 p, 1 l.   16ᵐ.
   1. Law reports, digests, etc.—Naples (Kingdom)   I. Grammatico,
Tommaso, 1473-1556, ed.

                                46–41261

NN   0017957   DLC MH-L

JN5289 Naples (Kingdom) Sacro regio consiglio.
.A5   Decisiones Sacri regii consilii neapolitani,
1588   per ... Thomam Grammaticvm ... ex causus per eum
Rare   in Sacro regio neapolitano consilio relatis summa
Bk   cura, summoq̃; iudicio selectae . His accessere,
   consilia qvædam pulcherrima, & quaestiones perquam vtiles eiusdem auctoris. Ad haec, index rerum, & verborum locupletissimus. Quae recenti,
   hac nostra editione diligentissimè expolita sunt, accuratissimeq̃; elaborata. Venetiis,
   Apud haeredes Petri Dehuchini, 1588.
   [188, 782 [2] p.   16 cm.
   1. Law reports,   digests. etc.—
Naples (Kingdom)

NN   0017958   ICU DCU

Law

Naples (Kingdom) Sacro regio consiglio.
   Decisiones Sacri regii consilii neapolitani,
per...Matthaevm de Afflictis...Caesars Vrsil-
lii...adnotationibus, casumq. nouis quibusdam
decisionibus separatim olim editis illustratae,
& quam diligentissime hac postrema editione re-
cogniatae. Cvm svmmariis, et indice ad singvlas
vtriusque decisiones locupletissimis. Venetiis,
apud Paulum Vgolinum, 1596.
   44 p.l., 351 l. 34 cm.
   1.Law reports, digests, etc.-Naples(Kingdom).I.
Afflito, Matteo d' 43(ca.)-1523. II.Title.

NN   0017959   DLC

VOLUME 405

KFX
ZNA
RNd
Naples (Kingdom) Sacro regio consiglio.
Decisiones Sacri regii consilii neapolitani,
avthore Vincentio de Franchis. Eisudem sacri
consilii consiliario, atque praeside, & vicepro-
thonotario, acin supremo Consilio Italiae apud
Catholicam Maiestatem Regente, electo... Item
praelvdia in vsvm Fevdorvm D. Iacobvtii de Franchis Regii Consiliarii. Venetiis, apud Iuntes,
1607.
260 p.

I. De Franchis, Vincentio. II. Title.

NN 0017960   CSt-Law

DG
403
C76
v.722
Naples (Kingdom) Sacro regio consiglio.
Decisiones Sacri regii consilii Neapolitani,
Matthaei de Afflictis ... His accessere aliàs
Thomae Grammatici, & Caesaris Vrsilli ... In
hac vero nostra editione nouissima, praeeditis
apprimè recognitis, perutiles celeberrimi
jurisconsulti Icannis Aloysii Riccii ...
Venetiis, apvd Ivntas, 1635.
860 p. [Consilia/statuti collection, v. 722]

1. Law reports, digests, etc - Naples (Kingdom)
I. Afflitto, Matteo d', 1443(ca.)-1523. II.
Riccio, Giovanni   Luigi, bp., d.1643. III.
Title.   IV. Series.

NN 0017961   CLU

Law

Naples (Kingdom) Sacro regio consiglio.
Decisiones Sacri regii consilii Neapolitani,Vincentio de Francis...collectae,ac in
qvatvor divisae partes. In quibus principa-
liores ac in foro frequentissiame juris mate-
riae tam canonicae quam civiles,criminales &
feudales,&...resolvntur. Vna cum praeludiis
& quaestionibus ad feudorum usus Jacobitii de
Franchis. Editio novissima...Cum adjecto copiosissimo indice totius operis. Francofurti,
Sumptibus Joannis Baptistae Schonwetteri,1672.

2 v. in 1.   34 cm.
Title in red in black.

1.Law reports,digests,etc.-Naples(Kingdom).
I.Franchi,Vincenzo de',1530-1601.II.Title.

NN 0017963   DLC T MH

7913
.6685q
Naples (Kingdom) Sacro regio consiglio
Decisiones Sacri regii consilii neapolitani,
Matthaei de Afflictis. His accessere aliàs
Thomae Grammatici, & Caesaris Ursilli...aureae
adnotationes, casuumq; novae quaedam decisiones
In hac verò editione novissima... perutiles...
Ioannis-Aloysii Riccii... decisiones...
Venetiis, Apud Juntas, 1635; et iterum Neap.,
Apud D. Raillard, 1719.
853 p. 35 cm.

NN 0017964   NjP

K
25
N16ca
1720
Naples (Kingdom) Sacro regio consiglio.
Decisiones Sacri regii consilii Neapolitani a
Vincentio de Franchis ... collectae; una cum praeludiis, & quaestionibus ad feudorum usus Jacobutii
de Franchis ... quarum novissima haec Veneta editio
dispersas in diversis voluminibus praeclarissimorum
jurisconsult. additiones Horatii Visconti, Flavii
Amendolae, Jo: Mariae Riccii, Jo: Mariae Novarii.
Sub sua dicisione dispositas continet; et scholia
ejusdem Amendolae ad feudorum praeludia, annotatio-
nesq; Petri Roitii ... necnon observationes in
singulas decisiones Caroli Antonii de Luca, cum
novissimis decisionibus ejusdem Sacri regii consilii,
ac Regiae Camerae summariae. Venetiis, apud Nicolaum
Pezzana, 1720.
4 v. in 3.

NN 0017965   CLU

Naples (Kingdom) Sacro regio consiglio.
Decisiones Sacri Regii Consilii Neapolitani,
a Vincentio de Franchis ... Collectae; una cum
praeludiis, & quaestionibus ad Feudorum usus
Jacobutii de Franchis ... quarum novissima haec
Veneta editio dispersas in diversis voluminibus
praeclarissimorum jurisconsult. additiones,
Horatii Visconti, Flavii Amendolae, Jo. Aloysii
Riciij, Jo. Mariae Novarii ... annotationesque
Petri Roitii ... necnon observationes in singulas
decisiones Caroli Antonii de Luca, cum novissimis

decisionibus ejusdem Sacri Regii Consilii, ac
Regiae Camerae Summariae... Venetiis, apud
Nicolaum Pezzana, 1747.

4 v. in 3.   36½cm.

Title vignettes.

NN 0017967   MH-L

Law

Naples (Kingdom) Sacro regio consiglio.
...Thomae Grammatici Neapolitani,regii con-
siliari decisiones,qvas ex cavsis potissimum
per eum in sacro regio neapolitano consilio
relatis selegit:ac consilia duo in materia
foriudicationis,qvaestionesq. aliotquot nota-
biles & quotidianq:nunc denuo per auctore
ipsum diligenter reconitae,ac plurimis in locis ampliatae. Qvibvs omnibvs dvae eivsdem
decisiones, videlicet CVI.& CVII.in hac secunda editione adiectae fuere. Cvm indice

locvpletissimo. Opus tam in foro uersantibus,
q de iure respondentibus maxime utile. Venetiis,apvd Ivntas, 1551.
[36],187 l.   31 cm.
L.Giunta's device on t.-p.and at end;ini-
tials.
In double columns.
1.Law reports,digests,etc.-Naples(Kingdom).
I.Grammatico,Tommaso,1473-1556. I.Title:De-
cisiones.

NN 0017969   DLC

Naples (Kingdom) Sacro regio consiglio.
Decisionvm sacri regii neapolitani
consilii, auctore Matthaeo de Afflictis ...
Nouis additionibus, annotationibus, casuum-
que variorum aureis decisionibus dn. Thomae
Grammatici & Caesaris Vrsilli ... illus-
tratarum ... Lvgdvni, ex officina haeredum
Symphoriani Beravd, 1608.

1 p.l., 679, [84], 156 p.   39cm.

"Additiones avreae decisionibvs Matthaei
de Afflictis noviter appositae" (156 p. at
end) has separate t.-p.

NN 0017971   MH-L

Law

Naples (Kingdom) Sacro regio consiglio.

FOR OTHER EDITIONS
SEE MAIN ENTRY

Carleval, Tomás, ca. 1576-1645.
Dispvtationvm ivris variarvm ad interpretationem regia-
rum legum Regni Castelle & illis similium tam ex iure
neapolitano quam ex vtroque communi ciuili & canonico
libri primi De ivdiciis tomvs prior,-posterior, Auctore
Thoma Carnevalio. Cum summis in cuiusque disputationis
capite, & suis locis insertis multis decisionibus eiusdem
Sacri Regij Consilij Neapolitani ... Neapoli, Ex Typo
graphia Regia A. Longhi, 1634-41.

DG
848.11
.A43
14--
Naples (Kingdom) Sacro regio consilio.
Fidelis traductio in formam impressa in alma
ciuitate Neap extracta de originali processu in-
formationum,ac inquisitionum factarum de ordina-
tione Sacre Regiae Maiestatis ... [15th cent.?]
[130] p.   25½ x 19½ cm.
Binder's title: Processo della Congiura de
baroni.
A manuscript copy,in several hands,of Processo
contro Pirri de Bautio ed altri congiurati
(Naples, Francesco del Tuppo, 1488) (H13383)
Italian text.
1.Naples--Kingdom--Hist. I.Title: Processo
contro Pirri de   Bautio.

NN 0017973   MiU

Naples (Kingdom) Sacro regio consiglio.
Selectarum et illustrium juris feudalium
conclusionum in s.r.c. neapolitano novissimè
decisarum compendium
see under Maradeus, Franciscus.

Law

Naples (Kingdom) Sacro regio consiglio.
Tabellae novae decisionvm d.Matthaei ab Afflictis. Farragohorvm propè omniū, que olim in
hoc floridissimo decisionum Neapolitanarum
opere valetissimus ille...Matthaeus ab Afflictis Parthenopeius consiliarius cumulatissimè
digestit,iamnunc in vrnum velut pugillum nota-
biliter congesta:seruato deltariorum ordine
in facie studiosorū prodeunt in lucem.[Lugdu-
ni],1537.
[60],342 l.   18 cm.
Colophon: Lugduni in Calcographia Joannis

Crespin alias du quarre Typographi solertissi-
mi Mense Februario. 1537.
Title in red and black within renaissance
ornamental border;initials.
Added illus.t.p.: Decisiones Neapolitanae.
In double columns.

1.Law reports,digests,etc.-Naples(Kingdom).
I.Afflito,Matteo d',1443(ca)-1523. II.Title:
Tabellae novae. III.Title:Decisiones.

NN 0017976   DLC

Naples (*Kingdom*) *Sacrum regium consilium*
see
Naples (*Kingdom*) *Sacro regio consiglio.*

Naples (*Kingdom*) *Sovereigns, etc.*
Capitoli e privilegi di Messina, a cura di Camillo Giardina.
Palermo, La R. Deputazione, 1937.

lxiv, 482 p. facsims. 25 cm. (R. Deputazione di storia patria
per la Sicilia. Memorie e documenti di storia siciliana. 2. Documenti,
v. 1)

Includes bibliographical references.

1. Messina — Charters, grants, privileges. 2. Messina — Hist.—
Sources. I. Giardina, Camillo, 1907– ed. II. Title. (Series:
Deputazione di storia patria per la Sicilia. Memorie e documen 1
di storia siciliana. 2. Documenti, v. 1)

55–55631

NN 0017978   DLC WaU

Naples (Kingdom) Sovereigns, etc.
Diplomatico aragonese
see under Aragon. Sovereigns, etc.,
1416-1458 (Alfonso)

Naples (Kingdom) Sovereigns, 12 -1266 (Manfredi
Il manifesto di Manfredi ai Romani
see under Manfredi, King of Naples and
Sicily, d. 1266.

Naples (Kingdom) Sovereigns, etc., 1266-1285
(Carlo I)
Actes et lettres
see under Carlo I, d'Anjou, King of
Naples, 1226-1285.

Naples (Kingdom) Sovereigns, etc., 1266-1285 (Carlo I)
Diplomi inediti di Re Carlo I.d'Angio riguardanti cose marittime. Pubblicati in occasione
del Congresso internazionale marittimo aperto
in Napoli li 30 giugno 1871. Napoli,stab. tip.
de fr.De Angelis,1871,
Ed. by Giuseppe del Giudice.
1.8°. pp.32.

NN 0017982   MH

Naples (Kingdom) Sovereigns, etc., 1343-1382
(Joanna I)
I diplomi Angioini dello Archivio di stato
di Palermo
see under Travali, Giuseppe.

VOLUME 405

Naples (Kingdom). Sovereign, 1458–1494 (Ferdinando I)
Codice aragonese; o sia, Lettere regie, ordinamenti ed
altri atti governativi de' sovrani aragonesi in Napoli riguardanti l'amministrazione interna del reame e le relazioni
all'estero. Per cura del cav. prof. Francesco Trinchera.
Con una introduzione ove a schiarimento degli atti qui
compresi, e del metodo usato nella compilazione si tocca di
tutte le epere del Grande Archivio. Napoli, Stab. tip. di
G. Cataneo, 1866–74.

   3 v. in 4.   24 cm.

   Vol. 3 has imprint : Napoli, Tip. di A. Cavaliere.

   "La raccolta ... contiene solo i tre volumi originali della Cancelleria aragonese, che sono intitolati Registri Exterorum, e questo
picciolo avanzo di tanti altri registri perduti contiene lettere del re
Ferdinando I."
   Vol. 1 contains documents of the period Jan. 1467 to June 1468;
v. 2 documents of the period Oct. 1491 to Jan. 1494; v. 3 documents
of the period Jan. 1491 to Aug. 1498 relating to local government.
   1. Naples (Kingdom)—History—Sources. 2. Law—Naples (Kingdom) I. Trinchera, Francesco, 1810–1874, ed. II. Title. III. Title:
Lettere regie, ordinamenti ed altri atti governativi de' sovrani aragonesi in Napoli.

DG848.115.N36   72–216687

NN 0017985   DLC MnU MH IU CU NNC

Naples (Kingdom). Sovereign, 1458–1494 (Ferdinando I)
Le Codice aragonese; étude générale, publication du
manuscrit de Paris; contribution à l'histoire des Aragonais de Naples, par Arm.-Ad. Messer ... Ouvrage illustré
de deux fac-similés et sept gravures dans le texte. Paris,
H. Champion, 1912.
   cxlviii, 524 p.   illus.   25 cm.   (Bibliothèque du XVᵉ ,i. e. Quinzième, siècle, t. 17)
   "Le Codice de Paris est ... un registre original, provenant de la
chancellerie du roi Ferrand Iᵉʳ de Naples."—p. xc.
   "Contains documents of the period 1458–1460.
   "Index bibliographique": p. xi.
   1. Naples (Kingdom)—History—Sources. 2. Aragon, House of.
I. Messer, Armand Adolphe, ed. II. Title. III. Series.

DG848.115.N35   18–13696

NN 0017986   DLC GU MH NjP NN CU ViU

       Naples (Kingdom) Sovereigns, etc., 1458–1494
         (Ferdinand I)
DG
848.11   Contribution a l'histoire des Aragonais de
+A42   Naples. Le Codice Aragonese, étude générale,
       publication du manuscrit de Paris, présentée
       par Arm. Ad. Messer. Dijon, Impr. Barbier,
       1909.
         cxliv, 522 p.   illus.   26 cm.

         Thèse - Dijon.
         Bibliographical footnotes.

         1. Naples (Kingdom) - Hist. - Sources.   I.
       Messer, Armand Adolphe, ed.

NN 0017987   WU

Naples (*Kingdom*) *Sovereigns, etc., 1458–1494* **(Fernando I)**
   Regis Ferdinandi primi Instructionum liber (10 maggio 1486-10 maggio 1488) Corredato di note storiche e
biografiche per cura di Luigi Volpicella. Napoli, Stab.
tip. L. Pierro & figlio, 1916.
   3 p. l., iix)-xxiv, 520 p.   34ᶜᵐ.   (*Added title-page*: Società napoletana
di storia patria. Monumenti storici, ser. 2. Documenti)
   Edizione di 150 esemplari.
   "Le Istruzioni ... portano tutte la firma del re e quella del segretario. ...
Sessantatrè ... cioè più della metà del loro numero, sono firmati da Giovanni
Pontano. ... Autori ... possono ... considerarsi il re e il segretario insieme
                       (Continued on next card)

   in opportuna collaborazione."—Prefazione, p. xiii.
   "Appendice. Trattato di pace fra Innocenzo VIII e Ferdinando I di Napoli
nel di 11 agosto 1486": p. [197]-210.
   "Note biografiche dei personaggi nominati nel libro del Istruzoni di Ferdinando I re di Napoli, compilate—da Luigi Volpicella": p. [211]-463.
   "Indice alfabetico delle abbreviazioni bibliografiche adoperate per le cita-
zioni nelle Note biografiche": p. [465]-473.
   1. Naples (Kingdom)—Hist.—Sources. 2. Naples (Kingdom)—Biography.
I. Volpicella, Luigi. II. Pontano, Giovanni Gioviano, 1426–1503.

NN 0017989   MiU ICU MH

                            (Charles II)
   Naples (Kingdom) Sovereigns, etc., 1734–1759
     [La proibiamo a assolutamente ne nostri
Dominj sotto la pena di dover essere i Liberi
Muratori puniti come perturbatori della pubblica
tranquillità ...
         see under   Naples (Kingdom) Laws,
   statutes, etc.

**Naples (Kingdom) Sovereigns, etc., 1759–1825
(Ferdinand I, of the Two Sicilies)**
   Ordinanza del re delle Sicilie che servir
de e d'istruzione, e di regolamento a'cadetti ...
        see under   Naples (Kingdom) Laws,
statutes, etc.

**Naples (Kingdom) Sovereigns, etc., 1759–1825
(Ferdinand I, of the Two Sicilies)**
   Ordinanza della amministrazione militare
del regno delle due Sicilie
        see under   Naples (Kingdom) Laws,
statutes, etc.

**Naples. Sovereigns, etc., 1759–1825
(Ferdinand I, of the Two Sicilies)**
   Ordinanza di sua maestà pel servizio delle
piazze de' suoi reali dominj
        see under   Naples (Kingdom) Laws,
statutes, etc.

**Naples (Kingdom) Sovereigns, etc., 1759–1825
(Ferdinand I, of the Two Sicilies)**
   Ordinanza di Sua Maestà per l'esercizio,
e per le manovre delle sue truppe di fanteria
        see under   Naples (Kingdom) Laws,
statutes, etc.

**Naples (Kingdom) Sovereigns, etc., 1759–1825
(Ferdinand I, of the Two Sicilies)**
   Ordinanza di Sua Maestà sulla giurisdizion
militare ...
        see under   Naples (Kingdom) Laws,
statutes, etc.

NAPLES (KINGDOM)   Sovereigns, 1830–1859
     (Ferdinand II).
[A collection of broadsides published in Pal-
ermo from 1849 to 1858, during the reign of
Ferdinand II, and five proclamations of Victor
Emmanuel II of the year 1861.]

   f°.

NN 0017996   MH

Naples(Kingdom) Sovereigns, etc.,1830–1859(Ferdinando II)
   [Decreti di Ferdinando II., Re delle Due Sicilie, e Ordinanze del
Luogotenente Generale Interim in Sicilia, pubblicati in Palermo
fra gli anni 1849 e 1858 per il governo dell' isola.]
— *Broadside proclamations.* Palermo. [1849–58.] (77) issues in
92 ff. Various sizes.
In portfolio.
Inserted is a manuscript table of contents.

N6535 — Sicily. Hist. — Broadsides.   Naples, Kingdom of. Hist. — Proclamations.

NN 0017997   MB

**Naples (Kingdom) Sovereigns, etc., 1830–1859
(Ferdinand II)**
   Ordinanza di sua maestà pel governo, il
servizio e la disciplina delle reali truppe nelle
piazze
        see under   Naples (Kingdom) Laws,
statutes, etc.

**Naples (Kingdom) Sovereigns, etc., 1830–1859
(Ferdinand II)**
   Ordinanza di sua maestà per gli esercizj e
le evoluzioni delle truppe di fanteria
        see under   Naples (Kingdom) Laws,
statutes, etc.

Naples (Kingdom) Stamperia reale.
   Épreuve des caractères de la Fonderie royale
de Naples. Naples, L'Imprimerie française,
1819.
   [38] l. specimens. 22cm.
   By the Fonderie royale

   1. Printing - Specimens. 2. Type and type-
founding.

NN 0018001   NNC

       Naples (Kingdom) Stamperia reale.
TypTS   Regno di Ferdinando Primo. Esposizione del
825   30 maggio 1822.
22.597F [Naples,1822]
       cover-title,20ℓ. 39cm.
       Leaves printed on 1 side only on paper of
       different colors; includes 7 leaves of
       ornaments & vignettes.
       Colophon: Dalla Stamperia reale.
       Original printed rose wrappers preserved;
       bound in half morocco.

NN 0018002   MH

   Naples (*Kingdom*)   *Summaria Audentia Rationum*
      see
   Naples (*Kingdom*)   *Camera della summaria.*

Naples (Kingdom) Treaties, etc.
   [Capitulation militaire pour un régiment d'in-
fanterie du canton de Berne conclue entre M. le
duc de Calvello, ministre plénipotentiaire de
S. M. le roi des Deux-Siciles, près la confédé-
ration suisse, et Messieurs Jean Rodolphe
Wurstemberger, Amédée Albert de Steiger, et
le Général Charles Louis de Watteville,
commissaires du louable canton de Berne,
sous réserve de la ratification de leurs hauts
commettans. Naples? 1828?]
   69 p. 4°.

   Text in French and German.
   Manuscript table inserted between p. 24 and 25.
   Without title-page; title taken from p. 3.

NN 0018005   MH

             Naples (Kingdom) Treaties, etc.
Law
    Naples (*Kingdom*) *Laws, statutes, etc.*
    Codice delle leggi del regno di Napoli, di Alessio de Sariis
... Napoli, V. Orsini, 1792–97.

   —— Epitome; o sia Indice generale de la Storia e del Codice
delle leggi del regno di Napoli, di Alessio de Sariis, Con
ordine alfabetico. Napoli, V. Orsini, 1797.

Naples(Kingdom) Treaties,etc.,1458–1494(Ferdinando I)
   Tratado de paz ó tregua entre Fernando I, el Bastardo, rey
de Nápoles, y Abuámer Otmán, rey de Túnez...1477... (In:
Centenario della nascita di Michele Amari. Palermo, 1910.
4°. v. 2, p. 373–386.)

   1. Tunis.—History, 1477. 2. Naples.   —History, 1477. 3. Ribera y Tar-
ragó, 1858, translator and editor.
N.Y.P.L.   August 7, 1916.

NN 0018008   NN

   Naples (Kingdom) Treaties, etc., 1734–1759
     (Charles IV of the Two Sicilies)
     Concordata inter Benedictum XIV... et
Carolum
     see under   Ceraso, Contradino.

VOLUME 405

Naples(Kingdom) Treaties, etc.,1734-1759 (Charles IV)
Tractaat van commercie, tusschen Sijne Majesteit den koning
der Beide Sicilien en de heeren Staaten generaal der Vereenigde
Nederlanden, &c.   's Gravenhage: J. Scheltus, 1753.   39 p.
21cm.
Treaty dated August 27, 1753.
With bookplate bearing initials: T. M.
VYP p.v.7
———————— 's Gravenhage: J. Scheltus, 1753.   39 p.
21cm.
At head of title: Num. 28.

1. Commerce—Treaties—Nether-   lands and Sicily, 1753. 2. Com-
merce—Treaties—Sicily and Nether-   lands, 1753. I. Netherlands (United
Provinces, 1581-1795). Treaties,   1753. II. Treaties, 1753, August 27.
N.Y.P.L.   *Revised*
                                                       November 30, 1938

NN 0018010   NN

Naples (Kingdom) Treaties, etc., 1734-1759
(Charles IV)
Trattato di accomodamento tra la S. Sede,
e la corte di Napoli
see under   Catholic Church. Treaties,
etc., 1740-1759 (Benedict XIV)

Naples (Kingdom) Treaties, etc., 1734-1759
(Charles IV)
Trattato perpetuo di commercio, e
navigazione conchiuso tra il Re Nostro Signore,
e la Corona di Danimarca da'rispettivi Ministri
plenipotenziarj in Madrid il dì 6. di aprile 1748.
Colle ratificazioni di Sua Maesta, e del Re di
Danimarca contracambiate il dì 20. agosto del
1748. Napoli, 1751.
1 p.l., 76 p. 25.5 x 19 cm.

NN 0018012   CtY

JX
717
1751   Naples (Kingdom) Treaties, etc., 1735-1751 (Charles IV)
Trattato perpetuo di commercio, e navigazione
conchiuso tra il Re Nostro Signore, e la Corona
di Danimarca da' rispettivi Ministri plenipotenziarj in Madrid il dì 6 di aprile 1748.
Colle ratificazioni di Sua Maesta e del Re di
Danimarca contracambiate il dì 20. agosto del
1748. In Napoli, Presso il Ricciardi stampatore
del real palazzo, 1751.
78 p., 1 l., 76 p. 23½ cm.

In French and   Italian.

NN 0018013   NNC CtY

Naples(Kingdom)Treaties,etc.,1734-1759 (Charles IV)
Trattato perpetuo di pace,navigazione,e
commercio concluso fra il re nostro signore,
e l'Impero Ottomano,da rispettivi ministri in
Costantinopoli,il giorno 7. di aprile dell'anno
1740;colle ratificazioni di sua maestà,e quelle
del gran signore,contracambiate il giorno 24.
settembre dell'istesso anno. Napoli,1740.
pp.40+(4). 12°.

NN 0018014   MH-L

Law   Naples (Kingdom) Treaties, etc., 1759-1825
(Ferdinand I of the Two Sicilies)

Catholic Church. *Treaties, etc., 1800-1823 (Pius VII)*
Concordato fra Sua Santità Pio VII, sommo pontefice, e
Sua Maestà Ferdinando I, re del Regno delle Due Sicilie, con
l'allocuzione pronunziata nel Concistoro de' 16 marzo 1818,
con le lettere e gl'indulti apostolici, co' documenti citati nel
Concordato, e co' decreti e le sovrane disposizioni finora pubblicate. Napoli, Stamperia della Società filomatica, 1818-

FOR OTHER EDITIONS
SEE MAIN ENTRY
Naples (Kingdom) Treaties, etc., 1759-1825
(Ferdinand I, of the Two Sicilies)
Gt. Brit. *Treaties, etc., 1760-1820 (George III)*
Supplementary treaty between His Majesty and the King
of the Two Sicilies; signed at Palermo, the 12th of Septem-
ber, 1812 ...   London, Printed by R. G. Clarke, 1812.

Naples (Kingdom) Treaties, etc., 1759-1825
(Ferdinand I, of the Two Sicilies)
Gt. Brit. *Treaties, etc., 1760-1820 (George III)*
Treaty of alliance and subsidy between His Majesty the
King of the United kingdom of Great Britain and Ireland,
and His Majesty the King of the Two Sicilies; signed at Pa-
lermo, the 13th May, 1809 ...   London, Printed by A. Strahan,
1811.

Naples (Kingdom) *Tribunale del sacro consiglio*
see
Naples (Kingdom) *Sacro regio consiglio.*

Law
Naples (Kingdom) Tribunale della gran corte
della vicaria.
Prosperi Caravita...commentaria super ritibus magnae curiae vicariae regni Neapolis. In
qvibus fere omnia, qvae ad praxim eiusdem
regni pertinent, & que a causarum patronis iudicibusq; desiderari possunt diligentissime
explicantur...His adiunximus commentaria Anni-
balis Troysij & Ioannis Francisci Scaglioni,
super eisdem ritibus. Opus summarijs auctum,
et nouo locupletissimoq; indice ornatum. Venetiis, apud Dominicum Nicolinum, 1572.

28 p.l., 233 l. 31 cm.

1.Law reports,digests,etc.-Naples(Kingdom).
I.Caravita,Prospero,fl.1550. II.Troisi,Anniba-
le,fl.1535. III.Scaglioni,Giovanni Francesco,
d.ca.1570. IV.Title.

NN 0018020   DLC

Law
Naples(Kingdom) Tribunale della gran corte
della vicaria.
Prosperi Caravitae Ebolitani provinciarvm
principatvs citra,& Basilicatae regij aduoca-
ti fiscalis commentaria super ritus magnae
Curiae vicariae regni Neapolis. In qvibus fere omnia,qvae a causarum patronis iudicibusq;
desiderari possunt diligentissimè explicantur.
Quibus multa hoc astersco*notata ab eodem authore dum viueret addita sunt. His adiunximus
commentaria dominorum,Annibalis Troysij Ca-
nensis,& Ioannis F   cisci Scaglioni, super

ni, provinciarvm principatvs...
eisdem ritibus. Opus summarijs auctum,et nouo,locupletissimoq,indice ornatum. Venetiis,
expensis Iacobi Anielli Mariae Bibliopolae
Naepolitani,1579.
2 p.l.,[48],231 l. 30 cm.
Colophon:Apud Dominicum Nicolinum.
1.Law reports,digests,etc.-Naples(Kingdom).
I.Caravita,Prospero,fl.1550. II.Troisi,Anni-
bale,fl.1535. III Title.

NN 0018022   DLC

Law   Naples (Kingdom) Tribunale della gran corte
della vicaria.

Anichini, Giovanni Giacomo, *d. ca. 1650.*
De praeventione instrvmentaria, ac de recta adversus instrv-
menta praeueniendi ratione. Tractatvs, sive Commentarivm ad
pragmaticam Malitijs, de praeuent. moder. & ritus Magnae curiae
vicariae, praeuentionem ordinantes. Avthore Io. Iacobo
Anichino... Adiecto triplici indice... Nvnc primvm in lvcem
prodit ... Neapoli, ex typographia Iacobi Gaffari, 1651.

Law
Naples (Kingdom) Tribunale della gran corte
della vicaria.
Decretorvm M.C. praxis criminalis cvm plv-
ribvs decisionibvs per regia tribvnalia pro-
latis; proprijs formulis dictorum decretorum,
aliarumue notabilium rerum, ac vtilibus anima-
duersionibus,breui,et eleganti methodo compo-
sita. Avthore Carolo Antonio de Rosa...Neapo-
li,apvd Hyacinthvm Passarvm,1680.
6 p.l.,212,[51],[11] p. 33 cm.
Title vignette(publisher's device).
I.Rosa, Carlo Antonio di,d.1712. II.Title.

NN 0018024   DLC

Naples (Kingdom) Tribunale della gran corte
della vicaria.
Estratti di un processo
see under   La Lumia, Isidoro, 1823-
1879.

Naples(Kingdom) Tribunale della gran corte della
Law   vicaria
Naples (Kingdom) Laws,statutes,etc.
Thomae Grammatici...in constitvtionibvs,ca-
pitvlis,et pragmaticis regni Neap.et ritibvs
Magnae curiae vicariae additions,& apostil-
lae,quas tum ipse lucubrarat,tum ex aliquot
ueterum,& modernorum iurisconsultorum uigiliis
uiuens congesserat. Accesserunt etiam aliquae
utillimae,et pulchrae questiones...Bartholo-
maei de Capua,et amplissimus totius uoluminis
index. Nvnc primvm in lvcem aeditae. Venetiis,
1562.

Naples (Kingdom) Viceroy.
Translation usz hispanischer sprach zů frantzö-
sisch gemacht so durch dể vice rey du Neopols
Fraw Margareten hertzogiñ in Burgundi zu geschri-
ben.[Dated: Validolyff, October 7th [15,22]

NN 0018027   NNH

Naples (Province)
Rapporto sul cholera di, S. Giov. a Teduccio
see under   Pepere, Pasquale.

Naples (*Province*) *Alto commissariato.*
Napoli, le opere del regime. 1925/27-
Napoli.
v. illus., maps. 35 cm. biennial.

1. Naples (Province)—Public works.

HD4195.N3A3   51-46832

NN 0018029   DLC NN

Naples (*Province*). **Camera di commercio ed arti.**
In 1910 the Camere di commercio ed arti changed their names to
Camere di commercio ed industria. Substituted in 1926 by Consigli
provinciali dell'economia. In 1944 the Consigli were abolished and
the Camere reintroduced as Camere di commercio, industria e agricoltura. The name was changed in 1967 to Camere di commercio,
industria, artigianato e agricoltura.
Works by these bodies are found under the following headings
according to the name used at the time of publication:

Naples (Province). Camera di commercio ed arti.
Naples (Province). Camera di commercio ed industria.
Naples (Province). Consiglio provinciale dell'economia.
Naples (Province). Camera di commercio, industria e agri-
coltura.

Naples (*Province*) **Camera di commercio ed arti.**
Il futuro ordinamento ferroviario ed il Mezzogiorno d'Italia; studii e proposte della Commissione speciale dei tras-
porti, 1905. [Napoli, 1905]
222 p. fold. plan. 24 cm.
Cover title.
At head of title: Camera di commercio ed arti di Napoli. Ufficio
di statistica.

1. Railroads—Italy. 2. Railroads and state—Italy.

HE3097.N2   11-5735 rev*

NN 0018031   DLC

VOLUME 405

Naples (Province) Camera di commercio ed arti.
Relazione della Camera di commercio ed arti di Napoli sul movimento commerciale e industriale della sua provincia nell'anno 1863. Napoli, Stab. tip. del cav. G. Nobile, 1864.
72 p. 26 cm.

1. Naples (Province)—Indus.

HF312.N2   10–19266 rev*

NN   0018032   DLC

587   Naples (Province) Camera di commercio ed arti.
N162s   Studii sul porto di Napoli per la camera di commercio ed arti.   Napoli, 1863.
v.p.

NN   0018033   IU

Naples (Province). Camera di commercio ed industria.
In 1910 the Camere di commercio ed arti changed their names to Camere di commercio ed industria. Substituted in 1926 by Consigli provinciali dell'economia. In 1944 the Consigli were abolished and the Camere reintroduced as Camere di commercio, industria e agricoltura. The name was changed in 1967 to Camere di commercio, industria, artigianato e agricoltura.
Works by these bodies are found under the following headings according to the name used at the time of publication:

Naples (Province). Camera di commercio ed arti.
Naples (Province). Camera di commercio ed industria.
Naples (Province). Consiglio provinciale dell'economia.
Naples (Province). Camera di commercio, industria e agricoltura.

Naples (Province) Camera di commercio ed industria.
Alcuni dati su l'attività produttrice della Campania in rapporto all'economia nazionale. Napoli, Stabilimento industrie editoriali meridionali, 1927–
v. map, tables. 26 cm.
At head of title: Camera di commercio di Napoli. Ufficio di statistica.
CONTENTS.—pt. 1. Sguardo generale alle industrie.

1. Campania—Indus.

HC307.C33N2   60–56810

NN   0018035   DLC NN

4HC   Naples (Province) Camera di commercio
504   ed industria.
L'attività economica della provincia di Napoli; rilievi e dati per l'anno 1924. Napoli, Stab. industrie editoriali meridionali, 1925.
228 p.

NN   0018036   DLC-P4 NN

4HE   Naples (Province) Camera di commercio
1072   ed industria.
I grandi porti commerciali del Nord. Napoli, Stab. cromo-tip. F. Razzi [Cover 1915–
v. 1

NN   0018037   DLC-P4

Law   Naples (Province) Camera di commercio ed
industria.
Italy. *Laws, statutes, etc.*
Leggi per Napoli. Napoli, Stab. industrie editoriali meridionali, 1927.

Naples (Province) Camera di commercio e industria.
...Prezzo corrente delle principali merci sulla piazza di Napoli... Anno

[Napoli,   f°.
Weekly.

1. Prices, Italy: Naples.
N.Y.P.L.   August 6, 1923.

NN   0018039   NN

Naples (Province). Camera di commercio, industria e agricoltura.
In 1910 the Camere di commercio ed arti changed their names to Camere di commercio ed industria. Substituted in 1926 by Consigli provinciali dell'economia. In 1944 the Consigli were abolished and the Camere reintroduced as Camere di commercio, industria e agricoltura. The name was changed in 1967 to Camere di commercio, industria, artigianato e agricoltura.
Works by these bodies are found under the following headings according to the name used at the time of publication:

Naples (Province). Camera di commercio ed arti.
Naples (Province). Camera di commercio ed industria.
Naples (Province). Consiglio provinciale dell'economia.

Naples (Province) Camera di commercio, industria e agricoltura.
Esposizione dell'artigianato artistico napoletano, 20 aprile–31 luglio, 1950. [Catalogo. Napoli, 1950]
58 p. plates. 22 cm.
"Bibliografia": p. 31–33.

1. Art industries and trade—Naples. 2. Art industries and trade—Exhibitions. I. Title.

Harvard Univ. Library   A 52–1928
for Library of Congress   [3]

NN   0018041   MH

Naples (Province) Camera di commercio, industria e agricoltura.
Industrializzazione del Mezzogiorno; legislazione vigente
see under   Italy. Laws, statutes, etc.

Naples (Province) Camera di commercio, industria e agricoltura.
Raccolta degli usi e delle consuetudini della provincia di Napoli, approvata dalla Giunta camerale con deliberazione n. 56 del 28 gennaio 1952. Napoli, Stab. tip. G. Montanino, 1952.
234 p. 25 cm.

1. Law merchant—Naples (Province)   I. Title.

55–40436 ‡

NN   0018043   DLC NN NNU

Naples (Province) Consiglio dell'economia
see **Naples (Province) Consiglio provinciale dell'economia.**

Naples (Province) Consiglio di sanità.
Gazzetta di medicina pubblica
see under title

Naples (Province) Consiglio provinciale.
... Sui progetti di modificazioni alle leggi concernenti la imposta sui redditi della ricchezza mobile e sui fabbricati. Osservazioni e voti rassegnati al governo ed al Parlamento.
A relazione del consigliere cav. E. Menichini. Napoli, F. Giannini, 1897.
1 p.l., 18 p. 30cm.

NN   0018046   MH-L

Naples (Province) Consiglio provinciale.
La viabilita minore nell'Italia meridionale ...
1942]
67 numb. l.

NN   0018047   DNLM

Naples (Province). Consiglio provinciale dell'economia.
In 1910 the Camere di commercio ed arti changed their names to Camere di commercio ed industria. Substituted in 1926 by Consigli provinciali dell'economia. In 1944 the Consigli were abolished and the Camere reintroduced as Camere di commercio, industria e agricoltura. The name was changed in 1967 to Camere di commercio, industria, artigianato e agricoltura.
Works by these bodies are found under the following headings according to the name used at the time of publication:

Naples (Province). Camera di commercio ed arti.
Naples (Province). Camera di commercio ed industria.
Naples (Province). Consiglio provinciale dell'economia.
Naples (Province). Camera di commercio, industria e agricoltura.

Naples (Province). Consiglio provinciale dell'economia.
...Bollettino mensile di statistica della provincia di Napoli.

[Napoli,   34½cm.

1. Economic history—Italy—   Naples (Province) 2. Naples
(Province)—Stat.   (Province)—Stat.
N.Y.P.L.   May 19, 1941

NN   0018049   NN

HC307   **Naples (Province) Consiglio provinciale**
.N3C6   **dell'economia.**
Corriere della borsa.
Napoli.

Naples (Province) Consiglio provinciale dell'economia.
...Monografie economiche. [no. 1]–
Napoli, 1932–   27cm.
no. 1. TESCIONE, G. L'arte della seta a Napoli e la colonia di S. Leucio.   1932.

1. No subject.
N.Y.P.L.   February 13, 1934

NN   0018051   NN

Naples (Province) Consiglio provinciale dell'economia.   FOR OTHER EDITIONS
SEE MAIN ENTRY
Assante, Arturo, 1898–
... Il porto di Napoli; saggio storico-geografico economico, guida descrittiva ... amministrativa, tariffaria e commerciale. Sotto gli auspici del Consiglio provinciale dell'economia corporativa di Napoli. Napoli, Editore "Il Porto", 1936.

VOLUME 405

Naples (*Province*) *Consiglio provinciale dell'economia.*
Relazione sull'attività economica della provincia di Napoli.
Napoli.

    v. tables (part fold.) 31-34 cm.

    Pub. under earlier names of the consiglio: 1930–   Consiglio provinciale dell'economia corporativa; 19   Consiglio provinciale delle corporazioni.

    1. Naples (Province)—Econ. condit.

    HC307.N3A3   330.9457   34–7310 rev*

NN   0018053   DLC NN

Naples (*Province*) *Consiglio provinciale dell'economia corporativa*
see **Naples** (*Province*) *Consiglio provinciale dell'economia.*

Naples (*Province*) *Consiglio provinciale delle corporazioni*
see **Naples** (*Province*) *Consiglio provinciale dell'economia.*

Naples (*Province*) *Economia, Consiglio provinciale dell'*
see **Naples** (*Province*) *Consiglio provinciale dell'economia.*

Naples (*Province*) *Ente per il turismo*
    see
    Naples (*Province*) *Ente provinciale per il turismo.*

Naples (*Province*) *Ente Provinciale per il Turismo.*
Alberghi della provincia di Napoli.

    ₍Milano₎

    v. 17 cm.

    1. Hotels, taverns, etc.–Italy—Naples (Province)

    TX910.I 8N3   56–50824 ‡

NN   0018058   DLC

Naples (Province) Ente provinciale per il turismo.
  Catalogo

  see under

  Naples. Mostra del Ritratto Storico.

Naples (Province) Ente provinciale per il turismo.
  Catalogo

  see under

  Naples. Mostra di Stampe e "Guazzi" Napoletani dell''800.

Naples(Province) Ente provinciale per il turismo.
    La Mostra della pittura napoletana dei secoli XVII– XVIII– XIX. ₍Napoli, F. Giannini & figli, 1938₎
    5 p. l., 13-349 p., 1 l. incl. illus., plates. 24°.

    "Questa Mostra ... promossa dall'Ente provinciale per il turismo di Napoli ..."
    1. Painting, Italian. 2. Painting - Naples.

        MiU CtY CLM
NN   0018061   NNC NcU CU NN ViU PPT CSt DLC-P4 NjP

---

                provinciale
Naples (*Province*) *Ente, per il turismo.*
    ... Mostra di stampe e disegni napoletani dell'ottocento; catalogo, a cura di Augusto Cesareo; ridotto del Reale teatro San Carlo, autunno XIX. ₍Genova, S. A. I. G. A., già Barabino & Graeve, 1941₎

    82 p., 1 l. 57 pl. on 29 l. 23ᵐ.

    At head of title: Ente provinciale per il turismo di Napoli.

    1. Engravings, Italian—Exhibitions. 2. Drawings, Italian—Exhibitions. 3. Engravings, Italian—Naples. 4. Drawings, Italian—Naples. I. Naples. R. Teatro San Carlo. II. Cesareo, Augusto.

                          45–26085
    Library of Congress   NE661.N3A5   1941
                  ₍3₎   769.94508

NN   0018062   DLC

Naples (Province) Ente provinciale per il turismo.

Rome (City) Mostra storica della canzone napolitana, 1955.
    Mostra storica della canzone napolitana. Ente provinciale per il turismo con la collaborazione del Comune di Roma. Palazzo delle esposizioni, 18 aprile–5 maggio 1955. ₍Roma, Atel, 1955₎

      Naples (Province) Ente provinciale per il
DG842   turismo.
.5
.F53   **Filippis, Felice de.**
    ... La Reggia di Napoli. ₍Napoli₎ Ente provinciale per il turismo di Napoli ₍1942₎

Naples (Province) Giunta preparatoria.
    Rapporto del delegato speciale presidente a S. E. il segretario di stato, ministro degli affari interni. [Napoli, 1820]
    1.8°.
    Without title–page. Caption title.
    Signed, p. viii: Il presidente, Tommaso de Liso.
    A statistical work listing election results in the province according to parishes and towns.

NN   0018065   MH

Naples (Province) Intendenza.
    Giornale dell'intendenza della provincia di Napoli, anno 1849, 1 giugno [–anno 1852, gennaio.] (Stabilimento tipografico del Dante), n. d.
    no. 1-41. 4°.
    n. t. p.

NN   0018066   MH-L

16
It18   Naples (Province) Ispettorato provinciale dell'
        agricoltura.
        Circolare.
    Napoli,
        1. Agriculture. Research. Naples (Province)

NN   0018067   DNAL

16
It18P   Naples (Province) Ispettorato provinciale dell'
        agricoltura.
        Pubblicazione.
    Napoli,
        1. Agriculture. Research. Naples (Province)

NN   0018068   DNAL

Naples (Province).Laws, statutes, etc.
    Le legge of luglio 1904, n. 351 sul risorgimento economico di Napoli e la sua applicazione. 1908.
    171 p.

NN   0018069   PP

Naples (*Province*) *Laws, statutes, etc.*
    ... Testo unico del Regolamento speciale ed organico del Manicomio provinciale di Napoli (approvato dalla Deputazione provinciale nell'adunanza del 30 luglio 1920) Napoli, Tip. ospedale psichiatrico "L. Bianchi," 1940.
    63 p. 26ᵐ.

    At head of title: Amministrazione provinciale di Napoli.

    1. Capodichino, Italy. Manicomio provinciale.   45–34298
    Library of Congress   RC532.N3A5   1940

NN   0018070   DLC

Naples(Province). Prefetto della provincia.
    Letters dell'ill. mo Sig. Prefetto della provincia al Sindaco di Napoli. 1909.
    21 p.

NN   0018071   PP

Naples (*Province*) *Prefettura.*
    ... Bollettino degli atti ufficiali ...

    Portici ₍19

        v. in   25ᵐ. semimonthly.

    Cover-title.

    1. Naples (Province)—Pol. & govt.

    J7.I 5N33   47–36245

NN   0018072   DLC

Naples (*Province*) *Prefettura.*
    ... Foglio annunzi legali ...

    ₍Naples,

        v. in   25ᵐ. semiweekly.

    Caption title.
    At head of title,   : Prefettura di Napoli.

    1. Naples (Province)—Pol. & govt.   I. Title.
                            46–34757
    Library of Congress   J7.I 5N34
                 ₍2₎   352.045

NN   0018073   DLC

Naples (*Province*) *Regia prefettura*
    see
Naples (*Province*) *Prefettura.*

Naples (*Province*) *Turismo, Ente provinciale per il*
    see
Naples (*Province*) *Ente provinciale per il turismo.*

VOLUME 405

Naples (*Province*) *Ufficio regionale per la conservazione dei monumenti delle provincie meridionali.*
... Monvmenti dell'Italia meridionale; relazione dell'Vfficio regionale per la conservazione dei monvmenti delle provincie meridionali ...
Roma, Officina poligrafica romana, 1902
v. illus. (incl. plans) plates. 32ᶜᵐ.

I. Architecture—Italy.   I. Avena, Adolfo, 1860-

Library of Congress   NA1111.A8   11—29350

NN   0018076   DLC InU MH OC1

Naples (*Province*) Ufficio sanitario del porto.
La sanità maríttima a Napoli
see under   Italy. Direzione generale della sanità pubblica.

Naples (*Province*) Unione fascista degli industriali
see   Unione degli industriali della provincia di Napoli.

Naples (*Province*) Unione industriale fascista
see   Unione degli industriali della provincia di Napoli.

Naples (*Province*) Unione regionale industriale
see   Unione degli industriali della provincia di Napoli.

Naples (Provinces, 1860-61)
Collezione delle leggi e de'decreti emanati nelle provincie continentali dell'Italia Meridionale durante il periodo della dittatura, da'7 settembre a'6 novembre 1860. Napoli, Tip. nazionale,1860.

Issued in 14 numbers.

NN   0018081   MH

Naples (*Provinces, 1860-1861*)
Collezione delle leggi e de' decreti emanati nelle Provincie continentali dell'Italia meridionale durante il periodo della luogotenenza ... Napoli, Tipografia nazionale, 1861-62.
2 v. fold. tab. 22ᶜᵐ.
CONTENTS.—v. 1. Da' 7 novembre 1860 a' 30 aprile 1861.—v. 2. Dal primo maggio al 31 ottobre 1861.
Issued in 57 parts. No. 1-56 have caption title: Collezione delle leggi e de' decreti emanati ... nelle Provincie napoletane. No. 57: Supplemento.
"Le presente collezione contiene, oltre gli atti governativi emanati dalla luogotenenza, anche parecchie leggi e decreti regii chiamati in osservanza nelle Provincie napoletane durante il periodo luogotenenziale."
I. Sardinia (Kingdom)   Laws, statutes, etc. II. Italy. Laws, statutes, etc. III. Title.

47—37580

NN   0018082   DLC MH DDO NAurW

Naples (Provinces, 1860-61) Commissione per gli studi legislativi.
Relazione presentata a S.A.R.il principe luogotenente [of the Neapolitan Provinces] dalla Commissione [!] per gli studii legislativi, instituita con decreto dei 6 febraio 1861. [Naples,1861?]

pp.15.

NN   0018083   MH

710.1   Naples, Fla. Ordinances.
N16p   Preliminary draft: amended zoning ordinance, Naples, Florida. Prepared for City Council and Zoning Commission by Harland Bartholomew & Associates. St. Louis [1953?]
67ℓ. fold.map (in pocket) 29cm.

1. Zoning law--Naples, Fla. I. Bartholomew (Harland) and Associates.

NN   0018084   IU

Naples, *Me.*
Annual report of the selectmen of the town ...

Portland, Me.,
v. tables. 23ᶜᵐ.
    has title: Annual report of the municipal officers of the town...

           CA 34-2027 Unrev'd
Library of Congress   JS13.N137   352.07419

NN   0018085   DLC

Naples. [Los Angeles: Le Berthon Publishing Company, Publishers. 190-?]
8 leaves (illus. in colors) Narrow folio.
Bound in green buckram, with original cream paper covers bound in.
On recto of last leaf is advertisement of Official Naples Company, and of Naples Extension Company.
Received from Mr. Huntington, Mar. 3, 1925.

NN   0018086   CSmH

Naples; histoire, monuments, beaux-arts, litterature.
See under
[Lefort, Louis Joseph]

Naples; political, social, and religious
see under   [Chichester, Frederick Richard, earl of Belfast] 1827-1853.

NAPLES and diplomatic intervention. [London, J.Chapman,1857].

pp.(28).
Caption-title.
The Westminster Review,new series,no.XXIII, July 1857,pp.186-213.
A review of the parliamentary papers on the treaty of Paris,and of the letters of Gladstone in regard to the Neapolitan government.

NN   0018089   MH

NAPLES and diplomatic intervention. [New York,L.Scott & Co.,etc.,etc.,1857].

1.8°. pp.(17).
Caption-title.
The Westminster Review,no.CXXXIII,American ed. vol.XLV,no.I,July 1857,pp.103-119.
A review of the parliamentary papers on the treaty of Paris,and of the letters of Gladstone in regard to the Neapolitan government.

NN   0018090   MH

Naples and the Campagna felice
see under   [Engelbach, Lewis]

Naples anti-cruelty society.
see
Società napoletana per la protezione degli animali.

Naples ce qu'il faut faire pour rendre ce Royaume florissant
see under   [Goudar, Ange] 1720-1791.

Naples- Characters
see under   [Dura, Gaet]

---

* F319
.N3N3   The Naples Company, Naples, Fla.
1888
    Naples, Florida; issued by the Naples Company. Naples, Fla. [Press of the Courier-Journal, Job Printing Co., Louisville] 1888.
30, [1] p. illus. 20cm.
"R. G. Robinson, Gen'l Manager."

1. Naples, Fla.—Descr

NN   0018095   ViU

D
393   Naples et le Piémont. Paris, E.Dentu, 1860.
.M52   32 p.
    No.4 in a vol.with binder's title: Mélanges politiques.

1.Naples (Kingdom)--Hist. 2.Piedmont--Hist.

NN   0018096   MiU NN

Naples & Venise
see   [Montaran,Marie Constance Albertine Moisson de Vaux, baronne de]
Fragmens. Naples & Venise.

... Naples, Pompeii, Pestum, Baia, Sorrento, Capri, Amalfi ...
see under   Fattorusso, Giuseppe, publisher.

Naples water works company limited.
Acquedotto di Napoli. Naples water works company limited concessionaria. Marzo 1885. [Padova, 1885] 46 p. illus. map. 32cm.

324242B. 1. Water supply—Naples.
N. Y. P. L.   March 29, 1946

NN   0018099   NN

Mhc9   Napleton, John, 1738?-1817.
N162   Advice to a minister of the gospel, in the
A41   United Church of England and Ireland. Being a continuation of Advice to a student in the University. To which is added, A sermon on the pastoral care ... Hereford,Printed by D. Walker:sold by S.Sael and co.,London;Hanwell and Parker,Oxford;and Allen,Hereford,1801.
v1,[2],[9]-111p. 21½cm. [Binder's title: Napleton's tracts]

NN   0018100   CtY IaU

VOLUME 405

x250
N162a

Napleton, John, 1738?-1817.
Advice to a student in the university, concerning the qualifications and duties of a minister of the Gospel in the Church of England. Oxford, Printed for Fletcher and Hanwell; sold by Mess. Rivington, London, 1795.
147p. 21cm.

NN 0018101   IU CU DLC NN CtY MH MB IaU

xC42
Ox2uNn

‹Napleton, John› 1738?-1817.
Considerations on the public exercises for the first and second degrees in the University of Oxford. ‹Oxford?› 1773.
‹3›, xiii, 61p. 20cm.

Attributed to John Napleton in Brit. Mus. Cat.
Error in paging: 2 (3d group) numbered 16.

NN 0018102   IU RPB NN

Lmd27
772n

[Napleton, John] 1739?-1817.
Considerations on the residence usually required for degrees in the University of Oxford. Oxford, Printed in the year 1772.
24p. 21½cm.
"Errata" mounted on verso of t.-p.

1.Oxford. University - Degrees. 2.Degrees, Academic. I.Title.

NN 0018103   CtY RPB

Mhc9
N162
A41

Napleton, John, 1738?-1817.
The duty of churchwardens respecting the church ... 3d ed. Glocester:Printed by D.Walker;sold by S.Sael and co.,London;Fletcher and Hanwell,Oxford;and J.Allen,Hereford,1805.
42p. 21½cm. [Binder's title: Napleton's tracts]

NN 0018104   CtY

Mhc8
1798
N16

Napleton, John, 1738-1817.
A sermon, preached at Lambeth chapel, on Sunday, March 4, 1798, at the consecration of the Right Reverend John Buckner ... By John Napleton ... Hereford,Printed by D.Walker;and sold by Messrs.Robson,Rivington, London;[etc.,etc.]1798.
24p. 22cm.

NN 0018105   CtY

Mhc9
N162
A41

Napleton, John, 1738-1817.
A sermon preached in St.Mary's church, in the University of Oxford, at the anniversary meeting of the governours of the Radcliffe infirmary, June XIX. M,DCC,XCII... Hereford: Printed by D.Walker;sold,for the benefit of the charity,by Messrs.Robson and Clark,London; Fletcher,and Prince and Cook,Oxford;and Allen, Hereford,1792.
32p. 21½cm. [Binder's title: Napleton's tracts]

NN 0018106   CtY

Mhc9
N162
A41

Napleton, John, 1738?-1817.
A sermon preached in the Cathedral church of Hereford at the meeting of the three choirs of Worcester Hereford and Gloucester September IX. MDCCLXXXIX ... Oxford:At the Clarendon press.Sold by D.Prince and J.Cooke,Oxford; T.Cadell;Messrs.Robson and Clarke,London,1789.
3p.ℓ.,[5]-25p. 21½cm. [Binder's title: Napleton's tracts]

NN 0018107   CtY

Mhc9
N162
A41

Napleton, John, 1738?-1817.
A sermon preached in the Cathedral church of Hereford, V. November M,DCCX ... Hereford: Printed by J.Allen;sold by W.Walker,London;and J.Allen,Hereford,1810.
18p. 21½cm. [Binder's title: Napleton's tracts]

NN 0018108   CtY MH-AH

Mhc9
N162
A41

Napleton, John, 1738?-1817.
A sermon, preached in the Cathedral church of Hereford, October XXV, MDCCCXI. Being the day of His Majesty's inauguration ... Hereford, Printed by E.G.Wright;sold by W.Walker,London, and J.Allen,Hereford,1812.
1p.ℓ.,iii,[5]-20p. 21½cm. [Binder's title: Napleton's tracts]

NN 0018109   CtY

Napleton, John, 1738?-1817.
Sermons for the use of schools and families. Glocester, printed by D. Walker, 1804-05.
2 vols.
Vol. I. is 3d ed. The title of vol. 2 is: Sermons for the use of colleges and schools, and families.

NN 0018110   MH

Law

Napley, David, ed.

Bateman, Joseph, 1797-1863.
Law of auctions. 11th ed. by David Napley. London, Estates Gazette ‹1954›

Law

Napley, David, joint author.

Grattan-Doyle, Howard Nicholas, d. 1947.
The law on the remuneration of auctioneers and estate agents, by H. N. Grattan-Doyle and David Napley. London, Estates Gazette ‹1947›

NAPODANO,Gabriele.
Appunti delle lezioni di dritto e procedura penale. Napoli,G.Argenio,1885.

8°.

NN 0018113   MH-L

Napodano, Gabriele.
Il concetto e la determinazione dello stato per ... Gabriele Napodano ... Napoli, G. Argenio, 1880.
68 p. 22½cm.

NN 0018114   MH-L

4K
1069

Napodano, Gabriele.
Del pubblico ministero nei popoli civili e delle sue condizioni in Italia. Napoli, Tip. di G. Argenio, 1880.
157 p.

NN 0018115   DLC-P4 MH

Napodano, Gabriele.
Dell'omicidio volontario. Lezioni due lette nella regia università di Macerata 1880. Napoli, 1888.
40 p.

NN 0018116   MH-L

NAPODANO,Gabriele.
Il diritto di punire e la imputabilità umana; prolusione letta nella regia università di Macerata come cominciamento al corso ordinario di dritto penale. Napoli,G.de Angelis e figlio, 1879.
pp.35. 8°.

NN 0018117   MH-L

4K
It
1625

Napodano, Gabriele.
Il diritto penale italiano nei suoi principii. Napoli, D. Cesareo, 1895-
v. 1

NN 0018118   DLC-P4

4K
4196

Napodano, Gabriele.
Il diritto penale romano nelle sue attenenze col diritto penale moderno. Napoli, Commend. G. de Angelis, 1878.
134 p.

NN 0018119   DLC-P4 MH-L MH

Napodano, Gabriele.
... L'eccezione di verità nel delitto di diffamazione secondo il diritto italiano. (In Pel cinquantesimo anno d'insegnamento di Enrico Pessina. Napoli, 1899. v. 2, p. ‹293›-311)

NN 0018120   NNC

Napodano, Gabriele.
Intorno alla proposta di legge dell'on. Luigi Lucchini; provvedimenti per la prevenzione della recidiva e per la riparazione degli errori giudiziari. Verona, Tipografia cooperative, 1903.
8° 18 p.
"Estratto dalla Ronda giudiziaria, anno 1, fasc. 20. "

NN 0018121   MH-L

4K
Ital.-
462

Napodano, Gabriele.
Manuale di procedura penale. Milano, F. Vallardi [191-
631 p.   (Biblioteca giuridica contemporanea)

NN 0018122   DLC-P4

VOLUME 405

Napodano, Gabriele.
  Note di giurisprudenza pubblicate nel Filangieri pel prof. Gabriele Napodano. Napoli, Società in accomandita A. Bellisario, 1888.
    62 p. 24cm.

NN 0018123   MH-L

Napodano, Gabriele.
  Posto che occupa il codice italiano del 1859 in mezzo alle legislazioni odierne e di fronte alla scienza del giure penale. Napoli, 1888.
    22 p.

NN 0018124   MH-L

Napodano, Gabriele.
  Problemi fondamentali di una filosofia del diritto. Napoli, G. de Angelis, 1873.
    8°

NN 0018125   MH-L

Napodano, Gabriele.
  Relazione intorno ai principii addottati dalla Commissione ministeriale per la riforma del Codice di procedura penale, letta dal prof. Gabriele Napodano alla Facoltà di giurisprudenza della Università di Pisa. Pisa, Vannucchi, 1901.
    61 p. 25cm.

NN 0018126   MH-L NN

[Napodano, Gabriele]
  ... Il sistema penale nel diritto positivo vigente in Italia ... [n.p., n.d.]
    12 p. 26½cm.
    Running title: Appendice ai capitoli V a IX.

NN 0018127   MH-L

NAPODANO, Gabriele.
  Il verbo novello nel dritto e nella procedura penale; studio critico intorno al positivismo moderno nella giustizia penale. Napoli, A. Bellisario, 1890.
    pp. 44. 8°.

NN 0018128   MH-L

Napodano, Luigi, 1844-
  ... Pel Signor Antonio Luigi Siniscalchi ... Roma, G. Balbi, 1895.
    cover-title, 20 p. 30cm.
    At head of title: Regia Corte di cassazione di Roma. 2ª Sezione penale. Udienza del 30 dicembre 1895.
    Signed at end: Avv. Luigi Napodano; Avv. Alfonso Mirenghi.

NN 0018129   MH-L

Napodano, Luigi, 1844-
  Per la Ditta A. Auverny e C. (parte civile) contro Fiorenzo Pez e Francesco Vinaccia innanzi l'Ecc.ma Corte di cassazione, 2ª Sezione penale. Udienza del 13 luglio 1893 ... Roma, G. Balbi, 1893.
    cover-title, 33 p. 30½cm.
    Signed at end: Avv. Luigi Napodano; Avv. Alfonso Mirenghi.

NN 0018130   MH-L

Napodano, Sebastiano, 1298-1362.
  Consvetvdines neapolitanae cvm glossa Napodani primvm authore Camillo Salerno additionibus sexdecim ill. iureconsultorum ... deinde alijs additionibus Vincentij de Franchis, Iacobi Anelli de Bottis, Foelicis de Rubeis ... ac Thomae Nauclerij... cum nouo indice, avthore Carolo de Rosa ... accessit in fine operis noua Glossographia eiusdem authoris ad easdem consuetudines. Neapoli, ex regia typographia Aegidij Longi, 1677.
    8 p. l., 384, 44, [46] p., 2 l., [3], 300, [47] p. 34.5 cm.
    Title-page printed in red and black; initials; tail piece.

    Carlo de Rosa's Glossographia has separate title-page printed in red and black with printer's mark and half-title.

NN 0018132   CtY-L

Italy Napadano, Sebastiano, 1298-1362.
46   Consuetudines neapolitanae cum glossa Napo-
N16 dani, primum a Camillo Slaerno suis, & quam-
+1775 plurium ill. JCC. ... additionibus auctae; postea Jac. Anelli de Bottis, Vinc. de Franchis, Fel. de Rubeis, Reg. Reverterii, & Th. Nauclerii aliis additionibus locupletatae; denique a Carolo de Rosa margineis notulis ... & decisionibus Minadoi, de Franchis, Gizzarelli, de Ponte, Capyciilatro, Sanfelicii, Merlini, & aliorum illustratae: nunc glossographia eiusdem Car. de Rosa ... & additionibus ... ad proprias sedes restitutis ... ab
    innumeris mendis purgatae ... Quibus accesserunt Nicolai Carletti ... excerpta; & novae additiones J.B.S. . . Neapoli 1775. Sumptibus Antonii Cervonii.
    2v. 37cm.

NN 0018134   CtY-L MH

Napodano, Sebastiano, 1298-1362.
  Consvetvdines neapolitane cvm glosis excellentissimi do. Neapolitani Sebastiani Neapolitani vna cum decisionibus sacri regii consilii ... Neapoli, apud Ioannem Paulum Suganappum, 1546.
    28 p. l., 117 numb. l., [2] p. 30.5 cm.
    Signatures: +⁴, a-f⁴, A-T⁶, U⁴.
    Woodcut arms of Spain on title-page; printer's mark on verso of last leaf; woodcut initials.
    Title-page and beginning of Prohemium printed in red and black.
    "Editum per ... Scipionem Ianuarium Neapolitanum": 2d prel. leaf.

NN 0018135   CtY-L

Napodano, Sebastiano, 1298-1362.
  Consvetvdines neapolitane cum glosis nobilis domini Neapolitani Sebastiani Neapolitani ... una cum decisionibus sacri regii cõsilii Neapolitani ... Neapoli, impressum per magistrum Antonium de Frizis sũptibus & expēsis d. Scipionis, 1518.
    38 p. l., 136 numb. l. 29.5 cm.
    Signatures: AA-EE⁶, FF⁸, A-V⁶, X-Y⁸.
    Errors in foliation: 60, 68, 69, 86, 87, 92,93 incorrectly numberd 59, 66, 61, 76, 78, 93, 83 respectively and corrected in manuscript.
    Title-page and Repertorium partly in red; the first two paragraphs of the Prohemium completely
    in red; woodcut initials.
    "Editum per ... Scipionem Ianuarium Neapolitanum": 3d prel. leaf.
    Contains marginal manuscript notes.

NN 0018137   CtY

Greenlee
4504
P855   NAPOLEADA ou sentimento dos povos da Catalunha. Traduzida do idioma hespanhol. 2.ed. Lisboa, Impressão Regia, 1808.
    12p. 20cm.

NN 0018138   ICN MH

Napoleão, Aluizio, 1914- comp.
  Arquivo do Barão do Rio-Branco
    see under Brazil. Ministério das Relações Exteriores. Divisão Cultural.

Napoleão, Aluizio, 1914-
  ... Os arquivos particulares do Itamaratí. Rio de Janeiro, Imprensa nacional, 1940.
    41, [1] p. 23ᶜᵐ. ([Brazil] Ministerio das relações exteriores. [Serviço de publicações. [Publicações] 6)
    "As atividades diplomáticas desses homens, cujo arquivos estão hoje depositados no Ministério das relações exteriores."—p. 41.
    CONTENTS.—Duarte da Ponte Ribeiro (barão da Ponte Ribeiro) 1795-1878.—Rodrigo de Souza da Silva Pontes, 1799-1855.—Francisco Adolpho de Varnhagen (visconde de Porto-Seguro) 1816-1878.—Francisco Ignacio de Carvalho Moreira (barão de Penedo) 1815-1906.—Joaquim Thomaz do Amaral (visconde de Cabo-Frio) 1818-1907.—José Maria da Silva Paranhos (visconde do Rio-Branco) 1819-1880.—José Maria da Silva Paranhos junior (barão do Rio-Branco) 1845-1912.—Joaquim Aurelio Nabuco de Araujo, 1849-1910.
    1. Brazil—For. rel. I. Title.
    [Full name: Aluizio Napoleão de Freitas Rego]
                            43-34002
    Library of Congress   JX1533.N3
    ——— Copy 2.   JX531.A26 no. 6

NN 0018141   DLC UU

Napoleão, Aluizio, 1914-
  Brazil. *Ministerio das relações exteriores.*
    ... Documentos e depoimentos sobre os trabalhos aéronauticos de Santos Dumont. Rio de Janeiro, Imprensa nacional, 1941.

Napoleão, Aluizio, 1914-
  ... Imagens da América (crônicas) Rio de Janeiro [Companhia brasileira de artes gráficas] 1945.
    6 p. l., 15-171 p. 19¼ᶜᵐ.
    "Algumas referências a outros livros do autor": p. [161]-171.
    1. U. S.—Descr. & trav. I. Title.
    [Full name: Aluizio Napoleão de Freitas Rego]
                            46-3400
    Library of Congress   E169.N25
                 [2]   917.3

NN 0018143   DLC PU

Napoleão, Aluizio, 1914-
  Rio-Branco e as relações entre o Brasil e os Estados Unidos. [Rio de Janeiro] Ministério das Relações Exteriores [1947]
    215 p. illus. 23 cm. (Comissão Preparatória do Centenário do Barão do Rio-Branco. Monografias, 2)
    1. U. S.—For. rel.—Brazil. 2. Brazil—For. rel.—U. S. 3. Rio Branco, José Maria da Silva Paranhos, barão de, 1845-1912.
    Full name: Aluizio Napoleão de Freitas Rego.
    F2537.R5748C6 No. 2   59-17768 ‡
    ViU FU NjP MH NcU ICU IEdS ICarbS CaBVaU
NN 0018144   DLC DPU CLU NNC CU NN CSt PU IU TxU

VOLUME 405

Napoleão, Aluizio, 1914–
Santos-Dumont and the conquest of the air, tr. by Luiz Victor Le Cocq d'Oliveira. Rio de Janeiro, National Print. Off., 1945.
2 v. illus., plates, ports., facsims. 25 cm. (Ministry of State for Foreign Affairs of Brazil. Division of Intellectual Co-operation. Brazilian studies collection, 1)
Vol. 2, "Documents and testimony on the aeronautical work of Santos Dumont," part in French, part in English, part in Italian, part in Portuguese.
1. Santos-Dumont, Alberto, 1873–1932. 2. Aeronautics—Hist. I. Le Cocq d'Oliveira, Luiz Victor. (Series: Brazil. Ministerio das Relações Exteriores. Divisão de Cooperação Intelectual. Brazilian studies collection 1)
Full name: Aluizio Napoleão de Freitas Rego.
TL540.S25N312   629.1309   47–6007*

ICN NNC NBC ViU MiHM NcD TxU CtY WaTC OrCS WaWW NN MiEM NcRS NcU PPT PPL PPD PU NcD CU IU PWcS NjP
NN 0018145   DLC MtBC IdPI CaBVaU IdU CaBVa CaBViP

NAPOLEÃO, ALUIZIO, 1914–
Santos-Dumont and the conquest of the air; translated by Luiz Victor Le Cocq d'Oliveira. Rio de Janeiro, National print. off., 1945. 2 v. illus., port. 25cm. (Brazilian studies collection. 1)
Microfiche (Negative). 12 sheets. 11 x 15cm. (NYPL FSN 1099)
Bibliographical footnotes.
1. Santos-Dumont, Alberto, 1873–1932. 2. Aeronautics—Hist.
I. Series.

NN 0018146   NN

Napoleão, Aluizio, 1914–
... Santos Dumont e a conquista do ar. Rio de Janeiro, Imprensa nacional, 1941.
270 p. 23cm. (Brazil) Ministerio das relações exteriores. Serviço de publicações. (Publicações) 16)
1. Santos-Dumont, Alberto, 1873–1932. 2. Aeronautics—Hist.
(Full name: Aluizio Napoleão de Freitas Rego)
Library of Congress   43–34034
——— Copy 2.   TL540.S25N3
JX531.A26 no. 16

NN 0018147   DLC DHEW MH–BA RPB

Napoleão, Aluizio, 1914–
... Santos-Dumont y la conquista del aire. Traducción de Alarcón Fernández ... Rio de Janeiro, Imprensa nacional, 1942–43.
2 v. illus., plates, ports., facsims. 24½cm. (Brazil) Ministerio de relaciones exteriores. División de cooperación intelectual. Colección de estudios brasileños, 1)
Vol. 2, "Documentos y testimonios sobre los trabajos aeronáuticos de Santos-Dumont," part in French, part in English, part in Italian, part in Portuguese.
1. Santos-Dumont, Alberto, 1873–1932. 2. Aeronautics—Hist.
I. Alarcon Fernandez, ———, tr.
(Full name: Aluizio Napoleão de Freitas Rego)
45–18068
Library of Congress   TL540.S25N317
(3)   629.1309

NN 0018148   DLC DPU NN TxU CU IU OCU

Napoleão, Aluizio.
... Segredo; contos; illustrações de Santa Rosa. Rio (de Janeiro) C. Mendes Junior, 1935.
5 p. l., (13)–169 p., 2 l. illus. 18½cm.
I. Title.
37–31178
Library of Congress   (PQ9697.N2S4
(2)   869.3

NN 0018149   DLC PU

Napoleão, Aluizio, 1914–
... O segundo Rio-Branco, o homem e o estadista; ensaio. Rio de Janeiro, Editôra A Noite (1941)
194 p., 2 l. plates, ports. maps. 18cm.
Appendices (p. (153)–(189)): Datas.—Trabalhos de Rio Branco.—Bibliografia.—Arquivos consultados.
1. Rio Branco, José Maria da Silva Paranhos, 2. barão do, 1845–1912. I. Title.
Library of Congress   F2537.R596   42–15868
(2)   923.281

NN 0018150   DLC CtY IU CIU LNHT NcU TxU FTaSU DPU

NAPOLEÃO, ARTHUR, 1843–1925.
Caissana brasileira. Rio de Janeiro, Typ. de Jornal do commercio, 1898. x,406 p. illus. 23cm.
Bibliography, p. [391]–404.
1. Chess—Problems, 1898.

NN 0018151   NN OCl CtY NjP

Napoleão, Arthur, 1843–1925.
...Feu follet; mazurka de concert pour piano, par Arthur Napoléon. Op. 31. Lisbonne: Sassetti & cie (189–?). Publ. pl. no. S. e Ca. 814. 15 p. f°.
1. Piano.—Mazurkas. 2. Title.   DREXEL MUSICAL FUND.
N. Y. P. L.   March 1, 1922.

NN 0018152   NN

[NAPOLEÃO, Arthur] 1843–1925.
Primeiro torneio de problemas de xadrez. Promovido pelo "Journal do Commercio" do Rio de Janeiro no anno de 1887. [Rio de Janeiro], J. Villeneuve & C., [1887].
16 cm. pp.6,(66),13. Illustr.
"Catalogo",13 pages at end.
"A scarce and interesting little collection of problems and one of the few books on chess published in South America." - Howland catalogue

NN 0018153   MH NjP OCl NN

[NAPOLEÃO, Arthur] 1843–1925.
Problemas,enigmas,esphinges e fantasias. Xadrez. Publicados no "Jornal do commercio" do Rio de Janeiro (Ate Dezembro de 1886). [Rio de Janeiro],Typ.imp.e Const.de J.Villeneuve & c., [1887].
16 cm. Illustr.
"Catalogo",pp.(2),10 at end.

NN 0018154   MH NjP OCl

Napoleão, Benedito Martins, 1903–
Opus 7 (i. e. sete) Poemas. Rio de Janeiro, Livraria Editôra Coelho Branco, 1953.
164 p. 19 cm.
I. Title.
PQ9697.N213O6   56–44814 ‡

NN 0018155   DLC

Napoleão, Benedito Martins, 1903–
...Poesias (1871–1889)
see under Area Leão, Raimundo de.

Napoleão, Hugo
see
Napoleão do Rego, Hugo.

Napoleão de Freitas Rego, Aluizio
see
Napoleão, Aluizio, 1914–

Napoleão de Victoria, Frederico
see Victoria, Frederico Napoleão de.

Napoleão do Rego, Hugo.
Banco do Brasil, pareceres (por) Hugo Napoleão, consultor jurídico. Prefácio do autor. Ementário alfabético e notas do dr. Paulino de Araujo Jorge ... Edição privada. Rio de Janeiro, A. Coelho Branco F.°, 1944.
301 p., 1 l. 23½cm.
On cover: 1.ª série.
1. Commercial law—Brazil—Addresses, essays, lectures. I. Banco do Brasil, Rio de Janeiro (1905–   )
45–21498

NN 0018160   DLC

Napoleão do Rego, Hugo.
... Discursos parlamentares. Camara federal, novembro de 1927 a dezembro de 1929. Rio de Janeiro, Typog. do Jornal do commercio, Rodrigues & c., 1930.
282 p., 2 l. 23½cm.
At head of title: Hugo Napoleão ...
1. Brazil—Pol. & govt.—1889–1930. 2. Piauhy, Brazil (State)
44–26472
Library of Congress   F2537.N3
(3)   981

NN 0018161   DLC

Napoleão dos Santos, Arthur
see
Napoleão, Arthur, 1843–1925.

Napoleon I, *Emperor of the French,* 1769–1821.
Works by this author printed in America before 1801 are available in this library in the Readex Microprint edition of Early American Imprints published by the American Antiquarian Society.
This collection is arranged according to the numbers in Charles Evans' American Bibliography.

NN 0018163   DLC

Napoleon I, *emperor of the French, 1769–1821.*
Œuvres.
Paris. Panckoucke. 1821, 22. 6 v. in 5. Portrait. Facsimile. 20 cm., in 8s.
Contents.—1. Généalogie de Napoléon Bonaparte. — Précis chronologique et historique de la vie de Napoléon Bonaparte. 2. Première campagne d'Italie, 1796, 1797. 3. Lettre à Matteo Buttafoco, le 23 janvier, l'an II. — Le souper de Beaucaire, 29 juillet 1793. — Première campagne d'Italie (suite), 1797, 1798. — Expédition d'Égypte, 1798, 1799. 4. Expédition d'Égypte (suite), 1799. — Consulat, 1799–1804. — Empire, 1804, 1805. 5. Empire (suite), 1805–1811. 6. Campagne de Russie, 1812. — Campagne de Saxe, 1813, 1814. — Campagne de France, 1814. — [Campagne de 1815.]
Vol. 6 is bound with vol. I.

NN 0018164   MB CtY NN RPB

VOLUME 405

845N16   Napoleon I, emperor of France.
I1822   Oeuvres de Napoléon Bonaparte.
     Paris, 1822.
     5v.

NN   0018165   IU OC1

944.05   Napoléon I, Emperor of the French, 1769-1821.
N216w   Werke. Nach den vorhandenen Quellen chrono-
logisch geordnet. Deutsch von L. von Alvensleben. Als Supplement zu Heyne's Geschichte
Napoleons. Chemnitz, Gedsche, 1840.
     432 p. illus.

     Imperfect copy: p. 261-268 wanting.

     1. France - Hist. - Consulate and Empire,
1799-1815. I. Alvensleben, Ludwig von, ed. and
tr. II. Heyne, C.T. Geschichte Napoleon's.

NN   0018166   TxCsA CU

Napoléon I, emperor of the French, 1769-1821.
     A l'armée. Imprimerie de
Poulet, n.d.   4to.

     Address.

NN   0018167   MWiW-C

Napoleon I, Emperor of the French, 1769-1821.
     Abrégé de l'art de la guerre
     see under title

Room

B138a   Napoléon I, emperor of the French, 1769-1821.
800   An account of the French expedition in
Egypt, written by Buonaparte and Berthier.
With Sir Sidney Smith's letters from Egypt.
Also, an appendix containing the life of
General Buonaparte, brought down to the end
of November, 1799, in which is given a sketch
of the revolution begun November 9; by
Buonaparte, Sieyes, &c. Leeds,E.Baines[1800?]
     62p. 21cm.
     Caption-title: French expedition in Egypt.

NN   0018169   CtY MH

Napoléon I, Emperor of the French, 1769-1821.

     Acte de médiation, fait par le premier
consul de la République Française, entre
les partis qui divisent la Suisse. Berne,
F. Fischer, 1803.
     118 p. 19cm. (Joseph Cabell Collection
Pamphlets, v. 5, no. 3)

     1. Switzerland—Constitutional law. 2. Constitu-
tions, State—Switzerland. 3. Switzerland—Hist.—
Under Mediation act, 1803-1814. I. France. II.
Switzerland. Con   stitution. III. Title.

NN   0018170   ViU

Napoleon I, *emperor of the French*, 1769–1821.
     ... Acte de médiation fait par le premier consul de la Ré-
publique française, entre les partis qui divisent la Suisse ...
₍Paris? 1803?₎

     120 p. 32ᶜᵐ.

     Caption title.
     At head of title: Au nom du peuple français. Bonaparte 1.ᵉʳ consul
de la république.

     1. Switzerland—Constitutional law. 2. Constitutions, State—Switzer-
land. 3. Switzerland—Hist.—Under Mediation act, 1803-1814. I.
France. II. Switzerland. Constitution. III. Title.

                       41–42054

     Library of Congress   JN8741 1803

NN   0018171   DLC ViU

Napoléon I, *emperor of the French*, 1769–1821.
     Napoleon's addresses; selections from the proclama-
tions, speeches and correspondance of Napoleon Bonaparte; ed. by Ida M. Tarbell. Boston, J. Knight company, 1897.

     xxvi, ₍27₎-147 p. front. (port.) 16½ᵐ.   (*On cover:* Famous men series)

     I. Tarbell, Ida Minerva, 1857– ed.   4–15683

     Library of Congress   DC214.N213

NN   0018172   DLC MB OC1

Napoléon I, emperor of the French,
     1769-1821
     Adieux de N. Bonaparte a la France et
a l'Europe, laissés en manuscrit à l'Ile
d'Elbe a son départ, en 1815. Paris,
J.Dentu,1848.
     Cover title. 16p. 22cm.

NN   0018173   OC1WHi

Napoléon I, emperor of the French, 1769-1821,
     supposed author.
     Les adieux de Napoléon Bonaparte, à l'impera-
trice Marie-Louise ...
     see under title

---

ar V   Napoléon I, Emperor of the French, 1769-
4428   1821.
no.5   Aforismi politici e pensieri morali e
filosofici di Napoleone Bonaparte estratti
da più di 80 opere originali per cura del
conte Augusto di Liancourt. Traduzione dal
francese. Torino, Ferrero e Franco, 1850.
     90 p. 20cm.

     No. 5 in a vol. with binder's title:
Miscellanea. Storia.

NN   0018175   NIC

Napoleon I, Emperor of the French, 1846-1906.
     Alexander Iᵉʳ et Napoléon d'après leur
correspondance inédite 1801-1813 ...
          see under   Tatishchev, Sergiĕi Spiridonovich,
1846-1906.

Napoléon I, *emperor of the French*, 1769–1821.
     ... Allocutions et proclamations militaires, pub. pour la
première fois d'après les textes authentiques par Georges
Barral ... Paris, E. Flammarion ₍1895₎

     xxxviii, ₍39₎-252 p. 17ᶜᵐ.

     At head of title: Napoléon Iᵉʳ.
     Title vignette.

     1. France—History—Consulate and empire, 1799-1815. 2. France—His-
tory, Military—1789-1815. 3. France—Army—History. I. Barral,
Georges, 1842– ed. II. Title.

                       A 18–187

     Title from Peabody Inst.,   Baltimore. Printed by L. C.

NN   0018177   MdBP NN

Napoleon I, emperor of the French. 1769-1821.
                FOR OTHER EDITIONS
                SEE MAIN ENTRY

₍Doris, Charles, de Bourges₎
     Amours secrettes de Napoléon Buonaparte; par l'au-
teur du Précis historique et des Mémoires secrèts. 2. éd.
rev. et cor.   Paris, G. Mathiot, 1815.

B137a   Napoléon I, emperor of the French, 1769-1821.
2   Analyse da correspondencia de Napoleão com
v.8   Azanza; ultimamente interceptada, e publicada:
que contém tres documentos, a saber: I. He a
abdicação voluntaria do intruso José. II. A
consulta do Conselho d'estado de Madrid. III.
A proclamação do Corso aos habitantes de peninsula. Lisboa,Na Impressão regia,1811.
     15p. 23cm. [Binder's title: Epoca franceza,
1808-1813. VIII]

NN   0018179   CtY

Napoleon I, Emperor of the French, 1769-1821.
     Anteckningar rörande Napoleon...
     see under title

Napoléon I, *emperor of the French*, 1769–1821.
     Aphorismes politiques, pensées morales et philosophi-
ques de l'empereur Napoléon; recueillis ... par Cᵗᵉ. Aᵘᵗᵉ.
G. de Liancourt, Mr. J. A. Manning, éditeur ... Londres,
T. C. Newby, 1848.

     xii p., 1 l., 271 p. 20½ᵐ.

     Added t.-p. in English; French and English on opposite pages.

     1. Aphorisms and apothegms.   I. Godde de Liancourt, Caliste Au-
guste de, comte, b. 1805, comp. II. Manning, James Alexander, ed.

                       11–2201

     Library of Congress   JC230.N2

NN   0018181   DLC PLF TxU CtY

Napoleon I, Emperor of the French, 1769–1821.
     The aphorisms of Napoleon. Les aphorismes de Napo-
léon. Translated by James Alexander Manning. London,
Ackermann ₍1852₎

     vi, 60 p. 19 cm.

     I. Manning, James Alexander, ed. II. Title. III. Title: Les
aphorismes de Napoléon.

     DC214.M2613   72–253774
                                  MARC

NN   0018182   DLC

NAPOLEON I,emperor of the FRENCH.
     Napoleon's appeal to the British nation,on
his treatment at Saint Helena;the official
memoir,dictated by him [to the Count of Montho-
lon] and delivered to Sir Hudson Lowe. London,
W.Hone,1817.

     pp.8.
     Published in London by G.N.Santini on his
arrival there from St.Helena in 1817.

NN   0018183   MH

YA   Napoleon I, Emperor of the French, 1769-1821.
23910   Napoleon's argument for the divinity of Christ,
and the scriptures,/in a conversation with
General Bertrand, at St.·Helena. [n.p., n.d.]
     8p.

     (American tract society, no. 477)

NN   0018184   DLC

YA   Napoleon I, Emperor of the French, 1769-1821.
23941   Napoleon's argument for the divinity of Christ,
and the scriptures, in a conversation with
General Bertrand, at St. Helena. Translated
from the French. [New York, Amer.Tract Soc.,1842?]
     8p. 12°. (American tract society, no. 477)

NN   0018185   DLC NN

VOLUME 405

* NAPOLEON I, emperor of the French.
'Napoleon's argument for the divinity of
Christ and the Scriptures. Translated from
the French. With a statement by Professor de
Felice, attesting the authenticity of the
narrative.] N.Y.,Mil.Post Library Assoc.,[1870

32°. pp.20.

NN   0018186   MH

Napoleon I, emperor of the French,
1769-1821
Au Quartier-Général d'Alexandrie, le
18 Messidor, an 6 de la Rép. Bonaparte,
membre de l'Institut national, Général
en chef; au Directoire Exécutif.
[au Caire, de l'Impr. de Marc Aurel,
imp. de l'Armée,1798]
3p.   23cm.
Caption title.
Printed text of an official report
made by Napoleon when he landed his
troops in Africa, narrating the advance

of the Army from Malta to Alexandria,
and the capture of the city. The original
report was signed by both Napoleon and
Berthier, chief-of-staff of the Army of
Bonaparte.

NN   0018188   OClWHi

Napoleon I, emperor of the French,
1769-1821
...Au Quartier-Général du Kaire, le
premier Messidor an 7. Bonaparte,
Général en Chef, au Directoire Exécutif.
[au Kaire, de l'Imp. nationale,1799]
8p.   21½cm.
Caption title.
At head of title: République française.
Liberté, Egalité.
Printed text of an official report
made by Bonaparte and sent to the
Executive Director in Paris, relative

to the military events which took place
in lower Egypt during his invasion of
Syria. The original report was signed
by both Napoleon and Berthier, chief-
of-staff of the Army of Bonaparte.

NN   0018190   OClWHi

944.05 Napoléon I, Emperor of the French, 1769-1821.
N16Wn1Gk Ausgewählte Correspondenz Napoleons I. Mit
Ermächtigung der zur Veröffentlichung
derselben bestellten Staatscommission aus dem
französischen übersetzt von Heinrich Kurz.
Hildburghausen, Verlag des Bibliographischen
Instituts, 1868-70.
3v. fold.col.map. 19cm.

I. Kurz, Heinrich, 1805-1873, ed.

NN   0018191   IU CU

Napoléon I, emperor of the French, 1769-1821.
Authentic copy of Napoleon's memorial concerning
the treatment he has experienced from Sir Hudson
Lowe, British governor of the Island of St. Helena
and his protest against the Treaty of August 3, 1815,
by General Count Montholon, as dictated by
Napoleon. To which is added important particulars,
by M. Santine. London, J. Fairburn [1816?]
16 p.   22 cm.
1. Napoléon I. Captivity, 1815-1821.
I. Montholon, Charles Jean Tristam, Marquis de,
1783-1853. II. Santini, Jean Noel.

NN   0018192   NcU

Napoleon 1, emperor of the French.
Autobiography of Napoleon Bonaparte. N. Y.
Cosmopolitan, 1898.
v.p. O.

NN   0018193   PP

Napoléon I, *emperor of the French*, 1769-1821.
Napoleon's autobiography; the personal memoirs of Bona-
parte, compiled from his own letters and diaries by Professor
F. M. Kircheisen; translated by Frederick Collins, B. A.; with
an introduction by Henry Irving Brock. New York, Duffield
& company, 1931.
2 p. l., viii, [1], 5-288 p. front., ports. 24½cm.
Lettered on cover: Memoirs of Napoleon I.
London edition (Hutchinson & co. ltd.) has title: Memoirs of Na-
poleon I.
I. Kircheisen, Friedrich Max, 1877– ed. II. Collins, Frederick, tr.
III. Title.
Library of Congress   DC213.2.A4 1931   31-6874
———— Copy 2.
Copyright A 35274   [5]   923.144

NN   0018194   DLC PHC NN PPL NcD

Napoléon I, emperor of the French, 1769-1821.
Bataille de Preussisch-Eylau...
see under title

Napoléon I, emperor of the French, 1769-1821,
supposed author.
La bataille de Waterloo: poème par Napoléon,
envoyé de Londres ...
see under title   [Supplement]

DC214 Napoléon I, emperor of the French, 1769-1821.
.A13   Berühmte aussprüche und worte Napoleons von
Corsika bis St. Helena. [2. durchgesehene u.
verm. aufl., Leipzig, J. Zeitler, 1906.
[1], 323, [1] p. front.(port.)
"Gesammelt und herausgegeben von Robert Rehlen
[pseud.]"
I. Zeitler, Julius, 1874-   ed.

NN   0018197   ICU

Napoléon I, emperor of the French, 1769-1821.
Berühmte Aussprüche und Worte Napoleons von
Corsika bis St.Helena. Leipzig, J.Zeitler
[1927?]
[2] 323 p. 1 l. front.(port) 16 cm.
Half-title: Rehlen-Bücher.
"Die Worte Napoleons in 3.durchgesehener und
vermehrter Aufl. wurden gesammelt und herausge-
geben von Robert Rehlen" [pseud. for Julius
Zeitler].

NN   0018198   MH CU

Napoleon I, *emperor of the French*, 1769-1821.
Die bibliothek Napoleons I und der kaiserin Maria Luise;
ausstellung einer leihgabe veranstaltet vom Verein der freunde
der Staatsbibliothek. Berlin [Druck durch J. Beltz, Langen-
salza] 1931.
57, [1] p. 20½cm.
Announcement by the firm of Martin Breslauer that the library is
for sale: type-written leaf, laid in.
1. Bibliography—Rare books. I. Marie Luise, empress consort of
Napoleon I, 1791-1847. II. Verein der freunde der Staatsbibliothek. III.
Title.
Library of Congress   Z997.N21   31-25844
[2]   018.2

NN   0018199   DLC PU CU CtY IEN MH

Napoleon I, Emperor of the French, 1769-1821.
La bibliothèque de Napoléon à Sainte Hélène ...
see under   Advielle, Victor, 1803-1905.

TB4   Napoléon I, emperor of the French, 1769-1821.
N216b   Biographie des contemporains. Paris, Ponthieu, 1824.
363p. 21cm.

1. France - Biography. 2. Marshals - France.

NN   0018201   NcU MdBP MH CtY CtY-M

Napoléon I, Emperor of the French, 1769-1821.
Biographie des contemporains. Paris, Masson
et Yonet, 1829.
178 p. 24°. (OEuvres choisies de Napoléon
Bonaparte)

NN   0018202   MB

Napoléon I, Emperor of the French, 1769-1821.
Bonaparte and the French people under his
consulate
see under [Schlabrendorf, Gustav, graf von]
1750-1824.

Napoléon I, Emperor of the French, 1769-1821.
Bonaparte au Caire
see under [Laus de Boissy, Louis] b. 1747.

Napoléon I, Emperor of the French, 1769-1821.
Bonaparte au Directoire exécutif; au quartier-
général d'Alexandrie, le 10 thermidor an 7
[28 July 1799] [Paris, 1799]
[3]-6 p. 22h.
n. t. -p.

NN   0018205   NIC

DC213 Napoleon I, Emperor of the French, 1769-1821
K4   Bonaparte et le coup d'Etat. Paris, A.
v. 5   Méricant [1908?]
317 p. 19 cm. (Correspondance, bulletins
& ordres du jour de Napoléon, 5)
Edited with introductions by Alexandre
Keller.

NN   0018206   MeB

*pFB8   Napoléon I, emperor of the French, 1769-1821.
N1627   Bonaparte, his letter to the Prince Regent of
Z803c   England. Dated, "Rochefort, 13. July, 1815."
London:Published by W.Hone,53,Fleet street,
Sep.21-1815.
plate. 38x49cm.,mounted & bd.to 51x34cm.
"Engraved by George Blake King."
Text of the letter in French, followed by
English translation; imprint also appears in
French.
No.59 in a volume lettered on spine: Collec-
tion of broad-   sides.

NN   0018207   MH

Napoléon I, *emperor of the French*, 1769-1821.
The Bonaparte letters and despatches, secret, confidential, and official; from the originals in his private cabinet ... London, Saunders and Otley, 1846.
2 v. 22cm.
Covers period March 6, 1796, to Nov. 27, 1797.
4-15675
Library of Congress   DC213.B69

NN   0018208   DLC OClWHi CtY OrCS PPL

VOLUME 405

Napoléon I, emperor of the French. 1769-1821.
DC198
.R72
Rœderer, Pierre Louis, *comte*, 1754-1835.
Bonaparte me disait... conversations notées par le comte
P. L. Rœderer. Paris, Horizons de France [1942]

Napoléon I, emperor of the French, 1769-1821.

Wheeler, Harold Felix Baker, 1877-
The boys' Napoleon, by Harold F. B. Wheeler ... New York,
T. Y. Crowell & company [1910]

Z944.05
N16cjS
Napoleon I, emperor of the French, 1769-1821.
Bref från Napoleon till Josefina, och
från Josefina till Napoleon, samt till sin
dotter. Usversättning af J.A.F. Urebro,
N.M. Lindh, 1834.

184 p.   19cm.

I. Josephine, empress Consort of Napoleon I,
1763-1814.

NN   0018211   MnU

944.05
N216leNh
Napoléon I, emperor of the French, 1769-
1821.
Brever til Marie Louise; med kommentarer
av Charles de la Roncière, oversatt av Carl
Huitfeldt. Oslo, Gyldendal, 1935.
236 p. facsim., plates, ports. 23cm.

Translation of Lettres inédites de Napoléon 1er à Marie Louise.
"318 brever ... daterer sig fra ar: ...
februar-mars, 1810 ... august 1814."

I. Marie Louise, empress consort of Napoleon
I, 1791-1847. II. La Roncière, Charles Germain
Marie Bourel de, 1870-   ed.

NN   0018213   FU

Napoleon I, Emperor of the French, 1769-1821
Napoleons Briefe; ausgewählt und herausgegeben
von Friedrich Schulze. Leipzig, Insel Verlag, 1912
404p. illus. 21cm.

NN   0018214   OKentU WaS OC1 TU

Napoléon I, *emperor of the French*, 1769-1821.
Die briefe Napoleons I an Marie-Louise; mit kommentar von
Charles de la Roncière. Berlin, S. Fischer [1935]

3 p. l., 9-307, [3] p., 1 l. front., ports., facsim. 21½cm.

"Erste bis vierte auflage 1935."
"Deutsche übertragung von Georg Goyert."

I. Marie Louise, empress consort of Napoleon I, 1791-1847. II. La
Roncière, Charles Germain Marie Bourel de, 1870-   ed. III. Goyert,
Georg, 1884-   tr.
                                          36-8717

Library of Congress   DC213.L33
Copyright A—Foreign   30446
                                  [2]   923.144

NN   0018215   DLC

Napoléon I, emperor of the French, 1769-1821.
Briefe Napoleon I. an seine gemahlin Josephine,
und briefe Josephine's an Napoleon und ihre tochter,
die königin Hortense. Uebertragen, mit erläuternden
anmerkungen von Oscar Marschall v. Bieberstein.
Leipzig, Schmidt & Günther, 1901.
vi p., 1 l., 336 p. incl. front., illus., ports.
21 cm.
I. Marschall von Bieberstein, Oskar, tr. & ed.

NN   0018216   CU

944.05
N16nc
Napoleon I, Emperor of the French, 1769-1821.
Briefe Napoleons des ersten Auswahl aus
der gesamten Korrespondenz des Kaisers, hrsg.
von F. M. Kircheisen. Stuttgart, R. Lutz,
1909-1910.
3 v.

1. France - History - Consulate and empire,
1799-1815. 2. France - History - Revolution,
1789-1804 - Sources. I. Kircheisen, Friedrich Max, 1877-   1933.

NN   0018217   WaU CtY CaBVaU NcD

Napoleon I, emperor of the French, and
Joseph Bonaparte, king of Spain
Briefwechsel Napoleons mit seinem
bruder Joseph aus den jahren 1795 bis
1815.   1854. 2v.

NN   0018218   IaU

Napoléon I, Emperor of the French, 1769-1821.
Bulletins officiels de la grande armée
see under title

Napoléon I, Emperor of the French, 1769-1821.
Buonaparte au peuple français, suivi de ses
adieux a son armée. Paris, M. DCC. XIV
[i. e. 1814]
8 p. 22 cm.

NN   0018220   DLC

Napoléon I, emperor of the French, 1769-1821.
T .J   X   *l'aîné, de P.*
Buonaparte démasqué. Par J. X. T. l'aîné, de P. ...
Paris, Delaunay, Petit, 1814.

Napoléon I, Emperor of the French, 1769-1821.
Buonaparte peint par lui-même dans sa
carrière militaire et politique
see under   Coffinières, Antoine Siméon
Gabriel, 1786-1862.

Napoleon I, emperor of the French, 1769-1821.
Buonapartens, obergenerals der Orientalischen
armee und mitglieds des National-instituts, eigenes
merkwürdiges tagebuch während des feldzuges in
Egypten und Syrien, welches er dem Directorio bei
seiner ersten audienz übergeben. Nach der
französischen handschrift auszugsweise übersetzt.
[Paris] 1799.
1 p. l., iii, 132 p. 18 cm.
1. Napoléon I. Egyptian campaign, 1798-1799.
I. France. Directoire exécutif. II. Title.

NN   0018223   CU

Napoleon I, emperor of the French, 1769-1821.
Campagne de Thessalie. Chapitre onzieme
du précis des guerres de César, par
Napoleon.
p. [149-]162

NN   0018224   MiU

Napoleon I, Emperor of the French, 1769-1821.
Campagnes d'Egypte et de Syrie, 1798-99
see his   Guerre d' Orient.

Napoleon I.
Campagnes d'Italie, d'Égypte et de Syrie.
Paris. Hachette & cie. 1872. 3 v. [France. Ministère de la
guerre .Bibliothèque de l'Armée française.] 16°.
Contents.— 1. Campagnes d'Italie. 2. Campagne d'Égypte. 3. Campagne
de Syrie.

F7058 — S.r. — France. Hist. Milit. — France. Hist. First Empire, 1804-1814.

NN   0018226   MB FTaSU

Napoléon I, Emperor of the French, 1769-1821.
Campaigns of Napoleon Bounaparte
see under title

Napoléon I, Emperor of the French, 1769-1821.
Carnet d'un voyageur, ou recueil de notes
curieuses sur la vie, les occupations, les habitudes
de Bonaparte
see under title   [Supplement]

Greenlee
4504
P855
NAPOLEON I, emperor of the French, 1769-1821.
Carta de Napoleão a seu irmão José. Traduzida,
do Diario de Sam-Tiago. N.º 124. [Lisboa,
Typografia Lacerdina,1808]
7p. 22cm.

NN   0018229   ICN

Napoléon I, Emperor of the French, 1768-1821.
Carta de Napoleon primero a su Cuñado el Gran
de Berg. Buenos Ayres, Imprenta de Niños
Expósitos, 1809.
Furlong 1304.

NN   0018230   RPJCB

Napoléon I, emperor of the French, 1769-1821.
Bo671
B935n
Cartas de amor de Napoleón a Josefina; comenta-
das y anotadas por Matilde Muñoz. Barcelona,
Editorial Juventud,s.a.[1935]
2p.l.,7-145,[1]p. plates,ports. 22½cm.
"Primera edición."

NN   0018231   CtY MiD

VOLUME 405

944.05
N216lrSb

Napoléon I, Emperor of the French, 1769-1821.
Cartas de Napoleón á Josefina durante la
primera campaña de Italia, el consulado y el
imperio y cartas de Josefina á Napoleón y á
su hija. Vertidas al castellano por Francisco
Bellido. Paris, Garnier Hermanos [1908]
xxx, 330 p. facsims., port. 18cm.

At head of title: Memorias históricas y
militares; sobre la revolución, el consulado

y el imperio.
Translation of Lettres de Napoléon à
Joséphine et de Joséphine à Napoléon.

1. Joséphine, empress consort of Napoleon I,
1763-1814. I. Bellido, Francisco, ed. & tr.
II. Title.

NN   0018233   FU

1509
.18   Napoleon I, emperor of the French, 1769-1821
.669   Las cartas inéditas de Napoleón a María
.022   Luisa, comentadas por Charles de La Roncière.
.1935   Versión española de Emilio Gascó Contell.
         Madrid [Galo Sáez] 1935
         280 p. illus.,ports. 21 cm.

I. Marie Louise, Empress consort of
Napoleon I, 1791-1847 II. La Roncière, Charles
Germain Marie Bourel de, 1870-   III. T

NN   0018234   NjP

Napoleon I, Emperor of the French, 1769-1821.
A catalogue of an assemblage of valuable
property ... having been in the possession of the
Emperor Napoleon ...
see under   Lowe, Sir Hudson, 1769-1844.

Napoleon I, emperor of the French, 1769-1821.
A catalogue of the library of the late emperor Napoleon, removed from the island of St. Helena, by order of His Majesty's
government. Which will be sold by auction by Mr. Sotheby, at his
house...on Wednesday, the 23d of July, 1823... ₍London, J.
Compton, printer, 1823₎ 8 p. 20cm.

1. Napoleon I, emperor of the   French, 1769-1821—Relics, etc.
I. Sotheby, firm, auctioneers, London.   Card revised
N. Y. P. L.   October 30, 1945

NN   0018236   NN

Napoleon I, Emperor of the French, 1769-1821.
A catalogue of the library of the late emperor
Napoleon, removed from the island of St. Helena,
by order of His Majesty's government. Which will
be sold by auction by Mr. Sotheby ... on Wednesday,
the 23d of July, 1823 ... [London, J. Compton,
1823]
   2 p.l., 4-8 p.   20 cm.
   Photostat copy (negative) made in 1945.

NN   0018237   RPB

Napoleon I, Emperor of the French, 1769-1821.
A catalogue of the Napoleon Collection formed by
William Henry Hoffmann, 1867-1916
   see under   Brown University. Library.

017.2
N16c

Napoléon I, Emperor of the French, 1769-1821.
A catalogue of the remaining library of the
late Emperor Napoléon, removed from the Island
of St. Helena, by order of His Majesty's Government; also, his walking stick, formed of one
piece of tortoise-shell, with a musical head,
to which is added an interesting collection of
books, recently imported from Paris. Which will
be sold by auction by Mr. Sotheby ... on Wednesday
the 23d of July, 1823. ₍London, 1823₎
   12p. 23cm.

Some items priced in manuscript.
Bound with O'Meara, B. E. Mr. Geo. Robins'
second day's sale. ₍London, 1836₎ and Lowe,
Sir Hudson. A catalogue of an assemblage of
valuable property. ₍London, 1844₎
   Inserted at end of volume: Napoleon I, Emperor
of the French. A collection of valuable authen

tic relics of his last moments at St. Helena,
preserved by Lieut. G. H. Wood. pp.169-170 of
a catalogue of Maggs Brothers.

1. Libraries, Private. 2. Napoleon I, Emperor
of the French, 1769-1821—Museums, relics, etc.
I. Sotheby, firm, auctioneers, London. II. Wood
G. H.

NN   0018241   IU

NAPOLÉON I, emperor of the French.
Cent-quatre-vingt-trois lettres inédites
de Napoléon, année 1806. [Roma, Modes e Mendel,
etc.,etc.,1899].

Half title serves as title-page.
Cover: Miscellanea Napoleonica, a cura di
Alberto Lumbroso. Estratto dalla serie sesta.

NN   0018242   MH CU

Napoléon I, Emperor of the French, 1769-1821.
Chagrins domestiques de Napoleon Bonaparte à
l'isle Sainte-Hélène
   see under   [Doris, Charles, de Bourges]

Z944.05
N16ec

Napoleon I, emperor of the French, 1769-1821.
Choix de pensées de Napoléon. Londres,
L.B. Hill ₍1914₎

   90 p. 10cm.

NN   0018244   MnU

NAPOLÉON I.
"Citizens of London!"

Broadside.
This book is in the Amy Lowell Library.

NN   0018245   MH

Napoleon I, emperor of the French, 1769-1821.
Code Napoleon.

   see

France. Laws, statutes, etc.
   Code civil.

Napoléon I, emperor of the French, 1769-1821.
Collection générale et complète de lettres, proclamations, discours, messages &c. &c. &c. de Napoléon le
Grand ... rédigée d'après le Moniteur etc., classée suivant
l'ordre du temps (1796-1807), accompagnée de notes
historiques, pub. par Chr. Aug. Fischer ... Leipzig,
H. Gräff, 1808-13.
   2 v. 21½ᵐ.
   Vol. 2 has title: Collection ... rangée par ordre chronologique (1796-1812)
... t. 2. Contenant les années 1808, 1809, 1810, 1811 et 1812.
   Added t.-p.: Neues französisch-diplomatisches lesebuch, oder Sammlung
französischer original-aufsätze über diplomatisch-politische gegenstände der
neuesten zeit ...
   1. Fischer, Christian   August, 1771-1829, ed.   4-15677

   Library of Congress   DC213.F52

NN   0018247   DLC

Napoleon I, Emperor of the French, 1769-1821.
Collection nouvelle de documens historiques
sur Napoleon
   see under title

Napoleon I, Emperor of the French, 1769-1821.
... Comment parlait Napoléon
   see under   Cambon, Victor, 1852-1927.

Napoleon I, Emperor of the French, 1769-1821.
Commentaires ... suivis d'un résumé des
principes de stratégie du Prince Charles, par Le
Vasseur... Paris, Corréard, 1851.
   2 v. fold. maps. 21 cm.
   I. Le Vasseur, P   G.

NN   0018250   NjP

Napoléon I, emperor of the French, 1769-1821.
Commentaires de Napoléon premier ... Paris, Imprimerie impériale, 1867.
   6 v. double maps. 28½ᵐ.

   "Imprimé par ordre de l'empereur ... par les soins de M. Anselme Petetin."
   "Exemplaire no. 286."

   1. France—History, Military—1789-1815. 2. France—Hist.—Consulate &
empire, 1799-1815. I. Petetin, Anselme, 1807-1873, ed.

   CaOTP
NN   0018251   MiU ICU NjP CtY PPRF CSt ScU MB NcU

Napoléon I, emperor of the French, 1769-1821.
Confession de Bonaparte. ₍Paris? B. Cadet,
182-?₎
   8 p. ₍Bound with: Reynaud de Montlosier,
François Dominique, comte de. De la Monarchie
française au 1er juin 1821. 1821₎

   Caption title.

NN   0018252   CU

Napoléon I, Emperor of the French, 1769-1821.
Confession of General Buonaparte to the
Abbé Maury ...
   see under   Sarrazin, Jean, 1770-1850?

Napoléon I, emperor of the French, 1769-1821.
Les confessions de l'empereur Napoléon
   see under   [Lullin de Châteauvieux,
Frédéric] 1772-1841.

VOLUME 405

Napoléon I, *emperor of the French,* 1769–1821.
The confidential correspondence of Napoleon Bonaparte with his brother Joseph ... Selected and translated, with explanatory notes, from the "Mémoires du roi Joseph." London, J. Murray, 1855.
2 v. 22½ᶜᵐ.
Napoleon's letters only.
4–15676

Library of Congress   DC213.C73

    INS T NcU PPL TxU OCl
NN 0018255   DLC OClWHi OClW FTaSU OrCS OKentU CoU

NAPOLÉON I, emperor of the FRENCH, 1769–1821.
The confidential correspondence of Napoleon Bonaparte with his brother Joseph, sometime king of Spain. Selected and translated, with explanatory notes, from the 'Mémoires du roi Joseph'. 2d ed. London, J.Murray, 1856.

    2 vol. 23 cm.

NN 0018256   MH CoU MiU OCl OCU OU ICN

Napoléon I, *emperor of the French,* 1769–1821.
The confidential correspondence of Napoleon Bonaparte with his brother Joseph ... Selected and translated, with explanatory notes, from the 'Mémoires du roi Joseph' ... New York, D. Appleton and company, 1856.
2 v. fronts. (ports.) 19½ᵐ.
4–15678

Library of Congress   DC213.C74

    OO NjNbS PU PSC PPA MB IdPI
NN 0018257   DLC NjP MHi TU FMU OWorP NcD MWA MdBP

Napoléon I, *emperor of the French,* 1769–1821.
Confidential correspondence of the Emperor Napoleon and the Empress Josephine: including letters from the time of their marriage until the death of Josephine, and also several private letters from the emperor to his brother Joseph, and other important personages. With numerous illustrative notes and anecdotes. By John S. C. Abbott. New York, Mason brothers, 1856.
viii, [9]–404 p. 18ᵐ.
Published Paris, 1833, with title: Lettres de Napoléon à Joséphine [etc.] Ed. by Mᵐᵉ Salvage de Faverolles. cf. Kirchelsen, Bibl. Napoléons.
I. Joséphine, empress consort of Napoléon I, 1763–1814. II. Abbott, John Stevens Cabot. 1805–1877, ed.
4–25175

Library of Congress   DC213.A13

    PPA OCH LNHT NN MH MB InU FTaSU NcA-S AAP
NN 0018258   DLC OKentU IdU WaWW CoU ViU NcU PPL

Napoleon I, Emperor of the French, 1769–1821.
Confidential correspondence of the Emperor Napoleon and the Empress Josephine. With notes, etc. New York, 1857.
12°.

NN 0018259   NB

Napoleon I, Emperor of the French, 1769–1821.
—— Confidential correspondence of the Emperor Napoleon and the Empress Josephine, including letters from the time of their marriage until the death of Josephine, and also several private letters from the emperor to his brother Joseph, and other important personages, with numerous illustrative notes and anecdotes. New York, 1858. 12°. 5826

NN 0018260   MdBP

Napoleon 1, emperor of the French.
Confidential correspondence...with...notes... by J.S.C. Abbott. N. Y. Mason, 1860.
404 p.

NN 0018261   PU CtY

Napoléon I, emperor of the French, 1769–1821.
Constitution royale et imperiale des échecs ...
see under [Loysel, J   B   ]

Napoleon I, Emperor of the French, 1769–1821.
Contestación que Napoleon I°...
see under title

Napoléon I, Emperor of the French, 1769–1821.
Une conversation du comte Molé avec Napoléon Ier. [Paris, 1887]
p. [129]–135.   26 cm.
Caption title.
Article signed: Gustave Bord.
Extract from: Revue de la révolution, t. X, Nov. 1887.
I. Molé, Louis Mathieu, Comte, 1781–1855.
II. Bord, Gustave, 1852-   ed.

NN 0018264   CU

Napoléon I, emperor of the French, 1769–1821.
[Conversations of Napoleon with Canova. n.p. 1825?]
451–460p. ports. 22cm.

Caption title.

I. Canova, Antonio, 1757–1822.

NN 0018265   NcU

Napoléon I, emperor of the French, 1769–1821.
Conversations religieuses de Napoléon ...
see under Beauterne, Robert François Antoine de, b. 1748.

923.144 Napoleon I, Emperor of the French, 1769–1821.
N216   Conversazioni; raccolte, tradotte e
I-AE   illustrate da Raffaele Ciampini. [Firenze, Rinascimento del libro, 1929]
          lxi, 290 p. 20 cm. (Collezione "Grandi stranieri")
          Includes bibliography.

    1. Napoleon I, Emperor of the French, 1769–1821. I. Ciampini, Raffaele, 1895- comp.

NN 0018267   NcD PP

Napoleon I, Emperor of the French, 1769–1821
Copia di lettera scritta dal generale in capo dell' armata francese in Italia al sig.cardinale Mattei e di altre lettere acclusevi. np, nd.

15 p.
Includes letter from Cardinal Busca.

NN 0018268   MH

NAPOLEON I, emperor of the FRENCH.
Copie d'un manuscrit de la main de Napoléon Bonaparte, avec l'orthographe qui existe dans le manuscrit même. Paris, Truchy, 1841.

pp.15.
Caption-title: Position politique et militair du département de Corse au 1er juin 1793.

NN 0018269   MH MB

Napoleon I, emperor of the French, 1769–1821.
Copies des lettres originales de l'armée du Général Bonaparte en Egypte, interceptées par la flotte sous le commandement de l'Amiral Lord Nelson. London, Printed for J.Wright, 1799

v. 2

NN 0018270   MH

DC Napoléon I, Emperor of the French, 1769–1821.
213   Correspondance, bulletins & ordres du jour
.K32 de Napoléon [par] Alexandre Keller. Paris, A. Méricant [1909–10]
      5 v. maps 18cm.
      CONTENTS.--1. De Brienne au 13 vendémiaire.--2. Bonaparte et le Directoire.--3. Campagne d'Italie.--4. Expédition d'Egypte.--5. Bonaparte et le coup d'état.
      1.France--Hist.--Revolution,1789–1799--Sources. 2.France--Hist.--Consulate and Empire,1799–1815   --Sources. I.Keller,Alexandre,ed.

NN 0018271   MiU FTaSU NIC UU CU NNF IaU CtY MB

944.05 NAPOLÉON I, emperor of the French,
N16cke 1769–1821.
        Correspondance, bulletins & ordres du jour de Napoléon. [publiés par] Alexandre Keller... Paris, A. Méricant [193-?]
        5v. fronts. (v.1, 3) maps (part double) 18cm.
        Contents.— I. De Brienne au 13 vendémiaire.— II. Bonaparte et le directoire. III. Campagne d'Italie.— IV. Expédition d'Egypte.— V. Bonaparte et le coup d'état.
        1.France   Hist.,1789–1815. 2.Europe History,1789– 1815. Sources. 3.France History,Military,1789–1815. I.Keller, Alexandre,ed.   MnU 36–776 Sources.

NN 0018272   MnU NjP

Napoléon I, emperor of the French, 1769–1821.

Bail, Charles Joseph, 1777–1827, *ed.*
Correspondance de Bernadotte, prince-royal de Suède, avec Napoléon, depuis 1810 jusqu'en 1814; précédée de notices sur la situation de la Suède, depuis son élévation au trône des Scandinaves, pièces officielles recueillies et publiées par m. Bail ... Paris, Chez L'Huillier, 1819.

Napoleon I.
Correspondance de Napoléon avec le Ministre de la marine [Decrès], depuis 1804 jusqu'en avril 1815. Extraite d'un portefeuille de Sainte-Hélène.
Paris. Delloye & Lecou. 1837. 2 v. in 1. Portrait. 20½ cm., in 8s.
Contains only letters of Napoleon.

L385 — France. Ministère de la marine. — Decrès, Denis, Duc, 1762–1820.

NN 0018274   MB IU MtU NN ICN CU ICU NcD

VOLUME 405

NAPOLEON I, emperor of the French, 1769-1821.
Correspondance de Napoléon Bonaparte avec le comte Carnot, pendant les cent jours. Paris, chez Plancher, 1819.

21 cm.

NN   0018275   MH CU NcD

Napoléon I, *emperor of the French*, 1769–1821.
Correspondence de Napoléon 1er; publiée par ordre de l'empereur Napoléon III. Paris, H. Plon, J. Dumaine, 1858–70.
32 v. 22cm.

Vols. 29–32 have subtitle: Œuvres de Napoléon 1er à Sainte-Hélène. Edited by a commission headed by J. B. P. Vaillant.

Library of Congress   DC213.N21   1—20466

CU ICN MB FTaSU MiDW
OKentU CaBVaU CaBVa NjP CtY NN MH CU-S NcU MdBP
InU OU OCl WaU NcD NIC PHC PPL IaU PPRF INS GU
NN   0018276   DLC DNW PPT PU FU PBm ViU MH OClW MiU

NAPOLÉON I, emperor of the French, 1769-1821.
Correspondance de Napoléon; six cents lettres de travail (1806-1810) présentées et annotées par Maximilien Vox.   [Paris] Gallimard [1943]
xxii, 572 p. 23cm. (Mémoires du passé pour servir au temps présent. 3)

Index des correspondants, p. [569]-572.

I. Vox, Maximilien, ed.

NN   0018277   NN FTaSU

Napoléon I, *emperor of the French*, 1769–1821.
... Correspondance de Napoléon, six cents lettres de travail (1806–1810) présentées et annotées par Maximilien Vox. 6. éd. [Paris] Gallimard [1943]

2 p. l., [vii]–xxii p. 1 l., 572, [2] p. front. (port.) 23cm. (Mémoires de passé pour servir au temps présent, collection dirigée par Louis-Raymond Lefèvre)

I. Vox, Maximilien, ed.   44–28161

Library of Congress   DC213.V6   1943
[2]   923.144

NN   0018278   DLC NN ICU NcD AAP TU

DC
213
.V6
1943

Napoléon I, emperor of the French, 1769-1821.
Correspondance de Napoléon, six cepts lettres de travail (1806-1810) presentees et annotees par Maximilien Vox. 12. ed. [Paris] Gallimard [1943]
572 p. illus. 23 cm. (Memoires de passe pour servir au temps present, collection dirigee par Louis-Raymond Lefevre)

I. Vox, Maximilien, ed.   II. Title

NN   0018279   OKentU

DC
213
V6
1943

Napoléon I, emperor of the French, 1769-1821.
Correspondance de Napoléon, six cepts lettres de travail (1806-1810) presentees et annotees par Maximilien Vox. 14. ed. [Paris]Gallimard[1943]
572p. front.(port.) 23cm. (Memoirs de passe pour servir au temps present; collection dirigee par Louis-Raymond Lefevre)

I. Vox, Maximilien, ed. II. Title.

NN   0018280   LN

Napoléon I, emperor of the French, 1769-1821.
Correspondence inédit de l'empereur Napoléon avec le Cardinal Fesch.
Paris, 1855.

[DuCasse, A. Histoire des negociations, v. 1, p. 17-173]

NN   0018281   DLC

Napoléon I, *emperor of the French*, 1769–1821.
Correspondance inédite de l'empereur Napoléon avec le commandant en chef de l'artillerie de la grande armée. Pendant les campagnes de 1809 en Autriche, 1810–1811 en Espagne et 1812 en Russie. Avec un fac simile autographe de Napoléon, et des notes historiques et topographiques, par Adrien Pascal. Paris. Chez l'éditeur [etc.] 1843.
1 p. l., 97 p. facsim. 21cm. [With Pascal, Adrien. Les bulletins de la grande armée. Paris. 1844. f. 6]

1. France—Hist.—Consulate and empire. 1799–1815.

Library of Congress   DC152.P27   4—23213

NN   0018282   DLC MiU

Napoléon I, *emperor of the French*, 1769–1821.
... Correspondance inédite de Napoléon 1er, conservée aux Archives de la guerre; pub. par Ernest Picard ... et Louis Tuetey ... Paris, H. Charles-Lavauzelle [1912–
v. 25cm.
At head of title: Publié sous la direction de la Section historique de l'État-major de l'armée.
This collection is planned to include all the unpublished documents and letters now in the War archives written by Napoleon after Dec. 2, 1804— also a few letters published in collections now rare, or incorporated in historical works where they are likely to escape notice.
"Titres des principales publications consacrées à la correspondance de Napoléon 1er": v. 1, p. xx–xxii.
1. France—Hist.—Consulate and empire, 1799–1815. 2. France—History, Military—1789–1815. I. Picard, Ernest. II. Tuetey, Louis, 1869– III. France. État-major de l'armée. Section historique. IV. France. Archives de la guerre.
Library of Congress   DC213.P5   13–23905

NN   0018283   DLC CtY NIC MiU MB

Napoléon I, *emperor of the French*, 1769–1821.
Correspondance inédite officielle et confidentielle de Napoléon Bonaparte avec les cours étrangères, les princes, les ministres et les généraux français et étrangers, en Italie, en Allemagne, et en Égypte ... Paris, C. L. F. Panckoucke, 1809 (*i. e.* 1819)–20.
7 v. 20cm.

Edited by C. T. Beauvais de Préau. cf. Kircheisen. Bibl. Napoleons; and La nouvelle biog.

1. Beauvais de Préau, Charles Théodore. 1772–1830, ed.

Library of Congress   DC213.B38   1819   4–15673

NN   0018284   DLC NjP CtY NcU MdBP NWM MB

Napoléon I, *emperor of the French*, 1769–1821.
Correspondance inédite, officielle et confidentielle de Napoléon Bonaparte avec les cours étrangères, les princes, les ministres et les généraux français et étrangers, en Italie, en Allemagne, et en Égypte ... Paris, C. L. F. Panckoucke, 1819–20.
7 v. 20cm.

Vols. 1, 7, dated 1820; v. 2–6, 1819.
Edited by C. T. Beauvais de Préau. cf. Kircheisen. Bibl. Napoleons; and La nouvelle biog.

1. Beauvais de Préau, Charles Théodore. 1772–1830, ed.

Library of Congress   DC213.B38   1819 a   4–15674

NN   0018285   DLC KyLoU MiU NWM MB

DC213
C75

Napoléon I, Emperor of the French, 1769-1821.
Correspondance militaire, extraite de la correspondance générale et publiée par ordre du ministre de la guerre. Paris, Plon, 1876-97.
10 v. 19cm.

Vols. 4-7, 9-10: 2. éd.

1. France - Hist. - Consulate and Empire, 1799-1815. 2. France - History, Military - 1789-1815. I.   Title: Correspondance militaire de   Napoléon Ier.

NN   0018286   GU FTaSU NjP OCl ICN NIC CtY MH

DC 213
C376
1820:1

Napoléon I, Emperor of the French, 1769-1821.
Corrispondenza di Napoleone Bonaparte col conte Carnot, ministro dell' interno, durante i Cento Giorni. Tradotta in italiano del cittadino D* * O**. Napoli, Tip. di R. Orlando, si vende da L. Marotta, 1820.
71 p. 19 cm.

Bound with Fasti di Napoleone. Napoli, 1820.
I. Carnot, Lazare Nicolas Marguerite, comte, 1753-1823. II. Title.

NN   0018288   CaBVaU

Napoléon I, *emperor of the French*, 1769–1821.
The Corsican; a diary of Napoleon's life in his own words ... Boston and New York, Houghton Mifflin company, 1910.
vi, 526 p., 1 l. 20½ cm.

Compiled by R. M. Johnston.

I. Johnston, Robert Matteson, 1867–1920, comp.

DC203.N12   10—29715

OrCS OrU CaBVaU Or MtU CoU OrStbM
NN MB PBm PPT PP ViU PPD MU KyLx NNC NcD TU OrPR
NN   0018289   DLC NjNbS RPB PU AAP MH OU OO OCl MiU

92
N216-6
1911

Napoléon, Emperor of the French, 1769-1821.
The Corsican; a diary of Napoleon's life in his own words. London, G.Richards, 1911
vi,526p. 21cm.

Compiled by R.M.Johnston.

I.Johnston, Robert Matteson, 1867-1920, comp. VI.Title. VII.Title: A diary of Napoleon's life in his own words. LC

NN   0018290   CLSU MH

NAPOLEON I, emperor of the French, 1769-1821.
The Corsican; a diary of Napoleon's life in his own words. New ed., illustrated. Boston and New York, Houghton Mifflin Co., 1921[cop. 1910].

Port.and plates.
"10th impression."
Compiled by R.M.Johnston.   Fr 1405.225.10
(2cop.)

NN   0018291   MH OrSaW PU

Napoléon I, *emperor of the French*, 1769–1821.
The Corsican; a diary of Napoleon's life in his own words ... Boston and New York, Houghton Mifflin company, 1930.
508 p. 21 cm.

Compiled by R. M. Johnston.

NBuHi IU PHC MWelC CU
NN   0018292   LU NjR CLSU IU TxU WaTC WaS OrSaW

Napoleon I, Emperor of the French, 1769-1821.
Court and camp of Bonaparte
see under title

4D-1138   Napoléon I, Emperor of the French, 1769-1821.
Darstellung der Kriege Caesars, Turennes, Friedrichs des Grossen, vom Kaiser in seinen letzten Lebensjahren im Exil auf St. Helena geschrieben und kritisch erläutert. [Übers. und] hrsg. von Hans E. Friedrich.   Berlin, F. Vorwerk, 1938.
543 p.

NN   0018294   DLC-P4 NNC

VOLUME 405

Napoléon I, *emperor of the French,* 1769–1821.
... Darstellung der kriege Caesars, Turennes, Friedrichs des Grossen, mit einem anhang: Der angriffskrieg in weltgeschichtlichen beispielen, vom kaiser in seinen letzten lebensjahren im exil auf St. Helena geschrieben und kritisch erläutert. Übersetzt, erläutert und herausgegeben von Hans E. Friedrich. 2. aufl. Darmstadt/Berlin, Vorwerk-verlag, 1942.
528 p. illus. ports. maps (part fold.) diagrs. 22ᶜᵐ.
At head of title: Napoléon I.
"Die übertragung wurde auf grund der definitiven ausgabe der werke Napoleons I. 'Correspondance,' bd. 31 und 32, Paris, Plon, 1870 hergestellt. Den abschnitt 'Der angriffskrieg' übersetzte Walther Schürenberg."
1. Military history.   I. Friedrich, Hans Eberhard, ed. and
tr. II. Schürenberg,   Walther, tr. III. Title.
                                                46–28403
Library of Congress   D25.N32 1942
                             ₍2₎   355.48

NN 0018295   DLC CLU

Napoléon I, *emperor of the French,* 1769–1821.
... De Córcega a Santa Elena (escritos y discursos) traducción y prólogo de D. Franco. Madrid, Pegaso ₍1941₎
307 p. front. (port.) 20ᶜᵐ. ₍Ciencias del espíritu, vol. III₎
At head of title: Napoléon.

I. Franco, D., tr. II. Title.
                                                43–31457
Library of Congress   DC213.F7
                             ₍2₎   923.144

NN 0018296   DLC

F
394
.6103 NAPOLÉON I, emperor of the French, 1769–1821.
       Denkwürdigkeiten zur Geschichte Frankreichs
unter Napoleon; von ihm zu St. Helena den Generalen dictirt, die seine Gefangenschaft getheilt haben, und herausgegeben nach der von ihm eigenhändig verbesserten Handschrift. Anmerkungen und vermischte Aufsätze. Aus dem französischen Original übersetzt. Leipzig, G. Reimer, 1823–
v. 21cm.

Vol. "niedergeschrieben von dem General Montholon."

NN 0018297   ICN MnU DLC-P4

Napoléon I, Emperor of the French, 1769–1821.
Denkwürdigkeiten zur geschichte Frankreichs unter Napoleon; von ihm zu St. Helena den generalen dictirt, die seine gefangenschaft getheilt haben, und hrsg. nach der von ihm eigenhändig verbesserten handschrift. Anmerkungen und vermischte aufsätze, niedergeschrieben von dem general Montholon ... 5. theil. Aus dem französischen original übersetzt. Berlin, G. Reimer, ₁823.
1 v. 21 cm.
Title of the French original: Mémoires pour servir à l'histoire de France ... 1823–25.
1. France. Hist., Military. 2. Napoleon I,

Emperor of the French, 1769–1821. I. Montholon, Charles Jean Tristan, marquis de, 1783–1858.

NN 0018299   CU

Napoléon I, emperor of the French, 1769–1821.

Dernière confidence de Buonaparte dit Napoléon, au peuple français, en partant de Fontainebleau ... ₍Paris, Impr. de J. M. Eberhart, 1814₎

Napoléon I, *emperor of the French,* 1769–1821.
Dernières lettres inédites de Napoléon Iᵉʳ, collationnées sur les textes et publiées par Léonce de Brotonne. Paris, H. Champion, 1903.
2 v. 23¹ᶜᵐ.

Continued in next column

Continued from preceding column

I. Brotonne, Léonce de, 1854–   ed.

                                                3—29543
Library of Congress   DC213.B87

NN 0018301   DLC GU NcU FU NIC OU NBuG OC1 PU

Napoleon I, Emperor of the French, 1769–1821.
Description de l'Egypte; ou Recueil des observations et des recherches ...
see under France. Commission des monuments d'Egypte.

Napoleon I, Emperor of the French, 1769–1821.
Détail officiel envoyé par le général Bonaparte au Directoire exécutif, des ordres que ce général a donné pour brûler un village dont les habitants ont assassiné un aide-de-camp et sa suite. [Paris? Impr. de Lackave, 1798?]

4 p.

NN 0018303   MH

Napoléon I, emperor of the French, 1769–1821.

Stutterheim, Karl, *freiherr* von, 1774–1811.
A detailed account of the battle of Austerlitz, by the Austrian major-general, Stutterheim. Translated from the French by Major Pine Coffin ... London, T. Goddard, 1807.

Napoleon I, Emperor of the French, 1769–1821.
A diary of St. Helena, the journal of Lady Malcolm
     see under   Malcolm, Clementina (Elphinstone) Lady.

4DC
1114   Napoleon I, emperor of the French,
       1769–1821.
       Dictionnaire-Napoléon; ou, Recueil alphabétique des opinions et jugements de l'empereur Napoléon Ier. Avec une introd. et des notes par . Damas Hinard. 2. éd. Paris, Plon frères, 1854.
       556 p.

NN 0018306   DLC-P4 CtY NIC CLU MH IaU OC1 NNF

Napoleon I, Emperor of the French, 1769–1821.
Diplomaticheskīà snoshenīà Rossīi i Frantsīi
see under Nikolaĭ Mikhaĭlovich, grand duke of Russia, 1859-1919, ed.

Napoléon I, emperor of the French, 1769–1821.
Discours adressé par Bonaparte, premier consul de la Republique française, aux curés de la ville de Milan, le 5 juin 1800. Traduit de l'Italien, auquel on a joint des notes historiques. Saint-Quentin, Impr. de J.M. Delannoy-Houtoy [1800]

10 p. 19 cm.

NN 0018308   MH

Napoléon I, emperor of the French, 1769–1821
Discours de Buonaparte aux habitans de l'île d'Elbe. ₍Paris, n.d.₎
8 p. 22 cm.

NN 0018309   WU

Napoleon I, emperor of the French, 1769–1821.
Le discours de Lyon, par le lieutenant Napoléon Bonaparte. ₍Paris₎; A. Morancé₁, 1929?₎. 102 p. facsims. 12°. ("Pages napoléoniennes.")
no. 244 of 2000 copies printed.
Preface signed: Edouard Driault.

483392A. 1. No subject. I. Driault,   Edouard, 1864–
N. Y. P. L.   June 25, 1930

NN 0018310   NN MiU

NAPOLÉON I, emperor of the French, 1769–1821.
Discours de Napoléon sur les verités et les sentiments qu'il importe le plus d'inculquer aux hommes pour leur bonheur; suivi de pieces sur quelques époques importantes de sa vie publié par le général Gourgaud. Paris, Baudouin frères, 1826.

NN 0018311   MH PPAmP

347.6
N216   Napoleon I, emperor of the French, 1769–1821.
       Discours ... écrit en 1794 sur les vérités et les sentiments qu'il importe le plus d'inculquer aux hommes pour leur bonheur, ou, Ses idées sur le droit d'ainesse et le morcellement de la propriété, publié en 1826 par le Général Gourgaud. Paris, Maulde et Renou, 1856.
       39p. 23cm.

       Text in Hungarian and French, on opposite pages.

NN 0018312   LNHT

French
Rev.
DC
141   Napoleon I, Emperor of the French, 1769–1821.
F87+   Discours prononcé par le Général Bonaparte
v.381 au Conseil des Anciens réuni extraordinairement à St. Cloud, le 19 brumaire. ₍Paris? Digeon, 1799₎
       7 p. 21cm.

NN 0018313   NIC

Napoléon I, *emperor of the French,* 1769–1821.
La divinité de Jésus-Christ, démontrée par l'empereur Napoléon Iᵉʳ à Sainte-Hélène. Toulouse, Chez m. l'aumonier de l'Hôpital-militaire. 1863.
63, ₍1₎ p. 13¼ᶜᵐ. (*Binder's title:* Réfutations de la Vie de Jésus. ₍v. 16, no. 2₎)
"Extrait d'un ouvrage intitulé: Sentiments religieux de Napoléon 1ᵉʳ, par le chevalier de Beauterne."—Avis au lecteur.
Napoleon's opinions as reported by Lacordaire.
1. Jesus Christ—Divinity.   I. Lacordaire, Jean Baptiste Henri Dominique de, 1802–1861. II. Beauterne, Robert François Antoine de, b. 1748, ed. III. Title.
                                                34–25653
Library of Congress   BT301.R42R4 vol. 16, no. 2
                                                   (232.9) 232.8

NN 0018314   DLC NN

Napoléon I.
Document written and signed by Napoleon. Mantova, le 15 Ventose An 5 de la République. fol.

NN 0018315   MWiW-C

VOLUME 405

Napoléon I, <u>emperor of the French</u>, 1769-1821.
Bo671 Napoleon: documents, discours, lettres.
B921 Leipzig, Insel-Verlag, 1921.
320p. 21½cm. (Bibliotheca mundi)
"Curavit editionem, Paul Amann"

I. Amann, Paul, ed. II.Ser.

NN 0018316 CtY WaU

Napoleon, I,
Napoleon's dream book;

see *under title*.

Napoléon I, *Emperor of the French*, 1769-1821.
DC214 Écrits philosophiques et politiques. Préf. du prince Na-
.A17 poléon. ₁Bordeaux₁ Delmas, 1947.
230 p. 19 cm.
"Préambule" signed : Franz Toussaint.
CONTENTS.—Notes sur le Discours sur l'origine et les fondements de
l'inégalité parmi les hommes, par Jean-Jacques Rousseau.—Mes ré-
flexions sur l'état de nature.—Discours sur les questions posées par
l'Académie de Lyon.—Qu'importe-t-il le plus d'inculquer aux hommes
pour leur bonheur?—Dialogue sur l'amour.—La Corse.
I. Toussaint, Franz, 1879- ed. II. Title.
DC214.N175 944.04 49-13706*

NN 0018318 DLC ICU TxU

Napoléon I, Emperor of the French, 1769-1821.
Eight conversations held at the chateau of the
Tuileries in 1810. London, Treuttel and Wurtz,
Treuttel, Jun. and Richter, 1825.
91.p. ports. fold. facsim. 22 cm.
At head of title: Napoleon and Canova.
I. Canova, Antonio, 1757-1822. II. Title.
III. Title: Napoleon and Canova.

NN 0018319 NcU

Napoléon I, *emperor of the French*, 1769-1821.
L'empereur Napoléon aux Français. ₁Fontainebleau,
1814₁
4 p. 22½ᶜᵐ.
Caption title.
"Pièce supposée."—Cat. de l'hist. de France, t. 3.
No. 7 in a collection of pamphlets lettered : Buonaparte. 3.

1. France—Hist.—Invasion of 1814.

Library of Congress DC197.N22 4-27485†

NN 0018320 DLC

DC Napoléon I, Emperor of the French, 1769-
213 1821.
N32 En marge de la correspondance de Napoléon
I; pièces inédites concernant la Pologne,
1801-1815. Varsovie, Gebethner & Wolff,
1911.
99 p. 25cm.
Edited by Adam Skałkowski.
"Extrait de la revue 'Kwartalnik Historyczny,'
Lwów, 1910.'"

NN 0018321 NIC NN CU

Napoleon I, emperor of the French, 1769-1821.
Napoleons Englandkampf. Napoleon über Seekrieg und Kolo-
nialpolitik Englands. Zusammengestellt von Heinrich
Conrad ₁pseud.₁ Neuherausgegeben von Hans E. Friedrich. Stuttgart,
R. Lutz ₁1940₁ 121 p. 21cm.

1. Great Britain—Invasions— Attempts and projects, 1793-1805.
I. Conradt, Heinrich, 1866- , ed. II. Friedrich, Hans Eberhard, ed.

NN 0018322 NN

Napoleon I, *emperor of the French*, 1769-1821.
Napoleons Englandkampf, Napoleon über Seekrieg und
Kolonialpolitik Englands, zusammengestellt von Heinrich
Conrad. Neuhrsg. von Hans E. Friedrich. Stuttgart, R.
Lutz Nachfolger ₁1942₁
121 p. 21 cm.
"Aus 'Napoleons Leben. Von ihm selbst.' "

1. Gt. Brit.—For. rel.—1789-1820. 2. France—Hist.—Consulate and
empire, 1799-1815. I. Conradt, Heinrich, 1866- ed. II. Friedrich, Hans Eberhard, 1907- ed. III. Title.
DC202.A5 1942 50-41896 rev

NN 0018323 DLC ICRL

NAPOLEON I, emperor of the French, 1769-1821.
Napoleons Engladskampf, Napoleon über Seekrieg
und Kolonialpolitik Englands, zusammengestellt von
Heinrich Conrad. Neuhrsg. von Hans E. Friedrich.
Stuttgart, R. Lutz Nachfolger [1942] 121 p. 20cm.
Film reproduction. Negative.
"Aus 'Napoleons Leben. Von ihm selbst'. "
1. Great Britain--For. rel., 1789-1815. 2. France--For. rel.--Gt. Br.,
1789-1815. 3. Great Britain-- Invasions--Attempts and projects,
1793-1805. I. Conradt, Hein- rich, 1866- , ed.
II. Friedrich, Hans Eberhardt, ed.

NN 0018324 NN

Napoleon I.
Die Ermordung Klebers.
(In Deutsche Roman-Zeitung. Jahrgang 1912. Band 1, pp. 423-
427. Berlin. 1912.)
From "Napoleons Leben von ihm selbst."

H9161 — T.r. — France. Hist. Milit. — Kléber, Jean Baptiste. 1753-1800.

NN 0018325 MB

Napoléon I, emperor of the French, 1769-1821,
supposed author.
Bonnet, J Esprit.
Essai sur l'art de rendre les révolutions utiles. Par J. E.
Bonnet ... 2. éd. Paris, Chez Maradan, an x.—1802.

Napoleon I, emperor of the French, 1769-1821.
Erreur de Napoléon, ou réponse a un article du
Moniteur
see under title [Supplement]

Napoléon I, emperor of the French, 1769-1821.
191 Exposé de la situation de la république.
Paris, 1803.
20 p. 21 cm.
At head of title: Paris, le 2 Ventôse, an
XI de la République.
Signed at end: Le premier consul, signé
Bonaparte.
Bound with: Montgaillard, J. G. M. R. de,
comte. Mé- moire concernant la
trahison de Pichegru ... Paris, 1804.

NN 0018328 NcU

Napoléon I, Emperor of the French, 1769-1821.
Extrait des prévisions, prédictions et prophéties
de Napoléon à l'Ile Sainte Hélène. Philadelphia,
Hibermann [18--]
36 p. 18 cm.
I. Title: Prévisions ...

NN 0018329 NcU

Soc Napoléon I, Emperor of the French, 1769-1821.
DC Extraits de lettres écrites pendant la tra-
213 versée de Spithead à Sainte-Hélène, et durant
N21 quelques mois de séjour dans cette isle.
Paris, Gide, 1817.
136p.
Bound with Beaufort d'Auberval, A.A. La
France fière d'elle-même, ou Hommage libéral,
en vers, à ses grands hommes ... Paris,
1820.
I. Title.

NN 0018330 FTaSU

DC Napoleon I, Emperor of the French, 1769-1821.
203.9 Facsimiles of all the different signatures of
E75 the Emperor Napoleon I. 2d ed. London, Tegg,
1875.
11 p.

NN 0018331 MBU MdBP MH CtY

Napoléon I, Emperor of the French, 1769-1821.
Les "fonds secrets" de Napoléon

see under

Savant, Jean, ed.

E NAPOLÉON I, Emperor of the French, 1769-1821.
5 Gedanken, Betrachtungen, Grundsätze und
.N 16086 Ansichten Napoleons. Auszüge aus seinen
Schriften, Reden, Proclamationen, seinen Ansichten im Staatsrathe, seinen officiellen
Briefen, Tagesberichten, seiner Denkschrift
von St. Helena u. s. w.: gesammelt von Hektor
Chaussier. Rechtmässige deutsche Ausgabe von
Auguste v. Faurex. Dresden, P.G.Hilscher,
1828.
2v.in 1. 16cm.

NN 0018333 ICN

Napoléon I, emperor of the French, 1769-1821.
Napoleons gedanken und erinnerungen, St. Helena

see under Gourgaud, Gaspard, baron, 1783-
1852.

DC Napoléon I, Emperor of the French, 1769-1821
202.7 Geheimer Briefwechsel zwischen dem Kaiser
.N3 Napoleon und dem Papst Pius VII. Aus den
urkundlichen Akten gezogen, nebst dem Bericht
über die gewaltthätige Entführung Sr. Päpstl.
Heiligkeit nach Frankreich. ₁n. p.₂ 1814.
266 p. 18cm.

I. Pius VII, Pope, 1742-1823. II. Title.

NN 0018335 WU NjP

Napoléon I, emperor of the French, 1769-1821.

Borel, Jean.
... Gênes sous Napoléon 1ᵉʳ; introduction de G. Pessagno.
Illustré de 4 hors-texte ... Paris-Neuchâtel, V. Attinger, 1929.

VOLUME 405

Napoléon I, *emperor of the French*, 1769-1821.
Gespräche Napoleons des ersten ... Zum erstenmal ge-
sammelt und hrsg. von F. M. Kircheisen. Stuttgart, R.
Lutz, 1911-13.

3 v.   21½ᶜᵐ.

2 aufl.

1. Kircheisen, Friedrich Max, 1877-   ed.

NN   0018337   MiU CU CtY

Napoléon I, *emperor of the French*, 1769-1821.
Great thoughts from Napoleon, comp. by Dr. A. S.
Rappoport.   New York, Dodge pvblishing company
[ˆ1912]

75 p. incl. front. (port.) 17ᶜᵐ. $0.50

1. Rappoport, Angelo S., comp.

                                              12-15492
Library of Congress   DC214.N2

NN   0018338   DLC TxU

Z944.05   Napoléon I, emperor of the French, 1769-1821.
N16maxS   Grundreglor och tankar af fången på
S:t Helena. Manuskript funnit island. Las
Casas's papper. Öfversättning.   Stockholm,
Tryckte hos C. Deleen, 1825.

84 p. 20cm.
Translation of Maximes et pensées du
prisonnier de Sainte-Hélène.

I. Las Casas, Emmanuel, comte de, 1766-1842.

NN   0018339   MnU

Napoléon I, Emperor of the French, 1769-1821.
Napoleons grundsätze, ansichten und äusserungen
über kriegskunst, kriegsgeschichte und kriegswesen.
Aus seinen werken und seiner correspondenz
dargestellt von F. von Kausler ... 2. theil.
Leipzig, Baumgärtner, 1827.
1 v.   19 cm.
1. Military art and science. I. Kausler, Franz
Georg Friedrich von, 1794-1848, comp.

NN   0018340   CU

U   NAPOLÉON I, Emperor of the French, 1769-1821.
0   Napoleons Grundsätze des Kriegs, aus dem
.61   Französischen von *r., Verfasser des "Kriegs
der Franzosen und ihrer Alliirten 1812-1815."
Leipzig, Ponthieu, Michelsen und Comp., 1828.
136p. 17cm.

NN   0018341   ICN

Napoléon I, *emperor of the French*, 1769-1821.
Guerre d'Orient. Campagnes de Égypte et de Syrie,
1798-1799. Mémoires pour servir à l'histoire de Napoléon, dictés par lui-même à Sainte-Hélène, et publiés par
le général Bertrand. Avec un atlas de 18 cartes. Paris,
Comon et cⁱᵉ, 1847.

2 v. 21½ᶜᵐ. *and atlas of 10 fold. maps, 8 fold. plans. 42ᶜᵐ.*

1. Napoléon I—Egyptian campaign, 1798-1799. 2. Egypt—Hist.—French
occupation, 1798-1801. I. Bertrand, Henri Gratien, comte, 1773-1844, ed.
II. Title.

                                              4—22643
Library of Congress   DC225.N21

NN   0018342   DLC MdBP NWM MdAN NIC MH NN

Napoleon 1, emperor of the French.
Harangues et proclamations. Paris, Gautier, n.d.
32 p.

NN   0018343   PU

Napoléon I, Emperor of the French, 1769-1821.
Histoire de l'expedition Française en Egypte
d'après les mémoires, materiaux, documens
inedits
        see under   Saintine, Joseph Xavier Boniface,
known as, 1798-1865.

Napoléon I, Emperor of the French, 1769-1821.
Histoire de Napoléon d'après lui-même
        see under   Gallois, Léonard, 1789-1851.

Napoléon I, Emperor of the French, 1769-1821.
Histoire de Napoléon le grand, empereur des
Français, depuis sa naissance jusqu'à sa mort
        see under title

Napoléon I, Emperor of the French, 1769-1821.
Histoire de Napoléon, empereur des
Français, jusqu'à l'époque de son couronnement;
suivie des détails historiques de toutes les fêtes
auxquelles ce grand événement a donné lieu
        see under title

Napoléon I, emperor of the French, 1769-1821.
Historia del emperador Napoleon. Edicion
pintoresca y popular ...
        see under title

Napoléon I, emperor of the French, 1769-1821.
The historical and unrevealed memoirs of the
political and private life of Napoleon Buonaparte
        see under   Ancemont, R   d',
mademoiselle.

Napoleon I, *emperor of the French*, 1769-1821.
Historical memoirs of Napoleon. 1815. Translated from
the original manuscript, by B. E. O'Meara. Philadelphia,
Printed and published for Almon Ticknor. 1820.

2 p. L. [ix]-xvi. [1]-164. [8] p. 2 l. [181]-295 p. incl. tables. fold.
plan. 18ᶜᵐ.

Title vignette (coat of arms)
"Official papers": [8] p. 2 l. p. [181]-278.

1. France—History—Consulate and empire, 1799-1815.   I. O'Meara,
Barry Edward, 1786-1836, tr.

                                              A 34-1180
Title from N. Carolina   Univ. Printed by L. C
                                              [DC213   ]

NN   0018350   NcU OClWHi ICU NjNbS PSC LU

Bo671   Napoleon I, emperor of the French, 1769-1821.
D820gd   Historical memoirs of Napoleon. Book IX.
1815. Tr. from the original ms. by B.E. O'Meara,
with an appendix of proofs that the pretended
manuscript from St.Helena was not written by
Napoleon. London, Printed for Sir R.Phillips
and co., 1820.
xii, 371p. front. (fold.plan) tables (1 fold.)
24cm.
Title vignette (coat of arms)

NN   0018351   CtY PPL PPA MWA NN NcU MH OrCS

---

*pGBß   Napoléon I, emperor of the French, 1769-1821.
V6755R   Ein historisch-ehrenvolles Document des Kaisers
7.32.48   Napoleon an die P. T. Bewohner Wiens.
[Wien] Druck von J.Klopf sen.u.Alex.Eurich.
[1848]

broadside. 41x26cm.
Reprinting a proclamation dated "Schönbrunn
den 6ten Nivos Jahr 14 (i.e. 26 Dec. 1805);
preceded & followed by commentary.

NN   0018352   MH

Napoleon I, Emperor of the French, 1769-1821.
The history of Napoleon Bonaparte
        see under   Abbott, John Stevens Cabot,
1805-1877.

Napoleon I, Emperor of the French, 1769-1821.
History of the campaign of 1796...
        see under title

Napoléon I, Emperor of the French, 1769-1821.
History of the campaign of 1799 ...
        see under title

Napoleon I, *emperor of the French*, 1769-1821.
Montholon, Charles Jean Tristan, *marquis* de, 1783-1853.
History of the captivity of Napoleon at St. Helena. By
General Count Montholon, the emperor's companion in exile,
and testamentary executor ... London, H. Colburn, 1846-47.

Napoleon I, emperor of the French, 1769-1821.
Hulde aan Napoleon
        see under title

DC214   Napoléon I, Emperor of the French, 1769-1821.
V5   Hundert und etliche Fanfaronaden des Corsika-
nischen Abentheurers Napoleon Buona-Parte, Ex-
Kaisers der Franzosen.   Leipzig, F.Brockhaus,
1814.
viii, 174 p. 20cm.
Compiled by C.F.D. de Villers and Friedrich
Saalfeld.
"Cum notis variorum".
Text partly in French.
1.France – History – Consulate and Empire,
1799-1815. I.Villers, Charles François Domi-
nique de, 1765-   1815; comp. II.Saalfeld,
Friedrich, 1785-   1834, comp. III.Title.

NN   0018358   CSt CU

DC213   Napoléon I, Emperor of the French, 1769-1821.
.C5   ...Inédits napoléoniens. Paris, Fontemoing et cⁱᵉ, 1913-19.
2 v. 25ᵐ.
At head of title: Arthur Chuquet.
"Ce volume peut être regardé comme un complément de nos Ordres et apostil-
les."—Préf.
Cover of v. 2 dated: 1914-1920.

1. France—History, Military—1789-1815. 2. France—Army—Hist.—Sources.
3. France—Hist.—Consulate and empire, 1799-1815—Sources.

         ICN ScU KU CU
NN   0018359   ICU NcU MH PU NIC NNF NBuG NjP MB NN

Napoleon I, Emperor of the French, 1769-1821.
Intercepted fragment of instructions from
Bonaparte to one of his ministers
        see under title

VOLUME 405

Napoleon I, Emperor of the French, 1769–1821.
Interesting memoirs of Napoleone Bonaparte
see under title

Napoléon I, Emperor of the French, 1769–1821.
Island empire or The scenes of the first exile
of the Emperor Napoleon I
see under   [Wolff, Sir Henry Drummond]
1830–1908.

Napoléon I, Emperor of the French, 1769–1821.
Jern-buren; julklapp till Napoleon
see under title

U51
.U5
1943
Napoléon I, emperor of the French, 1769–1821.
U. S. *Military academy, West Point. Dept. of military art
and engineering.*
Jomini, Clausewitz and Schlieffen. West Point, N. Y., Dept.
of military art and engineering, United States Military academy, 1943 ₍i. e. 1944₎

NAPOLEON I, emperor of the French, 1769–1821.
Juicios de Napoleón, sobre sus contemporáneos y
sobre el mismo: obra compuesta de los únicos
documentos auténticos publicados despues del
cautiverio de este gran hombre.   Buenos-Ayres,
Impr. Argentina, 1828. 129 p. 20cm.

Belle & Kermit Roosevelt Coll.
1. Napoleon I, emperor of the   French, 1769–1821--Friends and
associates.   associates.

NN   0018365   NN

Napoléon I., *emperor of the French,* 1769–1821.
The last will and testament of Napoleon Bonaparte ...
as written with his own hand, and proved in the prerogative-court, doctors' commons; with a prefatory address
and copious notes, explanatory of many interesting points
adverted to in this singularly curious document. By
W. H. Ireland ... London, J. Fairburn ₍1821?₎
27 p. 21ᶜᵐ·

I. Ireland, William Henry, 1777–1835.

Library of Congress   DC203.9.N21   4–27178†

NN   0018366   DLC

4DC-713   Napoleon I, Emperor of the French, 1769–1821.
Napoleons Leben; von ihm selbst. Übers. und
hrsg. von Heinrich Conrad.   Stuttgart, R. Lutz
[Vorwork, 1910–12]
10 v.
--- ----- Ergänzungsbände.   Stuttgart, R. Lutz
[Vorwort 1913]
3 v.

NN   0018367   DLC-P4 CU

Napoléon I, Emperor of the French, 1769–1821.
La légende napoléonienne et ses renégats
see under title

NAPOLEON, Emperor of the French, 1769–1821.
Letter before he became Emperor.

This book is in the Amy Lowell Library]

NN   0018369   MH

Napoléon I, emperor of the French, 1769–1821.
Lettera del signor generale Bonaparte dal quartiere
generale di Montebello. [Genova, 1797]

[4] p.

NN   0018370   MH

Napoléon I, emperor of the French, 1769–1821.
Lettere ... a Giuseppina durante la prima
campagna d'Italia, il consolato e l'impero, e lettere
di Giuseppina a Napoleone, ed a sua figlia.   Bastia,
Fabiani, 1834.
295 p. col. front. (port.) 23.5 cm.
I. Joséphine, empress consort of Napoléon I,
1763–1814.

NN   0018371   NjP OC1

Z944.05
N16cjI   Napoleon I, emperor of the French,
1769–1821.
Lettere di Napoleone a Giuseppina,
durante la prima campagna d'Italia, il
consolato e l'impero; e lettere di
Giuseppina a Napoleone. Ed a sua figlia.
Bastia, Presso i Fratelli Fabiani, 1854.

295 p. col. port. 24 cm.

1. Joséphine, empress consort of
Napoleon I, 1763–1814.

NN   0018372   MnU

Napoléon I, *Emperor of the French,* 1769–1821.
Letters; selected, translated, and edited by J. M. Thompson. London, Dent; New York, Dutton ₍1954₎
312 p. 19 cm. (Everyman's library, no. 995)
Bibliography : p. 11–12.

I. Thompson, James Matthew, 1878–   ed. and tr.

AC1.E8 no. 995   923.144   54—2838

OrU MtBuM
MiU NcU N WaU IaU ScCleU CaBVa Or OrPR OrP Wa IdPI
NN   0018373   DLC KyU MH GU OC1 OOxM PP PPLas PWcS

Napoléon I, Emperor of the French, 1769–1821.
Letters from the Cape of Good Hope, in reply to
Mr. Warden; with extracts from the great work now
compiling for publication under the inspection of
Napoleon. London, 1817.
22 cm.
"To the bookseller" signed C.

NN   0018374   CtY

Napoléon I, *emperor of the French,* 1769–1821.
Letters of Napoleon; selected, translated, and edited by
J. M. Thompson ... Oxford, B. Blackwell, 1934.
xvi, 383 p. front. (facsims.) 23ᶜᵐ·

I. Thompson, James Matthew, 1878–   ed.

Library of Congress   DC213.T45   34–37808
₍5₎   923.144

NN   0018375   DLC CaBVaU CaBVa CtY NN

Napoléon I, *emperor of the French,* 1769–1821.
Letters of Napoleon to Josephine; complete collection, with
preface by Dr. Léon Cerf; translated by Henry W. Bunn.
New York, Brentano's ₍ᶜ1931₎
236 p. front., plates, ports. 21¼ᶜᵐ·
"Bibliography and sources" : p. 235–236.

I. Joséphine, empress consort of Napoleon I, 1763–1814. II. Cerf,
Léon, ed. III. Bunn, Henry Walter, 1874–   tr.
Library of Congress   DC213.C45   31–25509
--- --- Copy 2.
Copyright A 42637   ₍5₎   923.144

NN   0018376   DLC WaS NIC PPA PBm OC1 MB NN

Napoléon I, *emperor of the French,* 1769–1821.
The letters of Napoleon to Marie-Louise; with a commentary by Charles de La Roncière ... and an introduction by
Philip Guedalla. With 31 illustrations. London, Hutchinson
& co., ltd. ₍1935₎
289, ₍1₎ p. front., plates, ports., facsims. 23ᶜᵐ·
A collection of newly discovered letters now in the Bibliothèque
nationale, Paris.
American edition (New York, Farrar & Rinehart, incorporated) has
title: Napoleon's letters to Marie Louise.

I. Marie Louise, empress consort of Napoleon I, 1791–1847. II. La
Roncière, Charles Germain Marie Bourel de, 1870–   ed.

Library of Congress   DC213.L3 1935 a   35–16914
₍3₎   923.144

NN   0018377   DLC GU TxU LU AAP NmLcU NcU CtY

Napoléon I, *emperor of the French,* 1769–1821.
The letters of Napoleon to Marie-Louise; with a commentary by Charles de La Roncière ... and an introduction by
Arthur Bryant. With 31 illustrations. London, Hutchinson
& co., ltd. ₍1950₎
289, ₍1₎ p. front., plates, ports., facsims. 23ᶜᵐ·
A collection of newly discovered letters now in the Bibliothèque
nationale, Paris.
American edition (New York, Farrar & Rinehart, incorporated) has
title: Napoleon's letters to Marie Louise.
First published 1935.
I. Marie Louise, empress consort of Napoleon I, 1791–1847. II. La
Roncière, Charles Germain Marie Bourel de, 1870–   ed.

NN   0018378   CU–I

Napoléon I, *emperor of the French,* 1769–1821.
Napoleon's letters to Josephine, 1796–1812; for the first
time collected and translated, with notes social, historical,
and chronological, from contemporary sources, by Henry
Foljambe Hall ... London, J. M. Dent & co.; New York.
E. P. Dutton & co., 1901.
xxvii, 330 p. 3 port. (incl. front.) facsim. 22¼ᶜᵐ·

I. Hall, Henry Foljambe, ed. and tr.

Library of Congress   DC213.H17   2–12173

PPL ViU MB NN
NN   0018379   DLC WaT IU MsSM OC1 OC1W OO OU PU

Napoléon I, *emperor of the French,* 1769–
Napoleon's letters to Marie Louise; with a foreword and
commentary by Charles de La Roncière ... New York,
Farrar & Rinehart, incorporated ₍ᶜ1935₎
xxviii, 292 p. front., plates, ports., facsims. 24 cm.
A collection of newly discovered letters now in the Bibliothèque nationale, Paris.
London edition (Hutchinson & co., ltd.) has title: The letters of
Napoleon to Marie-Louise.

I. Marie Louise, empress consort of Napoleon I, 1791–1847. II. La
Roncière, Charles Germain Marie Bourel de, 1870–   ed.

DC213.L3   923.144   35–27179

Or WaSp WaS MtU CaBVa CaBVaU OrCS WaT UU ILfC IdU
OC1 OCU GU OEac ViU PBm PV KU CoU TU KyLx MoU
NN   0018380   DLC NcC NcD NcRS NIC NN MB DN OC1W

1836
2656.126
Napoleon I.
Lettre confidentielle et inédite de Napoléon au Comte de Cessac.
— Paris. Bureau de La Nouvelle Minerve. 1836. 95–100 pp. 8°.
Cut from La Nouvelle Minerve, April, 1836.

NN   0018381   MB

VOLUME 405

Napoleon I, Emperor of the French, 1769–1821.
Lettre d'un Français au général Buonaparte
see under title

Napoléon I, Emperor of the French, 1769–1821.
Lettre de Napoléon Buonparte, au Grand Turc,
datée de l'Ile d'Elbe
see under title

Napoleon I, *emperor of the French*, 1769–1821

[Lamare, Pierre Alexandre] 1766–1835.
Lettre du *général* Buonaparte, à l'empereur Napoléon. Réponse de Napoléon à Buonaparte, suivies d'un Miserere, récité par Napoléon Buonaparte, à Orgon, département des Bouches-du-Rhône. Par l'auteur du Petit homme rouge. [Paris, Impr. de J. M. Eberhart, 1814]

1. Cretet, Emmanuel, comte de Champmol, 1747–1809.

NN   0018385   CU

Napoleon I, Emperor of the French, 1769–1821.
Une lettre inédite de Napoléon Ier.   [Paris, N. Charavay, 1903]
p. [101]–104.   24 cm.
Caption title.
On cover: L'Amateur d'autographes, 36. année, no. 6, 15 juin 1903.
1. Cretet, Emmanuel, comte de Champmol, 1747–1809.

NN   0018385   CU

Napoleon I, Emperor of the French, 1769–1821.
Lettres à Joseph Bonaparte.   [Paris, 1895]
p. [225]–229.   26 cm.
Caption title.
Prefatory note signed: Gaston Vayssié.
Extract from La Revue de Paris, 2. année, 15 mars 1895.
Contents: Lettre de Napoléon Bonaparte. Lettre de Lucien Bonaparte.
1. Joseph Bonaparte, king of Spain, 1768–1844. I. Bonaparte, Lucien, prince de Canino, 1775–1840. II. Vayssié, Gaston, ed.

NN   0018386   CU

Napoléon I, *emperor of the French*, 1769–1821.
923.144   ... Lettres à Joséphine avant le mariage, sous
N216   le directoire, le consulat, l'empire et après
L.JO   le divorce; recueillies et commentées par
          Jacques Bourgeat.   Paris, Guy Le Prat [1941]
          xvi, 238 p.   facsims.   19 cm.   (Collection Jadis et Naguère)

Includes bibliography.

1. Joséphine, empress consort of Napoleon I, 1763–1814.

NN   0018387   NcD

E   NAPOLÉON I, emperor of the French, 1769–1821.
5   ...Lettres à Pasquale Paoli (1789) et à Matteo
.N 16036   Buttafuoco (1791) préface de Matteo Rocca.
          Ajacciu,A.Muvra,1938.
             37p.   (Cullana storica. XVIII)

NN   0018388   ICN

Napoléon I, *emperor of the French*, 1769–1821.
... Les lettres ardentes de Napoléon à Joséphine (1796–1797) Paris, Éditions Beer [1935]
61, [1] p. 19ᵐ.   ("Les documents curieux")
Portrait of Napoleon on cover bound in.

1. Joséphine, empress consort of Napoleon I, 1763–1814.   I. Title.
                                                    A C 36–1777
Title from Iowa State   Univ. Printed by L. C.

NN   0018389   IaAS

944.05   Napoléon I, emperor of the French, 1769–1821.
N16Wn1ℓe   ... Lettres, bulletins et proclamations; introduction et notes par Roger Peyre.   Paris, Hatier [1921]
          88p.   illus.(facsims.)   (On cover: Les classiques pour tous. no.26)

At head of title: Napoléon Ier.

1. France--Hist.--Consulate and empire, 1799–1815--Sources. I. Peyre, Roger Raymond, 1848–1923, ed.

NN   0018390   IU PSC MH

Napoléon I, Emperor of the French, 1769–1821.
... Lettres de Bonaparte et de sa famille, 1784–1848.   [Paris, n. d.]
p. 289–312.   21 cm.
Caption title.
Extract from Nouvelle revue rétrospective, no. 23.
1. Napoléon I, Emperor of the French, 1769–1821.

NN   0018391   CU

Napoléon I, Emperor of the French, 1769–1821.
Lettres de l'empereur Napoléon du 1ᵉʳ août au 18 octobre 1813 non insérées dans la correspondance. Publiées par X ...   Paris [etc.] 1909.
25 cm.

NN   0018392   CtY NIC MH ICN PU IaU

Film   Napoléon I, Emperor of the French, 1769–1821.
11538   Lettres de l'empereur Napoléon du 1 aôt
          au 18 octobre 1813 non insérées dans la correspondance; pub. par X.   Paris, Berger, 1909.
          260p.   tables.

Microfilm copy (negative) made by University of Iowa Microfilm Service, 1968. 1 reel.

1. Napoléon I, Emperor of the French, 1769–1821 - Biog.

NN   0018393   IaU

Napoléon I, *emperor of the French*, 1769–1821.
... Lettres de Napoléon à Joséphine, réunies et préfacées par le Dʳ Léon Cerf. Paris, Duchartre & Van Buggenhoudt [*1928]
2 p. l., xi, [1] 188 p. xvi pl. (incl. front., ports., facsims.) 21ᵐ. (Collection laque verte, histoire & mémoires)
Copyright date changed in manuscript to 1929.
"Bibliographie et sources": p. [1]–11.

1. Joséphine, empress consort of Napoleon I, 1763–1814. II. Cerf, Léon, ed.
                                                    29–27811
Library of Congress   DC213.C4

NN   0018394   DLC WaS TNJ KyU NcU OCU OCl MB

NAPOLÉON I, emperor of the French, 1769–1821.
Lettres de Napoléon à Joséphine, réunies et préfacées par Léon Cerf. Paris, Duchartre et Lettres & Van Buggenhoudt [1929] xi, ii, 188 p. plates, ports. 21cm. (Collection laque verte Histoire & mémoires)

Includes bibliographies.

1. Letters, French. 2. Joséphine, empress consort of Napoléon I, 1763–1814.
3. France--Hist. --Consulate and Empire, 1799–1815. I. Cerf, Léon, ed.
II. Collection laque verte: Histoire & mémoires.
III. Histoire & mémoires.

NN   0018395   NN

Napoléon I, *emperor of the French*, 1769–1821.
Lettres de Napoléon à Joséphine pendant la première campagne d'Italie, le consulat et l'empire; et lettres de Joséphine à Napoléon et à sa fille ... Paris, Firmin Didot frères, 1833.
2 v. fold. facsims. 22½ᶜᵐ.

1. France--Hist.--Consulate and empire, 1799–1815. 2. Hortense, queen consort of Louis, king of Holland, 1783–1837. I. Joséphine, empress consort of Napoleon I, 1763–1814.
                                                    18–11390
Library of Congress   DC213.F5

NN   0018396   DLC LU FTaSU OClWHi MdBP CtY ICU NN

Napoléon I, *emperor of the French*, 1769–1821.
Lettres de Napoléon à Joséphine pendant la première campagne d'Italie, le consulat et l'Empire et lettres de Joséphine à Napoléon et à sa fille. Paris, Garnier frères, 1895.
pp. (4), xxx, 307 +. 2 ports., and facsim. plates. (Mémoires historiques et militaires sur la révolution, le consulat et l'empire.)

||Joséphine|Series

NN   0018397   MH ICN ViU CtY NIC

Napoléon I, *emperor of the French*, 1769–1821.
...Lettres de Napoléon à Josephine pendant la première campagne d'Italie, le Consulat et l'Empire et lettres de Joséphine à Napoléon et à sa fille.   Paris: Garnier frères[, 192-?]. xxx, 307 p. facsims., front. 12°.

At head of title: Mémoires historiques et militaires sur la Révolution, le Consulat et l'Empire.

1. Hortense, queen consort of Louis,   king of Holland, 1783–1837. 2. Joséphine, empress consort of Napoleon I,   1763–1814.
N. Y. P. L.   August 6, 1926

NN   0018398   NN

Napoleon I., emperor of the French.
Lettres de Napoléon relatives à la Corse. [Edited by L. Letteron.] Bastia: C. Piaggi, 1911. 2 p.l., [7]-8, (1)174-276 p. 4°. (Soc. des sciences historiques et naturelles de la Corse.)

On cover: Bulletin. nos. 331-333.
In: DRT p. v. 1. no. 8.

1. Corsica.--History, 1796-1815.   2. Letteron, Lucien, abbé, editor
3. Société des sciences historiques et   naturelles de la Corse.
N. Y. P. L.   March 18, 1913.

NN   0018399   NN

Napoléon I, emperor of the French, 1769–1821.
..Napoléon; lettres, discours, proclamations, ordres, messages... Notice de J.-G.Prod'homme. Paris, Mercvre de France, 1938.
651 p. 1 illus. 19 ᶜᵐ. (Collection des plus belles pages)

"Bibliographie": p.639-651.

I.Prod'homme Jacques Gabriel,1871-

NN   0018400   NjP OClW FTaSU

VOLUME 405

NAPOLÉON I, emperor of the French, 1769-1821.
Lettres et notes de Napoléon Bonaparte à
Carnot, son ministre de l'intérieur pendant
les cent jours.   Bruxelles, P.J. de Mat, 1819.
56p. 22cm.

E
5
.N 160375

NN 0018401   ICN CtY

Napoléon I, *emperor of the French,* 1769–1821.
Lettres inédites de Napoléon Iᵉʳ (an VIII—1815) publiées
par Léon Lecestre ...   Paris, E. Plon, Nourrit et cⁱᵉ, 1897.
2 v. 23ᶜᵐ.

1. France—Hist.—Consulate and empire, 1799–1815—Sources. 2. Europe—Hist.—1789–1815—Sources. I. *Lecestre, Léon, 1861—   ed.

Library of Congress   DC213.L45   2–19425

NN   0018402   DLC FTaSU TNJ FU NBuG OCl OCU OClW MB

Napoléon I, *emperor of the French,* 1769–1821.
Lettres inédites de Napoléon Iᵉʳ (an VIII—1815) pub. par
Léon Lecestre ... 2. éd. Paris, E. Plon, Nourrit et cⁱᵉ, 1897.
2 v. 23ᶜᵐ.

CONTENTS.—t. 1. An VIII—1809.—t. 2. 1810–1815.

1. France—Hist.—Consulate and empire, 1799–1815—Sources. 2. Europe—Hist.—1789–1815—Sources. I. *Lecestre, Léon, 1861—   ed. II. Title.

Library of Congress   DC213.L45 1897 a   18—10529

NN   0018403   DLC CtY NcD NIC NcU PPL PU

Napoléon I, *emperor of the French,* 1769–1821.
Lettres inédites de Napoléon Iᵉʳ, collationnées sur les
textes et publiées par Léonce de Brotonne. Paris, H.
Champion, 1898.
xvi, 611 p. 24½ᶜᵐ.

1. France—Hist.—Consulate and empire, 1799–1815—Sources. 2. Europe—Hist.—1789–1815—Sources. I. Brotonne, Léonce de, 1854—   ed.

                                                      8—20517

Library of Congress   DC213.B84

NN   0018404   DLC NIC CtY PU PSC OCl

Napoleon I.
Lettres inédites de l'Empereur Napoléon Iᵉʳ à la reine Hortense.
(*In* Hortense, Queen of Holland, 1783–1837. Mémoires de la
reine Hortense. Vol. 1, pp. 345–365; vol. 2, pp. 367–385. Paris,
1927.)

a643.208

N7397 — Hortense, Queen of Holland, 1783–1837. — Letters. Colls.

NN   0018405   MB

Napoléon I, *emperor of the French,* 1769–1821.
... Lettres inédites de Napoléon Iᵉʳ à Marie-Louise, écrites
de 1810 à 1814; avec introduction et notes par Louis Madelin
... 8 planches en phototypie ... ₍Paris₎ Éditions des Bibliothèques nationales de France, 1935.
xxxix, 270, ₍2₎ 2 l. front., ports., facsims. 21½ᶜᵐ.
At head of title: Bibliothèque nationale.

I. Marie Louise, empress consort of Napoleon I, 1791–1847. II. *Madelin, Louis, 1871—   ed. III. Paris. Bibliothèque nationale.

                                                      35–25091

Library of Congress   DC213.M3
                         ₍3₎   923.144

                                          OrSaW IEN MB NN KU LU
NN   0018406   DLC ScU CtY CLU INS CU FTaSU NcD ViU

Napoléon I, *emperor of the French,* 1769–1821.
... Lettres, ordres et décrets de Napoléon Iᵉʳ en 1812–
13–14, non insérés dans la "Correspondance" recueillis
et pub. par M. le vicomte de Grouchy. Paris ₍etc.₎ Ber-
ger-Levrault et cⁱᵉ, 1897.
2 p. l., 99 p. 25ᶜᵐ. (Publications de la société "La Sabretache")

1. France—Hist.—Consulate and empire, 1799–1815—Sources. I. Grou-chy, Emmanuel Henri, vicomte de, 1839—   ed.

                                                      A 12–1232

Title from Univ. of Chicago   DC213.G88   Printed by L. C.

NN   0018407   ICU NIC MU

Napoléon I, *emperor of the French,* 1769–1821.

Bonaparte, Louis Napoléon, *prince,* 1914–   ed.
Lettres personnelles des souverains à l'empereur Napoléon
Iᵉʳ, publiées par le prince Napoléon et Jean Hanoteau ... Paris,
Plon ₍1939₎–

Napoléon I, *Emperor of the French,* 1769–1821.
Lettres sur quelques particularités secrètes de
l'histoire pendant l'interregne des Bourbons
        see under   Barruel-Beauvert, Antoine
Joseph, comte de, 1756–1817.

Napoleon I, Bonaparte, emperor of the French.
Liebesbriefe Napoleons; zusammengestellt und herausgegeben von Gertrude Kircheisen.   Berlin: Morawe & Scheffelt₍,
cop. 1912₎. 238 p. facsim., port. 12°.

1. Napoleon I, Bonaparte, emperor of   the French. 2. Letters.
N. Y. P. L.   March 9, 1933

NN   0018410   NN

Napoleon I, *emperor of the French,* 1769–1821.
The life and campaigns of Napoleon Bonaparte
... containing details of his military achievements ...
        see under title

NAPOLEON I, emperor of the French, 1769–1821.
A little book of Napoleon wisdom; collected by Harold
F.B. Wheeler...   New York: Brentano's[, 1917]. 94 p.
front. (port.) 16°.

637166A. 1. No subject. I. Wheeler, Harold Felix Baker,
1877—   , editor.

NN   0018412   NN

Napoléon I, *emperor of the french,* 1769–
1821.
The love letters of Napoleon to Marie
Louise. With commentary by Charles de La
Roncière.   New York, United Feature
Syndicate, 1935.
       1 v. (various pagings) illus. 29cm.

DC
213
L33
1935+

I. Marie Louise, empress consort of
Napoleon I, 1791–1847. II. La Roncière,
Charles Germ   ain Marie Bourel de,
1870–   ed.

NN   0018413   NIC

Napoleon I, Emperor of the French, 1769–1821.
Manches was Bonaparte als Consul, und Napoleon
als Kaiser, vormals gesagt hat. Der Vergessenheit
entrissen und mit Noten beleuchtet.   Madrid und
Moskau, 1812.
16 p. 16.5 cm. [Bound with: Pfuel, Ernst
Heinrich Adolf von, 1779–1866. Rückzug der
Franzosen bis zum Nieman ... [St. Petersburg?]
1813 copy 2]
      Page 16 contains advertising matter.
      Fictitious imprint?

NN   0018414   CtY

Napoléon I, Emperor of the French,
1769–1821
Manifesto de Napoleon, vindo da
Ilha de Santa Helena por hum modo
desconhecido. 4. ed. Lisboa, Na
Imp. de J. Nunes Esteves, 1835.
110 p.

4DC
1527

NN   0018415   DLC-P4

Napoléon I, emperor of the French, 1769–1821.
Manoscritto del prigioniere di Sant-Elena
        see under   [Lullin de Châteauvrieux,
Frédéric] 1772–1841.

Napoleon I, Emperor of the French, 1769–1821.
Manuel du chef; maximes napoléoniennes
choisies par Jules Bertaut. Paris, Payot, 1919
₍cover 1918₎
221 p. 17 cm.

DC214
.B47

I. Bertaut, Jules, 1877—   ed.
II. Title.

NN   0018417   NjR CLSU OrU

Napoléon I, emperor of the French, 1769–1821.
The manuscript of St. Helena
        see under   [Lullin de Châteauvieux,
Frédéric] 1772–1841.

Napoléon I, *emperor of the French,* 1769–1821.
A manuscript, found in the portfolio of Las Casas, containing maxims and observations of Napoleon, collected during the
last two years of his residence at St. Helena. Translated from
the French. London, A. Black, 1820.
iv, 138 p. front. (port.) 23ᶜᵐ.
"A journal, occupying a space of eighteen months, without date or
arrangement, consisting of sentences, bon-mots, and maxims, collected
by Las Casas, in his daily conversations with the prisoner Napoleon":
p. iv.

I. *Las Cases, Emanuel, comte de, 1766–1842. II. Title.   Trans-lation of Maximes et pensées du prisonnier de Sainte-Hélène.

                                                      45–46375

Library of Congress   DC214.N2115

NN   0018419   DLC DNW CtY NjP

Napoleon I, Emperor of the French, 1769–1821.
Manuscript transmitted from St. Helena
        see under   [Lullin de Chateauvieux, Frederic]
1772–1841.

Napoléon I, emperor of the French, 1769–1821.
Manuscript von St. Helena; oder, Bonaparte's
Biographie von ihm selbst
        see under   [Lullin de Châteauvieux,
Frédéric] 1772–1841.

VOLUME 405

SPECIAL COLLECTIONS
B944.059N
N16

Napoléon I, Emperor of the French, 1769-1821.
Manuscrit de l'Ile d'Elbe. Des Bourbons en
1815. Publié par le comte★★★★★★★★
Londres, Impr. pour J. Ridgway, 1818.
xv, 86 p. 23cm.

"Publié par le comte★★★★★★★★ ₍de Montholon et par le Dr. Edward O'Meara₎ (Introduction et table.—Attribué faussement au
comte Bertrand)" cf. Bibliothèque Nationale.

NN 0018422 NNC

Napoléon I, Emperor of the French, 1769-1821, supposed
author.
Manuscrit de l'île d'Elbe; des Bourbons en 1815,
publié par le comte ★★★★★★★★ (Bertrand) Londres, J.
Ridgeway, 1820.

xvi, 75 p.
Supposed to have been dictated by Napoleon to General
Montholon.
Imperfect: lacks p.iii(?)-vi, 73-75.

NN 0018423 MH

Napoléon I, emperor of the French, 1769-1821.
Le manuscrit de Sainte-Hélène
see under [Lullin de Châteauvieux,
Frédéric] 1772-1841.

Napoleon I, Emperor of the French, 1769-1841.
Manuscrit venu de St. Hélène...
see under [Lullin de Châteauvieux, Frédéric]
1772-1841.

Napoleon I, Emperor of the French, 1769-1821,
supposed author.
Manuscrito, o Resumen de la vida
política de Napoleon Buonaparte
see under Lullin de Chateauvieux,
Frederic, 1772-1841. [supplement]

Napoléon I, *Emperor of the French, 1769-1821.*
Manuscrits de Napoléon, 1793-1795, en Pologne. Publiés par
Simon Askenazy.
— Varsovie. Librairie ancienne scientifique polonaise. 1929. 117,
(1) pp. 6 colored plates. Facsimiles. 39 cm. In a box.
Nr. 439 of an edition of 820 copies.
Pasted over the imprint is a label bearing the words, Paris MCMXXXI.
Éditions du Trianon.
The title is repeated in Polish: Rękopisy Napoleona, 1793-1795, w Polsce.
The editor's work is in Polish and French.

N9295 —₎Askenazy, Szymon, ed. —   nd. Pol. hist. — Manuscripts. Facsimiles. French.'^

NN 0018427 MB NcU

Bo67c
1895nh

Napoléon I, emperor of tho French, 1769-1821.
... Manuscrits inédits, 1786-1791. Pub.
d'après los originaux autographos par
Frédéric Masson et Guido Biagi. Paris,Société
d'éditions littéraires et artistiques,
Librairie P.Ollendorff,1907.
2p.l.,xv,581p. fold.facsims. 23cm.
"La première éd. des Manuscrits de Napoleon a
été pub. par nous sous le titre: Napoléon
inconnu, papiers inédits (1786-1793), par
Frédéric Masson. Cos notes aujourd'hui détachéor
forment un volume distinct sous le titre N
Napoléon dans sa   jeunesse, 1769-1793."

NN 0018428 CtY NcD OCIW

E
5
.N 1655
v.1

NAPOLÉON I, emperor of the French, 1769-1821.
Manuscrits inédits, 1786-1791. Publiés
d'après les originaux autographes, par Frédéric
Masson et Guido Biagi.   Paris,Ollendorff,1908.
581p. (Masson, Frédéric. Études napoléoniennes. ₍v.1₎)
Imprint on cover dated 1907.
"La première édition des manuscrits de Napoléon a été publiée sous le titre: Napoléon inconnu, papiers inédits accompagnés de notes sur
La jeunesse de Napoléon par Frédéric Masson. Ces
notes aujourd'hui   détachées forment un volume distinct sous   le titre: Napoléon dans
sa jeunesse, 1769-1793."

NN 0018429 ICN

944.059N
N16233

Napoléon I, emperor of the French, 1769-1821.
Manuscrits inédits, 1786-1791. Publiés
d'après les originaux autographes par Frédéric
Masson et Guido Biage. Paris, Société d'éditions littéraires et artistiques, 1910.
xv, 581 p.

1. Napoléon I, emperor of the French,1769-
1821. I. Masson, Frédéric, 1847-

NN 0018430 NNC TxHU

DC213
M2

Napoléon I, emperor of the French, 1769-1821.
... Manuscrits inédits, 1786-1791, publies
d'après les originaux autographes par
Frédéric Masson et Guido Biagi.   Paris, Paul
Ollendorff, 1912.

2p.l.,xv,581p. 22½cm.

At head of title: Napoléon.

I. Masson, Frédéric, 1847-1923.
II. Biagi, Guido, 1855-1925.

NN 0018431 NBuG

Napoléon I, *emperor of the French, 1769-1821.*
... Manuscrits inédits, 1786-1791. Pub. d'après les
originaux autographes, par Frédéric Masson et Guido
Biagi. Paris, P. Ollendorff, 1914.
2 p. l., xv, 581 p. fold. facsims. 23ᶜᵐ.
Imprint on cover dated 1910.
"La première éd. des Manuscrits de Napoléon a été pub. par nous sous le
titre: Napoléon inconnu, papiers inédits (1786-1793) accompagnés de notes
sur La jeunesse de Napoléon (1769-1793), par Frédéric Masson. Ces notes aujourd'hui détachées forment un volume distinct sous le titre Napoléon dans sa
jeunesse, 1769-1793."
1. France—Hist.—Consulate and empire, 1799-1815—Sources. 2. Europe—
Hist.—1789-1815—Sources. 1. Masson, Frédéric, 1847-1923, ed. 11. Biagi,
Guido, 1855-1925, joint ed.

NN 0018432 MiU ViU NNF

DC
214
M3
1927

Napoleon I, Emperor of the French, 1769-1821.
Manuscrits inédits, 1786-1791. Publiés
d'après les originaux autographes par Frédéric
Masson et Guido Biagi. Paris, A. Michel
₍1927₎
xv, 581 p. facsims. 23 cm. (His Études
napoléoniennes, 2)

I. Masson, Frédéric, 1847-1923, ed. II.
Biagi, Guido, 1855-1922, ed.

NN 0018433 CU-S FTaSU

DC216
.2
.M38

Napoleon I, Emperor of the French, 1769-1821.

Marie Louise, *consort of Napoleon I, 1791-1847.*
Marie-Louise et Napoléon, 1813-1814; lettres inédites de
l'impératrice avec les réponses déjà connues de Napoléon de
la même époque, suivies en annexes de documents inédits
tirés des Archives Bernadotte. Réunies et commentées par
C. F. Palmstierna; notes biographiques de Jean Savant.
Paris, Stock, Delamain et Boutelleau ₍1955₎

923.144
N216
I-MXB

Napoleon I, Emperor of the French, 1769-1821.
Massime di Napoleone relativamente alla
guerra. Bastia, 1838.
484 p. plates. 24 cm.

1. Military art and science.

NN 0018435 NcD

Napoléon I, emperor of the French, 1769-1821.
Massime e pensieri del prigioniere di Sant-
Elena. Manoscritto trovato nelle carte di Las-
Casas; tr. dal francese da Felice Miola. Napoli,
Dalla tipografia di Porcelli, 1820.
115 p.

Bound with: Lullin de Châteauvrieux, J. F.
Manoscritto del prigioniere di Sant-Elena...
1820.

I. Las Cases, Emmanuel, 1768-1842, comp.
II. Miola, Felice.   M. Title

NN 0018436 MiD-B CU

Napoléon I, *emperor of the French, 1769-1821.*
Máximas de Napoleon sobre el arte de la guerra. Traduci-
das y anotadas por el general José Antonio Páez. Nueva
York, Impr. de S. Hallet, 1865.
275 p, 1 l. 13ᶜᵐ.
"Máximas de guerra de Napoleon" (I-LXXVIII) annotated by m.
Burnod.
CONTENTS.—Máximas de guerra de Napoleon.—Pensamientos de Na-
poleon primero; pte. 1. Pensamientos relativos al arte militar; pte. 2.
Pensamientos diversos.—Notas del general Páez.
1. Military art and science. I. Burnod. ———, ed. II. Páez, José
Antonio, pres. Venezuela, 1790-1873, tr.
Library of Congress   U19.N3   5-30738

NN 0018437 DLC

Napoleon I, *emperor of the French, 1769-1821.*
Maximas militares de Napoleon, traducidas al castellano.
Madrid: Miyar, 1828.   274 p. nar. 24°.

189688A. 1. Military art and science.
N. Y. P. L.

NN 0018438 NN

Napoléon I, *emperor of the French, 1769-1821.*
Maximas militares de Napoleon. Edicion ordenada por el
Ministerio de la guerra del estado de Honduras. Tegucigalpa,
Tipografía nacional, 1898.
1 p. l, ll, ₍3₎-42 p. 18ᶜᵐ.
Contains LXXVIII maxims.

1. Military art and science. I. Honduras. Ministerio de la guerra.
Library of Congress   U19.N24   6—22626

NN 0018439 DLC

944.059N
N16234

Napoléon I, emperor of the French, 1769-1821.
Máximas y pensamientos del prisionero de
Santa Elena. Traducción del ingles al fran-
ces, y de este al castellano por D. M. C.
Madrid, Villalpando, 1821.
115 p.

Collected by Las Cases.

I. Las Cases, Emmanuel, comte de, 1766-1842.
II. C., D. M. III.₍ Title.

NN 0018440 NNC

VOLUME 405

Napoléon I, *emperor of the French*, 1769–1821.
Maximas y pensamientos del prisionero de Santa Elena; tra-
duccion del ingles al frances y de este al castellano, por D. M. C.
Mexico, Reimpresas en la oficina de Ontiveros, 1822.
3 p. l., 127 p. 13½ᵐ.
Collected by Las Cases.

I. *Las Cases, Emmanuel, comte de, 1766–1842. II. C., D. M. III.
D. M. C. IV. Title.
12—28873
Library of Congress   DC214.N212₉

NN   0018441   DLC

Napoléon I, Emperor of the French, 1769-1821.
Maximes [de] Napoléon. London,
A. L. Humphreys, 1903.
2 p. l., 187 p.   17 cm.

NN   0018442   CtY CaBVaU NRU OC1WHi NcU

Napoléon I, *emperor of the French*, 1769–1821.
Maximes [de] Napoléon. London, A. L. Humphreys,
1906.
2 p. l., 187 p. 17ᵐ.
French and English on opposite pages.
"Reprinted from the collection of Napoleon's maxims made by A. G.
de Liancourt, and translated by J. A. Manning."

1. Aphorisms and apothegms.   I. Godde de Liancourt, Caliste Auguste, comte de, b. 1805, comp. II. Manning, James Alexander, tr.
12—23411
Library of Congress   DC214.N18

NN   0018443   DLC NjP CSmH

Napoléon I, *emperor of the French*, 1769–1821.
Maximes de Napoléon, publiées par K. J. Frederiks ...
La Haye, M. Nijhoff, 1922–
v. 21½ᵐ.

1. Aphorisms and apothegms.   I. Frederiks, Karel Johannes, ed. II. Title.
23–5717
Library of Congress   DC214.A2F7

NN   0018444   DLC CtY

Napoleon, I, *emperor of the French* 1769-
Maximes de guerre de Napoleon, Paris, Annelin,
1830.
2 p.l., 188 p. 10½ cm.

NN   0018445   DNW

[355 Napoléon I,   emperor of the French.
N16m2   Maximes de guerre de Napoléon. [2.
éd.]   Bruxelles, 1837.
188p.   (Bibliothèque portative de
l'officier)

NN   0018446   IU CtY

Napoléon I, *emperor of the French*, 1769–1821.
Maximes de guerre de Napoléon. 4. éd., augm. et suivie d'une table ... Paris, J. Dumaine, 1850.
236 p. 13½ᵐ.
"Annotateurs: 1. ptie. M. Burnod. 2. ptie. M. Husson."

Continued in next column

Continued from preceding column

1. Military art and science.   I. Burnod, ed. II. Husson, Eugène Alexandre, 1786–1868, ed.

Library of Congress   U19.N2   5–23009†

NN   0018447   DLC CU

U161   Napoléon I, emperor of the French, 1769–1821.
.P5   Maximes de guerre.
1943 Phillips, Thomas Raphael, 1892–   ed. FOR OTHER EDITIONS
SEE MAIN ENTRY
Roots of strategy; a collection of military classics ... edited
by Major Thomas R. Phillips. London, John Lane [1943]

Napoleon , I, emperor of the French 1769-
Maximes de guerre et pensées de Napoleon I. 5th ed.
rev. et aug. 2e tirage. Paris, J. Dumaine, 1874.
xiii 319 p 13½ cm.

NN   0018449   DNW

DC   [Napoléon I, emperor of the French] 1769-
239   1821.
N21   Maximes et pensées du prisonnier de Sainte-
1820 Hélène; manuscrit trouvé dans les papiers de
Las Casas. Traduit de l'anglais.   Paris,
chez L'Huillier, 1820.
120 p. 21cm.

Bound with his Mémoires pour servir à
l'histoire de France en 1815. Paris, 1820.

I. Las Cas   as, Emmanuel, comte de,
1766–1842.   II. Title.

NN   0018450   NIC FTaSU IaU

Napoleon I, Emperor of the French, 1769-1821.
Maximes napoléoniennes [repertoire militaire]
par le Général Grisot. Paris, Baudouin, 1897-1901

20 pt. in 1 v.
Some parts reprinted from the Journal des sciences
militaires

NN   0018451   MH DNW

Napoléon I, *emperor of the French*, 1769–1821.
The maxims of Napoleon ... Embellishments by Edgar
Wilson; introduction by H. F. B. Wheeler. San Francisco &
New York, P. Elder and company [190–?]
124, [2] p. front. (port.) 17ᵐ. (*On cover:* The Panel-books)
Printed in Great Britain.
Bibliography : [2] p. at end.

I. Wheeler, Harold Felix Baker, 1877–   comp. II. Title.
44–30920
Library of Congress   DC214.N2117

NN   0018452   DLC

DC214 Napoléon I, Emperor of the French, 1769–
.N2117 1821.
1907
Maxims. [Introduction by Harold F. B.
Wheeler] London, Sisley's [1907?]
124, [2] p. 16cm. (The Everyday books, a
library for the million)
Bibliography: p. [125–126]

I. Wheeler, Harold Felix Baker, 1877–   comp.

NN   0018453   ViU

x944.05 Napoléon I, Emperor of the French, 1769-1821.
N16m   Maxims of Napoleon. With an introd. by
1911 Harold F. B. Wheeler.   New York, G. P. Putnam's Sons [1911?]
v, 153p. port. 15cm.

Bibliography: p.151-153.

1. Aphorisms and apothegms. I. Title.

NN   0018454   IU IdPI

Napoléon I, *emperor of the French*, 1769–1821.
...Maxims of Napoleon.   Girard, Kan.: Haldeman-Julius
Co.[, 1924?] 57 p. 24°. (Little blue books. no. 155.)

399645A. I. Aphorisms, French.
N. Y. P. L.   January 29, 1929

NN   0018455   NN

[Napoléon I, Emperor of the French] 1769-1821.
Maxims, advice and instructions on the art of war
see under title

Napoléon I, Emperor of the French, 1769-1821.
Maxims and opinions of Napoléon.

NN   0018457   DNW

Napoléon I, *emperor of the French*, 1769–1821.
Napoleon's Maxims of war, with notes by General Burnod. Tr. from the French by Lieut.-Gen. Sir G. C.
D'Aguilar ... Kansas City, Mo., Hudson-Kimberly publishing co. [n. d.]
1 p. l., [5]–144 p. 15ᵐ.

1. Military art and science.   I. Burnod, ——. II. D'Aguilar, Sir
George Charles, 1784–1855, tr. III. Title.
War 18–13
Library, War College Div.   General Staff

NN   0018458   DNW DAL OC1

Rare Napoléon I, emperor of the French, 1769–1821.
Books   ... Maxims of war. Translated from the French by Colonel
Dept. D'Aguilar ...   New York, S. Redfield, 1845.
212 p. 12cm.

At head of title: The officer's manual.
"Bound [in full green crushed morocco] by donor, Mrs. Dorothy
Sheldon Scott, 1935": slip tipped in at front.

1. Military art and science. I. D'Aguilar, Sir George Charles,
1784–1855, tr.

NN   0018459   CU ViLxW OO

Napoleon I, emperor of the French, 1769–1821.
...Napoleon's maxims of war.   New York: J. G. Gregory,
1861. 186 p. 24°.

At head of title: The officer's manual.
Translated by Sir G. C. D'Aguilar.

GANSEVOORT-LANSING COLL.
49197A. 1. Military art and science.   2. D'Aguilar, Sir George Charles,
1784–1855, translator. 3. Title.
N. Y. P. L.   September 5, 1922

CtY MH
NN   0018460   NN NDW MiU ICN ViU OOxM OC1WHi NIC

VOLUME 405

U
.19
N21
1880
Napoléon I, Emperor of the French, 1769-1821.
Napoléon's Maxims of war, with notes by General Burnod. Translated from the French by Sir G. C. D'Aguilar. Philadelphia, D. McKay (188-?)
146 p. 17cm.

p. 51-66 lacking; p. 39-46 duplicated.

NN 0018461   NIC

Napoléon I, *emperor of the French*, 1769-1821.
Napoleon's Maxims of war, with notes by General Burnod. Tr. from the French by Lieut.-Gen. Sir G. C. D'Aguilar ... Kansas City, Mo., Hudson-Kimberly publishing co. (1902?)
1 p. l., (5)-144 p. 15ᵐ.

1. Military art and science.   I. Burnod, ———.   II. D'Aguilar, Sir
George Charles, 1784-1855, tr.   III. Title.
                                                        War 18-13
Library, U. S. Army   War College
Library of Congress   [U19.N   ]

NN 0018462   DNW ViU

Napoleon I, *Emperor of the French*, 1769-1821.   355.04 N161
Napoleon's maxims of war, with notes by General Burnod. Trans-
121697 lated from the French by Lieut.-Gen. Sir G. C. D'Aguilar, C.B.
Philadelphia, D. McKay, [1917].
[2], 5-146 p. 16½ᵐ.

NN 0018463   ICJ OrCS MtBC

Napoleon I.
Napoleon's maxims of war, with notes based on the civil war, by Capt. James D. Basey extract from Infantry Journal, August 1936.

NN 0018464   DNW

Napoléon I, Emperor of the French, 1769-1821.
... Napoléons maxims of war
see also his The officer's manual.

Napoleon I, emperor of the French, 1769-1821.
Medallic history of Napoleon Bonaparte, tr. by Miss Ann Mudie Scargill
see under title

DC213 Napoleon I, *emperor of the French*, 1769-1821.
.2   Memoiren Napoleons, zum erstenmale hrsg. von F. M.
.A25 Kircheisen ... Dresden, P. Aretz (°1927)
347, (4) p. front., pl., ports. 22½ᵐ.

1. France—Hist.—Consulate and empire, 1790-1815. 2. Europe—Hist.—1789-
1815.

NN 0018467   ICU OCl NN CtY NBC

DC146   Napoleon I, emperor of the French, 1769-1821.
.S13A2

(Saint-Elme, Ida) 1776-1845.
Mémoires d'une contemporaine, ou, Souvenirs d'une femme sur les principaux personnages de la république, du consulat, de l'empire, etc. ... Paris, Ladvocat, 1827-28.

Napoléon I, emperor of the French, 1769-1821.
Fleury de Chaboulon, Pierre Alexandre Édouard, *baron,*
1779-1835.
Mémoires de Fleury de Chaboulon, ex-secrétaire de l'empereur Napoléon et de son cabinet, pour servir à l'histoire de la vie privée, du retour et du règne de Napoléon en 1815, avec annotations manuscrites de Napoléon Iᵉʳ pub. par Lucin Cornet ... Paris, E. Rouveyre, 1901.

Soc
DC
213.2
A13
Napoléon I, Emperor of the French, 1769-1821.
Mémoires de Napoléon, écrits sous sa dictée a Sainte-Hélène, par un de ses valets-de-chambre. Paris, Philippe, 1829.
428p. port.

Les pp. 1 à 150 contiennent le texte du Manuscrit venu de Sainte-Hélène.

1. France - History - 1789-1815.
I. Title.

NN 0018472   FTaSU NMW

Napoleon I, Emperor of the French, 1769-1821.
Memoires de Napoleon Bonaparte ... 1834-35
see under [Lamothe-Langon, Étienne Léon, baron de] 1786-1864.

944.05 Napoléon I, emperor of the French, 1769-1821.
N16Wnlm   ... Mémoires de Sainte-Hélène; introduction et notes par Roger Peyre. Paris, Hatier (1921)
88p. 1 illus. (On cover: Les classiques pour tous. no.25)

At head of title: Napoléon Ier.

1. Napoléon I, emperor of the French--Captivity, 1815-1821. I. Peyre, Roger Raymond, 1848-1923, ed.

NN 0018474   IU MH

Napoléon I, Emperor of the French, 1769-1821.
Mémoires et anecdotes sur Napoléon. Manuscrit venu de Sainte-Hélène ...
see under [Lullin de Châteauvieux, Frédéric] 1772-1831.

DC214
.A2M3
Napoléon I, *emperor of the French,*
1769-1821
Mémoires et oeuvres de Napoléon. Illustrés d'après les estampes et les tableaux du temps et précédés d'une étude littéraire par Tancrède Martel (pseud.) Paris, A. Michel (1910)
xxvii,470 p.,1 l. plate,ports., facsim. 19½cm.

I. Martel, Tancrède, pseud. of J.F.L. Napoléon Gras, 1856-1928.

NN 0018476   OCU CtY ViU MoU GU

Napoleon I, *emperor of the* French, 1769-1821.
Mémoires et oeuvres de Napoléon. Illustrés d'après les estampes et les tableaux du temps et précédés d'une étude littéraire par Tancrède Martel. Paris, Albin Michel (1926)
xxvii, 470 p., 1 l. plate, ports., facsim.   21cm.
CONTENTS.—Napoléon écrivain.—Premiers écrits.—Let tres à Joséphine.—Proclamation.—Allocutions et ordres du jour.—Mémoires historiques.—Histoire des campagnes d'Egypte et de Syrie.—Messages et discours.—Lettres à divers.—Critique littéraire.—Fragments de critique d'art.—Philosophie et politique.
1. France—Hist.   Consulate and empire, 1799-
1815. I. Martel,   Tancrède, 1857-

NN 0018477   ViU FTaSU

Napoléon I, *emperor of the French,* 1769-1821.
Mémoires historiques de Napoléon. Livre IX. 1815. Londres, R. Phillips & co., 1820.
viii,332,[9]p.incl.tables(1 fold.) front. (fold.plan) 22cm.
Forms Book IX of his Mémoires pour servir à l'histoire de France sous Napoléon.
Preface signed by the editor, B.E.O'Meara.

NN 0018478   CtY MWA

(Napoléon I, *emperor of the French*) 1769-1821.
Mémoires pour servir à l'histoire de France en 1815, avec le plan de la bataille de Mont-Saint-Jean. Bruxelles, Impr. de H. Remy, 1820.
3 p. l., (5)-118 p. tab. (part fold.) fold. plan. 21½ᵐ.
"Avertissement de l'éditeur" signed C. B. i. e. Charles Barrois, the publisher of the Paris edition, 1820.

1. Napoleon I—Elba and the 100 days.
                                                        2—13952
Library of Congress   DC239.N21

NN 0018479   DLC

944.05 N12.100
Napoleon I, Bonaparte, 1769-1821.
Mémoires pour servir à l'histoire de France en 1815, avec le plan de la bataille de Mont-Saint-Jean.
Paris, Chez Barrois l'ainé, 1820.
336 p. illus.

A fragment of the Memoirs dictated by the Emperor at Saint Helena to the generals who shared his captivity.
"Advertissement de l'éditeur" signed C.B., i.e. Charles Barrois, the publishers. On spine: Mémoires à l'histoire en 1815.

1. Napoleon I, Bonaparte, 1769-1821—Elba and the 100 days.
I. Title.

NN 0018481   CaOTP CtY MH OCl NjP IRA IEN NIC NcU

Napoléon I, Emperor of the French, 1769-1821.
Mémoires pour servir a l'histoire de France en 1815. (Livre IX) Avec le plan de bataille de Mont-Saint-Jean. Paris, Les Marchands de nouveautés, 1820.
2p.l.,196p. tables(2 fold.) 21ᵐ.

"Avertissement de l'éditeur", signed: C.B.

NN 0018482   KU

Napoléon I, *emperor of the French,* 1769-1821.
Mémoires pour servir à l'histoire de France sous Napoléon, écrits à Sainte-Hélène, par les généraux qui ont partagé sa captivité, et publiés sur les manuscrits entièrement corrigés de la main de Napoléon ... Londres, M. Bossange et cᵒ. (etc.) 1823-24.
7 v. fronts., fold. maps, fold. tables, fold. facsims. 21½ᵐ.
Vol. 4 dated 1824.
Vol. 2-4, 6-7 have title : Mémoires ... écrits à Sainte-Hélène, sous la dictée de l'empereur ...
Vol. 1-2 ed. by Gourgaud; v. 3-7, by Montholon

CONTENTS.—t. I-IV. Mémoires.—(t. V-VII) Mélanges historiques: t. I ... Précis des événemens militaires, ou Essais historiques sur les campagnes de 1799 à 1814 (par Math. Dumas) ... Notes sur ... Les quatre concordats (de M. de Pradt) ... Notes sur ... Mémoires pour servir à l'histoire de la révolution de Saint-Domingue (par Pillet) ... Notes sur ... Mémoires pour servir à l'histoire de Charles XIV, Jean, roi de Suède. Notes sur ... Considérations sur l'art de guerre (par Rogniat) ... t. II. Suite des notes sur ... Considérations ... Notes sur ... Manuscrit venu de Sainte-Hélène d'une manière inconnue. Notes sur ... Mémoires pour servir à l'histoire de la vie privée, du retour et du règne de Napoléon en 1815. t. III. Précis des guerres du maréchal de Turenne. Précis des guerres de Frédéric II.
1. France—Hist.—1789-1815.   I. Gourgaud, Gaspard, baron, 1783-1852.
II. Montholon, Charles Jean Tristan, marquis de, 1783-1853.   4-15670
Library of Congress   DC213.2.A12

NN 0018484   DLC CaBVaU NN MdBP MB NIC FTaSU OCl NN

VOLUME 405

Napoléon I, *emperor of the French*, 1769–1821.
Mémoires pour servir à l'histoire de France, sous Napoléon, écrits à Sainte-Hélène, par les généraux qui ont partagé sa captivité, et publiés sur les manuscrits entièrement corrigés de la main de Napoléon ... Paris, F. Didot, père et fils [etc.] 1823–24.
7 v. fold. maps, fold. facsims. fold. tab. 20½ᶜᵐ.
Imprints of v. 2 and [7] vary slightly. v. 1–[5], [7], dated 1823; v. [6], 1824.
Vols. 1–2: Écrit par le général Gourgaud. v. [3]–[7] (numbered 1–5): Écrit par le général comte de Montholon.
Vols. [3]–[4] contain "Mélanges historiques."
Vol. [8] wanting.
1. France—Hist.—1789–1815.   I. Gourgaud, Gaspard, baron, 1783–1852.
II. Montholon, Charles   Jean Tristan, marquis de, 1783–1853.
III. Title.

CA 17–604 Unrev'd

Library of Congress   DC213.2.A122

NN   0018485   DLC PBm DNW ViU CaBVaU

Napoléon I, Emperor of the French, 1769–1821.
Mémoires pour servir à l'histoire de France, sous Napoléon, écrits à Sainte-Hélène, par les généraux qui ont partagé sa captivité, et publiés sur les manuscrits entièrement corrigés de la main de Napoléon. Ecrit par le général comte de Montholon. Paris, F. Didot, 1823–25.
8 v.   illus.
1. France. Hist. 1789–1815.   I. Montholon, Charles Jean Tristan, marquis de, 1783–1853.

NN   0018486   FTaSU CtY MB PKsL

Napoléon I, *emperor of the French*, 1769–1821.
Mémoires pour servir à l'histoire de France, sous le règne de Napoléon, écrits à Ste.-Hélène sous sa dictée, par les généraux qui ont partagé sa captivité. 2. éd., disposée dans un nouvel ordre, et augmentée de chapitres inédits, etc., etc. ... Paris, Bossange père [etc.] 1829–30 [v. 5, '29]
9 v.   20½ ᶜᵐ.
Dictated to Generals Gourgaud and Montholon.
1. France — Hist.—1789–1815.   I. Gourgaud, Gaspard, baron, 1783–1852. II. Montholon, Charles Jean Tristan, marquis de, 1783–1853.

DC213.2.A13
4–15668 rev

KyLoU
NN   0018487   DLC NcU OCU OCl OO MiU MdBP ICN MnU

Napoléon I, *emperor of the French*, 1769–1821.
... Mémoires pour servir à l'histoire de France, sous Napoléon, écrits à Sainte-Hélène, par les généraux qui ont partagé sa captivité, et publiés sur les manuscrits entièrement corrigés de la main de Napoléon ... [Paris, 1851]
vii, [9]–1058 p.   25¼ᶜᵐ.   (Added t.-p.: Bibliothèque historique et militair ... pub. par MM. Ch. Liskenne et Sauvan.   t. 6)

1 France—Hist.—1789–1815.
4–15671

Library of Congress   U15.B5

NN   0018488   DLC

1509   Napoléon I, emperor of the French, 1769–1821.
.18   Mémoires pour servir à l'histoire de France
.669   sous le règne de Napoléon, écrits à Sainte-
.0072   Hélène sous sa dictée par les généraux qui
        ont partagé sa captivité. Éd.nouv., avec in-
        troduction, notes et appendices par Désiré
        Lacroix. Paris, Garnier [1904]
        5 v. maps. 19 cm. (Bibliothèque des
        mémoires historiques et militaires sur la
        révolution, le consulat et l'empire)

NN   0018489   NjP

NAPOLÉON I, emperor of the FRENCH.
Mémoires pour servir à l'histoire de France sous le règne de Napoléon, écrits à Sainte-Hélène sous sa dictée. Ed. nouvelle avec intro-duction, notes et appendices par Désiré Lacroix. Paris, Garnier frères, [1905].

5 vol. Maps and plans.
(BIBLIOTHÈQUE de mémoires historiques et militaires sur la révolution, le consulat et l'empire.)

NN   0018490   MH CaQMM

Napoléon I, Emperor of the French, 1769–1821.
Memoires secrets sur Napoleon Bonaparte
see under   [Doris, Charles, de Bourges]

Napoléon I, Emperor of the French, 1769–1821.
Mémoires secrets sur Napoleon et Louis XVIII
see under title   [Supplement]

Napoléon I, Emperor of the French, 1769–1821.
Memoires sur la vie privée de Josephine, sa famille et sa cour
see under   Villemarest, Charles Maxime Catherinet de, 1785–1852.
Memoires de Mademoiselle Avrillion ...

Napoléon I, Emperor of the French, 1769–1821.
Mémoires sur Napoléon, l'imperatrice Marie-Louise et la cour des Tuileries
see under   Durand, Mme. Sophie (Cohoudet) 1772–1850.

Napoléon I, *emperor of the French*, 1769–1821.
Napoleon's Memoirs ... Edited by Somerset de Chair. [London] The Golden cockerel press, 1945.
2 v. fronts. (ports.) 32½ᶜᵐ.
Title vignettes.
"Limited to 500 copies, of which numbers 1–50 ... contain a collotype reproduction of a passage of the text written in the emperor's own hand."
Vol. 1 is a rearrangement of the translation published in 1823 with title: Memoirs of the history of France during the reign of Napoleon, dictated by the emperor at Saint Helena to the generals who shared his captivity and published from the original manuscripts corrected by him-self. Vol. 2 is a new translation by the editor from the French original

published anonymously in 1820, with title: Mémoires pour servir à l'his-toire de France en 1815.
Editor's maps on lining-papers.
CONTENTS.—I. Corsica to Marengo.—II. Waterloo campaign.

1. France—Hist.—1789–1815.   I. De Chair, Somerset Struben, 1911– ed. and tr.
New York. Public library   A 46–4951
for Library of Congress   DC213.2.A4 1945
[2]†   923.144

NN   0018496   NN CU–A ICU CtY DLC

Napoléon I, *Emperor of the French*, 1769–1821.
Memoirs; edited by Somerset de Chair. London, Faber and Faber [1948]
xxvii, 605 p. ports., maps (part fold.) facsim. 23 cm.
Part 1 is a rearrangement of the translation published in 1823 with title: Memoirs of the history of France during the reign of Napoleon, dictated by the emperor at Saint Helena to the generals who shared his captivity, and published from the original manuscripts corrected by himself. Part 2 is a new translation by the editor from the French original published anonymously in 1820, with title: Mémoires pour servir à l'histoire de France en 1815. Supper at Beaucaire was trans-lated into English for the first time by the editor and published separately in 1945.
CONTENTS.—Corsica to Marengo. — The Waterloo campaign. — Ap-pendixes: A. Tables. B. Supper at Beaucaire.
1. France—Hist.—   1789–1815.   I. De Chair, Somerset Struben, 1911–   ed.   and tr. II. Title: Supper at Beaucaire.
DC213.2.A4 1948   923.144   50—119

NcU MH CaBViP IdU Or WaT
NN   0018497   DLC KEmT TNJ PP PU OU OClW OClJC PPT

Napoléon I, *Emperor of the French*, 1769–1821.
Napoleon's memoirs; edited by Somerset de Chair. New York, Harper [*1948]
xxvii, 605 p. ports., maps (part fold.) facsim. 23 cm.
Part 1, Corsica to Marengo, is a rearrangement of the translation published in 1823 with title: Memoirs of the history of France during the reign of Napoleon, dictated by the emperor at Saint Helena to the generals who shared his captivity, and published from the original manuscripts corrected by himself. Part 2, The Waterloo campaign, is a new translation by the editor from the French original published anonymously in 1820, with title: Mémoires pour servir à l'histoire de France en 1815. Supper at Beaucaire was translated into English for the first time by the editor and published separately in 1945.
1. France—Hist.—1789–1815.   I. De Chair, Somerset Struben, 1911–   ed. and tr.   II. Title: Supper at Beaucaire.

DC213.2.D4
1948a   923.144   50–10376

NN   0018498   DLC PLF PP PPL TU IEN MH

DC213
.2   Napoleon I, Emperor of the French, 1769–1821.
.A4   Napoleon's memoirs; edited by Somerset de
1949   Chair. New York, Harper [1949, c1948]
          xxvii, 605 p. ports., maps (part fold.)
          facsim. 23cm.
          Part I, Corsica to Marengo, is a rearrange-
          ment of the translation published in 1823 with
          title: Memoirs of the history of France during
          the reign of Napoleon, dictated by the emperor
          at Saint Helena to the generals who shared his
          captivity, and published from the original manu-

          scripts corrected by himself. Part 2, The
          Waterloo campaign, is a new translation by the
          editor from the French original published anony-
          mously in 1820, with title: Memoires pour servir
          a l'histoire de France en 1815. Supper at Beau-
          caire was translated into English for the first
          time by the editor and published separately in
          1945.
          1. France—Hist.—1789–1815.   I. De Chair,
          Somerset Struben,   1911–   ed. and tr. II.
          Title: Supper at   Beaucaire.

NN   0018500   MB NcU ViU OrU WaS CaBVa

Napoléon I, Emperor of the French, 1769–1821.
Memoirs of Napoleon Bonaparte
see under   Bourrienne, Louis Antoine Fauvelet de, 1769–1834.

Napoléon I, Emperor of the French, 1769–1821.
Memoirs of Napoleon Bonaparte, in an account of St. Helena.   New York, 1815
see under title   [Supplement]

E   Napoléon I,   emperor of the French,
5   1769–1821.
N 160865   Memoirs of Napoleon I, compiled from
          his own writings by F.M.Kircheisen; tr.
          from the German by Frederick Collins…
          London[1927]

NN   0018503   ICN

Napoléon I, *emperor of the French*, 1769–1821.
Memoirs of Napoleon I, compiled from his own writings by F. M. Kircheisen, translated from the German by Frederick Collins, B. A., with fifteen plates. London, Hutchinson & co. ltd. [1929]
288 p. front., ports. 24ᶜᵐ.
American edition (New York, Duffield & company) has title: Na-poleon's autobiography.

I. Kircheisen, Friedrich Max, 1877–1933, ed.   II. Collins, Frederick, tr.
29–13748
Library of Congress   DC213.2.A4 1929

NN   0018504   DLC MtBC PPA IU KU WaU MiU

VOLUME 405

Napoleon I, emperor of the French, 1769–1821.
  Memoirs of Napoleon I; compiled from his own writings by
F. M. Kircheisen, translated from the German by Frederick
Collins...   New York: Duffield & Co., 1929.   288 p.   front.,
plates, ports.   8°.

  Printed in Great Britain.

418158A. 1. France—Hist., 1789–   1815. 2. Kircheisen, Friedrich Max,
1877–   , editor. 3. Collins, Frederick,   translator.
N. Y. P. L.   July 2, 1929

NN   0018505   NN CU NcU OrU NcC PU OCl OCU OClh MB

Napoléon I, *emperor of the French*, 1769–1821.
  Memoirs of the history of France during the reign of Napoleon, dictated by the emperor at Saint Helena to the generals
who shared his captivity; and published from the original
manuscripts corrected by himself ...   London, H. Colburn
and co. (etc.), 1823–24.
  7 v. fronts., fold. maps, fold. tables, fold. facsims. 22⁰ᵐ.
  Vol. 4 dated 1824 ; v. 5: 2d edition.
  Vols. 1–2 "dictated to General Gourgaud"; v. 3–7 "dictated to the
Count de Montholon."
  Vols. 5–7 have title: Memoirs ... Historical miscellanies, vol. I–III.
  1. France—Hist.—1789–1815. I. Gourgaud, Gaspard, baron, 1783–
1852. II. Montholon, Charles Jean Tristan, marquis de, 1783–1853.

  Library of Congress   DC213.2.A21   4–15669

      PPWi MH PPL PPA MdBP CoU
NN   0018506   DLC CtY NjP MB MU NIC PLF MH WaU FMU

Napoleon I, Emperor of the French, 1769–1821.
  Memoirs of the life and actions of Napoleon
Bonaparte, emperor of the French ...
      see under title

Napoleon I, emperor of the French, 1769–1821.
  Memoirs of the military and political life of
Napoleon Bonaparte ...
      see under title

Napoléon I, emperor of the French, 1769–1821.
  Memoirs of the public and private life of
Napoleon Bonaparte
      see under Reid, William Hamilton, d. 1826.

Napoléon I, emperor of the French, 1769–1821.
  Memoirs relative to Egypt
      see under Institut d'Egypte, Cairo
  (1798–1801)

Napoléon I, *emperor of the French*, 1769–1821.
  Memorandum of two conversations between the Emperor
Napoleon and Viscount Ebrington, at Porto Ferrajo, on the
6th and 8th of December, 1814.   2d ed.   London, J. Ridgway,
1823.
  iv, (5)–31 p.   22½ᵐ.

  1. Fortescue, Hugh Fortescue, 2d earl, 1783–1861. II. Title.

                                                      44–15044
  Library of Congress   DC214.N2123 1823

NN   0018511   DLC MH NN NNF PLF ViU

Napoléon I, emperor of the French, 1769–1821.

FOR OTHER EDITIONS
SEE MAIN ENTRY
Las Cases, Emmanuel, *comte* **de,** 1766–1842.
  Mémorial de Sainte-Hélène. Journal de la vie privée et
des conversations de l'empereur Napoléon à Sainte Hélène;
par le comte de Las Cases ...   Londres, H. Colburn et co.
(etc.) 1823.

Napoleon I, Emperor of the French, 1796–1821.
  Memorias históricas de Napoleon
      see under title

Napoléon I, Emperor of the French, 1769–1821.
  [Message announcing a victory near Birkat]
(In France – Directoire exécutif. Message
[13 vendémiaire] 1799)

NN   0018514   NIC

Napoléon I, Emperor of the French, 1769–1821.
  [Message announcing the capture of Aboukir]
(In: France – Directoire exécutif. Message
[18 vendémiaire] 1799)

NN   0018515   NIC

Napoléon I, emperor of the French, 1769–1821.
  ...Messages et discours politiques publiés pour
la première fois d'après les textes autheniques
par Georges Barral. Paris, E.Flammarion [n.d.]
254p. 17.5cm.
  Portrait on title-page.

  I. Barral, Georges, 1842–   ed. II. Title.

  Title from Fordham Univ.   DC214.A4B3

NN   0018516   NNF

U 102
N36
1880
        Napoleon I, Emperor of the French, 1769–1821.
          Militärische Schriften, erläutert und
        mit Anmerkungen versehen durch Boie.
        Berlin, Schneider, 1880.
          iii, 159 p. 20 cm. (Militärische Klass-
        iker des In- und Auslandes, 6. Heft)

          1. Military art and science. I. Boie,
        Bernhard. II. Title. III. Series.

NN   0018517   CaBVaU

U 102
N37
1881
        Napoléon I, Emperor of the French, 1769–
        1821.
          Militärische Schriften (Schluss),
        erläutert und mit Anmerkungen versehen
        durch Boie. Scharnhorst: Militärische
        Schriften I, erläutert und mit Anmerkun-
        gen versehen durch v. d. Goltz. Berlin,
        Schneider, 1881.
          p. 162–184, xxv, 124 p.   plans, maps.
        20 cm. (Militärische Klassiker des In-
        und Auslan-   des, 9. Heft)

          1. Military art and science. I. Boie,
        Bernhard. II. Goltz, Colmar, Freiherr
        von der, 1843–1916. III. Scharnhorst,
        Gerhard Johann David von, 1755–1813./
        Militärische Schriften I. IV. Title.
        V. Title: Militärische Schriften I. VI.
        Series.

NN   0018519   CaBVaU CU

4U–35   Napoléon I, Emperor of the French, 1769–1821.
          Militärische Schriften. Erläutert durch Boie.
        Militärische Schriften von Scharnhorst, erläutert
        durch Frhr. v. d. Goltz.   Dresden, C. Höckner,
        1893.
          2 v. in 1.   (Militärische Klassiker des In- und
        Auslandes)

NN   0018520   DLC-P4

Napoléon I, emperor of the French, 1769–1821.
  The military and political life, character,
and anecdotes of Napoleon Bonaparte, from
his origin, to his death on the rock of St. Helena
      see under title

Napoleon I, emperor of the French, 1769–1821.
  The military career and life of Napoleon
Bonaparte
      see under title

Napoleon I, emperor of the French, 1769–1821.
  The military carriage of Napoleon Buonaparte
      see under title

Rare
DC
225
B54
        Napoleon I, Emperor of the French, 1769–1821.
          Military journal of General Buonaparte;
        being a concise narrative of his expe-
        dition from Egypt into Syria, in Asia
        Minor ... The whole taken from the
        original and official documents. Trans-
        lated from the French.   Baltimore,
        Printed by Warner & Hanna, 1800.
          96 p. 22cm.

          Extra-illu   strated with front. and
        mounted plate

          No. 1 in vol. lettered: Berthier.
        Journal of Egyptian campaign.

          1. Napoléon I—Egyptian campaign,
        1798–1799.

NN   0018525   NIC CtY PPAmP MdBP N DLC

Napoléon I, *emperor of the French*, 1769–1821.
  Military maxims of Napoleon. Tr. from the French,
by J. Akerly ... New York, Wiley and Putnam, 1845.
  81 p., 1 l. 19ᵐ.
  Contains LXXVIII maxims, annotated by M. Burnod; the greater part of
the notes being omitted in this edition.
  Name of annotator spelled Barnow in preface..

  1. Military art and science. I. Burnod, ———, ed. II. Akerly, J., tr.
III. Title.
                                                      16–19342
  Library of Congress   U19.N23

NN   0018526   DLC WaS NN

Napoléon I, *emperor of the French*, 1769–1821.
  The military maxims of Napoleon; tr. from the French
by Lieut.-Gen. Sir G. C. D'Aguilar, c. b. Introduction by
the author of "An absent minded war." London, Free-
mantle & co., 1901.
  xliii, 190 p. front. (port.) 13ᵐ.
  Ornamental title in red and black.

  1. Military art and science. I. D'Aguilar, Sir George Charles, 1784–
1855, tr. II. Title.
                                                      A 14–3002
  Title from Univ. of Calif.   Printed by L. C.

NN   0018527   CU

VOLUME 405

Napoléon I, *Emperor of the French*, 1769–1821.
The mind of Napoleon; a selection from his written and spoken words, edited and translated by J. Christopher Herold. New York, Columbia University Press, 1955.
322 p. 23 cm.

ı. Title.

DC214.H4   308.1   55–9068 ‡
[67o5]

OrPS NSyU MB TU
KEmT OU INS NBuU FMU IdPI OrP OrPR Wa WaS MtU
NN NcGU NcD ViU PP PPD PPT OC1W-H PSC MiU AU
NN   0018528   DLC AAP GU FU TxU OC1W OC1 PBL CU

Napoléon I, Emperor of the French, 1769–1821.
The mind of Napoleon as revealed in his thoughts, speech and actions. Collected by Harold F. B. Wheeler ... London [1909]
19 cm.
Bibliography, p. 183–[186]

NN   0018529   CtY OC1W

Napoléon I, Emperor of the French, 1769–1821.
DC216 .2 .M39
Marie Louise, *consort of Napoleon i*, 1791–1847.
Mon cher ami, Marie-Louise och Napoleon, 1813–1815; brev sammanställda, översatta och kommenterade av Carl-Fredrik Palmstierna. Stockholm, Norstedt [1955]

Napoleon I, emperor of the French, 1769–1821[?] purported author.
Les monologues de Napoléon Ier
see under title

U19 .N3
Napoléon I, Emperor of the French, 1769–1821.
Napoleão e a guerra moderna. Rio de Janeiro, Companhia Editôra Americana, 1954.
276p. 19cm. (Biblioteca do exército, v.207)

1.Military art and science. 2.Strategy I.Lanza, Conrad Hammond, 1878– ed. II.Title.

NN   0018532   NNU

Z944.05 N16n
Napoléon, emperor of the French, 1769–1821.
Napoléon. Paris, Ch. Meyrueis et compagnie, 1854.

8 p. 17cm.

"Les documents que je publie, contiennent la pensée intime de Napoléon sur le christianisme, et spécialement sur la divinité de l'Homme-Dieu."- p.[3]

NN   0018533   MnU

Napoléon I, Emperor of the French, 1769–1821.
Napoléon. Paris, Bureaux de la vie contemporaine, 1894
see under title

Napoléon I, Emperor of the French, 1769–1821.
Napoléon. New York, London, The Macmillan Company, 1906
see under title

Napoléon I, Emperor of the French, 1769–1821.
Napoleon, die Memoiren seines Lebens; in neuer Bearbeitung hrsg. von Friedrich Wencker-Wildberg in Verbindung mit Friedrich M. Kircheisen. Wien, Gutenberg-Verlag [n. d.]
v. in illus. 23 cm.
I. Wencker, Friedrich, 1893–
II. Kircheisen, Friedrich Max, 1877–1933, jt. ed.

NN   0018536   KU NcU KMK

Napoleon 1. Bonaparte, emperor of the French.
Napoleon; eine Auswahl seiner Briefe, Proklamationen, Gespräche, [edited by] Wolfgang Goetz. Berlin: Deutsche Buch-Gemeinschaft[, 192–?]. 444 p. 12°.

1. Goetz, Wolfgang, editor.
N.Y.P.L.   January 29, 1929

NN   0018537   NN WaU NIC CaBVaU OC1

Napoléon I, emperor of the French, 1769–1821.
Napoléon. Ses opinions et jugemens sur les hommes et sur les choses. Recueillis par ordre alphabétique, avec une introduction et des notes, par M. Damas-Hinard ... Paris, Duféy, 1838.
2 v. 21 cm.

ı. Damas-Hinard, Jean Joseph Stanislas Albert, 1805–1891, ed.
4–15672 Revised
Library of Congress   DC214.A2D2

NN   0018538   DLC MH MdBP RPB FTaSU NIC

Napoléon I, emperor of the French, 1769–1821.
... Napoléon; textes choisis et commentés, par É. Guillon ... Paris, Plon-Nourrit et cⁱᵉ [1912]
3 p. l., 316 p. incl. front. (port.) 19 cm. (Bibliothèque française. xixᵉ siècle) fr. 1.50
"Bibliographie": p. [305]–309.

ı. Guillon, Édouard Louis Maxime, 1849– ed.
Library of Congress   DC214.N2125   13–2585

NN   0018539   DLC NNC FTaSU PBm PSC

Napoléon I, *Emperor of the French*, 1769–1821.
Napoléon. Textes inédits et variantes, publiés par Nada Tomiche Dagher. Genève, Droz [1955]
205 p. 19 cm. (Textes littéraires français, 67)
CONTENTS.—Lettres autographes de Napoléon à Joséphine.—Les dictées de Napoléon à Sainte-Hélène: La guerre de Vendée. Autour de la paix d'Amiens. Notes sur Louis, roi de Hollande. Question russe et polonaise. Conférence de Dresde. Le premier juin. Des Bourbons: Le retour de l'île d'Elbe. La constitution de l'an VIII. Souvenirs de Sainte-Hélène: Série de variantes sur la révolution de 1789.—Conclusion.—Bibliographie p. [179]–195)

ı. Tomiche Dagher, Nada, ed.
A 56–4449
Illinois. Univ. Library for Library of Congress [2]

CSt KU
CtY InU IU CU ICU IaU ICN MH OU NjP MiU FU MU CU-S
NN   0018540   ICRL OrU CaBVaU TU PU LU NcD FTaSU

Napoléon I, Emperor of the French, 1769–1821.
... Napoléon an Josephine. Wien und Leipzig, Wiener verlag, 1906.
1 p. l., 142 p. front. (port.) 17 cm.
(Liebesbriefe berühmter männer und frauen. [1. bd.])
1. Josephine, consort of Napoléon I, 1763–1814.
2. Napoléon I, Emperor of the French, 1769–1821.

NN   0018541   CU

Napoléon I, *Emperor of the French*, 1769–1821.
Napoleon an Josephine; Briefe der Liebe. [Übertragen von Hannah Szász. Vorwort von Léon Cerf] Freiburg, Urban-Verlag [1929]
237 p. plates, ports. 22 cm.
Bibliography: p. 229–231.

ı. Joséphine, consort of Napoléon I, 1763–1814. II. Cerf, Léon, 1868– ed. III. Szász, Hannah, tr.

DC213.C345   59–58404

NN   0018542   DLC OC1

DC 213 B4
Napoléon I, emperor of the French, 1769–1821.
Napoléon and Berthier; catalogue of autograph letters, manuscripts, historical documents, and maps relating to the battles of the Napoleonic wars, the expeditions to Egypt and San Domingo, English, Italian, Spanish, and German affairs, the campaign in Russia, the mission of Berthier to Vienna, 1810, papers relating to Chambord and Versailles, etc. The property of the descendants of Louis-Alexandre Berthier.

[London, 1938]
83p. illus.,facsims.
Auction catalog.

1. Napoléon I, emperor of the French, 1769–1821.

NN   0018544   UU

Napoléon I, Emperor of the French, 1769–1821.
Napoleon and Canova; eight Conversations
see his Eight conversations.

Napoléon I, *emperor of the French*, 1769–1821.
Napoleon and modern war; his Military maxims, revised and annotated by Conrad H. Lanza ... Harrisburg, Pa., Military service publishing company, 1943.
xiv, 158 p. front. (port.) 20½ cm. (Half-title: Military classics. v)

1. Military art and science. 2. Strategy. ı. Lanza, Conrad Hammond, 1878– ed. II. Title.
43–17693
Library of Congress   U19.N237
[10]   355.4

NN   0018546   DLC NcD NBuU MH OrU PSt OC1JC PPT NcD

Napoléon I, Emperor of the French, 1769–1821.
Napoleon and modern war, his military maxims; revised and annotated by Conrad H. Lanza. Harrisburg, Pa. Military service pub. co., 1949.
158 p. D.

NN   0018547   PP

355 N162n
Napoleon I, Emperor of the French, 1769–1821.
Napoleon and modern war; his military maxims. Rev. and annotated by Conrad H. Lanza. Harrisburg, Pa., Military Service Pub. Co. [1954, °1943]
xiii, 158 p. (Military classics)

1. Military art and science I. Lanza, Conrad H II. Title

NN   0018548   MiD ScU

VOLUME 405

Napoleon I, emperor of the French, 1769-1821.

O'Meara, Barry Edward, 1786-1836.
   Napoleon at St. Helena, by Barry Edward O'Meara ... London, R. Bentley & son, 1888.

---

x944:C5 Napoléon I, Emperor of the French, 1769-1821.
N16na   The Napoleon calendar. A quotation from
          the works and sayings of Napoleon for every
          day in the year, compiled by A. S. Rappoport.
          London, F. Palmer [1911]
          93p. ports. 17cm.

          I. Rappoport, Angelo Solomon, 1871-   comp.
          II. Title.

NN 0018550   IU

Napoléon I, Emperor of the French, 1769-1821.
   Napoleon I [i. e. der Erste] hrsg. von dr. Otto
Krack.   Berlin, H. Ehbock [1907]
   4 p. l., p. 9-110.   16 cm.
   1. Napoléon I, Emperor of the French, 1769-1821.
I. Krack, Otto, 1865-   ed.

NN 0018551   CU

Napoléon I, Emperor of the French, 1769-1821.
   Napoleon I [i. e. der Erste] Seine wichtigsten
ansichten und urteile aus seinen eigenen reden und
briefen; zusammengestellt von Paul Rogal.
Braunschweig, K. Pfankuch [1907]
   112 p.   20 cm.
   On cover: Also sprach Napoleon I. Eine auswahl
aus den reden, briefen und schriften des kaisers.
   1. Napoléon I, Emperor of the French, 1769-1821
I. Rogal, Paul, ed.

NN 0018552   CU

Napoléon I, Emperor of the French, 1769-1821.
   Napoléon I. und papst Pius VII. Die korrespondenz zwischen dem römischen und französisch-
kaiserlichen hofe. Dokumente zur anfangsgeschichte
des kulturkampfes in Frankreich. Hrsg. von
J. W----r.   Leipzig, Deutsche verlagsactiengesell-
schaft [1906]
   1 p. l., ii, 102 p.   20 cm.
   1. Napoléon I, Emperor of the French, 1769-1821.
I. Pius VII, pope, 1742-1823. II. W----r, J., ed.

NN 0018553   CU

Napoléon I, Emperor of the French, 1769-1821.
   Napoléon, der feldherr, staatsmann und mensch
in seinen werken
       see under   Kircheisen, Friedrich Max,
       1877-1933.

Napoléon I, Emperor of the French, 1769-1821.
   Napoléon devant ses contemporains
       see under   Ader, Jean Joseph, 1796-1859.

Napoléon I, Emperor of the French, 1769-1821.
   Napoleon en la Isla de Sta. Elena ...
       see under title

Napoléon I, Emperor of the French, 1760-1821.
   Napoléon et Joséphine

see under

Savant, Jean.

Napoléon I, Emperor of the French, 1769-1821.
   Napoléon I. et la Garde Imperiale
       see under   Fieffé, Eugène, 1821-1862.

DC   Napoléon I, emperor of the French, 1769-1821.
214   Napoléon, his maxims of life, selected and ar-
.A363   ranged by Alfred H. Hyatt ...   [London & Edin-
        burgh, T. N. Foulis, 1911]
           82, [1] p.   illus.   13 x 6½cm.   (Maxims of life
        series no.1)
           Added t.-p. on 2 leaves of heavy colored paper, with
        mounted colored illustration.
           Bound by Sangorski & Sutcliffe, London.

           1. Napoléon I, emperor of the French, 1769-1821. I.
        Hyatt, Alfred Henry, ed.

NN 0018559   MiU NcU

Napoleon I, emperor of the French, 1769-1821.
   Napoleon, his maxims of life selected and arranged by Alfred
H. Hyatt.   [Edinburgh: Morrison & Gibb Ltd., 1912.]   82 p.
col'd illus.   [2. ed.]   nar. 24°.   (Maxims of life series. no. 1.)

1. Aphorisms (French). 2. Hyatt,   Alfred H., editor. 3. Series.
N. Y. P. L.   May 17, 1922.

NN 0018560   NN CtY MH

Napoléon I, Emperor of the French, 1769-1821.
   Napoléon, illustrated with prints from
contemporary and other portraits ...
       see under   Baily, J   T   Herbert,
       1865-

Napoléon I, emperor of the French, 1769-1821.

O'Meara, Barry Edward, 1786-1836.
   Napoleon in exile; or, A voice from St. Helena. The
opinions and reflections of Napoleon on the most important
events of his life and government, in his own words. By
Barry E. O'Meara ...   New York, W. Gowans, 1853.

Napoléon I, emperor of the French, 1769-1821.

Shorter, Clement King, 1857-1926, ed.
   Napoleon in his own defence; being a reprint of certain letters written by Napoleon from St. Helena to Lady Clavering,
and a reply by Theodore Hook; with which are incorporated
notes and an essay on Napoleon as a man of letters, by Clement
Shorter. With five plates. London, New York [etc.] Cassell
and company, limited, 1910.

Napoléon I, emperor of the French, 1769-1821.
   Napoleon in his own words, from the French of Jules
Bertaut, tr. by Herbert Edward Law and Charles Lincoln
Rhodes. Authorized ed. Chicago, A. C. McClurg & co.,
1916.

   xxx p., 1 l., 166, [1] p. incl. front. (port.) illus.   18½ cm.
   French title: Virilités, maximes et pensées de Napoléon-Bonaparte.

   I. Bertaut, Jules, 1877-   comp. II. Law, Herbert Edward, 1864-
tr. III. Rhodes, Charles Lincoln, joint tr.

DC214.V7   16—15808

PU OrCS OrU
NN 0018564   DLC WaU ICU OCIW OCX OCl ViU RP NN MB

          Napoléon I.
DC214
.5   Zongo-Tee-Foh-Tchi, pseud.
.Z8   Napoleon in the other world. A narrative written by him-
        self: and found near his tomb in the island of St. Helena, by
        Xongo-Tee-Foh-Tchi, mandarin of the third class [pseud.] ...
        London, H. Colburn, 1827.

Napoléon I, emperor of the French, 1769-1821.
   Napoléon inconnu; papiers inédits (1786-1793) pub. par
Frédéric Masson et Guido Biagi, accompagnés de notes sur la
jeunesse de Napoléon (1769-1793) par Frédéric Masson ...
3. éd. Paris, P. Ollendorff, 1895.

   2 v. fold. facsims., fold. geneal. tab. 22m.
   In v. 1, "Troisième édition" appears on cover only.

   1. Napoléon I, emperor of the French, 1769-1821. I. Masson, Frédéric, 1847-   II. Biagi, Guido, 1855-1925.
                                                    4—13537

   Library of Congress   DC205.N21

OCIW NcD
NN 0018566   DLC NcU NIC NjP MdBJ CtW NjR RPB MB

Napoléon I, emperor of the French.
   Napoléon inconnu; papiers inédits (1786-1793) publiés
par Frédéric Masson et Guido Biagi, accompagnés de notes
sur la jeunesse de Napoléon (1769-1793) par Frédéric
Masson ... Paris, P. Ollendorff, 1895. 2 v.
   Vol. II, 4. éd.

NN 0018567   DLC MH PBm PPL

Napoléon I, Emperor of the French, 1769-1821.
   Napoléon inconnu; papiers inédits (1786-1793) pub.
par Frédéric Masson et Guido Biagi, accompagné de
notes sur la jeunesse de Napoléon (1769-1793) par
Frédéric Masson ... 6. éd.   Paris, P. Ollendorff,
1895.
   2 v. fold. facsims., fold. geneal. tab. 22 cm.
   [In v. 1, "Six ième édition" appears on cover only]
   Later editions have title: Napoleon. Manuscrits
inédits, 1786-1791.

NN 0018568   CtY CU NjP

Napoléon I, emperor of the French, 1769-1821.

Warden, William, 1777-1849.
   Napoléon jugé par un Anglais. Lettres de Sainte-
Hélène; correspondance de W. Warden, chirurgien de
S. M. à bord du Northumberland, qui a transporté Napoléon Bonaparte à Sainte-Hélène; tr. de l'anglais et
suivie des Lettres du Cap de Bonne-Espérance; réponses
de Napoléon aux lettres de Warden. Avant-propos, notes,
documents justificatifs et appendice; par le docteur Cabanès ... Paris, H. Vivien, 1901.

Napoléon I, Emperor of the French, 1769-1821.
   Napoleon peint par lui-même ... 1818
       see under title

Napoléon I, emperor of the French, 1769-1821.
   Napoléon Ier et le roi Louis, d'après les documents conservés ...
       see under   Rocquain, Félix, 1833-   ed.

Napoléon I, Emperor of the French, 1769-1821.
   Napoléon Ier, peint par lui-même, par
M. Raudot ...   Paris, E. Dentu, 1865.
   2 p. l., 260 p.   18, 5 cm.
   I. Raudot, Claude Marie, 1801-1879, ed.
   1. Napoléon I, Emperor of the French, 1769-1821.

NN 0018572   CU MB NNF CtY

VOLUME 405

Vatican Rm.
Microfilm
11417.2
Napoleon I, Emperor of the French,1769-
1821.
...Napoléon, raconté par lui-même.
Paris, E. Chiron ₍18--?₎
xiv, 496 p. ports. 29 cm.
At head of title: Jules D'Auriac.

1. Napoleon I, Emperor of the French,
1769-1821. I. Auriac, Jules Eugène d',
1854- ed. II. Title.

NN   0018573   MoSU

Napoleon I, Emperor of the French, 1769-1821.
Napoléon, raconté par lui-même. Paris, Mercure de
France, 1912.

2 v.
Contents:-[1] 1769-1806. -[2] 1807-1821.

NN   0018574   MH CtY NN OCU NcU

NAPOLÉON I,emp.of the French.
Napoléon raconté par.lui-même. [Compiled
by R.M.Johnston.] 2e éd. Paris,Mercure de
France,1912.

2 vol.
I.1769-1806.
II.1807-1821.

NN   0018575   MH

Napoleon I.
Napoléon raconté par lui-même. [Publié par] Jules d'Auriac.
— Paris. Chiron. [192-?] (3), xiv, 496, (1) pp. Portraits. 28
cm., in 8s.

M8029 — Double main card. — ₍₎ ₍₎ on I. (M1) — Auriac, Jules d', 1854-.
(M2) — T.r. (1) — Napoléon I. (2)

NN   0018576   MB CtY

Napoléon I, *emperor of the French*, 1769-1821.
Napoléon, recueil par ordre chronologique de ses lettres,
proclamations, bulletins, discours sur les matières civiles et
politiques, etc., formant une histoire de son règne, écrite par
lui-même, et accompagnée de notes historiques; par M. Kermoysan ... Paris, Firmin Didot frères, 1853-65.
4 v. 18ᶜᵐ.

1. France—Hist.—Consulate and empire, 1799-1815. I. France.
Laws, statutes, etc., 1799-1814 (Napoléon 1) II. Kermoysan, Jean, ed.

Library of Congress   DC213.K4   27-25869

NN   0018577   DLC NcU NN

Napoléon I, *emperor of the French*, 1769-1821.
Napoleon self-revealed, in three hundred selected letters,
translated and edited by J. M. Thompson ... Boston and
New York, Houghton Mifflin company, 1934.
1 p. l., xvi, 383 p. 21 cm.
Published in Great Britain (Oxford, B. Blackwell) under title:
Letters of Napoleon.
"List of the principal sources ... from which the letters ... have
been selected": p. xiii-xv.

I. Thompson, James Matthew, 1878- ed. and tr. II. Title.

DC213.T45 1934a   923.144   35—2294

KEmT CoDU ICU ODW OO OCl NN MB ViU PPA PP WaSp
NN   0018578   DLC OrStbM MtU WaTC WaS Or IdU MoU

Napoleon I, emperor of the French, 1769-1821.
Napoleon transcripts, 1790-1853
see under title

Napoleón I, Emperor of the French, 1769-1821.
Napoleón y el arte de la guerra; las famosas
lecciones del mas grande estratega de todos los
tiempos, comentadas por generales ingleses,
alemanes, franceses, italianos y rusos. [Buenos
Aires, Imp. Talleres gráficos "Yunque", 1944]

NN   0018580   MH

Napoléon I, emperor of the French, 1769-1821.
... Napoléon-briefe; gesammelt und hrsg. von
Hans Landsberg. Berlin, Pan-verlag, 1906.
xiii p., 1 l., 457 p., 1 l. 19 cm. (Napoleon-
bibliothek)
"Literatur": p. xiii.
1. Napoléon I, emperor of the French, 1769-1821.
I. Landsberg, Hans, 1875- ed.

NN   0018581   CU

Napoleon I, *emperor of the French*, 1769-1821.
...Napoléon-Briefe; gesammelt und hrsg. von Hans Lands-
berg. 5. ed. Berlin, Pan-Verlag, 1909. xiii, 473 p. 19cm.
(Napoleon-Bibliothek. ₍Bd. 1₎)
"Literatur", p. xiii.

376346B. 1. France—Hist.—Consulate   and Empire, 1799-1815. I. Landsberg, Hans, 1875- , ed.
N.Y.P.L.   September 23, 1947

NN   0018582   NN PP

                                    [191-?]
DC213
.A25   Napoléon I, emperor of the French, 1769-
1821.
Napoleon-briefe.   Berlin, Parnassos-
verlag ₍191-?₎
xiv,479,₍1₎p. 18cm.
"Siebente auflage, gesammelt und herausgegeben von Hans Landsberg."

I.Landsberg, Hans, 1875-

NN   0018583   NNU-W

Napoléon I, Emperor of the French, 1769-1821.
Napoleone I, sua autobiografia. Torino,
1869.
109 p.

NN   0018584   DCU-IA

Napoléon I, *emperor of the French*, 1769-1821.
New letters of Napoleon I, omitted from the edition
published under the auspices of Napoleon III; from the
French by Lady Mary Loyd. New York, D. Appleton
and company, 1897.
xviii, 380 p. front. (port.) 20½ᶜᵐ.

I. Loyd, Lady Mary Sophia (Hely-Hutchinson) 1853- tr.

Library of Congress   DC213.N22   4-15679

OCl NcU ViU NN PP PU PV
NN   0018585   DLC WaS OKentU AU PLF TU GU MiU OCU

Napoléon I, *emperor of the French*,1769-1821.
New letters of Napoleon I, omitted from the edition
published under the auspices of Napoleon III; from the
French by Lady Mary Loyd. London, W. Heinemann,
1898.
3 p. l., ₍vi₎-xviii p., 1 l., 380 p. front. (port.) 23ᶜᵐ.

I. Loyd, Lady Mary Sophia (Hely-Hutchinson) 1853-   tr.

                                                          12-21851

Library of Congress   DC213.N22 1898

NN   0018586   DLC CaBVaU WaTC INS PIm MB

DC
213
.N22
1898
Napoléon I, Emperor of the French,
1769-1821.
New letters of Napoleon I, omitted
from the edition published under the
auspices of Napoleon III. Edited by M.
Léon Lecestre...From the French by Lady
Mary Loyd. Second ed. New York, D.
Appleton, 1898.
xviii, 380 p. front. (port.) 21
cm.
"Authorized edition."
I. Loyd, Mary Sophia (Hely-
Hutchinson),   Lady, 1853-   tr.

NN   0018587   OKentU OClW MiU PKsL

DC
214
.D82
Napoléon I,Emperor of the French,1769-1821.
Notes inédites de l'empereur Napoléon Iᵉʳ
sur les mémoires militaires du général Lloyd
Publiées par Ariste Ducaunnès-Duval. Bordeaux,
Impr.G.Gounouilhou,1901.
22 p.
"Extrait du tome XXXV des Archives histori-
ques de la Gironde."
Contains Lloyd's text.
1.Military art and science. I.Ducaunnès-
Duval,Ariste,ed. II.Lloyd,Henry,1720?-1783.
Introduction à   l'histoire de la guerre
en Allemagne,   en 1756.

NN   0018588   MiU NIC CtY NcU

Napoléon I, *emperor of the French*, 1769-1821.
Napoleon's notes on English history, made on the eve
of the French revolution. Illustrated from contemporary historians, and refreshed from the findings of later
research, by Henry Foljambe Hall ... London, J. M. Dent
& co.; New York, E. P. Dutton & co., 1905.
xxvii, ₍1₎, 352 p. front. (port.) pl., facsim. 22ᶜᵐ.
Title in red and black.
CONTENTS.—Introduction.—pt. I. Napoleon's note-books.—pt. II. A.-
Barrow: his History and preface. B.-Britons, Romans, and Anglo-
Saxons.—pt. III. Conquests of Northmen, home and colonial.—pt. IV. Normans and early Plantagenets. The Tudors.—Notes to pt. IV.—Index.
1. Gt. Brit.—Hist. I. Hall, Henry Foljambe, ed. and tr.

Library of Congress   DA32.N23   6-1463

ICU PP PPL MiU OClW MB NN
NN   0018589   DLC TxU NIC FTaSU Vi OrCS WaTC IdU

Napoléon I, Emperor of the French, 1769-1821.
Nouvelle biographie critique et anecdotique des contemporains, par Napoléon. Paris: chez l'éditeur, 1826. 128 p. 32°.

Binder's title: Vie de Napoléon.
"M. Gallois a réuni sous ce titre ₍Biographie des contemporains₎ les divers
jugements prononcés par Napoléon sur ses contemporains et qui se trouvent con-
signés dans les ouvrages de MM. O'Méara, Las-Cases, Gourgaud, Montholon et
autres, en ajoutant en tête de chaque jugement une courte notice biographique sur
chaque personnage dont il est fait mention. Cet ouvrage ou pour mieux dire ces
jugements ont été réimprimés: 1° sous le titre de Profils des contemporains. Paris,
Pollet, 1824... 2° sous celui de Biographie critique et anecdotique des contemporains.
Paris, 1826..."— *Quérard's La France littéraire*.
With this is bound: Vie politique et militaire de Napoléon. Paris, 1826.

1. Europe.—Biography. 2. Napo-   leon I, emperor of the French,
1769-1821. 3. Title.
N.Y.P.L.   August 15, 1918.

NN   0018590   NN

NAPOLEON I,emperor of the FRENCH.
Obras escogidas de Napoleón,puestas en orden
y precedidas de un estudio literario por A.Pu-
jol. Traducidas para los suscritores del Heraldo. Madrid,Espinosa y comp.,1846.

NN   0018591   MH

VOLUME 405

Bo671
B911ℓ
Napoléon I, <u>emperor of the French</u>, 1769-1821.
   Oeuvres amoureuses de Napoléon d'après ses
lettres d'amour à Joséphine avec une introduction et des notes du bibliophile Pol
André [pseud. of Hector Fleischmann] Ouvrage
orné de nombreuses illustrations dans le texte
et hors texte. Paris, A.Michel[1911]
   2p.ℓ.,352p. illus.,plates,ports. 22cm.

   I.Fleischmann, Hector, 1882-1914, ed.
x.André, Pol. x.Pol André

NN 0018592   CtY FTaSU OCU

Napoleon I., emperor of the French, 1769–1821.
   Œuvres choisies de Napoléon Bonaparte.   Paris: Librairie
ancienne et moderne. 1827. 4 v. front. 32°.

   Contents: v. 1. Rapports au Directoire: Campagnes d'Italie; Campagnes
d'Égypte et de Syrie. v. 2. Campagnes d'Égypte et de Syrie. Proclamations, discours, dépêches et messages officiels. Les trente-cinq jours; ou, Mémoires politiques
sur la campagne de 1815. v. 3. Les trente-cinq jours. Opinions et jugemens sur
les anciens et les modernes. v. 4. Opinions et jugemens. Pensées et réflexions sur
divers sujets. Lettres. Testament de Napoléon.

1. French literature.—Collected   works.
N. Y. P. L.   July 11, 1918.

NN 0018593   NN IU IEN

B844
N16
Napoléon I, emperor of the French, 1769-1821.
   Oeuvres choisies de Napoléon Bonaparte... Paris,
Philippe, 1828.
   4 v. port. 11 cm.

   Constant Chantpie, imprimeur.

NN 0018594   NNC

Napoléon I, emperor of the French, 1769-1821.
   Oeuvres choisies de Napoléon, mises en ordre
et précédées d'une etude littéraire. Par A. Pujol.
Paris, 1843.
      xi, 504 pp.

   I. Pujol, Auguste, ed.

NN 0018595   PPL RPB

Napoléon I, *emperor of the French*, 1769–1821.
   Œuvres choisies de Napoléon, mises en ordre et précé-
dées d'une étude littéraire, par A. Pujol. Paris, Belin-
Leprieur, 1845.
   xi, 504 p. front. (port.) 17¼ᶜᵐ.
   Title vignette.

   I. Pujol, Auguste, ed.
                                                 18–8622
   Library of Congress   DC214.A2P8

NN 0018596   DLC FTaSU LU OC1W

Napoléon I, emperor of the French, 1769-1821.
   Oeuvres littéraires, publiées d'après les
originaux et les meilleurs textes avec une
introduction, des notes historiques et littéraires et un index par Tancrède Martel.
Paris, Nouvelle Librairie Parisienne, 1888.
   4 v. ports. 18½ cm.

   Vol. 4: port. wanting.
   Portraits by Th. Bérengier.

   I. Martel,   Tancrède, 1857-   ed.

NN 0018597   NjR DLC-P4 NIC CtY

DC213
.A1
1888
Napoléon I, emperor of the French, 1769-1821.
   Oeuvres littéraires. Publiées d'après les
originaux et les meilleurs textes avec une introd,
des notes historiques et littéraires et un index
par Tancrède Martel. [2.éd.] Paris, A. Savine,
1888.
   4 v. ports.
   "Memento bibliographique": v.4, p.[533]-536.

NN 0018598   ICU

Napoléon I, emp. of the French.
   Œuvres littéraires et politiques. Nouvelle éd. Paris, H. L.
Delloye, 1840.
   pp. xij, 275. Port. (Bibliothèque choisie.)

||Series

NN 0018599   MH FTaSU NjP

Napoléon I, Emperor of the French, 1769-1821.
   Observations occasioned by the remarks, on the
character of Napoleon Bonaparte
      see under   Henshaw, David, 1791-1852.
[Supplement]

Napoléon I, *emperor of the French*, 1769–1821.
   The officer's manual. Military maxims of Napoleon.
Tr. from the French by Colonel D'Aguilar ... Dublin,
R. Milliken and son; [etc., etc.] 1831.
   250 p. 14ᶜᵐ.
   Contains LXXVIII maxims, annotated by M. Burnod.

   1. Military art and science.   I. Burnod, ——, ed. II. D'Aguilar, Sir
George Charles, 1784–1855, tr.
                                                 16–19345
   Library of Congress   U19.N21

NN 0018601   DLC CaBVaU DN NWM PPL DN

Napoléon I, *emperor of the French*, 1769–1821.
   The officer's manual. Napoleon's maxims of war. Richmond,
Va., West & Johnston, 1862.
   159 p. 15ᶜᵐ.
   Contains LXXVIII maxims, annotated by M. Burnod and translated by
Sir George C. D'Aguilar.

   1. Military art and science.   I. Burnod, ——, ed. II. D'Aguilar,
Sir George Charles, 1784–1855, tr.
                                                 16–19344
   Library of Congress   U119.N235

NN 0018602   DLC IU NcU NcD GEU MBAt ViU OC1WHi

xU19
N4
Napoléon I, emperor of the French, 1769-
   1821
   The officer's manual. Napoleon's maxims
of war.   New York, Bradburn, 1865.
   186p. 14cm.

   Contains LXXVIII maxims, translated by
Sir George C. D'Aguilar.
   1. Military art and science. I. D'Aguilar,
Sir George Charles, 1784-1855, tr.

NN 0018603   IaU

Napoleon I, Emperor of the French, 1769-1821.
   The officer's manual
      see also his ... Napoleon's maxims of war.

Napoleon I, Emperor of the French, 1769-1821.
   Opinions et jugemens sur les hommes et sur les
choses
      see his Napoleon. Ses opinions et jugemens...

Napoléon I, *emperor of the French*, 1769–1821.
   The opinions and reflections of Napoleon, edited by Lewis
Claflin Breed ... Boston, The Four seas company [*1926]
   534 p. front., pl., ports. 21ᶜᵐ.
   "Authorities": p. 515–516.

   I. Breed, Lewis Claflin, ed. II. Title.
   Library of Congress   DC214.A2B7   27–4163
   —— Copy 2.

NN 0018606   DLC NIC MoU FTaSU OrU OKentU PPA PU MB

Napoléon I, Emperor of the French, 1769-1821.
   Opinions de Napoleon sur divers sujets de
politique et d'administration ...
      see under [Pelet de la Lozère, Privat
Joseph Claramond, comte] 1785-1871.

Napoléon I, Emperor of the French, 1769-1821.
   Ordres et apostilles de Napoléon, 1799-1815
      see under France. Sovereigns, etc. 1799-
1814 (Napoleon I)

Napoléon I, Emperor of the French, 1769-1821.
   Original journals of the eighteen campaigns of
Napoleon Bonaparte ... Trans. from the French.
Added, all the bulletins relating to each campaign ...
London, Davis, 1817.
   2 v. 8°.

NN 0018609   MB

Napoléon I, Emperor of the French, 1791-1821.
   Napoleon's own memoirs. Printed from a
manuscript transmitted from Saint Helena through
an unknown channel
      see under [Lullin de Châteauvieux,
Frédéric] 1772-1841.

Napoléon I, Emperor of the French, 1769-1821.
   Pages de l'épopée impériale

   see under

   Coppet, André de, 1892-1953.

Napoléon I, *emperor of the French*, 1769–1821.
   Les pages immortelles de Napoléon, choisies et expliquées par
Octave Aubry. Paris, Éditions Corrêa [1941]
   246 p., 2 l. incl. front. (2 port.) 18¼ᶜᵐ. (*On cover:* Les pages immortelles)

   1. France—Hist.—Consulate and empire, 1799–1815.   I. Aubry,
Octave, 1881-   ed. II. Title.
                                                 A 41–4453
   Harvard univ. Library
      for Library of Congress   [2]

NN 0018612   MH FTaSU

Napoleon I, emperor of the French, 1769-1821.
   Pamietniki Napoleona; rekopism nadeslany
z wyspy Sw Heleny ... przez Kazimierza
Ehrenberga. Warszaw, Fiszer, 1912.
   [119 p.]

NN 0018613   OC1

VOLUME 405

Napoleon I, emperor of the French, 1769-1821.
...Paroles de Napoleon; le moraliste - l'organisa-
tour - l'homme d'etat - le patriote - le librateur;
introduction par A. Augustin Rey... 2. ed.
Paris, 1917.

DC214
.A2R4

NN   0018614   DLC

Napoléon I, *emperor of the French*, 1769-1821.
... Paroles de Napoléon; le moraliste—l'organisateur—
l'homme d'état—le patriote—le libérateur; introduction
par A. Augustin Rey ... 5. éd. Paris, J. Meynial, 1917.
34 p., 1 l. 21ᶜᵐ. (La guerre européenne et les enseignements de l'histoire) fr. 1

I. Rey, A. Augustin, comp.

Library of Congress   DC214.A2R4 1917   18-7985

NN   0018615   DLC TxU

Napoleon I, Emperor of the French, 1769-1821.
Pensamientos y maximes militares de
Napoleon. Barcelona, Imp. de la revista
cientifico-militar 1909.
92 p.   16.5 cm.

NN   0018616   DNW

Napoléon I, *emperor of the French*, 1769-1821.
... Pensées pour l'action, recueillies et présentées par Édouard
Driault. Paris, Presses universitaires de France, 1943.
xx, 221, [1] p. 23ᶜᵐ.
At head of title: Napoléon.
"1ʳᵉ édition."

I. *Driault, Édouard, 1864–   ed. II. Title.
                                              46-13735
Library of Congress   DC214.A2D7
                           [2]   944.05

NN   0018617   DLC NBuU TxU MoSU OU

Napoleon I, Emperor of the French, 1769-1821.
Pensieri di Napoleone, intorno alla divinita'.
Raccolti a Sant'Elena dal conte di Montholon, e
pubblicati dal Cav. di Beauterne.   Roma,
Edizioni cosmopoli [1940]
96 p.

NN   0018618   DLC

Soc
DC
213
D54

Napoleon I, Emperor of the French, 1769-1821.
Pièces diverses relatives aux opérations
militaires et politiques du général Bonaparte
Paris, impr. de P. Didot, 1800.
3v in 1 (350p.)

1. France - History - Consulate and Empire,
1799-1815. 2. Napoleon I, Emperor of the
French, 1769-1821. I. Title.

NN   0018619   FTaSU MdBP NWM

Napoléon I., Emperor of the French, 1769-1821.
Political aphorisms, moral and philosophical
thoughts of the Emperor Napoléon. Collected from
upwards of eighty original works, by Cᵗᵉ. Aᵗᵉ.
G. de Liancourt, edited by James Alexander
Manning ... London, T. C. Newby, Publisher
[C. Buck, Printer, Bury] 1848.
xii, 271 p.   8 vo.   In 3/4 red calf.
Added title in French.
Text in parallel pages in French and in English.

NN   0018620   CSmH

Napoleon I, emperor of the French, 1769-1821.

Friedrich I, *king of Württemberg*, 1754–1816.
Politische und militärische correspondenz könig Friedrichs
von Württemberg mit kaiser Napoleon I., 1805–1813. Hrsg.
von dr. August von Schlossberger ... Stuttgart, W. Kohl-
hammer, 1889.

Napoléon I, Emperor of the French, 1769-1821.
Porte-feuille de Buonaparte, pris à
Charleroi le 18 juin 1815. La Haye,
Libraire Belgique [n.d.]

97-128 p. fold. facsim. 22 cm.

Bound with Carnot, Lazare Nicolas
Marguerite. Exposé de la conduite politique de Carnot. Paris, 1815.
"3me cahier".

NN   0018622   CaBVaU CtY

Bo73
3
4

Napoléon I, *emperor of the French*, 1769-1821.
Porte-feuille de Buonaparte, pris a Charleroi
le 18 juin 1815. A Montpellier, De l'Imprimerie
de Jean-Germain Tournel, 1815.
48p. 20cm. [Binder's title: Troubles civils.
Midi]

NN   0018623   CtY

Napoléon I, Emperor of the French, 1769-1821.
Le précis des événements militaires arrivés
pendant l'année 1798, d'après le manuscrit original
des commentaires de Napoléon. [n.p., n.d.]
xvi p. facsims. 28 cm.

NN   0018624   NcU

Napoleon I, Emperor of the French, 1769-1821.
Préceptes et jugements de Napoléon recueillis et
classés ...
see under Picard, Ernest.

Napoléon I, *emperor of the French*, 1769-1821.
Précis des guerres de César, par Napoléon, écrit par
M. Marchand, à l'île Sainte-Hélène, sous la dictée de
l'empereur; suivi de plusieurs fragmens inédits. Bruxelles, J. P. Meline, 1836.
271 p. 15ᶜᵐ. (*Half-title:* Mémoires pour servir à l'histoire de Napoléon)
Fragmens divers: Note sur le deuxième livre de l'Énéide de Virgile.—
Observations sur la tragédie de Mahomet, par Voltaire.—Note sur le
suicide.—Deuxième codicile.
1. Gaul—Hist.—B. C. 58–A. D. 511. 2. Rome—Hist.—Republic—Civil
war, B. C. 49-48. 3. Caesar, C. Julius. 4. Vergilius Maro, Publius. Aeneis.
5. Voltaire, François Marie Arouet de. Mahomet. I. Marchand, Louis
Joseph Narcisse, comte, 1791-1876.
                                                          18-20375
Library of Congress   DC62.N2 1836 a

NN   0018626   DLC

Napoléon I, *emperor of the French*, 1769-1821.
Précis des guerres de César, par Napoléon, écrit par
M. Marchand, à l'île Sainte-Hélène, sous la dictée de
l'empereur; suivi de plusieurs fragmens inédits. Paris,
Gosselin, 1836.
2 p. l., 260 p. fold. plan. 21½ᶜᵐ. (*Half-title:* Mémoires pour servir à
l'histoire de Napoléon)

Subject entries: 1. Gaul—Hist.—B. c. 58–A. D. 511. 2. Rome—Hist.—
Republic—Civil war, B. c. 49-48. 3. Caesar, C. Julius.   8-32241

Library of Congress, no.   DC62.N21.

NN   0018627   DLC FTaSU NWM NN OClWHi OCU CtY

Napoleon I.
Précis des guerres de Frédéric.
(In Frederick II., the Great. Œuvres historiques. Vol. 3, pp. 199-
348. Paris. 1872.)

G4 — Frederick II., the Great, of Prussia.

NN   0018628   MB

Napoléon I, emperor of the French, 1769-1821.

Machiavelli, Niccolò, 1469–1527.
... El príncipe; comentado por Napoleón Bonaparte. Madrid, Librería Bergua [1933]

Napoléon I, Emperor of the French, 1769-1821.
Private anecdotes of the court of Napoleon
see under title

Napoléon I, Emperor of the French, 1769-1821,
supposed author.
Proclamation de Napoléon Buonaparte à ses
nouveaux sujets. Constitution de l'isle d'Elbe
see under   L   , M   S.

Napoléon I, emperor of the French, 1769-1821.
Proclamations. Mayenne, J. Floch [1946]

131 p. illus. 29 cm.
On cover: Lithographies originales de Jean
Pichard.

NN   0018632   MH

Napoléon I, emperor of the French, 1769-1821.
Proclamations et harangues de Napoléon Bonaparte. Recueillies par Th. D. Paris, Lecointe
et Pougin, 1835.

xvi, 320 p. front. (port.) 21 cm.

NN   0018633   MoKU

Bo710
830Ba

Napoléon I, Emperor of the French, 1769-1821.
Proclamations et harangues de Napoléon
Bonaparte, avec le sommaire des événements
qui ont donné lieu à chacune d'elles ...
2. éd. Paris, Librairie Française et Étrangère, 1850.
258 p. 15 cm. [Binder's title: Brochures
politiques. République, 15]

NN   0018634   CtY

VOLUME 405

French
Rev.
DC
141
F87+
v.385

Napoleon I, Emperor of the French, 1769-1821.
    Quarante lettres inédites de Napoléon,
recueillies par L*** F****. 2e éd. Paris,
Ponthieu, 1825.
    68 p. 20cm.

    With this is bound: Lettre adressée à
Monseigneur le duc d'Orléans ₍Signed A.S.₎

    I. L*** F**** II. Le Four, attributed
author. III.   F****, L***

NN   0018635   NIC

Napoléon I, Emperor of the French, 1769-1821.
    Une quatrième maxime de Napoléon
       see under   Grouard, Auguste Antoine,
1843-1929. [Supplement]

Napoleon I.
    Rapport [de la] bataille d'Aboukir.
    (In Gros. Exhibition du tableau de la bataille d'Aboukir. Pp. 5-8.
Paris, 1829.)

E2153 — Aboukir. Battle of. 1799.

NN   0018637   MB

Napoléon I, Emperor of the French, 1769-1821.
    Rękopisy Napoleona, 1793-1795, w Polsce
       see his   Manuscrits de Napoléon, 1793-1795,
en Pologne.

Napoleon I, Emperor of the French, 1769-1821.
    Recueil de décrets, ordonnances, traités de paix,
manifestes, proclamations, discours ...
       see under   France. Laws, statutes, etc.
1799-1814 (Napoleon I)

DC
213.2
A26

Napoléon I, Emperor of the French, 1769-1821.
    Recueil de pièces authentiques sur le captif
de Ste.-Hélène; de mémoires et documens écrits
ou dictés par l'empereur Napoléon. Suivis de
lettres de MM. le grand-maréchal comte Bertrand,
le comte Las Cases, le général baron Gourgaud,
le général comte Montholon, les docteurs Warden,
O'Meara et Automarchi, et plusieurs personnages
de haute distinction. Paris, A. Corréard,
1821-25.
    12 v.   illus., fold. map, plan, ports., tables
(part fold.)
    Subtitle varies   slightly.
    1. Napoléon I,   Emperor of the French,
1769-1821--   Captivity, 1815-1821

NN   0018640   MiU MH DGU PBL IU NjR CtY

Napoleon I, Emperor of the French, 1769-1821.
    Recueil des manifestes, proclamations, discours,
decrets ...
       see under   France. Laws, statutes, etc.,
1799-1814 (Napoleon I)

Napoléon I, emp. of the French.
    Le registre de l'île d'Elbe; lettres et ordres inédits, 28 mai 1814–
22 fév. 1815. Publiés par Leon G. Pélissier. Paris, Thorin et fils,
1897.
    pp. (4), xxvi, 310 +. Port.

||Pélissier°

NN   0018642   MH NNF CtY MnU NIC CU CLSU NjP

Napoleon I, Emperor of the French, 1769-1821.
    Le registre de l'île d'Elbe: lettres et ordres in-
édits de Napoléon Ier (28 mai 1814 - 22 février 1815)
publiés par Léon G. Pélissier... 2. éd. Paris, A. Fontemoing, 1897.
    ? p. l., xxvi, 310p. front. (port.)   19.5cm.

    1. Napoléon I-Captivity, 1814-1815. I. Title.

Title from Fordham Univ.   DC211.P4

NN   0018643   NNF

Napoleon I, Emperor of the French, 1769-1821.
    Reglas de moral y politica escritas por Napoleon
Bonaparte en la Isla de Sta. Elena, y traducidas de la
ultima edicion francesa.   Madrid, E. Aguado, 1829.
    88 p.   24°.

NN   0018644   NN

Bo67a
869c

Napoléon I, Emperor of the French, 1769-1821.
    ... Règlement de la Calotte du régiment de la
Fère composé en 1788 par Napoléon Bonaparte.
Suivi de Origine et signification des noms de
Napoléon Bonaparte, par le bon de Coston.
Montélimar, Imprimerie et lithographie Bourron
[1869?]
    40p. 18cm. (On cover: Petite bibliothèque
historique et littéraire du Dauphiné, éd. par
C. Bourron)
    Imprint on cover: Grenoble, Maisonville et
fils et Jourdan
    At head of title   Documents historiques
inédits.

NN   0018645   CtY

Napoléon I, *emperor of the French*, 1769-1821.
    Rękopisy Napoleona, 1793-1795, w Polsce, wydał Szymon
Askenazy. Warszawa, Nakładem Polskiego antykwarjatu
naukowego H. Wildera, 1929.
    3 p. l., 9-117, ₍1₎ p. facsims. (part double) 40 cm.
    Added t.-p., in French.
    In case.
    Each manuscript is transcribed in French and is accompanied by
an explanation in French and Polish.
    "Dzieła tego odbito ... 820 egzemplarzy numerowanych, z których
do sprzedaży oddano 790. Papier czerpany Van Gelder zonen sporząd-
zono wyłącznie dla niniejszego wydawnictwa ze znakiem wodnym 'N'
... nr. 810."
    I. Askenazy, Szymon, 1867-1935, ed.   II. Title.

DC213.A7   CA 29—684 Unrev'd

NN   0018646   DLC MH WaU NcD ICN MiU NN

Napoléon I, Emperor of the French, 1769-1821.
    Relation circonstanciée de la dernière
campagne de Buonaparte
       see under   [Delbare, François Thomas]
1770-1855.

DC202
.7
.N6

Napoléon I, emperor of the French, 1769-1821.
    Nikolaï Mikhaïlovich, *grand duke of Russia*, 1859-1919, *ed.*
    Les relations diplomatiques de la Russie et de la France
d'après les rapports des ambassadeurs d'Alexandre et de Napoléon, 1808-1812 ... St. Pétersbourg, Manufacture des papiers
de l'état, 1905-08.

Napoléon I, Emperor of the French, 1769-1821.
    Remarks on the character of Napoleon
Bonaparte
       see under   [Channing, William Ellery]
1780-1842.

Napoleon I.
    Remarques . . . sur les commentaires de César.
    (In Caesar, Caius Julius. Commentaires sur la guerre des Gaules
. . . Pp. 379-389. Paris. [1876?])

G2438 — Caesar, Caius Julius.

NN   0018650   MB

Napoleon I., emperor of the French.
    Resumen de los Comentarios de Cesar, obra dictada por
Napoleon ₍to L. J. M. Marchand₎...y traducida del frances por J.
A. Facio. Van añadidos varios fragmentos de Napoleon con una
noticia biografica del traductor, escrita por J. F.   Paris: Libreria
de Rosa, 1837.   1 p.l., (i)vi-xxxix, 225 p.   8°.

1. Cæsar, Caius Julius. 2. Facio,   Jose Antonio, translator. 3. F., J.
4. Marchand, Louis Joseph Marie,   comte.   uly 17, 1912.
N. Y. P. L.

NN   0018651   NN

Napoléon I, Emperor of the French, 1769-1821.
    Revolution und Kaiserreich
       see under   Pflugk-Harttung, Julius Albert
Georg von, 1848-1918.

Napoléon I, *emperor of the French*, 1769-1821.
    Sayings of Napoleon. Selected and arranged by Jon.
B. Frost ... Atlanta, Ga., The Romance publishing co.
₍*1895₎
    cover-title, 8 p. 20¼ᶜᵐ.

    I. Frost, Jonathan Burwell, comp.   II. Title.

Library of Congress   DC214.N214   CA 15-969 Unrev'd

NN   0018653   DLC

Napoleon I, emperor of the French, 1769-1821.
    Napoleons schriften und gespräche hrsg. von
Hans Landsberg. Berlin, Pan-Verlag, 1909.
    213 p.

NN   0018654   PP

Napoleon I, emperor of the French, 1769-1821.
    ... Napoleons schriften und gespräche, hrsg. von
Hans Landsberg. 2. aufl.   Berlin, Pan-verlag,
1909.
    vii, [1], 213 p.   19 cm.
    "Literatur": p. [1]
    I. Landsberg, Hans, 1875-   ed.

NN   0018655   CU

Napoléon I, *emperor of the French*, 1769-1821.
    A selection from the letters and despatches of the first
Napoleon. With explanatory notes. By Captain the
Hon. D. A. Bingham ... London, Chapman and Hall,
limited, 1884.
    3 v. 22ᶜᵐ.

    1. Bingham, Denis Arthur, ed.

Library of Congress   DC213.B61   4—15684

                 OC1W CtY MH ICN PPL
NN   0018656   DLC CoD OC1WHi NcU DNW NjP OC1 OOxM

VOLUME 405

NAPOLÉON I, emperor of the FRENCH, 1769-1821.
Sentiment de Napoléon sur la divinité de Jésus-Christ. Pensées inédites recueillies à Ste.Hélène par le comte de Montholon et publiées par le cher[er] de Beauterne. [Paris], chez l'auteur, etc., 1841.

At head of title: Fragments religieux inédits.

NN   0018657   MH MnU

DC
214
B38
1845
Napoléon I, Emperor of the French, 1769-1821.
Sentiment de Napoléon sur le christianisme. Conversations religieuses recueillies à Sainte-Hélène, avec des documents inédits de la plus haute importance, et des lettres du Cardinal Fesch, de MM. de Montholon, Hudson Lowe et Marchant. 4. éd. · Poissy, Olivier-Fulgence, 1845.
xxxii, 221 p. 22cm.

1. Napoléon I--Religion and ethics.

NN   0018658   NIC OClWHi

Napoléon I, *emperor of the French, 1769-1821.*
Sentiment de Napoléon sur le christianisme. Conversations religieuses recueillies à Sainte-Hélène. Avec des documents inédits de la plus haute importance, et des lettres du cardinal Fesch, de MM. de Montholon, Hudson-Lowe et Marchant, par le chevalier de Beauterne. **6.** éd. Poissy, Olivier-Fulgence; [etc., etc.] 1845.
2 p. l., xxxii, 207, [2] p. 19[cm].

1. Jesus Christ - Divinity.   I. Beauterne, Robert François Antoine de, b. 1748, ed.   II. Montholon, Charles Jean Tristan, marquis de, 1783-1853, comp.   III. Title.

NN   0018659   PKsL

Napoléon I, *emperor of the French, 1769-1821.*
Sentiment de Napoléon sur le christianisme. Conversations religieuses recueillies à Sainte-Hélène. Avec des documents inédits de la plus haute importance, et des lettres du cardinal Fesch, de MM. de Montholon, Hudson-Lowe et Marchant, par le chevalier de Beauterne. **8.** éd. Poissy, Olivier-Fulgence; [etc., etc.] 1845.
2 p. l., xxxii, 207, [2] p. 19[cm].

1. Jesus Christ—Divinity.   I. Beauterne, Robert François Antoine de, b. 1748, ed.   II. Montholon, Charles Jean Tristan, marquis de, 1783-1853, comp.   III. Title.

Library of Congress   DC214.B4 1845

19-570

NN   0018660   DLC

Napoleon I, Emperor of the French, 1769-1821.
Sentiment de Napoléon 1er, sur le Christianisme d'après des témoignages recueillis... Paris: A. Bray, 1860. x, 236 pp. New ed. 24°.

NN   0018661   NN

DC214
B4
1864
Napoléon I, emperor of the French, 1769-1821.
Sentiment de Napoléon Ier sur le christianisme, d'après des témoignages recueillis par feu le chevalier de Beauterne. Nouv. éd. entièrement refondue, corrigée et complétée, par M. Bathild Bouniol. Paris, Ambroise Bray, 1864.
216 p. 19cm.

Héros chrétiens de l'Empire par M. Bathild Bouniol, p. [167]-211.

NN   0018662   GU MH NjP

NAPOLÉON I, emperor of the FRENCH.
Sept lettres inédites de Napoléon Ier. [Roma, Modes e Mendel, etc., etc., 1899]

Half title serves as title-page.
Cover: Miscellanea Napoleonica, a cura di Alberto Lumbroso. Estratto dalla serie sesta.

NN   0018663   MH

Napoléon I, emperor of the French, 1769-1821.

Phocion, *pseud.*
A sketch of the character of Gen. Bonaparte, in letters to the editor of the Lancaster gazetteer: with specimens of his speeches, proclamations, &c., and his letter to the king, on being called to the important trust of first magistrate of the French republic. Lancaster [Eng.] Printed by J. Jackson [1802]

DC214
.A32
Napoléon I, emperor of the French, 1769-1821.
... Le souper de Beaucaire. Avec une notice et un appendice par José de Bérys. Paris, E. Sansot, 1908.
78 p. (Petite collection "Scripta brevia")

1. France--Hist.--Revolution--1793.

NN   0018665   ICU NcU KyU

Film
3549
Reel
21
Item
7
Napoléon I, Emperor of the French, 1769-1821.
Le souper de Beaucaire. Avec une notice et un appendice par José de Bérys. Paris, E. Sansot, 1908.
78p. 16cm. (Petite collection, "Scripta brevia")

Microfilm. Lexington, Ky., Erasmus Press; available through General Microfilm Co., Cambridge, Mass. 1 reel (various items) 35mm. (French Revolution: critical and historical literature)

NN   0018666   TxU DLC ICRL CoU

Napoléon I, emperor of the French, 1769-1821.
...Le souper de Beaucaire, avec six eaux-fortes originales de G. Goor. Paris, Éditions de la Chronique des lettres françaises, 1927.
47p., 2l. illus. 20cm.

At head of title: Napoléon Bonaparte.

I. Goor, G., illus. II. Title.

NN   0018667   NNF

Napoleon I, emperor of the French, 1769–1821.
Le souper de Beaucaire, par le capitaine Napoléon Bonaparte. [Paris:] A. Morancé[, 1929?]. 48 p. 12°. ("Pages napoléoniennes.")

no. 292 of 2500 copies printed.

530079A. 1. France—Politics, 1793.   I. Title.
N. Y. P. L.   June 8, 1931

NN   0018668   NN OU DLC-P4

Napoléon I, *emperor of the French, 1769-1821.*
Le souper de Beaucaire, et Lettre à M. Matteo Buttafoco, par Napoléon Bonaparte. Extrait de ses œuvres ... [Paris] C. L. F. Panckoucke, 1821.
5 p. l., 71 p. 21[cm].

1. Buttafuoco, Matteo, 1730-1800.   2. France—Hist.—Revolution—1793.

Library of Congress   DC214.N216

8-14889†

NN   0018669   DLC

Napoleon I, Emperor of the French, 1769-1821.
Strategie napoléonienne. Maximes de guerre de Napoléon I
    see under   Grouard, Auguste Antoine, 1843-1929.
    Maximes de guerre de Napoléon I.

355
N16pI
[Napoleon I, emperor of the French]
Sunto delle guerre di Cesare, opera dettata da Napoleone a Marchand all'isola di S. Elena con alcuni frammenti inediti e autentici del medesimo. Versione italiana ...   Milano, 1838.
xvi, 110p. fold.pl.

NN   0018671   IU

Napoléon I, *emperor of the French, 1769-1821.*
Supper at Beaucaire, by Napoleon Bonaparte. Translated into English for the first time, by Somerset De Chair. London, Eng., The Golden cockerel press, 1945.
38 p., 1 l. incl. front. (port.) 14½ x 11[cm].

"Limited to 500 numbered copies, nos. 1-100 on Batchelor's handmade paper and bound in full vellum, nos. 101-500 on Fabriano's mouldmade paper and bound in cloth."

1. France—Hist.—Revolution, 1793.   I. De Chair, Somerset Struben, 1911-   tr.   II. Title.

DC214.N217   944.04   A 47–1164
Harvard univ.   Library
for Library of Congress   [3]†

NN   0018672   MH CU-A INS CU-S NBu CtY NNC DLC

Napoléon I, *emperor of the French, 1769-1821.*
Supplément à la Correspondance de Napoléon 1er; lettres curieuses omises par le Comité de publication; rectifications. Paris, E. Dentu, 1887.
2 p. l., 216 p. 18½[cm].

At head of cover-title: Baron A. Du Casse.

I. *Du Casse, Albert, baron, 1813-1893, ed.   II. Title.

Library of Congress   DC213.N213

2-15831

NN   0018673   DLC FU CtY MdBP PU NcD MH

4DC
1277
Napoléon I, Emperor of the French, 1769-1821.
Supplément à la correspondance de Napoléon I; l'empéreur et la Pologne. Paris, Au Bureau de l'Agence polonaise de presse, 1908.
51 p.

NN   0018674   DLC-P4 CtY FU MH NIC InU

JC393
.E3F7
1820
Napoléon I, emperor of the French, 1769-1821.

France. *Conseil d'État.*
A system of education for the infant King of Rome, and other French princes of the blood, drawn up by the Imperial council of state, with the approbation, and under the personal superintendance, of the Emperor Napoleon. London, Printed for Lackington, Hughes, Harding, Mavor, and Jones, 1820.

VOLUME 405

Napoléon I, *emperor of the French,* 1769–1821.
  The table talk and opinions of Napoleon Buonaparte ...
London, S. Low, son, and Marston, 1868.
  2 p. l., iii, 194 p. 15ᶜᵐ. (The Bayard series)
  Title vignette (portrait)
  Comp. by Edith Walford Blumer.

  I. Blumer, Mrs. Edith (Walford) comp. II. Title.
                                                    17–2903
  Library of Congress   DC214.N24

      NN   MB
NN 0018676   DLC RPB FTaSU MoSU PPL OO OCU CtY–M

Napoleon, I, emperor of the French, 1769–1821.
  The table talk and opinions of Napoleon
Buonaparte ... London, S. Low, son and
Marston, 1869. Ed. 2.
  2 p. l., iii, 194 p.

  (The Bayard series)

NN 0018677   OCl PBa

Napoleon 1, emperor of the French, 1769–1821.
  The table talk and opinions of Napoleon
Buonaparte... Lond., S. Low and son and Marston,
1870.
  199 p.

NN 0018678   PSC FMU MoSU

Napoléon I, emperor of the French, 1769–1821.
  The table talk and opinions of Napoleon Buonaparte. 4th ed. London, S. Low, Marston, Low,
and Searle, 1875.
  2 p. l., iii, 199 p. 15 cm. (The Bayard series)
  Title vignette (portrait); head and tail-pieces.
  Compiled by Edith Walford Blumer.
  With autograph of Ed. N. Eubank.

  1. Table-talk. I. Blumer, Edith (Walford)
comp.   DC214.N24 1875

NN 0018679   Vi NIC OCl

NAPOLEON I, emp. of the French.
  Table talk and opinions. 6th ed. London, S.
Low, Marston, Searle and Rivington, 1885.

  24°. Port.
  (Bayard series.)

NN 0018680   MH

Napoleon I, emperor of the French, 1769–1821.
  The table talk and opinions of Napoleon
Buonaparte ... Philadelphia, Porter &
Coates, 1889.
  192 p.

  (The Bayard series)
  Comp. by Edith Walford Blumer.
  7th ed.

NN 0018681   MiU FTaSU MoSU

Napoléon I, Emperor of the French, 1769–1821.
  Tableaux historiques des campagnes d'Italie
depuis l'an IV ...
      see under title

Napoléon I, Emperor of the French, 1769–1821.
  Talks of Napoleon at St. Helena ...
      see under Gourgaud, Gaspard, baron, 1783–
1852.

Ex
1509   Napoléon I, emperor of the French, 1769–1821.
.18   Tarih-i Isevinin bin sekiz yüz beş senesi
.669   ₍1805₎...França devleti ile Avusturya ve
.001   Moskof devletleri bayninda...vâki olan cenk ve
        sefere dair havadisnamelerin tercümesidir.
        ₍n.p., 18––₎
          275 p. 25 cm.

        Turkish translation of 37 dispatches from
        the Grande Armée during the German and Aus-
        trian campaign which ended in the battle of

        Austerlitz. At end is a translation of the
        treaty of Pressburg.
          Inscribed: Odessae 21ᵐᵒ die Iulii 1832.
          Ex libris Gulielmi Schauffleri ₍William Gott-
        lieb Schauffler₎
          1. Napoléon I – German and Austrian cam-
        paign, 1805. 2. Austerlitz, Battle of, 1805.
        I. France. Treaties,   etc., 1805–1815
        (Empire)

NN 0018685   NjP

Napoléon I, emperor of the French, 1769 – 1821.
  ...Tendresses impériales avec une lettre préface
par Abel Gri... Paris, E. Sansot & Cie, B13.
  156p., 1 . 19cm.

  At head of title: Napoléon Bonaparte.

  I. Joséphine, empress consort of Napoleon I, 1763–
1814. II. Gri, Abel, ed.

NN 0018686   NNF

DC   Napoléon I, Emperor of the French, 1769–1821
213   Testament de Napoléon. Bruxelles, A.
T4   Wahlen, 1824.
          28p. 23cm.

NN 0018687   WU

DC214   Napoleon I, emperor of the French,
T4   1769–1821.
          Testament de Napoleon ...   Bruxelles,
         Chez C. Remy, 1824.
          31 p. 19cm.

NN 0018688   RPB

NAPOLÉON I, emperor of the FRENCH, 1769–1821.
  Testament de Napoléon, avec une traduction
anglaise. Londres, J. Ridgway, 1824.

  20 cm. pp. iv, 58.
  Binder's title: Mélanges, 1. Histoire, 1.

NN 0018689   MH CtY

NAPOLÉON I, emperor of the FRENCH, 1769–1821.
  Testament de Napoléon. n.p., [19– ?].

  17 cm. pp. 34.
  Without title-page. Caption title.
  "Collationné d'après l'original déposé aux
Archives nationales (Désiré Lacroix)."

NN 0018690   MH

[Napoléon I, emperor of the French] 1769–1821.
  Le testament de Napoléon ... 1951
      see under Savant, Jean.

NAPOLÉON I.
  Testament de Napoléon, ex-empereur des Français, contenant les différens legs qu'il a
faits à ses amis, à ses anciens officiers, et
généralement à toutes les personnes qui compo-
saient sa maison à Sainte Hélène. Paris, 1822.

  8 p.

NN 0018692   MH–L

NAPOLÉON I, emperor of the French, 1769–1821.
  Testament de Napoléon; précédé des derniers
jours de sa vie à l'isle Sainte-Hélène; suivis
de pièces officielles tirées des mémoires écrit.
par les personnes qui ont partagé son exil.
Avec la topographie de Sainte-Hélène. Paris,
Tenon, etc., etc., [1822?].

  15 cm.

NN 0018693   MH

944.05   Napoléon I, Emperor of the French, 1769–1821.
N21t   Thoughts on love and life. London, A. L.
         Humphreys, 1908.
          263p. 17cm. (The Royal library; belles
         lettres series)

          French and English translation on opposite
         pages.

NN 0018694   IEN CtY RPB

Napoléon I, emperor of the French, 1769–1821.

  Tennant, Charles.
    A tour through parts of the Netherlands, Holland, Germany,
  Switzerland, Savoy, and France, in the year 1821–2. Including a description of the Rhine voyage in the middle of autumn,
  and the stupendous scenery of the Alps in the depth of winter.
  By Charles Tennant, esq. Also containing, in an appendix,
  fac-simile copies of eight letters in the hand-writing of Napoleon Bonaparte to his wife Josephine ... London, Printed for
  Longman, Hurst, Rees, Orme, Brown, and Green, 1824.

Napoléon I, Emperor of the French, 1769–1821.
  A true and full account of the death of Bonaparte
      see under title

4DC–344 Napoléon I, Emperor of the French, 1769–1821.
         Uebersicht der Kriege Cäsars, von Napoleon.
        Vom Kaiser auf St. Helena dictirt, niedergeschrieben
        von Marchand. Nebst mehreren bisher noch unge-
        druckten Fragmenten von Napoleon. Aus dem
        Französischen. Stuttgart, J. B. Metzler, 1836.
         248 p.

NN 0018697   DLC–P4 MiU

NAPOLÉON I, emperor of the FRENCH, 1769–1821.
  Ungedruckte Briefe Napoleons aus den Jahren
1796 und 1797. Im besitze des Haus- Hof- und
Staats-Archives in Wien von Hermann Hüffer.
Wien, K. Gerold's Sohn, 1873.

  24 cm. pp. 29.
  "Aus dem Archiv für österreichische Geschichte
XLIX, Bd. I, Hälfte, S. 267, besonders abgedruckt.

NN 0018698   MH CU

VOLUME 405

Napoléon I, *emperor of the French*, 1769–1821.
... Unpublished correspondence of Napoleon I, preserved in the War archives; pub. by Ernest Picard ... and Louis Tuetey ... tr. by Louise Seymour Houghton. New York, Duffield & company, 1913–
v. 24½ᵐ.

At head of title: Published under the superintendence of the Historic section of the Army staff.
This collection is planned to include all the unpublished documents and letters now in the War archives written by Napoleon after December 2, 1804—also a few letters published in collections now rare, or incorporated in historical works where they are likely to escape notice.

"Titles of the principal publications consecrated to the correspondence of Napoleon I": v. 1, 12–15.

1. France.—Hist.—Consulate and empire, 1799–1815. 2. France—History, Military—1789–1815. I. Picard, Ernest, 1863–1913. II. Tuetey, Louis, 1860– III. France. État-major de l'armée. IV. France. Archives de la guerre. V. Houghton, Mrs. Louise (Seymour) 1838–1920, tr.

13—23904

Library of Congress   DC213.P52

OOxM OCU MiU PP DNW OCl OO MB NN
NN 0018700   DLC NIC OKentU MeB CaBVa CoU ViU NcU

Napoléon I, Emperor of the French, 1769-1821.
Vie de Napoléon; écrite par lui-même ...
Bruxelles, G. Peeters, 1820.
105 p. front. (port.) 14 cm.

NN 0018701   OClWHi

Napoléon I, *Emperor of the French*, 1769–1821.
La vie de Napoléon, racontée par Napoléon. Textes rassemblés par Claude Roy. Paris, R. Julliard [¹1952]
255 p. 19 cm. (Collection Quel roman que ma vie)

1. Napoléon I, Emperor of the French, 1769–1821. I. Roy, Claude 1915– ed.
DC213.2.R55   55–26308 ‡

NN 0018702   DLC NBuU NN

Napoleon I, Bonaparte, *emperor of the French*.
Vie de Napoléon; rétablie d'après les textes, lettres, proclamations, écrits par lui-même. Paris: Librairie Gallimard[, 1930].
405 p. 12°. (Mémoires révélateurs.)

1. Napoleonic wars.
N.Y.P.L.   April 1, 1931

NN 0018703   NN CtY OCl

Napoléon I, *emperor of the French*, 1769–1821.
...Vie de Napoléon rétablie d'après les textes, lettres, proclamations, écrits par lui-même... Paris: Gallimard[, 1930]. 405 p. 8. ed. 12°. (Mémoires révélateurs.)

511991A. 1. France—Hist., 1789–   1815.
N.Y.P.L.   February 20, 1931

NN 0018704   NN

Napoleon I, Emperor of the French, 1769-1821.
Vie politique et militaire de Napoléon. 1827 and later
see under Jomini, Henri, baron, 1779-1869.

Napoléon I, *emperor of the French*, 1769–1821.
... Virilités: maximes et pensées; avec une introduction, par Jules Bertaut. Paris, E. Sansot et cⁱᵉ [1912]
202 p., 1 l. 19ᶜᵐ.

1. Maxims. I. Bertaut, Jules, 1877– comp. II. Title.
20–18880
Library of Congress   PN6302.N3

NN 0018706   DLC FTaSU

DC214 **Napoléon I,** *Emperor of the French*, 1769–1821.
.C85 Voix de Napoléon; paroles authentiques recueillies par Roederer, Molé, Talleyrand, Metternich, Narbonne, Caulaincourt, Benjamin Constant, etc., présentées par P.-L. Couchoud. Genève, Éditions du Milieu du monde [1949]
280 p. 21 cm.
Bibliography: p. 273–[275]

I. Couchoud, Paul Louis, 1879– ed. II. Title.
DC214.C58   944.05   50–22260

NN 0018707   DLC ICU OClW NcU

Napoléon I, *emperor of the French*, 1769–1821.
... Vues politiques. Avant-propos de Adrien Dansette. Paris, A. Fayard [1939]
2 p. l., xxi, 433 p., 1 l. 19 cm. (On cover: Les grandes études politiques et sociales)
At head of title: Napoléon.
"Sources principales": p. [ix]
CONTENTS.—Sentiments et idées de jeunesse. — La doctrine impériale: Vues sur le passé. La dictature impériale. Le pouvoir exécutif. Le pouvoir législatif. Le pouvoir judiciaire. La famille. La religion. L'aristocratie. L'instruction publique. L'économie nationale. La question juive. L'armée. La guerre. La politique extérieure. Vues d'avenir. Pensées de l'homme d'état.—L'homme et sa destinée.
I. Dansette, Adrien, 1901– ed. II. Title.
DC214.A2D23   308.1   40—8994

NN 0018708   DLC MH OCl CtY IdPI MiU

308.1 **Napoléon I,** *emperor of the French*, 1769–1821.
N.62 ... Vues politiques. Avant-propos de Adrien Dansette. Paris, A. Fayard [1945,©1939]
xxv, 362 p. 17 cm. (On cover: Les grandes études politiques et sociales)
At head of title: Napoléon.
"Sources principales": p. [ix]
CONTENTS. — Sentiments et idées de jeunesse. — La doctrine impériale: Vues sur le passé. La dictature impériale. Le pouvoir exécutif. Le pouvoir législatif. Le pouvoir judiciaire. La famille. La religion. L'aristocratie. L'instruction publique. L'économie nationale. La question juive. L'armée. La guerre. La politique extérieure. Vues d'avenir. Pensées de l'homme d'état.—L'homme et sa destinée.
I. Dansette, Adrien, 1901– ed. II. Title

NN 0018709   KyU

Napoléon I, emperor of the French, 1769-1821.
Napoleon's war maxims with his social and political thoughts, by Professor L.E.Henry ... London, Aldershot [etc.] Gale & Polden [1899]
xxiv,187p. 25cm.

NN 0018710   MoU CU DNW CtY DAL

845N16 **Napoléon I, emperor of the French, 1769-1821.**
LT17 The words of Napoleon, emperor of France,
1900 being selections from his addresses and letters. Edited by Ida M. Tarbell. Boston, L. C. Page & company, 1900.
64p. (Day's work series)

I. Tarbell, Ida Minerva, 1857– ed.

NN 0018711   IU MBU OCl

Napoléon I, Emperor of the French, 1769-1821.
A year of the life of Emperor Napoléon
see under [Monier, A   D   B   ]

Napoléon I, Emperor of the French, 1769–1821
see also
France. Sovereigns, etc., 1799–1814 (Napoléon I)
France. Sovereigns, etc., 1815 (Napoléon I)

Napoléon II, François Charles Joseph Bonaparte, *herzog von Reichstadt, called*
see
Bonaparte, François Charles Joseph, *herzog von Reichstadt, called* Napoléon II, 1811–1832.

Napoléon III, *emperor of the French*, 1808–1873.
Œuvres de Louis Napoléon Bonaparte, pub. par M. Charles Édouard Temblaire ... Paris, Librairie Napoléonienne, 1848.
2 v. 21½ᵐ.
CONTENTS.—t. 1. Vie politique de Louis-Napoléon. Rêveries politiques. Considérations politiques et militaires sur la Suisse. Idées napoléoniennes. Pièces à l'appui.—t. 2. Fragments historiques. Pièces à l'appui. Analyse des questions des sucres. État comparé de la culture des colonies. Nombre de fabriques et culture de la betterave en 1840. Sucres. Tableau A. Mouvement de la navigation avec les quatre colonies à sucre et navigation générale. Tableau B. Valeur du commerce de la France avec ses quatre colonies à sucre. Tableau C. Extinction du paupérisme. Quelques mots sur Joseph-Napoléon Bonaparte.
I. Temblaire, Charles Edouard, ed.
18–15402
Library of Congress   DC275.2.N3 1848

NN 0018715   DLC CU MdBP NN IU

Napoléon III, *emperor of the French*, 1808–1873.
Œuvres de Napoléon III. Paris, Amyot, 1854–69.
5 v. front. (port.: v. 2) 24ᶜᵐ.
CONTENTS.—t. 1. L'idée napoléonienne. Des idées napoléoniennes. Fragments historiques 1688 et 1830. Réponse à Lamartine. Rêveries politiques. Mélanges.—t. 2. Mélanges (suite) Extinction du paupérisme. Tableaux justificatifs. Analyse de la question des sucres. Projet de loi sur le recrutement de l'armée. Considérations politiques et militaires sur la Suisse. Quelques mots sur Joseph Napoléon Bonaparte. Le canal de Nicaragua.—t. 3. Discours, proclamations, messages, etc.—t. 4. Du passé et de l'avenir de l'artillerie. [Extraits]—t. 5. Discours, proclamations, messages, etc.
1. France—Hist.—1848–1870. 2. France—Pol. & govt.—1848–1870. 3. Military history.
F—3790
Library of Congress   DC275.2.N3

NIC NjP NNC WaU NNC MB
NN 0018716   DLC OrU MH CaBVaU IaU MdBP CtY ICU

DC 275.2 NAPOLÉON III, *emperor of the French*, 1808-1873
.N213 Oeuvres. Paris, H. Plon, 1869
5 v. port.

Contents: v.1. L'idée Napoléonienne. v.2. Mélanges (suite). v.3. Discours, proclamations, messages, etc. v.4. Du passé et de l'avenir de l'artillerie. v.5. Discours, proclamations, messages, etc.

1. Napoléon III, emperor of the French, 1808–1873.

NN 0018717   InU KyU FTaSU TNJ GU FU

Napoleon III, *emperor of the French*, 1808–1873.
Opere di Napoleone III. Versione italiana per cura di V. C. ... v. 1– Napoli: G. Sarracino, 1861– v. front. (port.) 18cm.
CONTENTS.—v. 1. L'idea napoleonica. Frammenti storici 1688 e 1830. Risposta a Lamartine. Meditazioni politiche. Miscellanea.

1. France—Hist., 19th cent.   2. Political science, 1750–1880.
I. C., V., tr.
N.Y.P.L.   May 17, 1940

NN 0018718   NN MH

Napoleon III, emperor of the French, 1808-1878.
Die Abdankung Napoleon III...
see under Die Abdankung Napoleon III...

VOLUME 405

Kress
Room
    Napoléon III, emperor of the French, 1808–1873.
        Analyse de la question des sucres par le
    Prince Napoléon Louis Bonaparte ... [Paris]
    Administration de librairie, 1842.
      vii, 120 p. 26 cm.

        1.Sugar - Taxation. 2.Sugar trade - France.
    I.Title.

NN 0018720   MH-BA PPF LU

Napoléon III, emperor of the French, 1808–1873.
    Analyse de la question des sucres, par le Prince
Napoléon Louis Bonaparte ... 2. édition.
₍Paris₎ Administration de librairie, 1843.
    xvi, 140 p. tables. 27 cm.

    1. Beets and beet sugar. 2. Sugar trade.

NN 0018721   NSchU MH-BA

Napoléon III, *emperor of the French, 1808-1873.*
    Annales de la présidence; ou, Recueil méthodique des dis-
cours du prince Louis-Napoléon du 10 décembre 1848 au 2 décembre 1851. Introduction et notes historiques par Bern.-Alf.
Boullenot. Paris, D. Giraud et J. Dagneau, 1852.

    3 p. l., 161 p. 18cm.

    With this is bound Révolution militaire, by Hippolyte de Mauduit.

    1. France. History. Restoration to 1852. I. Boullenot, Bernard
Alfred, ed.

NN 0018722   CtW MH

₍**Napoléon III**, *emperor of the French*₎ 1808–1873, *defendant.*
    ... Attentat du 6 août 1840 ... Paris, Imprimerie royale,
1840–41.

    6 v. in 2. 24 x 19½ᶜᵐ.

    At head of title, v. 1–5: Cour des pairs; v. 6: Cour des pairs de
France.
    Lettered on cover: Cour des pairs. v. 19–20.
    Vol. 6 has imprint: Paris, Impr. de Crapelet.
    "Sont accusés: Charles-Louis-Napoléon Bonaparte, Charles-Tristan,
comte de Montholon, Jean-Baptiste Voisin ₍et autres₎ ... d'avoir commis,
à Boulogne-sur-Mer ... un attentat dont le but était, soit de détruire,
soit de changer le gouvernement."—v. 2, p. 74.

    CONTENTS.—₍v. 1₎ Rapport fait à la cour par m. Persil.—₍v. 2₎ Arrêt
du mercredi 16 septembre 1840. Acte d'accusation.—₍v. 3₎ Interroga-
toires des inculpés.—₍v. 4₎ Réquisitoires et répliques de m. Franck
Carré, procureur général du roi.—₍v. 5₎ Procédure. Dépositions de té-
moins.—₍v. 6₎ Procès-verbal des séances relatives au jugement de cette
affaire.

    I. Montholon, Charles Jean Tristan, marquis de, 1783–1853, defendant.
II. Voisin, Jean Baptiste, b. 1780? defendant. III. Persil, Jean Charles,
1785–1870. IV. Franck-Carré, Paul François Carré, known as, 1800–
1862. V. France. Cour des pairs. VI. Title.

                          31–18322

NN 0018724   DLC NcD

Napoléon III, *emperor of the French*, 1808–1873.
    Auswahl aus den schriften Napoleons III. Aus dem
französischen von einem officier. Berlin, W. Moeser, 1856.
    viii, 215 p. 22ᶜᵐ.

    1. France.—Hist.—Second empire, 1852–1870. 2. France—Pol. &
govt.—1852–1870. 3. France—History, Military. 4. Napoléon I, emperor of the
French, 1759–1821. I. Title.

                          20–14183

    Library of Congress   DC275.2.N55 1856

NN 0018725   DLC

Napoleon III, Emperor of the French, 1769-1821.
    Authentic memoirs of Prince Napoleon Louis
Bonaparte
      see under Wheaton, Martha B.

DC280 Napoleon III, *emperor of the French*, 1808–1873.
.A13   Autograph letter from Napoleon III to M. Soggioli,
1846 April 15, 1846.
Mss room 2 l. 21ᶜᵐ.

     Signed: N B.
     Presented by Auguste Fabiani of Venaco, Corsica.

     1. Manuscripts, French.

NN 0018727   ICU

NAPOLEON III, emp. of the French.
    Aux électeurs. [P?1848.]

    1 page.

NN 0018728   MH

DG554   Napoléon III, *emperor of the French*, 1808–1873.
.F7
1863   **France.** *Dépôt de la guerre.*
        Campagne de l'empereur Napoléon III en Italie, 1859.
    Rédigée au Dépôt de la guerre d'après les documents officiels,
    étant directeur le général Blondel sous le Ministère de son
    excellence le maréchal comte Randon, 1860–1861. 2. éd.
    Paris, Imprimerie impériale, 1863.

Napoléon III, Emperor of the French, 1808–1873.
    Le canal de Nicaragua, ou Projet de jonction
des océans atlantique et pacifique au moyen d'un
canal. Par le prince Napoléon Louis Bonaparte,
1846.
    (Extrait de la Revue britannique, année 1849)
    In Belly (Félix) A travers l'Amerique centrale
t. 2. p. 424-464. Paris, 1867. 8°.

NN 0018730   NN

Napoleon III, Emperor of the French, 1808–1873.
    Le canal de Nicaragua, ou Projet de jonction des
océans atlantique et pacifique au moyen d'un canal.
Par le prince Napoléon Louis Bonaparte. 1846.

    Microfilm (Master negative)
    Extrait de la Revue britannique, année 1849(In: Belly
Félix. A travers l'Amerique centrale, t.2, p.424-464)
Paris 1867.

NN 0018731   NN

Napoleon III, *emperor of the French*, 1808–1873.
    Canal of Nicaragua; or, a project to connect the Atlantic
and Pacific oceans by means of a canal. By N. L. B. London,
Printed by Mills & son, 1846.

    2 p. l., viii, 70 p. 3 fold. maps. 23ᶜᵐ.

    1. Nicaragua canal.

    Library, U. S. Dept. of   State TC773.I 5 vol. 1, no. 4

                                  S D 33–16

NN 0018732   DNAL MH-BA ViU ICJ CSmH MH LNHT NN

Napoléon III, *emp. of the* **French.**
    Considérations politiques et militaires sur la Suisse. Paris, A.
Levavasseur, [1833?].
    pp. (6), 78.

    Switzerland–Hist. 1816–1

NN 0018733   MH

Napoleon III, emperor of the French, 1808–1873.

Wellesley, *Sir Victor*, 1876–   *ed.*
    Conversations with Napoleon III; a collection of documents,
mostly unpublished and almost entirely diplomatic, selected
and arranged with introductions, by Sir Victor Wellesley ...
and Robert Sencourt ₍pseud.₎ ... London, E. Benn, limited
₍1934₎

Napoléon III, Emperor of the French, 1808–1873.
    Correspondance du roi Louis et de Louis Napoléon
interceptée par la police de Metternich, 1833–1840
    see under Louis Bonaparte, King of Holland,
1778–1846.

Napoleon III, *emperor of the French*, 1808–1873, and **Napoléon
Joseph Charles Paul Bonaparte**, *prince.*
    Correspondance inédite de Napoléon III et du Prince Napo-
léon. (Revue des deux mondes. Paris, 1923–24. 8°.
Période 7, tome 18, p. 763–796; tome 19, p. 51–84, 519–545; tome 20,
p. 79–114, 319–352.)

    1. France.—History, 1837-49.   2. Napoléon Joseph Charles Paul
Bonaparte, prince, 1822–91.
N. Y. P. L.   July 14, 1924

NN 0018736   NN

Napoleon III, Emperor of the French, 1808–1873.
    Les derniers télégrams de l'empire ...
      see under title

E   NAPOLÉON III, emperor of the French, 1808–1873.
5   Des idées napoléoniennes, par le prince Na-
.N 16606 poléon-Louis Bonaparte. Bruxelles, Hauman, 1839.
     242p.

NN 0018738   ICN PPL

Napoléon III, *emperor of the French*, 1808–1873.
    Des idées napoléoniennes. Par le prince Napoléon-
Louis Bonaparte ... Bruxelles, Société typographique
belge, A. Wahlen et cⁱᵉ, 1839.

    vi, ₍7₎–190 p. 16ᶜᵐ.

    1. Napoléon I, emperor of the French, 1769–1821. 2. France—Pol. &
govt.—1799–1815.

                               19–6988

    Library of Congress   JN2491.N2 1839 b
                ₍2₎

NN 0018739   DLC CtY IaU NN PPL

Napoléon III, *emperor of the French*, 1808–1873.
    Des idées napoléoniennes; par le prince Napoléon-
Louis Bonaparte ... Londres, H. Colburn, 1839.

    viii, 229 p. 22ᶜᵐ.

    1. Napoléon I, emperor of the French, 1769–1821. 2. France—Pol. &
govt.—1799–1815.

                               9–33570†

    Library of Congress   JN2491.N22

NN 0018740   DLC CaBVaU NBuU NN

VOLUME 405

923.144
N216
N17d
Napoleon III, emperor of the French, 1808-1873.
Des idées napoléoniennes; par le prince
Napoléon-Louis Bonaparte ...   Paris, Chez tous
les marchands de nouveautés, 1839.
2p.ℓ., 75p. 21cm.

1. Napoléon I, emperor of the French, 1769-
1821. 2. France — Pol. & govt. I. Title.

NN 0018741   LNHT PPL OCl

JN2491
.N2
1839
NAPOLÉON III, emperor of the French, 1808-1873.
Des idées napoléoniennes; par le prince Napoléon-Louis Bonaparte... Paris, Paulin, 1839.
viii, 266 p. ports. 23½cm.

NN 0018742   ICU InU CtY

Napoléon III, *emperor of the French*, 1808-1873.
Des idées napoléoniennes. On the opinions and policy of
Napoleon. By Prince Napoleon-Louis Bonaparte. Translated
from the French ... London, H. Colburn, 1840.
xxii, [7]-175, [1] p. 23ᵐ.

1. Napoléon I, emperor of the French, 1760-1821. 2. France—Pol. &
govt.—1799-1815.   I. Title.
43-48509

Library of Congress   JN2491.N2 1840

NN 0018743   DLC PP ViU NN PPL ICN

JN
2491
N2
1860a
Napoléon III, Emperor of the French, 1808-1873.
Des idées Napoléoniennes. Par Napoléon
Louis Bonaparte. Berlin, J. Springer, 1860.
viii, 153 p. 18 cm.

1. Napoléon I, Emperor of the French, 1769-
1821. 2. France - Pol. & govt. - 1799-1815.

NN 0018744   CU-S

Napoléon III, *emperor of the French*, 1808-1873.
Des idées Napoléoniennes. Par Louis-Napoléon Bonaparte.
Avec un avertissement de l'éditeur. Londres, W. Jeffs, 1860.
xvi, 151, [1] p. 19½ᶜᵐ.

1. Napoléon I, emperor of the French, 1769-1821. 2. France—Pol. &
govt.—Consulate and empire, 1799-1815.
9—33483

Library of Congress   JN2491.N2 1860

NN 0018745   DLC MnU

Napoleon III, *emperor of the French*, 1808-1873.   320.9261 N16
Des idées napoléoniennes, par le prince Napoléon-Louis Bonaparte, ... Paris, Amyot, [etc.], 1860.
[4], 216 p. front. (port.) 18ᶜᵐ.
Second edition; the first was printed in London, in 1839.
Contents.—1. Les gouvernements en général.—2. Idées générales.—3. Question
intérieure.—4. Question étrangère.—5. But où tendait l'Empereur.—6. Cause de la
chute de l'Empereur.—7. Conclusion.—Pièces à l'appui: 1. Lettre écrite par Napoléon
au Ministre de l'Intérieur, au sujet des communes. 2. Extrait de l'Exposé de la situation de l'empire présenté au Corps législatif, dans la séance du 25 février 1813, par le
comte Montalivet, ministre de l'intérieur. 3. Budgets sous le consulat et l'empire.

NN 0018746   ICJ PSC NcD NBC

Napoléon III, emperor of the French, 1808-1873
Des idées napoléoniennes, par le prince
Napoléon-Louis Bonaparte. Paris, H. Plon, 1860.
216 p.

1. Napoléon I, emperor of the French, 1769-1821. 2.
France - Pol. & govt. - 1799-1815.

NN 0018747   GEU MH

Napoleon III, Emperor of the French, 1808-1873.
Des idees Napoleoniennes. The opinions and
policy of Napoleon, translated into English. By
James A. Dorr.   New York, 1859.
12 mo.

NN 0018748   NN

Bo79
178f
Napoléon III, emperor of the French, 1808-1873.
Dictionnaire politique napoléonien; opinions,
pensées, maximes extraties des ouvrages de
Louis-Napoléon Bonaparte ... et classées alpha-
bétiquement par Alfred d'Almbert. Paris,
Librairie Furne[etc.]1849.
viii,9-177,[2]p. 16½cm.

NN 0018749   CtY

Napoléon III, *emperor of the French*, 1808-1873.
Discours et messages de Louis-Napoléon Bonaparte, depuis
son retour en France jusqu'au 2 décembre 1852. Paris, Typographie Plon frères, 1853.
2 p. l., 251 p. 21¾ᶜᵐ.
Half-title: Quatre années de présidence de la République.

1. France—Pol. & govt.—1848-1852.
27-25661

Library of Congress   DC275.2.N53

NN 0018750   DLC NjP OU

Napoléon III. (CHARLES LOUIS NAPOLÉON BONAPARTE,
emp. of the French.)
Discours et proclamations ... depuis son retour en
France jusqu'au janvier 1852 ... 2 p.l., 222 pp.
Paris: Typographie Plon Frères, 1852. 8°.

NN 0018751   NN

Napoleon III, emperor of the French, 1810-73
Discours prononcé à l'ouverture de la session législa-
tive de 1860, le 1er mars 1860. [P, nd.]
7 p.
At head of title: Corps législatif.Session 1860. No.1

NN 0018752   MH

Napoleon III, Emperor of the French, 1810-73
Discours prononcé à l'ouverture de la session législa-
tive de 1862, le 27 janvier 1862. [P, nd.]
6 p.
At head of title: Corps législatif.Session 1862. No 1

NN 0018753   MH

NAPOLEON III, emp. of the French.
Discours prononcé à la réunion du sénat et
du corps législatif, dans sa séance impériale
du 29 nov.,1869. Boulogne,[1869].

Broadside.

NN 0018754   MH

Military
Historical
Society
DC
203.9
B65
Napoleon III, Emperor of the French,
1808-1873.
Discours prononcé par son altesse
impériale le prince Napoléon le 15 mai
1865, pour l'inauguration du monument
élevé dans la ville d'Ajaccio à
Napoléon Iᵉʳ et à ses frères. Paris,
Dentu, 1865.
32p.

NN 0018755   MBU

944.07
A p.v.11
no.8
Napoléon III, Emperor of the French, 1808-1873.
Discours prononcé par son Altesse Impériale le prince
Napoléon dans la séance du Sénat du 1. septembre 1869.
Paris, E. Dentu, 1869.
31 p. 26 cm.

1. France. Pol. & govt. Second Empire, 1852-1870. 2.
France. Constitution. I. France. Sénat, 1852-1870. II. Title.

NN 0018756   N

---

*NAPOLEON III, emperor of the French, 1808-1873.
[LA GUÉRONNIÈRE, Louis Étienne Arthur Dubreuil-
Hélion, vicomte de].
L'empereur Napoléon III et l'Italie. Nouvelle
éd. Paris, E. Dentu, etc., 1859

NN 0018757   MH

Napoléon III, emperor of the French, 1808-1873.
The Emperor Napoleon's new system of field
artillery, as submitted to the French service by
Captain Favé
see under   Favé Idelphonse, 1812-1894.

Napoléon III, emperor of the French, 1808-1873.

Legge, Edward.
The Empress Eugénie, 1870-1910: Her Majesty's life since
"the terrible year". Together with the statement of her case,
the Emperor's own story of Sedan, an account of his exile and
last days, and reminiscences of the Prince imperial, from authentic sources, by Edward Legge. With illustrations and facsimile letters. New York, C. Scribner's sons, 1910.

[Napoléon III, *emperor of the French*] 1808-1873.
Estudios politicos. De los gobiernos y de sus sostenes.
[n. p., 1850?]
8 p. 19ᶜᵐ.
No. 7 of a collection of pamphlets lettered: Coleccion de impresos.
Caption title.
Signed: Napoleon-Luis Bonaparte.
French original pub. in 1844.
10-26356

NN 0018760   DLC

VOLUME 405

Napoleon III, emperor of the French, 1808–1873.
Études sur le passé et l'avenir de l'artillerie, par le prince
Napoléon-Louis Bonaparte... Paris: J. Dumaine, 1846–1871.
6 v.   plans, plates, tables.   4°.

Autograph of General Favé. v. 4.
t.-p. of v. 3–4 read: Études sur le passé et l'avenir de l'artillerie, ouvrage con-
tinué à l'aide des notes de l'Empereur, par Favé... t.-p. of v. 5–6 reads: Études sur
le passé et l'avenir de l'artillerie, par le Général Favé.

1. Artillery.—History. 2. Favé,   Ildephonse, 1812-94.
N. Y. P. L.   November 10, 1922.

NN   0018761   NN NWM MH DNW DLC ICN DN

Bo71C   Napoléon III, emperor of the French, 1808-
830B   1873.
12   Extinction du paupérisme. Paris, Pagnerre,
        1844.
          53 p. 15 cm. [Binder's title: Brochures
        politiques. Gouvernement de Juillet, 12]

NN   0018762   CtY NcD

RARE BOOKS
COLLECTION
HD   Napoleon, III, Emperor of the French, 1808-1873.
1516   Extinction du paupérisme, par le prince
.F8   Napoleon-Louis Bonaparte. 2. éd. Paris,
N29   Pagnerre, 1844.
          53p. tables. 14cm.

          1. Agricultural colonies.   France.
        I. Title.

NN   0018763   OrU

C.6413 Napoléon III, emperor of the French, 1808-1873.
   Extinction du paupérisme par le prince Napoléon-Louis
   Bonaparte. 3.éd. Paris, Pagnerre, 1844.
   53, [9] p.incl. tables. 14 cm.

NN   0018764   MH-BA

Napoleon III, *emperor of the French,* 1808–1873.
Extinction du paupérisme, ou Projet d'organisation agricole pour
l'amélioration du sort des travailleurs, par Louis-Napoléon Bonaparte, ... Édition populaire. ... Paris, [Impr. Bonaventure
et Ducessois, 1848].
28, [4] p. incl. tables. 15ᵉᵐ.

NN   0018765   ICJ

Napoleon III, emperor of the French, 1808-1873.
   Extinction du paupérisme, par Louis Napoléon
Bonaparte, président de la république française.
10th éd. Paris, Librairie centrale de Napoléon
Chaix et cie., Vialat et cie., 1849.
   36 p. 16.5 cm.

   1. Agricultural colonies. 2. Agricultural
colonies – France'.   I. Title.
                HD1516.F8.N2 1849

NN   0018766   Vi DLC PU

HX696   Napoléon III, emperor of the French 1808–1873.
.M8   Extinction du paupérisme.

Morgan, John Minter, 1782–1854.
   The Christian commonwealth ... By John Minter Morgan. London, Longman, Brown, Green, and Longmans,
1849.

Napoleon III, 1808-1873.
   Extinction of pauperism.   Translated from the
French.
London, 1849.
23 p. fol.
[With Extinction du pauperisme]

NN   0018768   DLC

NAPOLEON III, emperor of the FRENCH, 1808-1873.
Extinction of pauperism. London, Cleave, 1847.

24°. pp.33,[2].

NN   0018769   MH

Napoléon III, *emperor of the French,* 1808–1873.
   The extinction of pauperism, by Prince Napoleon Louis
Bonaparte. Translated from the third Paris edition, by
James H. Causten, jr. Washington, W. M. Morrison &
co., 1853.
   35 p. 19ᶜᵐ.

   1. Agricultural colonies. 2. Agricultural colonies—France.   I. Causten,
James H., tr.

                                            9–5808†
Library of Congress   HD1516.F8N3

NN   0018770   DLC DNLM

942.06   Napoléon III, emperor of the French, 1808-
N216   1873.
          Fragmens historiques 1688 et 1830 par
        le prince Napoléon Louis Bonaparte. [Paris]
        Administration de librairie, 1841.
          133 p. illus. 24 cm.

          1. Gt.Brit. Hist. Stuarts, 1603-1714.
        2. Gt.Brit. Hist. 1714-1837. I. Title.

NN   0018771   N

JN2491 NAPOLÉON III, emperor of the French, 1808-1873.
.N2   Fragmens historiques 1688 et 1830 par le prince
1839   Napoléon Louis Bonaparte. 2.éd. [Paris] Adminis-
        tration de librairie, 1841.
          [3],133,[1] p. 23½cm. [With his Des idées na-
        poléoniennes. Paris, 1839]

          1.Gt.Brit.--Hist.--Stuarts,1603-1714. 2.Gt.Brit.
        --Hist.--1714-1837.

NN   0018772   ICU

Napoleon III, Emperor of the French, 1808-1873.
   Geheimes Testament and seine Gattin, Sohn und
Freunde.   Leipzig.
   48 p. 19.5 cm.   [In "French political tracts",
6]

NN   0018773   CtY

4DC-116 Napoleon III, Emperor of the French, 1808-1873.
   Geheime Memoiren Louis Napoleon Bonaparte's,
hrsg. von L. Schubar (Dr. Lubarsch) Einzig
rechtmässig deutsche Ausg.   Berlin, Lubarsch's
Selbstverlags-Expedition, 1860-65.
   10 v. in 13.

NN   0018774   DLC-P4

Napoleon III, *emperor of the French,* 1808–1873.
Geschichte Julius Cäsars. Vom verfasser autorisirte
uebersetzung. ... Wien, Verlag von C. Gerold's sohn;
[etc., etc.] 1865-66.
2 v. and atlas. 25ᶜᵐ

1. Caesar, C. Julius. 2. Rome—Hist.—Republic, B.C. 265-30.

NN   0018775   MiU ICU MH PU IU NIC

[Napoléon III] Emperor of the French, 1803-1873.
   Geschichte Julius Cäsars.   Berlin, Dümmler,
1867.
   2 v.

NN   0018776   PPG

Napoleon III, Emperor of the French, 1808-1873,
   supposed author.
      The great political pamphlet of the day on
European affairs
           see under title

Napoleon III emperor of the French, 1808-1873.
   Histoire de Jules César.   New York, Charles
Laddalle, 1865.

   396 p. front. (port.) map, 20 cm.

   1. Caesar, C. Julius. 2. Rome - History - Republic.
B.C. 265-30.

NN   0018778   PLatS

Napoleon III, *emperor of the French,* 1808–1873.
Histoire de Jules César. Par S. M. I. Napoléon III. ...
New York, D. Appleton et cie., 1865.
2 v. 20ᶜᵐ.

1. Caesar, C. Julius. 2. Rome—Hist.—Republic, B. C. 265-30.
                                                   4—35243
Library of Congress   DG261.N22

                NjN OLak
NN   0018779   DLC ICRL MdBP MeB NjNbS MWA MB ViU NN

DG261   Napoleon III, Emperor of the French, 1808-1873.
.N24   Histoire de Jules César.   Paris, G. Paetz,
        1865-66.
          2v.

          1. Caesar, C. Julius. 2. Rome - Hist. -
        Republic, 265-30 B. C.

NN   0018780   NcU MB

[Napoléon III, *emperor of the French,* 1808–1873.
Histoire de Jules César ... Paris, H. Plon, 1865-1866.
2 v. 23ᶜᵐ. *and* atlas (2 v.) 36½ᶜᵐ.

1. Caesar, C. Julius. 2. Rome—Hist.—Republic, B. c. 265-30.
I. Title.

Library of Congress   DG261.N21   4—36640

NN   0018781   DLC WaPS ICJ CU MU OC1 KyU WaU

VOLUME 405

q871 ₍Napoléon III, Emperor of the French₎ 1808-1873.
C2Wn   Histoire de Jules César.   Paris, Impr. impe-
1865   riale, 1865-66.
        2v. col.maps. 37cm.

        1. Caesar, C. Julius. 2. Rome—Hist.—Repub-
lic, B.C.265-30.   I. Title.

NN   0018782   IU DGW NjP NcD TxU CU NN

Napoléon III, Emperor of the French, 1808-1873.
    Histoire de Jules César, par S. M. I. Napoléon III...
t. 1-   San Francisco, H. Payot, 1865-
    1 v.   front. (port.) fold. maps.   21 cm.

NN   0018783   CU

Napoleon III, Emperor of the French, 180
    Histoire de Jules César.   New York, 1866-67.
    2 v. & atlas.

NN   0018784   NjP IaU OCl

Napoleon III, emperor of the French, 1808-1873.
    Histoire du canon dans les armées modernes, par le citoyen
Louis-Napoléon Bonaparte, représentant du peuple, précédée de
sa biographie; par un vieil ami de la liberté, son collègue à l'Assemblée nationale, et suivie d'une notice sur tous les membres
aujourd'hui vivants de la famille Bonaparte.   Paris: Martinon,
1848.   88 p.   16°.
    Extracts from v. 55 and 56 of the Dictionnaire de la Conversation.

1. Ordnance.—History. 2. Bona-   parte family.
N. Y. P. L.   September 25, 1923.

NN 0018785   NN MiU

Napoleon III, Emperor of the French, 1808-1873.
    Histoire secrète de Napoléon III
        see under title

₍Napoléon III, emperor of the French₎ 1808-1873.
    History of Julius Cæsar ... New York, A. Dowling, 1865.
    2 v. front. (port.) 25ᵐ.

1. Caesar, C. Julius. 2. Rome—Hist.—Republic, 265-30 B. C.
I. Title.

Library of Congress   DG261.N24   4—33944

NN 0018787   DLC KyLx NcU TxU MB Nh ViU

₍Napoléon III₎ emperor of the French, 1808-1873.
    History of Julius Cæsar ... London, Cassell, Petter,
and Galpin; ₍etc., etc., 1865-66₎
    2 v. 22ᵐ. and atlas. 36¼ᵐ.

1. Caesar, C. Julius. 2. Rome—Hist.—Republic, b. c. 265-30.   I. Title.
                                                             4—33943
Library of Congress   DG261.N23

NN 0018788   DLC MB KEmT NN PV VtY TU PSC PPLT MH

DG261 ₍Napoleon III, emperor of the French₎ 1808-1873
N24   History of Julius Caesar.   New York,
         Harper, 1865-1866.
         2v. front. (port.) 25cm.

        1. Caesar, C. Julius. 2. Rome. History.
Republic, 265-30 B.C. I. Title.

      WU NIC MeB
      DNW KAS ViU MH NjP NN T OrU LU WaSp WaTC MiD NjNbS
NN   0018789   IaU I MH AU OLak ViLxW IEG Vi CtY MB

Napoleon III, emperor of the French.
    History of Julius Caesar. N. Y., Harper, 1868.
    2 v.

NN   0018790   PHatU NjNbS

Napoleon III.
    "How we lost Sedan."
    (In Legge, E. The Empress Eugénie, 1870-1910. Pp. 143-150.
New York. 1910.)

NN   0018791   MB

Napoléon III, Emperor of the French, 1808-73.
    Ideas napoleonicas. Aumentadas con notas
relativas á Espana, un diálogo entre Napoleon
y Robespierre y las conversaciones de Canova.
Traducidas del frances por Manuel de la Escosura.
Barcelona, Saurí, 1839.

    225 p. port.

NN   0018792   MH

Napoléon III, Emperor of the French, 1808-1873.
    Ideas napoleónicas. [Traducción de C. Romane]
Buenos Aires, Espasa-Calpe Argentina [1947]
    150 p.   18 cm.   (Colección austral, no. 798)

NN   0018793   OU

944.05 Napoleon III, Emperor of the French,
N21Zna   1808-1873.
             Les idées napoléoniennes, par le
IN: Prince Napoléon-Louis Bonaparte.   Paris,
spec   Paulin, 1839.
             viii, 160 p. port. 17 cm.

         1. Napoléon I, Emperor of the French,
1769-1821 2. France--Politics and
government--1799-1815 I. TITLE.

NN   0018794   IEN

4DC **Napoléon III Emperor of the French,**
1681   **1808 - 1873.**
          Intorno alla direzione degli aero-
       stati. [18]
          178-195 p.

NN   0018795   DLC-P4

Beinecke Napoleon III, emperor of the French, 1808-1873
Library   Julius Caesars historia ... Svensk ofver-
DG261   sattning ... Stockholm, Adolf Bonner [etc.,etc.]
N361   [1865-66]
             2 v. 26 cm.
             Issued in parts; original covers bound in.

         1. Caesar, C. Julius. 2. Rome - Hist. - Re-
public, B.C. 265-30. 3. Fryxell, Anders, 1791-
1881 - Autograph.

NN   0018796   CtY

Napoleon III.
    Julius Cæsars Historie. Autoriseret Udgave.
    Kjøbenhavn. Delbanco. 1866, 1867. 2 v. Portrait. 24.5 cm.,
in 4s.
    The author's name appears only in vol. 1 at the end of the Fortale.
    Contents. — 1. Rom før Cæsar. — Julius Cæsars Historie. 2. Gallerkrigen.
— Oversigt over Gallerkrigen og Fremstilling af Begivenhederne i Rom i
Aarene 696-705.—Bilag.

E2011 — Denmark. Lang. Works in Danish. — Cæsar, Caius Julius. — Rome.
Hist.

NN   0018797   MB CtY

Napoleon III, emperor of the French, 1808-1873.
    A letter of Elizabeth Barrett Browning to Napo-
leon III...
        see under Browning, Elizabeth Barrett,
1806-1861.

NAPOLEON III,emp.of the French.
    Letter to Gen.Forey. The cardinal idea of
intervention in Mexico. What French non-in-
tervention means. Comment of the London
times,June 20th,1863. n.p.,[1866?]

    4°. pp.(3).

NN   0018799   MH

Napoleon III.
    [Letters.]
    (In Legge, Edmund. The comedy & tragedy of the Second Em-
pire. New York. 1911.)

H6600

NN   0018800   MB

Napoléon III, Emperor of the French, 1808-1873.
    Letters of "An Englishman" on Louis Napoleon
        see under title

Napoléon III, emperor of the French, 1808-1873.
    Lettre de Louis Napoleon au peuple de France.
Paris ₍1848?₎
    2p.

    Signed: Théodore Staines.

MF-186 ---- ---- Microfilm edition. 1958.

NN   0018802   ICRL

Napoléon III, emperor of the French, 1808-1873.
    Lettre de S. M. l'empereur au ministre des
affaires étrangères.
Sauclières, etc.
    Napoléon III et la question romaine; réponse à la lettre im-
périale du 20 mai 1862; par de Sauclières ... Leipzig, K. F.
Köller, 1862.

Napoleon III, emperor of the French, 1808-1873.
    Lettre sur l'histoire de France par Henri
d'Orléans
        see under Aumale, Henri Eugène Philippe
Louis d'Orléans, duc d', 1822-1897.

VOLUME 405

Napoléon III, emp. of the **French.**   **Afr 2025.7**
Lettre sur la politique de la France en Algérie, adressée par l'empereur au maréchal de MacMahon. Paris, Imprimerie impériale, 1865.
    1. 8°.   pp. 88.

NN   0018805   MH NBuU OC1 IEN

Napoléon III, *emperor of the French,* 1808–1873.
Lettres de Napoléon III à madame Cornu, en grande partie inédites; texte intégral publié et commenté par Marcel Emerit ... Paris, Les Éditions des Presses modernes [1937]
    2 v. port. 18½ᵐ.
    Cover-title: t. II has special t.-p.
    Bibliography: t. I, p. vi–xvi.
    Imperfect? Portrait (or portraits) and facsimile wanting? *cf.* Bibl. de la France. 1938, no. 596.

    1. Cornu, Mme. Hortense (Lacroix) 1812–1875.   I. Emerit, Marcel, ed.
                               41–34530
Library of Congress   DC275.2.N587
                     [2]   923.144

NN   0018806   DLC ICU PU CtY

Napoléon III, emperor of the French, 1808–1873.
Manifeste de Louis-Napoléon Bonaparte aux electeurs. Paris, 1848.
    1 l. illus.

MF-186 ---- ---- Microfilm edition. 1958.

NN   0018807   ICRL

Napoléon III, *emperor of the French,* 1808–1873.
Manuel d'artillerie à l'usage des officiers d'artillerie de la République helvétique. Par le prince Napoléon-Louis Bonaparte ... Zurich, Orell Fussli et comp.ᵉ; [etc., etc.] 1836.
    2 p. l., xxxiii, 528 (i. e. 536), 7 p. incl. tables. xxxix pl. (incl. plans, diagrs.) 20 cm.
    Six leaves with ms. notes, inserted.
    Note on half-title, written by the owner (A. Mordecai) in 1856, indicates that this copy, including the manuscript notes, was purchased at the sale of the author's effects, and that the ms. notes were written with intention of preparing a new edition.
    Bibliography included in "Avant-propos" (p. [iii]–v)
    L. C. copy imperfect: p. 41–118, 275–312, 345–352, 491–506, 515–516, 529?; plates xxx–xxxi, xxxvi wanting; p. 353–354, mutilated.

    1. Artillery.
    UF145.N23   48–30343

NN   0018808   DLC NcD OC1WHi DN

NAPOLEON III, emperor of the French, 1808–1873.
    Minuta originale del proclama di Napoleone III agli Italiani 8 giugno 1859, colle di lui correzioni e varianti autografe; conservata e donata dal M.R. prevosto di Magenta, D.G. Giardini e fratelli alla Biblioteca Ambrosiana. 2ᵃ ed. Facsimile in fotolitografia. Milano, A. della Croce, [1859].
    f°. pp. (3).
    Cover serves as title-page.

NN   0018809   MH CtY

Napoleon III, emperor of the French, 1808–1873, supposed author.
    The Napoleon ballads by Bon Gaultier [pseud.]
       see under   Martin, Sir Theodore, 1816–1909.

Napoléon III, *emperor of the French,* 1808–1873.
Napoléon III et le prince Napoléon; correspondance inédite publiée par Ernest d'Hauterive. Paris, Calmann-Lévy, 1925.
    2 p. l., x, 412 p., 1 l. 23ᶜᵐ.

Continued in next column

Continued from preceding column

    1. France—Hist.—Second empire, 1852–1870.   I. Napoléon Joseph Charles Paul Bonaparte, prince, 1822–1891.   II. Hauterive, Ernest d', 1864– ed.
Library of Congress   DC275.2.N6
                                  25–11257

NN   0018811   DLC TU CtY NcD PU ICU MiU NN

Napoléon III, emperor of the French, 1808–1873.
Giraudeau, Fernand, 1835–
    Napoléon III intime, par Fernand Giraudeau. Paris, P. Ollendorff, 1895.

Napoléon III, *emperor of the French,* 1808–1873.
Napoléon III on England. Selections from his own writings. Ed. and tr. by John Hawkins Simpson ... London, Saunders, Otley, and co., 1860.
    viii, 206 p. 17ᶜᵐ.

    1. France—Pol. & govt.—1799–1815. 2. Gt. Brit.—Pol. & govt.   I. Simpson, John Hawkins, ed. and tr.
                             9–33569†
Library of Congress   JN2491.N28

NN   0018813   DLC PPL

Napoleon III, emperor of the French, 1808–1873, and **Francis Joseph I.**
    Napoleone III e Francesco Giuseppe alla pace di Villafranca; un carteggio inedito... (Nuova antologia. Roma, 1923. 8°. 1923, Dec. 16, p. 289–311.)
    Edited by F. Salata.

    1. Villafranca (Treaty of).   2. Francis Joseph I, emperor of Austria, 1830–1916. 3. Salata,   Francesco, editor.
N. Y. P. L.   June 9, 1924

NN   0018814   NN

Napoléon III, *emperor of the French,* 1808–1873.
Napoleonic ideas. Des idées napoléoniennes, par le prince Napoléon-Louis Bonaparte. Brussels: 1839. Tr. by James A. Dorr. New York, D. Appleton & company, 1859.
    154 p. 19ᶜᵐ.

    1. Napoléon I, emperor of the French, 1769–1821. 2. France — Pol. & govt.—Consulate and empire, 1799–1815.   I. Dorr, James Augustus, tr. II. Title.
                             9–33484
Library of Congress   JN2491.N26

          PPLT PU ODW OC1 OCX MeB NN MB
NN   0018815   DLC NjR MWA RPB KU PLF KyU NjP ViU

JN2491   Napoléon III, Emperor of the French, 1808–1873.
.N2   Napoleonische Ideen, von Napoleon Louis Bonaparte. Freiburg im Breisgau, Herder'schen
1839a   parte. Freiburg im Breisgau, Herder'schen
Rare bk   Kunst- und Buchhandlung, 1839.
       vi, 86 p.

       1. Napoléon I, Emperor of the French, 1769–1821. I. Title.

NN   0018816   ICU

Napoléon III, emperor of the French, 1808–1873.
    Nouveau système d'artillerie de campagne de Louis-Napoléon Bonaparte
       see under   Favé, Ildéphonse, 1812–1894.

[Napoléon III] *emperor of the French,* 1808–1873.
    Note sur l'organisation militaire de la confédération de l'Allemagne du Nord. Wilhelmshœhe. Janvier 1871. [Bruxelles, Impr. de C. Lelong, 1871]
    85 p. 29½ᶜᵐ.
    Published anonymously.

    1. North German confederation, 1866–1870. Army.   I. Title.
                               5—2386
Library of Congress   UA710.N21

NN   0018818   DLC CtY

Napoléon III, emperor of the French, 1808–1873.
    Notes sur les amorces fulminantes et sur les attelages, ... Paris, Gaultier-Laguionie, 1841.
    16 p. illus., diagrs. 21 1/2 cm.

NN   0018819   DNW

Napoléon III, *emperor of the French,* 1808–1873.
Œuvres posthumes et autographes inédits du Napoléon III en exil, recueillis et coordonnés par le comte de La Chapelle ... Annotations de la main de S. M. l'empereur. Paris, E. Lachaud, 1873.
    viii, 276 p. front. (port.) facsims. 27½ᶜᵐ.

    1. Franco-German war, 1870–1871. 2. France—History, Military.   I. Lachapelle, Alfred de, comte, 1830– ed.
                             19–3646
Library of Congress   DC275.2.N3 1873

NN   0018820   DLC MdBP CtY MiU PPL

JN2491   Napoléon III, emperor of the French, 1808–1873.
N3   On the opinions and policy of Napoleon. Tr. from the French. London, H. Colburn, 1840.
       xxii, 175 p. 23cm.

       1. Napoléon I, emperor of the French, 1769–1821. 2. France - Pol. & govt. - 1799–1815. I. Title.   x: Bonaparte, Louis Napoleon.

NN   0018821   OrCS

Napoléon III, Emperor of the French, 1808–1873.
    Opere politiche di Napoleone III. 1ᵃ versione italiana di Giulio Grandi. Firenze, Tip. Fioretti, etc., 1858.
    2 vol.

NN   0018822   MH

Napoléon III, Emperor of the French, 1808–1873.
    Papiers et correspondance de la famille impériale
       see under   France. Commission chargée de réunir, classer et publier les papiers saisis aux Tuileries.

Napoléon III, *emperor of the French,* 1808–1873.
Belly, Félix, 1816–1886.
    Percement de l'isthme américain. Canal de Nicaragua; exposé de la question, par M. Félix Belly. 2. éd. Paris, Aux bureaux de la direction du canal, 1859.

FOR OTHER SEE MAIN

VOLUME 405

Napoléon III, *emperor of the French, 1808–1873.*
The political and historical works of Louis Napoleon Bonaparte ... now first collected. With an original memoir of his life, brought down to the promulgation of the constitution of 1852 ... London, Pub. at the office of the Illustrated London library, 1852.
2 v. front. (port.) 22ᶜᵐ. CONTENTS.
v. 1. Political life of Prince Louis Napoleon Bonaparte.—Political reveries—ideas of a new constitution, 1832.—Switzerland, political and military. Ideas of Napoleonism.—Historical fragments—the revolutions of 1688 and 1830.

v. 2. Analysis of the sugar question.—Extinction of pauperism.—A few words relating to Joseph Bonaparte.—Opinions on various political and administrative questions.—Of governments and of their supporters.—Reply to M. de Lamartine.—The past and future of artillery.—"L'idée napoléonienne."—The revision of the constitution.—Miscellaneous papers, &c.—Papers relating to the coup d'état.

1. France—Pol. & govt.—1848-1852—Sources.

8—17446

NN 0018826   DLC PHatU PHi PPL CtY NcU NcD NWM MB

325.344 Napoléon III, Emperor of the French, 1808-
N216p   1873.
Politique de la France en Algérie. Paris, Impr. Impériale, 1865.
68p. tables. 30cm.

Letter of June 20, 1865, addressed to Marshal MacMahon.

1. France - Colonies - Algeria. I. MacMahon, Marie Edme Patrice Maurice de, duc de Magenta, 1808-1893. II. Title.

NN 0018827   NcU MiU

Napoléon III, emperor of the French, 1808-1873.
La politique impériale, exposée par les discours et proclamations de l'empereur Napoléon III, depuis le 10 décembre 1848 jusqu'en juillet 1865. Paris, Henri Plon, 1865.
3 p. l. ₍3₎-448 p. 24 cm.

1. France--History--1848-1870. 2. France--Politics and government--1848-1870. I. Title.

NN 0018828   NSchU PU TU MH InU

Napoléon III, Emperor of the French, 1808-1873.
La politique impériale, exposée par les discours et proclamations de l'empereur Napoléon III, depuis le 10 décembre 1848 jusqu'en février 1868. Paris, H. Plon, 1868.
503 p. 23 cm.

NN 0018829   WU MH IaU

Napoléon III, *emperor of the French, 1808-1873.*
Posthumous works and unpublished autographs of Napoleon III. in exile. Collected and arranged by Count de La Chapelle ... London, S. Low, Marston, Low, & Searle, 1873.
viii, 268 p. facsims. (part fold.) 23ᶜᵐ.

1. Franco-German war, 1870-1871. 2. France—History, Military. I. Lachapelle, Alfred de, comte, 1830- ed.

8—17445

Library of Congress   DC275.2.N3

NN 0018830   DLC NIC PP PLF MdBP CtY

Napoléon III, Emperor of the French, 1808-1873, defendant.
Procès de Louis-Napoléon Bonaparte, jugé par la Chambre des pairs, sur l'attentat de Boulogne du 6 août 1840. 1. - livraison. Paris [1840?]
1 v. 17 cm.

NN 0018831   CtY

NAPOLÉON III, Defendant.
Procès du prince Napoléon Louis Bonaparte, condamné a une détention perpétuelle par la cour des pairs.

In Les FASTES criminels de 1840, v.1

NN 0018832   MH-L

Napoléon III, *Emperor of the French, 1808-1873,* **defendant.**
Procès et condamnation du prince Louis Napoléon Bonaparte; attentat de Boulogne. Bruxelles, P.-J.-D. de Somer, imprimeur, 1868–

v. in 14 cm. (Documents historiques, 2

I. France. Cour des pairs. II. Title: Attentat de Boulogne.

49-56877*

NN 0018833   DLC

344.07 Napoleon III, emperor of the French, 1808-1873,
N16Wna   defendant.
Processo di Luigi Bonaparte avanti la corte dei pari. n.p. ₍184-₎
259p. front.(port.)

Caption title.
Trial of Charles Louis Napoleon Bonaparte, C. T. Montholon and others, for the attempt at Bologna, in 1840, to overthrow the government of France.

NN 0018834   IU

Napoléon III, emp.of the French, 1808-73.
Proposition tendant a abroger la loi du 26 mai 1848 qui exile la famille d'Orléans. P, 1849.
[1 p.]

NN 0018835   MH

Napoléon III, emp.of the French, 1808-73.
Proposition tendant à abroger le décret du 10 avril 1832 qui bannit la branche aînée des Bourbons. P, 1849.
[1 p.]

NN 0018836   MH

Napoléon III, emp.of the French, 1808-73.
Proposition tendant à abroger les lois du 10 avril 1832 et du 26 mai 1848 qui excluent la famille des Bourbons et le décret du 27 juin 1848 relatif aux insurgés de juin [P, 1849]
2 p.

NN 0018837   MH

Napoléon III, emp.of the French, 1808-73.
Proposition tendant a rapporter le décret du 27 juin 1848 relatif aux insurgés de juin. P, 1849.
[1 p.]

NN 0018838   MH

NAPOLÉON III,emperor of the French,1808-1873, defendant.
Prozess des prinzen Ludwig Napoleon Bonaparte und seiner mitangeklagten vor dem pairshofe. Aus dem französischen von Eugen Huhn. Karlsruhe,C.Macklot,1841.
pp.vi,250. Port.of Louis Napoleon.
Original compiled by Albert Fermé.

NN 0018839   MH

Napoléon III,emperor of the French,1808-1873, defendant.
... Prozess Ludwig Napoleon's. Karlsruhe, C.Macklot, 1844.
2 v.in 1. front.(port.) 21ᶜᵐ. (Archiv für oeffentlichkeit und mündlichkeit im strafverfahren. Sammlung der denkwürdigsten kriminalprozesse. 2.bd.)
Paged continuously: vi,112 p.,1 l.,113-250 p.
"Vorwort" signed: Eugen Huhn.
Trial of Charles Louis Napoleon Bonaparte,Gen.Ch.T.Montholon,and others,for the attempt at Boulogne,in 1840,to overthrow the government of France.
I.Huhn, Eugen,tr. II.Montholon,Charles Jean Tristan, marquis de,1783-1853,defendant. III.France. Cour des pairs. IV.Title.

NN 0018840   MiU

Napoléon III, emperor of the French, 1808-1873.
La Question algérienne...
see under [Aumale, Henri Eugène Philippe Louis d'Orléans, 1822-1897]

Napoléon III, Emperor of the French, 1808-1873.
Recueil historique des pensées, opinions, discours, proclamations, lettres et beaux-traits de Napoléon III, empereur des Français sur l'armée, l'artillerie, l'administration, le paupérisme, l'economie politique et sociale précédé des maximes de Napoléon Iᵉʳ, etc. Paris, Au Dépot géographique, 1857.
Plate (folded at end) and facsimile plate.

NN 0018842   MH

Napoléon III, emp.of the French, 1808-73
Recueil officiel contenant les lettres de l'Empereur à Sa Sainteté le pape Pie IX et au ministre d'Etat. P, 1860.
8 p.

NN 0018843   MH

DC275.2 NAPOLEON III,emperor of the French,1808-1873.
.N214   Rede des Prinzen Napoleon, gehalten in der Sitzung des französischen Senats am 1. Marz 1861 Berlin, J. Springer, 1861.
6+82 p.

I. tc.

NN 0018844   InU MH

VOLUME 405

NAPOLÉON III, emp. of the French.
Réponse à M. Lamartine. Lettres au journal
le Loiret et aux ouvriers. Publiées par C.E.
Templaire. Paris, 1848.

pp. 16.

NN   0018845   MH

Bo71C
830Ba
23
Napoléon III, Emperor of the French, 1808-
1873.
Réponse de Louis-Napoléon Bonaparte à M.
Lamartine. [Paris? 1843]
14 p. 19 cm. [Binder's title: Brochures
politiques. République, 23]
Caption title.
Includes two additional letters of Napoléon.

1. Lamartine, Alphonse Marie Louis de,
1790-1896.

NN   0018846   CtY

Napoléon III, *emperor of the French*, 1808-1873.
The second empire and its downfall; the correspondence
of the Emperor Napoleon III and his cousin Prince Napoleon,
now published for the first time by Ernest d'Hauterive, and
translated from the French by Herbert Wilson. With two
illustrations. New York, George H. Doran company [1927]
292 p. 2 port. (incl. front.) 24 cm.
Printed in Great Britain.
1. France—Hist.—Second empire, 1852-1870. I. Napoléon Joseph
Charles Paul Bonaparte, prince, 1822-1891. II. Hauterive, Ernest d',
1864- ed. III. Wilson, Herbert, tr. IV. Title. *Translation of
Napoléon III et la prince Napoléon; correspondence inédite.*

DC275.2.N63   27—16270

FTaSU
NN   0018847   DLC OClJC PPA PU OC1 MoU NN ICN LU

Napoléon III, Emperor of the French, 1808-1873.
The secret of the coup d'état
see under   Lansdowne, Henry William
Edmond Petty Fitzmaurice, 6th marquis of,
1872-1936, ed.

Napoléon III, Emperor of the French, 1808-1873,
supposed author.
Souvenirs et notes intimes de Napoléon III à
Wilhelmshoehe
see under   Kock, Henry de, 1819-1892.

944.07
N16sp NAPOLEON III, emperor of the French,
1808-1873.
Speeches from the throne together with
proclamations and some letters of the
emperor; a brief chronological record of
European events and an appendix by
Robert Holmes Edleston.   Cambridge,
R. I. Severs, 1931.

360 p.   facsim.   18cm.
1. France. Hist. 1852-1870. I. Edleston.
Robert Holmes.

NN   0018850   MnU CtY

[Napoléon III, *emperor of the French*] 1808-1873, *supposed
author.*
Les titres de la dynastie napoléonienne ... Paris, Imprimerie impériale, 1868.
76 p. 27ᶜᵐ.
Attributed to Napoléon III.

Continued in next column

Continued from preceding column

1. Plebiscite. 2. France—Constitutional history. 3. Napoléon I, emperor of the French, 1769-1821. 4. Napoléon III, emperor of the French,
1808-1873. I. Title.

Library of Congress   JN2610.P5N3   45-49306

NN   0018851   DLC CtY MH

Napoléon IV, pseud.
L'ex-futur empereur des français aux membres
de l'Assemblée dite nationale.   Bruxelles.
1 p.   28.5 cm.   [In verse]   [In "French
political tracts, 1868-75"]

NN   0018852   CtY

Napoléon Eugène Louis Jean Joseph Bonaparte, prince
imperial.
See
Louis Napoléon, prince imperial of the French, 1856-1879.

Napoléon, Joseph Charles Paul Bonaparte, 1822-1891.
Catalogue of works of art from the collections ..
of ... Prince Napoleon ... sold by auction by ...
Christie, Manson & Woods ... May 9, 1872 ...
[London, 1872]
30 p.   8°.

NN   0018854   NN

Napoléon Joseph Charles Paul Bonaparte, prince,
1822-1891.
Bonaparte, Jérôme Napoléon, 1805-1870.
Cour impériale de Paris. Première chambre. Appel du
jugement de la première chambre du Tribunal de première
instance de la Seine, du 15 février 1861. M. Jérôme-Napoléon
Bonaparte et mᵐᵉ Élisabeth Patterson contre S. A. I. le prince
Napoléon. [Baltimore, J. S. Waters, 1861?]

[Napoléon Joseph Charles Paul Bonaparte] Prince,
1822-1891.
De la conduite de la guerre d'Orient;
expédition de Crimée
see under [Tavernier,   ]

Napoléon. Joseph Charles Paul Bonaparte, prince, 1822-1891.
Discorso di S. A. I. il principe Napoleone al Senato francese
nella seduta del 1° marzo 1861.   Torino: Unione tipografico-
editrice, 1861.   87 p.   16°.

1. France.—History: Second Em-   pire, 1852-70.
N.Y.P.L.   September 24, 1924

NN   0018857   NN MH

D
393
.M52
Napoléon Joseph Charles Paul Bonaparte, prince,
1822-1891.
Discours de S.A.I. le prince Napoléon.
Paris, Impr. de N. Chaix, 1861.
80 p.
No. 13 in a vol. with binder's title:
Mélanges politiques.
At head of title: Sénat, séance du vendredi
1ᵉʳ mars 1861.
1. France—Pol. & govt.—1852-1870.
2. Italian question. 1848-1870.

NN   0018858   MiU MH

Napoléon Joseph Charles Paul Bonaparte, prince, 1822-
1891.
Discours de S. A. I. le prince Napoléon, prononcé au
Sénat, dans la séance du vendredi 1ᵉʳ mars 1861. Paris,
E. Dentu, 1861.
77 p. 24½ cm.

1. France—Pol. & govt.—1852-1870. 2. Italian question, 1848-1870.
I. Title.
18-9326

Library of Congress   DC277.33.N3

NN   0018859   DLC CtY

BX
1530
N3
Napoléon Joseph Charles Paul Bonaparte, Prince,
1822-1891.
Discours de S. A. I. le prince Napoléon dans
la délibération des paragraphes sur le projet
d'Adresse.   Séance du samedi 1er mars 1862.
Paris, E. Panckoucke, 1862.
93 p.   21 cm.

On spine: Documents de la question romaine.
Cover title.
"Extrait du Moniteur universel du dimanche
2 mars 1862."

With this is bound, David, J. Discours.
Paris, 1862. and Dupanloup, F. A. P. La convention. Paris, 1865.
1. Church and state in France - Hist. -
Sources. 2. Catholic Church in France - Hist.
- Sources. I. France. Corps législatif, 1852-
1870.

NN   0018861   CU-S MH

Napoléon Joseph Charles Paul Bonaparte, prince, 1822-91
Discours prononcé par le prince Napoléon Bonaparte (Jé-
rome) à la Chambre des députés, le 24 novembre 1876. P,
1876

29 p.

NN   0018862   MH

Napoléon Joseph Charles Paul Bonaparte, prince,
1822-1891.
Discours prononcé par son altesse impériale
le Prince Napoléon, le 15 mai 1865, pour
l'inauguration du monument élevé dans la ville
d'Ajaccio a Napoléon Iᵉʳ et a ses frères.   Paris,
E. Dentu, 1865.
32 p.   26 cm.

1. Napoléon I, emperor of the French, 1769-1821.

NN   0018863   NSchU NN

Napoléon Joseph Charles Paul Bonaparte, prince,
1822-1891.
Discours prononcés par son altesse impériale
le Prince Napoléon dans la délibération des
paragraphes sur le projet d'adresse, séances des
22, 25 février et 1ᵉʳ mars 1862 ...   Paris, E.
Dentu, 1862.
104 p.   24 cm.

"Extraits du Moniteur."
With this is bound: Hubaine, Em. Le gouvernement temporel des   papes. Paris, 1862.
1. Popes--Tem   poral power. 2. Roman
question.

NN   0018864   NSchU

Napoléon Joseph Charles Paul Bonaparte, *prince,*
1822-1891.
Économie politique. Discours et rapports du Prince Napoléon.
[Paris, Imprimerie Ramboz & Schuchardt, 1864?.]
222 p. 22½ᶜᵐ.
Half-title.

NN   0018865   ICJ CU MH-BA

VOLUME 405

Napoleon Joseph Charles Paul Bonaparte, prince, 1822-1891.
[Hubaine, Em   ]
Le gouvernement temporel des papes jugé par la diplomatie française (recueil de documents) Paris, E. Dentu, 1862.

NN 0018867   MH

NAPOLEON [JOSEPH CHARLES PAUL BONAPARTE, Prince
Lettre du prince Napoléon à Jules Favre sur le 4 sep.et la commune. [Paris],chez tous les libraires,[1871].

pp.10.

NN 0018867   MH

Napoléon Joseph Charles Paul Bonaparte, *prince,* 1822–1891.
Napoleon and his detractors. By His Imperial Highness Prince Napoleon. Tr. and ed., with a biographical sketch and notes, by Raphaël Ledos de Beaufort... With two portraits and autograph. London, W. H. Allen and co., 1888.
3 p. l., 403, [1] p. front., port., facsim. 22ᶜᵐ.
CONTENTS. — Translator's preface. — Prince Napoleon; biographical sketch.—Author's preface.—M. Taine.—Prince Metternich.—Bourrienne.—Madame de Rémusat.—The abbé de Pradt.—Miot de Mélito.—Correspondence of Napoleon I.—The man and his work.—Appendix.
1. Napoléon I, emperor of the French, 1769-1821.   I. Ledos de Beaufort, Raphaël, ed. and tr.
4—13532
Library of Congress   DC203.9.N23

NcU CtY MdBP NjP RPB PLF PBm MiU OCl
NN 0018868   DLC OrCS CoU CSt MoKU FTaSU OClWHi

Napoléon Joseph Charles Paul Bonaparte, prince.
Napoléon et ses détracteurs.   Paris: C. Lévy, 1887.   vii, 313 p., 1 l. 12°.
Title-page missing.

1. Napoleon I., emperor of the French.
N. Y. P. L.   November 18, 1913.

NN 0018869   NN CtY NjP

Napoléon Joseph Charles Paul Bonaparte, *prince,* 1822–1891.
Napoléon et ses détracteurs, par le prince Napoléon. 3. éd. Paris, Calmann Lévy, 1887.
2 p. l., vii, 313 p., 1 l. 18ᶜᵐ.
CONTENTS.—Préface.—M. Taine.—Le prince de Metternich.—Bourrienne.—Madame de Rémusat.—L'abbé de Pradt.—Miot de Mélito.—Correspondance de Napoléon Iᵉʳ.—L'homme et son œuvre.—Appendice.

1. Napoléon I, emperor of the French, 1769–1821.
27–22979
Library of Congress   DC203.9.N22 1887

NN 0018870   DLC TU AAP NIC CU NcU

Napoleon, Joseph Charles Paul Bonaparte, prince, 1822-1891.
Napoleon et ses detracteurs, par le prince Napoleon. 7. ed. Paris,Calmann Levy, 1887.
313 p.

NN 0018871   MiU

NAPOLÉON [Joseph Charles Paul Bonaparte].
Napoléon et ses détracteurs. 8e ed. Paris. 1887.

Containing criticisms on writings of M.Taine Prince Metternich,Bourrienne,Madame de Rémusat the abbé de Pradt,and Milot de Melito.

NN 0018872   MH

Napoléon Joseph Charles Paul Bonaparte, prince, 1822–1891.
Napoléon et ses détracteurs ... 9. éd. Paris, Lévy, 1887.
7, 313 p.   18 cm.
1. Napoléon I, emperor of the French, 1769-1821.

NN 0018873   NjP

Napoleon Joseph Charles Paul Bonaparte, prince, 1822-1891.
Napoleon et ses detracteurs, par le prince Napoleon. 18. ed. Paris, Calmann Levy, 1887.
2 p. l., vii. 313 p.

NN 0018874   OCU

Napoleon, Joseph Charles Paul Bonaparte, prince, 1822-1891.
Napoleon et ses detracteurs ... nouvelle ed. Paris. C. Levy, 1891.
vii, 313 p.

NN 0018875   OCl

Napoléon Joseph Charles Paul Bonaparte, prince, 1822–1891.
Napoléon III, *emperor of the French,* 1808–1873.
Napoléon III et le prince Napoléon; correspondance inédite publiée par Ernest d'Hauterive. Paris, Calmann-Lévy, 1925.

Napoleon, Joseph Charles Paul Bonaparte, prince, 1822-1891.
Sainte-Beuve, Charles Augustin, 1804–1869.
Nouvelle correspondance de C.-A. Sainte-Beuve, avec des notes de son dernier secrétaire. Paris, Calmann Lévy, 1880.

RARE BOOK
DEPT.
XG
.860
.B23M
no.5
Napoléon Joseph Charles Paul Bonaparte, prince, 1822-1891.
Observations sur le projet de loi sur la Garde nationale, par Napoléon Bonaparte ... Paris, Chez Ledoyen,libraire,Palais-national, galerie d'Orléans,31. Octobre 1850.
86p. 22cm.
Printed buff wrappers preserved.

NN 0018878   MB

Napoleon, Joseph Charles Paul Bonaparte, prince, 1822-1891.
Pièces a consulter pour s.a.i.le prince Napoléon contre Elisabeth Pat[t]erson, Jérôme Bonaparte (Pat[t]erson). [Paris], n.d.

4°. 60 p.

NN 0018879   MH-L

DC
275
.N3
Napoleon Joseph Charles Paul Bonaparte, prince, 1822-1891.
Politique intérieure; choix de discours et de publications du Prince Napoléon. [Paris] imprimerie Ramboz et Schuchardt [1873?]
286 p.

1. France - Pol. & govt. - 1848-1870. I. Title.

NN 0018880   NNC

944.07
N162
Napoleon Joseph Charles Paul Bonaparte, Prince, 1822-1891.
La question italienne sous l'Empire: discours du Prince Napoléon au Sénat. [n.p., [186?]
239 p.   22 cm.

NN 0018881   KyU

NAPOLEON [Joseph Charles Bonaparte].
La question polonaise; discours prononcé au Sénat,séance du 18 mars 1863. Paris,E.Dentu, 1863.

pp.51.

NN 0018882   MH

Napoléon, Joseph Charles Paul Bonaparte, prince, 1822-1891.
Paris. Exposition universelle, 1855. *Commission impériale.*
Rapport sur l'Exposition universelle de 1855 présenté à l'empereur par S. A. I. le prince Napoléon, président de la commission. Paris, Imprimerie impériale, 1857.

Napoléon, Joseph Charles Paul Bonaparte, prince, 1822-1891. (Paris, 1855)
Paris. Exposition universelle, 1855. Commission impériale.
... Rapports du jury mixte international publiés sous la direction de s. a. i. le prince Napoléon, président de la Commission impériale. Paris: Imprimerie impériale, 1856.   lxxvi, 1574 p. 26cm.

1. Exhibitions—Paris, 1855.
N. Y. P. L.   Card revised November 19, 1942

NN 0018884   NN CtY ICN

Napoleon Joseph Charles Paul Bonaparte, prince, 1822-1891.
Napoléon III, *emperor of the French,* 1808–1873.
The second empire and its downfall; the correspondence of the Emperor Napoleon III and his cousin Prince Napoleon, now published for the first time by Ernest d'Hauterive, and translated from the French by Herbert Wilson. With two illustrations. New York, George H. Doran company [1927]

NAPOLEON,Joseph Charles Paul,Bonaparte,prince.
SOFISMI e sarcasmi del principe Napoleone nel suo discorso al senato francese nella tornata del 1 di marzo 1861. Torino,1861.

NN 0018886   MH

VOLUME 405

Napoléon. Joseph Charles Paul Bonaparte, prince,
1822-1891.
    Speech in the French Senate, on the Temporal
Power of the Pope. March, 1862.   London, 1862.
    84 p.   8°.   [In v. 327, College Pamphlets]

NN   0018887   CtY

Napoléon, Joseph Charles Paul Bonaparte, prince, 1822-1891.
    La vérité à mes calomniateurs. Par le prince Napoléon.
    Paris. Dentu. 1871. 16 pp. 22 cm.
    Relates to his alleged provocation of the Franco-German War, etc.

K3494 — Franco-German War, 1870-1871.

NN   0018888   MB MH

Napoléon. Joseph Charles Paul Bonaparte,
prince, 1822-1891.
₍Pascal, Adrien₎ d. 1865.
    Visites et études de S. A. I. le prince Napoléon au Pa-
lais de l'industrie; ou, Guide pratique et complet à l'Exposition universelle de 1855. Comprenant les vingt-sept
classes de l'industrie. Paris, Perrotin, 1855.

Napoléon   Louis Bonaparte
    see   Bonaparte, Louis Napoléon, prince,
    1914-

Napoléon   Victor Jérôme Frédéric Bonaparte,
prince, 1862-1926, ed.
Hortense, *queen consort of Louis, king of Holland*, 1783-1837.
    Mémoires de la reine Hortense, publiés par le prince Napo-
léon ... avec notes par Jean Hanoteau ... Paris, Plon ₍1927₎

Napoléon   Victor Jérôme Frédéric Bonaparte,
prince, 1862-1926, ed.
Hortense, *queen consort of Louis, king of Holland*, 1783-1837.
    The memoirs of Queen Hortense; published by arrangement
with Prince Napoleon, edited by Jean Hanoteau, translated
by Arthur K. Griggs ... New York, Comopolitan book corporation, 1927.

Napoléon, Arthur.
    See
Napoleão, Arthur, 1843-

Napoleon, Jerome
    see   Jerome Bonaparte, King of Westphalia,
    1784-1860.

Napoleon, Louis, respondent.
              FOR OTHER EDITIONS
              SEE MAIN ENTRY
E450   **New York** (*State*) *Court of appeals.*
.N56
1861   ... Report of the Lemmon slave case: containing points and
arguments of counsel on both sides, and opinions of all the
judges. New York, H. Greeley & co., 1861.

Napoleon, Phil.
    At dusk. Words and music by Phil Napoleon and Jerry
Colonna. New York, M. Witmark & sons, c1932.

First line: Ev'ry morning roses bloom anew.

1. Evening.   I. Colonna, Jerry.   Printed for the Music Division
N. Y. P. L.   II. Song index (2). February 13, 1948

NN   0018896   NN

Napoleon, Wagcinton
    Carta, cuentos a mi amigo el publico
    see under title

Napoleon-Murray, Jacques
         See
    Murray, Jacques Napoleon.

Le Napoléon; journal hebdomadaire, politique, littéraire et
scientifique. no. 1-20; 6 jan.-19 mai, 1850. ₍Paris, Imprimerie Plon frères, etc., 1850₎
    160 p. 39ᶜᵐ.
    Head-pieces.
    Caption title.
    Edited by Jacquier.
    No more published.

    1. France—Hist.—Second republic, 1848-1852—Period. 2. Napoléon
III, emperor of the French, 1808-1873.

Library of Congress   DC272.A2N8   40-23218

NN   0018899   DLC MH

Soc
DC
197
N25
    Napoléon. Journal anecdotique et bio-
      graphique de l'Empire et de la grande
      armée. Deuxième et troisième années.
    Paris, Bureau de Journal, 1835.
    672,288 columns.

    Title varies.
    Vol. 3 has title: Napoléon. Mémorial an-
    ecdotique et biographique de l'Empire et de
    la grande armée.

NN   0018900   FTaSU

Le Napoléon, journal mensuel. no.1-
    ₍oct.₎ 1848-   Paris, A.Pierre
    & cie., 1848-
    v. 45 cm.

    Publication discontinued with no.4, Jan.1849.

NN   0018901   MH-BA

NAPOLEON; la revue du XIXe siècle.

    See   Revue des études
Napoleoniennes.

Napoléon; publication mensuelle. 195 -
    Paris.

    "Ouverte aux travaux de l'Académie Napoléon."
    Issues for 195 -   have also individual title

NN   0018903   MiU

Napoléon; revue des etudes napoleoniennes
    see   Revue des études Napoléoniennes.

Bo67
894n
    Napoléon. Paris,Bureaux de La Vie contempor-
      aine, 1894.
    3p ℓ.,136p.,2ℓ. illus.,2 fronts.,ports.
    27cm.
    Reproduction of original texts and illustra-
    tions.
    "Édition de grand luxe ... No.76."
    Contents. - Devant un Raffet, par François
Coppée. Le dimanche de Napoléon, par Frédéric
Masson. Boutades militaires, par Général Drago
Napoléon et Moltke, par Général Baron vonder
Goltz. Buonaparte se révèle, par Germain Bapst.

    Avant le mariage, par Albert Vandal. La reine
Hortense, par Lucien Perey. Le masque de César,
par Henri Bouchet.
    Napoléon et la marine, par Maurice Loir. La
bibliographie napoléonienne, par Henry Houssaye.
Notes et croquis.

NN   0018906   CtY NjR MH

Napoleon. London, A.L. Humphreys, 1906
    see under   Lord, John, biographer.

₈₁₈₆₆   ... Napoleon. New York, London. The Macmillan Compa-
    ny, 1906.
    xxviii, 946 p. 25ᶜᵐ.   (*In* Cambridge modern history, vol. 9.)
    "Bibliographies," p. 773-893.
    "Chronological table of the principal events," p. 894-899.
    Contents. — 1. Pariset, G. The Consulate, 1799-1804.—2. Walker, T. A. &
Wilson, H. W. The armed neutrality, 1780-1801.—3. Guilland, A. The pacification of
Europe, 1799-1802.—4. *same*. France and her tributaries, 1801-3.—5. Pariset, G.
France under the Empire, 1804-14.—6. Fisher, H. A. L. The codes.—7. Legg,
L. G. Wickham. The concordats.—8. Wilson, H. W. The command of the sea, 1803-
15.—9-10. Lloyd, E. M. The third coalition, 1805-7.—11. Rose, J. H. The Na-
poleonic empire at its height, 1807-9.—12. Keim, A. The war of 1809.—13. Rose,
J. H. The continental system, 1809-14.

        — 14. The French dependencies and Switzerland,
1800-14. (1) Fisher, H. A. L. The French dependencies. (2) Guilland, A. Switzerland.—15. Oman, C. W. The peninsular war, 1808-14.—16. Stchepkin, E. Russia under Alexander I, and the invasion of 1812.—17. Pflugk-Harttung, J. von. The war of liberation, 1813 4.—18. Fisher, H. A. L. The first restoration, 1814-5.—19. Ward,
A. W. The Congress of Vienna. 1. 1814-5.—20. Oman, C. W. The hundred days,
1815.—21. Ward, A. W. The Congress of Vienna. ii. 1815. 22. Gooch, G. P.
Great Britain and Ireland, 1792-1815.—23. The British Empire, 1783-1815. (1)
Hutton, W. H. India and Ceylon. (2) Egerton, H. E. The colonies.—24. Fisher,
H. A. L. St. Helena.

NN   0018909   ICJ

944.05
N162Bna
    ₍Napoleon₎ London and New York, Society of
      Napoleonic Literature, 1902.
    32v. plates, facsims., ports. (Imperial
    edition)

    Title from spine.
    "Imperial edition limited to ten numbered
copies, of which this is no.2."
    Contents.- v.1-12. The life of Napoleon
Bonaparte, by William Hazlitt.- v.13-20.
Memoirs of Napoleon Bonaparte, by L.A.F. de
Bourrienne.- v.21-32. Memoirs of Madame Junot

    1. Napoleon I, Emperor of the French,
1769-1821. I. Hazlitt, William, 1778-1830.
The life of Napoleon Bonaparte. II. Bourrienne,
Louis Antoine Fauvelet de, 1769-1834. Memoirs
of Napoleon Bonaparte. III. Abrantès, Laure
Saint-Martin (Permon) Junot, Duchesse d',
1784-1838. Memoirs of Madame Junot. IV.
Society of Napoleonic Literature.

NN   0018911   TxFTC

... Napoléon. Paris, P. Lafitte & cie [c1913]
    see under   [Keim, Albert] 1876-

VOLUME 405

Napoleon. Paris, Boivin & Cie. 1921
see under   Montorgueil, Georges,
1857-1933.

[Napoleon: a back view]
see under   [Ibbetson, Denzil] 1788-1857,
attributed author.

Soc
DC
203.9   Napoléon ₍à₎ Fontainebleau ₍par Jean
N316   Savant et al.   Paris, Editions
         Napoléon, 1950₎
         99p. illus.,ports.

         Cover title.
         Special issue, no.4-5, Napoléon, Sept.,
         1950.

         1. Napoléon I, Emperor of the French,
         1769-1821. I. Savant, Jean
         II. Napoléon.

NN 0018915   FTaSU NIC

Napoleon a la faz de sus contemporaneos
see under   [Ader, Jean Joseph] 1796-1859.

ar W   Napoléon ₍à₎ Malmaison.   ₍Paris, Editions
1698   Napoléon, 1950?₎
        79 p. illus. 21cm.

        1. Napoléon I, emperor of the French,
        1769-1821.

NN 0018917   NIC FTaSU

Napoleon à Waterloo
see   Pontecoulant, Philippe Gustave Le
Doulcet, comte de, 1795-1874.
Souvenirs mititaires...

The Napoleon album; designed for the promotion
of trade. Salt Lake City, Magazine Printing Co.
[1893?]
[22] p. illus. 25 cm.

Cover title.
At head of title: Conference souvenir, October,
1893.

1. Napoléon I, Emperor of the French, 1769-
1821 - Iconography.

NN 0018919   NjP

Napoleon, an explanation of his theories of
government
see under   [Lullin de Châteauvieux,
Frédéric] 1772-1841.

Napoleon; an historical drama, in six acts.
London, C. Fox, 1842.
159 p.

NN 0018921   DLC NN

Napoleon and Goethe, description of Napoleon's
own copy of Werther
see under   [Laredo, Sarah de]

DC
203
.N3   Napoleon and his campaigns. Embracing a
       complete history of Bonaparte's great
       military operations throughout Europe, with
       the most important incidents of his private
       and political life. A graphic account of
       his army and his generals, and their
       unexampled military career, with a sketch of
       the French Revolution to which is added
       Bonaparte's last will and testament.
       Philadelphia, John E. Potter ₍1880?₎
       x, 422 p. illus. 20cm.

NN 0018923   GU PLF

C 203
3   Napoleon and his campaigns, embracing a complete
     history of Bonaparte's great military operations
     throughout Europe, with the most important inci-
     dents of his private and political life; a grap-
     hic account of his army and his generals, and
     their unexampled military career, with a sketch
     of the French revolution, to which is added
     Bonaparte's last will and testament. Phila-
     delphia, Keystone Pub., 1890.
     422, xp. front., illus. 20 cm.

     1. Napoleon I, Emperor of the French, 1769-
     1821. 2. France   - Hist. - Consulate
     and empire, 1799-   1815.

NN 0018924   GASC

Napoleon and his fellow travellers
see under   Shorter, Clement King,
1857-1926.

Napoleon and his marshals. Portraits and
autographs. With statements of their services.
Paris, ₍n.d.₎
27 ports. 36 1/2 cm.

NN 0018926   PBL

Napoleon and the Bourbons.   London, W. Hone,
1816.
16 p.   Port.

NN 0018927   MH

Napoleon, and the French people under his
empire
see under   Schlabrendorf, Gustav, graf
von, 1750-1824.

Napoleon and the marshals of the empire ...
see under   [Griswold, Rufus Wilmot]
1815-1857.

*FC8
B4688   Napoléon au champ de mai 1815. Discours en
B831m   vers.
         [Paris? 1815?]
         8p. 20cm.
         Caption title; signed at end: J.T.
         No.11 in a volume lettered on spine: Mélanges.
         Littérature.

NN 0018930   MH

Napoléon aux Invalides. Dédié à tous les Français. Paris,
F. Knab ₍1840₎
36 p. incl. front. plates, fold. maps. 23ᶜᵐ.

1. Napoléon I, emperor of the French, 1769-1821.

Library of Congress   DC212.N21   F-2319

NN 0018931   DLC

Napoleon banished

see under

Ussher, Sir Thomas, 1779-1848.

Napoleon Bonaparte.   London, 1823.
[6] p.   15 cm.   (Portraits and
biography of public characters, no. 6)

NN 0018933   RPB

Napoleon Bonaparte and his times;
including an historical sketch of the French
Revolution and the wars subsequent on that
event.   Glasgow, Blackie, Fullarton, 1829.
467p. port., maps. 22cm.

1.Napoleon I, Emperor of France
1769-1821 2.Europe. Hist. 1789-1815

NN 0018934   CoD

Napoleon Bonaparte and his times; including
an historical sketch of the French Revolution
and the wars subsequent on that event. Glasgow,
Blackie & Son, 1834.
467p. col. ports. 23cm.

NN 0018935   NcU

Napoléon Bonaparte and his times;
including an historical sketch of
the French Revolution and the wars
subsequent on that event.   Glasgow,
Blackie & son, 1838.
xvi, 467 p.   front.   22 cm.

NN 0018936   PLF

DC
203   Napoleon Bonaparte and his times; including an
.N3   historical sketch of the French Revolution and
       the wars subsequent on that event. Glasgow,
       Blackie & Son, 1841.
       xvi, 467 p. illus.

       1. Napoleon I, Emperor of the French, 1769-
       1821. 2. France--Hist.--1789-1815.

NN 0018937   INS

VOLUME 405

Napoleon Bonaparte as overcome by Marquis
Wellington...
     see under   [Voltz, Johann Michael] 1784-
1858.

... Napoleon Bonaparte. 1816 [New York, 1934]
     see under   Staël-Holstein, Anne Louise
Germaine (Necker) baronne de, 1766-1817.

Y825N161
I
     NAPOLEON Bonaparte; or, The fallen
monarch; a drama, in three acts. By
an Englishman.   Calcutta, 1819.

     6 p.l., 63 p.   15cm.

     1. Napoléon I. Drama. I. An English-
man.

NN   0018940   MnU NcU

Napoleon Bonaparte: sketches from his history. Adapted for the young. London, The Religious tract society;
Philadelphia, American Sunday-school union [1845]

124 p. incl. front., illus. 15ᶜᵐ.

1. Napoléon I, emperor of the French, 1769-1821.
               4-18202

Library of Congress   DC203.N21

NN   0018941   DLC

Napoléon Bonaparte. Souvenirs intimes de l'Empire
qui ne sont pas de Marco de Saint-Hilaire. Paris
[1848?]
4p.

MF-186 ---- Microfilm edition. 1958.

NN   0018942   ICRL

Napoleon Bonaparte und das französische volk
unter seinem consulate.
     see under   Schlabrendorf, Gustav, graf von,
1750-1824.

*pFB8
N1627
2815n
     Napoleon Buonaparte, und sein Anhang, in der
Gewalt der Engländer.
[Germany, 1815]

     plate. 18.5x23cm., mounted to 54.5x41cm.
Broadley E-65.
Engraving (hand-colored), unsigned.
A satire on Napoleon.

NN   0018944   MH

Napoleon Bonaparte's Book of fate
     see   Napoleon's Book of fate.

E
5
.N 16803
     NAPOLEON Bonapartes genealogie, med an-
maerkninger.   Kjøbenhavn, C. Steens forlag,
1830.

     16p. 18cm.   (with Louis Bonaparte, King
of Holland. Svar til Sir Walter Scott. 1829)

NN   0018946   ICN

Napoleon Buonaparte. Correct explanation of
the hieroglyphic portrait of Buonaparte
     see under   Voltz, Johann Michael]
1784-1858.

*pFB8
N1627
Z817n
     Napoleon Buonaparte. Sketched from the life
at St Helena, March 1817.
London, Published May 21, 1817, by F.P. Tomkins,
no. 53, New Bond street.

     plate. 27x19cm., mounted to 54.5x41cm.
Not in Broadley.
Engraving, unsigned.
A portrait, slightly caricatured.

NN   0018948   MH

DC203
.N243
     Napoleon Buonaparte nach seinem Leben und Wir-
ken, von seiner Jugend bis zu seiner Verban-
nung auf die Insel Elba. London, P. Rickley,
1815.
2 v. in 1.

     1. Napoléon I, Emperor of the French, 1769-
1821. 2. France--Hist.--1789-1815.

NN   0018949   ICU MnU

Napoleon Buonapartes geheime liebschaften
     see under   [Doris, Charles, de Bourges]

*
M1.
.S444
v.150
no.42
     Napoleon Buonapartes grand march.
Arranged for the piano forte. Philadelphia,
Geo. Willig, 171 Chesnut [sic] Street
[after 1819?]
     [1] p.   32cm.   [Sheet music collection, v. 150,
no. 42]
     Caption title.

     1. Marches (Piano).

NN   0018951   ViU

Napoléon captif à Sainte-Hélène. Mémorial
de Sir Hudson Lowe
     see under   Lowe, Sir Hudson, 1769-1844.

     Napoleon. Coleccion de anecdotas
autenticas relativas a este celebre
guerreo, a sus generales, oficiales
etc. Barcelona, I. Oliveres, [1834]
2 v.

NN   0018953   OC1

... Napoléon, d'après le Mémorial de Sainte-
Hélène...
     see under   Las Cases, Emmanuel, comte
de, 1766-1842.

Napoléon dans Balzac
     see under   Balzac, Honoré de, 1799-1850.

Napoléon dargestellt nach den besten quellen
von *7...
     see under   Becker, Gottfried Wilhelm]
1778-1854.

Napoleon den Store.   Kjøbenhavn, Thieles
Bogtrykkeri, 1859.
Illustr.

NN   0018957   MH

                                 2646.170
Napoleon III. als Meineidiger und Menschenschlächter angeklagt
und verurtheilt vor dem Forum des Weltgerichts. Offener Brief
an alle Nationen der Welt.
Berlin. Streerath. 1870. 16 pp. 8°.

     Signed B *--, G--- v.

F716 — Napoleon III. — Franco-German War, 1870, 1871.

NN   0018958   MB

Napoleon III., das politische Project
Heinrich's IV. gegen das Haus Oestreich und der
zukünftige europäische Areopag. Hamburg, Hoffmann und Campe, 1859.

     91 p.   18.5 cm.

NN   0018959   MH

NAPOLEON III; der mann der grössten attentat[
des neunzehnten jahrhunderts; von einem con-
servativen. Cöln, Peter Hammer, 1859.

     Pamphlet.

NN   0018960   MH

Napoleon III. in Ham und in Compiègne.
     See   under
[Bruckbräu, Friedrich Wilhelm, 1792-1874.]

4DC
1367
     Napoleon III, (Napoleon Ludwig Bon-
aparte) Präsident der französischen
Republik präsumtiver Kaiser der
Franzosen (rechtmässiger Thronerbe des
Kaisers); sein Leben, seine Schicksale
und sein Charakter, Geschichte des
Prozesses über die Aufstände Louis
Napoleons in Strassburg und Boulogne,
sowie seine Wahl zum Prästdentum der
Republik. Aus den besten französischer

     Quellen.   Leipzig, F. W. Goedsche,
1849.
     44 p.

NN   0018963   DLC-P4

VOLUME 405

Napoleon III. und die legitimen. Von ****. Schwerin, Oertzen & comp., 1860.
31 p. 19ᶜᵐ.

1. France—Pol. & govt.—1852-1870. 2. Europe—Politics—1848-1871. 3. Napoléon III, emperor of the French, 1808-1870. I. ****.

                36-32007

Library of Congress   DC277.3.N3
         [2]   944.07

NN 0018964   DLC

Napoleon III. und Preussen. Antwort eines deutschen Flüchtlings auf "Preussen in 1860" von Edmond About. London, A. Petsch & Co., 1860.
42 p. 12°.

NN 0018965   NN

Napoleon III und seine Geschichte Julius Cäsar's. Frankfurt a. M., F. Boselli (W. Rommel) 1865.
2 p. l., 47, [1] p. 18ᶜᵐ.

1. Napoléon III. Histoire de Jules César.

                18-20825

Library of Congress   DG261.N4

NN 0018966   DLC

NAPOLEON der Gaukler, oder: Glückseligkeit durch Zerstöhrung. [Leipzig?] 1814. viii, 48 p. 19cm.

673461A. 1. Napoleon I., emperor of the French, 1769-1821. 2. Germany—Hist., 1806-1815

NN 0018967   NN

YA 2843   Le Napoléon des écoles, par un ancien company d'armes... Paris, Eymery [184-]
152 p.

NN 0018968   DLC

Napoleon [; dessins de Jodel]. Paris: Tolmer [, 19—?]. col'd illus. obl. 8°.
  Unpaged.

1. Napoleon I, Bonaparte, emperor   of the French. 2. Jodel, illustrator.
N.Y.P.L.   August 31, 1933

NN 0018969   NN

Napoléon devant l'officialité de Paris
    see under   [Dudon, Paul] 1859-

Napoléon devant ses contemporains
    see under   Ader, Jean Joseph, 1796-1859.

The Napoleon dynasty
    see under   [Lester, Charles Edwards] 1815-1890.

DC216
.N3
Rare Bk
Coll

Наполеонъ, его родственники и исполнители воли его; историческое извѣстіе, взятое изъ тайнаго французскаго кабинета. Москва, Въ Тип. Н. С. Всеволожскаго, 1813.
14 p. port. 21 cm.

1. Bonaparte family.   *Title transliterated:* Napoleon, ego rodstvenniki i ispolniteli voli ego.

DC216.N3   57-51420

NN 0018973   DLC

DC203
.N24   Napoleon. Eine biographische skizze. Aus dem französischen übersezt und mit anmerkungen versehen ... Stuttgart und Tübingen, J.G.Cotta, 1821.
437,[1]p. front.(port.) 14cm.
Translated by K.F.Lebret.

1.Napoléon I,emperor of the French,1769-1821.

NN 0018974   ICU

---

*pFB8
N1627
Z806n   Napoleon. El primero y último, por la ira del cielo ...
[Madrid? 1814?]
broadside. illus. 40.5x27cm.,mounted & bd. to 50x40cm.
Not in Broadley.
Copy of Voltz's celebrated hieroglyphic portrait of Napoleon at head.
Dated in ms. by a contemporary hand: Año de 1814.
No.104 in a volume lettered on spine: Napoleonic cari-   catures.

NN 0018975   MH

Napoleön en Pit, of Wie zal ze gevieren? Opgesteld door den schrijver van het boek Napoleon. Uit het Hoogduitsch vertaald. Germaniën, 1805.
40 p. 8°.

NN 0018976   NN

AC.901
MS   Napoleon en la isla, romance, historico-comico-tragico, por Un patricio ... Valencia, Oficina del diario, 1809.
1 p. l. 11 p.

"Adventencia" signed: F.M.F. de R.

NN 0018977   OO DLC

Napoleon en la isla de Sta. Elena, escritor de su vida politica. Puebla, Imprenta liberal, 1820.
103 p. 14ᶜᵐ.
Caption title: Maximas politicas.
Preface signed: J. N. T.

1. Napoléon I, emperor of the French, 1769-1821.

                4-25183

Library of Congress   DC214.N22

NN 0018978   DLC NNC CU-B

Napoleon et Josephine; drame en 5 actes
    see under   [Dailliere, Julian] 1812-1887.

Soc
DC
790
A5
N3   Napoléon et l'Arc de triomphe du Carrousel. Paris, chez Gauthier, 1831.
10p. illus.

1. Arc du Carrousel. 2. Napoléon I, Emperor of the French, 1769-1821.

NN 0018980   FTaSU

Napoléon et la conquête du monde
    see under   [Geoffroy-Château, Louis Napoléon] 1803-1858.

Napoléon et la grande armée...
    see under Auguis, Pierre René, 1786-1846.

Soc
DC
203.9
N36   Napoléon et la médecine. [Catalogue de] l'Exposition organisée à la Salpêtrière du 3 au 10 octobre, 1954, à l'occasion des Entretiens de Bichat. [Paris, Expansion scientifique] 1954.
unpaged illus.

1. Napoléon I, Emperor of the French, 1769-1821. 2. Medicine, Military - France. I. Entretiens de Bichat, Paris, 1954.

NN 0018983   FTaSU

Napoleon et les Parthes
    see under Barbier, Louis Nicolas, 1799-1888.

Napoléon et ses contemporains
    see under Chambure, Laurent Auguste Pelletici de, 1789-1832.

Napoléon et ses neveux. Arrivée de Napoléon-Louis à Paris, son discours à l'Assemblée Nationale. Paris, 1848.
1 l. illus.

MF-186 ---- Microfilm edition. 1958.

NN 0018986   ICRL

Napoléon et Talma aux champs élysées
    see under [Bertu, Charles François]

944.05
N216n   **Napoleon**; extracts from the 'Times' and 'Morning Chronicle' 1815-1821 relating to Napoleon's life at St. Helena. London, A. L. Humphreys, 1901.
192 p. 24cm.

1. Napoléon I, emperor of the French, 1769-1821. 2. Napoléon I - Captivity, 1815-1821. 3. France - Hist. - Louis XVIII, 1815-1824. 4. Napoléon I - Elba and the 100 days, 1814-1815.

NN 0018988   NcU PSt CtY

VOLUME 405

[Napoleon forced into the grave by a military
world.]
[Germany? 1814]

*pFB8
N1627
Z806n

plate. 20.5x25cm.,mounted & bd.to 50x40cm.
Not in Broadley.
Engraving, unsigned & without title or
imprint; engraved on a stone in the lower right
corner is the date 1814.
No.18 in a volume lettered on spine:
Napoleonic caricatures.

NN   0018989   MH

Napoleon', Frantzia Birodalom tsászárának,
   's Olasz Ország királlyának élete
      see under   Nagy, Pál.

Napoleon Gallery.
   Catalogue of the Napoleon Gallery, now exhibiting...
New York: I. Sackett, 1851.   8 p.   8°.

1. Paintings.—Exhibitions, U. S.: N. Y.
N. Y. P. L.   August 13, 1914.

NN   0018991   NN

Napoleon gallery; or, illustrations of the
   life and times of the Emperor of France.
   Engraved by Reveil, and other eminent
   artists, from all the most celebrated pictures, etc. produced in France during
   the last forty years.   London, Tilt,
   1837.
   unpaged   chiefly illus.

Soc
DC
203.8
N3

   1. Napoleon I - Portraits, caricatures, etc.

NN   0018992   FTaSU CtY

The **Napoleon** gallery; or, Illustrations of the life and times of
the emperor of France. / Engraved by Réveil, and other eminent
artists, from all the most celebrated pictures, etc. produced in
France during the last forty years.   London: H. G. Bohn, 1846.
viii p., 89 l., 99 pl. (incl. front.)   16°.

Plates numbered irregularly.

1. Napoleon I., emperor of the French.   1769-1821.—Portraits and caricature. 2. Réveil, Achille, engraver.
N. Y. P. L.   December 24, 1915.

NN   0018993   NN MH CSmH

The **Napoleon** gallery; or, Illustrations of the life and
times of the emperor of France. Engraved by Reveil,
and other eminent artists, from all the most celebrated
pictures, etc. produced in France during the last forty
years. London, H. G. Bohn, 1852.

1 p. l., viii p., 88 l. 98 pl. (1 fold.; incl. front., ports.)   17½ᶜᵐ.
Plates numbered irregularly.

1. Napoléon I—Portraits, caricatures, etc.   I. Réveil, Étienne Achille,
b. 1800.

Library of Congress   DC203.8.N21   4—27183

NN   0018994   DLC OO MiU CSmH CtY PWW

Napoleon gallery; or, Illustrations of the life
& times of the Emperor of France engraved by
Reveil & other... artists, fr. the most celebrated
pictures, etc... Lond., Tilt, 1887.
unp.

NN   0018995   PU

The **Napoleon** gallery; or, Illustrations of the life an
times of the emperor of France engraved by Revei
and other eminent artists, from all the most celebrated
pictures in France.   Boston, Estes & Lauriat [1888]
vi p., 87 l.   95 pl.   23½ᶜᵐ.

1. Napoléon I—Portraits, caricatures, etc.   I. Réveil, Achille.

Library of Congress   DC203.8.N215   4—27185

NN   0018996   DLC CoU PP ScCleU

Napoleon Hill's magazine; a golden rule monthly edited by
Napoleon Hill. v. 1–2; Apr. 1921–May/June 1923. [Chi-
cago, Hill publishing trust, etc., 1921–22; New York, Hill
publishing trust, 1922–23]
2 v. illus. 30ᶜᵐ.
No numbers were issued for May and Dec. 1921.
Vol. 1, no. 1–11 and v. 2, no. 1–2 have title: Napoleon Hill's magazine.
No more published?

I. Hill, Napoleon, ed.

Library of Congress   AP2.N14   29–4279

NN   0018997   DLC NN

Napoleon: his army and his generals: their unexampled military   2659a.136
career. With a sketch of the French Revolution. By an American.
New York. Leavitt, Trow & Co. 1847. 422, x pp. Portraits.
Plates. 12°.

E3307 — Napoleon I. — France. Hist. Revolution. 1789–1795.

NN   0018998   MB OrCS CtY PPL MH

Napoleon: his army and his generals; their unexampled military career. With a sketch of the French revolution, by an
American. Illustrated with numerous elegant engravings.
New York, Leavitt, Trow & co., 1848.
x, [11]–422, x p. front., illus. 19½ᶜᵐ.
"This work advances no greater claim to public consideration than
that of a compilation ... the compiler has made numerous extracts from
the works of Scott, Lockhart, Clarke, and other English authors."—Pref.

1. Napoleon I, emperor of the French, 1769–1821. 2. France—History—
Consulate and empire, 1799–1815. 3. Europe—History—1789–1815.

NN   0018999   ViU NN CU

Napoleon; his army and his generals...
New York, 1851.

NN   0019000   KyLx

Napoleon: his army and his generals their
unexampled military career... by an American
New York, Leavitt, 1853.
   422 p.   col. plates.   19.5 cm.

NN   0019001   PLF

Napoleon: his army and his generals; their unexampled military career. With a sketch of the French revolution, by an
American. Illustrated with numerous elegant engravings.
New York, Leavitt & Allen, 1854.
x, [11]–422, x p. front., illus. 19½ᶜᵐ.
"This work advances no greater claim to public consideration than
that of a compilation ... the compiler has made numerous extracts from
the works of Scott, Lockhart, Clarke, and other English authors."—Pref.

1. Napoleon I, emperor of the French, 1769–1821. 2. France—History—
Consulate and empire, 1799–1815. 3. Europe—History—1789–1815.

                                             A 40–2810

Georgetown univ. Library   DC202.1.A35
   for Library of Congress   [2]

NN   0019002   DGU NN

NAPOLEON: his army and his generals: their
unexampled military career. With a sketch
of the French revolution, by an American.
New York, Leavitt & Allen, 1855.

   Plates.

NN   0019003   MH

Napoleon; his army and his generals: their unexampled military
career. With a sketch of the French Revolution. By an American. New York: Leavitt & Allen, 1856.   x, (1)12–422, x p.,
6 pl.   12°.

1. Napoleonic wars. 2. France—   History: Revolution.
N. Y. P. L.   January 15, 1914.

NN   0019004   NN FTaSU

Napoleon; his army & his generals; their unexampled military career, by an American. N. Y.,
World, 1875.
   422 p.

NN   0019005   PP

Napoleon, his army and his generals; their
unexampled military career. With a sketch of
the French Revolution, by an American. New York
World publishing house, 1876.

   Spine: The world edition.

NN   0019006   MH

Napoleon: his army and his generals;
   their unexampled military career.
   With a sketch of the French
   revolution, by an American. New
   York, World Publishing House, 1877.
   [11]–422 p. illus. 20 cm.

DC
202
.1
.A35
1877

   1. Napoleon I, emperor of the
French, 1769–1821. 2. France—History
—Consulate and empire, 1799–1815.
3. Europe—History—1789–1815.

NN   0019007   OKentU

Microfilm
9488

Napoleon his own historian. Extracts from the original manuscript of Napoleon Bonaparte, by an American.
London, H. Colburn, 1818.
8, 140 p. 22ᶜᵐ.
Pub. in French under title: Napoléon peint par lui-même ...

   L. C. Copy Replaced by Microfilm

1. Napoléon I, emperor of the French, 1769–1821.

Library of Congress   DC214.5.N22   4–35151

NN   0019008   DLC C

VOLUME 405

Napoleon his own historian.   Extracts from the original manuscript of Napoleon Bonaparte, by an American. London, H. Colburn, 1818.

8, 140 p.   22ᶜᵐ.

Pub. in French under title: Napoléon peint par lui-même ...

1. Napoléon I, emperor of the French, 1769–1821.   4-25181

Library of Congress   DC214.5.N22

NN   0019009   ICU PP NcU PLF CtY OrCS

Napoleon il grande, trad. del tedesco. Vienna, 1814.

8°.

NN   0019010   NN

944.05
N216z   **Napoléon** immortalisé, ou, Relation exacte de la présence d'esprit, des vertus et des bienfaits de cet homme extraordinaire. Par un de ses aides-de-camp.   Paris, Camuzeaux, 1835.

346p. 22cm.

1. Napoléon I, emperor of the French, 1769–1821.

NN   0019011   NcU

Napoleon in Dresden
      see under   [Dressler von Scharfenstein, F   von]

Napoleon in Dresden und auf Elba
      see under   [Dressler von Scharfenstein, F.   von]

Napoleon in exile, described in unpublished letters by British Officers
      see under   Price, Eleanor Catherine.

Napoleon in the other world
      see under   Zongo-Tee-Foh-Tchi, pseud.

DC203
.N25   **Napoleon** intime, tr. from the French.   Privately printed for subscribers only. [n. p., n. d.]

vii, 223 p. col. front., facsim. 23ᶜᵐ.

"This book bears no author's name for it is not the creation of any one."—Pref.

"Confession of General Bonaparte to the Abbé Maury [by Jean Sarrazin]": p. [135]-223.

1. Napoléon I, emperor of the French, 1769–1821.

NRU IEdS
NN   0019016   ICU OCU MH NjP AAP OClW NN CSmH CtY

Napoleon I, imperatul Francezilor; viata si faptele lui, de un francez; traducere de L, I. Nadejde. Bucarest, Alcalay, n.d. [192 p. il. por.]

I. Nadejde, L. I   , tr.

NN   0019017   OCl

Napoleon Lajoie's official base ball guide
      see under   Lajoie, Napoleon, 1875–

Napoléon ... la république, le consulat, l'empire, Sainte-Hélène. Paris, Hachette & cᴵᵉ [1895]

[160] p. illus., port., facsim. 28½ x 36ᶜᵐ.

Title vignette.
More than 600 reproductions of paintings, engravings, etc., each accompanied by brief descriptive text.   2-26610

Library of Congress. no.   DC2038.N22.

NN   0019019   DLC CtY PLatS

Napoleon le grande[!]...
      see under   [Rowlandson, Thomas] 1756-1827.

Napoléon le premier et le dernier...
      see under   [Voltz, Johann Michael] 1784-1858.

Napoleon library, De Paul university
      see
De Paul university, *Chicago. Library. Napoleon collection.*

NAPOLÉON Louis Bonaparte à Paris. P.,[1848]

Broadside. Woodcuts.

NN   0019023   MH

DC256
.8
N47   Napoléon, Louis XVIII et Bonaparte.   [Paris? Le Normant, 1815?]

56 p.   [Bound with: Nettement, Philippe. Le second retour des Bourbons. 1815]

Caption title.
Binder's title: Retour des Bourbons en 1815. [t.] 2.

1. Napoleon I, emperor of the French, 1769-1821. 2. Louis XVIII, king of France, 1755-1824.

NN   0019024   CU

The **Napoleon** Mining Co., Quartz mining district, Gunnison Co., Col....St. Louis, Woodward & Tiernan Printing Co. [1890?]

7 p. 23 cm.

Cover title.

1. Napoleon Mining Company.   2. Mines and mineral resources - Colorado.

NN   0019025   NjP

944.05
N216BcaS   **Napoleón.** Monografías históricas de la "Historia del mundo en la edad moderna," edición española de "The Cambridge modern history", publicada por la Universidad de Cambridge con la colaboración de los principales historicadores de Europa y América.   Barcelona, Ramon Sopena [19--]

2 v.

1. Napoleón I, Emperor of the French, 1769-1821.   I. Cambridge modern history.   II. Historia del mundo en la edad   moderna.

NN   0019026   ICarbS

Le Napoléon noir
      see under   [Gozlan, Leon] d. 1866.

865N154
On   **Napoleon,** ó el verdadero D. Quixote de la Europa, ó sean comentarios criticopatriótico-burlescos á varios decretos de Napoleon y su hermano José, distribuidos en dos partes y cincuenta capítulos, y escritos por un español amante de su patria y rey desde primeros de fabrero de 1809 hasta fines del mismo año. Madrid, Impr. de Ibarra, 1813.

8v. in 4. illus. 15cm.

Attributed to   José Clemente Carnicero.

NN   0019028   IU OO NcD

DC197
N2   **Napoleon Pamphlets.**
v.p., v.d.
39 vols. 8 vo.

(Assembled by L.C. from various sources)

NN   0019029   DLC

Napoléon par l'image populaire. Portraits, scènes, batailles. Réimpression sur bois du temps; coloris en conformité du coloris primitif.
Épinal,1912-13. 2 portfolios of 60 col.pl. 50x34 cm.
"Édition spéciale de l'Imagerie d'Épinal fondée en 1796.".
"Cet ouvrage a été tiré à trois cents exemplaires numérotés à la presse. Exemplaire no.165." v.2.

NN   0019030   CtY

Napoléon peint par lui-même.   Extraits du véritable manuscrit de Napoléon Bonaparte, par un Américain. Londres, Colburn, 1818.

viii, 108 p. 22ᶜᵐ.

Pub. in English under title: Napoleon his own historian ...

1. Napoléon I, emperor of the French, 1769-1821.   4-25182

Library of Congress   DC214.5.N21

NN   0019031   DLC CSt DeWI NIC

Napoléon, poème.   [Paris, 1836]
      see under   [Faucher, Léon Léonard Joseph] 1803-1854.

Napoléon, poème en dix chants
      see under   [Lorquet, Hubert Louis] b. 1768.

VOLUME 405

Napoleon portrayed. An epic heroic poem. In six cantos.
Canto I.   London, Saunders and Otley, 1841.
46 p.   17cm.

No more published?

NN   0019034   CU

DC   Napoléon I. à l'île d'Elbe; San Martino.
211   Pistoia, G. Flori, 1901.
G53   16 p.   25cm.

Bound with Giunti, Benvenuto. Il V. maggio
a Portoferraio. Pisa, 1902.

1. Napoléon I--Elba and the Hundred Days.
2. Elba--Hist. 3. Elba--Descr. & trav.
I. Title: San Martino.

NN   0019035   NIC CtY

Napoleon I. et l'Europe
see under   Doin, Alexandre.

Napoleon I et son temps. [Autographes et
gravures. A collection of 63 autograph
letters, 205 portraits (mostly colored)
and 13 plates illustrating scenes in the
emperor's life]   Paris, n.d.
unp. illus. plates. ports. (mostly col)
34 x 47 cm.
Autographs certified by Noel Charavay.

NN   0019037   RPB

944.05   Napoléon 1.; tableaux historiques.
N16   ¿Paris?, n.p., 19--?¿
C   1v. of 8 illus.   20 x 25cm.
N162
19--   Pictures only. No explanatory text.
            At head of title: Historical Board.

1. Napoleon I. Portraits, caricatures,
etc. 1. Title: Tableaux historiques.

NN   0019038   KU

Napoléon, sa famille, ses amis, ses généraux, ses
ministres et ses contemporains ...
see under   [Lamothe-Langon, Etienne Léon,
baron de] 1786-1864.

Napoléon, sa naissance, son éducation, sa carrière militaire, son gouvernement, sa chute, son
exil et sa mort... Par M. O******
Paris, 1821. 17cm.

NN   0019040   CtY

944.05   Napoleon; sborník prací. ¿Redigoval J. M.
N16Wnapo Augusta¿   Praha ¿Napoleonská společnost¿
         1932.
         279p. illus., fold.map, ports. 22cm.
         (Napoleonská bibliotheka, sv.1)

Articles in Czech, French, Russian, Italian,
Polish and Serbo-Croatian. Summaries in
French or Czech.

1. Napoléon I, Emperor of the French, 1769-
1821. I. Augusta, J. M., ed.

NN   0019041   IU

Napoléon, seine Generale und Soldaten.   Leipzig,
C. B. Lorck, 1846-47.
3 v. front. illus. ports.   26 cm.
Vol. 1 by P. M. Laurent, vol. 3 by Hippolyte
Bellange.
Contents. - v. 1. Geschichte des Kaisers Napoléon. - v. 2. Die Generale der französischen Republik und des Kaiserreichs. - v. 3. Die Soldaten
der französischen Republik und des Kaiserreichs.
1. France. Armée - Biography. 2. France -
Hist. - 1789-1815. I. Laurent, Paul Mathieu,
called de l'Ardèche, 1793-1877.

NN   0019042   NcU

Napoleon Smith
see   Arkell, William J

Napoleon Society.
Napoleon. Paris, 1895.
16 v. illus., ports.

1. Napoleon I, Emperor of the French, 1769-1821.
2. France - History - 1789-1815.

NN   0019044   WaU

The Napoleon songster. New York, St. Louis;
Nafis, Cornish, n. d.
33 ¿1¿ p.]^ 1/2 cm.

Without music.
Caption-title: The American songster.
Portrait on cover.

NN   0019045   MiD

Napoleon III y el clero ... San Salvador, Imprenta del gobierno, 1860.
21 p., 1 l. 20½ᵐ.
"De el 'Suplemento al comercio' de Valparaiso, de 15 de marzo de 1860."

1. Napoléon III, emperor of the French, 1808-1873. 2. Church and
state in France.
44-43291
Library of Congress   DC279.N3

NN   0019046   DLC

NAPOLEON I. [187-?].

Cut from the Encyclopaedia Britannica, 9th ed.
vol.17, pp.192-226.
25 cm.
Signed J. R. S.

NN   0019047   MH

Napoléon I, Emperor of the French, Scrap-book.
n.o., n.d.
1 fac-sim. 30 pl., 94 port.   f°.

NN   0019048   NN

Napoleon, the first emperor of France
see under   Thomason, Henry D
1858-

X944
N19   ... Napoleon the Great's Book of 'fate'. Without
consulting which he never went to battle.
Copied from the French.
¿50¿ p.

Manuscript.
At head of title: Agnes Glenalmond Coleman.
February 14th 1878.
"Fortune telling by cards": p. ¿41-50¿

1. Napoleon I, emperor of the French, 1769-1821.
I. Title: Book of fate   II. Title: Fortune telling
by cards.

NN   0019050   NNC

Napoleon the little in a rage with his French eagle!
see under   [Rowlandson, Thomas] 1756-1827.

Napoleon the Third and his court, by a retired diplo-
matist. London, J. Maxwell and company, 1865.
iv, 348 p. 19ᵐᵐ.
Preface signed : H. S.

1. Napoléon III, emperor of the French, 1808-1873. 2. France—Court
and courtiers.   4-25791

Library of Congress   DC280.4.S12

NN   0019052   DLC

Napoleon the Third at the tribunal of history. Translated from the
French. 3d edition.
London. Simpkin, Marshall & Co. 1871. 16 pp. 16°.

F4330 — Napoleon III.

NN   0019053   MB OC1W

Napoleon the Third: review of his life,
character, and policy; with extracts from his
writings and speeches, and references to contemporary opinions. By a British officer.
London, Longman, Brown, Green, Longmans, & Roberts,
1857.
xi, 426 p.   23ᶜᵐ.

1. Napoléon III, emperor of the French, 1808-1873. I.
A British officer.

NN   0019054   MiU MnU MB PPL

Napoleon III, Musée, Paris.

see

Paris. Musée national du Louvre.

38-257

Napoleon transcripts, 1790-1853.
27 items. handwritten. (photocopies)
Twenty-one letters of Napoleon Bonaparte to Josephine,
Talleyrand, and others, 1790-1814; and six letters of
Letizia Bonaparte, Eugene de Beauharnais, Thomas
Jefferson, and Robert E. Lee.

1. Bonaparte family. 2. Europe—Politics—1789-1815.
3. France—For. rel.—1789-1815. 4. France—Hist.—
1789-1815. 5. France—Hist.—Revolution, 1792-1799.
I. Barras, Paul François Jean Nicolas, vicomte de, 1755-
1829. II. Beauharnais, Eugène de, prince d'Eichstätt,
1781-1824. III. Berthier, Louis Alexandre, prince de
Neufchâtel et de Wagram, 1753-1815. IV. Bonaparte,
Maria Letizia (Ramolino) 1750-1836. V. Humboldt,
Alexander, freiherr von,   1769-1859. VI. Jefferson,
Thomas, Pres. U.S.,   1743-1826. VII.

NN   0019055   ViU

VOLUME 405

NAPOLÉON III devant les catholiques. Paris, E.Dentu,1867.

Pamphlet.

NN 0019057   MH

Napoleon III et l'Europe en 1867
see under   Bauër, Marie Bernard, 1829-1898.

Napoléon III et la France libérale...
see under   Senneval, C   de.

Napoléon III et la politique secrète du Second
Empire. - "Extrait de Mémoires secrets."
Bruxelles, 1868.
68 p.   8°.   [In "Brochures diverses, 1860-1869"]

NN 0019060   CtY

Napoléon III et la Prusse.   Paris, 1866.
32 p.   8°.   [In "Brochures diverses, 1860-1869"]

NN 0019061   CtY

Napoléon III, et son armée
see under   [Lédot-   jeune] ed.

NAPOLÉON III, la Pologne, et Alfred Ier
l'Angleterre. Paris, E.Dentu, 1862.

pp.30.

NN 0019063   MH

Napoleon III, roi des Belges! Le dossier Lessinnes
see under   L'Indépendance belge.

Napoléon III, sauveur de l'Italie. 1866
see under   Bonaparte, Pierre Napoléon, 1851-1881.

Napoléon III: tragédie en quatre actes et en vers,
pour être représentée dans cinquante ans; par
un inconnu. Nouv. éd. Paris, 1877.
72 p.   12°. (In "Théâtre", 11)

NN 0019066   CtY

Napoléon typographe
see under   Herhan, L   E

Napoleon und Laura, oder Das schöne mädchen von
Orgon. (Ganz frei nach dem französischen)
(*In* Pantheon. Stuttgart, 1831. 17½ᶜᵐ. v. 24, p. [83]-120)

1. Title.

CA 17-2479 Unrev'd

Library of Congress   PT1337.P3

NN 0019068   DLC

Napoleon und das Vergissmeinnicht ...
[Nuremberg, 1814]

*pFB8
N1627
Z806n

plate. 24.5x40cm., mounted & bd.to 50x40cm.
Broadley E-79.
Engraving, unsigned.
A satire on Napoleon's exile to Elba.
No.65 in a volume lettered on spine:
Napoleonic caricatures.

NN 0019069   MH

Napoleon unter den Händen der Aerzte.
by L.Schlemmer in Nürnberg.[1814]

*pFB8
N1627
Z806n

plate. 18.5x22.5cm.,mounted & bd.to 50x40cm.
Broadley E-83.
Engraving (hand colored), unsigned.
A satire on Napoleon.
No.69 in a volume lettered on spine:
Napoleonic caricatures.

NN 0019070   MH

... Napoleon unüberwindlich ...
in Wien herrausgegebn.[1813]

*pFB8
N1627
Z806n

broadside. illus. 33x19.5cm.,mounted & bd.to
50x40cm.
Not in Broadley or Schulze.
Large engraving (unsigned) at head, with 14
lines of verse following. Title from caption
under engraving. Verses begin: Vivat, Dir guten
Kaiser Franz! ...
The caption under the engraving explains
numbered figures. The number "1." precedes
"Napoleon".
A satire on   Napoleon and Marie Louise.
No.66 in a vol-   ume lettered on spine:
Napoleonic carica-   tures.

NN 0019071   MH

Napoléon-Vendée
see
La Roche-sur-Yon, *France.*

Napoleon von Corsica bis St. Helena; original
illustrationen nach berühmten gemälden von Meiss-
onnier, David, Vernet, Delaroche, Gerome, Gerard,
Gros und Steuben... Hamburg, Hansaf n.d.]
192 p.

NN 0019073   PP

Napoleon vor seinen Zeitgenossen
see under   Ader, Jean Joseph, 1796-1859.

The **Napoleonade**; or, Visions of Ham. A poem in eight
cantos (or vigils) London, Printed for the author [by
Cassell, Petter, Galpin & co.] 1879.
191, [1] p. 19ᶜᵐ.

1. Napoléon III, emperor of the French, 1808-1873.

16-981

Library of Congress   PR3991.A1N35

NN 0019075   DLC

[Napoleonana, 1815-1818.   n.p. 18   ]
1 v. (various pagings) illus. map. 21cm.

Title from spine.

1. Napoléon I, emperor of the French, 1769-1821.

NN 0019076   NcU

[Napoleonana. Extracted from various English
periodicals. n.p., n.d.]
1 v. (various pagings) port. 22cm.

Title from binder's title.

1. Napoléon I, emperor of the French, 1769-1821.

NN 0019077   NcU

[Napoleonana. Miscellaneous. n.p. 18]
1 v. (various pagings) col. front. 22cm.

Title from spine.

1. Napoléon I, emperor of the French, 1769-1821.

NN 0019078   NcU

Napoleone, Arthur.
See
Napoleão, Arthur, 1843-1925.

Napoleone, Joannes.
Carmen lustrale ... in certamine poetico
Hoeufftiano magna laude ornatum.   Amstelodami,
Academia regia disciplinarum nederlandica, 1928.
8 p.   26 cm.   (K. Akademie van wetenschappen, Amsterdam. Certamina poeseos
latinae, 1928)

NN 0019080   CtY PPAmP

Napoleone; rivista storica. 1-[2] anno.   Milano,
Curti, 1914-1915.
2 v.   25 cm.   Bi-monthly.
No more published.
1. Napoléon I, emperor of the French, 1769-
1821. - Period. 2. France - History - 1789-1815 -
Period.

NN 0019081   NjP

DC
211
N366
1831

NAPOLEONE a S. Elena; continuazi alla sua
vita politica e militare, narrata al tribunale di Cesare,Alessandro e Federigo
II. Londra, Tip. D. L. Ayné, 1831.
3 v. in 1. 15 cm.

1. Napoléon I, Emperor of the French,
1769-1821 - Captivity - 1815-1821.

NN 0019082   CaBVaU

*pFB8
N1627
Z814n

Napoleone all' Elba.
[Italy, 1814]

plate. 15.5x22.5cm.
Broadley F-41.
Engraving, unsigned.
A satire on Napoleon's exile at Elba.

NN 0019083   MH

VOLUME 405

*pFB8
N1627
Z816n

Napoleone all' isola di S. Elena ...
in Bassano [1816?]

plate. 22x32cm.,mounted to 54.5x41cm.
Not in Broadley.
Engraving, unsigned.
A satire on Napoleon's exile at St. Helena.

NN   0019084   MH

---

*pFB8
N1627
Z816n2

Napoleone che fa la rivista all' isola di
S. Elena ...
Bassano [1816?]

plate. 22x32cm.,mounted to 54.5x41cm.
Not in Broadley.
Engraving, unsigned.
A satire on Napoleon's exile at St. Helena.

NN   0019085   MH

NAPOLEONE III e l'Italia,ad uso degl'Italiani. Torino,tipog.Cerutti,Derossi e Dusso,
1860.

pp.56.

NN   0019086   MH

Napoleone III e l'Italia e la civiltà
cattolica; ossia, La vera situazione
dello Stato papale. [n.p.] Tip.italiana,
1859.
125 p.

1.Napoléon III, emperor of the
French, 1808-1873.

NN   0019087   NjP NN MH

Napoleone III in Italia
    see under   Maillot, Thomas Jules Richard,
1825-1899.

NAPOLEONE III.,l'Inghilterra e l'Italia;
discorso critico di C.M.R. [Bruxelles,1861.]

pp.40.
Half title-page serves as title-page.

NN   0019089   MH

Napoleonic and French revolution relics
    see under   Fowler, Charles Evan, 1867-

Napoleonic miscellany.
[n.p., n.d.]

DC197
5
.N3

NN   0019091   DLC

... The Napoleonic period. Edited by James Harvey Robinson ... Philadelphia, Pa., The Department of history of
the University of Pennsylvania; London, P. S. King & son,
1895.

cover-title, 32 p. 21½ cm. (Translations and reprints from the
original sources of European history. vol. II, no. 2)

CONTENTS.—I. Extracts from the Memoires of Miot de Melito.—II.
The treaties of Campo Formio and of Lunéville: The secret articles of
Campo Formio. The peace of Lunéville.—III. The dissolution of the
Holy Roman empire: Napoleon's note to the German Diet, August 1,
1806. The abdication of Francis II.—IV. Documents relating to the

continental system: English note to the representatives of neutral
powers, May 16, 1806. The Berlin decree. The English order in council of November 11, 1807. The Milan decree.—V. The Prussian reform
edict of October, 1807.—VI. Decree reuniting the Papal dominions to
the French empire.—VII. Bibliography.

1. France—Hist.—Consulate and empire, 1799-1815—Sources.
I. Robinson, James Harvey, 1863-   ed.

D101.P4   vol. 2, no. 2   C D 27—79

NN   0019093   DLC NNC MoU MiU OO OCU

... The Napoleonic period. [Revised. Edited by
James Harvey Robinson. Philadelphia, Pa.,
The Department of history of the University
of Pennsylvania, 1902]
32 p. 21½cm. (Translations and reprints from the
original sources of European history. vol. II, no. 2)
Caption title.
Bibliography: p. 32.
CONTENTS.—I. Extracts from the memoires of Miot de
Melito.—II. The treaties of Campo Formio and of Lune-
ville.—III. The dissolution of the Holy Roman empire.—
IV. Documents relating to the continental system.—V.
The Prussian reform edict of October, 1807.—VI. Decree
reuniting the papal dominions to the French empire.
1. France—Hist.—Consulate and empire, 1799-1815—
Sources. I. Robinson, James Harvey, 1863-1936,
ed. II. Ser.

NN   0019094   ViU

La Napoleonide, poème en douze chants...
    see under   [Peyre-Ferry, Alexandre Rene
Francois]

DC
157
E14

Les Napoléonides ou les forfanteries
politiques et militaires de Buonaparte.
Paris, Charles, 1814.
58 p.

[Signed: S.M.]

NN   0019096   MBU

An
A100
841n
Stark
Lib'y

Napoleonis reliquiae, a poem in six cantos, with
notes. London, J. Hatchard and Son, 1841.
4p.l.,xvijp.,1l.,152p. front.(port.), pl.
22½cm.

"Printed at Rouen by Nicétas Periaux."
With this is bound The battle of the nations;
as revealed in Daniel's last vision. London,
1853.

1. Napoléon I, Emperor of the French, 1769-
1821-Poetry.

NN   0019097   TxU MoU

Le Napoleonium. Monographie du Louvre et des
Tuileries reunis, avec une notice historique
et archeologique ...
    see under   [Leconte, Emile]

Napoleonkalender und Gedenkbuch der
Befreiungskriege auf das Jahr 1813
    see under   Kircheisen, Friederich Max,
1877-1933.

Napoleons afresa till Elba
    see under   [Fabry, Jean Baptiste Germain]
1780-1821.

---

*pFB8
N1627
Z814n2

Napoleons Ankunft in der Unterwelt.
[Germany, 1814?]

plate. 24x31.5cm.,mounted to 41x54.5cm.
Broadley E-85.
Engraving (hand-colored), unsigned.
No.19 of an unidentified series.
A satire on the fall of Napoleon.

NN   0019101   MH

Napoleon's appeal to the British nation, on
his treatment at Saint Helena
    see under   Napoleon I, Emperor of the
French, 1769-1821.

Napoléon's argument for the divinity of Christ,
and the scriptures ...
    see under   Napoleon I, Emperor of the
French, 1769-1821.

---

*pFB8
N1627
Z806n

Napoleons betrübte Augenblicke vor der
Einschiffung auf die Insel Elba ...
Wöhrd an Nürnberg bei C.Riedel.[1814]

plate. 20x23cm.,mounted & bd.to 50x40cm.
Not in Broadley or Schulze.
Engraving (hand-colored), unsigned.
A satire on Napoleon's exile to Elba.
No.72 in a volume lettered on spine:
Napoleonic caricatures.

NN   0019104   MH

Napoleon's book of fate. [n.p., n.d.]
Pp. [8]   18.8x10.6cm.

NN   0019105   CaOTP

---

531. NAPOLEON'S BOOK OF FATE. [Woodcut.]
W. & T. Fordyce, Printers & Publishers, 15
Grey street, Newcastle. n.d.
17 x 9.5 cm. 24 p.   * KVD p.v.16, no.24
In prose.

NN   0019106   NN

Ib94
tl
2

Napoleon's book of fate. C.Goulden,printer,
Guildhall street,Canterbury.[ca.1860?]
cover-title,[8]p. 19cm.
Caption title: Oraculum.
Pamphlet

NN   0019107   CtY

Napoleon's Book of fate.
Napoleon Bonaparte's Book of fate.   Glasgow [18—]   24 p.
15½cm.

829737. 1. Fortune telling.   2. Proverbs. I. Title.   *Revised*
N. Y. P. L.   *January 9, 1939*

NN   0019108   NN MnU ICN

Napoleon's book of fate, captured at the Battle of
Leipsic, with interpretations of dreams. The
original edition. London, the Booksellers,
[18-?]
vi, 7-256 p.   1 port. illus.   16°.

NN   0019109   NN

VOLUME 405

Napoleon's book of fate.
see also Kirchenhoffer, Hermann.
The book of fate
and
Napoleon's dream book and book of fate
and
Napoleon the Great's Book of fate.
and also Napoleon's Book of fate.
The cabinet: or, Philosopher's masterpiece.

Napoleon's centenary and the verdict of posterity, 1869.
London: The Peace Society, 1869. 16 pp. 8º

NN 0019111 NN

Soc
DC
230
T5
N3713
Napoleon's conduct towards Prussia since
the Peace of Tilsit. From the original
documents published under the authority
of the Prussian government. Translated
from the German. London, Printed for
Henry Colburn, 1814.
84p. port.

1. Treaty of Tilsit, 1807. 2. France -
For. rel. - Prussia. 3. Prussia - For. rel.
- France.

NN 0019112 FTaSU CtY NN PLF

B13
525
3-4
... Napoleon's court and cabinet of St.Cloud;
in a series of letters from a gentleman at
Paris to a nobleman in London ... Philadelphia,
G. Barrie & sons[1899?]
2v. col.fronts.,plates,ports. 21½cm.
(Secret memoirs of the courts of Europe from the
16th to the 19th century, v.III-IV)
Plates accompanied by guard sheets with
descriptive letterpress.
"Imperial edition."
Caption title: The secret history of the court
and cabinet of St.Cloud.

NN 0019113 CtY KyLoU PV

... Napoleon's court and cabinet of St. Cloud in a series of
letters from a gentleman at Paris to a nobleman in London ...
Philadelphia, G. Barrie & son [19--?]
v. col. fronts., plates, ports. (1 col.) 22½cm. (*Half-title:* Secret
memoirs of the courts of Europe from the 16th to the 19th century.
Vol. III, IV)
Title in red and black.
Plates and portraits accompanied by guard sheets, some with descriptive letterpress.
"This edition, printed on Japanese vellum paper, is limited to one
thousand numbered copies, no. 527."
1. Napoléon I, emperor of the French, 1769-1821. 2. France. Court
and courtiers.

Printed by Wesleyan   University Library

NN 0019114 CtW ViU

Napoleon's dream-book and book of fate containing
Napoleon's celebrated oraculum fortune-telling
by tea-leaves and dreams with their interpretation; ... including a sketch of Napoleon's
career and exile. New York, Dick & Fitzgerald
[190-?]
p. 3-66 16º.

NN 0019115 NN

Napoleon's dream-book and book of fate
see also Napoleon's book of fate.

Napoleon's dream book, containing full, plain and **accu-**
rate explanations of fortune-telling by dreams, **visions**
and reveries ... Comp. from original sources. Together with an anecdotal account of remarkable **visions**
and apparitions ... New York, Wehman bros., *1915.
127 p. 18ᵐ.

1. Dreams.

Library of Congress   BF1091.N17   15-7319

NN 0019117 DLC

Napoleon's European campaigns, 1796-1815
see under Maycock, Frederick William
Orby, 1877- comp.

Napoleons feldzug in Russland, 1812
see under Chambray, Georges, marquis
de, 1783-1850.

Napoleons feldzug 1796. Ein beitrag zu der frage,
inwieweit das feldherrngenie der ausbildung
bedarf. [Berlin, E.S. Mittler und sohn, 1889]
p. [129]-148 . fold. plan. 24 cm. (**Beiheft**
zum militär-wochenblatt. 1889, drittes heft.
[pt. 2])
Caption title.
1. Napoléon I - Italian campaign, 1796-1797.

NN 0019120 CU

Napoleon's grandnephew the bringer of peace
see under Kallionistes, pseud.

Napoleon's grave, a poem ...
see under [Furman, Garrit] 1782-1848.

Napoleons grosse auction montags den 18. januar d.
jahres und an den folgenden tagen früh von 9 bis 11 uhr
und nachmittags von 3 bis 5 uhr in Paris gehalten von
K. Monach, kaiserl. königl. auctionator in Paris. Aus
dem französischen mit bemerkungen. Paris, K. K. Staats-
druckerei [i. e. Leipzig, Rein, 1814]
32 p. 19ᶜᵐ.

1. Napoléon I—Satire. I. Monach, K., pseud.

                                                    18-9340

Library of Congress   DC203.9.N3

NN 0019123 DLC

Z839.5N162
I
Napoleons himmel på jorden; eller,
Continentalsystemet. Ofversättning.
Stockholm, Tryckt hos A. Gadelius, 1813.

27 p. 29cm.

1. Napoléon I. Drama.

NN 0019124 MnU

Napoleons lefnadshistoria
see under [Lullin de Châteauvieux,
Frédéric] 1772-1841.

Napoleon's maxims of war
see under Napoléon I, emperor of the
French, 1769-1821.

4DQ
161
Napoleons Misshandlungen der Schweiz,
ein historischer Commentar zu der von
den hohen verbündeten Mächten erlassen-
en Antwort auf die Schweizer Neutral-
itätsakte. Germanien [
] 1814.
79 p.

NN 0019127 DLC-P4

Napoleon's Oraculum and dream book. Containing the
great oracle of human destiny. Also the true meaning of
almost any kind of dreams, together with charms, ceremonies, and curious games of cards ... New York, F. Tousey
[1884]
62 p. 16ᵐ.

1. Dreams. 2. Fortune-telling.

Library of Congress   BF1091.N2   10-32427

NN 0019128 DLC

Napoleon's Oraculum and dream book
see also
Napoleon's book of fate.
and
Napoleon's dream book.

Napoleon's oraculum, or Book of fate ...

See *under*

[Kirchenhoffer, Herman]

Napoleon's own memoirs
see under [Lullin de Châteauvieux, Frédéric]
1772-1841.

Napoleons soldat i 1813
see under [Erckmann, Émile] 1822-1899.

Napoleons Strategie im Jahr 1813 von der Schlacht
von Gross-Görschen bis zur Schlacht von
Leipzig
see under [Müffling, Friedrich Karl
Ferdinand, Freiherr von] 1775-1851.

---

*pFB8
N1627
Z806n
[Napoleons Stufenjahre]
[Berlin? 1814]

plate. 19.5x33.5cm.,mounted & bd.to 50x40cm.
Not in Broadley (but cf.Broadley E-14,E-15,&
E-119); reproduced in Schulze, plate 9*.
Engraving (hand-colored), unsigned; numbered
"26".
A satire on Napoleon's rise and fall.
In this copy the gallows representing
Napoleon's "Ende" has been blocked out with
opaque paint.
No.32 in a vol-   ume lettered on spine:
Napoleonic cari-   catures.

NN 0019134 MH

VOLUME 405

Napoleonti [!], primo Gallorvm Imperatori,
   semper, avgvsto
     see under [Marron, Paul Henri] 1754–
1832.

Nápoles, Armando Ceballos y
   see
   Ceballos y Nápoles, Armando.

Napoles, José de Lemos de
   see   Lemos de Napoles, José de, 1842–

Napoles, Miguel Angel de
   see   Miguel Angel de Napoles, O.F.M.

Napoles, Oscar Mendez
   see   Mendez Napoles, Oscar.

Nápoles, Pablo Garzona
   see
   Garzona Nápoles, Pablo.

Napoles de Paiva, Ataulfo
   see
   Paiva, Ataulfo de, 1865–

Nápoles Fajardo, Juan Christóbal, *1829–1862.*
   Coleccion de poesías inéditas del popular vate cubano
D. Juan C. Nápoles Fajardo (El Cucalambé) 1. ed.
Gibara, Est. tip. á cargo de M. Bim, 1886.
   264 p. 17½ᵐ.

                     9–16548

  NN   0019142   DLC

Nápoles Fajardo, Juan Christobal, 1829–1862.
   Rumores del hórmigo. Poesias de Juan C.
Nápoles Fajardo, (El Cucalambé) 2a edicion.
Habana, Imprenta del Tiempo, Calle de Cuban,
110, 1858.

  NN   0019143   NNH

Nápoles Fajardo, Juan Cristóbal, 1829–1867.
   Rumores del hormigo; poesias de Juan C. Napoles Fajardo
(El Cucalambé)   Buenos Aires: Maucci hnos. e hijos [1859?]
317 p. 12°.

1. Poetry (Cuban). 2. Title.
N. Y. P. L.   June 25, 1943.

  NN   0019144   NN MH

Nápoles Fajardo, Juan Christóbal, 1829–1862
Lat.Amer.   Rumores del hormigo, poesias de Juan C. Napoles
NA6438r   Fajardo (El Cucalambé)   Habana, "La Moderna
1926   Poesia", 1926.
Harris   327p. 18cm.
Collection

  NN   0019145   RPB NcU

Nápoles Fajardo, Juan Cristóbal, 1829–1862.
   ... Rumores del hórmigo, corregido, explicado y ampliado
por José Muñiz Vergara (el capitán Nemo) La Habana
[Seoane, Fernández y cía, impresores] 1938.
   2 p. l., 7–379 p., 1 l. 21ᵐ.
   At head of title: Juan Cristóbal Nápoles Fajardo (El Cucalambé)
Poems.

   I. Muñiz Vergara, José, ed.
                         44–51921
   Library of Congress   PQ7389.N3A17 1938
                  [2]   861.5

  NN   0019146   DLC OKentU DPU CtY FMU

Nápoles Fajardo, Juan Christobal, 1829–1862.
   Seleccion de Rumores del hormigo por el Cuca-
lambe. Seleccion e introd. Samuel Feijoo. La
Habana, Ediciones Brunidor, 1948.
   vii,134 p. illus. 21 cm.

   Poems.

   I. Feijóo, Samuel, 1914–   ed. II. T.:
Rumores del hórmigo.

  NN   0019147   NjP RPB

G512
N162a
   Nápoles G   , Alfonso.
   ... Algebra elemental para escuelas secun-
darias, por Alfonso Nápoles G. ... México,
D.F., Lit. "El Cromo" Czda. gral., 1940–
   v. 22cm.

   1. Algebra – Text-books.

  NN   0019148   TxU

Nápoles Massa, Jose de Noronha
          see
Noronha Nápoles Massa, Jose de, 1824–1890

Napoletani, Edmondo
   Manuale di preparazione agli esami di
Vol. Vice Coadiutore aggiunto negli archivi notarili. (Gruppo C) 2. ed. aggiornata al 1. luglio 1953 [per] Edmondo
[e] Pina Napoletani.   Pisa, Michelozzi
[1953]
   157p.

  NN   0019150   NNU-W

DE   Napoletani, Giovanni.
3   Fermo nel Piceno. Roma, E. Loescher, 1907.
S927   vii, 191 p. illus., fold plan. 25cm.
no.7   (Studi di storia antica, fasc. 7)

   1. Fermo, Italy--Hist.

  NN   0019151   NIC CtY IU MH

NAPOLETANI! [par un emigrato.] Torino,1859

Pamphlet.

  NN   0019152   MH

Napoletano, Domenico.
   Collocamento e contratto di lavoro. Milano, A. Giuffrè,
1954.
   92 p. 25 cm.
   Bibliographical footnotes.

   1. Labor contract—Italy.   I. Title.
                        A 59–713
   New York Univ.   Libraries HD7811
   for Library of Congress   [8]

  NN   0019153   NNU-W MH

Napoletano, Domenico.
   Il lavoro subordinato. Milano, Giuffrè, 1955.
   296 p. 25 cm.

   1. Labor contract—Italy. 2. Master and servant—Italy.
   I. Title.
                       58–22885 ‡

  NN   0019154   DLC MH-L NIC

Napoletano, Domenico.
   Massimario delle qualifiche del lavoratore; raccolta di
giurisprudenza sistematicamente ordinata ed aggiornata al
31 dicembre 1954. [1. ed. Roma] Jandi Sapi editori [1955]
   xxvi, 258 p. 25 cm.
   Bibliography: p. 243–258.

   1. Italy—Occupations. 2. Collective labor agreements—Italy.
   3. Labor contract—Italy.   I. Title.
                       56–42368

  NN   0019155   DLC NNU-W MH-L

Napoletano, Domenico.
   Le quietanze liberatorie nel diritto del lavoro. Milano, A.
Giuffrè, 1953.
   189 p. 26 cm.
   Bibliographical footnotes.
   "Errata-corrige": slip laid in.

   1. Labor contract—Italy. 2. Receipts (Acknowledgments)—Italy.
   I. Title.
   New York Univ.   Libraries   A 54–5703
   for Library of Congress   [3]†

  NN   0019156   NNU DLC

Napoletano, Giuseppe
   ... Poche osservazioni sul proposto
monopolio degli alcool. [Roma?
1894?]
   15 p. 24cm.

   Signed at end. Giuseppe Napoletano.

  NN   0019157   MH-L

Napoletano, Mario.
   ... Colonie e fascismo. Napoli, A. Chiurazzi & figlio [1931]
   128 p. 19½ᵐ. (Half-title: Politica—economia—corporativismo, collana diretta da Renato Caniglia. vol. VIII)

   1. Italy—Politics and government—1922–   2. Italy—Colonies—
Administration. 3. Fascism—Italy. I. Title.   A C 33–4681
   Title from Wellesley   College. Printed by L. C.

  NN   0019158   MWelC NN

VOLUME 405

Napoletano, Nini Francesco
809.3   Punti escalamativi. Napoli, A. Guida
N216P   [1935]
          118 p. 20 cm.

1. Fiction. 19th cent. Hist. & crit.
2. Fiction. 20th cent. Hist. & crit.
I. Title.

NN 0019159 NcD

Napoletano, Romolo.
   La progettazione degli stampi per resine termoindurenti ...
Milano, Görlich [1951]
   87 p. illus. 24 cm.

1. Power presses. I. Title.

TJ1450.N25   52-43731 ‡

NN 0019160 DLC MiDW NN

Law   Napoletano, Vincenzo, ed.

Dizionario bibliografico delle riviste giuridiche italiane.

Milano, Giuffrè.

Napoli,Anton
Conversational Spanish drill units.
East Lansing,Mich.state college,Dept.
of foreign languages,c1947.
248p.   28cm.

Mimeographed copy.

NN 0019162 Mi

Napoli, Bartolomeo.
   Dei baccani che si fanno nelle nozze
de' vedovi, detti volgarmente cembalate,
o scampanate. Dissertazione teologica, e
istoricocritica... Lucca, Per S. e G.
Marescandoli e comp., 1772.
   8 ℓ.,276 p. 19½ cm.

1.Marriage customs and rites in Italy.

NN 0019163 NjP MH

Napoli, Bebè.
   Mia sorella!... Creazione originale per lo schermo. 1ª.
ed. Salerno, Il Progresso, 1947.
   19 p. 21 cm.

I. Title.

PN1997.N33   47-7994*

NN 0019164 DLC

Napoli, Bernardo da.
   see Bernardo da Napoli, Capuchin
monk

Law   Napoli, Bino.

   Sicily (*Region*) *Laws, statutes, etc.*
   Sgravi fiscali per le nuove costruzioni: Legge regionale 18
gennaio 1949, n. 2 riguardante sgravi fiscali per le nuove costruzioni edilizie; Regolamento per l'esecuzione della Legge
approvato con decreto del presidente della Regione 26 aprile
1949, n. 10 e modificato con successivo Decreto 25 maggio
1950, n. 22. Nota introduttiva di Bino Napoli. A cura
dell'Ufficio legislativo della Presidenza della Regione siciliana. Palermo [1951]

Napoli, Carlo di, d. 1648.
   ... Anaptyxis ad fastos Ovidianos cum addi-
tamento J. F. Palesii Patavini...   (In Gruter,
Jan. Lampas. Florentiae, 1737-51. 36 cm.
v. 1; 1 l., 199 [26] p. 2d paging)

NN 0019167 CtY

Napoli, Carlo di, d. 1648.
   Nuove inventioni di tubi ottici, dimostrate
nell' Accademia fisicomatematica romana...1686.
see under Ciampini, Giovanni Giustino,
1633-1698.

Napoli, Diego.
   ... La responsabilità fiscale dei liquidatori
delle società commerciali (Art, 45 R.D.L.
17-9-1931, n. 1608) Napoli, E. Jovene, 1938.
   107 p.

NN 0019169 DLC

Napoli, Enrico di.
   ... L'assistenza ospedaliera, suoi nuovi orientamenti nel
regime fascista. Palermo, Arti grafiche S. Pezzino & figlio
[1939]
   4 p. l., [11]-120 p., 2 l. 21½ cm.
   "Bibliografia": p. [117]-120.

1. Charities, Medical—Italy. 2. Hospitals—Italy. 3. Public welfare—
Italy.
                                         45-25072
Library of Congress   HV688.I 8N3
                       [2]

NN 0019170 DLC

QB   Napoli, Federico.
36   Della vita e delle opere di Giovan Bat-
024   tista Odierna astronomo fisico e naturalista
N21+   del secolo XVII; memoria.   Palermo, Tipo-
        grafia E. Ferrigno e F. Andó, 1881.
           50 p. 30cm.

        "Estratto dagli Atti dell'Accademia di
        scienze e lettere di Palermo, vol. VII
        1880-81."

        1. Odierna, Giovanni Battista, 1597-1660.

NN 0019171 NIC

Napoli, Federico.   (1865).
   Il poeta civile;...

NN 0019172 NIC

Napoli, Ferdinando de, 1874-1936.
   ... Da Malthus a Mussolini; "la guerra che noi preferiamo"
... Bologna, L. Cappelli [1934]
   2 v. in 1. 19 cm.
   Paged continuously.

1. Italy—Population. 2. Demography. I. Title.
                                         45-44393
Library of Congress   HB3599.N35

NN 0019173 DLC NcRS MH ICU DNLM

Napoli, Ferdinando de, 1874-1936.   616.951 R208
   ... Il "605" nel laboratorio e nella pratica. Contributo clinico-
sperimentale alla nuova terapia antisifilitica ed esposizione dettagliata dei metodi per attuarla, delle sue applicazioni cliniche e
dei risultati finora ottenuti. Con lettera e prefazione del Prof. P.
Ehrlich. Napoli, V. Idelson, 1912.
   xxiii, 184 p. 3 illus. 22½ cm.   (On cover: Biblioteca di medicina pratica e di
attualità scientifiche. N. 2.)
   At head of title: Dr. Ferdinando de Napoli, ...

NN 0019174 ICJ DNLM

Napoli, Ferdinando de, 1874-1936.
   ... Sesso e amore nella vita dell'uomo e degli altri animali,
sessuologia, sociologia, fisiopatologia, igiene, pedagogia, psicologia, etica e legislazione sessuale, con prefazione di Augusto
Murri. 2. ed. ... Milano, Fratelli Bocca, 1942.
   4 p. l., [vii]-xxii, 1043, [1] p. incl. forms. 24 cm.   (Biblioteca di scienze
moderne, n. 99-100)
   "Altre pubblicazione dell' autore": p. [xxi]-xxii.

1. Sex. 2. Sex (Biology) 3. Sexual ethics. 4. Love.
                                         46-29135
Library of Congress   HQ21.N25 1942
                       [2]   612.6

NN 0019175 DLC NcU

Napoli, Ferdinando de, 1874-1936.
   ... Sesso e amore nella vita dell'uomo e degli animali, sessuologia, sociologia, fisiopatologia, igiene, pedagogia, psicologia, etica e legislazione sessuale, con prefazione di Augusto
Murri. 3. ed. ... Milano, Fratelli Bocca [1943?]
   2 v. 24 cm.   (Biblioteca di scienze moderne, n. 99-100)
   "Altre pubblicazione dell'autore": v. 1, p. [xxi]-xxii.

1. Love. 2. Sex. I. Series.
                                         Med 48-260
U. S. Army Medical Libr   [WP1050N216s 1943]
  for Library of Congress   [1]

NN 0019176 DNLM DLC ViU

Napoli, Ferdinando de.   616.951 R406
   ... . La sifilide ereditaria ed i moderni messi di indagine e di
cura. (Ricerca della spirocheta pallida, sifilide sperimentale,
sieroreazione del Wassermann e terapia salvarsanica dell' Ehrlich.) ... . Napoli, V. Idelson, 1915.
   vii, 342, [2] p. 25 cm.
   At head of title: Dott. Prof. Ferdinando de Napoli, ...
   "Bibliographia," p. [311]-340.

NN 0019177 ICJ DNLM

WC   NAPOLI, Ferdinando de, 1874-1936
161   La sifilide ereditaria dal punto di
N216s   vista clinico sperimentale e sociale.
1929   [2. ed.] Milano, Istituto editoriale
        scientifico, 1929.
           xxviii, 409 p.
           1. Syphilis

NN 0019178 DNLM

NAPOLI, FILIPPO.
   Storia della città di Mazara.   Mazara, Stab. tip.
"Hopps", 1932. 271 p. 26cm.

   Bibliography, p. [253]-254.

1. Mazara del Vallo, Italy--Hist.

NN 0019179 NN

Napoli, Francesco, duca di Campobello
   see Campobello, Francesco de Napoli,
duca di.

VOLUME 405

NAPOLI,Franco di., 1897-
 Camillo e la nave saturnia;poema in 3 atti.
Roma,Casa ed.Accademia,[1930].

NN 0019181 MH

Napoli, Franco di, 1897-
 ... La divina passione; dramma sacro in 7 atti, con prologo
ed epilogo. Taranto, Pappacena, 1928.
 132 p., 2 l. 22½ᵐ.

 I. Title.

 Library of Congress PQ4831.A7D5 1928
 28-23564

NN 0019182 DLC

PN   Napoli, Franco di, 1897-
85   "La frusta letteraria"; scritti polemici, con
N3   articoli di Melafumo, N. Sansanelli, L. Tonelli
     ecc. ed uno inedito di Giuseppe Baretti. 2.
     ed., rifatta ed ampliata. Roma, Casa Editrice
     accademia, 1930.
        182p. 19cm. (Interpretazioni, n. 1)

        1. Criticism - Addresses, essays, lectures
     I. Title

NN 0019183 WU

Napoli, Franco di, 1897-
 ... Ivanoe nel tennis-club, commedia in 3 atti. Taranto,
Pappacena, 1928.
 112 p., 1 l. 21ᶜᵐ.
 On cover: Maschere giocose e doloranti. Teatro di Franco di Napoli.

 I. Title. II. Title: Maschere giocose et dolorenti.

 Library of Congress PQ4831.A7 I 8 1928 28-18723

NN 0019184 DLC

NAPOLI, FRANCO DI, 1897-
 ...Rita da Cascia; dramma storico in 3 atti e 5 quadri.
Torino: Soc. editrice internazionale, 1931. 69 p. 20cm.
(Teatro misto.)

700569A. 1. Drama, Italian. I. Title.

NN 0019185 NN

Napoli, Franco di, 1897-
 ...Ultime note; commedia drammatica in 3 atti. Taranto:
A. Mandese, 1935. 89 p. 20cm.

909173A. 1. Drama, Italian.   I. Title.
N. Y. P. L.   September 30, 1937

NN 0019186 NN

M1105   Napoli, Gaetano de.
.G4 I 5
          Ghedini, Giorgio Federico, 1892-
            [Invenzioni]
            Invenzioni, concerto per violoncello, archi, timpani e piatti.
          [Revisione violoncellistica a cura di Gaetano de Napoli]
          Partitura. Milano, New York, G. Ricordi, 1941.

Napoli, Gennaro.
 Scene infantili,suite per piccola orchestre.
Milano, Ricordi, 1929.
 25 p.

NN 0019188 PP

Napoli, Giovanni di.
 Il concetto di educazione; lineamenti di filosofia pedagogica. Roma, Editrice Studium [1952]
 297 p. 25 cm.

 1. Education—Philosophy. I. Title.

 LB775.N25   55-24117 ‡

NN 0019189 DLC InStme

Napoli, Giovanni di.
 La concezione dell'essere nella filosofia contemporanea.
Roma, Studium [1953]
 309 p. 25 cm.
 Bibliographical footnotes.

 1. Ontology. 2. Philosophy, Modern.

 Chicago. Univ. Libr.   A 54-1224
 for Library of Congress   [‡]

NN 0019190 ICU NN

Napoli, Giovanni di.
 La concezione dell'essere nella filosofia greca. Milano, C.
Marzorati [1953]
 290, 8 p. 25 cm.
 Summary in English.
 Bibliographical footnotes.

 1. Philosophy, Ancient. 2. Ontology.

 Chicago. Univ. Libr.   A 56-1383
 for Library of Congress   [‡]

NN 0019191 ICU NjP MH

B3623 Napoli, Giovanni di
N3   La filosofia di Pasquale Galluppi.
        Padova, CEDAM [1947]
        xii,298 p. (Problemi d'oggi. 2.ser.,
        12)
          "Bibliografia": p.[276]-294.

          1. Galluppi, Pasquale, 1770-1846.

NN 0019192 CU NcD MH NN MB NNC

Napoli, Giovanni di.
 Manuale philosophiae ad usum seminariorum. Taurini,
Marietti [1950-51]
 4 v. 21 cm.
 Bibliographies at ends of chapters.
 CONTENTS.—1. Introductio generalis, logica, cosmologia.—2. Psy-
chologia, gnoseologia, ontologia.—3. Theologia rationalis, ethica,
paedagogia, aesthetica, historiologia.—4. Supplementum.

 1. Philosophy.
 B69.N3   A 52-5312
 Catholic Univ. of   America. Library
 for Library of Congress   [1]†

NN 0019193 DCU OWorP NcD DLC

Napoli, Giovanni di.
 In pensiero di Gian Giacomo Rousseau. Brescia, La Scuola
[1953]
 261 p. 25 cm.

 1. Rousseau, Jean Jacques, 1712-1778. I. Title.

 B2137.N3   54-24890 ‡

NN 0019194 DLC MH NN

Napoli, Giovanni di.
 Pensiero contemporaneo e suo influsso
pedagogico, a cura del Centro studi dell'
associazione italiana maestri cattolici.
[195]
 107 p. (Collana "La Guida," 2)

NN 0019195 DLC

Napoli, Giovanni di.
 Tommaso Campanella, filosofo della restaurazione cattolica. Padova, CEDAM [1947]
 vii, 539 p. 26 cm. (Problemi d'oggi, collana di filosofia e storia
della filosofia. 2. ser., v. 10)
 Bibliography : p. [531]-532.

 1. Campanella, Tommaso, 1568-1639. (Series)

 B785.C24N3   49-26073*

MB ICU
NN 0019196 DLC NBuU CaBVaU MU CSt OU NcD NN NNC

Napoli, Giuseppe de
 ... La confisca delle armi. Roma,
Stab. tip. "Agricoltura, Industria e
Commercio," 1903.
 34 p. 25½cm.

NN 0019197 MH-L

Napoli, Giuseppe de
 Ricordando la Corte di appello di
Altamura nel primo centenario della
abolizione. Notizie giudiziarie e
cittadine raccolte e pubblicate dallo
avv. Giuseppe de Napoli ... Con prefazione del senatore Raffaele de
Cesare ... Roma, Cooperativa tip. centrale, 1918.
 viii, 66, [2] p. illus., ports.,
photos. 26½cm.

 Errata slip inserted.
 Illustrated title-page and cover.
 Author's autograph presentation copy
to Luigi Lucchini.

NN 0019199 MH-L

Napoli, Giuseppe di, 1844-1916.
 ... Discorsi intorno ad alcuni generi letterarii, con una lettera
di Mario Rapisardi su l'epopea. Caltanissetta, Stab. tip. Panfilo
Castaldi-Petrantoni, 1907.
 3 p. l., [5]-82, [4] p. 24½ᵐ.

 1. Literature—Addresses, essays, lectures. I. Rapisardi, Mario,
1844-1912.

 Library of Congress PN515.N3
 44-10921

NN 0019200 DLC

Napoli, Giuseppe de, 1871-
 Amilcare Ponchielli (1834-1886) La vita, le opere, l'episto-
lario, le onoranze; notizie e incisioni raccolte da Giuseppe de
Napoli ... e pubblicate dalla Amministrazione podestarile di
Cremona in ricorrenza del cinquantenario della morte del mu-
sicista. Cremona, Stabilimento tipografico Società editoriale
"Cremona nuova", 1936.
 2 p. l., 7-399 p. illus. (incl. ports., facsims. (incl. music)) 24½ᵐ.
 "Errata corrige": leaf inserted at end.
 1. Ponchielli, Amilcare, 1834-1886. 2. Music—Italy—Cremona.
3. Opera—Cremona. I. Cremona (City)

 Library of Congress ML410.P78N3 39-21023
 [2]   927.8

NN 0019201 DLC ICN NN

VOLUME 405

Napoli, Giuseppe de, 1871–
Pierluigi da Palestrina, la vita e le opere...
Milano, Casa Editrice Sonzogno della Società
Anonima Alberto Matarelli [1933]
62 p. illus., facsims. 17 cm. (Biblioteca
del Popolo, v. 35)
Bibliography: p. 62.
Cover title.
1. Palestrina, Giovanni Pierluigi da, 1525?–
1594.

NN 0019202 NcD NcU

Napoli, Giuseppe de, 1871–
La triade melodrammatica altamurana: Giacomo Tritto
(1733–1824), Vincenzo Lavigna (1776–1836), Saverio Mercadante
(1795–1870). Notizie raccolte e pubblicate da Giuseppe de Napoli
... in ricorrenza dell' inaugurazione del monumento a Mercadante
(22 novembre 1931). Milano: Industrie grafiche Rosio &
Fabe₁, 1931₁. 256 p. illus. (incl. facsims., music, ports.)
24cm.
"Cronologia delle opere melodrammatiche di Tritto rappresentate per la prima
volta," p. 45–46; "Elenco dei cantanti che interpretarono i melodrammi di Giacomo Tritto

rappresentati per la prima valta ₍sic₎," p. 46; "Elenco cronologico dei melodrammi di
Mercadante," p. 256.
Bibliographical footnotes.

628360A. 1. Tritto, Giacomo, 1733–   CARNEGIE CORPORATION OF NEW YORK.
1836. 3. Mercadante, Giuseppe   1824. 2. Lavigna, Vincenzo, 1776–
—Italy—Altamura.   Saverio Raffaele, 1795–1870. 4. Music
N. Y. P. L.   May 16, 1933

NN 0019204 NN

Napoli, Ioannes di
see Napoli, Giovanni di.

Napoli, Jacopo, 1911–
₁Un curioso accidente. Piano-vocal score. Italian₎

Un curioso accidente (dalla commedia omonima di **Carlo**
Goldoni) commedia lirica in tre atti di Mario Ghisalberti,
riduzione dell'autore per canto e pianoforte. **Milano, G.**
Ricordi, 1942.
262 p. 27 cm.
1. Operas—Vocal scores with piano.   I. Ghisalberti, Mario, 1902–
Un curioso accidente.
M1503.N19C8 1942   48–41681*

NN 0019206 DLC

Napoli, Jacopo.

... Der eingebildete kranke, komische oper in einem akt,
bestehend aus zwei bildern und einem intermezzo; text nach
der komodie Molières von Mario Ghisalberti; für die **deutsche**
bühne übertragen von Joachim Popelka; klavierauszug **vom**
komponisten ... Milano ₍etc.₎ G. Ricordi & c.; New York, G.
Ricordi & co., inc.; ₍etc., etc.₎ 1939.
5 p. l., 172 (i. e. 176) p. 28ᶜᵐ.
Publisher's plate no.: 124617.
1. Operas—Vocal scores—Pianoforte accompaniment.   I. Molière,
Jean Baptiste Poquelin. Le malade imaginaire.   II. Ghisalberti, Mario.
Il malato immaginario.   III. Popelka, Joachim, tr.   IV. Title.
Library of Congress   M1503.N19M25   42–726

NN 0019207 DLC

Napoli, Jacopo, 1911–
... Il malato immaginario, commedia lirica in un atto di due
quadri ed un intermezzo (dalla commedia di Molière) di Mario
Ghisalberti; riduzione dell'autore per canto e pianoforte ...
Milano ₍etc.₎ G. Ricordi & c.; New York, G. Ricordi & co., inc.;
₍etc., etc.₎ 1939.
6 p. l., 172 (i. e. 176) p. 28ᶜᵐ.
Publisher's plate no.: 124866.
"Prima rappresentazione Napoli, Real teatro di s. Carlo, stagione
dell' anno XVII, 1938–39."
1. Operas—Vocal scores—Pianoforte accompaniment.   I. Molière,
Jean Baptiste Poquelin. Le malade imaginaire.   II. Ghisalberti, Mario.
Il malato immaginario.   III. Title.
Library of Congress   M1503.N19M2   42–883

NN 0019208 DLC

Napoli, Jacopo, *1911–*
₁Il malato immaginario. Libretto. Italian₎

... Il malato immaginario, commedia lirica in un atto di due
quadri ed un intermezzo (dalla commedia di Molière) per la
musica di Jacopo Napoli. Milano ₍etc.₎ G. Ricordi & c.; New
York, G. Ricordi & co. inc.; ₍etc., etc.₎ 1939.
43 p. 20ᶜᵐ.
At head of title: Mario Ghisalberti.
Publisher's plate no.: 124367.
"Prima rappresentazione, Napoli, Real teatro di s. Carlo, stagione
dell' anno XVII, 1938–39."
1. ₁Operas—Librettos₎   I. Ghisalberti, Mario.   II. Il malato immaginario.
Library of Congress   ML50.N2M3   45–32653
                               ₍2₎   782.6

NN 0019209 DLC

Napoli, Jacopo, 1911–
₁Mas'Aniello. Libretto. Italian₎

Mas'Aniello; tragedia popolare in tre atti ₍di₎ **Vittorio**
Viviani. Milano, E. Novi ₍1953₎
84 p. 23 cm.
1. Masaniello, Tommaso Aniello, known as, 1620–1647—Drama.
₍2. Operas—Librettos₎   I. Viviani, Vittorio. Mas'Aniello.   II. Title.
ML50.N2M4 1953₎   53–29602 ‡

NN 0019210 DLC

Napoli, Jacopo, 1911–
₁Mas'Aniello. Piano-vocal score. Italian₎

Mas'Aniello; tragedia popolare in 3 atti. Milano, E. Novi
₍1953₎
191 p. 34 cm.
Libretto by Vittorio Viviani.
Imprint on mounted label.
1. Operas—Vocal scores with piano.   ' 2. Masaniello, Tommaso
Aniello, known as, 1620–1647—Drama.   I. Viviani, Vittorio.   Mas'-
Aniello.   II. Title.
M1503.N19M3 1953   M 53–580

NN 0019211 DLC

4F   Napoli, Michele
Bra-   La Colonia italiana di Rio de
zil   Janeiro con brevi cenni sulla emigra-
122   zione italiana al Brasile; monografia
         compilata per incarico del Comitato
         delle esposizioni di Torino e Roma
         1911.₍di₎ Michele Napoli e Natale
         Belli. ₍
              19   ₎
              173 p.

NN 0019212 DLC-P4 MH

Napoli, Nicola di
... I delinquenti minorenni. Tesi
di laurea. Nelfi, 1904.
58 p. 25cm.
Bibliographical footnotes.

NN 0019213 MH-L

F   NAPOLI, ORAZIO.
0635   Storia degli ordini equestri d'Italia.
.613   Milano, Istituto italiano del libro storico
         ₍193–?₎
         193p. 25cm.

NN 0019214 ICN

4JN   Napoli, Orazio
It.   Storia degli ordini equestri
65   d'Italia. 2. ed. Milano, Istituto
         italiano del libro storico, 1936.
         199 p.

NN 0019215 DLC-P4

Avery
A
8700   Napoli, Paolo
N16   Arte e architettura in regime fascista. Roma,
         anno XVII ₍1938₎
         143, ₍5₎ p. 25 cm.
         Bibliography: p. ₍145₎

         1. Fascism - Italy. 2. Art and state - Italy.
         Architecture and state - Italy. I. Title.

NN 0019216 NNC MH NIC

Napoli, Peter Joseph, 1914–
... Finger-painting and personality diagnosis ₍by₎ Peter J.
Napoli ... ₍New York₎ 1945.
Microfilm copy of type-written manuscript. Made in 1946 by Uni-
versity microfilms (Publication no. 801) Positive.
Collation of the original: 2 p. l., v. 159 numb. l., 2 l. incl. illus.
(incl. photos., part mounted)
Thesis (ED. D.)—New York university, 1945.
Abstracted in Microfilm abstracts, v. 7 (1946) no. 1, p. 39.
Bibliography: leaves ₍155₎–159.
1. Finger painting. 2. Personality. 3. Shaw, Ruth Faison.
Microfilm AC–1 no. 801   Mic A 46–125

Michigan. Univ. Libr.
for Library of Congress   ₍1₎†

NN 0019217 MiU DLC

Napoli, Peter Joseph, 1914–
Finger-painting and personality diagnosis. Province-
town, Mass., Journal Press, *1946.
131–230 p. illus. 25 cm. (Genetic psychology monographs, v. 34,
2d half)
"Based upon a document submitted in partial fulfillment ... for the
doctorate degree in ... New York University."
"References": p. 229–230.
1. Personality, Disorders of. 2. Finger painting.   (Series)
LB1101.G4   vol. 34, no. 2   137.8
—— Copy 2.   BF435.N3   48–398 rev*

NN 0019218 DLC PU PPT PSt OCU TxU ViU Mi NcGU

Napoli, Pietro de
see
Napoli-Signorelli, Pietro, 1731–1815.

NAPOLI, Quintino.
Canti popolari leccesi, Saggio. Lecce, 1881.
pp. 38.
"Pubblicato dalla Gazzetta de Napoli."

NN 0019220 MH

Napoli, Raffaele.
Istituzione di chimica generale. Napoli, 1851.
pt. 1. 8°.

NN 0019221 CtY

Napoli, Raffaele.
Sur la Corrélation les forces physiques par
W. K. Grove. Naples, 1857.
30 p.

NN 0019222 CtY

NAPOLI, RENATO.
...Pagine di vita fascista. Foligno: T. Sbrozzi & fi-
glio, 1931. 120 p. 24½cm.
Articles reprinted from "La Fiamma."

732922A. 1. Fascism.

NN 0019223 NN

VOLUME 405

Napoli, Rodolfo A
... Manual de derecho procesal del trabajo, instancia administrativa obligatoria, magistratura del trabajo, procedimiento judicial; prólogo del dr. Benito Pérez ... ¡La Plata, Talleres gráficos, calle 12 n° 760, 1945¡
cover-title, 1 p. l., 5-221 p., 1 l. 23ᶜᵐ. (Enciclopedia jurídica práctica)

1. Labor courts—Italy.
45-19863

NN   0019224   DLC NIC

945.91 Napoli, Tommaso.
N162c   Compendiosa descrizione corografico-storica della Sardegna per via di domande e risposte ad uso della studiosa gioventù sarda.   n.p., n.d.
134p.

Title-page mutilated.

NN   0019225   IU

QTA   NAPOLI, V   de
N216a   L'arte di saper vivere; ovvero, La
1887   vita dei centenarj. 2. ed. Napoli,
Giannini, 1887.
375 p.

NN   0019226   DNLM

DD   Napoli, Vincenzo di.
147   La colonna espiatoria di Corradino
.5   di Svevia nella R. Chiesa di S. Croce
C64   del Purgatorio al Mercato in Napoli.
N21+   Napoli, M. De Rubertis, 1888.
30 p. illus. 26cm.

1. Conradin of Hohenstaufen, 1252-1268.
2. Naples.   Chiesa di Santa Croce del Purgatorio.

NN   0019227   NIC

¡Napoli, Vincent G   ¡ 1880-
A symposium of occult informations¡¡ edited and annotated¡¡ by Lio Pan ¡pseud.¡ First series. San Francisco, Calif., 1940.
25 p. l., 125 (i. e. 133) numb. l. 21ᶜᵐ.
Reproduced from type-written copy.
"Errata" slip attached to recto of last leaf.

1. Occult sciences.   i. Title.
42-8549
Library of Congress   BF1411.N3
¡2¡   [150.961] 133

NN   0019228   DLC

Napoli Baudo, Giuseppe di
see
Napoli, Giuseppe di, 1844-1916.

Napoli Prario, Lucy.
Tre abiti bianchi per Alessandra, la marchesa Carlotti, nata di Rudinì. ¡1. ed. Milano, Mondadori ¡1954¡
382 p. 20 cm. (Le Scie)

1. Marie de Jésus, Mother, 1876-1931.   i. Title.

BX4705.M355N3   55-21976 ‡

NN   0019230   DLC RPB NN MH

271.9
M3343Tn   Napoli Prario, Lucy.
Tre abiti bianchi per Alessandra, la marchesa Carlotti nata di Rudini.   [Milano] Mondadori [1955]
382p. illus., facsims. 21cm.

1. Marie de Jésus, Mother, 1876-1931. I. Title.

NN   0019231   IEN

Napoli Prario, Lucy.
Tre abiti bianchi per Alessandra, la Marchesa Carlotti, nata di Rudinì. [2.ed. Milano] Mondadori [1955]

NN   0019232   MH

PN1654   Napoli-Signorelli, Pietro, 1731-*1815.*
.N22   Addizioni alla Storia critica de' teatri antichi e moderni di Pietro Napoli Signorelli ...
Rare   Napoli, M. Migliaccio, 1798.
Bk   ¡8¡, 344, ¡8¡ p. 19cm.
Supplementary material supplied by the author to his original work in 6 v., 1787-1790.

1. Drama--Hist. & crit. 2. Theater--Hist.

NN   0019233   ICU MB

Napoli Signorelli, Pietro, 1731-1815.

Cruz Cano y Olmedilla, Ramón Francisco de la, 1731-1794.
Coleccion de sainetes, tanto impresos como inéditos de D. Ramon de la Cruz, con un discurso preliminar de Don Agustin Duran y los juicios criticos de los Sres. Martinez de la Rosa, Signorelli, Moratin y Hartzenbusch. Madrid, Librería europea de Hidalgo ¡1843¡

Napoli-Signorelli, Pietro, 1731-1815.
...Del gusto e del bello; ragionamento di Pietro Napoli-Signorelli... Napoli: V. Orsini, 1807.   xii, 132 p.   8°.
"Edizione napoletana."

SPINGARN COLLECTION.
273215A. 1. Aesthetics.
N. Y. P. L.   April 12, 1927

NN   0019235   NN

P 8115   Napoli-Signorelli, Pietro, 1731-1815.
.N 3   Delle migliori tragedie greche e francesi.
1804   Traduzioni ed analisi comparative de Pietro Napoli Signorelli. Milano, Dalla Stamperia e Fonderia al Genio, 1804-1805.
3 v. in 1. 23cm.

1. Drama - Collections. 2. Italian drama - Translations from foreign literature.   I. Title.

NN   0019236   MdBJ ICU

Napoli-Signorelli, Pietro. 1731-1815.   **T.46.42
Discorso storico-critico . . . da servire di lume alla storia critica de' teatri, e di risposta all' autore del Saggio apologetico.
= In Napoli MDCCLXXXIII. Nella stamperia di Amato Cons. A spese di Michele Stasi . . . (8), 240 pp. 21 cm., in 8s.
A Spanish translation of Lampillas' Saggio apologetico, may be found on shelf-number **D.183.31.

J446 — Lampillas, Francisco Xavier. 1731-1810. — Drama. Hist. and crit.

NN   0019237   MB

Napoli-Signorelli, Pietro, 1731-1815.
Elementi di critica diplomatica con istoria preliminare.   Parma, Luigi Mussi, 1805.
200p 22cm

NN   0019238   MnCS MH

341.7   Napoli-Signorelli, Pietro, 1731-1815.
N16e   Elementi di diplomatica politica.   Napoli,
V. Orsino, 1808.
231p. 24cm.

Bibliographical footnotes.

1. Diplomacy.

NN   0019239   IU NjP MH-L

NAPOLI-SIGNORELLI, Pietro.   No. 2 in *2768.
Faustina, commedia.
Venezia, 1796. 80 pp. [Teatro moderno applaudito. T. 5.]

NN   0019240   MB

PQ4720   Napoli-Signorelli, Pietro, 1731-1815
-N2   La Faustina, commedia, che ha
F3   riportata la prima corona nel concorso dell'anno 1778 dalla R. Accademica Deputazione di Parma. Parma, dalla Stamperia Reale ¡1778¡
113p. front. 28cm.

Added illustrated t.-p.

NN   0019241   RPB

PQ   Napoli Signorelli, Pietro, 1731-1815.
4720   La faustina, commedia. Con due lettere critiche. Una dell' autore, e l'altra di Carlo Vespasiano. Lucca, 1778.
N162F2   viii, 40, 78, 75 p.

"Lettere critiche ad istruzione de'continuatori delle novelle letterarie di Firenze, e in difesa della commedia della Faustina" (75 p. at end) has special t. p. with imprint: Genova, 1779.

NN   0019242   CLU CU

Napoli-Signorelli, Pietro, 1731-1815.
Faustina; commedia del dottor Pietro
PG 1231   Napoli-Signorelli.   Venezia, 1796.
.A7 T4   80 p.   17½cm.   (Il teatro moderno
t. 5   applaudito. t. V [pt. 2])

I. Title.   II. Series.

NN   0019243   MdBJ

Napoli-Signorelli, Pietro, 1731-1815.
... La Faustina, del doctor don Pedro Napoli Signorelli. Traducida por Fermín del Rey. ¡Barcelona, Juan Francisco Piferrer, n.d.¡
¡24¡ p. 21cm. (Comedias ¡Teatro antiguo español¡)

At head of title: Comedia famosa. Núm. 79.

I. Rey, Fermín del, tr. II. Title.

NN   0019244   NcU MH

Napoli-Signorelli, Pietro, 1731-1815.
La Faustina. Comedia del doctor Pedro
Napoli-Signorelli. Traducida por Fermin del Rey. [In five acts and in verse. Madrid
R. Ruiz, 1799]
30 p.

NN   0019245   NN

VOLUME 405

PQ 4720
N2 F3
1800

Napoli-Signorelli, Pietro, 1731-1815.
La faustina. Comedia del doctor Don
Pedro Napoli-Signorelli. Traducida por
Fermin del Rey. [Madrid? Libreria de
Cerro, 1800?]
30 p. 22 cm.
Caption title.

NN 0019246   OU NcU MnU

[Napoli-Signorelli, Pietro] 1731-1815.
Geschichte der schaubühne und theaterdichter bey allen
völkern. Aus dem italiänischen ... Leipzig, In commission
bey Fleischer, 1791.
2 v. 16°.
First published under title: Kritische geschichte des theaters der
alten und neuen zeit, Bern, 1783. cf. Ersch, J. S. Handbuch der deutsch.
lit., neue ausg., Leipzig, 1840, v. 2, col. 465, no. 3590.
Translation by F. A. C. Werthes, F. A. Weber, Tscherning and Schübler of Storia critica de' teatri antichi e moderni, libri III. Napoli, 1777.
cf. Holzmann, M. Deutsch. anon.-lex., Weimar, 1928, VII, p. 187, and
Gradmann, J. J. Das gelehrte Schwaben [Ravensburg] 1802, p. 736,
no. 21.

1. Drama—Hist. & crit. 2. Theater—Hist. 3. Music—Hist. & crit.
4. Opera—Hist. & crit. I. Werthes, Friedrich August Clemens, 1748-
1817, tr. II. Weber, Friedrich August, 1753-1806, tr. III. Tscherning,
Bernhard Theodor, 1750 (ca.)-1785, tr. IV. Schübler, Christian Ludwig,
1754-1820, tr. V. Title.
                                       36-31302
Library of Congress   PN1720.N34 1791
          [2]   809.2

NN 0019248   DLC CLSU

Napoli-Signorelli, Pietro, 1731-1815.
Kritische geschichte des theaters der
alten und neuen zeit, von D. Pietro
Napoli-Signorelli, aus dem italiänischen
übersezt. Bern, Bey der neuen typo-
graphischen gesellschaft, 1783.
2 v. in 1. 16cm.

1.Drama-Hist. & crit. I.Title.

NN 0019249   NNU-W NjP

---

q854N16 Napoli-Signorelli, Pietro, 1731-1815.
K1812   Lezioni accademiche ... Napoli, 1812.
101p. pl.

Contents.- Sulla scrittura pensiero.- Sull'in-
venzione della bussola nautica ragionamento.-
Lezione economica.- Elogio alla memoria del sacerdote Vincenzio de Muro.

NN 0019250   IU

Napoli-Signorelli, Pietro.
Ne' funerali in morte del Caroli III. Orazione
de P. Napoli Signorelli. Napoli, 1789.

NN 0019251   PPL

Napoli-Signorelli, Pietro, 1731-1815.
Opuscoli vari di Pietro Napoli-Signorelli...
Napoli, Stamperia Orsiniana, 1792-95.
4 v. in 2. plates. 20 cm.
With v. 4 is bound: Barbato, G. Saggio di
poesie ed iscrizioni- 1797.

NN 0019252   CU

Napoli-Signorelli, Pietro, 1731-1815.
Satire di Pietro Napoli-Signorelli ... Napoli,
1793.
166 p. 22 cm.
With this are bd. his? Riflessioni politiche.
100 p. n.p., n.d.; and his? Opuscula, sive De
aequa dominationis potestate; de factorum recog-
nitione, disputationes duae; & Liber ad Marcum
fratrem. 88 p. Neapoli, ex Typographia
Simoniana, 1783.

NN 0019253   CU

PN
1720
N21

Napoli-Signorelli, Pietro, 1731-1815.
Storia critica de' teatri antichi e
moderni. Napoli, V. Orsino, 1787-90.
6 v. in 3. 20cm.

1. Drama--Hist. & crit. 2. Theater--
Hist. 3. Music--Hist. & crit. 4. Opera--
Hist. & crit.

NN 0019254   NIC NN MB NNC InU PU MH

Napoli-Signorelli, Pietro, 1731-1815.
Storia critica de' teatri antichi e moderni divisa in dieci
tomi, di Pietro Napoli-Signorelli ... Napoli, Presso V.
Orsino, 1813.
10 v. in 5. front. 20°.
Vol. 10 in 2 parts, each with special t.-p. and separate paging.
Imperfect: frontispiece wanting.

1. Drama—Hist. & crit. 2. Theater—Hist. 3. Music—Hist. & crit.
4. Opera—Hist. & crit. I. Title.
Library of Congress   PN1720.N3
—— Copy 2. 10 v.   10-11022
                          in 11. 19°.
                          ML1700.854

NN 0019255   DLC CSt OCU NcD

Napoli-Signorelli, Pietro, 1731-1815.
Storia critica de' teatri antichi e moderni divisa
in dieci tomi, di Pietro Napoli-Signorelli ...
Napoli, Presso V. Orsino, 1813.
11 v. front. 20 cm.

NN 0019256   CtY

Z808.2
N162

Napoli-Signorelli, Pietro, 1731-1815.
Storia critica de' teatri antichi e
moderni libri III. Napoli, Stamperia
Simoniana, 1777.

xx, 468 p. 22cm.

1. Drama. History and criticism. 2.
Theater. History and criticism.

NN 0019257   MnU IEN DLC-P4

Napoli-Signorelli, Pietro, 1731-1815.
Vicende della coltura nelle due Sicilie, o sia storia ragionata della
loro legislazione e polizia, delle lettere, del commercio, delle arti,
e degli spettacoli dalle colonie straniere insinoanoi.
Napoli, Flauto, 1784-85. 4 v. 18 cm., in 8s.

K8797 — Naples, Kingdom of. Hist.

NN 0019258   MB MH

945.8
N16

Napoli-Signorelli, Pietro, 1731-1815.
Vicende della coltura nelle due Sicilie,
o sia storia ragionata della loro legislazione
e polizia, delle lettere, del commercio, delle
arti, e degli spettacoli dalle colonie straniere insino a noi. Napoli, V. Flauto, 1784-86.
6 v.

Vol. 6: Supplemento.

NN 0019259   NNC CU

NAPOLI-SIGNORELLI,Pietro.
Vicende della coltura nelle due Sicilie.
2a ed.napoletana. Napoli,Vincenzo Orsini,
1810-11.

8 vol.

NN 0019260   MH CtY ICU IU

Napoli-Vita, V   di.
... Cristoforo Colombo: narrazione storica compilata
sulle opere di suo figlio Fernando; di Antonio Gallo, suo
contemporaneo e sugli scritti degli storici e critici posteriori: seguita da un inno popolare Colombiano musicato
dal M°. Giovanni Basso. Napoli, L. Chiurazzi; New
York, Eco d'Italia, 1892.
190, [2] p. front. (port.) fold. pl. 15½°.

Subject entries: Colombo, Cristoforo.   3-51822

Library of Congress, no.   E111.N21.

NN 0019261   DLC

Napoli; rivista municipale.
Napoli, F. Giannini & figli.
v. illus., plates, ports., tables. 26½-31½°. monthly.
Publication began 1875. cf. Consiglio nazionale delle ricerche. Periodici italiani, 1931.
Title varies: 1875-19   Napoli; rivista municipale.
            19   Napoli; Bollettino del comune di Napoli.
Each issue consists of a section of general articles and a section of
statistics.
1. Naples—Pol. & govt. 2. Naples—Stat.
Library of Congress   JS31.N355   46-33044
——2d set. Jan.-June   1931 [With Naples. Divisione statistica. Annuario statistico   del comune di Napoli, 1931]
                            HA1379.N3A32 1931
           [2]   914.573

NN 0019262   DLC NN

Napoli. np [1872?]

Collection of plates

NN 0019263   MH

Napoli. [Napoli? 1889?] photo. 31½ x 248cm. fold.
31½ x 34½cm.
Cover-title.
Panorama.

1. Naples—Views.
N. Y. P. L.   December 12, 1939

NN 0019264   NN

B3614
C74N3

Napoli a Benedetto Croce, discorsi pronunziati da A. Omodeo [et al.] Napoli, G.
Macchiaroli [1943?]
43 p.

1. Croce, Benedetto, 1866-
I. Omodeo, Adolfo, 1889-1946.

NN 0019265   CU NN MH ICU

Napoli d'oggi; scritti di Nicola d'Ari-
enzo, Roberto Bracco, Riccardo Carafa
[ed altri]... Napoli, Pierro, 1900.
447 p. illus.(incl.ports.,music)
24 cm.

1.Naples-Descr. I.Arienzo,Nicola d',
1842-1915.

NN 0019266   NjP IdU CU MH MU

Edh
803N

Napoli e suo contorno con un appendice.
Napoli,1803.
xvi,344,28p.,2l. 19cm.
Half-title: Breve descrizione di Napoli e
del suo contorno; da servire di appendice
alla descrizione geografica e politica delle
Sicilie.

NN 0019267   CtY

Napoli, i Borboni ed il governo italiano;
     see under   Barbaro di San Giorgio, Ramiro.

VOLUME 405

Napoli e i luoghi celebri delle sue vicinanze ... **Napoli** ₍Stab. tip. di G. Nobile₎ 1845.
2 v. 25 pl., map, 2 plans. 29½ᶜᵐ.
Compiled by order of the "Ministero e Real segreteria di stato degli affari interni," by G. B. Ajello, S. Aloe, R. d'Ambra, M. d'Ayala, C. Bonucci, C. Dalbono, F. Puoti, B. Quaranta.
CONTENTS.—Napoli: Introduzione. 1. Chiesa napolitana e suoi edifizi. 2. Ordini governativi, giudiziari e militari, e loro edifizi. 3. Istituti scientifici e letterari, pubblica istruzione, e loro edifizi. 4. Istituti artistici, pubblici spettacoli e loro edifizi. 5. Industria, ed istituti economici e loro edifizi. 6. Istituti di beneficenza e loro edifizi. 7. Regie ville, e giardino e passeggi pubblici. 8. Palagi de' privati, e loro musei, biblioteche e ville.—Le vicinanze.—Censo della città di Napoli e risultamenti statistici.

1. Naples—Descr.   4-11826

Library of Congress   DG843.N23

NN   0019269   DLC FU PSt CtY PU

Napoli e i napoletani; grande guida generale di Napoli.

Napoli, Edizione de "La Voce di Napoli" ₍19

v. 25½ᶜᵐ. annual.

1. Naples—Direct.   44-45835

Library of Congress   DG842.N3
            ₍2₎   914.57

NN   0019270   DLC

Napoli e suoi dintorni. [map] n. p., n. d.

NN   0019271   NjP

Napoli musicale. anno ₍ ₎-13, n. 19/24; ₍ ₎-31 dic. 1880. ₍Napoli₎
v. in   34 cm. semimonthly (irregular)
Began publication in 1863?
Publication suspended Jan.–Mar. 1880.
Edited by L. Mazzone.
No more published?

1. Music—Period. I. Mazzone, Luigi, ed.

ML5.N116   56-51681

NN   0019272   DLC

Napoli nella storia e nella vita
     see under   Naples.

Napoli nobilissima; rivista di topografia ed arte napoletana. v. 1–
gen. 1892–
Napoli, 1892–
v illus. 36ᶜᵐ. monthly.

1. Art—Naples. 2. Art—Period. 3. Naples.

                    14-6324

Library of Congress   N6921.N2A4

NN   0019274   DLC ICJ IdU MoU NIC NjP MiU

Art Library
N6921
N2
+N36
(LC)

Napoli nobilissima. v.1-15, 1892-1906; nuova serie, v.1-3, 1921-1923. Napoli, R. Ricciardi.
6 v. illus. 35 cm.

Subtitle varies slightly.

1. Art - Naples - Period.
2. Naples - Descr. - 1900-

NN   0019275   CtY

Napoliello, R   **Rosino,** 1870–
Love and pride. By R. Rosino Napoliello ₍a story₎. New York, The Abbey press ₍*1900₎
3 p. l., 5–108 p. 20½ᶜᵐ.

Library of Congress   PZ3.N163L   Jan. 10, 1901-71

NN   0019276   DLC

Napolini, Scipione
    see   Polinari, Scipione.

Napolino, Pietro Floridia
    see   Floridia, Pietro, 1860–1932.

Napolino, Virginio, ed.
Resoconto amministrativo-sanitario ...
    see under   Modica, Italy. Ospedal degli Onesti ed Albergo dei Poveri.

Le Napolitain, ou le defenseur de sa maitresse
    see under   ₍Germont,   de₎

Napolitan, L
The fruit growing industry in Kent. ₍Bristol, Univ. of Bristol, Dept. of Economics, 1947₎
223–318 p. maps. 22 cm.
Bibliography: p. 317–318.

1. Fruit-culture—England—Kent.

SB356.N3   634   49–12697*

NN   0019281   DLC CU

₍**Napolitan, Louis**₎ 1895–
Six thousand years of hair styling, by M. Louis ... ₍New York, Printed by the Polygraphic company of America, *1939₎
96 p. incl. illus., plates. 30½ x 23½ᶜᵐ.

1. Hair-dressing.   I. Title.
Library of Congress   GT2290.N3   39—25723
—— Copy 2.
Copyright A 133483   ₍40f3₎   391.5

FMU
NN   0019282   DLC WaS Or OrCS NBuG OLak PP PPD OCl

---

*
M1.
.S444   The Napolitan ₍sic₎ Swiss & Vienna waltzes,
v.66   arr. for the piano forte. Philad₍elphi₎a,
no.22   Geo. Willig, 171 Chesnut ₍sic₎ St. ₍18——₎
      ₍2₎ p. 35cm. ₍Sheet music collection, v. 66, no. 22₎
      Caption title.

      1. Waltzes (Piano) I. Title: Neapolitan, Swiss and Vienna waltzes. II. Title: Swiss waltz. III. Title: Vienna waltz.

NN   0019283   ViU

NAPOLITANI, G. di Stefano.

    See STEFANO NAPOLITANI, Guiseppi di.

Napolitani, Vincenzo, 1814–1886.
Degli atti dello stato civile. Napoli, 1860–
v.

NN   0019285   NjP

4K
Ital.-
158

Napolitani, Vincenzo, 1814–1886.
Degli effetti legali delle obbligazioni e dei contratti in generale fermati da nazionali in paese straniero, ovvero stabiliti in regno tra nazionali e stranieri, o tra nazionali fra loro. Napoli, Stab. Tip. di P. Androsio, 1857-58.
2 v.

NN   0019286   DLC-P4 MH-L MiU-L

Napolitani, Vincenzo, 1814–1886.
Diritto e giurisprudenza; rivista giuridica quindicinale civile, commerciale, amministrativa, penale. v. 1–
15 magg. 1885–
Napoli, Stab. tipog. "Diritto e giurisprudenza" ₍etc.₎ 1886–

Napolitani, Vincenzo, 1814-1886.
Lexicon Universi Corporis Juris. Naples, 1853.
2 v., 4 tom.

NN   0019288   PPB

I Napolitani, al cospetto delle nazioni civili. [Roma, 1861]
81, (2) p.
Half-title serves as title-page.

NN   0019289   MH NN

Napolitano, Alberto Rafael.
La torre ya no mira al río, novela. Ilus. de Herminio Héctor Rondano. Buenos Aires, Editorial Mundo Forense ₍1947₎
370 p. illus. 24 cm.

I. Title.   A 50–5823

New York. Public Libr.
for Library of Congress   ₍1₎

NN   0019290   NN

M1621
.N35

Napolitano, Emilio A
Flor de cancion; vidala para canto y piano. ₍Op. 2, no. 3₎ Buenos Aires, Ricordi Americana, 1941.
6 p. 32 cm.
Cover title.
Words also printed separately.

1. Songs with piano. 2. Dance music, Argentine. I. Title.

NN   0019291   MB

MT247
.N3

Napolitano, Emilio A
Gato; al estilo popular ₍para piano₎ Op. 8, No. 3. Buenos Aires, Ricordi Americana, °1946.
2 p. 32 cm. (Coleccion didactica de musica Argentina)
Caption title.
"Mediana dificultad"

1. Piano music—Instructive editions. 2. Dance music, Argentine. I. Title.

NN   0019292   MB

VOLUME 405

M1621
.N35M3 Napolitano, Emilio A
La mariposa; cancion para canto y piano. «Poesía
de Gaston Figueira. Op. 6, No. 1. Buenos Aires,
Ricordi Americana «C1944»
6 p. 32 cm.
Cover title.

1. Songs with piano. I. Title.

NN 0019293 MB

M1621
.N35P5 Napolitano, Emilio A
Picaflor; zamba al estilo popular, para canto
y piano «Poesía del Dr. Ataliva Herrera. Op. 2,
No. 4» Buenos Aires, Ricordi Americana, 1941.
6 p. 32 cm.
Cover title.
Text also printed separately.

1. Songs with piano. 2. Dance music, Argentina.
I. Title.

NN 0019294 MB

Napolitano, Emma.
see Napolitano de Sanz, Emma.

Napolitano, Enrique.
... Crítica contemporánea. Buenos Aires, Editorial "Buenos
Aires," 1941.
143, ₍5₎ p. illus. 20½ᵐ.
CONTENTS.—Prólogo.—Un secretario modelo.—De la flora política.—El
pituco.—Un "mateo" que no quiso ser chofer.—El guapo.—Tras cuernos,
palos.—Carta de un reformador.—El hombre que se tragó la espada.—
El hombre orquesta.—Un comisario.—Un hombre que no halló su destino.—El caudillo.—El candidato.—Crítica contemporánea y el actual dis-
conformista, por el dr. Carmelo Puciarelli.—Un artículo de "La Prensa."

I. Title.

43-30500
Library of Congress PQ7797.N33C7
₍2₎ 863.6

NN 0019296 DLC TxU

PQ7797 Napolitano, Enrique
.N33 El veraneo de don Juan Manuel (Escenario
V4 principal Mar del Plata) ... Buenos Aires,
1935.
141p. 19cm.

Author's autograph presentation copy.

I. Title. S Autograph

NN 0019297 PSt

Napolitano, Enrique F., editor.
"La República Argentina ilustrada"; historia, arte, letras,
comercio, industria y variedades. Obra editada bajo la dirección
de Enrique F. Napolitano. Buenos Aires ₍1914₎. 104 l., 1 map,
3 mounted, col'd port. illus. f°.
Advertising matter interspersed.
At head of title: 1913-1914.

1. Argentine Republic. 2. Industries and mechanic arts, Argentine
Republic. 3. Title.
N.Y.P.L. November 17, 1916.

NN 0019298 NN

Napolitano, Epicuro, pseud.
see Epicuro, Marc Antonio, 1472-1555.

Napolitano, Francesco.
... Mentre la Francia rivive, la latinità oggi.
Roma, Editoriale Arte e storia [1944]
62 p.

NN 0019300 DLC

Napolitano, Francesco.
... Perchè si combatte? (Ristampa) Milano-Roma, Editoriale Arte e storia, 1941.
3 p. l., 9-85 p., 1 l. 21½ᵐ.

1. World war, 1939- —Causes. I. Title.
45-46103
Library of Congress D741.N3
₍2₎ 940.5311

NN 0019301 DLC

HB177 Napolitano, Gaetano.
N216 Le corporazioni fasciste come nuovi sentieri
dell'economia. ₍Roma, 1933₎
215 p. diagrs. 22cm. (Biblioteca del secolo
fascista, ser.1, n.2)
Autographed copy.

Hoover
Library
1. Economics. 2. Fascism - Italy. I. Title.

NN 0019302 CSt-H

330 Napolitano, Gaetano
N162c Corso di economia politica svolto sui
1928 prinipî della "Carta del lavoro". Aspetto
economico della "Carto del lavoro" studi di
Giuseppe Bottai. Roma, Attilio
Sampaolesi, 1928.
328p. 24cm.

1. Economics. I. Title. II. Title: Carta
del lavoro. III. Bottai, Giuseppe. Aspetto economico della "Carta del lavoro."

NN 0019303 KU NN ICarbS

Napolitano, Gaetano.
... Dell' economia politica come scienza umana; discorso con
taluni di parer contrario. Roma, A. Sampaolesi, 1930.
8 p. 23ᵐ.

1. Economic policy. I. Title.
32-10001
Library of Congress HB71.N3
₍2₎ 330.1

NN 0019304 DLC NN

Napolitano, Gaetano.
... Instituciones de economía corporativa; traducción del
italiano por C. Massó; presentación al lector español de R. Gay
de Montellá. Barcelona, Bosch ₍1941₎
2 p. l., 383 p. 25½ᵐ.
"Índice de nombres, de obras o de temas tratados": p. ₍367₎-380.

1. Economics. 2. Gilds—Hist. 3. Trade and professional associations—
Italy. 4. Italy—Economic policy. I. Massó Escofet, Cristóbal, tr. II.
Title.
45-51445
Library of Congress HB177.N28
₍3₎ 330.1

NN 0019305 DLC

Napolitano, Gaetano.
... Istituzioni di economia corporativa. Padova, CEDAM,
Casa editrice dott. Antonio Milani, 1938.
1 p. l., ₍v₎-viii, 406 p. 25½ᵐ.
"Indice dei nomi delle opere o degli argomenti trattati": p. ₍387₎-401.

1. Economics. 2. Gilds—History. 3. Corporate state. 4. Italy—Economic policy. I. Title.
A C 39-2098
New York. Public library
for Library of Congress ₍3₎

NN 0019306 NN CtY

Napolitano, Gaetano.
Italy in Africa: an example of enlighted colonization.
Roma, Menaglia ₍195-?₎
27 p. 24 cm.

1. Italy—Colonies—Africa—Administration. I. Title.
JQ3580.A55 325.245096 57-30375 ‡

NN 0019307 DLC NN

Napolitano, Gaetano.
La libertà di stampa in Europa. ₍Roma?₎ SPI, Centro
studi, 1955.
137 p. (Collana di monografie sui problemi della stampa, 1)

1. Liberty of the press. I. Title. (Series)
55-56990

NN 0019308 DLC MoU

Napolitano, Gaetano.
... I nuovi sentieri dell' economia ... Roma: L' Economia
italiana, 1933. 118 p. 24½cm. (Raccolta di studi politici,
economici e sociali a cura della rivista "L' Economia italiana."
ser. 2, n. 8.)

1. Capitalism. 2. Bolshevism. 3. Fascisti. I. Ser.
N.Y.P.L. May 22, 1934

NN 0019309 NN

Napolitano, Gaetano, joint author.
Petrone, Corrado.
... Il nuovo diritto costituzionale e amministrativo. 5. ed.
riv. ed ampliata. Roma, A. Sampaolesi, 1930.

Napolitano, Gaetano.
... Premesse economiche all'espansione corporativa. Padova,
CEDAM, Casa editrice dott. A. Milani, 1941.
iv, 137 p., 1 l. 25½ᵐ.
"Questo lavoro trae origine dalla pubblicazione 'Problemi del corpora-
tivismo fascista nell'impero e nelle colonie'."—p. ₍iii₎
"Indice dei nomi e delle opere citate": p. ₍133₎-137.

1. Italy—Economic policy. 2. Italy—Commercial policy. 3. Italy—
Colonies. I. Title.
44-12417
Library of Congress HC305.N3
₍2₎ 330.945

NN 0019311 DLC MH IU

Napolitano, Gaetano.
... Principi di economia corporativa. Roma, A. Sampaolesi, 1930.
176 p. 24ᵐ.

1. Economics. 2. Italy—Economic policy. 3. Fascism—Italy.
I. Title.
32-10788
Library of Congress HB177.N3
₍2₎ 330.1

NN 0019312 DLC NN KU

Napolitano, Gaetano.
... Problemi del corporativismo fascista nell' impero e nelle
colonie ... Padova, CEDAM, Casa editrice dott. A. Milani,
1939.
2 p. l., 148 p., 1 l. 23½ᵐ.
"Opera ritenuta meritevole del 'Premio città di Faenza' di l. 10,000,
in onore di Alfredo Oriani per l'anno XVI."
"Indice dei nomi e delle opere citate": p. ₍143₎-146.

1. Colonies. 2. Corporate state. 3. Italy—Colonies. I. Title.
42-1540
Library of Congress JV2227.N3

NN 0019313 DLC

VOLUME 405

Napolitano, Gaetano.
  Questo incontentabile mezzogiorno.   Mazara, Società editrice siciliana [1947]
  105 p. 18 cm. (Inchieste d'attualità, 1)

  1. Italy, Southern—Intellectual life.   I. Title.
  DG829.N3   49–18411*

  NN 0019314   DLC NN

Napolitano, Gaetano.
  ... Scienza economica o scienza della prosperità dei popoli?   Roma, Editoriale romana [1944]
  1 p. l., [5]–210 p., 1 l. 23½ᵐ.
  Bibliographical foot-notes.

  1. Economics.   I. Title.
  Library of Congress   HB177.N33
                                    [2]   330.1

  NN 0019315   DLC IU NNC CU MH

Napolitano, Gaetano.
  La zona depressa del Mezzogiorno.   Roma, Edica [1949]
  21 p. 19 cm. (Discussioni e programmi, 1)

  1. Italy, Southern—Soc. condit.
  HN479.N3   50–37152

  NN 0019316   DLC MH-IR

Hd69   Napolitano, Gian Gaspare, 1907–
N163   La Mariposa. Tam tam Mayumbe. La volpe d'argento.   [Firenze] Vallecchi [1950]
M3   396p. 18cm. (Letteratura contemporanea)
           Errata slip inserted.

  NN 0019317   CtY NN RPB

D655N162
W
         Napolitano, Gian Gaspare
           ... Scoperta dell'America; romanzo.   Roma, Sapienzia, Edizioni dei dieci, 1930.
           4 p. l., [11]–310 p., 2 l. 19½ᵐ.

  NN 0019318   NNC

Napolitano, Gian Gaspare
  Tam-tam Mayumbe.   [Firenze] Vallecchi [1954]
  346 p. 17cm. (Contemporanea.6)

  I. Title. II. Contemporanea.

  NN 0019319   NN CtY RPB

Napolitano, Gian Gaspare, 1907–
  ... Troppo grano sotto la neve; un inverno al Canadà, con una visita a Ford.   Milano: Casa edit. Ceschina, 1936.   489 p.
  18 pl. 20½cm.
  "Questo libro è la testimonianza di un viaggio nel Canadà e negli Stati Uniti compiuto, al servizio della 'Gazzetta del popolo' dal novembre 1931 al maggio 1932."

  877387A. 1. Canada—Descr. and   trav., 1910–   . I. Title.
  N.Y.P.L.   April 21, 1937

  NN 0019320   NN DLC-P4 NNC WU MnU

Napolitano, Giovanni, 1883–
  L'abisso e la vetta; poesie di Giovanni Napolitano.   Napoli, Stabilimento poligrafico, 1912.
  166p., 1l. 20cm.

  NN 0019321   CtY

4PR-   Napolitano, Giovanni, 1883–
146   "L'amante di Lady Chatterley" o del pudore.   Napoli, Miccoli [1948]
           91 p.

  NN 0019322   DLC-P4 NN

Napolitano, Giovanni, 1883–
  ... Arte e artisti della parola; (16 tavole fuori testo)   Milano, U. Hoepli, 1940.
  2 p. l., vii–xi, 274 p., 1 l. ports. 20½ᵐ.

  1. Oratory. 2. Orators, Italian. 3. Lawyers—Italy.   I. Title.
  Library of Congress   PN4125.N3   43–36658
                                    [2]   808.5

  NN 0019323   DLC WaSpG CtY

808.5   **Napolitano, Giovanni, 1883–**
N216a   Arte e artisti della parola.   [Napoli]
            Istituto editoriale del Mezzogiorno [1954]
            xi,383p. illus.,ports. 22cm.

            1.Oratory. 2.Orators, Italian.
            3.Lawyers. Italy. I.Title.

  NN 0019324   IEN NN

NAPOLITANO, GIOVANNI.
  Un grande maestro: Vincenzo Ianfolla (a firma di G. Napolitano ed A. Guidone). Mario Rovani e la sua opera (saggio di R. Rossi)   Napoli, Società aspetti letterari [1955?] 32 p. 25cm. (Quaderni Lucani)

  Film reproduction. Positive.

  1. Ianfolla, Vincenzo, 1873–1943. 2. Rovani, Mario, d. 1954.
  I. Guidone, Alfredo. II. Rossi, Raffaele   III. Quaderni Lucani.

  NN 0019325   NN

NAPOLITANO, Giovanni.
  Intuizioni su l'eloquenza.   Napoli, Libreria della Diana, 1930.

  12°.
  Autograph dedication.

  NN 0019326   MH-L

Napolitano, Giovanni.   I 170-N
  Lumi di vita interiore.   Napoli: Gaspare Casella, 1923.
  120 p. 12°.

  1. Title. 2. Ethics.
  N.Y.P.L.   March 24, 1924.

  NN 0019327   NN

Napolitano, Giovanni, 1901–

  see

  Napolitano, Pasquale Giovanni, 1901–

Napolitano, I
  Le secret de la coupe

  see under

  Marquant-Métairie, Maria, 1909–

TT520   Napolitano, I.
.M33
1950   Marquant-Métairie, Maria, 1909–
            Traité théorique des vêtements de dames.   Éd. nouvelle de Mme Marquant-Métairie; suivant les bases de coupe de I. Napolitano et M. M. Gaudet & Métairie.   Paris, Éditions Napolitano, °1950.

Napolitano, I   L687 Q907
  Le trésor du tailleur. Plans économiques indiquant la meilleure manière de disposer les modèles sur l'étoffe pour employer le moins de tissu possible pour toutes sortes de vêtements d'hommes, de dames et d'enfants de toutes tailles, établis par I. Napolitano. L. Gaudet et J. Métairie, gendres et successeurs. ... .   Paris, [1909].
  [8], 52, [2] p. illus., 3 port. on 1 pl. 36 x 23ᶜᵐ.

  NN 0019331   ICJ

Napolitano, Leonardo F.
  ... Aportes a la historia patria, bregando por la verdad histórico, las figuras encumbradas de la independencia y de la emancipación, deben ser honradas con fervor sincero. Reconstrucción de lugares históricos. Evocaciones y homenajes a las figuras humildes y preclaras del pasado ilustre. Buenos Aires, Editorial Buenos Aires, 1940.
  158, [2] p. incl. illus. (facsim.) plates, ports., plans. 21ᵐ.
  Imprint covered by label: Buenos Aires, Librería del colegio, s. a.

  1. Argentine republic—Hist. 2. San Martín, José de, 1778–1850.
  I. Title.
  Library of Congress   F2831.N25   42–11107
                                    [2]   982

  NN 0019332   DLC NcU DPU

Napolitano, Leonardo F
  Del árbol espiritual; ramajes, frutos y flores de la poliédrica interior.   Mendoza, Editorial "Cuyo," 1946.
  222 p. 21 cm.

  I. Title.
                                                   A 49–6470*
  New York. Public Libr.
  for Library of Congress   [1]

  NN 0019333   NN DPU

Napolitano, Leonardo F.
  Del pasado mendocino; bregando por la justicia y la verdad historica. Exhumando valores olvidados. Evocaciones pintorescas y antañinas. Rezagos de la barbarie primitiva modernizados con la elegancia contemporánea.   [Buenos Aires] Editorial Buenos Aires, 1944.
  143 p. port. 21 cm.

  NN 0019334   DPU

Napolitano, Leonardo F.
  ... El drama familiar y social ...   Buenos Aires, Imp. Gir y Schaffner, 1939.
  160 p., 1 l. 19½ᵐ.

  1. Family. 2. Social ethics. I. Title.   41–17276
  Library of Congress   HM216.N3
                                    [2]   301

  NN 0019335   DLC DPU

VOLUME 405

Napolitano, Leonardo F.
... Egosofía. Exploraciones introspectivas. Por las selvas y mares de la vida interior. Debe catearse en las reservas morales de cada ser, para movilizar dinámicamente sus riquezas latentes y orientarlas hacia la auto disciplina. Buenos Aires, Imprenta S. Gir, 1937.
158, ii p. 18½ᵐ.

1. Moral education. 2. Social problems. I. Title.
40-22181

Library of Congress   B1084.N33E5
(2)   199.82

NN 0019336   DLC ICarbS DPU

Arg **Napolitano, Leonardo F**
G   Evolución histórica del turismo. La
155   región andina en la vida turística argen-
.N3   tina (la necesidad de crear la cátedra de
      turismo en nuestra Universidad) Mendoza,
      1953.
      26 p. 24 cm.

NN 0019337   DPU

Napolitano, Leonardo F.
    Evoluciones de la Democracia. Buenos Aires,
1925.

NN 0019338   NN

G342.82 **Napolitano, Leonardo F**
N162g   Gobernantes y gobernados; contribución al
         derecho constitucional. Buenos Aires, Napolitano
         Hnos., 1912.
         164p. 22cm.

         Author's autograph presentation copy to Vri
         and Angel Petroff.

1018638   1. State, The. 2. Argentine Republic -
Constitutional law. I. Title.

NN 0019339   TxU

Napolitano, Leonardo F
... Hacia el arquetipo social ... (Buenos Aires) Editorial Buenos Aires, 1942.
125 p., 1 l. 20½ᵐ.

1. Civilization. 2. Sociology. 3. Evolution. I. Title.
43-1709
Library of Congress   HM101.N3
(2)   301

NN 0019340   DLC

Napolitano, Leonardo F.
... Legislación social contemporánea; estudios y críticas de las leyes sociales sancionadas hasta el presente en la República Argentina. Mendoza-Buenos Aires, "La Quincena social", 1928.
152 p. 20ᵐ.

1. Labor and laboring classes—Argentine Republic. 2. Argentine Republic—Soc. condit. 3. Argentine Republic—Sanit. affairs. (3. Public health—Argentine Republic) I. Title.
29-15562

NN 0019341   DLC MH-L

Napolitano, Leonardo F
... Mendoza; historia de la nomenclatura de sus calles. Buenos Aires, Editorial "Buenos Aires," 1943.
124, (4) p. maps (part double) 20ᵐ.

1. Mendoza, Argentine republic (City)—Streets. 2. Argentine republic—Biog.
45-11387
Library of Congress   F3011.M45N3
(3)

NN 0019342   DLC DPU

Napolitano, Leonardo F.
... Raza vencida: Evocaciones de antaño.—Perfiles raciales.—Hábitos y sistemas de ayer.—Problemas sociales de hoy y esperanzas fundadas del mañana. 2. ed., rev., aum. y corr. Buenos Aires, Talleres gráficos S. Gir, 1936.
200, ii p. illus. 18½ᵐ.

1. Argentine republic—Civilization. 2. Argentine republic—Soc. condit. I. Title.
38-24459
Library of Congress   F2810.N33
(2)   918.2

NN 0019343   DLC

NAPOLITANO, LEONARDO F.
Sentires poeticos, de ayer y de hoy. Mendoza, 1953.
[50] p., 23cm.

1. Poetry, Argentine. I. Title.

NN 0019344   NN

Napolitano, Leonardo F
Treguas de combate, recopilación de artículos literarios, descriptivos, doctrinarios y sociológicos. Buenos Aires, Imp. A. Pedemonte, 1922.
174, [2] p. port. 21 cm.

NN 0019345   NcU

Napolitano, Luigi.
L'imposta genreale (sic) sull'entrata; commento sistematico, con appendice contenente tutti i testi legislativi aggiornati al luglio 1949. Pref. del prof. Ettore Scandale. Napoli, E. Jovene, 1949.
xv, 451 p. 19 cm.

1. Income tax—Italy—Law. I. Italy. Laws, statutes, etc.
51-22737

NN 0019346   DLC

Napolitano, Luigi.
L'imposta generale sull'entrata; commento sistematico, con appendice contenente tutti i testi legislativi aggiornati al settembre 1950. Napoli, E. Jovene, 1951.
xii, 508 p. 19 cm.
——— Appendice di aggiornamento al 1 Maggio 1952. Napoli, E. Jovene, 1952.
79 p. 19 cm.

1. Income tax—Italy—Law. I. Italy. Laws, statutes, etc. II. Title.
51-27592 rev

NN 0019347   DLC NNU-W

Napolitano, Luigi.
L'imposta generale sull'entrata; commento sistematico. Appendice di aggiornamento, al 1 maggio 1952. Napoli, E. Jovene, 1952.
76 p.

NN 0019348   NNU-W

Napolitano, Luigi.
La imposta sulle società. rref. di Edgardo Caste.'i. Milano, Giuffrè, 1955.
xix, 455 p. forms. 25 cm. (Commenti sistematici delle nuove leggi finanziarie, 1)
"L. 6 agosto 1954, n. 603: Istituzione di una imposta sulle società e modificazioni in materia di imposte indirette sugli affari": p. (257)-278.
Bibliographical footnotes.

1. Corporations—Italy—Taxation. I. Title. (Series)
56-38752

NN 0019349   DLC NNU-W MH-L

Napolitano, Luigi.
Il reddito nella scienza delle finanze e nel diritto tributario italiano. Milano, A. Giuffrè, 1953.
xii, 242 p. 25 cm.
Bibliographical footnotes.

1. Income tax. 2. Income tax—Italy—Law. I. Title.
A 53-6680
Chicago. Univ. Libr.
for Library of Congress (a)†

NN 0019350   ICU DLC

Napolitano, Maria Lo Gatto
see Lo Gatto Napolitano, Maria.

Napolitano, Maria (Martone) 1899– *ed.*
Autobiografia degli Stati Uniti, a cura di Maria Napolitano Martone. Milano, Gruppo editoriale Domus, 1942.
2 p. l., (7)-310 p., 1 l. plates, ports. 22½ cm. (*Half-title:* La Ruota della fortuna; raccolta di memorie, biografie, cronache, saggi e testimonianze, diretta da Filippo Piazzi. Vol. I)
"Cronache, confessioni e rapporti, dovuti, complessivamente, a diciannove tra scrittori e giornalisti e cinque anonimi, e per un modo o per l'altro costituiscono un' inchiesta sul costume degli Stati Uniti."—Pref.

1. U. S.—Civilization. 2. U. S.—Soc. life & cust. I. Title.
E169.1.N32   917.3   46-39842 rev

NN 0019352   DLC NcD

Napolitano, Maria (Martone) 1899–   tr.

Berg, Mary, 1924–
Il ghetto di Varsavia; diario di Mary Berg, presentato da S. L. Shneiderman. (Roma) De Carlo, 1946.

Napolitano, Maria (Martone) 1899– *ed. and tr.*
Novellieri inglesi e americani; panorama della letteratura novellistica inglese e americana, a cura di Maria Martone e Edoardo Bizzarri. Tavole fuori testo dei pittori Brini, Gramaticopolo e Ferrari. Roma, De Carlo, 1944.
898 p., 1 l. illus. 24½ cm. (*Half-title:* Enciclopedia della novella, diretta da Salvatore de Carlo)
"Le traduzioni ... sono dovute a Maria Martone per la parte americana e ad Edoardo Bizzarri per la parte inglese."

1. English fiction (Selections: Extracts, etc.) 2. American fiction (Selections: Extracts, etc.) 3. Italian fiction—Translations from English. 4. English fiction—Translations into Italian. 5. American fiction—Translations into Italian. I. Bizzarri, Edoardo, ed. and tr. II. Title.
PR1115.N3   823.082   45-21581 rev 2

NN 0019354   DLC

PR6015 Napolitano, Maria (Martone) 1899– tr.
.I 53R35
Hilton, James, 1900–
Prigionieri del passato, di James Hilton. Romanzo. Primo traduzione italiana di Maria Martone. Roma, De Carlo (1944)

Napolitano, Mario.
L'acquiescenza al provvedimento amministrativo. Milano, A. Giuffrè, 1955.
104 p. 25 cm.

1. Acquiescence (Law)—Italy. 2. Administrative law—Italy. I. Title.
58-34273 ‡

NN 0019356   DLC NNC MH-L CtY-L

VOLUME 405

Napolitano, Mario, writer on chess.
    Le mie venti partite del campionato
mondiale di scacchi per corrispondenza.
Milano, La Scacchiera ₁1953₁

        65, ₁2₁ p.   port.

NN   0019357   OCl

WU
500   NAPOLITANO, Mario, **writer on dentistry.**
N216o   Odontotecnica scientifica; matematica,
1955   fisica, chimica e tecnologia applicate
        all'odontotecnica per medici dentisti,
        specializzandi in odontojatria, odonto-
        tecnici, allievi degli istituti di odonto-
        tecnica ₁di₁ M. Napolitano ₁e₁ V. Cadeddu.
        Roma, 1953-55 ₁v. 1, 1955₁
            2 v.   illus.
            1. Dentistry - Mechanical I. Cadeddu,
        Vittorio   Title

NN   0019358   DNLM

Napolitano, Notturno, pseud.
        see Epicuro, Marc' Antonio, 1472-1555.

Napolitano, Pasquale Giovanni, 1901–
    Napolitano; fifteen reproductions of his work in oil, sgraf-
fito, fresco, drawing and mechanical design. An article by
Merle Armitage. A portrait by Brett Weston and an original
lithograph drawn on the stone by Giovanni Napolitano and
hand printed by Lynton R. Kistler. New York, E. Weyhe,
1935.
    4 p. l., 7 p., 1 l. front. (port.) illus. 15 pl. 21½ᵐ.
"This edition ... consists of 212 copies." This copy not numbered.
"The book was designed by Merle Armitage."
    I. Armitage, Merle, 1893–
                                                      W 36-38
Washington, D. C.   Public Library
                               [N6537.N   ]

NN   0019360   DWP MoSW CoU NjN NBu MB

HE2791   Napolitano, Pasquale Giovanni, 1901–   illus.
.A83
1948   **Armitage, Merle,** 1893–
            Operations Santa Fé; Atchison, Topeka & Santa Fé rail-
        way system. Ed. by Edwin Corle, drawings by P. G. Na-
        politano. ₁1st ed.₁ New York, Duell, Sloan & Pearce ₁1948₁

Napolitano, Pietro Settimo
A2605   Marco Vipsanio Agrippa nella famiglia
        di Augusto. Roma, F. Failli, 1941.
        43 p.

        Microcopy of the original.

            1. ₁Agrippa, Marcus Vipsanius.
        2. Augustus, emperor of Rome, 63 B. C.–14
        A. D.

NN   0019362   WaU

Napolitano, Rocco.
    Buon umore: tre farse comiche in un atto

        see under   title

Napolitano, Tomaso.
    ... La famiglia sovietica, l'istituto della famiglia nella **storia**
e nel diritto dell' URSS. ₁Roma₁ Edizioni della **Bussola**
₁1946₁
    267, ₁1₁ p. 22½ᵐ. (*Half-title:* Collana "Ieri e oggi," II)
"Bibliografia essenziale": p. 253–257.

    1. Domestic relations—Russia.   I. Title.

                                                      47-22345

NN   0019364   DLC ICU PU

Napolitano, Tomaso.
    Maternità e infanzia nell'U.R.S.S. (Saggi
di legislazione sovietica) Prefazione di
Gennaro Marciano. Padova, CEDAM, 1934.
    xii, 171 p.

NN   0019365   NNC DLC-P4

Napolitano, Tomaso.
    ... Maternità e infanzia nell' U.R.S.S. (saggio di **politica**
sociale) ... Firenze, F. Le Monnier, 1938.
    2 p. l., ₁vii₁–viii, 81 p., 2 l. 19ᵐ. (Biblioteca popolare di cultura poli-
tica, I)
    Supplements an edition published in 1934. *cf.* p. viii.
    CONTENTS. — Le leggi-propaganda. — La realtà d'ogni **giorno (docu-**
menti)

    1. Women in Russia. 2. Children in Russia.   I. Title.

                                                      45-44182
Library of Congress   HQ1062.N3 1938
                            ₁2₁   **396**

NN   0019366   DLC

HX626   Napolitano, Tommaso.
.N21   Le metamorfosi del bolscevismo (polemiche
        sull'U.R.S.S.) Milano, Fratelli Bocca, 1940.
            xxiii, 312 p. (Collezione La Russia con-
        temporanea, no. 9)
            Includes bibliography.

            1. Communism—Hist. I. Title.

NN   0019367   ICU

Napolitano, Tomaso.
    ... Il partito comunista dell' U. R. S. S. (I congressi e la **linea**
generale) Roma, L'APE ₁1945₁
    xxxii, 236 p., 2 l. 20ᵐ. (*On cover:* Documenti del bolscevismo)
"Bibliografia sovietica": p. ₁219₁–226.

    1. Vsesoîuznaîa kommunisticheskaîa partiîa (bol'shevikov) 2. Rus-
sia—Pol. & govt.—1917–   I. Title.
    DK266.N258   47-17860

NN   0019368   DLC CSt

Napolitano, Tomaso.
    ... La politica criminale sovietica ... 2. ed. rielaborata e
aggiornata. Padova, CEDAM, Casa editrice dott. A. Milani,
1936.
    3 p. l., ₁ix₁–xviii p., 2 l., ₁3₁–330 p., 1 l. 25ᵐ.
    Includes legislation.
"Errata-corrige": leaf inserted.

    1. Crime and criminals—Russia. 2. Punishment—Russia. 3. Criminal
law—Russia.   I. Russia (1923–   U. S. S. R.) Laws, statutes, etc.
II. Title.

                                                      45-50090

NN   0019369   DLC NN NNC

Napolitano, Tomaso.
    U.S.S. Wisconsin, BB-64

    see under   title

Napolitano, Vitantonio, 1901–
    ... 25 luglio. ₁Roma₁ Casa editrice "Vega" ₁1944₁
    2 p. l., ₁7₁–396 p., 2 l. 18ᵐ.

    1. Italy—Pol. & govt.—1922–   2. Fascism—Italy. 3. World war,
1939–   —Italy.   I. Title.
                                                      45-14805
Library of Congress   DG571.N25
                            ₁2₁   945.09

NN   0019371   DLC CLSU CSt NcU

Napolitano, Vittorio.
    Escursioni di un siciliano nell'isola e fuori.
Milano, Gastaldi [1955]
    173 p.   19 cm.   (Collana di "Cultura")
    1. Europe – Descr. and Trav., 1945–
    2. Sicily - Descr. and Trav., 1900–
    3. Sicily - Biog.

NN   0019372   NN

4PQ   Napolitano de Sanz, Emma
Sp   El despertar, novela. Buenos
Amer   Aires, Editorial G. Kraft ₁1953₁
1178   192 p.

        (Coleccion Vertice)

NN   0019373   DLC-P4 NN NIC

NAPOLITANO DE SANZ, EMMA.
    Francisco A. Sicardi, por Emma Napolitano.
Buenos Aires, Impr. de la Univ., 1942.   376–528 p.
front.   23cm. (Buenos Aires ₍City₎. Universidad nacional.
Instituto de literatura argentina, Sección de crítica, [Publicaciones]
t. 2, no. 6)

    1. Sicardi, Francisco   Anselmo, 1856–1927.
I. Ser.

NN   0019374   NN NNC NcD

G465.2
P162t   Napolitano de Sanz, Emma.
            ... Teoría y práctica de análisis sintác-
        tico (elemental y superior) Oración **simple.**
        [Buenos Aires] Editorial "Buenos Aires"
        [1950]
            1 p. l., 5–302, [4] p. 21cm.

            1. Spanish language - Syntax. I. **Title.**

NN   0019375   TxU

Napolitano Martone, Maria
    see Napolitano, Maria (Martone) 1899–

Napollon, Sanson
    see Nappolon, Sanson.

Napollon-Margarita, Ernesta, 1840–
    Novelle narrate da Ernesta Napollon-Margarita. Ge-
nova, Stab. tip.-lit. ved. Armanino, figli e Casabona, 1877.
    84 p. 21½ᵐ.
    CONTENTS.—Maria Wink; storia irlandese, 1690.—Il venditore di fiam-
miferi.

                                                      6-30291

NN   0019378   DLC

Napolska, Mary Remigia, *sister.*
    ... The Polish immigrant in Detroit to 1914, by Sister Mary
Remigia Napolska, Felician, o. s. f. Chicago, Ill., Polish
Roman Catholic union of America, 1946.
    110 p. front. (map) 1 illus. 21½ᵐ. (Annals of the Polish R. C.
union, Archives and museum. Vol. x. 1945–1946)
    Thesis (M. A.)—University of Notre Dame.
"List of sources and references": p. 108–110.

    1. Poles in Detroit.
                                                      46-6802
Library of Congress   F574.D4N3
                            ₁2₁   325.243809774

NN   0019379   DLC OKentU MB TxU ICN OCl ViU

VOLUME 405

AC
831
Napolski, Alexander von
   Beitrag zur kenntnis der gesteine der
Republik Honduras ... Leipzig, 1904. 46 p.
Inaug. Diss. -Tübingen, 1904.

NN   0019380   ICRL MH PU

NAPOLSKI, FRIEDRICH VON, 1891-
   Erfahrungen in der Auslandshandelskammer-Arbeit.
[Bonn, Druck: H. Köllen, 1951?] 64 p. 21cm.
(Deutscher Industrie- und Handelstag. Schriftenreihe. Heft 14)

1. Commerce--Assoc. and org.   --Germany. I. Series.

NN   0019381   NN

Napolski, Friedrich von, 1891–
   Die völkerrechtliche natur der kriegsgefangeneninter-
nierung, dargestellt an hand der rechtslage der internier-
ten deutschen kriegsgefangenen in der Schweiz ...
Waldshut, Druck von H. Zimmermann, 1919.

   x, 73 p. 22½ᶜᵐ.
   Inaug.-diss.—Marburg.
   "Literatur": p. vi-viii.

1. Prisoners of war. 2. European war, 1914-1918—Prisoners and prisons. 3. European war, 1914-1918—Switzerland. I. Title.

                                                    24-11057

Library of Congress   JX5141.N4

NN   0019382   DLC CtY-L PU ICRL ICU PU-L

Napolski, Friedrich von, 1891–
   ...Zollhandbuch für die Schweiz; Zolltarif vom 8. Juni 1921
nebst den wichtigsten für die Zollformalitäten, sowie die Ein- und
Ausfuhr in Betracht kommenden Bestimmungen und einer Über-
sicht über die handelspolitischen Beziehungen der Schweiz zum
Ausland, mit einem ausführlichen Warenverzeichnis, nach amtlichen Quellen bearbeitet von Dr. F. v. Napolski... Nach dem
Stande vom 1. November 1927. Berlin: R. Hobbing, 1927.
123 p. incl. tables.   4°.   (Zollhandbücher für den Welthandel.)

376280A. 1. Tariff—Switzerland,   1921.
N. Y. P. L.   September 27, 1928

NN   0019383   NN

NAPOLSKI, Friedrich von, 1891-, editor.
   Zollhandbuch für die Schweiz. Nach amtlichen
quellen bearbeitet von F.v.Napolski. 1.nach-
trag. Berlin, R.Hobbing, [1929].

   f°. pp.19.
   "Zollhandbucher für den welthandel."

NN   0019384   MH

Napolski, Max von, 1856–
   Leben und werke des trobadors Ponz de Capduoill ...
Marburg, 1879.

   29, [3] p. 21ᶜᵐ.
   Inaug.-diss.—Marburg.
   Lebenslauf.
   Chapter I of the author's work, published in full, Halle, 1880 (182 p.)
   Bibliography: page following p. 29.

1. Pons de Capdoill, 12th cent.

                                                    18-9249

Library of Congress   PC3330.P6N3

NN   0019385   DLC

PC3330
P6N3
1879
Napolski, Max von, 1856-
   Leben und Werke des Trobadors Ponz de
Capduoill. Halle, M. Niemeyer, 1879.
   152 p. 22 cm.

   Chapter 1 issued also as author's thesis,
Marburg.
   Includes bibliography.

   1. Pons de Capdoill, 12th cent.

         OC1W ICU OC1 ICN NIC
NN   0019386   MeB MdBP NRU NjP RPB OCU CU CtY PU

NAPOLSKI, Stanislaus von.
   Beiträge zur charakteristik mittelalterlich-
en lebens, etc. Inaug.-diss. Marburg, 1885.

NN   0019387   MH ICRL DLC NjP

S541
.M73
1954
Napol'skiĭ, M., ed.
   Moscow. Vsesoiuznaia sel'skokhoziaĭstvennaia vystavka,
1954-
   Научно-исследовательские учреждения; краткий путе-
водитель. [Ответственный редактор М. Напольский. Мо-
сква] Московский рабочий, 1954.

Napol'skiĭ, M   ed.
   По методам И. В. Мичурина; сборник статей. Москва,
Гос. изд-во сельхоз. лит-ры, 1955.
   92 p. 20 cm.

   At head of title: Всесоюзная сельскохозяйственная выставка.

1. Plant-breeding. 2. Michurin, Ivan Vladimirovich, 1855-1935.
I. Title.   Title transliterated: Po metodam I. V. Michurina.

         SB123.N3   58-42796

NN   0019389   DLC

TN871
.Z47
Napol'skiĭ, M. S., joint author.

   Zhdanov, Mikhail Alekseevich.
      Методы исчисления запасов нефти. Москва, Гостоптех-
издат, 1948.

336.1
N162
1814
Napomknienia względem dobra publicznego.
   Warszawa, Nakładem Zawadzkiego i Komp.,
1814.
   56p. 21cm.

   At head of title added in manuscript:
Julian Ursyn Niemcewicz.

   1. Public domain. 2. Economics.
   I. Niemcewicz, Julian Ursyn, 1758-1841.

NN   0019391   KU

(Napor Bosne i Hercegovine za oslobođenje i ujedinjenje)
Напор Босне и Херцеговине за ослобо ење и уједињење.
Обрадио Перо Слијепчеви и сарадници. [Сарајево]
Изд. Обл. одбора нар. одбране, 1929.

   400 p. illus. 21 cm.
   Includes bibliographical references.

   1. Bosnia and Herzegovina—Politics and government. 2. European
War, 1914-1918—Bosnia and Herzegovina.   I. Slijepčević, Pero,
1888-1964, ed.

         DB250.N3   74-202062

NN   0019392   DLC

Napori: France Stele

   see under

   Slovenska akademija znanosti in umetnosti,
Ljubljana. Razred za umetnost.

Naporko, Aleksandr Grigor'evich.
   Очерки развития железнодорожного транспорта СССР.
Москва, Гос. трансп. жел.-дор. изд-во, 1954.
   284 p. 23 cm.
   ———— Microfilm (negative)
   Made in 1955 by the Library of Congress.
                                    Microfilm Slavic 372 AC

   1. Railroads—Russia.   I. Title.
                        Title transliterated : Ocherki razvitiĭa zhe-
                        leznodorozhnogo transporta SSSR.

   HE3135.N3   55-23296

NN   0019394   DLC CaBVaU

TF85.
.P4
Naporko, Aleksandr Grigor'evich.
   Передовые методы работы железнодорожников; сборник.
Общая ред. А. Г. Напорко. Москва, Гос. трансп. жел.-дор.
изд-во [1946]

Napotnik, Mihael, 1850-
   Die Basilika zur Heiligen Maria, Mutter der Barmher-
zigkeit, in der Grazervorstadt zu Marburg von Michael
Napotnik. 2., verb. und verm. Aufl. mit vielen und
originellen Abbildungen ausgestattet. Marburg, im
Selbstverlage des Verfassers, 1909

   538 p. illus.
   Earlier ed. published under title: Einweihungsfeier
der neuerbauten Pfarrkirche zur Heiligen Maria, Mutter der Barmherzigkeit   der Grazervorstadt zu
Marburg.

NN   0019396   MH

PG 1661
.B7N2
Napotnik, Mihael, 1850-
   Kratek pregled bosanskega slovstva. V
Mariboru, 1884.
   84 p.

   1. Serbian literature--Bosnia and
Herzegovina--Hist. & crit. 2. Croatian
literature--Bosnia and Herzgovina--
Hist. & crit.

NN   0019397   ICU MH

Napp, Adolf Ernst, 1902–
   ... Der altar von Pergamon. Mit 32 bildtafeln. München,
F. Bruckmann ag. [1936]
   8 p. 32 pl. on 16 l. 24½ᶜᵐ.
   "Literatur": p. 8.

   1. Pergamum. 2. Berlin. Museen. Pergamon-museum. 3. Sculpture,
Greek. I. Title.
                                            A C 37-758

Vassar college. Library
for Library of Congress   [2]

NN   0019398   NPV NcU CU NcD PSC

Napp, Adolf Ernst, 1902–
   Bukranion und guirlande; beiträge zur entwick-
lungsgeschichte der hellenistischen und römischen
dekorationskunst ... von Adolf Ernst Napp. [Wer-
theim am Main, Bechstein, 1933]
   vi, 49, [2] p. 21ᶜᵐ.

   Thesis, Heidelberg.
   Bibliographical footnotes.

   1. Decoration and ornament, Greek. 2. Decoration
and ornament, Roman.

NN   0019399   NNC IU PBm MiU PU CtY

VOLUME 405

Napp, Ernst ¡Eugen Julius¡ 1855–
De rebvs imperatore M. Avrelio Antonino in Oriente
gestis ... Bonnae, typis J. F. Carthaus, 1879.

134 p. 22½ᵐ.

Inaug.-dis.—Bonn.
Vita.
Half-title: De rebus ¡etc.¡ Qvaestiones historicae atqve chronologicae de
bello armeniaco parthico et de Avidii Cassii seditione. Accedvnt appendices et conspectvs titvlorum.

1. Rome—Hist.—Marcus Aurelius, 161–180. 2. Avidius Cassius, fl. 175
3. Inscriptions, Greek. 4. Inscriptions, Latin.

Library of Congress   DG297.N2   4–35230†

NN   0019400   DLC NBuU MiU PU NjP CtY

W 4   NAPP, Ernst Hermann Friedrich, 1929–
M96   Die Ausscheidung von neutralen C 17-
1954   Keto-Steroiden im Harn der Frau während
        des normalen Menstruationscyclus.
        München, 1954.
            44 ℓ. illus.
            Inaug.-Diss.-Munich.
            1. Menstrual cycle 2. Steroids

NN   0019401   DNLM

Napp, Heinrich, 1910–
... Ueber Entzündungserscheinungen an den
Tonsillen Neugeborener und kleiner Kinder ...
Rostock,1934.
    Inaug.-Diss.-Rostock.
    Lebenslauf.
    "Literatur-Verzeichnis": p.17.

NN   0019402   CtY

Napp (Hermann) [1869–]. *Beiträge zur*
Symptomatologie und Epidemiologie des Icte-
rus catarrhalis bei Kindern. 30 pp., 1 l. 8°.
Bonn, J. Bach Wwe., 1893.

NN   0019403   DNLM MH

Napp, Ludwig, 1861–
Untersuchung der sprachlichen Eigenthümlichkeiten
des Livre des miracles de Notre Dame de Chartres ...
Würzburg, 1887.
    [2] 54 p.   23.5 cm.
    Inaug.-Diss.-Bonn.
    Vita.
    Le livre des miracles de Notre Dame de Chartes
    is the translation by Jehan le Marchant of a Latin
    prose text. - cf. book, p. [3]
        1. Jean le Marchant, fl. 1262. 2. Le livre des
    miracles de Notre Dame de Chartres.
    Full name: Ludwig Christian Napp.

NN   0019404   CtY MH IU

Napp (Otto). *Ueber die Bildung polyposer*
Adenome und Carcinome in atrophischer Magen-
schleimhaut. 37 pp. 8°. *Freiburg, Speyer &
Kaerner, 1900.*

NN   0019405   DNLM ICRL

Napp, Ricardo.
The Argentine Republic; written in German by Richard
Napp assisted by several fellow-writers for the Central Argen-
tine commission on the Centenary exhibition at Philadelphia
... Buenos Aires, Printed by the Sociedad anonima, 1876.

2 p. l., 463, xcvii p. fold. maps, tables. 22ᵐᵐ.

In English.

1. Argentine republic.   4–9076

Library of Congress   F2808.N21

PPAN OCl
DAS MeB ICJ MB Nh PPF CaBVaU CaOTP MWA TxU NcD OU
NN   0019406   DLC NcU ODW CU NNH MH DNLM DN-Ob

Napp, Ricardo.
Die Argentinische Republik. Im auftrag des Argentin. central comité's für die Philadelphia-ausstellung und
mit dem beistand mehrerer mitarbeiter bearb. von Richard Napp. (Mit 6 karten) Buenos Aires, Gedruckt in
der dampfbuchdruckerei der Sociedad anónima, 1876.

2 p. l., 360, xcvii, ¡361¡–495, ¡2¡ p. fold. pl., ¡ fold. maps, 9 fold. tab.
21ᵐ.

1. Argentine Republic.

A 14–1659

NN   0019407   CU NNH MH-A

Napp, Ricardo, ed.
El Economista, revista quincenal; estadistica, comercio,
industria, agricultura, inmigracion y colonizacion, &ᶜ.

Buenos Aires, 18

Napp, Ricardo, ed.
La Plata monatsschrift (revista alemana) publicacion
destinada esclusivamente a dar a conocer estos paises
en Europa ... 1.–   jahrg.   ;
jan. 1873–
¡Buenos Aires, Nolte'sche buch- und kunsthandlung,
1873–

F   Napp, Ricardo
2808   La República Argentina; obra escrita en
N163aS   alemán por Ricardo Napp con la ayuda de varios
        colaboradores y por encargo del Comité Central
        Argentino para la Exposición en Filadelfia.
        Buenos Aires, Impreso por la Sociedad Anónima,
        1876.
            482,xcvii p. fold.maps,tables(part fold.)
            Original title: Die Argentinische Republik.

            1. Argentine Republic.

PPL MWA CtY
NN   0019410   CLU TxU MiU FU CU NNH MiU MH MB PPAN

Napp, Ricardo.
La République Argentine par R. Napp aidé de plusieurs
collaborateurs. Ouvrage écrit par ordre du Comité central
argentin pour l'exposition de Philadelphie. (Avec addition
de plusieurs cartes inédites) Buenos Ayres, Impr. du "Cour-
rier de la Plata", 1876.

2 p. l., 523, xxx p. maps. 22ᵐ.

1. Argentine Republic.

Library of Congress   F2808.N22   2—11313

NN   0019411   DLC FMU NN CU MWA

AC   Napp, Rudolf, 1911–
831   Erwerbsverbote durch einstweilige verfügung.
    ... Giessen, 1934.   98 p.
        Inaug. Diss.-Giessen, 1934.
        Lebenslauf.
        Bibliography.

NN   0019412   ICRL

Napp, Victor Johan Adolf, 1901–
... Ueber Erfahrungen mit dem Ahlstroem'schen
Ring ...
    Hamburg,1925. 22cm.
    Inaug.-Diss.-Hamburg.
    At head of title: Aus der Universitäts-Frauen-
    klinik Hamburg-Eppedorf; Direktor Prof. Dr. Hey-
    nemann.
    Lebenslauf.

NN   0019413   CtY MiU

Napp-Zinn, Anton Felix, 1899–
Binnenschiffahrt und eisenbahn, werden, gestalt und pro-
blem ihres verhältnisses im Deutschen Reich, von dr. Anton
Felix Napp-Zinn ... Leipzig, G. A. Gloeckner, 1928.

vi p., 1 l., 126 p. 23½ᵐ. (Added t.-p.: Kölner wirtschafts- und social-
wissenschaftliche studien. Zweite folge. 3. heft)

"Literatur-verzeichnis": p. 123–126.

1. Inland navigation—Germany. 2. Railroads—Germany. 3. ¡Railroads and waterways—Germany¡   I. Title.

Title from Bureau of   Railway Economics   HE1049.N16
                            Printed by L. C.   A 30–136

NN   0019414   DBRE

Napp-Zinn, Anton Felix, 1899–
Binnenschiffahrtspolitik der Niederlande ... von prof. dr.
A. F. Napp-Zinn ... Jena, Gustav Fischer, 1938.

viii p., 1 l., 102 p. fold. map, tables. 23½ᵐ. (Studien zur verkehrswirtschaft der Niederlande. 1)

Added t.-p.: Verkehrswissenschaftliche abhandlungen; schriftenreihe
des Verkehrswissenschaftlichen forschungsrats beim Reichsverkehrs-
ministerium. hft. 5.
"Literatur": p. ¡100¡–102.

1. Inland navigation—Netherlands. 2. Canals—Netherlands.
                                        A C 38–2484

Michigan. Univ. Library   HE674.N22
for Library of Congress   [HE131.G45 hft. 5]
                    ¡2¡   (380.82)

NN   0019415   MiU DLC NN

NAPP-ZINN, ANTON FELIX, 1899–
Christian Eckert; Gedenkrede.   Mainz [Institut für Verkehrswirtschaft an der Universität Mainz] 1952.   16. [2] p.
mounted port.   23cm.

Bibliography included in "Anmerkungen", p. [17–18]

1. Eckert, Christian Lorenz Maria, 1874–1952. I. Mainz. Universität. Institut für Verkehrswirtschaft.

NN   0019416   NN ICU

Napp-Zinn, ¡Anton Felix, 1899–
Eisenbahn und kraftwagen; verhandlungen auf
der von dem verein zur wahrung der gemeinsamen
wirtschaftlichen interessen in Rheinland und
Westfalen und dem Institut fuer verkehrswissen-
schaft an der Universitaet Koeln...dr. A.F.
Napp-Zinn, Koeln, januar 1931. [1931?].

[Cologne. Universitaet. Institut fuer verkehrs-
wissenschaft. Buchreihe... nr.4.]

NN   0019417   DLC

Napp-Zinn, Anton Felix, 1889–   ed.
Festschrift zu Ehren des Herrn Geheimen
Regierungsrates... Christian Eckert
    see his Kultur und Wirtschaft im
rheinischen Raum.

Napp-Zinn, Anton Felix, 1899–
Friedrich List als Verkehrspolitiker. Mainz, F. Kupfer-
berg ¡1948¡

24 p. 21 cm. (Universitas Moguntina. Reden und Aufsätze,
Heft 2)

1. List, Friedrich, 1789–1846. I. Title. (Series: Mainz. Universität. Reden und Aufsätze, Heft 2)

HB107.L6N3   51–23703

NN   0019419   DLC NBuU CaBVaU NN MH

Napp-Zinn, Anton Felix, 1899–
100 [i.e. Hundert] Jahre Köln-Düsseldorfer
Rheindampfschiffahrt
    see under Köln-Düsseldorfer Rheindampf-
schiffahrt, G. m. b. H.

VOLUME 405

Napp-Zinn, Anton Felix, 1899–
Johann Friedrich von Pfeiffer und die Kameralwissenschaften an der Universität Mainz. Wiesbaden, F. Steiner, 1955.
xviii, 119 p. 26 cm. (Beiträge zur Geschichte der Universität Mainz, Bd. 1)
The author's previously unpublished thesis, Cologne 1921.
Bibliography: p. ₍xiii₎-xviii.

1. Pfeiffer, Johann Friedrich von, 1718-1787. 2. Mainz. Universität—Hist. (Series)
Harvard Univ. Library
for Library of Congress ₍2₎
A 56–5707

NN   0019421   MH IEN NN NNC NjR NIC NcD OU

Napp-Zinn, Anton Felix, 1899–   *ed.*
Kultur und Wirtschaft im rheinischen Raum. Festschrift zu Ehren des Herrn Geheimen Regierungsrates ... Christian Eckert ... anlässlich der Vollendung seines 75. Lebensjahres. Hrsg. im Auftrag des Herrn Oberbürgermeisters der Stadt Mainz und der Rechts- und Wirtschaftswissenschaftlichen Fakultät der Johannes Gutenberg-Universität Mainz von Anton Felix Napp-Zinn und Michel Oppenheim. Mainz, Selbstverlag der Stadt ₍1949₎
321 p. plates, port., maps (1 fold.) tables. 25 cm.
Contributions by various authors.
1. Rhine River and Valley—Hist.   2. Rhine River and Valley—Econ. condit.   3. Eckert, Christian Lorenz Maria, 1874–   I. Oppenheim, Michel, joint ed.   II. Title.
Harvard Univ. Library
for Library of Congress ₍1₎
A 51–5675

NN   0019422   MH CtY OrU LU NN OU

Napp-Zinn, Anton Felix, 1899–
Rheinschiffahrt, 1913–1925; ihre wirtschaftliche entwicklung unter dem einfluss von weltkrieg und kriegsfolgen, von dr. Anton Felix Napp-Zinn ... mit 1 skizze und 52 tabellen im text. Berlin, J. Springer, 1925.
vi p., 1 l., 222, ₍2₎ p. incl. map. 23½ᵐ.
"Quellenverzeichnis der tabellen": p. ₍205₎-207; "Literaturverzeichnis": p. 207-210.

1. Shipping—Rhine River and Valley.   2. Rhine River and Valley—Comm.   I. Title.
Library of Congress   HE669.5.R5N3
26–2832

NN   0019423   DLC CtY ICJ

Napp-Zinn, Johannes Nikolaus
see **Napp-Zinn, Klaus,** 1927–

Napp-Zinn, Klaus, 1927–
Anatomische und morphologische Untersuchungen an den Involucral- und Spreublättern von Compositen. Mainz, 1951.
168-170 p. illus. 24 cm.
Diss.—Mainz.
"Sonderabdruck aus Band 98, Heft 1-2, 1951 der Österreichischen botanischen Zeitschrift."
Title page and vita typewritten.
Bibliography: p. 168-170.
1. Flowers—Morphology.   2. Compositae.   I. Title.
Full name: Johannes Nikolaus Napp-Zinn.
QK653.N3
52–41146

NN   0019425   DLC

Nappan, N.S. Experimental farm
see
Canada. Experimental farm, Nappan, N.S.

Nappe, Walter, 1908–
831   Die synallagmatische verknüpfung der gesellschaftlichen beitragsleistungen. ...
Kiel, 1934.   96 p.
Inaug. Diss. - Kiel, 1934.
Lebenslauf.
Bibliography.

NN   0019427   ICRL

La nappe renversee chez Renard. En vers
⁺FC6   burlesques.
⁴456m   A Paris, M.DC.XLIX.
2525   4°.   8p.   21.5cm., in case 28cm.
Moreau 2525.
In folder; in case labeled: Mazarinades.

NN   0019428   MH WU ICN

671   **Nappée, J**
N16t   Travail mécanique des tôles; emboutissage, recuit, étamerie, émaillerie, décoration. Par J. Nappée ... préface de A. Portevin ... Avec 442 figures dans le texte.   Paris et Liége, Librairie polytechnique Ch. Béranger, 1935.
3 p.l., ₍v₎-xviii, 415p. illus., tables, diagrs. 24½cm.

1. Sheet-metal work.

NN   0019429   IU

Nappée, J
Travail mécanique des tôles; emboutissage, recuit, étamerie, émaillerie, décoration. Préf. de A. Portevin. 2. éd. mise à jour et augm. Paris, G. Béranger, 1952.
473 p. illus. 25 cm.

1. Sheet-metal work.   I. Title.
TS250.N23 1952   *671.82 621.792   53–24337 ‡

NN   0019430   DLC NN

Nappée, Marie Louise.
Les bandages en pratique hospitalière et en pratique d'urgence. Paris, Masson, 1952.
208 p. illus. 20 cm.

1. Bandages and bandaging.   I. Title.
RD113.N3   53–19335 ‡

NN   0019431   DLC DNLM

Nappée, Marie Louise.
Manuel pratique de l'infirmière soignante, par mˡˡᵉ M.-L. Nappée; préface du dʳ Delassus. Paris, Masson & cⁱᵉ, 1937.
2 p. l., 384 p. illus., diagrs. 19¼ᶜᵐ.

1. Nurses and nursing.   2. Operations, Surgical.   I. Title.
Library of Congress   RT41.N3   37–9679
Copyright A—Foreign   34791
₍2₎   610.7302

NN   0019432   DLC

Nappée, Marie Louise.
Manuel pratique de l'infirmière soignante ... 3. éd. rev., corr. et augm. Paris, Masson, 1946.
438 p. illus. 20 cm.

1. Nurses and nursing.   ₍1. Nursing₎
Med 47–2406
U. S. Army Medical Library   [WY100N217m 1946]
for Library of Congress   ₍2₎

NN   0019433   DNLM OU

WY   **NAPPEE, Marie Louise**
100   Manuel pratique de l'infirmière
N217m   soignante. 4. éd. rev. et corrigée.
1949   Paris, Masson, 1949.
438 p. illus.
1. Nursing

NN   0019434   DNLM

WY   **NAPPÉE, Marie Louise**
100   Manuel pratique de l'infirmière
N217m   soignants, assistante médicale. 5. éd.,
1953   refondue et complétée. Paris, Masson, 1953.
755 p. illus.
1. Nursing

NN   0019435   DNLM

Napper (Albert) [1815-94]. On the advantages derivable to the medical profession and the public from the establishment of village hospitals, with general instructions concerning costs, plans, rules, etc., and an appropriate dietary. 20 pp. 8°. *London, H. K. Lewis, 1864.* [P., v, 2291.]

NN   0019436   DNLM

1815- 1894.
Napper (Albert). On the advantages derivable to the medical profession and the public from the establishment of village hospitals, with general instructions concerning costs, plans, rules, etc., and an appropriate dietary. 3. ed. 20 pp. 8°. *London, H. K. Lewis, 1866.*

NN   0019437   DNLM

Napper, Edmund. 1579-1654.   *2504.181.1
Common-place book. The Napper family register. Extracts, with brief annotations, by Joseph Gillow.
(In Catholic Record Society. Miscellanea. Vol. I, pp. 133-137. London. 1905.)

G1451 — Napper family. — Genealogy. Napper. — Gillow, Joseph, ed.

NN   0019438   MB

Napper, Gertie McGee.
Some international aspects of the water problems of the lower Rio Grande valley ... by Gertie McGee Napper ... ₍Kingsville, Tex., 1939₎
1 p. l., iii, 50 numb. l. incl. maps. 29 x 22ᶜᵐ.
Thesis (M. s.)—Texas college of arts and industries.
Type-written (carbon copy)
Bibliography: leaves 48-50.

1. Water-rights—U. S.   2. Water-rights—Mexico.   3. Rio Grande.   4. Rio Grande valley.
Library of Congress   HD1694.A3 1939   43–27037

NN   0019439   DLC

Napper, H. F. British settlement between Lindfield and Horsted Keynes. 2 pp. (Sussex Archaeol. Soc. Coll. v. 34, 1886, p. 227.)—Additional notes on "The measurements of Ptolemy and of the Antonine itinerary," by G. M. Hills. 16 pp. (Sussex Archaeol. Soc. Coll. v. 34, 1886, p. 228.)

NN   0019440   MdBP

NAPPER, H.   F.
The Lord's table; its true rubrical position|
London, 1875.

pp.55.

NN   0019441   MH

Napper (James). *Observations pratiques sur l'entérite chronique des enfans. 30 pp. 4°. Paris, 1825, No. 221, v. 196.

NN   0019442   DNLM

VOLUME 405

Napper, John.
  Life drawing, by John Napper and Nicholas Mosley.
London, New York, Studio Publications ₁1954₎
  96 p. illus. 26 cm. (The How to do it series, no. 54)

1. Human figure in art. 2. Anatomy, Artistic. I. Mosley, Nicholas, joint author. II. Title.   (Series)

NC765.N35   743.4   54–14935

NN OU PPT PP CaBVaU
NN 0019443   DLC ViU KU CLSU Or OrP WaE Wa WaS MB

AC901   **Napper, William.**
.M5   An account of the causes and principles of the
          intended resignation of a parish.   Dublin, 1821.
            125 p. (Miscellaneous pamphlets, 77:7)

NN 0019444   DLC

Napper, W₍illiam₎.
  An answer to the Rev. A. O'Callaghan...on the tendency of
Bible societies, as affecting the established church, and Christianity
itself as a "Reasonable service." Dublin: R. Napper, 1816.
110 p. 8°.
  In: * YIA (Brit. and For. Bible Soc.) p. v. 2, no. 4.

1. O'Callaghan, A.: Thoughts on the   tendency of Bible societies. 2. Bible
societies (pro).   January 31, 1912
N. Y. P. L.

NN 0019445   NN MH–AH NcD PPPM

BX5149   **Napper, William**
.B2N21   An exposition of the doctrine of the United
1843   Church of England & Ireland concerning rein: generation and baptism, collected from the Book
SWTS   of Common Prayer and the Homilies, and com-
           pared with the Holy Scriptures. Dublin,
           William Curry, Jun.; London, Longman, Brown,
           1843.
             191p. 18cm.
             1. Baptism—Anglican Communion. 2. Re-
           generation (Theology) I. Title.

NN 0019446   IEG

Napper, William Marianus, 1619–1693, defendant.
  A brief account of the proceedings against
the six popish priests
        see under Anderson, Lionel Albert, 1620
(ca.)–1710, defendant.

Law   **Napper, William Marianus, 1619–1693, defendant.**

Anderson, Lionel Albert, 1620 (ca.)–1710, *defendant.*
  The tryals and condemnation of Lionel Anderson, alias Munson, William Russel, alias Napper, Charles Parris, alias Parry
₍and others₎, ... for high treason, as Romish priests, upon the
statute of 27. Eliz. cap. 2. Together with the tryal of Alexander Lumsden, a Scotchman, and the arraignment of David
Joseph Kemish for the same offence. At the sessions of Oyer
and terminer in the Old-Baily, on Saturday, January 17th.
1679. Published by authority. London, T. Collins and J.
Starkey, 1680.

Nappez (Paul). *Les ictères syphilitiques tertiaires et quaternaires avant et depuis la médication arsénobenzolique. 57 pp. 8°. Paris,
1920.   No. 533.

NN 0019449   DNLM CtY

Hb48   **Nappi, Camillo Francesco**
74r   ... Dizionario di vocaboli poco conosciuti
        della lingua italiano con prefazione di
        Gennaro de Filippis (Dolores). Napoli, S.
        Romano, 1923.
          2p.l., 80p. plates. 19½cm.

NN 0019450   CtY MH

NAPPI, Cesare.   2799b.21
  I negromanti. Novella. Edita per le nozze di Guglielmo Guerrini colla
Marchesina Ottavia Antinori. [Avvertimento di Olindo Guerrini.]
—   Bologna. Zanichelli. 1885. (1), 59 pp. L. 8°.

NN 0019451   MB MH

NAPPI, Cesare.
  Rime pubblicate per la prima volta per cura
di Ugo Bassini. Bologna, Nicola Zanichelli,
1886.
    1.8°. pp. (5), [iii]–xlvi+.

NN 0019452   MH

FG 1720   **Nappi, Emanuele.**
N24 D6   Don Chisciotte, poema del nobil uomo
1806   signor conte Emanuele Nappi, patrizio
          anconitano ... Ancona, Presso Niccola
          Baluffi, 1806–07.
            3 v. fronts. (incl. port.) pl. 19½cm.

            I. Cervantes Saavedra, Miguel de, 1547–
          1616. II. Title.

NN 0019453   MdBJ CoU

Nappi, Giambattista
      see
Nappi, Gian Battista.

Nappi, Gian Battista.
  ... Annullamenti di matrimonio ... Milano, U. Hoepli, 1937.
  4 p. l., ₍xi₎–xix, 663 p. 23ᶜᵐ.
  "Sezione III: Leggi civili, Codex juris canonici, convenzioni internazionali, giurisprudenza": p. ₍287₎–654.

  1. Marriage—Annulment. 2. Marriage law—Italy. 3. Marriage
(Canon law)   I. Italy. Laws, statutes, etc. II. Catholic church.
Codex juris canonici. III. Title.

                                              38–36073

NN 0019455   DLC CtY–L NNC

Law   **Nappi, Gian Battista, joint ed.**

Law   **Italy.** *Laws, statutes, etc.*
  Commentario al Codice di procedura civile, per il prof. avv.
Giuseppe Nappi, con la collaborazione del dr. Giambattista
Nappi ... Milano, Società editrice libraria, 1941–

Nappi, Gian Battista, ed.
  Disposizioni per l'attuazione e disposizioni
transitorie per il libro primo del Codice civile
        see under Italy. Laws, statutes, etc.

Nappi, Gian Battista.
  ... Ordinamento dello stato civile
        see under Italy. Laws, statutes, etc.

Nappi, Gian Battista.
  ... Trattato di diritto matrimoniale, concordatario e civile ...
Milano, Società editrice libraria, 1940.
  2 v. 25½ᶜᵐ.
  At head of title: Giambattista Nappi.
  Paged continuously.
  "Bibliografia": v. 2, p. ₍737₎–753.
  CONTENTS.—v. 1. Parte generale e diritto concordatario.—v. 2. Diritto
civile speciale e comune, azione e giurisdizione.

  1. Marriage law—Italy. 2. Marriage (Canon law) 3. Concordat of
1929 (Italy)

                                              44–43812

NN 0019459   DLC

Nappi, Giuseppe.
  ... I delitti e quasi delitti dei commercianti; se e quando le
obbligazioni ex delicto vel quasi possano assumere carattere
commerciale (art. 4 Cod. comm.) contributo alla teoria degli
atti di commercio. Milano, U. Hoepli, 1908.
  3 p. l., ₍9₎–134 p., 1 l. 23ᶜᵐ.
  "Autori consultati": p. ₍13₎–14.

  1. Commercial law—Italy.   I. Title.

                                              33–20768

NN 0019460   DLC

4K   **Nappi, Giuseppe**
6814   Prontuario per l'applicazione delle
       norme transitorie del Nuovo codice di
       procedure civile. Complemento del
       Commentario al Codice di procedura
       civile. Milano, Società editrice
       libraria, 1942.
         35 p.

NN 0019461   DLC–P4

Nappi, Giuseppe.
  ... Trattato di diritto e procedura penale militare ... Milano,
U. Hoepli, 1917–
  v. 23½ᶜᵐ. (Studi giuridici e politici)
  "Bibliografia": v. 1, p. ₍xiii₎–xix.

  1. Italy. Esercito—Crimes and misdemeanors. 2. Courts-martial and
courts of inquiry—Italy.
                                              18–22636
  Library of Congress   UB785.I 8N3

NN 0019462   DLC ICJ

                                              609.61
                                              R400
Nappi, Romeo.
  ... Agricoltura, industrie e commercio della Tripolitania.
₁₆₀₀₁ Relazione del cav. uff. Romeo Nappi ... Roma, Tipografia
nazionale di G. Bertero e C., 1914.
  [2], 124 p. illus. 24½ᶜᵐ.
  At head of title: Ministero delle colonie. Mostra coloniale di Genova.

NN 0019463   ICJ

Nappi, Romeo.
  ...Tripolitania. Agricoltura, industrie e commercio della
Tripolitania. Relazione del cav. uff. Romeo Nappi ... Roma:
G. Bertero e C., 1914. 1 p.l., 124 p. illus. 8°. (Italy
<1861– , kingdom>. Colonie, Ministero delle. Monografie e
rapporti coloniali. 1914, n. 1.)

1. Agriculture, Tripoli. 2. Indus-   tries, etc., Tripoli. 3. Commerce,
Tripoli. 4. Series.   June 8, 1923.
N. Y. P. L.

NN 0019464   NN

Nappi, Rosa.
  Lo spazio, il tempo e la matematica nell'empirismo inglese.
Napoli, Libreria scientifica editrice, 1951.
  72 p. 22 cm.

  1. Space and time.   I. Title.

BD632.N3   52–38650 ‡

NN 0019465   DLC NN

VOLUME 405

Nappi, Settimio Aurelio.
"Guerra?" ₍Tre atti₎ Milano, Gastaldi ₍1955₎ 46 p. 20cm.
(Teatro)

1. Drama, Italian. I. Title.

NN 0019466 NN

Nappi, Settimio Aurelio.
  ... Per la società odierna .... Torino, Roma, Roux e Viarengo, [1902].
  [4], 360, [2] p. 19⁴ᶜᵐ.

304 N16
40480

At head of title: Settimio Aurelio Nappi.
Contents.—L'uomo dirigente e la società.—Sciope e leghe.—Il momento attuale e
l'Italia per il presente e per l'avvenire.—Osservando: La donna.—L'arte drammatica.

NN 0019467 ICJ

Nappi, Settimio Aurelio.
  Per la vita. Roma : Desclée, Lefebvre e C., 1902. 173(1) p.,
1 l. 8°.

1. Aphorisms (Italian).
N. Y. P. L.
                   May 25, 1912

NN 0019468 NN

Nappier, William
    see
Napper, William Marianus, 1619–1693.

Nappo, Antonio.
  Canti. Edizione postuma. Milano,
Gastaldi [1951] 73 p. 19cm.
(Poeti d'oggi. 396)

NN 0019470 NN RPB

4PQ
Ital.-
264
  Nappo. Antonio
  Momenti; atomi di lirica, 1947. [1948]
  44 p.

NN 0019471 DLC-P4

Nappolon, Sanson.
  Discours au vray de tout ce qui s'est passé tant
au Voyage que le Sieur Sanson Nappolon, a fait à
Constantinople, par le commandement de Sa
Majesté, qu'à Thunis et Argers. [Danjou.
Archives curieuses. 2 sér. T. 4. Paris, 1838)

NN 0019472 MB

Nappy in tow
    see under [Cruikshank, Isaac]
1756?–1811?

Napragus Demetrius
  see Napragyi, Demeter, Bp., 1556–1619.

---

*ZHC5
N1633
5950
  Napragyi, Demeter, bp., 1556–1619.
    Hvngariae periclitantis legatorum, r'ndi
domini Demetrii Napragi ... & generosorum
dominorum Nicolai Zokolij de Kis Varda, &
Michaelis Kellemesi vicecomitis comitatus
Sáros, ad serenissimum potentissimum̃
Sigismvndvm tertivm, Poloniae et Svecine regem
... oratio, in comitiis generalibus Cracouiae
habita, die 2. mensis martij, anno Domini,
M.D.XCV.
    [Cracoviae,1595]

4°. 29,[2]p. 19.5cm.
Colophon: Cracoviae, in officina Lazari,
anno Domini, 1595.

NN 0019476 MH

W 1
NA169
  NÁPRAVNÁ pedagogika.
  Praha, 19
    v.
    Until bound and cataloged, issues of
the above publications will be available at
the Periodical Desk.

NN 0019477 DNLM

Napravnik, August, 1915–   joint author.

  Smith, Hilton Albert, 1908–
    ... The photochemical oxidation of hydrogen, by Hilton A.
Smith ... and A. Napravnik ... Bethlehem, Pa., Lehigh university ₍1940₎

Nápravník, Eduard Frantsevich, 1839–1916.
  Concerto symphonique (La mineur) pour piano et orchestre. Op.
27. Partition.
= Hamburg. Rahter. [1877.] (1), 234 pp. L.8°.

G5954 — Concertos. Pianoforte and orchestra. — Pianoforte. Music. **Pianoforte**
and orchestra.

NN 0019479 MB ICN

Nápravník, Eduard Frantsevich, 1839–1916.
  ₍Concerto symphonique. Op. 27. Arr. for 2 pianos₎
    ...Concerto symphonique, la mineur, pour piano et orchestre,
composée par Eduard Nápravnik. Op. 27... Hamburg, D.
Rahter ₍etc., etc., 1880₎ Publ.pl.no.2070. 59 p. 35cm.

Score: piano I–II.
Bookplate of Nelly Reuschel.

378275B. 1. Concertos (Piano)—
N. Y. P. L.   Piano acc.
                              December 31, 1947

NN 0019480 NN

Nápravník, Eduard Frantsevich, 1839–1916.
  Cossack cradle song. [With accompaniment for pianoforte.] Adaptation by Louis C. Elson.
= Boston. Schmidt. [1882.] 5 pp. [Europa: a collection of
foreign songs. No. 2.] 34½ cm.
    No. 6 in *8053.966.1

L6699 — T.r — Elson, Louis Charles, ed., 1848–1920. — Songs ref. made.

NN 0019481 MB

Napravnik, Eduard Frantsevich, *1839–1915*.   **M.405.42
  Danses nationales pour orchestre composées par E. Nápravnik. Op.
20. Partition.
    Hamburg. Rahter. [187–?] 6 v. in 2. 25.5 cm.
Contents. — 1. Polonaise. 2. Casatschick. 3. Danse russe. 4. Valse. 5.
Tarentelle. 6. Mazourka.
The title-page of vol. 1 is in French, the others in Russian.
The title used is on the cover.

E3149 — Russia. Folk-dances. — Folk dances.

NN 0019482 MB

Nápravník, Eduard, Frantsevitch, 1839–1915.
  Démon d'après le poème de Lermontoff; IIIe
symphonie pour l'orchestre. Op. 18. Partition.
Hamburg, etc. [1882]
    4°.
    The poem is prefixed, in Russian, German,
and French.

NN 0019483 MH–Mu NN

VM
1001
N 21s3
  NÁPRAVNÍK, EDUARD FRANZOVICH, 1839–1916.
    ₍Symphony, no.3, op.18₎ "Démon" (d'après le
poème de Lermontoff). IIIème symphonie pour
l'orchestre. Op.18. Partition. Hambourg,D.
Rahter₍189–₎
    score(173p.) 34cm.

    Title also in Russian.
    Poem in Russian, German and French: ₍3₎p.
preceding score.
    Plate nos.: 2067, 2068.

NN 0019484 ICN

VM
1045
N 21dpe
  NÁPRAVNIK, EDUARD FRANTSEVICH, 1839–1916.
    ₍Deux pièces espagnoles, op.51₎ Deux
pièces espagnoles. Nº 1. Romance. Nº 2. Fandango. Op.51. Moscou, P.Jurgenson₍188–?₎
    score(2v.in 1) illus. 28cm.

    Cover titles and added title-pages in Rus-
sian.
    Plate nos.: 17462, 17464.

NN 0019485 ICN

Nápravník, Eduard Franzovich, 1839–1916.
  ...Deux pièces espagnoles, composées par E. Nápravník. Op.
51, no. 1– Moscou: P. Jurgenson₍, etc., etc., 1892₎
Publ. pl. no. 17462– v. 28cm.

Full score.
Cover and added t.-p. in Russian.
CONTENTS.—1. Romance.

1. Orchestra—Full score.   JUILLIARD FOUNDATION FUND.
N. Y. P. L.   October 22, 1934

NN 0019486 NN

Nápravník, Eduard Franzevich, 1839–1916.
  ...Deux pièces russes pour grand orchestre... Composées par
E. Nápravník... Pour piano à 4 mains... Op. 74, no.
Moscou: P. Jurgenson ₍etc., etc., 1906₎ Publ. pl. no. 30636
no.   34½cm.

Arranged for piano, 4 hands.
CONTENTS.—no. 1. Fantaisie.

1. Piano—4 hands—Arr.   CARNEGIE CORP. OF NEW YORK.
N. Y. P. L.   March 25, 1938

NN 0019487 NN ICN

NÁPRAVNÍK, EDUARD FRANTSEVICH, 1839–1916.
  ₍QUARTET, STRINGS, OP. 28₎
    2. quatuor, la majeur, pour 2 violons, alto et
violoncelle, composé par E. Nápravník, op. 28.
Moscou, P. Jurgenson [1890?] Pl. no. 14127. 4 parts.
34cm.

  From the collection of the Flonzaley quartet.

1. Chamber music, 19th cent.--Quartets. 2. Violin in quartets (2 violins,
viola, violoncello)   I. Flonzaley quartet.
i. [Title] Deuxième.

NN 0019488 NN IEN

VOLUME 405

Napravnik, Éduard Frantsevich, 1839–1916.
₍Dubrovsky. Piano-vocal score. Russian₎
Дубровский; опера в 4-х действиях и 5-ти картинах, соч. 58. Либретто М. И. Чайковского по повести А. С. Пушкина. Москва, Гос. муз. изд-во, 1952.
386 p. 30 cm.
Opera.

1. Operas—Vocal scores with piano.   I. Chaĭkovskiĭ, Modest
Il'ich, 1850–1916. Dubrovskiĭ. II. Title.
Title romanised: Dubrovskiĭ.

M1503.N2D87 1952   78–259707

NN   0019489   DLC MH

M1503
N3D8
1895
Napravnik, Éduard Frantsevich, 1839–1916.
₍Dubrovsky; acc. arr. piano₎
Dubrovsky; Oper in 4 Akten. Op. 58. Musik von E. Napravnik. ₍Moscow, Jurgenson, 1895?₎ Pl. no. 803.
345 p.

Caption title.
Title page in Russian.
Imprint covered by label: Milano, A. Pigna.
German and Russian words.
Libretto by Modest Chaĭkovskiĭ, based on Pushkin's play of the same title.

NN   0019490   CU

M1503
N3D8
1900
Napravnik, Éduard Frantsevich, 1839–1916.
₍Dubrovsky, acc. arr. pino₎
Dubrowsky; Oper in 4 Akten und 5 Bildern. Libretto nach einer Puschkin'schen Erzählung von M. I. Tschaikowsky. Op. 58. Aus dem Russischen in's Deutsche umgedichtet von Philipp Bock; Arrangement für Gesang und Pianoforte vom Componisten. Moskau, P. Jurgenson ₍190–?₎ Pl. no. 26653–26678.
345 p.

Russian and German words.

NN   0019491   CU MiU

Nápravník, Eduard Frantsevich.   No. 3 in **M.407.19
Fantaisie russe pour piano et orchestre. Op. 39. Partition.
= Hambourg. Rahter. [1881.] 91 pp. L. 8°.

G6977 — T.r. — Pianoforte. Music. Pianoforte and orchestra.

NN   0019492   MB

Nápravník, Eduard Frantsevich, 1839–1916.
...Fantaisie sur des thèmes russes pour violon et orchestre, composée par E. Nápravník. Op. 30. Arrangement pour violon et piano... Berlin: E. Bote & G. Bock ₍ca. 1880₎. Publ. pl. no. 12228. 2 parts in 1 v. f°.

Arranged for violin and piano.
Violin and piano in score and violin part.

                                   BOEKELMAN COLLECTION.
1. Violin and piano. 2. Concertos.—   Violin and orchestra.
N. Y. P. L.   May 15, 1919.

NN   0019493   NN

VM
1012
N 21f
NÁPRAVNÍK, EDUARD FRANZOVICH, 1839–1916.
₍Fantaisie sur des thèmes russes pour violon et orchestre₎ Op. 30. Partitur. Berlin, E. Bote & G. Bock, 1881₎
70p. 34cm.

Title-page wanting; title supplied from Library of Congress. Orchestral music catalogue. Scores. 1912.
Plate no.: 12504.

NN   0019494   ICN

Nápravník, Eduard Frantsevich, 1839–1916.
..."Harold" dramatische Oper in 5 Akten und 9 Bildern. Das Libretto nach dem Drama E. v. Wildenbruch's verfasst von Peter Weinberg, die deutsche Uebersetzung von Dr. A. Petrick. Musik von E. F. Nápravník. Op. 45. Moscau: P. Jurgenson₍ 1887₎. Publ. pl. nos. 6701–6727. 363 p. 4°.

Vocal score. Russian and German.
First performed in 1886.
Overture, and no. 25, "musikalisches Gemälde," Act 5, arranged for piano, 4 hands.

1. Operas—Piano and voice.   2. Wildenbruch, Ernst von, 1845–
1909; Harold. 3. Weinberg, Piotr.   1830–1908. 4. Petrick, Alexander
Heinrich, 1846–1890, translator.   5. Title.
N. Y. P. L.   August 22, 1928.

NN   0019495   NN MB CU

M1503
N3F7
1902
Napravnik, Eduard Frantsevich, 1839–1916.
₍Francesca da Rimini; acc. arr. piano₎
Francheska da Rimini; opera v 4-kh dieĭstvifakh i 5-ti kartinakh, sﬂuzhet zaimstvovan iz tragedii soch. S. Fillipsa "Francheska i Paolo" sﬂenicheskaﬂ planirovka O. Palecheka. Tekst libretto E. Ponomapev. Soch. 7loe. Mockva, P. Iurgenson [1902]
234 p.

Russian words.
Text by O. O. Palecek and E. P. Ponomarev, based on the play by Stephen Phillips.

NN   0019496   CU

VM
1046
N 21m
NÁPRAVNIK, EDUARD FRANZVICH, 1839–1916.
Marcia funèbre pour orchestre. Op. 42 bis.
Partition d'orchestre.   Hamburg, D. Rahter₍18—₎
score(31p.) 27cm.

Plate no.: 868.

NN   0019497   ICN

Nápravník, Eduard Frantsevich.   No. 2 in **M.407.6
Marcia funèbre pour orchestre. Op. 42 bis. Partition.
= Hamburg. Rahter. [1906?] 31 pp. 8°.

G5960 — T.r. — Marches.

NN   0019498   MB

Nápravník, Eduard Frantsevich, 1839–1916.
...Mélancolie, composée par E. Nápravník. Op. 48, no. 3...
Moscou, P. Jurgenson ₍etc., etc., 1895?₎ Publ.pl.no. 13735.
6 p.   28cm.

Score: string orchestra.
Reissue of the 1888 edition.

1. Orchestra, String—Scores.   I. Title.
N. Y. P. L.   December 10, 1948.

NN   0019499   NN

Nápravník, Eduard Frantsovich.   No. 12 in *8052.1166
Mélancolie. [For pianoforte.] Op. 48.
= Boston. The B. F. Wood Music Co. [1896.] 7 pp. 34 cm.
Edited by John A. Preston.

L7461 — T.r. Pianoforte music. — Pianoforte. Music. — Preston, John A., ed.

NN   0019500   MB

Nápravník, Eduard Frantsevich, 1839–1916.
... Notturno (La réminiscence de Chopin) [Op. 48, No. 1]... [Ed. and fingered by Max Vogrich] New York, G. Schirmer [c1894]
7 p. (music) 34 cm. (Compositions for piano by Russian composers)
[Pianoforte collections, v. 5]

NN   0019501   CtY

786.8
N16n
Nápravnik, Eduard Frantsovich, 1839–
Notturno. La réminiscence de Chopin. Arranged for the organ by Richard Keys Biggs.   New York, J. Fischer & bro. c1914.
9p.   (Recital pieces for organ, 4th ser.)

NN   0019502   IU

V
8
.665
no.344
Nápravník, Eduard Frantsevich,   1839–1916.
₍Quartett E dur für 2 violinen, viola und violoncell₎ Op.16.   Lpz. n.d.   D.   ([Payne's] kleine partitur-ausgabe. no.344)

NN   0019503   ICN MH

-VM
178
E 88
no.344
NÁPRAVNÍK, EDUARD FRANZVICH, 1839–1915.
₍Quartet, string; no.1, E major, op.16₎
₍Quartett, E dur, für 2 violinen, viola und violoncell₎ Op.16.   Leipzig, Eulenburg₍1924₎
71p.   (Eulenburgs kleine partitur-ausgabe. no.344)

Miniature score.
Plate no.: W. 8042 B.

NN   0019504   ICN MB

Nápravník, Eduard Frantsovich.   No. 1 in **M.412a.10
Quatuor no. 2 (La-majeur) pour 2 violons, alto et violoncelle. Op. 28. Partition.
= Moscou. Jurgenson. [187–?] 61 pp. 12°.

G5952 — Chamber music. String quartets.

NN   0019505   MB NN

Napravnik, Eduard Frantsevich, 1839–1916
Quartets, strings, no.2
Quatuor no.2 (la-majeur) pour 2 violons, alto et violoncelle. Op.28. Moscou, Jurgenson [19– ?] Pl. no.25213

Miniature score (61 p.)

NN   0019506   MH-Mu

Nápravník, Eduard Frantsovitch.   No. 2 in **M.412a.10
Quatuor, No. 3 (C-dur) pour 2 violons, alto et violoncelle. Op. 65.
= Moscou. Jurgenson. [187–?] 49 pp. 12°.

G5952 — Chamber music. String quartets.

NN   0019507   MB

Napravnik, Eduard Frantsevich, 1839–1916
Quartets, strings, no.3
Quatuor no.3 (C-dur) pour 2 violons, alto et violoncelle. Op.65. Moscou, Jurgenson [19– ?] Pl.no.25214

Miniature score (49 p.)

NN   0019508   MH-Mu NN

Nápravnik, Eduard Frantsevich, 1839–1916.
... Scherzo [Op. 48, no. 2]... [Ed. and fingered by Max Vogrich] New York, G. Schirmer [c1894]
7 p. (music) 34 cm. [Compositions for piano by Russian composers)
[Pianoforte collections, v. 5]

NN   0019509   CtY

VOLUME 405

Nápravník, Eduard Frantsevich, 1839–
　... Six morceaux pour piano. Op. 61...
Hambourg [etc.] D, Rahter, c1898.
　6 v. (music)　34 cm. [Pianoforte
collections, v. 5]

NN　0019510　　CtY

Nápravník, Eduard Frantsevich, 1839–1916.
　Sérénade du ⟨1ᵉʳ quatuor pour deux violons, alto et violoncelle, composé par E. Napravnik. Op. 16⟩, arrangée pour l'orchestre par l'auteur... Sᵗ. Pétersbourg: W. Bessel et Cⁱᵉ ⟨ca. 1882⟩. Publ. pl. no. 1154. 63 p. 4°.

Arranged for orchestra.
Full score.

I. Orchestra (Full).
N. Y. P. L.　　　　　　　　　　　　　November 5, 1919.

NN　0019511　　NN

VM
219
N 21s　NÁPRAVNIK, EDUARD FRANTSEVICH, 1839–1916.
　⟨Sonata, violin, op.52⟩ Sonate pour violon et piano. Op.52. Moscou, P. Jurgenson⟨189–⟩
　score⟨69p.⟩ and 1 part. 35cm.

　Violin part (19p.) laid in.

NN　0019512　　ICN

VM
1003
N 21d　NÁPRAVNIK, EDUARD FRANTSEVICH, 1839–1916.
　⟨Don Juan. Suite, op.54⟩ Suite für grosses Orchester aus der Musik zu der dramatischen Dichtung "Don Juan" von Graf A. Tolstoj. Op.54. Partitur. Moscou, Jurgenson⟨188–?⟩
　score⟨142p.⟩ 28cm.

　Cover title, t.-p. in Russian.
　Contents.—Nᵒ.1. Ouverture.—Nᵒ.2. Gesang der Nachtigall.—Nᵒ.3. Bei der Fontaine.—Nᵒ.4. Melodrame.—Nᵒ.5. Fandango.

NN　0019513　　ICN

Nápravník, Eduard Frantsevich.　　No. 1 in **M.407.6
Suite für grosses Orchester aus der Musik zu der dramatischen Dichtung „Don Juan" von A. Tolstoj, componirt von E. Náprawnik. Op. 54. Partitur.
= Moscou. Jurgenson. [1893.] 142 pp. L. 8°.

G5960 — Don Juan. Suite. — Suites. Orchestra.

NN　0019514　　MB

Nápravník, Eduard Frantsevich, 1839–1916.
　...Suite für grosses Orchester aus der Musik zu der dramatischen Dichtung "Don Juan" von Graf A. Tolstoj, componirt von E. Náprawnik. Op. 54... Partitur. Moscou: P. Jurgenson⟨1901⟩. Publ. pl. nos. 17464, 26162, 26164, 26166, 26168. 142 p. 4°.

Full score.
Cover-title. t.-p. in Russian.
Contents: No. 1. Ouverture. No. 2. Gesang der Nachtigall. No. 3. Bei der Fontaine. No. 4. Melodrame. No. 5. Fandango.

1. Orchestra, Full—Suites. 2. Tolstoi, Alekseĭ Konstantinovich, graf, 1817–1875: Don Juan. 3. Title: Don Juan.
N. Y. P. L.
JUILLIARD FOUNDATION FUND.
September 8, 1926.

NN　0019515　　NN

Nápravník, Eduard Frantsevich.　　No. 1 in **M.410.50
Suite pour violon avec accompagnement d'orchestre. Op. 60. Partition.
= Berlin. Simrock. 1898. 62 pp. F°.

F6743 — Suites. Violin and orchestra. — Violin. Music. Violin and orchestra.

NN　0019516　　MB

---

*M312
N2　Napravnik, Eduard Frantsevich, 1839–
　⟨Trio, piano & strings, op. 24, G minor⟩
Trio (en Sol mineur – G moll) pour piano, violon et violoncelle, op. 24. Leipzig, F. E. C. Leuckart ⟨1915?⟩

　score⟨80p.⟩ and 2 parts⟨19p. each⟩ 34cm.

　1. Piano trios.—Scores and parts.

NN　0019517　　NBuG

Nápravník, Eduard Frantsevich, 1839–
　[Trio, piano & strings, no. 2, D minor, op. 62]
Trio no. 2, ré mineur pour piano, violon et violoncelle composé par Eduard Nápravnik. Op. 62. Hamburg & Leipzig, D. Rahter [1897?]
　50 p. & 2 pts. 34 cm.
　Parts for violin & violoncello in pocket in back cover.
　Publ. no. 971.

NN　0019518　　CtY

787.342M
N 163 S
no.2　Nápravník, Eduard Frantsevich, 1839–1916.
　⟨Suite, violoncello & piano, no.2, op.36, A major⟩

　2. ⟨i.e. Zweite⟩ Suite, Violoncello ⟨und⟩ Piano. Op. 36. ⟨Leipzig, D. Rahter. n.d.⟩
　Pl. no. 2174.
　score (37 p.) and part. 35cm.

　Caption title.
　Contents.—Polonaise.—Scherzo.—Romance.—Alla russe.

NN　0019519　　NcU

Nápravník, Josef.
　Das Fest, Drama in 3 Akten. Leipzig, Xenien-Verlag [1920]
　96 p.

NN　0019520　　NjP

Nápravník, Josef
Kniha sonetu. V Praze [Česka akademie věd a uměni]
1954

82 p.

NN　0019521　　MH

Naprawa rzeczypospolitej do elekcyi nowego krola. Krakow, K. J. Turowski, 1859.
　26 p. 20cm. (In Biblioteka polska, 1858–59)

　1. Poland – Politics and government – 1572–1763. SSL NUC SC EX TK

NN　0019522　　CSt

Naprawnik, E.
　　see Napravnik, Eduard Frantsevich, 1839–1916.

NAPRED; národní zábavník mládeže slovenskej na rok 1871. Sostavili Kolman Bansell a Pavol Orszégh. V. Skalici, J. Škarnicl, 1871.

NN　0019524　　MH

Напред; орган на югословенските революционерни емигранти во НР' Бугарија.
⟨София⟩
　　v. in 7 Illus., ports. 40–43 cm. biweekly.
Subtitle varies slightly.
Vols. 19. called also no.

　1. Yugoslavia—Pol. & govt.—1945–　—Period. 2. World politics—1945–　—Period.　　*Title transliterated: Napred.*

DR301.N3　　　　　　　　58–44624

NN　0019525　　DLC

Napred.
Српство у Африци. Споменица листа "Напред." Бизерта, Штампарија Српских инвалида, 1918.
xiii, 160 p. 14 cm. (Библиотека "Напред," 5)

　1. European War, 1914–1918—Poetry. 2. Serbian poetry (Collections) 3. European War, 1914–1918—Personal narratives, Serbian. I. Title.　　*Title transliterated: Srpstvo u Africi.*

PG1414.N28　　　　　　　68–47228 ‡

NN　0019526　　DLC

Napred k víťazstvu pokrokových metód na dedine. ⟨Bratislava, Slovenská rada družstiev, 1949⟩
60 p. illus. 21 cm.

　1. Agriculture, Cooperative—Slovakia.

HD1491.C82S56　　　　　53–24986

NN　0019527　　DLC

Napredak. Sydney, Australia.
Weekly.

NN　0019528　　NN

Napredak, hrvatski narodni kalendar
　　see Napredkova knjiga.

DB361
N36　Napredkova knjiga.
Sarajevo, Vreck.
　illus. 22cm. annual

　Published by Hrvatsko Kulturno Drustvo "Napredak," Sarajevo.
　Title varies: 1942, Napredak, hrvatski narodni kalendar.

I. Napredak, hrvatski narodni kalendar.
II. Hrvatsko Kulturno Drustvo Napredak, Sarajevo.

NN　0019530　　CtY

Napredna misel; časopis za napredno kulturo. Praga
Leto 1–2; 1912–1913/14
No more published after leto 2(1914) zv.4?
Edited by Mihajlo Rostohar

　1. Slovenia – Period.　　I. Rostohar, Mihajlo, ed.

NN　0019531　　MH NNC

PN5355
.S4A5
1949　Napredna štampa u Srbiji.

Serbia (*Federated Republic, 1945–　*) *Ured za informacije.*
Напредна штампа у Србији, 1871–1949. ⟨Редакциони одбор: Мира Медин и др.⟩ Београд, 1949.

VOLUME 405

424.8
N16
Napredno pčelarstvo.
⌐Beograd⌐ Savez pčelara NR Srbije.

1. Servia. Apiculture. Periodicals.
I. Savez pčelara NR Srbije.

NN   0019533   DNAL NIC

Napretkova božićna knjiga. g. 1
1934–
Sarajevo.
v. illus., ports. 24 cm. annual.
Published by Hrvatsko kulturno društvo "Napredak" in Sarajevo.
Editor: 1934–   A. Martinović.

1. Almanacs, Croatian.   I. Martinović, Ante, ed.   II. Hrvatsko
kulturno društvo "Napredak," Sarajevo.

AY1038.C7N37   53–52024

NN   0019534   DLC

Napretkova uskrsna knjiga. g. 1–
1935–
Sarajevo.
v. illus., ports. 23 cm. annual.
Published by Hrvatsko kulturno društvo "Napredak" in Sarajevo.
Editor: 1935–   A. Martinović.

1. Almanacs, Croatian.   I. Martinović, Ante, ed.   II. Hrvatsko
kulturno društvo "Napredak," Sarajevo.

AY1038.C7N375   53–52025

NN   0019535   DLC

Náprstek, Rudolf.
Nová daň z obratu. Zpracovali: R. Náprstek, V. Fleischlinger, J. Veselý. ⌐V Praze⌐ Tiskařské a vydavatelské družstvo československého obchodnictva ⌐194–⌐
112 p.   21 cm.   (Obchodní, daňová a právní knihovna)
"Zákon ze dne 21. února 1946 o dani z obratu": p. 81–112.

1. Sales tax—Czechoslovak Republic.   I. Czechoslovak Republic.
Laws, statutes, etc.   II. Title.

55–19801

NN   0019536   DLC

Náprstkovo české průmyslové museum, Prague.
Our mothers' work. A selection of Bohemian national embroidery from Náprstek's Bohemian Industrial Museum. ⌐Prague?, 1898?⌐   8 l., 25 pl.   f°.

Preface in English and French.
French preface signed: J. Koula.

(The museum became Náprstkovo muzeum asijských, afrických a amerických kultur, in 1962? The collections described in work above may now be in the Národní muzeum in Prague)

                              DRAPER COLLECTION.
1. Embroidery (Bohemian).   2. Koula, Jan, 1855– .
3. Title.
N. Y. P. L.   October 25, 1916.

NN   0019537   NN

---

*EC65
A100
658n

Naps upon Parnassus. A sleepy muse nipt and pincht, though not awakened. Such voluntary and jovial copies of verses, as were lately receiv'd from some of the wits of the universities, in a frolick, dedicated to Gondibert's mistress by Captain Jones and others. Wherounto is added for demonstration of the authors prosaick excellency's, his epistle to one of the universities, with the answer; together with two satyrical characters of his own, of a Temporizer, and an Antiquary, with marginal notes by a friend to the reader ...

Continued in next column

Continued from preceding column

*EC65
A100
658n

London, Printed by express order from the Wits, for N. Brook, at the Angel in Cornhill, 1658.
[87]p.   16.5cm.
Signatures: A–E⁸,F⁴,G⁸,H⁴ (G1–H3 advts.; H4 blank)
"Advertisement to the reader" signed: Adoniram Banstittle, alias Tinderbox.
Written to ridicule Samuel Austin, by Thomas Flatman, Samuel Woodford, Sylvanus Taylor and others.

*EC65
A100
658n

"The authors own verse and prose" and "Two exact characters" have special title-pages.
"Books printed for Nath. Brooks": [22]p. at end.

NN   0019540   MH MWiW–C

Naptár.
⌐Budapest?⌐
v. illus. 20 cm.

1. Almanacs, Hungarian.

AY814.N37   51–33494 ‡

NN   0019541   DLC

Naphtali, or the wrestlings of the Church of Scotland for the kingdom of Christ; contained in a true and short deduction thereof, from the beginning of the reformation of religion until the year 1667: together with the last speeches & testimonies of some who have died for the truth since the year 1660. Whereunto are also subjoined a relation of the sufferings and death of Mr. Hugh M'Kail, and some instances of the sufferings of Galloway and Nithsdale. With introductory remarks by the Rev. Henry Duncan. Reprinted from the first edition of 1667.   Dumfries, David Haiilday, 1845.
365p.

1. Church of Scotland – History.   2. Reformation – Scotland.

NN   0019543   CSaT

Napton, William Barclay, 1808–1883.
An address delivered before the Society of alumni of the University of Virginia, June 29, 1871, by Hon. William B. Napton ...   Published by order of the society.   Charlottesville, Chronicle printing and stationery house, 1871.
30 p.   22½ᶜᵐ.

1. Virginia—Pol. & govt.   I. Virginia. University. Society of alumni.

                                      34–30160
Library of Congress   F231.N26   975.5

NN   0019544   DLC ViU NcD Vi CSmH NjP

B974.4
N16

Napton, William Barclay, 1839–
Over the Santa Fe trail, 1857.   Kansas City, Mo., F. Hudson pub. co., 1905.
99 p.   illus.   17cm.

"Lewis & Clark's route retraveled; the upper Missouri in 1858": p. ⌐73⌐–99.

1. Santa Fé trail.   2. Missouri river.

                  WaTC TKL
NN   0019545   NNC CtY MnU NN ICN InU MtHi NjP MH

Napton, William Barclay, 1839–
Past and present of Saline County, Missouri, by Hon. William Barclay Napton ...   Indianapolis, Ind., Chicago, Ill., B. F. Bowen & company, 1910.
932 p.   front., pl., ports.   28ᶜᵐ.
Includes biographical sketches.

1. Saline Co., Mo.—Hist.   2. Saline Co., Mo.—Biog.   I. Title.
                                      18–15020

Library of Congress   F472.S35N2

NN   0019546   DLC ICU MWA

Napulj
    see **Naples.**

W 6
P3

NAPUTAK o načinu kojim se je pučanstvu vladati kad prieti ili bukne kratelj. Istruzione sul modo di contenersi della popolazione pel caso di minaccia e sviluppo del colera. ⌐Zara, Vitaliani & Janković, 1884⌐
13 p.
Text in Croatian and Italian.

NN   0019548   DNLM

نقد كتاب شعراء الحلة ، كتاب انتقادی ادبی تاریخی بقلم باحث
كبير .   بغداد ، مطبعة الزهراء ، ١٩٥٣/١٣٧٢ ⌐1953⌐
168 p.   21 cm.

1. al-Khāqānī, 'Alī, ed.   Shu'arā' al-Ḥillah.   I. Bāḥith kabīr.
Title transliterated: Naqd kitāb Shu'arā' al-Ḥillah.

PJ8047.H5K35   59–34993

NN   0019549   DLC

Naqi Saheb, Saiyadul Ulama Maulana S. Ali Mujtahid
    see Mujtahid, Saiyadul Ulama Maulana
S. Ali Naqi Saheb.

Naqib, Firdaus Ahmad
    see
Nakib, Firdaus Ahmad, 1924–

Naqibī, Parvīz.
محمد مسعود ، گلی که در جهنم رولید ، نوشته پرویز نقیبی .
⌐تهران⌐ چاپ تابان ⌐194–⌐
208 p.   18 cm.

1. Mas'ūd, Muḥammad, d. 1948.   I. Title.
Title romanized: Muḥammad Mas'ūd.

DS317.N33   N E 68–731

NN   0019552   DLC

Naqīb'zādah Mashāyikh Ṭabāṭabā'ī, Ḥusayn 'Alī.
(Sirr-i tawfīq dar rūḥ-i taʻlīm va tarbiyat)
سر توفیق در روح تعلیم و تربیت ، اثر فکر و اندیشه سید
حسینعلی نقیبزاده مشایخ طباطبائی .   ⌐تهران⌐ چاپ تابان
١٣٣٣ ⌐1954 or 5⌐.
108 p.   port.   25 cm.
At head of title: الله

1. Education—Addresses, essays, lectures.   I. Title.

LB41.N283   73–206640

NN   0019553   DLC

VOLUME 405

---

al-Naqshabandī, Dā'ūd ibn Sulaymān
see
al-Khālidī, Dā'ūd ibn Sulaymān, 1816 *or* 17–1882 *or* 3.

النقل الداخلى. السنة الأولى—
اغسطس/اكتوبر ١٩٦٣ —
القاهرة، المؤسسة المصرية العامة للنقل الداخلى.

v. illus. (part col.) ports. 28 cm. quarterly (irregular)

1. Transportation—Egypt—Period. ɪ. al-Mu'assasah al-Miṣrīyah al-'Āmmah lil-Naql al-Dākhilī.
Title transliterated: al-Naqi al-dākhilī.

HE283.N3   N E 64–3374

NN   0019554   DLC NSyU

نقّاد .
كراچى .

v. illus. 25 cm. monthly.
In Urdu.
Text partially vocalized.

1. Pakistan—Pol. & govt.—Period.
Title transliterated: Naqqād.

DS376.N3   S A 64–4413

NN   0019555   DLC NSyU

---

al-Naqqāsh, Jalāl al-Dīn. al-Nashīd al-waṭanī al-rasmī.
al-Mahdī, Ṣāliḥ.
L'hymne national tunisien. النشيد الوطنى الرسمى
كلمات جلال الدين النقاش. تلحين صالح المهدى. تونس،
الجمهورية التونسية، كتابة الدولة للمعارف ،195].

---

al-Naqqāsh, Salīm Khalīl.
(Miṣr lil-Miṣrīyīn)
مصر للمصريين، لسليم خليل النقاش. الاسكندرية، مطبعة
جريدة المحروسة — 1884.
v. 26 cm.
PARTIAL CONTENTS: جزء ٤. من عهد تولية محمد توفيق باشا مام
١٨٧٩ الى يونيو سنة ١٨٨٢ — جزء ٧-٩. عائكة العرابيين. —

1. Egypt—History—Tewfīk, 1879–1892. 2. 'Urābī, Aḥmad, 1840 or 41–1911. ɪ. Title.

DT107.4.N36   74–214916

NN   0019557   DLC

Naqqāsh, Shafīq.
الحركة الكشفية فى الاقطار العربية ،تأليف، شفيق نقاش
و،على خليفة. بيروت، مطبعة الكشاف، 1936-.
v. illus, facsim., ports. 25 cm.

1. Boy Scouts. ɪ. Khalīfah, 'Alī, joint author. ɪɪ. Title.
Title romanized: al-Ḥarakah al-Kashfīyah fī aqṭār al-'Arabīyah.

HS3316.A7N36   77–235879

NN   0019558   DLC

نقّش .
كراچى .

v. 24 cm. monthly.
In Urdu.
Text partially vocalized.

1. Urdu literature—Hist. & crit.—Period.
Title transliterated: Naqsh.

PK2151.N3   S A 64–4945

NN   0019559   DLC NSyU WU

---

al-Naqshabandī, Muḥammad ibn 'Abd Allāh
see
al-Khānī, Muḥammad ibn 'Abd Allāh, 1798 or 9–1862.

---

al-Naqshabandī, Nāṣir Maḥmūd.
الدينار الاسلامى فى المتحف العراقى، تأليف ناصر محمود
التشبندى. بغداد، مطبعة الرابطة، ١٣٧٢-
١٩٥٣] · —١٣٧٢/
مطبوعات المجمع العلمى العراقى، ١١]
v. illus., 8 plates, port., fold. map, tables. 27 cm.
Added cover title: The Islamic dīnar in the Iraq Museum.
Arabic and English.
Includes bibliographical references.
CONTENTS—
الجزء الاول: الدينار الامرى والعباسى
1. Dīnar. ɪ. Bagdad. al-Matḥaf al-'Irāqī. ɪɪ. Title: The Islamic dīnar in the Iraq Museum. (Series: al-Majma' al-'Ilmī al-'Irāqī. al-Maṭbū'āt. 11)
Title transliterated: al-Dīnār al-Islāmī fī al-Matḥaf al-'Irāqī.

CJ3412.N3   54–30660 rev

NN   0019562   DLC UU CU ICU

Naquard (Jean-Baptiste-François-Adolphe).
* Essai de gérocomie, ou hygiène des vieillards.
1 p. l., 30 pp. 4°. *Strasbourg,* 1830, v. 61.

NN   0019563   DNLM

Naquard (Paul-Emmanuel). * Étude sur les
luxations du cristallin. 40 pp. 4°. *Paris,* 1871,
No. 184.

NN   0019564   DNLM

Naquard (Pierre-Louis-Emmanuel). * I. Quelle
est la valeur des signes fournis par l'odeur de la
bouche? II. [etc.] 39 pp. 4°. *Paris,* 1844,
No. 199, v. 421.

NN   0019565   DNLM PPC

NAQUET, Alfred, Joseph, 1834–1916.
Alfred Naquet; autobiographie, publiée par
Émile Pillias. [Paris], Lib. du Recueil Sirey,
1939.

24 cm. pp. 30. Facsimile plate.
Paper cover serves as title-page.
"Revue d'histoire politique et constitu-
tionnelle."

NN   0019566   MH

Naquet, Alfred Joseph, 1834–1916.
... L'anarchie et le collectivisme. Paris, E. Sansot
et cⁱᵉ, 1904.
250 p. 18½ᶜᵐ.

1. Anarchism and anarchists. 2. Collectivism.

NN   0019567   MiU IU NN NBuU MH CU NIC

Naquet, Alfred Joseph, 1834–1916.
...La anarquia y el colectivismo; traducción de C. Rodríguez
Avecilla. Valencia, F. Sempere y cía. [191–?] ix, 12–213 p.
19cm.

At head of title: Alfredo Naquet.

308941B. 1. Anarchism. 2. Socialism,   1910–1917.
N. Y. P. L.   **December 17, 1945**

NN   0019568   NN

---

*FC9
D8262
Z895n
[Naquet, Alfred Joseph, 1834–1916.
Antisémitisme et histoire ...
En vente,9,rue du Croissant,9,Paris.1895.
cover-title,48p. 17.5cm.
Desachy 529.
Caption on p.[1]: Chambre des députés,séance
du 27 mai 1895 (extrait du compte-rendu
officiel).
Original printed yellow wrappers preserved;
bound in cloth.

NN   0019569   MH

Naquet, Alfred Joseph, 1834–
Application de l'analyse chimique à la toxicologie
[thèse] Paris, 1859.
sq. Q.

NN   0019570   RPB

HX266
.N23
C&Y
Naquet, Alfred Joseph, 1834–1916.
Collectivism and the socialism of the liberal
school; a criticism and an exposition ... tr.
by W. Heaford. London, S. Sonnenschein & co.,
1891.
2 p. l., [vii]–X, 158 p. 19 1/2ᶜᵐ. [Social
science series. 38]

1. Socialism. 2. Collectivism. ɪ. Heaford,
William, tr.

NN   0019571   MB WaWW TxU RP NjP Nh PHC

Naquet, Alfred Joseph, 1834–1916.
Collectivism and the socialism of the liberal school; a criticism and an exposition [by] A. Naquet ... Tr. by W. Heaford. London, S. Sonnenschein & co., 1895.
2 p. l., [vii]–x, 158 p. 19½ᶜᵐ. [Social science series. 38]

1. Socialism. 2. Collectivism. ɪ. Henford, William, tr.

Library of Congress   HX266.N23   6—14633
———— Copy 2.   H31.87 vol. 38

NN   0019572   DLC NcD TxU ICJ MH OC1W OU OOxM CaBVaU

W
600
N217p
1873
Naquet, Alfred Joseph, 1834–1916
Compendio de química legal; guía para la
investigación de los venenos, exámen de las
armas de fuego, análisis de las cenizas,
alteración de escritos, de monedas, de alea-
ciones, de las sustancias alimenticias y
determinación de las manchas, etc., en las
operaciones químico-legales para uso de los
médicos, farmacéuticos, abogados, químicos,
peritos, etc. Traducida y adicionada con
trabajos especiales de Fressenius [et al.]

por Vicente Martín de Argenta. Madrid,
Taller tipográfico del hospicio, 1873.
512 p. illus.

Translation of Précis de chimie légale.

I. Argenta, Vincente Martín de

NN   0019574   DNLM PU

Naquet, Alfred Joseph, 1834–1916.

Blanc du Collet, Charles.
... Contribution à l'histoire du rétablissement du divorce en
France en 1884; étude faite d'après les travaux préparatoires
de la Loi Naquet ... par Charles Blanc du Collet ... Digne
(Basses-Alpes) L'auteur,1939.

QD
N217d
1860
NAQUET, Alfred Joseph, 1834–1916
De l'allotropie et de l'isomérie.
Paris, Baillière, 1860.
98 p.

NN   0019576   DNLM

VOLUME 405

Naquet, Alfred Joseph, 1834–1916.
Des sucres, par A. Naquet... Paris, F. Savy, 1863. 82 p.
22cm.

1. Sugars (Organic chemistry).
N. Y. P. L.   March 27, 1945

NN   0019577   NN PPF DNLM LU PBL

JX
1974
N21

Naquet, Alfred Joseph, 1834–1916.
   Désarmement, ou, Alliance anglaise.
Paris, E. Sansot, 1908.
   259 p. 19cm.

1. Disarmament. 2. France--For. rel.--Gt.
Brit. 3. Gt. Brit.--For. rel.--France.
I. Title. II. Title. Alliance anglaise.

NN   0019578   NIC

DC
369
.N23

Naquet, Alfred Joseph, 1834–1916.
Désarmement ou alliance anglaise. Paris,
E.Sansot,1908.
   263 p.

1. France--For.rel.--1870-1940. 2. France--
For.rel.--Gt.Brit. 3. Disarmament. I. Title.

NN   0019579   MiU

Naquet, Alfred Joseph, 1834–1916.
   Discours prononcé le 29 juillet 1872. Par
MM. Naquet et Gambetta en rapport au rapport
de la commission des marchés. Paris, 1872.
   71 p.

NN   0019580   MH

NAQUET, Alfred Joseph, 1834–
Le divorce. Paris, 1877.
viii, 355 p.

NN   0019581   MH-L

Naquet, Alfred Joseph, 1834–1916.
   ... Le divorce. 2. éd. rev. et très augm. Paris, E. Dentu,
1881.
   2 p. l., 356 p. tables (part fold.) 18¼ᶜᵐ.

1. Divorce—France. 2. Marriage law—France.

Library of Congress   HQ815.N2   9—7252

NN   0019582   DLC OU CU-L

Naquet, Alfred Joseph, 1834–1916.
   Le divorce. Documents, rapports et discours
parlementaires produit au cours de la troisième
législature de la Chambre des députés ...
     see under   France. Assemblée nationale,
1871-1942. Chambre des députés.

Joseph
Naquet, Alfred. 1835-. Divorce: from a
French point of view. 10 pp. (*N. Am. Rev.* v. 155, 1886.
p. 731.)

NN   0019584   MdBP

Naquet, Alfred Joseph
   — and Stanton, Theodore. French elec-
toral system. 11 pp. (*N. Am. Rev.* v. 155, 1892, p. 466.)

NN   0019585   MdBP

NAQUET, Alfred. Joseph, 1834–
   General Boulanger. His case [By Alfred Na-
quet.] His impeachment. [By Camille Pelletan
London, etc., 1889].

   pp. (29).
The new review, 1889, 1.1-29.

NN   0019586   MH

---

ar V
19013

Naquet, Alfred Joseph, 1834–1916.
   Grundzüge der modernen Chemie; nach
der 2. Aufl. von A. Naquet's Principes
de chimie. Deutsch bearb. und hrsg.
von E. Sell. Berlin, A. Hirschwald,
1868-70.
   2 v. illus. 20cm.

   I. Naquet, Alfred Joseph, 1834–1916.
Principes de chimie fondée sur les théories
modernes--German.

NN   0019587   NIC NcU

540.2 M802

Naquet, Alfred Joseph, 1834–
   Grundzüge der modernen Chemie. Nach der zweiten Auflage
von A. Naquet's Principes de chimie deutsch bearbeitet und herausgegeben von Dr. Eugen Sell, ... Erster Band. Anor-
ganische Chemie. Mit vielen in den Text gedruckten Holzschnitten. Berlin, A. Hirschwald, 1868.
   iv, 454, [2] p. 41 illus. incl. diagrs. 1 fold. table. 19ᶜᵐ.

NN   0019588   ICJ NN

Naquet, Alfred Joseph, 1834–1916.
   L'humanité et la patrie [par] A. Naquet.
Paris, P.-V. Stock, 1901.
   lxx, 337 p. 19 cm. (Bibliothèque des
recherches sociales)
   "Errata": leaf inserted.
   Bibliographical footnotes.
   1. Internationalism. 2. Freedom of the will.
I. Title.

NN   0019589   NRU NIC NcD

CB71
.N22

Naquet, Alfred Joseph, 1834–
   ... L'humanité et la patrie. 3. éd. Paris, P.-V. Stock, 1901.
   lxx, 342 p. 18¼ᶜᵐ.
   At head of title: A. Naquet.
   "De cet ouvrage il a été tiré à part dix exemplaires sur papier de Hollande."

   1. Civilization. 2. Patriotism. 3. Nationalism and nationality.

NN   0019590   ICU

Naquet, Alfred Joseph, 1834–1916.
   Legal chemistry. A guide to the detection of poisons, exami-
nation of stains, etc. etc. as applied to chemical jurisprudence.
Tr. with additions from the French of A. Naquet ... by J. P.
Battershall ... With a preface by C. F. Chandler ... New
York, D. Van Nostrand, 1876.
   2 p. l., 178 p. illus. 19ᶜᵐ.
   Bibliography: p. [157]-174.

   1. Chemistry, Legal. 2. Poisons.   I. Battershall, Jesse Park, 1851-
1891, tr.   II. Title.

                         6—30713
Library of Congress   RA1221.N2

ICJ NjP
NN   0019591   DLC NIC NcD TU ICRL PPC PU OC1W-H ViU

Naquet, Alfred Joseph, 1834–
   Legal chemistry. A guide to the detection of
poisons, examination of...stains, etc. etc. as
applied to chemical jurisprudence. Tr. with
additions from the French of A. Naquet...by
J. P. Battershall... [With a preface by C. F.
Chandler,]... 2d ed. rev. with additions.
New York, D. Van Nostrand, °1876.
   2 p. l., 190 p. illus.

   Bibliography: p. 163-186.

NN   0019592   MiD PSC IU IaU MiU OU IU-M NcRS

Naquet, Alfred Joseph, 1834–1916.
   Legal chemistry. A guide to the detection of
poisons, examination of tea, stains, etc., as
applied to chemical jurisprudence. Tr. with additions from the French of A. Naquet by J. P.
Battershall. 2d ed., rev., with additions. New
York, D. Van Nostrand, 1884.
   190p. illus.

NN   0019593   ICRL IdU

Naquet, Alfred Joseph, 1834–
   ... La loi du divorce ... Paris, E. Fasquelle, 1903.
   2 p. l., xxv, 302 p., 1 l. 18¼ᶜᵐ.
   Bibliothèque-Charpentier.
   "Le livre ... est divisé en deux parties. Dans l'une j'ai cru devoir com-
pléter l'historique du divorce en France en analysant les phases par les-
quelles a passé cette réforme de 1876 à 1884. Les phases antérieures de
1792 à 1876 ont été exposées dans mon livre Le divorce, édition de 1881 ...
La seconde partie du livre est consacrée à la réforme nouvelle, et aux con-
troverses qu'elle suscite."—Pref.

   1. Divorce—France.   I. Title.

                       15-7228
Library of Congress   HQ884.N2

NN   0019594   DLC NN NIC

Naquet, Alfred. Joseph
   Néo-malthusisme et socialisme [par] Alfred Naquet
et G.Hardy. Paris, Edition de Génération consciente
1910

   32 p.

NN   0019595   MH

W
700
N217p
1873

NAQUET, Alfred Joseph, 1834–1916
   Précis de chimie légale; guide pour la
recherche des poisons, l'examen des
armes à feu, l'analyse des cendres,
l'altération des écritures, des monnaies,
des alliages des denrées et la détermination des taches dans les expertises
chimico-légales, à l'usage des médecins,
pharmaciens, chimistes, experts, avocats,
etc. Paris, Savy, 1873.
   191 p. illus.

NN   0019596   DNLM CtY-L PU

Naquet, Alfred, 1834–
   Principes de chimie fondée sur les théories
modernes. Paris, F.
Savy, 1865.
   pp. (4), iv, 691 +. Illus.

Chem 428.65

NN   0019597   MH CU PU

Naquet, Alfred Joseph, 1834–1916.
   Principes de chimie fondée sur les théories modernes, par
A. Naquet. 2. éd., rev. et considérablement augm. Paris,
F. Savy, 1867.
   2 v. illus., fold. tables. 18ᶜᵐ.

   1. Chemistry.

                       32-20710
Library of Congress   QD31.N18 1867   540

NN   0019598   DLC PPAmP MB MH WaU PU NcU

VOLUME 405

QD
31
N21
1875

Naquet, Alfred Joseph, 1834-1916.
Principes de chimie fondée sur les théories modernes, par A. Naquet ... 3. éd., rev. et considérablement augm. Paris, F. Savy, 1875.
2 v. illus., fold. tables. 19cm.

1. Chemistry.

NN 0019599 NIC OClW MH DCU-IA

NAQUET, A[lfred], Joseph
Principes de chimie fondée sur les théories modernes; par A.Naquet,M.Henriot. 5e éd. Paris,F.Savy,1890.

2 vol.

NN 0019600 MH-C

Naquet, Alfred Joseph, 1834-1916.
Principles of chemistry, founded on modern theories. By Mons'. A. Naquet ... Tr. from the 2d ed. by William Cortis ... Rev. by Thomas Stevenson ... London, H. Renshaw, 1868.
xxviii, 848 p. illus., diagrs. 23cm.

1. Chemistry.   I. Cortis, William, tr.   II. Stevenson, Thomas, ed.

Library of Congress   QD31.N21   5-38398

NN 0019601 DLC MiU MiHM DNLM PPPCPh CtY NjP MB

Naquet, Alfred Joseph   Jr 1730.156
Questions constitutionnelles. Paris, E. Dentu, 1883.
pp. (4), 132.

France—Constitutional law

NN 0019602 MH

ar V
13157

Naquet, Alfred Joseph, 1834-1916.
Religion, propriété, famille. Paris, Chez tous les libraires, 1869.
iii, 312 p. 19cm.

1. Sociology. I. Title.

NN 0019603 NIC NcD MiU MH

Naquet, Alfred Joseph, 1834-   304 N161
Religion, propriété, famille, par Alfred Naquet, ... Troisième édition. Bruxelles, H. Kistemaeckers, 1877.
[4], xii, [4], 347, [4] p. 18cm.

NN 0019604 ICJ

Naquet, Alfred Joseph, 1834-1916.   321.8 N300
La république radicale, par A. Naquet, ... Paris, Germer-Baillière, 1873.
[4], 246, [2] p. 19cm.

NN 0019605 ICJ MiU MsU MH ICN

Naquet, Alfred Joseph, 1834-
... Socialisme collectiviste et socialisme libéral. [2. éd.] Paris, E. Dentu, 1890.
x, 204 p. 18½cm.

Continued in next column

Continued from preceding column

1. Socialism. 2. Collectivism.

Library of Congress   HX266.N2   1-F-3747

NN 0019606 DLC CaBVaU NcD NIC

Naquet, Alfred Joseph, 1834-1916.
... Temps futurs; socialisme-anarchie. Paris, P. V. Stock, 1900.
2 p. l., xiv, 352 p. 18½cm. (Recherches sociales. no. 3)
Author's name at head of title.

I. Title.

Library of Congress   HX266.N24   2-4415 rev.

NN 0019607 DLC MiEM MiU NIC NjR ICJ

Naquet, Alfred Joseph, 1834-1916.
... Vers l'union libre. Paris [1908]
18.5 cm.

NN 0019608 CtY

Naquet, David.
Memoire Responsif, pour ... David Naquet ...
see under title

Naquet, Edmond Vidal-
see
Vidal-Naquet, Edmond.

Naquet, Eliacim, 1843-   ed.
Mourlon, Frédéric, 1811-1866.
Répétitions écrites sur l'organisation judiciaire, la compétence et la procédure en matière civile & commerciale, contenant l'exposé des principes généraux, leurs motifs, la solution des questions théoriques, suivies d'un formulaire; par M. Frédéric Mourlon ... 5. éd. entièrement refondue, complétée et mise au courant jusqu'à ce jour, par M. E. Naquet ... Paris, A. Chevalier-Marescq, 1885.

Naquet, Eliacim, 1843-
Traité théorique et pratique des droits d'enregistrement, par E. Naquet ... 2. éd. mise au courant de la législation et de la jurisprudence, rev., cor. et considérablement augm. ... Paris, L. Larose, 1899.
3 v. 22½cm.
"Tarif des droits d'enregistrement": v. 3, p. [505]-537.

1. Taxation — France — Law. [1. Taxation—France, 2. Fee system (Taxation) [3. Recording and registry acts — France]   I. France. Laws, statutes, etc.   II. Title.

7-28464

NN 0019612 DLC

Naquet, Félix.
Les bacchantes: ballet en deux actes et trois tableaux, d'après Euripide, poème de Félix Naquet et Alfred Bruneau, musique d'Alfred Bruneau; illustrations par Notor, d'après des documents authentiques des musées d'Europe. Paris, E. Fasquelle, 1912.
39 p., 2 l. incl. front., illus. 19cm.
Without music.

I. Bruneau, Alfred, 1857-   II. Title.

12-28457

NN 0019613 DLC

Naquet, Felix
Les bacchantes; ballet en deux actes et trois tableaux d'après Euripide. Poème de Félix Naquet et Alfred Bruneau. Musique d'Alfred Bruneau. Illustrations par Notor, d'après des documents authentiques des musées d'Europe. Paris, Fasquelle, 1912.
39p. illus.

Microcard edition.

NN 0019614 ICRL

Naquet, Félix.
Les bacchantes
For editions with music see under   Bruneau, Alfred, 1857-1934.

Naquet, Félix.
... Fragonard, par Félix Naquet. Paris, Librairie de l'art [1890]
78 p., 1 l. illus. (incl. port.) 26cm. (Les Artistes célèbres)
"Bibliographie": p. [73]-74. "Catalogue": p. [75]-76.

1. Fragonard, Jean Honoré, 1732-1806.

Library of Congress   ND553.F7N3   F-3748
——— Copy 3. [With   Rocheblave, S. Les Cochin. Paris,
[1893]   N40.A3 [vol. 3]

NN 0019616 DLC MWiCA NcU MdBWA MH NjP PP OU

Naquet, Félix.
Ste. Rose de Lima
see under   Breville, Pierre Onfroy de, 1861-

Naquet, Georges Vidal-
see Vidal-Naquet, Georges, 1900-

Naquet, Gustave, 1819-1889, tr.
Whitney, James Parker, d. 1913.
Le Colorado aux États-Unis d'Amérique; Liste des minerais fournis par diverses personnes à l'Exposition universelle de 1867 à Paris; avec des renseignements sur le pays et ses ressources, par J.-P. Whitney ... tr. par Gustave Naquet. Paris, Imprimerie parisienne, L. Berger, 1867.

NAQUET, Gustave, 1819-1889.
Révélations sur l'état de siége à Marseille. Paris, Bibliothèque républicaine, 1875.

pp.93

NN 0019620 MH

842.7
N217u

Naquet, Gustave, 1819-1889.
Ugolin, drame en cinq actes et en vers. Cambrai, Lesne-Daloin, 1833.
xii, 97 p.

"Le sujet de ce Drame est tiré du poème de l'Enfer de Dante Alighieri" (vii).

1. Dante Alighieri, 1265-1321. Divina commedia. Inferno.   I. Title.

NN 0019621 ICarbS

VOLUME 405

Naquet, Henri.
... Droit romain: Des impots indirects chez les Romains sous la république et sous l'empire ...   Paris, A. Parent, 1875.

Thèse—Faculté de droit de Paris.

Droit français: De la société en nom collectif, noted on t.-p. but not included in this issue.

1. Taxation—Rome.

NN   0019622   MiU IU

Naquet, Henri.   AH 7108.75
Des impôts indirects chez les Romains sous la république et sous l'empire.   Paris, E. Thorin, 1875.
pp. (4), 166.

Taxation-Rome (State)

NN   0019623   MH

Naquet, Henri Jean, 1915–
... Des métastases, en tant que premiers signes du cancer primitif du poumon ...   Alger, Imp. nord-africaine ¡1939?¡
63 p. 24ᵐᵐ. (Algiers (City) Université. Faculté mixte de médecine et de pharmacie. (Thèse) 1939. no. 71)

Thèse—Algiers.

1. Lungs—Cancer.   2. Cancer¡—Metastases¡   I. Title.
                                                Med 47–1326
U. S. Army medical library   [W4A39]
for Library of Congress   ¡2¡

NN   0019624   DNLM

Naquet, J.
... Des modifications aux statuts des sociétés par actions et du pouvoir qu'on les décide ...   Paris, A. Rousseau, 1910.
2 p. l., 545 p. 25ᶜᵐ.
Thèse—Univ. de Paris.
"Bibliographie": p. ¡531¡–537.

1. Corporation law — France. ¡1. Corporations—France¡ 2. Stock companies—France. ¡2. Joint-stock companies—France¡   I. Title.
                                                14–8035

NN   0019625   DLC

Naquet, [Joseph] A[lfred] 1834–
    see   Naquet, Alfred Joseph, 1834–1916.

Naquet, Napoléon.
Les peccadilles de Valentin; comédie- vaudeville en un acte ...   Paris, 1855.
36 p. 12°. [In Bibl. dram., t. 107]

NN   0019627   CtY

Naquet, Napoléon.
Thérèse Lambert; comédie en deux actes, mêlée de couplets ...   Paris, 1804.
71 p. 12°. [In Bibl. dram., t. 274]

NN   0019628   CtY

Naquet (Paul) [1867–]. *Contribution à l'étude des hernies de l'appendice vermiculaire et de leurs complications. 130 pp. 8°. *Paris 1900. No. 126.

NN   0019629   DNLM

Naquin de Lippens, ———, ed.
Association provinciale des architectes français.
Bulletin de l'Association provinciale des architectes français (fédération des sociétés d'architectes des départements)
Lyon

Naquin de Lippens,

Chomel, A¡ugustin¡
... Quelques notes en réponse à notre confrère et ami M. Naquin de Lippens à propos de sa conférence sur l'art nouveau. Par M. A. Chomel ...   Lyon, Impr. Mougin-Rusand, Waltener & cᵉ, sucᵐ, 1902.

Nāqūyuvāskī, Dārī
    see
    Naguevskiĭ, Dariĭ Il' ich, 1845–1918.

Naqvi, Ali Mehdi
Mutual magnetic interactions in p-electron configurations (with calculations of transition probabilities and astrophysical applications)

Thesis - Harvard, 1952

NN   0019633   MH

Naqvi, Raza
    see
    Naqvi, S   Mohd Raza.

Asia
NA6183   Naqvi, S   A   A
.D4N33   Delhi Humayun's tomb and adjacent
            buildings, by S. A. A. Naqvi. Delhi,
            Manager of Publications, 1947.
            24 p. illus.

            At head of title page: Archaeological
            Survey of India.

            1. Delhi –   Tombs. 2. Architecture – Del- ,   hi. 3. India –
            Antiq. I. India, ..chaeological Survey.

NN   0019635   HU

Naqvi, S   K   Irtiza.
Air transport in India. With a foreword by D. Pant
Allahabad, Kitab Mahal ¡1949?¡
7, 231 p. illus., maps. 19 cm.

1. Aeronautics, Commercial—India.   I. Title.

TL527.I 4N3   57–42135

NN   0019636   DLC MH-BA

Naqvi, S   Mohd Raza.
The law and procedure of income-tax

see under

Pakistan. Laws, statutes, etc.

Naqvi, S   Mohd Raza.
The law of sales-tax in Pakistan

see under

Pakistan. Laws, statutes, etc.

Naqvi, S. N.
Correlation between frost and the preceding meteorological conditions
see under
Ali, Barkat.

Naqvi, Syed Khurshaid Husain.
Husain in the plain of Karbala. Second edition.
Lucknow, U.P., (India) Imamia Mission, n.d.
24 p. (Imamia Mission series, no. 50)
1. Islam. 2. Husain, c. 629 A.D. - c. 680 A.D.
I. Series.

NN   0019640   MsSM

Nar, C. von.
Erläuterungen zu dem bayerischen Gesetze über Heimat, Verehelichung und Aufenthalt vom 16. April 1868.   Erlangen, 1869.
viii, 220 p.

NN   0019641   MH-L

Nar, Carl Theodor.
Grundlagen der Gasschmelzschweissung. Berlin, W. de Gruyter, 1944.
54 p. illus. 21 cm. (Lehrbücher der Luftwaffe, Phasenbildreihe 1)
"Diese Phasenbildreihe ist unter D (Luft) 6169 Beiheft 2 als Luftwaffendienstvorschrift erschienen."

1. Oxyacetylene welding and cutting.   (Series)
TS227.N24   A F 50–200
Iowa.   State Coll.   Libr.
for Library of Congress   ¡3¡†

NN   0019642   IaU DLC

Nar (Gustavus). *De diversis iridis inflammationibus. 14 pp. 8°. *Monachii, J. A. Giesser, 1834.

NN   0019643   DNLM

BT
897   **Nar, Johannes, 1890–**
.N21   Frohbotschaft; Kurzpredigten und Lesungen
            über das Vaterunser und die christliche
            Liebe. Freiburg i.B., Caritasverlag, 1936.
            44 p. 21cm.

            1. Lord's Prayer--Sermons. 2. Love
            (Theology)—Sermons. 3. Sermons, German.
            I. Title.

NN   0019644   DCU

Nar-bey de Lusignan, G   A
    see his real name
    Calfa, Ambroise, b. 1831.

Nar-Dos, *pseud.*
Երկերի լիակատար ժողովածու։ Խմբ. Ռուբէն Զարյանի,
Երևան, Հայպետհրատ, 1947–50։
7 v. port. 21 cm. (Հայ կլասիկներ)
The set, planned to be published in 8 v., was completed in 7.
L. C. set incomplete: v. 2–3 wanting.
CONTENTS.— Հ. 1. Բանաստեղծություններ, պատմվածքներ.—Հ. 2. Ֆելյետոններ.—Հ. 3. Դրամատիկական երկեր.—Հ. 4. Նոր դարում, Սպանված աղավնին, Մահն ապաշխարող.—Հ. 5. Սպանված աղավնին.—Հ. 6. Շունը.—Հ. 7. Մեր թաղը, Խոնարհ գաղափարներ, Լոր ձորում, Լոքումներ, Նամակներ.

I. Zaryan, Rhowben, ed.   (Series: Hay klasikner)
                Title romanized: Erkeri liakatar zhoghovatsow.

PK8548.N25 1947   76–212710

NN   0019646   DLC

VOLUME 405

Nar-Dos, pseud.
Erkeri zhoghovatsu. Erevan, Haypethrat, 1955.
v. port. 21 cm.

NN 0019647 MiU

Nar-Dos, *pseud.*
Սար․դոս ։ [Գաւթր , Հայպեթե , 1934.]
500 p. 20 cm.
Cover title.

ɪ. Title.
Title romanized: **Mahŝ.**

PK8548.N25M3 75-212726

NN 0019648 DLC

Nar-Dos, *pseud.*
Սեր Թաղր ։ Երեան, Հայպետհրատ, 1952։
100 p. illus., plates. 23 cm.
Contents.—[list of contents]

ɪ. Title.
Title romanized: **Mer t'aghŝ.**

PK8548.N25M4 75-212793

NN 0019649 DLC

Nar-Dos, *pseud.*
Повести и рассказы. Перевод с армянского. Москва,
Гос. изд-во худож. лит-ры, 1955.
316 p. illus. 21 cm.

Title transliterated: Povesti i rasskazy.
Real name: Mikael Ovanessian.

PK8548.N25A57 1955 57-29903 ‡

NN 0019650 DLC

NAR schlagern slog: Nils-Georgs jubileumsalbum,
1927-1952: 25 år, 25 melodier. [Stockholm,
N. Georgs musikförlags, 1952] 57 p. 31cm.

For piano, with interlinear words.

1. Songs, Swedish--Collec-   tions.

NN 0019651 NN

NARA, Aisaburo, 1867-
Ueber scopolanin und seine nebenwirkungen
in der augenheilkunde. Inaug.diss., Rostock.
1905.

NN 0019652 MBCo

Nara, Masamichi.
(Bukkenhō shinshaku) 物權法新釋 [上卷] 奈
良正路著 [東京] 法鉾閣 [昭和 9 i. e. 1934]
22. 18, 1163 p. 23 cm.

1. Property—Japan. ɪ. Title.

71-822988

NN 0019653 DLC WaU-L

Nara, Masamichi.
普選法則則の研究 奈良正路著 東京 法鉾閣
昭和 11 [1936]
4, 6, 268 p. 23 cm.

1. Elections—Japan—Corrupt practices. 2. Election law—Japan.
ɪ. Title.
Title romanized: Fusenhō bassoku no kenkyū.

J 65-2619

NN 0019654 DLC

Nara, Masamichi.
判例を中心としたる普選法 奈良正路著 東京
日本評論社 昭和 5 [1930]
7, 8, 550 p. 23 cm.

1. Election law — Japan — Cases. 2. Elections — Japan — Corrupt
practices. ɪ. Title.
Title romanized: Hanrei o chūshin
to shitaru fusenhō.

J 66-966

NN 0019655 DLC CtY

Nara, Masamichi.
(Iriaikenron) 入會權論 奈良正路著 東京 萬
里閣 [昭和 6 i. e. 1931]
16, 7, 412 p. 23 cm.

1. Commons—Japan. ɪ. Title.

70-821614

NN 0019656 DLC

Nara, Masamichi.
解雇退職手當請求權の理論と實際 奈良正路著
東京 法鉾閣 昭和 9 [1934]
4, 2, 238 p. 22 cm.

1. Wages—Dismissal wage—Japan. ɪ. Title.
Title romanized: Kaiko, taishoku, teate
seikyūken no riron to jissai.

J 66-949

NN 0019657 DLC

Nara, Masamichi.
[Kosakuhōan no gensei hihan]
小作法案の嚴正批判 奈良正路著 [東京] 叢
文閣 [昭和 3 i. e. 1928]
8, 5, 251 p. 19 cm.

1. Farm tenancy—Japan. 2. Land tenure—Japan—Law. ɪ. Title.
72-804372

NN 0019658 DLC

Nara, Yasunori.
臣道と教學 奈良靖規著 東京 三友社 昭和
14 [1939]
3, 3, 14, 302 p. 24 cm.

1. Ethics, Japanese. 2. National characteristics, Japanese. ɪ.
Title. *Title romanized:* Shindō to kyōgaku.
J 60-2223
Hoover Institution
for Library of Congress   [3]

NN 0019659 CSt-H

Nara Gakujin, pseud.
see
Ōya, Tokujō, 1882-1950.

Nara, Japan (City)
Catalogue of the art treasures of the ten great
temples of Nara
see under title

Nara, Japan (City) Cultural Properties Research Institute
see
Nara Kokuritsu Bunkazai Kenkyūjo.

Nara, Japan. (City) Horyuji Monastery
see Horyuji, Ikaruga, Japan [Supplement]

Nara, Japan (City) Imperial Museum
see Nara Kokuritsu Hakubutsukan.

Nara, Japan (City) Institute of Cultural Materials
see
Nara Kokuritsu Bunkazai Kenkyūjo.

Nara, Japan (City) Kokuritsu Bunkazai Kenkyūjo
see
Nara Kokuritsu Bunkazai Kenkyūjo.

Nara, Japan (City) Nara, hotel,
see Nara hotel, Nara, Japan.

Nara, Japan (City) National Cultural Properties Research
Institute
see
Nara Kokuritsu Bunkazai Kenkyūjo.

Nara, Japan (City) National Museum
see
Nara Kokuritsu Hakubutsukan.

Serial
N   Nara, Japan (City) Prefectural Medical College.
Medical Association.
[Nara igaku zasshi] The Journal of the Nara
Medical Association.
maki
Nara, Japan, Nara Igakkai.
v. illus. 26cm.

Began publication June 1950.
Text in Japanese with table of contents
and summaries also in English.

NN 0019670 NNC-M DNLM ICRL ICJ

Nara, Japan. Research Institute for Tuberculosis,
Tenri.
Nara, Japan, Research Institute for Tuberculosis
see under Annals of tuberculosis.

Nara, Japan (City) Shōsōin
see
Shōsōin, Nara, Japan.

VOLUME 405

Nara, Japan (City) State Institute of Cultural Materials
see
Nara Kokuritsu Bunkazai Kenkyūjo.

Nara, Japan (City) Women's University
see   Nara Joshi Daigaku.

DS894
.29
.N36Y35   Nara, Japan (Prefecture)
Orien   (Yamato shiryō)
Japan   大和志料 奈良縣編 〔編者・齋藤美澄 奈良〕 奈
            良縣教育會 〔弘道館發賣 大正4 i. e. 1915〕

Nara, Japan. (Prefecture)   Ab.
: Nara & vicinity. [Osaka, Printed by the Sanyusha,
19- ?]

    24 p. illus. (part col.)

NN   0019676   MH

Nara, Japan (Prefecture)
An official guide to Nara. Nara, Nara Prefectural Govt.
Off., 1925.
    75 p. illus. 19 cm.

    1. Nara, Japan (City)—Description—Guide-books.   I. Title.
DS897.N35A47   915.2'18   73-156877
                                                 MARC

      CaBVaU PPPM
NN   0019677   DLC MiU NBuG MH NNC NN MnCS WaU OrU

Nara, Japan (Prefecture) Agricultural
    Experiment Station
      see   Nara-ken Nogyo Shi kenjo.

Nara, Japan (Prefecture) Board of Education
see
Nara, Japan (Prefecture) Kyōiku Iinkai.

Nara, *Japan (Prefecture)* Kyōiku Iinkai.
奈良縣綜合文化調査報告書 吉野川流域龍門地
區 奈良 奈良縣教育委員會 昭和28 〔1953〕
    5, 373 p. illus., maps. 26 cm.

    1. Nara, Japan (Prefecture)   I. Title.
                            Title romanized: Nara-ken sōgō
                            bunka chōsa hōkoku sho.
                                      J 65-3561
Harvard Univ. Chinese-   Japanese Library 3447
for Library of Congress   〔4〕

NN   0019680   MH-HY

Nara, Japan (Prefecture) Prefectural Government
    Office
      see   Nara, Japan (Prefecture)

Nara, Japan (Province)
    see   Nara, Japan (Prefecture)

Nara. 〔Views of the city. 1915?〕

    Plates, accompanied by guard sheet, with
descriptive letter-press in Japanese and English,
and folded map.

NN   0019683   MiD

Nara Bunkazai Kenkyūjo
    see
Nara Kokuritsu Bunkazai Kenkyūjo.

Nara Cultural Properties Research Institute
    see
Nara Kokuritsu Bunkazai Kenkyūjo.

Nara-Hari
    see
Narahari.

Nara Hotel, Nara, Japan.   *3019.98
A guide to Nara and neighbourhood. 2d edition.
= [Nara. 1912.] 31, (2) pp. Illus. Plates. Maps. Plans. 15 cm.

D4889 — Nara, Japan. Descr. Guide-books.

NN   0019687   MB

Nara hotel, *Nara, Japan.*
Nara & its vicinity ... Nara, Japan, The Nara hotel, 1932.
cover-title, 50, (2) col. illus. (incl. maps, plan) diagr. 20½ x 22½".
Two columns to the page. Columns 49-52 on p. (3)-(4) of cover.

    1. Nara, Japan—Descr.—Guide-books.
                                            43-46067
Library of Congress   DS897.N35N3
                                 (2)   915.2186

NN   0019688   DLC

Nara igaku zasshi
      see under   Nara, Japan (City) Prefectural
Medical College. Medical Association.

Nara Igakkai
      see   Nara, Japan (City) Prefectural
Medical College. Medical Association.

Nara Joshi Daigaku. Seibutsu Gakkai.
Nara Joshi Daigaku Seibutsu Gakkai shi.
(Biological journal of Nara Women's University)
Nara.
    v. illus. annual.
    Began 1951.
    Includes English abstracts.

    x Nara Women's Univer-   sity. Biological
journal

NN   0019691   ICRL

Nara Jokōshi Fuzoku Chūgakkō Kōtō Gakkō Kyōiku
Kenkyūkai.
奈良ブランホームルーム 奈良女高師附属中学
校高等学校教育研究会著 東京 東洋圖書 〔1949〕
    6, 320 p. illus., forms. 22 cm.
    In colophon: 奈良女子高等師範學校附属中學校高等學校
教育研究會代表 春近池義隆
    1. Home room guidance. 2. Personnel service in secondary educa-
tion—Nara, Japan (City)—Case studies. I. Chikaike, Yoshitaka,
1897—   II. Title.
                            Title romanized: Nara puran hōmu rūmu.

LB1620.7.N3   77-815023

NN   0019692   DLC

Nara-ken, *Japan*
    see
Nara, *Japan (Prefecture)*

10
N1   **Nara-ken Nogyo Skikenjo.**
           Nōka shikei (Farmers' guide)
         [Tokyo]

             1. Agriculture. Research. Nara-ken, Japan.
         I. Nara-ken, Japan. Agricultural Experiment
         Station. Farmers' guide.

NN   0019694   DNAL

Nara Kokuritsu Bunkazai Kenkyūjo.
文化史論叢 小林剛〔等著〕 奈良国立文化財研究
所編 天理 養德社 昭和30 〔1955〕
    43, 177, 18 cm. illus., maps, plans. 27 cm.
緑究学報 第3冊〕
    Nara State Institute for Cultural Materials. Monograph no. 3.
    Summary in English, with added t. p.: Symposium of cultural his-
tory.
    1. Japan—Civilization—Addresses, essays, lectures. I. Kobayashi,
Takeshi, 1903—   II. Title. III. Title: Symposium of cultural history. (Series: Nara Kokuritsu Bunkazai Kenkyūjo. Nara Kokuritsu Bunkazai Kenkyūjo gakuhō, dai 3 satsu)
                                Title romanized: Bunkashi ronsō.

DS821.N37   J 60-132

NN   0019695   DLC CaBVaU

Nara Kokuritsu Hakubutsukan.
    Catalogue of the paintings in the Nara imperial
museum. [Nara, Japan] The museum, 1915.
    cover-title, 1 p. l., 69 p., 1 l.   17 cm.
    Lists Japanese, Chinese and Korean paintings.
    1. Paintings, Japanese. Catalogs. 2. Paintings
Chinese. Catalogs. 3. Paintings, Korean.
Catalogs.

NN   0019696   MB

Nara Kokuritsu Hakubutsukan.
    Illustrated catalogue; special exhibition
of the Shosoin treasures. 1953. [Nara,
Kyado printing industrial co., ltd., 1953]
    pamph. illus.
    Text in Japanese and English.

NN   0019697   PPPM

Nara Medical Association
      see   Nara, Japan (City) Prefectural
Medical College. Medical Association.

Nara National Cultural Properties Research Institute
    see
Nara Kokuritsu Bunkazai Kenkyūjo.

Nara-shi, *Japan*
    see
Nara, *Japan (City)*

VOLUME 405

(Nara sōki)
奈良叢記 ﹙仲川明・森川辰藏編著　大阪　晟々堂書
店　昭和17 i.e. 1942﹚
3, 3, 491 p.　illus.　22 cm.

1. Nara, Japan (City)—Addresses, essays, lectures.　2. Nara, Japan
(City)—Civilization—Addresses, essays, lectures.　I. Nakagawa,
Akira, 1899-　ed.　II. Morikawa, Tatsuzō, ed.

DS897.N35N329　　　　　　　　74-815127

NN　0019701　　DLC

Nara State Institute for Cultural Materials
see
Nara Kokuritsu Bunkazai Kenkyūjo.

Nara State Institute of Cultural Materials
see
Nara Kokuritsu Bunkazai Kenkyūjo.

Nara Teikoku Hakubutsukan
see
Nara Kokuritsu Hakubutsukan.

Nara Teishitsu Hakubutsukan
see
Nara Kokuritsu Hakubutsukan.

Nara Women's University
　　see　Nara Joshi Daigaku.

Nārada.
　The aphorisms of Narada, by Lala Kannoo Mal...　Madras: S. Ganesan, 1923.　x, 57 p.　12°.

1. Sutras.　2. Mal, Lala Kannoo,　　　　　editor.
N.Y.P.L.　　　　　　　　　　　　　　October 9, 1924

NN　0019707　　NN CU OCl ICU

BL
1215
B5
N32
1938
Nārada.
　Aphorisms on Bhakti.　Edited by Y.
Subrahmanya Sarma.　Holenarsipur, India,
Adhyatma Prakasha Karyalaya, 1938.
26 p.　19 cm.
　Text in Sanskrit and English.
　1. Bhakti.　I. Subrahmanya Sarma, Y
II. Title.

NN　0019708　　CaBVaU MoSU

Nārada.
　Aphorisms on the gospel of divine love, or, Nārada bhakti
sutras; with Sanskrit text, word-by-word meaning, English
rendering of the text and elaborate explanatory and critical
notes.　By Swami Tyāgisananda.　Mylapore, Madras, Sri
Ramakrishna Math, 1943.
x, 251 p.　19 cm.
　Cover title: Nārada bhakti sūtras.
　Title on spine: The gospel of divine love.
　Includes bibliographical references.
　1. Bhakti.　I. Tyāgiśānanda, Swami, ed.　II. Title.　III. Title:
Nārada bhakti sūtras.　IV. Title: The gospel of divine love.

BL1215.B5N33　1943　　　　　　　　73-180444
　　　　　　　　　　　　　　　　　　　　MARC

NN　0019709　　DLC

BL
1215
B5N32
1955
Narada.
　Aphorisms on the gospel of divine love;
or, Narada bhakti sūtras with Sanskrit text,
word-by-word meaning, English rendering of
the text and elaborate explanatory and
critical notes by Swami Tyāgisananda.　﹙3d ed.﹚
Madras, Sri Ramakrishna Math, 1955.
x, 257 p.　18 cm.

　1. Bhakti.　I. Tyāgisananda, swami.　II.
Title.

NN　0019710　　PPT RPB WU TxFTC ICU OO

Nārada.
　The Bhakti sūtras of Nârada; with explanatory notes and
an introduction by the translator.　Translated by Nandlal
Sinha.　Allahabad, The Pânini office, 1911.
　2 p. l., xv, 32, iii p.　25 cm.　(Added t.-p.: The sacred books of the
Hindus ...　Ed. by Major B. D. Basu ...　﹙vol. vii, pt. i﹚)
　On cover: May 1911, no. 23.
　Constitutes part 1 of the general work Bhakti sāstra, t.-p. of which
is dated 1912.
　Sanskrit text with English translation.
　May be regarded as a companion piece of the Bhakti mīmāṁsa of
Ṣāṇḍilya, an enquiry into the philosophy of devotion.　cf. Introd.
　1. ﹙Bhakti﹚　I. Sinha, Nandalal, tr.　II. Ṣāṇḍilya.

[BL1110.S3　vol. 7]　　　　　　　　A C 39—3245
Harvard Univ.　Library
for Library of Congress　　　　　﹙66c1﹚

NN　0019711　　MH OCl NN PP WaU PU

Narada
　The Bhakti sūtras, with explanatory notes and
an introduction by the translator, tr. by Nandalal
Sinha.　2d ed.　[4],xvii,[1],32,[2]p.　Allahabad, Pânini office, 1917.　(Sacred books of
the Hindus, v.7, pt.1)

　Contains also the Sanskrit text.
　Consists of no. 23.
　Bound with this are The Ṣandilya sûtram.　Allahabad, 1918; and The Bhakti-ratnavali.　Allahabad,
1918.

NN　0019712　　OCl

BL1215
.B5S2
　　　Nārada.　Bhakti sūtras.

Sadananda, Swami.
　Narada bhakti sutras, text and full commentary by
Swami Sadananda Saraswati.　﹙1st ed.﹚ Rishikesh, Yoga
Vedanta Forest University, Divine Life Society, 1952.

Narada
　Fünfzehn blätter einer nepalesischen palm-
blatt-handschrift; einleitung, text, anmerkung-
en... vorgelegt vom verfasser August Conrady.
26p.　Leipzig, Druck von G. Kreysing, 1891.

　Inaug.-diss. - Würzburg.
　Sanskrit text.

NN　0019714　　OCl PU ICRL CU MH

BL
1200
N37
G74
Nārada.
　The gospel of Narada ...　edited and newly
translated from the Sanskrit of Narada Pancaratra,
the Narada Bhakti Sutras and the Narada Gita,
with a running commentary and introduction by
Duncan Greenlees.　Adyar, Madras, The Theosophical Pub. House, 1951.
204 p.　18 cm.　(The World gospel series, 7)

　1. Bhakti.　2. Philosophy, Hindu.　I. Greenlees, Duncan, ed. and tr.　II. Title.　(Series)

NN　0019715　　WaSpG

PK4031
.N2
1885
Nārada.
　The Institutes of Nārada, together with copi-
ous extracts from the Nāradabhashya of Asahāya
and other standard commentaries.　Edited by
Julius Jolly.　Calcutta, Printed by J. W.
Thomas, at the Baptist Mission Press, 1885.
18, 231 p.
　Text in Sanskrit.

　1. Law, Hindu.　I. Asahāya, 8th cent.　Narada-
bhāshya.　II. Jolly, Julius, 1849-1932, ed.

NN　0019716　　ICU CtY

Narada.
　Institutes (The) of Nárada Smriti, with
extracts from the Náradabhashya of
Asahāya, and other commentaries...
Edited by J.Jolly.　Calcutta: Asiatic
Soc. of Bengal, 1885-86.
2v.　8°.　(Bibliotheca Indica.　Sanskrit
New Series.　v.151.)

NN　0019717　　NN MH DSI MdBP

Nārada.

Jolly, Julius, 1849-　　ed. and tr.
　The minor law-books, translated by Julius Jolly.　Part I.
Nárada.　Brihaspati.　Oxford, The Clarendon press, 1889.

Nārada.
　Nárada sûtra; an inquiry into love (Bhakti-jijñâsā)　Translated from the Sanskrit with an independent commentary, by
E. T. Sturdy.　London, New York ﹙etc.﹚ Longmans, Green, and
co., 1896.
3 p. l., 68 p.　20ᵐ.　(On cover: Indian ideals, no. 1)

　1. Yoga.　2. Love.　I. Sturdy, Ed. T., tr.　II. Title: Bhakti-jijñāsā.
　　　　　　　　　　　　　　　　　　　　　　42-49030
Library of Congress　　　B132.Y6N3

NN　0019719　　DLC MH-AH CoU CU OCU OCl MB ICN NN NjP

B132
.Y6N3
1904
Nārada.
　Nárada sûtra; an inquiry into love (Bhakti-
jijñāsā)　Translated from the Sanskrit with
an independent commentary, by E. T. Sturdy.
2d ed.　London, J. M. Watkins, 1904.
64 p　18cm.　(The Brucheion series. no. 1)

　1. Yoga.　2. Love.　I. Title: Bhakti-jijñāsā.

NN　0019720　　ViU MH-AH

B 132
Y6 N3
1926
Nārada.
　Nárada sûtra; an inquiry into love
(Bhakti-jijñāsā)　Translated from the
Sanskrit with an independent commentary by
E. T. Sturdy.　3d ed.　London, J. M.
Watkins, 1926.
64 p.

　1. Yoga.　2. Love.　I. Sturdy, Ed. T.,
tr.　II. Title.　III. Title: Bhakti-
jijñāsā.

NN　0019721　　CaBVaU

Nārada.
नारदस्मृति, टीकाश्रुतगत भावाश्रुवाद-सश्वलित.　सम्पादक ও অনুবাদক
ঔনারায়ণচন্দ্র স্মৃতিতীর্থ.　﹙Calcutta, Sanskrit College, 1951﹚
8, 189 p.　24 cm.

Bengali and Sanskrit.

　1. Hindu law.　I. Smṛtitīrtha, Nārāyaṇacandra, ed. and tr.
　　　　　　　　　　　　　　Title transliterated: Nāradasmṛti.

　　　　　　　　　　　　　　　　　　　S A 65-5835

NN　0019722　　DLC CaBVaU NNC ICU NcD NIC

Nārada.
　Náradíya dharmasástra; or, the Institutes of Nárada.
Translated, for the first time, from the unpublished Sanskrit
original, by Julius Jolly.　With a preface, notes chiefly
critical, an index of quotations from Nárada in the principal
Indian digests, and a general index.　London, Trübner,
1876.
xxxv, 143 p.　20 cm.

　1. Hindu law.　I. Jolly, Julius, 1849-1932, ed. and tr.　II. Title.
III. Title: Institutes of Nárada.

　　　　　　　　　　　　　　　　　　　62-55641

　　MH CtY TxU CU
NN　0019723　　DLC MiU-L PU IaU OO OCH OCl PBm ICN

VOLUME 405

Narada.
... The Nāradīyamanusamhitā, with the Bhāsya of Bhavasvāmin. Edited by K. Sāmbaśiva Sāstrī... Trivandrum, Government press, 1929.
    24 cm.   (Trivandrum Sanskrit series, no. 97)
    At head of title: Śri Setu Laksmi Prasādamālā; no. 9.
    Added t.-p. in Sanskrit.
    "It appears that the present work is an abridgment by Nārada, of the ancient Dharmaśāstra of Manu" cf. Introduction, p.2.

NN   0019724   CtY

Nārada.
    The philosophy of love, being the Narada sutras. Translated with an independent commentary by Hari Prasad Shastri. London, Shanti Sadan Pub. Committee, 1947.
    95 p.   15 cm.

    1. Bhakti. 2. God—Worship and love.   I. Shastri, Hari Prasad, 1882-   ed. and tr. II. Title.
    BL1215.B5N3313 1947   73–153300
                                                        MARC

NN   0019725   DLC CLSU MH NN PPT

PK2971
.G3
no. 16
Nārada, *supposed author.*
    ... Sangita-makaranda of Nârada, edited with introduction and appendices by Mangesh Râmakrishna Telang ... Baroda, Central library, 1920.
    2 p. l., xi, 4, 64 p. 25ᵐ.   (*Half-title:* Gaekwad's Oriental series ... no. xvi)
    Title and author's name in Sanskrit at head of t.-p.
    Sanskrit text with Sanskrit paging.
    "The present work ... is said to be the work of Nârada on the authority of the manuscript."—p. iii.
    1. Music, Hindu.   I. Telang, Mangesh Ramakrishna, 1850-   ed. II. Title.
                                                        A 44–4648
    Chicago. Univ. Library
    for Library of Congress   PK2971.G3 no. 16

NN   0019726   ICU DLC HU

892.191
N161
Narada.
    La version môṇe du Narada-jataka, par Pierre Dupont. Saigon, École française d'Extrême-Orient, 1954.
    281 p.

    Dupont's thèse complémentaire, Paris.
    Published also without thesis note.
    Includes bibliographical references.

NN   0019727   NNC MH CtY

BL1411
J3N354
Nārada.
    La version môṇe du Nārada-jātaka, par Pierre Dupont. Saigon, École française d'Extreme-Orient, 1954.
    281 p. 22cm.   (Publications de l'École française d'Extrême-Orient, 36)

    Issued also as Dupont's thèse complémentaire, Paris.
    Original text and French translation.
    Includes bibliographical references.

    1. Buddha and Buddhism. I. Dupont, Pierre. II. Title.   (Series: Ecole française d'Extrême-Orient. Publications, v. 36)

        CU-S DLC-P4 MH NcU NPurMC CLU NN   MiEM
NN   0019729   CoU HU NNC MiU NNU WU NIC CSt ICU

Narada, Bhikkhu
        see   Narada, Thera.

Nārada, *of Vajirārāma Pariveṇa, Bambalapitiya*
    see
    Nārada, *Thera.*

Narada, Thera,   ed. and tr.
    Abhidhammattha-sangaha...
        see under   Anuruddha

Narada,Thera.
    The Bodhisatta ideal. [Colombo] Ceylon Daily News, 1944.
    31 p. (Vajirarama publications series, 9)

NN   0019733   MH

BL 1470
N37
1942
Nārada, Thera.
    The Buddha-Dhamma; or, The life and teachings of the Buddha. With a foreword by Cassius A. Pereira. Palm Grove, Panadura, Published by the children of the late Dr. & Mrs. C. P. de Fonseka, 1942.
    337 p. (Vajirārāma publication series, no. 6)
    1. Buddha and Buddhism. I. Title.

NN   0019734   CaBVaU

BL 1451
N31
Nārada, Thera.
    Buddhism in a nut-shell, by Bhikkhu Nārada. Vajirārāma. Bambalapitiya. ‹Colombo?› Caxton Print. Works, 1933.
    56 p. 19 cm.

    Cover title.

    1. Buddha and Buddism. I. Title.

NN   0019735   OU

Narada, Thera.
    Buddhism in a nutshell ...   Vajirarama, Bambalapitiya, Vajirarama publications society, 1945.
    30 p. 18.5 cm.   (Vajirarama publication series, no. 10)

NN   0019736   NcD

---

*
DS489
.7
.N37
1954
Nārada, Thera.
    Buddhism in a nutshell. Vajirarama, Bambalapitaya, Vajirarama Publication Society, 1954.
    39 p. 19cm. (Vajirarama publication series, no. 11)

    1. Buddha and Buddhism.

NN   0019737   ViU CtY-D

Nārada,Thera.
    ...The Buddhist doctrine of rebirth, by Nārada Thera. Colombo: Printed at Messrs. W. E. Bastian and co., 1936. 70 p. charts. 18½cm.

    Cover-title.

    1. Buddhism.
    N.Y.P.L.   April 7, 1939

NN   0019738   NN

Nārada, Thera, ed. and tr.
BL1411
.D5E76
Dhammapada. *English.*
    The Dhammapada. Translated with notes by Nārada Thera. With a foreword by Bhikkhu Kassapa and introd. by E. J. Thomas. London, J. Murray ₁1954₎

BL
515
N373
1953
Narada, Thera.
    La doctrine bouddhique de la re-naissance, par Narada Thera. Traduction: A. Migot. [Paris, A. Maisonneuve] 1953.
    82 p. 17 cm.

    1. Reincarnation. 2. Buddha and Buddhism. I. Migot, André, 1892-   tr. II. Title.

NN   0019740   CaBVaU TNJ-R MH DLC-P4 NIC CtY

491.37015
N164
1953
Narada, Thera.
    An elementary Pali course. [2d ed. rev. and enl.] Colombo, Associated Newspapers of Ceylon [1953]
    ii, 187p. 19cm.

    1. Pali language - Grammar. 2. Pali language - Composition and exercises.

NN   0019741   TxU ICU CU LU MiU MH MoU CaBVaU

BL
1451
.N3
Narada, Thera
    A manual of Buddhism; a textbook of Buddhism for the S. S. C. Colombo, Associated Newspapers of Ceylon [1949]
    132 p. illus. 19 cm.

    1. Buddha and Buddhism.

NN   0019742   NBuU

Nārada, *Thera.*
    A manual of Buddhism; a textbook of Buddhism for the S. S. C. 2d ed., revised according to the new syllabus. Colombo, Associated Newspapers of Ceylon ₁1951₎
    156 p. illus. 19 cm.

    1. Buddha and Buddhism.

    BL1451.N3 1951   294.312   60–20205 ‡

NN   0019743   DLC NSyU PU

BL
1451
.N22
1953
Nārada,Thera.
    A manual of Buddhism; a textbook of Buddhism for the G.C.E.ordinary level. 4th ed.,revised according to the new syllabus. Colombo, Associated Newspapers of Ceylon ₁1953₎
    156,viii p. illus.

    1.Buddha and Buddhism.

NN   0019744   MiU CaBVaU CtY MH

Wason
Pamphlet
E
493
Narada , Thera.
    Nibbana, but suprême du Bouddhisme. Phnom-Penh, Impr. du gouvernement, 1931.
    52 p. port. 25cm.

    "Version Cambodgienne."
    Title and text in Khmer; added t.p. in French.

NN   0019745   NIC

VOLUME 405

4BP
203
Narada, Thera
A simple introduction to Abhidhamma.
Calcutta, Maha Bodhi Society, 1948.
14 p.

NN 0019746   DLC-P4

Narada Thero
see
Nārada, *Thera.*

Narada-jataka.
La version mône du Narada-jataka
see under   Narada.

281.9
N16
Narada Gospodarcza, Warsaw, 1936.
Rereraty wygłoszone przez przedstawicieli rol.w.
nictwa na Naradzie gospodarczej w dniach 28. II ¬
2. III. 1936 r.   Warszawa, Związek izb i organi-
zacyj rolniczych r.p.,1936.
131 p.   18cm.

NN 0019749   DNAL

Narada Informacyjna, *Warsaw, 1947.*
Narada informacyjna dziewięciu partii.   Warszawa,
Wydawn. czasopisma "Nowe Drogi," 1947.
108 p. 25 cm.

1. Communist parties. 2. World politics—1945—   I. Title.
HX40.N3 1947   59–44568 ‡

NN 0019750   DLC

Nāradapāñcarātra
see Pāñcarātra.

Naradija dharmasastra ...
see under   Narada.

Naradzie gospodarczey, Warszawa, 1936
see   Narada Gospodarcza, Warsaw, 1936.

(Naraex,/Tunfilo/de) d. 1528
Sommation a faire aux habitants des contrees
et provinces qui s'etendent depuis la riviere
des Palmes et le cap de la Floride.(1527)
(In Ternaux-Compans, Henri, ed. Voyages, relations et memoires originaux pour servir a
l'histoire de la decouverte de l'Amerique.
Paris, 1837-41. (t.20) p.(1)-7)

NN 0019754   MiU-C

Naraghi, Hossein,
... Contribution à l'étude des cancers primitifs
de l'épiglotte ...   Toulouse, 1934.
Thèse – Univ. de Toulouse.
"Bibliographie": p. [190]-198.

NN 0019755   CtY

Naragon, Ernest Ashley
The synthesis and polymerization of
butadiene. 123,41., tables diagrs.
Thesis – Ph.D. degree – Western reserve
university, May 15, 1940.

NN 0019756   OClW

Naragon, Harold Leroy
The Ohio gubernatorial campaign of
1863 ... by Harold L. Naragon ... [Columbus]
The Ohio state university. 1934.
3 p.

NN 0019757   OU

Narahara Gangadhara Apate
see
Apte, Narhar Gangadhar, 1900–

Narahara Kāśinātha Ghārapure
see
Gharpure, Narhar Kashinath, 1904–

Narahara Raghunātha Phāṭaka
see
Phāṭaka, Narahara Raghunātha, 1894–

Narahara Vishṇu Gāḍagīḷa
see
Gadgil, Narhar Vishnu, 1896–1966.

Narahari.
Bodhasār; a treatise on Vedānta, with a commen-
tary by author's pupil Divākar. Edited by Swāmi
Dayānand.   Benares, B.B. Das, sold by H.D.
Gupta, 1906 [i.e. 1904-06]
972 p. (Benares Sanskrit series [v.23])
Sanskrit title at head of t.p.: Sanskrit text.
Issued in parts.
1. Vedānta. I. Divākara, disciple of Narahari.
Arthadīptī. II. Dayānada Svāmi, disciple of
Govindānanda, ed. III. Title. Series.

NN 0019762   ICU WaU

TN103
.N3
1882
Narahari, *fl.* 1235-1250.
Die indischen mineralien, ihre namen und die ihnen zuge-
schriebenen kräfte. Narahari's Râganighantu, varga XIII.
Sanscrit und deutsch, mit kritischen und erläuternden anmer-
kungen, herausgegeben von dr. Richard Garbe ... Leipzig,
Verlag von S. Hirzel, 1882.
x, 104 p. 22cm.
"Die handschriften": p. [3]–4.
"Râganighantu varga XIII. Sanskrit text": p. 4–29.
"Übersetzung": p. [33]–92.
1. Mineralogy—Early works to 1800. 2. Precious stones.   I. Garbe,
Richard von, 1857–1927.
                                          G S 34—738
U. S. Geol. survey. Libr.   Geo. F. Kunz collection K104 N141
for Library of Congress   [a40k1]

NN 0019763   DI-GS CtY CU MH PU OCl ICU

[Narahari, fl. 1235-50]
The Rājanighanta [of Narahari] and the Dhanvantari-
nighanta; two treatises on medicine. Edited by Vaidya
Nārāyaṇa Shastri Purandare. Poona, Āpte, 1896

440, 135 p. (Ānandāśrama Sanskrita series, 33)
Added t.p. in Sanskrit; text in Sanskrit

NN 0019764   MH

Narahari, 1674–1790
see
Kṛshṇadayārṇava, 1674–1790.

Narahari, H   G ururaja, 1917–
Ātman in pre-Upanisadic Vedic literature / by H. G.
Narahari. — [Madras] : Advar Library, 1944.
xliii, 278 p. ; 22 cm. — (Adyar Library series ; no. 47)
Thesis (M. Litt.)—University of Madras.
Bibliography : p. [237]–248.
Includes index.

1. Ātman. 2. Vedic literature—History and criticism.
I. Title. II. Series.
B132.A8N35   126   74–189275
                                                MARC

NN 0019766   DLC HU CU PU IEN OCl MH

Narahari, H   Gururaja, 1917–   ed.
Dharmacauryarasāyana of Gopālayogīndra
see under   Gōpālayogīndra.

Narahari, H   Gururaja, 1917–
Kavya, Nataka and Alankara. [Adyar] 1951
xxix, 604 p. (Descriptive catalogue of Sanskrit
manuscripts in the Adyar library, 5)
Adyar Library series, 80

NN 0019768   MH

Narahari Dvārkādas
see   Parīkh, Narahari Dwarkadas, 1891–

Narahari Dwarkadas Parikh
see
Parikh, Narahari Dwarkadas, 1891–

Narahari Gopalakristnamah Chetty
see   Chetty, Narahari Gopalakristnamah.

Narahari Svāmi
see
Narahari.

Narahashi, Wataru.
Exécution des jugements étrangers au Japon, d'après les lois
japonaises d'exéquatur en vigueur et les jurisprudences et
doctrines européennes notamment celles de France, par Wataru
Narahashi ... Paris, Recueil Sirey, 1937.
239, [1] p. 21½cm.
"Bibliographie": p. 238-239.

1. Judgments, Foreign—Japan.   I. Title.
                                          45–32549

NN 0019773   DLC CtY MnU

VOLUME 405

Narahashi, Wataru.
(Narahashi Shi no kataru Ō–Bei Yudaya seiryoku)
栖橋氏ノ語ル歐米猶太勢カト滿鐵ノ國際的地位
₍大連　南滿洲鐵道株式會社₎調査部特別調査班
昭和14₍1939₎
1, 3 l.　26 cm.
Cover title.
At head of title: 秘 (rubber stamped)
十一月十四日社員會館テ₍栖橋渡₎氏ヲ中心トスル座談會ヲ開催シタカ
其ノ際二於ケル同氏ノ談話…₍ノ₎部分ヲ栖橋録シタノカ本ケテアル

1. Minami Manshū Tetsudō Kabushiki Kaisha.　2. Railroads—Manchuria—Finance. 3. Jews—Economic conditions.　4. Jews—Political
and social conditions. I. Minami Manshū Tetsudō Kabushiki Kaisha.
Chōsabu. Tokubetsu Chōsahan. II. Title.
HE3290.M5N36
72-808624

NN 0019775   DLC

Wason
DS575.5
C3N21
Narai, King of Siam, 1632?-1688.
Traduction exacte de la lettre du Roy
de Siam à N.S.P. le Pape Innocent XI.
Bordeaux, Matthieu Chappuis, 1689.
2 p. 23cm.

1. Thailand—For. rel.—Catholic Church.
2. Catholic Church-Relations (diplomatic)
with Thailand.　I. Innocentius XI, Pope,
1611-1689.

NN 0019776   NIC

Narain
see also   Narayan.

Ph.
2199
N164j
Narain, Anand.
Jo'e sher.　[Delhi?], 1949.
392 p.

NN 0019778   CLU

Narain, Barkat, 1899–
Nutrition, by B. N. Khan.　[New Delhi, 1946]
61 p.　illus., ports. 22 cm.

1. Deficiency diseases. 2. Nutrition.　I. Title.
Name originally: Bercut Narain Khan.
RC620.N28 1946   641.1   52-43941 rev

NN 0019779   DLC

Narain, Barkat, 1899–
Nutrition. 2d ed., illustrated, rev. and enl. Foreword
by Rajkumari Amrit Kaur. [New Delhi, foreword 1949]
75 p. illus., ports. 23 cm.

1. Deficiency diseases. 2. Nutrition.
Name originally: Bercut Narain Khan.
RC620.N28 1949   641.1   58-30537

NN 0019780   DLC

Narain, Brahmadeva.
Constitutional restrictions, incorporating the relevant portions of the Constitutions of America, Australia & Canada.
1st ed. Patna, International Book Company, 1953.
288 p. 25 cm.

Continued in next column

Continued from preceding column

1. India—Constitutional law.　I. Title.
54-39555 ‡

NN 0019781   DLC NN MH-L

HJ
2928
.N3
Narain, Brij.
The agricultural worker and the
Punjab Land Revenue Committee.
[Lahore, Institute of Agrarian Re-
form [1939]
72 p.

#Agriculture--Taxation--Punjab.
#Peasantry--India--Punjab.
(A)The agricultural worker and the
Punjab Land Revenue Committee.

NN 0019782   MoU WaU NcD

DS481
G34N29
Narain, Brij
Charkha Marxism, Indian socialism.　Lahore, Rama
Krishna, 1941.
195 p.

1. Socialism in India.　2. India - Politics and government -
1919-1947.　I. Title.

NN 0019783   CU

Narain, Brij.
Curve fitting for students of economics, by Brij Narain ...
Delhi and Lahore, S. Chand & co., 1944.
viii, 197 p. diagrs. 21½ᶜᵐ.
"First published 1944."

1. Statistics—Graphic methods.　I. Title.
46-17398
Library of Congress   HA31.N3
[2]   311.2

NN 0019784   DLC

Narain, Brij.
Economic structure of free India, by Brij Narain ...
Lahore, Indian book company ltd. [1946]
xiv p., 1 l., 168 p. 22½ cm.
"First impression."

1. India—Economic policy. 2. Economics.　I. Title.
HC435.N27   330.954   47—18961

NN 0019785   DLC NcD NN MiU FU ViU WaU

HD2075
.P8A4
n. s.,
no. 2
Narain, Brij.

Narain, Raj.
An economic survey of Gijhi, a village in the Rohtak
District of the Punjab. Inquiry conducted by Raj Narain
under the supervision of Brij Narain. [Lahore, "C. & M.
Gazette" Press] 1932.

Narain, Brij.
Eighty years of Punjab food prices, 1841–1920. [Lahore,
"C. & M. Gazette" Press] 1926.
64 p. diagrs., tables. 25 cm. (The Board of Economic Inquiry,
Punjab. Rural section publication, 13)
"Reprinted ... from the Indian journal of economics."

1. Prices—Punjab. 2. Agriculture—Economic aspects—India—Pun-
jab.　I. Title.　(Series: Board of Economic Inquiry, Punjab.
Publications, no. 13)
HB233.A3N3   50–41100

NN 0019787   DLC NN NcD MoU

Narain, Brij.
Essays on Indian economic problems, [by] Brij Narain...
Lahore: The Panjabee (Electric) Press [1919]. 3 p.l., ii p., 1 l.,
307 p. incl. tables. fold. diagrs. 12°.
Reprinted in part from various Indian periodicals.

1. Economic history, India.　2. Prices, India, 1914-19.　3. European war, 1914- .—Economic   aspects, India.
N.Y.P.L.   December 3, 1920.

NN 0019788   NN MH

HC435 **Narain, Brij.**
.N24   Essays on Indian economic problems [by] Brij Narain ...
Lahore, The Panjabee press [1920]
[5], ii, [1], 307, [1] p. incl. tables. 3 fold. charts. 18½ᶜᵐ.

1. India—Econ. condit.

NN 0019789   ICU

Narain, Brij.
...Essays on Indian economic problems, [by] Brij Narain...
Lahore: The Punjab Prtg. Works, 1922. x, 547 p. incl. tables.
12°.　(Indian economic problems. Part 1.)
Some of the essays previously published in author's Essays on Indian economic
problems (Lahore, 1919), and in Weltwirtschaftliches Archiv of Kiel.—*Cf. Pref.*

99191A. 1. Economic history, India.
N. Y. P. L.   September 13, 1923.

NN 0019790   NN

Narain, Brij.
India before and since the crisis ... by Brij Narain ... Allahabad, The Indian press, ltd., 1939.
2 v. diagrs. (part col., part double) 22½ᶜᵐ.
"Incorporates the substance of India in the crisis and India before the
crisis."—*Pref.*, v. 1.

1. India—Econ. condit.—1918–　I. Title.
46–36743
Library of Congress   HC435.N295
[2]   330.954

NN 0019791   DLC NSyU

Narain, Brij.
India before the crisis, by Brij Narain ... Allahabad, The
Indian press, ltd., 1935.
xiv p., 1 l., 465 p. 20 diagr. (part col., part double) 22ᶜᵐ.
Subsequently incorporated with the author's India in the crisis and
India before and since the crisis.

1. India—Econ. condit.—1918–　I. Title.
46–36708
Library of Congress   HC435.N28

NN 0019792   DLC

Narain, Brij.
India in the crisis, by Brij Narain ... Allahabad, The Indian press, ltd., 1934.
vii p., 1 l., 399 p. 21ᶜᵐ.

1. India—Economic conditions.　I. Title.
Agr 37-69
U. S. Dept. of agr. Library   280.182N16
for Library of Congress   [HC435   ]

NN 0019793   DNAL IU

VOLUME 405

Narain, Brij.
Indian economic life, past and present, by Brij Narain ...
Lahore, Uttar Chand Kapur & sons, 1929.
3 p. l., xxiii, 578 p. diagrs. 24ᵐ.
Bibliography: p. xvii–xix.

1. India—Econ. condit. I. Title.

[Name in transliteration: Vraja-Nārāyaṇa]

Library of Congress   HC433.N3

    31–2307

    [2]   330.954

NN   0019794   DLC NcD CoU OOxM MiU NN ICU

Narain, Brij.
Indian economic problems ... [by] Brij Narain ... Lahore, The Punjab printing works, 1922.
2 v. 18½ᵐ.
CONTENTS.—I. Essays on Indian economic problems.—II. Source book for the study of Indian economic problems.

1. India—Econ. condit.—1918–   2. Currency question—India. 3. India—Economic policy. 4. Tariff—India. I. Title.

          24–350

Library of Congress   HC435.N3

    [2]   Provisional

NN   0019795   DLC MiU PU

Narain, Brij.
Indian economic problems: pre-war, war and post-war ... by Brij Narain ... Lahore [etc.] Atma Ram & sons, 1944.
2 v. diagrs. 18ᵐ.
CONTENTS.—v. 1. pt. 1. Pre-war period.—v. 2. pt. 2. War economy. pt. 3. Post-war planning.

1. India—Econ. condit.—1918–   2. India—Economic policy. I. Title.

          46–16982

Library of Congress   HC435.N82

    [2]   330.954

NN   0019796   DLC CU

Narain, Brij.
Indian socialism, by Brij Narain ... Lahore, Atma Ram & sons, 1937.
xxiii, 158 p. incl. tables. 19ᵐ.
Bibliographical foot-notes.

1. Socialism in India. I. Title.

[Name in transliteration: Vraja-Nārāyaṇa]

          A 38–131

New York. Public library
for Library of Congress   [2]

NN   0019797   NN ICU MoU

Narain, Brij.
Marxism is dead, by Brij Narain... Lahore: Rama Krishna & sons, 1939. 265 p. incl. tables. chart. 19½cm.

Bibliographical footnotes.
"Supplement to Marxism is dead..." 30 p., inserted at end.

70816B. 1. Bolshevism. English.   2. Socialism, 1931–   3. Socialism—India. I. Title.
N.Y.P.L.   August 28, 1940

NN   0019798   NN CtY WU

Narain, Brij.
The population of India; a comparative study [by] Brij Narain ... Anarkali, Lahore, Rama Krishna & sons, 1925.
3 p. l., ii, v, 215 p. incl. tables. 21½ᵐ.

Continued in next column

Continued from preceding column

1. India—Population.   2. India—Statistics, Vital.   3. India—Econ. condit.—
1918–   I. Title.

[Name in transliteration: Vraja-Nārāyaṇa]

Library of Congress   HB3639.N3   26–20388

   MiU NN
NN   0019799   DLC CaBVaU WaU InU NcD CtY PU ICU OU

Narain, Brij.
Post-war planning of the Indian defence services, by Brij Narain. New Delhi, The Indian institute of international affairs [1946]
36 p. 22 cm.
"First published–November 1946."
"The paper first appeared in the Journal of the Indian institute of international affairs for January, 1945."

1. India—Defenses.   I. Indian institute of international affairs, Delhi. II. Title.

UA840.N35   355   47–28296

NN   0019800   DLC NN

Narain, Brij.
Principles of economics, by Brij Narain ... 2d ed. Delhi, Lahore, S. Chand & co. [1944]
2 p. l., ii–vi, [1], 425, *78, 4 p. diagrs. 22½ᵐ.
"First edition 1941."

1. Economics.

          A 45–3015

New York. Public library
for Library of Congress   [2]

NN   0019801   NN

Narain, Brij.
Principles of economics, by Brij Narain ... (3d rev. and enl. ed.) ... Delhi–Lahore, S. Chand & co., 1945.
2 p. l., ii–v, 483 p. diagrs. 22ᵐ.
"First edition 1941 ... Third edition 1945."

1. Economics.

          46–16983

Library of Congress   HB171.5.N26 1945

    [2]   330.1

NN   0019802   DLC ICU

HC433 **Narain, Brij.**
.N3   ... Source book for the study of Indian economic problems [by] Brij Narain ... Lahore, Punjab printing works, 1922.
   [5], xi, 435 p. 18½ᵐ. (Indian economic problems, pt. II)

1. India—Econ. condit.

NN   0019803   ICU NN

Narain, Brij.
... Tendencies in recent economic thought; lectures delivered as Sir Kikabhai Premchand reader, 1934, to the University of Delhi, by Brij Narain ... [Delhi] University of Delhi, 1935.
3 p. l., 213 p. 24ᵐ. (The Delhi university publications. no. 5)
Bibliographical foot-notes.

1. Economics. 2. Economics—History.   I. Title: Recent economic thought.

          Agr 38–524

U. S. Dept. of agr. Library
for Library of Congress   280N16
       [HB87   ]

NN   0019804   DNAL CaBVaU NSyU NN

Narain, Brij.
The Traders' Bank prize thesis, 1; on a detailed plan for the development of Indian joint stock banking with a special reference to the assistance banks can render in the growth and progress of Indian industry. Lahore, U. C. Kapur, 1945.
111 p. diagrs., tables. 25 cm.
Bibliographical footnotes.

1. Banks and banking—India. 2. Currency question—India. I. Title. II. Title: A detailed plan for the development of Indian joint stock banking.

HG3284.N28   58–45863

NN   0019805   DLC

Narain, Brij, 1882–1926.
सुबह-वतन; अर्थात्, ब्रजनारायण "चकबस्त" की स्फुट कविताओं के संग्रह, सुबह वतन, का कठिन शब्दों के अर्थसहित हिन्दी रूपान्तर. सम्पादक ब्रजकृष्ण गुर्टू. प्रयाग, इंडियन प्रेस, १९४४ [c1944]
227 p. 20 cm.
1. Patriotic poetry, Hindi.   I. Title.
Title transliterated: Subaha-vatana.

PK2098.N33S8   1944   S A 62–141 ‡

NN   0019806   DLC

QB335
M3   Narain, H., joint author.

Marshall, Charles Edward.
Regional gravity investigations in the eastern and central Commonwealth, by C. E. Marshall and H. Narain. [Sydney, University of Sydney, Dept. of Geology and Geophysics] 1954.

JQ231   Narain, Iqbal
A24   Appleby report on Public administration in India; a survey and
1953   assessment, with a foreword by Eddy Asirvatham. [Agra,
N36   Ram Narain Azad, foreword 1954]
     33 p.

     Bibliographical footnotes.

     1. India (Republic) Cabinet Secretariat. / Public administration in India.   2. India - Pol. & govt. - 1947–   3. Appleby, Paul Henson, 1891–   I. Title.

NN   0019808   CU CtY NN NNU MiU

4JQ   Narain, Iqbal
54   Appleby report on public administration in India; a survey and assessment. With a foreword by Eddy Asirvatham. [Rajamandi, R. N. Azad, 1955]
     38 p.

NN   0019809   DLC-P4

JQ
231   Narain, Iqbal.
A65   Appleby report on public administration in
N22   India, a survey and assessment. With a foreword by Eddy Asirvatham. [Rajamandi, Agra, Ram Narain Azad, 1955]
     33 p.
     Includes bibliography.

     1. Appleby, Paul Henson, 1891– Public administration in India.

NN   0019810   MiU

Narain, Jagat, 1895–
Law of elections and election petitions in India and Burma, by Jagat Narain ... Calcutta, Eastern law house [1937]
3 p. l., ii, [2], 7, xviii, 497, 529, xviii p. 25ᵐ.
"Appendices" (statutes, etc.) : 529 p.

1. Election law—India. 2. Election law—Burma.   I. India. Laws, statutes, etc. II. Burma. Laws, statutes, etc. III. Title.

          38–35010
          Provisional

Library of Congress   JQ295.N33

    [3]   324.54

NN   0019811   DLC

VOLUME 405

Narain, Jagat, 1895-   comp.
Reports of Indian election petitions. Allahabad, Allahabad Law Journal Press, 1929-   [v. 3, 1929]
v. 25 cm.
Vol. 2 has imprint: Calcutta, Eastern Law House.
Contents.—v. 1. 1920.—v. 2. 1923-25.—v. 3. 1926-28.

1. Election law—India—Cases. 2. Contested elections. I. Title.
32–13009 rev*

NN   0019812   DLC

Narain, Jai Prakash.
Cultural variation ... by J. P. Narayan ... 1929.
3 p.

NN   0019813   OU

JQ298   Narain, Jai Prakash
S6N36   Gandhiji's leadership and the Congress Socialist Party, by Jayaprakash Narayan.   Bombay, All India Congress Socialist Party [1940?]
12 p.   (Congress socialist tracts no. 1)
Cover title.

1. Socialist Party (India) I. Title.

NN   0019814   CU

Narain, Jai Prakash, ed.
The Hyderabad problem
see under   Socialist Party (India) Hyderabad Struggle Committee.

DS
480.45
.N32   Narain, Jai Prakash
In the Lahore fort [by] Jayaprakash Narayan. Patna, Sahityalaya [1947]
viii, 199 p.
His diary written in 1943 and 1944.

1. India - Pol. & govt. - 1919-1947. 2. Narain, Jai Prakash. I. Title.

NN   0019816   NNC

DS   Narain, Jai Prakash, 1902-
450   India and Pakistan [by] Jayaprakash Narayan,
P3   Rammanohar Lohia [and] Asoka Mehta. [Patna]
N3   Socialist Party [1950]
26p. 22cm. (Socialist Party. Publications Department, I, 4)

1. India - For. rel. - Pakistan 2. Pakistan - For. rel. - India 3. Mohammedans in India I. Lohia, Rammanohar, 1910-   , joint author II. Mehta, Asoka, 1911-   , joint author III. Socialist   Party (India) IV. Title

NN   0019817   WU

[Narain, Jai Prakash]
"J. P." India's revolutionary number one; comp. and ed. by B. N. Ahuja. [1st ed.] Lahore, Varma Pub. Co. [1947]
viii, 220 p. 19 cm.
"Jaya Prakash Narayan—a biographical sketch by B. N. Ahuja": p. 1-20.

Continued in next column

Continued from preceding column

1. India—Pol. & govt.—1919-   I. Ahuja, B. N., ed. II. Title:
India's revolutionary number one.
DS481.N3A3   954   47–29733*

NN   0019818   DLC MiU CU DAU NcD MoU

D922   Narain, Jai Prakash
N3   Jayaprakash Narayan on Some impressions of my European tour. Text of a speech delivered at Sapru House on September 22, 1958, under the auspices of the Office for Asian Affairs, Congress for Cultural Freedom. New Delhi [1958?]
35 p.

1. Europe - Descr. & trav. - 1945-

NN   0019819   CU

HX391   Narain, Jai Prakash
N36   Miscellaneous writings.   [New Delhi, etc., 1951-56]
3 no. in 1 v.
Title supplied by CU Library.
Contents. - New perspectives. - Political trends. - Isavandan.

1. Communism - India.

NN   0019820   CU

HX   Narain, Jai Prakash.
394   My picture of socialism. Madras [A.K.Chan-
.N22   drasekhara Mudaliar, 194-?]
17 p.   illus.

1. Socialism in India.

NN   0019821   MiU

HX394   Narain, Jai Prakash.
.N275   My picture of socialism. Madras. J. Prachuralayam, 1949.
16 p.

1. Socialism—India.

NN   0019822   ICU

DS481   Narain, Jai Prakash
G34N3   A picture of sarvodaya social order.   [2d ed.]   Tanjore
1955   (S. India) Sarvodaya Prachuralaya [1955]
50 p.   (Bhoodan series)
Cover title.

1. Land tenure - India.   2. Village communities - India.
3. India - Econ. condit. - 1945-

NN   0019823   CU DLC-P4

JQ   Narain, Jai Prakash.
298   Political trends. [Bombay, Published by
.S6   Madhu Limaye for the Socialist Party, 1951]
N22   18 p.

1. Socialist Party (India) 2. Communist Party of India.

NN   0019824   MiU

Narain, Jai Prakash

Political vacuum, by Jayaprakash Narayan. [Bombay, 1951] 9 p. 19cm. (Socialist publications)

1. India— Hist., 1947-

NN   0019825   NN

4-DS   Narain, Jai Prakash
Ind.   Socialism to Sarvodaya.   Madras,
187   Socialist Book Centre [19]
128 p.

NN   0019826   DLC-P4

JQ298   Narain, Jai Prakash
S6N364   Socialist unity and the Congress Socialist Party, by Jayaprakash Narayen. Bombay, Congress Socialist Party [1941]
46 p.
Cover title.

1. Socialist Party (India) 2. Communist Party of India. I. Title.

NN   0019827   CU

DS   Narain, Jai Prakash.
481   To all fighters for freedom. [1st ed.]
.N24   Lucknow, Ganga Fine Art Press, 1947]
A4   49 p.
At head of cover title: Towards socialism.

1. India--Pol. & govt.--1919-1947.

NN   0019828   MiU

Narain, Jai Prakash.
Towards struggle; selected manifestos, speeches & writings by Jaya Prakash Narayan. Edited by Yusuf Meherally. Bombay, Padma publications ltd. [1946]
244 p. 28 cm.
"First published, 9th August, 1946."
"Jaya Prakash by Yusuf Meherally" (p. 7-14) is reprinted, with slight changes, from v. 1 of Meherally's Leaders of India.

1. India—Pol. & govt.—1919-1947.   I. Meherally, Yusuf, ed.
II. Title.
DS448.N34   954   47—20812

IU IEN CaBVaU CLU NSyU ViU OCU DAU MiU NcD
NN   0019829   DLC WaU NN TxU GU CU ICU KMK CU-S MoU

JQ298   Naraian, Jai Prakash.
S6N365   Where leader ship failed?   Lahore, Socialist Literature House [1946-
v.

1. Socialist Party (India) 2. India - Pol. & govt. - 1919-1947.

NN   0019830   CU

Narain, Jai Prakash.
Why socialism? by Jayaprakash Narayan. Benares, All India Congress Socialist Party, 1936.
iii, 160 p. 19 cm.
Includes bibliographical references.

1. Socialist Party (India) 2. Socialism in India.   I. Title.
JQ298.S6N33   335'.00954   72–235536
MARC

NN   0019831   DLC NN IEN WU MiEM OKentU NN

VOLUME 405

Narain, Lakshmi.
Indian economy, 1952. ₁1st ed.₎ Meerut, Shri Prakashan ₁1953₎
369 p. 23 cm.

1. India—Econ. condit.—1945–   ɪ. Title.

HC435.N33   330.954   54–15622 ‡

NN   0019832   DLC CaBVa OrU NcD TxU CtY NN

Narain, Lakshmi.
Indian economy, 1952. ₁1st ed.₎ Meerut, Shri Prakashan ₁1953₎
360 p. 23 cm.

-- --- Supplement contains facts and figures up to June 1954. Meerut, Shri Prakashan ₁1954₎
78 p.   22 cm.
1. India—Econ. condit.—1945–

NN   0019833   MiU PU-W NN

Narain, Lallah Luchmi
see Luchmi Narain, Lallah.

Narain, Mahesh
see Narayan, Mahesh.

HD1425
.F583

Food and Agriculture Organization of the United Nations. *Economics Division.*
₁Méthodes d'établissement des statistiques agricoles courantes, par R. D. Narain, Division de l'économie. Rome, Organisation des Nations Unies pour l'alimentation et l'agriculture, 1955–

Narain, R. D.

HD1425
.F58

Food and Agriculture Organization of the United Nations. *Economics Division.*
₁Methods of collecting current agricultural statistics, by R. D. Narain, Economics Division. Rome, Food and Agriculture Organization of the United Nations, 1955–

Narain, R. D.

323.354
N2188

Narain, Radhka
Some aspects of rural economic conditions in Delhi province. Delhi, S. Chand ₁1935₎
iv, 89, xiv p. 25 cm.
Cover title.

1. Delhi (Province) Rural condit. I. Title. II. Title: Rural economic conditions in Delhi province.

NN   0019838   NcD

HC
437
.D3
.N37
1939

Narain, Radhka.
Some aspects of rural economic conditions in Delhi province. 2d ed., rev. and enl. Delhi, S. Chand [1939]
102 p.
#Delhi (Province)—Economic conditions.
(A)Some aspects of rural economic conditions in Delhi province.

NN   0019839   MoU

Narain, Raj.
An economic survey of Gijhi, a village in the Rohtak District of the Punjab. Inquiry conducted by Raj Narain under the supervision of Brij Narain. ₁Lahore, "C. & M. Gazette" Press₎ 1932.
313 p. maps (part fold.) diagr., geneal. table. 25 cm. (Punjab village surveys. ₁New ser.₎ 2)
Board of Economic Inquiry, Punjab. Rural section publications, 17.
1. Gijhi, India—Econ. condit.   ɪ. Narain, Brij.   (Series. Series: Board of Economic Inquiry, Punjab. Publications, no. 17)
HD2075.P8A4   n. s., no. 2   330.954   50–47512

NN   0019840   DLC

Narain, Ram.
The tigress of the harem ₁by₎ Ram Narain. New York, The Macaulay company ₁*1930₎
4 p. l., 7–388, ₁1₎ p. 19½ᶜᵐ.

ɪ. Title.
Library of Congress   PZ3.N165Ti   30–7425

NN   0019841   DLC OrU

Narain, Ram, Editor of "Practical Medicine"
see Ram Narayan.

Narain, Ramji, joint author.

Lander, Percy Edward.
... Soils of the Punjab, by P. E. Lander ... Ramji Narain ... and Mehta Mokand Lal ... Calcutta, Government of India central publication branch, 1929.

4BP
375

Narain, Sheo
Asoka. Calcutta, Maha Bodhi Society [19]
13 p.

(Maha Bodhi pamphlet series no₁ 17)

NN   0019844   DLC-P4

4BP
378

Narain, Sheo
Buddhism. Calcutta, Maha Bodhi Society of India, 1950.
60 p.

(Mahabodhi pamphlet series, no. 12)

NN   0019845   DLC-P4

BL
1451
N34

Narain, Sheo
Buddhism. 2d ed. Calcutta, Maha Bodhi Society, 1938.
62 p.   19 cm. (in binder, 22 cm.)
(Mahabodhi pamphlet series, no. 12)

Cover title.

1. Buddha and Buddhism   I. Title

NN   0019846   WU

DS486
.S3N2

Narain, Sheo.
...Sarnath ... 2d impression. Calcutta, Maha Bodhi society ₁19--₎
cover-title, 38 p. pl. ₁Maha Bodhi pamphlet series. no.10₎

1. Sarnath, India.

NN   0019847   ICU

Narain, Shiv.
Outlines of world peace. Delhi, Sarover Prakashan ₁1950?₎
ii, iii, 101 p. 19 cm.

1. Peace.

JX1953.N33   55–26174

NN   0019848   DLC

Narain, Shri
see
Shri Narain.

Narain Agarwala Prakash
see Agarwala Prakash Narain.

Narain Anant Mavlankar
see Mavlankar, Narain Anant.

Narain Chaudhuri, Jnanendra
see
Chaudhuri, Jnanendra Narain.

Narain Dass Ram
see Ram Narain Das.

Narain Gupta, Raj
see
Gupta, Raj Narain.

Narain Kapur, Karam
see
Kapur, Karam Narain.

Narain Lal, Jagat
see Lal, Jagat Narain.

Narain Lal Ram
see Lal, Ram Narain.

Narain Malaviya, Kashi
see Malaviya, Kashi Narain.

Narain Sewal, Anand
see Sewal, Anand Narain.

VOLUME 405

Narain Sinha, Har
     see   Sinha, Har Narain, 1900–

Narain Sinha, Rajeshwar Prasad
     see   Sinha, Rajeshwar Prasad Narain.

PK
3521
.I84N3
1929
Narain Swami, governor of Gurukul.
     A commentary on the Ishopanishat,
translated into English from the rev. and
enl. Arya Basha ed. 2d ed. Meerut,
Vidya Printing Press, 1929.
     98 p.

#Upanishads. Iśopaniṣad.

NN   0019862   MoU

Naraion Gongopadkhaïñ, *pseud.*
     see
Ganguli, Taraknath, 1918–

al-Narāḳī, Muḥamad al-Mahdī
     see
al-Nirāqī, Muḥammad Mahdī ibn Abī Dharr, *d.* 1794 *or* 5.

Naramata, B.C. Christian leadership training
     school.
     Annual meeting of the board of directors,
1951-   Naramata, B.C. The School, 1951-
     1 v.

NN   0019865   CaBViP

Naramata, B.C. - Christian leadership
     training school.
     Tour of Alberta and B.C. Kootenays by
class of '49.   [N.p. The School,1949].
     9p.sq.Q.

NN   0019866   CaBViP

Naramata irrigation district, Naramata, British
     Columbia.
     Annual statement of receipts and expenditure,
and balance sheet for the year ending February 15th,
1950– February 15th, 1951.   [Naramata, B.C.
n. pub.] 1950-51.
     2 v.   tables.   sq. Q.

NN   0019867   CaBViP

Naramore, Dewilda [Ellen]
     The arrière-ban in medieval France.

Thesis - Radcliffe, 1943

NN   0019868   MH

Naramore, Earl.
     Handloader's manual; a treatise on modern cartridge com-
ponents and their assembly by the individual shooter into accurate ammunition to best suit his various purposes, by Earl Naramore ... sketches by Lt. Col. Julian S. Hatcher ... Onslow
county, N. C., Small-arms technical publishing company [*1937]

     3 p. l., v, 369, [1] p. front., illus., xx pl. on 10 l., diagrs. 19½ᵐ.

"Book by Samworth."

     1. Cartridges. 2. Ammunition.   I. Hatcher, Julian Sommerville,
1888-   illus. II. Title.

Library of Congress   TS538.N3   40-1197
———— Copy 2.
Copyright A 134644   [3]   623.4558

NN   0019869   DLC OC1 DAL

Naramore, Earl.
     Principles and practice of loading ammunition; a treatise
on the loading of ammunition, with particular reference to
the individual who reloads his own cartridges, together with
an explanation of the underlying principles which govern
or limit such practice. Georgetown, S. C., Small Arms
Technical Pub. Co. [1954]

     952 p. illus. 25 cm. (A Samworth book)

     1. Ammunition.   I. Title: Loading ammunition.

UF700.N3   54-4008 ‡

NN   0019870   DLC PPPL WaSp CaBVaU Wa Or OC1 PP MB

Naramore, Elisabeth.
     Farm on Fifth Avenue, a collection of figures from the
Metropolitan Museum of Art, depicting farm folk, barnyard
animals, and wild creatures of field and stream; shepherded
by Elisabeth Naramore. [New York] Pantheon [1951]

     32 p. illus. 24 cm.

     1. Animals in art. 2. Art objects.   I. New York.   Metropolitan
Museum of Art. II. Title.

N7660.N29   704.9432   51-10123

NN   0019871   DLC Or OrP OrU WaS Wa

Naramore, Elisabeth.
     William and his friends; a group of notable creatures in
the Metropolitan museum of art, herded together by Elisabeth Naramore. New York, The Viking press, 1936.

     [28] p. illus. 18½ᵐ.
     Illustrated t.-p.

     1. Animals in art. 2. New York. Metropolitan museum of art.
I. Title.

N7660.N3   704   36—17795

NN   0019872
OO OC1 OC1h MiDA WaS WaSp OrU CU-M
DLC OrU AAP OrPR Or OrP NN PPT MB MH

Naramore, Gay H.
     Poems.   Cambridge, 1865, c64.
     104 p.   D.

NN   0019873   RPB

Naramore, Gay H.
     Poems. By Gay H. Naramore. 2d and enl. ed. New
York, Carleton, 1866.

     iv, [5]-198 p. 17½ᵐ.

     An earlier collection, 1857, appeared under pseudonyms "Gay Humboldt,
alias Burr Lington, D. L. L."

                                            24-21736

Library of Congress   PS2459.N25

NN   0019874   DLC PPL

[Naramore, Gay H   ]
     Poems and letters to Don Brown, by Gay Humboldt,
alias Burr Lington, D. L. L. [*pseuds.] Albany, E. H. Bender, 1857.

     x p., 1 l., 252 p. 17½ᵐ.

     I. Title.

                                            24-21737

Library of Congress   PS2459.N252

NN   0019875   DLC OU MB NBuG PU

NARAMORE, GAY H.
     Poems and letters to Don Brown, by Gay Humboldt,
alias Burr Lington [pseuds.] Albany, E.H. Bender,
1857. 252 p. 19cm.

     Film reproduction. Negative.

NN   0019876   NN

Naramore, Gay H.
     Queen Loo, and other poems. By Gay Naramore.
Philadelphia, J. B. Lippincott & co., 1873.

     82 p. 18ᵐ.

     I. Title.

Library of Congress   PS2459.N255   24-21734

NN   0019877   DLC NcU PHC

Naramore, Robert Curtiss, jr.
     In memoriam. Robert Curtiss Naramore, Jr.
     see under title

Naramore, Bain, Brady & Johanson, firm,
     architects.
     Public Safety Building, City of Seattle.
[By] Naramore, Bain, Brady & Johanson,
Young & Richardson [and] B. Marcus Priteca,
architects associated. Seattle, 1948.
     [161] L.

NN   0019879   WaU WaS MH

Naramoto, Tatsuya, 1913–
     維新史の課題 日本近世史研究 奈良本辰也著
京都 白東書館 昭和 24 [1949]

     199 p. 19 cm.
     Colophon inserted.
     Bibliographical footnotes.
     First ed. published in 1948 under title: 日本近世史研究

     1. Japan—Hist.—Meiji period, 1867–1912.   I. Title
                                Title romanized: Ishinshi no kadai.

DS882.N3 1949   J 61–1711

NN   0019880   DLC

Naramoto, Tatsuya, 1913–
     (Nihon keizai shi gairon)
     日本經濟史概論 奈良本辰也著 [東京] 日本
評論新社 [昭和 30 i. e. 1955]

     3, 4, 185 p. 22 cm.
     Bibliography: p. 183-185.

     1. Japan—Economic conditions—To 1868.   I. Title.
HC462.6.N36   74-817530

NN   0019881   DLC

VOLUME 405

Naramoto, Tatsuya, 1913–
(Nihon no shisōka) 日本の思想家 奈良本辰也編 ₍東京₎ 毎日新
聞社 ₍1954₎
373 p. illus. 19 cm. (毎日ライブラリー)
Colophon inserted.

1. Philosophers—Japan. 2. Philosophy, Japanese. I. Title.
B5241.N32   73-823508

NN 0019882 DLC

NARAMOWSKI, Adam [Ignacy]
Facies rerum Sarmaticarum in facie regni
Poloniae. Tom. I. Wratislaviae, Strahowsky,
sc., 1724.

4°. Engraved front. and port.
Title page is engraved.

NN 0019883 MH

F
2726
A77
N382
LAC
Narancio, Edmundo M
Artigas, jefe de los orientales.   Montevi-
deo, 1951.
8p. 20cm.

1. Artigas, José Gervasio, 1764-1850.
Sp.: Lucuix Collection.

NN 0019884 TxU

Narancio, Edmundo M   editor.
Artigas: estudios publicados en "El País"
see under ₊ᵢₜₗₑ.

DP
65
N382
LAC
Narancio, Edmundo M
Concepto de la monarquía española y la si-
tuación peninsular a fines del siglo XVIII,
por Edmundo M. Narancio y José M. Traibel.
Montevideo, Organización Taquigráfica Medina
₍1945₎
45p. 22cm. (Colección de esquemas y textos
de historia nacional y americana, dirigida
por José María Traibel, 3)

NN 0019886 TxU

Narancio, Edmundo M
... Historia y análisis estadístico de la población del Uru-
guay. Montevideo, Peña y cía., impresores, 1939.
3 p. l., ₍9₎-290 p., 1 l. incl. map. diagrs. (part fold.) 25½ cm.
(Biblioteca de publicaciones oficiales de la Facultad de derecho y
ciencias sociales de Montevideo, sección III, XVII)
At head of title: ... Seminario de economía política, profesor dr.
Agustín Ruano Fournier ₍y₎ Edmundo M. Narancio ₍y₎ Federico Capurro
Calamet.
"Bibliografía general": p. ₍283₎-290.
1. Uruguay—Population. 2. Uruguay—Statistics, Vital.   I.
Capurro Calamet, Federico, joint author. II. Ruano Fournier, Agus-
tín, 1808– III. Title.
HB3577.N3   312.0989   40—33823

NN 0019887 DLC OU NjP NIC CU IU NcD TxU

G982
N1641
Narancio, Edmundo M
Las ideas políticas en el Río de la Plata a co-
ienzos del siglo XIX. Montevideo, 1955.
97-183p. 24cm.
Cover title.
At head of title: Universidad de la República.
Facultad de Humanidades y Ciencias.
"Apartado del n.º 14 de la Revista de la Facultad
de Humanidades y Ciencias."
Includes bibliographical references.
1. Río de la Plata (Viceroyalty) – Pol. & govt.
I. Title.

NN 0019888 TxU ICarbS NN WaU

Narancio, Edmundo M
El origen del estado oriental [por] Edmund M.
Narancio. Con prólogo del Dr. Justino Jiménez
de Aréchaga.   Montevideo, Impresora L.I.G.U.,
1948.
44 p. 24 cm.
Cover title.
Apartado de "Anales de la Universidad",
entrega no. 162.
1. Uruguay – Hist. – 1810-1830. Sp.: Lu-
Cuix Collection.

NN 0019889 TxU

q
JV
4060
N384
LAC
Narancio, Edmundo M
Régimen colonial; esquema y desarrollo
del Prof. don Edmundo Narancio. Monte-
video, Mimeoprenta Ilustración, 1946.
64ℓ. 36cm.

1. Spain - Colonies - America - Administration. I. Title. Sp.: Lucuix
Collection.

NN 0019890 TxU

Narang, *Sir* Gokul Chand, 1878–
Message of the Vedas, by Sir Gokul Chand Narang, kt. ...
Lahore, New book society ₍1946₎
8 p. l., ₍25₎-276 p. front. (port.) 19ᶜᵐ.
Includes selections from the Vedas in Sanskrit accompanied by translations in English.
"1st edition 1906; 2nd edition 1946."

1. Vedas—Criticism, interpretation, etc.   I. Vedas. Selections.
Sanskrit and English. II. Title.
BL1115.N3 1946   294.1   47-4005

NN 0019891 DLC NN

DS
485
.P3N27
Narang, Sir Gokul Chand, 1878–
The plight of Punjab minorities
under the so called Unionist govt.
as revealed in the speech of
Gokul Chand Narang, delivered during the general discussion of the
budget of 1941-42 in the Punjab
Legislative Assembly. With notes
and comments by Ram Lal Tara.
₍Lahore, 1941₎
96 p.
#Punjab--Politics and government.
#Minorities--Punjab.
(A) The plight of Punjab minorities
under the so called Unionist
govt. as revealed in the
speech of Gokul Chand Narang.

NN 0019892 MoU

Narang, *Sir* Gokul Chand, 1878–
Real Hinduism. Foreword by Syama Prasad Mookerjee.
₍1st ed.₎ Lahore, New Book Society ₍1947₎
250 p. ports. 19 cm.

1. Hinduism.   I. Title.
BL2001.N3   294.5   51-30619

IEN NSyU CU ViU KMK NcD
NN 0019893 DLC ICU CLSU NIC MH NN CtY PSC LU MiU

BL
2001
.N3
Narang, Sir Gokul Chand, 1878–
Real Hinduism. Foreword by Syama Prasad
Mookerjee. Lahore, New Book Society
₍1947₎
224 p. illus.

#Hinduism.
Real Hinduism.

NN 0019894 MoU

DS 432
.S5 N22
NARANG,GOKUL CHAND,1878–
The transformation of Sikhism; or, How
the Sikhs became a political power. 1st ed.
Lahore, Printed at the "Tribune" Press, 1912.
197 p.

1. Sikhs. I. Title.

NN 0019895 InU PU

Narang, *Sir* Gokul Chand, 1878–
Transformation of Sikhism, by Sir Gokul Chand Narang,
kt. ... Foreword by Sir Jogendra Singh, kt. ... 2d ed., rev.
and enl. Lahore, New book society ₍1945₎
2 p. l., 400 p. incl. front. plates, ports. 19ᶜᵐ.
"First edition 1912."
Bibliography: p. ₍13₎-21.

1. Sikhs. I. Title.
DS432.S5N3 1945   954.5   47-2166

NN 0019896 DLC CtY

Narang, *Sir* Gokul Chand, 1878–
Transformation of Sikhism. Foreword by Sir Jogendra
Singh. 3d ed., rev. and enl. Lahore, New Book Society
₍1946₎
376 p. port. 19 cm.
Bibliography: p. ₍371₎-376.

I. Title.
DS432.S5N3 1946   954.5   54-16749

ICN CU WaSpG
NN 0019897 DLC OC1 DCU NN OU MH CSt-H DCU CtY-D

Narang, Sir Gokul Chand, 1878–
Transition of Sikhism into a political organ-
ization. ₍2₎,160p. Lahore, Printed at the
"Tribune" press, ₍1910₎
Inaug.-diss. - Bern.

NN 0019898 OC1 CU DLC PU

Narang, Jai Gopal.
Constituent assembly and our demand, by Jai Gopal Narang,
with a foreword by Jawahar Lal Nehru. Lahore, Minerva
book shop, 1940.
3 p. l., ix, ₍1₎, 94 p. 18½ᶜᵐ.
"First published, 1940."
"Issued by the Punjab assembly congress party." ..

1. India—Nationality.   I. Punjab assembly congress party.
II. Title.
Library of Congress   DS480.45.N3   43-22152
                               ₍2₎   342.5409

NN 0019899 DLC NNC ICU MiU HU

Narang, Jai Gopal.
U. S. S. R., what it stands for, by Jai Gopal Narang. Lahore, The Minerva book shop ₍1944₎
vi p., 1 l., 120 p. 18½ᶜᵐ.

1. Communism—Russia.
                                                        45-19516
Library of Congress   DK266.N26
                               ₍2₎   947.084

NN 0019900 DLC CaBVaU

VOLUME 405

Narang, Kirpal Singh.
History of the Punjab, 1526–1849, by K. S. Narang and P. C. Saxena. Rev. by H. R. Gupta. 1st ed. Delhi, Uttar Chand Kapur, 1953.
498 p. illus. 19 cm.

1. Punjab—Hist.   I. Saxena, P. C., joint author.

DS485.P2N35   60–41810 ‡

NN 0019901   DLC

Naraniengar, M. T., ed.

Indian mathematical society.
The journal of the Indian mathematical society. v. 1–
Feb. 1909–
Madras, 1909–

LD4461   **The Naranjado,** published by the associated
.P235   students of the College of the Pacific. 19–
N3   San José, Cal.
              v. front. illus., plates, ports. 24 cm.
           I. Stockton, Calif. College of the Pacific.

NN 0019903   DLC CU DHEW

Naranjo, Abelardo Gómez
see Gómez Naranjo, Abelardo.

Naranjo, Alfonso Mora
see Mora Naranjo, Alfonso.

Naranjo, Antonio José de Jesus.
De l'action physiologique du chloroforme et de son application aux accouchements. Paris, E. Boutmy, 1869.
68p. 25cm.

Vol.5,no.2, of a collection with binder's title: L'anesthésie obstétricale.
Thèse --Faculté de médecine de Paris, no.₍242₎

NN 0019906   KU-M DNLM

Naranjo, Emigdio Alfaro
see Alfaro Naranjo, Emigdio, 1892–

Naranjo, Emilio Gallegos
see Gallegos Naranjo, Emilio, 1836–1871.

Naranjo, Enrique
see Naranjo Martinez, Enrique.

Naranjo, Enrique Barrenechea
see
Barrenechea, Enrique, 1865–

Naranjo, Enrique Gallegos
see Gallegos Naranjo, Enrique, 1855–

Naranjo, Enrique M.
see Naranjo Martinez, Enrique.

NARANJO, F. D.
Una de tantas; zarzuela en un acto en y verso. San Antonio de la Baños, Cuba, "El Trabajo", de J. F. d'Toste,1910.

pp.50.

NN 0019913   MH

Naranjo, Francisco.
Cuentos nacionales, por Francisco Naranjo. ₍México, D. F.,₎ 1931₎
126 p., 1 l. 16½ᶜᵐ.
CONTENTS.—Veinte años después.—La inútil literatura.—Breviario sentimental.—Fatalismo.—El aviador.—Mi pecado.—La abnegación de Felipe.

I. Title.   35–18184

Library of Congress   PQ7297.N27C8   863.6

NN 0019914   DLC OOxM

Naranjo, Francisco.
Diccionario biográfico revolucionario, por Francisco Naranjo ... México, D. F., Imprenta Editorial "Cosmos" ₍1935₎
2 p. l., 7–317 p. 21ᶜᵐ.
"Bibliografía" : p. 12.

1. Mexico—Biog. 2. Mexico—Hist.—Revolution, 1910–   I. Title.
Library of Congress   F1205.N35   36–6722
                                ₍2₎   920.072

NN 0019915   DLC NcD CtY OCl MiU NIC GU NcU

YAR **Naranjo, Francisco.**
893   Helena Petrovna Hahn de Blavatsky
         Monterrey, N. L., 1928.
         65, [1] p.

1. Beavatsky, Helene Petrovna (Hahn Hahn) 1831-1891.

NN 0019916   DLC NN WaS

Naranjo, Gerardo Barriga
see Barriga Naranjo,Gerardo.

Naranjo, Gregorio Chil y
see Chil y Naranjo, Gregorio.

Naranjo, Heliodoro P
Ley de loteria de 7 de junio de 1909 y su reglamento
see under Cuba. Laws, statutes, etc.

Naranjo, Hostos Fidel Fernández
see
Fernández Naranjo, Hostos Fidel.

Naranjo, Humberto Gómez
see Gómez Naranjo, Humberto.

Naranjo, Joaquín García
see
García Naranjo, Joaquín, *1888–*

Naranjo, José Alamo
see
Alamo Naranjo, José

Naranjo, Leopoldo.
Lampazos. (Recopilación de documentos.—Reseña histórica desde su fundación.—Datos tomados directamente del archivo de la parroquia de este lugar, y del Archivo general de la nación.—Instancia, título, confirmación, informes, visitas, etc. ...) Sus hombres, su tiempo, sus obras; complementario (sinópsis del orígen de la fundación de los pueblos en el estado de Nuevo León) por el inspector de monumentos históricos y artísticos Leopoldo Naranjo; prólogo de Ernesto Zertuche. Monterrey, México, Talleres J. Cantú Leal, 1934.
325 p. incl. illus. (incl. facsims.) ports. 20ᶜᵐ.
"Omisiones, puntuaciones, erratas": 6 leaves inserted.
1. Lampazos, Mexico.   2. Cities and towns—Mexico—Nuevo Leon.
Library of Congress   F1391.L3N3   38–21574
                               ₍2₎   972.1

NN 0019924   DLC DPU

---

qG972.12   **Naranjo, Leopoldo.**
N164ℓ   Lampazos. (Recopilación de documentos.—Reseña
Photo-   histórica desde su fundación.—Datos tomados direc-
copy   tamente del archivo de la parroquia de este lugar,
              y del Archivo General de la Nación.— Instancia,
              título, confirmación, informes, visitas, etc.) Sus
              hombres, su tiempo, sus obras; complementario (si-
              nópsis del orígen de la fundación de los pueblos en
              el estado de Nuevo León) Prólogo de Ernesto Zer-
              tuche. Monterrey, Talleres J. Cantú Leal, 1934.
              325p. illus., ports.,facsims. 29cm.

"Omisiones, puntuaciones, erratas"; 6 leaves in-serted.
Photocopy (positive)

1. Lampazos, Mexico. 2. Cities and towns - Mexi-co - Nuevo Leon.

NN 0019926   TxU

Naranjo, Luis María Escobar.
See
Escobar Naranjo, Luis María.

Naranjo,Manuel Gallegos
see
Gallegos Naranjo, Manuel, *1845–*

Naranjo, Nemesio García
see
García Naranjo, Nemesio, 1883–1962.

VOLUME 405

Naranjo, Nicolás Fernández
see
Fernández Naranjo, Nicolás.

Naranjo, Pedro Alejandro Gómez
see
Gómez Naranjo, Pedro Alejandro, 1894–

368.409 Naranjo, Plutarco, 1921–
N16c   El campesino ecuatoriano y el seguro social
  obligatorio; investigaciones médico-sociales.
  Quito, Imp. Caja del Seguro ɾ1948ɿ
  48p. tables. 25cm.

  Bibliography: p.48.

NN 0019932   IU DPU

Naranjo, Plutarco, 1921–
  ɾLas heladas y la necrosis fría de las plantas. ɾColaboradores gráficos: J. Ernesto Llerena y Juan Erazoɿ Quito, Impr. de la Universidad, 1947.
  125 p. illus. 22 cm.

  Summary in English by M. Spencer.
  Bibliography: p. 120–122.

  1. Plants, Effect of cold on. 2. Frost—Ecuador. 3. Frost protection. I. Title.

QK756.N3   581.1'9165   51–18925

NN 0019933   DLC

RC   Naranjo ; Plutarco. 1921–
598   Polinosis; estudio clínico y botánico ɾpor]
P64   Plutarco Naranjo Vargas ɾyɿ Enriqueta Banda de
N363 Naranjo. Quito, Impr. de la Universidad,
LAC   1950.
  220p. illus. 22cm.

  Includes bibliographies.

  1. Allergy. 2. Pollen. I. Banda de Naranjo, joint author. I. Title.

NN 0019934   TxU ICarbS IU PPJ DPU DNLM

WL   Naranjo, Plutarco, 1921–
600   El sistema neurovegetativo. Quito,
N218s Imp. de la Universidad, 1948.
1948   152 p. illus.

  Bibliography: p. 137–144.

  1. Nervous system, Autonomic

NN 0019935   DNLM

Naranjo, Tomás María Carrasquilla
  see
  Carrasquilla, Tomás, 1858–1940.

Naranjo, Urbano José
  ... Esquema jurídico de la evolucion
del derecho ...

  (In Bogotá. Universidad Javeriana.
Tesis. 1943, v. I, p. ɾ79ɿ–106)
  "Bibliografía": p. 106.

NN 0019937   MH-L

Naranjo Alonso, Clodoaldo.
Solar de conquistadores; Trujillo, sus hijos y monumentos, por d. Clodoaldo Naranjo Alonso ... (con licencia eclesiástica)
2. ed. Serradilla (Cáceres) Sánchez Rodrigo, 1929.
xvi, ɾ1ɿ, 583 p., 1 l. port. 17¼ᵐ.

  1. Trujillo, Spain—Hist. 2. Trujillo, Spain—Biog. 3. America—Disc. & explor.—Spanish. I. Title.

Library of Congress   DP402.T9N3   30–28085
    ɾ2ɿ   946.2

NN 0019938   DLC TU

Naranjo Alonso, Clodoaldo
Trujillo y su tierra; historia, monumentos é hijos ilustres. Trujillo, Tip. Sobrino de B.Peña [1922–23]

2 v.
At head of title of vol.2: Folletín de La opinion

  1. Trujillo, Spain - History. 2. Trujillo, Spain - Biography

NN 0019939   MH

G986.207
N164v   Naranjo Campaña, José Aurelio.
  Verdades sobre la Revolución de Mayo; el
  Batallón de Infantería "Carchi" en la gloriosa efemérides del 28 y 29 de mayo de 1944,
  en Guayaquil. Quito, Editorial Escuela Central Técnica, 1945.
  42p. port. 19cm.
  Cover title.
unacc.   1. Ecuador - Hist. - 1944- 2. Ecuador.
  Ejército. Batallón de Infantería "Carchi".
  I. Title.

NN 0019940   TxU

807
N218t   Naranjo Galán, Raquel.
  Lecciones de preceptiva literaria. Guayaquil,
  Reed & Reed [1952?]
  531, xxii, p. illus. 19 cm.

  1. Literature--Study and teaching. I. Title.

NN 0019941   ICarbS

G983.063
N164c   Naranjo Jaúregui, Víctor.
  Crísis de hombres i la elección presidencial
  de 1915. Santiago de Chile, Impr. Universitaria 1915.
  94p. 19cm.

  Includes bibliographical references.

  1. Chile - Pol. & govt. - 1824–1920. I. Title.

NN 0019942   TxU

Naranjo López, Marco, ed.
Law

Colombia. *Laws, statutes, etc.*
  Código del trabajo y Código de cooperativas; codificación sistemática de las disposiciones nacionales sobre la materia, inclusive los fallos arbitrales, las convenciones colectivas y doctrinas más importantes, con modelos, concordancias y notas. 2. ed. Bogotá, Editorial "Ahora," 1947.

Naranjo López, Marco, ed.
Law
Colombia. *Laws, statutes, etc.*
  ... Código del trabajo y Código de cooperativas; jurisprudencia y modelos. Bogotá, La Gran Colombia, 1944.

F230
.M12N3   Naranjo Martínez, Enrique.
  Alexander Macaulay, an unknown hero; his
  family and early life, by Enrique Naranjo.
  Durham,N. C., 1945]
  cover-title, 529–535 p. 25 1/2cm.
  "Reprinted from the Hispanic American historical review, vol. 25, no. 4, November, 1945."
  Text on p. [2] of cover.
  1. Macaulay, Alexander, 1787–1813.

NN 0019945   MB

NARANJO MARTINEZ, ENRIQUE.
  Alexander Macaulay, heroe desconocido, su famil
  familia y antecedentes. (IN: Popayán, Colombia. Universidad del Cauca. Revista. Popayan. 24cm. no 7 (abr. - jun. 1945)
  p. [111]-124)
  Microfilm (negative)

  1. Macaulay, Alexander, 1787–1813. 2. Colombia--Hist.--War of independence, 1810–1822.

NN 0019946   NN

Naranjo Martínez, Enrique.
  ... Informe del intendente de la navegación del
Río Magdalena y sus afluentes al señor ministro
de obras publicas
    see under   Colombia. Intendencia de la
navegación del río Magdalena y sus afluentes.

Naranjo Martínez, Enrique.
  Irish participation in Bolívar's campaigns, by Enrique
Naranjo M. ɾWashington, Govt. print. off., 1927ɿ
  cover-title, 1 p. l., 9, ɾ1ɿ p. illus. (incl. ports.) 23½ᵐ.

  "This booklet is reprinted from the October, 1925, issue of the Bulletin of the Pan American union in honor of American citizens of Irish extraction."

  1. Colombia—Hist.—War of independence, 1810–1822. 2. Irish in Colombia. I. Title.

Library of Congress   F2274.N21   27–16390

NN 0019948   DLC DNW OO Or N NN MB

Naranjo Martínez, Enrique.
  Kaleidoscopio de la vida yankee. Barranquilla, Colombia, Ediciones Arte, 1950.
  182 p. 22 cm.

  1. U. S.—Soc. life & cust. I. Title.

E169.N26   52–30568 ‡

NN 0019949   DLC DPU IdU NN TxU

Naranjo Martínez, Enrique.   Periodical Room (*4311.161.51)
The Magdalena River.
  (*In* Pan American Union. Bulletin. Vol. 51, pp. 248–265. Illus. Plates. Map. Washington. 1920.)

M3643 — Magdalena River, Colombia.

NN 0019950   MB

ɾNaranjo Martínez, Enriqueɿ
ɾ Monografia del rio Magdalena, 1916 ɿ reseña historica del descubrimiento y de la navegacion del río. Datos y cuadros estadisticos referentes al movimiento de sus transportes. ɾBarranquilla? 1917ɿ
  cover-title, 1 p. l., 40 p. port. 29½ x 23¼ᵐ.
  "... Un extracto del informe que el señor Enrique Naranjo Martinez, intendente de la navegación del río Magdalena y sus afluentes, remitió al señor ministro de obras públicas en mayo de 1917, y se reproduce ... por orden y cuenta de la Junta de propaganda para la apertura de las bocas de Ceniza."—Prelim. leaf.
  1. Magdalena river. I. Title.
                  20—11958
Library of Congress   F2281.M23N3
    ɾa37b1ɿ

NN 0019951   MB DLC

VOLUME 405

Naranjo Martínez, Enrique.
... Puntadas de historia. Bogotá, Editorial A B C, 1940.
2 p. l., ₁viiᵢ-xiv p., 1 l., 270 p. 25ᶜᵐ.
"Artículos sueltos, escritos en diferentes épocas, publicados ya varios de ellos, inéditos hasta ahora algunos."—Introducción.

1. Colombia—Hist.—Addresses, essays, lectures.   i. Title.

Library of Congress   F2271.N27   42-3260
                                             ₂₁   986

NBC OC1 MH
NN   0019952   DLC CSt MoU IaU FU CU NBuU NcD CtY

Naranjo Martinez, Enrique.
The Spanish language and the historical Spanish background of the continent in connection with inter-American relations, by Enrique Naranjo Martinez... ₁New York? 1939₎ p. 572–583. 23cm.
"Read in Spanish at the annual meeting of the New England modern language association in Boston, May 14, 1938."
"Reprinted from the Modern language journal, vol. XXIII, no. 8, May, 1939."

1. America—Discovery.   2. Spanish language.
N. Y. P. L.   September 30, 1940

NN   0019953   NN

Naranjo Morales, Baltazar.
... El doctor Torre Díaz y su actuación. ₁n. p.₎ 1926₎
29 p. 19ᶜᵐ.
At head of title: Baltazar Naranjo.
No. ₁49₎ in a collection with binder's title: **Biographical pamphlets: Spanish America.**

1. Torre Díaz, Alvaro.   43-26243
                                                    Brief cataloging
Library of Congress   F1407.B48 no. 40

NN   0019954   DLC

Naranjo Ostty, Rafael.
Conferencia del dr. Rafael Naranjo Ostty, dictada en el Colegio de abogados del Distrito federal el 6 de mayo de 1944. Caracas, Editorial Bolívar, 1944.
26 p. 23ᶜᵐ.

1. Justice, Administration of—Venezuela. 2. Venezuela—Constitutional law.
                                                    46-13937

NN   0019955   DLC

Naranjo Puente, Hugo.
Nociones fundamentales de instrucción cívica, síntesis geográfica, resumen histórico y población del Ecuador según el censo de 1950.   Quito, Tall. Gráf. nacionales, 1955.
135 p. 15cm.
"Especial para el personal de tropa del Ejército y la Policía Nacional y para los alumnos de enseñanza primaria."

1. Ecuador.

Q986.2
N164n

NN   0019956   TxU PPiU

Naranjo Quaglia, Carmen Elsa.
... La Carta del Atlántico. Memoria de prueba para optar al grado de licenciado en la Facultad de ciencias jurídicas y sociales de la Universidad de Chile. ₁Santiago de Chile₎ Escuela nacional de artes gráficas, 1946.
139 p. 27½ᶜᵐ.
"Bibliografía": p. ₁9₎-11₎

Continued in next column

Continued from preceding column

1. Atlantic declaration, Aug. 14, 1941.

JX1392.5.N3   940.531   47-22641

NN   0019957   DLC

Naranjo Quaglia, Irma.
El Poder Legislativo y Ejecutivo. Valparaíso ₁Imp. Diario "El Heraldo"₎ 1951.
129 p. 26 cm.
Thesis (licenciatura en ciencias jurídicas y sociales) – Univ. de Chile.
"Bibliografía": p.[121]-122.

Chi
JL
2611
.N3

NN   0019958   DPU

Naranjo V   , Plutarco
see   Naranjo, Plutarco, 1921-

Naranjo Vargas, Plutarco
see
Naranjo, Plutarco, 1921-

Naranjo Villegas, Abel.
Filosofía del derecho. ₁Bogotá?₎ Librería y Ediciones Teoría, 1947.
270 p. 23 cm.
"Bibliografía": p. ₁265₎-266.

1. Law—Philosophy.
                                            49-53207*

NN   0019961   DLC DPU CtY NNC NBuU

Naranjo Villegas, Abel, *ed.*
... Helcías Martán Góngora
    see under   Martán Gongora, Helcías.

Naranjo Villegas, Abel.
Ilustración y valoración; una filosofía de la educación. ₁Bogotá, Ministerio de Educación Nacional, 1952₎
ix, 186 p. 20 cm. (Biblioteca popular de autores colombianos, 11)

1. Education—Philosophy.   i. Title.

LB775.N27   370.1   53-21896

FU WU
NN   0019963   DLC FTaSU ViU OU MH TxU IaU NN NBuU

Naranjo Villegas, Abel
"La mujer pobre"; adaptación para teatro radial de la novela de León Bloy "La femme pauvre". [Bogotá,1950] 36p. 25cm. (Revista de las Indias. Suplemento, no.112)
With Revista de las Indias, 2.epoca, t.36, no.112.

Colombia
A83
185
II.36(112)

NN   0019964   CtY

Naranjo Villegas, Abel, joint author.
Villegas, Silvio, 1900–
Panegíricos de Mariano Ospina Pérez y Laureano Gómez, por Silvio Villegas y Abel Naranjo Villegas. Bogotá, Editorial "Nuevo Mundo" ₁1950₎

F2277
.O 8V5

Naranjo Villegas, Jesús.
Naturaleza, régimen y remuneración del trabajo según la doctrina católica ₁por₎ Jesús Naranjo Villegas. Tesis con que su autor abtuvo ₁!₎ el grado de doctor en derecho y ciencias políticas, en la Universidad de Antioquia. Medellín, Tip. Sansón ₁1937₎
43, ₁1₎ p., 1 l. 24ᶜᵐ.
"Bibliografía": p. ₁45₎

1. Church and labor.   i. Title.   40-36783

Library of Congress   HD6338.N3
                                    ₁2₎   331

NN   0019966   DLC

Naranjo y Garza, Felipe.
Elementos de mineralogia general, industrial y agrícola ... Madrid, Impr. de la viuda de A. Yenes, 1862.
xii, 603 p. diagrs. 23cm.
Bibliography: p. ₁vii₎-viii.

1. Mineralogy.   2. Mineralogy—Spain.

549
N16e

NN   0019967   IU CtY

Naranjo y Garza, Felipe.
Manual de mineralogia general, industrial y agrícola ... Madrid, Impr. de la viuda de A. Yenes, 1862.
506 p. 23cm.
"Este Manual contiene, esencialmente, la misma doctrina é igual sistema que los Elementos de mineralogía."

1. Mineralogy.   2. Mineralogy—Spain.

549
N16e
1862

NN   0019968   IU

Naranjo, Costa Rica. Escuela "República de Colombia".
... Material de enseñanza elaborado por el personal docente en el curso lectivo 1940- [San José?] Imp. española [   ]
v. illus. 33 cm.
Mimeographed.

Cos
LE
81
.N3
.E8g
date

NN   0019969   DPU

Narañon y Posadillo, José Luis.
... Leyes penales de España conforme a los textos oficiales. Contiene este volumen: la Constitución, el Código penal, la Ley de enjuiciamiento criminal y la del jurado ...
    see under   Spain. Laws, statutes, etc.

Naranovich, Arsenii Andreevich, 1875–
... Il crollo dei Romanoff; narrazione di Vittorio Gonzi. Roma ₁Siena, Tipografia cooperativa Combattenti, 1934₎
4 p. l., 11–277, ₁1₎ p. plates, ports. 22ᶜᵐ.
At head of title: Arsenio Naranovitch.
"Arsenio Naranovitch, nei suoi appunti traccia un quadro esatto, di tutti gli avvenimenti svoltisi alla corte imperiale russa e vissuti da lui, fino alla caduta del regime zarista. Il mio compito, è stato di dare a questi, una forma di narrazione chiara e concisa."—Introductory note, signed: Vittorio Gonzi.

1. Russia — Description and travel. 2. Russia — Social life and customs. 3. Nicholas II, emperor of Russia, 1868–1918.   i. Gonzi, Vittorio.
    ii. Title.
                                                    A C 36-242
Title from N. Y. Pub.   Libr. Printed by L. C.

NN   0019971   NN

Naranovich, P
Замѣчанія по осмотру клиникъ въ Берлинѣ и учрежденію санитарной части въ Прусской арміи во время войны въ 1866 году. Санктпетербургъ, Тип. Я. Трея, 1866.
88 p. 25 cm.
"Изъ сентябрской книжки Военно-медицинскаго журнала 1866 г."

1. Berlin—Hospitals. 2. Prussia. Armee—Sanit. affairs.
                                            Title transliterated: Zamiêchaniîa po osmotru klinik v Berliniê.

RA989
.G6B42

RA989.G6B42   51-47995

NN   0019972   DLC

VOLUME 405

UH
N218s
1866

NARANOVICH, Pavel Andreev, 1801-1874
Das Sanitätswesen in der preussichen
Armee während des Krieges 1866. Berlin,
Stuhr, 1866.
54 p.
Translation of excerpts from Zamīĕ-
chaniīa po osmotru klinik v Berlinīĕ i
uchrezhdenīĭū sanitarnoĭ chasti v prusskoĭ
armīi vo vremīa voĭny v 1866 godu.

NN 0019973   DNLM

Naranzi (Demetrio). Dell' innesto vaccino;
lettera all'... Francesco Aglietti.
In: RAGGUAGLIO della vaccina [etc.] 8°. Udine, [1801].
209-249.

NN 0019974   DNLM

Năraparāju Kōdaņḍarāmayya
see
Kodanda Ramaiah, N

Nararini, Andrea.
Richerche, meditazioni e conclusioni sul
colera morbus.   Bassano, 1886.
30 p.   23.5 cm.

NN 0019976   MBCo

Nararaja Rao, A.
see   Rao, A. Nagaraja, 1906.

Narasaki, Asatarō, 1881-
(Gendai shinrigaku kan)
現代心理學觀:附 兒童の敎育心理學的研究 /
楢崎淺太郎著. — 東京:成美堂書店, 昭和13
[1938]
2, 12, 378 p. : ill. ; 23 cm.
Includes bibliographical references.

1. Psychology.   I. Title.
BF128.J3N37   74-819242

NN 0019978   DLC

Narasaki, Asatarō, 1881-
Kongo no kyōiku no susumikata to jikkenteki
kenkyū
see under title

Narasaki, Kan'ichi, 1885-1965.
[Shimbun kisha gojūnen]
新聞記者五十年 楢崎観一著 [東京] 毎日新
聞社 [1955]
6, 217 p. ports. 19 cm.

I. Title.
PN5406.N36S5   72-806366

NN 0019980   DLC

DS894
.A4
.N3

Narasaki, S
Study of Nishinoyama III tomb;
research of an ancient tomb at Takada
Village, Ako District, Hyogo Prefecture,
by S. Narasaki [and others. n.p.,
Archaeological Museum of Une, 1952.
48p. illus.,plates. 26cm. (Archaeological Museum of Une. Report no. 1)
Added t.p. in Japanese, text in
Japanese with English summary.
1. Tombs -   Japan - Nishinoyama.
2. Nishinoyamá.   Series.

NN 0019981   NNU

Narasaki, Toshio, 1891-
(Doitsu-koku kōtsū seisaku)
獨逸國交通政策 楢崎敏雄著 [東京] 恒春閣
[昭和 19 i. e. 1944]
4, 4, 386 p. 21 cm.
Includes bibliographical references.

1. Transportation and state — Germany. 2. Transportation and
state. I. Title.
HE249.N35   73-820613

NN 0019982   DLC

HE249
.T63
Orien
Japan

Narasaki, Toshio, 1891-
Tōa Kenkyūjo. Tokyo.   Tokubetsu Dai 1 Chōsa Iinkai.
[Doitsu ni okeru kōtsū jōsei oyobi kōtsū seisaku]
獨逸に於ける交通情勢及び交通政策 [東京]
東亞研究所 昭和18[1943]

HE243
.T63
Orien
Japan

Narasaki, Toshio, 1891-
Tōa Kenkyūjo. Tokyo.   Tokubetsu Dai 1 Chōsa Iinkai.
[Eikoku ni okeru kōtsū jōsei oyobi kōtsū seisaku]
英國に於ける交通情勢及び交通政策 [東京]
東亞研究所 昭和20[1945]

Narasaki, Toshio, 1891-
(Gaikoku bōeki no riron to mondai)
外國貿易の理論と問題 楢崎敏雄著 [東京]
千倉書房 [昭和16 i. e. 1941]
7, 6, 320 p. 22 cm.
附錄 スノウデン小傳: p. 291-320.

1. Commerce. 2. Commercial policy. 3. Snowden, Philip Snowden,
viscount, 1864-1937.   I. Title.
HF1007.N337   73-819248

NN 0019985   DLC

Narasaki, Toshio, 1891-
經濟思想史 楢崎敏雄著 東京 元々社 昭和
30 [1955]
357 p. 18 cm.
Includes bibliography.

1. Economics—Hist. I. Title. *Title romanized:* Keizai shisō shi.
HB75.N34   J 60-1149 ‡

NN 0019986   DLC

Narasaki, Toshio, 1891-
經濟學序說 楢崎敏雄著 東京 玄同社 1947.
309 p. 18 cm. (玄同文庫 E-1001)
Colophon inserted.

1. Economics. I. Title. *Title romanized:* Keizaigaku josetsu.
                                              J 61-4004
California. Univ. at   Los Angeles. Library
for Library of Congress   [3]

NN 0019987   CLU

Narasaki, Toshio, 1891- 廣域經濟と南方開發 楢崎敏雄著 東京 東洋
經濟新報社 昭和 17 [1942]
289 p. illus. 22 cm.

1. Asia, Southeastern — Econ. condit. 2. Asia, Southeastern —
Comm. I. Title.
                      Title romanized: Kōiki keizai to nampō kaihatsu.
HC412.N29   J 61-18 ‡

NN 0019988   DLC

Narasaki, Toshio, 1891-
(Kōiki keizai to zenkyū keizai)
廣域經濟と全球經濟 楢崎敏雄著 [東京] ダ
イヤモンド社 [昭和16 i. e. 1941]
3, 3, 220 p. 22 cm.

1. Natural resources—Asia. 2. Greater East Asia co-prosperity
sphere. 3. Geography, Economic. I. Title.
HC412.5.N36   73-818202

NN 0019989   DLC

Narasaki, Toshio, 1891- 航空經濟政策論 楢崎敏雄著 東京 有斐閣
昭和 7 [1932]
2, 7, 9, 427 p. 23 cm.

1. Aeronautics, Commercial. I. Title.
                      Title romanized: Kōkū keizai seisaku ron.
                                              J 60-2934
Harvard Univ. Chinese-   Japanese Library 4515
for Library of Congress   [3]

NN 0019990   MH-HY

Narasaki, Toshio, 1891-
(Kōkū yusō no jōshiki)
航空輸送の常識 楢崎敏雄著 [東京] 千倉書
房 [昭和16 i. e. 1941]
5, 5, 197 p. 20 cm.

1. Aeronautics, Commercial. 2. Aeronautics, Military. I. Title.
HE9776.N369   73-817851

NN 0019991   DLC

Narasaki, Toshio, 1891-
[Kūchū kōtsū ron]
空中交通論 楢崎敏雄著 東京 南海書院
[昭和3 i. e. 1928]
6, 2, 23, 13, 792 p. col. plates. 23 cm.
Colophon inserted.
Bibliography: p. 1-13 (4th group)

1. Aeronautics, Commercial. 2. Aeronautics, Military. 3. Aeronautics—Laws and regulations. I. Title.
HE9776.N37   72-806026

NN 0019992   DLC

Narasaki, Toshio, 1891-
空中戰爭論 楢崎敏雄著 東京 日本評論社
昭和8 [1933]
10, 258 p. 23 cm.

1. Air warfare. I. Title. *Title romanized:* Kūchū sensō ron.
                                              J 60-2935
Harvard Univ. Chinese-   Japanese Library 8999
for Library of Congress   [3]

NN 0019993   MH-HY

VOLUME 405

Narasaki, Toshio, 1891–
(Sekai kōtsū bunka hattatsu shi)
世界交通文化發達史 [楢崎敏雄執筆　東京]
東京日日新聞社 [昭和15 i.e. 1940]
3, 785 p.　illus.　27 cm.
Includes 119 p. of advertisements scattered throughout the text.

1. Transportation—History.　2. Communication and traffic—History.
3. Japan—Description and travel—1901–1945.　I. Tōkyō Nichinichi
Shimbun Sha.　II. Title.

HE151.N33   73–818297

NN   0019994   DLC

Narasaki, Toshio, 1891–
社會經濟思想史　楢崎敏雄著　東京　東京文化
研究所出版部　昭和24 [1949]
246, 119 p.　22 cm.
附錄　社會思想小說　然し可能性は存在する: p. [1–119
(2d group)

1. Economics—Hist.　I. Title.　II. **Title: Shikashi kanōsei wa
sonzaisuru.**
Title romanized: **Shakai keizai shisō shi.**

HB180.J3N4   J 65–153

NN   0019995   DLC

Narasaki, Toshio, 1891–
東亞廣域經濟論　楢崎敏雄著　東京　千倉書房
昭和15 [1940]
6, 7, 279 p.　tables.　23 cm.

1. East (Far East)—Econ. condit.　I. Title.
Title romanized: Tōa kōiki keizai ron.

HC412.N3   J 59–2552

Hoover Institution
for Library of Congress   [a]†

NN   0019996   CSt-H CtY DLC

Narasaki, Toshio, 1891–
東亞交通論　楢崎敏雄著　東京　千倉書房　昭
和14 [1939]
326 p.　illus.　23 cm.

1. Transportation—East (Far East)　I. Title.
Title romanized: Tōa kōtsū ron.

HE269.N3   J 61–17 ‡

NN   0019997   DLC NIC

Narasaki, Toshio, 1891–
圖南經濟論　楢崎敏雄著　東京　千
倉書房　昭和15 [1940]
8, 9, 321 p.　tables.　23 cm.

1. Asia, Southeastern—Econ. condit.　I. Title.
Title romanized: Tonan keizai ron.

                                                J 59–2093

Hoover Institution
for Library of Congress   [a]

NN   0019998   CSt-H

Narasayya, T   K   Venkata
see   Narasiah, T.K.V.

Narasiah, T.K.V.
War and the British raj.   Georgetown, 1915.

NN   0020002   NjP

Narasimh-Aiyangar, called Sri-Kalki, God
Incarnate
see   Narasimhiengar, M   T

Narasimh'-Aiyangar, M   T
Madhuravani, the Sanskrit poetess of Tanjore.
19p.   Madras, G. A. Natesan & co., 1908.

Cover-title.
"Reprinted from the Indian review, Feb., 1908."

NN   0020004   OC1

[Narasimha, *disciple of Gadādhara; 17th cent.*]
[... Tārā-Bhakti-Sudhārṇava, with an introduction in English; edited by Pañchānana Bhaṭṭāchārya ... Calcutta, Sanskrit book depot; London, Luzac & co., 1940.
26 p., 1 l., 4, 435 p.   25½ᶜᵐ.   [Tāntrik texts [edited by Arthur Avalon,
pseud.]   vol. xxi]
Text in Sanskrit, with Sanskrit t-p., and Sanskrit paging.
The author of this treatise is Narasimha.   cf. Introd.
Bibliography included in introduction (p. 25–26)

I. Pañchānana Bhaṭṭāchārya   ed.   II. Title.   A C 40–2625

New York.   Public library
for Library of Congress   [PK3051.A2   vol. 21]

NN   0020005   NN PBm

Narasimha, B   V   , swami
see   Narasimha Swami, B   V

Narasimha Acharya, K   N
Atlas of the Madras Presidency, compiled under the
superintendence of K. N. Narasimha Acharya, and pub-
lished under the direction of L. G. B. Firth.   Rev.   Madras,
Helio-zincographed at the Central Survey Office, 1932 [i. e.
1933]
[2], 1, 26 col. maps.   46 cm.
Cover title: Madras Presidency district atlas.
Map no. 15 dated 1933.
Typescript annotations relating to transfers of territory (2 of
which dated 1942) on labels pasted on some maps.
1. Madras (Presidency)—Administrative and political divisions—
Maps.   [I. Madras (Presidency). Survey Dept.   II. Title.   III.
Title: Madras Presidency district atlas.

G2283.M28N3 1933   912'.54'82   73–171036
                                                        MARC

NN   0020007   DLC

Narasimha Aiyar, Nāndivāda ʀ
see   Narasimmha Aiyer, N.R.

Narasimha Ayyangar, M   B   tr.
Vedāntasāra
see under
Ramanuja, founder of sect.

Narasimha Chintamaṇ Keḷkar
see
Kelkar, Narsinha Chintaman, 1872–1947.

Narasimha Gopalaswami Ayyangar, *Sir, diwan bahadur*
see
Gopalaswami Ayyangar, *Sir Narasimha, diwan bahadur,*
1882–

Narasimha Iyengar, B
see   Iyengar, B   Narasimha, 1882–

Narasimha Iyer, P
Iyer, P   Narasimha.

Narasimha Mehetā, 1414–1481.
આદિ-ભક્ત-કવિ નરસિંહ મહેતાનું મૂલસંબદ. સંશોધ્કર્તા અને સંશોધક હમ્બારામ
સૂર્વરામ દેસાઈ. [પ્રથમાશ્ચિ. મુંબઈ ગુઞ્જરાતી પ્રેસના માલીક, 1913.
75, 654 p.   illus.   20 cm.   [હ્ચ્ચારામ કાવ્યમાળા, 1]
Added t. p.: The poems of Narasinha Mehta.
In Gujarati.
I. Desai, Itcharam Suryaram, 1858–1912, ed.   II. Title.
Title transliterated: Ādi-bhakta-kavi Narasimha
Mehetākṛta kāvyasaṅgraha.

PK1859.N27A6   1913   S A 65–7309

NN   0020014   DLC

Narasimha Moorty, C., joint author.
HC438
.B3S7
Srinivasan, R   K
Labour and housing in Bangalore City, by R. K. Srini-
vasan and C. Narasimha Moorty.   Bangalore City, Printed
at the Bangalore Press, 1935.

Narasimha Moorthy, V
... Investigation of typhoid fever in Bangalore city (Octo-
ber–December 1938) by V. Narasimha Moorthy ...   Bangalore,
Printed by the superintendent at the Government press, 1940.
cover-title, ii, 48 p. incl. tables.   fold. map, fold. diagrs.   24½ᶜᵐ.
At head of title: Mysore state dept. of public health.

1. Typhoid fever—Bangalore, India.   I. Mysore.   Dept. of health.
                                                        44–46770

Library of Congress   RC195.I 4B35
                              [2]   614.511

NN   0020016   DLC

Narasimha Moorthy, V   L
The Mysore house rent & accommodation control order,
1948 [by] V. L. Narasimha Moorthy [and] Ratnabai Chittur.   [Bangalore, Chandra Print. and Pub. Co.] 1950.
iv, 101, iv p.   23 cm.

1. Rent control—Mysore.   I. Chittur, Ratnabai, joint author.
II. Mysore.   Laws, statutes, etc.   Mysore house rent and accommodation control order, 1948.   1950.   III. Title.

                                                72–180630
                                                        MARC

NN   0020017   DLC

Narasimha Murty, G   S   R
see   Narasimhamurty, G   S   R

Narasimha Sastri
see
Chandrasekhara Bharati, *Swami,* 1892–1950.

PK2916   Narasimha Sastri, C   R
N57   Studies in Sanskrit literature.   First
          series.   Mysore, Sree Panchacharya Electric
          Press, 1936.
          97, xix, ii p.

Contents.– Amaru.– Bhartṛhari.– A novel
view of Rasa.– Gāthā-Saptaśati.

1. Sanskrit poetry – Addresses, essays,
lectures.

NN   0020020   CU MH

VOLUME 405

Narasimha Sastri, Devudu, 1896–1963.
ಅಂತರಂಗ. ﾍﾠﾍﾠﾍﾠﾍﾠ. ﾍﾠﾍﾠﾍﾠﾍﾠﾍﾠ, ﾍﾠﾍﾠ,
1950.
vii, 170 p. 19 cm.
In Kannada.
A novel.

I. Title.
Title transliterated: Antaraṅga.

PL4659.N29A8　　　　　　　　S A 64–8827

NN　0020021　　DLC

Narasimha Sastri, Devudu, 1896–1963.
ಮಯೂರ. ﾍﾠﾍﾠﾍﾠﾍﾠ. ﾍﾠﾍﾠﾍﾠﾍﾠ, ﾍﾠﾍﾠﾍﾠﾍﾠ ·
ﾍﾠ ﾍﾠﾍﾠ, 1953.
ii, 248 p. 19 cm.
In Kannada.
A novel.

I. Title.
Title transliterated: Mayūra.

PL4659.N29M35　　　　　　S A 64–8632

NN　0020022　　DLC

Narasimha Sastri, Devudu, 1896–1963.
ಸೋಲೋ-ಗೆಲುವೋ. ﾍﾠﾍﾠﾍﾠﾍﾠ. ﾍﾠﾍﾠﾍﾠﾍﾠ, ﾍﾠﾍﾠﾍﾠ
ﾍﾠﾍﾠﾍﾠ, 1950.
iii, 108 p. 19 cm.
In Kannada.
Short stories.

Contents.—ಸೋಲೋ-ಗೆಲುವೋ.—ಇದು ನಿಜವೇ?—ಅದರ ಫಲ.

I. Title.
Title transliterated: Sōlō-geluvō.

PL4659.N29S6 1950　　　　S A 64–8609

NN　0020023　　DLC

BL
1175
S35
N21
Narasimha Swami, B　　V
　　Sage of Sakori. Madras, Kesari Printing
Works 1935.
　　iii, 177 p. illus. 19cm.

　　1. Sastri, Kasinath Govind Upasani, 1870–
I. Title.

NN　0020024　　NIC

Asia
B133
.R36N282
Narasimha Swami, B　　V
　　Self realisation; life & teachings of
Ramana Maharshi. Tiruvannamalai,
Niranjanananda Swami, 1931.
　　242 p. illus.

　　1. Ramana, Maharsi. I. Title.

NN　0020025　　HU

BL 1146
R36
27
1936
Narasimha Swami, B　　V
　　Self-realisation: life & teachings
of Ramana Maharshi. 3d ed. Tiruvannamalai, Niranjananda Swami, 1936.
　　264 p. illus.

　　1. Ramana, Maharsi. I. Title.

NN　0020026　　CaBVaU

Asia
BL1201
.N37
1944
Narasimha Swami, B　　V
　　Self-realisation; life and teachings of
Bhagawan Sri Ramana Mahari-shi. 4th ed.
Tivuvannamalai, Sri Ramanasramam, 1944.
　　316 p.

　　1. Hinduism. 2. Ramana, Maharishi.
I. Narasimha Swami, B.

NN　0020027　　HU CtY

B133
.R27Z7N2
Narasimha Swami, B　　V
　　Self-realisation; life & teachings of Sri
Ramana Mararshi. 5th ed. rev. from the 3d ed.
with an epilogue, by S. S. Cohen. Tiruvannamalai
T. N. Venkataraman, 1953.
　　272 p. illus., ports.

　　1. Rāmana, maharsi, 1879–1950. I. Title.

NN　0020028　　ICU CtY–D NSyU

PK
81
B5
no.160
Narasimha Vājapeyī.
　　Nityācārapradīpaḥ, by Narasimha Vājapeyin.
Edited by Paṇḍita Vinoda Vihāri Bhaṭṭācāryya.
Calcutta, Asiatic Society of Bengal, 1907–1928.
　　2 v. (Bibliotheca indica, no.160)

　　Vol.2 edited by Paṇḍita Vinoda Vihāri Bhattā-
cāryya and Mahāmahopādhyāya Sadāśiva Miśra.
In Sanskrit.
　　Issued in fascicles; new series, nos.1047,
1056, 1064, 1078, 1094, 1111, 1130 and 1160)

NN　0020029　　WaU

Narasimhācār, D　　L
　　see
Narasimhachar, D　　L　　1906–

Narasimhācār, P　　T
　　see
Narasimhachar, P　　T　　1905–

Narasimhachar, D.L., 1906–　　ed.
Pampârâmāyana saṅgraha
　　see under　Pampa, fl. 1100.

Narasimhachar, Lakshmi.
　　A guide to Halebid. Published for the Government of
Mysore. Rev. ed. Mysore, Printed by the Senior Asst. Director at the Govt. Branch Press, 1950.
　　17 p. illus. 19 cm.

　　1. Halebid, India—Descr.—Guide-books.
DS486.H29N32 1950　　　　55–35419 ‡

NN　0020033　　DLC

Narasimhachar, Lakshmi.
　　A guide to Talkad. Published for the Government of
Mysore. Rev. ed. Mysore, Printed by the Senior Asst. Director at the Govt. Branch Press, 1950.
　　20 p. illus. 18 cm.

　　1. Talkad, India—Descr.—Guide-books.
DS486.T18N32 1950　　　　55–35418 ‡

NN　0020034　　DLC

Narasimhachar, Lakshmi.
　　A guide to the Chennakesava Temple at Belur. Pub-
lished for the Government of Mysore. Rev. ed. Mysore,
Printed by the Senior Asst. Director at the Govt. Branch
Press, 1950.
　　19 p. illus. 18 cm.

　　1. Belur, India (Hassan District)
NA6008.B4N3 1950　　　　55–23652 ‡

NN　0020035　　DLC

Narasimhachar, P　　T　　1905–
ಈಚಲುಮರದ ಕೆಳಗೆ. ﾍﾠﾍﾠ ﾍﾠ. ﾖ. ﾍﾠﾍﾠﾍﾠﾍﾠﾍﾠﾍ. ﾍﾠﾍﾠﾍﾠ.
ﾍﾠﾍﾠﾍﾠﾍﾠ 1949
　　127 p. 19 cm. (ಕನ್ನಡ ಕಾವ್ಯಮಾಲೆ, ೪೯)
In Kannada.

I. Title.
Title transliterated: Icalumarada keḷage.

AC125.K3N3　　　　　　S A 64–8629

NN　0020036　　DLC

Narasimhachar, P　　T　　1905–
ಮಲೆದೇಗುಲ. ﾍﾠﾍﾠ ﾍﾠ. ﾖ. ﾍﾠﾍﾠﾍﾠﾍﾠﾍﾠﾍ. ﾍﾠﾍﾠﾍﾠ,
ﾍﾠﾍﾠﾍﾠﾍﾠ 1955
　　v. 60 p. 19 cm. (ಕನ್ನಡ ಕಾವ್ಯಮಾಲೆ)
In Kannada.

I. Title.
Title transliterated: Maledēgula.

PL4659.N293M28　　　　　S A 65–611

NN　0020037　　DLC

Narasimhachar, P　　T　　1905–
ಮಾಂದಳಿರು. ﾍﾠﾍﾠ ﾍﾠ. ﾖ. ﾍﾠﾍﾠﾍﾠﾍﾠﾍﾠﾍ. ﾍﾠ. ﾍﾠﾍﾠﾍﾠﾍ.
ﾍﾠﾍﾠ ﾍﾠ ﾍﾠ ﾍﾠﾍﾠﾍﾠ. ﾍﾠﾍﾠﾍﾠﾍﾠﾍﾠ, ﾍﾠﾍﾠ ﾍﾠﾍﾠﾍﾠ ﾍﾠﾍﾠﾍﾠﾍ,
1936
　　vi, 62 p. 19 cm.
In Kannada.
Poems.

I. Title.
Title transliterated: Māndaḷiru.

PL4659.N293M3　　　　　S A 65–610

NN　0020038　　DLC

Narasiṃhāchār, Rāmānujapuram Anandāṇ-Piḷḷai
　　see
Narasimhacharya, Ramanujapuram, 1860–1937.

Narasimhachar, So., ed.
The Apastamba-Sulbasūtra
　　see under　Apastamba.

Narasimhachar, So., ed.
Apastambiyam Srautasutram
　　see　Apastamba.

Narasimhachar, So., ed.
Srauta sūtra with the bhāṣya of Dhūrtaswāmi
and the vrtti of Rāmāgnicit
　　see under　Apastamba.

VOLUME 405

Narasimhacharya, Ramanujapuram, *1860-1937.*

... Architecture and sculpture in Mysore...
see under title

CN
+1175
+B75
N3
Narasimhacharya, Ramanujapuram, 1860-1937
Bodhan stone inscription of the reign of
Trailokyamalla (Somesvara I) A. D. 1056.
ₑHyderabad?ₑ 1925.
8 p. illus. 32cm. (in binder, 36cm.)
(Hyderabad archaeological series, no. 7)

1. Inscriptions, Kannada I. Title

NN   0020044   WU OCl PU-Mu

Narasimhacharya, Ramanujapuram

CN1173
.C3M9
Mysore. *Dept. of Archaeology.*
Epigraphia carnatica. By B. Lewis Rice, Director of
Archaeological Researches in Mysore. Bangalore, Mysore
Govt. Central Press, 1886-19

PL
4641
N28
Narasimhacharya, Ramanujapuram, 1860-1937.
History of Kannada language (Readership lectures) by
R. Narasimhacharya. Mysore, Printed by the Asst. Supdt.,
Govt. Branch Press, 1934.
xii, 171 p. 22 cm.
At head of title: University of Mysore.

1. Kannada language—Hist.   I. Title.

PL4641.N3   S A 66-1007

NN   0020046   DLC ICU WaU

Narasimhacharya, Ramanujapuram, 1860-1937.
History of Kannada literature (Readership lectures) by
R. Narasimhacharya. Mysore, Wesley Press and Pub.
House, 1940.
viii, 85 p. 22 cm.
At head of title: University of Mysore.

1. Kannada literature—Hist. & crit.   I. Title.

PL4650.N3 1940   894.81409   42-2096 rev*

NN   0020047   DLC WU PU CU OCl

NA6008
.B4
.N3
Narasimhacharya, Ramanujapuram, *1860-1937.*
The Kesava temple at Belur.
Bangalore, Mysore Government Press,
1919.
x,38p. plates,plan. 29cm. (Mysore
archaeological series. Architecture
and sculpture in Mysore, no.2)

1.Temples, Buddhist. I.Title.
Series.

NN   0020048   NNU CU IEN OCl MB MH CtY

Narasimhachar, Ramanujapuram, 1860-1937.
The Kesava temple at Somanathapur.
ix,[1],17p. plates, plan (fold.) Bangalore,
Printed at the Mysore government press, 1917.
(Mysore archaeological series: architecture and
sculpture in Mysore, v. 1)

"Published under the authority of the Government of His Highness the Maharaja of Mysore."

NN   0020049   OCl CtY NN PPPM

NA
5208
.D63
L25
Narasimhacharya, Ramanujapuram, 1860-1937.
The Lakshmidevi temple at Dodda-gaddavalli,
by R. Narasimhachar. Bangalore, Mysore Govt.
Press, 1919.
viii, 8 p. 14 plates. 29 cm. (Mysore
archaeological series. Architecture and sculpture in Mysore, no. 3)

Presentation copy.

1. Lakshmidevi Temple, Dodda Gaddavalli, India
2. Temples--India--Mysore. I. Title. II. Series. xNarasimhāch-   ārya, Rāmānujapuram
Ānandān-Pillāi.   xDodda Gaddavalli, India.
Lakshmidevi Temple.

NN   0020050   OrU MWiW OCl CtY OCU

BL
1215
S2
N3
Narasimhacharya, Srimushna.
A true interpretation of Vedic sacrifice
based on Rig & Yajur Vedas and the rituals.
Madras, Kandan Press, 1932.
xxiii,144,5 p.

1.Sacrifice. 2.Vedas--Criticism,interpreta-
tion,etc.   I.Title.

NN   0020051   NSyU

Narasimhadevara Sundara Rama Sastry
see
Sundara Rama Sastry, Narasimhadevara, 1908-

Narasimhaiya, Agaram Narasimha, *pandit*
see
Narasimhia, Agaram Narasimha, *pandit.*

PK2971
.G3
no. 47
Narasimhakavi, called Abhinava Kālidāsa.
Nañjarājayaśobhūṣaṇa of Abhinava Kālidāsa, critically
edited with introduction and index by Embar Krishnamacharya ... Baroda, Oriental institute, 1930.
xi, ₍13₎-47, 270 p. illus. 25ᶜᵐ. (*Half-title:* Gaekwad's Oriental series
... no. xlvii)
Sanskrit text with Sanskrit paging.

1. Sanskrit poetry—Hist. & crit.   I. Krishnamacharya, Embar, ed.
II. Title.   A 44-4671
Chicago. Univ. Library
for Library of Congress   PK2971.G3 no. 47

NN   0020054   ICU OCl HU DLC

Narasimhalu Nayudu, S   **P**
விவசாயசாயனசாஸ்திரச்சுருக்கம். இது தமிழ்நாட்டுக் குடிகளுக்கு
உபயோகமாக மேலும் படஉரல நரசிம்மலு நாயடு எழுதியது. ₍மதுரை₎
மதுரைத்தமிழ்ச்சங்கம், 1904.
71 p. 22 cm. (செந்தமிழ்ப் பிரசுரம் 11)
In Tamil.

1. Fertilizers and manures — India — South India. 2. Soils —
India—South India.   I. Title.
Title romanized: Vivacāyaracāyapacāstiraccurukkam.

S633.5.I4N37   72-206881

NN   0020055   DLC

Narasimham, P
Interpretation of Indian statutes and of the Government of
India act, 1935, by P. Narasimham ... Madras, The Madras
law journal office, 1940.
xxxviii, 646 p. 22ᶜᵐ.

1. Law—Interpretation and construction. 2. Law—India.   I. India.
Laws, statutes, etc. II. Title: Government of India act, 1935.

43-35485

NN   0020056   DLC

Narasimham, Sarat C   V
Liaquats in America. (Newsman's diary)
Karachi, Madina press, 1950.
180 p. ports. 19 cm.

NN   0020057   PU

Narasimhamurty, G.S.R.
Studies in the rate of fall of liquid droplets.
[Cincinnati, 1954]
xii, 152 l. illus. 29 cm.
Thesis (Ph.D.) - Univ. of Cincinnati, 1954.
Bibliography: l. 124-127.

NN   0020058   OCU

M/1710
N218
Narasimhan, M.
Agricultural meteorology: The prediction of the
minimum temperature on clear days at selected
stations in India, by M. Narasimhan and L. A.
Ramdas. Delhi. 1937.
745-761. map, tabs., diagrs. 24½cm.
(Reprinted from The Indian journal of agricultur-
al science. v.7, pt.5. Oct., 1937.)

NN   0020059   DAS

Narasimhan, M.J., joint author.

Coleman, Leslie C.
... Black rot or koleroga of coffee in Mysore, by Leslie
C. Coleman ... M. K. Venkata Rao ... and M. J. Narasimhan ... Bangalore, Printed at the government press,
1923.

HD2072
.N34
Narasimhan, P. S., joint author.
FOR OTHER EDITIONS
SEE MAIN ENTRY
Narayanaswami Naidu, Bijayeti Venkata, 1901-
The economics of Indian agriculture, by B. V. Nara-
yanaswamy and P. S. Narasimhan. 2d ed., rev. Madras,
Rochouse, 1944.

Narasimhan, R   *ld.*
Gurudev Tagore ₍by₎ Tan Yun Shan ₍and others₎ Edited
by R. Narasimhan. ₍Bombay, V. Kulkarni, Hind Kitabs,
1946₎
vi, 132 p. 18 cm.
Includes bibliographical references.

1. Tagore, Sir Rabindranath, 1861-1941 — Addresses, essays, lectures.   I. T'an, Yün-shan, 1900-

PK1725.N28   891'.44'14   74-175140
                                                      MARC

NN   0020062   DLC OCl CoU NjP MH CU

Narasimhan, V. K., ed.
HG3283
.I5
The Indian bankers' annual. 1950-
Madras, Indian Press Publications.

Narasimhan, V.M.
A guide to art
see under Madras, All-India Khadi,
Swadeshi and Industrial Exhibition, 1952-53.

Narasimhaśāstri, Dēvuḍu
see
Narasimha Sastri, Devudu, 1896-1963.

VOLUME 405

Narasimhasvāmi, K   S
see
Narasimhaswamy, K   S   1915–

Narasimhaswamy, K   S   1915–
ದೀಪದ ಮಲ್ಲಿ. ಲೇಖಕ್ ಕೆ. ಎಸ್. ನರಸಿಂಹಸ್ವಾಮಿ. ಮೈಸೂರು,
ಕಾವ್ಯಾಲಯ [1955]
95 p. 18 cm.
In Kannada.
Poems.

I. Title.

Title transliterated: Dīpada malli.

PL4659.N297D5

S A 65–609

NN   0020067   DLC

LA
1051
N373
1947
Narasimhayya, P
Education in Asia, by P. Narasimhayya.
New Delhi, Indian Council of World Affairs, 1947.
19 p.   25 cm.

Cover title.
At head of title: Asian Relations Conference, March-April 1947.

1. Education - Asia.   I. Asian Relations Conference, Delhi, 1947./ II. Title.

NN   0020068   CaBVaU

Narasimhia, Agaram Narasimha, *pandit.*
... A grammar of the oldest Kanarese inscriptions, by A. N.
Narasimhia ... Mysore, The University of Mysore, 1941.
4 p. l., xxi p., 1 l., 375 p. 22ᵐ. (University of Mysore. Studies in
Dravidian philology—No. 1)
"Thesis presented to the Faculty of arts of the University of London,
June 1933, in partial fulfilment of the requirements for the degree of
doctor of philosophy."
Bibliography: p. 366–374.

1. Kanarese language—Grammar. 2. Inscriptions, Kanarese.
44–17857
Library of Congress   PL4643.N3
[2]   494.8145

NN   0020069   DLC CU CtY NN WaU

NARASIMHIENGAR, M.T.
The Brahmanaic systems of religion and
philosophy. Madras, S.P.C.K. press,1911.

pp. 25.
Cover title.
"Reprinted from the "Quarterly Journal
of the Mythic Society, Bangalore",
for April 1911".

NN   0020070   MH

Narasimhiengar, M   T
The divine doctrine; or, Universal religion.
By H.H. Sri-Kalki, G.I. (Prof. M. T.
Narasimhiengar) ... Bangalore, 1931.
v, [2], 93, ix, viii p. port. 19 cm.

NN   0020071   CtY

DS 486
.B15N21
Narasimiah, S. K.
The founder of Bangalore, or Magadi
Kempe Gowda and his ancestors,
successors and collaterals. [Translated
by S.G. Govindaraja Iyengar] Bangalore,
Vokkaligara Sangha Press, 1924.
vi, 54 p.

1. Kempe Gowda. 2. Bangalore, India
(City)--Hist.

NN   0020072   ICU

4K
Ind.
313
Narasimmha Aiyer, N.R.
The case law of Hindu law, being
an abstract of the decisions on Hindu
law, by N. R. Narasimmiah and P. Sama
Row. 1st ed.   Madras, Printed by
Srinivasa, Varadachari, 1893.
283 p.

NN   0020073   DLC-P4

Narasimmha Aiyer, N. R.   andSama Rau, P.
Mahamadan Law chiefly based upon MacNaughten's
Treatise and the decided cases.   4th ed.
Madras, 1890.

8⁰   v.p.

NN   0020074   MH-L

Narasimmha Aiyer, N.R.
Principles of Hindu Law; chiefly based upon
Sir Thomas Strange. Mr. Mayne, Mr. Siromani,
Tagore Law lecture, and cases of the four High
Courts in India and of the Privy Council, to
the end of 1891, with introduction, appendix,
and an abstract of cases. 3d ed., Madras,
1893,

(2)+2+(1)+vi+iv+viii+lxviii+357+283+
ix+iv+xxiiip.
8 vo.

NN   0020075   MH-L

Narasimmiah, N.R.
see   Narasimmha Aiyer, N.R.

Narasinga Rao, A., ed.
The **Mathematics** student; a quarterly dedicated to the service of students and teachers of mathematics in India.
v. 1–   Mar. 1933–
Madras, Srinivasa Varadachari & co.; [etc., etc., 1933–

Narasinga Rao, C   V
... The specific relief act (Act I of 1877) by
C.V. Narasinga Rao ... 1st ed., 1915, together
with a supplement incorporating the legislative
changes and bringing down the case-law to end of
July, 1922. By S. Kasturi Rangachariar ...
Madras, Printed and published by the Law printing
house, and Lawyer's companion office, 1923.
2 p.l., 94, 351 [i.e. 451] p.   25 cm. (The
Lawyer's companion series)
p. 406-451 in- correctly numbered p. 306-351.

NN   0020078   CtY

Narasinga. Rao, T.V.
Madras. Government museum.
... Catalogue of the wood specimens exhibited in the
Economic section. Madras, Government press, 1916.

Narasinh Narayan Godbole
see
Godbole, Narasinh Narayan, 1888–

Narasinha Chintaman Kelkar
see   Kelkar, Narsinha Chintaman,
1872-1947.

Narasinha Mehta
see
Narasimha Mehetā, 1414–1481.

Narasu, Pokala Lakshmi
see
Lakshmi Narasu, Pokala.

Narat, Joseph K   1888–
[Collected papers on medicine and surgery]

NN   0020084   ICJ

Narath, Albert, 1864-1924.
Beiträge zur Therapie der Luxatio Coxae
Congenita. Wien, Braumüller, 1903.
214 p. illus. plates. 25.5 cm. (Arbeiten
aus dem Gebiete der klinischen chirurgie)

NN   0020085   MBCo

Narath, Albert, 1864–1924.
Der Bronchialbaum der Säugethiere und des Menschen. Eine
vergleichend anatomische und entwicklungsgeschichtliche Studie.
Von Dr. Albert Narath, ... Mit 242 Figuren im Text und VII
Doppeltafeln. Stuttgart, E. Nägele, 1901.
viii, 380 p. 242 illus., VII fold. col. pl. 31⁴ᵐᵐ. (*In* Bibliotheca medica, Ab-
theilung A, Anatomie, A, Heft 3.)
"Literatur-Verzeichnis," p. [373]-376.

NN   0020086   ICJ MB MdBJ CtY MH CtY-M DNLM PU NIC

NARATH, Albert,1900–
Die innere reibung von gasen und ihre zusam-
menhang mit der komplexbildung der Molekeln.
Inaug. diss., Heidelberg. Leipzig, J.A.
Barth,1926.
pp.(4). [637]-672.
"Lebenslauf", at end.
"Sonderdruck aus 'Annalen der physik"
bd. 79, heft 7, 1926, " pp.[637]-672.

NN   0020087   MH ICRL CtY

TR897
.L5
1943
Narath, Albert, joint author.
1900–
Lichte, Hugo, 1891–
Physik und technik des tonfilms, von dr. Hugo Lichte und
dr. habil. Albert Narath ... 2., erweiterte aufl. Mit 296 abbildungen. Leipzig, S. Hirzel, 1943.

Narath, Albert, 1900–
Terminologie der Mikrodokumentation.
Nachrichten für Dokumentation, vol. 1 no.
3/4, December1950, p. 99-102.
[4]pp. photocopied.

"Classified definition of 19 terms in
German." (Wagner bibliography)

NN   0020089   OClW

Narath, Alfred, 1891–
Die Kochkost und Rohkost des Nieren- und
Blasenkranken. Stuttgart, J. Püttmann, 1928.
154 p.
1. Cookery for the sick. I. Title.

NN   0020090   CU-I

VOLUME 405

Narath (Alfred) [1891–   ]. *Ueber Entstehung der anämischen Lebernekrose nach Unterbindung der Arteria hepatica und ihre Verhütung durch arterio-portale Anastomose. [Heidelberg.] 75 pp., 1 l. 8°. Leipzig, F. C. W. Vogel, 1916.

NN   0020091   DNLM CtY

HF1027
.M35

Narath, Friedrich, joint author.

Mayer, Emil, *teacher.*
Die Wirtschaftsgebiete und Wirtschaftsgüter der Erde; ein wirtschaftsgeographisches Lehrbuch für Wirtschaftsschulen, von Emil Mayer und Friedrich Narath. Dortmund, L. Lensing [Vorwort 1952–53]

Narath, H
Fein- und feinstbearbeitungs- maschinen, von H. Narath, VDI.   Leipzig, J.J. Arnd, 1941.
136 p.

NN   0020093   NNE

Narath, H
Geräte zum prüfen und messen in der werkstatt, von H. Narath, VDI.   Leipzig, J. J. Arnd, 1941.
123 p. illus. 20ᵐ.

1. Measuring instruments.

		44–24059
Library of Congress	TJ1313.N3	
	[2]	621.9

NN   0020094   DLC

4TA
238

Narath, H
Prüfgeräte für die Werkstoffprüfung in der Metallbearbeitung. Leipzig, J. J. Arnd, 1941.
156 p.

NN   0020095   DLC-P4

Narath, Heinz Jordan
see Jordan-Narath, Heinz.

Narath, Peter A
Renal pelvis and ureter. New York, Grune & Stratton, 1951.
429 p. illus. 26 cm.

1. Pelvis. 2. Ureters. 3. Urinary organs.   I. Title.

QM401.N3	611.96	51–6845 †

MBCo CaBVaU OrU-M
NN   0020097   DLC DNLM ICU ICJ TxU-M NjR NbU NbU-M

Narath, Rudolf, *1903–*
... Die union von Südafrika und ihre bevölkerung. Leipzig und Berlin, B. G. Teubner, 1930.
3 p. l., 262 p. 22ᵐ. (Geographische schriften ... hft. 6)
"Die vorliegende arbeit [ist] eine Heidelberger geographische dissertation."—Vorwort.
"Literaturverzeichnis": p. 261–262.

1. Anthropo-geography—Africa, South.   I. Title.

		32–4327
Library of Congress	GF721.S6N3	
	[2]	916.8

NN   0020098   DLC CU TNF NN ICU

U854
.B4

Narath, Rudolf, 1903–   tr.

Behmer, Elis G   1904–
Das zweischneidige schwert der germanischen völkerwanderungszeit, von Elis Behmer ... [Stockholm, Tryckeriaktiebolaget Svea, 1939]

A narative of some of the sufferings of J.P. in the city of Rome
see under   [Perrot, John] d. 1671?

Naravane, D   N.
The Indian states in the federation of India (memoir presented for the diploma of the Institut universitaire de hautes études internationales, Geneva) by D. N. Naravane ... with a foreword by Sir Manubhai N. Mehta, kt. ...   Bombay, Karnatak publishing house, 1939.
xvi, 248 p. 19ᵐ.
"Select bibliography": p. [246]–248.

1. India—Pol. & govt.—1919– government. I. Title.	2. India. Constitution. 3. Federal	
		42–497
Library of Congress	JQ215.1939.N3	
	[2]	342.54

NN   0020101   DLC NSyU ICU CaBVaU MiU CtY NN

Naravane, Vishwanath S
Rabindranath Tagore; a philosophical study. Allahabad, Central Book Depot [19–]
iii, ii, 238 p. 22 cm.
Includes bibliographies.
"Based upon a thesis entitled 'The philosophy of Rabindranath Tagore' which was accepted by the University of Allahabad in 1946 for the D. Phil. degree."

1. Tagore, Sir Rabindranath, 1861–1941.

B133.T34N3	181.4	58–34237

NN   0020102   DLC CtY ICU MH WU

LA1152
N4
Educ.
Library

Narawane, V   N
Primary education in India in 1931-41.   Bombay, Local Self-Government Institute, 1948.
168 p. tables.

Cover title.
Bibliography: p. 167-168.

1. Education - India. 2. Education, Elementary. I. Title.

NN   0020103   CU

Narawangsa Tun Nambang.
Malay annals
see under   Sejarah Malayu. English.

Náray, Antal,
Légitámadás! irta vitéz Náray Antal és ifj. vitéz Berkó István. [Budapest] A Magyar könyvbarátok számára kiadja a Kir. magy. egyetemi nyomda [1936] 304 p. illus., plates, tables. 20½cm.

"Irodalom," p. [290]–292.

876330A. 1. Defense—Hungary.   I. Berkó, István, jt. au. II. Title.
N.Y.P.L.   April 7, 1937

NN   0020105   NN MH

4QD
149

Náray-Szabó, István.
Szerves anyagok röntgenvizsgálata; a Mérnöki Továbbképző Intézet 1942. évi tanfolyamainak anyaga. Budapest, Királyi Magyar Egyetemi Nyomda, 1943.
27 p.

(A Mérnöki Továbbképző Intézet kiadványai, 28. köt., 31. füzet)

NN   0020106   DLC DLC-P4

Narayan, A. L.
Absorption spectra and their bearing on the structure of atoms and molecules; being the Sir Subrahmanya Aiyar lecture, delivered...11th December, 1924, by Dr. A. L. Narayan... [Madras,] The University, 1925.   25 p. incl. diagrs., tables.   8°. (Madras Univ. Sir Subrahmanya Aiyar lecture. 1924.)

1. Spectra, Absorption. 2. Atoms.
N.Y.P.L.   October 19, 1929

NN   0020107   NN OrU

Narayan, A   L
... On the resonance lines of thallium and their probable absence in the sun, by A. L. Narayan... Madras, Printed by the Superintendent, Govt. press, 1933.
p. 311-316. diagrs. 31 cm. (Kodaikanal observatory. Bulletin no. XCIX)
Caption title.
"References": p. 316.

NN   0020108   DN-Ob

QC462
.P8N2

Narayan, A   L.
A study of the optical properties of potassium vapour ...   Madras, Printed by the superintendent, government press, 1925.
v, [1], 30 p. 9 pl., fold. diagr. 24½ᶜᵐ.
Thesis—Madras.
Thesis note mounted on t.-p.

1. Spectrum analysis. 2. Potassium.

NN   0020109   ICU CU

Pamph.
BL
1265
.S4
Z92

Narayan, Bikashendra, 1885–
Reminiscences of my life. [n.p.] 1953.
37 p. 19 cm.

1. Narayan, Bikashendra, 1885–
2. Sen family.

NN   0020110   MH-AH

Narayan, Bramdeva
see
Narain, Brahmadeva.

Narayan, Brij
see
Narain, Brij.

BX
4705
A18N21

Narayan, J   Stephen, 1898–
Acquaviva and the Great Mogul. Patna, Catholic Book Club [1945]
233 p. 19cm.

1. Acquaviva, Rodolfo, 1550-1583.
2. Jesuits in India. 3. Missions--India.

MH
NN   0020113   NIC WaSpG OWorP NcD NcWsW NSyU InStme

Narayan, J   Stephen, 1898–
From Hinduism to Catholicism via Anglicanism, by J. Stephen Narayan, B. D. 3d completely rev. ed. Ranchi, Catholic press, 1943.
2 p. l., 69 p. 18½ᵐ. [Light of the East series, no. 2]

1. Converts, Catholic.   I. Title.

		46–41778
Library of Congress	BX4668.N3 1943	
	[2]	922.254

NN   0020114   DLC

VOLUME 405

Narayan, Jagat
see Narain, Jagat, 1895-

Narayan, Jaya Prakash
see
Narain, Jai Prakash.

QK827 Narayan, Kadur Narasimhappa, 1913-
N3   Cytogenetic studies of apomixis in
Pennisetum. ₍Davis, 1951₎
11,121 ℓ. illus.

Thesis (Ph.D.) - Univ. of California,
Davis, June 1951.
Bibliography: p.90-98.

1. Pennisetum. 2. Fertilization of
plants.

NN 0020117   CU

915.41 Narayan, Kailaspati, rai sahib
N218B   Bihar and Orissa in 1935-36. Patna,
Superintendent, Govt. Print., Bihar, 1938.
xi, 148, xxiv p. illus., ports., fold.
col. map, diagrs. 24 cm.

1. Bihar and Orissa. I. Title.

NN 0020118   NcD CU

954.14 Narayan, Mahesh.
N16p   The partition of Bengal; or, The separation
of Behar? Being the exposition of an ideally
perfect scheme for the partition of the lower
provinces of Bengal, Behar and Orissa, by Mahesh
Narain and Sachchidananda Sinha.   ₍Allahabad,
Hindustan Review₎ 1906.
iv, 41p. 25cm.

Cover title.
"Reprinted with additions from the Hindustan
review."

NN 0020119   IU

Narayan, R   K   1906-
An astrologer's day, and other stories. London, Eyre &
Spottiswoode ₍1947₎
vi, 229 p. 19 cm.
"Most of these stories were first published in the Hindu of Madras."

I. Title.
PZ3.N166As

47-27903*

NcD IEN CaBVa CaBVaU
NN 0020120   DLC NcU IU CSt CtY NcGU MH PU CU KU

Narayan, R   K   1906-
The bachelor of arts, a novel by R. K. Narayan, with an
introduction by Graham Greene. London, New York ₍etc.₎
T. Nelson and sons, limited ₍1937₎
x, 11-265 p. 19½ᶜᵐ.

I. Title.
37-34173
Library of Congress   PZ3.N166Bac

NN 0020121   DLC NBuT IU CU N

PR   Narayan, R   K   , 1906-
9799   The bachelor of arts; a novel.
N21B12   London, Eyre & Spottiswoode,₍1948₎
1948   134 p. 19cm.

NN 0020122   NIC IU PU MH NRU

Narayan, R   K   1906-
The bachelor of arts, a novel. East Lansing, Michigan
State College Press, 1954.
166 p. 21 cm.
Bound with the author's Swami and friends. East Lansing, 1954.

I. Title.
PZ3.N166Sw 4

54-4796 ‡

ScU ICU NcD NN TxU MiU OO OrU OrCS CaBVaU
NN 0020123   DLC DAU NBuU IU HU KEmT ViU OrU FU GU

Narayan, R   K   1906-
The dark room; a novel, by R. K. Narayan. London, Macmillan and co., limited, 1938.
2 p. l., 209, ₍1₎ p. 19¼ᶜᵐ.

I. Title.
38-38056
Library of Congress   PZ3.N166Dar

NN 0020124   DLC HU IaU NIC

Narayan, R   K   1906-
Dodu and other stories. Mysore, Indian Thought Publications ₍19—₎
145 p. 17 cm.

I. Title.
PR6027.A68D6

823.91   51-36782

NN 0020125   DLC

Narayan, R   K   1906-
The English teacher, by R. K. Narayan. London, Eyre &
Spottiswoode ₍1945₎
183, ₍1₎ p. 19ᶜᵐ.
"First published in 1945."

I. Title.
46-2676
Library of Congress   PZ3.N166En

NN 0020126   DLC CaBVaU MH CSt NcU LU

Narayan, R   K   1906-
The English teacher; a novel. Mysore,
Indian Thought Publications ₍1955₎
210 p.

NN 0020127   WaU PU-SRS

Narayan, R   K   1906-
The financial expert, a novel; with an introd. by Graham
Greene. London, Methuen ₍1952₎
217 p. 19 cm.

I. Title.
PZ3.N166Fi

52-67531 ‡

NN 0020128   DLC OrCS CU ViU OEac PU TxU MH NN IaU

Narayan, R   K   1906-
The financial expert. ₍A novel. East Lansing₎ Michigan
State College Press, 1953.
178 p. 23 cm.

I. Title.
PZ3.N166Fi 2

53-1131 ‡

WaSp CaBVaU Or OrP WaS WaT
TxU OO NcD PP PHC OC1 MiU ICU MB TNJ MtBC CaBVa
NN 0020129   DLC ScU MoU GU CaOTP GU CLU IaU MU RP

Narayan, R   K   1906-
Grateful to life & death. ₍East Lansing₎ Michigan State
College Press, 1953.
218 p. 23 cm.
First ed. published in 1945 under title: The English teacher.

I. Title.
PZ3.N166Gr

53-3348 ‡

OrP DAU OrMonO IdB WaT WaS MtBC OrU NcGU
OC1 NN OOxM ViU TNJ MU MB KMK AAP CaBVa CaBVaU Or
NN 0020130   DLC AU MoU HU GU NBuU ICU MiU NcD TxU

PR6027 Narayan, R   K   1906-
A68L3   Lawley Road and other stories. Delhi,
Hind Pocket Books ₍n.d.₎
159p. 17cm. (Orient paperbacks)

NN 0020131   IaU

PR6027 Narayan, R   K   1906-
A68M57   Mr.Sampath. London, Eyre & Spottiswoode
₍1949₎
219p. 19cm.

NN 0020132   IaU CaBVa NIC PU NN MH IEN

DS485 Narayan, R   K   1906-
.M85N35 Mysore. Mysore, Government Branch Press,
1939.
127 p. plates.

1. Mysore--Descr. & trav.

NN 0020133   ICU

Narayan, R   K   1906-
Mysore, by R. K. Narayan. 2d ed. Mysore, Indian thought
publications, 1944.
vi, 114 p. plates. 18ᶜᵐ.

1. Mysore--Descr. & trav.
46-16421
Library of Congress   DS485.M85N3 1944
₍2₎   915.48

NN 0020134   DLC

Narayan, R   K   1906-
Swami and friends. With 20 sketches by R. K. Laxman.
₍1st Indian ed.₎ Mysore, Indian Thought Publications
₍1944₎
197 p. illus. 19 cm.

I. Title.
PZ3.N166Sw

54-49954

NN 0020135   DLC

VOLUME 405

Narayan, R   K   1906–
Swami and friends, a novel of Malgudi. East Lansing,
Michigan State College Press, 1954.

179 p. 21 cm.

Bound with the author's The bachelor of arts. East Lansing, 1954.

ɪ. Title.

PZ3.N166Sw 4   54–8878 ‡

IdPI OrCS NcD
ViU AAP OrU MU IU IEN WaChenE CaBVaU CaBVa WaS OrP
NN   0020136   DLC TxU OO ICU NN HU MoU NBuU GU KEmT

Narayan, R   K   1906–
Waiting for the Mahatma. ₍Lansing₎ Michigan State
University Press, 1955.

241 p. illus. 22 cm.

1. Gandhi, Mohandas Karamchand, 1869–1948—Fiction.   ɪ. Title.

PZ3.N166Wai   55—11689 ‡

CaBVa OrU MoU MU WaE OrMonO WaS
WaSp ViU AAP MB MtU AU FU GU Or OrP CaBVaU NBuC
MiU NcD IU CU TxU OO OC1 NcU ICU NIC PU NN WaT
NN   0020137   DLC TNJ OU ScU NcU DAU WaU FU OOxM

PR 9796.5
N373   Narayan, R   K   1906–
W3   Waiting for the Mahatma. London,
1955   Methuen [1955]
       256 p. 20 cm.

1. Gandhi, Mohandas Karamchand, 1869–
1948 – Fiction. I. Title.

NN   0020138   CaBVaU

Narayan, Ram
See
Ram Narayan.

517.1   Narayan, Shanti.
N16c   A course of mathematical analysis. ₍2d
1949   ed.₎   Delhi, S. Chand ₍1949₎
       iv, 304p. 25cm.

1. Functions of real variables.

NN   0020140   IU GU NN NcD CU RPB

QA331.5
.N3   Narayan, Shanti.
      A course of mathematical analysis.
      ₍3d ed.₎   Delhi, S. Chand & Co. ₍1953₎
      361 p. 22 cm.

1. Functions of real variables.
I. Title. II. ₍Tit₎le: Mathematical analysi

NN   0020141   TU ICarbS

QA 300   NARAYAN, SHANTI.
.N218   A course of mathematical analysis. ₍4th
      ed.₎   Delhi, S. Chand ₍1955₎
      5+404 p. illus., ports.

1. Calculus. 2. Functions.

NN   0020142   InU

512.3   Narayan, Shanti.
N164t   A text book of matrices.   Fountain, Delhi,
S. Chand [1953]
     1p.ℓ., vii, 289p. 19cm.

Cover title: Matrices.
Bibliography: p. [286]

1. Matrices.

NN   0020143   WU ICarbS NcRS IU TU TxU MnSST OC1W

512.895   Narayan, Shanti
N164t   A text book of vector algebra (with
1954   applications)   Delhi, S. Chand, 1954.
      iv, 190p. illus. 20cm.

1. Algebra, Universal. 2. Vector
analysis. I. Title.

NN   0020144   KU IU NNC ICarbS OU NcRS NcD

Narayan, Shiv.
... Electric generators, motors and circuits. Important facts,
figures and formulæ. By Shiv Narayan ... Roorkee, Printed
at the Photo-mech. & litho. dept., Thomason college, 1924.

32 p. incl. plates. diagrs. 21½ᶜᵐ. (Electrical engineering booklets for
Indian students, engineers and industrialists. no. 1)

1. Electric machinery—Direct current.   2. Electric circuits.

                                41–37583
Library of Congress   TK2612.N3
                     ₍2₎   621.3182

NN   0020145   DLC

Narayan, Shiv.
Electric railways in India (with relevant facts about electric
traction in other countries and some statistics about Indian
railways in general) ... By Shiv Narayan ... Poona, India,
B. Narayan & co., 1940.

iv, ₍4₎, 128 p. incl. illus., tables. pl., diagrs. (1 fold.) 24½ᶜᵐ.

1. Electric railroads—India.   2. Railroads—Electrification.   ɪ. Title.

                                41–245
Library of Congress   TF1108.N3
                     ₍2₎   621.330954

NN   0020146   DLC

Narayan, Shiv.
Hydro-electric installations of India. A treatise for students.
Useful to engineers, industrialists and others. A practical and
popular account of the salient features of the hydro-electric plants
and projects of British India and the Indian states... By Shiv
Narayan... Gwalior: Y. T. Mangaokar, 1922. 302 p. incl.
tables. illus. (incl. maps, plans.) 8°.

108034A.   1. Electricity.—Power   plants and stations, India.
2. Water power.—Plants and   companies, India.
N. Y. P. L.   November 12, 1923.

NN   0020147   NN IU

Narayan, Shiv.
Indian water power plants; a companion volume to Hydro-
electric installations of India, including chapters on 'Water-
power projects of Burma', 'Achievements and tendencies
abroad'. Twenty chapters, six appendices, three dozen tables,
three dozen illustrations. By Shiv Narayan ... Poona, B.
Narayan, 1937.

1 p. l., viii, ₍2₎, 172 p. incl. illus. (incl. maps) 2 pl. on 1 l., tables.
2 fold. diagr. 25ᶜᵐ.

1. Water-power electric plants—India.   ɪ. Title.

                                40–11606
Library of Congress   TK1508.N3
                     ₍2₎   621.3121340954

NN   0020148   DLC

Narayan, Shiv.
... Lightning, lightning conductors, protectors and arresters.
How to guard buildings and machines, telegraph and transmis-
sion lines and systems. Erection and testing of lightning con-
ductors. By Shiv Narayan ... Roorkee, Printed at the
Photo-mech. & litho. dept., Thomason college, 1924.

2 p. l., 8–35 p. incl. 5 pl. 21½ᶜᵐ. (Electrical engineering booklets for
Indian students, engineers and industrialists. no. ɪɪɪ)

1. Lightning-conductors.   2. Lightning-arresters.
                                41–37575
Library of Congress   TH9057.N3
                     ₍2₎   621.31982

NN   0020149   DLC

Narayan, Shriman
Shriman Narayan, 1912–

Narayan, T   G
... Famine over Bengal, with a foreword by Vijaya Lakshmi
Pandit. Calcutta, The Book company, ltd. ₍1944₎

viii p., 1 l., 234 p. 18¾ᶜᵐ.

1. Bengal—Famines.   ɪ. Title.
                                46–20382
Library of Congress   HC439.N3
                     ₍2₎   338.15

NN   0020151   DLC WaU ICU NcD TxU ViU

Narayan, T   G
... Famine over Bengal, with a foreword by
Vijaya Lakshmi Pandit. Calcutta, The Book
company, ltd. [1944]
      viii p., 1 l., 234 p. 18.5 cm.
      Microfilm. Washington, Library of Congress,
Photoduplication Service, 1965. 1 reel.

NN   0020152   MiU

Nārāyan Aiyangār
see   Aiyangār, Narayan.

Narayan Aiyer, A   K   Yegna
see   Aiyer, A   K   Yegna Narayan, 1878–

Narayan Anant Gore
see
Gore, Narayan Anant.

Narayan Anant Mavlankar
see   Mavlankar, Narain Anant.

Narayan Bahl, Karm
see   Bahl, Karm Narayan, 1891–

Narayan Balkrishna Godbole
see
Godbole, Narayan Balkrishna.

VOLUME 405

Narayan Bapuji Utgikar
see
Utgikar, Narayan Bapuji.

Narayan Bhaskar Khare
see
Khare, Narayan Bhaskar, 1884–

Narayan Bhavanrao Pavgee
see   Pavgee, Narayan Bhavanrao, 1854–

Narayan Chaudhuri, Harendra
see   Chaudhuri, Harendra Narayan.

Narayan Chaudhuri, Nagendra
see   Chaudhuri, Nagendra Narayan.

Narayan Dajiba Wadegaonkar
see
Wadegaonkar, Narayan Dajiba, 1871–1950.

Narayan Das
see
Nābhādāsa, *fl.* 1585.

Narayan Daso Banhatti
see
Banhatti, Narayana Daso.

Narayan Ganesh Goray
see
Goray, Narayan Ganesh, 1907–

Narayan Gangopadhyaya, *pseud.*
see
Ganguli, Taraknath, 1918–

Narayan Ganguli, *pseud.*
see
Ganguli, Taraknath, 1918–

Narayan Gopal Tavakar
see
Tavakar, Narayan Gopal, 1895–

Narayan Gour, Prabhu
see   Gour, Prabhu Narayan, ed.

Narayan Gupta, Ram
see   Gupta, Ram Narayan.

Narayan Jagat
see   Narain, Jagat, 1895–

Narayan Keshao Mahajan
see
Mahajan, Narayan Keshao, 1913–

Narayan Keshav Behere
see
Behere, Narayan Keshav, 1890–1958.

Narayan Keshav Bhagwat
see   Bhagwat, Narayan Keshav.

Narayan Lal, Aditya
see   Lal, Aditya Narayan.

Narayan Malhar Joshi
see
Joshi, Narayan Malhar, 1879–1955.

Narayan Menon, Vallathol
see   Menon, Vallathol Narayan, 1879–

Narayan Nathaji Kulkarni
see   Kesava Misra.

Narayan Prasad, Purnendu
see   Prasad, Purnendu Narayan.

Narayan Prasad Mishra
see
Mishra, Narayan Prasad.

Narayan Prosad Dulia
see   Dulia, Narayan Prosad, plaintiff.

Narayan Raghunath, Deshpande
see
Deshpande, Narayan Raghunath.

Nārāyan Rām, Achārya
see   Rām Achārya, Nārāyan.

Narayan Rao, M   Anant.
Arunachala, or a short history of hill and temple in Tiruvannamalai, North Arcot district, Madras presidency, S. India. ₍Tiruvannamalai₎ Published by the author, 1947.
11, 87 p. illus. (plates) fold. plan. 19cm.

"Errata" on l. following p. 87.
"List of books consulted": p. ₍86₎–87.

NN   0020186   NNC NN

Narayan Rao, M   Anant.
... Observations on the morphology and life-cycle of *Filaria recondita* Grassi, by M. Anant Narayan Rao ... Calcutta, Superintendent government printing, India, 1923.
1 p. l., 7 p., 2 pl., diagr. 25ᶜᵐ. (Pusa. Agricultural research institute. Bulletin no. 144)

1. Filaria and filariasis.

                                                                    Agr 24–147
Library, U. S. Dept. of   Agriculture 22P97 no. 144

NN   0020187   DNAL

Narayan Rao, Nidadavolu Nara, 1926–
The high-tension spark plug, its evolution, present state of development and manufacture. Edited by H. A. Havemann. Bangalore, Indian Institute of Science ₍1955₎
x, 149 p. diagrs., tables. 25 cm. (Memoirs of the Indian Institute of Science, new ser., no. 2)
Bibliography: p. 139–145.

1. Spark-plugs.   I. Title.   (Series: Indian Institute of Science, Bangalore. Memoirs, new ser., no. 2)

TJ787.N28   58–55280

NN   0020188   DLC NN

Narayan Sadashiv Bapat
see
Bapat, Narayan Sadashiv.

Narayan Sanyal
see
Sanyal, Narayan.

Narayan Singh
see
Singh, Narayan.

Narayan Singh, Avadhesh
see
Singh, Avadhesh Narayan.

Narayan Singh, Pratap, Bahadur of Ayodhya
see   Pratap Narayan Singh, Bahadur of Ayodhya.

Narayan Singh, Shyam
see   Singh, Shyam Narayan.

VOLUME 405

Narayan Sinha, Akhauri Basudev
see
Sinha, Akhauri Basudev Narayan, 1889–

Narayan Vaman Tilak
see
Tilak, Narayan Vaman, 1862?–1919.

Narayan Vinayak Kanitkar
see
Kanitkar, Narayan Vinayak, 1887–

Narayan Visanji Thakkur
see
Thakkur, Narayan Visanji, 1884–1938.

Narayan Vishnu Joshi
see
Joshi, Narayan Vishnu.

PK3798
.N28T3
Nārāyaṇa, *15th cent.*
तन्त्रसमुच्चयः. श्रीनारायणप्रणीतः. ... ...
... ...
... ... 1945-62.

    3 v. 23 cm. (अनन्तशयनविश्वविद्यालय: अनन्तशयनसंस्कृतग्रन्थावलि:,
प्रन्थाङ्कः १५१, १९९, २००)
    Vol. 1 has added t. p., in English; v. 2-3 have cover titles in English.
    Vol. 1 edited by V. A. Ramaswami Sastri; v. 2, by K. S. D. Mahadeva Sastri; v. 3, by K. Raghavan Pillai.
    In Sanskrit; pref. and introd. in English.

    1. Temples—India. I. Saṅkara, son of Nārāyaṇa. Vimarśinī. II. Kṛṣṇa, 16th cent., supposed author. Vivaraṇa. III. Ramaswami Sastri, V. A., ed. IV. Mahadeva Sastri, Kilnattam Sundara Dikshitar, 1902– ed. V. Raghavan Pillai, K., 1920– ed. VI. Title. (Series: Trivandrum Sanskrit series, no. 151 [etc.])
                 Title transliterated: Tantrasamuccayaḥ.

PK3798.N28T3 1945   S A 65-2134

NN   0020201   DLC CU

PK2971
.T8
no.67
etc.
Nārāyaṇa, *15th cent.*
    The Tantrasamuchchaya; with the comentary Vimarsinī of Sankara. Edited by T. Ganapati Sāstrī. Trivandrum, Printed by the Govt. Press, 1919-21.
    2 v. (Trivandrum Sanskrit series, no. 67, 71)
    Added t.p. and text in Sanskrit.
    Contents.--Pt.1. Patalas 1-6.--Pt.2. Patalas 7-12.
    1. Tantrism. 2. Rites and ceremonies--India. I. Saṅkara, son of Nārāyaṇa of Jayanta-Maṅgala. Vimarsinī. II.   Title.

NN   0020202   ICU CtY

Asia
PK4031
.N28V92
1941
Nārāyaṇa, pupil of Vijñaneśvara.
    Vyavahāraśiromani, of Nārāyaṇa. Edited by T. R. Chintamani. [Madras] University of Madras, 1941.
    56 p.

    "Reprinted from the 'Annals of Oriental Research'."

    1. Hindu law.   I. Chintamani, T. R., ed.   II.   Title.

NN   0020203   HU

Nārāyana, son of Divākara.
    [Aśvālayana-Gṛihyasūtra. With the commentary of Nārāyaṇa, son of Divākara. With the commentary of Nārāyaṇa, son of Divākara. Followed by the Gṛihyaparisishta and the Gṛihyakarikas of Kumārila see under   Aśvālayana.

PK3798
.S77N313
1934
Nārāyaṇa, son of Narasiṁha Vedarakara.
    Śrīharṣa, *12th cent.*
    The Naishadhacarita of Śrīharsha (cantos I–XXII) For the first time translated into English with critical notes and extracts from unpublished commentaries, appendices and a vocabulary, by Krishna Kanta Handiqui. Lahore, Motilal Banarsi Dass. Punjab Sanskrit Book Depot, 1934.

Nārāyāna, son of Śrīratnakara.
Upanishads.
    ... Eleven Âtharvaṇa upanishads with dīpikâs. Ed., with notes, by Colonel G. A. Jacob ... Bombay, Government central book depôt, 1891.

Nārāyāna, son of Śrīratnākara.
Upanishads. *Mahānārāyaṇā-upanishad.*
    ... The Mahānārāyaṇa-upanishad of the Atharvaveda, with the dīpikā of Nārāyaṇa, edited by Colonel G. A. Jacob ... Bombay, Government central book depôt, 1888.

Nārāyaṇa, Son of Śrīratnakara.
    Tantra sāra saṅgraha; with commentary; a treatise teaching formulae and rites for the attainment of health and happiness and even of Super-human power, edited with introd. in English & Sanskrit by M. Duraiswami Aiyangar. Madras, Govt. Oriental Manuscripts Library, 1950

    34, 512 p. (Madras Government oriental series, 15)
    Text in Sanskrit

NN   0020208   MH ICU MiU

Narayana, swami, 1781-1830
    see   Sahajananda, swami, 1781-1830.

B132
D5N25
Narayana,   Bhagavan
    Sanatana dharma sootras of Bhagavan Sri Narayana. Prefaced, transliterated and translated in English by Sri Janardana. Mylapore, Madras, Suddha Dharma Office [1918?]
    viii, 78 p. (Suddha dharma mandalam series, no. 11)

    1. Dharma. 2. Philosophy, Hindu. I. Title.

NN   0020210   CU

NARAYANA, Bhagavan.
    Yoga deepika of Bhagavan Narayana and the comentary of Hamsa Yogi, edited by Pandit K.T. Sreenivasachariar, with an English translation. Foreword by Sir S. Subrahmanya Iyer. Madras. Law Printing House, 1916.

    Plate.
    "Suddha Dharma Mandala series, 2."
    Label pasted over imprint: London, Arthur Probsthain.

NN   0020211   MH

Nārāyana, G. Veṅkata, joint author.

Taduliṅgam, Chinnakavanam, 1878–
    A handbook of some south Indian weeds containing complete descriptions and short notes on some of the common weeds indigenous and introduced in south India (with illustrations) By C. Taduliṅgam ... and G. Veṅkaṭanārāyaṇa ... Foreword by R. D. Anstead ... Madras, Printed by the superintendent, government press, 1932.

Narayana, K. Lakshmi
see
Lakshminarayana, Kodali, 1908–

Narayana, Kini, Kulai
    see   Kini, Kulai Narayana, 1891–

Narayana, Lakshami
    see   Lakshminarayana, Kodali, 1908–

Narayana, Meherban Babasaheb
    see   Meherban Narayanrao Babasaheb, chief of Ichalkararji, 1870–

Nārāyaṇa, R   K
see
Narayan, R   K   1906–

Asia
BL1135
P75N28
Narayana, Vadhoola.
    A new approach to Devi Mahatmyam (Chandy Sapthasathy); introduction. [Madras] 1947.
    37 p.

    1. Puranas. Markandeyapurana.

NN   0020218   HU

Narayana Aiyar, Ananta
see
Aiyar, Ananta Narayana.

Nārāyaṇa Aiyar, C   V
    see   Sadananda, Swami.

615.1
N164p
Pharm
Lib'y
Narayana Aiyer, K   S
    Pharmacognosy of ayurvedic drugs, Kerala, by K. Narayana Aiyer and M. Kolammal. ser.1–

    Trivandrum Dept. of Pharmacognosy, University of Kerala, 1951–
       v. illus., part col.) 25cm.

    Title varies: ser.1, no.1-2, Pharmacognosy of ayurvedic drugs of Travancore-Cochin.
    Ser.1, no.1-3 issued by the Central Research Institute, Univer-   sity of Travancore.

NN   0020221   TxU

VOLUME 405

BV4828
.T3
1911
Orien
Tam

ǃNarayana Ayer, P., tr.
Ēcukitistu eppār oḻukikkāṭṭiya oḻukkamuraiṉūl.
Imitatio Christi. Tamil.
எசுகிறிஸ்து என்பார் ஒழுகிக்காட்டிய ஒழுக்கமுறைநூல். The imitation of Christ. தமிழ் மொழிபெயர்ப்பு: ப. நாராயண அய்யர். ஸ்ரீரங்கம்,
ஸ்ரீ வாணீ விலாஸ் பிரஸ், 1911.

DS421
.B5618
Orien
Tam

Narayana Ayer, P., tr.
Piracina...
Besant, Annie (Wood) 1847–1933.
பிராசீன தர்மங்களின் உயர்வும் இக்கால ஆசாரங்களும். அந்நிபெ
ஸன்ட் அம்மையாரது ஆங்கில உபந்தியாசங்களின் மொழிபெயர்ப்பு.
மதுரை, பிரஹ்மஞான மந்திரம், 1905.

Narayana Ayer, P., tr.
Avvaiyār.
... Yoga aphorisms of Avvayar, tr. into English, by
P. Narayana Ayer ... Madura, Printed at the Viveka
Bhanu press, 1909.

B132
.Y6B4359
Orien
Tam

Narayana Ayer, P., tr.
Yoka upanyasankaḷ.
Besant, Annie (Wood) 1847–1933.
யோக உபந்யாஸங்கள்; இது...அந்நிபெஸண்டு அம்மை 1907ஆ
டிஸம்பர்மீ 27, 28, 29, 30உகளில் காசி ஷேஒத்திரத்தில் கூடிய பிரஹ்மஞ்
ஞான ஸபையின் 32ஆம்த்தின் சபைக்கூடத்தில் ஆங்கிலத்தில் செய்த
உபந்யாஸங்களின் தமிழ் மொழி பெயர்ப்பு. ப. நாராயண ஐயர் அவர்
களால் செய்யப் பெற்றது. சென்னை, சச்சிதாநந்தம் பிரஸில் பதிப்பிக்
கப் பெற்றது, 1913.

Narayana Ayyangar, Kadaba
see
Narayana Iyengar, Kadaba, 1878–

Nārāyaṇa Ayyar, A   A
On the displacements at the sun's limb of lines sensitive to
pressure and density. By A. A. Narayana Ayyar. ₍Madras:
Gov. Press, 1914.₎ 113–116 p. 4°. (Kodaikanal Observatory. Bull. v. 3⁴⁴.)

Caption-title.

1. Sun.—Spectrum, 1914.   2. Series.
N. Y. P. L.   January 6, 1917.

NN   0020227   NN

Narayana Ayyar, C   C
see Sadananda, Swami.

Narayana Ayyar, L   Anantakrishna
see Iyer, Lakshinarayanpuran Anantkrishna Narayana,
rao bahadur.

Nārāyaṇa Bālakṛṣṇa Gōḍabōle
see
Godbole, Narayan Balkrishna.

Nārāyaṇa Bāpū-jī Uṭgīkar
see
Utgikar, Narayan Bapuji.

Asia
PK3798
.N3P722
1931

Nārāyaṇa Bhaṭṭa
Prakriyāsarvasva of Śrī Nārāyaṇa Bhaṭṭa,
with commentary. Edited by
K. Sambasiva Sastri. Trivandrum,
Superintendent, Government Press, 1931–
v.   (Trivandrum Sanskrit series,
no. 106,

Sri Setu Laksmī Prasādamālā, no.
XVIII.

NN   0020232   HU PU CU

Asia
PK3798
.N3P722

Nārāyaṇa Bhaṭṭa.
Prakriyāsarvasva (Taddhita)/by Nārāyaṇa
Bhaṭṭa. Edited by C. Kunhan Raja.
₍Madras₎ University of Madras, 1941.
xxxii, 193, 155 p. (Madras University.
Oriental Research Institute. Sanskrit
Dept.// Sanskrit series, no. 15)

I. Kunhan Raja, Chittenjoor, ed.
II. Title. III.   Series.

NN   0020233   HU MH NNC ICU

Narayana Bhatta, called Mrigarājalakshma
see   Narayana Bhatta, fl. 1060.

Narayana Bhatta, of Kerala
see   Nārāyanabhattapāda.

PK
4191
.N35
M83

Nārāyaṇa Bhaṭṭa, son of Ananta
Muhūrtamārtaṇḍa of Nārāyaṇa Daivajña.
Edited with Mārtaṇḍa prakāsikā Sanskrit
and Hindi commentaries by Kapileshwara
Sāstrī. Benares, Jaya Krishna Das Hari Das
Gupta, 1947.
4, 170 p. 23 cm. (The Kashi Sanskrit
Series, 145; Jyautiśa section, 10)

Text in Sanskrit; commentary in Sanskrit and Hindi.

1. Astrology, Hin-   du. I. Title.

NN   0020236   WU

Narayana Bhatta, son of Matrdatta
see   Narayana Bhatta, fl. 1060.

Nārāyaṇa Bhaṭṭa, son of Rameśvara Bhaṭṭa.
Prayogaratna ... ceremonies of Hindus.
Bombay, 1861.

NN   0020238   NjP

F64
345

Nārāyaṇa Bhaṭṭa, son of Rameśvara Bhaṭṭa.
Prayogaratna./ ₍Bombay, Published by Tukaram
Javaji,1915₎
2p.ℓ.,15,213 numb.ℓ., 1ℓ. incl.front.,illus.
13x27cm.
Sanskrit foliation; the 2d part has also
individual foliation: ℓ.1-55.
Edited by Vasudeva Lakshmaṇa Pansikar.

I. Vasudeva Lakshmana Pansikar,   ed.
x Sanskrit language - Texts & translations.
Narayanabhatta   x Title.

NN   0020239   CtY

PK
3591
K38
no.10

Nārāyaṇa Bhaṭṭa, 9th cent.
The Stava-Chintāmaṇi of Bhaṭṭa Nārāyaṇa,
with commentary by Kṣhemarāja. Edited with
notes by Mukunda Rāma Shāstrī. Published under
the authority of the Government of His Highness Lieut.-General Mahārāja Sir Pratāp Singh
Sāhib Bahādur, Mahārāja of Jammu and Kashmir
State. Srinagar, Printed at the "Kashmir
Pratap Steam" Press, 1918.
3, 155 p. (Kashmir series of texts and
studies, no.10)

In Sanskrit.
"Published by the Research Department,
Srinagar, Kashmir".

NN   0020241   WaU ICU OCl CtY MH

Narayana Bhatta, fl. 1060.
Hitopadesa
see under Hitopadeśa.

PK3798
.N29
V47T2

Nārāyaṇa Bhaṭṭa, fl. 1060.
Stanzas from Veṇi saṃhāra nātaka, set to
music by Sourindro Mohun Tagore. Calcutta,
Printed by I. C. Bose, 1893.
32 p. music.
Includes Sanskrit text with English translations.

I. Tagore, Sir Sourindro Mohun, 1840–1914.
II. Title: Veṇi   saṃhara nataka.

NN   0020243   ICU

Am
PK3798
.N3V425

Nārāyaṇa Bhaṭṭa, fl. 1060.
Veṇīsamhāra: die Ehrenrettung der Königin.
Ein Drama in 6 Akten. Kritisch mit Einleitung
und Noten hrsg. von Julius Grill. Leipzig,
Fues, 1871.

xxxvi, 181 p. 27cm.

I.Grill, Julius von, 1840–1930, tr. II.
Title.

NN   0020244   MnU CaBVaU HU OCl

Nārāyaṇa Bhaṭṭa, fl. 1060.
The Veṇīsamhāra of Bhaṭṭa Nārāyaṇa; edited
by B. T. Dravid alias Sheshadri Iyer and S. T.
Dravid. Poona, Sathaye, 1896.
1 v. (various pagings)

NN   0020245   WaU

NĀRĀYANA BHATTA, fl. 1060.
The Veṇīsamhāra, with the commentary of
Jagaddhara, and various readings. Edited
by K.P.Parab and K.R.Mādgāvkar. Bombay,
1898.

nar.1.12°.

NN   0020246   MH CU

Narayana Bhatta, fl. 1060.
The Veṇīsamhāra of Bhatta Nārāyaṇa. Edited
with the commentary of Jagaddhara, curtailed or
enlarged as necessary, various readings, a literal
English translation and critical and explanatory notes
in English by M. R. Ka'le. 2d ed. (thoroughly rev.)
Bombay, Gopal Narayan & Co., 1919.
114 p.
1. Ka'le, Moreshvar Ramchandra, tr. II. Title.

NN   0020247   CtHC

VOLUME 405

PK 3798 N3 V45 1936
Nārāyana Bhaṭṭa, fl. 1060.
    The Venisamhara of Bhatta Narayana.
Edited with the commentary of Jagaddhara,
curtailed or enl. as necessary, various
readings, a literal English translation
and critical and explanatory notes in
English by M.R. Kale. 3d ed. (thoroughly
rev.) Bombay, Gopal Narayan, 1936.
    17, 3, 171, 130 p. 22 cm.
    I. Kale, Moreshvar Ramchandra, ed. and
tr. II.   Title.

NN 0020248   CaBVaU

PK 3798 .N3 .V4 1940
Narayana onatta, fl. 1060.
    [Venisamhara. / Edited with trans-
lation into English, notes and
appendices by A. B. Gajendragadkar.
3d ed. Bombay?, Aryabhushan Press,
194-?]
    1 v. (various pagings)
    Text in Sanskrit; notes in
English.
    Title page wanting.
    PARTIAL CONTENTS.--Venisamhara: a
critical study, by A. B.
Gajendragadkar.
    (A)Gajendragadkar, Aswathama
        balacharya, 1892-   tr.
    (A)Gajendragadkar, Aswathama

        Balacharya, 1892-
        Venisamhara: a critical
        study.
    (A)Venisamhara.

NN 0020250   MoU

PK 3798 .N3 V4 1953a
Nārāyana Bhaṭṭa, fl. 1060.
    Veṇīsamhāram. Edited with an introd.,
a literal English translation, exhaustive
grammatical critical and exegstical [sic]
notes, and useful appendices, by G. V.
Devasthali. [Bombay] D. M. Tilak, 1953]
    xxvi, 396 p. 23 cm.

    Text in Sanskrit and English.

NN 0020251   WU

PK3791 .N3V4 1909 (S)
Nārāyaṇa Bhaṭṭa, fl. 1060.
    ... Venisanhara. A drama by Shi¡l¡ Bhatta Narayana,
with a Sanskrit commentary named Balabodhini by Shri
Appashastri Rashivadekar ... and with English notes by
Prof. K. N. Dravid ...   Kolhapur, Printed at Shri Venka-
teshwar and Shri Jainendra press; ¡etc., etc.¡ 1909-10.
    ¡48¡, 342, ¡186¡ p. pl. 21ᵐᵐ.
    Various paging at beginning and end; 342 p. in Sanskrit numerals.

NN 0020252   ICU MH NN

Nārāyaṇa Bhaṭṭa, fl. 1060.
    Veṇí-sanhára nátaka; or, The binding of the braid, a
Sanskrit drama, by Bhatta-Náráyaṇa. Done into English
by Sourindro Mohun Tagore. Calcutta, 1880.
    72 p. geneal. table. 21 cm.

    I. Tagore, Sir Sourindro Mohun, 1840-1914, tr. II. Title.
    III. Title: The binding of the braid.
    PK3798.N277V413   S A 64-7890

NN 0020253   DLC OC1

Nārāyaṇa Bhavānrāu Pāvgī
    see
Pāvgee, Narayan Bhavanrao, 1854-

Nārāyana-Chandra Vandyopādhyāya
    see
Banerjee, Narayanchandra, d. 1943.

Nārāyaṇa Cheṭṭiyār, Ṣaṅkara, P
    see
Sankaranarayana, Paluri.

Nārāyaṇa Dājībā Vāḍegāvakara
    see
Wadegaonkar, Narayan Dajiba, 1871-1950.

Nārāyaṇa Dāsa, *munshi*
    see
Das, Narayan, *munshi*.

Nārāyaṇa Daṣo Banhaṭṭi
    see
Banhatti, Narayana Daso.

Nārāyaṇa Dīkshita, Kāsīnātha
    see
Dikshit, Kashinath Narayan, 1889-

Nārāyaṇa Gaṇeṣa Chandāvaṛkar
    see
Chandavarkar, *Sir* Narayan Ganesh, 1855-1923.

Nārāyaṇa Gaṇeśa Gore
    see
Goray, Narayan Ganesh, 1907-

Nārāyaṇa Gaṅgōpādhyāya, *pseud.*
    see
Ganguli, Taraknath, 1918-

Narayana Iyar, C   V
    see
Sadananda, *Swami*.

Narayana Iyengar, Kadaba, 1878-
    Notes on building materials for Indian students. 2d ed.
¡Mysore, Printed at the Wesley Press and Pub. House¡ 1937.
    110 p. illus.

    1. Building materials. 2. Building—India.

    TA404.I 5N3 1937   58-52833

NN 0020265   DLC

Nārāyaṇa Iyer, C   V
    see Sadananda, Swami.

Narayana Iyer, K
    see Narayanaswami Aiyar, K

Narayana Iyer, Lakshinarayanpuran A
    see Iyer, Lakshinarayanpuran Anantkrishna Narayana,
rao bahadur.

Narayana Iyer, P   R
    Estate duty act (act XXXIV of 1953)

    see under

    India (Republic) Laws, statutes, etc.

Nārāyaṇa Keśava Mahājana
    see
Mahajan, Narayan Keshao, 1913-

PL 4718.5 N34 Z53 1939
Narayana Kurup, P
    K. C. Narayanan Nambiar; a poet of
kerala, by P. Narayana Kurup. [Madras]
1939.
    42 p. 19 cm.

    1. Narayanan Nambiar, K. C.   I. Title.

NN 0020271   CaBVaU

Narayana Menon, 1911-
    see
Narayana Menon, Vatakke Kurupath, 1911-

Narayana Menon, B   K
    see Menon, B⁻ K   Narayana.

Narayana Menon, Nalapat, 1888-1955.
    Chakravalam (Horizon). Translated from Malayalam
by N. Balamani Amma. Bombay, International Book
House ¡1940¡
    viii, 22 p. 20 cm.

    I. Balamani Amma, Nalappat, 1909-   tr. II. Title. III. Title:
Horizon.
    PL4718.9.N298C313   44-17855
                      rev   MARC

NN 0020274   DLC NN OC1

Narayana Menon, Vatakke Kurupath, 1911-
    The development of William Butler Yeats, by V. K. Nara-
yana Menon. With a pref. by Sir Herbert J. C. Grierson.
Edinburgh, Oliver and Boyd, 1942.
    xiv, 98 p. port. 23 cm.

    1. Yeats, William Butler, 1865-1939.

    PR5906.N3 1942   821.91   43-3984 rev*

        OC1 O OC1W PRosC PU IdU ICU LU ViU OO
NN 0020275   DLC MU TxU CU WaSp CaBVaU OrU NcU ScU

Narayana Murti, Bhaskarla Surya
    see
Murti, Bhaskarla Surya Narayana.

VOLUME 405

Nārāyaṇa Narasiṃha Bedarkar
see
Nārāyaṇa, *son of Narasiṃha Vedarakara.*

Nārāyana Pandita
    see   Nārāyaṇa-pandita, fl. 1356.

Narayana Panicker, R
ഗവേഷണവും ചരിത്രനിമിഷതിയും . Lectures on the
mediaeval period in Malayalam literature, by R. Narayana Panicker. ₁Trivandrum₁ University of Travancore ₁19—₁

170 p. 25 cm.
Cover title.
In Malayalam.

1. Malayalam literature—Hist. & crit.   I. Title.
                    Title transliterated: Gaveṣaṇavuṃ caritranirim-
                                                mittiyuṃ.

PL4718.1.N33   S A 66-7803

NN   0020279   DLC

Narayana Pillai, P. K., ed.

Z6605
.M3T7   Trivandrum, India (City) University of Kerala. *Oriental
         Manuscripts Library.*
            Index of Malayalam manuscripts, edited by P. K. Nara-
         yana Pillai. Trivandrum, Printed at the Alliance Print.
         Works, 1951.

Narayana Pillai, P.K., ed.
    Jaiminiyasūtrārthasangraha of Rsiputra
Paramesvara
        see under   Jaimini. Mīmāṃsa sūtra.
Sanskrit.

Narayana Pillai, P   K   ed.
    Kerala studies; Prof. A. Gopala Menon commemoration
volume. With a foreword by K. P. Kesava Menon. Trivandrum, 1955.

vi, vi, 177 p. illus. 25 cm.

CONTENTS.—Parsʼurāma and the Koṅkaṇ, by A. D. Pusalkar.—
Kerala and Parasʼurāma tradition, by M. R. Balakrishna Warrier.—
Kerala in early days, by P. J. Thomas.—St. Thomas tombs, skeletons
and bodies, by T. K. Joseph.—Dutch relations with the northern
princes of Malabar, by T. I. Ponnen.—Malabar in Anandaraṅga Pillaiʼs
diary, by V. Raghavan.—Malabar and the English East India Company, by K. M. Varma.—Pandit Sankarnath Jyotsiar, by S. Para-
mesvaran Pillai.—Srī Chaitanya in Kerala, by P. Seshadri.—A critical recension
of the Adhyātma, by P. K. Narayana Pillai.

tar.—Material culture of the primitive races in South India, by L. A.
Krishna Iyer.—Sylvan civilization of Kerala, by P. Damodaran Pillai.—The Kaṇṇaki legend and the tottam pāṭṭus, by P. Ananthan
Pillai.—Saṅkarācārya's philosophy of action, by A. S. Narayana Pillai.—Srī Chaitanya in Kerala, by P. Seshadri.—A critical recension
of the Adhyātma, by P. K. Narayana Pillai.

1. Kerala—Hist.—Addresses, essays, lectures. 2. Gopala Menon, A.
I. Title.

DS485.K4N3   S A 63-1539

NN   0020283   DLC MoU CtY HU PU-SRS CU

Asia
B132   Narayana Pillai, P   K
.M5N333   Mīmāṃsā in Kerala. Introduction to the
         Jaiminīya–Sūtrārtha–Saṅgraha, T. S. S.
         no. 156, edited by the author. ₁n.p.,
         n.d.₁
            65 p. (Studies in Kerala Sanskrit,
         no. 1)

            1. Mimamsa. 2. India – Religion.   I.
         Paramesvara.   Jaiminiya–sutrartha–
         sangraha. II.   Title. III. Series.

NN   0020284   HU

Nārāyaṇa Prasāda Miśra
see
Mishra, Narayan Prasad.

Narayana Rad hika
    see Narain, Radhka

HC   Narayana Rao, A
497   Indian labour in Burma ₁by₁ A. Narayana
B9   Rao. ₁Rangoon, 1933₁
N3   231p. illus. 19cm.

            1. Burma – Econ. condit. 2. Labor and
         laboring classes – India I. Title

NN   0020287   WU

Narayana Rao, Chilukuri, 1890-1952.
ఆంధ్రభాషాచరిత్రము. కర్త చిలుకూరి నారాయణరావు. వాక్టేరు,
1937-
    2 v. (xxii, iv, 1750 p.) illus., map, diagrs., tables. 26 cm.
    (ఆంధ్ర విశ్వకళాపరిషద్ (గ్రంథమాల, 18)
    Added t. p.: History of Telugu language, by C. Narayan Rao.
Includes bibliographies.

    1. Telugu language—Hist.   I. Title.   (Series: Andhra Univer-
sity series, no. 18)
                    Title transliterated: Āndhrabhāṣacaritramu.

PL4771.N3   S A 64-809

NN   0020288   DLC

Narayana Rao, Chilukuri, 1890-1952.
    An introduction to Dravidian philology. Lectures delivered
on behalf of the Oriental Research Institute, Madras University,
on the 29th Jan. 1929 and the succeeding days. By C. Narayana
Rao... Anantapur: The Sadhana Pub. House, 1929. ii,
214 p. 12°.

    "The following is the second of the four lectures delivered by Mr. C. Narayana Rao
under the auspices of the Madras University as a part of the scheme of the Oriental
Research Institute attached to the university."

529916A. 1. Dravidian languages.   I. Madras University. Oriental
Research Institute.   June 9, 1931
N.Y.P.L.

NN   0020289   NN ICU CtY

WZ   NARAYANA RAO, D   1878-
70   Ayurveda; a survey, being a brief
J14   historical and scientific outline of the
N2a   indigenous system of medicine ... ₁New
         Delhi, Majumdar, 1950-
                v.   illus., port.
            1. Medicine - Hindu

NN   0020290   DNLM

Narayana Rao, D., 1878-
HD2346
.I 52M3   Madras (*Presidency*)
1929   Preliminary report on the survey of cottage industries in
         the Chingleput ₁Chittoor, Coimbatore, East Godavari,
         Kistna and West Godavari, North Arcot, Salem, Tanjore
         and South Arcot,

            districts. Madras, Printed by the Superintendent, Govt.
         Press, 1929.

Narayana Rao, D   1878-
    Preliminary report on the survey of cottage industries
in the Kurnool district, by D. Narayana Rao. Madras,
Printed by the Supt., Govt. Press, 1927.

    19 p. 25 cm.

    1. Cottage industries—Karnul district.

HD2346.I 5N28   73-159594
                                                    MARC

NN   0020292   DLC

QE756   Narayana Rao, S. R., joint author.
.I 4A4
vol. 29, Sripada Rao, K
no. 2   ... The fossil *Charophyta* of the Deccan intertrappeans near
         Rajahmundry (India) by K. Sripada Rao ... and S. R. Na-
         rayana Rao ... Calcutta, Geological survey of India, 1939.

Narayana Rao, U   B
see
Narayanrao, U   B

Narayana Rao Huilgola, Krishnarao
see
Huilgol, Narayanarao Krishnarao, 1884-

Narayana Row, S   A   L
    Estate duty simplified, an exposition of Indian estate duty
law in simple language. 2d enl. ed. Allahabad, Ram Narain Lal ₁1955₁

6, ii, ii, 371 p. 19 cm.

"The act at a glance": fold. leaf inserted.
Includes legislation.

    1. Inheritance and transfer tax—India.   I. India (Republic)
Laws, statutes, etc. Estate duty act. II. Title.

                                                    61-40247

NN   0020296   DLC MH

Nārāyaṇa Sadāśiva Bāpaṭa
see
Bapat, Narayan Sadashiv.

Nārayaṇa Sastri, T   S
    The Makutabhisheka mahotsava or Imperial coronation.
With a free poetic translation in English by M.Kris-
hnamacharya. Madras, Printed by Rama Iyar, 1911

V. I.   illus. (Vidvan Mano Ranjani series, 9)
Cover title; t.p. in Sanskrit
Text in Sanskrit and English

NN   0020298   MH

Narayana Shastri Purandare, ed.
    The Rājanighanta [of Narahari] and the Dhanvan-
tarinighanta
        see under [Narahari] fl. 1235-50]

Nārāyaṇa Sheshādrī,
    The darkness and the dawn in India; two
missionary discourses by Nārāyan Sheshādri ...
and John Wilson ... Edinburgh,W.Whyte and co.
₁etc.,etc.₁1893.
    126p. 18cm.

NN   0020300   NNUT

Nārāyaṇa Sheshādri.
    The native missionary. Remiscences of the
Rev. Dr. Narayan Sheshadri. n.p., n.d.

NN   0020301   PPPrHi

Nārāyaṇa Siṃha, *Kaliyā, of Jodhpur*
see
Singh, Narayan.

VOLUME 405

Nārāyaṇa Siṃha Pūrṇendu
see
Pūrṇendu Nārāyaṇa Siṃha.

Nārāyaṇa Sītārāma Phaḍke
see
Phadke, Narayan Sitaram.

Nārāyana-svāmi Nāyuḍu, B. V.
see Narayanaswami Naidu, Bijayeti Venkata, 1901–

Narayana Swami, Rasipuram Krishnaswami Iyer
see
Narayan, R K 1906–

PK3921   Narayana Tirtha, Swami.
.S17T58   The Bhakti chandrikā (commentary on Sandilya
N2   sūtra), Edited with introd. etc, by Gopi Nath
Kaviraj. Benares, Sarasvati Bhavana, 1924–38.
2 v. (2, 255, 7, 9, 2, 6, 3 p.) (The Princess
of Wales Sarasvati Bhavana texts, no.9, pts.1–2)
Sanskrit title at head of t.p.; Sanskrit text.
Vol. 2, edited by Anant Shastri Phadke.

   1. Sāṇḍilya. Bhaktisūtra. I. Kaviraj, Gopi
Nath, Mahamahopadhyaya, ed. II. Phadke, Anant
Shastri, ed. III.   Title. Series.

NN   0020307   ICU CtY HU

PK3921   Narayana Tirtha, Swami.
.N22B5   The bhaktyadhikaranamala of Srimannarayana
1936   Tirtha; edited with the Sandigdhartha prakasini
commentary by Ananta Shastri Phadke. Benares
City, Printed at the Eureka Printing Works,
1936–
v. ( ) (The Princess of Wales Sarasvati Bhavana texts, no. 63, pts. 1–
Sanskrit title at head of t.p.; Sanskrit text.

   1. Bhakti. I. Phadke, Anant Shastri, ed. II.
Title. Series.

NN   0020308   ICU HU

Nārāyana Vaidya.
Srī Nīlakanta Tīrthaswāmicharyā, by Kavīdipa
Nārāyana Vaidya, and Srīsivaprāsadah. With
introd. by K. Saṅkara Pīllai. Cattanuam Muri,
Dist. Travankore, Govindam, 1911.
28 p.

NN   0020309   MH

Nārāyaṇa Vāmana Ṭiḷak
see
Tilak, Narayan Vaman, 1862?–1919.

Nārāyaṇa Vināyaka Kāniṭkar
see
Kanitkar, Narayan Vinayak, 1887–

Nārāyaṇa Vināyaka Kulakarṇī
see
Kulakarṇī, Nārāyaṇa Vīnāyaka, 1892–1948.

Nārāyaṇa Visanajī Ṭhakkura
see
Thakkur, Narayan Visanji, 1884–1938.

PK2971   Nārāyanabhaṭṭapāda.
.T8   The Mānameyodayā of Nārâyaṇa Bhatta and
no.19   Nārāyaṇa Pandita. Edited by T. Ganapati Sāstrī.
Trivandrum, Printed at the Travancore Govt.
Press, 1912.
ii, 2, 140 p. (Travandrum Sanskrit series.12
no.19)
Added t.p. and text in Sanskrit.

   1. Mīmāṃsa. I. Nārāyaṇa Paṇḍita, joint author
II. Title.

NN   0020314   ICU CtY PU

Nārāyaṇabhaṭṭapāda.
Māṅameyodaya; an elementary treatise on the Mīmāṁsā,
by Nārāyaṇa. Edited with an English translation by
C. Kunhan Raja, and S. S. Suryanarayana Sastri. With
a foreword by S. Kuppuswami Sastri. Madras, Theosophical Pub. House, 1933.
ii, 349 p. 22 cm.
English and Sanskrit.
Bibliography : p. [xxxi]–xxxiii.

   1. Mīmāṃsā. I. Kunhan Raja, Chittenjoor, tr. II. Suryanarayana Sastri, Satalur Sundara, 1894– tr. III. Title.
B132.M5N37   74–152081
                                    MARC

NN   0020315   DLC NNC OCl NcD ICU

PK3591   Nārāyaṇabhaṭṭapā:
T85   Nārāyaṇīya, with the commentary, Bhaktapriyā,
no.18   of Desamangala Varya. Edited by T. Ganapati
Sāstrī. Trivandrum, Printed at the Travancore Govt. Press, 1912.
ii,2,6,375 p. (Trivandrum Sanskrit series,
no.18)

Added title page in Sanskrit.
"Summarizes, in order, the whole story of
Srīmad-Bhāgavata." – Pref.
Bibliography of Nārāyaṇa Bhaṭṭa's works:
p.ii.

NN   0020316   CU

Narayanamurthy Rajagopala Rao
see
Rajagopala Rao, Narayanamurthy, 1925–

Narayanamurti, D   1904–
Preliminary studies on improved
wood. Dehra Dun, Forest Research
Inst., 1943–1948.
v.4 (Dehra Dun, India. Forest
Research Institute. Indian forest
leaflet, no.98)

Contents
pt.4 Impregnation of wood with urea-
formaldehyde resins, by D.
Narayanmurti & J. George.

NN   0020318   OrP

Narayanamurti, D   1904–
Preservative treatment of bamboos, by
D. Narayanamurti, A. Purushotham & J.N. Pande.
Dehra Dun, India, Forest Research Institute, 1947.
pt. diagrs. (Indian forest bulletin, no. 137)
Contents – pt. 1. Treatment of green bamboos
with inorganic preservatives.

NN   0020319   OrP

AC   Narayanamurti, D., 1904–
831   Versuche über die feuchtigkeitsbewegung in
holz und anderen körpern beim trocknen und über
das wärme leitvermögen feuchten holzes. ...
Inaug. Diss. – Techn. Hochschule Danzig, [1935?]
Lebenslauf.

NN   0020320   ICRL

Narayanamurti, N., ed.
HD875
.R33   Ranga, N G
The modern Indian peasant, a collection of addresses,
speeches and writings of Prof. N. G. Ranga ... Madras, Kisan
publications [1936]

Narayanan, Edatata.
Praja socialism: monopoly's pawn. Bombay, People's
Pub. House, 1952.
74 p. 19 cm.

   1. Praja Socialist Party. 2. Communism—India.
JQ298.P7N3   58–22909

NN   0020322   DLC CtY CU NN MiU WU MH NcD

XT
L506   Narayanan, N
V22   Modern Indian worthies. Madras, Macmillan,
1926.
136 p. illus.

   1.India--Biog. I.Title.

NN   0020323   MiU

PL4758   Narayanan, N
.5   Notes on the Tiruvacakam of St. Māṇikkavacaka.
.T608N9   Jaffna, Ceylon, Published by the editor at the
"Ardralaya," 1939.
v.

   I. Māṇikkavacakar, 9th cent. II.Tirumurai.
Tiruvācakam.

NN   0020324   ICU

Nārāyaṇan, P
see
Narayana Ayer, P

B132   Narayanan, R., 1896– ed.
.Y6P264   Pakavāṉ Patañcali Maharisi aruḷicceyta
1912   Yōkacūttiram.
Orien   Patañjali.
Sans   பகவான் பதஞ்சலி மஹரிஷி அருளிச்செய்த யோகசூத்திரம். இது ஸ்ரீ ... 1912.

PR6063   Narayanan, V., tr.
.A32T519   Tillaik Kōvintaṉ.
Orien   Madhaviah, A
Tam   தில்லைக் கோவிந்தன். எழுதியவர் அ. மாதவையா. மொழிபெயர்த்தவர் வே. நாராயணன். சென்னை, தினமணி காரியாலயம், 1944.

Nārāyaṇan Nampūtiri, Cennās
see
Nārāyaṇa, *15th cent.*

VOLUME 405

Narayanan Sivaraja Pillai, K
see
Sivaraja Pillai, K Narayanan, 1875-*1941*

290
(N164g
Narayanananda, Swami.
The gist of religions. [1st ed.]
Rishikesh, U.P., India, N.K. Prasas
[1955]
136p. port.

1. Religions. I. Title.

NN 0020330 TxFTC

DLC-P4
4BL
205
Narayanananda, *Swami.*
The ideal life and moksha (freedom).
[1st ed.] Rishikesh, U. P., Himalayas,
N. K. Prasad, 1951.
208 p.

NN 0020331 DLC-P4 NN

Narayanananda, *Swami.*
The mysteries of man, mind and mind-functions; a masterly treatise on psychology. Rishikesh, N. K. Prasad, 1951.
xx, 656 p. port. 19 cm.

1. Hinduism. I. Title.

BL1202.N33 1951 150 71-258463
MARC

NN 0020332 DLC

4BL-
173
Narayanananda, Swami.
The primal power in man or the Kundalini
Shakti. Rishikesh (U.P.) N.K. Prasad, 1950.
155 p.

NN 0020333 DLC-P4 MH NN

Narayanananda, *Swami.*
Revelation. [1st ed.] Rishikesh, U. P., N. K. Prasad, 1951.
267 p. illus. 19 cm.

1. Philosophy, Hindu. I. Title.

B133.N3R4 55-26094 ‡

NN 0020334 DLC NBuU NN

181.4
N218
Narayanananda, Swami.
The secrets of mind-control (a masterpiece on the subject) [1st ed.] Himalayas, India, N.K. Prasad [1954]
280 p. ports. 19cm.

1.Philosophy, Hindu. 2.Intellect.

NN 0020335 CSt

4BL
570
Narayanananda, Swami.
The way to peace, power, and long
life. 2d enl. & rev. ed. Rishikesh,
N. K. Prasad, 1950.
190 p.

NN 0020336 DLC-P4

Nārāyaṇapaṇḍita, fl. 1356.
Gaṇita kaumudī, Nārāyaṇapaṇḍitakṛitā. Padmākaradvivedinā saṃskṛitā. The Ganita Kaumudi. [Allahabad, Superintendent, Govt. Print.] 1936-42.
2 v. 22 cm. (The Princess of Wales Saraswati Bhavana texts, no. 57, pts. 1-2)
In Sanskrit; v. 2 has introd. in English.

1. Mathematics, Hindu. 2. Magic squares. I. Dvivedi, Padmakara, ed. II. Title. III. Series: The Princess of Wales Saraswati Bhavana texts series, no. 57, pts. 1-2.

QA32.N3 60-57303

NN 0020337 DLC ICU HU

Nārāyaṇaprasāda Miśra
see
Mishra, Narayan Prasad.

Narayanarao Krishnarao Huilgol
see
Huilgol, Narayanarao Krishnarao, 1884-

Nārāyaṇārya, 11th cent?
Nītimālā. By Nārāyaṇārya. Edited with introduction and notes by R.Ramanujachari and K.
Srinivasachari. [Annamalainagar,published by
the University,1938-39.]
24 cm. pp.(5),[19],1-24,[75]-78.
Issued as separate signatures with the
Journal of the Annamalai University,vol.VII,no.
2,vol.VIII,no.2,1938-39.
Sanskrit text.

NN 0020340 MH

Asia
B132
.A3N332
Nārāyaṇārya, 11th cent?
Nītimālā, by Nārāyaṇārya. Edited with
introduction and notes by
R. Ramanujachari and K. Srinivasacharya.
[Annamalainagar, Annamalai University]
1940.
lxxxii, 29, 92 p. (Annamalai University
philosophy series, no. 2)

1. Advaita. 2. Vedanta. I.
Ramanujachari, R., ed. II.
Srinivasacharya, K., jt ed.

NN 0020341 HU CtY ICU

Nārāyaṇarāya, Huyilugōḷa
see
Huilgol, Narayanarao Krishnarao, 1884-

Narayanasami, W M
see Narrainsawmy, W M

Nārāyaṇasiṃha, *Kaliyā, of Jodhpur*
see
Singh, Narayan.

Nārāyaṇasvāmi Aiyar, K
see
Narayanaswami Aiyar, K

Nārāyaṇasvāmi Aiyar, R,
see
Narayanaswami Iyer, R.

Nārāyaṇasvāmi Aiyar, T S
see Narayanaswami Iyer, T S

Narayanaswami, K
see
Narayanaswami Aiyar, K

QK358
.A4
vol. 11,
no. 1
Narayanaswami, V., joint author.

Calder, Charles Cumming, 1884-
... (1) List of species and genera of Indian phanerogams not included in Sir J. D. Hooker's Flora of British India, by C. C. Calder, V. Narayanaswami and M. S. Ramaswami. (2) *Loranthaceae* [!] of southern India and their host plants, by C. E. C. Fischer, I. F. S. Calcutta, Government of India central publication branch, 1926.

Narayanaswami, V
A revision of the Indo-Malayan species of *Glycosmis.*
With a foreword by K. Biswas. Delhi, Manager of Publications, 1941.
72 p. illus. 25 cm. (Records of the Botanical Survey of India, v. 14, no. 2)
Bibliography: p. 70-71.

1. Glycosmis. 2. Botany—Malay Peninsula. (Series: India (Republic) Botanical Survey. Records, v. 14, no. 2)
A 60-5669

Illinois. Univ. Library
for Library of Congress [2]

NN 0020350 IU

NARAYANASWAMI AIYAR,K
The Hindu god universal. Adyar,Madras,
Published by the author,Theosophical Society,
1915.
pp. .,11, ,131. 19 cm.

NN 0020351 MH-P

Narayanaswami, Aiyar, K.
Maha-bharata or Karma-yoga. The second
volume of the permanent history of Bharata-
varsha. Trivandrum, [Bhaskara", press]
1916-18.
2 pt.

NN 0020352 MH CtY

Narayanaswami Aiyar, K
The Permanent history of Bharata Varsha, by K. Narayana Iyer. [1st ed. Trivandrum] 1915-
v. 19 cm.

1. Hinduism—Sacred books—History and criticism. 2. Philosophy, Hindu. I. Title.

BL1110.N36 S A 68-14268
MARC

NN 0020353 DLC NN OCl MiU IU

Narayanaswami Aiyar, K
Professor Bergson and the Hindu Vedanta... [Adyar,
Madras: Vasanta Press, 1914?] 1 p.l., 35 p. 16°.
Repr.: The Theosophist. v. 35, April-June, 1914.

1. Bergson, Henri Louis, 1859– 2. Vedanta philosophy.
N. Y. P. L. June 30, 1921.

NN 0020354 NN

VOLUME 405

Narayanaswami Aiyar, K
   The Purānas in the light of modern science, by K. Nārāyaṇa-swami Aiyar... Adyar, India: Theosophical Soc., 1916. xv, 294 p., 1 l. illus. 2. ed. 12°.

1. Puranas.
N. Y. P. L.   February 21, 1923.

NN 0020355   NN

BL1120   *Narayanaswami Aiyar, K*   *tr.*
.A3N3
         Upanishads. *English.*
            Thirty minor Upanishads, translated by K. Nārāyaṇasvāmi Aiyar ... Madras [Printed by Annie Besant at the Vasanṭā press] 1914.

Narayanaswami Aiyar, K
   Vāsudevamana, the meditations of Vasudeva
         see under Vāsudeva Yati, Parama-hamsa
Parivrājakāchārya.

Law   Narayanaswami Iyer, R., joint author.

          Chitale, V   V
             The civil digest, (1911–1923.) ... By V. V. Chitale ... and R. Narayanaswami Iyer ... Mylapore, Madras, The Madras law journal office, 1924–25.

Law   Narayanaswami Iyer, R., joint author.

          Chitale, V   V
             The criminal and revenue digest, 1911–1923 ... By V. V. Chitale ... and R. Narayanaswami Iyer ... Mylapore, Madras, The Madras law journal office, 1924.

Narayanaswami Iyer, R   *comp.*
   The decennial digest, civil, criminal and revenue (1921–1930) by R. N. Iyer and V. V. Chitaley ... Mylapore, Madras, The Madras law journal office, 1931.
      4 v. 25¼ᵐ.
      Addenda slip inserted in v. 1.

   1. Law reports, digests, etc.—India.   I. Chitale, V. V., joint comp.
   II. India. Courts. III. Title.
                                [Name in transliteration: Nārāyaṇasvāmi Aiyar, R.]
                                                42–40450
                                                Provisional

NN 0020360   DLC CtY

Narayanaswami Iyer, R   *comp.*
   The quinquennial digest, (1921–1925.) ... By R. Narayana-swami Iyer ... and V. V. Chitaley ... Mylapore, Madras, The Madras law journal office, 1926.
      2 v. 25ᵐ.

   1. Law reports, digests, etc.—India.   I. Chitale, V. V., joint comp.
   II. India. Courts.
                                                39–14515 Revised
                                                Provisional

NN 0020361   DLC MH

India   Narayanaswami Iyer, R   comp.
40   The quinquennial digest, 1936–1940. Mylapore,
N164   Madras Law Journal Office, 1941.
1936–40   2 v. 25cm.

Continued in next column

Continued from preceding column

   1. India - Digests
   I. India. Reports (Digests)
   II. Madras law journal
   III. Title

NN 0020362   CtY-L

Narayanaswami Iyer, R   *comp.*
   The quinquennial digest (1941–1945) Madras, Madras Law Journal Off., 1946–
      v. 25 cm.

   1. Law reports, digests, etc.—India.   I. India. Courts.
                                                48–20786*

NN 0020363   DLC

Narayanaswami Iyer, R.
   The subject-noted index of cases overruled, followed, etc., by R. Narayanaswami Iyer ... vol. I–
Mylapore, Madras, The Madras law journal office, 1927–
      v. 25¼ᵐ.
   "No report, official or non-official up to January, 1927, has been omitted."—Pref.

   1. Law—India—Indexes. 2. Annotations and citations (Law)—India. 3. Law reports, digests, etc.—India.   I. Title.
                                                2. 1380

NN 0020364   DLC

FL8   Narayanaswami Iyer, R
I4.68   The subject-noted index of cases (overruled,
N218s   followed, etc.) 3d ed. rev. and brought up to end
1954   of 1952. Madras, Madras Law Journal Office,
        1954–57.
           3 v. 26ᵐ.

        1. India - Law - Indexes. 2. Annotations and
        citations - India. 3. Reports, digests, etc. -
        India - Indexes. I. Title.

NN 0020365   MiU-L MH-L

Law   Narayanaswami Iyer, R., ed.

          The "Yearly digest" of Indian & select English cases ... reported in all the important legal journals.

          Mylapore, Madras, The Madras law journal office [19

Narayanaswami Iyer, T. S.
   A guide to Hindu astrology, by T. S. Narayanaswami Iyer... Madras: Addison & Co., 1889. 2 p.l., ii, 150 p. diagr., tables. 8°.

1. Astrology (Hindu).
N. Y. P. L.   November 27, 1917.

NN 0020367   NN MH ICN

281.182   *Narayanaswami Naidu, Bijayeti Venkata, 1901–*
N16   The economics of Indian agriculture.
         Madras, Rochouse, 19

Continued in next column

Continued from preceding column

      1. Agriculture. Economic aspects. India.
      2. India. Agriculture. I. Narasimhan, P
S   joint author. II. Title.

NN 0020368   DNAL

Narayanaswami Naidu, Bijayeti Venkata, 1901–
   The economics of Indian agriculture, by B. V. Narayana-swamy and P. S. Narasimhan. Madras, Rochouse, 1943–44.
      2 v. (ii, iv, 648 p.) 19 cm.

   1. Agriculture—Economic aspects—India.   I. Narasimhan, P. S., joint author. II. Title.

   HD2072.N33   338.1   49–41781*

NN 0020369   DLC

Narayanaswami Naidu, Bijayeti Venkata, 1901–
   The economics of Indian agriculture, by B. V. Narayana-swamy and P. S. Narasimhan. 2d ed., rev. Madras, Rochouse, 1944.
      2 v. (viii, 288, [299]–643 p.) 19 cm.
      Vol. 2: 1st ed.

   1. Agriculture—Economic aspects—India.   I. Narasimhan, P. S., joint author. II. Title.

   HD2072.N34   338.1   49–41690*

NN 0020370   DLC DNAL

Narayanaswami Naidu, Bijayeti Venkata, 1901–
   The economics of Indian agriculture, by B. V. Narayanaswamy and P. S. Narasimhan. 4th ed. Madras, Rochouse [1948]
      2 v. (viii, 389 p.)

   1. Agriculture - Econ. aspects - India.
   I. Narasimhan, P   S   jt. auth.

NN 0020371   NNC

338.1   Narayanaswami Naidu, Bijayeti Venkata,
N164   1901–
        The economics of Indian agriculture,
        by Rao Bahadur B.V. Narayanaswamy
        and P.S. Narasimhan. [6th rev. ed.]
        Madras, Rochouse [1955]
           2 pt. in 1 v. (478 p.) 22cm.
           Earlier editions by B.V. Narayana-
        swamy and P.S. Narasimhan. This ed.
        rev. by V.G. Ramakrishna Iyer. cf.
        Pref.

NN 0020372   MnU

Narayanaswami Naidu, Bijayeti Venkata,
   1901–
   Fundamentals of business organisation by Dr. B.V. Narayanaswami Naidu...and
H.K. Datta. Madras, Seshachalam, 1954.
   599 p. [2½ ᵐ]

   3d ed., rev. and enl.

   1. Business - Study and teaching.

NN 0020373   NjP

VOLUME 405

Narayanaswami Naidu, Bijayeti Venkata, 1901–
Groundnut (marketing and other allied problems) by B. V. Narayanaswamy Naidu ... and S. Hariharan ... ₍Annamalainagar₎ Annamalai university, 1941.
xi, 147 p. illus. (map) plates, diagrs. 25ᵐ. (*Half-title:* Annamalai university economic series–no. 7)
Bibliography : p. 145.

1. Peanuts. ɪ. Hariharan, S., joint author.

44–32493

Library of Congress   HD9235.P32 I 65
₍2₎   338.175659

NN   0020374   DLC DNAL PU CU

Narayanaswami Naidu, Bijayeti Venkata, 1901–
The Madras agriculturists' relief act; a study, by B. V. Narayanaswamy Naidu and P. Vaidyanathan. Annamalainagar, ₍Annamalai₎ University 1939.
viii, 28, 113 p. forms. 25 cm. (Annamalai University. Bulletin of the Dept. of Economics, no. 2)
Half title: The Madras agriculturists' debt relief act: a study.
1. Agricultural credit — Madras (Presidency) 2. Debtor and creditor—Madras (Presidency) I. Vaidyanathan, P., joint author. II. Madras (Presidency). Madras agriculturists relief act, 1988. 1939. III. Title. IV. Title: The Madras agriculturists' debt relief act; a study. V. Series: Annamalai University. Dept. of Economics. Bulletin, no. 2.

H31.A7 no. 2   72–207031

NN   0020375   DLC

Narayanaswami Naidu, Bijayeti Venkata, 1901–
Madras finance. ₍Madras₎ Madras University, 1948.
140 p. illus. 25 cm. (Sir William Meyer endowment lectures, 1947–48)

1. Finance, Public—Madras (Presidency)   ɪ. Title.

HJ1320.M3N3   59–35109 ‡

NN   0020376   DLC MiU ICU MH CU

Narayanaswami Naidu, Bijayeti Venkata, 1501–
The Madras general sales tax act, a study, by Dr. B. V. Narayanaswamy Naidu ... and S. Thiruvengadathan ... Foreword by Rai Bahadur Sir Kurma Venkata Reddi Naidu ... Annamalainagar, The University, 1940.
viii, 220 p. incl. tables, forms. 25ᵐ. (*Half-title:* ₍Annamalai university. Chidambaram, India. Dept. of economics₎ Bulletin .... no. 4)
Bibliography : p. ₍218₎

1. Sales tax—Madras (Presidency)   ɪ. Thiruvengadathan, S., joint author. ɪɪ. India. Laws, statutes, etc. ɪɪɪ. Title.

44–36753

Library of Congress   H31.A7 no. 4
₍2₎   (330.82) 336.2713

NN   0020377   DLC MnU

Narayanaswami Naidu, Bijayeti Venkata, 1901–   *ed.*
Rajah Sir Annamalai Chettiar commemoration volume ₍presented ... on his sixty first birthday by the members of the university. Annamalainagar₎ Annamalai University, 1941.
xx, 1187 p. illus., plates, ports. (part col.) diagrs., tables. 25 cm.
Contributions in English, Tamil, Sanskrit, Hindi, Kanarese, Telegu, or Malayalam.
Includes bibliographies.

1. Chettiar, Sir Annamalai, Raja, 1881–1948.

AC11.N3   58–53886

NN   0020378   DLC

Narayanaswami Naidu, Bijayeti Venkata, 1901–
... Report of the economist for enquiry into rural indebtedness, 1946 ₍by₎ Rao Bahadur Dr. B. V. Narayanaswami Naidu ... Madras, Printed by the superintendent, Government press, 1946.
iv, 110 p. incl. incl. tables. fold. map, diagrs. 24½ᵐ.
At head of title : Government of Madras.

Continued in next column

Continued from preceding column

1. Agricultural credit—India—Madras (Presidency) (Presidency)   ɪ. Madras

HG2051.I 5M35   332.71   47–21368

NN   0020379   DLC DNAL

H31
.A7
no. 3
Narayanaswami Naidu, Bijayeti Venkata, 1901–
Jagannathachari, C
Report on the working of prohibition in the Salem district, by C. Jagannathachari ... directed and guided by Dr. B. V. Narayanaswamy Nayudu ... ₍Annamalainagar₎ Annamalai university, 1939.

HC
435
.N35
Narayanaswami Naidu, Bijayeti Venkata, 1901–
State and economic life, by B. V. Narayanaswamy Naidu. [Delhi] Delhi University, 1947. 140 p. (Sir Kirkeebhai Premchand readership lectures. 1947)

#India—Economic policy.
#Agriculture and state--India.
#Industry and state--India.
State and economic life.

Delhi. University.
Sir Kikabhai Premchand readership lectures. 1947.

NN   0020381   MoU IU MiD CU MH NN DLC–P4 CaBVaU

Narayanaswami Naidu, Bijayeti Venkata, 1901–   *tr.*
Bharata Muni, *supposed author.*
Tāṇḍava Lakṣaṇam; or, The fundamentals of ancient Hindu dancing, being a translation into English of the fourth chapter of the Nāṭya śāstra of Bharata, with a glossary of the technical dance terms compiled from the eighth, ninth, tenth and eleventh chapters of the same work, illustrated with original photographs of the sculptured dance poses in the great temple of Śiva Naṭarāja at Cidambaram, and containing special appendices of aesthetic and archaeological interest. By Bijayeti Venkata Narayanaswami Naidu ... and Pasupuleti Srinivasulu Naidu ...

and Ongole Venkata Rangayya Pantulu ... Madras (India) G. S. press, 1936.

Narayanaswamy, B. V.
see **Narayanaswami Naidu, Bijayeti Venkata,** 1901–

Narayanaswamy, G
A journey to Japan, by G. N. Sam ₍pseud.₎ Coimbatore, Topical Book Co. ₍ᶜ1951₎
63 p. illus. 22 cm.

1. Japan—Descr. & trav.—1945–   ɪ. Title.

DS811.N37   915.2   54–15902 ‡

NN   0020385   DLC

Narayanaswamy Rangiah, Pagadala
see
Rangiah, Pagadala Narayanaswamy, 1908–

Narayanchandra Banerjee
see
Banerjee, Narayanchandra, d. 1943.

Narayani Handiqui historical institute.

DS485
.B47M5
Mīrzā Nathan, *fl.* 1642.
Bahāristān-i-Ghaybī, a history of the Mughal wars in Assam, Cooch Behar, Bengal, Bihar and Orissa during the reigns of Jahāngīr and Shāhjahān, by Mīrzā Nathan; translated from the original Persian by Dr. M. I. Borah ... Gauhati, Assam, The Government of Assam, Dept. of historical and antiquarian studies, Narayani Handiqui historical institute, 1936.

Narayaniah, J   *plaintiff.*
In the court of the district judge of Chingleput. J. Narayaniah - plaintiff versus Mrs. Annie Besant - defendant. ₍Madras, Vasanta press, 1912₎
26 p., 22ᶜᵐ.

NN   0020389   NjPT

Narayanrao, U   B
Indigenous medicinal specialties. Introd. by K. S. Mhaskar. Bombay, Medical digest, 1953.
304 p. 17 cm.

1. Materia medica—India. 2. Therapeutics.   ɪ. Title.

RS180.I 3N3   56–46435 ‡

NN   0020390   DLC DNLM MiU

Narayanrao, U   B
Materia medica of pharmaceutical combinations and specialities. With an introd. by G.V. Deshmukh. ₍1st ed.₎ Girguam, Rayan Pharmacy, 1932.
xliii, 249 p.
615.1

NN   0020391   ICJ

Narayanrao, U   B
Materia medica of pharmaceutical combinations and specialities, by U. B. Narayanrao. 5th ed. Bombay, Medical Digest, 1954.
lvii, 421 p. 25 cm.
————— Supplement. With an introd. by G. V. Deshmukh. Bombay, Medical Digest, 1961.
xxix, 89 p. 25 cm.   RS125.N28 1954 Suppl.
1. Medicine—Formulae, receipts, prescriptions. 2. Materia medica. 3. Drugs.   I. Title.

RS125.N28 1954   72–206940
                                            MARC

NN   0020392   DLC MiU DNLM MnU

Narayanrao Babasaheb, Meherban, chief of Ichalkaranji
see Meherban Narayanrao Babasaheb, chief of Ichalkaranji, 1870–

Narayanswami, C   K
Create your own jobs. Bombay, All India Khadi & Village Industries Board, Ministry of Production ₍1955?₎
48 p. 20 cm.

1. India—Occupations.   ɪ. Title.

HF5382.5.I 4N3   57–35515 ‡

NN   0020394   DLC

Narayanswami, Rasipuram Krishnaswami
see **Narayan, R   K**   1906–

VOLUME 405

Narayen (Gopal) and Company.
Gopal Narayen & Co.'s general catalogue of books. Bombay, G. Narayen, 1883.
76 p. 22 cm.
Cover title.

Z999.N22   48-41337*

NN 0020396   DLC

Narayen Ganesh Chandavarkar
see
Chandavarkar, *Sir* Narayan Ganesh, 1855-1923.

Narayen Gokhale, Ganapati
see Gokhale, Ganapati Narayen.

Nārāyun, pundit.
Rajneeti; or, Tales exhibiting the moral doctrines and civil and military policy of the Hindoos. Tr. from the original Sunskrit of Narayun pundit, into Brij bhasha, by Sree Lulloo Lal Kub, Calcutta, 1827.
26 cm.

NN 0020399   CtY

Narazaki, Muneshige, 1904–
北齋論 楢崎宗重著 東京 アトリエ社 昭和 19 ₍1944₎
4, 15, 25, 120, 460 p. illus., plates (part col.) tables. 22 cm.

1. Katsushika, Hokusai, 1760-1849.   I. Title.
Title romanized: Hokusai ron.
J 63-76

| Harvard Univ. Chinese- for Library of Congress | Japanese Library 6288.6 ₍3₎ |

NN 0020400   MH-HY

Narazaki, Toshio
see
Narasaki, Toshio, 1891–

Narb, Max, tr.
France, Anatole, 1844-1924.
... Anatole France in pantoffeln. Berlin, Verlag für kulturpolitik, 1925.

Narbáez, Luis de
see
Narváez, Luis de, *16th cent.*

Narbais, Luys
see
Narvaez, Luis de, *16th cent.*

Narbaïts, André, 1912–
Respiration et exercices physiques.
Bordeaux, Delmas, 1942.
73 p. illus. (Bordeaux. Université. Faculté de médecine et de pharmacie. Thèse. 1941/42. no. 41)

Bibliography: p. ₍71₎-73.

W 4 B72 1941/42

NN 0020405   DNLM

Narbal Fontes
see Fontes, Narbal, 1899–

Narbekov, Vasiliĭ, tr.
Photius I, Patriarch of Constantinople, ca. 820–ca. 891.
₍Nomokanon₎
Номоканонъ Константинопольскаго Патрiарха Фотiя, съ толкованiемъ Вальсамона. ₍Русскiй переводъ съ предисл. и примѣчанiями₎ Василiя Нарбекова. Казань, Типо-лит. Имп. Университета, 1899.

BX343 .P5617 1899

NN 0020408   DLC

Narbekov, Vasiliĭ.
₍Tolkovanie Val'samona na Nomokanon Fotiia₎
Толкованiе Вальсамона на Номоканонъ Фотiя. Казань, Тип. Имп. Университета, 1889.
365, 20, ii p. 26 cm.
Includes bibliographical references.

1. Nomocanon. 2. Balsamon, Theodorius, Patriarch of Antioch, 12th cent. 3. Photius I, Saint, Patriarch of Consatintinople ca. 820 -ca. 891.   I. Title.

BX343.N37   73-200907

NN 0020408   DLC

Narbel (C.) *Recherches sur l'éclairage natarel dans les écoles de Neuchâtel.* [Bern.] 64 pp., 8 pl. 8°.   *Verey, A. Roth, 1894.*

NN 0020409   DNLM

Narbel, Catherine.
Exercices de mémoire ... Par Catherine Narbel. Berlin, A. Duncker, 1843-46.
2 v. in 1. 17ᶜᵐ.
CONTENTS.—Première partie, mise à la portée des enfants.—Seconde partie, destinée particulièrement à la jeunesse.

1. French poetry (Collections)   I. Title.
                                                              19-908
Library of Congress   PQ1165.N3

NN 0020410   DLC

Narbel, Cathérine.
Nouveau récueil de comédies, proverbes et charades dramatiques à l'usage des maisons d'éducation et des familles. .[4],307p. Berlin, J. Springer, 1863.

NN 0020411   OCl

Narbel, Catherine.
Récueil de comédies, proverbes et charades dramatiques à l'usage des maisons d'éducation et des familles, par Catherine Narbel. 3. éd. Leipzig, A. Oehmigke (M. Geissler) ₍1872₎
2 p. l., ₍3₎-237, ₍1₎ p. 19ᶜᵐ.
CONTENTS.—Valentine.—A qui mal veut.—Comme on fait son lit on se couche.—Le reste du gigot.—La treille du roi.—Blanche de Césanne.—La rosière, ou Trop parler nuit.—Une représentation à Saint-Cyr.—Les talismans.—Le prix de famille.—Bonne volonté ne suffit pas.—Charade en trois tableaux.

1. Children's plays, French. 2. Schools—Exercises and recreations.
                                                          37-11321
Library of Congress   PZ27.N3 1872

NN 0020412   DLC NcU ICU

Narbel, François
... Contribution à l'étude du traitement chimiothérapique de la blennorragie ...
Bâle, 1941.
Thèse - Univ. de Lausanne.

T113 I37 1941

NN 0020413   CtY

Narbel, Henri.
Emmanuel Petavel-Olliff
see under Petavel-Olliff, Emmanuel, 1836-1910.

Narbel, Jean.
Quelques aspects des transformations des démocraties contemporaines. Lausanne, 1935.
111 p. 24ᶜᵐ.
Diss. - Lausanne.
"Bibliographie des ouvrages cités": p.107-109.

JC273 S9N97

Hoover Library

1.State, The. 2.Democracy. I.Title.

NN 0020415   CSt-H

Narbel, Marguerite
La cytologie de la parthénogenèse chez Apterona helix Sieb. (Lepid. Psychides) Genève, 1946
Thèse - Lausanne.
"Revue suisse de zoologie. Tome 53, no.30, octobre 1946."

NN 0020416   CtY

Narberhaus, Josef.
Benedikt von Aniane, werk und persönlichkeit, von Josef Narberhaus. Münster in Westf., Aschendorff, 1930.
vi p., 1 l., 80 p. 25½ᶜᵐ. (Added t.-p.: Beiträge zur geschichte des alten mönchtums und des Benediktinerordens ... hft. 16)
"Quellen und literatur": p. ₍77₎-80.

1. Benedictus, Saint, of Aniane, d. 821.   I. Title.
                                                              31-29540
Library of Congress   BX2410.B4 hft. 16
                           ₍2₎   (271.08) 922.244

NN 0020417   DLC MH MiU NN InStme ICU

Narberth, Pa. Presbyterian Church.
Church register, 1891-1924, 1924-1949, 1950-1962, 1955-1962.
4v. mss. and bound
(Dates in vols. 3 and 4 overlap)

NN 0020418   PPPrHi

Narbeshuber, Karl.
... Aus dem leben der arabischen bevölkerung in Sfax (regentschaft Tunis) von dr. med. Karl Narbeshuber ... mit einem beitrage von prof. Hans Stumme ... Leipzig, R. Voigtländer, 1907.
44 p. 27 cm. (Veröffentlichungen des Städtischen museums für völkerkunde zu Leipzig. hft. 2)
CONTENTS.—I. Werbung, verlobung, hochzeitsfeierlichkeiten. (Arabische textstücke in transkription und in arabischer schrift, nebst übersetzung und anmerkungen)—II. Liebeszauber.—III. Böser blick.—IV. Regen, regenzauber und verwandtes.—V. Die 'aïsâwîs.—Anhang. Von universitätsprofessor dr. Hans Stumme.

1. Sfax, Tunis—Soc. life & cust. 2. Folk-lore—Tunis—Sfax. I. Stumme, Hans, 1864-1936.
                                                          13—25370
Library of Congress   DT269.S4N3

PU-Mu PPDrop
NN 0020419   DLC CU MoU LU CoU CSt CU ICJ OCl NN

VOLUME 405

4PT
Ger.365
Narbeshuber, Max.
Camachos Hochzeit; Komödie. Berlin,
A. Langen/G. Müller.
172 p.

NN 0020420   DLC-P4

4PT
Ger.366
Narbeshuber, Max.
Don Juan; Drama in 5 Akten. Berlin,
A. Langen/ G. Müller.
153 p.

NN 0020421   DLC-P4

WB
16303
Narbeshuber, Max
Europa hinter dem Walde.Roman. Graz,
Verlag Stiasny[c1953]

NN 0020422   CtY

Narbeth, B   M
Some notes upon technical education; being a
report presented to the Council of the Durban
technical institute upon matters connected with
technical education observed in Britain and
America in 1914. Durban, P.Davis & sons, ltd.,
1915.

85 p. 21 cm.

NN 0020423   MH

Narbeth, Horace, 1906-
see
Roye, pseud.

Narbey, C. abbé.
Acta sanctorum quotquot toto orbe coluntur
see under Acta sanctorum.

NARBEY, C   abbe .
Episodes de la persecution religieuse
dans les hautes montagnes du Doubs.
Locle, Suisse, Imp. Courvoisier,1868.

pp.97.

NN 0020426   MH

NARBEY , C. abbé.
Histoire de l'ancien Clichy et de ses
dependance; Monceau, Le Rouble, la rue
de Clichy, etc., Depuis les origines jusqu'en
93. Clichy, chez l'auteur, etc., etc.,
[1908]

Pan and other illustr.

NN 0020427   MH

Narbey, C., abbé, ed.

Acta sanctorum.
Supplément aux Acta sanctorum pour des vies de saints
de l'époque mérovingienne par M. l'abbé C. Narbey.
Paris [etc.] Le Soudier [etc.] 1899–19

Narbey, Geneviève.
Quelques recherches sur l'*Aspergillus niger*, son développe-
ment dans quelques sirops officinaux, par Mlle. **Geneviève**
Narbey ... Montpellier, Imprimerie E. Montane, 1926.
44 p. diagrs. 25ᶜᵐ.

1. [Aspergillus niger]

Agr 28–1628

Library, U. S. Dept. of   Agriculture 462N16

NN 0020429   DNAL CtY

Narbherām Narharrām
see Narharrām Narbherām.

Narbona, Alfonso de, 1563 or 4–1611.
D. dn. Alphonsi Narbona ... Commentaria in tertiam partem
Nouæ recopilationis legum Hispaniæ. Siue in leges sub vno-
quoque Nouæ recopilationis titulo quaternionibus duobus vlti-
mis additas, à nullo hactenus expositas, nunc primùm in praxis,
& theoricæ vtilitatem explanatas. Vberiùs tamen, legem illam
seu concordiam inter regium, & supremum Sanctæ inquisitionis
tribunal circa numerum, qualitatem, ius, ac exemptionem eiusdem Sanctæ inquisitionis familiarium ... Toleti, apud Dida-
cum Rodriguez, typ. regium, 1624.

Vol. 2 has title: D. dn. Alphonsi Narbona ... Commentaria ad l. xv. tt. ı.
lib. 4. Nouæ recopilationis legum Hispaniæ. Siue ad concordiam fami-
liarivm Sanctae inqvisitionis ...

1. Law—Spain. ı. Spain. Laws, statutes, etc. Nueva recopilación.
ıı. Inquisition. Spain.

46–41393

NN 0020432   DLC

Narbona, Benjamin
see Narbona Arnau, Benjamin.

Narbona, Didacus de
see Narbona, Diego de, 1605?-1650.

Narbona, Diego de, 1605?-1650
... Annales iuris de aetate
ad omnes hvmanos actus requisita ...
avtore Don Didaco de Narbona ... Mantva
Carpentana, Didacvs Diaz, 1642.
14 p.l., 697 p., [96] p., 1 l. port.
30cm.
Engraved t.-p.

NN 0020435   MH-L

BV
192
.B2
N21
fol.
Narbona, Diego de, 1605?-1650.
Annales tractatus iuris de aetate ad omnes
humanos actus requisita ... auctore insigni et
celebri I.C.D. Didaco de Narbona Toletano
Romae, sumptibus Iosephi Corbi, 1649.
Xii, 560 p. 32 cm.

1. Age (Canon law).

NN 0020436   DCU

BX1935
N219
1669
Narbona, Diego de, 1605?-1650.
Annales tractatvs ivris de aetate ad omnes
hvmanos actvs reqvisita... Romae, svmptibvs
Iosephi Corbi, 1669.
l, [12] 560 [72] p.

Printer's device on title page and end page.

1. Canon law. 2. Ecclesiastical law.
I. Title.

NN 0020437   CU-L NjP MH CLU

NARBONA, Diego de, 1605?- 1650.
Horographia juris, seu de legitimis horarum
intervallis juridica descriptio. Matriti,
1652.

f°.

NN 0020438   MH-L

Narbona, Eugenio de.
Doctrina política civil escrita en aphorismos por el doctor Eugenio Narbona ... El concejo y consejeros del
principe por Fadrique Furió Ceriol ... Madrid, Impr. de
A. de Sotos, 1779.
22 p., 1 l., 424 p. 14½ᶜᵐ.
"Concejo y consejeros del principe" with special t.-p.

1. Political science. ı. Furió Ceriol, Fadrique, d. 1592.
10-4269†

Library of Congress   JC189.N3

NN 0020439   DLC MH-L

Narbona, Eugenio de.
Dotrina Politica Civil, escrita por Aphorismos:
sa cados de la dotrina de los Sabios, y exemplos
de la experiencia. Por el D. Evgenio Narbona
natural de Toledo. A la Magestad catolica del
Rey de las Españas don Felipe. IIII. nuestro
soberano señor. Con privilegio. Y censura de los
Calificadores del Supremo Consejo de la Inquisicion,
y con su licencia impressa. En Madrid, Por la
viuda de Cosme Delgado. Año M.DC.XXI.

NN 0020440   NNH

Narbona, Eugenio de.
Historia de la recuperacion del Brasil
hecha por las armas de España y Portugal ...
por el dr. Eugenio de Narbona y Zuñiga.
(in Rio de Janeiro. Bibliotheca nacional.
Annaes. 1950. v. 69, p. [161]-231.)

1. Brazil - History.

NN 0020441   NNC

Narbona, Francisco
see Narbona González, Francisco.

868
M540
N22
Narbona,Rafael.
El aliento de un siglo,Menéndez Pelayo.
Portada de Eduardo Narbona. Madrid, V.
Suarez [c1942]
111 p. port.(on cover) 20 cm.

1.Menéndez y Pelayo,Marcelino,1856-1912.
I.Title.

NN 0020443   MiU NN WU IU OO NNC IEN MoU

VOLUME 405

Narbona, Rafael.
El aliento de un siglo: Menéndez Pelayo.
Portada de Eduardo Narbona.   Madrid, V. Suárez
[1946]
111 p.   port. on cover.   20 cm.
Author's inscription on first leaf.

NN   0020444   NcU

Narbona, Rafael.
Ausencia sin retorno, sinfonía en gris; novela. ₍1. ed.₎
Madrid, Ediciones A. Z. ₍1953₎
222 p.   20 cm.

ɪ. Title.
                A 53–5185

Illinois. Univ. Library
for Library of Congress   ₍₎

NN   0020445   IU NN

860
N219
tC
Narbona, Rafael.
La ciudad de los sueños.   Madrid, Editora
Nacional, 1947.
181p. 17cm.

NN   0020446   CLSU ViU InU NcU IEN TU

Narbona, Rafael.
Una luz en la sombra, novela.   3. ed.   Madrid, C. Jaime
₍1945₎
263 p.   port.   23 cm.

ɪ. Title.
PQ6625.A65L8 1945   836.6   48–20585*

NN   0020447   DLC NN

Narbona, Rafael.
... Palacio Valdés; o, La armonía.   Madrid, V. Suarez, 1941.
251 p., 2 l.   19ᶜᵐ.
On spine: 1.ᵃ edición.

1. Palacio Valdés, Armando, 1853–1938.
                A 42–404
New York. Public library
for Library of Congress   ₍2₎   M 1 U

IaU CLU UU MtU MiU
NN   0020448   NN CU NIC IU FMU TxU NcU PPT OC1 NcD

Narbona, Vicente
see Narbona Jiménez, Vicente.

WJ
358
N219p
1953
NARBONA ARNAU, Benjamin
Poliquistosis y quistes serosos renales.
Barcelona, Editorial Científico Medica,
1953.
ix, 197 p. illus.
1. Cysts 2. Kidney diseases

NN   0020450   DNLM ICJ

4HD–
463
Narbona Gómez, Jorge.
El problema del vino.   Santiago de Chile,
1948.
63 p.

NN   0020451   DLC-P4 DNAL

Narbona González, Francisco.
Manolete, riesgo y gloria de una vida. ₍1. ed.   Fotogra-
fías de José M.ª Lara y Luis Arenas.   **Portada e ilus. de
Sáez₎**   Madrid, Ediciones Espejo ₍1948₎
319 p.   illus., ports.   20 cm.

1. Rodríguez Sánchez, Manuel Laureano, 1917–1947.   2. Bull-fights.

GV1107.N28   927.918   49–27782*

NN   0020452   DLC NN

946.08
N219q
Narbona González, Francisco.
La quema de conventos por Francisco
Narbona.   Madrid, Publicaciones españoles,
1954.
29 p.   illus.   (Temas españoles, no. 129)

Title and imprint on p. [2] of cover.

1. Spain--Hist.--Civil War, 1936-1939.
2. Spain--Hist.--Civil War, 1936-1939--
Religious aspects.   3. Catholic church in
Spain.   I. Title.

NN   0020453   PrU

PQ7001
.A62N8
Narbona Jiménez, Vicente.
Folklore español.   Un libro de cantares de Andalucía.
Portada de Eduardo Narbona.   Madrid, 1948.
182 p.   20 cm.

1. Folk songs, Spanish--Andalusia.   ɪ. Title.   ɪɪ. Title: Un libro
de cantares de Andalucía.
                A 52–2598
New York. Public Libr.
for Library of Congress   ₍₎

NN   0020454   NN IU DLC

Narbona Jiménez, Vicente.
Sevilla, ciudad de Invierno plan de mejoras y
reformas necesarias para la consecucion de este
fin por Vicente Narbona Jiménez.   Lema
Felices los pueblos que procu ran su engrandeci-
miento!
Obra premiada por el ateneo y sociedad de
escursiones de Sevilla, en el certamen público de
sus juegos florales celebrados con motivo de las
fiestas de primavera de ...   en el mes de
abril del año de 1900.   1901 estab. tip. de el
progreso, Julio Cesar 12.   Sevilla.

NN   0020455   NNH

Narbona Jiménez, Vicente.
El sueño de la loca; monólogo dramático, sin tesis, original de
D. Vicente Narbona Jiménez...   Sevilla: Estab. Tip. de El
Progreso, 1905.   15 p.   8°.

1. Monologues (Spanish). 2. Title.
N. Y. P. L.   January 19, 1918.

NN   0020456   NN OO

4X
1563
Narbona Salinas, Fernando
El perdón judicial.   Santiago de
Chile, 1929.
52 p.

NN   0020457   DLC-P4

Narbona Toletano, Dídaco de
   see   Narbona, Diego de, 1605?-1650.

Narbone, Alessio, 1789–1860.
Bibliografia sicola sistematica, o apparato metodico
alla storia letteraria della Sicilia, di Alessio Narbone ...
Palermo, Stamperia di G. Pedone ₍etc.₎ 1850-55.
4 v.   22ᶜᵐ.

1. Sicily--Bibl.   4–15691

Library of Congress   Z2364.S5N2

NN   0020459   DLC MiU MB

Narbone, Alessio, 1789-1860, ed.
Dell' origine, progressi e stato attuale d'ogni
letteratura
     see under   Andrés, Juan, 1740-1817.

Narbone, Alessio, 1789-1860.
Dieci glorie dell'angelico giovane S. Luigi
Gonzaga esposte ai suoi divoti.   Napoli, A.
Festa, 1852.
Collezione di buoni libri a favore della verita
e della virtú, XXIX.
Series number from half-title; name of series
from recto of last leaf.

NN   0020461   MH

PQ
6920
N37
Narbone, Alessio, 1789- 1860.
Istoria della letteratura siciliana.   Palermo,
Carini, 1852-1863 ₍v.12,1859 ₎
12 v. in 6.
Each vol. has added t.p.: Storia letteraria della
Sicilia.
Bibliographical footnotes.

1. Italian literature--Sicily--Hist.& crit.
I. Title.   II. Title: Storia letteraria della
Sicilia.

NN   0020462   NSyU InU NjP NNC MH

Narbone, Alessio, 1789-1860, ed.
Storia d'ogni matematica
     see under   Andrés, Juan, 1740-1817.

Narbone, Alessio, 1789-1860.

Andrés, Juan, 1740-1817.
Storia d'ogni teologia, di Giovanni Andres, ᴅ. ᴄ. ᴅ. ɢ., bre-
viata e annotata per Alessio Narbone, ᴅ. ᴍ. ᴄ. Palermo, Stamperia G. Pedone, 1841.

Narboni (Albert) [1865–].   *Considérations
sur les récidives de la fièvre typhoïde.   70 pp.
4°. *Paris,* 1894, No. 356.

NN   0020465   DNLM

VOLUME 405

Narboni, David, 1892–
Contribution à l'étude de la typhlite aiguë primitive (Forme ulcéro-gangreneuses) ... Alger [1921]
24 cm.
Thèse - Univ. d'Alger.

NN 0020466   CtY

Narboni (Georges) [1892–]. *Contribution à l'étude de l'aérophagie bloquée. 50 pp., 1 l. 8°. Paris, 1920. No. 57.

NN 0020467   DNLM CtY

NARBONI ,Luc.
Contribution a l'etude de la fievre recurren te en Algerie. Relation d'une epidemie a Alger.— Paris, 1912.

[161 p.] Paris, Th. med. 1911–1912. N° 166.

NN 0020468   MBCo DNLM

Narboni, Moses
see Moses ben Joshua, *of Narbonne, 14th cent.*

Narboni, Raymond, 1915–
... Étude des granulations "pathologiques" des polynucléaires neutrophiles au cours de la tuberculose expérimentale ...   Paris, 1939.
Thèse - Univ. de Paris.

NN 0020470   CtY

PQ1496 .N7 12— Mss room
LES NARBONNAIS (Chanson de geste)
⌈Fragments of the chanson de geste Guillaume d'Orange: Les Narbonnais and Siège de Barbastre French manuscript of the late 13th century⌉
4 l. 14 cm.
Manuscript on vellum; accompanied by typewritten transcription (11 l.)

1. Manuscripts, French. I. Siège de Barbastre.

NN 0020471   ICU

Les Narbonnais (*Chanson de geste*)
Les Narbonnais; chanson de geste, publiée pour la première fois, par Hermann Suchier ... Paris, Firmin Didot et cⁱᵉ, 1898.
2 v. facsim. (6 p.) 23½ cm. (*Half-title:* Société des anciens textes français)
Treated by Gautier (Épopées fr., 1. & 2. éd.) as two chansons, the Département des enfans Aimeri and the Siège de Narbonne. Suchier applies the title, Département des fils d'Aimeri, to fragment in ms. fr. 1448 in the Bibliothèque nationale.
"Bibliographie du fragment ⌈latin⌉ de La Haye": t. 2, p. lxix–lxxi.

Appendices: III. Département des fils d'Aimeri ⌈Bibl. nat. fr. 1448⌉—IV. Les rubriques du roman en prose de Guillaume d'Orange.—v. Chap. xvi et xvii du roman en prose de Guillaume d'Orange.—VI. Fragment de La Haye.—VII. Fac-similé du fragment de La Haye.
CONTENTS.—t. 1. Texte des Narbonnais.—t. 2. Introduction. Appendices.

1. Guillaume d'Orange (Chanson de geste)   I. Département des fils d'Aimeri. II. Suchier, Hermann, 1848–1914, ed.
Johns Hopkins Univ.   Library   A 13—2673
for Library of Congress   ⌈PQ1496.N3 1898⌉

PHC OOxM PSC OrU GU
NN 0020473   MdBJ FU NcU MU CU MB MiU OCl OO OU ViU

PQ4204 .A3C5 vol.47–49
Les Narbonnais (Chanson de geste)
Andrea *da Barberino, b. ca.* 1370.
Le storie nerbonesi; romanzo cavalleresco del secolo xiv, pubblicato per cura di I. G. Isola ... Bologna, G. Romagnoli, 1877–87.

Narbonne, A. V. D. P. Fabre de
see
Fabre de Narbonne, A. V. D. P.

Narbonne, Aimeri de
see
Aimeri de Narbonne.

Narbonne, Bérenger, Vicomte de
see Bérenger, Vicomte de Narbonne, 11ᵗʰ cent.

Narbonne, Edouard
see Narbonne-Lara, J   E   d'A de.

Narbonne, Gerhard von Pelet-
see Pelet-Narbonne, Gerhard von, 1840–1909.

---

4 K Alger-1
Narbonne, Henri.
Répertoire de jurisprudence algérienne, contenant l'analyse sommaire et le classement méthodique de toutes les décisions importantes rendues par la Cour d'Appel d'Alger et les diverses autres juridictions de l'Algérie en matière civile, commerciale, criminelle et administrative pendant les années 1857 à 1876, avec annotations, tables et renvois au Journal de la Jurisprudence de la Cour d'Alger, à l'usage des tribunaux des administrations, du barreau, des officiers publics et ministériels, des commerçants, et de tous les

hommes d'affaires. Alger, A. Jourdan, 1877. 557 p.

NN 0020481   DLC-P4

H31 .F6 no. 72
Narbonne, Jacques, joint author.
Dogan, Mattei.
Les Françaises face à la politique, comportement politique et condition sociale ⌈par⌉ Mattei Dogan et Jacques Narbonne. Préf. de François Coguel. Paris, A. Colin, 1955.

Narbonne, Jean Charles Darré-
see Darré-Narbonne, Jean Charles.

Narbonne, Jean Joseph Brierre
see Brierre Narbonne, Jean Joseph.

Narbonne, Louis.
La cathédrale Saint-Just de Narbonne, guide historique, archéologique et descriptif, par m. Louis Narbonne ... Narbonne, F. Caillard, imprimeur, 1901.
vi, 471 p., 1 l. illus. (incl. plans) 25ᶜᵐ.

1. Narbonne. Saint-Just (Cathedral)
                                              5–15320 Revised
Library of Congress   BX4629.N3J8

NN 0020485   DLC NjP

Narbonne, Louis de
see Narbonne-Lara, Louis Marie Jacques Amalric, comte de, 1755–1813.

Narbonne (Paul). *De la cure radicale de la hernie crurale par le procédé du Clou. 64 pp. 8°. Toulouse. 1909. No. 820.

NN 0020487   DNLM ICRL CtY

Narbonne (Paul) [1873–]. *Kystes du canal de Nück. 73 pp. 8°. Paris, 1899, No. 223.

NN 0020488   DNLM

DC 130 .N22 A3 1866
Narbonne, Pierre.
Journal des règnes de Louis XIV et Louis XV, de l'année 1701 à l'année 1744. Recueilli et édité avec introd. et notes par J.-A. Le Roi. Paris, A. Durand et Pedone Lauriel, 1866.
659 p.

1. France—Hist.—Louis XIV, 1643–1715.
2. France—Hist.   —Louis XV, 1715–1774.
I. Title.

NN 0020489   MiU NjR IEN OCl NNU-W CtY InU MH

Narbonne, René de, 1912–
... Les ailes qui poussent. Paris, Baudinière ⌈1935⌉
2 p. l., ⌈7⌉–222 p., 1 l. 19ᶜᵐ.
"Une suite d'articles, certains présentés sous forme d'interview, qui mettent en scène quelques-uns de nos grands pilotes les font agir et parler devant nous."—Préf.

1. Aeronautics—France. I. Title.
                                              38–24809
Library of Congress   TL526.F8N3
                             ⌈2⌉   629.130944

NN 0020490   DLC NN

Narbonne, René de, 1912–
Aviation de France, textes du lieutenant René de Narbonne et du lieutenant-colonel Robert Gaujour. Illustrations de: A. Brenet, Lucien Cavé, Géo. Ham ... ⌈etc.⌉ Lyon, Paris, Éditions Mirambeau, 1945?⌉
3 p. l., 3–108 (i. e. 116), ⌈2⌉ p., 1 l. illus. (incl. facsim.) col. plates 20½ x 23½ᶜᵐ.
Includes extra numbered pages (58 (1)–58 (8))
Originally published under the occupation without the chapter: Les gardiens de la flamme.
Errata slip inserted.
CONTENTS.—Les conquérants.—Les cocardes, 1914–1942.—L'essor.

1. Aeronautics—France. I. *Gaujour, Robert, 1906–

TL526.F8N315 1945   629.130944   A F 47–3756
Seattle. Public library
for Library of Congress   ⌈2⌉†

NN 0020491   WaS DLC

VOLUME 405

Narbonne, René de, 1912–
... Baliseurs de ciels. Paris, Flammarion [1945]
205, [1] p. illus. (maps) 18¼ᵐ.

1. Aeronautics—Biog. 2. Aeronautics—Flights.   I. Title.
TL539.N3   A F 47–3212
Hoover library, Stanford   univ.
for Library of Congress   [2]†

NN 0020492   CSt-H DLC

Narbonne, René de, 1912–
...Baliseurs de ciels.   Paris, Flammarion [1947]   205 p.
maps.   19cm.

434548B. 1. Aeronautics—France.
N. Y. P. L.   April 23, 1948

NN 0020493   NN

Narbonne, René de, 1912–
... Le destin des ailes. Paris, Baudinière [1943]
255, [1] p. 18¼ᵐ.
At head of title: R. de Narbonne.

1. Aeronautics—France.   I. Title.
Library of Congress   TL526.F8N32   46–13184
                            [2]   629.130944

NN 0020494   DLC

Narbonne, René de, 1912–
...Le destin des ailes.   Paris, Éditions Baudinière [1945]
249 p.   19cm.
2. ed.

380127B. 1. Aeronautics—Hist.
N. Y. P. L.   April 7, 1947

NN 0020495   NN

Narbonne, René de, 1912–
Un pilote m'a dit ... Ce que fut l'épopée héroïque de la
"Ligne." Préf. de Didier Daurat. Paris, Baudinière [1948]
253 p. illus., ports., fold. col. map. 19 cm. (Bibliothèque de
l'aviateur)

1. Aeronautics—Biog. 2. Aeronautics—France. 3. Air lines—
France.   I. Title.
TL539.N32   387.7   49–52555*

NN 0020496   DLC OrU NN IEN

Narbonne-Lara, J   E   d'A   de.
. . . L'aimable compagnon; anecdotes, traits de sa-
tire et propos comiques. 2. éd. Montreal, Typographie
L. Perrault et cie., 1870.
363, [1] p. 21¼ᵐ.
Author's name at head of title.
                                        2–8958

NN 0020497   DLC

Narbonne-Lara, J   E   d'A   de.
Esquisses poétiques, par M. de Narbonne-Lara.   Montréal,
E. Senécal, 1875. 255 p. 22cm. (Oeuvres. t. 2.)

NN 0020498   NN CaBVaU CaOTU

PC   Narbonne-Lara, Louis Marie Jacques Amalric,
3428   comte de, 1755-1813.
N3   Calquis bers d'uno muso gascouno, par le
A6   comte de Narbonne-Lara. Toulouse, Delboy,
1856   1856.
              15 p. 20 cm.

1. Gascon poetry.

NN 0020499   CU-S

Narbonne-Lara, Louis Marie Jacques Amalric, comte de, 1755-1813.
Declaration de M. Louis de Narbonne...dans le procès du roi.
Londres: Les marchands de nouveautés, 1793. 16 p. 8°.

103132A. 1. Louis XVI, king of   France, 1754-93.
N. Y. P. L.   January 9, 1924.

NN 0020500   NN WU

Bo61   Narbonne-Lara, Louis Marie Jacques Amalric,
910ℓ   comte de, 1755-1813.
1792n   Discours de M. de Narbonne, ministre de la
          guerre, à l'Assemblée nationale, dans la séance
          du lundi 23 janvier 1792. [Paris,Impr. de Du
          Pont,1792]
              7 p. 21½cm.
              Caption title.
              [Pamphlet]

NN 0020501   CtY

Narbonne-Lara, Louis Marie Jacques Amalric,
    comte de, 1755-1813.
    Laurent le Cointre à Caritat, dit Condorcet
    see   Lecointre, Laurent, d. 1805.
    Lettre à L. Narbonne.

Narbonne-Lara, Louis Marie Jacques Amalric,
    comte de, 1755-1813.
    Le ministre de la guerre se proposoit
d'adresser à la Garde Nationale de Strasbourg
    see under   France. Ministère de la
guerre.

CD   Narbonne. Archives communales.
+1217   Inventaire des Archives communales antérieures
+N34   à 1790. Rédigé par German Mouynès. Narbonne,
A47   E. Caillard, 1871-79.
              6v. in 5. 32cm.
              Contents.— [t.1] Série AA.— [t.2.] Annexes
          de Série AA.— [t.3.] Série BB, t. I.— [t. 4.]
          Annexes de Série BB, t. I.— [t.5.] Série BB,
          t.II.— [t.6.] Annexes de Série BB, t.II.—
              1. Narbonne - Hist. - Sources - Bibl.
              I. Mouynès, Germaine II. Title

NN 0020504   WU CU

Narbonne. Bibliothèque municipale.
    Catalogue de la Bibliothèque publique de la ville de Nar-
bonne, par M. J. Tissier ... Narbonne, Impr. F. Caillard, 1891.
    2 v. 25ᵐ.

1. Narbonne—Bibl.   I. Tissier, Jean Joseph, 1859-1923.
                                        7-10136 Revised
Library of Congress   Z927.N28

NN 0020505   DLC

Narbonne. Bibliothèque publique

see

Narbonne. Bibliothèque municipale.

Narbonne. Chambre de commerce.
La belle Aude

see under

Aude, France (Department). Conseil général.

Narbonne. Commission archeologique
    see   Commission archeologique de Narbonne

Narbonne. Musée archéologique et des beaux-arts.
    Catalogue de la céramique au Musée de Narbonne [par]
Paul Paloque. Narbonne, Commission archéologique, 1951.
    155 p. 25 cm.

1. Pottery—Narbonne—Catalogs.   I. Paloque, Paul.
NK3730.N35N3   52–44263 ‡

NN 0020509   DLC MH NN OrU

Narbonne. Musée archéologique et des beaux-arts.
...Catalogue descriptif et annoté des peintures et sculptures,
par M. Louis Berthomieu...   Toulouse: É. Privat, 1923.
xxxvii, 240 p.   plan, plates, ports.   8°.

197735A. 1. Art—Collections—   France—Narbonne. 2. Berthomieu,
N. Y. P. L.   Louis Victor, 1870- , editor.
                                        September 25, 1925

NN 0020510   NN CU MH

Narbonne.- Musée archéologique et des beaux-arts.
    ... Trésors d'orfèvrerie des églises
du Roussillon et du Languedoc méditerranéen,
maijuin 1954. Narbonne, Musée des beaux
arts de Narbonne, 1954.
    [99] p. 100 illus. on pl. 21cm.

    "Réferences bibliographiques" p. [99]
    Text signed: Jacques Dupont, Jean
Thuile, Jean Claparède, Marcel Durliat.

NN 0020511   OC1MA

Narbonne. Musée des beaux arts
    see   Narbonne. Musée archéologique et
des beaux-arts.

Narbonne. Syndicat d'initiatives de
Narbonne et des Corbières-Minervois

See

Syndicat d'initiatives de Narbonne et des Corbières-Minervois.

BX 1532   Narbonne   (Archdiocese)
N3   Livre vert de l'archevêché de Narbonne,
A3   publié par Paul Laurent. Paris, A. Pi-
1886   card, 1886.
              xlv, 160 p. 25 cm.
              Text in Latin.
              Compiled under the archbishopric of
          Pierre de la Jugie and preserved by dint
          of a copy executed in 1649 under the or-
          ders of   Claude de Rebé.

Continued in next column

VOLUME 405

Continued from preceding column

1. Church lands - France - Narbonne (Archdiocese) 2. Ecclesiastical law - Narbonne (Archdiocese) I. Laurent, Paul, ed. II. La Jugie, Pierre de, Cardinal, Abp. of Narbonne, d. 1376. III. Rebé, Claude de, Abp. of Narbonne. IV. Title. a.

NN 0020515 CaBVaU MH NNH MdBWA

Narbonne; guide illustré
see Guide de Narbonne.

Narborough, Frederick Dudley Vaughan, 1895–
The Christian faith and social objectives; five broadcast addresses, by Rev. F. D. V. Narborough... Preface by the Right Rev. C. S. Woodward... ₁London₁ Industrial Christian fellowship ₁1945?₁ 24 p. 18cm.

1. Sociology, Christian.
N. Y. P. L. May 6, 1949

NN 0020517 NN

Narborough, Frederick Dudley Vaughan, 1895– ed.
Bible. *N. T. Hebrews. English. 1930. Revised.*
... The Epistle to the Hebrews, in the revised version, with introduction and commentary, by F. D. V. Narborough ... Oxford, The Clarendon press, 1930.

(The Clarendon Bible)

Narborough, Frederick Dudley Vaughn, 1895–

Rawlinson, Alfred Edward John, *bp. of Derby,* 1884– ed.
Essays on the Trinity and the incarnation, by members of the Anglican communion, edited by A. E. J. Rawlinson ... London, New York ₁etc.₁ Longmans, Green and co., ltd., 1928.

G170
.A173
Rare Bk.
Coll.
Narbrough, Sir John, 1640–1688.
An **Account** of several late voyages and discoveries: I. John Narbrough's voyage to the South-Sea by the command of King Charles the Second ... II. Captain J. Tasman's discoveries on the coast of the south terra incognita. III. Captain J. Wood's attempt to discover a northeast passage to China. IV. F. Marten's observations made in Greenland and other northern countries ... London, D. Brown ₁etc.₁ 1711.

FOR OTHER EDITIONS
SEE MAIN ENTRY
Narbrough, Sir John, 1640–1688.

An **account** of several late voyages & discoveries to the South and North ... By Sir John Narborough, Captain Jasmen Tasman, Captain John Wood, and Frederick Marten ... London, Printed for S. Smith and B. Walford, 1694.

Narbrough, Sir John, 1640–1688.
Journal du voyage du capitaine Narbrough à la mer du Sud, par ordre de Charles II. roi de la Grand' Bretagne.
(*In* Coreal, Francisco. Voyages ... aux Indes Occidentales ... Paris, 1722. 16½cm. v. 2, p. 139–318)

1. Magellan, Strait of. 2. Chile—Descr. & trav.
2-74 Revised
Library of Congress F221.C80 vol. 2

NN 0020522 DLC CtY

Narbrough, Sir John, 1640–1688.
Journal du voyage du capitaine Narbrough à la mer du Sud, par ordre de Charles II. roi de la Grand' Bretagne.
(*In* Coreal, Francisco. Voyages ... aux Indes Occidentales. Amsterdam, 1722. 16cm. v. 3, p. 1–200)

1. Magellan, Strait of. 2. Chile—Descr. & trav.
2-75 Revised
Library of Congress F2221.C79 vol. 3

NN 0020523 DLC MdBP

British
Tracts
1676
+N164
Narbrough, Sir John, 1640–1688.
A **particular** narrative of the burning in the port of Tripoli, four men of war ... by Sir John Narbrough ... on the 14th of January, 167⅞. Together with an account of his taking afterwards five barks ... [London] Printed by Tho: Newcomb, 1676.
8 p. front.(fold.plan) 28½ cm.
Signed: John Narbrough.
Plan engraved by Wenceslaus Hollar.
I. Hollar, Wenceslaus, 1607-1677, illus. II.Title
chronology

NN 0020524 CtY ICN CSmH DN

G160
A43
v.12
x
Narbrough, Sir John, 1640-1688.
Reise des Ritters Johann Narborough.
(*In* Allgemeine Historie der Reisen zu Wasser und Lande. 25cm. v.12 (1754) p 29-49)

1. Magellan, Strait of. 2. Chile - Description and travel.

NN 0020525 CU-B

Narbrough, Sir John, 1640–1688.
Coreal, Francisco, 1648?–1708.
Relation des voyages de François Coreal aux Indes Occidentales, contenant une description éxacte de ce qu'il y a vû de plus remarquable pendant son séjour, depuis 1666. jusqu'en 1697 ... Bruxelles, Chez F. Foppens, 1736.

Narbrough, Sir John, 1670–1688.
Coreal, Francisco, 1648?–1708.
Voyages de François Coreal aux Indes Occidentales, contenant ce qu 'il y a vû de plus remarquable pendant son séjour depuis 1666. jusqu 'en 1697. Traduits de l'espagnol avec une Relation de la Guiane de Walter Raleigh & le Voyage de Narborough à la mer du Sud par le détroit de Magellan. Tr. de l'anglois. Amsterdam, J. F. Bernard, 1722.

Narbut, Egor Ivanovich
see
Narbut, Georgiǐ Ivanovich, 1886–1920.

CR2047
.U4N3
Narbut, Georgiǐ Ivanovich, 1886–1920.
Гербы гетмановъ Малороссіи. ₁Рисовалъ Е. И. Нарбутъ. Издалъ С. Н. Тройницкій. Петроградъ, 1915₁
14 l. coats of arms. 24 cm.
"Отпечатано въ количествѣ пятидесяти экземпляровъ въ Тип. Сиріусъ."

1. Heraldy—Ukraine. I. Troǐnǐtsǐǐ, Sergeǐ Nikolaevich, 1882– II. Title.
Title transliterated: Gerby getmanov Malorossii.

CR2047.U4N3 66–55859

NN 0020529 DLC

Narbut, Heorhiǐ Ivanovych
see
Narbut, Georgiǐ Ivanovich, 1886–1920.

Narbut, I͡Uriǐ
see
Narbut, Georgiǐ Ivanovich, 1886–1920.

BT
4174
.N22
Narbutas, Titas.
La reforma del Breviario romano por Pio X. Santiago de Chile ₁Imprenta "Relampago,"₁ 1949.
153 p. 19 cm.

"Bibliografía": p. ₁11₁-₁15₁

1. Breviarium romanum - History. 2. Liturgy - History - 20th cent. I. Title.

NN 0020532 DCU DLC-P4

Narbutt, Ignacy.
Ludzie i wydarzenia. ₁n. p.₁ Książka, 1947. 116 p. 21cm.

1. World war, 1939-1945—Personal narratives, Polish. I. Title.

NN 0020533 NN DLC-P4

Narbutt, J
Les chaleurs specifiques et les chaleurs de la fusion d'une serie de dihalogenobenzenes. Dorpat., Mattiesen, 1916.
183 p

NN 0020534 PU

Narbutt, Justyn, 1776-1845.
Dzieje wewnętrzne narodu litewskiego z czasów Jana Sobieskiego i Augusta II, królów panujących w Polsce; wyciąg z różnych notacyów i manuskryptów. Wyd.2. Wilno, W Drukarni A.Dworca, 1843

2v. in 1
1.Lithuania - Hist. - 1569-1772

NN 0020535 MH

947.5
N16d
Narbutt, Teodor, 1784-1864.
Dzieje narodu litewskiego w krótkości zebrane. Z dołączeniem potoku pochodzeń ludów narodu litewskiego i 4 tablic rodowych xiążąt litewskich. Wilno, Nakł. R. Rafałowicza, 1847.
vii, 244p. geneal.tables. 21cm.

1. Lithuania—Hist. I. Title.

NN 0020536 IU MH PU CtY

947.5
N164d
1835
Narbutt, Teodor, 1784-1864.
Dzieje starożytne narodu litewskiego. Wilno, A. Marcinowski, 1835-41.
9v. plates,ports.,fold.maps,geneal. tables. 23cm.

Title varies: v.4-9, Dzieje narodu litewskiego.

1. Lithuania. History. I. Title. II. Title: Dzieje narodu litewskiego.

NN 0020537 KU CtY CoU MH PU

VOLUME 405

DK511
L2N27
Narbutt, Teodor, 1784-1864.
    Pomniejsze pisma historyczne szczególgni do historyi Litwy
odnoszące się. Wilno, Nakł. T. Glücksberga, 1856.
    300 p. plates, facsim.

    1. Lithuania - Hist.   I. Title.

NN   0020538   CU MH PU

Narbutt, Teodor, 1784-1864.
    Rys historyczny ludu cygańskiego.
Wilno, A. Marcinowski, 1830.
    176 p.

NN   0020539   OCl

PG
7158
.N21
W2
Narbuttówna, Krystyna
    W Ameryce; powieść na tle życia spółcznego
w Stanach Zjednoczonych. Warszawa, Nakł.
Gebethnera i Wolffa, 1875.

    251p. 17cm.

    1. Poles in U.S.A. - Fiction.

NN   0020540   PCamA

Narc
   see
National Association for Retarded Children

Narceate, Dalisto, pseud.
    see   Casotti, Giovanni Battista, 1669-1737.

Narcejac, Pierre
   see
Narcejac, Thomas, 1908–

Narcejac, Thomas, 1908–
    The art of Simenon. [Translated by Cynthia Rowland]
London, Routledge & Paul [1952]
    178 p. 19 cm.
    Translation of Le cas "Simenon."

    1. Simenon, Georges, 1903–   I. Title.
    PQ2637.I 53Z653 1952   843.91   52—67326 ‡

NN   0020544   DLC GU NN MH CtY FMU CoU UU

PQ2637
.I 53Z65
Narcejac, Thomas, 1908–
    Le cas "Simenon." Paris, Presses de la Cité, 1950.
    191 p. ports. 18 cm.

    1. Simenon, Georges, 1903–

                     A 51-2664
    Illinois. Univ. Library
    for Library of Congress   [1]

NN   0020545   IU TxU ScU NcU IEN CaBVaU OCl DLC

PQ2603
.O27C4
Narcejac, Thomas, 1908–   joint author.

   Boileau, Pierre, 1906–
       Celle qui n'était plus ... Roman [par] Boileau [et]
Narcejac. [Paris] Denoël [1952]

PQ2603
.O27D4
Narcejac, Thomas, 1908–   joint author.

   Boileau, Pierre, 1906–
       ... d'entre les morts [par] Boileau [et] Narcejac. Paris,
Denoël [1954]

Narcejac, Thomas, 1908–
    Esthétique du roman policier. Paris, Le Portulan [1947]
    201 p. 19 cm.

    1. Detective and mystery stories—Technique.   I. Title.
    PN3448.D4N3   808.3   47-7966*

NN   0020548   DLC CtY NcU OU CaBVaU NjP CLSU NBuU

PS374
.D4N3
Narcejac, Thomas, 1908–
    La fin d'un bluff; essai sur le roman policier noir améri-
cain. [Paris] Portulan [1949]
    178 p. 19 cm. (La Mauvaise-chance)

    1. Detective and mystery stories—Hist. & crit.   I. Title.
    (Series)
                                    A 50-3548
    Illinois. Univ. Library
    for Library of Congress   [2]

NN   0020549   IU NN DLC

Narcejac, Thomas, 1908–
    Le grand métier. Paris, Presses de la cité [1955]
    218 p. 19 cm.

    I. Title.
    PQ2627.A675G7   55-42227 ‡

NN   0020550   DLC

Narcejac, Thomas, 1908–
    Liberty ship. Paris, Presses de la cité, 1953.
    224 p. 19 cm.

    I. Title.
    PQ2627.A675L5   54-38467 ‡

NN   0020551   DLC NN

PQ2603
.O27L6
Narcejac, Thomas, 1908–   joint author.

   Boileau, Pierre, 1906–
       Les louves, roman [par] Boileau [et] Narcejac. Paris,
Denoël [1955]

Narcejac, Thomas, 1908–
    Le mauvais cheval. Paris, Presses de la cité, 1950 [*1951]
    222 p. 18 cm.

    I. Title.
    PQ2627.A675M3   54-39945 ‡

NN   0020553   DLC

Narcejac, Thomas, 1908–
    La mort est du voyage. Paris, Librairie des Champs-
Élysées [1948]
    243 p. 18 cm. (Le Masque; collection de romans d'aventures)

    I. Title.   (Series)
    PQ2627.A675M6   49-24539*

NN   0020554   DLC TxU

Narcejac, Thomas, 1908–
    La nuit des angoisses. Paris, S. E. P. E. [1948]
    189 p. 19 cm. (Le Labyrinthe)

    I. Title.   (Series: Collection "Le Labyrinthe")
    PQ2627.A675N8   48-22330*

NN   0020555   DLC

Narcejac, Thomas, 1908–
    La police est dans l'escalier. Paris, Portulan [1947]
    250 p. 18 cm. (La mauvaise chance, 16)

    I. Title.   II. Series.
    PQ2627.A675P6   47-29189*

NN   0020556   DLC

Narcejac, Thomas, 1908–
    Une seule chair. Paris, Presses de la cité, 1954.
    222 p. 19 cm.

    I. Title.
    PQ2627.A675S4   54-37181 ‡

NN   0020557   DLC NN

PQ2603
.O27V5
Narcejac, Thomas, 1908–   joint author.

   Boileau, Pierre, 1906–
       Les visages de l'ombre; roman [par] Boileau [et] Narcejac.
Paris, Denoël [1953]

PZ3
.B63573
Wo
Narcejac, Thomas, 1908–   joint author.

   Boileau, Pierre, 1906–
       The woman who was no more, by Pierre Boileau and
Thomas Narcejac; translated from the French by Geoffrey
Sainsbury. New York, Rinehart [1954]

VOLUME 405

...El **Narcete**. En cinco actos. Corregida y enmendada en esta segunda impresion... ¡Barcelona: J. F. Piferrer, 1800?¡ 28 p. 2. rev. ed. 8°.

Caption-title.
At head of title: No. 96. Tragedia.
In verse.

1. Drama (Spanish).
N. Y. P. L.   October 24, 1921.

NN 0020560   NN MH

---

el-Narchakhy, Mohammad
see
al-Narshakhī, Muḥammad ibn Ja'far, *d*. 959.

Narcisco, bp.
    see   Narcissus, bp. of Kentus, pseud.

NARCISO, Saint, *d*. 307
    See NARCISSUS.

Narciso, Adolfo.
    ...Lo char à bancs dei comici. Con prefazione di Carlo Nazzaro. Napoli: Casa editrice "Audaces," 1929. 294 p. 19½cm.

180747B.   1. Fiction, Italian.   I. Title.
N. Y. P. L.   December 30, 1942

NN 0020564   NN

PQ   Narciso, Adolfo
4831   Varietà dell'Ottocento. Napoli, Adriana,
.A8   1944.
A16   352 p.

       1. Naples - Addresses, essays, lectures.
    I. Title.

NN 0020565   DGU

Narciso, Armando, joint author.
García Ayuso, Juan de Dios.
    ... Tratamiento hidromineral y climático de las enfermedades de la piel; su base objetiva y sus aplicaciones practicas, con la colaboración del profesor Armando Narciso ... 1. ed. Madrid, Morata, 1946.

Narciso, Armando da Cunha, 1890-1948.
    Le climat des Açores
    see under   Agostinho, Jose, 1888-

DP702   Narciso, Armando da Cunha, 1890-1948.
A86N3   Terra açoreana; monografía romántica.
       ¡Lisboa¡ Ediçoes Paulo Guedes ¡1932¡
       122p. 18cm.

       1. Azores - Descr. & travel. I. Title.

NN 0020568   IaU MB

Narciso, John Carmine, 1924-
    The effect of sleep on learning. Austin, Tex., 1952.
    44,[1]ℓ. 29cm.

    Thesis (Ph.D.) - University of Texas, 1952.
    Vita.
    Bibliography: ℓ.43-44.

    1. Learning, Psychology of. 2. Sleep. I. Title.

NN 0020569   TxU

F   Narciso, Vicente A
1469   Album de recuerdos: Expedición musical al
P4   Petén y Belize, 1910-1911; notas, impresiones,
N373   estudios, recuerdos, por Veani. Guatemala
LAC   Impr. de Siguere ¡1911?¡
        94p. illus. 22cm.

        1. Petén, Guatemala (Dept.) I. Title.
    Sp.: Taracena Flores Collection.

NN 0020570   TxU MH LNHT

Narcisco, Vicente A.
    Siquil huál (Klagegesang) der Pokonchi-Indianer von S. Cristobal [with musical notes] (Internationaler Amerikanisten. Kongress. 14. Tagung. Stuttgart 1904. 2. Hälfte. p. 415-417. Stuttgart, 1906. 8°.)
    Text in Pokonchi and Spanish.

NN 0020571   NN

Narciso, Vicente A.   *4317.94.2
    Sitten und Gebräuche der Pokonchi-Indianer . . . mitgeteilt von Karl Sapper.
    (*In* International Congress of Americanists. 14th session. 1904. Vol. 2, pp. 403-417. Music. Stuttgart. 1906.)

M1584 — Pokonchi Indians. — Sapper, Carl, ed.. 1866-

NN 0020572   MB NN

Narcisco Campillo, D
    see   Campillo y Correa, Narcisco, 1838?-1900.

Narciso Chavarria, Rodolfo, 1901-
    El ruiseñor verapaz; capricho... [n.p., 1950] 4 ℓ. port. 34cm.

    Serenata for picolos de marimba and piano.

    1. Marimba and piano. I. Title.

NN 0020574   NN

Narciso da Silva, Joaquim Possidonio
    see   Silva, Joaquim Possidonio Narciso da, 1806-1896.

Narciso Renato Descartes Baptista, Joaquim
    see
Renato Baptista, Joaquim, 1855-1900.

Narciso Teletor, Celso
    see
Teletor, Celso Narciso.

4PQ   Narciso, antologia della poesia trentina. [Illus-
Ital.   trazioni di Roberto Iras Baldessari. Rovereto]
143   Delfino, 1946.
      60 p.

NN 0020578   DLC-P4

Narciso, drama da rappresentarsi nel Regio Teatro d'Haymarket, per la Reale Accademia di Musica. Londra, per Giovanni Packard, 1720.
1p.ℓ., 32 numb. ℓ.
Libretto, Italian and English.

NN 0020579   DFo

NARCISO il parrucchiere ad una gran festa da ballo Farsa in un atto (Traduzione dal francse Firenze, [1875]

    24°. pp. 30.
    ([Salani, Adriano]. Collezione di farse italiane e straniere, 90)

NN 0020580   MH

Narciso Monturiol; inventor del primer submarino (biografía del sabio español y explicaciones sobre su Ictíneo) Buenos Aires, Editorial Tór, 1916.
124, ¡3¡ p. 18cm. (*On cover:* Lecturas españolas. núm. 2)

"Hemos creido oportuno reunir en las Lecturas españolas algunos de los trabajos que han visto la luz pública en nuestra prensa, desde 1860 a 1915, hablando del primer invento español en la materia."—Nota preliminar.
    Apparently reprinted with the articles rearranged and slightly revised from the compilation of Jerónimo Estrany: Narciso Monturiol y la navegación submarina, Barcelona, 1915.

    1. Monturiol, Narciso, 1819-1885. 2. Submarine boats. I. Estrany, Jerónimo.

                                                        18-27448
    Library of Congress   VM365.E75

NN 0020581   DLC NN

Narciso; poéticas mexicanas modernas
    see under   Martínez, José Luis, ed.

Narciss, Georg Adolf, 1901-
    Deutsche Entscheidungen im Osten; ein geschichtlicher Querschnitt. Mit 28 Karten von Arthur Hackenberg. Unter Mitarbeit von Hermann Aubin ¡et al.¡ Geleitwort ¡von¡ Joseph Wagner. Breslau ¡Landesgruppe Schlesien des Bundes Deutscher Osten¡ 1938.
    90 p. maps. 21 cm. (Schriftenreihe der Landesgruppe Schlesien des Bundes Deutscher Osten)

    "Erschien ursprünglich im Zusammenhang mit einer Ausstellung ¡i. e. Ausstellung der Landesgruppe Schlesien des Bundes Deutscher Osten¡"
    "Schrifttum" : p. ¡67¡-88.

    1. Drang nach Osten. 2. Germany, Eastern—Hist. 3. Germans in foreign countries.   I. Bund Deutscher Osten. Landesgruppe Schlesien, Deutsche Entscheidungen im Osten. II. Title.   (Series: Bund Deutscher Osten. Landesgruppe Schlesien. Schriftenreihe)
    DD119.2.N3   A 54-1893
    Harvard Univ. Library
    for Library of Congress   ¡2¡†

NN 0020584   MH CtY NNC N ICU WU IaU WaU CU NN DLC

PT2388   Narciss, Georg Adolf, ed.
.K9R4
1944   Kurz, Hermann, 1813-1873.
       ... Reichsstädtische erzählungen. Breslau, W. G. Korn
       ¡1944¡

Hkb4   Narciss, Georg Adolf, 1901-
40n   ... Studien zu den Frauenzimmergesprächspielen
       Georg Philipp Harsdörfers (1607-1658) ...
       [Leipzig]1927.
       2p.ℓ.,221,[1]p. 23cm.
       Inaug.-Diss. - Greifswald.
       Lebenslauf.
       "Bibliographie": p.189-218.

       1.Harsdörfer, Georg Philipp, 1607-1658.

NN 0020586   CtY CSt

VOLUME 405

Narciss, Georg Adolf, 1901–
... Studien zu den Frauenzimmergesprächspielen Georg Philipp Harsdörfers (1607–1658) ; ein beitrag zur deutschen literaturgeschichte des 17. jahrhunderts. Leipzig, H. Eichblatt, 1928.

4 p. l., 221, [1] p. 23ᶜᵐ. (*Added t.-p.:* Form und geist; arbeiten zur germanischen philologie ... hft. 5)

Issued also as the author's thesis, Greifswald, 1927.
"Die werke Harsdörfers": p. 189–214; "Schriften über Harsdörfer": p. 214–216; "Häufiger benützte werke": p. 216–218.

1. Harsdörfer, Georg Philipp, 1607–1658. Frauenzimmer gesprächspiele.

A O 37–722

Yale univ. Library
for Library of Congress   [2]

NN 0020587   CtY NcU ICN CU ICU MH NN PU TxU

FILM
832H25
OfYn
1928

Narciss, Georg Adolf, 1901–
Studien zu den Frauenzimmergesprächspielen Georg Philipp Harsdörfers (1607–1658); ein beitrag zur deutschen literaturgeschichte des 17. jahrhunderts. Leipzig, H. Eichblatt, 1928.
4 p.l., 221, [1] p. 23cm. (Form und geist; arbeiten zur germanischen philologie — hft. 5)
Issued also as the author's thesis, Greifswald, 1927.
Microfilm (negative) Chicago, University of Chicago Library,   1972. 1 reel. 35mm.

NN 0020588   IU

Narcisse, Alphonse, 1909–
L'ombre de la morte. Paris, Plon [1954]
219 p. 19 cm. ([Collection] Roman)

I. Title.

PQ2627.A676O5   55–17880 ‡

NN 0020589   DLC CaBViP CaBVa IU NN PP

Narcisse, Franck D
De nos institutions communales; plan général d'organisation, suivi de la solution de questions intéressant nos municipalités. Port-au-Prince, E. Chenet, 1919.

94 p. fold. table. 25cm.

1. Local government – Haiti. 2. Municipal government – Haiti. I. Title.

NN 0020590   FU DPU

Narcisse. Eine Englische Wertheriade. Leipzig, in der Weygandschen Buchhandlung, 1793.
384 p. incl. front. 16.5 cm.

NN 0020591   CtY

Narcisse, ou l'amant...
see under   [Caminade De Castres,   ]

Narcisse, ou le chateau d'Arabit
see under   [Castera, Désirée de]

Narcisse dans l'isle de Venus: poëme en quatre chants
see under   [Malfilâtre, Jacques Charles Louis de Clinchamp de] 1733–1767.

[Narcisso, Giovanni Andrea]
Libro chiamato Fortunato figliol de Passamonte elquale fece vendetta de suo padre contra de Magancesi. [Vinegia, Impresso per Ioanne Tacuino de Trino, 1519] 38 l. illus. 22cm. (4°.)

Sander 4931. Essling 1621.
A poem.
Illustrations: large woodcut (depicting Renaldo) on t.-p., previously used in the Sessa 1515 edition of Inamoramento de Rinaldo (Essling 1858), and numerous small woodcuts in the text. Printer's mark on l. 38ᵇ.

The Heber copy.
Binding, 18th century French, of mottled calf, gilt.

1. Wood engravings, Italian.   2. Bindings, 18th cent., French.
I. Title. II. Title: Fortunato,   figliol de Passamonte,

NN 0020596   NN

Narcissus, bp. of Kentus, pseud.
L'epistola di Narciso Vescovo [intorno] all'apparizione del tentatore testo Siviaco con traduxione e introduxione, per il dr. prof. Italo Pizzi ... 1886.

NN 0020597   MiU

Narcissus, Ferdinandus Georgius, respondent.
De Chaerephyllo
see under   Hellwig, Christoph, 1642–1690, praeses.

Narcissus (Ferdinandus Georgius). *Diss. sistens circa nitrum observationes physico-medicas. 2⁰ pp. sm. 4⁰. Halæ Magdeb., lit. C. Hreckelii, [17??].

NN 0020599   DNLM

W 4
L68
1742
N. 1

NARCISSUS, Franz Jakob
Dissertatio medica inauguralis de generatione & receptaculis chyli ... Lugduni Batavorum, Conrad. et Georg. Jac. Wishoff, 1742.
24 p. plate. 21 cm.
Diss. - Leyden.

NN 0020600   DNLM

Narcissus.
Narcissus, a Twelfe Night merriment played by youths of the parish at the College of S. John the Baptist in Oxford, A. D. 1602, with appendix; now first ed. from a Bodleian ms. by Margaret L. Lee. London, D. Nutt, 1893.
xxxii, 51, [1] p. 26½ᶜᵐ. (*Half-title:* The Tudor library. [v. 4])
"Five hundred copies of this edition are printed."
The "Appendix" (p. 28–36) contains four pieces from the same ms.: A speech made for the foresaid porter ...; A speech delivered by Francis Clarke to the Ladie Keneda; A speech spoken by Francis Clarke in the behalfe of the freshmen; A letter composd for Francke Clarke, the porter of S. John's ...
1. Oxford. University. St. John Baptist college.   I. Lee, Margaret L. ed.

1–5470

Library of Congress   PR2411.N15

OOxM KEmT ViU PU
OrU NIC NcU NcGU NcD NjP WaU TxU PHC PSC MiU OU
NN 0020601   DLC CU-S IU FTaSU MoU CoU NNC CaBVaU

Narcissus.
Narcissus, a Twelfe Night merriment. Edited from a Bodleian MS. by Margaret L. Lee. London, 1893.
(In Three centuries of drama: English, 1512–1641)
Microprint.

1. Narcissus--Drama. I. Lee, Margaret L., ed.

NN 0020602   MoU CaBVaU CSt

Narcissus Scrap-Book
see under   Hazeltine, Charles.

Narcissus. *Words of the choruses*
see under   [Butler, Samuel] 1835–1902.

Narciza Amalia
see   Campos, Narciza Amalia de.

Narcof, Onil Pidoca, pseud.
see   Picado Franco, Lino Matias.

Narcotic addiction; a bibliography
see under   New York Academy of Medicine. Library.

Narcotic drug control
see under   Carnegie Endowment for International Peace.

RA402
.A3N3

Narcotic drug control league.
...Narcotic drug addiction; its meance to our country and how it must be met. [New York, 192– ?]
[4]p.

NN 0020609   DLC

W2
MU5
E19n

Narcotic drugs; summary of reports on illicit transactions and seizures received by the Secretary-General. [United Nations]
Geneva, United Nations Economic and Social Council 194
v.
1. Narcotic Trade - stat. I. United Nations. Economic and Social Counci

NN 0020610   DNLM

... Narcotic education; published by the World conference on narcotic education and the International narcotic education association. v. 1–   July 1927–
New York, N. Y. [etc.], 1927–
v.   illus. (incl. ports.) 31ᶜᵐ. quarterly.
Title varies: July 1927–Apr. 1929, Narcotic education; bulletin of the World conference on narcotic education and the International narcotic education association.
July 1929–   Narcotic education, published by the World conference on narcotic education and the International narcotic education association.
"Published ... at the Washington branch of the secretariat ... Washington, D. C.," July 1927–Apr. 1928; "at the New York branch of the secretariat ... New York, N. Y.," July 1928–
1. Narcotics–Period.   I. World conference on narcotic education.
II. International narcotic   education association.
31–20968
Library of Congress   HV5800.N3
[2]   178.805

NN 0020611   DLC DNLM MH-L MB PPC NN OCl ICJ

The Narcotic review; to suppress the use of habit forming drugs. v. 1–

Chicago, 1935–   v. illus. 28–30cm.

Quarterly (irregular).
Various mistakes in numbering.
Published by Inter-state narcotic association.
Occasional issues are propaganda sheets with title Bulletin.

1. Narcotics–Per. and soc. publ.   I. Interstate narcotic association, inc.
N. Y. P. L.—   August 23, 1944

NN 0020612   NN ICRL DNLM

VOLUME 405

178.8 ₍Narcotics; miscellaneous pamphlets on narcotics
N165 and control of the narcotics traffic. v.p.,
v.d.
v.p.
pamphlets in loose-leaf binder.
Contents. The opium traffic ... report of the
Secreaty of state relative to the control of the
opium traffic.1911.- Milestones in the war against
the narcotic peril, by Walter F. Lineberger, 1925.-
Control of drug addiction mainly a police problem,
by H. S. Cumming, 1925.- The purpose of Narcotic
education week, by Richmond Pearson Hobson.

NN 0020613 WaPS

BV4470 Narcotics: the churches and the problem of
.N22 narcotic addiction. ₍New York, National
1952 Council of the Churches of Christ in the
U.S.A., Department of Pastoral Services and
₍In: Social Welfare, ₍c.1952, 1954₎
CTS 15p. 21cm.
Text prepared by Paul Tilden.
Bibliography: p.₍16₎
Cover-title.
1. Church work with narcotic addicts. ₍I.₎
Tilden, Paul. II. National Council of Churches
of Christ in the U.S.A. Dept. of Pastoral Ser-
vices and Social Welfare.

NN 0020614 IEG

Narcotics the modern menace; a guide for teachers
and study clubs
see under Froula, Vaclav Karel, 1873-

RARE Narcotique. ₍A Berne et à Lausanne. Chez
BOOK les Sociétés typographiques, 1780₎
p.188-192. 21cm.
Extract from Encyclopédie, ou Dictionnaire
raisonné des sciences, des arts et des
métiers ... par m. Diderot ... et ... par
m. d'Alembert. v.22, pt.2, 1780.

NN 0020616 IEN-D

Narcy, Charles. Compte-rendu des principales herborisa-
tions faites dans le Cher en 1802 sous la direction de M.
Le Grand. ₍Bourges. 1803.₎ l. 8°.
*Mémoires de la Société historique, littéraire, artistique et scientifique du
Cher, 1803, 4e sér., ix, 119-146.

NN 0020617 MH-A

Narcy ₍Charles₎ ₍1886- ₎. *Contribution à
l'étude du sang adulte. 142 pp. 8°. Paris,
1913. No. 52.

NN 0020618 DNLM CtY

Narcy, Philippe.
Les bitumes, définition, bitumes proprement dits pyro-
schistes et rétinasphaltes, par Philippe Narcy ... Paris,
P. Vicq-Dunod et cⁱᵉ, 1898.
142 p. 24½ᶜᵐ.
1. Asphalt.
G S 17-267
Library, U. S. Geological Survey 465 N17

NN 0020619 DI-GS NIC ICJ

₍Narcyz Kwiatek₎ *pseud., ed.*
Antologja poezji współczesnej, wydana w podziemnej Warszawie. Glasgow, Książnica polska ₍1942₎
55, ₍1₎ p. incl. facsim. 18¼ᶜᵐ.
On facsimile of original t.-p.: Zebrał Narcyz Kwiatek.
"Wydane staraniem Ministerstwa spraw wewnętrznych Rządu polskiego."
1. Polish poetry (Collections) ₁. Title.
44-33779
Library of Congress PG7137.N3

NN 0020620 DLC CtY OCl NNC CSt

914.641 Nard, Francisco.
N223G Guia de Aranjuez. Madrid, D. R. J.
Dominguez, 1851.
183 p. illus., fold. map. 15 cm.
1. Aranjuez, Spain. Description.
I. Title.

NN 0020621 NcD

Nard, J
Chasse pratique; bréviaire du Nemrod. Illus. de M.
Brulard. Paris, Maison rustique ₍1947₎
232 p. illus. 19 cm.
1. Hunting. ₁. Title.
New York. Public Libr. A 52-2369
for Library of Congress ₍3₎

NN 0020622 NN

Nard, Léonce Léonard, 1888-
... Sur le ganglion de troisier (étude diagnosti-
que et thérapeutique chirurgicale) ... Bordeaux,
1922.
25.5 cm.
Thèse - Univ. de Bordeaux.

NN 0020623 CtY

Nardain, B
Les francs-tireurs et partisans français et l'insurrection
nationale, juin 1940-août 1944. Présenté par l'Association
nationale des anciens francs-tireurs et partisans français.
Préf. de Marcel Prenant. Paris, Éditions internationales de
presse et de publicité ₍1947₎
63 p. illus., port., facsims. 21 cm. (Les Documents de notre
époque, no 3)
1. Francs-tireurs et partisans français. 2. France—Hist.—German
occupation, 1940-1945.
D761.9.F7N35 49-21744*

NN 0020624 DLC IaU CLU

Nardain, B
... Vers l'armée de la république. Paris, Éditions France
d'abord ₍1945₎
3 p. l., 9-124 p., 2 l. illus. (incl. facsims.) 19ᶜᵐ.
"L'essentiel demeure": ₍2₎ p. laid in.
1. France. Armée. 2. World war, 1989-1945—France. ₁. Title.
UA702.N3 355 A F 46-725
Yale univ. Library
for Library of Congress ₍4₎†

NN 0020625 CtY NN MH CLSU DLC

₍Nardal₎
...Martinique₍, par Mlle Nardal₎; Guadeloupe; Guyane₍, par
le docteur G. Devez₎; St Pierre-Miquelon₍, par P. Roussier₎.
Paris: Soc. d'éditions géographiques, maritimes et coloniales,
1931. 74, 66, 56, 34 p. maps, plans, plates. 16cm. (Guides
des colonies françaises. ₍Tome, 5.)
Plates printed on both sides.
Two maps in pocket on inside of back cover.
Includes bibliographies.
603037A. 1. Martinique—Guidebooks, 1931. 2. Guadeloupe, W. I.—Guidebooks, 1931.
3. Guiana, French—Guidebooks, 1931. 4. Saint Pierre and Miquelon
—Guidebooks, 1931. I. Devez, G. 1931. 4. Saint Pierre and Miquelon
III. Guadeloupe. IV. Title. II. Roussier, Paul, 1882-
St-Pierre-Miquelon. V. Ser. Martinique, Guadeloupe, Guyane,
N. Y. P. L. October 5, 1932

NN 0020626 NN DLC CU

NARDECCHIA, Attilio.
Catalogo d'una ricca raccolta Carducciana.
Roma, Nardecchia, 1907. 18 p. 21cm.
Cover title.
1. Carducci, Giosuè, 1835-1907--Bibl.

NN 0020627 NN MH

NARDECCHIA, Attilio, compiler.
Catalogo dei duplicati della biblioteca da
vendersi alla publica auzione. 1913-14.

NN 0020628 MH

Nardecchia, Attilio.
Catalogo di libri d' occasione.
Rome, 1904.

NN 0020629 NIC

Nardecchia, Attilio.
Catalogo di libri d' occasione vendibili.
Rome ₍1897₎

NN 0020630 NIC PU

Nardecchia, Attilio.
... Catalogue of a rich collection of
books relating to America... 96p. Rome,
Author, 19-6.

NN 0020631 OCl

NARDECCHIA, Attilio.
Catalogus librorum.
Rome, 1904.

NN 0020632 MH

Nardecchia, Attilio.
Vendita all'asta pubblica della ricca biblioteca di
Francesco Crispi
see under Crispi, Francesco, 1819-1901.

Nardecchia, Elvira.
Aletos ₍por₎ Elvira Nardecchia ₍et al.₎ Ilustró Elsa
Carafi de Marchand. Montevideo, Consejo Nacional de
Enseñanza Primaria y Normal, Dept. Editorial, 1947.
117 p. illus. 27 cm. (Colección Ceibo, v. 20)
"₍Libro₎ de lectura para el primer año de las escuelas primarias."
1. Spanish language—Chrestomathies and readers. ₁. Title.
PC4115.N24 372.4 49-28113*

NN 0020634 DLC

VOLUME 405

Nardecchia, Elvira.
Semillita ¡por¡ Elvira Nardecchia ¡et al.¡ Ilustró Elsa Caraff de Marchand. Montevideo, Consejo Nacional de Enseñanza Primaria y Normal, Dept. Editorial, 1947.
99 p. illus. 27 cm. (Colección Ceibo, v. 18)

"¡Libro¡ de lectura para el primer año de las escuelas primarias."

1. Spanish language—Chrestomathies and readers.   I. Title.

PC4115.N25   372.4   49–28087*

NN   0020635   DLC

Nardecchia, *firm, booksellers, Rome.*
(1930. *Libreria già Nardecchia*)
... 600 serie di periodici italiani ... Roma, Libreria già Nardecchia, 1930.
cover-title, 47 p. 21ᶜᵐ.

At head of title: Nuova serie n. 10. Supplement to Catalogue nuova serie n. 9, "742 serie di periodici italiani."

1. Italian periodicals—Bibl.

Library of Congress   Z2345.N3   44–20245

NN   0020636   DLC

Nardella, Arduino.
Arduino Nardella. Milano, Edizione del Milione, 1952.
xxvii p. 24 col. plates. 35 cm.

ND623.N37A15   [759.5] 927.5   53–27433

NN   0020637   DLC

Nardella, Tidelfo.
...La seconda Roma; storia della città dalla caduta dell'Impero romano alla fine del regno pontificio (476–1870)... Milano, Edizioni "Corbaccio", 1927.
2 v. 19 ᶜᵐ. (Cultura contemporanea. v.20–21)

1.Rome (City)—Hist.

NN   0020638   NjP MH

¥   **Nardelli,**
4   Sul trattamento dell'empiema tubercolare.
qP12   Padova, CEDAM, 1931.
1931   44 p.

Tesi delle Scuole di perfezionamento, R. Università di Padova.

NN   0020639   DNLM

NN   0020640   DNLM

Nardelli, Antonio.
Per un caso di spondilite cervicale. Nota.
Bologna, ditta N. Zanichelli, 1892.
16 p. 8°.

NN   0020641   DNLM

Nardelli, Berenice.
Brunetto Latini.
Alba, 1887.

NN   0020642   NIC

BR65
.A9N3   **Nardelli, Ercole.**

...Il determinismo nellz filosofia di S.Agostino...   Torino ¡etc. ¡ G.B.Paravia e comp., 1905.
x p.,2ℓ.,¡3¡–216,¡1¡ p.   20cm.(Half-title: Biblioteca di filosofia e pedagogia (Collezione Paravia) ¡96¡)

1.Augustinus, Aurelius, Saint, bp.of Hippo.2.Free will and determinism. I.Title.

NN   0020643   OCU PU

PQ
4804   **Nardelli, Federico Vittore, 1891-**
N3   L'arcangelo; vita e miracoli di Gabriele
1931a   d'Annunzio. [Roma]A. Stock[1931]
394p. 25cm.

1. Annunzio, Gabriele d', 1863-1938. I.Title.

NN   0020644   MU PPT InU CU CaBVaU

855An7   **Nardelli, Federico Vittore, 1891-**
BN16   D'Annunzio, a portrait, by Federico Nardelli
1931a   and Arthur Livingston.   London, J. Cape ¡1931¡
320p. ports. 21cm.

Published in New York with title: Gabriel the archangel.

1. Annunzio, Gabriele d', 1863-1938. I. Livingston, Arthur, 1883-   joint author.

NN   0020645   IU OO CaBVaU

D855N16
Q
Nardelli, Federico Vittore, 1891-
Europa; 33 temi ¡di¡ Nardelli. ¡Roma, Edizioni Europa, 1930¡
cover-title, 4 p. l., XXXIII numb. l., ¡6¡ p. 36½ cm.

No. 8 of 200 numbered copies.

NN   0020646   NNC

Nardelli, Federico Vittore, 1891-
Gabriel the archangel 〈Gabriele d'Annunzio〉 ¡by¡ Federico Nardelli and Arthur Livingston. New York, Harcourt, Brace and company ¡1931¡
6 p. l., 3–336 p. front., plates, ports. 22ᶜᵐ.

1. Annunzio, Gabriele d', 1863-1938.   I. *Livingston, Arthur, 1883- joint author. II. Title.

Library of Congress   PQ4804.N3

————— Copy 2.   31–11367

Copyright A 35057   ¡a38r33m2¡   928.5

PBm ViU MiU OCl OrSaW MB NN MH
NN   0020647   DLC WaSp WaS WaU NjN LU TxU MB CU

858
P664Z   **Nardelli, Federico Vittore, 1891-**
N16Y   El hombre secreto; vida y tormento de Luigi Pirandello. Traducción de José Blaya Lozano.   Buenos Aires, Corinto ¡1944¡
269 p. illus., ports. 24cm.

Translation of L'uomo segreto.

1. Pirandello, Luigi, 1867-1936. I. Title.

NN   0020648   AU NN

Nardelli, Federico Vittore, 1891-
L'homme secret (L' uomo segreto) ¡by¡ F. V. Nardelli; traduit de l' italien par A. E. Guillaume. Paris: Gallimard ¡1937¡ 252 p. 12°. (Les contemporains vus de près, 2ᵉ ser. no. 2.)

1. Pirandello, Luigi. 2. Title.
N. Y. P. L.   March 7, 1938

NN   0020649   NN

Nardelli, Federico Vittore, *1891-*   2799B.582
La Panarda. Romanzo.
— Milano. Treves. 1927. (6), 215 pp. 18 cm., in 8s.

NN   0020650   MB WaT NN N

Nardelli, Federico Vittore, 1891-
... L'uomo segreto; vita e croci di Luigi Pirandello. ¡Milano¡ A. Mondadori ¡1932¡
4 p. l., ¡11¡–291, ¡2¡ p., 1 l. 24 pl. (incl. front., ports., facsims.) on 13 l. 23ᶜᵐ. ¡"Le scie"; collana di epistolari, memorie, biografie e curiosità¡

1. Pirandello, Luigi, 1867-1936.   I. Title.   33—15706

Library of Congress   PQ4835.I 7Z7
¡a37c1¡   928.5

MB IEN MiU IU NRU CaBVaU
NN   0020651   DLC ViU InU CSt CU PU NN OCl MiU OClW

921
P664lna2   **Nardelli, Federico Vittore, 1891-**
L'uomo segreto; vita e croci di Luigi Pirandello. 2. ed. ¡Milano¡ A. Mondadori ¡1944¡
257 p. 24 pl. (incl. front., ports., facsims.) on 13 l. ¡"Le scie"; collana di epistolari, memorie, biografie e curiosità¡

1. Pirandello, Luigi, 1867-1936. I. Title.

NN   0020652   WaU NcD NNC NN NIC IaU

NARDELLI, Francesco.
Giurisdizione e competenza della corte dei conti in materia contabile; legislazione, dottrina e giurisprudenza.   Napoli,1901.

NN   0020653   MH-L

Nardelli, Francesco.
Raccolta delle leggi, decreti, e regolamenti sulle ferrovie dello stato, commentata ed annotata dall' avv. Francesco Nardelli. Torino-Roma, Società tipografico-editrice nazionale, 1907.
131 p., 1 l. 19½ᵐᵐ. (*On cover:* Biblioteca del cittadino italiano. 90–91)

1. Railroad law—Italy. 2. Railroads and state—Italy.   I. Italy. Laws, statutes, etc.   8–13955

Library of Congress   HE3093.N2

NN   0020654   DLC NN

4K
Ital.-   **Nardelli, Francesco.**
313   Il ricorso alla IV sezione del consiglio di stato, secondo la legge e la dottrina degli scrittori e commentato colla giurisprudenza della stessa IV sezione e della corte di cassazione di Roma. Napoli, N. Jovene, 1902.
442 p.

NN   0020655   DLC-P4 MH

VOLUME 405

Nardelli, Franklin.
   Bastardo; dramma in tre atti.   Milano: C. Barbini, 1910.
73 p.   16°.   (Biblioteca ebdomadaria teatrale.   fasc. 947.)

1. Drama (Italian).   2. Title.
N. Y. P. L.   February 27, 1912.

NN   0020656   NN

NARDELLI, Gaetano.
   Et, que, etque, ac.   Isservazioni intorno
all'uso delle congiurzioni copulative latine.
Roma, E. Loescher & co., 1899.

   Pamphlet.

NN   0020657   MH

831.09   Nardelli, Gaetano.
N223P   Le primavere liriche della Germania.
         Roma, G. B. Paravia, 1891.
            183 p.   23 cm.

         1. German poetry.   Hist. & crit.   I. Title.

NN   0020658   NcD

Nardelli, Giuseppe, 1875-
   ... Il conducente una pubblica tramvia
elettrica non è pubblico ufficiale ...
Roma, Tip. Italiana, 1909.
   11 p.   31½cm.
   At head of title: Istanza diretta
all'ecc.mo procuratore del Re di Roma
per la scarcerazione di Fabrizi Flavio
illegalmente detenuto.

NN   0020659   MH-L

Nardelli, Giuseppe, 1875-
   ... In difesa di Carlo Zancolla.
Arringa pronunciata alla Corte di
assise di Roma il 27 settembre 1922.
Con prefazione di Francesco Geraci.
Piacenza, Società tip. editoriale
Porta, 1923.
   7 p.l., 53 p.   port.   25½cm.

NN   0020660   MH-L

Nardelli, Giuseppe, 1875-
   ... La libertà della stampa ed i reati commessi a mezzo della
stampa.   Roma, Fratelli Treves, 1924.
   145 p., 1 l.   24½ᵐ.

   1. Liberty of the press—Italy.   2. Press law—Italy.   I. Title.
                                                   38-86099

NN   0020661   DLC MH

NARDELLI, Giuseppe, 1875-
   Nei tribunali.   Roma, C.Oriani,1914.
   8°.

NN   0020662   MH-L

WQ   NARDELLI, Honorato F
150   El problema de las madres.   3. ed.
N223p   Buenos Aires, Editorial Mundo Moderno
1953   [1953]
            127 p.   illus.
            1. Obstetrics - Popular works   Title

NN   0020663   DNLM

WR   NARDELLI, Leonardo
205   La psoriasi.   Roma, Abruzzini [1955]
qN223p   viii, 148 p.
1955   1. Psoriasis

NN   0020664   DNLM PPC

Nardelli, Matteo.
   ...Fascismo, idea universale.   Prefazione dell' on. prof. Paolo
Orano...   Trento: Edizione di "Trentino," Anno XIV [1936]
235 p.   20½cm.

902505A.   1. Fascism.   2. Fascism   —Italy.
N. Y. P. L.   October 19, 1937

NN   0020665   NN MH

Nardelli, Raffaele

——.   Igiene o medicina curativa.   23 pp.   8°.
   Arezzano, Angelini & Pietrocola, 1885.

NN   0020666   DNLM

Nardelli (Raffaele).   Ira o epilessia larvata ?
Perizia freniatrica in causa d' assassinio.   45 pp.
8°.   *Alba, Paganelli, 1890*

NN   0020667   DNLM

Nardelli (Raffaele).   Tre perizie medico-legali.
50 pp., 1 l.   8°.   *Arezzano, Angelini & Pietrocola,
1884.*

NN   0020668   DNLM

308t   Nardelli, Robert Raymond
N2236   A study of some aspects of creative reading.
         [Berkeley, 1953]
            vii,132 l.   tables.

            Thesis (Ph.D. in Education) - Univ. of
         California, Sept. 1953.
            Bibliography: p.105-109.

NN   0020669   CU

Narden, P   A.
   ... Статистика табаководства и табачного производства в
дореволюционной России (за годы 1877-1916)   Составил
П. А. Нарден.   Москва, Ленинград, Акционерное "Про-
миздат" общество, 1927.
   26, [1] p.   20½ᵐ.
   At head of title: Бюро с'ездов гос. табачной промышленности.

   1. Tobacco manufacture and trade—Russia—Stat.   I. Büro s"ezdov
gosudarstvennoi tabachnoi promyshlennosti, Moscow.   II. Title.
                                                   40-17175
   Library of Congress   HD9145.R92N3

NN   0020670   DLC

[Nardi, *pseud.*]
   Poems.   Cedar Rapids, Ia., Priv. print., 1921.
   44 p.   20½ᶜᵐ.

   I. Title.

   Library of Congress   PS3500.N3P6 1921   21-18539

NN   0020671   DLC

Nardi, Agostino.
   Casimira la cieca ...
      see under   Persiani, Luigi Giulio.

Nardi, Agostino.
   Compònimenti teatrali ad uso dei collegi e
seminari.   Torino, P. di G. Marietti, 1869.
   250 p., 1 l.   8°.

NN   0020673   NN

NARDI, Agostino.
   Rime.   Venetia,appresso G.B.Crotti,1613.
   13 x 7 cm.
   Engraved title-page,with ornamental border.

NN   0020674   MH

[NARDI, Agostino, compiler]
   La tromba del illustriss. sig. Benedetto
Corraro formata di poesie diverse.   Vicenza,
appresso G. Greco,1598.
   4°.pp.(8). 62.
   A collection of poems by various authors
in praise of Benedetto Corraro.
   Dedication signed: Agostino Nardi.

NN   0020675   MH

Nardi (Alfonso).   Annotazioni relative ad alcuni
casi di clinica chirurgica e di operativa.   42 pp.
4°.   *Bologna, Gamberini & Parmeggiani 1882*

NN   0020676   DNLM

332.4945 Nardi, Arnoldo.
N16c   Condizioni economiche in cui trovossi in Tosca-
         na l'industria mineralogica durante il medio
         evo.   Con tavole dimostrative del valore de' gener
         e note ...   Livorno, Tipografia Tedeschi, 1847.
         161p.

         1. Money--Tuscany.

NN   0020677   IU

Nardi, Baldassare
   Apologia contro le vane ragioni con
le quali, alcune scritture, che sono da
Venetia uscite, impugnano le censure del
Papa.   Con due discorsi politici,
intorno allo stato presente delle cose
de i signori Venetiani.   Napoli, G. I.
Carlino, 1607.
   30, 46p.   21cm.

NN   0020678   WU

878   Nardi, Bruno.
V7Wna2   ...Breve guida al paese natio di
         Virgilio.   Mantova, Bedulli, 1930.
            19p.   illus.,maps.   D.
Class.   At head of title: Bimillenario Virgili-
         ano.

NN   0020679   IaU

1019   Nardi, Bruno.
D202   ... Il canto XI dell 'Inferno'
         Roma. A. Signorelli, 1941.
            31 p.   25cm.   (Nuova 'lectura Dantis')

            1. Dante Alighieri.   La Divina
         commedia.   Inferno.

NN   0020680   NIC

VOLUME 405

PQ4445   Nardi, Bruno
11thN3   Il canto XI dell' 'Inferno'.   Roma, A.
          Signorelli, 1951.
          31 p.   (Nuova 'Lectura Dantis', a cura
          di Siro A. Chimenz)

          "Lettura tenuta alla 'Casa di Dante' in
          Roma il 28 gennaio 1951."
          Text of canto XI: p.21-24.

NN   0020681   CU OrU MiU RPB NN MH

          Nardi, Bruno.
              Il canto XI dell''inferno', con nota
          aggiuntiva di A. Chimenz. 2. ed. Roma,
PG 1459   A. Signorelli [1955]
.N8 A1   24 p.   25cm. (Nuova 'Lectura Dantis')
11th N
          Bibliographical references included in
          "Nota" (p. 20-24)

          1. Dante Alighieri, 1265-1321. Divina
          Commedia. In-   ferno: XI.

NN   0020682   MdBJ OrU

          Nardi, Bruno.
              La crisi del Rinascimento e il dubbio cartesiano. A cura
          del dott. Tullio Gregory. Anno accademico 1950-51. Roma,
          La Goliardica [1950?]

              95 p. 25 cm.

          At head of title: Università degli studi di Roma. Facoltà di let-
          tere e filosofia.

              1. Science—Methodology. 2. Descartes, René, 1596-1650.
          I. Title.
                                                          A 53-4883
          Harvard Univ. Library
          for Library of Congress   [1]

NN   0020683   MH

          Nardi, Bruno.
PQ4380   Il culto di Dante nel mondo (relazione...
N3   al 47° Congresso: Ravenna, 7-9 settembre
          1952) Roma, Tip. Editrice Italia, 1953.
          9 p.   27 cm.

          Cover title.
          At head of title: Società Dante Alighieri.

          1. Dante Alighieri--Addresses, essays,lectures

NN   0020684   RPB

          NARDI, Bruno.
              Dante e Alpetragio. Firenze, L.S. Olschki,
          1926.

              f°. pp.15.
          "Estratto dal vol. xxix, quad, 1, del
          Giornale dantesco".

NN   0020685   MH

          Nardi, Bruno.
              ... Dante e la cultura medievale, nuovi saggi di filosofia
          dantesca. Bari, G. Laterza & figli, 1942.
              xii, 334, [2] p. 20ᵐ. (Half-title: Biblioteca di cultura moderna, n.
          368)

              1. Dante—Philosophy. 2. Philosophy, Medieval.
                                                          46-30905
          Library of Congress   PQ4412.N3
                                   [2]   851.15

NN   0020686   DLC CtY IU NjP NN NcD TU OrU CLU ICU

          Nardi, Bruno.
              Dante e la cultura medievale; nuovi saggi di filosofia
          dantesca. 2. ed. riv. e accresiuta. Bari, Laterza, 1949.
              xvi, 423 p. 21 cm. (Biblioteca di cultura moderna, n. 368)
          Bibliographical footnotes.

              1. Dante—Philosophy. 2. Philosophy, Medieval.
              [PQ4412.N]   (851.15)   A 50-5267
          Chicago. Univ. Library
          for Library of Congress   [1]

NN   0020687   ICU AU WaU PBm IaU CSt CU NcRS PU MB
              MoSU NjPT ICN CtY CaBVaU MtU

          Nardi, Bruno.
              Dante e la cultura medievale; nuovi saggi di filosofi
          dantesca. 2. ed. riv. e accresiuta. Bari, Laterza, 1949.
              xvi, 423 p. On film (negative) (Biblioteca di cultura moderna
          368)
          Microfilm. Original in Univ. of Chicago Library.
          Includes bibliographical references.

NN   0020688   CU

          Nardi, Bruno
Hc35   La filosofia di Dante. Milano, C. Marzorati
N16   [1952]
          106 p. 25 cm.
          Bibliography: p. [105]-106.

          1. Dante - Philosophy.

NN   0020689   CtY CaBVaU PBm

PQ4412   Nardi, Bruno
N32   La filosofia di Dante.   Milano, C. Marzorati, 1954.
          [1149]-1253 p.

          Cover title.
          "Estratto dalla Grande antologia filosofica."
          "Nota bibliografica": p. 1252-1253.

          1. Dante Alighieri - Philosophy.

NN   0020690   CU

          NARDI, Bruno.
              La giovinezza di Virgilio. Mantova, lib.
          ed. U. Mondovi, 1927.

              Cover: Il millenio Virgiliano, a cura de
          comune de Virglio.

              Sheet of "Errata" inserted between pp.
          118-119.

NN   0020691   MH

          Nardi, Bruno.
              Le meditazioni di Cartesio; A cura del dott. T.Gregory.
          Roma, La Goliardica [1952]

              51 p.

NN   0020692   MH

PQ4339   Nardi, Bruno.
.N37   Nel mondo di Dante. Roma, Edizioni di Storia
          letteratura, 1944.
          382 p. 26cm. (Storia e letteratura, 5)
          Bibliographical footnotes.

              1. Dante Alighieri, 1265-1321.   I. Title.
          II. Series.

          InU NjR OCU NcU NNC OO CtU OrU CaBVaU PU MnCo11S
          ViU NRU NBuU CoU MH ICN NjP RPB OU NcD CtY ICU CU
NN   0020693   MB IaU MiU DLC-P4 IU WaU CSt NIC MeB

          Nardi, Bruno, ed.

          Thomas Aquinas, Saint, 1225†-1274.
              ... Opuscoli e testi filosofici, scelti e annotati da Bruno
          Nardi ... Bari, G. Laterza & figli, 1915-17.

          Nardi, Bruno.
              Il problema della verità. Soggetto e oggetto del conoscere
          nella filosofia antica e medievale. [Roma] Universale di
          Roma [1951]
              66 p. 24 cm.
          At head of title: Centro romano di studi.
          "Il presente saggio precede la pubblicazione del 2° volume degli
          Atti del Centro romano di studi su 'Il problema della verità.'"
          Bibliographical footnotes.

              1. Knowledge, Theory of.   I. Rome (City) Centro romano di
          studi. II. Title.
              BD164.N25   121   A 52-5910 rev
          Chicago. Univ. Libr.
          for Library of Congress   [r53b†]†

NN   0020695   ICU NN NIC DLC

          Nardi, Bruno.
              ... Saggi di filosofia dantesca.
          Milano, Società anonima editrice
          Dante Alighieri, 1930

              xii,380p. 19cm. (Biblioteca peda-
          gogica antica e moderna italiana e
          straniera.   v.LVII)

NN   0020696   CLSU CU CLU NIC PU MH MdBJ NcD NNF IU

          Nardi, Bruno.
              Sigieri di Brabante nel pensiero del Rinascimento italiano.
          Roma, Edizioni italiane [1945]
              183 p. 23 cm.
          Bibliographical footnotes.

              1. Siger de Brabant, 13th cent. 2. Philosophy, Medieval. 3. Phil-
          osophy, Renaissance.
              B765.S54N3   189.4   A F 48-2766*
          Chicago. Univ. Libr.
          for Library of Congress   [2]†

NN   0020697   ICU OrU NNC OU ICN MH CtY DLC

B765   Nardi, Bruno
.S54   Sigieri di Brabante; nel pensiero del Rinas-
N2   cimento Italiano. Roma, Edizione italiane
          .1949]
          183p. 23cm.

          Author's autograph copy.
          Bibliographical footnotes.

              1.Siger de Brabant, 13th cent. 2.Renais-
          sance - Italy.

NN   0020698   NcU

          Nardi, Bruno,
851.15   Sigieri di Brabante nella Divina commedia e
DN223   le fonti della filosofia di Dante.   Spianate
          (Pescia) Presso l'autore, 1912.
              viii, 70 p. 25°.
          "Estratto dalla 'Rivista di filosofia neosco-
          lastica' (aprile e ottobre 1911, febbraio e
          aprile 1912)"
          Bibliographical footnotes.

              1. Dante - Philosophy. 2. Siger de Brabant,
          13th cent. 3. Philosophy, Medieval. 4. Philoso-
          phy, Renaissance.

NN   0020699   CSt MH CtY

          Nardi, Bruno.
              Soggetto e oggetto del conoscere nella filosofia antica e
          medievale. 2. ed. riv. e accresciuta di una appendice su Gio-
          vanni Rodington e il dubbio iperbolico di Cartesio. Roma,
          Edizioni dell'Ateneo [1952]
              92 p. 23 cm.
          At head of title: Centro romano di studi.

Continued in next column

VOLUME 405

Continued from preceding column

1. Knowledge, Theory of. 2. Joannes Rodingtonus, d. 1348.

A 53–4187

Chicago. Univ. Libr.
for Library of Congress   ₁₁₎

NN   0020700   ICU RPB OC1W NN OU

NARDI, Bruno.
   Vittorino da Feltre al paese natale di
Virgilio. [Rome],Istituto di Studi Romani,1938.
   pp.7.
   Cover serves as title-page.
   "Estratto dagli 'Atti del IV Congresso na-
zionale di studi romani'."

NN   0020701   MH

Nardi, Bruno.
   The youth of Virgil, by Bruno Nardi; translated by **Belle
Palmer Rand**, with a preface by Edward Kennard **Rand.**
Cambridge, Harvard university press, 1930.
   xii, 189 p. front. 19½ᵐ.
   "List of works frequently cited": p. ₁ix₎

1. Vergilius Maro, Publius.   i. *Rand, Belle (Palmer) tr.

30—15178

Library of Congress   PA6825.N3
                         ₁a44k1₎   928.7

        IdU
        WaU ViU NN OCU OOxM PSC PU PV TxU OrU MB OrSaW
NN   0020702   DLC PPD CU KEmT OKentU NIC MeB MU

Nardi, Carlo.
   ... Augusto, il suo tempo e la sua opera. Con 21 tavole. Milano, S. a. Fratelli Treves editori ₁1939₎
   3 p. l., 301 p. front., plates, ports., fold. geneal. tab. 20ᵐ.
   Bibliography: p. 273–298.

1. Augustus, emperor of Rome, B. C. 63–A. D. 14. 2. Rome—History—
Augustus, B. C. 30–A. D. 14.

A C 40–1288

Michigan. Univ. Library   DG279.N22
for Library of Congress   ₁2₎

NN   0020703   MiU CU PU OC1 ICU CLU

Nardi, Carlo.
   Augusto. ₁1939₎

   Microcopy of the original.

Nardi, Carlo.
   ... In solitudine, liriche ...   Genova, Libreria
editrice moderna, 1924.
   54 p., 1 l. 19 cm.

NN   0020705   CU

Nardi, Carlo.
   Il liutaio Cesare Candi e il violino di Paganini. Genova,
Di Stefano ₁1949₎
   62 p. illus., port. 25 cm.

1. Violin—Construction. 2. Candi, Cesare, 1869–1947. 3. Paganini,
Nicolò, 1782–1840.   i. Title.

ML830.N27   A 50–888

Oregon. Univ. Libr.
for Library of Congress   ₁₁₎†

NN   0020706   OrU CLU DLC

Nardi, Carlo.
   Notizie di Montalto in Calabria. Roma, Giordano [1954]
   617 p. illus.

NN   0020707   MH

Nardi, Carlo.
   Il processo di Gesù, "Il re dei Giudei." Genova, Di Stefano ₁1948₎
   394 p. plates. 22 cm.

1. Jesus Christ—Trial.   i. Title.

BT440.N3   232.962   49–16687*

NN   0020708   DLC TxU CU-L NNC

Nardi, Carlo.
   La vita e le opere di Francesco Saverio Salfi
(1759-1832) Genova, 1925.
   403 p.
   "Elenco cronologico delle opere edite ed inedite
di Francesco Saverio Salfi": p. [xi]-xiv..

NN   0020709   IU CtY MH

929.75 Nardi, Carlo, 18ᵗʰ cent.
N166d   De'titoli del re' delle due Sicilie
        colle spiegazioni.   Napoli, 1747.
        213p. fold.geneal.tables.

NN   0020710   IU

929.2   Nardi, Carlo, 18ᵗʰ cent.
G439n   Della famiglia Giovene de' duchi di
        Girasole ragguaglio storico-genologico.
        Lucca, 1736.
        212p. pl., fold.geneal.tab.

NN   0020711   IU

Nardi, Carlo, 18ᵗʰ cent. Discendenza della
famiglia Volpi. 46 pp. (Volpi, G., Dell' istoria de' Visconti. v. 2, p. i.)

NN   0020712   MdBP

471.7   Nardi, Carlo Maria, fl. 1735.
N16i   Caroli - M. Nardi ... Inscriptionum specimen ap-
        positis annotationibus, atque excursibus illus-
        tratum ...   Neapoli, apud Vincentium Pauriam,
        1763.
        xxiv, 260p.

        1. Inscriptions, Latin.

NN   0020713   IU ICU

Nardi, Carlo Maria, fl. 1735.
   Istorie della citta di Firenze di Iacopo Nardi
      see under   Nardi, Jacopo, 1476–ca. 1563.

Nardi, Dino.
   Art and esthetics; brief syntheses of old and new concepts.
Rome, Rome Daily American ₁1954₎   35 p.   24cm.

1. Aesthetics.

NN   0020715   NN

Nardi (Dominicus). Dissertatio de onanismo
conjugali. 146 pp. 8°. Tolosa, E. Frisat, 1870.

NN   0020716   DNLM

Nardi, Enzo.
   ... I casi di indegnità nel diritto successorio romano. Milano,
A. Giuffrè, 1937.
   4 p. l., ₁vii₎–xv, 380 p. 25½ᵐ. (R. Università di Roma, pubblicazioni
dell' Istituto di diritto Romano dei diritti dell' oriente Mediterraneo e di
storia del diritto, II)
   "Bibliografia": p. ₁vii₎–xii.

1. Inheritance and succession (Roman law) 2. Domestic relations
(Roman law)   i. Title.

39–9006

NN   0020717   DLC CtY

Nardi, Enzo.
   ... La reciproca posizione successoria dei coniugi privi di
conubium. Milano, A. Giuffrè, 1938.
   viii, 100 p., 1 l. 25½ᵐ. (R. Università di Roma. Pubblicazioni del-
l'Istituto di diritto romano, dei diritti dell' Oriente mediterraneo e di
storia del diritto, VII)

1. Husband and wife (Roman law) 2. Inheritance and succession
(Roman law)   i. Title.

43–11164

NN   0020718   DLC WaU-L CtY-L NIC

K   Nardi, Enzo
N22   Ritenzione e pegno gordiano. Milano,
        A. Giuffrè, 1939.
        viii, 108 p. 25cm. (₁Rome (City)₎
        Università. Istituto di diritto romano,
        dei diritti dell'Oriente mediterraneo e di
        storia del diritto. Pubblicazioni, 13)

NN   0020719   NIC MiU-L MH CU-L WaU-L

Nardi, Enzo.
   La rivalsa del concedente per i contributi agricoli unifi-
cati. Milano, A. Giuffrè, 1950.
   56 p. 24 cm. (Rivista di diritto del lavoro. Quaderno 1)
   Bibliographical footnotes.

1. Agricultural laborers—Italy. 2. Insurance, Social—Italy.
3. Métayer system—Italy.   (Series)

A 53–7641

New York Univ. Wash.   Sq. Library
for Library of Congress   ₁₁₎†

NN   0020720   NNU-W DLC CtY-L

Nardi, Enzo.
   Studi sulla ritenzione in diritto romano. Milano, Giuffrè,
1947–57.
   3 v. 25 cm. (Collana della "Fondazione G. Castelli," 21)
   Vols. 2–3 published as Università di Parma. Pubblicazioni della
Facoltà di giurisprudenza, 1, 4.
   Bibliographical footnotes.

1. Liens (Roman law)   (Series: Parma. Università. Facoltà
di giurisprudenza. Pubblicazioni, 1 ₁etc.₎)

58–41887 rev

NN   0020721   DLC NNC NjP MH-L CtY-L MiU-L OU NNC-L

4K   Nardi, Enzo.
1955   Sui divieti matrimoniali delle
        leggi Augustee. Roma, Apollinaris
        [194]
               37 p.

NN   0020722   DLC-P4

VOLUME 405

Nardi (Ernesto). Rendiconto igienico-sanitario dell' orfanotrofio maschile di Milano nel triennio 1886-8. 30 pp., 1 l., 5 tab. 8°. *Milano, G. Agnelli,* 1889.

NN　0020723　DNLM

Law

Nardi, Federico, ed.

Italy. Laws, statutes, etc.
Codice delle leggi di spropriazione e servitù per pubblica utilità; raccolta completa di tutte le leggi, le provvisioni e i decreti in vigore sulla materia, ordinata da Federico Nardi ... Napoli, R. Marghieri di Gius., 1888.

NN　0020725　NIC

BV
192
T2
N22
Nardi, Francesco, 1808-1877.
Diritto matrimoniale cattolico, aggiuntevi Le leggi intorno al matrimonio promulgate nell'Impero d'Austria. Padova, P. Prosperini, 1857.
397 p. 21 cm.

1. Marriage (Canon law). 2. Marriage law - Austria.

NN　0020726　DCU PLatS MH

NARDI, Francesco, 1808-1877.
Elementi di diritto ecclesiastico, aggiuntevi le norme politiche e civili austriache in oggetti misti. Venezia, 1846.

vol. 1.

NN　0020727　MH-L

BV
190
.N22
E3
1854
Nardi, Francesco, 1808-1877.
Elementi di diritto ecclesiastico, aggiuntevi le norme politiche e civili in oggetti misti. 2. ed. aum. e corr. Padova, Tipi del Seminario, 1854.
3 v. fold. table. 22 cm.

1. Ecclesiastical law. I. Title.

NN　0020728　DCU PLatS

Nardi, Francesco, 1808-1877.
Intorno alla Sacrae Congregationis dell' indice... Roma, Sinimberghi, 1865.
15 p

NN　0020729　PU

Nardi, Francesco, 1808-1877.
Das oecumenische concil und die rechte des staates... antwort auf das buchlein, Le concile oecumenique et les droits de l'etat aus dem italienischen übers. von Theophil Landmesser. Berlin, W. Moeser, 1869.
38 p

NN　0020730　PHC

Nardi, Francesco, 1808-1877.
Parole dette al tumulo nel dì delle solenni esequie del conte Carlo Bernardini, maresciallo d'alloggio nell'artiglieria pontificia, morto nella battaglia di Mentana, nella chiesa dei Lucchesi in Roma il giorno 16 novembre 1867. [Roma, coi tipi dell'Osservatore romano, 1867]
10 p.

NN　0020731　MH

NARDI, Francesco, 1808-1877.
Pel natale di Roma; discorso. [Rome, 1861].

pp. 14.

NN　0020732　MH

[Nardi, Francesco] 1808-1877.
Roma e i suoi nemici al signor de la Guéronnière. n.p., n.d.
26 p.
Signed: Francesco Nardi.

NN　0020733　MH MC

[NARDI, Francesco] 1808-1877.
Il Santo Padre in Anagni il 20 maggio. Roma, dalla tipografia Sinimberghi, 1863.

pp. 31.

NN　0020734　MH

Nardi, Francesco, 1808-1877.
Scritti a difesa della Santa Sede. Torino, coi tipi di Pietro di G. Marietti, 1862.

NN　0020735　MH

Bonaparte
Collection
No. 5125
[Nardi, Francesco]　1808-1877.
Studii sui dialetti della lingua italiana; lettura accademica pubblicata per le felici nozze del nob. Signor dott. Nicolò Nardi colla nob. Signora Lucia Malvolti. Padova, 1852.　O.

Author's dedication to his brother signed: Francesco Nardi.

NN　0020736　ICN

[NARDI, Francesco] 1808-1877.
Studii sui dialetti della lingua italiana. n.p., [186-?]

pp. 23.

NN　0020737　MH

457
N159s
1872
Nardi, Francesco, 1808-1877.
Sui dialetti d'Italia; discorso accademico. Nuova ed. accresciuta. Roma, Tip. e Libreria di Roma, 1872.
22p. 22cm.

1. Italian language--Dialects. I. Title.

NN　0020738　IU

NARDI, Francesco, 1808-1877.
Sul significato d'alcune parole; discorso tenuto all'Accademia Pontificia Tiberina il 6 maggio 1867. Roma, Fratelli Monaldi, 1871.

Pamphlet.

NN　0020739　MH

Nardi, Francesco, 1808-1877.
Sul tentativo anti-cattolico in Inghilterra, e l'opuscolo dell'on. mo sig. Guglielmo Gladstone; osservazioni. Roma, Tip. della pace, 1875.
(1), 74 p.

NN　0020740　MH

Nardi, Francesco, 1808-1877.
Sulla scoperta delle origini del Nilo fatta da Speke e Grant; memoria di Monsign. F. Nardi. Roma, Tip. delle Belle arti, 1864.
11 p. 28½ cm.
"Estratta dagli Atti della Accademia pontificia de' Nuovi Lincei, sessione II, del 3 gennaro 1864, tomo XVII."

1. Nile River.

9-13359

Library of Congress　　GB1363.N3

NN　0020741　DLC

Nardi, Francesco, 1808-1877.
Sur les principes de 89. Discours lu à l'Académie pontificale de la religion catholique le 12 juin 1862, et traduit par l'abbé L. Godard. P, 1862

32 p.

NN　0020742　MH

NARDI, Francesco, 1808-1877.
Viaggio al Giordano e al Mar Morto, pubblicato dal Dr. Domenico Lucheschi, Padova, P. Prosperini, 1858.

f°. pp. (4). 24.

"Per le nozze Miari-Rota".

NN　0020743　MH

Nardi, Francesco, 1808-1877.
Un viaggio da Amburgo a Copenhagen, lettura accademica dell'ab. dott. Francesco Nardi ... pubblicata per le fauste nozze del dr. Luigi Pivetta colla contessa Marina Arnaldi. Padova, coi tipi del Seminario, 1851.
34 p. 21 cm.

NN　0020744　CtY

F1233
I3
no.2
x
Nardi, Francesco, 1808-1877.
Visita dell'Imperatore e Imperatrice del Messico al S. Padre. Rome, Tip. Sinimbergh, 1864.
22 p. 20cm.　[Imperio de Mexico, no.2]

1. Maximilian, Emperor of Mexico, 1832-1867. 2. Charlotte, Empress Consort of Maximilian, Emperor of Mexico, 1840-1927. I. Title.

NN　0020745　CU-B

QH
331
N223g
1948
NARDI, Francesco, 1912-
Grenzgebiete des Lebendigen. [Köln] Staufen [1948]
153 p. illus.
1. Life　　　Title

NN　0020746　DNLM

VOLUME 405

Nardi, Francesco, 1912–
    Organismus und gestalt von den formenden kräften des lebendigen, von F. Nardi. München und Berlin, R. Oldenbourg, 1942.
    251, [1] p. illus. 20ᵐ. (*Half-title:* Einheit des wissens, hrsg. von Max Bense)

    1. Morphology (Animals) 2. Embryology. 3. Regeneration (Biology)
    I. Title.

    Library of Congress   QL799.N3   44–46243
                                    [2]   591.4

NN   0020747   DLC MH IU NNC OkU

Nardi, George L
    The utilization of radioactive glycine in the livers of normal and depleted mice. Oak Ridge, Tenn., Technical Information Division, ORE, Oak Ridge, Tenn. AEC, 1950.
    4 p. 27ᶜᵐ.
    At head of title: United States Atomic Energy Commission. AECU-177 (UCRL-305)
    "References": p. 4.
    1. Glycocoll—Physiological effect. I. Title. II. Ser.

NN   0020748   ViU

WZ   NARDI, Giovanni, ca. 1580– ca. 1655
250   ... Apologeticon in Fortunii Liceti mulctram, vel de duplici
N224a   calore [Florentiae, Typis Amatoris Massae, & soc., 1638]
1638   [1], 537, [7] p. 24 cm.

    I. Liceti, Fortunio, 1577-1657

NN   0020749   DNLM

Nardi, Giovanni, ca. 1580–1655.
    De igne svbterraneom physica prolvsio. [Colophon:] Florentiae, Excudebant Amator Masta, & Laurentius de Landis, 1641.
    152 p.

NN   0020750   PPAmP

WZ   NARDI, Giovanni, ca. 1580-ca.1655.
250   ... De prodigiosis vulnerum curationibus.
T375   605-608 p. 21 cm. (In Theatrum sympatheticum auctum.
1662   Norimbergae, 1662.
    Caption title.

NN   0020751   DNLM

MN   Nardi, Giovanni, ca. 1580– ca. 1655.
610   De rore disquisitio physica. Florentiae, Typis A.
N223   Massae & L, de Landis, 1642.
    8, 212 p. engr. front. 24 cm.

    1. Medicine. Early works to 1800. I. Title.

NN   0020752   N CLU-M

WZ   NARDI, Giovanni, ca. 1580- ca. 1655.
250   Lactis physica analysis ... [Florentiae, Typis Petri Nestii,
N224ℓ   1634]
1634   [16], 342, [18] p. 23 cm.
    Engraved title page.

NN   0020753   DNLM CLU-M

Nardi, Giovanni, ca. 1580-1655.
    Noctes geniales Avctore D. Ioanne Nardio Florentino Annvs Primvs.   Bononiae, Io. Baptistae Ferronij, 1655.
    6 p.l., 748 p., 20 l.
    Book-pl. of Marchionis Salsae.
    The book is principally valuable for the priority of the discovery of the circulation of the blood as between Cesalpinus and Harvey. Also contains a very early reference to the microscope.
    (Small 4to. Old marbled paper wraps)
    1. Medicine. 15th-18th cent. 2. Blood. circulation. 3. Microscope and micros copy.

    Early works to 1800. I. Harveana.

NN   0020754   KU-M CtY-M

Nardi, Giovanni, ca. 1580-ca.1655.
    Noctes geniales ... Annus primus.   Bononiae, Typis Jo, Baptistae Ferronii, 1656.
    [12], 748, [40] p.   22 cm.
    Edited by Elias Schottelius.
    Dedicatory epistle signed by Filippo Nardi, the author's son.
    I. Nardi, Filippo, fl. ca. 1655. II. Schottelius, Elias, fl. ca. 1655, ed.

NN   0020755   DNLM CLU-M PPC

Law   Nardi, Giovanni de, joint ed.

    Italy. *Laws, statutes, etc.* (*Indexes*)
    ... Indice sistematico cronologico della legislazione italiana; leggi, decreti e regolamenti dal 1861, ordinato per materia alfabeticamente con copiose note analitiche e di riferimento ... Belluno, S. E. B. A., Società editrice bellunese (accomandita)
    19

Nardi, Giovanni Domenico.   *5340.10.11
    Sui mezzi più efficaci ad impedire che qualche figlio illegittimo rimanga occulto, ossia non iscritto nei registri civili ...
    (In Reale istituto veneto di scienze, lettere ed arti. Memorie. Vol. 11, pp. 201–217. Venezia, 1862.)

E4451 — Illegitimacy.

NN   0020757   MB

PN6475   Nardi, Giuseppe   comp.
R3N3   Proverbi, frasi e modi proverbiali del ravennate, raccolti e spiegati. Con prefazione del prof. Santi Muratori.   Imola, P. Galeati, 1922.
    xiii, 287 p.

    1. Proverbs, Italian.

NN   0020758   CU MH OC1 NN

Nardi, Giuseppe di.
    La banca. [Torino] Edizioni Radio italiana [1955]
    57 p. 17 cm. (Classe unica, 34)
    Bibliography: p. 57.

    1. Banks and banking.   I. Title.

    HG1607.N35   67-125071

NN   0020759   DLC

Nardi, Giuseppe di.
    Le banche di emissione in Italia nel secolo XIX. [Torino] Unione tipografico-editrice torinese [1953]
    xii, 436 p. diagrs. 25 cm. (Storia e dottrine economiche, 8)
    Bibliographical footnotes.

    1. Banks and banking—Italy.   I. Title.

    HG1870.I 8N3   A 55-3357
    New York Univ. Wash.   Sq. Library
    for Library of Congress   [2]†

    NNU-W
NN   0020760   DLC NNU ICU CU MH NcD TxU NN IaU OrU

Nardi, Giuseppe di.
    Economia dello scambio. [2. ed.] Bologna, C. Zuffi, 1952.
    x, 312 p. 25 cm.
    A revision of the author's Lezioni di economia politica, vol. 1.
    Includes bibliographies.

    1. Exchange.   I. Title.

                                    A 52-10152
    Chicago. Univ. Libr.
    for Library of Congress   [2]

NN   0020761   ICU NN NNU

Nardi, Giuseppe di.
    Economia dello scambio. 3. ed. riv. Napoli, E. Jovene, 1955.
    x, 326 p. diagrs. 24 cm.
    A revision of the author's Lezioni di economia politica, v. 1.
    "Bibliografia" at end of each chapter.

    1. Commerce. 2. Economics.   I. Title.

    [HB771.N   ]   A 57-4596
    New York Univ.   Libraries
    for Library of Congress   [3]

NN   0020762   NNU MH TxU

HD 2735   Nardi, Giuseppe di.
.N22   L'indeterminazione nel monopolio bilaterale. Bari, Tip. Cressati, 1934.
    60 p.

    1. Monopolies. 2. Exchange. I. Title.

NN   0020763   ICU

Nardi, Giuseppe di.
    Lezioni di economia politica. Bari, Istituto di economia politica, Università degli studi [1950–
    v. illus. 25 cm.
    Includes bibliographies.
    CONTENTS.—v. 1. Introduzione. Teoria dello scambio.

    1. Economics.   A 51-6260
    Chicago. Univ. Libr.
    for Library of Congress   [3]

NN   0020764   ICU

NARDI, GIUSEPPE DI.
    ...I limiti di oscillazione del salario nei rapporti collettivi di lavoro.   Bari: L. Macri, 1938.   94 p. 25cm.

    "Estratto dalla 'Rivista di diritto corporativo e del lavoro' n. 5, maggio 1938."

    1. Wages. 2. Wages—Italy. 3. Labor contracts, Collective. 4. Labor contracts, Collective—Italy.

NN   0020765   NN ICU

NARDI, GIUSEPPE di.
    ...Il sistema bancario nell'ordine corporativo.   Bari: Casa edit. tip. Cressati, 1938.   68 p. 25½cm.

    Also paged [67]–132.
    Bibliographical footnotes.

    1. Banks and banking—Italy. 2. Credit—Italy.

NN   0020766   NN ICU

Nardi, Giuseppe Michele
    see Nardi, Michele Giuseppe.

VOLUME 405

NARDI,Gustavo.
Raccolta sistematica della legislazione
vigente sulla istruzione elementare. Leggi,rego-
lamenti,circolari emanate dal 1859 al 1919;cenni
storici;commenti;massime di giurisprudenza. Con
appendice contenente le modificazioni e aggiunte
fino a tutto il 1922. Torino,etc.,G.B.Paravia
& C.,[1923].

NN   0020768   MH

NARDI,Gustavo.
Il regolamento generale sull'istruzione
elementare,approvato con r.decreto 26 aprile
1928. Cenni storico dei vari istituti guiri-
dici,commento per articoli,[etc.]. Torino,
etc.,G.B.Paravia & c.,1928.

"Pubblicato sulla 'Gazzetta ufficiale' n.167
del 19 luglio 1928 (supplemento)."

NN   0020769   MH

Nardi, Gustavo.
Il testo unico delle leggi sull'istruzione
elementare, approvato con R.D. 22 gennaio 1925,
N.432... Torino, Paravia, n.d.
195 p

NN   0020770   PU

Nardi, Helen C
The Central Valley Project of California

see under

California. Legislative Counsel Bureau.
Library.

Nardi, Iacopo
see   Nardi, Jacopo, 1476-ca. 1563.

Nardi, Isidoro.
Genealogia della famiglia Valignana, descritta da D.
Isidoro Nardi ... Roma, Nella stamperia della Reu.
Camera apost. [1686]

20 p. l., 220, [4] p. ports., coats of arms. 25^{cm}.

Head-pieces; initials.
Portraits engraved by Girolamo Frezza.

1. Valignana family.   I. Frezza, Giovanni Girolamo, 1659–1728.

26–21697

Library of Congress   CS769.V3N3

NN   0020773   DLC IU

Y
9935
.607   NARDI, ISIDORO.
Modo e formole di scrivere viglietti tanto
di complimento, quanto di negozio, con una scala
de'termini più pratticati nella segretaria, e
con un titolario per un prelato principe: ag-
giuntovi un saggio di lettere di complimento
per la terza parte del segretario principiante
ed istruito, ed un'altro saggio di lettere latine... Roma, Per il Placho,1718.
240p. front. 15cm.

NN   0020774   ICN

808.6
.N223se
1710   Nardi,Isidoro.
Il segretario principiante,ed istruito.
Diviso in due parti di lettere in questa
terza impressione,ricorretto,ed accresciuto
di nuove lettere,di titolario,e di formole
di patenti,e di altre spedizioni. Roma,
Stamperia di G.Placho, 1710.
2 v.in 1.
1.Letter-writing.   2.Letter-writing,
Italian.   I.Title.

NN   0020775   MiU

808.6
.N223se
1711   Nardi,Isidoro.
Il segretario principiante,ed istruito.
Diuiso in due parti di lettere. Corretto,
ed accresciuto di nuove lettere,di titolario,
e di formole di patenti,e di altre spedizioni.
Bologna, Longhi, 1711.
586 p.

1.Letter-writing.   2.Letter-writing,
Italian.   I.Title.

NN   0020776   MiU

Nardi, Isidoro.

Il segretario principiante ed istruito,
diviso in due parti di lettere, corr., ed
accresciuto di nueve lettere, di titolario,
e di formole di patenti, e di altre spedizioni.
Con nuova, e brieve aggiunta per regolarsi
sopra la introduzione moderna de.' titoli.
Bologna, Nella stamperia del Longhi, 1735.
596 p. 14 cm.
1. Letter-writing, Italian.   I. Title.

NN   0020777   NcD NjP

Y
9935
.61   Nardi, Isidoro.
Il segretario principiante, ed in-
struito. Lettere moderne... Venezia,
n.d.   2v.in 1.

NN   0020778   ICN

Nardi, Isidoro.
Il segretario principiante ed istrutto. Lettere moderne. Ed.
novissima. Venezia, F. Storti, 1757.
nar. 16°. pp. 480.

NN   0020779   MH

Nardi, Isidoro.   4789a.22
Il segretario principiante ed istrutto. Lettere moderne. Col titolario, formole di patenti, spedizioni ec. ed alcune utilissime osservazioni intorno il regolato comporre, e scrivere una lettera. Edizione novissima accresciuta di una raccolta di lettere mercantili
...
Bassano. Remondini. 1814. 360 pp. 14½ cm., in 18s.

.

L8351 — T.r. — Letter-writing.

NN   0020780   MB

Nardi, Isidoro.
Vita di S. Rosa viterbese del terz'Ordine di S. Francesco. Composta dal canonico D. Isidoro Nardi... Roma, Nella Stamperia
del Varese, 1686. 336 p. front. 21cm.

350117B. 1. Rose of Viterbo, Saint,   13th cent.
N. Y. P. L.   May 26, 1947

NN   0020781   NN

---

x853N16   Nardi, Jacopo, 1476-ca. 1563.
Oa   Comedia di amicitia. [Florence, Lorenzo
Morgiani and Johannes Petri, ca.1496-97?]
[20]l. 19.7cm.

Leaf [1ª] (t.p.): ¶COMEDIA DI AMICITIA.
Hain. Repertorium, 11673; Goff. Third
census, N4.
Brit. Mus. Gen. Cat of Printed Books gives
imprint: [Florence? 1510?] The play was most
likely performed 1502-12. Cf. Radcliff-Um-
stead, Douglas. The birth of modern comedy in
Renaissance Italv (1969), p.110.

NN   0020782   IU CtY MH PU

Nardi, Jacopo, 1476-ca.1563.
Bm52   Delle istorie della città di Firenze, di
126   Iacopo Nardi. Libro inedito tratto ora in
luce da'codici originali e annotato per cura
e opera di Lelio Arbib.
Firenze,A spese della Società editrice delle
storie del Nardi e del Varchi,1841. 23½cm.
"Vita di Iacopo Nardi, gentiluomo, poeta ed
istorico fiorentino, scritta da D.Carlo-Maria
Nardi"2. ed.: [3p.l.,lxxiii pp.

NN   0020783   CtY

Nardi, Jacopo, 1476-ca.1563.
I due felici rivali,commedia inedita di Jacopo Nardi,pubblicata da Alessandro Ferrajoli.
Roma, Forzani e c., 1901.
xlvii,72 p.,1 l. 26½^{cm}.

Half-title: Nozze Pizzirani-Sterbini,xxix aprile mcmi.
"Il testo da noi seguito 'e tratto da un ... manoscritto ... che si conserva in Roma nella biblioteca dei
principi Barberini (segnato XLV,5)"—Introd.,p.ix.
Editor's autographed presentation copy.

1.Nozze,Per. Pizzirani-Sterbini. I.Ferrajoli,Ales-
sandro,marchese,1846-1919, ed. II.Title.

NN   0020784   MiU ICN ICU PU NN NcD IU MH PBm

Nardi, Jacopo, 1476–*ca.* 1563.
Le historie della citta di Fiorenza, di M. Iacopo Nardi
cittadino fiorentino. Le quali con tutta quella particolarità che bisogna, contengono quanto dal' anno 1494. fino
al tempo del' anno 1531. è successo. Con vn catalogo de
gonfalonieri di giustitia, che hanno seduto nel supremo
magistrato della citta di Fiorenza. Et nella fine vn Discorso sopra lo stato della magnifica città di Lione [di
Francesco Giuntini]. Nuouamente poste in luce. Lione,
Appresso T. Ancelin, 1582.
4 p. l., 232 numb. l., 36 l. 24^{cm}.
Title within ornamental border.
Dedication signed: Francesco Giuntini.
1. Florence—Hist.   2. Lyons—Déscr.   I. Giuntini,
Francesco, 1523?–1590,   ed.
                                        18–19689

Library of Congress   DG736.N2 1582

MWelC PPPD CLU IU
NN   0020785   DLC PPPD NjP NNC DFo NNG MB MnU

Nardi, Jacopo, 1476–*ca.* 1563.
Istorie della città di Firenze di Iacopo Nardi, ridotte
alla lezione de' codici originali con l'aggiunta del decimo
libro inedito e con annotazioni per cura e opera di Lelio
Arbib ... Firenze, A spese della Società editrice delle
storie del Nardi e del Varchi, 1838–41.
2 v. front. (port.) 24^{cm}.
"Vita di Iacopo Nardi ... scritta da D. Carlo-Maria Nardi": v. 1, p.
[xi]-lxxxix.
1. Florence—Hist.   I. Arbib, Lelio, ed.   II. Nardi, Carlo Maria, fl.
1735.
                                        18–5026

Library of Congress   DG736.N2 1838

NN   0020786   DLC

Nardi, Jacopo, 1476–*ca.* 1563.
Istorie della città di Firenze di Iacopo Nardi, ridotte alla
lezione de' codici originali con l'aggiunta del decimo libro
inedito e con annotazioni per cura e opera di Lelio Arbib ...
Firenze, A spese della Società editrice delle storie del Nardi
et del Varchi, 1842.
2 v. front. (port.) 23^{cm}.
"Vita di Iacopo Nardi ... scritta da D. Carlo-Maria Nardi": v. 1,
p. [xl]-xciii.
1. Florence—Hist.   I. Arbib, Lelio, ed.   II. Nardi, Carlo Maria,
fl. 1735.
                                        28–1347

Library of Congress   DG736.3.N2 1842

NN   0020787   DLC WU NIC NcD MH

VOLUME 405

Nardi, Jacopo, 1476–*ca.* 1563.
Istorie della città di Firenze di Iacopo Nardi, ridotte alla lezione dei codici originali coll' aggiunta del decimo libro e con annotazioni per cura e opera di Lelio Arbib ... Torino, Societa' editrice del Monitore e biblioteca dei comuni italiani [1852]
2 v. in 1. 19^{cm}.

1. Florence—Hist.   I. Arbib, Lelio.

27–19989

Library of Congress   DG736.3.N2 1852

NN   0020788   DLC OC1

945.51 Nardi, Jacopo, 1476–*ca.* 1563.
N16h   Istorie della città di Firenze ri-
1853   dotte alla lezione dei codici originali coll'aggiunta del decimo libro e
con annotazioni per cura e opera di
Lelio Arbib.   Torino, 1853.
2 v.

"Vita di Iacopo Narbi scritta da
Carlo Nardi": v.1, p.[7]–77.

NN   0020789   IU

Nardi, Jacopo, 1476–*ca.* 1563.
Istorie della città di Firenze di Iacopo Nardi, pub. per cura di Agenore Gelli. Firenze, F. Le Monnier, 1858.
2 v. 19^{cm}.

Half-title: Opere di Iacopo Nardi.

1. Florence—Hist.   I. Gelli, Agenore, b. 1829, ed.

Library of Congress   DG736.3.N2 1858   8–37139

NN   0020790   DLC WaU PV CtY NIC PU NN NjP MiU

Nardi, Jacopo, 1476–*ca.* 1563.
Istorie della città di Firenze, di Iacopo Nardi. Secondo il testo pubblicato per cura di A. Gelli. Firenze, Successori Le Monnier, 1888.
2 v. 17½^{cm}. (Biblioteca nazionale economica)

1. Florence—Hist.   I. Gelli, Agenore.

Library of Congress   DG736.3.N2 1888   2—2525

NN   0020791   DLC CU MeB WaU

PA6456   Nardi, Jacopo, 1476–*ca.* 1563, tr.
.N33
Livius, Titus.
... Roma contro Cartagine; prefazione di Manlio Lupinacci.
Torino, G. Einaudi, 1942 [i. e. 1943]

Nardi, Jacopo, 1476–*ca.* 1563.
Le storie della citta di Firenze di m. Iacopo Nardi ... Doue con tutte le particolarità, che si possono disiderare si contiene cio che dall'anno 1494. sino all'anno 1531. e successo. Con la tauola delle cose notabili, e co'sommari à ciascun libro; aggiuntoui vn istruzione per leggere le storie ordinatamente. Firenze, Stamperia di B. Sermartelli, 1584.
8 p. l., 390, [18] p. 22^{cm}.

Dedication signed: Bartolommeo Sermartelli.
First published 1582.

1. Florence—Hist.   I. Sermartelli, Bartolomeo, ed.

Library of Congress   DG736.3.N2 1584   45–29845

InU NSchU PP PU ICN MiU WaU
NN   0020793   DLC CU MiDW MH CSt MCM DFo CtY ICU

Nardi, Jacopo, 1476–*ca.* 1563.
Vita d'Antonio Giacomini Tebalducci Malespini, scritta da Iacopo Nardi. Fiorenza, Ne le case de Sermartelli, 1597.
4 p. l., 77, [7] p. 22½^{cm}.

Title vignette (device of Sermartelli)
Edited by L. Giacomini Tebalducci Malespini.

1. Giacomini Tebalducci Malespini, Antonio, 1453?–1517.   I. Giacomini Tebalducci Malespini, Lorenzo, d. 1599, ed.

18–6457

Library of Congress   DG738.14.G5N3 1597

NN   0020794   DLC CtY NcD PU MWelC

DG738 Nardi, Jacopo, 1476–*ca.* 1563.
.14   Vita d'Antonio Giacomini Tebalducci Malespini, scritta
.G43N22 da Jacopo Nardi. Lucca, F. Bertini, 1818.
xii, 140 p. 22½^{cm}.

NN   0020795   ICU

Nardi, Jacopo, 1476–*ca.* 1563.
Vita d'Antonio Giacomini Tebalducci Malespini, scritta da Jacopo Nardi. Pisa, Presso N. Capurro, 1818.
xii, 140 p. 22½^{cm}.

1. Giacomini Tebalducci Malespini, Antonio, 1453?–1517.

18–5024

Library of Congress   DG738.14.G5N3

NN   0020796   DLC CU IaU NjP NN CtY

Nardi, Jacopo, 1476–ca. 1563. La vita di
Antonio Giacomini.

Porzio, Camillo, 1526?–1580?
La congiura de' baroni del regno di Napoli, di Camillo Porzio. La vita di Niccolò Capponi, di Bernardo Segni. La vita di Antonio Giacomini, di Jacopo Nardi. Milano, G. Silvestri, 1821.

Bm52   Nardi, Jacopo, 1476–*ca.* 1563.
95   Vita di Jacopo Nardi, scritta da
Jacopo Nardi, ridotta a corretta lezione sui
manoscritti e annotata per cura di Agenore
Gelli ... Firenze, Tipografia Galileiana, 1854
2 p. l., [3]–106 p., 1 l. 20½ cm.
"Edizione fatta su quella degli Opuscoli
scelti annessi alle Letture di famiglia."

NN   0020798   CtY IU ICN

Nardi, Jacopo, 1476–ca.1563.
Vita di Antonio Giacomini e altri
scritti minori... Firenze, Barbèra, 1867.
32,528 p. 11 ^{cm}.

NN   0020799   NjP

Nardi, Joannes
see Nardi, Giovanni, ca. 1580–1655.

Nardi, Jole.
D'Annunzio ed alcuni scrittori francesi. Cesena, Editrice Orfanelli Addolorata [1951]
viii, 144 p. 24 cm.

"Errata corrige": [2] p. tipped in.
Bibliographical footnotes.

1. Annunzio, Gabriele d', 1863–1938.

Full name: Jole Ghini Nardi.

A 53–1609

Harvard Univ. Library
for Library of Congress   [2]

NN   0020801   MH IU CU NN OU OrU

4QO   Nardi, L
729   Elementi di aerologia; corso
allievi piloti, anno 1928–1929.
Merate, Ditta Fratelli Airoldi [192]
30 p.

NN   0020802   DLC-P4

BX   Nardi, Luigi, 1777–1837.
1915   Articolo estratto dal Giornale ecclesiastico
N166a   di Roma; lettera miscellanea. 2. ed. con
1825   aggiunte. Pesaro, Tip. Nobile, 1825.
68 p.

Includes bibliographical references.

1. Catholic Church – Clergy. 2. Mirrors.
3. Combs. I. Title.

NN   0020803   CLU

922.2 Nardi, Luigi, 1777–1837.
N16c   Cronotassi dei pastori della s. chiesa riminese
aumentata e corretta dal ... Luigi Nardi.   Rimino,
Dai tipi albertiniani, 1813.
334p.

Bibliographical foot-notes.

NN   0020804   IU

---

q292   Nardi, Luigi, 1777–1837.
N16d   Dei compiti, feste e givochi compitali degli antichi e dell'antico compito savignanese in Romagna
Pesaro, Dalla Tipografia di A. Nobili, 1827.
176p.

"Alcuni uomini illustri nelle lettere dell'antico distretto compitano": p.144–165.
Bibliographical foot-notes.

1. Ludi compitalicii. 2. Savignano, Italy--
Biog.

NN   0020805   IU PU ICN

BV   Nardi, Luigi, 1777–1837.
192   Dei parrochi, opera di antichita sacra e dis
.L2   ciplina ecclesiastica, del parroco D. Luigi Nardi
N22   ... Pesaro, Coi tipi di Nobili, 1829–30.
2 v. 28 cm.

Bibliographical footnotes.

1. Pastors (Canon law) 2. Parishes (Canon law)
3. Clergy (Canon law)

NN   0020806   DCU MBtS IU CU

Nardi, Luigi, 1777–1837.
Descrizione antiquario-architettonica; con
rami dell'Arco di Augusto, Ponte di Tiberio e
Tempio Malatestiano di Rimino. Rimino, Nella
stamperia Marsoner e Grandi, 1813.
81 p., 17 plates (incl.plans) 40cm.

1.Italy – Antiquities. 2.Architecture, Roman
– History. 3.Rome – Antiquities.   I.TITLE.
SSL NUC SC

NN   0020807   CSt MB IU ICU NjP CtY NcD CaBVaU

NARDI, Luigi, 1777–1837.
Memoria sopra alcune parole italiane,
e sopra la terzina di Dante [Purg. XXXI.
130–132. Roma, 1824]

pp.[23].
Giornale arcadico, 1824, xxiv. 343–365.

NN   0020808   MH NIC

VOLUME 405

[Nardi, Luigi] 1777-1837.
Porcus troianus, o sia la Porchetta. Cicalata ne le
nozze di Messer Carlo Ridolfi, Veronese, con Madonna
Rosa Spina, Riminese. Altra edizione. [Milano] Da tipi
Nobili. CIↃ IↃ CCC XXI.
1 p. l., xvi, 134 p. 20ᶜᵐ.
Dedication "A ser Maggiro, cuoco dello sposo, Giri di Luna [anagramma di Luigi Nardi] salute," p. iii-xvi.—Cicalata, p. 1-55.—Testamento di Marco Grunio Corocotta Porcello ("Marcvs. Grvnivs. Corocotta. Porcellvs. Testamentvm. Fecit" [etc.]) p. 56-58.—Annotazioni alla Porchetta, p. 59-130.—Approvazione (signed Milano, 25 luglio, 1813 "noi il Poligrafo. B. segretario ad hoc.") p. 131-133.—Errata, p. 134.
First published, Arimino, dai tipi Albertiani, CIↃIↃCCCXIII, without the "Testamento" and without the valuable notes.
3-23261

NN   0020809   DLC NcD OC1

Nardi, Luigi, 1777-1837,
Sopra alcune parole italiane antiche ...
Roma, 1824.

NN   0020810   NIC

Nardi, Marcia.
Beatrice; opera in three acts
see under Hoiby, Lee, 1926-

WJA   NARDI, Mauro.
N223d   Dissertatio de onanismo conjugali.
1876   Tolosae, Privat, 1876.
      146 p.

NN   0020812   DNLM

RG51   Nardi, Michele Giuseppe.
.N22   Il pensiero ostetrico-ginecologico nei secoli.
      Pref. del Cesare Decio. Milano, Thiele [1954]
      540 p. illus., ports.
      Issued in 23 pts., 1953-54.
      Includes bibliographies.

      1. Obstetrics--Hist. 2. Gynecology--Hist.

NN   0020813   ICU PPC

Adelmann
QL   Nardi, *Michele Giuseppe.*
953   Problemi d'embriologia umana antica e
N22   medioevale. Firenze, G. C. Sansoni, 1938.
      126 p. 20cm. (Biblioteca italiana, 10)
      By Giuseppe Michele Nardi.

      1. Embryology--Hist. I. Series.

NN   0020814   NIC CU DNLM NNC PPC

M1850
.N25 I 8   Nardi, Nachum, 1901-
      Israel, an album of Hebrew songs.
      Words by M. Avigal [and others].
      English adaptations by Olga Paul.
      Cover design and book illustrations
      by Saul Raskin. New York, E. Marks
      Music Corp. c1952.
      40 p. illus. port. 31cm.
      Words in English and Hebrew.

      1. Songs, Jewish. I. Title.

NN   0020815   MB OrP CaBVa

M1850
.N25L3   Nardi, Nachum, 1901-
Hebraic   למתנדבים בעם, שמונה שירים. תל־אביב, תש״ג.
Sect.   [Tel-Aviv, 1942]
      20 p. 16 cm.
      All but one of the songs are unaccompanied.
      CONTENTS.—
דרכן ע. מאת ח.נ. ביאליק.—שיר החללה. מאת מרים ולקפראומטש.
—לחיל העברי, מאת ראובן גרוסמן.—שי לחיל, מאת לוין קיפניס.—חיילה עברית הני,
מאת אסתר אוקסמן.—נודד חילים יהודים, מאת בן־ירושלם.—אני־על־עד־כך, מאת דוד
המע׳טוביץ.—שיר למולדת. מאת יעקב ליכטמן.
      1. Songs, Jewish.   I. Title.
      Title transliterated: La-mitnadvim ba-'am.
      Name originally: Nachum Naroditzky.

M1850.N25L3   48-20415*

NN   0020816   DLC

Nardi, Nachum, 1901-
... Mi yivneh, Who will build ...
see under title

M1850
.N25S4   Nardi, Nachum, 1901-
      שירי נחום נרדי. רמן, הוצאה למוסיקה.
      [Rennen, Palestine, 1947-]
      v. illus. 25 cm.
      Melodies unacc.
      Errata slip inserted.
      CONTENTS.— שירי ילדים. 75 א. קובץ
      1. Songs, Jewish. 2. Children's songs, Jewish
      Title transliterated: Shire Naḥum Nardi.
      Name originally: Nachum Naroditzky.

M1850.N25S4   49-16920*

NN   0020818   DLC

Nardi, Naum
see Nardi, Nachum, 1901-

NARDI, Noach, 1902-
Education in Israel. Enlarged reprint
from Child Care in Israel, Jerusalem, 1950,
p.1-15.

1.Israel-Education.

NN   0020820   NNJ

Nardi, Noach, 1902-
Education in Palestine, 1920-1945, by Noah Nardi. [Washington] Zionist organization of America, 1945.
xv, 255 p. 23ᶜᵐ.

1. Jews in Palestine—Education. 2. Education—Palestine. I. Zionist organization of America. II. Title.
                     46-142
Library of Congress*   LA1441.N3
               [5]   370.9569

      OC1Tem OC1 NNZI MB PSt PPDrop
NN   0020821   DLC OrP OrU Or WaS MiU NcC ICJS NRU

Nardi, Noach, 1902-
פסיכולוגיה של הלמידה. תל־אביב. הוצאת "אורים." תשי״ג.
[Tel-Aviv, 1952/53]
      36 p. illus. 19 cm.   [ספריה פדגוגית קטנה, יז]
      Bibliography: p. 35-36.

      1. Learning, Psychology of.
      Title transliterated: Psikhologiyah shel ha-lemidah.

LB1051.N3   54-55604 ‡

NN   0020822   DLC

Nardi, Noach, 1902-
הפסיכולוגיה של הילד. תל־אביב. י. צ׳צ׳יק, תשט״ו.
[Tel-Aviv, 1954/55]
      251 p. 23 cm.

      1. Child study.   I. Title.
      Title transliterated: ha-Psikhologiyah shel ha-yeled.

LB1115.N3   56-52534 ‡

NN   0020823   DLC

Nardi, Noach, 1902-
הפסיכולוגיה והחינוך. תל־אביב. י. צ׳צ׳יק, תשט״ו.
[Tel-Aviv, 1954/55]
      400 p. 24 cm.
      Bibliography: p. 363-385.

      1. Educational psychology. 2. Education—Israel. I. Title.
      Title transliterated: ha-Psikhologiyah veha-ḥinukh.

LB1051.N32   57-50334

NN   0020824   DLC NB

Nardi, Noach, 1902-
Zionism and education in Palestine, by Noach Nardi ...
New York city, Teachers college, Columbia university, 1934.
ix, 99, [1] p. 22½ᶜᵐ.
Thesis (PH. D.)—Columbia university, 1935.
Vita.
Published also as Teachers college, Columbia university, Contributions to education, no. 629.
Bibliography: p. 93-99.

      1. Jews in Palestine—Education. 2. Jews—Restoration. 3. Education—Palestine. I. Title.
                     35-7338
Library of Congress   LC747.P3N3 1935
Columbia Univ. Libr.   [2]   370.9569

NN   0020825   NNC DLC

Nardi, Noach, 1902-
Zionism and education in Palestine, by Noach Nardi ...
New York city, Teachers college, Columbia university, 1934.
ix, 99 p. 23½ᶜᵐ.   (Teachers college, Columbia university. Contributions to education, no. 629)
Issued also as thesis (PH. D.) Columbia university.
Bibliography: p. 93-99.

      1. Jews in Palestine—Education. 2. Jews—Restoration. 3. Education—Palestine. I. Title.
                     35-7337
Library of Congress   LC747.P3N3 1934
——— Copy 2.   LB5.C8 no. 629
Copyright A 82432   [13]   370.9569

      ViU WaS MtU DHEW
NN   0020826   DLC KEmT PSt OCH OCU OC1 PBm PPT MB

Nardi, Noah
see Nardi, Noach, 1902-

B878N21
R7   Nardi, Paolini, 16th cent.
1557   D. Pavlini Nardi Bononiensis De prvdentia
      oratio ... Bononiae, Ex officina Victorij
      Benatij, 1596.
      [12] p. 21cm.

      Printer's device on title page.
      Bound with Natta, Marcantonio. In Divi Hieronymi Stridonensis natale, oratio. 1557.

NN   0020828   NNC

VOLUME 405

Nardi, Piero, 1891–
... Antonio Fogazzaro. Con quaranta tavole fuori testo e quattro autografi. Milano, A. Mondadori [1938]

5 p. l., [3]–722 p. front., xxxix pl. (incl. ports.) on 20 l., 4 facsim. (1 fold.) 22½ᵐ. [Le scie"; collana di epistolari, memorie, biografie e curiosità]

"1ª edizione—febbraio 1938."
"Cronologia della vita e degli scritti di Antonio Fogazzaro": p. [665]–690.
"Nota bibliografica": p. [691]–695.

1. Fogazzaro, Antonio, 1842–1911.
              A C 38–2864 Revised

Illinois. Univ. Library
for Library of Congress   PQ4688.F6Z94
Copyright A—Foreign   45023
                [r40c2]   928.5

NN 0020829   IU OrU NcD CU MoU MB MiU NjP DLC

PQ4688 Nardi, Piero, 1891–
F6Z94   Antonio Fogazzaro. Con quaranta tavole
1945   fuori testo e quattro autografi. [3.ed.
      Milano] Casa editrice Mondadori [1945]
        720p. XXXIX plates (incl.ports.) 4
      facsims (1 fold.) 23cm.

        "1ª edizione, febbraio 1938."
        Includes bibliography.

        I. Fogazzaro, Antonio, 1842–1911.

NN 0020830   IaU OU NIC ICU CSt

NARDI, Piero, 1891–
Fogazzaro, su documenti inediti.
Vicenza, E. Jacchia, 1929.

Facsimile plate.

NN 0020831   MH CU NcD WU RPB

D855F68
DN
    Nardi, Piero, 1891–
    ... Fogazzaro, su documenti inediti. 2. ed.
    riveduta con nuovi documenti. Vicenza, Jacchia,
    1930.
      4 p. l., [xi]–xx, 350 p., 2 l. port., facsim.
    19ᶜᵐ.

      "Nota bio-bibliografica": p. [343]–350.
      1. Fogazzaro, Antonio, 1842–1911.

NN 0020832   NNC PU MH CtY ICU ViU MU

Nardi, Piero, 1891–
Giuseppe Giacosa, Luigi Albertini, ritratti di Piero Nardi e Ettore Janni. In occasione delle celebrazioni commemorative tenutesi a Colleretto Parella e a Ivrea il 12 ottobre 1952, a cura del Comitato promotore canavesano. [Torino, Stamperia artistica nazionale, 1952] 70 p. illus., ports. 22cm.

Contents.—Presentazione.—A Giuseppe Giacosa, di G. Pascoli.—Ritratto biografico di Giuseppe Giacosa, di P. Nardi.—"Come le foglie," dopo mezzo secolo, di P. Nardi.—"Elogio" di Luigi Albertini, di E. Janni.

1. Giacosa, Giuseppe, 1847–1906.   2. Albertini, Luigi, 1871–1941.
I. Janni, Ettore, 1879– . II. Title.

NN 0020833   NN RPB

PQ4087 Nardi, Piero, 1891–
.N3   Novecentismo; abbozzi e cartoni. Milano,
      Societa editrice "Unitas" [1926]
      221 p.

        1. Italian literature—20th cent.—Hist. and
    crit. I. Title.

      OU CoU CU IEN
NN 0020834   ICU DLC-P4 NcD PU OC1 NjP IU ViU CSt

PQ4688   Nardi, Piero, 1891–   ed.
.D55A6
1940   Dossi, Carlo, 1849–1910.
      Le più belle pagine di Carlo Dossi, scelte da Piero Nardi.
    [Milano] Garzanti [1940]

Nardi, Piero, 1891–   ed.

I promessi sposi

see under

Manzoni, Alessandro, 1785–1873.

PQ4841 Nardi, Piero, 1891–
E76Z76   Renato Serra. Milano, Sezione del Nastro
      Azzurro, 1930.
      56 p. 20cm. (I quaderni del nastro
    Azzurro)

      1. Serra, Renato, 1884–1915.

NN 0020837   CoU

850.9 Nardi, Piero, 1891–
N166s   Scapigliatura da Giuseppe Rovani a Carlo
      Dossi. Bologna, N. Zanichelli [1924]
      336 p.

      Bibliography: p.[321]–336.

      1. Italian literature – 19th cent. –
    History and criticism. I. Title.

NN 0020838   WaU CU NcD ICU PP PU ICU

Nardi, Piero, 1891– ed.

Fogazzaro, Antonio, 1842–1911.
Tutte le opere di Antonio Fogazzaro; a cura di Piero Nardi ... [Milano, A. Mondadori, editore, 1931–35]

PQ4684 Nardi, Piero, 1891–   ed.
.B23
1942   Boito, Arrigo, 1842–1918.
      Tutti gli scritti, a cura di Piero Nardi. [1. ed.] [Milano]
    A. Mondadori [1942]

Nardi, Piero, 1891–
... Vita di Arrigo Boito. Con 60 illustrazioni fuori testo e 10 facsimili. [Milano] Mondadori [1944]

753, [1] p. incl. front. plates, ports., facsims. (incl. music) 20ᵐ. [Le Scie," collana di epistolari, memorie, biografie e curiosità]

"1ª edizione, dicembre 1942; 2ª edizione, novembre 1944; ristampa 30 novembre 1944."

1. Boito, Arrigo, 1842–1918.
ML410.B694N3   927.8   A F 47–154
Newberry library
for Library of Congress   [4]†

      OU TxU VtMiM DLC IaU
NN 0020841   ICN MdBP NcU NN NRU NcU NcD CLU ICU

NARDI, PIERO, 1891–
Vita di Arrigo Boito. 2. ed. Con 60 illus. fuori testo e 10 facsimili. [Milano] Mondadori [1944]
753 p. plates, ports., facsims. (incl. music) 20cm. ["Le Scie," collana di epistolari, memorie, biografie e curiosità]

Film reproduction. Negative.

1. Boito, Arrigo, 1842–1918.

NN 0020842   NN

Nardi, Piero, 1891–
La vita di D. H. Lawrence. [1. ed. Milano] A. Mondadori [1947]
898 p. 20 cm. (Tutte le opere di David Herbert Lawrence, v. 1)
I Classici contemporanei stranieri.

1. Lawrence, David Herbert, 1885–1930.
PR6023.A93A12   vol. 1   50–17313

      TxU
NN 0020843   DLC PSt OrU CU-S OU CU IEN NN NNU-W

Nardi, Piero, 1891–
Vita e tempo di Giuseppe Giacosa. [1. ed. Milano] Mondadori [1949]
xi, 926 p. illus., ports., facsims. 20 cm. (Le Scie)

1. Giacosa, Giuseppe, 1847–1906.   I. Title.

PQ4692.G6Z75   928.5   50–27658

NN 0020844   DLC ICU NN RPB PU OC1W NBuU CSt MB

Nardi, Pietro de, 1847–1905.
Amori celebri dei poeti e degli artisti italiani. Milano, Tipeditrico Dante Alighiere, 1872.
368 p

NN 0020845   PU NIC

Nardi, P[ietro] de, 1847–1905.
Antonio Rosmini ed i Gesuiti dinanzi a San Tommaso d'Aquino; colla confutazione del nuovo libro del p. Cornoldi Sul Rosminianismo. Risposta prima alla Civiltà cattolica. Torino, stamperia dell' Unione tipografico-editrice, 1882.
pp. 263 +.

Rosmini-Serbati,   Antonio|Thomas Aquinas, Saint

NN 0020846   MH

NARDI, Pietro de, 1847–1905.
L'assoluto inconoscibile di Herbert Spencer, esposizione, storia e critica. Forli, Tip. Sociale (Suc. Bordandini), 1904.

NN 0020847   MH

NARDI, Pietro de, 1847–1905.
Caratteri della filosofia di Giovanni Locke e del sensismo in generale; in risposta al Prof. Sante Ferrari. Firenze, coi tipi di M.Cellini e c., 1889.

pp.24.

NN 0020848   MH

NARDI, Pietro de, 1847–1905.
Del rinnovamento della dottrine di Gall e Broussais di Locke, Hume e Reid per opera della filosofia positiva, francese ed inglise, a complemento della memoria.; Caratteri della filosofia di Giovanni Locke, etc., Firenze, coi tipi di M. Cellini e c., 1890.

pp.12.

NN 0020849   MH

VOLUME 405

027.245
M637d
Nardi, Pietro de, 1847-1905.
Della Biblioteca nazionale di Brera
in Milano ...   Milano [1878?]
22p.

"Articoli estratti dal Monitore dei
collegi e delle scuole."

NN 0020850 IU

NARDI, Pietro de, 1847-1905
La filosofia di Antonio Rosmini-Serbati,
prete roveretano difesa contro in neoscolastici
del canton Ticino. Pt. I. Bellinzona, Tip.
Cantonale, 1881.

No more published.

NN 0020851 MH

Nardi, Pietro de, 1847-1905.
Giuseppe Mazzini, la vita, gli scritti, le dottrine, per Pietro
de-Nardi. Milano, Tipografia editrice Dante Alighieri, 1872.

796 p. incl. illus., plates, ports. 23ᶜᵐ. [With Balbiani, Antonio. Il
messia dei popoli oppressi, scene storiche della vita politica e militare
del generale Giuseppe Garibaldi. Volume terzo. Milano, 1872]

Portrait of Mazzini on t.-p.

1. Mazzini, Giuseppe, 1805-1872. 2. Italy—Hist.—1815-1870.

34-3389

Library of Congress   DG552.8.G2B3

NN 0020852 DLC NN CtY MH

NARDI, P[ietro] de, 1847-1905.
Petarca e Laura; storia dellaloro vita
e dei loro amori. Milano, C.Barbini,1873.

pp.91.

NN 0020853 MH

NARDI, Pietro de, 1847-1905.
Rosmini e Kant; studio comparativo e critico
Forli, tip. sociale, 1902.

pp.60.

NN 0020854 MH

Nardi, Rafaela Chacón
see   Chacón Nardi, Rafaela.

Nardi, Shulamith Schwartz.
The J N F's share in Tel Aviv, by Sulamith Schwartz. Describing the part played by the Jewish national fund «Keren kayemeth
leisrael» in the founding and development of the first Jewish city
of modern times.   Jerusalem: Issued by the Head off. of the
Keren kayemeth leisrael ltd. ⟨Jewish national fund⟩, 1936.   4 p.
front. (plan.)   30cm.

Cover-title.
Reproduced from typewritten copy.

1. Tel-Aviv, Palestine—Hist.   I. Jewish national fund.
N. Y. P. L.   August 17, 1939

NN 0020856 NN

Nardi, Tilde.
PQ4831
A74
Q47
Le quattro stagioni.   Milano, Gastaldi [1951]
34p.   19m. (Poeti d'oggi. n.204)

NN 0020857 RPB

NARDI, Vincenzo.
Chi piu dura la vince Proverbio in un atto
in versi. Firenze, [1876]

24°. pp.19.
([Salani, Adriano]. Collezione di farse
italiana e straniere,191]

NN 0020858 MH

Nardi, Vittorio, 1879-
Rime paesane. Con pref. di Plinio Bulleri. Mercato S.
Severino, Edizioni Moriniello [1952]
271 p. 18 cm. (Collana "Paestum" di poesia, n. 5)

I. Title.

PQ4831.A75R5   55-41442

NN 0020859 DLC IEN RPB

[Nardi-Beltrame, Achille.]
...La Camera agrumaria ed il suo funzionamento; relazione
a S. E. il ministro per l'industria, il commercio ed il lavoro. Roma:
L. Cecchini, 1917. 224 p. incl. tables. 4°. (Italy. Credito
e delle assicurazioni private, Direzione generale del. Annali. ser.
2, v. 19.)

"Relazione del Comm. Nardi." — p. 6.

1. Citrus fruits—Italy. 2. Acid,   Citric. 3. Ser.
N. Y. P. L.   August 11, 1927

NN 0020860 NN

4TL-
30
Nardi-Bernardi, E
Al ragazzi d'Italia, la gloriosa trasvolata di
S.E. il gen. Italo Balbo per il cieli sconfinati.
Firenze, Arti Grafiche Ammannati
99 p.

NN 0020861 DLC-P4

NARDI DEI, Silvio Maria.
Graziano; Cenni biografici. Roma, F.
Cuggiani, 1894.

Pamphlet.

NN 0020862 MH

NARDI-GRECO, Carlo.
Sociologia giuridica (contributo)
Torino, [etc.] 1905.

NN 0020863 MH-L

Nardi-Greco, Carlo.
... Sociologia giuridica (contributo) con prefazione del
prof. A. Asturaro ... Torino [etc.] Fratelli Bocca, 1907.
xxxviii p., 1 l., 480 p. diagr. 24½ᶜᵐ. (On cover: Biblioteca di scienze
sociali, vol. LIV)

Bibliographical foot-notes.

1. Sociology. 2. Law—Hist. & crit. 3. Ethnopsychology. I. Title.

14-20156

Library of Congress   HM34.N3

NN 0020864 DLC ICU ICJ

Nardi-Greco, Carlo.
... Sociología jurídica, por Carlos Nardi-Greco, con prólogo
de A. Asturaro; traducción por Eduardo Ovejero. Madrid, La
España moderna [1909?]
583 p., 1 l. diagr. 22ᶜᵐ. (Biblioteca de jurisprudencia, filosofía é
historia)

1. Sociology. 2. Law—Hist. & crit. 3. Ethnopsychology. I. Asturaro, Alfonso, 1854-1917. II. Ovejero y Maury, Eduardo, tr.

44-43254

Library of Congress   HM34.N33

NN 0020865 DLC

Nardi-Greco, Carlo.
Sociología jurídica. [Versión castellana por E. Ovejero,
rev. y corr. por C. de las Cuevas] Buenos Aires, Editorial
Atalaya [1949]
318 p. 23 cm.

1. Sociology. 2. Law—Hist. & crit. 3. Ethnopsychology.

HM34.N33 1949   301   50-1649

NN 0020866 DLC

Nardi-Greco, Nicolo.
Prolegomeni allo studio della divina commedia
di Dante Alighieri;...
Napoli, 1870.

NN 0020867 NIC

Nardin, Charles.
... Por los parques del amor. Novela. Montevideo [I. L. E.]
1944.
119, [1] p. 20ᶜᵐ.

I. Title.   A 45-3877

New York. Public library
for Library of Congress   [2]

NN 0020868 NN TxU

Nardin (Charles). * Sur l'électrothérapie dans
l'incontinence nocturne de l'urine. 36 pp. 4°.
Paris, 1864, No. 113.

NN 0020869 DNLM

912.6
N224a
Nardin, E
L'Afrique actuelle; nouvelle carte
physique et politique dressée d'après
les documents les plus récents par E.
Nardin et Th. Protin.   Paris, Garnier
[1910]
col.map 89 x 68cm. fold. to 19 x 12cm.

Scale 1:125,000,000.

1. Africa.   Maps. I. Protin, Th.
II. Title.

NN 0020870 IEN

[Nardin, Frances Louise] 1878-
The bugle calls the children; a pageant for playtime. [Co-
lumbia, Mo.] Woman's committee, Council of national defense,
Missouri division [°1918]
[12] p. 23ᶜᵐ.

"Copyright ... by F. Louise Nardin."

1. Pageants. I. U. S. Council of national defense. Committee on
women's defense work. Missouri division. II. Title.

19-5225 Revised

Library of Congress   PN6120.A5N3

NN 0020871 DLC

VOLUME 405

Nardin, Frances Louise, 1878–
How may the freshman be more easily and quickly adjusted to college life?

(*In* National education association of the United States. Addresses and proceedings, 1919. p. 415–420)

1. Students. ₍1. College students—Freshmen₎ 2. Woman—Education—U. S.

Library, U. S. Bur. of   Education   E 20–124

NN 0020872   DHEW OU OO

Nardin, Frances Louise, 1878–
The makers of America; a civic ritual, by F. Louise Nardin ... Bureau of community development, University extension division, the University of Wisconsin, Madison ... ₍Madison, University of Wisconsin₎ 1920.
23 p. diagr. 19ᶜᵐ. (Bulletin of the University of Wisconsin, serial no. 1050. General series, no. 834)

1. Americanization. I. Wisconsin. University. University extension division. Dept. of general information and welfare. Community development bureau. II. Title.

Library of Congress   PN4241.N3   20–27227

NN 0020873   DLC

Nardin, George Frederic, joint author.

McKee, Paul Gordon, 1898–
How to speak and write; a junior handbook, by Paul McKee ... Harriet E. Peet ... ₍and₎ George F. Nardin. Boston, New York ₍etc.₎ Houghton Mifflin company ₍*1940₎

Nardin, George Frederic.

U. S. *Council of national defense. Committee on women's defense work. Missouri division.*
Mother Goose in war time. ₍Columbia, Mo., Columbia printing co., *1918₎

Nardin, George Frederic.
... The new viewpoint in reading by George F. Nardin and O.C. Whitney ... Boston, New York ₍etc.₎ Houghton, Mifflin co. ₍c1925₎
₍13₎ p. incl. diagrs. 18½cm. (Educational progress vol. 5, no. 1)

Lbe33
925n

NN 0020876   CtY

Nardin, Georges.
Les métiers; rondels. Paris: A. Lemerre, 1911. 2 p. l., iv, 81 p., 1 l. 12°.

1. Poetry (French). 2. Title
N. Y. P. L.   June 21, 1912.

NN 0020877   NN

Nardin, Honorio, illus.
La ciudad de los ojos alegres
see under   Montiel Ballesteros, Adolfo, 1888–

Nardin, Honorio, illus.
Pitití, el hombre más chiquito del mundo
see under   Montiel Ballesteros, Adolfo, 1888–

PS3999   Nardin, James Thompson, 1921–
A study in popular American farce, 1865–1914. 1949.
152 l.

Typewritten.
Thesis—Univ. of Chicago.

1. Farce. 2. American drama—Hist. & crit.

NN 0020880   ICU

W 4
G32
1946
Nardin, Jean
Contribution à l'étude de la stérilisation extemporanée de l'eau de boisson. Genéve, Impr. genevoise, 1946.
48 p. (Geneva. Université. Faculté de médecine. Thèse. M. D. no. 1859)

Bibliography: p. ₍43₎–48.

NN 0020881   DNLM

Nardin, Jean Frédéric, 1687–1728.
Le prédicateur évangélique; ou, Sermons de Jean-Frédéric Nardin ... Tome 1– Paris: Bureau des archives du christianisme, 1821. v. 4. ed. 8°.

1. Sermons (French).
N. Y. P. L.   November 30, 1921.

NN 0020882   NN CtY MH

WB
34968

WB
34968a
Nardin, Jean-Frédéric, 1687–1728.
Le prédicateur évangélique; ou, Sermons pour les dimanches et les principales fêtes de l'année, précédés de sa Vie par J.-J. Duvernoy. Avec une introd., une notice bibliographique par A. Maulvault. 7. éd. revue et corrigée. Toulouse, Société des Publications Morales et Religieuses, 1910.
6 v.
— —— Supplément. Toulouse, Société des Publications Morales et Religieuses. 1911.
48 p.

NN 0020883   CtY

Nardin, Léon, 1857–1930.
Archives et archivistes de la principauté de Montbéliard; notice ornée d'un portrait de Jacques Loeffler (1583–1638) chancelier de Montbéliard, par Léon Nardin ... ₍et₎ Julien Mauveaux ... Paris, H. Champion, 1918.
2 p. l., 72 p., 1 l. port. 25½ᶜᵐ.
CONTENTS.—Les archivistes de la principauté.—Le partage des archives de la principauté de Montbéliard entre Paris, Besançon, Montbéliard, Vesoul et Colmar.—Autres sources manuscrites de la principauté de Montbéliard.—Documents.

1. Archives—France. 2. Archives—France—Montbéliard. I. Mauveaux, Julien, joint author. II. Title.

Library of Congress   CD1216.M6N3   19–19123

NN 0020884   DLC NN CtY MiU

Nardin, Léon, 1857–1930.
Histoire des corporations d'arts et métiers des ville et comté de Montbéliard et des seigneuries en dépendant, d'après les papiers inédits de ces sociétés et les archives de la principauté, avec une planche de sceaux. Par Léon Nardin ... ₍et₎ Julien Mauveaux ... Paris, H. Champion, 1910.
2 v. 25½ᶜᵐ.

1. Montbéliard, France—Gilds. I. Mauveaux, Julien, joint author.

12–16121

Library of Congress   HD6466.M7N3

NN 0020885   DLC CtY NcD ICJ NN

Nardin, Léon, 1857–1930.
... Jacques Foillet, imprimeur, libraire & papetier (1554–1619); ses peregrinations à Lyon, Genève, Constance, Bâle, Courcelles-les-Montbéliard, Besançon & Montbéliard d'après des documents inédits, avec l'inventaire de ses biens, le catalogue détaillé de sa librairie, des fac-similés d'autographe, les filigranes de ses papeteries, etc., le tout accompagné de notes, commentaires et éclaircissements. Paris, H. Champion, 1906.
1 p. l., 283 p. illus., xvi pl. (incl. facsims. (part double)) 22ᶜᵐ.
Published originally in "Mémoires de la Société d'émulation du Doube" 1905, 7th ser., v. 9, p. 263–546.
"Catalogue des ouvrages imprimés par Jacques Foillet": p. 185–223.
1. Foillet, Jacques, printer, 1554–1619. 2. Printing—Hist.—Montbéliard, France.

33–35899

Library of Congress   Z232.F6N2   926.55

NN 0020886   DLC TxU NNC MB

Nardin P., joint author.

Trillat, Jean Jacques.
... Recherches sur l'activité de l'huile de ricin, par J. J. Trillat ... ₍et₎ P. Nardin ... Préface de m. E. Darmois ... Paris, E. Blondel La Rougery ₍etc.₎ 1939.

Nardin, Paul D   1855–
Paul D. Nardin
see under title

Nardin, Pierre.
... La langue et le style de Jules Renard ... par Pierre Nardin ... Paris, E. Droz, 1942.
2 p. l., 351 p. 25ᶜᵐ.
Thèse—Univ. de Paris.
"Bibliographie": p. ₍337₎–342.

1. Renard, Jules, 1864–1910.

PQ2635.E48Z75   840.81   47–33004

OCU ICU NN MA RPB PU CtY MdBP NNC
NN 0020889   DLC NBuU FU CSt NcU MiU WaU OU TxU

Nardin, Pierre.
... Lexique comparé des fabliaux de Jean Bedel ... par Pierre Nardin ... Paris, E. Droz, 1942.
xii, 161, ₍3₎ p. 25ᶜᵐ.
Thèse complémentaire—Univ. de Paris.
"Bibliographie": p. ₍158₎–161.

1. Bedel, Jean, 13th cent.

PQ1427.B65N3   47–33552

NN 0020890   DLC WaU IaU TNJ CLU CU CtY PU

Nardin, Pierre.
... Lexique comparé des fabliaux de Jean Bedel. Paris, E. Droz, 1942.
xii, 161 p., 1 l. 25½ᶜᵐ.
"Bibliographie": p. ₍158₎–161.

1. Bedel, Jean, 13th cent.

PQ1427.B65N3 1942a   841.19   A F 47–4083

Princeton univ. Library
for Library of Congress   ₍2₎†

NN 0020891   NjP CU OU LU ICU CtY LU NNC TxU DLC

Nardin, Ulysse
Chronométrie Ulysse Nardin. - La Maison Ulysse Nardin S.A. fondée en 1846 Le Lockle & Geneve. (La Chaux-de-Fonds, 1924.)
il., 32 p. 22cm.

Caption title:
Le "Revue Internationale de l'Horlogerie" 15 février-1ᵉʳ Mars 1924.

NN 0020892   DN-Ob

VOLUME 405

HD9282 Nardin, W   T
.U4N2   Memorandum on Federal trade investigation of
         milk manufacturers ₍by₎ W. T. Nardin. 1919.
         84 p. tables,diagrs.(part.fold.) 25 cm.

              1.Milk trade - U.S. 2. Milk supply - U.S. I.
         U.S. F.T.C. II.Titl₎

    NN 0020893   DFT

Nardin academy, Buffalo.
    Cormariae
       see under title

Nardin quarterly.
    Buds of promise; a garland of verses by high school
students, reprinted from the Nardin quarterly, with a
foreword by Mary Synon. Buffalo, N. Y., The Nardin
academy, 1923.
    7 p. l., 3-156 p. illus 19¾ᶜᵐ.

    i. Nardin academy, Buffalo. ii. Title.

    Library of Congress   PS591.S3N3   23-18301

    NN 0020895   DLC

274.5311 ₍Nardini, Antonio₎
N166s   Series historico-chronologica præfectorum, qui
         ecclessiam titulo s. Demetrii mar. Thessaloni-
         censis fundatam deinceps s. Bartholomæi apostoli
         de Rivoalto reparatam rexerunt ab ecclesia con-
         dita, anno DCCCXXXX, tunc Petro Tradonico duce
         venetiarum, et Urso participatio episcopo olivo-
         lensi r. r. a ræædificatione, anno MLXX sub Do-
         minico Sylvio duce venetiarum, et Dominico Con-
         tareno episc. olivolensi peracta, usque ad annum
         bissextilem MDCCLXXXVIII auspicantibus Paulo
         Rainerio, duce venetiarum, et Friderico Maria

Giovanelli, patriarcha venetiarum Dalmatiæque
primate. ₍Venetiis, 1788₎
    lxii p. front.

Dedication by Antonio Nardini.

    1. Venice--Church history. I. Title.

    NN 0020897   IU

Nardini, Antonio Bernieri
    see Bernieri Nardini, Antonio.

₍Nardini, Bartolomeo₎
    Les exploits et les amours de frère Diable, général de
l'armée du cardinal Ruffo. Tr. de l'italien de B. N.
Par A. C. E. Paris, Ouvrier, an ix—1801.
    2 p. l., 179 p. front. 14¾ᶜᵐ.

    i. Égron, Adrien César, tr. ₍ii. Title.

                                              18-3963
    Library of Congress   PQ4720.N25E9

    NN 0020899   DLC

₍Nardini, Bartolomeo₎
    Mémoires pour servir a l'histoire des derniéres
révolutions de Naples, ou détail des événemens
qui ont précédé ou suivi l'entrée des Français
dans cette ville, recueillis par B. N...
Paris, De l'imprimerie de A. Égron, 1803.
    128p.   20 1/2 cm.

    Bound with: Laujon, A.P.M. Précis historique
de la derniere expédition de Saint-Domingue.[1805]

    1. Naples---Hist.   I. Title.

    NN 0020900   LNHT

Case   ₍NARDINI, BARTOLOMEO₎
MS   Memorie per servire alla storia dell'
5A   ultime rivoluzioni di Napoli;ossia, Det-
28   taglio degli avvenimenti che hanno prece-
         duta, e seguita l'entrata de Francesi nella
         città di Napoli nell'anno 1799. Raccolti
         da B. N. testimonio oculare, e tradotti
         da Raffaele d'Ambrosio, Duca di Quadri.
         ₍motto: 2 lines₎   Napoli, 1808.
            ₍117₎₺. 28cm.

    NN 0020901   ICN

₍Nardini, Bartolomeo₎
    Mes périls pendant la révolution de Naples, ou
récit de toutes les horreurs commises dans cette
ville par les Lazzarronnis et les Calabrois; suivi
d'une notice exacte sur los moeurs des habitans de
la Calabre; par N... Précédé d'une esquisse des
moeurs napolitaines. Paris, Chez Bacot, 1806.
    xxxij,107p.   20 1/2 cm.

    At end: Table des matieres and Errata, p.377-
80, from Virgil's Aeneid.
    Bound with: Laujon, A.P.M. Précis historique
de la derniére expédition de Saint-Domingue. ₍1805₎

    1. Naples---Hist.   I. Title.

    NN 0020902   LNHT MH

Nardini, Bruno, 1921-
PQ4831   La terra di Nod, con otto incisioni
A75   di Renzo Grazzini. ₍Firenze₎ Vallecchi
T3   ₍1952₎
            77p. illus. 24 cm.

         Biblical poem.

    NN 0020903   RPB WU DLC-P4 NN

Nardini, Bruno, 1921-
PQ4831   Variazioni del sangue. ₍Firenze₎ Vallecchi
A75   ₍1950₎
V35   60p. 19m. (Collezione di letteratura
         contemporanea. Serie poesia)

    NN 0020904   RPB NN

Z6621   Nardini, Carlo, comp.
.F605A3
         Florence. Biblioteca moreniana.
            I manoscritti della Biblioteca moreniana. Firenze, Tip.
         Galletti e Cocci, 1903-

Nardini, Clemente.
    Domenico di Ubaldo Guidi da Mandolfo. [Roma,
Gaetano A. Bertinelli, 1847]
    (4) p.
    Without title-page. Caption title.
    "Articolo estrato dal N. 14 del Contemporaneo.
Signed Clemente Nardini.

    NN 0020906   MH

NARDINI,Domenico Antonio.
    Il calcio del caval Pegaseo;risposta alla let-
tera del signor Antonio Luciani sullo spirito
della poesia,ed influenza di essa nel secolo
XVIII,al signor Domenico Cedrari. Roma,V.Pog-
gioli,1825.

    19 cm. pp.29,(1).

    NN 0020907   MH

NARDINI, Domenico.Antonio.
    Saggj poetici e letterarj. la ed., riveduta
e corretta dall'autore. Massa, L. Frediani,
1823.

    Consists mainly of Italian translations
from various Latin and French authors.

    NN 0020908   MH

PQ 4831 Nardini, Emilio.
A8   Versi friulani. Udine, Carducci, 1922.
V47   124 p. (Scrittori friulani, 2)
1922
              1. Italian language - Dialects - Friuli
         I. Title.

    NN 0020909   CaBVaU

Gs13   Nardini, Famiano.
41   L'antico Veio de Famiano Nardino. Discorso
         inuestigatiuo del sito di quella citta all'
         eminmo e reumo. Sig.card. Antonio Barberino.
         Roma,V.Mascardi,1647.
            4p₺.,210,[10]p. fold.map. 23cm.
         Engr. t.-p.

    NN 0020910   CtY NNU ICU OCU

Nardini, Famiano,
    Roma antica. In Roma, Per il Falco,
A spese di B.Diuersino e F.Cesaretti,
1666.
    10 ₺., 546,24 p. illus.,plates(part
fold.,incl.maps,plans) 23 ᶜᵐ.

    "Discorso d'Ottavio Falconieri intorno
alla piramide di C.Cestio, & alle
pitture..": 24 p.at end.
    Imperfect: has only p.9-12 of the
"Lettera al signor C.Dati."

         MdBJ
    NN 0020911   NjP MoU MH CSt ICU NSyU MnU CU DDO

Nardini, Famiano.
    Roma antica di Famiano Nardini ... Edizione 2a.
Roma, G. Andreoli, 1704.
    9 p. l., 583, 24 p. illus. (incl. plans) fold. plates, maps (1 fold.) 23½ᶜᵐ.

    "Discorso d'Ottavio Falconieri intorno alla piramide di C. Cestio ... Lettera
. . . al Signor C. Dati sopra l'iscrizione d'un mattone cavato dalle ruine d'un
muro antico . ." p. ₍557₎-583.
    "Memoria di varie antichità trovate in diversi luoghi della città di Roma,
scritte da Flaminio Vacca ...": 24 p. at end.
    Printed in Rome by Gaetano Zenobi.
    1. Rome (City)—Antiq. 2. Rome (City)—Descr. i. Falconieri, Ottavio,
d. 1676. ii. Vacca, Flaninio.

    NN 0020912   CU MdBP NNC MoSW NNU-W MiU NcD IaU

Nardini, Famiano,
    Roma antica. Ed.3. romana, con note,
ed osservazioni storico-critiche. In
Roma, Nella stamperia di L.Capponi, 1771.
    4 v. illus.,plates(part fold.;incl.
port.,maps,plans) 17 ᶜᵐ.

    Paged continuously.
    Vol.4 contains also "Discorso di
Ottavio Falconieri intorno alla piramide
di C.Cestio," and his "Lettera al signor

                    Continued in next column

VOLUME 405

Continued from preceding column

Carlo Dati sopra l'iscrizione di un
mattone cavato dalle ruine d'un muro
antico…" Also "Memorie di varia antichità
trovate in Roma, scritte da Flaminio
Vacca."

NN 0020914   NjP PPD OCU MdBJ ICU CtY IU CU

Nardini, Famiano.
Roma antica di Famiano Nardini. Ed. 4. romana
riscontrata, ed accresciuta delle ultime scoperte, con note
ed osservazioni critico antiquarie di Antonio Nibby … e
con disegni rappresentanti la faccia attuale dell'antica
topografia di Antonio de Romanis … Roma, Stamperia
de Romanis, 1818–20.
4 v. in 2. front. (port.) fold. maps, plans. 23ᶜᵐ.
Contents.—t. 1–3. Nardini, F. Roma antica; libri 8.—t. 4. Falconieri, O.
Discorso intorno alla piramide di C. Cestio; Lettera al Signor C. Dati sopra
l'iscrizione di un mattone cavato dalle ruine d'un muro antico. Vacca, F.
Memorie di varie antichità trovate in Roma. Nibby, A. Delle vie degli
antichi.
1. Rome (City)—Antiq. 2. Rome (City)—Descr. I. Nibby, Antonio,
ed. II. Falconieri, Ottavio. III. Vacca, Flaminio.
Library of Congress   DG63.N22
                        4—31282

NN 0020915   DLC CaBVaU CtY NjP PPL OClW PBm MB NN

Nardini, Famiano.
Roma Vetus; libri viii. Ex Italica in Latinum
linguam translati a J. Tollio.
[Graevius, Thesaurus Ant. Rom., v. 4]

NN 0020916   DLC

Nardini, Famiano.
Veji antiqui. Seu Dissertatio, investigans
veram ejus urbis situm. Latine ex Italico
vertit… Abrahamus Preigerus. Lugduni
Batavorum, sumptibus Petri vander Aa [1723]
4 p., 104 col. map. 40cm. (In
Graevius, J.G. Thesavrvs antiqvitatvm et
historiarvm Italiae. v.8, pt.3)
1.Veii, Italy. I.Preigerus, Abrahamus, tr.

NN 0020917   MnU

Nardini, Ida Fiore
see Fiore Nardini, Ida.

Nardini, Leonardo.
Dictionnaire françois-italien de M. l'abbé
François Alberti de Villeneuve…
see under Alberti di Villanova, Francesco
d', 1737–1800.

Nardini, Leonardo, comp.
Favole scelte. Londra, A. Dulau, 1800.
xxiv, 258 p. 16cm.
1. Fables, Italian. I. Title.

NN 0020920   NIC

Nardini, Leonardo   ed.
Novelle scelte degli autori più celebri
italiani, raccolte e di note gramaticali
illustrate da Leonardo Nardini, ad uso degli
studiosi della lingua italiana. Londra,E.A.
Dulau e co.,1802.
3p l.,2,229,[1]p.,1l. 16cm. (His Novelle
degli autori più celebri italiani, pte.1)
Contents. - Delle novelle del P.Soave. -
Dell'Albergati Capacelli. - Dell'Altanesi. -
Del Lodoli. - Del Manni. - Di anonimo. - Del
Padovani. - Del   Gozzi.

NN 0020921   CtY

Nardini, Leonardo, comp.
Poesie del magnifico Lorenzo de'Medici …
see under Medici, Lorenzo de', il
Magnifico, 1449–1492.

[Nardini, Leonardo, ed.]
Saggi di prose e poesie de'più celebri
scrittori d'ogni secolo …
In Londra:Per Cooper e Graham.Stampato a
spese degli editori;e si vende da G.Polidori e
co.no.12.Cockspur street,dirimpetto a Pall-Mall.
1796–98.
6v. 21.5cm.
Half-title in v.1: Saggi di prose e poesie
raccolte dagli editori L. Nardini e S.
Buonaiuti.

Contents: v.1. Secolo XVIII.--v.2. Secolo
XVII.--v.3. Secolo XVI.--v.4. Secolo XV.--v.5.
Secolo XIV.--v.6. Secolo XIII.
From the library of H. W. Longfellow, with
his autograph in all vols. & with several ms.
notes scattered throughout.

NN 0020924   MH PPL NIC

[Nardini, Leonardo]   comp.
Scelta di lettere familiari degli autori
più celebri, con note ed accenti che indicano
la pronunzia. Ad uso dei licei del regno.
Milano,Stamperia reale,1810.
xii,419,[1]p. 14½cm.
"Compilato, corretto e stampato da L.Nardini."

NN 0020925   CtY

[Nardini, Leonardo]
Scelta di lettere familiari degli autori più
celebri. Con note de accenti che indicano
la pronunzia. Ad uso delle scule d'italia.
Turin,V.Pomba,1818. xii,297p. 17cm.

NN 0020926   MWelC

NARDINI, Leonardo.
Scelta di lettere familiari degli autori
piu celebri, con note ed accenti che indiacano
la pronunzia. 9a ed., Milano, G.Silvestri,
1829.

NN 0020927   MH

Nardini, Leonardo,   ed.
Teatro italiano; ossia, Commedie e tragedie degli autori più
celebri. Raccolte da Leonardo Nardini… Londra, A Dulau
e co. [etc.] 1800. 3 v. 16cm.
Contents.—Tomo 1. Rossi, G. G. de: Il cortigiano onesto. L'astratto geloso.
Albergati Capacelli, Francesco, marchese: Il ciarlator maldicente.—Tomo 2. Goldoni,
Carlo: La Scozzese. Il matrimonio per concorso. La donna di maneggio. Maffei, F. S.,
marchese: Le cerimonie.—Tomo 3. Alfieri, Vittorio: Polinice. Oreste. Virginia. Monti,
Vincenzo: Aristodemo. Maffei, F. S., marchese: Merope.
265191–3B. 1. Drama, Italian—   Collections.
N. Y. P. L.   March 31, 1944

NN 0020928   NN IU

Nardini, N.
Cracovia. Losanna, 1847.
8°

NN 0020929   NN

sVM
221
S 69a NARDINI, PIETRO, 1722–1793.
Adagio… [London,Augener & co.,1889]
p.8-10. 31cm. (Classische violin musik
berühmter meister des 17. und 18. jahrhunderts)
Caption title.
Bound with Somis, Giovanni Battista. Adagio
& allegro… [1889]
Violin part laid in.

NN 0020930   ICN

M1145
.N21A2 Nardini, Pietro, 1722–1793.
[Adagio, string orchestra]
Adagio, per orchestra d'archi ed organo ad
libitum. [Elaborazione di] Ettore Bonelli.
Padova, G. Zanibon, 1937.
score (4 p.)
1. String-orchestra music.

NN 0020931   ICU ICN NN

Nardini, Pietro, 1722–1793.
…Allegro vivamente [par] Pietro Nardini… Berlin: E. Bote
& G. Bock [etc., etc., 1909] Publ. pl. no. B. & B. 16810. 2 parts.
34cm. (Moffat, A. Six pièces du XVIII siècle. 6.)
Score (5 p.): violin and piano (realized from basso continuo). Violin part.
"Arrangé par Alfred Moffat."
1. Violin and piano—To 1800. I. Moffat, Alfred Edward, 1866-
N.Y.P.L.   arr.   September 17, 1936

NN 0020932   NN

M1013
.N36N3 Nardini, Pietro, 1722–1793.
1914   [Concerto, violin, A major; arr.]
Concert in A dur; bearb. von Tivadar
Nachèz [für Violine und Klavier. Mayence,
B. Schott's Söhne, 1914]
score (21 p.) and part. 34cm. (Concertos
classiques pour violon, orchestre à cordes et
orgue d'après la basse chiffrée. 5.)
[Caption title.
1. Concertos (Violin)—To 1800—Solo with
piano.

NN 0020933   ViU LU NcD

Nardini, Pietro, 1722–1793.
Concert von Pietro Nardini (componirt 1760) für Violine zum
Concertvortrage eingerichtet von M. Hauser… Für Violine mit
Pianoforte… Leipzig: F. E. C. Leuckart [188–?]. Publ. pl.
no. F. E. C. L. 3427. 2 parts in 1 v. f°.
Violin and piano in score, and violin part.
1. Violin and piano. 2. Concertos.—   Violin and orchestra. 3. Hauser,
Miska, 1822–87.
N.Y.P.L.   May 16, 1919

NN 0020934   NN

f785.6
N22c.H Nardini, Pietro, 1722–1793.
…Concerto (E minor) for violin
and piano; ed. by Miska Hauser.
New York, Fischer [c1915]
2v. F. (Carl Fischer's music library.
no.598)
"Concerto by Pietro Nardini" signed:
Gustav Saenger.
Contents: [v.1 Score for violin and
piano]-[v.2.] Violin.

NN 0020935   IaU

VOLUME 405

M1013
.N36P4
1911
Nardini, Pietro, 1722-1793.
ιConcerto, violin, E minorι

Concerto en mi mineur pour violon et piano. Revue et augmenté d'une cadence par Emilio Pente. Mainz, B. Schott's Söhne ι1911ι
score ι15 p.ι and part. 31cm. ιEdition Schott No. 853ι

1. Concertos (Violin)—To 1800—Solo with piano.

NN   0020936   ViU

*M1106
N2
Nardini, Pietro, 1722-1793.
ιConcerto, violin, E minor; arrangedι
Concerto in E minor for violin and piano. Arranged by M. Hauser. Ed. by Sam Franko. New York, Schirmer, c1908.

score(11p.) and part(5p.)   30½cm. (Schirmer's library of musical classics, vol. 934)

Originally for violin with string orchestra.

NN   0020937   NBuG OU ICN WaBeN

M
1013
N37
C6
Nardini, Pietro, 1722-1793.
ιConcerto, violin, E minor; arrι
Concerto in E minor for violin and piano ιin a special concert arrangement by Miskaι Hauser. New York, C. Fischer ιc1910ι
score (11 p.) and part. 31cm. (Carl Fischer music library, 593)

1. Concertos (Violin) - To 1800 - Solo with piano.

NN   0020938   CoU

qM787.1
N16c
1920
Nardini, Pietro, 1722-1793.
ιConcerto, Violin, E Minor; arr.ι
Concerto in E minor, arr. ιfor violin & pianoι by Miska Hauser; rev. and ed. by Émile Sauret. ιLondon, Augenerι c1920.
score (11p.) and part. 31cm. (Augener's edition no.7952)
Caption title.

1. Concertos (Violin)--To 1800--Solo with piano I. Hauser, Miska, 1822-1887, arr. II. Sauret, Émile, 1852-1920, ed.

NN   0020939   IU

M785.63
N224CE
Nardini, Pietro, 1722-1793.
ιConcerto, E-minor, arr. pf. & vln.ι
...Concerto in E minor for violin and piano ιbyι Pietro Nardini. Arranged for concert use by M. Hauser. Edited by Sam Franko. New York, G. Schirmer, c1936.   Publ.pl.no.20277.
2pts.in 1v. 30cm. (Schirmer's library of musical classics, vol.934.)

Violin part in pocket.

NN   0020940   NcD NcU OO

Nardini, Pietro, 1722-1793.
ιConcerto, violin, E minor; arrangedι

Concerto in E minor for violin, by Pietro Nardini; arranged for violin and pianoforte by Wilfred Ridgway. London, Novello and company, limited ι1938ι
1 p. l., 14 p. 30½ x 24cm.
Publisher's plate no.: 16478.

1. Concertos (Violin with string orchestra), Arranged—Solo with piano.   I. Ridgway, Wilfred, arr.
                                    46-28651
Library of Congress   M1106.N2   E min.

NN   0020941   DLC

Nardini, Pietro, 1722-1793.
ιConcerto, violin, E minor; arrangedι

Concerto in E minor for violin, by Pietro Nardini; arranged with accompaniment for string orchestra by Wilfred Ridgway. Score.   London, Novello and company, limited ι1938ι
, 2 p. l., 15 p. and pt. 30½ x 24cm.
Publisher's plate no.: 16477.

1. Concertos (Violin with string orchestra). Arranged—Scores.
I. Ridgway, Wilfred, arr.   46-28650

Library of Congress   M1105.N27   E min.

NN   0020942   DLC NN

Nardini, Pietro, 1722-1793.
ιConcerto, violin, E minor; arr.ι

Concerto in G minor. ιLondon, Oxford University Press ι1950ι
score (16 p.) and part. 31 cm. (Transcriptions for viola & piano by Watson Forbes and Alan Richardson, no. 10)

Cover title.
"The piano part is not a reduction from the orchestral score, but a free arrangement suitable for concert use."
Duration: 11 minutes.

1. Viola and piano music, Arranged.   (Series: Transcriptions for viola & piano, no. 10)

M228.N   51-40823

NN   0020943   DLC

M1013
.N36B3
1910
Nardini, Pietro, 1722-1793.
ιConcerto, violin, A major; arr.ι

Concerto in La maggiore. Cadenze, accompagnamento di pianoforte, digitazione ed ornamenti di Cesare Barison. ιLeipzig, C. Schmidl, 1910ι
score (24 p.) and part. 32cm. (Edition Schmidl no. 4596)
"Tesori musicali italiani raccolta di composizioni per violino scelte fra i capolavori dei grandi maestri italiani antichi ..."
Caption title.
1. Concertos (Violin)—To 1800—Solo with piano.

NN   0020944   ViU

qM785.6
N16c
Nardini, Pietro, 1722-1793.
ιConcerto, violin, E minorι
Concerto in mi minore ιdiι Nardini-Pente. Mainz, B. Schott's Söhne, c1925.
score (20p.) and   parts. 37cm.

1. Concertos (Violin)--To 1800--Scores and parts.   I. Pente, Emilio, 1860-1929, ed.

NN   0020945   IU

8A
2050
NARDINI, PIETRO, 1722-1793, supposed composer.
30 ιi.e.Dreissigι Capricen für Violine allein. Bearb. und hrsg. von Andreas Moser. Berlin, M.Hesses Verlag ι1925?ι
63p. 35cm.

Authorship uncertain, cf.MGG,Bd.9, col.1266.

NN   0020946   ICN

Nardini, Pietro, 1722-1793.
ιSonatas. Violin & piano. (Walsh) no. 5, 3. Selectionsι
5te Sonate (D dur), von Pietro Nardini... Bearbeitung von A. Moffat.   Berlin: N. Simrock, G.m.b.H., cop. 1905.   Publ. pl. no. 12029.   2 parts in 1 v. 34cm.   (Meister-Schule der alten Zeit: Sammlung klassischer Violin-Sonaten. 25.)

Score (11 p.) : violin and piano (realized from basso continuo). Violin part. Made up of the first 2 movements of sonata 5 and the first movement of sonata 3 of his: Six solos for a violin with a bass for the harpsichord or violoncello.   London: J. Walsh ιca. 1765ι and the last movement of sonata 4 of his: Six solos for the violin

with a bass... Opera V.   London: H. Fougt ιca. 1760ι—cf. Pfäfflin. *Pietro Nardini. p. 26.*
Caption-title.

1. Violin and piano—To 1800.   I. Moffat, Alfred Edward, N. Y. P. L.   2. Sonatas—Violin and piano—To 1866-   , ed.   November 18, 1936

NN   0020948   NN

M1012
.N3S5
n.d.
Nardini, Pietro, 1722-1793.
ιConcerto, violin, E minor; arr.ι

Konzert. ιLeipzig, C. G. Röder, n. d.ι Pl. no. 3427.
14 parts. 34cm.
Caption title.
Violin solo ed. by Miska Hauser, rev. by G. Havemann; orchestral parts arr. by Hans Sitt.

Parts: violin solo, vl. I, vl. II, vla., cello, bass, fl. I, fl.II, ob, I, ob. II, bn. I, bn. II, hn. I, hn. II.
1. Concertos   (Violin with chamber orchestra), Arrang   ed—Parts.

NN   0020949   ViU

Nardini, Pietro, 1722-1793.
ιConcerto, violin, E minor; arr.ι

Konzert e-moll, für Violine und Orchester. Eingerichtet von M. Hauser und Hans Sitt; Solostimme von Gustav Havemann. München, F. E. C. Leuckart ι195-?ι
score (11 p.) and part. 31 cm. (Alte Musik für verschiedene Instrumente, Nr. 7ιbι)
Acc. arr. for piano.

1. Concertos (Violin)—To 1800—Solo with piano.   (Series)

M1013.N25H35   65-32948/M

NN   0020950   DLC OU NcD

Nardini, Pietro, 1722-1793.
ιConcerto, violin, E minor; arr.ι

Konzert für Violine und Orchester in E moll (komp. 1760) Eingerichtet von M. Hauser und Hans Sitt; Solostimme von Gustav Havemann. Leipzig, F. E. C. Leuckart ι195-?ι Pl. no. F. E. C. L. 3484.
score (31 p.) 34 cm. (Alte Musik für verschiedene Instrumente, Nr. 7)
Caption title.
Duration : 13 min.
1. Concertos (Violin)—To 1800—Scores.   (Series)

M1012.N24 E min.   65-53161/M

NN   0020951   DLC OU NjP NcD CU-SB

M1160
.N3N3
1914
Nardini, Pietro, 1722-1793.
ιConcerto, violin, A major; arr.ι

Konzert in A dur für Violine, Streichorchester und Orgel nach dem Autograph mit nicht beziffertem bass zum erstenmahl bearb. von Tivadar Nachéz. Mainz, B. Schott's Söhne ι1914ι
6 pts. 34cm.
Parts: violin solo, vl.I, vl.II, vla., bass, organ.
1. Concertos (Violin with string orchestra), Arranged—Parts.   I. Nachéz, Tivadar, 1859-, arr.

NN   0020952   ViU

Nardini, Pietro, 1722-1793.
ιQuartets. Strings. no. 1-6ι
...Sechs Streichquartette. Heft I-ιIIIι...   Leipzig: Breitkopf & Härtel ι1937ι   Publ. pl. no. 30822, 30827-30828.   3 no. in 1 v. 33cm.   (Collegium musicum. Nr. 63-65.)

Parts only: violin I-II, viola and violoncello.
His: Sei quartetti per due violini, viola e violoncello.   ιFirenze: G. Poggiali inc., 1782?ι—cf. Pref.; Pfäfflin. *Pietro Nardini. p. 37.*

"Herausgegeben von Wilh. Altmann."
Cover-title.
At head of title: Breitkopf & Härtels Kammermusik-Bibliothek. Nr. 1964a/b-ι1966a/bι
Each Heft contains 2 quartets.

925061A. 1. Chamber music, 18th   cent.—Quartets. 2. Violin-
Quartets—2 violins, viola and violon-   cello—To 1800. I. Altmann,
Wilhelm, 1862-   , ed. II. Ser.
N. Y. P. L.   August 19, 1938

NN   0020954   NN ICU MH IU

VOLUME 405

Nardini, Pietro, 1722–1793.
ₐSolos, violin & continuo (Walsh)ₐ

Six solos for a violin with a bass for the harpsichord or violoncello. London, I. Walsh ₐca. 1760ₐ
score (26 p.) 33 cm.
Each solo has caption : Sonata.

1. Sonatas (Violin and harpsichord)—To 1800.

M219.N224S5   47–42700 rev*/M

NN   0020955   DLC

Nardini, Pietro, 1722–1793.
ₐSolos, violin & continuo, op. 5ₐ

Six solos for the violin, with a bass. Opera v. London, Printed and sold by H. Fougt ₐ1769ₐ
score (31 p.) 34 cm.

1. Sonatas (Violin and harpsichord)—To 1800.

M219.N224 op. 5   45–28140 rev*/M

NN   0020956   DLC

Nardini, Pietro, 1722–1793.

Six sonatas for two German flutes or two violins and a bass. Composed by Sigᵗ P. Nardini. London, R. Bremner ₐ1770?ₐ
3 pts. 32ᶜᵐ.

1. Trio-sonatas.

Library of Congress   M317.N25T7   46–42029

NN   0020957   DLC ViU CtY

Nardini, Pietro, 1722–1793.

Six sonatas or duets for two violins, op. 2, by Sigr. Nardini and Ferari. London, I. Walsh [c1765]
Parts only.

NN   0020958   CU

Nardini, Pietro, 1722–1793.
ₐSonates avec les adagios brodés, violin & continuo. No. 2ₐ

Sonata, D major, for violin and piano. Edited by Theodore Spiering. New York, C. Fischer ₐ1916ₐ
score (15 p.) and part. 30 cm. (Carl Fischer's music library, no. 772)

"According to the Venetian edition of 1760 by Ferdinand David."

1. Sonatas (Violin and harpsichord)—To 1800.

M219.N224S62 1916   65–41795/M

NN   0020959   DLC OrU OO NN

Nardini, Pietro, 1722–1793.
ₐSonates avec les adagios brodés, violin & continuo. No. 2ₐ

Sonata in D for violin and figured bass. Arranged for violin and piano by Ferdinand David. Edited and fingered by Henry Schradieck, with biographical sketch of the composer by Theo. Baker. New York, G. Schirmer, ᶜ1898.
score (15 p.) and part. 31 cm. (Schirmer's library of musical classics, v. 511)

"Arranged ... from the Venetian edition of 1760."

1. Sonatas (Violin and harpsichord)—To 1800.

M219.N224S62 1898   65–41797/M

NN   0020960   DLC CtY NcU MdBP OU NN

Nardini, Pietro, 1722–1793.
ₐSonates avec les adagios brodés, violin & continuo. No. 2; arr.ₐ
Sonata in D major. Transcribed for viola and piano by Milton Katims. New York, International Music ₐᶜ1948ₐ
score (15p.) and part. 35cm.

NN   0020961   WaBeN

M
219   Nardini, Pietro, 1722–1793.
N37   [Sonata, violin & continuo, D major]
D maj.   Sonata in D major for violin and piano. Edited by Theodore Spiering. New York, C. Fischer ₐc1916ₐ
score (13 p.) and part. 31cm.

1. Sonatas (Violin and harpsichord) – To 1800.

NN   0020962   CoU

M228   Nardini, Pietro, 1722–1793, supposed composer.
.N21S6   Sonata in F minor for viola and piano. Edited by L. A. Zellner. London, Crans ₐn.d.ₐ
score (11 p.) and part.

1. Sonatas (Viola and piano), Arranged.
I. Zellner, Leopold Alexander, 1823–1894, ed.

NN   0020963   ICU

Nardini, Pietro, 1722–93.
Sonatas, violin & continuo, G major
Sonata in G-dur. [Arrangement von A. Moffat] Mainz, Schott, c1909 [i.e. c1910]

Score (13 p.) & 1 pt. (Kammer-Sonaten für Violine & Klavier, bearb. von A. Moffat, 15)

NN   0020964   MH

Nardini, Pietro, 1722–1793.
[Sonata, violin & continuo, D major]
Sonate, D dur * D major * Ré majeur. Für Violine und unbezifferten Bass. Leipzig, Breitkopf & Härtel [n.d.]
score (15 p.) and part.
For violin and piano.

NN   0020965   OU

Nardini, Pietro, 1722–1793.
ₐSonatas. Violin & piano.ₐ
Sonate ₐD dur, von Pietro Nardini... Bearbeitung von A. Moffat. Berlin: N. Simrock, G.m.b.H., 1899, Publ. pl. no. 11227. 2 parts in 1 v. 34cm. (Meister-Schule der alten Zeit: Sammlung klassischer Violin-Sonaten. 14.)

Score (including realized basso continuo) and violin part.
No. 3 of his: Sei sonate per violino solo e basso. ₐParis? 1765?ₐ—cf. Brit. Mus. Cat. of music. Accessions. Part 11; Brit. Mus. Cat. of printed music (1487–1800).
Caption-title.

1. Violin and piano. 2. Sonatas—   Violin and piano. I. Moffat, Alfred
Edward, 1866–   , ed.
N. Y. P. L.   March 4, 1936

NN   0020966   NN

Nardini, Pietro, 1722–1793.
...ₐSonatas, Violin. D maj.ₐ Sonate D dur (Flesch)...
Leipzig: C. F. Peters₍, cop. 1931₎. Publ. pl. no. 10861. 2 parts in 1 v. 30½cm. (Meister Weisen. No. 9.)

Violin (or viola) and piano (realized from basso continuo), in score. Violin part. no. 2 of his: Sei sonate per violino solo e basso, Venice 1760. Third movement, Larghetto, interpolated from Sonata no. 1 in Bb. On editions published in Berlin and Amsterdam, ca. 1765, the six sonatas were called Op. 2.
"Herausgegeben von Carl Flesch."
Edition Peters Nr. 4167.

1. Violin and basso continuo   (harpsichord or piano). 2. Viola
and basso continuo (harpsichord or   piano). 3. Violin—Sonatas.
I. Flesch, Karl, 1873–   , editor.   II. Ser.
N. Y. P. L.   October 21, 1932

NN   0020967   NN

M
787.1   Nardini, Pietro, 1722–1793.
N166s   ₐSonata, violin & continuo, D majorₐ
Sonate D dur, Violine und Klavier. ₐHrsg. von Carl₎ Flesch. ₐNew York, C. F. Peters, c1931₎
score (15 p.) and part. (Edition Peters, no. 4167)

Meister Weisen aus älteren und neueren Werken für Violine und Klavier.
Cover title.

NN   0020968   WaU

Nardini, Pietro, 1722–1793.
ₐSonates avec les adagios brodés, violin & continuo. No. 2₎

Sonate en ré majeur, pour violon avec une basse chiffrée. Transcrite pour violon avec accompagnement de piano et revisée par Joan Manén. Wien, New York, Universal-Edition, ᶜ1926.
score (19 p.) and part. 31 cm. (Universal-Edition, Nr. 8444)

1. Sonatas (Violin and harpsichord)—To 1800.

M219.N224S62 1926   65–41796/M

NN   0020969   DLC

Nardini, Pietro, 1722–1793.
ₐSonata, violin & continuo, op. 2, no. 5, D major₎

Sonate en ré majeur, pour violon solo et basse. Harmonisée d'après la basse chiffrée de l'auteur par Eugène Ysaÿe. Bruxelles, Éditions Ysaÿe, ᶜ1924₎
score (15 p.) and part. 35 cm.
At head of title: Répertoire classique et moderne du violon.
The figured bass of the original realized for piano.

1. Sonatas (Violin and harpsichord)—To 1800. I. Ysaÿe, Eugène, 1858–1931, ed.

M219.N224 op. 2, no. 5 1924   65–41798/M

NN   0020970   DLC

Nardini, Pietro, 1722–1793.
ₐSonates avec les adagios brodés, violin & continuo. No. 2₎.

Sonate für Violine mit unbeziffertem Bass, nach der venezianischen Ausg. von 1760 für Violine und Pianoforte bearb. von Ferd. David. Leipzig, Breitkopf & Härtel ₐ1867₎ Pl. no. 11318.
score (15 p.) and part. 34 cm. (Die Hohe Schule des Violinspiels, Werke berühmter Meister des 17ten u. 18ten Jahrhunderts, No. 7)
Caption title.

1. Sonatas (Violin and harpsichord)—To 1800. I. David, Ferdinand Victor, 1810–1873, ed.

M219.N224S62 1867   65–41801/M

NN   0020971   DLC PU

---

sVM   NARDINI, PIETRO, 1722–1793.
219   ₐSonata, violin; no.   D major₎ ...Sonate für
N 22s   violine und unbezifferten bass. Nach der venezianischen ausgabe von 1760 bearbeitet von Ferd. David. Neue revidierte ausgabe von Henri Petri. Leipzig, Breitkopf & Härtel₍18--₎
15p.   (Breitkopf & Härtel's violin-bibliothek)

Caption title.
For violin with piano accompaniment.
Plate no.:   11318.

NN   0020972   ICN

Nardini, Pietro, 1722–1793.
ₐSonatas. Violin & piano.₎
...Sonate...G-dur... Mainz: B. Schott's Söhne ₐetc., etc., 1910₎ Publ. pl. no. 28742. 2 parts in 1 v. 31cm. (Kammer-Sonaten des 17ten und 18ten Jahrhunderts. 15.)

Score (including realized basso continuo) and violin part.
No. 2 of his: Sei sonate per violino solo e basso. ₐParis? 1765₎—cf. Brit. Mus. Cat. of music. Accessions. Part 19; Brit. Mus. Cat. of printed music (1487–1800).
"Arrangement von Alfred Moffat."
"Edition Schott... No. 815."

1. Violin and piano. 2. Sonatas—   Violin and piano. I. Moffat, Alfred
Edward, 1866–
N. Y. P. L.   March 4, 1936

NN   0020973   NN

VOLUME 405

Nardini, Pietro, 1722–1793.
Sonate in D-dur für Violine mit beziffertem
Bass. Bearbeitung für Violine und Klavier von
Alfred Moffat. Hamburg, N. Simrock [c1933]
score (11 p.) and 1 part. 36 cm.
For violin and piano; originally violin with
figured bass.
Pl. no. 11227.

NN   0020974   OOxM

Nardini, Pietro, 1722–1793.
₍Sonata, violin & continuo, op. 2, no. 2, G major₎
Sonate, Sol majeur, harmonisée pour violon avec accompagnement de piano par J. Salmon. Paris, Société anonyme
des éditions Ricordi, ᶜ1921.
score (14 p.) and part. 35 cm.
Cover title.
Figured bass of the original realized for piano.
With an added movement, the Adagio from the 6th of the Solos
for violin & continuo, op. 5.
1. Sonatas (Violin and harpsichord)—To 1800. 2. Sonatas (Violin
and harpsichord)—To 1800—Excerpts. I. Nardini, Pietro, 1722–
1793. Solo, violin & continuo, op. 5, no. 6, C minor. Adagio.

M219.N224 op. 2,   65–41794/M
no. 2 1921

NN   0020975   DLC

Nardini, Pietro, 1722–1793.
₍Solos, violin & continuo. Selections₎
Sonate, ut majeur, harmonisée pour violon avec accompagnement de piano par J. Salmon. Paris, Société anonyme
des éditions Ricordi, ᶜ1921.
score (12 p.) and part. 35 cm.
Cover title.
Figured bass of the original realized for piano.
The 1st 3 movements are from the composer's Solos, violin & continuo (Walsh): the 1st 2 from no. 5 and the 3d from No. 3 (Adagio).
The 4th movement is the 2d Allegro from No. 4 of the Solos, violin &
continuo, op. 5. The whole is transposed 1 tone lower from the original.
1. Sonatas (Violin and harpsichord)—To 1800—Excerpts.

M219.N224S49   65–41793/M

NN   0020976   DLC

M
231
.N37   **Nardini, Pietro,** 1722–1793.
Cmaj.   ₍Sonata, violoncello & continuo, C major₎
Sonate, Ut majeur, harmonisée pour violon-
celle avec accompagnement de piano par J. Salmon.
Paris Société Anonyme des Éditions Ricordi, ᶜ1931
score (12 p.) and part.

1. Sonatas (Violoncello and harpsichord) -
To 1800.

NN   0020977   INS

---

m781.3   **Nardini, Pietro,** 1722–1793.
N224s3   [Sonata, violin & piano, B major]
Sonaten für Violine und Pianoforte.
Hrsg. von Hans Sitt. Leipzig, C.F.
Peters [n.d.] Pl.no. 7316.
score (27p.) and part. 31cm. (Edition Peters,
no.2476)

CONTENTS.—Sonate in B dur (Bᵇ major).—Sonate in D dur
(D major)

1.Sonatas (Violin and piano) - To 1800.
I.Nardini, Pietro, 1722–1793. Sonata,
violin & piano,   D major.

*

NN   0020978   CLSU

Nardini, Pietro, 1722–1793.
Sonaten für Violine und Pianoforte, von Pietro Nardini; her-
ausgegeben von Hans Sitt... Leipzig: C. F. Peters₍, 1889₎.
Publ. pl. no. 7316. 2 parts in 1 v.   f°.
Violin and piano in score and violin part.
On cover: Edition Peters. no. 2476.
Contents: Sonate in B dur. Sonate in D dur.

1. Violin and piano. 2. Violin—   Sonatas. 3. Sitt, Hans, 1850–1922,
editor.
N. Y. P. L.   January 15, 1929

NN   0020979   NN ICN

Nardini (V.) Dell' utero didelfo in rapporto
alle funzioni fisiologiche. 48 pp. 8°. *Modena*,
1808.

NN   0020980   DNLM

Nardini, Vincenzo, 1830–1913.

Lacordaire, Jean Baptiste Henri Dominique de, 1802–1861.
La inquisicion, santo Domingo y su orden, segun el r. p.
Lacordaire; extraido de "La Rosa del Peru". Lima, Tipo-
grafia indusrial ₍1₎ 1886.

---

4   Nardini, Vincenzo Maria
Rare   Inno alle Muse. Con l'aggiunta
Bks   della traduzione della decima Egloga
di Virgilio. 2. ed. Lucca, Presso
F. Bertini, 1829.
15 p.

Bound with Cicci, M. L. Poèsie.
Parma, 1796.

NN   0020982   DLC-P4

NA1121   Nardini Despotti Mospignotti, Aristide,
F632.25   1826–1903.
D86f   Appendice agli studi di Aristide
N37a   Nardini Despotti Mospignotti sulla
facciata del Duomo di Firenze.
Livorno, Tip. di F. Vigo, 1864.
12 p. front. 30cm.

Cover title.
Author's autograph inscription.

NN   0020983   MWiCA

NARDINI DESPOTTI MOSPIGNOTTI, Aristide.
Il campanile di Santa Maria del Fiore.
Firenze, etc., [1887?]

pp. 74.
"Estratto dalla Rassegna nazionale,
anno, VII".

NN   0020984   MH NjP

NA1121   Nardini Despotti Mospignotti,
M637.25   Aristide, 1826–1903.
D86   Del Duomo di Milano e della sua
N37   nuova facciata; studi di Aristide
Nardini Despotti Mospignotti...
Milano, B. Saldini, 1889.
188 p. 5 fold. plates. 30cm.

Label on cover: Firenze, Loescher
& Seeber, 1889.

NN   0020985   MWiCA MB IU

NA1113   Nardini Despotti Mospignotti, Aristide.
.N16f
(SA)   Della facciata del duomo di
Firenze, studi. Livorno, Vigo, 1864.
78 p. 1 plate. 48½ ᶜᵐ.

1.Florence. Santa Maria del Fiore
(Cathedral)

NN   0020986   NjP IU MWiCA

Nardini-Despotti ₍Mospignotti₎, Aristide.
Della razionalità architettonica. Firenze, a spese dell'autore,
1853.
4°. pp. (6), 138 +. Plates.

NN   0020987   MH

NA1121   Nardini Despotti Mospignotti, Aristide,
F632.25   1826–1903.
D86f   Due disegni per la facciata del Duomo
N37d   di Firenze. Livorno, Tip. di F.
Vigo, 1867.
19 p. 30.5cm.

Author's autograph inscription.
With this are bound four handwritten
pages and Del Concorso per la facciata
di S. Maria del Fiore. Rapporto.
Firenze, 1863.

NN   0020988   MWiCA MH

NA1121   Nardini Despotti Mospignotti,
F632.25   Aristide, 1826–1903.
D86f   Il Duomo di Firenze, il Setticelli,
N37s   e il Nardini Despotti Mospignotti.
Livorno, Tip. di F. Vigo, 1873.
22 p. 18cm.

Text signed: A. Nardini Despotti
Mospignotti.
From the library of Ugo Ojetti.-
included inside Holstein, J., firm,
Frankfurt am Main. Katalog 33, item
no. 123.

NN   0020989   MWiCA

Nardini Despotti Mospignotti, Aristide.
... Il Duomo di San Giovanni, oggi Battistero di Firenze;
con trenta illustrazioni e due tavole fuori testo. Firenze, Tip.
di S. Landi, 1902.
xii p., 1 l., 181 p. illus., II pl. (incl. front.) port. 26½ᶜᵐ.
Cover imprint: Firenze, Fratelli Alinari, 1902.

1. Florence. San Giovanni (Baptistery) 2. Architecture—Florence.
                            3–28874 Revised
Library of Congress   NA5621.F6N3

NN   0020990   DLC NSyU MH MB NjP CtY

DG133   Nardini Despotti Mospignotti, Aristide.
.N25   Il Pantheon, Agrippa, Adriano ... e Settimio
Severo? Milano, Tip. e litografia degli ingegneri, 1899.
29 p. plate.
"Estratto dal periodico Il Politecnico ...
anno 1899."

1. Rome (City) Pantheon.

NN   0020991   ICU

Jad72   **Nardini Despotti Mospignotti, Aristide.**
F68   Il sistema tricuspidale e la facciata del
871N   Duomo di Firenze; studj di Aristide Nardini
Despotti Mospignotti. Livorno, Tip. F. Vigo,
1871.
165 p. 24 cm.

1. Florence, Santa Maria del Fiore
(Cathedral)

NN   0020992   CtY IU

Avery
AA
5621   Nardini-Saladini, Raffaello
M77   La cappella espiatoria di Monza. Bergamo,
N16   Istituto italiano d'arti grafiche, 1912.
1 case (63 p. illus., mounted col. plates.
26 cm. and 53 mounted plates (chiefly photos.)
41 cm.)

On cover: Omaggio dell'arch. Guido Cirilli.

1. Monza, Italy. Cappella espiatoria.
I. Title.

NN   0020993   NNC CtY

VOLUME 405

Nardis, Angelus
Ad Leonem P. M. Ode. [By Angelus Nardis.] Porticibus: Typis Spedaliere, 1902. 8 p. 4°.

NN 0020994 NN

781.3 Nardis, Camillo de, 1857-
D391L Lezioni di armonia. Napoli, l'Autore,
[n.d.]
4v. 32cm.

1. Harmony.

NN 0020995 CLSU

Nardis, Camillo de, 1857-
... Messa per tenori e bassi, di Camillo de Nardis... Napoli:
R. Izzo [189-?] Publ. pl. no. 1076. 24 p. f°.
Latin words.

1. Masses, with organ accompaniment.
N.Y.P.L. February 21, 1923.

NN 0020996 NN

Nardis, Camillo de, 1857-
"1911." Ouverture eroica. Riduzione per banda del M°. Luigi   **M.462.162
Santori ... [Partitura.]
— Napoli. Izzo. 1913. (2), 60 pp. 38 cm.

N2429 — T.r. — Band music. — Overtures. — Santori, Luigi, ed., 1875–

NN 0020997 MB

Nardis, Camillo de, 1857-
... Partimenti dei maestri; Cotumacci—Durante
—Fenaroli—Leo—Mattei—Platania—Sala—Scarlatti—Tritto—Zingarelli. Milano, G. Ricordi
& c., 1933.
1 p. l., 91 p. 27 1/2cm. (E. R. 1586)

1. Thorough-bass. 2. Harmony. I. Title.

NN 0020998 MB

NARDIS, CAMILLO DE, 1857-1951.
[SCENE ABRUZZESI]
Scene abruzzesi; 1. suite per orchestra. Napoli,
R. Izzo, c1901. Pl. no. 1812 b. score (78 p.) 35cm.

Microfilm.
CONTENTS.--Adunata.--Serenata.--Pastorale.--Saltarello e
temporale.

1. Suites (Orchestra). I. Title.

NN 0020999 NN

M1003 Nardis, Camillo de, 1857-1951.
.N22S2 [Scene abruzzesi. Suite, no.2]
Scene abruzzesi; 2a suite per orchestra.
Partitura. Milano, New York, G. Ricordi,
c1921.
score (48 p.)
Contents.--Processione notturna del Venerdì
Santo.--San Clemente a Casauria.--Serenata
agli sposi.--Festa tragica.

1. Suites (Orchestra) I. Title.

NN 0021000 ICU

---

o5.2 Nardis, Camillo de, 1857-
N16s Scene abruzzesi. 2) suite per orchestra _
Milano [etc.] G. Ricordi e c., 1929.
48p.

Miniature score.

NN 0021001 IU PP

NARDIS, CAMILLO DE, 1857-1951.
Sogno d'un soldato; fantasia per orchestra.
Napoli, R. Izzo [190-?] Pl. no. 1249. score(29 p.)
35cm.

Microfilm (master negative)
Positive in *ZB-361.

NN 0021002 NN

Nardis, Camillo de, 1857-
[Stella. Piano-vocal score. Italian]

Stella; dramma lirico in tre atti di Paolo d'Elsa [pseud.]
da un dramma di F. G. Starace. Musica di Camillo de Nardis.
Riduzione per canto e pianoforte. Milano, E. Sonzogno,
1899.
235 p. 30 cm.

1. Operas—Vocal scores with piano.   I. Pagliara, Rocco E., 1856-
1914. Stella. II. Title.

M1503.N224S7 1899   M 54-1849

NN 0021003 DLC MB CLU

NARDIS, Domenico, de barone,   de
Omero e Dante ne' loro tempi . . . Libera trad. di Vincenzo
Baroni de Nardis.
[Roma.] n. d. 13 pp. 8°.
In Romaic with Italian translation.

NN 0021004 MB

Nardius, Joannes
see Nardi, Giovanni, ca. 1580-ca. 1655.

Nárdiz, Francisco de.
La España universal de Felipe II. Madrid, 1944.
45 p. 19 cm. (Consejo Superior de Investigaciones Científicas.
Cursos para extranjeros)
"Conferencia inaugural del XVI Curso para extranjeros en Santander, 1. de agosto de 1943."

1. Spain—Hist.—Philip II, 1556-1598.   I. Title.   (Series:
Spain. Consejo Superior de Investigaciones Científicas. Cursos para
extranjeros)
DP178.N27   55-51353

NN 0021006 DLC CU WaU NRU InU MH TxU IaU

Nárdiz, Francisco de.
... Figuras. Santander [Imp. y enc. de la "Librería moderna"], 1931.
122 p., 3 l. mounted plates. 16¼ᶜᵐ.
CONTENTS.—Princesa Silvia.—El hidalgo y el pastor.—Astolfo.—Don
Filiberto.—Los tres amigos de Teodoro.—Monna Lisa.

I. Title.
                                                        32-32333
Library of Congress   PQ6625.A7F5 1931
                        [2]   863.6

NN 0021007 DLC NcD

Serat toentoenan sekar lagoe maos dolanan
lan gérong tanpa goeroe. Djil. I. Kaismpoen
déning Nardjikoen. Ngajogjakarta [194-]
17 p. illus. 22cm.
Cover title.
No more published?
Unacc. melodies with added numeral
notation.
1. Songs, Javanese. 2. Music, Javanese.
3. Gamelan. I. Title.

NN 0021008 NIC

Nardjoe, As
see
Nardju, As

Nardju, As.
Mustika budi; menudju kesempurnaan
hidup. Djakarta, "Pustaka Islam", [1953]
105 p. 20cm.

Indonesian and Arabic.

1. Conduct of life. 2. Character.
I. Title.

NN 0021010 NIC

Nardo, Angelo de.
Comitato per le onoranze a Guido Bergamo.
Vita di Guido Bergamo [di] Angelo de Nardo [et al.]
Montebelluna [1954]

Nardò, Angliberto del Balzo, duca di
see
Balzo, Angliberto del, duca di Nardò, d. 1487.

Nardo, Antonio di.
Farm houses, small chateaux and country churches in France,
by Antonio di Nardo; with a preface by Paul P. Crét, photographs by C. D. Arnold and A. di Nardo. Cleveland, O., J. H.
Jansen, 1924.
173 p. incl. front., illus., plates. 41½ᵐ.

1. Architecture—France.   I. Arnold, Charles Dudley, 1844-
II. Title.
                                                        24-28971
Library of Congress   NA1041.N3

                                OU OCU OC1 PP ViU MiU WaS OrU OC1MA OrCS IdU
NN 0021013   DLC NBuU LU PU-FA PU NIC KMK NcRS CoU

NARDO, CESARE DE.
...Cromwell. Napoli: A. Chiurazzi & figlio, 1936.
54 p. ports. 22½cm.

1. Cromwell, Oliver, 1599-1658.

NN 0021014 NN

Nardo, Giandomenico
see Nardo, Giovanni Domenico, 1802-1877.

VOLUME 405

40   Nardo, Giovanni Domenico, 1802–1877.
           Alcune osservazioni chimico-geologichs sul
       potere aggregatore del ferro, e sulla formazione
       del cosi detto ca ranto nel bacino Adriatico.
       [Venezia, tip. Cecchini, 1852]
           4 p.   unp. 8°.   [Geological pamphlets.
       v. 17: 14]

NN   0021016   DLC

Nardo, Giovanni Domenico, 1802–1877.
    Annotazioni illustranti cinquantaquattro
specie di crostacei (podottalmi, stomapodi,
edriottalmi e succhiatore) del mare Adriatico,
proceduti dalla storia antica e recente della
carcinologia adriatica. Venezia, 1869.

    127 p. 4 plates.. 4°.
    Mem.R.Ist.Veneto. XIV.

NN   0021017   MH-Z

Nardo, Giovanni Domenico, 1802–1877.
    Considerazione sulla famiglia dei pesci, Mola.
1840.
    (I.P. vol. 9)

NN   0021018   PPAN

Bonaparte
Collection NARDO, GIOVANNI DOMENICO, 1802–1877.
No.5126   Considerazioni filologiche sull'importanza
        dello studio comparativo dei dialetti rustici,
        e sulla riuscita di alcuni saggi di versione
        tentati in qualche dialetto veneto, del canto
        della Divina commedia in cui trovasi descritta
        la morte del conte Ugolino.   Venezia, Tipogra-
        fia del commercio, 1869.
            34p.   24cm.
            Text of Dante from canto 33 of the Inferno,
        accompanied by 4 Venetian versions: p.11-26.
            "Versione libera   di Federico Federigo nel
        dialetto veneziano":   p.[32]-34.

NN   0021019   ICN NIC

Nardo, Giovanni Domenico, 1802–1877.
    De proctostego, novo piscium genere, specimen ichthyo-
logicum anatomicum quod pro summis honoribus in medicina rite assequendis indicit Joan. Dominicus Nardo
Clodiensis ... Patavii, Typis Crescinianis, 1827.
    17 p. pl. 29cm.

    1. Apodes.

                                            A 18-1593

    Title from Harvard Univ.   Printed by L. C.

NN   0021020   MH ICJ PPAN

NARDO, Giovanni Domenico, 1802–1877.
    Imitazioni di canti popolari chioggiotti.
Nuovamente pubblicate sulla prima edizione
dell'anno 1871. Venezia, stabilimento
tipografico fratelli Visentini, 1885.

    31 p.

NN   0021021   MH

[Nardo, Giovanni Domenico] 1802–1877.
    Lettera al signor Fortunato Luigi Naccari sulla
preparazione e conservazione dei crostacei.
Treviso, F. Andreola, 1822.
    3 l.   8°.
    Repr. from: Gior. d. sc. e. lett. d. Prov.
Venete, No. xi.

NN   0021022   DNLM

Nardo, Giovanni Domenico, 1802-1877.   *5340.10.11
    Norme quale devono essere ordinate le statistiche relative all'
andamento economico amministrativo ed all' esercizio della beneficenza negli istituti degli esposti, onde ricavarne utili e sicure
induzioni morali, economiche e sanitarie.
    (In Reale istituto veneto di scienze, lettere ed arti. Memorie.
Vol. 11, pp. 357-374. Venezia, 1862.)

E4357 — Foundling hospitals. — Statistics.

NN   0021023   MB

Nardo, G[iovanni] Domenico, 1802–1877.
    Notizie sullo sferococco confervoide delle venete lagune
e sugli usi suoi terapeutici ed economici con avvertenze
sul modo di raccoglierlo e conservarlo, sulla formazione
de' bagni algosi, ecc. Del Dr. G. Domenico Nardo ...
Venezia, G. Antonelli, 1853.

    7 p. 22cm.

    [Botanical pamphlets, v. 4, no. 2]
    Estratto dal Diz. arti e mestieri, fasc. 146.

    1. Sphaerococcus confervoides.

    Library of Congress   QK3.B77   5-35874†

NN   0021024   DLC

Nardo, Giovanni Domenico, 1802–1877.
    Nuove osservazioni anatomiche sul sistema cutaneo e
sullo scheletro del prottostego del dott. Gio. Domenico
Nardo ... Estratte dal bimestre v.–vi. 1840 degli Annali
delle scienze del regno Lombardo-Veneto. Padova, Tipi
di A. Sicca, 1840.

    8 p. 29cm.

    [Ichthyological pamphlets, v. 5, no. 7]

    1. Ausonia. 2. Fishes—Anatomy.

                                                11-4301
    Library of Congress   QL612.I 22 vol. 5

NN   0021025   DLC

Nardo, Giovanni Domenico, 1802-1877.   *5340.10.2
    Osservazioni anatomiche comparative sull' intima struttura delle
cartilagini dei condrotterigi.
    (In Reale istituto veneto di scienze, lettere ed arti. Memorie.
Vol. 2, pp. 201-211. Venezia, 1845.)

E5284 — Cartilage. — Histology. — Selachians.

NN   0021026   MB PPAN

Nardo, Giovanni Domenico, 1802- 1877.   *5340.10.5
    Osservazioni chimico-geologiche sul potere aggregatore del ferro e
sulla formazione del cosi detto caranto nell' adriatico bacino.
    (In Reale istituto veneto di scienze, lettere ed arti. Memorie.
Vol. 6, pp. 1-23. Venezia, 1856.)

E4724 — Iron. — Hard-pan, Formation of.

NN   0021027   MB

Nardo, Giovanni Domenico, 1802–1877.
    Osservazioni ittiologiche comunicate alle Assemblee
italiane de' scienziati, dal dottor Gio. Domenico Nardo ...
[n. p., n. d.]
    [8] p. 25cm.
    Unpaged.
    [Inserto nel tim. 1. 1843, degli Annali degli scienze del regno Lom-
bardo-Veneto.]
    CONTENTS.—Nuove osservazioni sul *Lepadogaster piger* (Nardo) e con-
siderazioni sul posto che occupar dovrebbero i lepadogastri nel sistema
naturale de' pesci.—Proposizione per la formazione di un nuovo genere di
pesci intitolato *Brachychirus*.—Proposizione per la formazione di un
nuovo genere di *Salachi* chimato *Caninoa o Caninotus* ...
    1. Fishes.
                                                A 18-2011
    Library, U. S. National   Museum

NN   0021028   DSI PPAN NIC

PC   Nardo, Giovanni Domenico, 1802–1877.
1843   La pesca del pesce ne' Valli della Veneta
N22   Laguna al tempo delle prime buffere inver-
       nali detto volgarmente (Fraima) monologo
       didascalico in versi nel dialetto de' pesca-
       tori chioggiotti colla versione nella lin-
       gua comune d'Italia. Venezia, M. Visentini,
       1871.
           xxiv, 103 p. 25cm.

       1. Italian   language--Dialects--
       Chioggia. I.   Title.

NN   0021029   NIC PU NjP NRU MH

Nardo, Giovanni Domenico, 1802–1877.
    Prospetto analitico rischiarante l' etiologia e
la diagnostica dei mali nervosi, specialmente
isterici ed ipocondriaci. Venezia, G. Cecchini &
Comp., 1842.
    9 p., 1 tab. 8°.

NN   0021030   DNLM

Nardo, Giovanni Domenico, 1802-1877.
    ——. Quali sieno i fatti principali che condur-
rebbero a supporre essere una miscellanea venefica
la causa efficiente del cholera-asiatico; ricerche;
con note illustrative. 50 pp. 8°. *Venezia, G.
Cecchini, 1865.*

NN   0021031   DNLM

NARDO, Giovanni Domenico, 1802–1877.
    Relazione di quanto ha potuto operare la
direzione del Comizio agrario e di piscicoltura del prima distretto della provincia di
cio che sarebbe necessario per renderlo vera-
mente utile ed assicurare i mezzi di sua esistenza. Con un' appendice che fa conoscere le
attuali sue condizione economiche; Il programma che si e prefisso, e le leggi sovrane
dalle quali sono regolati i comisj,del dott.
Giandomenico Nardo. Venezia, tip. Grimaldo
e c., 1875.
    1 p. l., 39 p.20 cm.

NN   0021032   MH

QL32   Nardo, Giovanni Domenico.
.C6   Rischiarimenti e rittifcazioni ai generi ed a
       qualche specie della famiglia de zoofitari sarcinoidi
       od alcionari. (Inserto nel bien. 1 e 2. 1845.
       degli Annali delle scienze del regno Lambardo-
       Veneto) Vicenza, 1845.
           12 p. 4°. [Zoological pamphlets, v. 1]

NN   0021033   DLC

Nardo, Giovanni Domenico, 1802 - 1877.
    Rischiarimenti e retrificazioni ai generi
ed a qualche specie della famiglia de
zoofitari sarcinoidi alcionari, stabilita dal
Sig. De Blainville. 1848.

NN   0021034   PPAN

NARDO, Giovanni Domenico, 1802–1877.
    Sinonimia moderna delle specie registrate
nell' opera intitolaata;Descrizione de'crostacei,de' testacei e de' pesci che abitano le
lagune et golfo veneto,rappresentati in figure
a chiaroscuro ed a colori, dall' abate Stefano
Chiereghini,Ven. Clodiense. Applicata per
commissione governative dal Dr. Gio. Domenico
Nardo... Venezia, Nell' I.R.Priv. stabilimento
Antonelli, 1847.
    XI, 128 (i. e. 64). p. 25 cm.
    Two numbers given to each page.

NN   0021035   MH

VOLUME 405

Nardo, Giovanni Domenico, 1802-1877.
Sopra un nuovo genere di spongiali silicei intitolata viva il qualo vive nell'interni delle pietre e dei gusci marine perforandoli in mille guise. Venezia, 1840.

NN 0021036   PPAN MH

Bonaparte
Collection NARDO, GIOVANNI DOMENICO, 1802-1877.
No.4945   Studj filologici e lessicografici sopra alcune recenti giunte ai Vocabolarj italiani, sopra voci e maniere di dire additate dal Monti, dal Brambilla, dal Tommaseo e dal Fanfani, e sopra taluna delle dichiarazioni erronee od imperfette che trovansi ancora ne'Vocabolarj. Con un discorso, Sui mezzi indicati da M.Cesarotti per avviare l'italiana favella alla desiderata perfezione. Venezia,G.Cecchini,1855.
xxvi,204p. 25cm.

Bibliography: p.xxi-xxv.

NN 0021037   ICN MU DNLM

AS   Nardo, Giovanni Domenico, 1802-1877.
222   Sui mezzi più efficaci ad impedire che
V45   qualche figlio illegittimo rimanga occulto,
M5++   ossia non iscritto nei registri civili, e
v. 11 quindi senza tutela legale, e che qualche
no. 5 figlio legittimo sia trasmesso come esposto
       all'Istituto de Trovatelli.

(In Istituto veneto di scienze, lettere ed arti. Memorie. Venezia. 32cm. v. 11 (1862) p. ₍201₎-217)

NN 0021038   NIC

NARDO, Giovanni Domenico,1802-1877.
Sull'esistenza dell' organo del gusto in alcune specie di cani marini. Osservazioni anatomiche del dott. Gio. Domenico Nardo. Venezia, Presso la segretaria dell' I.R.Istituto,1851.

4 p. 32 cm.
"Inserite nel volume IV delle Memoire dell' I.R. Istituto veneto di scienze, letterer ed arti".

NN 0021039   MH

Nardo, Giovanni Domenico.   *5340.10.4
Sull' esistenza dell' organo del gusto in alcune specie di cani marini: osservazioni anatomiche.
(In Reale istituto veneto di scienze, lettere ed arti. Memorie. Vol. 4, pp. 109-113. Venezia, 1852.)

E5100 — Selachians. — Taste.

NN 0021040   MB NIC

NARDO, Giovanni Domenico,1802-1877.
Sull'indirizzo preso dal Comizion agrario e di piscicoltura veneta per meglio soddisfare al proprio mandato qual e di rendere il suolo maggiormento produttivo e piu ubertosa la pescagione della laguna. Con appendice descrittiva una barca detta tartana da pesca, del dott., Gio. Domenico Nardo. Venezia, G. Antonelli,1870.

24 p. folded table. 20 1/2 cm.
"Estr. dal vol. XV, serie III degli Atti dell' Istituto ve neto di scienze, lettere ed arti."

NN 0021041   MH

Nardo, Giovanni Domenico, 1802-1877.
Sulla coltura degli animali acquatici nel veneto dominio, considerazioni del D.ʳ Gio. Domenico Nardo ... Parte prima riguardante la piscicoltura e le pesche di acqua dolce e della veneta laguna. Con copiose note illustrative. Venezia, G. Antonelli, 1864.

₍4₎ 158, ₍1₎ p. 1 fold. table, II fold. diagrs. on 1 leaf. 22ᶜᵐ.

NN 0021042   ICJ MH

Nardo, Giovanni Domenico, 1802-1877.   *5340.10.9
Sulla identità personale dei figli abbandonati, sulle questioni giuridiche che su di essa potrebbero insorgere e sul valore de' mezzi finora proposti onde guarentirla.
(In Reale istituto veneto di scienze, lettere ed arti. Memorie. Vol. 9, pp. 135-165. Venezia, 1860.)

E4676 — Foundlings.

NN 0021043   MB

AS   Nardo, Giovanni Domenico, 1802-1877.
222   Sunto di alcune osservazioni anatomiche
V45   sull'intima struttura della cute de'pesci
M5++   comparativamente considerata e sulle cause
v. 5   fisiologiche e fisico-chimiche della loro
no. 4 colorazione e decolorazione.

(In Istituto veneto di scienze, lettere ed arti. Memorie. Venezia. 32cm. v. 5 (1855) p. ₍243₎-276)

NN 0021044   NIC

Nardo, Guido di.
Alchimia e cabala alla luce della scienza (La pietra filosofale) Con un appendice sugli elementi della "Lingua sacra." Napoli, Istituto della stampa, 1950 ₍i. e. 1951₎
158 p. illus., map. 26 cm.
Bibliographical footnotes.

1. Alchemy. 2. Cabala.
                                        A 54-873
Harvard Univ. Library
for Library of Congress   ₍3₎

NN 0021045   MH

Nardo, Guido di.
Mito e preistoria alle origini di Roma.
₍Roma, 1936₎
₍9₎ p

NN 0021046   PBm

Nardo, Juan B   de.
Metalurgia física y sus aplicaciones industriales. 1. ed. Buenos Aires, J. Montesó, 1946.
518 p. illus., tables. 24 cm.
"Bibliografía": p. ₍479₎-486.

1. Metallurgy. 2. Physics.

TN690.N3   669   49-18976*

NN 0021047   DLC

WX   NARDO, Luigi
N224c   Come si provvega a migliorare lo
1863   Spedale civile generale di Venezia in armonia al progresso dei tempi; cenni. Venezia, Longo, 1863.
xxvi, 50 p.
1. Venice. Ospedale civile 2. Venice. Spedale civile 3. Venice. Spedale civile provinciale

NN 0021048   DNLM

Nardo (Luigi)   Della vita e degli studi di Francesco Enrico Trois. 28 pp. 4°.
Venezia. P. Naratovich, 1856.

NN 0021049   DNLM

Nardo, Luigi. Su alcuni usi ed applicazioni economiche del Pinus maritima e della sua corteccia; memoria chimico-tecnica. Venezia. 1834. 8°. pp. 20.

NN 0021050   MH-A

Nardo, Luigi Umberto de.
Dosage du carbone dans la terre végétale et dans les produits organiques purs au moyen de l'oxydation par l'anhydride permanganique. illus.
Ann. sci. agron. année 46, p. 9-13.   Paris, 1929.

1. Carbon—₍Determination₎
                                        Agr 29-1260
Library, U. S. Dept. of   Agriculture 14An75 année 46

NN 0021051   DNAL

Nardo, Luigi Umberto de.
Guida alla soluzione dei quesiti di estimo ordinario e catastale per ingegneri, agronomi, geometri e per i candidati agli esami di abilitazione professionale e di concorso ai pubblici uffici. 11.ed., riv. e corr. Udine ₍1950₎
282 p.

NN 0021052   ICU ICRL

Nardo, Luigi Umberto de.
Lezioni di estimo ordinario e catastale, precedute da un sunto di economia politica e agraria, da richiami di matematica finanziaria e corredate da numerose esemplificazioni e illustrazioni; con tavole finanziarie, tabelle, modelli catastali, tipi di frazionamento ecc. in appendice, per allievi geometri, periti agrari e industriali. Udine, Del Bianco ₍1950₎
510 p. diagrs., forms, fold. plan. 25 cm.
Errata leaf laid in.
——— Appendice. Udine, Del Bianco ₍1958₎
77 p. diagrs., forms, plan. 25 cm.
1. Assessment. 2. Valuation.
                                        A 51-8060 rev
New York Univ.   Libraries HJ3241
for Library of Congress   ₍r59b8₎

NN 0021053   NNU

Nardo, Luigi Umberto de.
... Nozioni di agronomia e zootecnica, secondo la riforma dei programmi ministeriali, ad uso degli allievi geometri, dei professionisti e degli agricoltori. 4. ed. completamente rifatta ... Udine, IDEA ₍1942-43₎
2 v. illus., forms, diagrs. 25ᶜᵐ.
At head of title: L. U. de Nardo.
Paged continuously.

1. Agriculture. 2. Stock and stock-breeding. 3. Fruit-culture—Italy.
ɪ. Title.
S493.N27   A F 47-773
Illinois. Univ. Library
for Library of Congress   ₍4₎†

NN 0021054   IU DLC NIC DNAL

30   Nardo, Luigi Umberto de.
N16   Nozioni di agronomia e di zootecnica, secondo i
Ed. 6 programmi ministeriali, ad uso degli allievi geometri, dei professionisti e degli agricoltori.
6. ed.   Udine, Del Bianco Editore [1947-50]
2 v.
Vol 2. is 5th ed., published 1947.

NN 0021055   DNAL

VOLUME 405

Nardo, Michele di.
   Dante e Tommaseo. Milano, U. Hoepli,
1941.
   62 p.
   "Estratto dal volume Studi su Dante, vol.
vi, luglio 1941".
   Bibliographical references included in note,
p. [56]-62.
   1. Tommaseo, Niccoló, 1802-1874. 2. Dante -
Criticism and interpretation. I. Title.

NN 0021056   CLU

Nardo, Michele di.
   ...Per un famoso passo del Tommaseo. Udine,
Tipografia Arti grafiche friulane, 1949. 15 p.
24cm.

   1. Tommaseo, Niccolò, 1802-1874.

NN 0021057   NN RPB

Nardo, Vincenzo de.
   Statistica e demografia
      see under   Istituto nazionale per le
relazioni culturali con l'estero.

Nardo-Cibele, Angela.
   leggende bellunesi. 18 pp. (Archiv. studio tradiz. po-
   polari, v. 7, 1888, p. 233.)   *Acque. Pregiudizi e*
   by Angela Nardo-Cibele and G.C.Buzzeti.

NN 0021059   MdBP

X NARDO-CIBELE, ANGELA.
71818   Studi sul dialetto di Burano.   Venezia,
.133   Visentini, 1898.
        98p. 24cm.

        "Estratto dall'Ateneo Veneto, anno XXI,
vol.1."

NN 0021060   ICN IU

Nardo-Cibele, Angela, editor.
   Zoologia popolare veneta, specialmente bellunese. Credenze,
leggende e tradizioni varie. Palermo, L. P. Lauriel, 1887.
   pp. xi, 168. (Curiosità popolari tradizionali, 4.)

Folklore--Italy--Venice |Do. (2)-Animals||Series

NN 0021061   MH ICN MiU NN CtY

Nardoianni, Raffaele.
   ...Piedimonte San Germano nella voragine di
Cassino.   Cassino, A. Malatesta & figli, 1950.
100 p.   illus. 24cm.

   1. World war, 1939-1945—Italy—Piedimonte San
Germano. 2. Piedimonte San Germano, Italy. 3. Monte
Cassino (Benedictine abbey)—Siege, 1944.

NN 0021062   NN

Nardon, Gaston.
   ... Vade-mecum du musicien. Principes élémentaires
de la musique à l'usage des professeurs et des élèves par
demandes et par réponses, par Gaston Nardon ... Paris,
Costallat & c^{ie} [¹1918]
   104 p., 1 l. illus. (music) 18^{cm}.   fr. 2

   1. Music—Manuals, text-books, etc.   I. Title.
                                                   19-4585
Library of Congress   MT6.N17

NN 0021063   DLC

Nardou-Durosier (Félix). *Étude sur la
péritonite après l'ovariotomie. 138 pp. 4°.
Paris, 1860, No. 188.*

NN 0021064   DNLM

F   Nardone, Benito.
2710   Chico Tazo procesa a "El Día"; el pleito
N382   del Molino de la Aguada.   Montevideo [Diario
LAC   Rural] 1954.
           191p. 20cm.

           1. Uruguay - Rural conditions. 2. Uruguay
         - Economic conditions. I. Title. Sp.:
         Lucuix Collection.

NN 0021065   TxU

989.5   Nardone, Benito.
N16c   Chico Tazo procesa a "El Día"; fracaso del
         estatismo.   Montevideo, 1955.
           190p. 20cm.

           1. El Día, Montevideo. 2. Uruguay--Pol. &
         govt.--1830-   I. Title.

NN 0021066   IU NcD DPU NN

PQ8519   Nardone, Benito.
N33J6   José Artigas; [animación de la vida del héroe en sesenta y
         cuatro episodios basados en documentos históricos] Escribió
         Chico-Tazo [pseud.]   Montevideo [Tall. Gráf. Diario Rural]
         1951.
           544 p.

           1. Artigas, José Gervasio, 1764-1850 - Drama.

NN 0021067   CU NcU ICU

Nardone, Benito.
   Jose Artigas;... Escribió Chico-Tazo(pseud.)
Montevideo Tall. Graf. Diario Rural 1951.
544 p.

   Film reproduction

NN 0021068   NN

851.7   Nardone, Costantino, fl. 1825.
N224b   La baccheide.   Napoli, Stamperia della
         Società filomatica, 1825.
           235p. 18cm.

           Poems.

NN 0021069   IEN

Nardone, Domenico.
   ... Notizie storiche sulla città di Gravina
(455-1860)   Gravina, L. Attolini, 1922.
   2 p.l., [vii]-xviii, 204 p., 1 l.   25 cm.
   Bibliographical foot-notes.
   1. Gravina, Italy - Hist.

NN 0021070   CU

Nardone, Pietro.
Genova e pisa.
Prato, 1923.

NN 0021071   NjP WU

Nardone, William Frederick.
   Industrial manganese poisoning, by William F.
Nardone.   (Cincinnati, 1952)
   75, (17) l.   29 cm.

NN 0021072   OCU

BX   Nardoni, Carlo.
2541   Notizie storiche-tradizionali del Santuario
S8   della SS. Trinità sul Monte Autore e notizie
Z6   sulle origini e vicende storiche di Vallepietra.
S2   [Tivoli] Aldo Chicca, 1954.
N2   34 p. 22 cm.

           "Bibliografia": p. 34.

           1. Santissima Trinità sul Monte Autore
         Vallepietra, Italy. 2. Vallepietra, Italy -
         Hist. 3. Trinity Shrines.

NN 0021073   DCU

NARDONI, Leone.
   L'antico oratorio di sant'Agnese in
monasterio [S.Prassede], con pitture cristiane
del secolo nono; indicazione. Roma, G.
Aurelj,1870.

   op.7+.

NN 0021074   MH

NARDONI, Leone.
   Dell'antica chi sa di S.Stefano gia
esistita ad Acquatraversa sulla via Cassia;
memoria. n.p., [1859]

   pp.6+.

NN 0021075   MH

NARDONI, Leone.
   Di alcune sotterranee confessioni nelle
antiche basiliche di Roma sconosciute per
varii secoli. [Roma,1881?]

   1.8°. pp.(11)
   Extracted from a larger work.

NN 0021076   MH

Nardoni, Leone.
   Di alcuni oggetti di epoca arcaica rinvenuti
nell'interno di Roma. Memorie di Leone Nardoni
e Michele Stefano de Rossi.   Roma, 1874.
   28 p., 11 folded pl.
   "Estratto dal giornale Il Buonarroti, Serie II,
Vol. IX. Marzo 1874".

NN 0021077   MH-P

VOLUME 405

Nardonnet, Jeanne, 1912-
... Contribution à l'étude du diagnostic étiologique des annexites chroniques ... Paris, 1939.
Thèse - Univ. de Paris.

NN 0021078 CtY

Nardowni, Shawarsh, 1898–1968.
Բաներ, բաներ, ինչ բաներ. արձակ բանաստեղծութիւն եւ հէքեաթ։ Paris, Գրատուն Գարամեան [1941]
191 p. 23 cm.

I. Title.
Title romanized: Baner, baner, inch' baner.

PK8548.N27B3 72–211247

NN 0021079 DLC

Nardowni, Shawarsh, 1898–1968.
(Hanown Mesrob Mashtots'i)
Յանուն Մեսրոպ Մաշտոցի. պաշտպանութիւն հայ լեզուի։ Անթիլիաս, Տպարան Կաթողիկոսութեան Հայոց Մեծի Տանն Կիլիկիոյ, 19
v. 24 cm.

1. Armenian language—Addresses, essays, lectures. I. Title.

PK8002.N26 73–219070

NN 0021080 DLC

Nardowni, Shawarsh, 1898–1968.
Մեղեդիներ, մեղեդիներ. հէքեաթ եւ բանաստեղծութիւն։ Փարիզ [Դիմել] Direction du journal "Haratch", 1933։
218 p. 23 cm. (Մատենաշար "Յառաջ," թիւ 1)

I. Title.
Title romanized: Meghediner, meghediner.

PK8548.N27M4 72–204714

NN 0021081 DLC

Nardowni, Shawarsh, 1898-1968, ed.
Metsarank'arh Erowand Tēr-Andrēasian
see under title

NARDROFF, Robert von,1895-
The refraction of x-rays in pyrites.
Thesis, Columbia University. n.p., [1924]

pp.(11).
"Vita", at end.
"Reprinted from Physical Review, pp.143-151. no.2, Aug, 1924"

NN 0021083 MH

Narducci, Enrico, 1832–1893.
Die Benedetto Micheli poeta, musico e pittore romano del secolo XVIII, e di un suo poema inedito in dialetto romanesco intitolato: "La libbe 'à romana". Memoria del socio Enrico Narducci letta nella seduta del 19 maggio 1878.
(In Atti della R. Accademia dei Lincei. Memorie della Classe di scienze morali, storiche e filologiche. Roma, 1878. 29½cm. ser. 3, vol. II, p. 589–608)
Also issued separately.
A discussion of the text of La libbertà romana in ms. 426 in the collection of manuscripts belonging to prince Baldassare Boncompagni-Ludovisi, followed by annotated lists of Benedetto Michele's published and unpublished works.
Bibliographical foot-notes.
1. Micheli, Benedetto, 18th cent. 2. Boncompagni-Ludovisi, Baldassare, principe, 1821–1894.
Illinois. Univ. Library A C 37–2391
for Library of Congress [AS222.R645 ser. 3, vol. 2]
[2] (063)

NN 0021084 IU MH MoU OCl OU OCU

Narducci, Enrico, 1832–1893.
Bibliografia romana. Osservazioni di Enrico Narducci. Estratto dal Popolo romano (1, 3, 5 marzo 1880) Roma, Stabilimento tipografico del Popolo pomano [!] 1880.
16 p. 18cm.
Notes on the plan and scope of the projected Bibliografia romana, to be issued by the Ministerio di agricoltura, industria e commercio (of which the first and only volume appeared in 1880), with incidental references to existing Italian bibliographies.

1. Bibliografia romana, 1880.

Library of Congress Z2364.R7B45 3—7367

NN 0021085 DLC

Narducci, Enrico, 1832-1893, ed.

Il Buonarroti; scritti sopra le arti e le lettere di Benvenuto Gasparoni continuati per cura di Enrico Narducci. [Ser. II] v. 1–14, 1866–80; ser. III, v. 1–4, 1882–94. Roma, Tip. delle scienze matematiche e fisiche, 1866–90 [i. e. 1894]

Narducci, Enrico, 1832–1893.
Catalogo dei codici Petrarcheschi delle biblioteche Barberina, Chigiana, Corsiniana, Vallicelliana e Vaticana e delle edizioni Petrarchesche esistenti nelle biblioteche pubbliche di Roma; comp. da Enrico Narducci ... Roma [etc.] E. Loescher, 1874.
vii, 101 p. 22cm.

1. Petrarca, Francesco—Bibl. I. Rome (City) Biblioteca Barberiniana. II. Rome (City) Biblioteca Chigiana. III. Rome (City) Biblioteca Corsiniana. IV. Rome (City) Biblioteca Vallicelliana. V. Vatican. Biblioteca Vaticana.

Library of Congress Z8676.N22 5–12774

NN 0021087 DLC NcU NcD OCU MiU CtY NIC

Narducci, Enrico, 1832–1893.
Catalogo delle pubblicazioni, di Enrico Narducci ... (30 anni di lavoro) Roma, Tipografia delle scienze matematiche e fisiche, 1887.
2 p. l., 16 p. 33cm.

1. Narducci, Enrico, 1832–1893—Bibl. 2. Italian literature—Hist. & crit.—Bibl.

Library of Congress Z8614.N2 5–3369

NN 0021088 DLC

Narducci, Enrico, 1832–1893, comp.

Boncompagni-Ludovisi, Baldassarre, *principe*, 1821–1894.
Catalogo di edizioni del secolo XV. possedute da D. Baldassarre Boncompagni; comp. da Enrico Narducci. Roma, Tip. delle scienze matematiche e fisiche, 1893.

Narducci, Enrico, 1832–1893.
Boncompagni-Ludovisi, Baldassarre, *principe*, 1821–1894.
Catalogo di manoscritti ora posseduti da d. Baldassarre Boncompagni, compilato da Enrico Narducci. 2. ed., notabilmente accresciuta, contenente una descrizione di 249 manoscritti non indicati nella prima, e corredata di un copioso indice. Roma, Tip. delle scienze matematiche e fisiche, 1892.

Narducci, Enrico, 1832-1893.

Rome (City) Biblioteca Angelica.
Catalogus codicum manuscriptorum, praeter graecos et orientales, in Bibliotheca Angelica olim coenobii Sancti Augustini de Urbe. Integrum confecit, adnotationibus instruxit, indicibus locupletavit, privatis impensis, publicae studiosorum commoditati edidit Henricus Narducci. Tomus prior, complectens codices ab instituta bibliotheca ad 1870. Romae, typis Ludovici Cecchini, 1892.

Narducci, Enrico, 1832-1893, comp.

Z6621
.R74N2

Rome (City) Università. *Biblioteca Alessandrina.*
Catalogus codicum manuscriptorum praeter orientales qui in Bibliotheca Alexandrina Romae adservantur. Confecit Henricus Narducci ... Romae, ex typographia romana, sumptibus Fr. Bocca, 1877.

(Narducci, Enrico) 1832-1893.
I codici petrarcheschi delle biblioteche,...
Rome, 1874.

NN 0021093 NIC

Narducci, Enrico, 1832-1893, ed.

Ristoro *d'Arezzo, 13th cent.*
La composizione del mondo di Ristoro d'Arezzo, testo italiano del 1282, pub. da Enrico Narducci. Roma, Tip. delle Scienze matematiche e fisiche, 1859.

Narducci, Enrico, 1832–1893.
Dell'uso e della utilità di un catalogo generale delle biblioteche d'Italia; relazione e proposta a S. E. il Sig. comm. prof. Guido Baccelli, ministro della istruzione pubblica, seguita dalla prima sillaba dello stesso catalogo per cura di Enrico Narducci ... Roma: Tipografia delle scienze matematiche e fisiche, 1883. xix p., 136 col. [137]–169 p. 30cm.
Bibliographical footnotes.

904010A. 1. Cataloguing, Co-operative. I. Title.
N. Y. P. L. July 13, 1938

NN 0021095 NN CU MH TxHU MB IU

Narducci, Enrico, 1832-1893.

Cicero, Marcus Tullius.
Des presbyter Hadoardus Cicero-excerpte, nach E. Narducci's abschrift des Cod. vat. reg. 1762 [fol. 1–155] mitgetheilt und bearbeitet von Paul Schwenke.
(In Philologus ... Supplementband. Göttingen, 1889. 22cm. v, p. [397]–588)

Narducci, Enrico, 1832–1893.
... Di Benedetto Micheli, poeta, musico e pittore romano del secolo XVIII e di un suo poema inedito in dialetto romanesco intitolato La libbertà romana. Memoria del socio Enrico Narducci. Roma, Coi tipi del Salviucci, 1878.
22 p. 30 x 22cm.
At head of title: Reale accademia dei Lincei, anno CCLXXV (1877–78) "Serie 3a.—Memorie della Classe di science morali, storiche e filologiche. vol. II°.—Seduta del 19 maggio 1878."—verso of t.-p.

1. Micheli, Benedetto, 18th cent.

Library of Congress PQ4720.M17N3 11—32685

NN 0021097 DLC

Narducci, Enrico, 1832-1893.
Discorso del modo di formare un catalogo...
(Roma, 1867).

NN 0021098 NIC

Narducci, Enrico, 1832-1893
Due capitoli;...
(Rome, 1858)

NN 0021099 NIC

NARDUCCI,Enrico,1832-1893,editor.
Due capitoli:l'uno inedito di Francesco d'Arezzo a detestazione della invidia,l'altro di Maestro Simone da Siena,fatto per la morte di Dante. Pubblicati per cura di Enrico Narducci. Roma,Tip.delle scienze matematiche e fisiche,1859.
21 cm. pp.29,(1).
"Estratto dal Giornale arcadico,tomo CLVI."

NN 0021100 MH PU NIC

VOLUME 405

QA 32   NARDUCCI, ENRICO, 1832-1893.
.N22   Due trattati inediti d'abaco contenuti in
         due codici vaticani del secolo XII e pubbli-
         cati da Enrico Narducci.   Roma, Tipografia
         delle Scienze Matematiche e Fisiche, 1882.
         54 p.

            Estratto dal Bullettino di bibliografia
         di storia delle scienze matematiche e fische,
         t. XV, Marzo 1882.

            1. Mathematics--Early works to 1800.

    NN   0021101   InU MH

Narducci, Enrico, 1832-1893.
   Giunte all'opera "Gli scrittori d'Italia" del conte Giammaria
Mazzuchelli, tratte dalla Biblioteca Alessandrina e presentate
dal socio corrisp. Enrico Narducci nella seduta del 16 gennaio
1881.
   *(In Atti della R. Accademia dei Lincei. Memorie della Classe di
scienze morali, storiche e filologiche. Roma, 1884. 29½cm. ser. 3,
vol. XII, p. ₍3₎-120)*
   This, like the work supplemented, does not go beyond 1750 and covers
only A-B.
   1. Italy--Bio-bibliography. 2. Italian literature--Bibliography. I.
Mazzuchelli, Giovanni Maria, conte, 1707-1765. Gli scrittori d'Italia. II.
Rome (City) Università. Biblioteca Alessandrina.
                                                A C 40-2069
Illinois. Univ. Library
   for Library of Congress   [AS222.R645 ser. 3, vol. 12]
                                    ₍2₎   (065)

    NN   0021102   IU MoU NcU OU

Narducci, Enrico, 1832-1893.
   ... Giunte all'opera "Gli scrittori d'
Italia" del conte Giammaria Mazzuchelli,
tratte dalla Biblioteca Alessandrina, per
cura del socio corrispondente Enrico
Narducci. Roma, Coi tipi del Salviucci,
1884.
   Microfilm copy, made in 1958, of the
original in Vatican. Biblioteca vaticana.
Positive.
   Negative film in Vatican. Biblioteca
vaticana.

   Collation of the original, as determined
from the film: 120 p.
   At head of title: Reale accademia dei
Lincei (anno CCLXXI, 1883-84)
   "Serie 3.ᵃ--Memorie della Classe di scienze
morali, storiche e filologiche. Vol. XII.-
seduta del 16 Gennaio 1881."--verso t.-p.
   This, like the work supplemented, does
not go beyond   1750 and covers
only A-B

   «Manuscripta, microfilms of rare and out-of-
print books. List 3, no. 11»
   1. Italy--Bio-bibliography. 2. Italian
literature--Bibliography. I. Mazzuchelli,
Giovanni Maria, conte, 1707-1765. Gli
scrittori d'Italia. II. Rome (City)
Università. Biblioteca Alessandrina.
(Series: [Manuscripta, microfilms of rare
and out-of-print   books. List 3,
no.11])

    NN   0021105   MoSU ViU OU

Narducci, Enrico, 1832-1893.
   Intorno a due edizioni della Summa de arithmetica di
fra Luca Pacioli; nota di Enrico Narducci. Roma, Tipografia delle scienze matematiche e fisiche, 1863.
   16 p.   23ᶜᵐ.

   1. Paccioli, Luca, d. ca. 1514. Summa de arithmetica. 2. Arithmetic--Be-
fore 1846.

    NN   0021106   MiU ICN CU

NARDUCCI, Enrico, 1832-1893.
   Intorno ad alcune lettere inedite del card.
Pietro Bembo e d'altri illustri italiani,
pubblicate dal prof. Giuseppe Spezi; notizia.
Roma, Tipografia delle Scienze matematiche
e fisiche, 1862.

   pp.11.

    NN   0021107   MH

Narducci, Enrico, 1832-1893.
   Intorno ad una traduzione italiana fatta
nell' anno 1341 di una compilazione astronomica
di Alfonso X. Re di Castiglia. Nota di Enrico
Narducci.   Roma, Tipografia dell scienze
matematiche e fisiche, 1865.   34p. 24cm.

   "Estratto dal Giornale Arcadico, tomo 137,
gennaio e febbraio, 1864."

   1. Astronomy. Early works to 1800. 2. Alfons
X, el Sabio, king of Castile and Leon, 1221-1284.
Trattato della Sfera. 3. Vatican. Biblioteca
Vaticana, Mss. no.   8174.

    NN   0021108   MWelC

Narducci, Enrico, 1832-1893.
   Intorno all'autenticità di un codice vaticano contenente il
trattato di Boezio "De consolazione philosophiae" scritto di
mano di Giovanni Boccaccio. Memoria del socio corrisp. Enrico Narducci, seguita da un' appendice di documenti riguardanti le ambascerie di Bernardo Bembo, letta nella seduta del
19 febbraio 1882.   (Con una tavola)
   *(In Atti della R. Accademia dei Lincei. Memorie della Classe di
scienze morali, storiche e filologiche. Roma, 1883. 29½cm. ser. 3,
vol. VIII, p. 243-264. pl. (facsims.))*
   "Occasione del presente scritto è un recente processo svoltosi innanzi
alla 5ᵃ sezione del Tribunale correzionale di Roma, per furto del codice

vaticano n.º ₍lat.₎ 3362, contenente il trattato De consolazione philosophiae
di Boezio. Oggetto dello scritto medesimo è di dimostrare che questo codice
₍Vat. lat. 3362₎, ... è realmente scritto di mano di Giovanni Boccaccio."--
p. 243.
   "Credo mio dovere di premettere che i documenti in questa memoria
allegati ... ₍furono₎ tratti dagli archivi di stato di Firenze e di Venezia."--
p. 243.
   Bibliographical foot-notes.

   1. Boethius, d. 524. De consolatione philosophiae. 2. Boccaccio, Giovanni, 1313-1375. 3. Vatican. Biblioteca vaticana. Mss. ₍Lat. 3362₎
4. Bembo, Bernardo, 1433-1519.
                                                A C 38-3823
Illinois. Univ. Library
   for Library of Congress   [AS222.R645 ser. 3, vol. 8]
                                    ₍4₎   (065)

    NN   0021110   IU NcU MoU MH OU DLC

Narducci, Enrico, 1832-1893.
   Intorno alla vita del conte Giammaria Mazzuchelli ed
alla collezione de' suoi manoscritti ora posseduta dalla
Biblioteca Vaticana, notizie raccolte da Enrico Narducci
... Roma, Tip. delle scienze matematiche e fisiche, 1867.
   1 p. l., 70 p.   22½ᶜᵐ.
   "Estratto dal Giornale arcadico, tomo cxcvII, LII della nuova serie."
   "Questa raccolta composta di 24 buste, e di 11 altri volumini."--p. 19.
   "Indice generale di tutto ciò che si contiene nella raccolta di manoscritti
Mazzuchelliani (codici vaticani, n.⁴ 9260-9294)": p. 47-64.

   Subject entries: 1. Mazzuchelli, Giovanni Maria, conte, 1707-1765. 2.
Rome. Biblioteca Vaticana. 3. Manuscripts. Italy.
                                                          2-8525
   Library of Congress, no.   Z6616.M47N.

    NN   0021111   DLC NN

NARDUCCI, ENRICO, 1832-1893.
   Intorno alla vita del conte Giammaria Mazzuchelli
ed alla collezione de' suoi manoscritti, ora posseduta
dalla Biblioteca Vaticana. Roma, Tipografia delle
matematiche e fisiche, 1867.   79 p.   23cm.

   Microfiche (neg.) 2 sheets. 11 x 15cm. (NYPL FSN 12, 267)
   "Estratto dal Giornale Arcadico tomo 197, 52 della nuova serie."
   Includes bibliographical references.

   1. Manuscripts--Collections--   Italy--Rome.
   2. Mazzuchelli, Giovanni   Maria, conte, 1707-1765.

    NN   0021112   NN

Narducci, Enrico, 1832-1893.
   Lettera sopra due sonetti,...
      1865.

    NN   0021113   NIC

NARDUCCI, Enrico, 1832-1893.
   Italy. *Direzione generale della statistica.*
   ... Monografia della città di Roma e della Campagna
romana ... Roma, Tip. Elzeviriana, 1881.

Narducci, Enrico, 1832-1893.
   Nota delle edizioni della divina commedia...
Rome, 1867.

    NN   0021115   NIC CtY

Narducci, Enrico, 1832-1893.
   Notizie della Biblioteca Alessandrina nella R. Università di Roma raccolte dal bibliotecario Enrico Narducci.
Roma, Tipog. delle scienze matematiche e fisiche, 1872.
   50 p. 22½ᶜᵐ.

   Subject entries: Rome. R. Università. Biblioteca Alessandrina.
                                                          2-13993
   Library of Congress, nc.   Z810.R71N.

    NN   0021116   DLC MdBP

[NARDUCCI, Enrico, 1832-1893].
   Le opere volgari a stampa dei secoli XIII e
XIV, indicate e descritte da Francesco Zambrini.
Bologna, Tipi Fava e Garagnini, 1866. [Review.
Roma, 1866].

   22 cm. pp. ₍3₎.
   Without title-page. Caption title.
   "Estratto dal Buonarroti, tomo III, quaderno X,
e dal Giornale arcadico, tomo CXCIV della nuova
serie."
   Signed at end: E. Narducci.

    NN   0021117   MH

Narducci, Enrico, 1832-1893, ed.
Giordano da Rivalto, 1260-1311.
   Prediche inedite del b. Giordano da Rivalto dell'ordine
de' predicatori, recitate in Firenze dal 1302 al 1305, e pubblicate per cura di Enrico Narducci. Bologna, G. Romagnoli,
1867.

Narducci, Enrico, 1832-1893.
   Prose e versi stampati da Achille Monti.
      (In Magni, B. Vita di Achille Monti,
Roma, 1880. p. 16-36)

    NN   0021119   MH

Narducci, Enrico, 1832-1893.
   Saggio di bibliografia del Tevere, presentato alla Società geografica italiana, nella tornata del 13 febbraio
1876 dal socio Enrico Narducci ... Roma, G. Civelli,
1876.
   viii, 69 p. 22½ᶜᵐ.
   412 titles, annotated.
   "Estratto dal Bollettino della Società geografica italiana, fascicolo 5º."
   Also issued the same year in Francesco Brioschi's Le inondazioni del
Tevere in Roma.

   Subject entries: Tiber River--Bibl.
                                                          2-8505
   Library of Congress, no.   Z2304.T5N2.

    NN   0021120   DLC VtU

VOLUME 405

Bonaparte
Collection NARDUCCI, ENRICO, 1832-1893.
No.4946   Saggio di voci italiane derivate dall'arabo...
Roma,Tipografia delle scienze matematiche e fisi-
che,1858.
55p. 23½cm.

A vocabulary covering the letters A-D. Continued by Secondo saggio, published in 1863.

NN   0021121   ICN

Narducci, Enrico, 1832-1893, ed.

Dati, Leonardo, d. 1425, supposed author.
La sfera, libri quattro in ottava rima scritti nel secolo xiv
da F. Leonardo di Stagio Dati. Aggiuntivi due altri libri e la
Nuovo sfera pure in ottava rima di F. Gio. M. Tolosani da
Colle. L'America di Raffaello Gualterotti, con altre poesie
del medesimo. Raccolta già pubblicata in Firenze nel 1859
dall'avvocato Gustavo Camillo Galletti, ed ora in nuova e più
breve forma ristampata. Milano, G. Daelli e comp., 1865.

Narducci, Enrico, 1832-1893.
Studj bibliografici e biografici sulla storia della geografia in
Italia pubblicati per cura delle Deputazione ministeriale
istituita presso la Società geografica italiana. Roma, Tip.
Elzeviriana, 1875.

---

*fIC8
N1667
882s
Narducci, Enrico, 1832-1893.
Sui presunti obelischi dei circhi di
Alessandro Severo e di Adriano e sul "Mercurio
errante" di Pietro Rossini da Pesaro, note
archeologico-bibliografiche di Enrico Narducci
seguite da un'appendice sulla parte nascosta
dell'obelisco solare del campo Marzio, di
Costantino Maes.
Roma,Tipografia delle scienze matematiche e
fisiche,via Lata n? 3.1882.

24p. 27.5cm.,in case 29cm.
"Saggio di bibliografia degli obelischi":
p.24-30.
Original printed yellow wrappers; in cloth
case.

NN   0021125   MH

Narducci, Enrico, 1832-1893.
Tre prediche inedite del beato ...
see under   Giordano da Rivalto, 1260-1311.

Narducci, Enrico, 1832-1893.
Un vers de "l'Enfer" du Dante,...
1869.

NN   0021127   NIC

Narducci, Enrico, 1832-1873, ed.
Vita di Pitagora
see under   Baldi, Bernardino, 1553-1617.

Narducci, Enrico, 1832-1893, ed.

Baldi, Bernardino, 1553-1617.
Vite inedite di matematici italiani, scritte da Bernar-
dino Baldi e pubblicate da Enrico Narducci ... Roma,
Tip. delle scienze matematiche e fisiche, 1887.

Narducci, Guglielmo.
... La colonizzazione della Cirenaica nell' antichità e nel presente. Bengasi, Stabilimento tipografico Fratelli Pavone, 1934.
4 p. l., 3-195 p. 24½cm.
"Bibliografia": p. [163]-189.

1. Cyrenaica—Colonization.

Library of Congress   DT238.C8N3

45-47016

NN   0021130   DLC IEN OCU

Narducci, Guglielmo.
La colonizzazione della Cirenaica nell'
antichità e nel presente. Bengasi, Stabilimento tipografico Fratelli Pavone, 1934.
195p.

Microfilm ed., positive and negative copies.
Negative does not circulate.

NN   0021131   ICRL

Narducci, Guglielmo.
Storia della colonizzazione della Cirenaica. Milano, Editoriale Arte e storia, 1942.
239 p. plates, fold. map. 23 cm.
"Bibliografia generale": p. 209-237.

1. Cyrenaica—Hist. 2. Cyrenaica—Econ. condit.

DT238.C8N317

49-40118*

NN   0021132   DLC CSt-H NN IEN

Narducci, Guglielmo.
Storia della colonizzazioni della Cirenaica.
Milano, Editoriale Arte e storia, 1942.
239p. illus.

Microfilm ed., positive and negative copies.
Negative does not circulate.

NN   0021133   ICRL

Z
810
S32N16
Narducci, Luigi.
Notizie storiche della Biblioteca Comunale
di Sandaniele del Friuli. Venezia, Tip.
M. Visentini, 1875.
43 p.

Cover title: Per le nozze Narducci-Bonin.

1. San Daniele del Friuli, Italy. Biblioteca Comunale Guarneriana. I. Title.

NN   0021134   CLU

Narducci, Luigi
Prontuario pel calcolo e l'esecuzione del
cemento armato nelle costruzioni civili. Torino,
Lattes, 1920.
160 p

NN   0021135   PP

691.3
N16p2
Narducci, Luigi.
... Prontuario pel calcolo e l'esecuzione del cemento armato nelle costruzioni civili per ingegneri, progettisti,
costruttori, ecc. ... 2.ed. rifatta ed
aumentata. Torino, 1930.
310p. tables, diagrs.

NN   0021136   IU

Narducci (Marianus). Manustuprationis cri-
ticæ historia.
In: Rac. di opusc. med.-prat. Firenze, 1775. ii, 245-261.

NN   0021137   DNLM

Narducci, Pietro.
Sulla fognatura della città di Roma; descrizione tecnica. Roma,
Forzani e c. 1889.
l. 8°, pp. 124, and atlas of 14 plates and plan, obl. f°.

Sewerage—Rome

NN   0021138   MH NN IU DNLM

Narducci, Pompeo, appellant.
... Memoria difensionale per il cav.
Pompeo Narducci
see under   Monti-Guarnieri, Stanislao,
1867-

Narducci, Tommaso, 1679-1766.
Il paragone de' canali, considerazione necessaria per ben regolare gli scoli delle campagne.
(In: Raccolta d'autori che trattano del moto dell'
acque. Firenze, 1767. 2. ed. 4°. Tomo 3.
1. 145-182, plates.)

NN   0021140   NN

QA35
.G7
Rare bk.
coll.
Narducci, Tommaso, 1679-1766, tr.

Grandi, Guido, 1671-1742.
I fiori geometrici del padre abbate d. Guido Grandi, tra-
dotti e spiegati in grazia della studiosa gioventù da Tomaso
Narducci ... Con l'aggiunta di alcune dimostrazioni del-
l'istesso autore. Lucca, F. Marescandoli a Pozzotorelli,
MDCCXXIX.

Narducci, Tommaso, 1679-1766.
Il paragone de' canali. Considerazione necessaria per ben regolare
gli scoli delle campagne. Diagrams.
(In Cardinali, Francesco, compiler. Raccolta d'autori italiani che
trattano del moto delle acque. Vol. 4, pp. 343-366. Bologna.
1822.)

G9441 — Water. Flow.

NN   0021142   MB

3942.11.4

Narducci, Tommaso, 1679-1766.
La quantità del moto, o sia La forza dell' acque correnti, dimostrata ne' diversi stati, e supposti delle me-
desime da Tomaso Narducci ... con alcune considerazioni
sopra la superficie, e pressioni delle acque, tanto nel
fondo, che ne' ripari de' fiumi. Lucca, F. Marescandoli
a Pozzotorelli, 1733.
200 p. 4 fold. diagr. 22cm.

1. Hydraulics.

18-9059

Library of Congress   TC175.N35

NN   0021143   DLC IaU

PG3453
.A7A6
1923
Narducci, Virgilio, tr.

Apukhtin, Aleksiei Nikolaevich, 1841-1893.
... Prose e poesie, traduzione dal russo di Virgilio
Narducci. Prefazione di Ettore Lo Gatto. Napoli, R.
Ricciardi, 1923.

VOLUME 405

Narduzzi, Nestore.
Classi di redditieri ed integrazione di economie [problemi di politica economica posti dalle teorie e dai fatti contemporanei] Milano, A. Giuffrè, 1954.
[213]-299 p. 24 cm.
"Estratto dagli 'Annali della Facoltà di scienze politiche ed economia e commercio' della Università degli Studi di Perugia- anno accademico 1952-53".
Bibliographical footnotes.
1. Classes, social. 2 .. Wealth and income. Distribution.

NN 0021145   NN MH

Narduzzi, Nestore.
...Le sanzioni nelle origini, negli sviluppi e nei risultati. Roma: Soc. edit. di "Novissima," a. XIV [1936] 135 p. incl. map, tables. 23½cm.

877935A. 1. Sanctions (International law). 2. Italy—For. rel., 1922– N.Y.P.L.   April 21, 1937

NN 0021146   NN

Nardy, Adolpho.
... Notas sobre o seguro social no Brasil, apresentado á douta congregação da Faculdade de direito da Universidade de São Paulo, no primeiro concurso para preenchimento da cathedra de legislação social. São Paulo, Empreza graphica da "Revista dos tribunaes," 1938.
4 p. l., 135 p. 23ᵐ.
At head of title: Adolpho Nardy Filho.

1. Insurance, Industrial—Brazil. 2. Insurance, State and compulsory—Brazil. 3. Employers' liability—Brazil. 4. Old age pensions—Brazil.
Library of Congress   HD7154.N3   42-45423

NN 0021147   DLC

Nardy Filho, Francisco.
... A cidade de Ytu ... S. Paulo, Escolas profissionaes salesianas, 1928–
v. 23ᵐ.

1. Ytú, Brazil—Hist.   I. Title.
Library of Congress   F2651.Y9N22   31-11852
[2]   981

NN 0021148   DLC

Narea, Erma Esquivel
see
Esquivel Narea, Erma

Nareb   see National Association of Real Estate Boards.

Naredo, César González
see González Naredo, César.

[Naredo, José María]
Biografía del sr. d. Gabriel Barranco, notable pintor orizabeño. Año de 1887. Orizaba, 1887.
15 p. 21ᵐ.
Signed: José María Naredo.
No. [66] in a collection with binder's title: Biographical pamphlets: Spanish America.

1. Barranco, Gabriel, 1796–1886.   43-26260
                                               Brief cataloging
Library of Congress   F1407.B48 no. 66

NN 0021152   DLC

[Naredo, José María]
Biografía del Sr. D. José Nicolás del Llano, cura párroco de la ciudad de Orizaba. Escrita por J. M. N. Orizaba: G. G. Guapillo, 1885. vi, 33, vi-vii p. front., port. 8°.
Preface signed: José María Naredo.

1. Llano, Nicolás del, 1798?–1850?
N.Y.P.L.   December 19, 1924

NN 0021153   NN

Naredo, José María.
Estudio geográfico, histórico y estadístico del cantón y de la ciudad de Orizaba, escrito por José María Naredo ... Orizaba, Imprenta del hospicio, 1898.
2 v. 24ᵐ.

1. Orizaba, Mexico. 2. Orizaba, Mexico (Canton)
                                               2-20358
Library of Congress   F1371.N22

NN 0021154   DLC CtY WU

Rare Books Dept.
[Narée,   de] Mémoire dans lequel on établit les avantages du nettoiement de la rivière d'Authion, le desséchement des marais & communes du Comté de Beaufort, & les moyens de faire ces travaux sans lever aucunes contributions en argent. [n. p., 1783]
20 p. 24cm. [Bound with: Perronet, Jean Rodolphe. Mémoire lû à la rentrée publique de l'Academie Royale des Sciences, le 15 novembre 1775. 1776]

Caption title.

1. Authion River. *I. Title.

NN 0021155   CU

4BP-   Narendra Ananda Saraswati, Swami.
121   Disquisition of divine life. [1.ed.] Bezwada, Hindu Vijnana Prachara Samiti, 1949.
23 p.

NN 0021156   DLC-P4

4BP·   Narendra Ananda Saraswati, Swami.
122   The problem of life. 1st ed. Bezwada, Hindu [!] Vijnana Prachara Samiti, 1949.
43 p.

NN 0021157   DLC-P4

Narendra Ananda Saraswati, *Swami.*
Spiritual renaissance. Vijayawada, Hindu Vignana Prachara Samiti, 1949.
vii, vi, 109, vii, iv p. 19 cm.

1. Philosophy, Hindu.   I. Title.
B133.N35S7   59-30488

NN 0021158   DLC

Narendra Ananda Saraswati, *Swami.*
Synopsis of philosophy of Dayananda. Foreword by K. S. Ramaswamy Sastry. [1st ed.] Vijayavada, Hindu Vijnana Prachara Samithi, 1950.
[23], 105 p. illus., fascims. 19 cm.

1. Dayananda Sarasvati, Swami, 1824–1883.
B133.D38N3   59-30489

NN 0021159   DLC NN

Narendra Deva
see
Deva, Narendra, *Acharya*, 1889–1956.

Narendra-krishna Simha
see
Sinha, Narendra Krishna.

Narendra Kumar Roy
see
Roy, Narendra Kumar.

Narendra Mitra
see
Mitra, Narendranath, 1916–

Narendra Nath Das
see
Das, Narendra Nath.

Narendra Nath Dutt
see
Vivekananda, *Swami*, 1863–1902.

Narendra Nath Law
see Law, Narendra Nath, 1889–

Narendra Nath Sen Gupta
see
Sengupta, Narendranath.

Narendra-nātha Lahā
see Law, Narendra Nath, 1889–

Narendra Śarmā
see Sharma, Narendra, 1913–

Narendra Singh Sodhi
see Sodhi, Narendra Singh, 1882–

VOLUME 405

Narendrananda Sarswati, *Swami*
see
Narendra Ananda Saraswati, *Swami*.

Narendranath Bhattacharjee
see
Roy, Manabendra Nath, 1893–1954.

Narendranath Mitra
see
Mitra, Narendranath, 1916–

Narendranath Sengupta
see
Sengupta, Narendranath.

Narendranātha Datta
see
Vivekananda, *Swami*, 1863–1902.

Narendranātha Mitra, *Kavirāja*
see
Mitra, Narendranātha, 1916–

Narendranātha Senagupta
see
Senagupta, Narendranātha.

Narendraprabha Sūri.
Alaṅkāramahodadhi. Ed. critically with an introd. in Sanskrit, indices and appendices by Lalchandra Bhagawandas Gandhi. Baroda, Oriental Institute, 1942.

41, 418 p. facsims. 24 cm. (Gaekwad's Oriental series, no. 95)
Sanskrit text, paged with Sanskrit numerals.

I. Gandhi, Lalchandra Bhagawandas, ed. II. Title. III. Series.
PK2971.G3 no. 95   A 48–787*
Cleveland. Public Libr.
for Library of Congress   ₍2₎†

NN 0021178   OCl HU PU DLC

Nareno, Karmen.
PQ4831
A77   Pagine piacevoli utili. ₍Firenze, Tip. A. Conti
P3   1949₎
        124p. 18cm.

Contents.–Vecchi impossibili amori.–L'arte d'amare (Ovidio).–La persona perfetta, civile, educata, a modo, per bene.

NN 0021179   RPB

Nareus (Xaverius). "De peripneumonia chronica ac imprimis illius symptomatum accurata expositio. 21 pp. 4°. *Parisiis*, 1817, No. 11, v. 129.

NN 0021180   DNLM

PN
1621   Narensky.
S691   Songs, duets, choruses, &c. &c. in the new serio-comic opera, called Narensky; or, The road to Yaroslaf: as performed at the Theatre Royal, Drury-Lane ... London, J. Cawthorn, 1814.
        15 p. 22cm.

        No. 12 in vol. lettered: Songs, duets, etc.

NN 0021181   NIC

₍Nares, Edward₎ 1762–1841.
Denk ich bei mir selbst, eine ernsthaft-scherzhafte, tragi-komische geschichte, geschrieben von—Denk ich bei mir selbst :—Wem? ₍pseud.₎ Aus dem englischen übersetzt nach der zehnten Londner ausgabe von 1826. Mit zwei kupfer-stichen und einem facsimile. Berlin, In der Vossischen buchhandlung, 1827.

xvi, 404 p. front., 1 mounted illus., fold. facsim., diagr. 16¼ᶜᵐ.

I. Title.

                                        30–33913
Library of Congress   PR5102.N6T53   827.7

NN 0021182   DLC InU

JK45
N16   Nares, Edward, 1762–1841.
          Discourses on the three creeds, and on the homage offered to our Saviour, on certain and particular occasions during His ministry, as expressed in the evangelical writings, by the Greek term Broskyneo, preached before the University of Oxford, at St. Mary's in the years 1816, 1817. With a copious and distinct appendix to each set of sermons. London, Printed for Baldwin, Cradock, and Joy, 1819.
          vii, 343p.

          1. Creeds - Addresses, essays, lectures. 2. Sermons, English. I. Title.

NN 0021184   CSaT N

D21   Nares, Edward, 1762–1841.   FOR OTHER EDITIONS SEE MAIN ENTRY
.W85
1830a   Woodhouselee, Alexander Fraser Tytler, *lord*, 1747–1813.
          Elements of general history, ancient and modern; with a continuation terminating at the demise of King George III, 1820, by Edward Nares. To which are added a succinct history of the United States, with additions and alterations, by an American gentleman. With an improved table of chronology, a comparative view of ancient and modern geography and questions on each section, adapted for the use of schools and academies, by an experienced teacher. Concord, N. H., H. Hill ₍1830?₎

By34   Nares, Edward, 1762–1841.
1   A few observations on the Edinburgh review of
36   Dr. Nares's Memoirs of Lord Burghley. No.CIX. April 1832. In a letter from the author of that work, to a particular friend. London,J.F.Dove, 1832.
          21,₍2₎p. 25ᶜᵐ
          "List of publications, by the Rev. Edward Nares ... " ₍2₎p. at end.

NN 0021186   CtY

Sem
113   Nares, Edward, 1762–1841.
N16e   'Εις Θεός, εἰς Μεσίτης; or, An attempt to shew how far the philosophical notion of a plurality of worlds is consistent, or not so, with the language of the Holy Scriptures. London, Printed for F. and C. Rivington [etc.] by R. Rickaby, 1801.

          xviii, 406 p.
          Title transliterated: Heis Theos, heis Mesitas.

NN 0021187   CLamB MH

₍Nares, Edward₎ 1762–1841.
Heraldic anomalies; or Rank confusion in our orders of precedence. With disquisitions, moral, philosophical and historical, on all the existing orders of society. By it matters not who. London, G. and W. B. Whittaker, 1823.

2 v. 19ᶜᵐ.

1. Precedence. 2. Titles of honor and nobility. I. Title.
                                        21–11826
Library of Congress   CR3535.N3

NN 0021188   DLC MU CU MdBP TxU PU PHi NN MB

₍Nares, Edward₎ 1762–1841.
Heraldic anomalies ... 2d ed. London, G. and W. B. Whittaker, 1824.
2 v. 19ᶜᵐ.

1. Precedence. 2. Titles of honor and nobility. I. Title.
                                        21–13202
Library of Congress   CR3535.N3 1824

NN 0021189   DLC WaS CaBVaU NcU OCl CU PU OU PPL MB

Nares, Edward, 1762-1841, ed.
  The Holy Bible... With historical prefaces by the Rev. Edward Nares... London, T. Cadell, 1816-24.
    see under
Bible. English. 1816-24. Authorized.

PR5102
.N6I7   ₍Nares, Edward₎ 1762–1841.
1812   I says, says I; a novel by Thinks-I-to-Myself. First American, from the 2d London ed. Corrected. Boston, Published by Bradford and Read...1812.
            2v. in one. 18cm.

            I. Title. II. Thinks-I-to-Myself.

NN 0021191   IEG PPL CtY RPB MB NN IU WU

Nares, Edward, 1762-1841.
  Man, as known to us theologically and geologically. By the Rev. Edward Nares ... London, Printed for J. G. & F. Rivington, 1834.
    2 p. l., 255, ₍1₎ p. 1 illus. 20ᶜᵐ.

    1. Man (Theology) 2. Bible and geology. 3. Religion and science—1800–1859. I. Title.
                                        30–34014
Library of Congress   BL256.N4   215

NN 0021192   DLC NjNbS PPL

VOLUME 405

Nares, Edward, 1762–1841.
Memoirs of the life and administration of the Right Honourable William Cecil, lord Burghley ... Containing an historical view of the times in which he lived, and of the many eminent and illustrious persons with whom he was connected; with extracts from his private and official correspondence, and other papers, now first published from the originals. By the Rev. Edward Nares ... London, Saunders and Otley, 1828–31.
3 v. 4 port. (incl. fronts.) facsims. 28½ x 22ᶜᵐ.
Vols. 2–3 have imprint: London, Colburn and Bentley, 1830–31.
1. Burghley, William Cecil, baron, 1520–1598. 2. Cecil family.
9–29016
Library of Congress   DA358.B9N3

OCl MdBP MB NN NjP NjNbS PPPD
NN 0021193   DLC TU WaU NcD CtY NNUT T PHi PP OU MiU

[Nares, Edward] 1762–1841.
The preface to the Iron Chest. A Satyrical poem. Written by Thinks-I-to-Myself. London, J. Roach, n.d. [1796]
12 p. front. (pl.) octavo. unbound.
Note: Wendell sale, Oct. 1919, no. 696.
References. D.N.B. 14:91; Cushing. I. & P. 1st series. p. 282.

NN 0021194   CSmH

Nares, Edward, 1762–1841.
Remarks on the version of the New Testament, edited by the Unitarians, with the title of "An improved version upon the basis of Archbishop Newcome's new translation ... London, 1808" ... With a letter ... to the Rev. Francis Stone ... 2d edition. London, Cadell & Davies, 1814. xliii, (7), 336 pp. 8°.
The version referred to is on shelf-numbers 7411.53, etc.
3462.13

G1592 — Bible. N. T. English. Newcome's translation, 1796. Works about.—
Stone, Francis, Rector of Cold-Norton, Essex.

ICMcC
NN 0021195   MB NjNbS PPLT DLC CtY NjPT NNUT NjR

Nares, Edward, 1762–1841.
Syllabus of lectures on political economy, by Professor Nares, 1817. [Oxford, Printed by S. Collingwood, 1817?]
7 p. 21 cm.

Caption title.

NN 0021196   MH-BA CtY

[Nares, Edward] 1762–1841.
Thinks-I-to-myself: a serio-ludicro, tragico-comico tale, written by Thinks-I-to-myself, who? 10th ed. London, Sherwood and co. [n.d.]
1 p. l., 371 p.

NN 0021197   LU

[Nares, Edward] 1762–1841.
Thinks I to myself. A serio-ludicro, tragico-comico tale, written by Thinks I to myself, who? [pseud] ... New York, J. Miller [n.d.]
2 v. in 1. 16.5 cm.

NN 0021198   ViW NjP

[Nares, Edward] 1762–1841.
Thinks-I-to-myself; a serio-ludrico, tragico-comico tale; written by Thinks-I-to-myself Who? New York: James Miller [18—?]. 234 p. 16°.

NN 0021199   NN NNC

[Nares, Edward] 1762–1841.
Thinks-I-to-myself. A serio-ludicro, tragico-comico tale; written by Thinks-I-to-myself, who? Two volumes in one ... Baltimore, J. N. Lewis [18—]
234 p. 13ᶜᵐ.

I. Title.

Library of Congress   PR5102.N6T5   37–14768
[2]   827.7

NN 0021200   DLC InU

827.7
N22t2   [Nares, Edward] 1762–1841.
LIMITED   Thinks-I-to-myself. A serio-ludicro, tragico-
CIRCULATION comico tale written by Thinks-I-To-Myself Who?
In two volumes. [Volume number] Second edition, with additions. London, Printed for Sherwood, Neely, and Jones, 20, Paternoster Row; J. Hatchard, Piccadilly; and J. Asperne, Cornhill; By Law and Gilbert, St. John's-Square, Clerkenwell, 1811.
2 v. 18cm.

Notes in ms. on front endpapers: C. White to

Caroline Leigh 1843; M. J. Wilkes nee Leigh 1897.
Brit. Mus. gen. cat. v.168, col.737.

NN 0021202   FU CtY PU TU ScU GEU IU

Nares, Edward, 1762–1841.
Thinks I to myself. ... Baltimore, A. Miltenberger, 1812.
2 v in 1

NN 0021203   PHC

Nares, Edward, 1762–1841.
Thinks-I-to-myself...
Boston, 1812

NN 0021204   NjR

[Nares, Edward, 1762–1841]
Thinks-I-to-myself. A serio-ludicro, tragico-comico tale, written by Thinks-I-to-myself who? Two volumes in one ... Second American edition.
Boston: Published by Bradford & Read, and by A. Finley, Philadelphia. 1812. Lincoln & Edmands, printers.
2v. in 1. 17.5cm.
The two volumes have continuous signatures & paging.
*EC8
N1673
811tf

NN 0021205   MH

[NARES, Edward, 1762–1841.]
Thinks-I-to-myself; a serio-ludicro, tragico-comico tale. Written by Thinks-I-to-myself who? 1st American from the 4th London ed. Boston, Bradford & Read, 1812.

2 vol.

NN 0021206   MH PPL MB

Nares, Edward, 1762–1841.
Thinks-I-to-myself; a serio-ludicro, tragico-comico tale, written by Thinks-I-To-Myself. Who? To which is added, a preface, concerning the author, with replies to reviewers, thanks to the public, and various other particulars. London: Thomas Allman [1812]
264 p. plate. 14cm.

NN 0021207   ViU

[NARES, EDWARD] 1762–1841.
Thinks-I-to-myself; a serio-ludicro, tragico-comico tale, written by Thinks-I-to-myself, who? [pseud.] To which is added, a preface concerning the author; with replies to reviewers, thanks to the public, and various other particulars. London, Dove [1812]
264p. (Dove's classic edition)
Y
155
.N 159

NN 0021208   ICN

PR5102
.M6   Nares, Edward, 1762–1841.
T5   Thinks-I-to-myself. A serio-ludicro, tragi-
1812   co-comico tale, written by Thinks-I-to-myself
Who? [pseud.] 6th ed. London, Printed for Sherwood, Neely, and Jones, [etc.] 1812.
2v.

NN 0021209   NcU

3A
3240   [NARES, EDWARD] 1762–1841.
Thinks-I-to-myself. A serio-ludicro, tragico-comico tale, written by Thinks-I-to-myself who?... 7th ed. London, Printed for Sherwood, Nelly, and Jones, 1812.
2v. front. 19cm.

NN 0021210   ICN NjP

[Nares, Edward] 1762–1841.
Thinks-I-to-myself. A serio-ludicro, tragico-comico tale, written by Thinks-I-to-myself, who? [pseud.] 2d American from the 4th London ed. New-York: Printed and published by J. Oram, 1812.
2 v. in 1 (215 p.) 19 cm.

NN 0021211   NcD CtY

[Nares, Edward] 1762–1841.
Thinks-I-to-myself. A serio-ludicro, tragico-comico tale. Written by Thinks-I-to-myself who? ... New-York: Published by Richard Scott, 276 Pearl-street. 1812.
2 v. in 1. front. 13½ᶜᵐ.
Paged continuously.

I. Title.   42–26381
Library of Congress   PR5102.N6T5 1812
[2]

NN 0021212   DLC CSmH MB ViU ViW MiU

[Nares, Edward] 1762–1841.
Thinks-I-to-myself. A serio-ludicro, tragico-comico tale, written by Thinks-I-to-myself who?... Philadelphia: A. Finley, 1812. 2 v. in 1. 16°.
Continuously paged.
2. Amer. ed. from the 6. enl. London ed.

235236A. 1. Wit and humor, Eng-   lish. 2. Fiction, English.
3. Title.   October 14, 1926
N. Y. P. L.

NN 0021213   NN PPL NcD

[Nares, Edward] 1762–1841.
Thinks-I-to-myself. A serio-ludicro, tragico-comico tale, written by Thinks-I-to-myself who? Two volumes in one. First Wilmington - from the fourth London enlarged edition. Wilmington: printed by R. Porter ..... 1812.
216 p. 14.5 cm.

Imperfect: upper corner of p. 23-24 torn off.
Error in pagination: 34 numbered 43.
Bookplate: From the library of Gen. John E. Roller ... by his daughter.

NN 0021214   Vi MnU

VOLUME 405

[Nares, Edward,] 1762–1841.
  Thinks-I-to-myself. A serio-ludicro, tragico-comico tale, written by Thinks-I-to-myself, who?   Brattleborough: W. Fessenden, 1814. 2 v. in 1. 24°.

Paged continuously.

1. Fiction (English). 2. Title.
N. Y. P. L.   July 9, 1920.

NN 0021215   NN MWA ICU

---

823   [Nares, Edward] 1762–1841.
N167t   Thinks-I-to myself; a serio-ludicro, tragico-
1816 comico tale, written by Thinks-I-to-myself, who?
  To which is added, a preface concerning the author,
  with replies to reviewers, thanks to the public, a
  letter relative to the portrait, and various other
  particulars. 9th ed.   London, Sherwood, Neely,
  and Jones, 1816.
    2v. port. 18cm.

NN 0021216   TxU

[Nares, Edward,] 1762–1841.
  Thinks I to myself. A serio-ludicro, tragico-comico
tale, written by Thinks I to myself, who? [pseud.] ... Philadelphia, A. Sherman, agt., R. Wright, printer, 1824.
  2 v. in 1. front., illus. 16½ᶜᵐ.
  Added t.-p., engr., with vignette.

  I. Title.

                                                22–1839
  Library of Congress   PR5102.N6T5 1824

NN 0021217   DLC NN NcU PP

[Nares, Edward] 1762–1841.
  Thinks-I-to-myself: a serio-ludicro, tragico-comico tale,
written by Thinks-I-to-myself, who? 10th ed. London,
Sherwood and co.,   1826.
  1 p. l., 371 p. 19½ᶜᵐ.

NN 0021218   GU

[NARES, EDWARD] 1762–1841.
  Thinks-I-to-myself. A serio-ludicro, tragico-comico tale;
written by Thinks-I-to-myself, who?... Boston: J.P.Peaslee,
1827. 2 v. in 1. 13½cm.

Paged continuously.

780058A. 1. Wit and humor, English. 2. Fiction, English.
I. Title.

NN 0021219   NN CaBVaU CtY MH MnU MWA ViU NcD

[Nares, Edward] 1762–1841.
  Thinks-I-to-myself: a serio-ludicro, tragico-comico tale,
written by Thinks-I-to-myself, who? 10th ed. London,
Sherwood and co.,. 1829.
  1 p. l., 371 p. 19½ᶜᵐ.

  I. Title.

                                           7—23115
  Library of Congress   PR5102.N6T5 1829

NN 0021220   DLC

---

*
PR5102   [Nares, Edward,] 1762–1841.
.N6T5
1836   Thinks-I-to-myself. A serio-ludicro,
  tragico-comico tale; written by Thinks-I-
  to-Myself Who? Exeter: J. & B. Williams,
  1836.
    2 v. in 1. (192 p.) 13cm.
    Paged continuously.

NN 0021221   ViU CtY NNC OC1

NARES, Edward, 1762-1841.
  Thinks-I-to-myself. A serio-ludicro, tragico-comico tale, written by
Thinks-I-to-myself, who?
       London. Scott, W. & G. 1840. 264 pp. Pl. 24°.

NN 0021222   MB

---

040   Nares, Edward, 1762–1841.
A p.v.1   Thinks-I-to-myself: A serio-ludicro,
no.8 tragico-comico tale, written by Thinks-I-to-
  myself, who? [pseud.] ... New York, M. W. Dood,
  1843.
    156 p. 18 cm.

NN 0021223   N NN

[Nares, Edward,] 1762–1841.
  Thinks-I-to-myself. A serio-ludicro,
tragico-comico tale; written by Thinks-I-
To-Myself, who? Philadelphia, Wm. A. Leary,
1848.
  2 v. in 1. (237 p.) front. 13cm.

NN 0021224   ViU

[Nares, Edward] 1762–1841.
  Thinks-I-To-Myself. A Serio-Ludicro, Tragico-
Comico tale ... Philadelphia, Published by
Daniels & Getz, Successors To W.A. Leary &
Co., 1853.
  2 volumes in 1.   stamped roan. sm 8vo.

NN 0021225   CSmH

---

*
PR5102   [Nares, Edward,] 1762–1841.
.N6T5
1854   Thinks-I-to-myself. A serio-ludicro,
  tragico-comico tale; written by Thinks-I-
  to-myself, Who? Philadelphia: Leary & Letz,
  1854.
    2 v. in 1. front. 13cm.

NN 0021226   ViU

[Nares, Edward] 1762–1841.
  Thinks-I-to-myself. A serio-ludicro, tragico-comico tale;
written by Thinks-I-to-myself Who? Two volumes in one.
Philadelphia: Moss & Brother. 1856. 234 p. 16°.

1. Wit and humor (English). 2. Fic-   tion (English). 3. Title.
N. Y. P. L.   March 19, 1912.

NN 0021227   NN

---

*
PR5102   [Nares, Edward,] 1762–1841.
.N6T5
1858   Thinks-I-to-myself. A serio-ludicro,
  tragico-comico tale; written by thinks-I-to-
  myself, who? [pseud.] Philadelphia: Leary
  & Getz, 1858.
    2 v. in 1. front. 13cm.

NN 0021228   ViU

[Nares, Edward] 1762–1841.
  Thinks-I-to-myself. A serio-ludicro, tragico-
comico tale; written by Thinks-I-to-myself, who?
Philadelphia: J. B. Smith & co., 1859.
  1 p.l., 4-237 p. front.(col.) 17 1/2 cm.

  Bound with this is: The life and adventures of
Peter Wilkins, by Robert Paltock.

NN 0021229   ViLxW

[Nares, Edward] 1762–1841.
  Thinks-I-to-myself. A serio-ludicro, tragico-
comico tale; written by thinks-I-to-myself, who?...
Philadelphia, J.B. Smith & co., 1860.
  2 v. in 1. col. front. 17 cm.
  Continuous pagination.
  Issued with this is: [Paltock, Robert] 1697-
1767. The life and adventures of Peter Wilkins...
Philadelphia, 1860.

NN 0021230   CtY

[Nares, Edward] 1762–1841.
  Thinks-I-to-myself, a serio-ludicro, tragico-comico tale;
written by Thinks-I-to-myself who? Two volumes in one.
Philadelphia, Moss & co., 1864.
  234 p. 16ᵐ.

  I. Title.

                                               27–16329
  Library of Congress   PR5102.N6T5 1864

NN 0021231   DLC NcD MWA

---

*
PR5102
.N6T5   Nares, Edward, 1762–1841.
1872
     Thinks-I-to-myself: a serio-ludicro,
  tragico-comico tale; written by Thinks I
  to myself, who? [pseud.] New York, M.
  Doolady, 1872.
    2 v. in 1. illus. 16½cm.
    Bookplate of Woodberry Library.

NN 0021232   ViU CtY

PR 5102 [Nares, Edward] 1762–1841.
N22 T4   Thinks-I-to-myself, a serio-ludicro, tragico-comico tale;
1876 written by Thinks-I-to-myself who? Two volumes in one.
  New York, J. Miller [1876?]
    2 v. in 1 (234 p.) 18 cm.

NN 0021233   OU

Nares, Edward, 1762–1841.
  Tytler's general history
     see under Woodhouselee, Alexander
Fraser Tytler, lord, 1747-1813.

Nares, Edward, 1762–1841.

Woodhouselee, Alexander Fraser Tytler, lord, 1747–1813.
  Universal history, from the creation of the world to the
decease of George III., 1820. By the Hon. Alexander Fraser
Tytler, and Rev. Edward Nares, D. D. Ed. by an American ...
New York, Harper & brothers, 1839.

Nares, Edward, 1762–1841.
  A view of the evidences of Christianity at the close of the
pretended age of reason : in eight sermons preached before the
University of Oxford, at St. Mary's, in the year MDCCCV., at
the lecture founded by the Rev. John Bampton ... By Edward Nares ... Oxford, The University press for the author;
[etc., etc.,] 1805.
  xi, [1], 543 p. 22ᵐ.

  Binder's title: Bampton lectures. 1805.

  1. Apologetics—19th cent. 2. Rationalism—Controversial literature.
3. Philosophy and religion. 4. Church of England—Sermons. 5. Sermons, English.   I. Title.
  Library of Congress   BR45.B3 1805
                                           38–16051
  [3]   (230.082) 280

ODW CU NIC
NN 0021236   DLC NjNbS CtY PHi RPB GEU ICN PP MH

VOLUME 405

Nares, Sir George Strong, 1831-1915.
Artic expedition. Results derived from the
Arctic expedition, 1875-76
see under Gt. Brit. Admiralty.

Nares, Sir George Strong, 1831-1915.

Gt. Brit. *Admiralty.*
Arctic expedition, 1875-6. Journals and proceedings
of the Arctic expedition, 1875-6, under the command of
Captain Sir George S. Nares ... ⟨In continuation of parliamentary papers C 1153 of 1875 and C 1560 of 1876.⟩
London, Printed for H. M. Stationery off., by Harrison &
sons ₁1877₎

Nares, Sir George Strong, 1831-1915.
H.M.S. Challenger. Reports of Captain G.S.
Nares, R.N. With abstract of soundings & diagrams of ocean temperature in North and South
Atlantic oceans. 1873. [London, Printed by
G.E. Eyre and W. Spottiswoode, for H.M.
Stationery off., 1873]
cover-title, 15 (i.e. 17), 7 p. 6 fold. col.
charts. 32.5 cm.
1. Atlantic ocean. 2. Challenger expedition,
1872-1876.

NN 0021239 ICU MH

Nares, *Sir* George Strong, 1831-1915.
Narrative of a voyage to the Polar Sea during 1875-6
in H. M. ships 'Alert' and 'Discovery.' By Capt. Sir
G. S. Nares ... With notes on the natural history, edited
by H. W. Feilden ... London, S. Low, Marston, Searle,
& Rivington, 1878.
2 v. fronts., illus., plates, photos., fold. map. 22½ᶜᵐ.

1. Arctic regions. 2. Natural history—Arctic regions. 3. Alert (Ship)
4. Discovery (Ship) I. Feilden, Henry Wemyss.
5—19312

Library of Congress G670.1875.A36

MiU OCU OClWHi NjP CaBViPA Wa CaBVaU RPJCB
NN 0021240 DLC WU WaU NIC CtY MdBP OU PPAN PPL

VK
541
N22

Nares, *Sir* George Strong, 1831-1915.
The naval cadet's guide; or, Seaman's companion. Containing practical rules for fitting and placing riggings, managing sails,
&c.; complete illustrations of all the standing
riggings, the knots, bends, and hitches
in use; and a catechism on rigging ships, &c.
By George S. Nares. Portsea ₁Eng.₎ J. Griffin, 1860.
vii, 141 p. illus., plates (part fold., part
col.) 23 cm.

"Used on board H. M. S. Britannia, with the sanction of the Lords Commissioners of the Admiralty."
Later editions were published under title: Seamanship.

1. Masts and rigging. 2. Seamanship. I. Title.

NN 0021242 Vi CU PPFr CtY

NARES, Sir GEORGE STRONG, 1831-1915.
The official report of the recent
Arctic expedition. By Captain Nares ...
London, J. Murray, 1876.
1 p.ℓ., 96 p. front. (map) 8vo

Bound in half morocco over marbled
boards; original blue printed paper
wrappers bound in.

NN 0021243 InU CaBViPA CtY OClWHi NNC ICN CU MnHi

Nares, Sir George S[trong] 1831-1915.
On the north circumpolar sea. n.p., n. pub.,
1877.
p. 96-106. O.
Extract from the Royal Geographical soc.
Proceedings. 1877.
Bound in Arctic etc. v.2.

NN 0021244 CaBViPA

Nares, Sir George Strong, 1831-1915.

Gt. Brit. *Hydrographic office.*
... Report on ocean soundings and temperatures ... ₁ob-
tained by H. M. S. Challenger during the years 1873-76₎
₁London, Printed for H. M. Stationery off., by G. E. Eyre
and W. Spottiswoode, 1874-76₎

Q115
.C4

Nares, Sir George Strong, 1831-1915.

Gt. Brit. *Challenger office.*
Report on the scientific results of the voyage of H. M. S.
Challenger during the years 1873-76 under the command of
Captain George S. Nares ... and the late Captain Frank
Tourle Thomson, R. N. Prepared under the superintendence
of the late Sir C. Wyville Thomson ... and now of John
Murray ... Published by order of Her Majesty's govern-
ment. ₁Edinburgh₎ Printed for H. M. Stationery off. ₁by
Neill and company₎ 1880-95.

VK541
.N23
1862

Nares, Sir George Strong, 1831-1915.
Seamanship. By Lieut. George S. Nares, R. N.
2d ed. with upwards of three hundred and fifty
illus., from drawings by J. Murray, Jun. Used
on board H. M. training ship Britannia, by
sanction of the Lords Commissioners of the Admiralty. Portsea, J. Griffin; London, Longman, Green Longman, and Roberts. ₁Pref. 1862₎
ix, ₁1₎, 230p. front., plates (part fold.,
part col.) 23cm.
Bookplate: "From the library of Mark F. Boyd".
1. Navigation. I. Title.

NN 0021247 FMU MB Vi

Nares, Sir George Strong, 1831-1915.
Seamanship; including names of principal
parts of a ship; mast, sails, yards, &c. ...
By Commander G.S.Nares,R.N. ... 3d ed.,with
three hundred and fifty illustrations, also
coloured sheets of signal flags ... Portsea,
J.Griffin and co.; ₁etc.,etc.₎ 1865.
1 p.ℓ.,8,185-200 p. col.front., illus.,
plates (part fold., part col.) 22½cm.

NN 0021248 CtNlCG

Nares, Sir George Strong, 1831-1915.
Seamanship: including names of principal parts of a ship;
masts, sails, yards, &c.; knots and splices ... by Captain G. S. Nares
... Portsmouth: Griffin & Co., 1876. xiv, 256 p. incl. diagrs.,
tables. col'd front., plates (part col'd). 5. ed., rev. and enl.
8°.
Revised by Captain Robert Harris. — *cf. Pref.*

1454/5A. 1. Seamanship. 2. Naval art and science. 3. Harris, Sir
Robert Hastings, 1843– , editor.
N. Y. P. L. September 19, 1924

NN 0021249 NN RPB

Nares, *Sir* George Strong, 1831-1915.
Seamanship: ... . Sixth edition. enlarged and revised by Lieut.
Arthur C. B. Bromley. xi,[1],291 p. il. 140 pl. O. New York:
E. & F. N. Spon. 1882.

NN 0021250 ICJ PPL

Nares, *Sir* George Strong, 1831–
Seamanship: including names of principal parts of a
ship; masts, sails, yards, etc. ... by Captain Sir George
S. Nares ... 6th ed. enl. and rev. by Lieut. Arthur C. B.
Bromley, R. N. With four hundred and twenty illustrations, and coloured sheets of national ensigns for men-
of-war and mercantile marine—signal flags ₁etc.₎ Portsmouth. Griffin & co., 1882.
xi, ₁1₎, 291 p. col. front., illus., plates (part fold., part col.) 22ᶜᵐ.

1. Navigation. I. Bromley, Arthur Charles Burgoyne, d. 1909, ed.
II. Title.
13-13304

Library of Congress VK541.N23 1882

NN 0021251 DN-Ob MB DLC

Nares, *Sir* George Strong, 1831-1915.
Seamanship... 6 th ed. enl. Portsmouth,
Griffin, 1886
291 p

NN 0021252 PP

Nares, *Sir* George Strong, 1831-1915.
Seamanship: including names of principal parts of a
ship ... glossary of sea terms, etc., etc., etc.; by Vice-
Admiral Sir George S. Nares ... 7th ed., enl. and rev.
by Commander T. P. Walker ... Portsmouth, Griffin &
co., 1897.
viii p., 1 l., ₁2₎ p., 1 l., 334 p. illus., plates (partly col.) 22ᶜᵐ.

1. Navigation. I. Walker, Thomas Philip. II. Title.
4-17753

Library of Congress VK541.N24

NN 0021253 DLC CaBViP NIC ICJ NN

Nares, *Sir* George Strong, 1831-1915.
Traité de manœuvre et de matelotage: suivi de quelques renseignements utiles sur la construction des navires, l'arrimage de
la cale, la manœuvre des embarcations, le sauvetage des naufragés,
etc... Par Sir George S. Nares... Traduit de l'anglais et annoté
par Edmond Tiret... Portsmouth: Griffin et Cie.₁, 188–?₎
vii, 305 p. diagrs., front., illus., plates. 2. ed. 8°.

1. Masts and rigging. 2. Seaman- ship. 3. Tiret, Edmond,
translator.
N. Y. P. L. October 6, 1926

NN 0021254 NN

919.8
N16nFb

Nares, *Sir* George Strong, 1831-1915.
Un voyage à la mer polaire sur les navires de
S. M. B. l'Alerte et la Découverte (1875 à 1876),
suivi de notes sur l'histoire naturelle, par H.
W. Feilden. Ouvrage traduit de l'anglais avec
l'autorisation des auteurs, par Frédéric Bernard.
Paris, Hachette, 1880.
xxiii, 572p. illus., fold.map, plates, port.
24cm.

Translation of Narrative of a voyage to the
Polar sea.

NN 0021255 IU CaOTP CtY

Nares, Gordon.
Arbury Hall
see under
Country Life, ltd., London.

Nares, Gordon.
Country houses open to the public; a concise guide to all
the greater country houses and to many lesser houses of
architectural or historic interest which are now open to the
public in England. London, Country Life ₁1951₎
83 p. illus. 22 cm.

1. Gt. Brit.—Historic houses, etc. I. Title.

DA660.N3 942 51-34686 ‡

NN 0021257 DLC CaBVa MWiCA CaBViP

VOLUME 405

Nares, Gordon.
    Country houses open to the public; a concise guide to all
the greater country houses and to many lesser houses of
architectural or historic interest which are now open to the
public in England. [3d ed.] London, Country Life [1953]
    100 p. illus. 21 cm.

    1. Gt. Brit.—Historic houses, etc.   I. Title.

    DA660.N3 1953   942   53–35088 †

NN   0021258   DLC PP MB

Nares, Gordon.
    Country houses open to the public; a concise guide to all
the greater country houses and to many lesser houses of
architectural or historic interest which are now open to the
public in Great Britain. [4th ed.] London, Country Life
Limited [1954]
    127 p. illus. 21 cm.

    1. Gt. Brit.—Historic houses, etc.   I. Title.

    DA660.N3 1954   942   54–31733 †

NN   0021259   DLC CtY LU

Nares, Gordon.
    Royal homes; Buckingham Palace, Windsor Castle, the
Palace of Holyroodhouse, St. James's Palace, Clarence
House, Balmoral Castle, Sandringham House. London,
Country Life [1953]
    112 p. illus. 29 cm.

    1. Palaces—Gt. Brit. 2. Castles—Gt. Brit.   I. Title.

    NA7745.N37   725.17   53–34136 †

        NcD PPD TU PBm MB NN CSt Wa WaS Or LN
NN   0021260   DLC CaBViP CaBVa IaU OO PP OC1W OOxM

Nares, James, *1715–1783.*
    Behold how good and joyful. Anthem [A. B. Accomp. for organ].
    (In Stevens. Sacred Music. Vol. 2, pp. 60–67. London. [18–?])
                                    No. 10 in **M.234.4.2
    Same. (In his Twenty Anthems. Pp. 8–13. 1778.)
                                    No. 2 in **M.236.33

E5825 — T.r. — Church music. Anthems, &c.

NN   0021261   MB

Nares, James, *1715–1783.*   No. 19 in **M.190.5
    Behold! now praise the Lord. Full anthem with duett [S. S.].
The organ accomp. by W. H. Longhurst.
London. Novello. [1845.] 56–59 pp. F°.

E6809 — T.r. — Longhurst, William Henry, ed. — Church music. Anthems, &c.

NN   0021262   MB

Nares, James.
    Blessed is he that considereth the poor. Anthem [S.S.A.T.B.
Accomp. for organ].
    (In Musical Times. [Music.] Vol. 3, pp. 47–49. London.
[1850.])   No. 14 in **M.175.1.3
    Same. (In Hullah. The Singer's Library. Sacred. Pp. 9–12.
[186–?])   No. 30 in **M.157.3

E5825 — T.r. — Church music. Anthems. &c.

NN   0021263   MB

Nares, James.   No. 11 in **M.220.10
    By the waters of Babylon. Canon, 3 in 1.
    (In Warren. Vocal Harmony. Pp. 16, 17. London. [1765.])

E5825 — T.r. — Church music. Anthems, &c.

NN   0021264   MB

Nares, James.
    By the waters of Babylon. Duet [S. S. Accomp. for organ].
    (In Ayrton. Sacred Minstrelsy. Vol. 2, pp. 170–173. London,
1835.)   No. 63 in **M.290.22.2
    Same. (In his Twenty Anthems. Pp. 42–47. 1778.)
                                    No. 7 in **M.236.33

E5825 — T.r. — Church music. Anthems, &c.

NN   0021265   MB

M1578   Nares, James.
.C74   A collection of catches, canons and glees by
case   Dr. Nares organist, composer &c. to His Majesty...
vol.12   London, Printed by Welcker in Gerrard Street
        St. Ann's Soho, (c.1775) 41p.

NN   0021266   DLC

Nares, James.   No. 20 in **M.430.1.11
    Come follow, follow me. Canon four in two.
    (In Catch Club. Original manuscript collection. Vol. 11, pp.
47–49. [London. 1773.])

K5639 — T.r. — Part songs.

NN   0021267   MB

Nares, James, 1715–1783.
    A concise, and easy treatise on singing, addressed to
the delettanti in music, who are desirous of performing
duets, or any vocal music in parts ... with a set of English
duets for beginners, by Dr. Nares ... London, Printed for
the author, and sold by J. Preston [17—]
    1 p. l., 2–33 p. 26½ x 36ᶜᵐ.
    Engraved throughout.

    1. Singing and voice culture.

                                    CA 17–806 Unrev'd

Library of Congress   MT885.N28

NN   0021268   DLC MiU C

Nares, James, 1715–1783.
    Eight setts of lessons for the harpsichord, composed by Mʳ.
James Nares ... London, Printed for the author by J. Johnson in Cheapside, 1747.
    3 p. l., 2–45 p. 26½ x 36ᵐᵐ. [With Nares, James. A concise, and easy
treatise on singing. London [178–?]]
    Engraved throughout, with exception of 3d preliminary leaf (list of
subscribers)
    Title within ornamental border.

    1. Harpsichord—Instruction and study.

                                    28–12678

Library of Congress   MT885.N28

NN   0021269   DLC NN ViWC

Nares, James.
    Fear no more. Elegy [A. T. B.].
    (In Warren. Collection of Catches. Vol. 1, pp. 338–341. London.
[1770.])   No. 206 in **M.220.9.1
    Same. (In Flowers of Harmony. Vol. 1, pp. 49–56. [17–?])
                                    No. 38 in **M.157.18.1
    Same. (In The Harmonist. Vol. 7, pp. 64–68. [179–?])
                                    No. 16 in **M.218.8.7
    Same. (In Clementi. Vocal Harmony. Vol. 1, pp. 98–101.)

E5824 — T.r. — Part songs.

NN   0021270   MB

Nares, James.   No. 36 in **M.290.22.2
    Have mercy upon me. Duet [S. S. Accomp. for organ].
    (In Ayrton. Sacred Minstrelsy. Vol. 2, pp. 88, 89. London, 1835.)

E5824 — T.r. — Church music. Anthems, &c.

NN   0021271   MB

Nares, James.   No. 13 in **M.430.1.11
    I call and cry to Thee. Canon [T.T.B.].
    (In Catch Club. Original manuscript collection. Vol. 11, pp.
32, 33. [London. 1773.])

K5639 — T.r. — Church music. Anthems, etc.

NN   0021272   MB

M7   Nares, James, 1715–1783.
.W48 0 4
no.18   ... Introduction and fugue in A, composed by
        Dr. James Nares. London, Novello & co., ltd.,
        c1906
            1 p. l., 11 p. 30 1/2cm. (Old English organ
        music, edited by John E. West. No. 18)
            Publisher's plate no.: 12220.

            1. Canons, fugues, etc. (Organ)—To 1800.
            2. Organ music—To 1800.

NN   0021273   MB IU

---

q786.8   Nares, James, 1715–1783.
W52o   ... Introduction and fugue in E flat, composed
no.17   by Dr. James Nares ... London, Novello & co.,
        ltd., c1906.
            7p.   (Old English organ music, edited by John
        E. West. no.17)

            Plate no.: 12219.

            1. Organ music. 2. Fugue.

NN   0021274   IU CLSU

M   Nares, James, 1715–1783.
23   [Lessons, harpsichord, op. 2]
N22++
op.2   Lessons for the harpsichord, with a sonata
        in score for the harpsicord or organ, op. 2,
        London [1749?]
            53 p. 26 x 34cm.

            The sonata is for harpsichord, 2 violins
        and violoncello.

NN   0021275   NIC

Nares, James.   No. 1 in **M.380.56
    A morning and evening service consisting of Te Deum, Jubilate,
Magnificat & Nunc Dimittis together with six anthems in score
for two, three, four & five voices, the three last of which require
only a bassoon or other bass accompaniment. [With figured
bass.]
= London. Printed & sold by J. Preston. 1788. (4), 62 pp. F°.

G3232 — T.r. — Church music. Anthems, etc.

NN   0021276   MB NN FU

Nares, James.   No. 10 in **M.290.22.1
    O come hither and hearken. Anthem. [Accomp. for pianoforte.]
    (In Ayrton. Sacred Minstrelsy. Vol. 1, pp. 28–31. London, 1834.)

E5826 — T.r. — Church music. Anthems, &c.

NN   0021277   MB

VOLUME 405

Nares, James.
O fairest maid. [Catch for 4 voices.]
(In Warren. Collection of Catches. Vol. 1, p. 48. London.
[1764.])   No. 54 in **M.220.9.1
Same. (In Webbe, Jr. Convito armonico. Vol. 2, p. 149. [1828?]
                                                    No. 11 in **M.234.3.2

E5826 — T.r. — Part songs.

NN   0021278   MB

Nares, James.
O'er Handel's tomb. Elegy [A.T.B.].   No. 26 in **M.430.1.11
(In Catch Club. Original manuscript collection. Vol. 11, pp.
64–70. [London. 1773.])

K5618 — T.r. — Part songs.

NN   0021279   MB

Nares, James, 1715–1783.
Il principio, or A regular introduction to playing on
the harpsichord or organ, by D‍r. Nares ... London,
Welcker [1759?]
2 p. l., 2–35 p. 24 x 33½cm.
Engraved throughout.

                                                    CA 17–807 Unrev'd
Library of Congress   MT243.A2N2

NN   0021280   DLC

Nares, James.
Reason ne'er in fetters bind. Glee [A. T. B.].   No. 76 in **M.220.10
(In Warren. Vocal Harmony. Pp. 121–133. London. [1765.])

E5826 — T.r. — Part songs.

NN   0021281   MB

Nares, James.
Rejoice in the Lord. Solo [A. or Bar. Accomp. for organ].
(In Ayrton. Sacred Minstrelsy. Vol. 2, pp. 22–24. London,
1835.)   No. 8 in **M.290.22.2
Same. (In his Twenty Anthems. Pp. 19–23. 1778.)
                                                    No. 4 in **M.236.33

E5826 — T.r. — Church music. Anthems, &c.

NN   0021282   MB

M1625   Nares, James, 1715–1783.
.N3   The royal-pastoral, a dramatic ode set
R6   to musick by Dr. Nares. London, Welcker
         [1769]
             score (108p.) 40cm.

             1. Monologues with music (Orchestra)
         I. Title.

NN   0021283   NcU

FILM   Nares, James, 1715–1783.
A989   The royal pastoral, a dramatic ode set to music by Dr.
M   Nares.   London, Printed by Welcker [1769]
            score (108 p.) On film (negative)

            Microfilm. Original in the British Museum.
            For solo voices, chorus, and orchestra.
            The text is by Daniel Bellamy. Cf. Brit. union-cat.
        of early music.

NN   0021284   CU

Nares, James, 1715–1783.
[The royal-pastoral]
    The royal-pastoral, a dramatic ode, set to musick by Dr.
Nares. London, Printed by Welcker [1770?]
2 p. l., 108 p. 37½cm.
Signature on lining-paper: John Alcock, 1770.

1. Operas—Scores.   44–15108
Library of Congress   M1500.N255R6

NN   0021285   DLC

Nares, James.
    The royal pastoral, a dramatic ode.
Set to musick by Dr. Nares. [Full
score]. London: Printed by Welcker,
[1790?]. 2 p.l., 108 p. 38cm.

NN   0021286   NRU--Mus

Nares, James.
Single chant [in A].   No. 65 in **M.111.4.2
(In Turle and Taylor. The People's Music Book. Vol. 2, p. 279.
London, 1844.)

E5822 — Chants.

NN   0021287   MB

Nares, James.
    Six fuges (!) with introductory voluntary's for
the organ or harpsichord. London, Welcker [1772]

NN   0021288   PU

Nares, James.
Some say 'tis ambition. Catch [for 4 voices].   No. 39 in **M.220.10
(In Warren. Vocal Harmony. Pp. 60. London. [1765.])

E5826 — T.r. — Part songs.

NN   0021289   MB

Nares, James.
The souls of the righteous. Anthem [S. S., and chorus. Accomp.
for organ].
(In Ayrton. Sacred Minstrelsy. Vol. 1, pp. 180–184. London,
1834.)   No. 64 in **M.290.22.1
Same. (In his Twenty Anthems. Pp. 94–99. 1778.)
                                                    No. 15 in **M.236.33
Same. (In Novello's Collection of Anthems. Vol. 7, pp. 99–107.
[187–?])   No. 9 in **M.195.2.7

E5826 — T.r. — Church music. Anthems, &c.

NN   0021290   MB

Nares, James.   **M.233.14.1
Te Deum, Jubilate, Kyrie, Nicene creed, Sanctus, Magnificat, and
Nunc dimittis in F. [Accomp. for organ.]
(In Novello. Cathedral Choir Book. Vol. 1. London. [184–?])

E5827 — T.r. — Church music. Anthems, &c.

NN   0021291   MB

VM   NARES, JAMES, 1715–1783.
22   These lessons for the harpsichord, with a
N226t   sonata in score for the harpsichord or organ
        are – dedicated to – the Countess of Car-
        lisle – Opera II.   London, Printed for the
        author & sold at Johnson's Music Shop [ca. 1759]
        [2]l., 53p. 26x35cm.

            Consists of 5 lessons for harpsichord solo
        and a sonata for solo harpsichord, 2 violins,
        and continuo.
            Autograph of Robert Cooke on fly-leaf.
            Bookplates: Julian Marshall; W H C [i.e.
        Wilhelm Heyer,   Cöln;
            Bound by F.   Bedford.

NN   0021292   ICN ICU ViWC

Nares, James.
To all lovers of harmony. Glee [A. T. B.].
(In Warren. Collection of Glees. Vol. 2, pp. 1–5. London.
[1771.])   No. 1 in **M.220.9.2
Same. (In Clementi. Vocal Harmony. Vol. 2, pp. 120–125.
[181–?])   No. 3 in **M.235.9.2

E5827 — T.r. — Part songs.

NN   0021293   MB

Nares, James.   No. 35 in **M.157.34
To God the mighty Lord. [Anthem. Accomp. for organ.]
(In Metcalfe. Fifty Metrical Anthems. Pp. 55, 56. London.
[1858.])

E5827 — T.r. — Church music. Anthems, &c.

NN   0021294   MB

SC   Nares, James, 1715–1783.
Nk42   A treatise on singing, in which is exhibited
N167   and explained by examples all the known rules
        of solmisation, or learning to sing by notes,
        with directions for the delivery & management
        of the voice ... London, Welcker [177–?]
            1 p.l., 40 p. music. 17 x 25 cm.

            1. Singing—Instruction and study—To
        1800. 2. Solmization. I. Title. I.I.
        3s.

NN   0021295   CtY-Mus

Nares, James, 1715–1783.
    A treatise on singing in which is exhibited and explained
by examples all the known rules of solmisation, or learning to sing by notes with directions for the delivery &
management of the voice. drawn from observations on
nature as well as art. highly usefull in all societies where
singing by notes is necessary, being adapted to make that
study easy & clear, by D‍r. Nares ... London, Printed by
Longman and Broderip [ca. 1780?]
1 p. l., 40 p. 18 x 26cm.
Engraved throughout.
1. Sight-singing. 2. Singing and voice culture.
                                                    17–17453
Library of Congress   MT830.A2N2

NN   0021296   DLC

VOLUME 405

Nares, James.
Try me, O God. Anthem. [Accomp. for organ.]
(In Hullah. Part Music. Sacred. Vol. 2, pp. 73-75. London, 1845.)
No. 25 in **M.157.28.2
Same. (In Same. New edition. Vol. 1, pp. 139-141. 1868.)
No. 32 in 8043.28.1

E5827 — T.r. — Church music. Anthems, &c.

NN 0021297   MB

NARES, James.   **M.236.3;
Twenty anthems. In score for 1, 2, 3, 4 and 5 voices [with figured bass]
London. The author. 1778. (8), 140 pp. Fº.
Contents. — Behold, O God our Defender [S. T. B.]. — Behold how good and joyful [A. B.]. — Lord, how long [A. B.]. — Rejoice in the Lord [S. or T.]. — Arise, Thou Judge [S. T. B.]. — Not unto us [A. T. and chorus]. — By the waters of Babylon [S. S. or T. T.]. — O Lord my God [B. solo and chorus]. — Turn Thee again [A. T. B.]. — Come, let us sing [S. S. or T. T. and chorus]. — Unto Thee, O God [S. A. T. B.]. — Awake up, my Glory [A. solo and chorus]. — God is our hope [S. A. T. and chorus]. — Hide not Thy face [A. T. and chorus]. — The souls of the righteous [S. S. and chorus]. — The Lord is my strength [A. B. and chorus]. — It is a good thing [S. S. B. and chorus]. — S. S. A. T. B.]. — O give thanks [S. A. and chorus]. — The Lord is righteous [S. S. and chorus]. — Call to remembrance [S. S. A. T. B.].

NN 0021298   MB CtY NN

Nares, James.
Wherewithal shall a young man. Anthem. [Accomp. for organ.]
(In Ayrton. Sacred Minstrelsy. Vol. 1, pp. 86-89. London, 1834.)

E5827 — T.r. — Church music. Anthems, &c.

NN 0021299   MB

Nares, James, *1715-1783.*
While we thus our time. Canon, 3 in 1.   No. 126 in **M.220.10
(In Warren. Vocal Harmony. P. 220. London. [1765.])

E5827 — T.r. — Part songs.

NN 0021300   MB

Nares, James, *1715-1783.*
Why should mortals sigh for gold? Duet [S. A. Accomp. for   No. 39 in **M.235.18.2
pianoforte].
(In Musical Library. Vol. 2, pp. 96-99. London, 1854.)

E5824 — T.r. — Duets. Vocal.

NN 0021301   MB

Nares, James, *1715-1783.*
Wilt thou lend me thy mare? [Catch for 3 voices.]
(In Warren. Collection of Catches. Vol. 1, p. 54. London. [1764.])   No. 68 in **M.220.9.1
Same. (In Sibbald. Collection of Catches. Vol. 1, p. 27. Edinburgh. [1780.])   No. 24 in **M.392.49.1
Same. (In The Harmonist. Vol. 8, p. 59. London. [179-?])   No. 17 in **M.218.8.8
Same. (In Clementi. Collection of Catches. Vol. 1, p. 27. [179-?])   No. 24 in **M.110.1.1=No. 24 in **M.110.2.1
Same. (In Social Harmony. P. 116. [1818.])

E5824 — T.r. — Part songs.

NN 0021302   MB

Nares, John.
A summary of the law on penal convictions. London, Printed by A. Strahan for J. Butterworth, 1814.
168 p. 21 cm.

1. Judgments—Gt. Brit. 2. Criminal procedure—Gt. Brit.

55-47139 †

NN 0021303   DLC NcD

B   **Nares, Owen,** 1889-1943.
N227n1   Myself and some others; pure egotism.
London, Duckworth [1925]
204p. port. 19cm.

1. Actors—Correspondence, reminiscences, etc. I. Title.

NN 0021304   IU CLSU PU MH OU

Nares, Robert, 1753-1829, ed.

The **British** critic, and quarterly theological review. v. 1-42, May 1793-Dec. 1813; new ser., v. 1-23, Jan. 1814-June 1825; [3d ser.] v. 1-3, Oct. 1825-Oct. 1826; [4th ser.] v. 1-34, Jan. 1827-Oct. 1843. London, Printed for F. and C. Rivington [etc.] 1793-1843.

Nares, Robert, 1753-1829.

British museum. *Dept. of manuscripts.*
A catalogue of the Harleian manuscripts in the British museum. With indexes of persons, places, and matters ... Printed by command of His Majesty King George III. in pursuance of an address of the House of commons of Great Britain. [London, G. Eyre and A. Strahan] 1808-12.

Nares, Robert, 1753-1829.
Catalogue of the valuable and extensive library of the late Very Rev. Archdeacon Nares, including Stephani Thesaurus Graecus, a Barker et Valpy[etc., etc.],which will be sold by auction by Mr. Evans, at his house on November 25, and seven following days (Sunday excepted). [London, W. Nicol] 1829.

23 cm. pp.(2), 75.
Priced.

NN 0021307   MH NN

Nares, Robert, 1753-1829.

A connected and chronological view of the prophecies relating to the Christian church; in twelve sermons: preached in Lincoln's-Inn chapel, from the year 1800 to 1804, at the lecture founded by the Right Rev. William Warburton ... By Robert Nares ... London, F. C. and J. Rivington [etc.] 1805.
9 p. l., [3]-371, [1]p. 22cm.

1. Bible. Prophecies. I. Warburton lectures. II. Title.

Printed by Wesleyan   University Library

NN 0021308   CtW

Nares, Robert, 1753-1829.
Elements of orthoepy: containing a distinct view of the whole analogy of the English language; so far as it relates to pronunciation, accent, and quantity. By R. Nares ... London, Printed for T. Payne and son, 1784.
xxvi p., 1 l., 372, [44] p. 22ᶜᵐ.

1. English language—Pronunciation. 2. English language—Accents and accentuation. 3. English language—Syllabication. I. Title.

11—8537

Library of Congress   PE1137.A2N35

ViU MdBP IaU
NN 0021309   DLC NcD CU NcU NIC CtY PPL PU OU MiU

Nares, Robert, 1753-1829.
An essay on the demon or divination of Socrates. London, Printed for T. Payne and Son, 1782.
53 p. 18 cm.
With this is bound 14 other pamphlets on various subjects.

1. Socrates. 2. Imprints--17th century.
(checklist) I. Title. II. Title: The demon or divination of Socrates.

NN 0021310   KAS CU IU MH PU CtY MdBP

824.7   **Nares, Robert,** 1753-1829.
N227   Essays and other occasional compositions, chiefly reprinted. By the Rev. R. Nares. London, Printed by W. Bulmer; sold by F.C. and J. Rivington, 1810.
2v. 19cm.

NN 0021311   ICarbS CtY ODW NjP IU DLC

3528   **Nares, Robert,** 1753-1829.
.669   General rules for the pronunciation of the English language; with complete lists of the exceptions.. London, Printed for E. Jeffery, 1792.
26,372,[44] p. 21½ cm.

1. English language—Pronunciation.

NN 0021312   NjP NjR CtY OO

Nares, Robert, 1753-1829.
A glossary; or, collection of words, phrases, names, and allusions to customs, proverbs, &c., which have been thought to require illustration, in the works of English authors, particularly Shakespeare, and his contemporaries ... By Robert Nares ... London, R. Triphook; [etc., etc.] 1822.
viii, 583, [1] p., 1 l. 29 cm.

1. English language—Glossaries, vocabularies, etc. 2. English language—Obsolete words. 3. Shakespeare, William—Dictionaries, indexes, etc.

PE1667.N3 1822   17—10836

OC NcD
NN 0021313   DLC MtU OU NIC InU MdBP NN CtY MH-AH

PR   **Nares, Robert,** 1753-1829.
2892   A glossary; or, collection of words, phrases,
.N23   names, and allusions to customs, proverbs, &c.
1825   which have been thought to require illustration, in the works of English authors, particularly Shakespeare, and his contemporaries ... By Robert Nares ... Stralsund, C. Loeffler, 1825.
viii, 912 p. 22½ᶜᵐ.

1. English language—Glossaries, vocabularies, etc. 2. English language—Obsolete words. 3. Shakespeare, William—Dictionaries, indexes, etc.

NN 0021314   MiU TxU OO

Nares, Robert, 1753-1829.
A glossary; or, Collection of words, phrases, names, and allusions to customs, proverbs, etc., which have been thought to require illustration in the works of English authors, particularly Shakespeare and his contemporaries ... A new edition, with ... additions both of words and examples, by J. O. Halliwell and T. Wright ... London, J. R. Smith, 1849.
2 v. 8°.

NN 0021315   NN

VOLUME 405

PE
1667
N3
1859

Nares, Robert, 1753-1829.
A glossary; or, collection of words, phrases, names, and allusions to customs proverbs, etc., which have been thought to require illustration, in the works of English authors, particularly Shakespears and his contemporaries. By Robert Nares. A new ed., with considerable additions both of words and examples, by James O. Halliwell and Thomas Wright London, J. R. Smith, 1859.

2 v. 23 cm.
Paged continuously.

1. English language—Glossaries, vocabularies, etc. 2. English language—Obsolete words. 3. Shakespears, William—Dictionaries indexes, etc. I. Hallewell-Phillipps, James Orchard, 1820-1889, ed. II. Wright, Thomas, 1810-1887, joint ed.

PP NjP MB
NN   0021317   IEdS OC TxU GU ICN NjNbS OC1 MH CtY LU

Nares, Robert, 1753-1829.
A glossary; or, collection of words, phrases, names, and allusions to customs, proverbs, etc., which have been thought to require illustration, in the works of English authors, particularly Shakespeare and his contempora- ries. By Robert Nares ... A new ed., with considerable additions both of words and examples, by James O. Hal- liwell ... and Thomas Wright ... London, J. R. Smith, 1867.
2 v. 22½ᵐᵐ.
Paged continuously.
1. English language—Glossaries, vocabularies, etc. 2. English language—Obsolete words. 3. Shakespeare, William—Dictionaries, indexes, etc. I. Halliwell-Phillips, James Orchard, 1820-1889, ed. II. Wright, Thomas, 1810-1877, ed.
25-6607
Library of Congress   PE1667.N3 1867

MB NN
NN   0021318   DLC NSyU OrU NIC CU OCU MiU MdBP TxU

Nares, Robert, 1753-1829.
A glossary; or, collection of words, phrases, names, and allusions to customs, proverbs, etc., which have been thought to require illustration, in the works of English authors, par- ticularly Shakespeare and his contemporaries. By Robert Nares ... A new ed., with considerable additions both of words and examples, by James O. Halliwell ... and Thomas Wright ... London, J. R. Smith, 1872.
2 v. 23ᵐᵐ.
Book-plate of Dr. Ernest Lewis McEwen.
1. English language—Glossaries, vocabularies, etc. 2. English lan- guage—Obsolete words. 3. Shakespeare, William—Dictionaries, indexes, etc. I. Halliwell-Phi- lipps, James Orchard, 1820-1889. ed. II. Wright, Thomas, 1810- 1877. joint ed.
32-32819
Library of Congress   PE1667.N3 1872   427

NN   0021319   DLC OrCS INS KU AAP NRCR DSI

PE
1667
N3
1876

Nares, Robert, 1753-1829.
A glossary; or, Collection of words, phrases, names and allusions to customs, proverbs,etc., which have been thought to require illustration, in the works of English authors, particularly Shakespeare and his contemporaries. A new ed., with considerable additions both of words and examples, by James O. Halliwell and Thomas Wright London, J. R. Smith, 1876.
2 v. (981 p.)

NN   0021320   KMK MH

Nares, Robert, 1753-1829.
A glossary; or, Collection of words, phrases, names, and allusions to customs, proverbs, etc., which have been thought to require illustration, in the works of English authors, par- ticularly Shakespeare and his contemporaries. A new ed., with considerable additions both of words and examples, by James O. Halliwell and Thomas Wright. London, J. R. Smith, 1882.
2 v. (ix, 981 p.) 23 cm.
1. English language—Glossaries, vocabularies, etc. 2. English lan- guage—Obsolete words. 3. Shakespeare, William—Dictionaries, in- dexes, etc.
PE1667.N3 1882   59-56023

NN   0021321   DLC OU NjP CoU

Nares, Robert, 1753-1829.
A glossary; or, Collection of words, phrases, names, and allusions to customs, proverbs, etc., which have been thought to require illustration, in the works of English authors, par- ticularly Shakespeare and his contemporaries. By Robert Nares ... A new ed., with considerable additions both of words and examples, by James O. Halliwell ... and Thomas Wright ... London, Reeves and Turner, 1888.
2 v. 23ᵐᵐ.
Paged continuously.
1. English language—Glossaries, vocabularies, etc. 2. English lan- guage—Obsolete words. 3. Shakespeare, William—Dictionaries, indexes, etc. I. Halliwell-Phillipps, James Orchard, 1820-1889, ed. II. Wright, Thomas, 1810-1877, ed.
4-22031
Library of Congress   PE1667.N3 1888

OC1W ViU
NN   0021322   DLC CaBVaU MtU NIC PPLas MB OCU OC1

Nares, Robert, 1753-1829.
A glossary, or collection of words, phrases, names, and allusions to customs, proverbs, etc., which have been thought to require illustration in the works of English authors particularly Shakespeare and his contemporaries. A new ed., with considerable additions both of words and examples, by James O. Halliwell and Thomas Wright, London, Gibbings, and co., ltd., 1901.

2 v. 22.5 cm.
Contents: 1. A-J.   2. K-Z.

NN   0021323   MH OC1StM TU PSC WaS WaSpG

Nares, Robert, 1753-1829.
A glossary of words, phrases, names and allusions ... George Routledge & Sons, Ltd. 1904.
(1), ix, 981, (2) p.   21 cm., in 8s.

NN   0021324   MB PP

Nares, Robert, 1753-1829.
A glossary of words, phrases, names and allusions in the works of English authors; particularly of Shakespeare and his contemporaries, by Robert Nares... New edition with consid- erable additions both of words and examples, by J. O. Halliwell... and Thomas Wright... London: G. Routledge & Sons, Ltd., 1905. ix, 981 p. 8°.

60638A. 1. English language.—Dic- Obsolete words. 3. Shakespeare, well-Phillips, James Orchard, 1820-89, 1810-77, jt. editor.
N.Y.P.L.
tionaries. 2. English language.— William.—Concordances. 4. Halli- editor. 5. Wright, Thomas,
October 24, 1922.

NN   0021325   NN MiD ViU WU KMK WaT OC1 OOxM PU NjP

Nares, Robert, 1753-1829.
... An historical account of the discoveries made in palimp- sest manuscripts. Communicated by Archdeacon Nares ...
(*In* Royal society of literature of the United Kingdom. London. Essays by divers hands, being the transactions. London, 1829. 27½ᵐᵐ. vol. I, pt. I, p. 122-133)
"Read March 3rd and 17th, 1824."

1. Manuscripts (Palimpsests)
No. Carolina. Univ. Libr for Library of Congress
A C 39-2726
[PN22.R6 vol. 1, pt.1]
(2)
(806.242)

NN   0021326   NcU DLC

Nares, Robert, 1753-1829.
... On the religion and divination of Socrates. By Archdea- con Nares ...
(*In* Royal society of literature of the United Kingdom. London. Essays by divers hands, being the transactions. London, 1829. 27½ᵐᵐ. vol. I, pt. II, p. 106-113)
"Read April 19th, 1826."

1. Socrates.
No. Carolina. Univ. Libr. for Library of Congress
A C 39-2745
[PN22.R6 vol. 1, pt. 2]
(2)
(806.242)

NN   0021327   NcU DLC

J
54555
.258
1793
no.27

NARES, ROBERT, 1753-1829.
... Principles of government, adapted to general instruction and use. By the Rev. R. Nares, A.M. author of a tract, entitled Prin- ciples of government, deduced from reason, &c. From which this is abridged. With a new intro- duction. London, Printed for John Stock- dale, 1793.
24p. 22cm.
At head of title: Abridgement.

NN   0021328   ICN

Nares, Robert, 1753-1829.
Principles of government deduced from reason, sup- ported by English experience, and opposed to French errors. By the Rev. R. Nares ... London, Printed for J. Stockdale, 1792.
xviii, (2), 160 p. 21½ᵐᵐ.

1. Political science.
9-25492†
Library of Congress   JF45.N2

NN   0021329   DLC CtY MH CaBVaU PHi

JF45
.N25

NARES,ROBERT,1753-1829.
Principles of government deduced from reason, sup- ported by English experience,and opposed to French er- rors. By the Rev.R.Nares... Dublin Printed for B. Dornin,1793.
xii,[1],86 p. 20½cm.

1.Political science.

NN   0021330   ICU

Bx
5133
.N23
P8

Nares,Robert,1753-1829.
Protestantism the blessing of Britain; a fast sermon,preached in the Cathedral at Lichfield on Wednesday,February 28,1810. London, Printed for the author,and sold by F.C.and J.Rivington, 1810. 31 p.

NN   0021331   MiU

[Nares, Robert] 1753-1829.
Remarks on the favourite ballet of Cupid and Psyche; with some account of the pantomime of the ancients, and other ob- servations. London, Printed for J. Stockdale, 1788. 63 p. 15cm.

For authority of main entry, *cf. Watt, R. Bibliotheca britannica.* 695j.

266601B. 1. Ballet. I. Title.
N. Y. P. L.
II. Title: Cupid and Psyche.
September 13, 1944

NN   0021332   NN

Nares, Robert, 1753-1829.
Sermons preached before the Honourable Society of Lincoln's Inn. 2 p.l., 350 pp. *London: F. & C. Riv- ington, 1794. 8°.*

NN   0021333   NN

XG
.789
.A10R
no.3

[Nares, Robert] 1753-1829, supposed author.
A short account of the character and reign of Louis XVI. Shewing how little he deserved, from his ungrateful people, the name of tyrant. To which is subjoined, a corrected translation of his last will.
London: Printed for J.Downes,No.240,Strand. 1793.

2p.l.,28p. 21cm.(8vo)

NN   0021334   MB

VOLUME 405

BS2560
.N22
1816
Nares, Robert, 1753-1829.
   The veracity of the evangelists demonstrated, by a comparative view on their histories. London, printed for F.C. and J. Rivington, 1816.
   xv, 288p. folded chart. 22cm.

   1. Bible. N.T. Gospels—Harmonies.
   I. Title.

NN   0021335   IEG PPL NjP

Nares Chandra Sen Gupta
see
Sen Gupta, Nares Chandra, 1882–

F868
F8N3
Nares and Saunders, Fresno, Calif.
   A different California: Laguna de Tache Grant. Fresno, Calif. [Fresno Republican Print., 1899?]
   22 columns. illus. 23cm.

   Cover title.

   1. Real estate business – Fresno Co., Calif. 2. Real estate business – Kings Co., Calif. 3. Rancho Laguna de Tache. I. Title.

NN   0021337   CU-B

F868
.L1N2
Nares & Saunders, Fresno, Calif.
   The laguna de Tachegrant, the heart of California. Nares & Saunders, managers, Laton, Fresno County, California. San Francisco, Sunset Photo Engraving Co. and Sunset Press [1904]
   40 p. incl. illus., 2 maps. 22.5 x 20 cm. fold. to 22.5 x 10 cm.

NN   0021338   DLC

Nareśa Candra Senagupta
see
Sen Gupta, Nares Chandra, 1882–

Nareśa-Chandra Rāya
see
Roy, Naresh Chandra.

Naresh Chandra Roy
see
Roy, Naresh Chandra.

4DS
Ind.
580
Naresh.
   Empire number of Naresh. [Lahore 193]
   1 v. (unpaged)

NN   0021342   DLC-P4

PL6271
N28
x
Naresian te nankerian fei Iehova. Samoa, Printed at the London missionary society's press, 1845.
   10 p. 17cm. in cover 20cm.
   Presentation copy to A. Pinart from the Rev. George Turner.
   In one of the dialects used on the island of Tanna in the New Hebrides.

NN   0021343   CU-B

Naret, Edward.
   History of the French settlers at Gallipolis, Ohio, in 1790. By the late Edward Naret, M. D. Cincinnati, Keating & co. [n. d.]
   39, [2] p. incl. plates. 22cm.

   1. Gallipolis, O.—History. 2. French in Ohio.
                                          A 20-1370
Title from Western   Reserve Hist. Soc. Printed by L. C.

NN   0021344   OC1WHi OC1 OC

Naret (Georges-Léon). *Des paralysies consécutives à la diphthérie. 44 pp. 4°. Paris, 1892, No. 196.

NN   0021345   DNLM

Naret (Henri-Alphonse-Joseph) [1874–].
*Contribution à l'étude de la tuberculose pulmonaire chez les tuberculeux chirurgicaux adultes. 61 pp. 8°. Lille. 1906. No. 3.

NN   0021346   DNLM

Naret, Henry.
   Contribution à la radiesthésie médicale, plan d'examen méthodique. Paris, Maison de la radiesthésie [1944]
   94 p. diagrs. 25 cm. (Collection Alfred Lambert. "Arts, sciences et philosophies")

   1. Radiesthesia. (Series)

   RZ999.N3   616.0757   48–37740*

NN   0021347   DLC DNLM

Naret-Koning, Johann Josef David.   No. 10 in M.392.42.3
   Einheit und deutsche Treu! [Männerchor.]
   (In Abt. Deutsche Sängerhalle. Vol. 3, pp. 31, 32. [Leipzig, 187–?])

   E5824 — T.r. — Part songs.

NN   0021348   MB

NARET-KONING, Johann Josef David.   No. 10 in **M.3[
   Vier Lieder für Männerchor (und Solostimmen).
= Mannheim. Sohler & Donecker. [187–?] 21 pp. L. 8°.
   Contents. — Schlummerlied. — Abendfeier. — Zwiegesang. — Gesellenlied.

   Sheet D 3284   Aug. 23, 189[

NN   0021349   MB

PG3328
Z6N3
Naretto, Michele.
   Personaggi-idee in Dostoievski. Torino, Edizioni di "Filosofia" [1950]
   19 p. (La Filosofia nella letteratura, 5)

   Cover title.

   1. Dostoevskiĭ, Fedor Mikhaĭlovich, 1821-1881 - Characters.

NN   0021350   CU

Naretto, Michele.
   Personaggi-idee in Dostoievski. Torino [1952]
   19 p. (La filosofia nella letteratura, 5)

NN   0021351   MH

Narewczewitz, Albert, 1894–   Wandlung und Schadensersatz. [In Maschinenschrift.] 67 S. 4°(2°). — Auszug: [Marburg 1921]. 2 Bl. 8°
Marburg, Jur. Diss. v. 21. Dez. 1919 [1921], Ref. Leonhard
[Geb. 22. Okt. 94 Eschwege; Wohnort: Eschwege; Staatsangeh.: Preußen; Vorbildung: G. Eschwege Reife 13; Studium: Berlin 4, Marburg 2 S.; Rig. 20. Nov. 19.]
                                                   [U 21. 1504

NN   0021352   ICRL

Narewczewitz, Georg: Ueber Silikatzemente, unt. bes. Berücks. einer neuen, für die Praxis wichtigen Untersuchungsmethode. [Maschinenschrift.] 35 S. 4° [Lag nicht vor.] — Auszug: o. O. u. J. 2 Bl. 8°
Erlangen, Med. Diss. v. 5. Dez. 1922 [1923]   [U 23. 1765

NN   0021353   ICRL

Narewski, Eugen, 1882 –   Schleimhautveränderungen des Mundes während der Schwangerschaft. [In Maschinenschrift.] 29, IV S. 4°(2°). — Auszug: Bonn 1921: Carthaus. 2 Bl. 8°
Bonn, Med. Diss. v. 22. Juli 1921, Ref. Kantorowicz
[Geb. 17. Okt. 82 Berlin; Wohnort. Bonn; Staatsangeh.. Preußen; Vorbildung.: G. Friedberg. Hessen bis Prima 02; Studium: Bonn 8 S.; Coll. 22. Juli 21: Zahnärztl. Approb. 22. Juli 05.]
                                                   [U 21. 2758

NN   0021354   ICRL

W 4
eL89
1740
N.1
NAREZ, Ursmer, 1678-1744, praeses.
   Disputatio medica de glandularum fabrica et usu ... Lovanii, Typis Petri Augustini Denique [1740]
   broadside. 44 x 35 cm.
   Diss. - Louvain (J. Stapleton, respondent)

   I. Stapleton, John, respondent

NN   0021355   DNLM

W 4
eL89
1742
N.1
NAREZ, Urmer, 1678-1744, praeses.
   Disputatio medica de perspiratione ... Lovanii, Typis Petri Augustini Denique [1742]
   broadside. 54 x 43 cm.
   Diss. - Louvain (G. Joris, respondent)

   I. Joris, Gérard, respondent

NN   0021356   DNLM

W 4
eL89
1741
N.1
NAREZ, Urmer, 1678-1744, praeses.
   Disputatio medica de sanguine,... Lovanii, Typis Petri Aug. Denique [1741]
   broadside. 43 x 35 cm.
   Diss. - Louvain (J. J. Thiebaut, respondent)

   I, Thiebaut, Jacob Joseph, respondent

NN   0021357   DNLM

PG3337
.N3B8
1895
Narezhnyĭ, Vasiliĭ Trofimovich, 1780-1825.
   Бурсакъ; романъ. Изд. 4. С.-Петербургъ, Изд. А. С. Суворина [1895]
   388 p. 16 cm. (Дешевая библіотека, № 5)

   I. Title.   *Title transliterated: Bursak.*
   PG3337.N3B8 1895   60-56924 ‡

NN   0021358   DLC

VOLUME 405

Narezhnyĭ, Vasiliĭ Trofimovich, 1780–1826.
Избранные романы; подготовка текста к печати, вступ. статья и примечания В. Ф. Переверзева. ;Москва; Academia, 1933.
904 p. port. 18 cm.
"Литература о Нарежном": p. ;892;
Contents. — Аристион; или, Перевоспитание. — Бурсак. — Два Ивана; или, Страсть к тяжбам.
I. Pereverzev, Valerian Fedorovich, 1882– ed. II. Title: Aristion. III. Title: Bursak. IV. Title: Dva Ivana.
Title transliterated: Izbrannye romany.

PG3337.N3A6 193   48–37836*

NN 0021359   DLC NIC

Narezhnyĭ, Vasiliĭ Trofimovich, 1780–1826.
Романы и повѣсти. Сочиненія Василія Нарѣжнаго. Изд. 2. Санктпетербургъ, Въ Тип. А. Смирдина, 1835–36 ;v. 1, 1836;
10 v. 18 cm.
Contents.—ч. 1–2. Бурсакъ; малороссійская повѣсть.—ч. 3–4. Два Ивана; или Страсть къ тяжбамъ.—ч. 5. Аристіонъ; или Перевоспитаніе—ч. 6–7. Черный годъ; или Горскіе князья—ч. 8. Богатый бѣдникъ.—ч. 9. Марія.—ч. 10. Славенскіе вечера.

Title romanized: Romany i povĭesti.

PG3337.N3 1835   68–142232

NN 0021360   DLC MH

Narezhnyĭ, Vasiliĭ Trofimovich, 1780–1825.
(Rossiĭskiĭ Zhilblaz;
Россійскій Жилблазъ; или, Похожденія князя Гаврилы Симоновича Чистякова. Сочиненіе Василія Нарѣжнаго. Санктпетербургъ, Въ Тип. Воен. министерства, 1814–
v. in   18 cm.

I. Title.

PG3337.N3R67   74–214359

NN 0021361   DLC

Narezo, Gabriel García
see
García Narezo, Gabriel, 1916–

Narfin, Roland, 1911–
... Contribution à l'etude des modifications du rythme cardiaque pendant l'effort sportif ... Paris, 1939.
Thèse - Univ. de Paris.

NN 0021363   CtY

Narfon, Julien de, 1863–1919.
...Les catholiques italiens, la question romaine et la guerre; 19ᵉ des conférences d'union sacrée donnée à la Fraternité de l'ascension...le dimanche 10 février 1918 sous la présidence de M. le pasteur Auguste Weber... Paris: La Fraternité, 1918. 40 p. 16°.

1. European war, 1914– .—Catholic state, Italy, 1870–1918. 3. Catholic N.Y.P.L.   Church (Roman). 2. Church and Church (Roman), Italy, 1870–1918. November 26, 1919.

NN 0021364   NN

[NARFON, Julien de]
La creation d'une union pour l'etude du droit des gens, d'apres les principes chretiens. Brignais,1912.

24 p.

NN 0021365   MH-L

Narfon, Julien de, 1863–1919.
Léon XIII intime. Paris, F. Juven ;1898?;
276 p. illus., ports. 20½cm.

1. Leo XIII, pope, 1810–1903. I. Title.

NN 0021366   NCH

DC255   Narfon, Julien de, 1863–
M7   Montalembert et Louis Veuillot. Avec une
N32   préf. Les deux écoles, et, en appendice, la
reproduction des dernières polémiques sur
Louis Veuillot. Paris, G. Crès [1914]
94 p. 23 cm.
At head of title: Deux grands journalistes.

1. Montalembert, Charles Forbes René de Tryon, Comte de, 1810–1870. 2. Veuillot, Louis François, 1813–1883.

NN 0021367   CtY MiU NN InU IU

Narfon, Julien de, 1863–1919.
Pope Leo XIII, his life and work, by Julien de Narfon; translated from the French by G. A. Raper ... London, Chapman & Hall, ld., 1899.
xii, 237, ;1; p. incl. front., illus., plates, port. 20½ᵐ.

1. Leo XIII, pope, 1810–1903. I. Raper, George A., tr.

Library of Congress   BX1374.N3   1–3438

NN 0021368   DLC MeB CtY-D CtY PP NjP ICN MB NN

Narfon, Julien de, 1863–1919.
Pope Leo XIII, his life & work, tr. fr. the Fr. by G.A. Raper ... Phil., Chapman, 1899.
2–237 p. il. por. O.

NN 0021369   OCl

Narfon, Julien de, 1863–1919.
... La presse et la guerre ...
see under Le Figaro, Paris.

Narfon, Julien de, 1863–
La séparation des églises et de l'état, origines—étapes—bilan, par J. de Narfon. Paris, F. Alcan, 1912.
2 p. l., iii, 317 p. 22ᵐ. (*On cover:* Bibliothèque générale des sciences sociales. XL)

I. Title.

14–2539

NN 0021371   DLC ICJ

DC59   Narfon, Julien de, 1863–1919.
.5   Vers l'Église libre. 3.ed. Paris, Librairie
.N23   Mutuelle, 1905.
xxviii, 404 p.
Imprint covered by label: Paris, Dujarric, 1906.

1. Church and state in France. 2. Catholic church in France. 3. Concordat of 1801.

NN 0021372   ICU MH

Nargaud (Arthur-Léon). * Suppuration chronique des voies séminales. 36 pp. 4°. Paris, 1873. No. 164.

NN 0021374   DNLM

Nargeot (Albert). *Hépatisation pneumococcique terminée par gangrène pulmonaire. 76 pp. 8°. Paris, 1910. No. 201.

NN 0021375   DNLM

Nargeot, Julien
see Nargeot, Pierre Julien, 1799–1891.

Nargeot, Pierre Julien, 1799–1891.
Los contrabandistas
For libretti see under Thierry, Emile.

M1503   Nargeot, Pierre Julien, 1799–1891
N33D3   [Dans le pétrin; acc. arr. piano]
Dans le pétrin; folie-opérette en un acte, Paroles de Mr. de Sorant. Partition chant et piano avec livret. Paris, F. Mackar et Gresse [1866?] Pl.no.F.M. et G.1000. 40 p.

Vocal score with piano accompaniment. French words.

I. Sorant, J   A   de. II. Title.

NN 0021378   CU NN NcU

Nargeot, Pierre Julien, 1799–1891.
Dans le pétrin
For libretti see under Rostan,
J   M   A   de, Baron.

M1503   Nargeot, Pierre Julien, 1799–
N33D6   [Le docteur Frontin; acc. arr. piano]
Le docteur Frontin; opéra comique [en un acte] Poème de Marc Constantin. Paris, Choudens [186–?] Pl.no.A.A.1458. 74 p.

Vocal score with piano accompaniment. French words.

I. Constantin, Marc, 1810–1888. II. Title.

NN 0021380   CU

Nargeot, Pierre Julien, 1799–1891.
Les enfers de Paris ...
see under Beauvoir [Eugène Auguste Roger de Bully] called Roger de, 1809–1866.

VOLUME 405

M1503
N33E8
Nargeot, Pierre Julien, 1799–
[Les exploits de Sylvestre; acc. arr. piano]
Les exploits de Sylvestre; opérette en un acte de M.J.A. de
Sorant. Partition piano & chant avec le livret. Paris, E.
Challiot, E. Coudray [1866?] Pl. no. E.C. 3257.
37 p.

Vocal score with piano accompaniment. French words.

I. Sorant, J.A., de.   II. Title.

NN   0021382   CU

Nargeot, Pierre Julien, 1799–1891.   No. 1 in **M.393-47
Jeanne, Jeannette & Jeanneton. Opérette en un acte. Paroles de
Marc Constantin & Émile Abraham. Musique de J. Nargeot.
[Partition chant et piano.]
Paris. Bathlot. 1876. (3), 59 pp. L. 8°.

E6808 — Operas. — Constantin. Marc. and Émile Abraham. — Jt. auth.

NN   0021383   MB

M1509
N32M3
Nargeot, Pierre Julien, 1799–1891.
[Le mari d'Andréa; acc. arr. piano]
Le mari d'Andréa; duo comique. Paroles de Lucien Cardoze.
Paris, E. Challiot, 1863.
20 p.

Vocal score with piano accompaniment. French words.

I. Cardoze, Lucien   II. Title.

NN   0021384   CU

Nargeot, Pierre Julien, 1799–1891.
Mignon
For editions without music see under
Montheau, Gaston, de, d. 1867.

M1509
N32M6
Nargeot, Pierre Julien, 1799–
[Un monsieur bien servi; acc. arr. piano]
Un monsieur bien servi [jocrissiade musicale] Jocrissiade de
Ch. Delange. Paris, Choudens [1886?] Pl. no. A.C. 1709-1710.
15 p.

Vocal score with piano accompaniment. French words.

I. Delange, Charles   II. Title.

NN   0021386   CU

M1509
N32O9
Nargeot, Pierre Julien, 1799–
[Les ouvrières de qualité; acc. arr. piano]
Les ouvrières de qualité; vaudeville en un acte. Paroles de
M.J. Duflot. Airs nouveaux de M.J. Nargeot. Paris, Bureaux,
1857-58.
16 p.   (Magasin des demoiselles, 14me année, album no. 10)

Vocal score with piano accompaniment. French words.

I. Duflot, Joachim   II. Title.

NN   0021387   CU

Nargeot, Pierre Julien, 1799–1891.
Les ouvrières de qualité. Vaudeville en un acte. Paroles de J.
Duflot. Airs nouveaux de J. Nargeot. [Partition chant et
piano.]
= Paris. Magasin des demoiselles. 1858. 32 pp. L. 8°.
No. 2 in **M.393-47

NN   0021388   MB

Nargeot, Julien, 1799–1891.
Paris asleep ...
For libretti   see under   Delacour, Alfred Charlemagne
Lartigue, known as, 1817–1883.   [supplement]

Nargeot, Julien, b. 1799.
Paris qui dort, scènes de la vie nocturne en
cinq actes
For libretti see under   Delacour, Alfred
Charlemagne Lartigue, known as, 1817–1883.

NARGEOT, Pierre Julien.   No. 3 in **M.267.21
[Pêcheurs et pêcheresses. Opérette-bouffe en 1 acte. Paroles de J.A. de
Sorant. Musique de J. Nargeot. Partition piano et chant.]
= [Paris. Aubry. 1873.] (1), 7, 32 pp. L. 8°.
The title-page is missing.

NN   0021391   MB

Nargeot, Pierre Julien, 1799–1891.
Un roi malgré lui
see under   Montjoye, Armand.

Nargeot, Pierre Julien, 1799–1891.
Les variétés de 1852 ...
For libretti   see under   Guénée, Adolphe, 1818–

Nargeot, Pierre Julien, 1799–1891.
Le voyage aérien de Madame Pincebec.
[Scène comique] Musique de Nargeot. Acct.
par Mce. de Raoulx.   [Paris] Impie. Cayrol
et Cie ... n.d.
3 l. (incl. pictorial title)   4 to.   unbound as
issued.]
[caption]
Maggs' Bibliotheca Aeronautica, no. 407.

NN   0021394   CSmH

Nargis, pseud.
see   Dowland, Jessie E.

Nargue du chagrin
see under   [Blocquel, Simon] 1780–1863,
comp.

Nargus
see
National association of retail grocers of the United States.

Narhar Balwant Chandurkar
see
Chandurkar, Narhar Balwant, 1902–

Narhar Ganesh Abhyankar
see **Abhyankar, Narhar Ganesh.**

Narhar Gangadhar Apte
see –
Apte, Narhar Gangadhar, 1900–

Narhar Gopal Sardesai
see **Sardesai, Narhar Gopal.**

Narhar Kashinath Gharpure
see
Gharpure, Narhar Kashinath, 1904–

Narhar Vishnu Gadgil
see
Gadgil, Narhar Vishnu, 1896–1966.

Narhari
see   **Narahara.**

Narharrām Narbhorām.
The student's companion in the acquisition of a
practical knowledge of English and Gújaráti grammar
and idioms.   (2),vii,(3),[252]p.   Ahmedabad,
Printed at the "United printing press," 1869.

NN   0021405   OC1

Nari, Colombo.
Manuale dei giuochi di prestigio e calcolo colle
carte ...   Milano, A. Bietti e C 1905.
128 p.   16°.

NN   0021406   NN

GV1549
.H6
v. 4 no. 16
Houdini
Coll.
Nari, Colombo.
Manuale dei giuochi di prestigio e calcolo colle
carte con figure intercalate nel test accuratamente
raccolti e diligentemente spiegati [!] da
Colombo Nari.   Milan, A. Bietti etc., 1905.
143 p.   illus.   15.5 cm.   [Houdini
pamphlets: card tricks, v. 4, no. 16]

NN   0021407   DLC

Nariad, India (Bombay)
see
Nadiad, India (Bombay)

Naric
see
National rice and corn corporation (*Philippines*)

VOLUME 405

The Naric. v. 1–   no. 1–
May/June 1941–
Manila, Philippines ₍1941₎
     v. illus. (incl. ports.) 23ᶜᵐ. monthly.
     Official organ of the National rice and corn corporation.
Supersedes Naric service recorder.

     1. Rice and rice culture—Period. 2. Maize—Period. 3. Rice and rice culture—Philippine islands. 4. Maize—Philippine islands.   I. National rice and corn corporation (Philippines)

                                         44–11182

     Library of Congress   SB191.R5A25
                      ₍3₎   633.1805

   NN   0021410   DLC CU

Gz
076.8
N167
    Las Narices. Papel semipolítico y semiliterario; de buen humor y criticón. t.1 (núm.1   ); oct. 1, 1867–
     Morelia [Tip. I. Arango]
       v. 31cm.

     Vol. 1, no.1-2 have subtitle: Papel anti-Torreño y disparatado que saldrá a la calle siempre que haga mal temporal para que le de catarro.
     Some numbers have supplements.

   NN   0021411   TxU

Narich, Bélisaire Jacob, 1856–

     ——. A propos d'une opération de céphalotripsie sans broiement chez une femme à bassin oblique-ovalaire. Petite modification dans le cranioclaste. 46 pp., 5 pl. 8°. *Paris, A. Delahaye & E. Lecrosnier, 1882.*

   NN   0021412   DNLM

     Narich (Bélisaire-Jacob) [1856–   ]. *Expériences avec le cranioclaste de Karl Braun (de Vienne) dans les bassins très rétrécis, et proposition d'un nouveau procédé d'extraction du fœtus avec le même instrument. 90 pp., 5 l., 4 pl. 4°. Paris, 1882. No. 3.*

   NN   0021413   DNLM PPC

     Narich (Joseph) [1880–   ]. *Du phlegmon ligneux. 41 pp., 1 l. 8°. Montpellier, 1904. No. 1.*

   NN   0021414   DNLM

Narichania, V   N   C   ed.
     International insurance intelligence
       see under title

Narichkine, Natalie (Rostopchine)
     see **Naryshkina, Nataliíà Fedorovna (Rostopchina)**
     1797–1863.

Narici, Leopoldo,
     ...L'Italia fascista, inizia la civilta dell umanesimo... Napoli, Tipografia del progresso, 1927.
       64 p

   NN   0021417   PHC

Narici, Leopoldo.
     ... La scienza del processo storico-politico diretto da Roma, eterna metropoli dell'orbe. Roma, Casa editrice Leonardo da Vinci ₍1932₎
     xiii p., 1 l., 153 p., 1 l. 22½ᶜᵐ.
     Date on cover: 1933.

     1. Political science. 2. State, The. 3. Rome—Pol. & govt.   I. Title.

                                   35–20016

     Library of Congress   JC265.N3   320.1

   NN   0021418   DLC

Narici, Louis, arr.
     ... Cosi fan tutte ...
       see under   Mozart, Johann Chrysostom Wolfgang Amadeus, 1756–1791.

M32
N37D3
     Narici, Louis.
     [Danse des abeilles]
     Danse des Abeilles. Paris, F. Durdilly [n.d.] Pl. no. C. 5848 H.
     5 p.   35cm.
     Cover title.

     1. Waltzes (Piano)   I. Title.

   NN   0021420   CoU

Narici, Louis, arr.
     Don Juan ... [1898?]
       see under   Mozart, Johann Chrysostom Wolfgang Amadeus, 1756–1791.

Narici, Louis.
     Messaline... transcription pour chant et piano de L. Narici. 1899
       see under   De Lara, Isidore, 1858–1935.

Narici, Louis, arr.
     Les noces de Figaro ...
       see under   Mozart, Johann Chrysostom Wolfgang Amadeus, 1756–1791.

Narici, Louis, arr.
     La prise de Troie... Partition chant et piano reduction de L. Narici. 1899
       see under   Berlioz, Hector.

Narielwala, P   A
     Report
       see under   India. Essential Oil Committee
(Exploratory)

Narielwala, P   A
     Report (exploratory)
       see under   India. Essential oil advisory committee.

Narĭezhnyĭ, Vasiliĭ Trofimovich
     see
     Narezhnyĭ, Vasiliĭ Trofimovich, 1780–1825.

YA
18671
     Narik, Horace R.
     A victim of the duchess of fie and of the London police (Scotlandyard). [Smyrna, Turkey [1906]
     95p.

   NN   0021428   DLC

Narikawa, Keiji.
     (Gaikoku kawase no jissai)
     外國爲換の實際　成川圭司著　[東京]　大日本圖書　[大正11 i.e. 1922]
     6, 5, 183 p.   14 illus. (in pocket)   23 cm.
     Bibliography: p. 180–183.

     1. Foreign exchange.   I. Title.

     HG3851.N377   73–822075

   NN   0021429   DLC

Nariman, Gushtaspshah Kaikhushro, *1873–1933*
     Literary history of Sanskrit Buddhism. (From Winternitz, Sylvain Levi, Huber) By G. K. Nariman ... Bombay, D. B. Taraporevala sons & co., 1920.
     2 p. l., xiii, 382 p., 1 l. 23ᶜᵐ.
     "Abbreviations" : p. ₍ix₎

     1. Sanskrit literature—Hist. & crit. 2. Buddha and Buddhism.   I. Winternitz, Moriz, 1863–   II. Levi, Sylvain, 1863–   III. Huber, Eduard, 1879–1914.

     Library of Congress   PK2907.N3
                                 21–7634 Revised

   NN   0021430   DLC MoU NcD CtY ICU MiU OCl TU

PK
2907
N3
     Nariman, Gushtaspshah Kaikhushro, d. 1933.
     Literary history of Sanskrit Buddhism. (From Winternitz, Sylvain Levi, Huber) Bombay, Indian Book Depot, 1923.
     xiii, 383 p.

     1. Sanskrit literature – History and criticism. 2. Buddha and Buddhism. I. Winternitz, Moriz, 1863–1937.   II. Levi, Sylvain, 1863–1935. III. Huber, Edward, 1879–1914. IV. Title.

   NN   0021431   WaU

891.2
N167
     NARIMAN, Gushtaspshah Kaikhushro.
     Literary history of Sanskrit Buddhism (from Winternitz, Sylvain Levi, Huber) Bombay, Indian book depot, 1923.

     xiii, 393 p.   25cm.
     1. Sanskrit literature. History and criticism. 2. Buddha and Buddhism. I. Winternitz, Moriz, 1863–   II. Levi, Sylvain, 1863–   III. Huber, Edward, 1879–1914.

   NN   0021432   MnU MH CU IU CaBVaU

[Nariman, Gushtaspshah Kaikhushro] *d. 1935*
     Nawruz. 24,8,[2]p. [n.p., 1881]

     Caption-title.
     Contains a Persian description of the New Year by Khusrau, ed. by M. A. Mazandi, and a free English translation.

   NN   0021433   OCl

VOLUME 405

Nariman, Gushtaspshah Kaikhushro, *d*. 1933.
Persia & Parsis. Bombay, Published under the patronage
of the Iran League, 1925–
v. port. 24 cm. (The Marker literary series for Persia,
no. 2)
Contents.—1. Introduction, by G. K. Nariman. Persia—Historical
and literary sketch, by Darmesteter. The influence of Parsism on
Islam, by Goldziher. Note on Influence of Parsism on Islam, by G. K.
Nariman. Who destroyed the fire temples of Iran? By G. K. Nariman. Rivayats, part 1–2, by G. K. Nariman.
1. Parsees. 2. Iran—Civilization. I. Darmesteter, James, 1849–
1894. Persia; a historical and literary sketch. II. Goldziher, Ignác,
1850–1921. Influence of Parsism on Islam. (Series)

DS432.P3N3   58–54319

NN   0021434   DLC OU OC1 NN IU CU

Nariman, Gushtaspshah Kaikhushro, 1873–1933.
Posthumous works of G. K. Nariman ...
(Woman in Sassanian law and English translation
from Barthold's Iran in Russian) Compiled by
S. H. Jhabvala.   [Bombay, S. H. Jhabvala, 1935]
318 p.
1. Iran – Hist.   2. Jhabvala, S. H.

NN   0021435   KMK

AC
8   Nariman, Gushtaspshah Kaikhushro, d.1933.
N22p   Posthumous works. Compiled by S.H.Jhabvala.
       [Bombay, S.H.Jhabvala, 1938?]
       10,318,A-H p. 19cm.

       I. Jhabvala, Shavaksha Hormusji, comp.

NN   0021436   NRU

PK3794 Nariman, Gushtaspshah Kaikhushro, d. 1933, tr.
.H3P6
1923   Harṣavardhana, *king of Thānesar and Kanauj*, *fl.* 606–647.
       Priyadarśikā, a Sanskrit drama, by Harsha ... translated
       into English by G. K. Nariman ... A. V. Williams Jackson ...
       and Charles J. Ogden ... with an introduction and notes by
       the two latter, together with the text in translation.   New
       York, Columbia university press, 1923.

BL1570 Nariman, Gushtaspshah Kaikhushro, d. 1933,
.T5   ed. and tr.
       Tiele, Cornelis Petrus, 1830–1902.
       The religion of the Iranian peoples (from the German)
       with Darmesteter's sketch of "Persia," and Goldziher's "In-
       fluence of Parsism on Islam" (from the French) translated
       by G. K. Nariman.   Bombay, "The Parsi" Pub. Co., 1912–

AC
8   Nariman, Gushtaspshah Kaikhushro, d.1933.
N22w   Writings of G.K.Nariman ... Compiled by
       R.B.Paymaster.   [Bombay, Published by the
       compiler, 1935?]
       x,iii,252p. 24cm.

       I. Paymaster, Rustum Barjort, comp.
       II. Title.

NN   0021439   NRU ICU CtY

NARIMAN, *Khurshed Framji, 1883–*
   Address of Sjt.K.F.Nariman, the chairman of the Reception Committee, 48th sessions of the Indian National Congress, Bombay. 26th October, 1934...   [Bombay: S.K.
Pati, 1934] 20 p. 21½cm.

   Cover-title.

858022A. 1. India—Govt., 1929–   . I. Indian National
Congress. 48th, Bombay, 1934.

NN   0021440   NN

DS   Nariman, Khurshed Framji, 1883–
480.45   What next? by K. F. Nariman.   Bombay,
.N3   Bombay Book Depot, 1934.
       368 p.   19 cm.

       1. India – Pol. & govt. – 1919–1947.
       2. Nationalism – India. 3. Nationalism
       and socialism.   I. Title.

NN   0021441   WU CaBVaU NNC KMK NSyU IU

Nariman, Khurshed Framji, 1883–
   "Whither congress?" 'Spiritual idealism' or 'political
realism,' some random thoughts on the Poona conference and
after. [Bombay, D. R. Dewoolkar] 1933.
   xvi, 143 p. 19 cm.
   Errata slip inserted.

   1. India—Pol. & govt.—1919–1947. 2. Indian National Congress.
I. Title.
DS480.8.N3   *954.08   54–46255

NN   0021442   DLC WaU NSyU KMK MoU MiU NcD CU

R
608   Nariman, Sam D
.N23   Dr.Sir Temulji Bhicaji Nariman,kt; a short
N25   sketch of his life. [Bombay, Printed at
       Mody's Diamond Print.Works, 1941]
       93 p.   illus.

       1.Nariman,Sir Temulji Bhicaji,1848–1907.

NN   0021443   MiU ICU

Nārīmān Ḥusayn Fahmī Ṣādiq
   see
   Ṣādiq, Nārīmān, 1933–

Nārīmān Ṣādiq
   see
   Ṣādiq, Nārīmān, 1933–

Narimanidze, Niko.
   [Quartet, strings, no. 3, G major]
   Квартет № 3 (соль-мажор) для двух скрипок, альта и
виолончели. Партитура. Москва, Музыкальный фонд
СССР, 1955.
   score (46 p.) 30 cm.

   1. String quartets—Scores.
             Title transliterated: Kvartet no. 3 (sol'-mazhor)
M452.N234 no. 3   M 58–48

NN   0021446   DLC

Narimanidze, Niko.
   Воспоминание, для скрипки и фортепиано. Москва,
Искусство, 1939.
   score (13 p.) and part. 31 cm.
   For violin and piano.

   1. Violin and piano music.   I. Title.
             Title transliterated: Vospominanie.
M221.N   M 56–1304

NN   0021447   DLC

DS356
.N3
       Narimanov, L
       Афганистан в огне гражданской войны. [Ленинград]
       Прибой, 1929.
       98 p. 17 cm.

       1. Afghanistan—Hist.
                       Title transliterated: Afganistan v ogne
                       grazhdanskoĭ voĭny.
                                       51–45199

NN   0021448   DLC

Narimanov, Nariman N., 1872–1925.

       Ленин и Восток; сборник статей М. Рафаила, М. Павловича
[*pseud.*] Н. Нариманова и А. Ходорова. 2. дополненное
изд. Москва, Научная ассоциация востоковедения Союза
ССР, 1925.

PL   Narimanov, Nariman N., 1872–1925.
314   Nadir shah. 3d edition.   Baku, 1926.
N129n   61 p.
1926
       Play.

       1. Nadir Shah, shah of Persia, 1688–1747 –
       Drama.   I. Title.

NN   0021450   CLU

Narimanov, Nariman N., 1872?–1925
   see also Moscow. Institut vostokovedeniia.

Narīmanov, S., joint comp.

Dubenskiĭ, Leonid Dmitrievich, *comp.*
   Положение о сельских советах, с постатейным коммен-
тарием и приложением главнейших партийных директив,
законов и ведомственных распоряжений по 1 декабря 1932
года; составили Л. Дубенский, А. Завитаев, С. Нариманов,
под общей редакцией М. Вербицкого. Москва, Издательство "Власть советов" при Президиуме ВЦИК, 1932.

Narina, the story of a little princess,
and her silver-feathered shoes, with other
moral tales. Boston, T. H. Carter & Co.,
(18–).
   Front. and other illustr. nar. 16°

NN   0021453   MH

Narindar Nath
   see
   Nath, Narindar, 1927–

Narinder Sharma
       see Sharma, Narendra, 1913–

Narindr Devi, princess.
   Phra Rajavicarana. The record kept by the
Princess Narindr Devi from 1767–1820. Edited
by Chulalonkorn, king of Siam, from a unique
MS. with an explanatory commentary and state
papers relating thereto. Bangkok, 127 (1908)

   Various pagings. fold. table. 23.5 cm.
   Siamese text and title page, added English
title page.
   (Royal historical research society, Siam)

NN   0021456   MH CtY DLC

VOLUME 405

Narine & Co., printers.
Schedule of printing types; consisting of
ornaments, borders, dashes, rules, and plain
and ornamental types of almost every variety
and size. New York, 1852.
133 1. specimens (part col., part fold.)
23cm.

1. Printing - Specimens. 2. Type and type-
founding.

NN 0021457   NNC

PG3476
.N366F4
Narin'iani, Semen.
Фельетоны. Москва, Советский писатель, 1952.
156 p. 20 cm.

I. Title.   *Title transliterated:* Fel'etony.

PG3476.N366F4   52-38316

NN 0021458   DLC

Narin'iani, Semen.
Life in review, and other Soviet sketches.
New York, International publishers [194-?]
70 p. illus.

I. Title: Life in review.

NN 0021459   NNC CtY MH

Narin'iani, Semen.
Магнитогорский металлургический комбинат. [Москва]
Московский рабочий, 1931.
15 p. 17 cm. (Книжка-копейка, № 17)

1. Magnitogorskiĭ metallurgicheskiĭ kombinat.
                        Title transliterated: Magnitogorskiĭ
                        metallurgicheskiĭ kombinat.

HD9526.R94M35   61-57685 ‡

NN 0021460   DLC

Nariño, Antonio, 1765-1823.
... Antonio Nariño, F. de P. Santander y Julio Arboleda.
[Bogotá. Editorial Minerva, s. a., 1936]
1 p. l. [7]-143 p. 1 l. 20cm. (Biblioteca aldeana de Colombia [Elo-
cuencia. nᵒ 71])

CONTENTS.—Nariño, Antonio. Su defensa ante el Senado.—Santander,
F. de P. Su defensa ante la Cámara.—Arboleda, Julio. Discurso como
presidente del Congreso al dar posesión de la presidencia al doctor
Manuel María Mallarino.

1. Colombia—Pol. & govt.—1810-   I. Santander, Francisco de Paula,
pres. New Granada. 1792-1840. II Arboleda, Julio, 1817-1862.

Library of Congress   F2273.N36
                                              37-29454
———— Copy 2.   [2]   986

          OCU NjP ICN OrU
NN 0021461   DLC DPU CSt MU NN NNC PP OOxM OCl

F 2273 NARIÑO, ANTONIO, 1765-1835.
.N231   Antonio Nariño, F. de P. Santander y Julio
           Arboleda. Bogotá, Editorial Minerva, 1937.
           205 p. (Selección Samper Ortega de
           literatura colombiana, no. 71. Sección 8.
           Elocuencia)

           Contents: NARIÑO, A. Su defensa ante el
           Senado. SANTANDER, F. DE P. Su defensa ante la
           Cámara. ARBOLEDA, J. Discurso como presidente
           del Congreso al dar posesión de la presidencia
           al doctor Manuel   María Mallarino.

NN 0021462   InU

Nariño, Antonio, 1765-1823.
La bagatela. [Bogotá, 1947]
224 p. 20 cm. (Biblioteca popular de cultura colombiana, t. 114)

A reissue of the weekly (irregular) periodical, published in Santa
Fé, July 14, 1811-Apr. 12, 1812 (38 no., with supplements to no. 3-5,
7, 9 and 24)
Reissued also in his Vida y escritos.

I. Title.   (Series)
PQ8179.N34B3 1947   52-18378

NN 0021463   DLC NcU NBuU DPU TU TxU

Bell
F
2274
N2D4
Nariño, Antonio, 1765-1823.
Defensa del general Nariño. [Bogota,
Espinosa, 1823]
89 p. 22 cm.

Title page lacking.

1. Colombia - Pol. & govt. - 1810-
I. Title.

NN 0021464   NBuU NcU

Nariño, Antonio, 1765-1823.
... Escritos varios. 3. ed. ...   Bogota,
Colombia, Librería nueva, 1897.
cover-title, [65]-103, [1] p. 18 cm.
(Biblioteca popular, no. 3)

NN 0021465   CtY

Nariño, Antonio, 1765-1823.
Le procès de Nariño
see under   Clavery, Edouard, 1867-

Nariño, Antonio, 1765-1823.
Proceso de Nariño; fiel copia del original que existe en el
Archivo general de Indias de Sevilla, cuidadosamente confron-
tada y publicada por José Manuel Pérez-Sarmiento ... Cádiz
(España) Impr. de M. Alvarez, 1914
v. plates, port. 28cm.
CONTENTS.—T. 1. Al lector, por J. M. Pérez-Sarmiento. Discurso pronunciado por H. Holguín y Caro, al descubrirse la estatua de Nariño, en
Bogotá. Oración fúnebre, pronunciada por R. M. Carrasquilla, al inaugurar el sepulcro del general Nariño en la catedral de Bogotá. Causa al
autor del papel titulado "Derechos del hombre" ... reos: d. Antonio Nariño y d. José Antonio Ricaurte ... 1794 á 1807 [documentos].
      1. France. Déclaration des droits de l'homme.   I. Ricaurte y Lo-
zano, Antonio, 1786-1814. II. Pérez-Sarmiento, José Manuel, ed. III. Holguín y Caro, Hernando,   1871-1921. IV. Carrasquilla, Rafael
María, 1857-1930. v. Title.
                                              18-9402 Revised
Library of Congress   F2274.N24

                  NcD CU MH IU MiU
NN 0021467   DLC IaU NIC CoU FMU NBuU CtY   OU MB

986.103
N167v
1859
Nariño, Antonio, 1765-1823.
Vida i escritos del jeneral Antonio Nariño
Tomo 1.   Bogotá, Impr. de Pizano i Perez,
1859.
257p. 20cm.

Vol. 1 contains essays and letters through
no.38 of La Bagatela (12 de abril de 1812).
Vol. 2 was to contain his writings from 1812
to 1824. No more published? No biography
included.
Preface signed   by editor: J.M. V. i V.

NN 0021468   KU MH

Nariño, Antonio, 1765-1823.
... Vida y escritos del general Antonio Nariño ... 2. ed.
[Bogotá, Imprenta nacional, 1946]
1 p. l. [v]-viii, 342 p. 19½cm. (Biblioteca popular de cultura colom-
biana)
Name of editor, José María Vergara y Vergara, on cover.

1. Colombia—Pol. & govt.—1810-   I. Vergara y Vergara, José
María, 1831-1872, ed.
F2274.N243   923.286   47-20703

                  CU TU TxU ICU DPU OCl IU MnU NNC
NN 0021469   DLC LNHT OU NBuU OCU CaBVaU LU PSt

Nariño, José Antonio Ignacio Vicente

See

Nariño, Antonio, 1765-1823.

Nariño, Luis Gomez
see   Gómez Nariño, Luis.

Nariño de Campos, José
see
Campos, José Nariño de.

Narino e Silva, Antonio
see
Silva, Antonio Narino e, 1921-

Nariño y Alvarez, Antonio
see
Nariño, Antonio, 1765-1823.

Nariño y Alvarez, José Antonio Ignacio Vicente.

see

Nariño, Antonio, 1765-1823.

Nariño, Colombia (Dept.)
A la memoria del general Alejandro de la
Rosa Arroyo ...
see under title

J222
.N3R2
Nariño, Colombia (Dept.)
Acuerdos departamentales.

NN 0021477   DLC

Nariño, Colombia (Dept.)
Biblioteca de autores nariñenses
see under title

Nariño, Colombia (Dept.)
Boletín oficial; organo de la gobernación del
Departamento ...
Colombia
)14
367
+N2b
Pasto, (Colombia)
35cm.

Caption title.
"Bajo la dirección de la Secretaría privada
de la gobernación."

NN 0021479   CtY NN

VOLUME 405

Nariño, *Colombia* (*Dept.*)
El departamento de Nariño en la Exposición nacional de
1919 ... Bogota, Casa editorial de Arboleda & Valencia,
1920.
144 p. incl. illus., pl. fold. pl. 24ᶜᵐ.
Colored coat of arms of the city of Pasto mounted on cover.

1. Bogota. Exposición nacional, 1919—Nariño. I. Title.

Library of Congress   T452.1919.F3N3   21–1245

NN   0021480   DLC MH DNAL TxU NN

Nariño, *Colombia* (*Dept.*)
... Documentos historicos de los hechos ocurridos en Pasto
en la guerra de la independencia. Publicación oficial. **Pasto**,
Impr. del Departamento, 1912.
viii, 145 p. 26¼ᶜᵐ.
At head of title: República de Colombia—Departamento de Nariño.

1. Colombia—Hist.—War of independence, 1810–1822—Sources.
2. Pasto, Colombia—Hist.—Sources. I. Title.

20—23612

Library of Congress   F2291.P28N3

NN   0021481   DLC NcD NcU

Nariño, Colombia (Dept.)
...Especificaciones técnicas sobre acueductos
y alcantarillados
    see under   Colombia. Ministerio de tra-
bajo, higiene y prevision social. Departamento
de ingenieria sanitaria.

Nariño, *Colombia* (*Dept.*)
... Gaceta departamental ...
Pasto ₍19
v. 35ᶜᵐ. irregular.
Caption title.

1. Nariño, Colombia (Dept.)—Pol. & govt.

42–41827

Library of Congress   J6.CSN3

NN   0021483   DLC NN

Col
F2277   **Nariño, Colombia (Dept.)**
0547   Homenaje del departamento de Nariño a la
memoria del doctor Enrique Olaya Herrera.
Boletín oficial, edicion extraordinaria.
Pasto, Imprenta del departamento, 1937.
71 p. 24 cm.

NN   0021484   DPU

Narino, Colombia ₍Dept.₎
...Liquidación adicional al presupuesto de 1910,
y presupuesto de rentas y gastos, correspondiente
a los meses de enero a abril de 1911, practicada de
acuerdo con el decreto numero 463 de 31 de diciembre
de 1910, en plata.
Pasto, 1911.

HJ34
.Z9N5

NN   0021485   DLC

Nariño, Colombia (Dept.)
Presupuesto de rentas y gastos ...
    see under   Nariño, Colombia (Dept.)
Secretaria de Hacienda.

Narino, *Colombia* ₍Dept.₎
... Primer centenario de la emancipación de Colombia en
Pasto. Ed. oficial, arreglada por Gonzalo Torres A. ₍Pasto?₎
Imprenta del Departamento ₍1910?₎
₍64₎ p. 26½ x 12¼ᶜᵐ.
Unpaged.
At head of title: 1810–1910.
Includes Decreto numero 152 de 1910 (14 de abril) sobre celebración
del centenario de la independencia. El gobernador del Departamento de
Nariño ₍Eliseo Gomez Jurado₎

1. Colombia—Centennial celebrations, etc. 2. Pasto, Colombia—Centennial celebrations, etc. I. Torres A., Gonzalo. II. Title.

CA 17—2022 Unrev'd

Library of Congress   F2274.N26

NN   0021487   DLC

Colombia   **Nariño, Colombia (Dept.) Asamblea.**
07222   ... Anales de la Asamblea ...
N2
+H3   Pasto,
             35cm. irregular.

Caption title.
At head of title:
República de Colombia. Departamento de Nariño;
    , Libre de Porte.
República de Colombia. Departamento de Nariño.

NN   0021488   CtY NN

Nariño, *Colombia* (*Dept.*) *Asamblea.*
Reglamento para el régimen interior de la Asamblea del
departamento de Nariño. Ed. oficial. Pasto, Imprenta del departamento, 1911.
40 p. 22ᶜᵐ.

1. Nariño, Colombia (Dept.) Asamblea—Rules and practice.
I. Title.

33–39409

Library of Congress   JL2899.N3A5 1911   352.086

NN   0021489   DLC

Col
JL   **Nariño, Colombia (Dept.) Asamblea.**
2899   ... Reglamento para el régimen interior de
.N3A5   la Asamblea del departamento de Nariño. Nueva
1939   ed., con las reformas vigentes introducidas por
la corporación. Pasto, Imprenta del departamento, 1939.
56 p. 24 cm.
At head of title: República de Colombia.

NN   0021490   DPU

4F   **Nariño, Colombia (Dept.) Comision de**
Col   **Cultura Aldeana.**
27   Esquema para una interpretacion
sociologica del Departamento de Nariño.
Informe que rinde al señor Ministro de
Educación Nacional, el relator litera-
rio y perito en sociología de la
Comision de Cultura Aldeana. [
      Impr. Nacional, 19]
      249 p.

NN   0021491   DLC-P4

HJ34
.Z9N3   **Nariño, Colombia (Dept.) Contaduría general.**

Nariño, *Colombia* (*Dept.*) *Contraloría general.*
Informe.
₍Pasto₎ 19

Nariño, *Colombia* (*Dept.*) *Contaduría general*
    see also
Nariño, *Colombia* (*Dept.*) *Contraloría general.*

Nj34   **Nariño, Colombia (Dept.) Contraloría general.**
N2   ... Boletín de la Contraloría; organo oficial
A22   del Departamento de contraloría de Nariño ...
Pasto, Imprenta del departamento
      fold.tab. 24cm.
    At head of title: República de Colombia.
Departamento de Nariño.

NN   0021494   CtY

Nariño, *Colombia* (*Dept.*) *Contraloría general.*
Informe.
₍Pasto₎ 19
      v. tables, diagrs. 24ᶜᵐ. annual.
   At head of title   –1984/35: República de Colombia.
19   issued by the Contaduría general; 1935/36–   **by the**
Contraloría general.
   Part of the illustrative material is folded.

1. Finance—Nariño, Colombia (Dept.) I. Nariño, Colombia (Dept.)
Contaduría general.

44–1458.

Library of Congress   HJ34.Z9N3

NN   0021495   DLC NN

Nariño, *Colombia* (*Dept.*) *Contraloría General.*
Informe financiero.
₍Pasto₎
      v. 25 cm. annual.   **LACAP 68–2985**

1. Finance, Public—Nariño, Colombia (Dept.)

HJ34.Z9N34   73–378117

NN   0021496   DLC TxU

Nariño, *Colombia* (*Dept.*) *Contraloría general*
see also
Nariño, *Colombia* (*Dept.*) *Contaduría general.*

Nariño, *Colombia* (*Dept.*) *Cooperativa de empleados*
de la zona de carreteras de Pasto, ltd.
    see
Cooperativa de empleados de la zona de carreteras de
Pasto, ltd.

Nariño, *Colombia* (*Dept.*) *Coordinación y Propaganda,*
Oficina de
see **Nariño**, *Colombia* (*Dept.*) *Oficina de Coordinación*
y Propaganda.

Colombia   **Nariño, Colombia (Dept.) Dirección de educación**
L94   **pública.**
S67o   ... Informe ...
A21   Pasto, Colombia, Imprenta del Departamento,
         fold.tables. 24½cm.
    Cover-title, 1939-
    Title on t.-p. of 1939 reads: La educación
pública en el Departamento de Nariño.
    1937 issued by the Director de educación
nacional del Departamento de Nariño.

NN   0021500   CtY NcD OCl DLC OrU

Nariño, *Colombia* (*Dept.*) *Dirección de Estadística.*
Anuario estadístico.
₍Pasto₎
      v. 34 cm.

1. Nariño, Colombia (Dept.)—Stat.

HA1017.N3A33   55–54003 ‡

NN   0021501   DLC CtY DPU NN

VOLUME 405

Nariño, *Colombia (Dept.) Dirección de estadística.*
... Boletín de estadística departamental ...
Pasto ₁1933-
    v. plates (part fold.) ports., tables (part fold.) 34ᶜᵐ.

1. Nariño, Colombia (Dept.)—Stat.   ɪ. Title.

Library of Congress   HA1017.N3A3   34–12939
                                                  ₍2₎   318.6

NN 0021502   DLC

Nariño, *Colombia (Dept.) Dirección general de obras públicas.*
Informe.
Pasto,
    v. maps, tables. 23½ᶜᵐ.
Part of the illustrative material is folded.

1. Nariño, Colombia (Dept.)—Public works.

Library of Congress   TA46.N3A3   43–36425

NN 0021503   DLC DPU NN

Nariño, *Colombia (Dept.) Dirección general de obras públicas*
    see also
Nariño, *Colombia (Dept.) Secretaría de obras públicas.*

Nariño, Colombia (Dept.) Estadística, Dirección de
        see   Nariño, Colombia (Dept.) Dirección de estadística.

Nariño, Colombia (Dept.) Gerencia de rentas.
Colombia   ... Informe ...
N j34   Pasto, Imprenta del Departamento,
N2   34½ᶜᵐ.
+A31   Functions under the Secretaría de hacienda.

NN 0021506   CtY NN DPU

Nariño, *Colombia (Dept.) Gobernador.*
    ... Actividades de la gobernación de Nariño en relación con
el fomento de la economía departamental. Pasto, Imprenta del
departamento, 1940.
    30 p. 24ᶜᵐ.
    At head of title: Colombia. Nariño.

1. Nariño, Colombia (Dept.)—Econ. condit.
                                                  44–44688
Libra y of Congress   HC108.N3A5 1940

NN 0021507   DLC DPU

Nariño, Colombia (Dept.) Gobernador.
Boletin oficial
    see under   Nariño, Colombia.

Nariño, Colombia (Dept.) *Gobernador.*
    Memoria que el gobernador del departamento de
Nariño presenta al senor ministro de hacienda y
tesora de Colombia sobre las oportunidades para la
inversion de capitales extranjeros en esta seccion
de la republica.
J222
.N3N5

NN 0021509   DLC

Nariño, *Colombia (Dept.) Gobernador.*
Mensaje.
Pasto, Nariño, Colombia, 19
    v. in   tables (part fold.) 23½ x 31½ᶜᵐ.
Title varies: Informe que el gobernador de Nariño presenta
al Consejo administrativo del departamento.
            Mensaje a la Asamblea departamental (varies slightly)
            Memoria del gobernador a la Asamblea departamental.
            Mensaje del gobernador de Nariño a la Asamblea de-
partamental.

1. Nariño, Colombia (Dept.)—Pol. & govt.
                                                  43–19376

Library of Congress   J222.N3N16

NN 0021510   DLC NcD NN

Col   Nariño, Colombia. (Dept.) Gobernador, 1939–
J   (Montezuma H.)
222   ... Alocucion del gobernador del
.N32   departamento doctor Alberto Montezuma H.
1940   Pasto, Imprenta del Departamento [1940]
ja. 1   cover-title, [4] p.   24 cm.

NN 0021511   DPU

Nariño, Colombia (Dept.) Gobernador, 1939–
    (Montezuma H.)
        see also   Montezuma Hurtado, Alberto.

Nariño, Colombia (Dept.) Gobierno, Secretaría de
        see   Nariño, Colombia (Dept.) Secretaría
de gobierno.

Nariño, Colombia (Dept.) Hacienda, Secretaría de
        see   Nariño, Colombia (Dept.) Secretaría
de hacienda.

Nariño, *Colombia (Dept.) Higiene y Asistencia Pública,
Secretaría de*
    see Nariño, *Colombia (Dept.) Secretaría de Higiene y
Asistencia Pública.*

Col   Nariño, Colombia (Dept.) Inspección nacional
HV   de cedulacion.
6078   ... Informe de los inspectores nacionales
.N3   de cedulacion, al ministro de gobierno, de
1936   conformidad con el artículo 16 del decreto 3035
de 1936. (diciembre 16)   Pasto, Imprenta del
Departamento, 1937.
    28 p.   fold. tabl.   24 cm.
    At head of title: República de Colombia.
Depto. de Nariño. Inspección nacional de
cedulacion.

NN 0021516   DPU

Nariño, *Colombia (Dept.) Laboratorio de higiene*
    see
Pasto, Colombia. Laboratorio de higiene de Nariño.

Nariño, Colombia (Dept.) Laws, statutes, etc.

₁Guerrero, Florentino₁ comp.
    ... Compilación de disposiciones sobre régimen político y mu-
nicipal. 2. ed. Pasto, Imprenta del departamento, 1939.

Col   Nariño, Colombia (Dept.) Laws, statutes, etc.
LB   ... Decreto n. 405 de 1940 por el cual se
3479   reorganiza el funcionamiento de los restaurantes
.N3   escolares en el Departamento y se dictan algunas
1940   disposiciones sobre granjas.   Pasto, Imprenta
del Departamento [1940?]
    cover-title, 8 p.   24 cm.
    At head of title: Colombia. ₁ Departamento de
Nariño.

NN 0021519   DPU DNAL

Nariño, Colombia (Dept.) Laws, statutes, etc.
    ... Disposiciones sobre baldíos
        see under   Colombia. Laws, statutes, etc.

324.861   Nariño, Colombia (Dept.) Laws, statutes,
C718d   etc.
        Disposiciones sobre cuestiones electorales.
Pasto [Colombia] Imprenta del Departamento,
1949.
    48 p.   23cm.

    Cover title.
    At head of title: República de Colombia. –
Departamento de Nariña. Secretaría de
Gobierno.

    1. Election   law - Colombia.
I. Title.

NN 0021521   FU

Nariño, *Colombia (Dept.) Laws, statutes, etc.*
    ... Disposiciones vigentes sobre fraudes a las rentas deptales.
Pasto, Imprenta del departamento ₁1936₁
    35 p. 16½ᶜᵐ.
    At head of title: Colombia. Nariño.

1. Taxation—Nariño, Colombia (Dept.)—Law. 2. Fraud — Nariño,
Colombia (Dept.) ɪ. Title.

Library of Congress   HJ3434.N3A5 1936   42–35543

NN 0021522   DLC

Nariño, *Colombia (Dept.) Laws, statutes, etc.*
    ... Disposiciones vigentes sobre tránsito de automóviles.
Contiene: Decreto nº 520 de 1927, Ordenanza nº 11 de 1918,
Ordenanza nº 43 de 1927, Ordenanza nº 42 de 1930, Decreto
nº 531 de 1930, Ordenanza nº 52 de 1931. Pasto, Imprenta
departamental, 1933.
    66 p. 16ᶜᵐ.
    At head of title: Colombia—Nariño.

1. Automobiles—Laws and regulations—Nariño, Colombia (Dept.)
ɪ. Title.
                                                  34–21013

NN 0021523   DLC

Nariño, *Colombia (Dept.) Laws, statutes, etc.*
    ... Disposiciones vigentes sobre vagancia y ratería. Pasto,
Imprenta del depto., 1933.
    41 p. 24ᶜᵐ.
    At head of title: República de Colombia. Departamento de Nariño.

1. Tramps—Colombia—Nariño (Dept.) 2. Larceny—Nariño, Colombia (Dept.) ɪ. Title.

Library of Congress   34–14268
———— Copy 2.   ₍2₎   362.51

NN 0021524   DLC

VOLUME 405

Nariño, *Colombia (Dept.)* *Laws, statutes, etc.*
... Disposiciones y resoluciones importantes sobre minas y
baldíos ... Pasto, Imprenta del departamento, 1939.
137 p. diagrs. 24⁰ᵐ.
At head of title: República de Colombia, Departamento de Nariño ...
Secretaría de hacienda. Sección de minas y baldíos.
"Contenido": p. ₍₃₎ of cover.

1. Mining law—Nariño, Colombia (Dept.)   I. Nariño, Colombia
(Dept.) Secretaría de hacienda. Sección de minas y baldíos.
                                                            44–52213
Library of Congress   TN239.C62N3 1939

NN   0021525   DLC NcU CSt NN DPU CtY

Nariño, Colombia (Dept.)   Laws, statutes, etc.

Pasto, Colombia. Escuela de artes y oficios.
... Importantes disposiciones y reglamento de la Escuela de
artes y oficios de Pasto. Ed. oficial. Pasto, Imprenta del departamento, 1934.

Nariño, *Colombia (Dept.)* *Laws, statutes, etc.*
... Límites de los municipios de Nariño y disposiciones
legales que los fijan. Pasto, Imprenta departamental, 1941.
26 p. 23½⁰ᵐ.
At head of title: República de Colombia. Departamento de Nariño.

1. Cities and towns—Colombia—Nariño (Dept.)
                                                            44–39528
Library of Congress   JS2520.N3A5 1941

NN   0021527   DLC

Nariño, Colombia (Dept.). Laws, statutes, etc.
Ordenanza de código fiscal del Departamento de Nariño.
Pasto, Impr. del Departamento, 1939.
100 p. 24 cm.

1. Taxation—Nariño, Colombia (Dept.)—Law.   I. Title.
                                                            74–216251

NN   0021528   DLC DPU MH-L CtY

Nariño, Colombia (Dept.) Laws, statutes, etc.
Pamphlet   ... Ordenanza número 43 de 1933 sobre penali-
Colombia dad por fraudes en materia de rentas e impuestos
1933   departamentales, y decretos reglamentarios nú-
N162   meros 484, 531 y 571 de 1933. Ed.oficial. Pasto,
          1933.
          At head of title: Colombia - Nariño.

NN   0021529   DNAL

Colombia Nariño, Colombia (Dept.) Laws, statutes, etc.
Neb44   ... Ordenanza no. 43 de 1936 por la cual se
S67   reglamenta el servicio de tránsito en el departa-
1   mento. Pasto, Imprenta del departamento,1938.
1938   Pamphlet
          At head of title: Colombia - Departamento de
          Nariño.

NN   0021530   CtY

Nariño, *Colombia (Dept.)* *Laws, statutes, etc.*
... Ordenanzas expedidas por la Asamblea de **Nariño**
y decretos reglamentarios. Pasto, Imprenta del departamento,
v. 24⁰ᵐ.
At head of title: República de Colombia.

I. Title.
                                                            34–25284

NN   0021531   DLC ICarbS NN

Nariño, *Colombia (Dept.)* *Laws, statutes, etc.*
... Proyecto de ordenanza sobre presupuesto de rentas y
gastos ...

Pasto
v. tables. 16½ x 24½⁰ᵐ.
Cover-title.
At head of title,   : República de Colombia. Departamento
de Nariño. Secretaría de hacienda, Sección ordenadora.

1. Budget—Nariño, Colombia (Dept.)   I. Nariño, Colombia (Dept.)
Secretaría de hacienda.
                                                            44–32002
Library of Congress   HJ34.Z9N43

NN   0021532   DLC DPU

Col   Nariño, Colombia (Dept.) Laws, statutes, etc.
GV   ... Reglamento de foot-ball. Pasto, Imprenta
955   del Departamento [1939]
.N2   cover-title, 1 p.l., ii, [3]–59 p. ports.
1939   24 cm.
       At head of title: República de Colombia.
Comisión departamental de educación física de
Nariño.

NN   0021533   DPU

Col   Nariño, Colomiba (Dept.) Laws, statutes, etc.
GV   ... Reglas oficiales de basket-ball. Pasto,
885   Imprenta del Depto. [1939]
.N2   1 p. l., ii, [3]–30 p. ports., diagr. 24 cm.
1939   At head of title: República de Colombia.
Comisión deptal. de educación física de Nariño.

NN   0021534   DPU

Nariño, *Colombia (Dept.)* *Obras públicas, Secretaría de*
see
Nariño, *Colombia (Dept.)* *Secretaría de obras públicas.*

**Nariño, Colombia (Dept.) Oficina de Coordinación
y Propaganda.**
Boletín informativo.

NN   0021536   DLC

Nariño, *Colombia (Dept.)* *Secretaría de gobierno.*
Informe.

Pasto, 19
v. tables (part fold.) 24⁰ᵐ. annual.
Report year irregular.

1. Nariño, Colombia (Dept.)—Pol. & govt.
                                                            44–27269
Library of Congress   J222.N3R25

NN   0021537   DLC NN

Nariño, *Colombia (Dept.)* *Secretaría de Gobierno. Oficina
de Coordinación y Propaganda*
see **Nariño,** *Colombia (Dept.)* *Oficina de Coordinación
y Propaganda.*

Nariño, Colombia (Dept.) Secretaría de hacienda.
... Boletín de estadística fiscal. no.1-
nov.1939-
Pasto,Imprenta departamental,1939-
30½cm.

NN   0021539   CtY

Nariño, *Colombia (Dept.)* *Secretaría de hacienda.*
Informe. 19
Pasto, 19
v. tables (part fold.) 23–34⁰ᵐ. annual.

1. Finance—Nariño, Colombia (Dept.)
                                                            43–47967
Library of Congress   HJ34.Z9N33

NN   0021540   DLC NN

Colombia Nariño, Colombia (Dept.) Secretaría de hacienda.
Nj34   ... Presupuesto de rentas y gastos ...
N2   Pasto,Imprenta del Departamento,
A14   17x25cm.
          At head of title: República de Colombia.
Departamento de Nariño. Secretaría de hacienda.
Sección ordenadora.
          19 -1937 have title: Ordenanzas sobre asig-
naciones civiles y presupuesto de rentas y
gastos ...

NN   0021541   CtY DLC NN

HJ34   Nariño, Colombia (Dept.) Secretaría de
Z9N43   hacienda.
Nariño, *Colombia (Dept.)* *Laws, statutes, etc.*
... Proyecto de ordenanza sobre presupuesto de rentas y
gastos ...

Pasto

Nariño, *Colombia (Dept.)* *Secretaría de hacienda. Dirección general de obras públicas*
see
Nariño, *Colombia (Dept.)* *Dirección general de obras públicas.*

TN239   Nariño, Colombia (Dept.) Secretaría de
.C62N3   hacienda. Sección de minas y baldíos.
1939   **Nariño,** *Colombia (Dept.)* *Laws, statutes, etc.*
... Disposiciones y resoluciones importantes sobre minas y
baldíos ... Pasto, Imprenta del departamento, 1939.

G338.2 Nariño, Colombia (Dept.) Secretaría de Hacien-
N1671   da. Sección de Minas y Baldíos.
1941   Informe que rinde el jefe de la Sección de
Minas y Baldíos al señor secretario de hacien-
da, correspondiente al año de 1941. Pasto,
Imprenta del Departamento, 1942.
24p. 24cm.
Cover title.
At head of title: Julio César Medina.
1. Mines and mineral resources - Colombia -
Nariño (Dept.)   I. Medina, Julio César.

NN   0021545   TxU

Nariño, Colombia (Dept.) Secretaría de higiene
    see Nariño, Colombia (Dept.) Secretaría
de Higiene y Asistencia Publica.

RA   Nariño, Colombia (Dept). Secretaría de Higiene
215   y Asistencia Pública.
.N2   Informe. 19-   Pasto.
B1
        v. tables.

1. Public health- Nariño, Colombia (Dept.)
2. Communicable diseases- Nariño, Colombia
(Dept).

NN   0021547   DPAHO NN DPU

VOLUME 405

Nariño, *Colombia (Dept.) Secretaría de obras públicas.*
Informe.
Pasto, 1938–
   v. tables. 24½ᶜᵐ.

   1. Nariño, Colombia (Dept.)—Public works.

Library of Congress   TD45.N3A3   43–44195

NN   0021548   DLC

Nariño, *Colombia (Dept.) Secretaría de obras públicas.*
  ... Reglamento de trabajo. Pasto, Imprenta del departamento, 1938.
   6 p. 17ᶜᵐ.
   At head of title: República de Colombia. Departamento de Nariño. Secretaría de obras públicas.

   1. Labor and laboring classes—Nariño, Colombia (Dept.) 2. Nariño, Colombia (Dept.)—Public works.
                           43–29837

Library of Congress   HD8023.C7N3   1938

NN   0021549   DLC

Nariño, *Colombia (Dept.) Secretaría de obras públicas*
  see also
Nariño, *Colombia (Dept.) Dirección general de obras públicas.*

49.9
C712
   Nariño, Colombia (Dept.) Sector Agrícola de Ipiales.
   Boletín de información agropecuaria.
   [Tpiales?]
   1. Colombia. Departamento de Nariño. Domestic animals. 2. Colombia. Departamento de Nariño. Agriculture.

NN   0021551   DNAL

Nariño, *Colombia (Dept.) Tribunal Superior*
  see **Colombia.** *Tribunal Superior (Pasto)*

Nariño, Universidad de.
   see
Pasto, Colombia. Universidad de Nariño.

CT99
.N23128
1911
   Nariño y los derechos del hombre ... Pasto, Imprenta del departamento, 1911.
   1 p.l., 16 p. 22cm.

   Signed: X

   1. Nariño, Antonio, 1765–1823.

NN   0021554   DLC

Narinori Okoshi,
   ... A sketch of the fisheries of Japan, by Narinori Okoshi. London, W. Clowes and sons, ltd., 1883.
   39 p. incl. tables. 21½ᶜᵐ. (International fisheries exhibition, London, 1883)
   (DLC: SH341.I6 1883)

Continued in next column

Continued from preceding column

   1. Fisheries—Japan.
                        F 17–173

   Library, U. S. Bur. of   Fisheries

NN   0021555   DI MH DLC

Narinyani, Semyon
   see Narin'íàni, Semen.

W 6
P3
   NARIO, Alfredo.
     Nuevas observaciones sobre el tratamiento de las hemoptisis por el clorhidrato de heroína. Montevideo, Impr. Latina, 1927.
     15 p.
     Title

NN   0021557   DNLM

Nario, Alfredo.
   ... Sanatorio y hospital sanatorio. Montevideo, 1935.
   110 p. illus., plans.

   "Bibliografía": p. 102–105.

   1. Tuberculosis - Hospitals and sanatoriums.

NN   0021558   NNC

Nario, Juan Carlos.
   ... De la entrega efectiva de la herencia. Montevideo, Peña & cía., impresores, 1941.
   120 p. 24ᶜᵐ. (Biblioteca de publicaciones oficiales de la Facultad de derecho y ciencias sociales de Montevideo. Sección III, XXII)
   At head of title: Dr. Juan C. Nario.
   "Autores consultados": p. 117.

   1. Inheritance and succession—Uruguay. I. Title.
                       42–22300

NN   0021559   DLC

Narishkine, M   B
   see Naryshkin, Vasiliĭ L'vovich, 1841–1906.

Narischkine, Natalie (Rostopchine)
  see Naryshkina, Nataliîà Fedorovna (Rostopchina) 1797–1863.

Narischkine, Vera (Witte)
  see Naryshkina, Viera Sergieevna (Witte)

Narischkine-Witte, Vera
  see
Naryshkina, Viera Sergieevna (Witte)

Nariscus, Johannes [pseud.]
  see Hortig, Johann Nepomuk, 1774–1847.

Narishkin-Kurakin, Elizabeth
  see
Naryshkina, Elizaveta (Kurakina)

LB1570
I 84
Orien
Japan
   Narita, Katsuya, 1925–
     Itō, Tadahiko, 1924–
     新教育計画―カリキユラム構成―伊藤忠彦•成田克矢共著 東京 明治図書出版社 [1949]

Narita, Kiyofusa, 1884–
   Japanese paper-making. Tokyo, Hokuseido Press; [on label: distributed by P. D. and Ione Perkins, South Pasadena, Calif.] 1954.
   60 p. illus. 19 cm.

   1. Paper making and trade—Japan. I. Title.

TS1095.J3N3   *676.2   55–21910 ‡

     ViU FTaSU MiDA KEmT Or OrP WaS
NN   0021567   DLC CaBVa PSt PSC OCl PP PPD IU MB

Narita, Kiyofusa, 1884–
   (Ki kara kami ni naru made)
   木から紙になるまで 成田潔英著 東京 丸善出版 [昭和24 i. e. 1949]
   3, 3, 160 p. illus., map(on lining paper) 22 cm.
   Bibliography: p. 158.

   1. Paper making and trade—Japan. I. Title.

TS1095.J3N312   71–799357

NN   0021568   DLC

Narita, Kiyofusa, 1884–
   九州の製紙業 成田潔英著 東京 丸善出版 [1949]
   3, 2, 2, 9, 202 p. illus., ports. 21 cm.
   Colophon inserted.

   1. Paper making and trade—Kyushu. I. Title.
                     Title romanized: Kyūshū no seishigyō.

TS1095.J3N313   76–818345

NN   0021569   DLC

Narita, Kiyofusa, 1884–
   紙業提要 成田潔英編 訂正版 東京 丸善出版 [1949]
   7, 365 p. illus. 19 cm.

   1. Paper making and trade—Handbooks, manuals, etc. I. Title.
                     Title romanized: Shigyō teiyō.

TS1105.N27   1949   70–814730

NN   0021570   DLC

Narita, Minoru.
   マレー戦記 成田穣著 東京 那珂書店 昭和17 [1942]
   4, 3, 235 p. illus., map. 19 cm.

   1. World War, 1939–1945—Campaigns—Malay Peninsula. 2. World War, 1939–1945—Personal narratives, Japanese. I. Title.
                     Title romanized: Marē senki.

D767.5.N3   J 64–704

NN   0021571   DLC

VOLUME 405

Narita, Seita.
(Gakai)
瓦解　満洲始末記　成田精太著　[東京]　北隆
館　[昭和25 i.e. 1950]
2, 6, 337 p.　map.　19 cm.
Colophon inserted.

1. World War, 1939-1945—Personal narratives, Japanese.　2. Japanese in Manchuria.　I. Title.　II. Title: Manshū shimatsuki.

DS784.2.N37　　　　　　　　　　71-788686

NN　0021572　　DLC

Narita, Seita.
ソ連國力の解剖　成田精太著　[東京]　北隆館
[1949]
2, 6, 327 p.　maps.　19 cm.
Subtitle on cover: ソ連敗れしなば

1. Russia—Econ. condit.—1945-1955.　I. Title.
Title romanized: Soren kokuryoku no kaibō.

HC335.N33　　　　　　　　　　J 68-1955

NN　0021573　　DLC

DS798
.M525
Orien
Japan
Narita, Seiyū.
**Minami Manshū Tetsudō Kabushiki Kaisha.　Hokuman
Keizai Chōsajo.**
(Gaimō sekka no shinsō)
外蒙赤化の眞相　[哈爾濱　南滿洲鐵道株式會
社]北滿經濟調査所　康德3[1936]

GB1338
.A7M5
Orien
Japan
Narita, Seiyū.
**Minami Manshū Tetsudō Kabushiki Kaisha.　Hokuman
Keizai Chōsajo.**
(Man-So kokkyō Arugungawa chōsashi)
滿蘇國境額爾古納河調査誌　[成田精雄執筆
哈爾濱　南滿洲鐵道株式會社]北滿經濟調査所
康德2[1935]

HF3626
.M474
Orien
Japan
Narita, Seiyū.
**Minami Manshū Tetsudō Kabushiki Kaisha.　Hokuman
Keizai Chōsajo.**
(Sobieto Rempō no gaikoku bōeki)
ソウイエト聯邦ノ外國貿易　[撮當者　成田吉
雄・エヌ・イ・ニキーフオロフ・石田喜奥志　哈爾濱
南滿洲鐵道株式會社]北滿經濟調査所　昭和11
[1936]

Narita, Setsuo.
(Kakyō shi)
華僑史　成田節男著　増補　東京　螢雪書院
[昭和17 i.e. 1942]
2, 4, 475 p.　illus.　18 cm.
Includes bibliographical references.

1. Chinese in foreign countries—History.　2. Chinese in Southeastern Asia—History.　I. Title.

DS732.N34　　　　　　　　　　74-819256

NN　0021577　　DLC

Narita, Shigeru, 1894-
農產物及畜產物の販賣事情　成田繁・鶴田祥平共
著　東京　養賢堂　昭和4[1929]
2, 6, 208 p.　diagrs., tables.　23 cm.

1. Produce trade—Japan.　I. Tsuruta, Shōhei, 1900-　joint author.　II. Title.
Title romanized: Nōsanbutsu oyobi chikusanbutsu no hambai jijō.

Hoover Institution
for Library of Congress　　　[A]

J 59-2291

NN　0021578　　CSt-H

Narita, Sōichirō.
(Jitsumujō yori mitaru shuppanhō ryakugi)
實務上より見たる出版法略義　附出版關係法令
集　成田總一郎著　中村忠序　東京　丸ノ内出版
社　[昭和8 i.e. 1933]
8, 145 p.　19 cm.
Includes legislation.

1. Printing industry—Law and legislation—Japan.　2. Press law—Japan.　I. Title.　II. Title: Shuppanhō ryakugi.

70-797357

NN　0021579　　DLC

Naritasan shi.
成田山史　[成田町(千葉縣)]　成田山開基一千
年祭事務局　[昭和13 i.e. 1933]
24, 42, 952 p.　illus.　23 cm.
At head of title: 成田山開基一千年祭記念
Errata slip inserted.
Bibliography: p. 939-948.

1. Narita.　Shinshōji—History.

BQ6353.N376S56　　　　　　　72-808171

NN　0021580　　DLC

Narita-san Shinshoji.
Educational and social work carried on by the Naritasan Shinshoji Temple. [Chiba?] Japan, 1937
Text also in Japanese characters

NN　0021581　　MH

Naritelli, Raúl Molina
see
Molina Naritelli, Raúl.

Nariyuki, Koda
see　Kōda, Rohan, 1867-1947.

Nariz del diablo; publicación mensual de los empleados del Ferrocarril de Guayaquil a Quito.
Año.

Quito, 192
v.　illus.　　　　　　　　　　4°.
Numbering continuous.
Cover-title reads: Nariz del diablo; revista mensual illustrada. Organo de los empleados de la Compañia del ferrocarril del sur.

1. Railways—Employees—Ecuador.
N.Y.P.L.

February 28, 1930

NN　0021584　　NN CSt InU

Narizhnyĭ, Symon, 1898-
Харківське історично-філологічне товариство.　Прага, Вид. Укр. історично-філологічного т-ва, 1944.
16 p.　25 cm.
At head of title: Société des sciences historiques et philologiques ukrainienne[s] à Prague.

1. Kharkov.　Universitet.　Istoriko-filologicheskoe obshchestvo.
Title romanized: Kharkivs'ke istorychno-filolohichne tovarystvo.

PG3801.K43N3　　　　　　　73-207259

NN　0021585　　DLC

Narizhnyĭ, Symon, 1898-
15 літ діяльности Українського історично-філологічного товариства в Празі (1923-1938).　Прага, 1940.
16 p.　26 cm.

1. Ukraïns'ke istorychno-filolohichne tovarystvo v Prazi.　I. Title.
Title romanized: P'iatnadtsiat' lit diial'nosty Ukraïns'koho istorychno-filolohichnoho tovarystva v Prazi.

PG3801.U43N3　　　　　　　73-207258

NN　0021586　　DLC

DK508
.7
.N3
Narizhnyĭ, Symon, 1898-
Розвідування московських посланців на Україні в другій половині XVII віку.　Прага, Вид. Укр. історично-філологічного т-ва в Празі, 1941.
22 p.　29 cm.

1. Espionage, Russian—Ukraine.　I. Title.
Title transliterated: Rozviduvannià moskovs'kykh poslantsiv.

DK508.7.N3　　　　　　　　65-58816

NN　0021587　　DLC

Narizhnyĭ, Symon, 1898-
Українська еміграція; культурна праця української еміграції між двома світовими війнами.　Прага, 1942-
v.　plates, ports., fold. map.　25 cm.　(Студії Музею визвольної боротьби України, т. 1

1. Ukrainians in foreign countries.　I. Title.　(Series: Prague.　Muzeĭ vyzvol'noĭ borot'by Ukrainy.　Studiĭ, t. 1
Title transliterated: Ukraïns'ka emigratsiia.

DK508.44.N25　　　　　　　53-18285

NN　0021588　　DLC IaU

Narizhnyĭ, Vasyl'
see
Narezhnyĭ, Vasiliĭ Trofimovich, 1780-1825.

---

al-Narizi
see　　Abu'l 'Abbas al-Tadhl ibn Hatim
al-Narizī [supplement]

Narjes, Jan Ludwig, 1900-
Zum problem des gesetzes in der wirtschaftswissenschaft.　Auszug.
Inaug. diss. Kiel, 1924.

NN　0021591　　ICRL

VOLUME 405

ar W
1713
Narjes, Wolfgang, 1914–
Die Zulässigkeit der Blankozession bei
den verbrieften Grundstückspfandrechten.
Düsseldorf, G. H. Nolte, 1938.
ix,53 p. 22cm.

Diss.—Göttingen.

1. Mortgages.

NN 0021592   NIC

Narjot, G., ed.

Ortolan, Joseph Louis Elzéar, 1802–1873.
Cours de législation pénale comparée. Introduction
historique. Histoire du droit criminel en Europe, depuis
le XVIII° siècle jusqu'à ce jour. Par M. Ortolan ... Analyses du cours de 1839–1840; recueillies et publiées par
M. G. Narjot. Paris, Joubert, 1841.

Narjoux, André, 1867–1935.
L'architecture du XVIII° siècle ₍par₎ André Narjoux ...
Paris, C. Schmid ₍1900₎
1 p. l., 50 pl. (incl. plans) 45ᶜᵐ.
L. C. copy imperfect: 22 pl. wanting.

1. Architecture—France.   1. Title.   ₍Full name: André Félix Narjoux₎
Library of Congress   NA1046.N3   44–46328

NN 0021594   DLC

N
7443
E78
v.2
no.7
Narjoux, André, 1867–1935.
Église St-Pierre de Montmartre. Paris,
Aulanier ₍1897₎
37 p. illus. 25cm.

1. Paris. Saint Pierre de Montmartre
(Church) I. Title.

NN 0021595   NIC

Narjoux, André, 1867–1935.
Restitution du Château de Marly le Roi, par André
Narjoux ... Paris, A. Guérinet ₍1902₎
1 p. l., 23 pl. (incl. t.-p., plans) on 18 l. 40½ᶜᵐ.
In portfolio.

1. Marly-le-Roi. Château de.
14–6347
Library of Congress   NA7736.M3N3

NN 0021596   DLC OC1 NNC TNJ

Narjoux, Félix, 1836–1891.
Architecture communale ... par M. Félix Narjoux ...
avec une préface de M. Viollet-Le-Duc. 1.–3. sér. ...
Paris, Vᵉ A. Morel et cⁱᵉ, 1870–80.
3 v. 223 pl. (incl. plans) 36 × 30ᶜᵐ.
CONTENTS.—1.–2. sér. Hôtels de ville, mairies, maisons d'école, salles
d'asile, presbytères, halles et marchés, abattoirs lavoirs, fontaines, etc.—
3. sér. Architecture scolaire: écoles de hameaux, écoles mixtes, écoles de
filles, écoles de garçons, groupes scolaires, salles d'asiles, écoles profession-
nelles, écoles normales primaires.

1. Public buildings. 2. School-houses. 3. Architecture—Designs and
plans.
10–29189
Library of Congress   NA4283.N2

NN 0021597   DLC CtY NIC CU MB

Narjoux, Félix, 1836–1891.
... Les écoles normales primaires. Construction et installation. Paris, C. Delagrave ₍etc.₎ 1880.
2 p. l., 316, 19, ₍1₎ p. incl. illus., plates, plans. 23½ᶜᵐ.
Annexe: Enseignement primaire; Commission des bâtiments scolaires;
Projet de règlement pour la construction et l'ameublement des écoles normales: 19, ₍1₎ p. at end.

1. Normal schools—Europe. 2. Primary education—Europe.
E 8–557
Library, U. S. Bur. of   Education LB2059.N23

NN 0021598   DHEW

LB3219
.F8N25
NARJOUX, FÉLIX, 1836–1891.
Écoles primaires et salles d'asiles, construction et
installation; à l'usage de MM. les maires, délégués can-
tonaux et membres de l'enseignement primaire, par Félix Narjoux... Paris, C. Delagrave₍etc.₎1879.
₍3₎,260 p. incl. illus., plates, plans, tables. 18cm.

1. School-houses--France.

NN 0021599   ICU

Narjoux, Félix, 1836–1891.
... Les écoles publiques, construction et installation en Belgique et en Hollande; documents officiels—services intérieurs
et extérieurs—bâtiments scolaires—mobilier scolaire—services
annexes. Paris, Vᵉ A. Morel et cⁱᵉ, 1878.
2 p. l., xii, 253 p., 1 l. incl. illus., plans, diagrs. 24ᶜᵐ.

1. School-houses—Belgium. 2. School-houses—Netherlands.
E 10–1331
U. S. Off. of educ.   Library   LB3219.B4N2
for Library of Congress   ₍a37b1₎

NN 0021600   DHEW CtY KU MH MB

Narjoux, Félix, 1836–1891.
... Les écoles publiques, construction et installation en
Suisse; documents officiels—services intérieurs et extérieurs—bâtiments scolaires—mobilier scolaire—services
annexes. Paris, Vᵉ A. Morel et cⁱᵉ, 1879.
2 p l., vii, 265 p., 1 l., incl. illus., plates, plans. 24ᶜᵐ.

1. School-houses—Switzerland.
E 11–702
Library, U. S. Bur. of   Education LB3219.S9N2

NN 0021601   DHEW KU CtY MB

Narjoux, Félix, 1836–1891.
Les écoles publiques en France et en Angleterre, construction et installation; documents officiels—services extérieurs—services intérieurs—salles d'asile—mobilier
scolaire—services annexes, par Félix Narjoux ... Paris,
Vᵉ A. Morel et cⁱᵉ, 1877.
2 p. l., viii, 339 p. illus. (incl. plans) diagrs. 24ᶜᵐ.

1. Public schools—France. 2. Public schools—Gt. Brit. 3. Education—
France. 4. Education—Gt. Brit. 5. School-houses.
E 10–1083
Library, U. S. Bur. of   Education LC75.N2

NN 0021602   DHEW CtY MH MB PU

---

4 DD–967
Narjoux, Félix, 1836–1891.
En Allemagne; la Prusse et ses annexes; le
pays, les habitants, la vie intérieure. Ouvrage
illustré de 16 dessins par l'auteur. Paris,
Librairie Plon, 1884.
405 p.

NN 0021603   DLC-P4 CU

Narjoux, Félix, 1836?–1891.
... Francesco Crispi. L'homme public.—L'homme
privé. Paris, A. Savine, 1890.
333 p., 1 l. front. (port.) 19ᶜᵐ.
On cover: 2. éd.

Subject entries: Crispi, Francesco, 1819–1901.
3–4036

NN 0021604   DLC MB MH MU

Narjoux, Félix, 1836–1891, joint author.

Viollet-Le-Duc, Eugène Emmanuel, 1814–1879.
Habitations modernes, recueillies par E. Viollet-Le-
Duc, avec le concours des membres du Comité de rédaction
de l'Encyclopédie d'architecture, et la collaboration de
Félix Narjoux ... Paris, Vᵉ A. Morel et cⁱᵉ, 1875–77.

Narjoux, Félix, 1836–1891.
... Histoire d'un pont, par Félix Narjoux...
Paris, Hachette et cie, 1884.
3 p. l., ₍1₎–11, 282, ₍1₎ p. incl. illus., plates
18 1/2cm. (Bibliothèque des merveilles)

1. Bridges - History.

NN 0021606   DP DSI

Narjoux, Félix, 1836–1891.
L'Italie des Italiens, par Félix Narjoux. Paris, Librairie
des imprimeries réunies, 1888.
3 p. l., 356 p., 1 l. illus., port., plan. 20½ᶜᵐ.
On cover: 2. mille.
CONTENTS.—En Italie.—En voyage.—Le pays, les habitants.—Les villes
transformées.—Les habitations.—La vie intérieure.—La rue.—Les caractères.—La religion.—La famille royale.—Les théâtres.—Les plaisirs.

Subject entries: 1. Italy—Descr. & trav. 2. Italy—Soc. life & cust.
3–5218
Library of Congress. no.   DG427.N23.

NN 0021607   DLC NIC

Narjoux, Félix.
Le ministère de Martial Ravignac.
Paris, Plon, ₍n.d.₎
296p. 19cm.

NN 0021608   MeWC

Narjoux, Félix.
Monsieur le député de Chavone. Paris,
Plon, 1885.
277p. 19cm.

NN 0021609   MeWC

Narjoux, Félix, 1836–1891.
Notes & sketches of an architect taken during a journey
in the north-west of Europe; tr. from the French of Félix
Narjoux by John Peto. With 214 illustrations. London,
S. Low, Marston, Searle & Rivington, 1876.
xviii, 403 p. illus., plates, plans. 23ᶜᵐ.

1. Architecture — Netherlands. 2. Architecture—Germany. 3. Architecture—Denmark. 1. Peto, John, tr.
11–28650
Library of Congress   NA950.N3

NN 0021610   DLC NcD CtY PU MB

VOLUME 405

NA
950
N23nE
1877
Narjoux, Félix, 1836–1891.
Notes and sketches of an architect
taken during a journey in the northwest
of Europe; translated from the French by
John Peto. Author's ed., from advance
sheets. Boston, J.R.Osgood, 1877.
442p. illus.,plans. 22cm.
Translation of Notes de voyage d'un
architecte dans le Nord-ouest de l'Europe.

1. Architecture – Netherlands.
2. Architecture – Germany. 3. Architecture –
Denmark.

CtY MB CU PSt MU TxU MoU NjP
NN 0021612 NRU MiU OC1 ICN NjP OC1W NBuG OOxM

Narjoux, Félix, 1836–1891.
Notes de voyage d'un architecte dans le Nord-ouest de
l'Europe, par Félix Narjoux. Croquis et descriptions.
Paris, A. vᵉ Morel et cⁱᵉ, 1876.
2 p. l., 467 p. illus., plates, plans. 28½ᶜᵐ.

1. Architecture—Netherlands. 2. Architecture—Germany. 3. Architecture—Denmark.
11–30720
Library of Congress   NA950.N2

NN 0021613 DLC CaBVaU CtY PPD PP MB

Narjoux, Félix, 1836–1891.
Paris; monuments élevés par la ville, 1850–1880; ouvrage
publié sous le patronage de la ville de Paris par Félix Narjoux
... Paris, Vᵛᵉ A. Morel et cⁱᵉ, 1880–83.
9 pt. in 8 v. illus., 304 pl. (incl. plans) 46½ᶜᵐ.
CONTENTS.—,sér. I, Édifices administratifs. 1881.—,sér. II, Édifices religieux.—,sér. III, Édifices consacrés à l'instruction publique. 1888.—,sér. IV, Édifices consacrés aux beaux-arts. 1882.—,sér. V, Édifices décoratifs. 1882.—,sér. VI, Édifices judiciaires. 1880.—,sér. VII, Édifices de la force publique. 1883.—,sér. VIII, Édifices sanitaires. 1883.—,sér. IX, Édifices d'utilité générale. 1883.
1. Paris—Public buildings. 2. Architecture—Paris. I. Title.
11–34285
Library of Congress   NA4298.P2N2

NN 0021614 DLC CtY MB PP MiU NN MWiCA MU NIC

617.71 Narjoux, Joseph, 1867–
N231d De la syphilis secondaire de la conjonctive.
Lyon, A. Rey, 1895.
74p. 26cm.
Thèse—Faculté de médecine et de pharmacie
de Lyon.
"Bibliographie": p.₍73₎–74.

1. Eye—Syphilis. 2. Conjunctiva—Diseases.

NN 0021615 IU-M DNLM

QI-250
.N6 Narjoz, M
N3 Étude anatomique des hybrides du genre Epilobium. Le Mans, Impr. Monnoyer, 1913.
85 p., 3 plates. 24 cm.
Thèse – Besançon.
Bibliography: p.81–82.

1. Epilobium – Anatomy. 2. Onagraceae.
i. t.

NN 0021616 NNBG CtY

Narka, Ram Swarup
see
Swarup, Ram.

Narkevičius, Aleksandras.
... Zuzi šoka; romanas.

NN 0021618 OC1

Narkiewicz, Witold Jodko
see   Jodko, Witold Narkiewicz.

Narkiewicz-Jodko, Antoni, 1843–1892.
Zarys dziejów malarstwa od najdawniejszych czasów do
końca XVIII stulecia... ,Tom, ,Lwów: Gubrynowicz
i Schmidt, 1888–89., v. illus. 8°.
t-p. missing.
Title from British Museum catalogue.
Bibliography at head of each chapter.

1. Art, Ancient.
N.Y.P.L.   November 17, 1926

NN 0021620 NN

Narkiewicz-Jodko, Konstanty, 1901–
W walce o szczyty Andów... ,Warszawa, Nakładem głównej księgarni wojskowej,
1935,
2 p. ℓ., ,9,–239 p. incl. plates (1
fold.) maps.
1. Andes- Desc. + travel. I. Title.

NN 0021621 WU

TA439
.N3 Narkir'er, D   I
Установка для вакуумирования бетона. Под ред. В. Т.
Федорова. Москва, Гос. научно-техн. изд-во машиностроит. лит-ры, 1952.
51 p. illus. 20 cm. (В помощь стройкам коммунизма)
Erratum slip inserted.

1. Concrete. 2. Vacuum-pumps.   I. Title.
Title transliterated: Ustanovka dlia vakuumirovaniia betona.
54–17579
NN 0021622 DLC

Narkirier, Marie.
Ueber Yoghurt.   Zürich, Gebr. Leemann &
Co., 1911.
27 p. 8°.
Dissertation.

NN 0021623 DNLM

Narkiss, David.
העקבות מולכים אל ... תל-אביב. י. צ׳יק, תשי"ב-י"ד.
,Tel-Aviv, 1951/52–53/54,
3 v. in 1 (240 p.) illus. 18 cm.
Stories.
הבית הנודד.—המסתרת הירוקה.—לקרקס בוניציה.
CONTENTS.—

I. Title.   Title transliterated: ha-'Akevot molikhim el.
PZ90.H3N34   53–54964 rev ‡

NN 0021624 DLC

Narkiss, David.
מסע ילדי א. ר. ל. ב. ה. מתל-אביב לאפריקה ובחזרה. תל-
אביב. י. צ׳יק, ,Tel-Aviv, 1955,
144 p. illus. 23 cm.

I. Title.   Title transliterated: Masa' yalde A. R. L. B. H.
PZ90.H3N35   57–53779 ‡

NN 0021625 DLC

Narkiss, Mordecai.
The Herman Shulman hall
see under   Jerusalem. Bezalel museum.

ND699
.C514 Narkiss, Mordecai.
Igud ha-muze'onim be-Yisrael.
מארק שאגאל; יצורתו 1908-1951. ,הקטלוג נערך ונכתב בידי
מ. נרקיס. ,Jerusalem, 1951.

NN 0021628 DLC CU ICU CLU

Narkiss, Mordecai, 1898-1957.
... מטבעות ארץ-ישראל ... ירושלם, תרצ"ו-
,Jerusalem, "The Bialik foundation," 1936-
v. illus., plates. 18ᶜᵐ.   סמרת לידיעת ארץ-ישראל של
החברה העברית לחקירת ארץ-ישראל ועתיקותיה. א-ב,
At head of title: נרקיס.
Added t-p.: ... Coins of Palestine ... (Library of Palestinology of
the Jewish Palestine exploration society. I/II–
Includes glossaries and bibliographies.
CONTENTS.—ספר א'. מטבעות יהודה
1. Numismatics—Palestine. 2. Numismatics—Jews. I. Title.
Title transliterated: Matbe'oth Erez-Yisrael.
45–45188
Library of Congress   CJ1875.N3

NN 0021629 DLC MH

Narkiss, Mordecai.
מלאבת-האמנות של יהודי תימן. ירושלים, תש"א.
,Jerusalem, 1941,
40 p.; vii p. illus. 17 cm. (מחקרי בית תנבות הלאומי בצלאל. א')
Added t. p.: The artcraft of the Yemenite Jews.
"הערות" (partly bibliographical): p. 32–37.

1. Art industries and trade—Yemen. 2. Art, Jewish.   (Series:
Jerusalem. Bezalel Museum. Meḥkere ... 1)
Title transliterated: Melekhet ha-omonut
shel Yehude Teman.
NK1038.N3   54–49746

BM657
.H3N3 Narkiss, Mordecai.
מגרת החנוכה, מאת מ. נרקיס, ירושלים, בהוצאת "בני
בצלאל" ובסיוע מוסד ביאליק שליד הסוכנת היהודית לארץ
ישראל, ,ת"ש. ,Jerusalem, Bney Bezalel publishing co., 1939,
18, 102 p., 1 l.; n p. illus., 65 pl. 32 x 25ᶜᵐ. (Added t-p.: ספר בית הנקת
הלאומי בצלאל בירושלים. ספר א')
Preliminary matter paged with Hebrew characters.
Added t.-p.: The Hanukkah lamp, by M. Narkiss.
Bibliography: p. 82–83.
1. Hanukkah lamp. I. Title.   (Series: Bet ha-nekhot
ha-le'umi le-omanut Betsal'el   Title transliterated: Menorath ha-Ḥanukah
Kitve Bet ha-nekhot, sefer 1)
45–44231
Library of Congress   BM657.H3N3

NN 0021630 DLC

Z118
.N3
,Hebraic Narkiss, Mordecai.
Sect. מלון למונחי הגרפיקה. ירושלם. מוסד ביאליק ע"ידי ועד הלשון
העברית. תרצ"ז. ,Jerusalem, 1937,
7, 294 p. illus. 22 cm.
Added t. p.: Dictionary of graphic arts.
The Hebrew terms and definitions are arranged under their German equivalents.

1. Printing—Dictionaries. 2. Art—Dictionaries.   I. Va'ad ha-lashon ha-'Ivrit be-Erets-Yisrael.
Title transliterated: Milon le-munaḥe ha-grafikah.
Z118.N3   55–47275

NN 0021631 DLC

Narkiss, Mordecai.
One nation out of many people
see under   Jerusalem. Bezalel Museum.

Narkiss, Mordecai, 1898-1957.
The "Yahuda Haggada"

see under

Jerusalem. Bezalel Museum.

VOLUME 405

Narkissos, by W. London, K. Paul, Trench,
Trübner, 1909.
53 p. 20 cm.
I. W.

DK268
.O7N3
Нарком стахановцев. Стахановцы страны о Серго Орджо-
никидзе. Москва, Гос. социально-экон. изд-во, 1937.
60 p. illus. 21 cm.

1. Ordzhonikidze, Grigoriĭ Konstantinovich, 1886–1937.
Title transliterated: Narkom stakhanovt͡sev.

DK268.O7N3   54–47964 ‡

Narkomfin RSFSR
see **Russia** (*1917–*   *R. S. F. S. R.*) *Narodnyĭ komissariat finansov.*

Narkomfin SSSR
see **Russia** (*1923–*   *U. S. S. R.*) *Narodnyĭ komissariat finansov.*

Narkomfin Z. S. F. S. R.
see **Transcaucasia** (*S. F. S. R.*) *Narodnyĭ komissariat
finansov.*

Narkomi͡ust USSR
see **Ukraine.** *Narodnyĭ komissariat i͡ustit͡sii.*

Narkomkhoz RSFSR
see
Russia (*1917–*   *R. S. F. S. R.*) *Narodnyĭ komissariat
kommunal'nogo khozi͡aĭstva.*

Narkomles RSFSR
see **Russia** (*1917–*   *R. S. F. S. R.*) *Narodnyĭ komissariat lesnoĭ promyshlennosti.*

Narkommash
see **Russia** (*1923–*   *U. S. S. R.*) *Narodnyĭ komissariat
mashinostroenii͡a.*

Narkommestprom RSFSR
see
Russia (*1917–*   *R. F. S. S. R.*) *Narodnyĭ komissariat
mestnoĭ promyshlennosti.*

Narkomnat͡s
see
Russia (*1917–*   *R. S. F. S. R.*) *Narodnyĭ komissariat
po delam nat͡sional'nostei.*

Narkomos USRR
see
Ukraine. *Narodnyĭ komissariat osvity.*

Narkompishcheprom RSFSR
see **Russia** (*1917–*   *R. S. F. S. R.*) *Narodnyĭ komissariat pishchevoĭ promyshlennosti.*

Narkompishcheprom SSSR
see **Russia** (*1923–*   *U. S. S. R.*) *Narodnyĭ komissariat pishchevoĭ promyshlennosti.*

Narkompishcheprom USSR
see **Ukraine.** *Narodnyĭ komissariat pishchevoĭ promyshlennosti.*

Narkompochtel' SSSR
see
Russia (*1923–*   *U. S. S. R.*) *Narodnyĭ komissariat pocht
i telegrafov.*

Narkomprod RSFSR
see
Russia (*1917–*   *R. S. F. S. R.*) *Narodnyĭ komissariat prodovol'stvii͡a.*

Narkomput'
see **Russia** (*1923–*   *U. S. S. R.*) *Narodnyĭ
komissariat puteĭ soobshchenii͡a.*

Narkomrabkrin SSSR
see **Russia** (*1923–*   *U. S. S. R.*) *Narodnyĭ
komissariat raboche-krest'i͡anskoĭ inspekt͡sii.*

Narkomsnab SSSR
see
Russia (*1923–*   *U. S. S. R.*) *Narodnyĭ komissariat snab-
zhenii͡a.*

Narkomsobes RSFSR
see
Russia (*1917–*   *R. S. F. S. R.*) *Narodnyĭ komissariat
sot͡sial'nogo obespechenii͡a.*

Narkomsovkhoz SSSR
see **Russia** (*1923–*   *U. S. S. R.*) *Narodnyĭ komissariat zernovykh i zhivotnovodcheskikh sovetskikh khozi͡aĭstv.*

Narkomstroĭ SSSR
see **Russia** (*1923–*   *U. S. S. R.*) *Narodnyĭ komissariat po stroitel'stvu.*

Narkomtorg RSFSR
see
Russia (*1917–*   *R. S. F. S. R.*) *Narodnyĭ komissariat
torgovli.*

Narkomtorg SSSR
see
Russia (*1923–*   *U. S. S. R.*) *Narodnyĭ komissariat
torgovli.*
Russia (*1923–*   *U. S. S. R.*) *Narodnyĭ komissariat
vneshneĭ i vnutrenneĭ torgovli.*

Narkomtorg USSR
see
Russia (*1923–*   *U. S. S. R.*) *Narodnyĭ komissariat torgovli.*

Narkomtrud RSFSR
see
Russia (*1917–*   *R. S. F. S. R.*) *Narodnyĭ
komissariat truda.*

Narkomtrud SSSR
see
Russia (*1923–*   *U. S. S. R.*) *Narodnyĭ komissariat
truda.*

Narkomvneshtorg RSFSR
see
Russia (*1917–*   *R. S. F. S. R.*) *Narodnyĭ komissariat
vneshneĭ torgovli.*

Narkomvneshtorg SSSR
see
Russia (*1923–*   *U. S. S. R.*) *Narodnyĭ komissariat vneshneĭ torgovli.*

Narkomvnudel RSFSR
see
Russia (*1917–*   *R. S. F. S. R.*) *Narodnyĭ komissariat
vnutrennikh del.*

Narkomvnudel SSSR
see **Russia** (*1923–*   *U. S. S. R.*) *Narodnyĭ komissariat vnutrennikh del.*

Narkomvod SSSR
see
Russia (*1923–*   *U. S. S. R.*) *Narodnyĭ komissariat vod-
nogo transporta.*

Narkomzdrav SSSR
see
Russia (*1923–*   *U. S. S. R.*) *Narodnyĭ komissariat zdra-
vookhranenii͡a.*

VOLUME 405

Narkomzem (*R. S. F. S. R.*)
  see
Russia (*1917–*   *R. S. F. S. R.*) *Narodnyĭ komissariat*
zemledelii︠a︡.

Narkomzem (*U. S. S. R.*)
  see
Russia (*1923–*   *U. S. S. R.*) *Narodnyĭ komissariat*
zemledelii︠a︡.

Narkomzem Kryma
  see **Crimean A. S. S. R.** *Narodnyĭ komissariat zemlede-*
lii︠a︡.

Narkose und Anaesthesie. Zeitschrift und
  Zentralorgan für das Gesamtgebiet der
  Schmerzlinderung und- Verhütung. Jg.
  1 heft 1–jg. 2 heft 6. Berlin, Georg
  Stilke, 1928–1929.
   2 v. illus. 24 cm.
   Combined with Der Schmerz to form
  Schmerz, Narkose, Anaesthesie.
   1. Anesthesiology. Per.

NN 0021671   IParkA DNLM MBCo

Nářky husitské. Querelae Hussitarum, r. 1438–
  1443. [Žaloby pana Oldřicha z Rožmberka na
  Táborské, žaloby Táborských na pana Oldřicha
  a odpory obojí strany. Vyd. František Teplý]
  V Praze, Nakl. Tiskove Ligy, 1915.
   104 p. (Husitství ve světle pravdy.
  Roč. 12, čis. 2–4)

NN 0021672   MH

Narlikar, V   V
  Wave mechanics. ₍Patna₎ Patna University, 1942.
   vii, 160 p. 25 cm. (Sukhraj Rai readership lectures, 1939–40)
   Includes bibliographies.

   1. Wave mechanics.   (Series)

QC174.2.N37   77–276298
               MARC

NN 0021673   DLC

Narmad
  see
  Narmadashankar Lalshankar, 1833–1886.

Narmadāśaṅkara Vallabhajī Dvivedī
  see
  Dvivedī, Narmadāśaṅkara Vallabhajī, 1892–

Narmadashankar Devshankar Mehta
  see Mehta, Narmadashankar Devshankar.

Narmadashankar Lalshankar, 1833–1886.
  Dharmavicāra. Lakhanāra Kavi Narmadāśaṅkara Lāla-
  śaṅkara. Āvṛtti trijī. Mumbaī, "Gujarātī" Prĕsa, 1914.
   6, 220 p. 22 cm.
   In Gujarati.

   I. Title.

   PK1859.N3D5   54–23656

NN 0021677   DLC

Narmaev, Morkhadzhi Bambaevich.
Dosbergenov, Ti︠u︡lebek.
  В горах Тянь-Шаня. ₍Рассказ Т. Досбергенова записал
  и литературно обработал М. Б. Нармаев. Москва₎ Профиздат, 1955.

PL5089   **Narmin Suti.**
N23A5   Angan2 dan peristiwa. Medan, Saiful ₍1955?₎
     68 p. illus. 18 cm. (Roman populer
     "Gelora". Tahun 1, no. 1)

NN 0021679   NIC

STC   **Narne, William,** 1583?–1653.
18359   Christs starre: or, A Christian treatise for
   our direction to our sauiour, and for our conjunction with him. Declaring Christs excellencie,
   our necessitie of him, his great loue and manifold mercies bestowed vpon vs; as also some of
   our duties ... London, Printed by I. L. for Philemon Stephens and Christopher Meredith, 1625.

   A^2, ¶–2¶^{2}, B–2H^4, 2h^2, 2I–3E^4. (¶1 signed
   ¶3.) 4to.
   Harmsworth copy.

NN 0021680   DFo NNUT MH MBrZ

AW   Narne, William, 1583?–1653.
1   Christs starre: or, A Christian treatise for our
R475: direction to our Saviour, and for our conjunction with
1250   him ... also some of our duties ... By W. Narne ...
   London, Printed by I. L₍egat₎ for P. Stephens and C.
   Meredith, 1625.
    Microfilm of original in the Harvard University
   Library; t.p., prelim. material, p. 1–7, 228–257 from
   British Museum copy filmed at end. Ann Arbor, Mich.,
   University Microfilms, 1971. (Early English books,
   1475–1640, reel 1250)
Micro/ STC no. 18359.   Microfilm.
    I. Title.

NN 0021681   MiU WaPS CaBVaU

STC   **Narne, William,** 1583?–1653.
18360   The pearle of prayer most pretious, and
   powerfull, or, A Christian treatise most
   necessarie for all these that desire to
   eshew that wrath to come ... and who doe
   long for Gods favour ... Edinburgh, Printed
   by Iohn Wreittoun, 1630.

   ₍A₎^{8}, A–2E^8, 2F^4. 8vo.
   Harmsworth copy.

NN 0021682   DFo

Narnese Romano.
  Sonetti. [Milan, Phil. de Mantegaliis,
  ca. 1498]
  Goff: N–5.

NN 0021683   DLC

Narnette, (Mrs.) Eva (Magruder) de
  see De Narnette, (Mrs.) Eva (Magruder)

NARNI, Cassio da.

  See CASSIO DA NARNI.

BZ   **Narni, Girolamo Mantini da** 1562?–1632.
27   Prediche fatte nel palazzo apostolico.
N23   3. ed. romana. Rome, typis Vaticanis, 1639.
1639   12 p. l., 700, [120] p. 20 cm.

   1. Sermons, Italian.
   I. Seventeenth century books

NN 0021686   IMunS

Narni, Reale Fusoritto da
  see
Fusoritto da Narni, Reale.

Narni, Italy.
  Leoni XIII consecrationis episcopalis annum L
  see under title

Narni   Italy. Giunta Comunale.
  Risposta in confutazione della relazione del ragioniere di Prefettura Signor Enrico Tusa in data 16 aprile 1906 circa la sua ispe-
  zione al comune di Narni. ₍Maggio 30, 1906.₎ Narni: Tipografia Economica, 1906. 34 p., 2 l. pap. 8°.

  1. Municipal finance, Italy: Narni,   1906.
  N. Y. P. L.   June 26, 1912.

NN 0021689   NN CtY

Narni, Italy. Laws, statutes, etc.
  Statuta illustrissimae civitatis Narniae ...
  [Narniae, typis haeredum Corbelletti, 1716]
   20 p. l., 280, [5] p. port. 31 cm.
   Initials; printer's ornaments.
   Imperfect: Title-page damaged; portrait of
  S. Giovenale lacking.

NN 0021690   CtY

MT42   Naro, Bernardino.
N664   Vita del venerabil servo di Dio Cardinale
Xn16v Roberto Nobili, Bibliotecario della Santa
   Romana Chiesa. Pronepote del sommo pontefice
Restricted Giulio III. Urbino, Nella stamperia della Ven.
Circulation Cappella del SS. Sagramento per A. Fantauzzi,
  MDCCXXVIII.
   4 p. l., 91 p. 27 cm.

   Title vignette.
   Added t.p. engraved: Compendio di vita del
  venerabile servo di Dio Cardinale Roberto
  Nobili ... da   Bernardino Naro.

   1. Nobili, Roberto de', 1577–1656. 2. Catholic
  Church – Missions – India. 3. India – Missions
  4. Jesuits in India.

NN 0021692   CtY-D

Naro-Montoro, Maddalena (Gondi) marchesa
  Patrizi
   see Patrizi-Naro-Montoro, Maddalena
  (Gondi) marchesa.

G3201   Narochnit︠s︡kiĭ, A. L.
.S6
194–   **Russia** (*1923–*   *U. S. S. R.*) *Glavnoe upravlenie geode-*
.R8   *zii i kartografii.*
    Колониальные владения с 1789 по 1876. Составлено и
   оформлено Научно-редакционной картосоставительской
   частью ГУГК. Автор А. Л. Нарочницкий; ответственные
   редакторы Л. П. Четверикова и Т. Н. Бекова. ₍Москва?
   194–?₎

VOLUME 405

G3201
.S8
1950
.R8

Narochnitskiĭ, A. L.

Russia (1923-   U. S. S. R.) *Glavnoe upravlenie geode-
zii i kartografii.*
Территориально-политический раздел мира с 1876 по
1914 г. Составлено и оформлено Научно-редакционной
картосоставительской частью ГУГК. Автор Нарочницкий
А. Л. Ответственный редактор Бекова Т. Н. Москва, 1950.

NAROD

V Londýně

NN   0021696   InU

Per
N232

Národ. roč.1-3; 8.břez.1917-31.pros.1919
3v. facsim. weekly.

Edited by J. Kamelský (and K. Paul, 7.list.-
31.pros.1919)

V Praze

I.Kamelský, Jan,   ed.

NN   0021697   NcU InU

NÁROD; česko-americký kalendář. Chicago.
1, 1896-
1-56, 1896-1949 as Katolík

NN   0021698   ILS IEdS

Slavic-
American
Imprints
Coll.
420.11
N376
1951

Národ; česko-americký kalendář na občanský
rok 1951. Obsahuje část kalendářní, poučné
čtení, povídky, básně, kroniky, adresáře,
žerty pro zasmání a různá vyobrazení. Chicago, Tiskárna českých benediktinů [1951?]
[19] 20-240 p. illus. 26 cm.
English translation of title: Nation; Czech-American almanac for the common year 1951. Contains a calendar, instructive reading, short stories, poems, chronicles, directories, laughable jokes and various illustrations.

PARTIAL CONTENTS: Duchovní stav. (The clergy) Napsal
(by) D. Kvítek, pp. 113-120.—Kronika. (Chronicle) pp.
167-196.—Adresář českých katolických kněží v Americe. (The
directory of Czech Catholic priests in America) pp. 197-201.
Adresář českých katolických osad v Americe. (The directory
of Czech Catholic parishes in America) pp. 210-213.

NN   0021700   IEdS

Slavic-
American
Imprints
Coll.
420.11
N376
1952

Národ; česko-americký kalendář na přestupný
rok 1952. Obsahuje část kalendářní, poučné
čtení, povídky, básně, kroniky, adresáře,
žerty pro zasmání a různá vyobrazení. Chicago, Tiskárna českých benediktinů [1952?]
213 [23] p. illus. 26 cm.
English translation of title: Nation; Czech-American almanac for the leap-year 1952. Contains a calendar, instructive reading, short stories, poems, chronicles, directories,
laughable jokes   and various illustrations.

PARTIAL CONTENTS: Ježíš Kristus...včera i dnes i na vě-
ky. (Jesus Christ...yesterday, today and to all eternity)
Napsal (by) W. Hradecký, pp. 22-24.—Kronika. (Chronicle)
pp. 143-193.—Adresář českých katolických kněží v Americe.
(The directory of Czech Catholic priests in America) pp.
194-198.—Adresář českých katolických osad v Americe. (The
directory of Czech Catholic parishes in America) pp. 198-
208.

NN   0021702   IEdS

Slavic-
American
Imprints
Coll.
420.11
N376
1954

Národ; česko-americký kalendář na mariánský
rok 1954. Obsahuje část kalendářní, poučné
čtení, povídky, básně, kroniky, adresáře,
žerty pro zasmání a různá vyobrazení.
Chicago, Tiskárna českých benediktinů
[1954]
252 p. illus. 26 cm.
English translation of title: Nation; Czech-American almanac for the Marian year 1954. Contains a calendar, instructive reading, short stories, poems, chronicles, directories, laughable   jokes and various illustrations.

PARTIAL CONTENTS: Kázání loupežníkum. (Preaching to rob-
bers) p. 83.—Kronika. (Chronicle) pp. 141-177.—Jubilejní svatoprokopský rok ve svobodném světě. (St. Procopius
jubilee year in the free world) pp. 178-182.—Protest kněží-
exulantů Spojeným Národum proti náboženskému pronásledování v
Československu. (Protest of exiled priests to United Nations
against the persecution of religion in Czechoslovakia) p.
185.—Projev soudce Frank H. Bicka po posvěcení svatoprokop-
ské školy. (The declaration of Judge Frank H. Bicek after
the consecration   of St. Procopius School) p. 187.—

Adresář českých katolických kněží v Americe. (The directory
of Czech Catholic priests in America) pp. 192-200.—Adresář
českých katolických osad v Americe. (The directory of Czech
Catholic parishes in America) pp. 200-229.—České katolické
ústavy v Americe. (Czech Catholic institutions in America)
p. 229.—Vyšší učiliště. (Academies) p. 229.—České katolické časopisy v Americe. (Czech Catholic periodicals in A-
merica) p. 230.—Seznam česko-katol. jednot ve Spoj. Statech
a adresář jejich úředniků. (The list of Czech Catholic unions
in the United   States and the directory of their
officials) p.   230.

NN   0021705   IEdS

Slavic-
American
Imprints
Coll.
420.11
N376
1955

Národ; česko-americký kalendář na mariánský
rok 1955. Obsahuje část kalendářní, poučné
čtení, povídky, básně, kroniky, adresáře,
žerty pro zasmání a různá vyobrazení. Chicago, Tiskárna českých benediktinů [1955?]
237 [1] p. illus. 26 cm.
English translation of title: Nation; Czech-American almanac for the Marian year 1955. Contains a calendar, instructive reading, short stories, poems, chronicles, directories, laughable jokes and various illustrations.

PARTIAL CONTENTS: Kronika. (Chronicle) pp. 140-190.—
Adresář českých katolických kněží v Americe. (The directory of Czech Catholic priests in America) pp. 196-204.—
Adresář českých katolických osad v Americe. (The directory
of Czech Catholic parishes in America) pp. 204-224. rw

NN   0021707   IEdS

Narod; česko-americký kalendář..,
see also Katolík česko-americký kalendář ...

Slavic-
American
Imprints
Coll.
420.18
N375

Národ [český katolický polotýdeník] Chicago [Benediktinské opatství svatého
Prokopa] 1894-
v. illus. 57 x 46 cm.

English translation of title: The nation, Czech Catholic semi-weekly. rw

NN   0021709   IEdS

AP56
.N27

Narod. The Nation.
Oakland.
v. in illus., ports. 41 cm. monthly.
Some articles in English.

I. Title: The Nation.
AP56.N27   64-58379

NN   0021710   DLC

DK52
.N3

Народ-богатырь, IX-XIII в.в. [сборник. Москва, Воен.
изд-во, 1948.
97 p. illus. 20 cm.
Sequel: За родную землю.

1. Russia—History, Military.   *Title transliterated: Narod-bogatyr'.*

DK52.N3   51-28949

NN   0021711   DLC

DK52
Z2

Narod-bogatyr'.
За родную землю; XIV-XVII века. Москва, Воен. изд-во,
1949.

HD9259
.B3C46

Народ Гватемалы и "Юнайтед фрут компани." Перевод с
испанского Н. А. Бунтман и Е. П. Клусова. Предисл.
С. А. Гонионского. Москва, Изд-во иностранной лит-ры,
1954.
50 p. 20 cm.
Includes bibliography.

1. United Fruit Company.   *Title transliterated: Narod Gvatemaly
i "IŪnaĭted frut kompani."*

HD9259.B3C46   60-36566 ‡

NN   0021713   DLC

Národ legiím. 1914,1915,1916, 1917. [Úvod Masaryk
T.G.] V Praze, Nákl. Odboru Národ Legiím[1920-1921]
175 p. illus.
Suppl. Čestní dárcové díla Národ Legiím, Praha, 1921
(20 p.) inserted
1.World War, 1914-1919(5) - Czechoslovakia 2.
Československé legie I.Odbor Národ Legiím II.
Masaryk, Tomáš Garrigue, *Pres. Czechoslovak Republic, 1850-1937.*

NN   0021714   MH OC1

Slavic-
American
Imprints
Coll.
425.24
N37

Národ Polski; urzędowy organ Zjednoczenia
polskiego rzymsko-katolickiego w Ameryce. Chicago, Zjednoczehie Polskie Rzym-
sko katolickiego w Ameryce, 1886-
v. illus. 39 x 30 cm.
English translation of title: The Polish Nation; official organ of the Polish Roman Catholic Union of America.
Published semi-monthly.
Periodical in Polish and English.

NN   0021715   IEdS

Naród polski w walce o pokój i plan sześcioletni. Warszawa,
Książka i Wiedza, 1951.
54 p. 21 cm.

1. Poland—Economic policy.

HC337.P7N35   53-27839

NN   0021716   DLC MiU NN

Národ slovenský.
Memorandum národa slovenského (1861)
see under   Národné slovenské shromaždenie v Turčianskom sv. Martine, 1861.

Národ sobě. Národní divadlo a jeho umělecké
pklady. Mikoláš Aleš et al. V Praze, Melantrich c1940.
170 p. plates (part col.) 31cm.

1. Prague. Národní Divadlo. 2. Architecture—
Prague. 3. Paintings—Prague. 4. Czech language—Texts. I. Aleš, Mikoláš, 1852-1913.

NN   0021718   MB IU

VOLUME 405

Národ sobě. Národní divadlo a jeho umělecké **poklady**
Mikoláš Aleš ₍et al.₎ 2. vyd. V Praze₎ Melantrich ₍1941₎
170 p. plates (part col.) 31 cm.

1. Prague. Národní divadlo. 2. Architecture—Prague. 3. Paintings—Prague. ɪ. Aleš, Mikuláš, 1852-1913.
NA6840.C9P7 1941   53-53513

NN   0021719   DLC GU

NA 6840 Národ sobě. Národní divadlo a
.C92P9 jeho umělecké poklady.
        Mikoláš Aleš ₍et al.₎ 3. vyd. ₍V
        Praze₎ Melantrich ₍1950₎
        170 p. plates (part col.)

1. Prague. Národní divadlo. 2.
Architecture—Prague. 3. Paintings—
Prague. ɪ. Aleš, Mikuláš,
1852-1913.

NN   0021720   ICU

Naród w walce
        see under   Kurdybacha, Łukasz, ed.

Naroden arkheologicheski muzeĭ, *Plovdiv*
  see
Plovdiv, Bulgaria. Narodna biblioteka i muzeĭ.

Naroden arkheologicheski muzeĭ, *Sofia*
  see Sofia. Naroden arkheologicheski muzeĭ.

Naroden etnografski muzeĭ, Sofia
  see Sofia. Naroden etnografski muzeĭ.

GV204
.B8N3
Naroden fizkulturen sŭiŭz.
  Правилник за физкултурните колективи на НФС,
които се изграждат при дружествата на Съюза на народната младеж. София, 1948.
  15 p. 100 mm.
  Cover title.

1. Physical education and training—Societies. 2. Physical education and training—Bulgaria.
        Title transliterated: Pravilnik za fizkulturnite kolektivi na NFS.
        50-30509

NN   0021725   DLC

GV1133
.N35
Naroden fizkulturen sŭiŭz.
  Състезателни правила по бокс. ₍София₎ Физкултура ₍1949₎
  49 p. illus. 16 cm.

1. Boxing.   ɪ. Title.
        Title transliterated: Sŭstezatelni pravila po boks.
GV1133.N35   54-32189 ‡

NN   0021726   DLC

Naroden fizkulturen sŭiŭz.

Bulgaria. *Vŭrkhoven komitet za fizicheska kultura i sport.*
  Състезателни правила по лека атлетика. ₍София₎ Физкултура ₍1949₎

GV204
.B8N3
1948a
Naroden fizkulturen sŭiŭz.
  Устав. ₍Приет на 2. редовен конгрес на НФС, състоял се на 7, 8 и 9 март 1948 г. София, Българска наука₎ 1948.
  31 p. 11 cm.

1. Physical education and training—Bulgaria.
        Title transliterated: Ustav.
GV204.B8N3 1948a   51-31152

NN   0021728   DLC

JN9679
.M3F7
Naroden front na Makedonija. Glaven odbor.
  Фронтовски весник. г. 1-   1950-
  ₍Скопје₎

DR701
.M4K584
1949
Naroden front na Makedonija. Glaven odbor.
Konferencija na begalcite od Egejska Makedonija, *1949.*
  Од Конференцијата на бегалците од Егејска Македонија. Посветена на истгодишнината на НР Македонија. Скопје, Издава Главниот одбор на Народниот фронт на Македонија, 1949.

Naroden front Skopje.
  Пет години слободно Скопје ₍1944-1949₎. Скопје, 1949₎
  95 p. illus. 24 x 31 cm.

1. Macedonia—Descr. & trav.—Views.   ɪ. Title.
        Title transliterated: Pet godini slobodno Skopje.
DR701.M15N27   55-27617 ‡

NN   0021731   DLC

Slavic- Naroden Glas; Bulgarski Naroden Nezavisim
American Ilyustrovan Vestnik. Redaktor: Vasil
Imprints Stefanov. Granite City, Ill., Naroden Glas
Coll.   Publishing Co.
421.26
N376   v. illus. 59 x 45 cm.
          English translation of title: National
        Herald; Bulgarian National Illustrated Independent Newspaper. Managing editor: Vasil Stefanov.

NN   0021732   IEdS

Naroden glas.
  Българо-американски календарь-алманахъ за 1920- Редакция, издание и печатъ на в-къ "Народенъ гласъ" ... Bulgarian-American calendar-almanac for 1920-
  ₍Granite City, Ill.₎ "Naroden glas" ₍1920₎

Naroden glas.
  25-годишенъ алманахъ на в-къ "Народенъ гласъ," най стария български вестникъ въ Америка, 1908-1933. 25-th anniversary jubilee almanac. ₍Редакторъ Василъ Стефановъ. Granite City, Ill., 1933?₎
  575 p. illus. 23 cm.

1. Bulgarians in the U. S. 2. Macedonians in the U. S.   ɪ. Stefanov, Vasil, ed.   ɪɪ. Title.
        Title transliterated: Dvadeset i pet godishen almanakh.
E184.B8N3   63-56088 rev ‡

NN   0021734   DLC

E184
.B8N32
Naroden glas.
  Юбилеенъ сборникъ на вѣстникъ "Народенъ гласъ," 1907-1918. Jubilee almanac of "Naroden glas." Издаденъ по случай 10-годишнината на вѣстника. Съставили: Василъ Стефановъ и Василъ Граматиковъ. ₍Granite City, Ill.,₎ 1918₎
  266 p. illus., port. 27 cm.

1. Bulgarians in the U. S.   ɪ. Stefanov, Vasil, ed.   ɪɪ. Gramatikov Vasil, ed.   ɪɪɪ. Title.
        Title transliterated: Jubileen sbornik na vestnik "Naroden glas."
E184.B8N32   20-1778 rev*

NN   0021735   DLC

Naroden lovno-ribarski sŭiŭz.
  Правилник за ловно-рибарските дружинки. София, 1947.
  14 p. 18 cm.

1. Fishing—Bulgaria. 2. Hunting—Bulgaria.   ɪ. Title.
        Title transliterated: Pravilnik za lovno-ribarskite druzhinki
SH613.B8N3   59-32641 ‡

NN   0021736   DLC

Naroden morski sŭiŭz
  see also
Naroden sŭiŭz za sport i tekhnika.

Naroden muzeĭ, *Sofia*
  see
Sofia. Naroden arkheologicheski muzeĭ.

Народен пастир; месечник за пастирско служение.
  София.
        v. in   illus., ports. 50-57 cm.
  Frequency varies.
  Subtitle varies slightly.
  Organ of Sveshtenicheski sŭiŭz v Bŭlgariĭa,   ; issued by Sveti Sinod of the Bulgarian Orthodox Church, Sept. 1935-

1. Orthodox Eastern Church, Bulgarian—Period.   ɪ. Sveshtenicheski sŭiŭz v Bŭlgariĭa.   ɪɪ. Orthodox Eastern Church, Bulgarian. Sveti Sinod.   *Title transliterated:* Naroden pastir.
BX650.N3   60-35752

NN   0021739   DLC

Naroden sŭiŭz za sport i tekhnika.
  Основни въпроси по авиацията. ₍Под ред. на Захари Захариев₎ ₍София₎ Физкултура ₍1949₎
  288 p. illus. 23 cm.

1. Aeronautics.   ɪ. Zakhariev, Zakhari, ed.   ɪɪ. Title.
        Title transliterated: Osnovni vŭprosi po aviatsiĭata.
TL515.N26   54-40334 ‡

NN   0021740   DLC

Naroden sŭiŭz za sport i tekhnika
  Правилник и програма на популярните курсове по морско дело. София, 1948.
  15 p. 19 cm.
  At head of title: Народен съюз за спорт и техника. Комитет по морско дело.

1. Naval education—Bulgaria.   ɪ. Title.
        Title transliterated: Pravilnik i programa ... po morsko delo.
V621.N3   59-34109 ‡

NN   0021741   DLC

VOLUME 405

Naroden sŭfûz za sport i tekhnika.
Правилник и програма за курсове по парашутизъм за подготовка на любители-парашутисти. София, 1948.
24 p. forms. 10 cm.
At head of title: Народен съюз за спорт и техника—София. Комитет за въздушен спорт.

1. Parachuting.   *Title transliterated:* Pravilnik i programa.

TL750.N3   59-33893

NN   0021742   DLC

Naroden sŭfûz za sport i tekhnika.
Правилник за Секциите спорт и техника на НССТ при дружествата на Съюза на нар. младеж в България. София, 1948.
22 p. 09 mm.
At head of title: Народен съюз за спорт и техника. И. К. Съюз на народната младеж. И. К.

1. Physical education and training—Bulgaria. I. Title.
Title transliterated: Pravilnik za Sektsiite sport i tekhnika na NSST.

GV281.A4 1948   52-67244 rev

NN   0021743   DLC

GV281
.S6
Naroden sŭfûz za sport i tekhnika.
Спорт и техника. г. 1–
1948–
[София]

Naroden sŭfûz za sport i tekhnika
see also
Dimitrovski komunisticheski mladezhki sŭfûz.

Naroden sŭfûz za vŭzdushen sport
see also
Naroden sŭfûz za sport i tekhnika.

Naroden sŭfûz "Zveno."
Национална конференция 3 януари 1948 година. София, 1948.
64 p. 21 cm. (Библиотека "Звено," кн. 12)

1. Bulgaria—Pol. & govt. *Title transliterated:* Natsionalna konferentsiia.

JN9609.A8N3 1948   53-32104

NN   0021747   DLC

Naroden sŭfûz "Zveno."
Нови политически моменти; [доклад от политическия секретар на народния съюз Г. Кулишев] София, 1948.
23 p. 21 cm. (Библиотека "Звено," кн. 14)

1. Bulgaria—Pol. & govt. I. Kulishev, Georgi. II. Title.
Title transliterated: Novi politicheski momenti.

JN9609.A8N3   54-29929

NN   0021748   DLC

Narodetzki (Aaron) [1864–] . De l'arrachement sous-cutané des insertions des tendons extenseurs des doigts sur la phalangette.
48 pp. 4°. *Paris.* 1891. No. 371.

NN   0021749   DLM

Narodetzki, Aaron, 1864–
Livre de santé et d'hygiène; la médecine végétale et le régime biologique, par le docteur A. Narodetzki ... Traité illustré de médecine, d'hygiène et de pharmacie ... Ouvrage de 1.000 pages, illustré de plus de 600 gravures d'anatomie et de dessins de plantes, avec 24 pages en couleurs hors texte, contenant un atlas anatomique. 998° mille. 100. éd. Paris, 1922.
1000 p. illus., col. plates. 22½ᶜᵐ.

1. Therapeutics. 2. Materia medica. 3. Botany, Medical.
Library of Congress   RM127.N3   22-14988

NN   0021750   DLC

WB
120
N232L
1924
NARODETZKI, Aaron, 1864–
Livre de santé et d'hygiène; la médecine végétale et le régime biologique. Montréal, Produits Français, [1924?]
950 p. illus.
Title   Title: La médecine végétale et le régime biologique

NN   0021751   DNLM

Narodetzki, Aaron, 1864–
Livre de santé et d'hygiène; la médecine végétale et le régime biologique. Traité illustré de médecine, d'hygiène et de pharmacie. Paris, [193–?]
1008 p. illus. 22 cm.
1. Therapeutics. 2. Materia medica, Vegetable. 3. Botany, Medical.

NN   0021752   NIC

Narodetzki, Aaron, 1864–
... La médecine végétale illustrée; traité pratique de médecine d'hygiène et de pharmacie Maladies régimes – traitements... Paris [P. Dupont,1913]
1000p. illus.,col.plates. 22cm.
Cover-title.

1.Therapeutics. 2.Materia medica. 3.Botany Medical.

NN   0021753   CtY-M

448
N16
1925
Narodetzki, Aaron, 1864–
... La médecine végétale et le régime biologique ... Cent cinquième édition ... Paris, [Orléans, Pigele t, 1925]
1000 p. illus. 21 cm.
At head of title: Livre de santé et d'hygiène.
1. Materia medica and therapeutics.
2. Medical botany. 3. Pathology.

NN   0021754   DNAL

Narodetzki, André.
Devant la guerre: la faillite des trois internationales; l'internationale des nations, l'internationale catholique, l'internationale ouvrière; leur origine, leur doctrine pacifique, leur fonction et leur action en 1914, par André Narodetzki ... Paris, A. Pedone, 1922.
155 p., 2 l. 26ᶜᵐ.

1. Peace. 2. International cooperation. 3. Catholic church. 4. The International. 5. International socialist congress. I. Title.
Library of Congress   JX1948.N3   25-15376

NN   0021755   DLC CaBVaU CtY ICU NN

Narodetzki, André.
... Les internationales et la guerre mondiale... Paris, 1921.
25 cm.
Thèse – Univ. de Paris.
Published also without thesis note, with title: Devant la guerre: la faillite des trois internationales.
Contents: Introduction. –L'internationale des nations. –L'internationale catholique. –L'internationale ouvrière. –Conclusion.

NN   0021756   CtY MH

Narodetzki, André.
Le remède secret; législation et jurisprudence de la Loi du 21 germinal an xi au Décret du 13 juillet 1926, par André Narod Narodetzki ... Paris, Librairie générale de droit et de jurisprudence, 1928.
216 p., 3 l. 23ᶜᵐ.
"Liste des principaux ouvrages et documents consultés": 2d–3d leaves at end.

1. Medicines, Patent, proprietary, etc. 2. Pharmacy—Laws and legislation—France. I. Title.
[*Full name:* André Narod Narodetzki]
Library of Congress   RA401.F7N3   44-19385

NN   0021757   DLC CtY MiU

W
4
P232
1937/38
Narodetzki, Pierre.
Sur l'établissement d'une technique pour étudier les doses homoeopathiques. Paris, Jouve, 1938.
62, [1] p. (Paris. Université. Faculté de pharmacie. Thèse. 1937/38. sér. U. no. 17)

NN   0021758   DNLM CtY

Narodetzky, M.
Stresses in a non-homogeneous cylinder, by M. Narodezky. Academy of sciences, USSR v 58 pp 1305–8, 1947. Translated from the Russian by G. Volkoff.
The organization, Melbourne. 8p. 1954. TD-834.288

NN   0021759   CoDBR

Law
Narodifskiĭ, M   D
Организация проката кинофильмов в СССР; практическое пособие для работников проката и кинофикации. Москва, Госкиноиздат, 1947.
127 p. forms. 19 cm.
Includes legislation of the U.S.S.R.

1. Moving-pictures—Law—Russia. I. Russia (1923– U.S. S.R.) Laws, statutes, etc. II. Title.
Title transliterated: Organizatsiia prokata kinofil'mov v SSSR.
51-39414

NN   0021760   DLC

LA832
.N3
Narodifskiĭ, M   D
Всеобщее обязательное начальное обучение в РСФСР на новом этапе. Под ред. и с предисл. К. С. Чужко. Москва, Гос. учебно-педагог. изд-во, 1931.
75 p. 22 cm.

1. Education—Russia. *Title transliterated:* Vseobshchee obiazatel'noe nachal'noe obuchenie v RSFSR.
51-46922

NN   0021761   DLC

Naroditzky, Nachum
see his later name **Nardi, Nahum,** 1901–

U4
.N34
Народна армија; централни орган оружаних снага ФНРЈ. г. 1– (бр. 1–) ; 2 окт. 1945– Београд.
v. illus. 56 cm. semiweekly.
Issued by Ministarstvo narodne odbrane.

1. Yugoslavia. Armija—Period. I. Yugoslavia. Ministarstvo narodne odbrane. *Title transliterated:* Narodna armija.
53-39908

NN   0021763   DLC

VOLUME 405

Narodna armija, *Belgrad.*
Kalendar. 1953-
Beograd.
v. illus., ports., maps (part col.) 20 cm.

1. Yugoslavia—Armed Forces—Yearbooks.
U10.N3   58-48193

NN 0021764   DLC

Narodna banka FNRJ
Agenda for the ... annual meeting ... [of the
National bank of the Kingdom of Yugoslavia]

NN 0021765   OC1FRB OU

Narodna banka FNRJ.
Banque nationale du royaume de Yougoslavie.

Beograd.
v. in   31 cm.
Title varies: 19   Banque nationale du royaume des
Serbes, Croates et Slovènes.
Vols. for   issued by the bank under an earlier name:
Narodna banka kraljevine Jugoslavije.

1. Banks and banking—Yugoslavia.
HG3236.A33   S D 41–73 rev 2*‡
U. S. Dept. of State.   Library
for Library of Congress   [r54e]‡

NN 0021766   DS FTaSU CU ICJ NN DLC

HG37
.Y8N29   **Narodna banka FNRJ. Bilten.**

Narodna banka FNRJ. *Odeljenje za analize i ekonomska*
izučavanja.
Bilten Odeljenja za analize i ekonomska izučavanja
Narodne banke FNRJ.

Beograd.

Narodna banka FNRJ.
Bulletin trimestriel. Quarterly bulletin. [1.]-   année;
jan./mars 1929-
Beograd.
r. in   maps, diagrs. 28–31 cm.
Vol. for 1929 issued without English title.
Issued by the bank's Service des études économiques under the
bank's earlier name: Narodna banka kraljevine Jugoslavije.
Separately paged supplements accompany some numbers.

HG3233.A34   332.120949   44–37839 rev*

NN 0021768   DLC ICRL CU MdBJ

Law

Narodna banka FNRJ.

Yugoslavia. *Laws, statutes, etc.*
Devizni propisi Jugoslavije, sa komentarom, sudskim
odlukama, zbirkom rješenja Ministarstva financija i okružni-
cama Narodne banke. Rikard Fuks. Zagreb, Tisak "Tipo-
grafije," 1938.

Narodna banka FNRJ.
Ekonomsko-finansiski elaborat o obrtnim sretsvima.
Beograd, 1955.
26 p. illus. 20 cm.
At head of title: Narodna banka FNRJ. Glavna centrala.

1. Capital—Yugoslavia.   I. Title.
HG4234.6.N3   58-25128

NN 0021770   DLC

Narodna banka FNRJ.
Гласник.
Београд.
v. in   30 cm. monthly.
Began publication with Apr. 1947 issue.

Title transliterated: Glasnik.
HG3232.N324   54–35191

NN 0021771   DLC CU

HG3233
.A5   **Narodna banka FNRJ. Glasnik. Supplement.**

Narodna banka FNRJ.
Obaveštenja komitentima. g. 1-
11 avg. 1954-
[Beograd]

Narodna banka FNRJ.
Imenik sedišta Narodne banke FNRJ. Beograd, 1950.
32 p. 24 cm.

1. Banks and banking—Yugoslavia—Direct.   I. Title.
HG3231.N3   55-20410 ‡

NN 0021773   DLC

Narodna banka FNRJ.
Indices de l'activité économique en Yougoslavie. [1.]-
année; 1934-
[Beograd]
v. in   diagrs. 48 x 64 cm. monthly.
Each issue consists of a single sheet.
Issued by the bank's Service des études économiques under the
bank's earlier name: Narodna banka kraljevine Jugoslavije.

1. Yugoslavia—Econ. condit.   2. Yugoslavia—Stat.
HC407.Y6A14   330.9497   42–11405 rev*

NN 0021774   DLC CU NN DL OO DNAL

Narodna banka *F N R J.*
Loi sur la Banque nationale du royaume de Yougoslavie du
17 juin 1931... Beograd: Imprimerie d'état du royaume de
Yougoslavie, 1931. 37 p. 22½ cm.
"Cette loi a été publiée dans le no 137 – XLV de la 'Gazette officielle' du 20 juin
1931."

694067A. 1. Banks and banking—   Jurisp.—Yugoslavia, 1931.
N. Y. P. L.   May 8, 1934

NN 0021775   NN

Narodna banka FNRJ.
Metodološki materijali.
[Beograd]
v. illus. 20 cm.

1. Finance—Yugoslavia.
HG3231.N33   61–39395 ‡

NN 0021776   DLC

Narodna banka FNRJ.
Народна банка, 1884–1934. Топчидер, Завод за израду
новчаница [1935?]
vi, 336 p. illus. (part col.), ports. 32 cm.

I. Title.
Title romanised: Narodna banka.
HG3233.A5 1935   70–229377

NN 0021777   DLC MU

HC407
.Y6N27   **Narodna banka** *FNRJ.*

Народна привреда. 1-   1935–
Топчидер, Завод за израду новчаница.

Narodna banka FNRJ.
National bank of the Kingdom of Jugoslavia
see its   [Report]

Narodna banka FNRJ.
Obaveštenja komitentima. g. 1-
11 avg. 1954-
[Beograd]
v. in   tables. 29 cm. irregular.
Supplements accompany some issues.
Issued as a supplement to the Bank's Glasnik.

I. Narodna banka FNRJ. Glasnik. Supplement.
HG3233.A5   64-38564

NN 0021780   DLC

Narodna banka FNRJ.
Plan računa. 5. izd. Cirkular br. 305/16 od 14 dec. 1953 g.
Beograd, 1953.
54 p. 20 cm.

1. Accounting.
HF5653.N24 1953   59–18147 ‡

NN 0021781   DLC

Narodna banka FNRJ.
Plan računa; cirkular br. 202/14 od 14 juna 1955 g. 6. izd.
Beograd [Zavod za izradu novčanica] 1955.
60 p. 20 cm.

1. Yugoslavia—Economic policy.
HC407.Y6N25 1955   56–20978 rev ‡

NN 0021782   DLC

Narodna banka FNRJ.
Potsjetnik za dugorocno kreditiranje. [Zagreb, 1953]
24 p. 21 cm.
Cover title.

1. Credit—Yugoslavia.   I. Title.
HG3729.Y82N3   59–17027

NN 0021783   DLC

4HG   **Narodna banka FNRJ.**
347   **Potsjetnik za štedne referente.**
[n. p. n. d.]
23 p.

NN 0021784   DLC-P4

Narodna banka FNRJ.
Правила о агенцијама. Београд, 1924.
11 p. 23 cm.

I. Title.   *Title transliterated:* Pravila o agencijama
HG3233.A5 1924   48–37968 rev*

NN 0021785   DLC

VOLUME 405

Narodna banka FNRJ.
　　Правила о комисионим пословима, о давању зајмова на залоге, и о оставама у готову по текућим рачунима. Београд, 1920.
　　14 p. 16 cm.

　　　　　ɪ. Title.　　　*Title transliterated:* Pravila o komisionim poslovima.

　　HG3233.A5　1920　　　　　　45–41021 rev*

NN　0021786　　DLC

Narodna banka FNRJ.
　　Правила о кредитовању и есконтовању. Београд, 1924.
　　14 p.　23 cm.

　　　　ɪ. Title.　　　*Title transliterated:* Pravila o kreditovanju.

　　HG3233.A5　1924º　　　　　　48–37969 rev*

NN　0021787　　DLC

Narodna banka FNRJ.
　　Правила о ломбардовању рецеписа утоварене робе у тпенове. Београд, 1925.
　　7 p.　15 cm.

　　　　ɪ. Title.　　　*Title transliterated:* Pravila o lombardovanju.

　　HG3233.A5　1925a　　　　　　43–34878 rev*

NN　0021788　　DLC

Narodna banka FNRJ.
　　Pravila o organizaciji i poslovanju deviznih obracunskih mesta. Beograd, 1952.
　　10 p.　20 cm.

　　　　1. Foreign exchange—Law—Yugoslavia.　2. Foreign exchange administration—Yugoslavia.　ɪ. Title.

　　　　　　　　　　　　　　　　　　　59–38639 ‡

NN　0021789　　DLC

HG3233
.A5
1923

Narodna banka FNRJ.
　　Правила за жиро-послове. Београд, 1923.
　　13 p.　15 cm.

　　　　ɪ. Title.　　　*Title transliterated:* Pravila za žiro-poslove.

　　　　　　　　　　　　　　　　　　　45–40467 rev*

NN　0021790　　DLC

Narodna banka FNRJ.
　　Правилник о наплати провизија и трошкова. Београд, 1925.
　　18 p.　22 cm.

　　　　ɪ. Title.　　　*Title transliterated:* Pravilnik o naplati provizija.

　　HG3233.A5　1925　　　　　　48–37972 rev*

NN　0021791　　DLC

Narodna banka FNRJ.
　　Priručnik za poslovanje po potrošačkim kreditima. Beograd, 1953.
　　63 p.　illus.　21 cm.

　　　　1. Consumer credit—Yugoslavia.　ɪ. Title.

　　HG3755.N3　　　　　　　　58–32601 ‡

NN　0021792　　DLC

Narodna banka FNRJ.
　　Привилегована Народна банка краљевине Србије, 1884–1909. У Београду, 1909.
　　224 p.　tables, diagrs.　32 cm.

　　　　ɪ. Title.　　*Title transliterated:* Privilegovana Narodna banka

　　HG3233.A5　1909　　　　　　45–40469 rev
　　Library of Congress

NN　0021793　　DLC

Law

Narodna banka FNRJ.
　　Прописи о штедно-кредитном пословању земљорадничких задруга. ₍Београд, Изд. "Службеног листа ФНРЈ"₎ 1949.
　　54 p.　17 cm.

　　　　1. Agricultural cooperative credit associations—Yugoslavia.　ɪ. Title.
　　　　　　　Title transliterated: Propisi o štedno-kreditnom poslovanju zemljoradničkih zadruga.

　　　　　　　　　　　　　　　　　　　55–26520

NN　0021794　　DLC

Narodna banka FNRJ.　Quarterly bulletin
　see its　Bulletin trimestriel.

Narodna banka FNRJ.
　　Razvoj narodne privrede u Jugoslaviji
　　see under title

Narodna banka FNRJ.
　₍Report₎
　₍Beograd₎
　　v.　illus.　26–35 cm.　annual.
　　Began publication in 1920. Cf. Serial publications of foreign governments.
　　Vols. for 19　　–28 issued by the bank under its earlier name: Narodna banka Kraljevine Srba, Hrvata i Slovenaca; 1929– Narodna banka Kraljevine Jugoslavije.

　　　　1. Yugoslavia—Econ. condit.

　　HF3233.A36　　　330.9497　　44–34907 rev 2*

NN　0021797　　DLC IU NSyU NN MH–BA ICU MiU OC1

Narodna banka FNRJ.
　　Spisak vrsta robe i osnovnih koeficijenata za obračun razlike u cenama po uvozu i izvozu za 1954 god. Beograd, 1954.
　　64 p.　24 cm.

　　　　1. Yugoslavia—Comm.　2. Prices—Yugoslavia.　ɪ. Title.

　　HF3732.5.N3　　　　　　　59–27043 ‡

NN　0021798　　DLC

HG3232
.N33

Narodna banka FNRJ.　Statistički bilten.

Narodna banka FNRJ. *Služba društvenog knjigovodstva.*
　　Statistički bilten Službe društvenog knjigovodstva pri Narodnoj banci FNRJ. g. 1–　1955–
　₍Beograd₎

Narodna banka FNRJ.
　　Статути од 25 јуна 1931 године, са изменама и допунама од 16 септембра 1940 године. Београд, 1940.
　　37 p.　20 cm.

　　　　　　　　　　　Title transliterated: Statuti.

　　HG3236.A5　1940'　　　　　　42–26839 rev*

NN　0021800　　DLC

Narodna banka *FNRJ.*
　　Statuts de la Banque nationale du royaume de Yougoslavie. Beograd: Imprimerie d'état du royaume de Yougoslavie, 1931.
　　39 p. incl. forms.　22½ cm.

　　694067A.　1. Banks and banking—　　Yugoslavia.　　May 8, 1934
　　N. Y. P. L.

NN　0021801　　NN

Narodna banka FNRJ.
　　Statuts de la Banque nationale du Royaume des Serbes, Croates et Slovènes. Belgrade, Imp. "Dossitié Obradovitch," 1922.
　　42 p.　23 cm.

　　HG3236.A5　1922　　　　　　27–21354 rev 2*

NN　0021802　　DLC CtY

Narodna banka FNRJ.
　　Tarifa provizija i troškova za usluge u bankarskim poslovima. ₍Beograd₎ Izd. Službenog lista FNRJ, 1952.
　　14 p.　23 cm.

　　　　1. Banks and banking—Service charges.　2. Banks and banking—Yugoslavia.　ɪ. Title.

　　HG3232.N329　　　　　　　59–26620 ‡

NN　0021803　　DLC

Narodna banka FNRJ.
　　Upravljanje bančinim osnovnim sredstvima sa uputstvima za knjiženje; cirkular br. 11/2 od 13 januara 1955 god. Beograd, 1955.
　　41 p.　20 cm.
　　At head of title: Narodna banka FNRJ. Glavna centrala.

　　　　1. Capital—Yugoslavia.　ɪ. Title.

　　HG4234.6.N36　　　　　　59–26671 rev ‡

NN　0021804　　DLC

Narodna banka FNRJ.
　　Uputstva za izvršenje budžeta. Cirkular br. 280/41 od 1 jula 1954. Beograd, 1954.
　　117 p.　21 cm.

　　　　1. Budget—Yugoslavia.　ɪ. Title.

　　HJ2146.5.N3　　　　　　　59–17028 ‡

NN　0021805　　DLC

VOLUME 405

Narodna banka FNRJ.
  Upu?tstva za naplatu faktura (računa) Beograd, 1951.
  42 p. 21 cm.

  I. Title.

  HG3236.A53   53–29317

NN 0021806   DLC OrU

Narodna banka FNRJ.
  Uputstva za odobravanje kredita individualnim poljo-
privrednim proizvođačima. Cirkular br. 254/19 od 6 jula
1954 god. Beograd, 1954.
  55 p. 20 cm.
  At head of title: Narodna banka FNRJ. Glavna centrala.

  1. Agricultural credit—Yugoslavia.   I. Title.

  HG2051.Y8N3   58–36977 rev ‡

NN 0021807   DLC

Narodna banka FNRJ.
  Uputstva za rad po II narodnom zajmu u sedištima Narodne banke FNRJ. Beograd, 1950.
  19 p. 21 cm.

  1. Debts, Public—Yugoslavia.   I. Title.

  HJ8753.N28   59–28200 ‡

NN 0021808   DLC

Narodna banka FNRJ.
  Упутства за рад штедних каса. 2. изд. Београд, 1950.
  36 p. 20 cm.

  1. Savings-banks—Yugoslavia.   I. Title.
        Title transliterated: Uputstva za rad štednih kasa.
  HG1939.Y82N3 1950   55–15554

NN 0021809   DLC

Narodna banka FNRJ.
  Uputstva za rad u unutrašnjem platnom prometu. Beograd, 1955.
  200 p. 20 cm.
  At head of title: Narodna banka FNRJ. Glavna centrala.

  1. Money—Yugoslavia.   I. Title.

  HG1182.N3   58–25129 ‡

NN 0021810   DLC

Narodna banka FNRJ.
  Uputstvo o isijecanju kupona sa potrošačkih karata
radnicima, službenicima i članovima njihove obitelji u
slučaju neopravdanog izostanka sa posla. (Sl. list FNRJ,
broj 60/49) ₍Zagreb, 1950₎
  15 p. 14 cm.

  1. Labor discipline—Yugoslavia.   I. Title.

  HF5549.5.L3N3   59–26570 ‡

NN 0021811   DLC CLU

Narodna banka FNRJ.
  Uputstvo za primenu Tarife provizija i troškova za usluge
u bankarskim poslovima. ₍Beograd₎ Izd. Službenog lista
FNRJ, 1952.
  11 p. 20 cm.

  1. Banks and banking—Yugoslavia.   I. Title.

  HG3232.N3   59–19460 ‡

NN 0021812   DLC

Narodna banka FNRJ.
  Uputstvo za primenu uredbe o izradi i odobrenju in-
vesticionog programa i o polaganju depozita za obezbeđenje
isplate nivesticionih radova. Cirkular Glavne centrale br.
294/25 od 18 avg. 1955 g. Beograd, 1955.
  28 p. 21 cm.
  At head of title: Narodna banka FNRJ. Glavna centrala.

  1. Saving and investment—Yugoslavia.   I. Title.

  HG5682.N2   59–18148 ‡

NN 0021813   DLC

Narodna banka FNRJ.
  Uputstvo za rad na poslovima po unutrašnjim državnim
zajmovima. Beograd, 1954.
  56 p. 20 cm.

  1. Debts, Public—Yugoslavia.   I. Title.

  HJ8753.N3   59–18150

NN 0021814   DLC

Narodna banka FNRJ.
  Uputstvo za rad sa domaćim akreditivima. Beograd, 1950.
  16 p. 20 cm.

  1. Letters of credit—Yugoslavia.   I. Title.

  HG3745.N3   58–33762 ‡

NN 0021815   DLC

Narodna banka FNRJ.
  Uputstvo za tehniku rada po zajmovima za investicije;
cirkular br. 292/36-1-24-8 od 28 jula 1954 god. Beograd,
1954.
  49 p. 20 cm.

  1. Credit—Yugoslavia.   I. Title.

  HG3729.Y82N34   59–26661 ‡

NN 0021816   DLC

Narodna banka FNRJ.
  Uputstvo zemljoradničkim zadrugama za rad na odobra-
vanju investicionih zajmova individualnim poljoprivred.
proizvođačima. Beograd, 1954.
  15 p. 21 cm.

  1. Collective farms—Yugoslavia—Finance.   I. Title.

  HD1491.Y8N28   58–33233 ‡

NN 0021817   DLC

Law   Narodna banka FNRJ.

Yugoslavia. *Laws, statutes, etc.*
  Закон о Народној банци краљевине Југославије од 17
јуна 1931 године, са изменама и допунама према Уредби о
изменама и допунама тога закона, М. с. бр. 1202 од 14 септембра 1940 године. Београд, Штампа Државне штампа-
рије, 1940.

Narodna banka FNRJ.
  Zbirka propisa o službenicima Narodne banke FNRJ; sa
komentarom. Beograd, Narodna banka FNRJ–"Glasnik,"
1954.
  128 p. 20 cm.

  1. Bank employees—Yugoslavia.   I. Title.

  HD8039.B27Y85   58–32602 ‡

NN 0021819   DLC

Narodna banka FNRJ
  see also
  Državna investiciona banka FNRJ, *Belgrad.*

Narodna banka FNRJ
  see also
  Poštanska štedionica FNRJ.

Narodna banka FNRJ. *Centrala za LR Slovenijo, Lju-
bljana.*
  Bančni vestnik.
  ₍Ljubljana₎
    v. in illus., tables. 30 cm. monthly.
  Began publication in 1951. Cf. New serial titles, 1950–60.

  1. Banks and banking—Slovenia—Period.

  HG3234.S5N3   64–38558

NN 0021822   DLC

Narodna banka FNRJ. *Centrala za LR Slovenijo, Ljubljana.*
  Imenik lastnikov tekočih računov. Ljubljana, 1953.
  209 p. illus. 24 cm.

  1. Slovenia—Comm.—Direct.   I. Title.

  HF5167.S53N3   57–27362 ‡

NN 0021823   DLC

Narodna banka FNRJ. *Centrala za LR Slovenijo, Ljubljana.*
  Plan računa. Ljubljana, 1951.
  44 p. 29 cm.

  1. Accounting.

  HF5653.N28   59–18017 ‡

NN 0021824   DLC

Narodna banka FNRJ. *Centrala za LR Slovenijo, Ljubljana.*
  Priročnik navodil za finansiranje investicijske opreme iz
investicijskih kreditov in lastnih sredstev podjetij. Ljubljana, 1952.
  14 p. 21 cm.
  At head of title: Narodna banka FLRJ. Centrala za LRS.
Direkcija stanovanjskih kreditov in fondov.

  1. Capital investments—Yugoslavia.   I. Title.

  HG4234.6.N33   59–18149

NN 0021825   DLC

VOLUME 405

Narodna banka FNRJ. *Centrala za Lu Slovenijo, Ljubljana.*
Priročnik navodil za kreditiranje dovršitve stanovanjskih
zgradb. Ljubljana, 1952.
24 p. 21 cm.
At head of title: Narodna banka FLRJ. Centrala za LRS. Direkcija stanovanjskih kreditov in fondov.

1. Housing—Slovenia—Finance.

HD7337.S6N3   59–26660 ‡

NN   0021826   DLC

                              LR Slovenijo, Ljubljana,
4HG   Narodna banka FNRJ. Centrala za,
8   Priročnik za sestavo analiz za
         reprezentativna podjetja. Ljubljana,
         1952.
                19 p.

NN   0021827   DLC-P4

Narodna banka FNRJ. *Direkcija društvene evidencije.*
Navodilo za gospodarska podjetja v zvezi z vodenjem
družbene evidence. Beograd, 1952.
12 p. 21 cm.
At head of title: Narodna banka FLRJ. Glavna centrala. Direkcija za družbeno evidenco in proračune.

1. Accounting.   I. Title.

HF5653.N295   59–28198 ‡

NN   0021828   DLC

Narodna banka FNRJ. *Direkcija društvene evidencije.*
Uputstvo po poslovima društvene evidencije; ₍cirkular br.
370/34 od 8 oktobra 1954. Beograd, 1954₎
167 p. illus. 21 cm.
At head of title: Narodna banka FNRJ. Glavna centrala. Direkcija društvene evidencije. Br. 370/34. K. br. 158. Važi za sve banke, br. 1.

1. Accounting.   I. Title.

HF5653.N3   58–22033 ‡

NN   0021829   DLC

Narodna banka FNRJ. *Direkcija emisije i trezora.*
Uputstva za poslovanje sa taksenim i poreskim vrednosnicama. ₍Beograd, 1955–
1. v. (loose-leaf) 20 cm.

1. Negotiable instruments—Yugoslavia.   I. Title.

                                                        61–30880

NN   0021830   DLC

Narodna banka FNRJ. *Direkcija za društveno evidenco in
proračune*
see
Narodna banka FNRJ. *Direkcija društvene evidencije.*

Narodna banka FNRJ. *Odeljenje za analize i ekonomska
izučavanja.*
Bilten Odeljenja za analize i ekonomska izučavanja
Narodne banke FNRJ.
Beograd.
v. in   28 cm. monthly.
Published 1946–54.
Issued, 19 –52 as Bilten of the Narodna banka FNRJ.
Superseded by Statistički bilten of the bank's Služba društvenog knjigovodstva.
Vols. -0 called also no. –342.
1. International finance—Period. 2. Economic history—1945—
Period. 3. Finance—Yugoslavia—Period.   I. Narodna banka FNRJ.
Bilten.

HG37.Y8N29   64–48654

NN   0021832   DLC

Narodna banka FNRJ. Odeljenje za analize i
ekonomska izučavanja.
Bulletin timestriel
see under   Narodna banka FNRJ.

Narodna banka FNRJ. *Odeljenje za analize i ekonomska
izučavanja.*
Народна привреда.
Топчидер, Завод за израду новчаница.
v. illus. 31 cm. quarterly.
Issued, 19   by the bank under its earlier name: Narodna
banka kraljevine Jugoslavije. Odeljenje za ekonomska izučavanja.

1. Yugoslavia—Econ. condit.—period.   I. Title.
                           Title transliterated: Narodna privreda.

HC407.Y6A143   64–58816

NN   0021834   DLC

        Narodna banka FNRJ. Odeljenje za analize i
HC407   ekonomska izučavanja.
.Y6A17   Развој народне привреде у Југославији. L'activité écono-
         mique en Yougoslavie.
         Београд.

Narodna banka FNRJ. *Odeljenje za ekonomska izučavanja*
see
Narodna banka FNRJ. *Odeljenje za analize i ekonomska
izučavanja.*

Narodna banka FNRJ. *Service des études économiques*
see
Narodna banka FNRJ. *Odeljenje za analize i ekonomska
izučavanja.*

Narodna banka FNRJ. *Služba društvenog knjigovodstva.*
Statistički bilten Službe društvenog knjigovodstva pri
Narodnoj banci FNRJ. g. 1– 1955–
₍Beograd₎
v. 28 cm. monthly.
Issued, 1955–62 as Statistički bilten of the Narodna banka FNRJ.
Supersedes Bilten of the bank's Odeljenje za analize i ekonomska
izučavanja, published 1946–54.

1. Finance—Yugoslavia—Period.   I. Narodna banka FNRJ.
Statistički bilten.

HG3232.N33   64–48655

NN   0021838   DLC MiU

Narodna banka Kraljevine Jugoslavije, *Belgrad*
see
Narodna banka FNRJ.

Narodna banka Kraljevine Srba, Hrvata i Slovenaca, *Belgrad*
see
Narodna banka FNRJ.

Narodna banka Kraljevine Srbije, *Belgrad*
see
Narodna banka FNRJ.

Narodna biblioteka, *Belgrad*
see
Belgrad. Narodna biblioteka.

Narodna biblioteka, *Cetinje*
see
Cetinje, Yugoslavie. Centralna narodna biblioteka NRCG.

Narodna biblioteka, *Sofia*
see
Sofia. Narodna biblioteka

Narodna biblioteka Narodne Republike Srbije,
Belgrad
see   **Belgrad. Narodna biblioteka.**

Narodna biblioteka v Plovdiv
see   **Plovdiv, Bulgaria. Narodna biblioteka i muzeL.**

Narodna čitalnica v Kranju
see   Kranj, Yugoslavia (City). Narodna
čitalnica.

WM   NARODNA čitanka o alkoholu. 3. izd.
274   Zagreb, ₍Izd. Društva za borbu protiv
N232   alkoholizma u NR Hrvatskoj₎ 1954.
1954   133 p. illus., port.
          Contributions in Serbian, Croatian,
          Slovenian, or Macedonian.
          1. Alcoholism   I. Društvo za borbu
          protiv alkoholizma u NR Hrvatskoj

NN   0021848   DNLM

Narodna država; mesečnik za pitanja državne uprave i
privrede.
Beograd.
v. 24 cm.
Began publication with July 1946 issue.
Issued July 1946–1948 by Savezna kontrolna komisija of Yugoslavia ; 1949–   by Savet za zakonodavstvo i izgradnju
narodne vlasti (called to Apr. 1950 Komitet za zakonodavstvo i
izgradnju narodne vlasti)
Subtitle varies slightly.
1. Yugoslavia—Pol. & govt.—1945–   —Period. 2. Law—Yugoslavia—Period.   I. Yugoslavia. Savezna komisija državne kontrole.
II. Yugoslavia. Savet za zakonodavstvo i izgradnju narodne vlasti.

DR364.N28   54–15188

NN   0021849   DLC CtY NN

... **Narodna enciklopedija srpsko-hrvatsko-
slovenačka** ...
see under   Stanojević, Stanoje, 1874–1937,
ed.

                    Narodna fronta Vojvodine.
DR381
.V6H7   **Hrvatska riječ.**
        Subotica.

Narodna galerija, *Ljubljana*
see
Ljubljana. Narodna galerija.

Narodna galerija u Pragu
see
Prague. Národní galerie.

VOLUME 405

Narodna hrvatska zajednica
see
Croatian Fraternal Union of America.

Narodna i univerzitetska biblioteka SR Makedonije
see
Skopje, Yugoslavia. Narodna i univerzitetska biblioteka.

Narodna in univerzitetna knjižnica, *Ljubljana*
see Ljubljana. Narodna in univerzitetna knjižnica.

Narodna knjiga; bibliografski časopis. g. 1–
1948–
Zagreb.
    v. illus., ports. 21 cm. monthly.

    1. Croatia—Imprints.

Z2124.C7N3   **64–48008**

NN   0021857   DLC MH

Narodna književnost
    see under Matica hrvatska, Zagreb.

Narodna knjižnica. Celji, Tiskal in založil Dragotin
Hribar

2 (1893) - Vošnjak, Jože, 1834-1911
   . Zbrani dramatični in pripovedni spisi

NN   0021859   MH

Narodna knjižnica. Ljubljana, Založil A.Trstenjak

1 (1889) - Vošnjak, Jože, 1834-1911
    Pobratimi

NN   0021860   MH

Narodna krila. g. 1–   1947–
Beograd.
    v. illus., maps, ports. 28 cm.
    Monthly, 19 –51; bimonthly, 1953–
    Publication suspended July 1951-Dec. 1952.
    Journal of Vazduhoplovni savez Jugoslavije.
    Supplements accompany some issues.

    1. Aeronautics—Period. 2. Aeronautics—Yugoslavia.   ɪ. Vazdu-
hoplovni savez Jugoslavije.

TL4.N28   **64–48294**

NN   0021861   DLC

Narodna milicija.
  Beograd.
    v. in   illus., ports., maps, facsims. 24–34 cm. monthly.
    Began publication in 1948.
    Journal of Državni sekretarijat za unutrašnje poslove FNRJ.
    Serbian or Croatian.
    Supplements: "Odgovori na postavljena pitanja," accompany **some**
    issues; Informativni prilog, called no. 12, accompanies v. **13**, no. **12.**

    1. Police—Period. 2. Police—Yugoslavia—Period.   ɪ. Yugoslavia.
Državni sekretarijat za unutrašnje poslove. ɪɪ. Title: Informativni
prilog.

HV7551.N27   63–28516

NN   0021862   DLC

Narodna misao...
    see under Bañanin, Jovo.

Narodna mladezh
    see
    Dimitrovski komunisticheski mladezhki sŭfŭz.

Narodna odbrana, Maribor.
    Koroški Slovenci in plebiscit leta 1920. Maribor
1930
    20 p.

NN   0021865   MH

Narodna odbrana, Maribor.
  Mi in naši Nemci. Maribor, 1928

  31 p.
    1.Germans - Slovenia I.Title

NN   0021866   MH

Народна омладина. г. 1–   нов. 1947–
  ₗБеоградₗ
    v. 20 cm.
    Bimonthly (irregular) 1947-50; monthly, 1951–
    Issues for 1947-49 also called no. 1-12.
    Issued 1947-48 by Centralno veće of Narodna omladina Jugoslavije;
    1949– by its Centralni komitet.

    1. Youth—Yugoslavia—Period.   ɪ. Narodna omladina Jugoslavije.
Centralno veće. ɪɪ. Narodna omladina Jugoslavije. Centralni komitet.
            Title transliterated: Narodna omladina.

HQ799.Y8N28   53–37225

NN   0021867   DLC

HE 3244 NARODNA OMLADINA BOSNE I HERCEGOVINE, Central-
.B6 N23 ni komitet.
    Omladina domovini ; ₗzbirka članaka i repor-
taža o naporima omladine i njenom udjelu u so-
cijalističkoj izgradnji naše zemljeₗ Sarajevo, 1951.
    93 p. illus.

    In Cyrrilic and Latin characters.
    1. Railroads--Bosnia and Hercegovina. 2. La-
bor service--Yugoslavia. I. Title.

NN   0021868   InU

PG560   Narodna omladina Bosne i Hercegovine. Centralni
.Z6   komitet.
    Zora; omladinski časopis za književnost i kulturu. god. 1–
    jan. 1948–
    Sarajevo.

PG560   Narodna omladina Bosne i Hercegovine. **Zemaljsko**
.Z6   **vijeće.**
    Zora; omladinski časopis za književnost i kulturu. **god. 1–**
    jan. 1948–
    Sarajevo.

Narodna omladina Hrvatske. *Centralni komitet*
    Borbeni put SKOJA; fragmenti iz borbe mladih. ₗUre-
dili Vladimir Mirković i Vojislav Živkovićₗ Zagreb,
Mladost, 1953.
    117 p. illus., facsims. 24 cm.

    1. Savez komunističke omladine Jugoslavije.   ɪ. Mirković, Vla-
dimir, ed. ɪɪ. Živković, Vojislav, ed. ɪɪɪ. Title.

HQ799.Y8S372   65–49610

NN   0021871   DLC

4DR   Narodna omladina *Hrvatske.* Central-
Yugo   ni komitet.
116   Narodna vlast omladini. Zagreb,
1950.
    1 v. (unpaged)

NN   0021872   DLC-P4

GV287   Narodna omladina Hrvatske. Centralni komitet.
.C7A58
    Croatia (*Federated Republic, 1945–*   ) *Savjet za pro-
svjetu, nauku i kulturu.*
    Srednjoškolske igre. ₗZagreb, 1953ₗ

NARODNA OMLADINA JUGOSLAVIJE.
    Doboj—Banja Luka 1951. [n. p., 1951] 32 p. illus. 24 cm.

    1. Industrial army—Yugoslavia. 2. Youth—Yugoslavia. 3. Državne
železnice Jugoslavije. Pruga   Doboj—Banja Luka .

NN   0021874   NN

HQ799   Narodna omladina Jugoslavije.
.Y8S374
    Savez komunističke omladine Jugoslavije.
    Конгрес СКОЈ-а и Народне омладине Југославије.
Београд, Центр. ком-т Нар. омладине Југославје, 1949.

HQ799   Narodna omladina Jugoslavije.
.Y8N323
    Предлог Статута са образложењем. Београд, 1953.
    23 p. 20 cm.

              Title transliterated: Predlog Statuta.

                            54–44212

NN   0021876   DLC

Narodna omladina Jugoslavije.
    The Šamac-Sarajevo; youth railway. ₗn. p., 1947?ₗ
    unpaged. illus. 29 cm.

    ɪ. Title.

HE3245.N3A3   51–36285 ‡

NN   0021877   DLC

VOLUME 405

Narodna omladina Jugoslavije.
  Statut. Zagreb, Centralni komitet Narodne omladine Hrvatske ₍cover 1950₎
  72 p. 15 cm.
  "O projektu statuta Narodne omladine Jugoslavije," by Brana Perović: p. 3–30.

      I. Perović, Brana.

      HQ799.Y8N315   54–30174

  NN   0021878   DLC

Narodna omladina Jugoslavije.
  Статут. Цетиње, Центр. ком-т Народне омладине Црне Горе, 1951.
  62 p. 12 cm.

         Title transliterated: Statut.

      HQ799.Y8N322   55–30687 rev ‡

  NN   0021879   DLC

Narodna omladina Jugoslavije.
  Статут. Усвојен на v конгресу Народне омладине Југославије, одржаном од 6–9 марта 1953 г. у Београду. ₍Сарајево, Изд. Омладинске књижаре, 1953₎
  16 p. 12 cm.

         Title transliterated: Statut.

      HQ799.Y8N324   54–43400

  NN   0021880   DLC

Narodna omladina Jugoslavije.
  Statut. ₍Beograd, 1953₎
  7 p. 17 cm.

      HQ799.Y8N3243   56–26244 ‡

  NN   0021881   DLC

Narodna omladina Jugoslavije.
  Статут Народне омладине Југославије. Резолуција v конгреса Народне омладине Југославије. Београд, 1953.
  16 p. 14 cm.

        I. Narodna omladina Jugoslavije. 5. kongres, Belgrad, 1953.
        Title transliterated: Statut Narodne omladine Jugoslavije.

      HQ799.Y8N2342   58–25519 ‡

  NN   0021882   DLC

Narodna omladina Jugoslavije.
  Statute of the People's youth organization of Yugoslavia. Belgrade, Central committee of the People's youth organization of Yugoslavia, 1949.
  73 p. 14 cm.

      1. Youth movement—   Yugoslavia.

  NN   0021883   NN OCl CtY MH

HX365.5
N231
  Narodna Omladina Jugoslavije.
  Statuts de la Jeunesse populaire de Yougoslavie. Belgrade? ₎ Édition du Conceil ₍? ₎ central de la Jeunesse populaire de Yugoslavie, 1946.
  29 p. illus. 20 cm.

      1. Communism - Yugoslavia. 2. Youth movement - Yugoslavia. I. Title.

  NN   0021884   CSt-H

Narodna omladina Jugoslavije
  see also
  Savez komunističke omladine Jugoslavije.

Narodna omladina Jugoslavije. Centralni Komitet.
  Le Congrès commun de l'Union de la jeunesse communiste et de La jeunesse populaire de Yougoslavie. Belgrade, 1949.
  122 p. 20 cm.
    1. Youth. Congresses. Yugoslavia. Belgrade, 1948.

  NN   0021886   NN

Pam.
Coll.
  Narodna omladina Jugoslavije. Centralni komitet.
45197
  Memorandum of the Central Committee of the People's Youth of Yugoslavia to the Executive Committee of the World Federation of Democratic Youth. ₍Walthamstow, Eng., Printed by the Walthamstow Press, 1950?₎
  23 p. 21 cm.

      1. World Federation of Democratic Youth. 2. Youth. Yugoslavia.

  NN   0021887   NcD

Narodna omladina Jugoslavije. *Centralni komitet.*
  Народна држава народној омладини; приручник омладинског руководиоца у агитацији за изборе народних посланика за Народну Скупштину ФНРЈ. ₍Београд₎ 1950.
  56 p. 20 cm.

      1. Narodna omladina Jugoslavije. I. Title.
     Title transliterated: Narodna država narodnoj omladini.

      HQ799.Y8N3274   58–29158 ‡

  NN   0021888   DLC

HQ799
.Y8P5
  Narodna omladina Jugoslavije. Centralni komitet.
  Пионирски руководилац.
  ₍Београд₎

NARODNA OMLADINE JUGOSLAVIJE. *Centralni Komitet.*
  Reports and resolutions [of the] Congress of the People's youth of Yugoslavia.
  Belgrade.   v.   29 cm.

    Issued by its Central committee.

    1. Youth--Congresses--Yugoslavia.

  NN   0021890   NN

Narodna omladina Jugoslavije. *Centralni komitet.*
  Town of solidarity. ₍Belgrade, 1950₎
  30 p. illus. 21 cm.

      I. Title.

      HQ799.Y8N328   57–32373 ‡

  NN   0021891   DLC

Narodna omladina Jugoslavije. *Centralni komitet*
  see also **Narodna omladina Jugoslavije.** *Centralno veće.*

Narodna omladina Jugoslavije. *Centralno veće.*
  Девети пленарни састанак Централног већа Народне омладине Југославије. ₍У Београду₎ 1948.
  78 p. 21 cm.

       Title romanized: Deveti plenarni sastanak.

      HQ799.Y8N329   78–268739

  NN   0021893   DLC

Narodna omladina Jugoslavije. *Centralno veće.*
  Молодежная железная дорога. ₍n. p., 1947?₎
  unpaged (chiefly illus.) 33 cm.

      1. Omladinska pruga Brčko-Banovići. I. Title.
     Title transliterated: Molodezhnaia zheleznaia doroga

      HE3245.O6N3   52–44426 rev ‡

  NN   0021894   DLC

Narodna omladina Jugoslavije. *Centralno veće.*
  Youth Railway. V Ljubljani ₍Central Council of the People's Youth of Yugoslavia, 1947₎
  ₍90₎ p. (chiefly illus., ports., map) 33 cm.

      1. Youth Railway, Sumac-Sarajevo, Yugoslavia.

      HE3244.B6N3   625.1   52–64917 rev

  NN   0021895   DLC NN MH

Narodna omladina Jugoslavije. *Centralno veće*
  see also **Narodna omladina Jugoslavije.** *Centralni komitet.*

Narodna omladina Jugoslavije. *Kongres.*
  ₍Izveštaj₎
  Beograd, Kultura.
    v. illus., ports. 20 cm.
  Croatian or Serbian.
  Vols. 19   lack title.
  Vol. 6–   issued in series : Politička dokumentacija, 2.

      1. Youth—Yugoslavia—Societies, etc.

      HQ799.Y8N33   55–27101 rev

  NN   0021897   DLC

HQ799
.Y8N2342
  Narodna omladina Jugoslavije. 5. kongres, Belgrad, 1953.

Narodna omladina Jugoslavije.
  Статут Народне омладине Југославије. Резолуција v конгреса Народне омладине Југославије. Београд, 1953.

Narodna omladina Jugoslavije. *5. kongres, Belgrad, 1953.*
  v Congress of the People's Youth of Yugoslavia, March 6–9, 1953 : reports and resolutions. Belgrade, Central Committee of the People's Youth of Yugoslavia, 1953.
  52 p. 29 cm.

      1. Youth—Yugoslavia—Societies, etc.

      HQ799.Y8N33   1953g   57–28507

  NN   0021899   DLC

VOLUME 405

Narodna pjesmarica, isdala matica Dalmatinske. Ed. 7. [336p.] Zagreb, Tisak Dionicke tiskare. 1912.

NN   0021900   OC1

Narodna pripovijetke po Karadzicu, Stojanovicu, Valjavcu i drugima. [148p.] Zagreb 19-6.

NN   0021901   OC1

Народна привреда. 1-   1935-
Топчидер, Завод за израду новчаница.
    v. charts, tables. 30 cm.
    Issued by Narodna banka of Yugoslavia (called 1929–41 Narodna banka Kraljevine Jugoslavije)

    1. Yugoslavia—Econ. condit.—Period. 2. Yugoslavia—Stat.
    I. Narodna banka FNRJ.
                    Title transliterated: Narodna privreda.

HC407.Y6N27   64–58501

NN   0021902   DLC

(Narodna prosveta)
Народна просвета.
₍София₎
    v. 26 cm. monthly.
    Organ of Ministerstvo na narodnata prosveta and Tsentralen komitet of Sŭiûz na bŭlgarskite uchiteli.
    Summaries in Russian.

    1. Education—Bulgaria—Addresses, essays, lectures.   I. Bulgaria. Ministerstvo na narodnata prosveta. II. Sŭiûz na bŭlgarskite uchiteli. Tsentralen komitet.

LA950.N67   74–640331
                                             MARC-S

NN   0021903   DLC

Народна просвета ; педагогическо списание.
София.
    v. illus., ports. 23 cm. monthly.
    Began publication in 1945. Cf. Български книгопис, 1945–1950, № 487.
    Organ of Profsŭiûz na rabotnitsite po prosvetata i pechata.
    Tables of contents also in French and Russian

    1. Education—Period. 2. Education—Bulgaria—Period.   I. Profsŭiûz na rabotnitsite po prosvetata i pechata.
                    Title transliterated: Narodna prosveta.

L51.N28   59–19924

NN   0021904   DLC

370.9497
N167   Narodna prosvjeta. god. 1-
            listopad 1944-
        ₍Zagreb₎
            v. 31cm.

        Organ of Ministarstvo prosvjete Narodne republike Hrvatske (varies slightly)

NN   0021905   IU

JN9659
.A45N3
        Narodna radikalna stranka.
            Рад прве главне скупштине странке држане 26. 27. и 28. јула 1882. год. у Крагујевцу. Београд, 1882.
            255 p. 20 cm.
            Cover title.

            1. Serbia—Pol. & govt.
                    Title transliterated: Rad prve glavne skupštine stranke.

                                            51–53531

NN   0021906   DLC

Narodna radikalna stranka u egzilu
    see
Narodna radikalna stranka u izgnanstvu.

Narodna radikalna stranka u izgananstvu.

JN9659
.A45R3
        Радикал.   г. 1-   1952-
        ₍Paris₎

DR55
.N3
        Народна република България ₍историко-географски и културен очерк. н. р., 194-₎
        19 p. 29 cm.
        Cover title.

        1. Bulgaria.   *Title transliterated:* Narodna republika Bŭlgariíà.

DR55.N3   51–53121

NN   0021909   DLC

Народна Република България. ₍п. р.₎ 1946.
    1 v. (various pagings) illus., col. maps. 28 cm.
    Cover title.

    1. Cities and towns—Bulgaria. 2. Bulgaria—Administrative and political divisions.
                Title romanized: Narodna Republika Bŭlgariíà.

HT145.B8N3   72–225933

NN   0021910   DLC

Narodna Republika Crna Gora
    see   **Montenegro** (*Federated Republic, 1945-   *)

Narodna Republika Hrvatska
    see   **Croatia** (*Federated Republic, 1945-   *)

DB366   Narodna Republika Hrvatska; informativni
N37   priručnik. Zagreb [Izdavač: Ured za Informacije Izvršnog Vijeća Sabora NRH] 1953.
            424, 164 p. illus. 24 cm.

            1. Croatia.

NN   0021913   CtY

Narodna Republika Makedonija
    see   **Macedonia** (*Federated Republic, 1945-   *)

Narodna Republika Srbije
    see   **Serbia** (*Federated Republic, 1945-   *)

370.943735
N167   Národná škola slovenská. roč. 1-17; jan.
            1923-20. dec. 1938. Bratislava.
            17v. illus. 24cm.

            Organ of Svāz slovenského učitel'stva.
            Frequency varies.

NN   0021916   IU

Народна Скупштина FNRJ
    see
Yugoslavia. *Savezna Skupština.*

Народна Србска Скупштина, 1-га и 3-га мая 1848. у Карловци държана, пређашня политика дворска, и садашня политика нове мацарске владе. Одъ Єдинога православнога родолюба. У Београду, У Книгопечатни княжества Србскога, 1848.
    60 p. 21 cm.

    1. Voivodina—History. 2. Serbs in Voivodina. 3. Hungary—History—Uprising of 1848–1849.   I. Jedan pravoslavni rodoljub.
                Title romanized: Narodna Srbska Skupština.

DR381.V67N3   75–262954

NN   0021918   DLC

Narodna starina; časopis za historiju i etnografiju južnih Slovjena. knj. 1-   (sv. 1-   ) 1922-
U Zagrebu.
    v. in   illus., ports., maps (part fold., part col.) music. 25 cm. irregular.
    Subtitle varies slightly.
    Journal of Muzej grada Zagreba and other museums.
    Summaries in French.
    Editors: 1922-   J. Matasović and others.

    1. Yugoslavia—Hist.—Period.   I. Matasović, Josip, 1892-   ed.
    II. Zagreb. Muzej grada.

DR301.N35   60–58405

        MdBJ OrPS NcD
NN   0021919   DLC MH NN CSt ICU OU DDO FTaSU NIC INS

Narodna tehnika Jugoslavije
    see
Narodna tehnika, Savez za tehničko vaspitanje.

T4
T2277   Narodna tehnika, Savez za tehničko vaspitanje.
vol. 8-9   Službeni glasnik.

        ₍Beograd ?₎
            v. in   13 cm. irregular.
            Vols.   bound with Tehničke novine, v.
            Croatian or Serbian.

            1. Technical societies—Period.   I. Tehničke novine. Supplement.
            II. Title.

T4.T2277 vol. 8-9   58–47621

NN   0021921   DLC

T4
.T2277   Narodna tehnika, Savez za tehničko vaspitanje.

        Tehničke novine.

        ₍Beograd₎

T4
.T2283   Narodna tehnika, Savez za tehničko vaspitanje.

        Tehnika narodu; tehnika, nauka, privreda, sport.

        Beograd.

        Savez za tehničko vaspitanje.
        Narodna tehnika, Centralni odbor.
        Plenum.

NN   0021924   DLC-P4

        Savez za tehničko vaspitanje.
4T   Narodna tehnika, Centralni odbor.
149   Statut Narodne tehnike. Beograd,
            1949.
            29 p.

NN   0021925   DLC-P4

VOLUME 405

Narodna tehnika, Savez za tehničko vaspitanje. *2. kongres,*
Sarajevo, 1954.
   Materijal sa II Kongresa Narodne tehnike održanog u
Sarajevu 2 i 3 februara 1954 god. Beograd, Narodna teh-
nika, 1954.
   133 p. illus. 17 cm.

   1. Technology—Yugoslavia.   I. Title.

T26.Y8N3 1954   59–37829 ‡

NN   0021926   DLC

Narodna uprava: časopis za pitanja izgradnje narodne vlasti.
god. 1–   1950–
Sarajevo.
   v. in   tables.   24 cm.

   Bimonthly, 1950–   ; monthly, 195
   Issued by Savjet za zakonodavstvo i izgradnju narodne vlasti.
   Serbian or Croatian.

   1. Law—Period.—Bosnia and Herzegovina.   I. Bosnia and Herzegovina (Federated Republic, 1945–) Savjet za zakonodavstvo i
izgradnju narodne vlasti.

                        58–47048

NN   0021927   DLC CU

  DB379   **Narodna vlada hrvatske, formirana u gradu**
  N232   Splitu dnna 14. travnja, 1945.   ₍Zagreb₎
            Državno nakl. poduzece hrvatske, 19
            v.   plates,ports.   20ᶜᵐ.

     1. Croatia - Pol. & govt.

NN   0021928   CSt-H

  4DR   **Narodna vlada Hrvatske, formirana u**
  Yugo   **gradu Splitu dana 14. travnja 1945.**
  114   ₍Split?₎ Državno nakladno poduzece
           Hrvatske, 1945.
           107 p.

NN   0021929   DLC-P4 MH InU CSt-H NNC

Narodna zaštita, Zagreb.
   ...Almanah, 1914.–1924.   ₍Zagreb:₎ Izdali saradnici i prija-
telji Narodne zaštite, 1924.   158 p.   illus., ports., tables.   8°.

   1. Social work—Yugoslavia.
   N.Y.P.L.   October 27, 1931

NN   0021930   NN

Narodna zaštita, Zagreb.
   ...Kako je osnovana i što je učinila Narodna zaštita, 1914.–
1924. (Izvještaj o desetgodišnjem radu.)   Zagreb, 1926.   95 p.
incl. tables.   illus. (ports.)   16°.   ("Slovo" socijalna knjižnica Narodne zaštite.   Svezak 15–16.)

   1. Social work—Yugoslavia.   1914–1924. I. Ser.
   N.Y.P.L.   February 9, 1932

NN   0021931   NN

Narodnaíà armiíà V'etnama
    see
    Vietnam (*Democratic Republic, 1946–*   ) *Army.*

Народная энциклопедія научныхъ и прикладныхъ знаній.
Москва, Тип. И. Д. Сытина, 19
   v.   25 cm.
   At head of title, v.   : Харьковское общество распространенія
въ народѣ грамотности.

   1. Jurisprudence.   I. Khar'kovskoe obshchestvo rasprostranenīa
v narode gramotnosti.
       Title transliterated: Narodnaíà ėnt͡siklopedī-
íà nauchnykh i prikladnykh znanīĭ.

                     55–53228

NN   0021933   DLC KU

Narodnaíà gazeta, *Moscow.*
   Изборникъ. кн. 1–   февр. 1906–
   Москва.
    v.   illus. (part col.)   ports.   28 cm.   monthly.

   1. Orthodox Eastern Church, Russian—Period.
        Title transliterated: Izbornik.

   BX460.N3   51–32520

NN   0021934   DLC

Народная месть. ₍Куйбышев₎ Огиз, Куйбышевское издательство, 1942.
   46, ₍2₎ p.   19¾ᶜᵐ.
   "Сборник очерков, печатается по газетам 'Правда,' 'Известия,'
'Красная звезда,' 'Комсомольская правда' за ноябрь, декабрь 1941 г.,
январь, февраль 1942 г."

   1. World war, 1939– .   —Russia.   2. Guerrillas.
        Title transliterated: Narodnaíà mest'.
   Library of Congress   D764.N34
                      44–46808

NN   0021935   DLC

Narodnaíà molodezh' Bolgarii
    see
    Dimitrovski komunisticheski mladezhki sǔíûz.

Narodnaíà molodezh' IÛgoslavii
    see   **Narodna omladina Jugoslavije.**

  DK511   **Narodnaíà partiíà gortsev Kavkaza.**
  .C3G6
        Горцы Кавказа.   Les Montagnards du Caucase.

        Paris.

Народная поэзия Таджикистана. ₍Сталинабад₎ Госиздат
Таджикской ССР, 1949.
   175 p.   20 cm.
   Errata slip inserted.

   1. Tajik poetry—Translation into Russian.   2. Russian poetry—
Translation from Tajik.
        Title transliterated: Narodnaíà poėzīíà Tadzhikistana.

   PL55.T27N3   50–30546

NN   0021939   DLC

Narodnaíà politicheskaíà konsul'tativnaíà konferentsiíà
Kitaíà
   Chung-kuo jên min chêng chih hsieh shang hui i.

Народная правда. People's truth.   г. 1–   № 1–
   1948–
New York.
   v.   29–45 cm.   biweekly (irregular)
   Organ of the Russkoe narodnoe dvizhenie.
   Editor: 1948–   R. C. Gul'.
   No. 1–16, published in Paris, have title also in French.

   1. Russia — Pol. & govt.—1917–   Period. 2. Russia—Soc.
condit.—Period.   3. Russians in foreign countries—Period.   I. Gul',
Roman Borisovich, ed.   II. Russkoe narodnoe dvizhenie.
        Title transliterated: Narodnaíà pravda.

   DK266.A2N3   53–32067

NN   0021941   DLC NN InU WaU

Narodnaíà Respublika Albaníà
    see
    Albania.

(Narodnaíà Respublika Bolgaríà)
Народная Республика Болгария; историческая библиография.   Москва, Изд-во Академии наук СССР, 1954–
   v.   27 cm.   36.50rub (v. 1)   varies   Bu 72–1616 (v. 3)
   Added t. p. in Bulgarian: Народна република България.
   On leaf preceding t. p., vols. 1–2: Фундаментальная библиотека
общественных наук Академии наук СССР. Болгарский библио-
графический институт имени Елина-Пелина; vols. 3– : Народна
библиотека "Кирил и Методий." Фундаментална библиотека
за обществени науки към Академията на науките на СССР.
   Vols. 3– have t. p. in Bulgarian and added t. p. in Russian.
   Vols. 3– have imprint: София. Народна библиотека "Кирил
и Методий."

       CONTENTS: т. 1. Иванов, Д. Д. 1944–1947.—т. 2. Иванов,
Д. Д. 1948–1952.—т. 3. Кунчева-Едрева, П. Г. 1953–1957.

   1. Bulgaria—Bibliography.   I. Ivanov, Dmitriĭ Dmitrievich,
1896– .   II. Edreva, Pavlina.   III. Akademīíà nauk SSSR. Fundamental'naíà biblioteka obshchestvennykh nauk.   IV. Sofia. Narodna
biblioteka.   V. Title: Narodna republika Bǔlgaríà.

   Z2896.N37   55–27091

NN   0021944   DLC

Народная Румыния; общественно-политический и литера-
турный журна.
 ₍Бухарест₎
   v.   illus., ports., maps.   33–41 cm.   monthly.
   Began publication with May, 1950 issue.
   Vols. for 1950–   called also no.
   Title varies: 1950–   Народно-демократическая Румыния.

   1. Rumania.   *Title transliterated:* Narodnaíà Rumyníà.

   DR201.N3   60–44844

NN   0021945   DLC

  HE7051
  .N3
       Народная связь.
       Москва.
         v.   27 cm.   annual.
         Report for 19   issued by Narodnyĭ komissariat pocht i
       telegrafov SSSR.

        1. Postal service—Russia.   2. Telegraph—Russia.   3. Telephone—
       Russia.   I. Russia (1923–) Narodnyĭ komissariat
       pocht i telegrafov.   *Title transliterated:* Narodnaíà svíàz'.

                      51–24453

NN   0021946   DLC

Narodnaíà volíà (*Political party*)
   Литература партіи Народной воли; 2. ₍i. e. 3.₎ приложе-
ніе къ сборникамъ "Государственныя преступленія въ
Россіи," издающимся подъ ред. Б. Базилевскаго ₍pseud.₎
Paris, Société nouvelle de librairie et d'édition, 1905.
   IV, 978 p.   19 cm.   (Русская историческая библиотека, № 6)
   At head of title: La littérature du partie ₍sic₎ de la "Volonté du
peuple."   Réédité par B. Basilevsky ₍pseud.₎
   1. Russia—Pol. & govt.—1855–1881.   I. íÀkovlev, Vasiliĭ íÀko-
vlevich, 1861–1915, ed.   Gosudarstvennyíà prestuplenīíà v Rossii.
   II. Title.   (Series: Russkaíà istoricheskaíà biblioteka, no. 6)
        Title transliterated: Literatura partīi Narodnoĭ voli.

   JN6598.S6N3   1905   8–2170 rev 2*

NN   0021947   DLC CtY NNC NN CLU NhD MnU TU

VOLUME 405

Narodnaiã volía (*Political party*)
Литература соціально-революціонной партіи "Народной воли." ₁n. p.₎ Тип. Партіи соціалистовъ-революціонеровъ, 1905.
II, 978 p. 19 cm.
At head of title: Партія соціалистовъ-революціонеровъ.
Another ed., published in Paris in the same year under title: Литература партіи Народной воли, was issued as 3d supplement to Государственныя преступленія въ Россіи, edited by V. IA. IAkovlev.
1. Russia—Pol. & govt.—1855–1881.   I. Partiîã sofsialistov-revoliûtsionerov.   II. IAkovlev, Vasiliĭ IAkovlevich, 1861–1915, ed.   Gosudarstvennyiã prestupleniîã v Rossii.   III. Title.
Title transliterated: Literatura sofsial'no-revoliûtsionnoĭ partiî "Narodnoĭ voli."

JN6598.S6N3   1905a   52–51247

NN   0021948   DLC KU CaBVaU TU

Narodnaiã volía (*Political party*) Viêstnikъ (*transliterated:* Viêstnik)
see Viêstnikъ Народной воли (*transliterated:* Viêstnik Narodnoĭ voli)

Narodnaiã volía (*Political party*)
see also
Partiîã sofsialistov-revoliûtsionerov.

Národné divadlo, *Bratislava*
see
Bratislava. Národné divadlo.

4GV
519
Narodne igre Bosne i Hercegovine.
Prva zbirka: Sarajevsko polje.
[1. izd. Sarajevo] Izd. Saveza
Kulturno-prosvjetnih društava
Bosne i Hercegovine [1950]
38 p.

NN   0021953   DLC-P4

Народне јуначке песме. књ. 1–
Београд, 1951–
v. illus. 21 cm. (Моја књига, 2–
Editor: v. 1–   V. Ђурић.

1. Serbian ballads and songs.   I. Ђurić, Vojislav, ed.
Title transliterated: Narodne junačke pesme.

PG1464.N28   54–37912

NN   0021954   DLC

Народне јуначке песме средњих времена. Приредио Војислав Ђурић. Београд, Знање, 1954–
v. 17 cm. (Школска библиотека, 58–
CONTENTS.—1. О Хајдуцима.

1. Folk-songs, Serbian.   2. Serbian ballads and songs.   I. Ђurić, Vojislav, ed.
Title transliterated: Narodne junačke pesme srednjih vremena.

PG1464.N283   55–40946 ‡

NN   0021955   DLC

(Narodne lirske pesme)
Народне лирске песме. ₁Избор извршио, текст за штампу приредио, белешке и речник написао Војислав Ђугић₎ Београд, Ново поколење, 1953.
499 p. 20 cm. (Југословенски писци)

1. Folk-songs, Serbian.   2. Serbian ballads and songs.   I. Ђurić, Vojislav, 1912–   comp.

PG1464.N2839   1953   55–20614 ‡

NN   0021956   DLC

Law
Narodne novine. Supplement.

Pribićević, Adam, 1880–   *defendant.*
Obtužnica, koju je Kr. državno odvjetničtvo u Zagrebu dne 12. siečnja 1908. podiglo protiv Adama Pribićevića i 52 druga radi zločina veleizdaje. ₁U Zagrebu, 1909?₎

Law
Narodne novine. Supplement.

Pribićević, Adam, 1880–   *defendant.*
Stenografski zapisnik, sastavljen kod Kr. sudbenog stola u Zagrebu 3. ožujka 1909. i slijedećih dana o glavnoj raspravi povodom optužnice, koju je podnielo Kr. državno odvjetničtvo u Zagrebu dne 12. siječnja 1908. broj I. 1263–08. protiv Adama Pribićevića i 52 druga radi zločinstva veleizdaje ₁§. 58. sl. c₎ kaz. zakona. U Zagrebu, 1909?

Narodne novine; list južnoslovenskih trudbenika u Mađarskoj.
Budimpesta.
v. illus., ports., maps. 44 cm. weekly.
Title varies: , Naše novine.
Croatian or Serbian.

AP56.N3   58–45137

NN   0021959   DLC

Národné noviny. National news.
Pittsburgh.
v. in   illus., ports. 43 cm. biweekly.
Organ of the National Slovak Society, 19
Includes an English Section.

1. Slovaks in the U. S.—Period.   I. National Slovak Society of the United States of America.   II. Title: National news.

E184.S64N27   64–38849

NN   0021960   DLC IU IEdS NN

Народне песме, 1941–1951. Крагујевац, Светлост, 1952.
78 p. illus. 17 cm.

1. Folk-songs, Serbian.   *Title transliterated:* Narodne pesme.

PG1464.N287   56–19530

NN   0021961   DLC

(Narodne pesme o kraljeviću Marku)
Народне песме о краљевићу Марку. Београд, Дечја књига ₁1951₎
244 p. illus. 21 cm.
Compiled by V. Ђurić.

1. Marko, Prince of Serbia, 1335?–1394—Poetry.   2. Folk-songs, Serbian.   I. Ђurić, Vojislav, 1912–   comp.

PG1464.N288   1951   55–20639 ‡

NN   0021962   DLC

Narodne piesme bosanske i hercegovačke
see under   Kunić, O. Filip.

Народне пјесме. Загреб, Просвјета, 1950.
283 p. 20 cm. (Библиотека "Просвјете," коло 1, књ. 8)

1. Serbian ballads and songs.   *Title transliterated:* Narodne pjesme.

PG1464.N29   55–25050 ‡

NN   0021964   DLC

Narodne pjesme izdala Matica Dalmatinska o svom trošku. U Zadru, Tiskom Demarki-Ružierovim, 1865.

NN   0021965   MH NSyU

Narodne pjesme o boju na Kosovu godine 1389 ...
see under   Pavić, Armin, 1844–1914.

GR 261 NARODNE PJESME O 1000-GODIŠNJICI HRVATSKOG
.C8 N2 Kraljevstva,925–1925. Zagreb, "Lino-tip"
        ₁1926–
        v. illus.

        Contents: ₁knj.₎ 1. Herojske. ₁knj.₎ 2.
Lirske.

        1. Folk-songs—Croatian. Folklore cds.

NN   0021967   InU

Narodne pjesme Muhamedovaca u Bosni i **Hercegovini.**
Sarajevo, Zemaljska štamparija, 1888–89.
2 v. 26 cm.
L. C. set imperfect: all after p. 288, v. 2, wanting.

1. Folk-songs, Serbian—Bosnia and Herzegovina.   2. Folk-songs, Croatian—Bosnia and Herzegovina.   3. Epic poetry, Serbian—Bosnia and Herzegovina.   4. Epic poetry, Croatian—Bosnia and Herzegovina.   I. Hörmann, Kosta, comp.

PG1417.B6N33   75–472655

NN   0021968   DLC

GR 261 NARODNE PRIPOVIJETKE. ILUSTRIRAO LJUBA BABIĆ.
.C8 N3 Zagreb, Izvanredno izd. Matice hrvatske,1911–
        v. illus.

        1. Tales—Croatian. Folklore cds.

NN   0021969   InU

DB678 NÁRODNÉ SLOVENSKÉ SHROMAŽDENIE V TURČIANSKOM
.N23   SV. MARTINE, 1861.
       Akty Slovenského národného shromaždenia v
Turčianskom sv. Martine dňa 6. a 7. júna 1861.
Z naloženia Matice slovenskej ariadil a sostavil
Andrej Sládkovič. ₁V Turčianskom sv. Martine,
Matica slovenská, 1941₎
       297 p. facsims.
       Pref. signed: Fr. Hrušovský.
       1. Slovakia—Hist.

NN   0021970   ICU

VOLUME 405

Národné slovenské shromaždenie v Turčianskom sv. Martine, 1861.
　　Memorandum národa slovenského.
　　(V) Budíne, 1861.

NN 0021971   OC1BHS

DB678
.S53
　　Národné slovenské shromaždenie v Turčianskom sv. Martine, 1861. Memorandum národa slovenského.

Škultéty, Jozef, b. 1853.
　　Slovenské memorandum roku 1861, na 50-ročnú rozpomienku. Sprílohou Memoranduma. V Turčianskom sv. Martine, Nákl. Kníhtlačiarského účastinárského spolku, 1911.

Národné výbory.
　　Bratislava.
　　　v. 30 cm. monthly.
　　　Began publication in 1945?
　　　Official organ of Poverenictvo vnútra.

　　1. Local government — Czechoslovak Republic. I. Slovakia.
Poverenictvo vnútra.

JS4721.N3   56–46682

NN 0021973   DLC

HX
260
S55
N35
1945
　　NÁRODNE výbory ako orgány štátnej moci. L'udové súdy, ich význam a úloha. Bratislava, Vydavatelstvo Pravdy, 1945.
　　　20 p. 17 cm.

　　1. Communism - Slovakia. 2. Slovakia - Pol. & govt. I. Title.a: Ludove sudy, ich vyznam a uloha.

NN 0021974   CaBVaU

Národné zhromaždenie, Turčiansky sv. Martin, 1861
　　see Národné slovenské shromaždenie v Turčianskom sv. Martine, 1861.

Národní a universitní knihovna, *Prague*
　　see
Prague. Národní a universitní knihovna.

Narodni adresar, hrvata-slovenaca-srba; the national directory of the Croat-Slovene-Serb organizations, institutions, business, professional and social leaders in the United States and Canada, édited and published by Ivan Mladineo. New York (*1937)
　　xxxi, (1) p., 1 l., 4–891 numb. col., 1 l., 895–1244 p. 20^{cm}.
　　Maps on lining-papers.
　　"First edition."
　　Includes advertising matter.
　　1. Croats in the U. S.—Direct. 2. Slovenes in the U. S.—Direct. 3. Serbs in the U. S.—Direct. 4. Croats in Canada—Direct. 5. Slovenes in Canada—Direct. 6. Serbs in Canada—Direct. I. Mladineo, Ivan, ed.
                                         38—1471
　　Library of Congress   E184.C93N27
　　—— Copy 2.
　　Copyright A 112544   (40c2)   325.2497097

NN 0022002   DLC WaS MiU FTaSU NcD OC1 OO PP

Národní album; sbírka podobizen a životopisů českých lidí prací a snahami vynikajících i zasloužilých. S ornamentem J. Filipiho (et al. Životopisy pro dílo napsali: Benešovský-Veselý J. J. et al.) V Praze, J. R. Vilímek (1899)
　　280 p., 354 columns. illus., ports. 28 x 36 cm.

　　1. Bohemia—Biography—Portraits. I. Filipi, J., illus. II. Benešovský-Veselý, J. J.

DB202.N28   76–234887

NN 0022003   DLC NN InU TxU OC1

Národní banka československá.
　　Annual report of the National bank of Czechoslovakia ... and minutes of the ... annual general meeting ... 192
(Prague, 192
　　　v. 30^{cm}.
　　　192   has title: Annual report and accounts ... minutes of the ... annual general meeting ...

　　1. Banks and banking—Czechoslovak republic. 2. Finance—Czechoslovak republic.
                                         31–21698
　　Library of Congress   HG3019.C95N25
　　—— 2d set.   (2)   332.1109437

NN 0022004   DLC OC1 CU

Národní banka československá.
　　Bulletin. Oct. 1926–Dec. 1949. Prague.
　　　v. in   maps, diagrs. 26–30 cm. monthly.
　　　Issues for Oct. 1926–   called also no. 1–
　　　Publication suspended 1942–46.
　　　Issue for Nov. 1926 not published.
　　　Supplements, Foreign exchange regulations in Czechoslovakia, accompany most numbers.
　　　Includes legislation.
　　　English, French, and German.
　　　L. C. set incomplete: vols. for 1940–41 wanting.
　　　1. Czechoslovak Republic—Econ. condit.—Period. 2. Foreign exchange—Law—Czechoslovak Republic. I. Czechoslovak Republic. Laws, statutes, etc. II. Title: Foreign exchange regulations in Czechoslovakia.

HC267.B2N3   53–36133

NN 0022005   DLC OC1FRB

Národní banka československá.
　　Czechoslovakia: foreign exchange regulations
　　　see under Czechoslovak Republic. Laws, statutes, etc.

Národní banka československá.
　　Deset let Národní banky československé; jubilejní publikace o československé měně, o činnosti Národní banki československé, o stavu a vývoji národního hospodářství Československé republiky. V Praze, 1937.
　　　445 p. illus., ports., fold. col. map. 19 cm.

　　1. Banks and banking—Czechoslovak Republic. 2. Finance—Czechoslovak Republic. I. Title.

HG3019.C95N32   51–46254

NN 0022007   DLC NSyU ICU

Národní banka československá.
　　... Government announcement dated April 12, 1933, No. 59 of the Code of laws and regulations, of banking competition norms, so far as the interest agreement is concerned, fixed by the Advisory board on banking matters. (Prague, "Orbis", 1933)
　　　10 p. incl. tables. 30cm. (Bulletin of the National Bank of Czechoslovakia, No. 78 (4), Special Annex, April, 1933)

NN 0022008   MH-L

Národní banka československá.
　　Jahresbericht.
　　Prag.
　　　v. tables, maps (part col.) 30 cm.
　　　Began publication in 1926. Cf. Serial publications of foreign governments.
　　　Merged with the bank's Výroční zpráva to form its Zpráva a výroční účty.
　　　Issued, 1939–40 by the bank under its wartime name: Národní banka pro Čechy a Moravu.
　　　Vols. for 19 –39 include section Jahresrechnungen.
　　　———— Jahresrechnungen.
　　Prag.
　　　v. 30 cm.
　　　1. Finance—Czechobanking—Czechoslovak   HG186.C9N312   2. Banks and   slovak Republic.   Republic   60–55014

NN 0022009   DLC

Národní banka československá.
　　Jahresbericht und Jahresrechnungen
　　see its
　　Zpráva a výroční účty.

Národní banka československá.
　　Jahresrechnungen
　　see its
　　Jahresbericht.

Národní banka československá.
　　Měsíční zpráva
　　see its
　　Monatsbericht.

Národní banka československá.
　　Monatsbericht. 1939, no.   –1941, no. 7. Prag.
　　　v. in   illus. 29 cm. monthly.
　　　Vols. for 1939–41 called also no.   –177.
　　　Absorbed by the bank's Monatsbericht. Měsíční zpráva.
　　　Issued by the bank under its wartime name: Národní banka pro Čechy a Moravu.
　　　Includes legislation.
　　　Supplements accompany some issues.
　　　1. Finance—Czechoslovak Republic. 2. Banks and banking—Czechoslovak Republic. I. Czechoslovak Republic. Laws, statutes, etc.

HG186.C9N32   60–55186

NN 0022013   DLC WU

Národní banka československá.
　　Monatsbericht. Měsíční zpráva.
　　Praha.
　　　v. illus., ports., maps. 20 cm. monthly.
　　　Began publication in 1926. Cf. Serial publications of foreign governments.
　　　Issues for 19 –July 1941 (no –177) in Czech, with title: Zprávy.
　　　Issued, 1939–   by the bank under its wartime name: Národní banka pro Čechy a Moravu.
　　　Includes legislation.
　　　Supplements accompany most issues.
　　　1. Finance—Czechoslovak Republic. 2. Banks and banking—Czechoslovak Republic. I. Czechoslovak Republic. Laws, statutes, etc.

HG186.C9N33   60–55185

NN 0022014   DLC WU

[Národní banka československá]
　　The most important economic data relating to the new Czecho-Slovakia. [Praha, 1939]
　　　28 p. incl. tables. 30 cm.
　　　1. Industries - Stat. - Czecho-Slovakia.

NN 0022015   NN MH

Narodni banka ceskoslovenská.
　　National bank of Czechoslovakia.   Prague: "Orbis" Pub. Co.(, 1925.) xxiii, 51 p. incl. tables. 8°.

486970A. 1. Banks and banking—   Czecho-Slovakia.
N. Y. P. L.   August 19, 1930

NN 0022016   NN

Narodni banka československá.
　　The National Bank of Czechoslovakia.
　　Speeches made at the constituent general meeting
　　　see under Englis, Karel, 1880–1961.

Národní banka československa.
　　Obchodní sprava. Praha.
　　Title also in German: Geschäftsleitung.

NN 0022018   WU

284.9
N16P
　　Národní banka československá.
　　　La première période décennale de l'activité de la Banque nationale de Tchécoslovaquie; publication jubilaire sur la monnaie tchécoslovaque, l'activité de la Banque, la situation et l'évolution de l'économie tchécoslovaque. Prague, Banque nationale de Tchécoslovaquie, 1937.
　　　496 p., 1 l. incl. illus., ports. maps. 19cm
　　　"Ouvrages en langue étrangère sur la Tchécoslovaquie": p.495–(497).

NN 0022019   DNAL CSt CSt-H

VOLUME 405

Národní banka československá.
... Report
see its Annual report.

Narodni banka ceskoslovenska.
... Speeches made at the constituent general
meeting on 21st March 1926 ...
see Engliš, Karel, 1880–1961.
The national bank of Czechoslovakia. Speeches
made at the constituent general meeting.

Národní Banka Československá.
Statement of condition.

Praha.
v. 30 x 46 cm. weekly.

Includes report on the condition of Czechoslovak state notes debt.

HG3019.C95N315 48–39076*‡

NN 0022022 DLC

Národní banka československá.
Ten years of the National bank of Czechoslovakia; jubilee
publication; currency, activities of the National bank, economic conditions and development of the Czechoslovak republic. ₁Praha₁ Pub. by the National bank of Czechoslovakia,
1937.
3 p. l., 11–486, ₁1₁ p. incl. illus., plates, diagrs. front., ports., double
map, fold. tables. 19ᶜᵐ.
Folded map forms front lining-paper.
"Publications in foreign languages dealing with Czechoslovakia":
p. 485–₁487₁
Published simultaneously in German.
1. Banks and banking—Czechoslovak republic. 2. Finance—Czechoslovak republic. I. Title.
Library of Congress HG3019.C95N33
38–25812
—————— Copy 2. ₁2₁ 332.1109437

ViU NN NNC DNAL OkU MiU
NN 0022023 DLC OrU NcU NcD CtY PU PPT PHC OC1 CU

Národní banka československá.
Zehn jahre Čechoslovakische nationalbank; die čechoslovakische währung, die tätigkeit der Čechoslovakischen nationalbank, die lage und entwicklung der nationalwirtschaft der
Čechoslovakischen republik. Festschrift. Prag, Hrsg. von
der Čechoslovakischen nationalbank, 1937.
542 p. incl. front., illus., plates, diagrs. ports., double map, fold. tab.
19ᶜᵐ.
Folded map forms front lining-paper.
"Fremdsprachige publikationen über die Čechoslovakei": p. 539–542.
Published simultaneously in English.
1. Banks and banking—Czechoslovak republic. 2. Finance—Czechoslovak republic. I. Title.
Library of Congress HG3019.C95N34
38–25813
₁2₁ 332.1109437

NN 0022024 DLC NN MU IU ICU

Národní banka československá.
Zpráva a výroční účty. 1941–
V Praze, Tisk "Politika."
v. tables. 30 cm. annual.
Supersedes the bank's separate publications: Výroční zpráva and
Jahresbericht.
Vols. for 1941– have also title: Jahresbericht und Jahres-
rechnungen.
Czech and German.
Issued by the bank under its wartime name: Národní banka pro
Čechy a Moravu.

HG3019.C95N316 60–55013

NN 0022025 DLC

Národní banka československá.
Zprávy
see its
Monatsbericht.

Národní banka československá
see also
Státní banka československá.

Národní banka pro Čechy a Moravu
see
Národní banka československá.

Národní banka v Praze
see
Národní banka československá.

Národní dělnictvo československa.
České dělnické listy.
see under title

Národní dělnictvo československé
Ceský dělník
see under title

Národní Demokrat. Berwyn, Ill., Felix
Harvánek [1952 ?]
v. illus. 27 cm.
English translation of title: National
Democrat.

NN 0022032 IEdS

Národní divadlo, *Prague*
see Prague. Národní divadlo.

Národní divadlo; list divadelní práce.
Praha.
v. in illus., ports., facsims. 21 cm.
Vols. for 19 1958/59, no. 9 called also v. –34.

1. Prague. Národní divadlo.

PN2616.P8N22 62–43175

NN 0022034 DLC

Národní epika bosenských Mohamedánů
see under Holeček, Josef, 1853–1929, tr.

Narodni etnografski muzej, *Split*
see Split, Yugoslavia. Narodni etnografski muzej.

Narodni front.
₁Београд₁
v. 20 cm. monthly.
Organ of Savezni odbor za organizaciona pitanja of the Narodni
front Jugoslavije.

1. Yugoslavia—Pol. & govt.—1945— —Period. I. Narodni
front Jugoslavije. Savezni odbor za organizaciona pitanja.
DR364.N33 57–42537

NN 0022037 DLC

Narodni front Beograda.
О раду народних одбора у Београду. Београд, 1950.
52, ₁3₁ p. 17 cm. (Потсетник агитатора, 8)
Bibliography : p. ₁55₁

1. Belgrad—Econ. condit. I. Title.
Title transliterated: O radu narodnih odbora u Beogradu.

HC409.B4N3 58–48375

NN 0022038 DLC

Narodni front Beograda.
Пета градска конференција Народног фронта Београда.
₁Београд, Изд. Градског одбора Нар. фронта, 1950₁
44 p. 21 cm.

1. Belgrade—Pol. & govt. I. Title.
Title transliterated: Peta gradska konferencija.

JS6939.B4N3 54–21807

NN 0022039 DLC

Narodni front Beograda. *Gradski odbor.*
Београд 1949; Народни Фронт у борби за изградњу со-
цијализма. ₁Београд, 1950?₁
1 v. (unpaged chiefly illus.) 33 cm.

1. Belgrad—Descr.—Views. I. Title.
Title transliterated: Beograd hiljada devet
stotina četrdeset i deveta.

DR386.N3 54–37978 ‡

NN 0022040 DLC

Narodni front Bosne i Hercegovine.
Правилник о изборима у организацијама ... фронта.
Сарајево, 1951.
13 p. 16 cm.

I. Title.
Title transliterated: Pravilnik o izbo-
rima u organizacijama ... fronta.

JN9679.A5N26 55–23210 ‡

NN 0022041 DLC

Narodni front Bosne i Hercegovine.
Statut. ₁Sarajevo, 1951₁
₁15₁ p. 14 cm.

JN2269.A5N3 57–15133 ‡

NN 0022042 DLC

Narodni front Bosne i Hercegovine.
Statut. Sarajevo, 1951.
₁12₁ p. 21 cm.

JN2269.A5N3 1951a 58–23557 ‡

NN 0022043 DLC

Narodni front Crne Gore. *Komisija za agitaciju i propagandu.*
Материјали за кружоке и курсеве у масовним организацијама. Титоград, 19
v. 17 cm.

1. Communism—Montenegro. I. Title.
Title transliterated: Materijali za kružoke
i kurseve u masovnim organizacijama.

JN9679.A8N3 59–41171

NN 0022044 DLC

VOLUME 405

Narodni front Hrvatske
see also
Socijalistički savez radnog naroda Hrvatske.

Narodni front Hrvatske. *Glavni odbor.*
Pravilnik o izboru organa Narodnog fronta Hrvatske. ₍Osijek, 1951₎
8 p. 15 cm.

1. Croatia—Pol. & govt.   I. Title.

JN2199.C46N3   58–40338 ‡

NN   0022046   DLC

Narodni front Hrvatske. *Glavni odbor. Komisija za agitaciju i štampu*
see
Narodni front Hrvatske. *Komisija za agitaciju i štampu.*

Narodni front Hrvatske. *Gradski odbor, Zagreb*
see
Narodni front Hrvatske. *Odbor grada Zagreba.*

Narodni front Hrvatske. *Komisija za agitaciju i štampu.*
Naša industrija. ₍Zagreb, 1950₎
1 v. (unpaged, chiefly illus.)   19 x 20 cm.

1. Yugoslavia—Economic policy.   I. Title.

HC407.Y6N3   54–40921 ‡

NN   0022049   DLC

Narodni front Hrvatske. *Komisija za agitaciju i štampu.*
Naša kultura prosvjeta. ₍Zagreb, 1950₎
1 v. (unpaged, chiefly illus.)   19 x 21 cm.

1. Croatia—Intellectual life.   I. Title.

DB370.5.N37   55–30162 ‡

NN   0022050   DLC

JN
2199
C46
N37
1946
Narodni front Hrvatske. 1. kongres, Zagreb, 1946.
Prvi kongres Narodne fronte Hrvatske. Zagreb, Izdanja Propagandnog odjela Narodne fronte Hrvatske, 1946.
102 p. illus. 23 cm.

1. Croatia - Pol. & govt.   I. Title.

NN   0022051   CaBVaU

Narodni front Hrvatske. *Odbor grada Zagreba.*
O razvoju i radu Narodnog odbora grada Zagreba. ₍Zagreb, 1952₎
72 p. 17 cm.

1. Zagreb—Econ. condit.   I. Title.

HC268.Z3N3   57–48827 ‡

NN   0022052   DLC

4–HX–372   **Narodni front** *Hrvatske. Odbor grada Zagreba.*
Šesta godišnja konferencija Narodnog fronta grada Zagreba, 4.–5. velj. 1950. godine.
Zagreb, 1950.
48 p.

NN   0022053   DLC-P4

AP58
.B8G5
Narodni front Jugoslavije.
Глас на Българите в Югославия; вестник на Народни фронт.
г. 1–   1949–
₍Белград₎

Narodni front Jugoslavije.
Izborni proglas. Sarajevo ₍Izdaje Komisija za agitaciju i štampu Glavnog odbora NF-a Bosne i Hercegovine₎ 1950.
12 p. 20 cm.

1. Yugoslavia—Pol. & govt.—1945–   I. Title.
     Title transliterated: Izborni proglas.

JN9679.A5N282   54–33232

NN   0022055   DLC

Narodni front Jugoslavije.
Изборни проглас. Сарајево ₍Издаје Комисија за агитацију и штампу Главног одбора НФ-а Босне и Херцеговине₎ 1950.
12 p. 20 cm.

1. Yugoslavia—Pol. & govt.—1945–   I. Title.
     Title transliterated: Izborni proglas.

JN9679.A5N28   54–33409

NN   0022056   DLC

Narodni front Jugoslavije.
Југославија—доследан борац за мир. Београд, 1950.
27 p. 18 cm. (*Its* Политичка библиотека, 10)

1. Yugoslavia—For. rel.—1945–   2. World politics—1945–
I. Title.   *Title transliterated:* Jugoslavija—dosledan borac za mir.

DR370.N27   53–30139

NN   0022057   DLC

NARODNI FRONT JUGOSLAVIJE.
Materijali za ideološki odgoj članova Narodnog fronta.
[Zagreb] 1949.   1 v.   20cm.

Dio 2.
By Tito and others.

1. Bolshevism—Yugoslavia. I. Tito, Josip Broz, known as, 1892–

NN   0022058   NN

JN9679
.A5N37
Narodni front *Jugoslavie.*
Kardelj, Edvard, 1910–
Narodni front Jugoslavije; zadaci, program, statut. Beograd, Kultura, 1945.

Narodni front Jugoslavie.
Реферати со дискусија од седницата на Извршниот одбор на НФЈ и Резолуција за задачите на НФЈ што се во тек. Скопје, Изд. Глав. одбор на Народниот фронт на Македонија, 1950.
56 p. 20 cm. (Политичка библиотека, 3)

     Title transliterated: Referati so diskusija od sednicata na Izvršniot odbor na NFJ.

JN9679.A5N285   59–29435 ‡

NN   0022060   DLC

Narodni front Jugoslavije.
Rezolucija i referati sa sjednice Izvršnog odbora Narodnog fronta Jugoslavije, održane 23. i 24. januara 1950. ₍Zagreb₎ Vjesnik NF Hrvatske, 1950.
39 p 22 cm.

1. Yugoslavia—Pol. & govt.—1945–

JN9679.A5N29   55–33428

NN   0022061   DLC

JN9679
.A5N3
Narodni front Jugoslavije.
Седница Извршног одбора Народног фронта Југославије; реферати и резолуција. Београд, 1950.
35 p.   22 cm. (*Its* Политичка библиотека, 7)

1. Yugoslavia—Pol. & govt.—1945–   I. Title.
     Title transliterated: Sednica Izvršnog odbora Narodnog fronta Jugoslavije.

     53–24058

NN   0022062   DLC

Narodni front Jugoslavije.
Spoljna trgovina FNRJ. ₍Beograd₎ Savezni odbor Narodnog fronta Jugoslavije ₍1950₎
24 p. 17 cm. (Materijali za izbornu agitaciju)

1. Yugoslavia—Comm.   I. Title.

HF3732.N3   55–35119

NN   0022063   DLC

4HX–406   **Narodni front Jugoslavije.**
Temeljna in organizacijska načela. V Ljubljani, Slovenski knjižni zavod, 1945.
16 p.

NN   0022064   DLC-P4

Narodni front Jugoslavije
see also
Socijalistički savez radnog naroda Jugoslavije.

Narodni front Jugoslavije. 2. kongres, Belgrad, 1947.
Drugi Kongres Narodnog fronta Jugoslavije. Referati: Maršala Tita, Sretena Žujovića, Vladimira Bakariča. ₍Beograd₎ Izd. Nar. fronta Jugoslavije, 1947.
51 p. 24 cm.

1. Yugoslavia—Politics and government—1945–   —Congresses. I. Tito, Josip Broz, Pres. Yugoslavia, 1892–   II. Žujović, Sreten. III. Bakarić, Vladimir.

JN9676.N35   1947   76–278683

NN   0022066   DLC

JN9679
.A5N35
1947f
Narodni front Jugoslavije. 2. kongres, Belgrad, 1947.
Tito, Josip Broz, *Pres. Yugoslavia,* 1892–
Народный фронт как всенародная политическая организация; доклад на II конгрессе Народного фронта Югославии 27 сентября 1947 года. Резолюция II конгресса Народного фронта Югославии. Белград ₍Изд-во Союза об-ва журналистов ФНРЮ₎ 1947.

VOLUME 405

Narodni front Jugoslavije. *2. kongres, Belgrad, 1947.*
Die Volksfront Jugoslawiens. Referate auf dem 2. Kongress, 26–28 Sept. 1947. Beograd ₍Jugoslovenska knjiga₎ 1947.
150 p. 19 cm.

1. Yugoslavia—Pol. & govt.—1945–
JN9679.A5N35 1947

52–27899 rev

NN 0022068   DLC

Narodni front Jugoslavije. *4. kongres, Belgrad, 1953.*
IV конгрес Народног фронта Југославије (Социјалистичког савеза радног народа Југославије) 22–25 фебруар 1953. Београд ₍Култура ₁1953₎
149 p. 21 cm.

1. Communism—Yugoslavia—Congresses. 2. Yugoslavia—Pol. & govt.—1945–   I. Socijalistički savez radnog naroda Jugoslavije.
Title transliterated: Četvrti kongres Narodnog fronta Jugoslavije.
JN9679.A5N35 1953

55–35502

NN 0022069   DLC

JN9679
.A5N38
Narodni front Jugoslavije. Savezni odbor za organizaciona pitanja.
Ljudska fronta. leto 1–   avg. 1949–
₍V Ljubljani₎

Narodni front Jugoslavije. Savezni odbor za organizaciona pitanja.
Narodni front
   see under title

Narodni front Makedonije
see
Naroden front na Makedonija.

AP58
.U5R8
Narodni front na Rusinokh u Voĭvodine.

Руске слово.
Руски Керестур.

Law
Národní fronta.

Na ochranu republiky; řeč ministra spravedlnosti **Alexeje** Čepičky, projevy poslanců Národní fronty v Národním shromáždění 6. října 1948. ₍1. vyd. Praha?₎ Ministerstvo informací a osvěty, 1948.

---

4 DB
Cz
108
Národní fronta.
Národný front účinným nástrojom pracujúceho ľudu. Z prejavov predsedu ÚAV NF Antonína Zápotockého a predsedu Národného shromaždenia a generálineho tajomníka ÚAV NF Oldřicha Johna. [Praha? 1950]
56 p.

NN 0022075   DLC–P4

Národní fronta.
Národní fronta účinným nástrojem pracujícího lidu; z projevů předsedy vlády a předsedy ÚAVNF Antonína Zápotockého a generálního tajemníka ÚAVNF Oldřicha Johna. ₍Vyd. 2. V Praze₎ Ústřední akční výbor Národní fronty ₍1951₎
56 p. 22 cm.

1. Czechoslovak Republic—Pol. & govt.—1945–   —Addresses, essays, lectures.   I. Zápotocký, Antonín, Pres. Czechoslovak Republic, 1884–   II. John, Oldřich.
DB215.5.N22 1951

65–66952 ‡

NN 0022076   DLC

Národní fronta.
Program československé vlády Národní fronty Čechů a Slováků, přijatý na prvé schůzi vlády dne 5. dubna 1945 v Košicích. ₍1. vyd. V Praze₎ Ministerstvo informací ₍1945₎
29 p. 19 cm. (Ministerstvo informací. Publikace, čís. 2/45)

I. Title.
JN2229.A5N2

54–36625 ‡

NN 0022077   DLC NSyU

Národní fronta .
   Program nové československé vlády Národní fronty Čechů a Slováků...
      see under   Czechoslovak Republic.

Národní fronta.
Program prvé domácí vlády Republiky, vlády Národní fronty Čechů a Slováků; sbírka dokumentů. ₍Praha₎ Ministerstvo informací ₍1945₎
48 p. 21 cm. (Ministerstvo informací. Publikace, čís. 2/45)

JN2229.A5N22

54–36624 ‡

NN 0022079   DLC

Národní fronta.
Program vlády Národní fronty přednesený předsedou vlády Viliamem Širokým dne 13. prosince 1954 v Národním shromáždění. ₍1. vyd.₎ Praha, Orbis, 1954.
28 p. 21 cm.

1. Czechoslovak Republic—Pol. & govt.—1945–   —Addresses, essays, lectures.   I. Široký, Viliam.   II. Title.
DB215.5.N26

65–82175 ‡

NN 0022080   DLC

BX 1612
.C9 N3
NÁRODNÍ FRONTA.
Zrada Vatikánu a biskupů. V Praze, Vydal Ústřední akční výbor Národní fronty, 1949.
48 p.

1. Church and state in the Czechoslovak Republic
2. Catholic Church in the Czechoslovak Republic
I. Title.

NN 0022081   InU CSt–H

---

4 K
Cz
142
Národní fronta. Ustrední akční výbor.
Naše nové občianske právo; prejavy prednesené v pléne Národného shromaždenia dňa 25. októbra 1950. [Praha? 1950]
64 p.

NN 0022082   DLC–P4

Národní fronta. Ústřední akční výbor.

Přehled státně politických akcí, významných výročí a jubileí.
Praha, Orbis.

AYS09
S5S6
Narodni fronta. Ústřední akční výbor.

Slovenský ľudový kalendár
Bratislava, Ústredný akčný výbor NF.

Národní galerie, Prague
See
Prague. Národní galerie.

NARODNI Glasnik, Chicago.

Chicago.   v.   illus., ports.   57cm.

Film reproduction. Positive.
Weekly.

1. Croatians in the U. S. --Per.   and soc. publ.

NN 0022086   NN

Národní hlásnik; noviny pre slovenský lud.
Turčiansky Svatý Martin.
v.

NN 0022087   MiU

Národní jednota československých protestantů v Americe a v Kanadě
see National Union of Czechoslovak Protestants in America.

Národní jednota dcer americanské revoluce
see
Daughters of the American Revolution.

DB 200.7 NÁRODNÍ JEDNOTA PRO VÝCHODNÍ MORAVU, OLOMOUC
.A2 N2   Zprava
192
V Olomouci
   v. illus.

· 1. Minorities--Czechoslovak Republic

NN 0022090   InU

Slavic-   Národní Jednota Sokolská ve Spojených Státech.
American   Cvičení prostná stanovená ku sletu
Imprints   Slovanského Sokolstva v Americe a závodům
Coll.   Národní Jednota Sokolská. New York,
420.33   Národní Jednota Sokolská, 1909.
C953
            5 p. illus. 35 cm.

            English translation of title: Calisthenics for the Slet of Slavic Sokols in America and the contests of National Sokol Union.

NN 0022091   IEdS

Národní jednota sokolská ve Spojených Státech.
Památník Národní jednoty sokolské ve Spojených Státech; na oslavu 25-letého trvaní. ₍Chicago, 1904₎
223 p. illus. 31 cm

1. Národní jednota sokolské ve Spojených Státech—History.
2. Czechs in the United States.   I. Title.
GV203.N3726

74–231158

NN 0022092   DLC OC1

VOLUME 405

Národní Jednota Sokolská *ve Spojených Státech.*
  Stanovy Národní Jednoty Sokolske ve
Spojených Státech; přijaté na sjezdu v
Detroit, Michigan, v měsíci říjnu 1908.
Chicago, Ill., Národní Jednota Sokolská
ve Spojených Státech, 1908.
  79 p.   15 cm.
  English translation of title: By-Laws of
National Sokol Union in United States; adopted
at the Convention at Detroit, Michigan on
October 1908.

NN   0022093   IEdS

Národni Jednota v Racine, Wis.
  Stanovy Národni Jednoty v Racine, Wis.
Racine, Wis., 1916.
  26 [3] p.   14 cm.
  English translation of title: Statute of
National Union at Racine, Wis.
  Contents. –Stanovy Národní Jednoty v Racine,
Wis., přijaté dne 1. unora 1885. (Statute of
National Union at Racine, Wis., approved on
February 1, 1885) – Vedlejší pravidla, přijatá
v řádne schuzi dne 5. prosince, 1915. (By-rules
approved at the regular meeting on December 5,
1915)

NN   0022094   IEdS

  AY
  809   NÁRODNÍ kalendár. V B. Bystrici,
  S5   Matica Slovenská, 1866–
  N37   v. illus. 20 cm. (Matica
            Slovenská, Turčiansky sv. Martin./
            Spisy, čis. 10. etc)

          1. Almanacs, Slovak. 2. Literary
        calendars. I. Series.

NN   0022095   CaBVaU MH

Narodni kalendar.
  Sarajevo, Seljačka knjiga.
    ¡v. illus., ports. 23 cm.
  Croatian and Serbian.

      1. Almanacs, Croatian. 2. Almanacs, Serbian.   I. Seljačka knjiga,
    Sarajevo.
    AY1038.C7N39   58–30402

NN   0022096   DLC

Národní klenotnice. č. 1–
  New York City ¡etc.¡ 1949–
    no. in   v. 27 cm. irregular.
    Editor: 1949–   O. Odložilik.

      1. Czech literature—Period.   I. Odložilik, Otakar, 1899–   ed.
    PG5020.N34   65–30128

NN   0022097   DLC DDO

Národní knihovna, *Prague*
  see **Prague. Národní knihovna.**

Národni koledar in Letopis Matice Slovenske zaleto
    1867–68
      see under   Slovenska Matica v Ljubljani.

Národní komise vědecké organizace, Prague.
  Veroeffentlichungen des Tschechoslowakischen Nationalko-
mitees für wissenschaftliche Organisation.
  no. 1

Prag, 1930   8°.
  no.

    Contents:
  no. 1a. TRNKA, F. Über den durch Unfälle verursachten volkswirtschaftlichen Verlust.
    1930.

NN   0022101   NN

  DB 205   NÁRODNÍ KRONIKA ČESKÁ. REDIGUJE FRANTIŠEK
  .N23   Roubík. Praha, J. Elstner, 1941–
              v. illus.

          Each vol. has also special title.

            1. Bohemia––Hist. I. Roubík, František,
          1890–   , ed.

NN   0022102   InU CLU

      Narodni list, New York. 1908–lip. 1911, 1912
        18, 1920–21 (Incomplete) New York, N. Y.
        illus.

        Microfilm. Daily.

          1. American newspapers (General) –
        Croatian.

NN   0022103   NN

  PE1129   Narodni list, New York.
  .S73B7   FOR OTHER EDITIONS
  1914   SEE MAIN ENTRY
    ¡Brozović, Stjepko¡ 1874–
        Gramatika hrvatsko-englezka. Razgovori za sve prilike
      života i englezko-hrvatski te hrvatsko-englezki riečnik.
      Izdalo uredničtvo "Narodnog lista." New York, N. Y.,
      Croatian printing & publishing co., 1914.

      Narodni list, *New York.*

      Hammerling, Louis Nicholas, 1874–
        A menace to Americanization. New York, N. Y., Na-
      rodni list, 1919.

      Narodni list, *New York.*
        Ratne pjesme o ratovanju i junačtvu hrvata i hrvatskih regi-
      menta u krvavom svjetskom ratu. Sabralo za hrvate u Americi.
      Uredničtvo "Narodnog lista." N¡ew¡ Y¡ork¡ Naklada tiskare
      "Narodnog lista," "Croatian printing & publishing co." ¡°1915¡
        352 p. 23½°°.

        1. Croatian literature—U. S. 2. Croatian poetry. 3. European war,
      1914–1918—Poetry.   I. Croatian printing and publishing co., New
      York. II. Title.
                                              15—20555
        Library of Congress   PG1681.N3

NN   0022106   DLC

      Narodni list (*Zadar*)
        Jubilarni broj Narodnoga lista (Il Nazionale) 1862–1912.
      Zadar, 1912.
        116 p. illus., ports. 58 cm.

        PN5355.C7N3   57–51080

NN   0022107   DLC

  AN 52   NÁRODNÍ listy. roč. 1–81; 1861–1941.
  N3   V Praze.
              v. illus. 58 cm. daily.

NN   0022108   CaBVaU

  Národní Listy, Prague. červen-list., 1906. V
    Praze. 1 reel. 47–58 cm.

  Microfilm. Daily.

      1. Czechoslovak newspapers (General)

NN   0022109   NN

  Národní listy.
    Jubilejní sborník, 1861–1941
      see   Národní listy, 1861–1941; jubilejni
    sborník.

  Národní listy.
    Literaní listy
      see under title

  PN 5169   NÁRODNÍ LISTY.
  .P89 N23   Půl století "Národních listů"; almanach
              ¡1860–1910¡   V Praze, Tiskem a nákl. Pražské
            akciové tiskárny ("Narodni listy") ¡1910¡
              245 p. illus.,ports.

          1. Czech newspapers. I. Title.

NN   0022112   InU MB

  Národní listy.
    Půl století "Národních listů"; almanach.
  V Praze, Tiskem a nákladem pražské akciové
  tiskarny ("Národní listy") ¡1911¡
    244 p. plates, port.

      1. Czech literature - Collections. I. Title.

NN   0022113   NNC MH

  Národní listy, 1861–1941; jubilejní sborník.
  Praha ¡Tiskem a nákladem Pražské akciové
  tiskárny¡ 1941.
    253 p. illus., ports.

    Title on spine reads: Sborník národních
  listů, 1861–1941.

NN   0022114   NNC MH MiU NcU InU ICU CtY NNMM IU

  Narodni muzej ...

    People's museums with names beginning as indicated above are
  entered under the name of the city, e. g. Belgrad. Narodni muzej.

  057.86   Národní myšlenka; revue českého nacionalismu.
  NAR   roč. 1–14; 1923/24–1936/37.   V Praze.
              14v. 23cm.

NN   0022116   IU

VOLUME 405

Lilly
AN 52
.P8 N23
NÁRODNÍ NOWINY. dub.5,1848-led.17, 1850
W Praze, Wojtech H. Deym, 1848-50.
3v. in 2   42-47 cm.   daily

Publication suspended, June 10-25, 1848.
Supplements to nos.6,13,17,24,30,32,42,
48,55,66,78 of v.2, bound to follow v.3,no.17.
Edited by Karel Havlíček.
Contains also Sotek,Příloha k Národním
Novinám
Bound in quarter calf and marbled boards.

NN   0022117   InU IU NNC

NÁRODNÍ nowiny. Číslo. 1-
dub. 5 1848-led. 1850.
Praha, W. Deym.

reels.

Microfilm copy (negative) of the original
in the New York Public Library.
Collation of the original: v.
Daily except Monday (slightly irregular);
not published June 11-23, 1848.
Editor: Karel Hawliček et al.

Various nos. include supplements.
Suppressed by the government in Jan. 1850.

1. Bohemia - Hist. - Revolution, 1848 -
Sources. 2. Austria - Hist. - Revolution,
1848-1849 - Sources. 3. Newspapers -
Bohemia. I. Havlíček, Karel, ed.
1821-1856

NN   0022119   CaBVaU

Národní nowiny.
Duch národnich novin
    see under   Havlíček, Karel, 1821-1856.

Narodni odbor grada Kragujevca
    see
Kragujevac, *Yugoslavia. Narodni odbor.*

Narodni odbor grada Pule
    see
Pula, *Yugoslavia (City) Narodni odbor.*

Narodni odbor grada Zenice
    see
Zenica, *Yugoslavia. Narodni odbor.*

Narodni odbor Sreza Crnogorskog
    see
Crna Gora, *Serbia (District) Narodni odbor.*

Narodni odbor Sreza Pančevačkog
    see
Pančevo, *Serbia (District) Narodni odbor.*

Národní písně.   v Praze, A. Reinwart, [1877].
    pp. 138 +.   (Sbírky prostonárodní.)

Ballads–Bohemian||Series

NN   0022126   MH

Narodni pisnicky; vydala česko-americka
matice skolska.   [48p.]   [N.Y. Hlava, n.d.]

NN   0022127   OC1

Slavic-
American
Imprints
Coll.
420.33
P573
Národní písničky.   New York?, Česko-Americká
Matice Skolská [1910?]
    47 p.   23 cm.

English translation of title: National
songs.

NN   0022128   IEdS

NÁRODNÍ písničky.   [New York] Vydala
Česko-americká matice školská [1913?-17?]
    2 v.   28cm.   (Sbírka Česka škola. sv. 14/15, 19/20)

Unaccompanied melodies.
[Sv. 1.] edited by L. Urban; sv. 2. edited by Václav Kopřiva and
others.
1. Folk songs, Czechoslovakian. I. Urban, Ladislav, ed. II. Kopřiva,
Václav, ed. III. Sbírka Česka škola. IV. Kopřiva, Václav.

NN   0022129   NN

Národní podnik Československá pošta, *Prague*
    see
Československá státní pošta, národní podnik, *Prague.*

Národní podnik Československá státní pošta, *Prague*
    see
Československá státní pošta, národní podnik, *Prague.*

Národní podnik Přerovské strojirny
    see
Přerovské strojirny, Národní podnik.

Národní pohádky a pověsti.   v Praze, A. Reinwart, [18—].
    sq. 16°.   pp. (8), 147 +.   (Sbírky prostonárodní.)

Folklore–Bohemia

NN   0022133   MH

Národní pohádky o zvířátkách a dětech. Zobrazil Rudolf Mates.
— V Praze. Weinfurter. [1930.] 63, (1) pp. Colored illus. Colored
plates. Decorated title-page. Illustrated end-papers. 26½ cm.

N7886 — Bohemia. Folk-lore.   — Animals. Stories and anecdotes.
— Mates, Rudolf, illus.— Bohemia. 1.   Works in Bohemian.— Picture books
for children.

NN   0022134   MB

DB379
N37
Narodni pokret u Hrvatskoj u prvoj polovici 19. stoljeća.
Napisao J. Š.   Zagreb, Tisak Hrvatske pučke seljačke
tiskare, 1909.
    61 p.   (Mala knjižnica, sv. 5 i 6)

1. Croatia, Austria - Pol. & govt.   2. Croatia, Austria -
Hist.   I. Š., J.

NN   0022135   CU

AP
52
.N3
Národní rada; (Čechoslovák a Naše zahraničí).
roč. 14-18.
1934-1938.
Praha, Národní rada československá.
5 v.   21cm.   monthly (irregular).

Formed by the union of Čechoslovák and Naše
zahraničí, and continues the volume numbering
of the former.
Title varies slightly.
Vol. 14-18 called also v. 1-5.
Ceased with   v. 18, no. 2.

NN   0022136   NNC MH InU

Národní rada.
Anketa o českém vystěhovalectví, uspořádaná Zahra-
ničním odborem Národní rady české. Přehled odpovědí
podávají Jan Auerhan, Jan Hejret a Alois Svojsík. V Praze,
1912.
    33 p.   24 cm.
"Otištěno z Vlčkovy osvěty 1912."

1. Czechoslovak Republic—Emig. & Immig.   I. Auerhan, Jan.
II. Title.

JV7890.C92N3   60-55607

NN   0022137   DLC NN

Národní rada.
Gutachten der Národní rada česká (des Böhmischen na-
tionalrates) über die Bienerth'sche regierungsvorlage
eines reichsgesetzes über die regelung des sprachenge-
brauches bei den staatlichen behörden im königreiche
Böhmen—mit rücksichtnahme auf den gleichzeitigen ge-
setzentwurf über die kreisregierungen im königreiche
Böhmen und die hiedurch notwendigen änderungen in der
organisation der politischen verwaltung. Genehmigt in
der plenar-jahresversammlung der Národní rada česká
am 4. juli 1909. Übersetzung des böhmischen originals.
Prag, Verlag der Národní rada česká [etc.] 1910.
    115 p.   23cm.
1. Bohemia—Pol. & govt.   I. Bohemia.   Laws, statutes, etc.
II. Title.

Library of Congress   DB205.7.A5 1910   CA 25-603 Unrev'd

NN   0022138   DLC CSt-H

Národní rada.
Národní rada česká. [V Praze, Tiskem "Unie", 1907]
    10 p.   illus.

NN   0022139   MH

Národní rada.
Die nationale steuerleistung und der landeshaushalt im
königreiche Böhmen. Antwort auf die erwägungen des
prof. dr. freih. Wieser. Hrsg. auf anregung der "Národní rada česká." Übersetzt von judr. Georg Hoetzel
... Prag, "Národní rada česká," Commissionsverlag
Bursík & Kohout, 1905.
    3 p. l., [5]-113, [1] p.   2 tab. (1 fold.)   24cm.
CONTENTS.—Vorrede der redaktion.—I. Allgemeine erwägung.—II. Der
inhalt der Wieserschen abhandlung.—III. Zur frage der nationalen steuerleistung in Böhmen, von dr. Theodor Živansky.—IV. Sind die Deutschen in
unserem landeshaushalte verkürzt? Erwägungen der dr. Dobroslav Krejčí.
1. Wieser, Friedrich, freiherr von, 1851-   Die deutsche steuerleistung und der öffentliche haushalt in Böhmen. 2. Finance — Bohemia.
3. Taxation—Bohemia.   I. Hoetzel, Georg, tr.

Library of Congress   HJ2638.B3A4   10-1385

NN   0022140   DLC MH OO ICJ

Národní rada.
Pani Renáta Tyršová
    see under   Czechoslovac Republic.   Národni
rada československá.

VOLUME 405

Národní radá.
DB200.7 Pokyny pro sčítání lidu po stránce národ-
N233 nostní ve smyslu porad sčítací komise menši-
nového odboru Národní rady české; připojen
překlad důvěrných protičeských oběžníků
"Deutscher Volksrat." V Praze, 1910.
45 p. 19cm.

1. Bohemia - Population. 2. Germans in
Bohemia. I. Title.

NN 0022142 CSt-H MH

Národní rada:
Posudek Národní rady české o vládní osnově Bienert-
hové; stran zákona říšského týkajícího se úpravy jazyka
úřadů státních v Království českém ... schválený valným
shromážděním Národní rady české dne 4. července 1909.
V Praze, Nákladem Národní rady české, 1909.
90 p. fold. map. 23ᵐ.

1. Bohemia—Languages. 2. Bohemia—Nationality. 3. Germans in Bohemia. i. Title.

24-27918

Library of Congress DB200.7.A4 1909

NN 0022143 DLC CSt-H MiU

Národní rada.
Příloha k dotazníku Národní rady české ze dne 2.května
1910 ohledně národní daně. [V Praze, 1910]

(7) p. 31 cm.
Title taken from caption.

NN 0022144 MH

Národní rada.
Slovensko po oslobodení
see under Gessay, Ignác.

Národní rada.
Stanoviska Národní rady české v otázce našeho
národohospodářského posílení. [V Praze, Tiskem
Rolnické tiskárny, 1909]

8 p. (Informace odborům Národní rady české,1)

Slav 7326.38.5
Another issue, with imprint "Knihtiskárna
Zmatlik a Palička", and unnumbered series note

NN 0022146 MH

Národní rada.
Základní řády Národní rady české. V Praze,
[1912?]

15 p. 17 cm.
Paper cover serves as title-page.
With corrections in pen. On cover, in pen:
1906-1912.

NN 0022147 MH

Národní rada
see also
Czechoslovak National Council.
Czechoslovak National Council of America.
Czechoslovak Republic. Národní rada česko-
slovenská.

D727 Národní Rada. Slovenská Odbočka.
N37 Slovensko proti revizii Trianonskej smluvy.
Sostavila a vydala: Slovenská odbočka čsl.
národnej rady v Bratislave. Bratislava, 1929.
234 p. 23 cm.

1. Europe - Politics - 1918-1945 - Sources.
2. Trianon, Treaty of, June 4, 1920 (Hungary)
3. Rothermere, Harold Sidney Harmsworth, 1st
viscount, 1868- 4. Slovakia - Hist. I.Title

NN 0022149 CtY

Národní rada badatelská
see Československá národní rada badatelská.

Národní rada česká
see
Národní rada.

Národní rada československa v Římě
see Národní rada.

Národní rada českých zemí
see Národní rada.

Národní rada zemí české
see Národní rada.

Slavic- Národní Síň v Edwardsville, Ill.
American Protokoly sboru ředitelů Národní síně
Imprints v Edwardsville, Ill. Edwardsville, Ill.,
Coll. 1912-
Manuscript
no.21 v. 33 x 19 cm.
The minutes of the board of directors
of the National Hall at Edwardsville, Ill.

NN 0022155 IEdS

Národní souručenství.
Rok Národního souručenství; právní, organisační a pra-
covně programová .základna české národní pospolitosti.
[Praha, Propagační Komise N. S.,1940]
62 p. 17 cm. (Propagační knižnice Národního souručenství, sv. 2)

(Series)

JN2229.A5N26 59-57470

NN 0022156 DLC

Národní správa studentského majetku v Čechách.
Informace vysokoškolákům. V Praze, 1948.
61 p. 15 cm.
Cover title: NSSM podává informace vysokoškolákům.

1. Students—Czechoslovak Republic. 2. Universities and colleges—
Czechoslovak Republic. i. Title. ii. Title: NSSM podává informace vysokoškolákům.

LA688.7.C95N26 53-35438

NN 0022157 DLC

Národní Stanovy Socialistické Strany v Americe;
přijaty na národní konvenci v Indianapolis,
Indiana, 12-17. května 1912 a Pravidla Českého
Odvětí Socialistické Strany v Americe.
Chicago, České Odvěti Socialistické Strany
v Chicago, Ill. [n.d.]
54 p. 15 cm.
National By-Laws of Socialist Party in
America; adopted on the national convention
at Indianapolis, Indiana, May 12-17, 1912
and the Regulations of Czech Branch of Socialist Party in America.

NN 0022158 IEdS

Народни стихови из борбе и изградње. Цетиње, Народна
књига, 1950-
v 17 cm. (Библиотека Културно-просвјетног савеза Црне
Горе)

1. Serbian poetry
Title transliterated: Narodni stihovi iz borbe i izgradnje.

PG1414.N3 52-31170

NN 0022159 DLC

Národní strana svobodomyslná

See
Československá národní demokracie.

Národní střed; čs. živnostník vexilu. Číslo 17-
date;1 ed. 1951-date
Paris, Washington. no. 27-28cm.

Monthly.
"Informační a hospodářská služba Čs. ŽOS v exilu."
*QVA
1. Artisans.—Czecho-Slovakia. 2. Czechs in foreign
countries. 3. Slovaks in foreign countries.
I. Československá živ- nostensko-obchodnická
strana stredostavovs- ká v exilu.

NN 0022161 NN

Narodni šumar; stručni list za šumarstvo i drvnu industriju.
Sarajevo.
v. illus., ports. maps. 23 cm. monthly (Irregular)
Began publication in 1947.
Subtitle varies slightly.
Issued by Sekcija Šumara of the Društvo
inženjera i tehničara Bosne i Hercegovina; Apr. 1951- by
Društvo inženjera i tehničara šumarstva i drvne industrije NR Bosne
i Hercegovine.
Tables of contents also in English, French, and German; summaries
in English, French, and German.
1. Forests and forestry—Period. 2. Forests and forestry—Yugoslavia—Period. i. Društvo inženjera i tehničara Bosne i Hercegovine. Sekcija Šumara. ii. Društvo inženjera i tehničara šumarstva
i drvne industrije NR Bosne i Hercegovine

SD1.N24 60-33720

NN 0022162 DLC

Tzz Narodni svaz českých katoliku v Texas.
282 "Naše dějiny", sestavil a vydává Národní svaz
N167n českých Katolíku v Texas. Granger, Texas,
Tiskem časopisu "Našinec," 1939.
718p. illus.,ports. 24cm.

1. Catholic Church in Texas. 2. Czechs in
Texas. I. Title.

NN 0022163 TxU TxCM

VOLUME 405

D651
G4N232
₍Narodni svet v Ljubljani, Laibach. Pokrajinski
odsek, Gorizia₎
Mémorandum présenté par les Slovènes du pays
de Gorice₁au Conseil national de Ljubljana.
Lioubliana, 1919.
cover-title, 1 l., 7 p.   22ᵐ.

At end: Gorice, le 17 octobre 1918. Comité
nationale, section locale.
Published also in Slovenian.

1. European war, 1914-1918 - Territorial
questions -   Gorizia. 2. Slovenes.
I. Title.

NN   0022164   CSt-H

M30
.N23
Národní tance na Moravě, sebrali a vydali
Lucie Bakešová, Xav. Běhálková, Martin Zeman
a Leoš Janáček. 2.vyd. Praha, Státní nakl.
krásné literatury, hudby a umění, 1953.
44 p. illus.
"Příloha: Čtyřruční klavírní úpravy" (15 p.)
inserted.
For piano; the suppl. for piano, 4 hands.

1. Dance music, Moravian. 2. Piano music
(4 hands), Arranged. 3. Folk dance music,
Moravian. I.   Bakešová, Lucie,
comp.

NN   0022165   ICU

Národní technické museum, *Prague*
see Prague. Národní technické museum.

Narodni univerzitet, *Belgrad*
see
Belgrad. Narodni univerzitet.

Народни војник.
Београд ₍etc.₎
v. in   illus.,ports. 50 cm.
Frequency varies.
Organ of the Vojna oblast of Serbia.

1. Military art and science—Period.   I. Yugoslavia. Armija.
Vojna oblast (Serbia)
                    Title transliterated: Narodni vojnik.

UA829.Y8N35   64-35668

NN   0022168   DLC

Národní výbor pro oslavu svatováclavského tisíciletí.
Svatováclavský sborník, na památku 1000. výročí smrti
knížete Václava svatého. ₍Redigovali Karel Guth et al.₎ V
Praze, 1934-
v. illus. 26 cm.

1. Wenceslaus, Saint, Duke of Bohemia, 907?-935?   I. Guth, Karel,
ed. II. Title.

BX4700.W4N3   55-48869 ‡

NN   0022169   DLC NN MnU IU NcU WU NIC OrPS

Národní výbory; časopis pro poslance a pracovníky NV. 2.
led. 1952-
₍Praha₎
v. in   illus., ports., tables. 22-31 cm.
Frequency varies.
Vols for 1952-   called also v. 1-
Subtitle varies.
Issued 1952-   by Ministerstvo vnitra; 195   by Úřad
předsednictva vlády (with its various sections)
Includes legislation.
Supplements accompany some issues.
1. Local government—Czechoslovak Republic—Period. 2. Czechoslovak Republic—Economic policy—1945—   I. Czechoslovak Republic. Ministerstvo vnitra. II. Czechoslovak Republic. Úřad předsednictva vlády. III. Czechoslovak Republic. Laws, statutes, etc.

JS41.N33   63-47998

NN   0022170   DLC MH-L

Narodni zemaliski muzej, Agram
see   Zagreb. Hrvatski narodni muzej.

Národní zlatodol. Beletristický zlomek českých
národohospodářských snah. Napsal Autor
Nejmenovaný. Praha, Nákl. Václava
Rezníčka, 1896.
118 p.   (Modré knihovny č. 28; Patého
ročníku č. 2)
I. Title: Beletristický zlomek českých
národohospodářských snah.

NN   0022172   NSyU

Národní zpěvníček [1947-48]
see under   Czechoslovak Republic.
Ministerstvo informacf. [supplement]

Národní zpěvníček česko-americký obsahující
zpěvy ku nápěvum ve sbírce písní národních
a vlasteneckých upravené pro piano a harmonium. Věnováno mládeži česko-americké.
3. vyd. Omaha, Národní Tiskárna, 1907.
93 p.   15 cm.
English translation of title: Czech-American
national book of songs containing words to the
melodies in the collection of national and
patriotic songs arranged for the piano and
harmonium. Dedicated to Czech-American
youth.

NN   0022174   IEdS MnHi

Narodni zpěvníček česko-Americký sbírce píšni.
Omaha, Neb., Národní Tiskarny, 1907.
93 p.

NN   0022175   OCl

Národní zpěvník česko-americký;
nejúplnější sbírka všech známých českých
písní národních, vlasteneckých, společenských
i milostných a velmi mnohých písní amerických
v znění anglickém i pěkném překladu původním.
[383p.]
Omaha, Národní Tiskárny, 1909

NN   0022176   OCl

Narodniia musei, Sofia
see   Sofia. Naroden arkheologicheski muzéi.

Národnj báchorky
see under   Mikšicek, M[atej], 1815-1892, ed.

HC407
.Y6A144
Народно благостање. год. 1-
9 фебр. 1929-
Београд.
v. 30 cm. weekly.
Edited by V. J. Bajkić.

1. Yugoslavia—Econ. condit.—Period.   I. Bajkić, Velimir,
1875-   ed.   *Title transliterated:* Narodno blagostanje.

HC407.Y6A144   55-49155

NN   0022179   DLC

Narodno bogatstvo; list za promicanje industrijske agrarne
i šumske proizvodnje. god. 1-
1. Aug. 1922-
Zagreb.
v. in   illus., ports. 30 cm. bi-weekly.

1. Yugoslavia—Indus.—Period.

HC407.Y6A145   51-25715

NN   0022180   DLC

079.497 Narodno jedinstvo. god. 1-   28 ožuj.
NA   1914-
U Zagrebu
v. 52cm. weekly.

NN   0022181   IU

Narodno jedinstvo, ilustrovani zvanični almanah-kalendar
Drinske banovine. god. 1-
1929-
Sarajevo. Izd. Kraljevske banske uprave Drinske banovine.
v. illus., ports., fold. maps, tables. 28 cm.
Serbian or Croatian.

1. Drinska banovina, Yugoslavia. 2. Almanacs, Yugoslav—Drinska
banovina.

DR381.D7N3   38-34149 rev

NN   0022182   DLC

Народно календарче Есперанто.
₍София₎
v. 18 cm. annual.
Cover title.   : Есперанто.
Issued by Bŭlgarski esperantski sŭiuz.

1. Esperanto—Yearbooks. 2. Almanacs, Bulgarian.   I. Bŭlgarski
esperantski sŭiuz.
                    Title transliterated: Narodno kalendarche Esperanto.

PM8201.N3   55-26507 ‡

NN   0022183   DLC

PN2007
.K3
Narodno kazalište, Osijek.
Kazalište.
₍Osijek, Narodno kazalište₎

Narodno kazalište, *Pula*
see
Pula, Yugoslavia (City) Narodno kazalište.

Narodno kazalište, *Šibenik*
see
Šibenik, Yugoslavia (City) Narodno kazalište.

Narodno kazalište, *Split*
see
Split, Yugoslavia. Narodno kazalište.

Народно-хозяйственный план.
Москва ₍etc.₎
v. in   15-24 cm.
Issued by Gosudarstvennaia planovaia komissiia.
Vol. for 1932 consists of reports to and decisions of TSentral'nyi
ispolnitel'nyi komitet SSSR.
Some vols. issued in revised editions.

1. Russia—Economic policy—1917—   I. Russia (1923-
U. S. S. R.) Gosudarstvennaia planovaia komissiia. II. Russia (1923-
U. S. S. R.) TSentral'nyi ispolnitel'nyi komitet.
                Title transliterated: Narodno-khoziaistvennyi plan.

HC331.A35913   51-29951 rev

NN   0022188   DLC

VOLUME 405

Narodno oslobodilačka armija i partizanski odredi Jugo-slavije
see
Yugoslavia. *Armija.*

Народно-отлободилачка борба у заробљеничким логорима, 1941–1945. Београд, Простовета, 1945.
98 p. facsims. 19 cm.
At head of title: Антифашистички одбор бивших заробљеника.

   1. World War, 1939–1945—Prisoners and prisons, Germans.
2. Antifašistički odbor bivših zarobljenika.   *Title romanised:* Narodno-oslobodilačka
       borba u zarobljeničkim logorima.

D805.G3N357   75–243960

NN   0022190   DLC

Narodno osvobodilna vojska in partizanski odredi Jugo-slavije
see
Yugoslavia. *Armija.*

PN2007   Narodno pozorište, Tuzla.
.P63   **Pozorište.**

     ₍Tuzla, Narodno pozorište₎

Narodno-sofsialisticheskaíà partiíà Kuby
see
Partido Socialista Popular (*Cuba*)

Народно стопанство. год. 1, кн. 1–9/10; ноем. 1946– ноем./ дек. 1947. София.
1 v. maps, tables. 28 cm. monthly (irregular)
Organ of Vŭrkhovna stopanska kamara of Bulgaria.

   1. Bulgaria—Econ. condit.—Period.   I. Bulgaria. Vŭrkhovna stopanska kamara.   *Title transliterated:* Narodno stopanstvo.

HC407.B9N27   54–25979

NN   0022194   DLC

NARODNO stvaralaštvo Istre.
Zagreb.

Issued by Institut za narodnu umjetnost Zagreb.

1. Folk lore--Istria.   I. Institut za narodnu umjetnost, Zagreb, Yugoslavia.

NN   0022195   NN

Narodno sveučilište
see
Obrazovanje odraslih.

Narodno sveučilište, *Rijeka*
see
Rijeka, Croatia (City) Narodno sveučilište.

Narodno-trudovoĭ soíûz.
Что мы должны знать.; сокращенный курс национально-политической подготовки. ₍n. p., 1939?₎
80 p. 14 cm.
Issued by the society under its earlier name: Nafsional'no-trudovoĭ soíûz.

   1. Russia—Pol. & govt.—1917–1953.   I. Title.
           Title transliterated: Chto my dolzhny znat'.

DK266.N263   43–37195 rev 2*

NN   0022198   DLC

Narodno-trudovoĭ soíûz.
Dokumente zur Entführung von Dr. Alexander Truschno-witsch. ₍Frankfurt/Main₎ 1954. 37 p. port. 30cm.

   1. Trushnovich, Aleksandr Ru-   dol'fovich, 1893–

NN   0022199   NN

Narodno-trudovoĭ sofûz.
Курсъ національно-политической подготовки. ₍Бѣл-градъ, Изд. Исполнительнаго бюро совѣта союза, 1937–
v. 24 cm.
"На правахъ рукописи."
Bibliography: v. 4, p. 155–159.
Issued by the society under its earlier name: Nafsional'no-trudovoĭ sofûz.

   1. Social sciences. 2. Russia—Pol. & govt.—1936–1953.   I. Title.
           Title transliterated: Kurs national'no-politicheskoĭ podgotovki.

H91.N3   51–40617 rev

NN   0022200   DLC

Narodno-trudovoĭ sofûz.
Основы дела Национально-трудового союза. ₍n. p., n. d.₎
24 p. 21 cm.

   1. Russia—Pol. & govt.—Societies, etc. 2. Russia—Pol. & govt.—
1945-   3. Russians in foreign countries—Societies, etc.   I. Title.
           Title transliterated: Osnovy dela Nafsional'no-trudovogo sofûza.

DK272.5.N3   52–48841 rev

NN   0022201   DLC

AP50   Narodno—trudovoĭ sofûz.
.P66

Посев; голос российского революционного движения.

Frankfurt/Main ₍etc.₎

Narodno-trudovoĭ sofûz.
Программа. ₍Limburg₎ 1947.
45 p. 30 cm.
Issued by the society under its earlier name: Nafsional'no-trudovoĭ sofûz.

   1. Russia—Pol. & govt.—1915–
           Title transliterated: Programma.

DK272.5.N32   51–37924 rev *

NN   0022203   DLC

DK266   **Narodno-trudovoĭ sofûz. Institut izucheniíà**
.A2O2   **SSSR.**
       Обновленная Россия. 1–
       ₍Frankfurt am Main₎ 1953–

Narodno-trudovoĭ sofûz rossiĭskikh solidaristov
see
Narodno-trudovoĭ sofûz.

D651   ₍Narodno vijeće Rijeka-Sušak, Fiume₎
J2P232   Protestation of Fiume against the Italian annexationist projects. Washington, 1919.
     3 *l.* 27^{cm}. ₍With Paris. Peace Conference, 1919. Yugoslavia. Memorandum on the Serbo-Bulgarian relations. Washington, 1919₎
     At head of title: Kingdom of the Serbs, Croats and Slovenes. Official information Bureau, Washington.
     The Jugoslav National Council of Fiume (Sushak) has addressed to ₍the₎ Prime Minister of the Kingdom of the Serbs, Croats and Slovenes, the following protestation against the legislative measures taken by the Italian National Council of Fiume.
   1. European War, 1914–1918 – Territorial questions - Fiume. 2. Fiume. Consiglio na-zionale italiano.   I. Title.

NN   0022206   CSt-H

D643.A7   **Narodno vijeće Rijeka-Sušak, Fiume.**
DP6J9   To the Senate of the United States of
N232   America. ₍Washington?₎ 1919.
     7 *l.* 18^{cm}. ₍Delegation propaganda: Jugo-slavia. Miscellanea₎
     At head of title: Jugoslav National Council of Fiume-Sushak.
     Processed.
     Reply "to the messages addressed to the United States Senate by the 'Italian National Council' of Fiume": *l.* 1.
   1. Fiume. 2. European War, 1914–1918 – Ter-ritorial ques   tions - Fiume. I. Fiume. Consiglio naz   ionale italiano. II. Title.

NN   0022207   CSt-H NN

Народно задругарство.

Београд ₍Пољопривредно издавачко предузеће₎
v. tables. 21 cm. monthly.
Serbian and Croatian.
Includes legislation.

   1. Collective farms—Yugoslavia—Period.   I. Yugoslavia. Laws, statutes, etc.   *Title transliterated:* Narodno zadrugarstvo.

HD1491.Y8N3   58–28013

NN   0022208   DLC

Narodno zdravlje.

Beograd, Medicinska knjiga.
    v. illus., ports., maps. 29 cm. monthly.
Began publication with Jan. 1945 issue.
Organ of Ministarstvo narodnog zdravlja, March 1945- ;
of Komitet za zaštitu narodnog zdravlja, 194
Tables of contents also in English and French; summaries in Eng-lish and Russian.
Croatian or Serbian.
Includes legislation.
   1. Hygiene, Public— Period. 2. Hygiene, Public — Yugoslavia—Period.   I. Yugoslavia. Komitet za zaštitu narodnog zdravlja. II. Yugoslavia. Ministarstvo narodnog zdravlja. III. Yugoslavia. Laws, statutes, etc.

RA421.N22   58–46773

NN   0022209   DLC NSyU InU

Narodno zdravlje u Sovjetskom savezu. Zbornik, sa 21 slikom. Zagreb, Hrvatska naklada, 1940.
3 p. l., 9–331 p., 2 l. illus., diagrs. 20^{cm}. (Hrvatska naklada, 15)
"Ovaj je zbornik pripremio za štampu Redakcioni odbor lekarskog sindikata (Beograd) : dr. Miloš Popović, dr. Sima Milošević, dr. Velizar Kosanović, dr. Dejan Popović, dr. Ljuba Živković, dr. Mlodrag Jovano-vić, dr. Nenad Parenta, dr. Milutin Zečević."—Verso of t.-p.

   1. Hygiene, Public—Russia.   I. Popović, Miloš D., 1876–   ed. II. Milošević, Sima, ed.

Library of Congress   RA513.N3   42–27199

NN   0022210   DLC

Народное дѣло. № –5;   –іюнь 1904. ₍Женева?₎
v. 17 cm.
Began publication with Aug. 1902 issue.
Issued by Partíía sofsialistov-revoliûfsionerov.

   1. Russia—Pol. & govt.—Period.   I. Partíía sofsialistov-revoliû-fsionerov.   *Title transliterated:* Narodnoe dêlo.

DK1.N27   55–45304

NN   0022211   DLC WaU InU

VOLUME 405

Народное искусство СССР в художественных промыслах.
Москва, Искусство, 1940–
v. illus. (part col.) 35 cm.
At head of title, v. 1– : Научно-исследовательский институт художественной промышленности Всекопромсовета.
CONTENTS.—Т. 1. РСФСР. v.

1. Folk art—Russia. 2. Art industries and trade, Russian. I. Moscow. Nauchno-issledovatel'skiĭ institut khudozhestvennoĭ promyshlennosti.
Title romanized: Narodnoe iskusstvo SSSR v khudozhestvennykh promyslakh.

NK975.N3   76–273419

NN   0022212   DLC

Народное хозяйство Казакстана. г. 1–   1926–
Кзыл-Орда.
v. in   fold. map. 27 cm. irregular.
Organ of Gosudarstvennaia planovaia komissiia KSSR, 1926–

1. Kazakhstan—Econ. condit.—Period. I. Kazakh S. S. R. Gosudarstvennaia planovaia komissiia.
Title transliterated: Narodnoe khozīaĭstvo Kazakstana.

HC488.K3N3   48–40380*

NN   0022213   DLC

(Narodnoe khozīaĭstvo Latviĭskoĭ SSR)
Народное хозяйство Латвийской ССР.
Рига, Лиесма ɪetc.ɪ
v. graphs. 22 cm. annual.
Vols. for   issued by TSentral'noe statisticheskoe upravlenie.

1. Latvia—Statistics.   I. Latvian S. S. R. Centrālā statistikas pārvalde.
HA1448.L3N37   74–647529
                                        MARC-S

NN   0022214   DLC

Народное хозяйство СССР.   г. 1–
1920–
Москва, Экон. жизнь ɪetc.ɪ
v. 25 cm. annual.
Title varies: v. 1, Народное хозяйство.—v. 2–3, Народное хозяйство России.

1. Russia—Econ. condit.—Yearbooks. 2. Russia—Econ. condit.—1918–
Title transliterated: Narodnoe khozīaĭstvo SSSR.
HC331.N32   47–44625*

NN   0022215   DLC

Народное хозяйство СССР; сборник. № 1–
Москва, Госпланиздат, 1947–
v. 26 cm.

1. Russia—Econ. condit.—1918–
Title transliterated: Narodnoe khozīaĭstvo SSSR.
HC331.N34   49–24960*

NN   0022216   DLC CaBVaU

Народное хозяйство Средней Азии (*transliterated:* Narodnoe khozīaĭstvo Sredneĭ Azii)
see Sredne-Aziatskiĭ ėkonomicheskiĭ sovet. *Gosudarstvennaia planovaia komissiia.* Контрольные цифры народного хозяйства Средней Азии (*transliterated:* Kontrol'nye fsifry narodnogo khozīaĭstva Sredneĭ Azii)

Народное хозяйство Томской области; статистический сборник.
Москва ɪetc.ɪ, Статистика, etc.ɪ
v. 15–22 cm.
At head of title: ЦСУ-СССР;   ЦСУ РСФСР.
Issued by Statisticheskoe upravlenie Tomskoĭ oblasti.

1. Tomsk, Siberia (Province)—Statistics.   I. Tomsk, Siberia (Province) Oblastnoe statisticheskoe upravlenie.
Title transliterated: Narodnoe khozīaĭstvo Tomskoĭ oblasti.
HA1907.T6N3   58–42771

NN   0022218   DLC

Народное хозяйство в 1920 г. и первую половину 1921 г.
Москва, 1921.
85 p. 25 cm.
At head of title: Российская Социалистическая Федеративная Советская Республика.

1. Russia—Economic conditions—1918–1945.
Title romanized: Narodnoe khozīaĭstvo.
HC335.2.N34   78–263050

NN   0022219   DLC

Народное образование.
Москва.
v.   ports. 26 cm. monthly.
Organ of Narodnyĭ komissariat po prosveshcheniu RSFSR, 1941–46, no. 2; Ministerstvo prosveshcheniu RSFSR, 1946, no. 3–19
Editors: 1946–48, no. 2, A. G. Kalashnikov.—1948, no. 5–19 I. P. Kondakov.

1. Education—Period. 2. Education—Russia.   I. Kalashnikov, Alekseĭ Georgievich, 1893–   ed.   II. Kondakov, I. P., ed.   III. Russia (1917–   R. S. F. S. R.) Narodnyĭ komissariat po prosveshcheniu.   IV. Russia (1917–   R. S. F. S. R.) Ministerstvo prosveshcheniu.
Title transliterated: Narodnoe obrazovanie.
L51.N205   49–26363*

NN   0022220   DLC CaBVaU

Народное образование въ Острогожскомъ уѣздѣ, съ планами школъ и картою грамотности. Воронежъ, Изд. Воронежскаго губ. земства, 1887.
150, 45 p.   map. 26 cm.

1. Education—Russia—Ostrogozhsk (Uezd)—History. 2. Illiteracy—Russia—Ostrogozhsk (Uezd)—History.
Title romanized: Narodnoe obrazovanie v Ostrogozhskom uĕzdĕ.
LA853.O83N3   72–209368

NN   0022221   DLC

Narodnoe pitanie, Vsesoiuznoe paevoe tovarishchestvo
see
Vsesoiuznoe paevoe tovarishchestvo "Narodnoe pitanie."

Narodne predpriatie K. TSeiss, Jena
see
Zeiss (Carl) Jena, VEB.

Народное просвещение в СССР. 1920/21–
Москва.
v. in   tables. 26–30 cm.
Title varies: 1920/21–26/27, Народное образование в СССР.
Official publication of different sections of TSentral'noe statisticheskoe upravlenie.   Issued in 1920/21–25/26 as v. 12 and v. 28 of its Труды (HA1431.A37)

1. Education—Russia—Stat.   I. Russia (1923–   U. S. S. R.) TSentral'noe statisticheskoe upravlenie.   II. Russia (1923–   U. S. S. R.) TSentral'noe statisticheskoe upravlenie. Trudy, t. 12, 28.
Title transliterated: Narodnoe prosveshchenie.
L451.N3   33–38038 rev*

NN   0022224   DLC

Narodnogospodarski vestnik.
letnik 1–2.
10 maj, 1901–15 marc, 1903.
V Ljubljani, Merkur, 1901–03.
2 v. 33cm. monthly.
Organ of Slovensko trgovsko društvo "Merkur".
Superseded in 1904 by Slovenski trgovski vestnik (192 –   Trgovski tovariš)

NN   0022225   NNC

Narodnooslobodilačka vojska Jugoslavije.
Leto borb ob Soči, September 1943–1944
see under title

Narodnostna karta Koroške. — Lastno štetje—Leta 1910 . . . Merilo 1:350.000 . . . [n.p., 1919?]
col. map. 20½ x 42 cm. in folder 27½ cm.

NN   0022227   CSt-H

Národnostní obzor. roč. 1–9; 1930–39.   Praha.
9 v.   quarterly.
Editor: 1930–39 E. Sobota.
Vols. 1–2 published by Československá společnost pro studium menšinových otázek. Vols. 3–9 published by Československá společnost pro studium narodnostních otázek.
1. Minorities – Czechoslovak Republic – Period. 2. Minorities – Europe – Period. 3. Czechoslovak Republic. – Pol. & gov't. – Period. I. Sobota, Emil, 1892–   ed.

NN   0022228   NcU NNC IU MH-L

Národnostní otázky. sv. 1–
V Praze, Orbis, 1933–
Issued by Československá Společnost pro Studium Národnostních Otázek v Praze.

NN   0022229   CtY

Národnostní poplatnost a zemské hospodářství v Král. českém ...
see under   Dvořak, Ladislav Frantíšek, 1888–   ed.

Narodny, Ivan.
American artists, by Ivan Narodny; introduction by Nicholas Roerich ...   New York, Roerich museum press, 1930.
x, 110 p. plates. 19½ cm.   (*Half-title:* New era library. ser. 1– "Lights of America", book 1)
Series title in part on t.-p.
Published 1929.
CONTENTS.—Robert W. Chanler.—John E. Costigan.—Leon Dabo.—Howard Everett Giles.—Eugene Higgins.—Charles W. Hawthorne.—Rockwell Kent.—Leon Kroll.—Gari Melchers.—Eugene Speicher.

1. Painters, American. 2. Artists, American.
Library of Congress   ND212.N3   30–700

NN CaBViP Wa
Or WaT GU OU NcC TNJ NcD PPT PPGi OC1h MB PP NcU
NN   0022231   DLC OrCS FTaSU IdB WaS OrU NjR LU IdU

Narodny, Ivan.
The art of Robert Winthrop Chanler, by Ivan Narodny. Fourteen plates of full color, twenty-seven halftone illustrations.   New York, W. Helburn, inc., 1922.
93 p. incl. illus., plates. 14 col. pl. (1 fold.; incl. front.) 44 cm.
Plates accompanied by guard sheets with descriptive letterpress. Initials.

1. Chanler, Robert Winthrop, 1872?–1930. 2. Art, Decorative. 3. Mural painting and decoration.   I. Chanler, Robert Winthrop, 1872?–1930, illus.
Library of Congress   ND237.C45N3   23—6384

OU OC1MA OC1 ViU PPPM
NN   0022232   DLC CaBVaU KU OrP WaS OrU UU NBB PP

VOLUME 405

Narodny, Ivan.
　　The art of Robert Winthrop Chanler...
Special memorial ed. New York, Roerich
museum press, 1931.
　　93 p.incl.illus.,plates, 14 col.pl.
(1 fold.; incl.front.)

　　1.Chanler,Robert Winthrop,1872?-1930.

NN　0022233　NjP PP

Narodny, Ivan, ed.
　...The dance; introd. by Anna Pavlowa. N. Y.,
The National society of music, °1916.
　284 p. illus. ports. (Art of music, v.10)

NN　0022234　MiD OU

Narodny, Ivan.
　　Echoes of myself; romantic studies of the human soul,
by Ivan Narodny; illustrated by Eugene Higgins. [Stu-
dio ed.] New York & London, The Liberty publishing
company [1909]
　　6 p. l., 11–231 p. front., 3 pl. 22½ᶜᵐ. $3.00
　　"Limited to 999 numbered copies." This copy not numbered.

　　　　　　　　　　　　　　　　　　　9–28955
　　Library of Congress　　PZ3.N168E

NN　0022235　DLC OKentU NcU MiU NN

Narodny, Ivan.
　　Fortune favors fools, a musical comedy at the court of
the Czar, by Ivan Narodny. Tr. from the Russian by
Maria Ossipovna Mieler.
　　(*In* Poet lore. Boston, 1912. 25ᶜᵐ. vol. XXIII, no. V, p. 305–319)

　　ɪ. Mieler, Maria Ossipovna, tr. ɪɪ. Title.
　　　　　　　　　　　　　　　　　　　C D 17–481
　　Library of Congress (Card Division)　　PN2.P7 vol.23

NN　0022236　DLC CaBVaU PU MB ODW OCU NN

Narodny, Ivan.
　　Fortune favors fools, a musical comedy at the court of
the Czar, by Ivan Narodny. Tr. from the Russian by
Maria Ossipovna Mieler. [Boston, R. G. Badger] °1912.
　　p. 315. 25½ᶜᵐ. (Poet lore plays)
　　Reprinted from Poet lore, 1912, vol. XXIII, no. v.

　　ɪ. Mieler, Maria Ossipovna, tr. ɪɪ. Title.
　　　　　　　　　　　　　　　　　　　A 20–1109
　　Title from St. Paul Pub.　　Libr. Printed by L. C.

NN　0022237　MnS ViU WaS PPL MiU MB

Narodny, Ivan.
　　Roerich, Nikolaï Konstantinovich, 1874–
　　... Himalaya, a monograph; articles by Frances R. Grant,
Mary Siegrist, George Grebenstchikoff, Ivan Narodny, and
"Banners of the East", by Nicholas Roerich, with 24 color-
plates and 78 halftones. New York, Brentano's [°1926]

NARODNY, IVAN
　　...How Esthonians are conquering Russia by means of
democracy. New York, N.Y.: Amer. Esthonian league
[1919] 2 l. 26½cm.

　　Caption–title.
　　Reprinted from Estonia.

　　1. Bolshevism—Esthonia. 2. Russia—Hist. 1917–1923—
Civil war. 3. Esthonians in Russia.

NN　0022239　NN

Narodny, Ivan.
　　The inner meaning of Roerich's art.
　　(*In* Roerich, Nikolai Konstantinovitch. Himalaya. . . . Pp. 65–
70. Illus. Plate. New York. [1926.])

NN　0022240　MB

DK267　Narodny, Ivan.　　　　　　　　FOR OTHER EDITIONS
.C63　　　　　　　　　　　　　　　　SEE MAIN ENTRY
1943 a　Cole, Margaret Isabel (Postgate) 1893–
　　　Our soviet ally; essays by Margaret Cole [and others] ...
Edited for the Fabian society by Margaret Cole. London,
G. Routledge & sons, ltd. [1943]

Narodny, Ivan.
　　The skygirl, a mimodrama, in three acts on a star, prologue & epilogue on the earth; dramatic episodes of a life
fifty thousand years ahead of ours, by Ivan Narodny;
foreword by John D. Williams; scenes and costumes by
David Burliuk, Vladimir Bobritsky, Constantine Aladja-
lov and N. Cickovsky. London, New York, The Britons
publishing company [°1925]
　　103 p. incl. front., 1 illus., plates. 25¼ᶜᵐ.

　　ɪ. Title.
　　　　　　　　　　　　　　　　　　　25–15777
　　Library of Congress　　PR6027.A7S5 1925

NN　0022242　DLC

Narodny, Leo H
　　Vanilla cultivation in Dominica, by Leo H. Narodny... A
collection of notes gathered by the author, intended to serve as
a brief guide to those interested in vanilla cultivation in Dominica,
B. W. I. Roseau, Dominica, B. W. I., 1943 [i. e. 1945] 16 l.
22cm.

　　"Errata" corrects imprint date.
　　"Appendix: Constitution of the Dominica vanilla growers association," 3 l., at end.

　　1. Vanilla—Dominica. ɪ. Do-　　　minica vanilla growers' association.
N. Y. P. L.　　　　　　　　　　　February 23, 1949

NN　0022243　NN

Národný americko-slovenský kalendár.
　　Pittsburgh.
　　　v. illus., ports., music. 26 cm.
　　　Title varies: , Kalendar of the Národný slovenský spolok.
　　19　　have also title: Almanac National Slovak Society.
　　　Issued by Národný slovenský spolok v Spojených Štátoch ame-
rickych.
　　　Slovak and English.
　　　Vols. for　　　　　　　　　called also roč.

　　1. Almanacs, Slovak—U. S. ɪ. National Slovak Society of the
United States of America.

　　AY76.N35　　　　　　　　　　58–28913

NN　0022244　DLC NSyU NN

Národný hlásnik. Rocnik I. Budín, Uhorská
Kral. Univ., 1869.

　　　Editor: Feriencik Mikuláš.

NN　0022245　OClBHS

Narodný kalendar pre reimsko a greckokatolikov
a evanjelikov na obyčajný rok ...
　　　see Národný americko-slovenský kalendár.

Národný pracovník; časopis slovenskej osvety.
　　V Bratislave, Štátné nakladatel'stvo.
　　　v. ports., maps, tables. 23 cm. monthly (except July and
Aug.)
　　　Subtitle varies.
　　　Vols. for
　　Ustredná osvetová komisia; Oct. 1941–　　—Sept. 1941, issued by
　　Issues for 1942–　　　　by Osvetové ústredie.
　　Supplement accompanies v. 2, no. 6.　without monthly designations.

　　ɪ. Slovakia. Osvetové ústredie. ɪɪ. Slovakia. Ústredná osvetová
komisia.

　　AP58.S55N3　　　　　　　　· 51–25686

NN　0022247　DLC

Národný slovenský spolok v Spojených Štátoch America-
kých
　　see National Slovak Society of the United States of
America.

Národný spevníček; sto slovenských ľudových
piesní
　　see under Czechoslovak Republic. Ministerstvo informacíí.

Národný sväz slovenských evanjelikov
　　see
National alliance of Slovak Lutherans.

Národný umelec Fraňo Král'
　　see under Lajčiak, Milan, ed.

Národný výbor československý...
　　see under [Československa kolonia v Paříži]

(Narodnye artisty Soûza SSR)
　　Народные артисты Союза ССР. [Текст П. Маркова]
Москва, Искусство, 1937–
　　　v. ports. 36 cm.
　　　CONTENTS: вып. 1. Станиславский, Немирович-Данченко, Ка-
чалов, Москвин, Леонидов, Корчагина-Александровская, Блюмен-
таль-Тамарина, Нежданова, Щукин, Литвиненко-Вольгемут, Сак-
саганский, Васадзе, Хорава, Байсеитова.

　　1. Actors—Russia. ɪ. Markov, Pavel Aleksandrovich, 1897–

　　PN2727.N35　　　　　　　74–213981

NN　0022253　DLC

Народные мстители; сборник литературно-художествен-
ных произведений для самодеятельности, театров и эстрады. Москва–Ленинград, Государственное издательство
"Искусство," 1943.
　　　100, [2] p. 16 x 13ᶜᵐ.
　　　Includes music.

　　　1. World war, 1939–　—Poetry. 2. World war, 1939–　—Fiction.
3. Patriotic poetry, Russian. 4. World war, 1939–　—Songs and
music.　　　　　　　　　*Title transliterated:* Narodnye mstiteli.
　　　　　　　　　　　　　　　　　　　44–40894
　　Library of Congress　　D745.7.R9N3 .

NN　0022254　DLC

Народные песни. [Москва] Военмориздат, 1942.
　　cover-title, 50, [2] p. 14 x 11ᶜᵐ.

　　1. Russian ballads and songs.　*Title transliterated:* Narodnye pesni.
　　　　　　　　　　　　　　　　　　　44–50881
　　Library of Congress　　M1756.N37

NN　0022255　DLC

Narodnyĭ bank, *Moscow*
　see
Moskovskiĭ narodnyĭ bank.

VOLUME 405

Народний декляматор. Коломия, Накладом Я. Оренштайна, 1903.
x, 306 p. 16 cm.

1. Ukrainian poetry (Collections)
Title romanized: Narodnyĭ deklamator.

PG3934.N3   79-229564

NN   0022257   DLC

Народный календарь Союза коммун Северной области.
1.–   ; 1919–
Петроград.
.v. illus. 29 cm.

1. Almanacs, Russian.   I. Soiûz kommun Severnoĭ oblasti.
Title transliterated: Narodnyĭ kalendar'
Soiûza kommun Severnoĭ oblasti.

AY944.N26   54-23380 ‡

NN   0022258   DLC

Narodnyĭ kalendar' Soiûza kommun Severnoĭ oblasti.
... Zur geschichte und tätigkeit der sowjets in Russland;
aus dem Volkskalender des Petrograder sowjets 1919; mit
einem vorwort von M. J. Braun. ¡Berlin¿ Verlag Rote fahne
g. m. b. h., 1919.

1 p. l., iv, 49 p. 22 cm. (Kommunistische bibliothek, nr. 6)

NN   0022259   CSt-H

Narodnyĭ kalendar' Soiûza kommun Severnoĭ oblasti.
... Zur geschichte und tätigkeit der sowjets in Russland;
aus dem Volkskalender des Petrograder sowjets 1919; mit
einem vorwort von M. J. Braun. ¡Berlin¿ Verlag Rote fahne
g. m. b. h., 1919.

1 p. l., iv, 49 p. 22 cm. (Kommunistische bibliothek, nr. 6)

LC copy replaced by microfilm

I. *Soviets.* Hist.—Revolution, 1917-1921. 3. Communism—Russia.   2. Russia—
Hist.—Revolution, 1917-1921. 3. Communism—Russia.   I. Braun,
M. J.
⌈DK266.A3K6 nr. 6⌉   39-30443 rev 2

NN   0022260   DLC

Народный Китай.
¡Пекин, Изд-во лит-ры на иностранных языках¿
.v. illus. 27 cm. semimonthly.
Began publication Nov. 1, 1950.
Issued also in English.

1. China—Hist.—Period.   *Title transliterated:* Narodnyĭ Kitaĭ.

DS701.N25   55-27118

NN   0022261   DLC

Narodnyĭ komissariat gosudarstvennogo prizreniia
RSFSR
see
Russia *(1917–   R. S. F. S. R.) Narodnyĭ komissariat
sotsial'nogo obespecheniia.*

Narodnyĭ komĭssarĭat po Ĭnostrannym
delamRSFSR

see

Russia (1917-   R.S.F.S.R.) Narodnyĭ
komĭssarĭat po Ĭnostrannym delam.

Narodnyĭ komĭssarĭat po Ĭnostrannym
delamSSSR

see

Russia (1923-   U.S.S.R.) Narodnyĭ
komĭssarĭat po Ĭnostrannym delam.

Narodnyĭ komissarĭat prodovol'stviia RSFSR
see Russia (1917-   R. S. F. S. R.)
Narodnyĭ komĭssarĭat prodovol'stviia.

Narodnyĭ komĭssarĭat snabzheniia
see Russia (1923-   U. S. S. R.) Narodnyĭ
komĭssarĭat snabzheniia.

Narodnyĭ komissariat sotsial'nogo obespecheniia RSFSR
see
Russia *(1917–   R. S. F. S. R.) Narodnyĭ komissariat
sotsial'nogo obespecheniia.*

Narodnyĭ komĭssarĭat tiazheloĭ promyshlennostĭ. Sektor nauchno-Ĭssledovatel'skĭĭ Ĭ tekhnĭcheskoĭ propagandy

see

Russia (1923- U. S. S. R.) Narodnyĭ kom
Ĭssarĭat tiazheloĭ promyshlennostĭ.
Sektor nauchno-Ĭssledovatel'skĭĭ Ĭ tek
hnĭcheskoĭ propagandy.

Narodnyĭ komissariat torgovli RSFSR
see
Russia *(1917–   R. S. F. S. R.) Narodnyĭ komissariat
torgovli.*

Narodnyĭ komissariat truda Tatarskoĭ SSR
see **Tatar A. S. S. R.** *Narodnyĭ komissariat truda.*

Народный русскій календарь.
Владимірова бу Свящника. Русск. церков. тчп.
illus. 22 cm.

1. Orthodox Eastern Church. Liturgy and ritual—Calendar. 2.
Orthodox Eastern Church—Catechisms and creeds—Church Slavic.
Title transliterated: Narodnyĭ russkiĭ kalendar'.

BX350.N28   62-19832

NN   0022271   DLC KU

Народный театр; комедии ... ¡Москва¿ "Красная новь,"
1923.
173 p. 22½ᵐ.

Contents.—Ан-скій, С. А. На конспиративной квартире.—Галкин,
Г. Опасное время.—Неверов, А. Смех и горе.—Чижевский, Дм. Си-
волапинская комедия-буффонада.—Шишков, Вяч. На птичьем поло-
жении.

1. Russian drama (Comedy)   *Title transliterated:* Narodnyĭ teatr.
44-22507

Library of Congress   PG3253.N3

NN   0022272   DLC

Народный театръ; сборникъ. Москва ¡Изд. Е. В. Лавро-
вой и Н. А. Попова, 1896¿
256, lxxviii p. illus. (1 fold.) 25 cm.

1. Theater—Russia—Addresses, essays, lectures.
Title romanized: Narodnyĭ teatr.

PN2723.N3   70-286494

NN   0022273   DLC

Narodnyĭ universitet, *Moscow*
see Moscow. Gorodskoĭ narodnyĭ universitet imeni
A. L. Shaniavskogo.

Narodnyĭ universitet imeni A. L. Shaniavskogo, *Moscow*
see
**Moscow. Gorodskoĭ narodnyĭ universitet imeni A. L. Sha-
niavskogo.**

Narodnyia iûzhnorusskiia piêsni
see under   Metlinskiĭ, Amvrosiĭ Luk'iano-
vich, 1814-1870, ed.

Narodnyia skazki, izdannyia Vilandem
see under   Musäus, Johann Karl Aubust,
1735-1787.

Národohospodářská propagace Československa.
Uherský Brod; město a okres
see under   Jarušek, Robert, 1889-   ed.

Národohospodářský ustav při České akademii věd
a umeni v Praze
see   Česká akademie věd a umění, Prague.

Národopis lidu československého.
díl 1-
V Praze, 1922-
v. illus., plates (part col.) maps
(part fold. col.) music, plans (part col.)
tables. 31-32cm.

Issued by Národopisná společnost českoslovan-
ská, československé zemědělské museum a Archeo-
logická komise České akademie věd.
Díl 1, sv. 1 published in 1923.
Summaries in French and German.
Editor: díl 1-   Karel Chotek.

NN   0022281   NNC CtY MH NN

Narodopisje Slovencev. S sodelovanjem Antona Breznika
¡et al.¿ Ljubljana, 1944-52.
2 v. illus. 26 cm. (Klas, znanstvena knjižnica, 1)

Vol. 1 edited by R. Ložar; v. 2, by I. Grafenauer and B. Orel.
Vol. 2 published in parts by Državna založba Slovenije, without
series statement.
Includes bibliographies.

1. Slovenes.   I. Breznik, Anton. II. Ložar, Rajko, ed.
III. Grafenauer, Ivan, ed.

DB34.S6N3   57-43648

MiU CtY KU MiEM IU
NN   0022282   DLC MB OU WaU NNC ICU NN NSvU NIC

VOLUME 405

DB 919 Národopisná mapa Uher podle
.N23　　úředního Lexikonu osad z roku
　　　　1773. Sestavil A. Petrov. V Praze,
　　　　Nákl. České akademie věd a
　　　　umění, 1924.
　　　　132 p. map on 4 sheets (in portfolio)
　　　　The map was prepared by the
　　　　Vojenský zeměpisný ústav in
　　　　Prague.
　　　　1. Ethnology--Hungary--Maps. 2.
　　　　Hungary--Nationality. I. Petrov,
　　　　Aleksei Leonidovich, 1859-1932, comp.
　　　　II. Vojenský zeměpisný ústav,
　　　　Prague. III. Title: Lexicon osad z roku
　　　　1773. IV. Title: Lexicon universorum
　　　　Regni Hungariae locorum populosorum. V.
　　　　Title: Lexicon locorum populosorum.

NN　0022283　　ICU

Národopisná společnost československá,
Prague.

Prague. Národopisná výstava československá, 1895.
　　　Národopisná výstava československá v Praze 1895. Vydali
Výkonny výbor Národopisné výstavy československé a Ná-
rodopisná společnost československá prací spisovatelův a
umělců českých. Pořádají K. Klusáček ｛et al.｣ V Praze,
Nákl. J. Otty ｛pref. 1895｣

Národopisná společnost československá, Prague.

Nárcdopisný sborník československský.

V Praze, 18

DB191　Národopisná společnost československá, Prague.
.N25
Národopisný věstník československský. Revue d'ethnographie
tchécoslave.

V Praze, 19

Národopisná společnost československá, *Prague.*
　　　Sborník prací věnovaných Prof. Dr. J. Polívkovi k šedsá-
tým narozeninám Společností Národopisného musea českoslovanského v Praze. Uspořádal Jiří Horák. Praha, 1918.
　　　258, 7 p. port. 27 cm.
　　　CONTENTS.—Haškovec, P. M. Vzpomínka.—Horák. J. Soupis prací
prof. dra J. Polívky.—Máchal, J. Literárně-historické práce Polívkovy.—Paul, K. Třicetileté jubileum.—Tille, V. Polívkovy studie se
srovnávací literatury.—Weingart, M. Jiří Polívka a slovanská lido-
věda.
　　　1. Polívka, Jiří, 1858-1933. i. Polívka, Jiří, 1858-1933. ii. Horák, Jiří, ed. iii. Title.

PG34.P6N3　　　　　　　　　　　　66-54308

NN　0022287　　DLC CtY NIC WU MiU TxU NNC

398.04　Narodopisná společnost československá, Prague.
N167s
　　　Sborník prací věnovaných Prof. Dr. Václavu
Tillovi k šedesátým narozeninám, 1867-1927.
pořádali Jiří Polívka ｛et al.｣ Vydala Národo-
pisná společnost československá v Praze. V
Prase, Nakl. "Orbis", 1927.
　　　271p. 25cm.
　　　Added t.p.: Mélanges publiés en l'honneur de
M. le professeur Václav Tille.
　　　Contributions in Czech, French, German, and
Russian; summaries in French.
　　　　　　　　　　　　　　　　　12-1J

　　　"Soupis prací prof. Dr. V. Tille": sestavili
Dr. Jiří Ježek a Josef Kvapil": p.241-267.

NN　0022289　　TxU InU MH

GN2　Národopisná společnost československá, Prague.
.N3　　Stanovy Národopisné společnosti československé.
　　　V Praze, 1896.

NN　0022290　　DLC

Národopisná společnost československá, *Prague*
　　see also
Prague. Národopisná výstava československá, 1895.

Národopisná výstava československá, *Prague*
　　see
Prague. Národopisná výstava československá, 1895.

069.09437
N16r　Národopisné a průmyslové museum města Prostě-
　　　jova a Hané.
　　　Ročenka. roč. 1-　　　　1924-
　　　V Prostějově.
　　　　v. illus. 25cm.

　　　"Vydává Kuratorium."

NN　0022293　　IU

Národopisné museum českoslovanské, *Prague*
　　see
Prague. Národopisné museum českoslovanské.

Národopisný sborník.

Bratislava.
　　v. illus., music. 25 cm. annual.
　　Issued by Slovenská akadémia vied a umení.
　　Summaries in Russian and German.

　　　1. Ethnology—Period. 2. Ethnology—Slovakia—Period. i. Slovenská akadémia vied a umení, Bratislava.

GN1.N28　　　　　　　　　　　　58-23781

NN　0022295　　DLC

GN 1　NARODOPISNÝ SBORNIK, sv.
.N231.4　19
　　　｛V Turčianskom sv. Martine｝
　　　　v. in　　illus.

　　　Issued by Matica Slovenská　　Turčiansky
sv. Martin.

NN　0022296　　InU

Národopisný sborník českoslovanský.

V Praze, 18
　　v. illus., plates, ports. 26 cm.

　　Began publication in 1897.
　　Issued by Národopisná společnost českoslovanská (called Společnost
Národopisného musea českoslovanského); with
Národopisné museum českoslovanské
　　Includes music.
　　Superseded by Národopisný věstník českoslovanský.

　　1. Ethnology—Bohemia—Period. i. Národopisná společnost
českoslovanská, Prague. ii. Prague. Národopisné museum českoslovanské.

GN1.N3　　　　　　　　　　　　54-46721

NN　0022297　　DLC NcU CtY MB CU MiU InU

DB 785　Národopisný sborník okresu
.H81N23　Hořického. Vydán péčí
　　　Redakčního komitétu
　　　Národopisného odboru v
　　　Hořicích. V Hořicích, 1895.
　　　423 p. illus., ports., maps.
　　　"Věnováno památce
Národopisné výstavy
československé v Praze, roku 1895."

　　　1. Hořický okres. 2. Hořice--
Descr. I. Národopisný odbor v
Hořicích.

NN　0022298　　ICU

Národopisný věstník českoslovanský. Revue d'ethnographie
tchécoslave.

V Praze, 19
　　v. in　　illus., plates, ports., diagrs. 27ᶜᵐ. quarterly.
　　Supersedes Národopisný sborník českoslovanský. cf. Union list of
serials.
　　19　　published by the Národopisná společnost českoslovanská.

　　1. Ethnology—Czechoslovak republic. 2. Ethnology—Period.
i. Národopisná společnost českoslovanská, Prague.

　　　　　　　　　　　　　　　　　　44-38053
Library of Congress　　DB191.N25

NN　0022299　　DLC NIC NcU IU CU MiU ViBlbV

Narodopravstvo
　　see
Union "Russian commonwealth" ("Narodopravstovo")

Народоволецъ. № 1-4; апр. 1897-авг. 1903. Лондонъ.
　　4 no. in 1 v.　19 cm.
　　Publication suspended Nov. 1897-July 1903.
　　Edited by V. L. Burťsev.

　　1. Russia—Pol. & govt.—Period.　i. Burťsev, Vladimir L'vovich,
1862-1942, ed.　Title transliterated: Narodovoleťs.
DK1.N28　　　　　　　　　　　　55-45302

NN　0022301　　DLC

Narodowa Demokracja.
　　Deklaracja programowa stronnictwa Demokratyczno-Naro-
dowego.　Warszawa: F. Wyszyński i S-ka, 1918.　14 p.　8°.

　　1. Parties (Political), Poland.
N. Y. P. L.　　　　　　　　　　　　August 23, 1922.

NN　0022302　　NN CSt-H

Narodowa Demokracja. 2. Kongres.
　　Intelligencja i postepowe mieszczánstwo ...
see under　Chajn, Leon.

Narodowe Muzeum Przyrodnicze, *Warsaw*
　　see
Warsaw. Państwowe Muzeum Zoologiczne.

Narodowiec.

Lenc ｛France｝

illus.　daily.

NN　0022305　　MnU

Narodowiec, Paris. 1940 (Incomplete) Paris.
illus. 60 cm.

　　Microfilm. "Niezależny dziennik
demokratyczny dla obrony socjalnych i
kulturalnych interesów wychodżtwa."

　　1. French newspapers (General) - Polish.

NN　0022306　　NN

VOLUME 405

q
HG
1870
.P6
N3

Narodowy Bank Polski.
The banking system in Poland. [n.p.,n.d.]
27, [1] p.

1. Banks and banking - Poland. I. Title.

NN   0022307   DGU NN

Narodowy Bank Polski.
Rocznik informacyjny.
Warszawa.
  v. 30 cm.
  Issued also in English.

  1. Poland—Economic conditions—1945— —Periodicals.
  2. Finance—Poland—Periodicals.

HC337.P7N36   79-615767

NN   0022308   DLC

Narodowy Bank Polski.
Technika operacyjna i rachunkowość w Narodowym
Banku Polskim. Opracował zespół pracowników NBP, pod
kierownictwem Kazimierza Madury. Warszawa, Polskie
Wydawn. Gospodarcze, 1954.
  290 p. 25 cm.

  i. Madura, Kazimierz, ed. ii. Title.

HG3138.N3   57-41828

NN   0022309   DLC

Narodowy Bank Polski.
Wiadomości. r. 2, nr. 5–
czerw. 1946–
Warszawa [Polskie Wydawn. Gospodarcze]
  v. tables. 30 cm. monthly.
  Vol. 2, no. 5 called also no. 9.
  Vols. 1–2, no. 4 never published; issued for the use of the bank only.

  1. Poland—Econ. condit.—1945— —Period. 2. Economic history—1945— —Period.

HC337.P7A17   58-31404 rev

NN   0022310   DLC FU TxU NN

Narodowy Klub Żydowksi Posłow Sejmowych przy
Tymczasowej Żydowkiej Radzie Narodowej
      see   Klub Posłow i Senatorów Żydowskiej
Rady Narodowej.

JN6769   Narodowy związek robotniczy.
A5N2A2   Program Narodowego związku robotniczego. Warszawa, 1914.
  8 p. 22ᶜᵐ

  1.Political parties- Poland.

NN   0022312   CSt-H

Народи-брати; літературно-репертуарний збірник. [Упо-
рядкували Ф. Надененко (пісні), Б. Степанюк (поезію), Ф.
Сидоренко (прозу)] Київ, Мистецтво, 1954.
  219 p. 23 cm.
  "1654–1954."
  Includes choral pieces (2–4 voices) with piano by various composers.

      Continued in next column

Continued from preceding column

  1. Ukrainian literature (Collections) i. Nadenenko, F., comp.
                          Title transliterated: Narody-braty.

PG3932.N3   54-42796

NN   0022313   DLC

Народы СССР о сталинской Конституции; к годовщине
принятия Конституции СССР. Москва, Государственное
социально-экономическое издательство, 1937.
  xlvii, [1], 253, [3] p. front. (port.) 22½ᶜᵐ.
  "Все материалы привлечены в книгу из центральных, республикан-
ских, краевых и областных газет."—p. [iv]
  Errata slip inserted.

  1. Russia (1923–   U. S. S. R.) Constitution.

                                 41-31943

NN   0022314   DLC CaBVaU

Narokov, Nikolaĭ, 1887–
  Мнимые величины; роман. Нью-Йорк, Изд-во им. Че-
хова, 1952.
  411 p. 22 cm.

  i. Title.   *Title transliterated: Mnimye velichiny.*

PG3549.N3M5   52-42420 †

     CaBVa
NN   0022315   DLC OrPR OrU OrCS CLSU WaT CaBVaU

F
6605   Naroll, Raoul.
          Clio and the constitution: the influence of
        the study of history on the Federal convention
        of 1787. 1953.
          ix, 267 l.

          Thesis, University of California, Los Angeles.
          Bibliography: l. 251–267.
          Microfilm (positive) Los Angeles, University
        of California Library, 1969. 1 reel.

NN   0022316   NNC ICU

Nāropā
  see
Naḍapāda.

Narosny, Eleanor Helen.
  A comparative study of the performance of
juvenile delinquents and educational problem
children in the Stanford-Binet and Grace
Arthur scales ... by Eleanor H. Narosny ...
[Columbus] The Ohio state university, 1937.
  7 p. 2–45 nu,b.

NN   0022318   OU

Narot, Joseph R[   ].

  Four high holiday sermons... given at
Temple Beth Israel, Atlantic City, N.J.,
5707...   n.t.-p. [Atlantic City:
Palmer Press,1946.] 1 p.L.,18 p.   8.

NN   0022319   OCH

Narot, Joseph R
  Three High Holy Day sermons. [Miami, Fla.]
1953.
  12 p.   23 cm.

NN   0022320   OCH

Narot, Joseph R
  Three High Holy Day sermons ...   [Miami,
Fla., 1954]
  11 p. 24 cm.

NN   0022321   OCH

Narot, Joseph R
  Three High Holy Day sermons. [Miami, Fla.]
1955.
  12 p. 23 cm.

NN   0022322   OCH

Narot, Joseph R.
  Visions of faith, by Joseph R. Narot.   New York, Bloch pub.
co. [1943] 26 p. 24cm.

  1. Sermons, Jewish, in English.
N. Y. P. L.   June 29, 1945

NN   0022323   NN OCH

JQ205   Narotam, Desai.
.N23   A dictionary of law terms & phrases, with
        special reference to the law in force in
        British India. 2d ed., rev. and enl. Bom-
        bay, Printed at the "Tatva-Vivechaka" Press,
        1916.
          469 p.

          1. Law--Dictionaries. 2. Law--India--Terms
        and phrases.

NN   0022324   ICU

Narotam, Desai.
  The Indian easements act. 1910
      see under   India. Laws, statutes, etc.

Narotam, Desai.
  Indian registration act. 1916
      see under   India. Laws, statutes, etc.

Narotam, Desai.
  The Negotiable instruments act.. 1913
      see under   India. Laws, statutes, etc.

Narotam Singh Bindra
  see
Bindra, Narotam Singh.

Nāroṭapa
  see
Naḍapāda.

[Narottama] Desai
      see Desai.

VOLUME 405

Narōttamadāsa, fl. 1545.
Narōttamadāsa-kṛta Sudāmā-carita. Sampādaka. Badrī-
prasāda Sārasvata. ṛTṛtīya saṃskaraṇaṛ Āgarā, Sāhitya-
Ratna-Bhaṇḍāra ṛ1947?ṛ
76 p. 18 cm.
A poem.

ɪ. Sārasvata, Badrīprasāda, 1915–   ed. ɪɪ. Title: Sudāmā-carita.
                                                    A 60–2397
Pennsylvania. Univ.   Library
for Library of Congress   ṛ5ṛ

NN   0022331   PU

Narovchatov, Sergeĭ Sergeevich, 1919–
Солдаты свободы. ṛМосква, Молодая гвардия, 1952.
55 p. 17 cm.
At head of title: Сергей Наровчатов.
Poems.

ɪ. Title.
                        Title romanized: Soldaty svobody.
PG3476.N3664S6   53–27642

NN   0022332   DLC

Naroyian, Mesrop, 1875–1944.
Նշխարներ. Մեսրոպ Արքեպիսկ. Նարոյեանի (Հաշ֊մակ֊
գրական գործերը: Իֆանպուլ, Becid Basımevi, 1948:
398 p. illus. 22 cm.
Collection of articles.
Includes bibliographical references.

1. Armenian Church—Addresses, essays, lectures. 2. Theology—
Addresses, essays, lectures. ɪ. Title.
                          Title romanized: Nshkharner.
BX126.N37 1948   72–211124

NN   0022333   DLC

Narp (Gustave). *De l'eczéma du sein. 30 pp.
4°. Paris, 1872. No. 346.

NN   0022334   DNLM

Narp, Mme.   Lory de
    see   Lory de Narp, Mme.

Narpit
    see
Vsesoiûznoe paevoe tovarishchestvo "Narodnoe pitanie."

Narr, Friedrichṛ, 1844–1893
Einleitung in die theoretische mechanik. Leipzig, B. G. Teubner, 1875.
pp. xii, 350. Diagrs.

NN   0022337   MH CtY OO MiU MB

Narr, Joh., 1802–69.
——. De processu hæmorrhoidali. Diss. path.
14 pp. 4°. Monachii, sumpt. A. Weber, 1828

NN   0022338   DNLM

Narr (Joh.) [1802–69]. *Ueber die Natur und
das Wesen des Friesels. 77 pp. 8°. München,
Leutner, 1827.

NN   0022339   DNLM PPC

Narr, Karl J
Alt- und mittelpaläolithische Funde aus rheinischen Frei-
landstationen, mit Beiträgen von E. Kahrs und H. Hofer.
(In Bonner Jahrbücher des Rheinischen Landesmuseums in Bonn
und des Vereins von Altertumsfreunden im Rheinlande. Kevelaer,
Rhld. 28 cm. Heft 151 (1951) p. ṛ5ṛ–51. illus.)

1. Stone age—Rhine Province.
[DD491.R4B7 Heft 151]   A 54–4715
Chicago. Univ. Libr.
for Library of Congress   ṛ2ṛ

NN   0022340   ICU OU

Narr, Karl J
Feuersteinartefakte von Lüxheim und Gladbach (Kreis
Düren) und Rheydt-Odenkirchen.
(In Bonner Jahrbücher des Rheinischen Landesmuseums in Bonn
und des Vereins von Altertumsfreunden im Rheinlande. Kevelaer,
Rhld. 28 cm. Heft 153 (1953) p. ṛ5ṛ–12. illus.)

1. Stone implements—Germany—München-Gladbach.   ɪ. Title.
[DD491.R4B7 Heft 153]   A 54–6886
Chicago. Univ. Libr.
for Library of Congress   ṛ1ṛ

NN   0022341   ICU OU

Narr, Karl J
Das Rheinische Jungpaläolithikum Zugleich ein
Beitrag zur Chronologie der späten Altsteinzeit
Mittel- und Westeuropas von Karl J. Narr.
Bonn, R. Habelt, 1955.
265 p.   illus.   (Bonner Jahrbücher,
Beiheft, 4)
Paleolithic period – Europe. Paleolithic
period – Rhine Valley. Rhine Valley – Anti-
quities.
(A) Das Rheinische Jungpaläolithikum
Zugleich ein Beitrag zur Chronologie der späten
Altsteinzeit Mittel --und Westeuropas von

Karl J. Narr. (S) Bonner Jahrbücher. Beiheft. 4.

NN   0022343   MoU NNC CtY IEN ICU MH NN MiU

[Narr, P   A   ]
Schattenbilder am Rhein [von] Pan [pseud.]
[Wien, Waldheim-Eberle a.g., 1919]
6 p.l., [15]–133 p. illus. 27cm.

NN   0022344   NcD

Narr, Paul, 1866–
Schwierigkeiten in der gynäkologischen Diagnostik mit
besonderer Berücksichtigung der Darmtumoren, die vom
Genitale ausgehende Geschwülste vortäuschen. Prag:
Selbstverl. 1911: Bellmann. 19 S., 3 Taf. 8° [Umschlagt.]
¶(Aus: Prager med. Wochenschrift. 36.)
Gießen, Med. Diss. v. 8. März 1911. Ref. v. Franqué
[Geb. 14. Jan. 66 Zirndorf; Wohnort: Stromberg, Hunsrück; Staatsangeh.:
Bayern; Vorbildung: Gymn. Erlangen Reife Aug. 86; Studium: Würzburg 8,
Erlangen 4. Würzburg 7 S.; Coll. 11. Nov. 10; Approb. 28. Dez. 95.]
                                            [U 11.1245]

NN   0022345   ICRL MBCo DNLM

Narr, Paul Johann Friedrich
    see   Narr, Paul, 1866–

AC   Narr, Willy, 1911–
831   Das problem des firmenwertes. ... Wuerzburg,
      1937.   87 p.
      Inaug. Diss. – Tuebingen, 1937.
      Lebenslauf.
      Literaturverzeichnis.

NN   0022347   ICRL CtY NNC

The Narr. June 30–July 2, 1909. Bedford Springs, Pa.,
1909.
ṛ12ṛ p. illus. (incl. ports.) 56½ᶜᵐ.
Various pagings.
Published daily during the sessions of the Pennsylvania state bar
association.

ɪ. Pennsylvania bar association.
                                            10—539

NN   0022348   DLC

PT2440   Narr Jak ṛpseud.ṛ
.N16W5   Welt und Hof; ein satyrischer Roman, voll
1788   Wahrheiten aus dem achtzehnten Jahrhundert,
          obgleich überirdische Geschichte. Berlin, 1788.
          2 v. in 1.

NN   0022349   ICU

... Narraçaõ da vinda dos judeos espanhoes a Amsterdam;
with introduction by J. S. da Silva Rosa ... Amsterdam, Facsimile print: N. v. "A. H. O.". Algemeene handelsonderneming,
1933.
2 p. l., x p., facsim.: 8, ṛ8ṛ p. 18ᶜᵐ. (Reprints and texts from the
library of the Portuguese Jewish seminary Ets Haim, Amsterdam.
vol. 1)
"Edition limited to 100 numbered copies. no. 25."
First published in Amsterdam (?) 1710 (?) under title: Memoria para
os siglos futuros. The second edition, Amsterdam, 1768, to which a
Hebrew translation by Isaac Cohen Belinfante was appended, and of

which this is a facsimile, has title: Narraçaó, da vinda dos judeos
espanhoes a Amsterdam, conforme a tradiçaõ verdadeira, que recebeo
de seus genitores, o senhor Ury de Aharon a Levy, e o publicou a o
mundo no a°. 5471. E agora traduzido no nosso sacro idioma por, &
impresso por ordem, & despeza de Mosseh Levy Maduro. cf. p. iv.
Hebrew section paged with Hebrew numerals.

1. Jews in Amsterdam.   ɪ. Silva Rosa, Jacob S. da, 1866–
ɪɪ Belinfante, Isaac Cohen, d. 1780, tr.

Library of Congress   DS135.N5A55   34–10110
                              ṛ2ṛ   296.06492

NN   0022351   DLC CtY PPDrop

Narraçaõ do jantar patriotico no dia 15 de Setembro de 1821 na caza do izidro em Lisboa.
[Lisboa, 1821]
19p.

NN   0022352   DCU-IA

NARRAÇAÕ do que se passou na cidade do
Porto por occasiaõ da morte da senhora D.Maria
Primeira,rainha de Portugal,Brazil,e Algarves.
s.s.s. Lisboa,na Impressaõ Regia,1816.

pp.15.

NN   0022353   MH DCU-IA

Greenlee   NARRAÇÃO dos applausos com que o juiz do
4639   povo e Casa dos Vinte-Quatro festeja a feli-
N23   cissima inauguração da estatua equestre onde
1775   tembem se expõem as allegorias dos carros,
            figuras, e tudo o mais concernente ás ditas
            festas. Lisboa,Na Regia Officina Typografica,
            1775.
            120p. 20cm.

NN   0022354   ICN

VOLUME 405

Narração dos applausos com que o Juiz do Povo e Casa dos Vinte-Quatro festeja a felicissima inauguração da estatua equestre onde tambem se expoem as allegorias dos carros, figuras, e tudo o mais concernente ás ditas festas.   Lisboa Na Regia Officina Typografica.Anno 1775.
123,[2]p.   21cm.
Signatures: a-q⁴(q₄ blank)
The statue was that of King José I.
Mostly (p.43-[125]) in verse, including several pieces by Domingos Caldas Barbosa.

NN   0022355   CtY InU MH

Narrache, Jean, *pseud.*
see
Coderre, Émile, 1893–

Narración biográfica del Gran Mariscal D. José de La-Mar
    see under   Villarán, Manuel Vicente.

Narración circunstanciada de la deplorable catastrofe sufrida en la ciudad de Lima ...
    see under   [Llano y Zapata, José Eusebio de] fl. 1744-1769.

... Narración de la batalla de Jutlandia
    see under   Gt. Brit. Admiralty.

Narración de la maravillosa aparicion, qve hizo el Arcangel S. Migvel á Diego Lazaro de S. Francisco.   Sevilla, 1692
    see under   Florencia, Francesco de, 1619-1695.

Narracion de la venida del Rey Don Fernando VII á la Universidad de Alcalá y arenga que hizo a S. M. el Dr. D. Nicolas Heredero y Mayoral, del Gremio y Claustro, y Catedrático de Elocuencia de la misma Universidad, Cura Propio de la Parroquial de Santa María la Mayor de dicha Ciudad.

NN   0022361   NNH

NN   0022362   CU-B

... Narración de los viajes de levantamiento de los buques de S. M. "Adventure" y "Beagle" en los años 1826 á 1836 ...
    see under   [Fitzroy, Robert] 1805-1865, ed.

Narracion exegetica de los casos rateros de la corba-alana, prometidos al final de la Conversata dramatica, "para que le sirviese de apendice" de los dos palanganas, Veterano, y Bisoño, sobre la detestacion del nombre de Salas, celebrada, en el phontisterio de las gradas de la Iglesia mayor.   Ambato [1775] [25] p.   20 cm.   [Bound with Drama de los palanganas Veterano, y Bisoño ... [Lima, 1776]]
    Half title.

NN   0022364   CtY

Narración Heroyca ...
    see under   Juárez de Orozco, Marcos. [supplement]

282.46 N234
Narración histórico-juridica de el derecho de el Real Patronato; titulos en que se afianza, y extensión de ellos, que dirige el zelo, y amor a la augusta Magestad de España.   [n. p., n. d.]   130 p.   24 cm.
    1. Patronage, Ecclesiastical. Spain
    2. Prerogative, Royal. Spain 3. Patronage, Ecclesiastical (Canon law)

NN   0022366   NcD

Narración Poetica ...
    see under   Bruno de Aranda Saavedra Puerta Guzmán, Francisco. [supplement]

Narracion sucinta de los fundamentos de hecho, y de derecho ...
    see under   [Muñoz Zejudo, Geronymo]

Rare Book Room Bn6 621 22
Narracion verdadera de todo lo que ha passado Sabado a 30. de Iulio en el sitio de Tonneins, y defecha de las tropas del Señor de La Force. Traduzida de frances en castellano por Iuan Luna. [Colophon: Con licencia en Barcelona por Esteuan Liberos,en la calle de Santo Domingo. Año 1622]
    [4]p. 1 illus. 20cm.
    Caption title.

NN   0022369   CtY

PQ 6174 .N3
Narraciones, v.1-   Madrid, Taurus, 19 -
    1. Spanish literature-20th cent.-Collections.

NN   0022370   DAU.

G868.8308 N1667
Narraciones americanas, por Tomás Argüelles [et al.] Con un prólogo de A.R.Ll. Ilus. de A. Utrillo. Barcelona, Durán, 1893.   189p. illus.,col. plates. 19cm. (Biblioteca ilustrada)
    CONTENTS.--Alegoria de la época indígena: Angela; o, La hidalga heroína de Tzintzuntzan, por T. Argüelles. Tapaligui, por R. Fernández Guardia.--Alegoria de la época colonial: Una vida por una honra, por R. Palma. El fiscal; tradición bogotana, por J. Caicedo Rojas.→
Alegoria de la época moderna: Constancia filial, por H. Vázquez. Natalia, por E. Posada. Una china presumida, por B. Fernández Medina.
    1. Short stories, Spanish-American. I. Argüelles, Tomás.

NN   0022372   TxU NBuU RPB

---

17 B.19
Narraciones biblicas. (2a ed.) [anon]   New York, N. Ponce de Leon, 1880.   88 p., 1 l.   12°.

NN   0022373   DLC

Narraciones de Cuartel
    see under   Ceballos Quintana, Enrique.

Narraciones de las Fiestas en Zaragoza ...
    see under   Abas y Nicolau, Gabriel Manuel.

Narraciones de un Montero
    see under   Covarsi, Antonio.

Narraciones Extremeñas
    see under   Barrantes y Moreno, Vicente, 1829=1898.

Narraciones Feudales Leyendas en verso
    see under   Gómez de Tejada, Julio S.

Narraciones históricas ó Coleccion de hechos heroicos, rasgos notables y virtudes de los españoles
    see under   Pontes, José Maria.

Narraciones históricas ó Coleccion de los hechos mas notables de la antigüedad para uso de la juventud; traducidas del italiano por D. F.A... Indocti discant et ament meminisse periti. Aprendan los ignorantes, y complázcanse los sabios en el recuerdo.   Madrid, Imprenta y casa de la Union Commercial, 1844.

NN   0022380   NNH

Narraciones históricas tomadas de los mejores Hablistas Castellanos
    see under   González de Tejada, José.

Narraciones Infantiles.   Madrid, 1895
    see under   Mesa de la Peña, Rafael.

Les narraciones mas extraordinarias
    see under   Solero, Francisco Jorge.

Narraciones populares catalanas
    see under   Farnés, Sebastián.

VOLUME 405

NARRACIONES tapatías. t. 1-
[Guadalajara? 195-?]   v.   illus.   23cm.

Editor: v. 1-   , E.F. Camarena.

1. Guadalajara, Mexico--Per. and soc. publ. I. Camarena, Enrique
Francisco, ed. II. Camarena, Enrique Francisco.

NN   0022385   NN

NARRACIONES tragicas, por varios autores.
Mexico, linotipia de "El Mundo" y "El
Imparcial", 1901.

pp.39.
At head of title:- Biblioteca de "El
Mundo".   SAL 1664.2.23

NN   0022386   MH

Narracions populars.   Barcelona.

NN   0022387   MiU

Narracott, Arthur Henson, 1905–
Air power in war, by A. H. Narracott ... with a foreword
by Air Chief Marshal Sir Arthur Tedder ...   London, F.
Muller ltd. [1945]
168 p. plates. 19ᵐ.
"First published ... June 1945."

1. Air warfare. 2. World war, 1939-1945—Aerial operations.
46–5135
Library of Congress   UG630.N35
[4]   358.4

NN   0022388   DLC PU CtY MH NNC TxU

Narracott, Arthur Henson, 1905–
How the R. A. F. works, by A. H. Narracott ... With a fore-
word by the Rt. Hon. Sir Archibald Sinclair ...   London,
F. Muller ltd. [1941]
158 p. plates, port. 19ᵐ.
"First published ... in October 1941."

1. Gt. Brit. Royal air force. 2. World war, 1939-   —Aerial operations. I. Title.   A 42-1421 Revised
Harvard univ. Library
for Library of Congress   UG635.G7N37 1941
[r44d2;†   358.40942

NN   0022389   MH NcD OU DLC CaBVaU

Narracott, Arthur Henson, 1905–   comp.
In praise of the few, a battle of Britain anthology. London, F. Muller [1947]
[64] p. ports. 14 cm.
Verse and prose.

1. World War, 1939-1945—Aerial operations, British. 2. Gt. Brit.
Royal Air Force. I. Title.
D745.2.N3   940.544   48-12749*

NN   0022390   DLC MH

Narracott, Arthur Henson, 1905–
Unsung heroes of the air, by A. H. Narracott ... With a
foreword by the Director-general of civil aviation, W. P. Hil-
dred ...   London, F. Muller, ltd. [1943]
168 p. plates, ports. 19ᵐ.
"First published ... in 1943."

Continued in next column

Continued from preceding column

1. World war, 1939-   —Aerial operations. 2. Air pilots—Gt. Brit.
3. Aeronautics—Gt. Brit.   I. Title.
A 43-3017
Harvard univ. Library
for Library of Congress   [3]

NN   0022391   DLC NN OC1 CtY MH

Narracott, Arthur Henson, 1905–
War news had wings, a record of the R. A. F. in France, by
A. H. Narracott ...   London, F. Muller ltd. [1941]
xviii, 19-224 p. front, plates. 22½ᵐ.
"First published ... in 1941."

1. Gt. Brit. Advanced air striking force. 2. World war, 1939-   —
Aerial operations. 3. World war, 1939-   —Campaigns—France. I.
Title.
41–12359 Revised
Library of Congress   D786.N3
[r44d3;   940.544942

NN   0022392   DLC KU

Narragansett, *pseud.*
see
Hazard, Thomas Robinson, 1784–1876.

Narragansett, Young, *pseud.*
Hon. Elisha R. Potter. An address to the
people of Rhode-Island
see under title

Narragansett, *R. I.*
A list of persons, corporations, companies and estates,
assessed in accordance with the town tax.
Wakefield, R. I., 18
v.   21-23ᵐᵐ.
Cover-title: Tax book.

1. Taxation—Narragansett, R. I.
11–6537
Library of Congress   HJ9013.N14 g

NN   0022395   DLC

Narragansett, R.I.
A manual of sanitary rules and regulations
relative to the health of the ..., made by the
council of said district June 25, 1889. With
directions for making and the use of disinfec-
tants, by W. Thornton Parker, health officer.
Wakefield, Times Print, 1889.
17 p.   12°.

NN   0022396   DNLM

Narragansett, R.I.
Records of the proprietors of the Narragansett
see under   Proprietors of lands in the
Narragansett country.

Narragansett, *R. I.*
see also Narragansett Pier, R. I.
North Kingstown, R.I.

Narragansett, R. I. Chamber of Commerce.

G3774
.N234
1950
.J6
Joss, John.
Narragansett Pier, Rhode Island. [Narragansett, Narra-
gansett Chamber of Commerce, °1950.

Narragansett, R.I. French Church.
Records of the French church at Narragansett, 1686-1691; tr.
and ed. by L. Effingham de Forest ...   New York, Huguenot
soc. of America [1940?]   23 p.   26cm.
"Reprinted from the July, 1939, October, 1939, and January, 1940, issues of the
New York genealogical and biographical record."

1. Huguenots in the U. S.—Rhode   Island. I. De Forest, Louis Effingham,
1891-   II. Huguenot society of   America.
N.Y.P.L.   June 19, 1947

NN   0022400   NN

Narragansett, R.I. Marine Laboratory
see
Rhode Island. University. *Narragansett Marine Laboratory.*

Narragansett, R.I. Ordinances, etc.
Ordinances of the District of Narragansett.
[Wakefield, R.I., 1890?]
13 p.   18 cm.

NN   0022402   RPB

Narragansett, R. I. St. Paul's Church.
The old Narragansett church (St. Paul's)
built A.D. 1707 ...
see under Lawrence, H   Newman.

Narragansett, R. I.   St. Paul's Church.
Records of St. Paul's Church, Narragansett. Entries in the Narra-
gansett parish register, April 14, 1718 – November 6, 1774.
(In Updike, Wilkins. A history of the Episcopal Church in Nar-
ragansett. 2d edition. Vol. 2, pp. 459-605. Boston. 1907.)
Transcribed and edited by Mary Harris Rollins.

G7045 .J [Rollins, Mary Harris, ed.

NN   0022404   MB

Narragansett, R.I. School committee.
Report ...   Wakefield, R.I.,
v.   19-22 cm.

NN   0022405   RPB

Narragansett, R.I. Treasurer.
... Report of the District of Narragansett ...
Wakefield, R.I.
v.   25 cm.

NN   0022406   RPB

Narragansett archaeological society of Rhode Island.
The Jones pond shell heap; an excavation by the Narragansett
archaeological society of Rhode Island.   [Providence?] 1939.
26 p. illus. (incl. charts.)   24cm.

1. Mounds—U. S.—Rhode Island.   2. Narragansett bay—Archaeology.
I. Title.
N.Y.P.L.   September 17, 1942

NN   0022407   NN FU PBm

VOLUME 405

Narragansett association
    see   Baptists. Rhode Island. Narragansett
association.

Narragansett Baptist association
    see   Baptists. Rhode Island.
Narragansett association.

*D731
.N34   Narragansett Bay defenses digest. v. 1;
1942-43   no. 1-17, 19-20, 25-40; 42-45; Feb 13, 1942-
Folio   Jan. 29, 1943. Boston, Army Post Newspapers
    of New England, 1942-43.
    1 v. illus. 43cm. weekly.
    No more published?

    1. World War, 1939-1945—Period. 2. Period-
icals, English.

NN   0022410   MB NN CtY

Narragansett Bay yacht racing association.
    Constitution and by-laws and racing rules of the Nar-
ragansett Bay yacht racing association   ...
Inter-bay cabin catboat association rules ... ₍Provi-
dence₎ R. I.₎ Narragansett Bay yacht racing association,
    v. 20ᶜᵐ.
    On cover: Year book 1910.
    Compiler: A. W. Harris.
    Editor: W. L. Frost.

    ɪ. Harris, A. W., comp. ɪɪ. Frost, W. Louis, ed.

    Library of Congress   GV823.N3A4

                                                10-13147

NN   0022411   DLC

The Narragansett blue book ...
    see under   [Reid, James Allen] comp.

Narragansett Boat Club, Providence.
    Constitution, by-laws, and racing rules ...
adopted Dec. 3, 1879 ...   Providence, 1880.
    47 p.   16 cm.

NN   0022413   RPB

UA25
.N37   Narragansett Brewing Company, Cranston, R. I.
    Your army, navy and marine corps, a government
service handbook. Cranston, R. I. [c1941]
    31 p.   illus., ports. 24cm.

    1. U. S. Army. 2. U. S. Navy. 3. U. S.
Marine Corps. I. Title.

NN   0022414   MB

Narragansett brick company.
    Charter and by-laws.   Providence, 1865.
    8 p.   19 cm.

NN   0022415   RPB

[Narragansett club, Providence]
*AP85   [Circulars, prospectuses, order forms, etc.]
N1678c   [Providence,1865-72]

    9 pieces.   23cm.,in folder 24cm.

NN   0022416   MH

CT258   Narragansett Club, Providence.
P23   George Taylor Paine, [Providence, 1906]
N3   8 p. 23cm.
             Founder of the Club for Colonial Reprints.
John Carter
Brown Library

    1. Paine, George Taylor, ?   -1903.
    I. Club for Colonial Reprints.

NN   0022417   RPJCB

Narragansett club, *Providence.*
    Publications of the Narragansett club.   (First series) v.
1-6. Providence ₍Providence press co., printers₎ 1866-74.
    6 v.   22½ x 18½ cm.
    Subscribers' edition.
    Limited edition: v. 1-3, 200 copies each; v. 4, 5, and 6, 170, 130, and
160 copies respectively.
    Chiefly reprints, including reproductions of the title-pages, of the
original editions of the works of Roger Williams.
    No more published.

    CONTENTS.—v. 1. Biographical introduction, by R. A. Guild. A
key into the language of America, ed. by J. H. Trumbull. Letter of
John Cotton and Roger Williams's reply, ed. by R. A. Guild. 1866.—
v. 2. John Cotton's answer to Roger Williams, ed. by J. L. Diman.
Queries of highest consideration, ed. by R. A. Guild. 1867.—v. 3. The
bloudy tenent of persecution, ed. by S. L. Caldwell. 1867.—v. 4. The
bloody tenent yet more bloody, ed. by S. L. Caldwell. 1870.—v. 5.
George Fox digg'd out of his burrowes, ed. by J. L. Diman. 1872.—
v. 6. The letters of Roger Williams, 1632-1682. Now first collected.
Ed. by J. R. Bartlett. 1874.

    1. Rhode Island—Hist.—Colonial period.

    F76.N2j   3—20323
    ———— 2d set.   v. 1-3, 5-6.
                                  ₍a53b4₎

    NcD OO MWA ICN RPJCB OCU OrU
    MiU-C CSmH MH Nh NjP OC1W DSI OU ViW NjPT LU KyU
NN   0022419   DLC CU ViU OCl DFo PHi PPL MWA NNC NN

Micro
Film
D50   Narragansett club, Providence.
reel   Publications of the Narragansett club.   (First
437   series) v.6. Providence ₍Providence press co.,
no.4   printers₎ 1874.
         (On American culture series, reel 437, no.4)
         Subscribers' edition.
         Limited edition: v.1-3, 200 copies each; v.4, 5,
      and 6, 170, 130, and 160 copies respectively.
      Chiefly reprints, including reproductions of the
      title-pages of the original editions of the works
      of Roger Williams.
      No more publis   hed.

         Contents.- v.1. Biographical introduction, by
      R.A. Guild. A key into the language of America,
      ed. by J.H. Trumbull. Letter of John Cotton
      and Roger Williams's reply, ed. by R.A. Guild.
      1866.- v.2. John Cotton's answer to Roger
      Williams, ed. by J.L. Diman. Queries of
      highest consideration, ed. by R.A. Guild. 1867.-
      v.3. The bloudy tenent of persecution, ed. by
      S.L. Caldwell.   1867.- v.4. The bloody
      tenent yet more   bloody, ed. by S.L.

      Caldwell.- v.5. George Fox digg'd out of his
      burrowes, ed. by J.L. Diman. 1872.- v.6.
      The letters of Roger Williams, 1632-1682. Now
      first collected. Ed. by J.R. Bartlett. 1874.
      Microfilm (positive). 35mm. Ann Arbor,
      Mich.. University Microfilms, 1970.
      Collation of the original: 6v. 23x19cm.
      V.1-5 not film   ed.
      1. Rhode Island   - Hist. - Colonial period.
      I. Title.

NN   0022422   PSt

Narragansett county. Proprietors.

         see

Proprietors of lands in the Narragansett country.

E99
.N16N3 The Narragansett dawn ...

    [Oakland, R. I., 1935-36]
        v.   22½cm.

    "Published monthly in the interest of the
Narragansett tribe of Indians."

    1. Narragansett Indians.

NN   0022424   DLC NN

Narragansett Electric Lighting Company.
    ...Annual report and statements.

₍Providence,   ₎ no.   diagrs., illus.   8°.

1. Electricity.—Lighting: Com-   panies, U. S.: R. I.: Providence.
N. Y. P. L.   May 25, 1922.

NN   0022425   NN

Narragansett electric lighting company.

Providence.
    Lighting contract and franchise agreement between the
city of Providence and the Narragansett electric lighting
company.   Providence, Loose leaf manufacturing co.,
city printers, 1912.

Narragansett Fire and Marine Insurance Company,
    Providence.
         Charter.   Providence, 1864.
         11 p.   17 cm.
         Cover-title.

NN   0022427   RPB

The **Narragansett** historical register, a magazine devoted to
    the antiquities, genealogy and historical matter illustrating
    the history of the state of Rhode Island and Providence
    Plantations ... James N. Arnold, editor. v. 1-8, v. 9, no. 1-
    2; July 1882-Apr. 1891. Providence, The Narragansett his-
    torical publishing company, 1882-91.
    9 v. illus., pl., ports. 23½ᶜᵐ. quarterly.
    July 1882-Apr. 1883, title reads: The Narragansett register,
    a magazine devoted to the antiquities ... of the Narragansett country or
    southern Rhode Island.
    Official organ of the Rhode Island citizens historical association,
    1886-88.
    Issued in Hamilton, R. I., July 1882-Jan. 1886.
    No more published.
    1. Rhode Island—Hist.—   Period. 2. Rhode Island—Geneal.—
    Period. 3. Rhode Island—   Antiq. ɪ. Arnold, James Newell,
    1844-1927, ed. ɪɪ. Rhode   Island citizens historical association.
    Library of Congress   F76.N23   Rc—2942

    NcD
NN   0022428   DLC Nh MH Vi NN NcU LU OC1WHi MWA NIC

A Narragansett idyl...
    see under   Donaldson, Frank ₍M. D.₎

Narragansett library association, *Peace Dale, R. I.*
    Books added.
    ₍Peace Dale,
        v. 21½ᶜᵐ.

                                                CA 15-682 Unrev'd

    Library of Congress   Z881.P37A

NN   0022430   DLC

VOLUME 405

Narragansett library association, *Peace Dale, R. I.*
Bulletin.
Peace Dale, 19
v. pl. 21½ᶜᵐ.
Contains the annual reports of the librarian.

8-25030†

Library of Congress   Z733.P368

NN   0022431   DLC MB

Narragansett Litho, inc., *Providence.*

G3700
.S1
1950
.H4

Hetherington, Herbert W
Complete historical map of the United States. Providence, Narragansett Litho. Co., ᶜ1950.

725:85 **Narragansett machine co.,** *Providence, R.I.*
N16c   Catalog of gymnastic apparatus made by the
Narragansett machine co., Providence, R.I., U.S.A.
Factory — Pawtucket, R.I.   Chicago [etc.]
c1928.
162p. illus.

"Catalog of anthropometric apparatus": p.[151]-
162.
With this is bound: Narragansett machine co.,
Providence, R.I. Gymnastic construction. Providence, c1928.

NN   0022433   IU

W   **NARRAGANSETT Machine Company,**
26   **Providence.**
qN234   [Catalogs of medical equipment]

A file of these publications will be
found on the shelves under the above
call number.
1. Medical instruments - Catalogs

NN   0022434   DNLM

Narragansett machine co., Providence.
Catalogue of gymnastic apparatus made by the
Narragansett machine co... [Catalogue 77]
[Providence?] 1905.

GV410
.N24   46 p. illus. 30 cm.

NN   0022435   DLC CU

Narragansett machine co., *Providence, R. I.*
Catalogue of gymnastic apparatus; made by the Narragansett machine co., Providence, R. I., U. S. A. ... [Taunton, Mass., C. A. Hack & son, inc.] 1916.
140 p. incl. illus., pl. 23½ᶜᵐ.

1. Gymnasiums—Apparatus and equipment. [1. Gymnastic apparatus]

S G 16-272

U. S. Surg.-gen. off. Library
for Library of Congress   [a7841]

NN   0022436   DNLM DHEW KEmT KMK

Narragansett Machine Company, *Providence, R. I.*
Catalogue of gymnastic apparatus made by the Narragansett
Machine Co.   Providence, R. I.[, 1922.]   158, 24, 78 p.   illus.
(incl. plans.)   [13. ed.]   8°

"Catalogue of anthropometric apparatus made by the Narragansett Machine Company," p. [147]-158.
Includes: Standard steel lockers; and, Gymnasium construction: each with separate t.-p. and paging.
Appended: Price list of gymnastic apparatus. 8 p.

288739A. 1. Gymnastics—Apparatus.
N. Y. P. L.   May 9, 1927

NN   0022437   NN

Narragansett machine co., *Providence, R. I.*
Catalogue of scientific gymnasium goods ...   Providence, R. I., Narragansett machine co., 1889.
17 x 23½ᶜᵐ.
Cover-title.

8-14671

NN   0022438   DLC NN

Narragansett machine co., Providence, R. I.

[Storey, Thomas Andrew] 1875-
Chest weight exercises, from the Department of hygiene of the College of the city of New York ... Providence, R. I., Narragansett machine company [ᶜ1914]

Narragansett Machine Company, Providence, R. I.
Guide book to Dr. Maingot's musico-calisthenics
see under title

Narragansett machine co., *Providence, R. I.*
Gymnasium construction ... Providence, R. I., Chicago [etc.]
Narragansett machine company, ᶜ1919.
1 p. l., 78 p. illus. (incl. plans) 23½ᶜᵐ.

1. Gymnasiums. I. Title.
19—8227
Library of Congress   GV405.N3

NN   0022441   DLC NN OrU ICJ

796.4
N167c
1927   NARRAGANSETT MACHINE CO., Providence, R.I.
Women's   Gymnasium construction, Narragansett machine
Gym.Col company, Providence, R.I., U.S.A.   Chicago, New
York, c1927.
1p.l.,78p. illus.,diagrs. 23½cm.

Bound with its Catalog of gymnastic apparatus.
Chicago, 1927.

1. Gymnasiums. I. Title.

NN   0022442   TxU

Narragansett machine co., *Providence, R. I.*
... Playground apparatus. Providence, R. I., Chicago
[etc.] Narragansett machine company [ᶜ1914]
36 p. 17½ x 23½ᶜᵐ.
At head of title: Catalog H4.

1. Playgrounds. I. Title.

Library of Congress   GV426.N3
14-11262

NN   0022443   DLC

Narragansett Marine Laboratory
see
Rhode Island. University. *Narragansett Marine Laboratory.*

NARRAGANSETT MILLS, R. I.

See NORTH KINGSTOWN, R. I.

Narragansett; or, The Plantations; a story of 177–...   London:
Chapman and Hall, 1860. 3 v. 8°.

1. Fiction (English).
N. Y. P. L.   September 3, 1915.

NN   0022446   NN CtY MB

Narragansett park association.
Record of races at Narragansett park.
[Providence, Providence press co., printers, 186
v. front. 13½-14ᶜᵐ.
Comp. by George H. Smith.
Title varies.

1. Horse-racing—Rhode Island. I. Smith, George H., comp.
CA 15-439 Unrev'd
Library of Congress   SF325.N3

NN   0022447   DLC

Narragansett Park association.
Rules and regulations ...   [n.p.] [n.d.]
72 x 56 cm.
Poster.

NN   0022448   RPB

Narragansett park association.
Rules and regulations ...   [Boston, 1869]
17 p. 14 cm.
Caption-title.

NN   0022449   RPB

Narragansett Pier, *R. I.*
see also **Narragansett,** *R. I.*

Narragansett Pier, R. I. First Baptist Church.
Calendar ... [Wakefield, R.I., 1896]
9 p. 16 cm.

NN   0022451   RPB

... **Narragansett Pier,** [New York, 1879]
see under [Carroll, Charles] d. 1889.

Narragansett Pier, R. I., Illustrated. Published by the
Hotel men's association. [N. Y., Press of the Moss
eng. co., 1891]
[69] pp. illus. obl. 8°.
F89.NN2
1-Ro-2017

NN   0022453   DLC MB

Narragansett Pier, Rhode Island. Street scenes, hotels, residences and places of interest. Providence, R. I., D. Rubin,
1900.
1 p. l., 33 pl. 13½ x 19½ᶜᵐ.
Half-tone illustrations by Reeves engraving co.

1. Narragansett Pier, R. I.—Descr.—Views.
Library of Congress   F89.N2N3   0-5496 Revised

NN   0022454   DLC

VOLUME 405

Narragansett pier railroad company.

Potter, Elisha Reynolds, 1811–1882.
Important correspondence between Judge Elisha R. Potter and R. G. Hazard, esq. ... Central Falls, R. I., E. L. Freeman & co., book, job and lithographic printers, 1876.

Narragansett racing association, inc.

Chafee, Zechariah, 1885–
... State house *versus* Pent house; legal problems of the Rhode Island race-track row, by Zechariah Chafee, jr. ... Providence, R. I., The Booke shop, 1937.

[Narragansett steam boat company]
To the public [concerning the rate war between the owners of the steam boats "Kingston" and "Providence."] Providence, 1838]
8 p. illus. 22 cm.

NN 0022457 MH-BA

Narragansett Steamship Company
see also
Fall River Line.
Old Colony Steamboat Company.

641.5 The Narragansett Terrace Association,
N16t Riverside, R.I.
Terrace cook book, compiled by the Women's Auxiliary of the Narragansett Terrace Association. Riverside, R.I., 1946.
69 l. illus. 21 cm.

Cover title.

1. Cookery, American--Rhode Island. I. Title.

NN 0022459 LU

M15.2 The Narragansett Times, Wakefield, R.I.
N234c Carol was here... A pictorial chronicle of the hurricane in South County August 31, 1954. ...And look what happened! [Wakefield, R.I.], Narragansett Times, Inc., c1954]
cover-title, 36 p. illus., diagrs., photos. 27cm.

NN 0022460 DAS

Narragansett Times, Wakefield, R. I.
...Narragansett pier special edition. Wakefield, 1887. 2 l. illus. 85cm.

Film reproduction. Positive.

Issue of April, 1887.

1. Narragansett, R. I.

NN 0022461 NN

Narragansett Wheelmen, Providence.
Programme of the grand fair ... Music hall, Providence, R.I., Dec. 17–22, 1894. [Providence, 1894]
[11] p. 17¯x 28 cm.

NN 0022462 RPB

Narragon, Frederic R
An evaluation and classification of technical terms in algebra ... by F. R. Narragon ... 1928.
1 p.

NN 0022463 OU

BX2439 Narragonia monachorū/ zu tütsch. [Colophon]: Getruckt
.A2N2 Rare bk zu Basel durch Jo[hann] Beb[el], 1523 ?]
room [110] p. 1 illus. 19ᶜᵐ.

Signatures: A-O⁴ (blank leaf at end wanting)
A dialogue between a monk and a priest. For full description *see* Weller, Repertorium typographicum, no. 2621.

1. Monasticism and religious orders. 2. Catholic church—Doctrinal and controversial works—Protestant authors. 3. Reformation—Pamphlets to 1530.

NN 0022464 ICU

Narrainsawmy, W M
Select Tamil tales, with free translations in English and Teloogoo, to which are added a vocabulary (from good manuscripts) in English and Teloogoo, and a choice number of Dr. Marshman's dialogues in English and Tamil. Madras, Printed by C. Sample, at the American mission press, 1839. [8],190,[1]p.

NN 0022465 OC1 CtY MH WU

Narramore, Clyde Maurice, 1916–
A Christian answers Kinsey. Wheaton, Ill., Van Kampen Press [1954]
32 p. illus. 19 cm.

1. Indiana. University. Institute for Sex Research. Sexual behavior in the human female. 2. Sexual ethics. 3. Sex and religion. I. Title.

HQ18.U5 I 67   392.6   55–16499 rev ‡

NN 0022466 DLC CLSU NN

HX 263 Narrat, Georges.
N37 Milieux libres, quelques essais contem-
1908 porains de vie communiste en France par Georges Narrat. Paris, F. Alcan, 1908.
230 p.
Thèse - Paris.

1. Socialism in France. I. Title.

NN 0022467 CaBVaU CtY MH-BA

Le Narrateur, journal politique, d'annonces etc. du département de la Meuse. t. 1–
27. sept. 1804–
Commercy, Chez Denis [1804–
v. tab. 21]ᵐᵐ.
Once in 4 days, Sept. 1804-Dec. 1805; 3 numbers in 2 weeks, Jan. 1806-June 1824; weekly, July 1824.
Caption title, Sept. 1804– Le Narrateur de la Meuse. Title-page reads, Sept. 1804–June 1824: Le Narrateur, journal du département de la Meuse; July 1824– Le Narrateur, journal politique, d'annonces etc. du département de la Meuse.
DC611.M597N3

—— Supplément ...
Commercy, Impr. de Denis, 18
v. 21½ᵐᵐ. irregular.
From 18 to 18 title reads: Affiches, annonces et avis divers, pour le département de la Meuse; supplément ...

1. Meuse, France (Dept.)

CA 9–5834–5 Unrev'd
Library of Congress   DC611.M597N3 suppl.

NN 0022469 DLC

Narratio actionis solennis Conventv theologico Vniversitatis scholasticae Lipsicae
see under Leipzig. Universität. Theologische Fakultät.

Narratio ōdis D. D. Ioannis Stephani Dvrantii ... et Iacobi D'Affisii. Toulouse, 1567.

NN 0022471 WU

Narratio de capta Famagusta ...
see under Benedetti, Rocco.

NARRATIO de colloquio imperatoris Turcici cum mercatore Germano ab alio Germano mercatore scripta. E Germanico sermone in Latinum translata. Epistola de regno Fessano in Africa ad Christum converso. [Constantinopoli, 1560]

ff.(15).
Nunciata ex Hispaniis de regno Fessano in Africa, ab idololatria Turcica ad religionem Christianem nuper converso. ff.(11–14).

NN 0022473 MH

Bd.w. Narratio de colloquio imperatoris Turcici cum
BX mercatore Germano, mira & tristis: ab alio
1805 Germano mercatore scripta ex vrbe Cōstantinopoli,
F57 ad quendam amicum: nuperrimè à literato quodam
1554a viro, è Germanico sermone in Latinum translata.
Cage Epistola de regno Fessano in Africa ad Christum conuerso [Leipzig? 1560]

A-B⁸. 8vo.
Possibly by Georgius Sabinus. Signed on sig. B2r: N.

NN 0022474 DFo

Narratio De fvroribvs gallicis ...
see under [Hotman, François, sieur de Villiers Saint Paul] 1524–1590.

Narratio de iis quae Christo nato in Persia acciderunt
see Religious conference at the court of the Sassanidae.

Narratio de imperatoribus domus valentinianae et theodosianae.
Chronicon imperiale.
Chronica gallica a. CCCCLII et DXI.
(*In* Mommsen, Theodor, ed. Chronica minora saec. IV. V. VI. VII. Berolini, 1892. 30ᶜᵐ. vol. 1, p. [615,–666)

Narratio de itinere navali peregrinorum Hierosolymam tendentium et Silviam capientium, A. D. 1189. [Edited by] Charles Wendell David ... [Philadelphia? 1939?]
cover-title, p. 501–676. front. (facsim.) maps. 25½ᶜᵐ.

"Edited from the unique manuscript in the library of the Turin academy of sciences."
"Reprinted from Proceedings of the American philosophical society, vol. 81, no. 5, 1939."
Bibliographical foot-notes.

1. Silves, Portugal—Siege, 1189. 2. Crusades—Third, 1189–1192. I. David, Charles Wendell, 1885– ed. II. Accademia delle scienze di Torino. Biblioteca. Mss. (MM. V. 11)

A C 40–2423

Northwestern univ. Libr.
for Library of Congress [2]

NN 0022478 IEN DDO PU CSmH

VOLUME 405

Narratio de miracvlo a Michaele Archangelo
Chonis patrato; adiecto Symeonis Meta-
phrastae de eadem re libello; edidit Max
Bonnet. Paris, Librairie Hachette et cie,
1890.
xlvi, [2], 33, [3]p.   illus. (diagr.)
map. 25cm.
Texts proper paged in duplicate.
Reprinted in part from Analecta Bollan-
diana. Paris,1889. 8:[287]-328. The latter
also includes a Latin translation of the
two texts.   (p. 317-328)
Bibliography: p. xlvi.

NN   0022479   OCU MH ICU PU

Narratio de Praeliis Gestis inter Polonvm ...
see under Titlewski, Mattias.

La Narratio de rebus Armeniae; éd. critique et commentaire. Louvain, L. Durbecq, 1952.
xliv, 483 p.   25 cm.   (Corpus scriptorum Christianorum orienta-
lium, v. 132.   Subsidia, t. 4)
Bibliography : p. ix-xliv.

1. Armenian Church—Hist.—Sources.   i. Garitte, Gérard, ed.
(Series)
[BR60.C5S85 vol. 4]   A 53-5754

Catholic Univ. of   America. Library
for Library of Congress   [2]

          CtY-D MoSC CU-SB NcD UU OU TNJ-R PPiPT
NN   0022481   DCU MH InStme RPB ICU OC1 NN CU NIC

NARRATIO | Fidelis Et Svccincta | De Nvpera Illa | Proditione
Longe | Immanissima, A Iesvitis | Et Conivratis In Magnvm | Magnæ
Britanniæ Regem | Intentata, | Ex Commentarijs Anglicis, publica
authoritate | editis, in unum Historiæ corpus congesta. | (device).
Lvgdvni Batavorvm, | Prostant apud Ioannem Orlers, | Anno MDCVII. | 18.2x
14.3 cm. 38p.

NN   0022482   NNUT-Mc

Narratio historica eorvm, qvae Societas Iesv in
Nova Francia fortiter egit ...
see under [Ragueneau, Paul] 1608-1680.

Narratio historica vicissitvdinis rervm ...
see under Vermigli, Pietro Martire,
1500-1562, supposed author.

Narratio itineris navalis ad Terram Sanctam.

Chroust, Anton, 1864-   ed.
Quellen zur geschichte des kreuzzuges kaiser Friedrichs I.
Herausgegeben von A. Chroust. Berlin, Weidmannsche buch-
handlung, 1928.

NARRATIO Oder Erzelung darin War und Herlich
vorgestelt was sich in Franckreich sieder dess
Hertzogen von Parma ankunfft Nechst verlauffenen
Augustmond September vnd October Gedenckwürdiges
begeben. Mitt Einen Appendice darin vornembste Geschichte in Polen die Belägerung vnd eröberung der
Statt Corbueil vnd der Anschlag dess Hertzogen von
Parma auff Chalon in seiner Reiss auff Nieder-
landt erkläret vnnd gehandelt wird. Auss dem

Latein in Teutsch Vertirt durch Thomam Sigfridum...
Gedruckt zu Franckfort am Mayn durch Peter Schmidt.
Anno M.D.XCI.   8 l.   21cm.

1. Alexander Farnese, duke of Parma and Piacenza,
1545-1592. 2. Henry IV, king of France, 1553-1610.
3. France—Hist.—Henry IV, 1589-1610. I.Sigfrid,
Thomas, ed.

NN   0022487   NN

Rd.w.   Narratio, vere & grauiter exponens quid in Gallia
DA   post ducis Parmensis aduentum proximis mensibus,
36.22   Augusto, Septembri, & Octobri, memorabile actum
D7   sit. Auctore D.R.A. Francofurti ad Moenum, Impensis
B8   Pauli Brachfeldii, 1591.
1590
Cage   A-B⁴. 4to.

NN   0022488   DFo

Narration authentique de l'échange des prisonniers
faits aux Cèdres pendant la guerre américaine de 1775;
tr. de l'anglais par Marcel Ethier ... Montréal, E. Senécal, 1873.
44 p. 23ᶜᵐ. (*In* Verreau, H. A. J. B., comp. and ed. Invasion du
Canada. 1873. iv. 2,)
Translation of a tract published in London in 1777 under title "Authentic narrative of facts relating to the exchange of prisoners taken at the
Cedars."
1. U. S.—Hist.—Revolution—Prisoners, Exchange of. 2. Canadian invasion, 1775-1776.   i. Ethier, Marcel, tr.
                                                        2—4643
Library of Congress   E231.V55 vol. 2
  MB __ Copy 2.   E281.A93

        CaNSWA
NN   0022489   DLC CtY DNW RWoU CaBVaU MiU-C MB

A narration, briefely contayning the history of
the French massacre
see under [Bruyn, Ambrosius de]

PQ   Narration en vers de dix-huit principaux
1947   traits de l'histoire de Suisse, et
C3   Mélanges curieux de littérature légère,
N3   d'histoire naturelle & de morale agréable,
        par A. M. C**. Lausanne, Hignou, 1796.
        160p. 20cm.

1. Switzerland - Hist. - To 1648 - Poetry
I. C**, A. M. II. Title: Mélanges curieux
de littérature légère

NN   0022491   WU

Narration of certain uncommon things that did formerly happen to me,
Herbert Willis, R.D. 61 pp.
(In Tales from Blackwood. Vol. 7. Edinburgh. [1861.])
A story of the reign of James II.

G9913 — Great Britain. Hist. Fict. James II., 1685-1688.

NN   0022492   MB

A Narration of the Captivity of John Fillmore,
and his escape from the Pirates. [Double rule]
Printed at Portland, by B. Titcomb, Jun. 1792.
16 p.   12.5 x 21 cm.

NN   0022493   MWA

A narration of the captivity of John Fillmore
and his escape from the pirates. Suffield [Conn.]:
Printed by Edward Gray. 1802.
20 p. 18cm.
"The substance of the ... relation was verbally
delivered to the editor,by the Honorable Increase
Moseley. Esq. who was intimately acquainted with
Mr.John Fillmore."-Advertisement,p.[2].
John Fillmore was the great-grandfather of Pres.
Millard Fillmore.-See Appleton's Cyclopaedia of
American biography,1887,vol.2,p.452.

NN   0022494   MiU-C

A narration of the captivity of John
Fillmore and his escape from the pirates.
Johnstown.   William Child.   1805.

31 p.

NN   0022495   OC1WHi

Narration of the captivity of John
Fillmore and his escape from the pirates.
[Johnston, 1806]
16p. 18cm.

NN   0022496   PBL MWA

A narration of the captivity of John Fillmore, and his
escape from the pirates. Johnstown 2d ed. Johnstown
[N. Y.] Printed and sold by A. Taylor, 1809.
18 p. 22½ᶜᵐ.
"The substance of the following relation was verbally delivered to the
editor, by the Hon. Increase Moseley, esq. who was intimately acquainted
with Mr. John Fillmore ... Mr. Fillmore ... being dead, the editor has
chosen to deliver the story as though it was written by the sufferer himself ..."—Advt.
First edition, Suffield, Conn., 1802.
1. Fillmore, John, 1702-1777. 2. Phillips, John, d. 1724. 3. Pirates.

Library of Congress   G537.F5N3   8-12061

NN   0022497   DLC MB NjPT MiU-C MWA

A narration of the expedition to Taunton; the
raising the siege before it, and the condition
of our forces, and the enemies, at this present
in the West. Sent from a Commander in the
army, and dated at Chard, May 18, 1645.
Published by authoritie.   London,
S. Gellibrand, 1645.
8 p.   18.5 x 14.5 cm.

NN   0022498   CtY

*E065   A narration of the great victory, (through
B7763   Gods providence) obtained by the Parliaments
644t   forces under Sir William Waller, at Alton in
         Surrey the 13. of this instant December, 1643.
         against the Cavaliers: where were taken neer
         a thousand prisoners, a thousand arms, two
         hundred horse, with divers officers of great
         quality ...
         [London] Printed for Edward Husbands,Dec.16.
         [1643]
         8p. 20cm.
         Bound with J.   Avery's Two letters of
         great conse-   quence, sent from
         Hamborovgh,   1644.

NN   0022499   MH

A narration of the grievovs visitation, and dreadfvll desertion of
Mʳ. Peacock, in his last sicknesse: together with the sweet and
gracious issue, in his comfortable restauration, to the joy of Gods
salvation, before his most blessed end, and heavenly death,
Decemb. 4. 1611...   London: Printed by R. H. for R. Milbourn,
1641.   18 p.l., 104 p., 2 l.   14½cm. (12°.)
First leaf blank: "imprimatur," leaf 1 at end.
Epistle "To the Christian reader" signed: I. C.
Last (blank?) leaf wanting.
1. Peacock, Thomas, d. 1611.   I. C., I.   *Revised*
N. Y. P. L.   *September 30, 1937*

NN   0022500   NN

A narration of the late accident in the New Exchange, on the 21. and 22. of November, 1653
see under Sá, Pantaleão.

A narration of the life, service and sufferings,
of... John Peters... Lond., 1709.

NN   0022502   PHC

A narration of the lives of the thirteen compilers of
the liturgy of the Church of England
see under [Downes, Samuel]

VOLUME 405

[A narration of the most material parliamentary proceedings of this present Parliament and their armies, in their civil and martial affairs. Which Parliament began the third of November, 1640. and the remarkable transactions are continued until this year ... London? 165-?]
1 p.l.,30,32 p. illus. 18½cm. [With A narration of the most material parliamentary proceedings of this present Parliament ... London, 1651]

Signatures: A-D⁴, *4, a⁴, C⁴, D-E² (A₁, title-page, wanting)
Imperfect copy: title-page (sig.A₁) wanting; margins closely trimmed.
Title supplied from earlier edition (London, 1651)
Attributed to John Vicars.

Published also (London, 1656) under title: Former ages never heard of, and after ages will admire. Or, A brief review of the most materiall parliamentary transactions.

NN 0022506   CLU-C

A **narration** of the most material parliamentary proceedings of this present Parliament and their armies, in their civil and martial affairs. Which Parliament began the third of November, 1640. and the remarkable transactions are continued until this yeer. Published as a breviary, leading all along successively, as they fell out in their several yeers ... London, Printed for T. Jenner, 1651.
1 p. l., 30, 32 p. 11 illus., 1 pl. 20 x 15½cm.
Leaves, closely trimmed, approximating 16½ x 12ᶜᵐ, inlaid to 19½ x 15ᶜᵐ.
Subject entries: Gt. Brit.—Hist.—Charles I, 1625-1649.
2-28656

Library of Congress, no.   DA412.N23.

NN 0022507   DLC CLU-C CtY

---

*EC65
A100
652n

A narration of the most material Parliamentary proceedings of this present Parliament and their armies, in their civil and martial affairs. Which Parliament began the third of November, 1640. and the remarkable transactions are continued until this yeer. Published as a breviary, leading all along successively, as they fell out in their several yeers. So that if any man will be inform'd of any remarkable passage, he may turn to the yeer, and so see in some measure in what moneth thereof it was accompaished. And for information of   such as are altogether

ignorant of the rise and progress of these times, which things are brought to pass, that former ages have not heard of, and after ages will admire ...
London.Printed for Th.Jenner,at the south-entrance of the Royal Exchange,MDCLI[1652].
1p.l.,30,36p. illus. 19cm.
The illustrations are engraved; in this copy there is no illustration on p.17 (2d count).

NN 0022509   MH

Narration of the proceedings of the Scottish army, and a **vindication** of the parliament of England. London, 1646.

NN 0022510   PPL

A narration of the siege and taking of the town of Leicester the last of May, 1645 by the kings forces; together with other proceedings of the committee...
London, Ptd. by G.Miller 1645.
12p. 22.5cm.
Photostat reproduction of original in British Museum. E.289.   (6)

NN 0022511   CSmH CtY

A narration of the wonders of grace. In verse...
see under   [Dutton, Mrs. Anne]

Narration; or (Second part of Amboyney) of sundry ...
see   [Darell, John]
A true and compendious narration; or (Second part of Amboyney)

Narration scale,
n.p.   1 l. (fold.)   Q

6 compositions.

NN 0022514   OO

Narratione del marauiglioso torneo rappresentato...
see under   [Cirni, Antonfrancesco]

NARRATIONE della felice vittoria, che ha conseguito l'armata christiana contra quella di Selim imperatore de Turchi. Nuovamente posta in ottava rima. [Venezia, 1571]

24°. pp.(16). Vign.

NN 0022516   MH

NARRATIONE delli meravigliosi prodigi apparsi nella citta di Baiona in Francia, dove s'intende li stupendi segni veduti nell'aria, con il nascimento di un figliuolo, che haveva 33 occhi. Napoli,1622.

p;(8).

NN 0022517   MH

NARRATIONE delli prodigiosi portenti & ispressio ni metheorologiche occorsi nella Citta di Costantinopoli nelli 18 di marzo fino alli 7 di maggio del presente anno 1646. Napoli, etc., per il Gariboldi, [16-]

ff.4

NN 0022518   MH

NARRATIONE veridica di quanto succede gjornalmente ne'presenti tempi di Guerra in Costantinopoli con le ribelione de Turchi e loreo confusioni. Venetia,1690.

Wdcts.

NN 0022519   MH

Law
Case
Narrationes (Anglo-Norman law text)

Natura breuium. ‖ The olde tenures. ‖ Lyttylton tenures. ‖ The new talys. ‖ The articles vppon ‖ the new talys. ‖ Diuersyte of courtes. ‖ Justyce of peace. ‖ The chartuary. ‖ Court baron. ‖ Court of hundrede. ‖ Returna breuium. ‖ The ordynaunce for ‖ takynge of fees in ‖ the escheker. ‖ And fyrste a table to ‖ all these .xii. bokes. ‖ Cum priuilegio. ‖ ₍Colophon₎ ... Prentyd ‖ by W. Rastell ‖ in Fletestreete in ‖ saynt Brydys chyrche ‖ yarde, the yere of ‖ oure lorde ‖ 1534 ‖ ·.· ‖₎

Narrationes de recto cum sequentibus
see
Narrationes (*Anglo-Norman law text*)

NARRATIONES de vita et conversatione beatae Mariae virginis et de pueritia et adolescentia Salvatoris ex codice Gisensi edidit Oscar Schade. Commentatio. Halis Saxonum,Libraria Orphanotrophei,1870.

4°. pp.28.

NN 0022522   MH

Narrationes Dvae *Admodum Memorabiles*...
see under   Bigges, Walter, d. 1582?

Narrationes duae facinorum atrocium atque saevorum
see under   [Camerarius, Joachim] 1500-1574.

Narrationes; recueil de récits, extraits principalement de Tite-Live. Texte latin publié avec des notices biographiques, des remarques grammaticales, des notes explicatives, un appendice critique, des cartes et des plans, par O.Riemann et I.Uri. 2.éd., revue et corrigée. Paris, Hachette et cie., 1898.

NN 0022525   MH

Narrationes rervm Indicarvm ex litteris patrvm societatis Iesv desumptae ... Lovanii, 1589
see under   Jesuits. Letters from missions (The East)

Narrationis amatoriae ...
see under   [Achilles Tatius]   [Supplement]

Narrations d'Omai ...
see under   [Baston, Guillaume André René] 1741-1825.

Narratiuncula de Indulgentia Portiunculae ex libro "Compendium theologiae pauperis" deprompta. [Edidit Bonaventura Kruitwagen.]
— Ad Claras Aquas. Typ. Collegii S. Bonaventurae. 1909. 407-411 pp. 24 cm.
Bound with the original paper covers.
"Extractum ex periodico 'Archivum franciscanum historicum,' an. 2, fasc. 3."

E.3560 — Compendium theologiae   pauperis. — Portiuncula Indulgence.
— Kruitwagen, Bonaventura, Pater, O.F.M., ed.

NN 0022529   MB

VOLUME 405

DA
448
.N23
Narrativ of the plott. [A collection of 29
titles relating to the "popish plot". London, 1679-83]
29 pieces in 1 v.   31 cm.
Binder's title.

1. Popish Plot, 1678.

NN   0022530   MiU

Narrativa da perseguição de Hippolyto Joseph da
Costa Pereira Furtado de Mendonça ...
see under   Costa Pereira Furtado de
Mendonça, Hippolyto José da, 1774-1823.
[Supplement]

Narrativa de viagem de um naturalista inglês ao
Rio de Janeiro ...
see under   Bunbury, Sir Charles James
Fox, 1809-1866.

NARRATIVA Della Gverra Principiata contra il gran Turco, per gli Illustrissimi Signori Venetiani, doue si
comprende asalti per terra, mouimenti per Mare...
La superba imbasiata del gran Turco, & la honorata
Risposta fattali dal Senato, La creatione & partita
del Generale, & l'ordine de l'armata, nome...del-
li Signori ... tanto, genti e denari...& alcune
noue di Francia.   Viterbo [Agostino Colaldi, 1570]
4 l.   21cm.(4°.)

NN   0022533   NN MH

Narrativas e lendas da historia patria. Lisboa, A. David,
Encadernador [19—]-
v. illus., ports. 17 cm. (Bibliotheca da infancia, 1
CONTENTS.—[1] Conquista e organização do Reino de Portugal.

1. Portugal— *History - Juvenile literature.*
DP540.N4   58-37218

NN   0022534   DLC GU NIC

Narrativas insulanas
see   Ervedal da Beira, Visconde do.
[Supplement]

Narrativas militares..,

See *under*

[ESCHAGNOLLE] TAUNAY, Alfredo de] 1843-1899.

---

*EB65
A100
681n
The narrative.
London: Printed for Anthony Jackson, 1681.
broadside. 31.5x19.5cm.
In verse, beginning: Come prick up your ears,
if they are not gone.

NN   0022537   MH

A narrative. A short and thrilling narrative of a few of
the scenes and incidents that occurred in the sanguinary and
cruel war of 1812-14, between England and the United States;
written by one who ... passed through or was an eye-witness
to nearly every scene and incident here related. Published by
the author. Norway [Me.] Advertiser press, 1853.
62 p. 21cm.

1. U. S.—Hist.—War of 1812— Personal narratives.
Library of Congress   E361.N23   1-27860

NN   0022538   DLC MeB

1730
+N16
The narrative and affidavit-men detected:
or, Collcott and Robin put to the blush ...
[London, A. Moore, 1730]
5p. 32cm.
Caption title.

1. Collcott, George   2. Jones,
Robert

NN   0022539   CtY CLU-C

Narrative and confessions of Lucretia P. Cannon, who
was tried, convicted, and sentenced to be hung at Georgetown, Delaware, with two of her accomplices. Containing an account of some of the most horrible and shocking
murders and daring robberies ever committed by one of
the female sex. New York, Printed for the publishers,
1841.
24 p. incl. front. 22½cm.

1. Cannon, Mrs. Lucretia P. (Hanly)
                                        22-14006
Library of Congress   HV6248.C16N3

NN   0022540   DLC N CU NNC ViU

Narrative and confessions of Lucretia P.
Cannon... [Georgetown, Del., Sussex
Countian] [19-?]
20p

"First printed for the New York
publisher in 1841."

NN   0022541   DeWI

Narrative and correspondence concerning the
removal of the deposites, and occurences
connected therewith
see under   [Duane, William John] 1780-1865.

Narrative and critical history of America
see under   Winsor, Justin, 1831-1897, ed.

RARE
DA
412
1648
.N3
A Narrative and declaration of the
dangerous design against the Parliament & Kingdom, carried on in the
County of Kent and elsewhere, under
the specious pretence of petition-
ing. Also a declaration (published
in the name) of the counties of
Kent, Essex, Middlesex, Surrey, to
the Army under the command of the
Lord Fairfax. Together with
several papers of dangerous consequence, and observations thereupon.
Ordered by the Commons assembled in
Parliament, that this narrative,
papers and observations be forthwith
printed and published. London, E.

Husband, Printer to the Honorable
House of Commons, 1648.
22 p.
#Kent, England--History--Sources.
#Great Britain--Politics and gov-
ernment--1642-1649--Pamphlets.
#Great Britain--History--Civil
War, 1642-1649--Pamphlets.
(A)Great Britain. Parliament, 1648.
(A)Great Britain. Army.

NN   0022545   MoU CSmH MH MnU CtY CU NNUT

A narrative and defence of the proceedings of the
Methodist Episcopal Church in Baltimore city
station ...
see under   [Bond, Thomas Emerson]
1782-1856.

AC901
.M5
Narrative and extracts of the proceedings relative
to the election of a member of parliament for
the city of Edinburgh, on the 16th september
1780; and subsequent election of magistrates
of that city, and second election of a member
of parliament attempted on the 7th October
1780. [Edinburgh? 1781]
111 p. 4°. [Miscellaneous pam. v. 280]

NN   0022547   DLC

RA792.09421
C873n
[Narrative and letters regarding a contract
dispute between W. C. MacReady and the
proprietors of Covent Garden Theater.
London, Printed by Gold and Walton, 1823]
[3]-19[1]p. 22cm.

Title page lacking.

1. London. Covent Garden Theatre.
2. Theater--London. 3. Actors, English.
I. MacReady, William Charles, 1793-1873.

NN   0022548   OC

The narrative & reasons of the Honourable House
of Commons, concerning the tryal of the lords
in the tower ...
see under   Gt. Brit. Parliament, 1679.
House of Commons.

Narrative & report of the causes and circumstances of the
deplorable conflagration at Richmond. ⟨Virginia.⟩ From
letters and authentic documents. [Richmond] Printed for the
public, January 12th, 1812.
72 p. 14cm.

1. Richmond—Theater disaster, 1811.   A 33-3332
Title from Virginia State   Libr. F234.R5N2 Printed by L. C.

NN   0022550   Vi MiU-C NIC NcD

The narrative and resolution, with the rules of the
Society for reformation of manners ...
see under   Society for Reformation and
Manners.

Narrative and romantic poems of the Italians
see under   [Foscolo, Ugo] 1778-1827.

A narrative and testimony concerning Grace
Watson, daughter of Samuel and Mary Watson:
who departed this life at London, on the
twentieth day of the sixth month, 1688 ...
London, Printed for Thomas Northcott in
George-yard in Lumbard-street, 1690.
2 p.l., 19 p. 18.5 cm.
Testimonies from Charles Marshal,
Elizabeth Moss, Sameul Watson, Mary Watson,
Mary Moss, and Benjamin Antrobus.

NN   0022553   PSC-Hi PHC

Narrative and writings of Andrew Jackson, of
Kentucky
see under   Jackson, Andrew, b. 1814.

VOLUME 405

The narrative ⟨Autobiographical sketch⟩
see under [Fancourt, Samuel] 1678-1768.

The Narrative Bible
see under Johnson, Clifton, 1865-1940, ed.

The NARRATIVE companion; or, Entertaining
moralist. Containing choice of novels and
allegories, from the best English writers.
London, printed for T.Becket,1760.

2 vol.

NN 0022557 MH

A NARRATIVE concerninge the salt of South
and North Shields,Sunderland,Blyth,and other
places within the counties of Durham and Northumberland . From a MS. in the Lansdowne
collection. Newcastle,1847.

pp.24. (Reprints of rare tracts, etc.,
Historical III. [iii.]).
"Only 100 copies printed"

NN 0022558 MH

A narrative containing notices of facts, opinions,
principles and persons, as exhibited and
developed during the late election for the
city of Oxford ... Oxford [etc.] 1835.

NN 0022559 CtY

A narrative. [Correspondence between Isaac
Newton and the Century Club] 1884
see under Booth, George.

Narrative episodes from the Old Testament ...
Boston, Palmer, 1910
see under Bible. O.T. English.
Selections. 1910.

Narrative for youthful inquirers. [anon.]
Boston, Mass.,S.S.S. 1839.
32 p. 32°.

NN 0022562 DLC

A narrative, founded on facts: in a series of
most interesting events, anecdotes, &c.
particularly describing the amazing fortune
acquired by a person that came into a noble
family as a footman, who was raised by his
noble master to the employment of steward;
his peculations, behaviour, and methods
pursued, in acquiring a fortune of upwards
of ten thousand pounds per annum ...
London [pref. 1786]
2 p.l., 82 p. 21 cm.

NN 0022563 CtY

Narrative history of "G" and 7th tank battalion,
1919
see under Gt. Brit. Army. 7th tank
battalion.

The **narrative** history of King James, for the first fourteen
years. In four parts. I. The state of England at His Majesties
entrance, and relation it had to other parts ... II. The proceedings touching the divorce betwixt the Lady Frances Howard,
and Robert earl of Essex ... III. A declaration of His Majesties
revenue ... IV. The commissions and warrants for the burning
of two hereticks ... London, Printed for Michael Sparke at
the sign of the Bible in Green-Arbour, 1651.

6 p. l., 192 p., 2 l., 72 p., 1 l., 18, ₍8₎ p. 2 port. (incl. front.) 19ᶜᵐ.
Parts 1 and 2 paged continuously; pt. 2-4 have each a special t.-p.
Collation: 1st prelim. leaf: recto blank, verso "The emblematical title

explained" (in five rimed stanzas); 2d p. l.: illus. t.-p., engraved "Trvth
brought to light and discovered by time or A discourse and historicall narration of the first XIIII yeares of King Iames reigne. London, Printed by
Richard Cotes and are to be sold by Michaell Sparke at the Blew Bible in
Green 1651 Arber, Iohn Droeshout sculp. Lon." vᵒ blank; 3d p. l.: rᵒ
blank, vᵒ portrait of Sir Thomas Overbury (engr.); 4th p. l.: title-page
(printed); 5th-6th p. l. (sig. a-a2): "The stationer to the impartial
reader, gentlemen or others" (signed: Ml. Scintilla); p. 1-74 (sig. B-L₄)
in fours): A historical narration of the first xiv. years of King James";
p. ₍75₎-192 (sig. ₍L₂₎-Z, Z* in fours, Y in two excepted): "Truth brought
to light by time. The proceedings touching the divorce between the Lady
Frances Howard, and Robert earl of Essex ... London, Printed by R. C.
for Michael Sparke, 1651" (with fold. engr. port. of the Earl of Essex and
his wife); "An abstract or brief declaration of the present state of His

Majesties revenew ... London, Printed for M. S. 1651" and "The contents" (2 p. l. without sig., followed by text, p. 1-72 with sig. A*-I* in
fours); "A true relation of the commissions and warrants for the condemnation and burning of Bartholomew Legatt and Thomas Withman ...
London, Printed for Michael Spark, 1651" (1 p. l. and p. 1-18 with sig.
Aa*-Bb* in fours, Cc* in two); "A compleat table of the several chapters
of this Historical narration" ₍etc.₎ (i. e. of the first part of the book, ₍8₎
p. with sig. a)
"A historical narration of the first xiv. years of King James" (p. 1-74)
slightly abridged, and "Sʳ Francis Bacon, his speech at the arraignment
of the Earl of Somerset" (p. 165-176) were published in 1643 under the
title: The five years of King Iames, or, The condition of the state of
England, and the relation it had to other provinces. Written by Sʳ
Foulk Grevill, late Lord Brook."

1. Gt. Brit.—Hist.—   James I, 1603-1625.
                                                    9-17822
Library of Congress   DA391.N2

DFo MWiW-C CSt PSt NIC CU
NN 0022567   DLC CtY WU PU-F MB NjP IaU MH CSmH TU

Narrative hymns for village schools
see under [Alexander, Mrs. Cecil
Frances (Humphreys] 1818-1895.

A **narrative** in justification of injured innocence. Wherein
cowardice, fraud, tyranny, and oppression are detected and exposed... To which is annexed, a chart of the Streights of Gibraltar, and the adjacent coasts. Written by a country gentleman...
London, W. Webb, 1749.   viii, 120 p.   chart.   21cm.

491670. 1. Navy, British, 1740-1748.   2. Warships, British—Elizabeth.
3. Sbirel, John. 4. Lingen,   Joseph. I. A country gentleman.
N. Y. P. L.   *Card revised*
                                                June 20, 1946

NN 0022569   NN

A **narrative**, in two parts: written in 1812. London,
Printed by J. Compton, 1813.

1 p. l., 238 p. fold. map. 22ᶜᵐ.
Travels in Europe.

Subject entries: Europe—Descr. & trav.

                                                    8-19101
Library of Congress, no.   D919.N23.

NN 0022570   DLC

The narrative of a commuted pensioner
see under [Williamson, John] d. 1840.

Narrative of a journey from Lima to Para, across
the Andes and down the Amazon
see under Smyth, William, 1800-1877.

Narrative of a journey from Santiago de Chile to
Buenos Ayres ...
see under [Hibbert, Edward]

E490   Narrative of a journey from Southampton to
N37   Bombay, via Paris, Brussels, the Rhine, part of
       Switzerland and Savoy; south of France, Malta,
       upper Egypt, and Aden, performed between the
       12th October and the 13th December, 1842: with
       an appendix, by an officer of His Highness the
       Nizam's army. Madras, B. Lacey, 1843.
       70 p. illus., plates, 3 fold.maps. 21 cm.

       1. Voyages and travels - 1800-1850.

NN 0022574   CtY

Wason   Narrative of a journey in the interior of
DS703   China, and of a voyage to and from that
Z114   country, in the years 1816 and 1817
       ₍a review₎. London, 1819₎
       67-91 p. 21cm.

       Detached from the Quarterly review,
       XXI, 1819.
       In vol. lettered: Miscellaneous on China.

       1. Abel, Clarke. Narrative of a journey
       in the interior   of China.

NN 0022575   NIC

Narrative of a journey through India. By T. D. L. ...
Westminster, Printed by T. Brettell, 1857.
viii, ₍2₎ 118 p. col. front. 20½ᶜᵐ.

I. India- Descr. & trav.   I. L., T. D. II. T. D. L.

                                                    20-3543
Library of Congress   DS412.N3

NN 0022576   DLC CtY CU

Narrative of a journey to the north of Ireland, in
1802. London, 1803.
96 p. O.

NN 0022577   RPB

Narrative of a late expedition against the Indians
see under [Brackenridge, Hugh Henry]
1748-1816, ed.

The narrative of a late horrid
murther, committed by Robert Watts
of Norwich upon the person of Mary
Watts his wife, for which he was
condemned at the assize there, and
was executed before his own house,
August the 30th, 1701 ... London, 1701.
16p., illus.

t.-p.mutilated cutting off name of
publisher.

NN 0022579   CaBVa

A narrative of a light company soldier's service,
in the 41st regiment of foot, during the late
American war ...
see under [Byfield, Shadrach] b. 1789.

Narrative of a miraculous cure of a
decrepid maid, on a new-year's day, 1705-6,
by faith, prayer, and anointing with oil.

NN 0022581   PPL

VOLUME 405

Narrative of a mission of inquiry to the Jews from
the Church of Scotland
    see under   [Bonar, Andrew Alexander] 1810-
1892.

The narrative of a mission to Nova Scotia
    see under   [Marsden, Joshua] 1777-1837.

A narrative of a new and unusual American
imprisonment of two Presbyterian ministers...
    see under   [Makemie, Francis]
1658-1708.

Narrative of a prisoner in the war of 1812 ...
    see under   [Denison, Isaac] 1790-1865.

Narrative of a private soldier in His Majesty's 92d
regiment of foot. Written by himself. Detailing many
circumstances relative to the insurrection in Ireland in
1798; the expedition to Holland in 1799; and the expedition to Egypt in 1801; and giving a particular account
of his religious history and experience. With a preface
by the Rev. Ralph Wardlaw, D. D. 1st American ed.
Philadelphia, Pub. for the benefit of the United foreign
missionary society, 1822.
    ix, [11]–216 p. 15ᶜᵐ.
    Signed: G. B.
    1. Gt. Brit.—History,   Military—1789-1820.   I. B., G.
    II. G. B.
                                    22–11135
    Library of Congress   DA68.N3

NN   0022586   DLC PMA

Narrative of a residence in Belgium during the
campaign of 1815 ...
    see under   [Watts, Jane (Waldie)] 1793-
1826.

A narrative of a revival of religion in Springfield,
Vermont
    see under   [Morton, Daniel Olus.] 1788-
1852.

Narrative of a singular escape from a Portuguese
convent. With an introductory address by the
Rev. W. Carus Wilson. m.a. Rector of
Whittington. Kirby Lonsdale, A. Foster,
1835.
    xli (1), 58 p. 16°.
    I. Wilson, William Carus, 1792-1859, ed.

NN   0022589   NN

Narrative of a singular imposition practised
by Mary Willcocks. London, 1817.
    68 p

NN   0022590   PHi

The narrative of a soldier
    see under   [Coates, Joseph]

A narrative of a strange and sudden apparition
of an arch-angel at the Old-Bayly ...
    see under   Hickes, George, 1642-1715.

Narrative of a ten years residence at Tripoli...
    see under   [Tully, Miss   ] fl. 1783-
1795.

Narrative of a three months' march in India
    see under   [Ashmore, Harriette]

Narrative of a three years' residence in Italy,
1819-1822
    see under   [Martin, Selina]

Narrative of a tour in North America
    see under   Tudor, Henry.

Narrative of a tour in the summer of 1817

      see under   [Storrow, Samuel Appleton]
d. 1837.

A narrative of a tour in the west of England;
and a short visit through several of the
Midland counties, for the purpose of ascertain-
ing the religious and moral state of the inhabitants, and Hints on the formation and encouragement of Sabbath schools & village
preaching. Second edition, corrected. By an
old traveller. London, Published by John
Offor, 1823.
    viii, 116 p.   13. 2 x 8. 4 cm.

NN   0022598   CaOTP

A **narrative** of a tour of observation, made during the summer of 1817, by James Monroe, president of the United States,
through the north-eastern and north-western departments of
the Union: with a view to the examination of their several
military defences. With an appendix. Philadelphia: Published by S. A. Mitchell & H. Ames, Clark & Raser, Printers.
1818.
    xii, [13]–228, xxxvi p. 18ᶜᵐ.
    Half-title: The president's tour.
    Not the same as Waldo's Tour of James Monroe, though involving
much the same material. cf. p. vii of Waldo's Tour of James Monroe,
Hartford, 1818.
    1. Monroe, James, pres.   U. S., 1758–1831. 2. U. S.—Defenses.
                                                      2–17205
    Library of Congress   E371.N23

    ICN MWelC MiU-C OC PSt PPL NcD PHi ICN MH
    CaBViP OCU AAP T IC MiU InU PBL TxU PMA PU ICN
NN   0022599   DLC NjR ViU OOxM OFH PSt NcD KEmT

Narrative of a tour taken in the year 1667, to La
Grande Chartreuse and Alet. 1813
    see under   Schimmelpennick, Mary Anne
(Galton) 1778-1856.

Narrative of a tour through some parts of the
Turkish empire
    see under   [Fuller, John] fl. 1829.

Narrative of a trip/ to the/ falls of Shewinagam./ [n.p. n.d.]
    [3]p. 4to. Caption title. A reminiscence of a trip in 1830 or somewhat later.
27.5 x 21.6 cm.

NN   0022602   CaOTP

915.91   Narrative of a two months' cruise amongst the
N234   islands of the Mergui Archipelago. [Lon-
           don, H. S. King][n.d.]
           39p. 26cm.

           Cover title: The Tenasserim Archipelago.

NN   0022603   IU

Narrative of a visit to Brazil, Chile, Peru ...
    see under   Mathison, Gilbert Farquhar.

Narrative of a voyage by Captain Ross, in the years 1829, 30, 31,
32, and 33, to discover a north-west passage from the eastern to
the western ocean; in which is given detailed particulars of the
many unparalleled sufferings experienced by himself and his un-
daunted crew, during his abode in tohse [sic] extremely inclement
regions; the loss of the Victory steam ship; the discovery of the
North Pole; and the happy rescue of Captain Ross and his crew
by the Isabella, a whale ship from Hull, by which they safely returned to their native country.   London: W. Mason[, 1835?].
24 p.   front.   8°.

    587360A. 1. Arctic expeditions,   1829–1833. 2. Ross, Sir John,
    1777–1856.
    N. Y. P. L.   June 21, 1932

NN   0022605   NN

Narrative of a voyage from Valparaiso to the South
Sea Islands in Her Majesty's ship Actæon, **towards the**
end of the year 1836.
    (In United service journal and naval and military magazine. **London,**
1838. 21½ᶜᵐ. v. 26, p. 492-500)

    1. Ethnology—Oceanica. 2. Actæon (Ship)

                                                   CA 18-731 Unrev'd
    Library of Congress   U1.U6
    —— Copy 2, separate.   DU620.6.N32

NN   0022606   DLC

Narrative of a voyage to Brasil.   London, 1805
    see under   Lindley, Thomas.

Ayer
150.5   Narrative of a voyage to Maryland,
M3   1705-1706.   [New York,1907]
N2   p.327-340.
1907

         Caption title.
         "From a manuscript in the British
    museum (Sloane MS. 2291, fol.1) to which
    the attention has been called by Pro-
    fessor C.M.Andrews. The author's name
    is not known."
         Extract from the American historical
    review, vol.12.

NN   0022608   ICN

Narrative of a voyage to Spitzbergen in the year
1613 ...
    see under   [Fotherby, Robert]

VOLUME 405

Narrative of a voyage to the Spanish Main, in the ship "Two friends"; the occupation of Amelia island by M'Gregor, &c.—sketches of the province of East Florida; and anecdotes illustrative of the habits and manners of the Seminole Indians: with an appendix, containing a detail of the Seminole war, and the execution of Arbuthnot and Ambrister ... London, Printed for J. Miller. 1819
1 p. l., [v]-ix, [6], 328 p., 1 l. 22 cm.
The Seminole war—Execution of Arbuthnot and Ambrister, etc.: p. 196-312.
1. Florida—Hist.—Spanish colony, 1784-1821. 2. Amelia island, Fla.—Hist. 3. Two Friends (Ship) 4. Venezuela—Hist.—War of independence, 1810-1823.   5. Seminole war, 1st, 1817-1818. 6. Arbuthnot, Alexander, 1748?-1818. 7. Ambrister, Robert Christie, 1785?-1818.   8. Spanish Main.
F314.N23
1—21778

NN 0022610
NcD FTaSU OFH IHi PPL PU-Mu FMU
DLC RPJCB NN MB GU-De ViU OC CtY NcD

PR 975 N166
Narrative of a voyage towards the South Pole, in the years 1773 and 1774. Recommended to all seamen. Dublin, Printed by M. Goodwin, 1824.
12 p.

NN 0022611 CLU

Narrative of a yacht voyage in the Mediterranean
see under [Westminster, Elizabeth Mary (Leveson-Gower) 2d marchioness] 1796 or 7-1891.

A narrative of affairs lately received from His Majesties island of Jamaica
see under Jamaica. Governor, 1682-1684? (Sir Thomas Lynch)

A NARRATIVE of all the proceedings in the draining of the great level of the fens, extending into the counties of Northampton, Lincoln, Norfol, Suffolk, Cambridge, and Hunting don; and the isel of Ely; from the time of Queen Elizabeth, until May, 1661. By N.N. L. 1661.

(Arber, Edward, editor. An English garner, etc., 1877, etc., 313-320)

NN 0022614 MH MB MnU

A narrative of all the proceedings in the draining of the great level of the fens extending into the counties of Northampton, Lincoln ... London, the Author, 1661.
(In: An English garner. [v. 6] Social England.   Westminster, 1903.   8°.
p. 407-414)
By N.N.

NN 0022615 NN

A narrative of all the robberies, escapes, &c. of John Sheppard ...
see under [Defoe, Daniel] 1661?-1731.

A narrative of an ascent to the summit of Mont Blanc, made during the summer of 1827
see under [Hawes, Sir Benjamin] 1797-1862.

A narrative of an attempt made by the French of Canada upon the Mohaque's country ...
see under [Bayard, Nicholas] 1644?-1707.

Narrative of an excursion from Corfu to Smyrna...
see under [Jolliffe, Thomas Robert] 1780-1872.

A narrative of an excursion to Ireland
see under [Gorst, Gilpin]

Narrative of an expedition across the great southwestern prairies, from Texas to Santa Fé
see under Kendall, George Wilkins, 1809-1867.

Narrative of an expedition against Fort Shelby, on the Mississippi, one league above the entrance of the Wiskonsin, under the command of Lieutenant Colonel McKay, then Major of the Michigan Fencibles; from the Journal of an officer who was an eye witness. Written for the 22 and 23 nos. of the Canadian Magazine. (March and April, 1828, pages 133-170.)
— [Green Bay, Wis.] 1925. 16 pp. Portrait. Facsimile. [Green Bay Historical Society. Green Bay historical bulletin. Vol. 1, no. 3.] 22½ cm.
Edited by Lieut. Col. McKay.

N2379 — S.r.c. — United States. Hi. War of 1812. Personal narratives. — McKay, Lieut. Col. William, ed.

NN 0022622 MB

Narrative of an expedition of five Americans, into a country of wild animals, without any aid of government, and solely on their own resources ... 5th thousand. London, J. Blackwood [1853]
iv, [5]-114 p. front., plates. 18½ʲᵐ.

1. Randolph Co., W. Va.
13-19345
Library of Congress   F247.R2N2

NN 0022623 DLC

Narrative of an expedition of five Americans into a country of wild animals, (such as panthers, bears, wolves, elk, deer, otter, badger, etc.) without any aid of government, and solely on their own resources. Illustrated by Watts Phillips. London, J. Blackwood, 1854.
2 p.l., [iii]-iv, 160 p.   front., illus., pl.   16.5 cm.
Added title-page, illustrated.

NN 0022624 NcD

Narrative of an expedition to explore the river Zaire, usually called the Congo ...
see under Tuckey, James Kingston, 1776-1816.

Narrative of an official visit to Guatemala from Mexico.   London, 1829
see under Thompson, George Alexander.

A narrative of Captain Cook's voyages round the world
see under [Kippis, Andrew] 1725-1795.

The narrative of Captain David Woodard and four seamen
see under Woodard, David.

Narrative of Captain James Cook's voyages round the world.
see under [Kippis, Andrew] 1725-1795.

Narrative [of Colonel Ethan Allen's captivity, 1775-1778]
see under [Allen, Ethan] 1737-1789.

The **narrative** of Col. Tho. Blood concerning the design reported to be lately laid against the life and honour of His Grace George, Duke of Buckingham, wherein Colonel Blood is charged to have conspired with Maurice Hickey, Philip Le Mar and several others to suborn the testimony of Samuel Ryther and Philemon Coddan to swear buggery against the said duke. Together with a copy of the information exhibited in the Crown-Office against the said Colonel Blood, Hickey, Le Mar and the rest. London, Printed by R. Everingham, 1680.
4, 4, 32 p. 32 cm.
1. Blood, Thomas,   1618?-1680. 2. Buckingham, George
Villiers, 2d duke of, 1628–   1687.
DA447.B5N3
48-33097*

NN 0022631 DLC IU DFo MB PU PPULC CSmH MnU

Narrative of conversations held with Christopher Davis and Wm. Clarke, who were executed January 27th, 1832, for the part they took in the Bristol riots: to which is added, a letter by W. Clarke, finished on the day of his execution, on the evils of Sabbath-breaking and drunkenness. By a layman.   Bristol, J. Chilcott, 1832.   31 p.   18cm.

Dedication signed: J. S. H.

1. Davis, Christopher, d. 1832.   2. Clarke, William, d. 1832.
3. Gregory, Thomas, d. 1832. 4. Kayes,   Joseph, d. 1832. 5. Riots—Gt. Br.—
Eng.—Bristol, 1831. I. A layman.   II. H., J. S.
N.Y.P.L.   June 26, 1950

NN 0022632 NN OCl CtY

Narrative of Dimmock Charlton, a British subject, taken from the brig "Peacock"
see under [Cox, Mary L   ] ed.

Narrative of discovery and adventure in the Polar seas and regions
see under [Leslie, Sir John] 1766-1832.

Narrative (A) of Dr. Livingston's discoveries in South-Central Africa, from 1849 to 1856... *London: Routledge & Co.*, 1857. 64 pp., 1 map. 16°.
Repr.: "British Banner" newspaper.
In: *C p. v. 1197.
Gift of Mrs. Henry R. Hoyt.

NN 0022635 NN NcA-S

The narrative of Edward Crewe; or, Life in New Zealand
see under [Baines, William Mortimer]

Narrative of Elizabeth Vermeule
see under American tract society.

VOLUME 405

Narrative of Emily Graham. Revised by the
Committee of Publication. Philadelphia, American Sunday School Union ₍182-₎
33 p. front.

Contents suggest an English origin.
"No. 137. V. series."
Inscription on inside of cover: "Lydia Carew
from her friend Miss Susan Gray, Norwich, Connecticut, January 11th, 1829".

NN 0022638   NNC ICU

NARRATIVE of Emily Graham. Philadelphia,
Published by the Sunday and adult school union; R.
Piggot, agent; I. Ashmead & Co., printers. 1823.
1 p.l., (1)6-36 p. front. 14cm.

Fiction.
In original printed blue paper covers.

I. Sunday and adult school   union, Philadelphia.

NN 0022639   NN

Narrative of events affecting the position and
prospects of the whole Christian Church
see under   Woodhouse, Francis V.

A narrative of events connected with the
acceptance, and resignation of the Rectorship
of St. Paul's Church, Boston
see under   [Jarvis, Samuel Farmar]
1786-1851.

Narrative of events in Afghanistan from the spring of
1872 to April 1874 ₍and April 1874 to May 1875₎
(Chapters IX and X of Cabul precis) ₍n. p., 1874?₎

1 v. (various pagings) 35 cm.
Caption title.

1. Afghanistan—Politics and government.   I. Title: Cabul
precis.
DS364.N37   72-182563
                                         MARC

NN 0022642   DLC

Narrative of events in the several cruises of
Captain Lambert Wickes ...
see under   [Hardy, Henry] of Washington, D.C.₎

A narrative of events, that have lately taken place
in Ireland among the society called Quakers ...
see under   [Rathbone, William] 1757-1809.

A Narrative of events which have recently occurred
in the Island of Ceylon, written by a gentleman on
the spot.   London, 1815.
73 p.   8°.   [In vol. 840, College Pamphlets]

NN 0022645   CtY

Narrative of facts and circumstances that have
tended to produce a secession from the Society
of Friends ...
see under   Friends, Society of. New England
Yearly meeting.

Narrative of facts and events connected with the origin and history of
the West Reformed Dutch Church. By a friend.
New York. 1852. 36 pp. 12°.   *7544.170

G6855 — New York, City. Churches. West Reformed Dutch Church.

NN 0022647   MB

Narrative of facts and incidents in the life of John
Meshullam. Philadelphia, C.Sherman, printer [1850]

35 p. 15 cm.
Cover-title.

NN 0022648   MH

Narrative of facts connected with the abuses that have
prevailed in the treasury and police departments
[at] Bombay. [Bombay? 1810?]
16 p.   12°.

NN 0022649   NN

A narrative of facts connected with the change effected
in the political condition and relations of Paraguay,
under the directions of Dr. Thomas ₍!₎ Francia, by an
individual who witnessed many of them, and obtained
authentic information respecting the rest ... London,
Printed for the author by R. Greenlaw; pub. by W.
Mason, 1826.

55, ₍1₎ p. 22¾ᶜᵐ.

1. Francia, José Gaspar Rodriguez, dictator of Paraguay, d. 1840.
2. Paraguay—Hist.—1811-1870.

                                         16-19531

Library of Congress   F2686.F8

NN 0022650   DLC

Narrative of facts in the case of Passmore Williamson.
Philadelphia, Pub. by the Pennsylvania anti-slavery society, 1855.

24 p. 17¾ᶜᵐ.
The escape of Jane Johnson and two children, slaves of John H. Wheeler,
the trial of Williamson and others concerned, and refusal of state Supreme
court to issue writ of habeas corpus.

1. Williamson, Passmore. 2. Johnson, Jane, b. 1820? 3. Slavery in the
U .S.—Legal status of slaves in free states.

                                         10—34487

Library of Congress   E450.N23

NN 0022651   DLC NIC TxU NjP MiU OO OClWHi NNC NcU

A narrative of facts leading to the trials of
Maha Rajah Nundocomar and Thomas ₍i. e. Joseph₎
Fowke for conspiracies against Governor
Hastings and Richard Barwell, esqrs., members
of the Supreme Council at Bengal; and to the
trial of Maha Rajah Nundocomar, for forgery;
with some extraordinary anecdotes pending and
subsequent to those prosecutions; in which
are introduced the genuine addresses of the
grand jury, European and Armenian inhabitants
of Calcutta, to Sir Elijah Impey, knt., chief

justice, and the other judges of the Supreme
Court of Judicature; with their lordships'
answers: also, some pertinent remarks on
trade in Bengal. By a gentleman, resident in
Calcutta. London, Sold by J. Bew, 1776.
31 p. 26 cm.
Name of author (?) in MS. on t. p.: Joseph
Price.
No. ₍3₎ in a   volume with binder's
title: India   tracts.

1. Nanda Kumāra, Mahārāja, d. 1775. 2.
Fowke, Joseph. 3. Hastings, Warren, 1732-1818.
4. Trials (India) I. Price, Joseph, supposed
author. II. A gentleman, resident in Calcutta.

NN 0022654   NcD MH OCl MdBP

Narrative of facts; relating to the plunder of the
English merchants by the Arabs
see under   [Baldwin, George] 1743?-1826.

Narrative of facts relative to American
affairs.   *fAC7
₍London,1768?₎   A100
f°. 1p.ℓ.,15p. 33.5cm.   768n
Resumé of dispatches dealing with events of
1768 from the governors of the American
colonies; inscribed on t.-p. in contemporary
hand: This paper is given with the utmost
confidence in your secrecy, attended with an
earnest desire that you will not communicate it
to any person whatever.

NN 0022656   MH

A narrative of facts relative to the conduct of some of the
members of the legislature of Pennsylvania, professing to be
Democrats, at the election of a senator to represent this state
in the Senate of the United States, on the 13th of January,
1807. Philadelphia: May, 1807.

16 p. 23ᶜᵐ.
₍Political pamphlets, v. 105, no. 8₎
An exposure of some of the political acts of Michael Leib.

¯1. Leib, Michael, 1759-1822.   I. Pennsylvania. General assembly.
                                         19—15280

Library of Congress   JA36.P8 vol. 105

NN 0022657   DLC PP PPL

A Narrative of facts, relative to the conduct of some
of the members of the legislature of Pennsylvania,
professing to be Democrats, at the election of a
senator to represent this state in the Senate of the
United States, on the 13. of January, 1807.
Philadelphia, 1807.
16 p. 8°.
2. ed.

NN 0022658   NN PPAmP PHi

A narrative of facts relative to the conduct of
Vice-Admiral Gambier...
see under   Gambier, James, captain,
defendant.

A narrative of facts, relative to the massacre of the
Irish protestants. 1846
see under   Musgrave, Sir Richard, bart.,
1757 ?-1818.

A narrative of facts relative to work done
for Christ, in connection with the orphan homes
of Scotland, for fifty-second year, ending 31st
October, 1923. Also Consumption sanatoria of
Scotland and Colony of mercy for epileptics.
Glasgow, Aird and Coghill ltd., 1923.
68 p. illus.   D.

NN 0022661   OO

Narrative of facts, respecting Alanson Work,
Jas. E. Burr and Geo. Thompson, prisoners in
the Missouri penitentiary ...
see under   Quincy, Ill. Anti-Slavery concert
for prayer, 1842.

A NARRATIVE of facts: supposed to throw light   Y
on the history of the Bristol-stranger; known by   762
the name of the Maid of the hay-stack. Translated .I 31
from the French.   London,H.Gardner₍etc.₎1785.
xxviii,76p.

Translator's preface signed: Philalethes
₍pseud. of George Henry Glasse₎
Later published under title: Louisa, a narrative of facts.
Translated from the anonymous French work

"L'inconnue, histoire veritable". An attempt to
prove that a mysterious refugee at Bristol was
identical with Felix-Julienne de Schönau, otherwise Freulen, who declared herself to be the
natural daughter of the emperor Francis I, and
who was the unnamed heroine of the French work.—
cf. Dict. nat. biog.

NN 0022664   ICN OU

VOLUME 405

A narrative of five youth from the Sandwich Islands...
    see under   [American board of commissioners
for foreign missions]

Narrative, A, of "Griswold," the African youth from the mission school **3539-¹³⁵**
    at Cape Palmas, who died in Boston, May 16, 1844.
= Boston. Published by a friend of missions. 1845. 16 pp. 24°.

E₃₁₅₂ — Griswold, Alexander Viets, (Wana Hobah).

NN   0022666   MB

Narrative of intended conspiracy and
invasion. London, 1751
    38p. 12°

NN   0022667   MWA

Narrative of James Williams, an American slave
    see under   [Whittier, John Greenleaf] 1807-
1892.

The narrative of Jean Hornn, military coachman to
    Napoleon Bonaparte
    see under   Hornn, Jean, b. 1787.

Narrative of John Trust
    see under   [Carne, William Francis] 1883-
1910.

Narrative of Joseph Gray, a revolutionary soldier
    see under   Gray, Joseph, 1751-

    A narrative of late difficulties in
the South church in Reading, Mass. including the covenants of the church; a
result of a ministerialconference, and a
remonstrance on the subject of infant
baptism....
North Wrentham, Mass., New England telegraph press, 1835. 5- p. 0.

NN   0022672   OO OClWHi

Narrative of Le Moyne, an artist who accompanied
    the French expedition to Florida ...
    see under   Le Moyne de Morgues, Jacques,
d. 1588.

Narrative of Lieut. Gen. Sir Henry Clinton ...
    campaign in 1781
    see under   Clinton, Sir Henry, 1738?-1795.

The narrative of Lieut. Gen. Sir William Howe,
    in a committee of the House of Commons
    see under   Howe, William Howe,
5th viscount, 1729-1814.

Case
E
5
.B 996   NARRATIVE of Lord Byron's voyage to Corsica
and Sardinia, during the summer and autumn of the
year 1821. Compiled from minutes made during the
voyage by the passengers, and extracts from the
journal of His Lordship's yacht, the Mazeppa,
kept by Captain Benson, R.N., commander.   London, J.Limbird, 1824.
    viii,79p. front.(port.)

    Ms. notes.

NN   0022676   ICN PU CtY NcD InU NjP

PR4381
.N3   Narrative of Lord Byron's voyage to Corsica and
Sardinia, during the summer and autumn of the year
1821. Compiled from minutes made during the voyage
by the passengers, and extracts from the journal of His
Lordship's yacht, the Mazeppa, kept by Captain Benson
... Paris, A.and W.Galignani, 1825.
    xii,94 p. 18cm.
    "A fabrication."--Brit.mus. Cat.
    1.Byron,George Gordon Noël Byron,6th baron,1788-
1824.

NN   0022677   ICU InU NIC NjP IaU

Narrative of M. de Chaumeveix, who escaped
from the massacres of Aurai & Vannes... with observations on the public opinion in Brittany...
Lond., 1795.

NN   0022678   PPL

The narrative of Marie Le Roy and Barbara
    Leininger,
    see under   Le Roy, Marie.

A narrative of memorable events in Paris,
    preceding the capitulation, and during the
    occupancy of that city by the allied armies
    see under   [Underwood, T   R   ]
1772-1835.

Narrative of messrs. Moody, and Sankey's labors
    in Scotland
    see under   Randolph, Anson Davies Fitz,
1820-1896.

BV
4904
N3   Narrative of Miss Catherine Y---, in letters
from her aunt, with whom she resided. From the London
Christian Observer.   New York, American Tract Society
[180-?]
    12 p. 17cm.   ([Tract] no. 261)

    Cover title.

    1. Consolation.

NN   0022682   CBGTU

A Narrative of Mr. Adam Rankin's Trial, and rema[r]ks on
the same, with some observation on his vindication, and a Concluding Address, to professors of the Presbyterian Denomination. Published by order of the Transylvania Presbytery. *Lexington:
Printed by W. Maxwell & Co.* M,DCC,XCIII. 8vo, pp. 41.
                                        PRESB.HIST.SOC. 96459
"Title from a facsimile of the title page in McMurtrie's "Antecedent Experience in
Kentucky of William Maxwell," 1932. As Evans in his no. 27545 gives an edition
printed by J. Bradford, Lexington, 1794, without location or collation, it is probable
that he had found a reference to the above issue and assumed that the printer would
be Bradford, the only important printer in Kentucky at the time.

NN   0022683   PPPrHi

285.1
N167   A narrative of Mr. Adam Rankin's
trial, and remaks [sic] on the same; with
some observation on his vindication. And a
concluding address to professors of the
Presbyterian denomination. Published by order of the Transylvania Presbytery.   Lexington [Ky.,]Printed by W.Maxwell, 1793.
    41 p.   26 cm.

    Photocopy (positive)

NN   0022684   KyU

The narrative of Mr. John Soren, a native of the
    United States, piratically captured on the
    high seas
    see under   Soren, John.

A narrative of Mr. Joseph Rawson's case: or, An
    account of several occurrences relating to the
    affair of his being excluded from communion
    see under   [Taylor, John] 1694-1761.

Narrative of Mrs. Scott and Capt. Stewart's
    captivity
    see   A true and wonderful narrative of the
suprising captivity and remarkable deliverance of
Mrs. Frances Scott ...

A narrative of occurrences and transactions relating to the Royal
Family privateers and their prizes in the last war, extracted from
journals, invoices, letters, and other authentic vouchers, compared
with the testimonies of living witnesses... With some references
to a pamphlet lately publish'd, entitled The managers defence...
By an impartial hand...   London: Printed for the editor[, 1756?].
2 p.l., 82 p.   19cm. (8°.)

                                    PROUDFIT COLLECTION.
                                    1739-1747. 2. Walker, George,
sv8054A. I. Privateering—Gt. Br.,
d. 1777. I. An impartial hand.
N. Y. P. L.   September 21, 1932

NN   0022688   NN DN

DA
87.1
.W3
N37   A Narrative of occurences and transactions
relating to the royal family privateers and
their prizes in the last war, extracted from
journals, invoices, letters, and other authentic vouchers ... with some references to a
pamphlet lately publish'd, entitled: the
managers defence, etc. etc. by an Impartial
Hand. Printed for the Editor, and to be had
at the Pamphlet Shops of London and Westminster
[ca. 1775]
    82 p.

    Includes re-   ports about George
Walker.

NN   0022689   NNC

VOLUME 405

Narrative of occurrences relative to Major
General Stuart from the time of his being put
in arrest by order of the Select Committee of
Fort St. George on the 17th September, 1783 to
that of his embarkation for Europe on the 14th
October following.   [1783?]
   [66]p.

   Manuscript.

NN 0022690   OC1

A narrative of occurrences in the Indian countries of
North America ...
      see under   [McGillivray, Simon] supposed
author.

Narrative of occurrences that took place...
      see under   [Cunningham, Sir Charles] 1755-
1834.

A Narrative of Part of the Life and Adventures of Joseph Andrews, Particularly of his Piracy and the Murder of
Capt. Duryee and his Company, for
which he was tried on the 17th Instant
and condemn'd to be hang'd this Day,
the 23rd of May 1769.
pp.(20

NN 0022693   PPL PPULC

Narrative of privations and sufferings of United
States officers and soldiers while prisoners of
war ...
      see under   United States sanitary commission.

Narrative of proceedings connected with the
exhumation and removal of the remains of the
late Emperor Napoleon. By a Resident.
St. Helena, for the proprietor, by William
Bateman, 1840.
   38 p.   Small octavo in twos.   3/4 dark blue
morocco.
   Note: From the Library of F. R. Marvin,
April, 1919.
   1. Napoleon I, Emperor of the French, 1769-
1821.

NN 0022695   CSmH

Narrative of proceedings in both Houses of
Parliament, during the years 1859 ... —66,
which resulted in the act ... "to render it
unnecessary to make and subscribe certain
declarations...
   32 p.   8°.   [In College Pamphlet, v. 1738]

NN 0022696   CtY

A narrative of proceedings, tending towards a
national reformation, previous to, and consequent upon, His Majesty's royal proclamation, for the suppression of vice and immorality
      see under   [Glasse, Samuel] 1735-1812.

Narrative of Ransom Clark... 1839
      see under   Clark, Ransom.

The narrative of R-b-rt Cl-b-ry Gl-nn, m.d.
concerning the strange and deplorable franzy of
R-ch-rd W-ts-on, d.d. 1781
      see under   Mathias, Thomas James.

A Narrative of recent occurrences in Posen.
Accompanied by official documents, letters from
an English lady resident in Posen, transmitted
through Dr. Whately, archbishop of Dublin, and
a report of the discussion in the House of Lords
on Lord Kinnaird's motion.   London, E. Detkens,
1848.
   55 p.   8°.

NN 0022700   NN

Narrative of Ribaut's whole and true discovery
of Terra Florida
      see under   [Laudonnière, René Goulaine de]
16th cent.

Narrative of services in the liberation of Chili, Peru,
and Brazil, from Spanish and Portuguese domination
      see under   Dundonald, Thomas Cochrane,
10th earl of, 1775-1860.

A narrative of Sir George Rooke's late voyage
to the Mediterranean, where he commanded as
admiral of the confederate fleet. With a description of Gibraltar; and observations on the
usefulness and importance of that place; which
was attack'd and taken by the said fleet, and
now remains in the possession of the allies. An
account also of the naval battel fought betwixt
the confederates and French king's fleets: with
a judgment of the event. In a letter to a person of quality. London, Printed for Benj.

Tooke, 1704.
   29 p.   21cm.

   1. Gibraltar expedition, 1704.

NN 0022704   MB TxU MH CSmH ICN

A narrative of Sir Henry Clinton's cooperations
with Sir Peter Parker, on the attack of Sullivan's
island
      see under   [Clinton, Sir Henry] 1738?-1795.

Narrative of Sir William Keith's coming to the
government of Pennsylvania ...
      see under   [Hamilton, Andrew]
1676(Ca.)-1741, supposed author.

Narrative of Sojourner Truth ,...
      see under   [Gilbert, Olive]

A Narrative of some late injurious proceedings of
the managers of the Royal infirmary, against the
students of medicine in the University of
Edinburgh ...   [Edinburgh] published by the
students [1785]

NN 0022708   NNNAM

Narrative
   of some occurrences intervening between
   the time of the fall of first Adam and
   resurrection of second, etc. n.t.p.
   139p. 12°

NN 0022709   MWA

A narrative of some of the adventures, dangers
and sufferings of a revolutionary soldier ...
      see under   [Martin, Joseph Plumb] 1760-
1850.

A narrative of some of the sufferings of J. P. in the
city of Rome
      see under   [Perrot, John] d. 1671?

A narrative of some passages in or relating to the
Long Parliament, by a person of honor
      see under   [North, Dudley North] 4th baron,
1602-1677.

Narrative of some passages in the history of
Van Diemen's Land
      see under   [Franklin, Sir John] 1786-
1847.

Narrative (A) of some proceedings in the management of Chelsea Hospital as far as relates to
the appointment and dismission of Samuel Lee,
surgeon. 5-95 pp. 8°. London, W. Owen, 1753.

NN 0022714   DNLM CtY

A narrative of some recent occurrences in the
Church of the Puritans, New York; with documents
relaying thereto
      see under   New York (City) Church of the
Puritans (Congregational)

Witchcraft
BF   A narrative of some strange events that took
1581   place in Island Magee and neighbourhood,
Z7   in 1711; in consequence of which several
1711   persons were tried and convicted at Carrick-
         fergus, for witchcraft. By an eye witness.
         Belfast, Printed by J. Smyth, 1822.
         57 p. 19cm.

         Appendix (p. [47]-57); Dr. Wm. Tisdall's
         account of the trial of eight reputed witches
         at Carrickfergus, March 31st, 1711. (Copied
from the   Hibernian magazine, for
Jan. 1775,   p. 52.)

NN 0022716   NIC MH PU PP

Narrative of some things of New Spain and of the great
city of Temestitan, Mexico, written by the anonymous conqueror, a companion of Hernan Cortes; tr. into English and
annotated by Marshall H. Saville. New York, The Cortes
society, 1917.
   93 p. 1 illus., pl. 21 cm. (*Half-title:* Documents and narratives
concerning the discovery and conquest of Latin America ... no. 1)
   "Edition limited to 250 copies of which ten are Kelmscott paper.
This copy is number 51."

Continued in next column

VOLUME 405

Continued from preceding column

The original Spanish text is lost. An Italian translation by G. B. Ramusio was published in his "Terzo volvme delle navigationi et viaggi ... Venetia, 1556." It was translated from the Italian into Spanish by Joaquin García Icazbalceta, and published in his "Coleccion de documentos para la historia de Mexico," v. 1, Mexico, 1858. The present English translation is from this Spanish text. *cf.* Introd., p. 11-13.

1. Mexico—Hist.—Conquest, 1519-1540. i. Saville. Marshall Howard, 1867-   ed. and tr. ii. Cortes society, New York.

18—15279

Library of Congress   F1230.D63 no. 1
——— Copy 2.   F120.N23

CoU OrPS WaS WaTlC IdU IdPl
OO ODW CU-B MB PSC MiU-C RPJCB MWA NcD PPT TxU MU
NN   0022718   DLC OrU Or TU NIC DAU OU MiU MeB OCl

Narrative of sudden outbursts of gas in collieries
working the Barnsley thick coal and the Silk-
stone coal
       see under   [Midland Institute of Mining,
Civil and Mechanical Engineers, Barnsley , Eng.]

A narrative of the adventures and experience of
Joseph H. Jackson
       see under   Jackson, Joseph H

Narrative of the adventures and experiences of
Mrs. Josephine Clare ...
       see under   [Clare, Josephine]

Narrative of the adventures of an American navy
officer, who served during part of the American
revolution under the command of Com. John Paul
Jones ...
       see under   [Fanning, Nathaniel] 1755-1805.

Narrative of the adventures of Col. Daniel Boon ...
       see under   [Filson, John] 1753?-1788.

A narrative of the adventures of Lewis
*E065   Marott, pilot-royal of the galleys of France.
A100   Giving an account of his slavery under the
677n   Turks, his escapes out of it, and other strange
occurrences that ensued thereafter. Translated
from the French copy.
London: Printed for Edward Brewster, at the
Crane in St. Pauls church-yard. 1677.
1p.l., 86p. 15cm.
Errata: p. 86.

NN 0022724   MH MB

A narrative of the affair between Mr. Brown,
and the Inspector. Wherein all the facts are
set in their true light. With some observations
on the Inspector's own accounts of it ... London: Printed for S. Clay ... 1752.
24 p. 20½cm. [With Hill, John. The Inspector
... London, 1751. 20½cm.]

First edition.
Signatures: 1 leaf unsigned, B-C⁴, D⁵.

NN 0022725   CLU-C CSmH MH

A narrative of the affair between Mr. Cresswell,
and Miss Sc[rop] e ...
       see under   [Cresswell, Thomas Estcourt]
d. 1788

Narrative [of the appearance of cholera at
Kirkintilloch]. 22+pp. 8°. [*s. p., s. d.*] [P.,
v. 1061.]

NN   0022727   DNLM

A | NARRATIVE | Of The | Apprehending, Commitment, | Arraign-
ment, Condemnation, | And Execution of | John James | Who Suffered
at Tiburne, Novemb. | the 26th. 1661. | With several occasional Pas-
sages and Speeches, | faithfully Collected from such as were | Eye and
Ear Witnesses. | Also, An Account of the Death of several Persons |
since the Execution of John James, known to | be active and diligent
in that matter. | . . . (1 line).
London, Printed in the year, 1662. | Line border. 18.4x13.6cm. 47p. 1-2 blank.

NN   0022728   NNUT-Mc

A narrative of the apprehending of the arch-
Jesuite Blundel, who as Mr. Oates hath
deposed, used before the plot was discovered
under the pretence of charity to visit the
condemned malefactors at Newgate, being
titular ordinary of that goal ... [London,
1680?]
4 p. 30ᶜᵐ.

Bound in half brown calf.

Wing N-176

NN   0022729   CLU-C

Narrative of the arrest, trial, & condemnation of
Colonel Türr ...
       see under   Türr, István, 1825-1908.

A **Narrative** of the atrocities committed by the crew of the
piratical brig "El Defensor de Pedro," with a brief account
of the trial and execution of the pirates. To which is prefixed the confession of the crew. With a port. of Benito
Soto, their leader, who was executed at Gibraltar, Jan. 25,
1830. London, E. Wilson, 1830.
35 p. port. 22 cm.
The dedication signed: A. B.

1. Soto, Benito, d. 1830. 2. El Defensor de Pedro (Brig)
i. A. B. ii. B., A.

G537.S67N3   75-248009

NN   0022731   DLC CU MB NN

---

*Defoe   A narrative of the barbarous and unheard of
30   murder of Mr. John Hayes, by Catherine his wife,
.726   Thomas Billings, and Thomas Wood, on the 1st of
.A10N   March at night ... Published with the approba-
tion of the relations and friends of the said
Mr. John Hayes. The third edition. London:
Printed for, and sold by Thomas Warner, E. Nutt,
A. Dod, and by the booksellers of London and
Westminster. 1726.
32 p., incl. front. 19.5cm.

NN   0022732   MB

PR   Narrative of the barbarous murder of Madame
975   Mazel, a French lady of distinction, with
N167   an account of the trial, torture, and death,
of her valet de chambre, Le Brun; who was
declared, on presumptive evidence, to be
guilty of the murder, or accessary thereto;
also, the confession and execution of the
real murderer, who was miraculously discovered some time afterwards. London, Hodgson [n.d.]
24 p. fold. col. front.

NN   0022733   CLU NjP

Narrative of the Barbarous Treatment experienced
by American prisoners in England ... 1816
       see under   [Coleman, Simeon]
A concise narrative of the Barbarous Treatment ...

A narrative of the battle of Bladensburg ...
       see under   [Parker, Thomas] 1753-1820,
supposed author.

A narrative of the Battle of Hanau, and other events
connected with the retreat of the French Army
from Leipzig to the Rhine, forming a continuation
of the Narrative of the battles of Leipzig. By an
eye-witness. London, J. Cawthorn, 1814.
xi, 82 p. 24 cm.
Portrait of Napoleon bound in.
1. Leipzig, Battle of, 1813.

NN   0022736   OrCS MH

A **narrative** of the battles of Bull run and Manassas junction, July 18th and 21st, 1861. Accounts of the advance of
both armies, the battles, and the defeat and rout of the enemy.
Compiled chiefly from the detailed reports of the Virginia and
South Carolina press. Charleston. Press of Evans & Cogs-
well, 1861.
cover-title, 32 p. 23½ᶜᵐ.

1. Bull run, 1st battle, 1861.

Library of Congress   E472.18N23   2—26040

NN   0022737   DLC NcD

Narrative of the battles of Drumclog, and Bothwell
Bridge ...
       see under   [Brownlee, Thomas, laird of
Torfoot]

A narrative of the bloudy murders committed by
Sir John Fites alias Fitz, 1605
       see under   Halliwell-Phillipps, James
Orchard, 1820-1889, ed.

A Narrative of the Briton's Voyage to Pitcairn's
Island ...
       see under   Shillibeer, John.

Narrative of the burning of the "Sarah Sands"
screw steam ship ...
       see under   Schlotel, Frederick.

A narrative of the campaign of the British
Army in Spain ...
       see under   Moore, James Carrick,
1763-1834.

A narrative of the campaigns of the British army
at Washington and New Orleans, under General
Ross, Pakenham, and Lambert, in the years
1814 and 1815
       see under   [Gleig, George Robert] 1796-
1888.

A narrative of the campaigns of the Loyal Lusitanian
legion
       see under   [Lillie, Sir John Scott] 1790-
1868, supposed author.

VOLUME 405

Narrative of the captivity and escape of
    Mrs. Frances Scott
      see   A remarkable narrative of the captivity
    and escape of Mrs. Frances Scott.

Narrative of the captivity and extreme sufferings of Mrs.
Clarissa Plummer...who, with Mrs. Caroline Harris...were, in
the spring of 1835, with their unfortunate families, surprised and
taken prisoners by a party of the Camanche tribe of Indians, while
emigrating...to Texas...   New-York: Perry and Cooke, 1838.
23(1) p.   4°.

1. Indians (N.A.).—Captivities. 2.   Indians (N.A.): Comanche. 3.
Harris, Mrs. Caroline.
N.Y.P.L.   June 4, 1914.

NN   0022746   NN MWA CSmH InU CLCM

Narrative of the captivity and extreme
sufferings of Mrs. Clarissa Plummer, wife of
the late Mr. James Plummer, of Franklin County,
state of New York; who, with Mrs. Caroline
Harris ... were in the spring of 1835, with
their unfortunate families, surprised and taken
prisoner by a party of the Camanche [sic]
tribe of Indians. New-York, Perry and Cooke,
1838.
    Microcard edition (Plains and Rockies, 71) micro-
    printed by LCP, 1961.
    1. Indians of North America—Captivities. 2.
Plummer, Clarissa.   I. Ser.

NN   0022747   ViU MoU NNC IdPI

Narrative of the captivity and extreme sufferings of
Mrs. Clarissa Plummer, wife of the late
Mr. James Plummer, of Franklin County, State of
New-York; who, with Mrs. Caroline Harris, wife
of the late Mr. Richard Harris, were, in the
spring of 1835, with their unfortunate families
surprised and taken prisoners by a party of the
Camanche tribe of Indians, while emigrating from
said Franklin County (N. Y. to Texas; and after
having been held nearly two years in captivity, and
witnessed the deaths of their husbands, were
fortunately redeemed from the hands of the savages
by an American fur trader, a native of Georgia.

Mrs. Plummer was made prisoner and held in
bondage at the same time with the unfortunate
Mrs. Harris, whose narrative the public
have been recently presented.   New York,
Perry and Cooke, publishers, 1839.
    1 p. l., [5]-23, [1] p.   front.   23 x 14.9 cm.
Sig. in fours.

NN   0022749   ICN TxFTC

Narrative of the captivity and providential escape of
    Mrs. Jane[!] Lewis ...
      see under   [Lewis, Mrs. Hannah]

A narrative of the captivity and sufferings of
    Benjamin Gilbert and his family
      see under   [Walton, William] 1740-1824.

Narrative of the captivity and sufferings of
    Mrs. Hannah Lewis ...
      see under   [Lewis, Mrs. Hannah]

Narrative of the captivity of an officer, who fell into
    the hands of the Burmähs during the late war
      see under   [Bennett, Richard]

... Narrative of the captivity of John Ortiz
      see under   [Drake, Samuel Gardner]
    1798-1875.

A narrative of the captivity of Mrs. Horn...
      see under   [Horn, Sarah Ann]

A narrative of the captivity of Mrs. Johnson
      see under   [Hastings, Susannah (Willard)
    Johnson] 1730-1810.

Narrative of the capture and providential escape of
Misses Frances and Almira Hall, two respectable young
women (sisters) of the ages of 16 and 18—who were taken
prisoners by the savages, at a frontier settlement, near
Indian Creek, in May last ... Likewise is added, the
interesting narrative of the captivity and sufferings of
Philip Brigdon, a Kentuckian, who fell into the hands of
the merciless savages ... Communicated by persons of
respectability living in the neighborhood of the captives.
[New York] 1832.
    24 p. incl. front. 24ᶜᵐ.

    Copyrighted by William P. Edwards.
    Cover-title: War and pestilence! Capture of two young ladies by the
savages ...
    The names of the girls were Rachel Hall (afterwards Mrs. Munson)
and Sylvia Hall (afterwards Mrs. Horn) cf. Baldwin, Hist. of La Salle
County, Ill. and Moses, Illinois, historical and statistical.

    1. Indians of North America—Captivities. 2. Black Hawk war, 1832.
3. Munson, Mrs. Rachel (Hall) d. 1870. 4. Horn, Mrs. Sylvia (Hall)
1813-1899. ɪ. Edwards, William P.

    Library of Congress   E83.83.N23

                                   3-11791

        OO ICN IHi ViU
NN   0022758   DLC MiU-C RPB OC PHi MnHi IaU OClWHi

Narrative of the capture and providential escape of Misses
Frances and Almira Hall, two respectable young women (sisters) of the ages of 16 and 18—who were taken prisoners by
the savages, at a frontier settlement, near Indian Creek, in
May last ... Likewise is added, the interesting narrative of
the captivity and sufferings of Philip Brigdon, a Kentuckian,
who fell into the hands of the merciless savages ... Communicated by persons of respectability [l]iving in the neighborhood
of the captives. [New York?] 1833.
    24 p. incl. front. 24½ᶜᵐ.

    Illustrated covers.
    Copyrighted in 1832 by William P. Edwards.
    The real names of the two girls were Rachel Hall (afterwards Mrs.
Munson) and Sylvia Hall (afterwards Mrs. Horn) cf. Baldwin, Hist.
of LaSalle County, Ill., 1877, p. 95-104.

    1. Indians of North America—Captivities. 2. Black Hawk war, 1832.
ɪ. Horn, Mrs. Sylvia (Hall) 1813-1899. ɪɪ. Munson, Mrs. Rachel (Hall)
d. 1870. ɪɪɪ. Edwards, William P. ɪᵥ. Brigdon, Philip.

                                   16—9483

    Library of Congress   E83.83.N24

NN   0022760   DLC NNC IaU MoU CtY KyU MiU-C MWA ICN

Narrative of the capture and providential escape of Misses Frances
and Almira Hall, two respectable young women (sisters) of the
ages of 16 and 18, who were taken prisoners by the savages, at
a frontier settlement, near the Indian Creek, in May, 1832, when
fifteen of the inhabitants fell victims to the bloody tomahawk and
scalping knife; among whom were the parents of the unfortunate
females. Likewise is added the interesting narrative of the captivity and sufferings of Philip Brigdon; a Kentuckian, who fell
into the hands of the merciless savages in their return to their

settlement, three days after the bloody massacre. Also a particular account of the war with Black Hawk... [New York?
1833.]   26 p. (incl. front.)   [3. ed.?]   4°.

    Copyrighted in 1832 by William P. Edwards.
    Cover-title: Horrible Indian outrages, and massacre!

1. Indians, N.A.—Captivities. 2. In-   dians, N.A.—Wars, 1832—Black
Hawk war.   3. Horn, Sylvia (Hall),   1814-1899. 4. Munson, Rachel (Hall),
1816-1870.   5. Brigdon, Philip.   6. Edwards, William P.
N.Y.P.L.   October 22, 1925

NN   0022762   NN IaU PPRF ICN

    NARRATIVE of the capture and providential
escape of Misses Frances and Almira Hall...like-
wise is added the interesting narrative of the
captivity and sufferings of Philip Brigdon...
[n.p.]1834.
    24p. illus. 24cm.

    Bookplate of Frank C. Deering.
    In box.

NN   0022763   ICN OCl

    NARRATIVE of the capture and providential
escape of Misses Frances and Almira Hall...like-
wise is added the interesting narrative of the
captivity and sufferings of Philip Brigdon...
[n.p.]1835.
    13,[1]p. front. 26cm.

NN   0022764   ICN

Narrative of the capture and providential escape of
Misses Frances and Almira Hall, two respectable young
women (sisters) of the ages of 16 and 18, who were taken
prisoners by the savages, at a frontier settlement, near
the Indian Creek, in May, 1832 ... Likewise is added the
interesting narrative of the captivity and sufferings of
Philip Brigdon, a Kentuckian, who fell into the hands of
the merciless savages ... Communicated by persons of
respectability living in the neighbourhood of the captives.
[New York] 1835.
    1 p. l., [7]-21 p. incl. pl. front. 26ᶜᵐ.

    Cover-title: War and pestilence! Horrible and unparalleled[!] mas-
sacre! ...
    Illustrations on cover.
    The real names of the two girls were Rachel Hall (afterwards Mrs.
Munson) and Sylvia Hall (afterwards Mrs. Horn) cf. Baldwin, Hist. of
La Salle County, Ill., 1877, p. 95-104.

    1. Indians of North America—Captivities. 2. Black Hawk war, 1832.
ɪ. Horn, Mrs. Sylvia (Hall) 1813-1899. ɪɪ. Munson, Mrs. Rachel (Hall)
d. 1870. ɪɪɪ. Brigdon, Philip.

                                   24-8637

    Library of Congress   E83.83.N25

NN   0022766   DLC IaU

    Narrative of the capture and providential
escape of Misses Frances and Almira Hall, two
respectable young women, (sisters,) of the
ages of 16 and 18, who were taken prisoners
by the savages, at a frontier settlement, near
the Indian Creek, in May, 1832 ... Likewise
is added, the interesting narrative of the
captivity and sufferings of Philip Brigdon,
a Kentuckian, who fell into the hands of the
merciless savages ... Also, a particular account of the war with Black Hawk. Portland,
S.H. Coleswort[h?], 1845.

    24 p. incl. front. illus. 21 cm.

    Copyrighted by William P. Edwards in 1832.
    The names of the girls were Rachel and Silvia
Hall. cf. Baldwin, Hist. of La Salle County,
Ill., 1877, p. 95-104.

NN   0022768   CtY

A narrative of the capture of certain Americans, at
Westmorland, by savages; and the perilous escape which
they effected, by surprising specimens of policy and heroism. To which is subjoined, some account of the religion, government, customs and manners of the aborigines of North-America. Hartford: Printed and sold near
the bridge [1780?]
    24 p. 19ᶜᵐ.
    Brinley, 5579.
    1. Indians of North America—Captivities. 2. Westmoreland Co., Pa.

                                 4-28491†

    Library of Congress   E85.N24

NN   0022769   DLC NN ICN

VOLUME 405

Ayer
255
N2
1784

A NARRATIVE of the capture of certain Americans at Westmoreland by savages, and the perilous escape which they effected by surprising specimens of policy and heroism, to which is subjoined, Some account of the religion, government, customs, and manners of the aborigines of North-America. New-London, T. Green, 1784.
16p. 19cm.

Attributed to M. Van Campen by Evans.
Bookplate of ⌐Frank C. Deering.

NN 0022770   ICN PPiU

A **narrative** of the capture of the United States' brig Vixen, of 14 guns, by the British frigate Southampton; and of the subsequent loss of both vessels, on a reef of rocks, off Conception Island. With some account of the sufferings of the crew; their manner of deliverance; and final deposit in the prison-ships at Port-Royal, Jamaica. The whole interspersed with various remarks, relative to the treatment shown to, and conduct observed by, the prisoners. By one of the Vixen's crew, in a letter to a friend. New York, Printed and sold at the office of "The war", 1813.

35 p. 18ᵐ. (In Bubble   & squeak; or, A dish of all sorts ...
New York, 1814)
1. Vixen (Brig)   2. Southampton (Frigate)
Library of Congress   PS991.A1B75   22-1840

NN 0022771   DLC CtY NNH NjP PU

A narrative of the capture of the United States' brig Vixen, of 14 guns, by the British frigate Southampton; and of the subsequent loss of both vessels, on a reef of rocks, off Conception island. With some account of the sufferings of the crew; their manner of deliverance; and final deposit in the prison-ships at Port-Royal, Jamaica... By one of the Vixen's crew, in a letter to a friend. New York: Printed and sold at the office of "The War," 1813 ⌐repr. West Chester, Pa., 1884⌐ 36 p. 24cm.

See: Sabin 100636.
"50 copies printed. Copy no. ⌐50⌐ For ⌐self.⌐"
"Reprinted for private circulation, through the courtesy of the proprietor of the West Chester Local News."—Note, p. ⌐2⌐, signed: Wm. Reed Lewis, and dated: Devon P. O., Penna., 1st of April, 1884.
Narrative signed: ******* *********.
Bound in are eleven letters and cards of acknowledgement from persons and institutions to whom copies of the pamphlet had been presented by Lewis.

53R0583. 1. Warships, U.S.—Vixen.   2. Warships, British—Southampton.
3. United States—Hist.—War of 1812   —Prisoners and prisons. I. Lewis,
William Reed.

NN 0022773   NN PHi PPL PU NBu

A **narrative** of the case of a considerable number of the Associate Congregation of Edinburgh, who are debarred from sealing ordinances, because they cannot in conscience acquiesce in an Act of the Associate Synod, of April 9. 1767. With a detection of some gross falsehoods and misrepresentations relating to them, advanced by the Rev. Mr. Adam Gib, in his Refuge of lies. Humbly offered to the consideration of the Rev. the Associate Synod, to meet at Edinburgh, April 5. 1768... Edinburgh: Printed, and sold by all booksellers, 1768. 32 p. 8°.

421436A. 1. Gib, Adam, 1714-   1788: A refuge of lies swept away.
2. Secession Church, Scotland—Hist.,   1768.
N. Y. P. L.   July 30, 1929

NN 0022774   NN

A NARRATIVE of the case of Mr. Jackson being refus'd the sacrament of the Lord's supper at Bath, by Mr. Coney. With observations upon it, etc., L., 1736.

pp. 22.   Tr 86

NN 0022775   MH

A narrative of the case of Salomé Müller ...
see under Müller, Salomé, plaintiff.

Case
E
5
.T 4157

A NARRATIVE of the case of the Reverend Mr. Roger Throp, decˢ'd, lately rector of Killcornan, in the diocese of Limerick. Taken from a manuscript drawn up by him in his life-time, to which is added, an account of the proceedings in that case since his death. Together with an account of the life and character of Mr. Throp. ⌐London?⌐ 1739.

Attributed to Jonathan Swift in a contemporary hand.
Numerous ms.   notes.
Bookplate of   Clement K. Shorter.

NN 0022777   ICN

British
Tracts
1677
N16

A narrative of the cause and manner of the imprisonment of the lords: now close prisoners in the Tower of London ... Amsterdam, 1677.
22 p. 18½ cm.

Signed: J.E.

I. E., J.

NN 0022778   CtY CSmH MH

---

*E065
M100
659n

A narrative of the causes and events of civil-war between princes and people. Together with the manner how the people of Rome, and of the Netherlands rejected and abjured their King and kingly government; with the form of their oaths of abjuration, extracted out of the Roman and Netherlands history. As likewise, some objections now in contest concerning the taking of the like oath in this common-wealth, examined and answered, if not for satisfaction, at least for information of such as are concerned. By F.M.
London: Printed   for the authour, 1659.
20p. 18cm.
Page 14 misnum-   bered 13.

NN 0022779   MH

A narrative of the causes which led to Philip's Indian war of 1675 and 1676 ...
see under Easton, John, 1617-1705.

Maryland
BX
7676
.A3N3
1852

A narrative of the causes which led to the separation of the Society of Friends in America, and the means that were employed to effect it, by a member of the Society of Friends. 2d ed. Baltimore, Printed by Wm. Wooddy & Son, 1852.
51 p. 22 cm.

1. Friends, Society of - Gt. Brit. 2. Friends, Society of - U. S.

NN 0022781   MdU MdBP PHi PHC NcD

A narrative of the celebrated Dyde supper
see under [Rose, William L   ]

---

v.789

A narrative of the celebration of Peace at Cambridge ... Tuesday, July 12, 1814 ... Cambridge, Printed by J. Smith, for W. Gibson [1814?]
2p.ℓ., 45, [3]p. fold. plan. 22½cm.

1. Cambridge, Eng.

NN 0022783   CtY

NARRATIVE of the circumstances of and attending the sinking of, the Spanish galleons, with the treasure on board, in the harbor of Vigo, Spain, in the year 1702, with a view to a proper understanding and appreciation of the project formed for the recovery of the treasure. New York, S. Hamilton & Sons, 1874.

pp. (2). 23.

NN 0022784   MH

A narrative of the circumstances that led to the attempt, and the particulars of the boarding and capturing of the Hermione frigate in 1799
see under [Hamilton, Sir Edward, bart.] 1772-1851.

A narrative of the circumstances which attended the separation of Lord and Lady Byron; remarks on his domestic conduct, and a complete refutation of the calumnies circulated by public writers ... London, Printed for the author and sold by R. Edwards, 1816.
22 p. 8vo (Binder's title: Byron tracts, v. 3 ⌐no. 6⌐)

Bound with C. Gordon, Life and genius of Lord Byron.

NN 0022786   InU NjP

... Narrative of the circumstances which led to an interview between the Emperor Napoleon and George Sinclair
see under Sinclair, George.

NARRATIVE of the civil and military services of W. H. Harrison. Compiled from the most authentic authorities. Cinn., 1836.

pp. 72. Port., engraving, and 2 woodcuts.

NN 0022787   MH OCHP

Narrative of the combat experiences of Battery "B," 537th AAA AW bn during continental operations. ⌐n. p., 1945⌐ 30 p. illus., map. 20cm.

Caption-title.
On cover: Undo Baker (code name of unit).
"Battery roster," p. 26-30.

1. World war, 1939-1945—Regt.   hist.—U. S.—537th anti-aircraft
artillery battalion. Battery B.
N. Y. P. L.   July 24, 1950

NN 0022788   NN

Narrative of the conduct of Dr. James Gregory, towards the Royal College of Physicians of Edinburgh, drawn up and published by order of the College, in consequence of the various printed papers circulated by him relative to their affairs. Edinburgh, Printed for Peter Hill, Manners & Miller, and A. Constable, 1809.
⌐8,98,42p. 27cm.

NN 0022789   KU-M PPC DNLM

A NARRATIVE of the conduct of the corporation of Harvard College, relative to the late disorders perpetrated by the students. Cambridge, printed by W. Hilliard, 1807.

23 cm. pp. 18.

NN 0022790   MH

VOLUME 405

A narrative of the conduct of the tea-dealers ...
    see under   Committee of tea-dealers,
London.

Narrative of the confinement and exile of William
    Steel Dickson ...
       see under   Dickson, William Steel, 1744-
1824.

Narrative of the conquest of Finland by the Russians
in the years 1808-9. From an unpublished work by a
Russian officer of rank. Ed. by Gen. Monteith ... London, L. Booth, 1854.
    viii, 245 p. fold. map. 20^{cm}.

    1. Finland—Hist.   I. Monteith, William, 1790-1864, ed.

    Library of Congress   DK457.N2   5-13672†

    NN   0022793   DLC CU NN

                   A narrative
of the consecration of Christ church cathedral,
Fredericton, N. B. Wednesday, August 31, 1853.
N.Y., Churchman off., 1853. 24 p. 22½ cm.

    NN   0022794   CaNSWA

    NARRATIVE ot the consecration ot tne Rev. H.
Tully Kingdon, as Bishop co-adjutor of the Diocese of Fredericton ... St. John, Sun pub. co.,
1882. 22 p. 20½ cm.

    NN   0022795   CaNSWA

E
5   **NARRATIVE** of the consecration of the Rev.
.O 567   Henry U.Onderdonk, D.D., with the address of the
presiding bishop.   Philadelphia,J.Harding,
printer,1827.
    22p. 23cm.

    NN   0022796   ICN PPAmP

A narrative of the conspiracy, for the forcible
    abduction of Miss Maria Glenn ...
       see under   [Tuckett, George Lowman]

A Narrative of the conversion and sufferings of
    Sarah Doherty, illustrative of popery in Ireland,
    1st American from the 3d. Edinburgh, ed.
    New York, American Protestant society, n. d.
    128 p.

    NN   0022798   PPPrHi

BV4935
.Z9N3   A narrative of the conversion and sufferings of Sarah
Doherty, illustrative of popery in Ireland, and of the power
of evangelical truth. New York, American and foreign
Christian union, 1854.
    128 p. 15½^{cm}.
    "The narrative was first published in this country in 1839, in the Protestant
vindicator ... and subsequently in a volume ... by the American Protestant
society and ... carried ... through several editions."—Introd. note.

    1. Catholic church—Doctrinal and controversial works—Protestant authors.

    NN   0022799   ICU NNUT

A Narrative of the conversion of George Story,
    who died in London, 1818. [London? B.
Bensley, 18—]
    16 p. 18 cm.

    Caption title.
    At head of title: No. 173.
    Imperfect: p. 15-16 mutilated.

    1. Story, George, 1738-1818.   I. Story,
George, 1738-1818.

    NN   0022800   NcD

A narrative of the conversion of John Price... Revised by the
Committee of publication of the American Sunday-school union.
Philadelphia: Amer. Sunday-school union [183-?] 16 p. front.
12cm.

    1. Juvenile literature, Religious.   I. American Sunday-school union.
N. Y. P. L.   May 6, 1943

    NN   0022802   NN

A Narrative of the cruel, and unjust suffering of the
    people of God in the nation of Ireland, called
Quakers. London, 1659.
    (2), 14 p.

    NN   0022803   PPL

*EC65   [A] narrative of the cruelties & abuses acted
F9155   by Isaac Dennis keeper, his wife and servants,
684n   in the prison of Newgate, in the city of
Bristol: upon the people of the Lord in scorn
called Quakers, who were there committed for the
exercise of their consciences towards God.
With an account of the eminent judgments of God
upon him, and his end. Published for a warning
to others, by some of those people who were
sufferers under him ...
    [London,1684]
    27,[1]p.   18.5cm.
    Dated (p.27):   ... the 6th of the 12th
moneth, 1682.
    Imperfect: upper edges cropped.

    NN   0022804   MH DFo CtY PHC

A narrative of the cruelties inflicted upon Friends of
    North Carolina ...
       see under   Friends, Society of. North
Carolina Yearly meeting.

Narrative of the cruise of the Alabama, and list of her
officers and men, by one of the crew. London, 1864.
    16 p. 20^{cm}.

    Subject entries: Alabama (Privateer)

                                  3-15808

    Library of Congress, no.   E599.A3N2.

    NN   0022806   DLC CtY PHi OClWHi

A narrative of the cruise of the yacht Maria
       see under   [Greig,   ]

A narrative of the dangerous journey of Mrs.
    Caroline Cedarholm
       see under   Cedarholm, Caroline.

A Narrative of the dangers and distresses which befel
    Isaac Morris and seven more of the crew belonging
to the Wager Store-Ship...
       see under   Morris, Isaac.

A narrative of the debate in the General assembly
    of the Church of Scotland ...
       see under   [Erskine, John] 1721-1803, ed.

The narrative of the Deluge
       see under   [Arnold, Henry Vernon] 1848-

A narrative of the descendants of Richard Harris
       see under   [Foster, Joseph] 1844-1905.

A narrative of the descendants of Samuel Harris
    of Fordingbridge...
       see under   [Foster, Joseph] 1844-1905.

Narrative of the destruction by fire of H. M. S.
    Queen Charlotte
       see under   Braid, John.

A narrative of the diabolical, appalling,
    horrible and bloody murder of Mr. Weare ... with
lives of the Thurtells, Hunt and Probert, and
every particular relative to the transaction.
Illustrated with four views ... London,G.
Smeeton [1823]
    8p. fold. front. 22cm.
    [DLC: Political pamphlets, v.67]

    NN   0022815   CtY DLC MH-L

*EC65   A narrative of the disease and death of that
A100   noble gentleman John Pym esquire, late a member
643n   of the Honourable House of commons. Attested
under the hands of his physitians, chyrurgions
and apothecary ...
    London,Printed for Iohn Bartlet,at the signe
of the Gilt-cup at Austins gate,1643.
    1p.l.,5p. 19cm.
    Title vignette.

    NN   0022816   MH CtY NNC

A narrative of the disease and death of that
noble gentleman John Pym Esquire, late a member
of the honourable House of commons, Attested
under the hands of his physitians.
London, John Bartlet, 1643.
    1 p.l., 5 p. 22 cm.
    Photostat reproduction of original in British
Museum.

    NN   0022817   CSmH

A narrative of the disinterment of Milton's coffin,
    in the parish-church of St. Giles
       see under   [Neve, Philip]

Narrative of the dispute between the Bishop of Ontario and the congregation of St. George's, Kingston, relative to the appointment of Dr.
Lauder. *Toronto: W.C. Chewett & co., printer, King street east. 1863.*
    32 p. 8vo. 21.7 x 14 cm. Bound with original gray paper covers, front cover
bearing within a frame, a reprint of the t.-p. and the words: Price 12½ cents.
                                              Gagnon.

    NN   0022819   CaOTP

VOLUME 405

Narrative, A, of the dispute in the corporation of Kinsale. In a letter from a buff at Kinsale to his friend in Dublin.   Dublin, 1756.   24 p.   12°.   (Patriot miscellany. v. 2.)

1. Ireland.—Politics, 1756.
N. Y. P. L.   May 25, 1912

NN 0022820   NN CtY InU ICN

Narrative of the dreadful disasters occasioned by the hurricane, which visited Liverpool and various parts of the kingdom, on the nights of Sunday and Monday, January, 6th and 7th, 1839. Liverpool, Printed by E. Smith and co., 1839.
108 p. 18½cm.

1. Storms—Gt. Brit.
                                                        35-30740
Library of Congress   QC959.G7N3

NN 0022821   DLC

DA
690
.B8
T8

A narrative of the dreadful riots and burnings, which occurred in Bristol, on Saturday, Sunday, and Monday, the 29th, 30th, and 31st of October, 1831, and the destruction of property and lives consequent upon them. ₍Bristol, Rose, printer, 1831?₎
82 (i.e.28) p.   18½cm.
Caption title.
With Trials of the persons concerned in the late riots, before Chief Justice Tindal. 1832.

1. Bristol—Riot, 1831.

NN 0022822   MiU

A narrative of the Earl of Clarendon's settlement and sale of Ireland
see under   [French, Nicholas, bp. of Ferns]
1604-1678.

A narrative of the early days and remembrances of Oceola Nikkanochee ...
see under   [Welch, Andrew]

Narrative of the early life, travels, and gospel labors of Jesse Kersey ...
see under   Kersey, Jesse, 1768-1845.

---

*H.86
.109

A narrative of the election of Dr. Hough, president to St. Mary Magdalen Colledge, Oxon. 1687. [London, Printed for R. Baldwin, 1688?]
66 p.   20cm.
Caption title.
Not in Wing?

1. Hough, John, Bp. of Worcester, 1651-1743.
2. Oxford. University. Magdalen College—Hist.

NN 0022826   MB

Case
D
2896
.612

A NARRATIVE of the events connected with the election of an assistant bishop for Illinois. By a presbyter of the diocese.   ₍Peoria Co., Ill.₎ Jubilee College, 1848.
12p. 21cm.

Cover-title.
Signed: D.C.

NN 0022827   ICN ICHi IHi NN IU

... Narrative of the events of the Siege of Lyons
see under   [Beraud, Paul Émilion]
1751-1836.

Narrative of the events which led to the declaration of war by Chili against Bolivia and Peru
see under   [Chile. Ministerio de relaciones exteriores]

A narrative of the excommunication upon seven persons (for conscience sake)
see under   [Thacher, Charles Stone]
1802-1869.

A narrative, of the excursion and ravages of the King's troops under the command of General Gage...
see under   Massachusetts (Colony) Provincial congress.

A narrative of the exercise of soul and distress of body, of Noah Hatheway ...
see under   [Hatheway, Philip]

A narrative of the expedition of Hernando de Soto into Florida. By a gentleman of Elvas. Published at Evora 1557.   Translated from the Portuguese by Richard Hackluyt. London, 1609.
(In French, B. F. Historical collections of Louisiana ... Philadelphia, 1850. 23]ᵗᵐ. pt. 2, p. 111-220)
The 1609 ed. of this trans. of the anon. "Relaçam verdadeira ..." bore the title "Virginia richly valued, by the description of the maine land of Florida, her next neighbour ..."
French has omitted Hakluyt's dedicatory letter to the counsellors of the Virginia company. The spelling has also been modernized, and most of the marginal notes omitted.
1. Florida—Hist.—Colonial period. 2. Soto, Hernando de, ca. 1500-1542.

Library of Congress   F366.F87
                                                        2-14277

NN 0022833   DLC MiU-C MWH

The narrative of the expedition of Hernando de Soto, by the Gentleman of Elvas.   (In: Spanish explorers in the southern United States. New York, 1907. 8°. p. 127-272. map.)
"...The English translation by Buckingham Smith...is followed in the present volume..."
Introduction signed: T. Hayes Lewis.

1. Soto, Hernando de, ca. 1500-42.   2. Florida.—History (Colonial).
3. Elvas, Gentleman of. 4. Smith,   Thomas Buckingham, 1810-71, translator. 5. Lewis, Theodore Hayes,   1856-   , edit.
N. Y. P. L.   October 3, 1923.

NN 0022834   NN PPL PU

Narrative of the expedition of the Marquis de Nonville against the Senecas, in 1687
see under   Denonville, Jacques René de Brisay, marquis de, d. 1710.

A narrative of the expedition to, and the storming of Buenos Ayres, by the British army, commanded by Lieutenant-General Whitelocke. By an officer, attached to the expedition. Bath, Printed by W. Meyler, 1807.
2 p. l., [3]-38 p. plan. 21½cm.

1. Buenos Aires—Hist. 2. Argentine Republic—Hist.—English invasion, 1806-1807.

Library of Congress   F2845.N23
                                                        4-22932

NN 0022836   DLC CtY

A narrative of the expedition to Dongola and Sennaar ...
see under   [English, George Bethune] 1787-1828.

NARRATIVE of the expedition to the Baltic; with an account of the siege and capitulation of Copenhagen, including the surrender of the Danish fleet. By an officer employed in the expedition. London, printed by Brettell & co., for W. Lindsell, 1808.

Plan and map.

NN 0022838   MH NN PBL

A Narrative of the expedition to the Rivers Orinoco and Apuré
see under   Hippisley, Gustavus.

986.3
N16

Narrative of the expedition under General MacGregor against Porto Bello: including an account of the voyage; and of the causes which led to its final overthrow... By an officer who miraculously escaped. London, Printed for C. and J. Ollier... and T. and J. Allman, 1820.
55p. 17cm.

1. Colombia—Hist.—War of independence, 1810-1822.
2. MacGregor, Sir Gregor, 1786-1845. I. An officer who miraculously escaped.

NN 0022840   LU

Narrative of the expedition which sailed from England in 1817, to join the South American Patriots
see under   Hackett, James.

A NARRATIVE of the experience and happy death of James Tilghman Hemsley. By an episcopal clergyman. Baltimore, 1824.

pp. 48.

NN 0022842   MH

A narrative of the extraordinary adventures of Donald Campbell, Esq.
see under   Campbell, Donald, 1751-1804.

Narrative of the extraordinary adventures of four Russian sailors.
Litchfield, n.d.
pp. 15.   12°

NN 0022844   PBL

VOLUME 405

A NARRATIVE of the extraordinary adventures of four Russian sailors who were cast away on the desert island of East- Spitzbergen. To which is added A droll story of a fisherman. Stirling, C. Randall, n. d.

pp. 24.
Interleaved.   25276.23*

NN   0022845   MH

A narrative of the extraordinary adventures of four Russian Sailors, who were cast away, and lived six years, on the Desert Island of East-Spitzbergen as related by themselves. Norwich, John Trumbull, 1785
16p.

NN   0022846   OClWHi

A NARRATIVE of the extraordinary case of George Lukins, of Yatton, Somersetshire, who was possessed of evil spirits for near eighteen years. Also an account of his remarkable deliverance, in the vestry-room of Temple Church in the city of Bristol. Extracted from the manuscripts of several persons who attended. To which is prefixed a letter from the Rev. W.R.W.   [Bristol?pref. 1788]
23p. 20cm.
1. Lukins, George.
I.W., W.R., reverend. II.W.R.W., reverend.
III. Provenance. Baker, Ernest E. Bookplate.

NN   0022847   CtY-M IEG CtY MnU MH

A narrative of the extraordinary case of George Lukins, of Yatton, Somersetshire, who was possessed of evil spirits, for near eighteen years. Also an account of his remarkable deliverance, in the vestry-room of Temple church, in the city of Bristol, extracted from the manuscripts of several persons who attended. To which is prefixed, a letter from the Rev. W.R.W. Bristol, printed—Philadelphia: Reprinted and sold by Parry Hall, n°. 149, Chesnut street near Fourth street. 1792.
19 p. 22cm.
I Lukins, George.   I. W., W. R.   II. W. R. W.

CA 25-295 Unrev'd

Library of Congress   BF1559.N3

NN   0022848   DLC MWA MH Mi PHi NN

W6   A narrative of the extraordinary case of George Lukins
P3   (of Yatton, Somersetshire) who was possessed of evil spirits, for
v. 2470 near eighteen years.--Also an account of his remarkable
no. 1   deliverance ... To which is prefixed a letter from the Rev. W.
         R. W[ild] Philadelphia, T. T. Stiles, 1805.
         24 p.
         Reprinted from the Bristol, 1788 edition.

         1. Lukins, George.   I. Wild, W. R.

NN   0022849   DNLM

A Narrative of the extraordinary effects of a medicine well known all over Europe ... London, W. Nicoll ... [176- ?]

NN   0022850   NNNAM

A Narrative of the extraordinary effects of a medicine well known all over Europe by the name of Le Lievre's Baume de vie ... London, Pr. for W. Nicoll [1780?]
vi, [62?] p. 19.6cm.

All after p. 38 wanting; "Alphabetical list ..." facing p. vi, calls for 62 p.

NN   0022851   CSmH

Narrative of the extraordinary life of John Conrad Shaf-ford, known by many by the name of the Dutch hermit ... New York, C. L. Carpenter, 1840.
24 p. front. (port.) 24½cm.

1. Shafford, John Conrad, 1756-1840. 2. Indians of North America—Captivities.

10-14040

Library of Congress   E87.S47N3

NN   0022852   DLC PU OClWHi ICN NBuHi

920
Zs45n2   Narrative of the extraordinary life of John Conrad
            Shafford, known by many by the name of the Dutch Hermit,
            who for the last 50 years has lived a secluded and lonely
            life, in a log hut, in a remote part of the village of Dundee,
            Lower Canada, where he died on the 24th of April last,
            1840, at the age of between 80 and 90 ... New York,
            C. L. Carpenter, 1841 [°1840]
            24 p. front. 22 cm.

            1. Shafford, John Conrad, d. 1840.

NN   0022853   N ICN NjP OU

Narrative of the extraordinary life of John Conrad Shafford, known by the name of the Dutch hermit ... [New York: C. L. Carpenter, 1844.] 22 p., 1 l. incl. front. 8°.

1. Shafford, John Conrad, 1756-1840.   2. Indians, N. A.—Captivities.
N. Y. P. L.   October 21, 1925

NN   0022854   NN

A narrative of the facts and circumstances relating to the kidnapping and presumed murder of William Morgan, and of the attempt to carry off David C. Miller, and to burn or destroy the printing office of the latter, for the purpose of preventing the printing and publishing of a book, entitled "Illustrations of Masonry." Prepared under the direction of the several committees appointed at meetings of the citizens, of the counties of Genesee, Livingston, Ontario, Monroe, and Niagara, in the state of New York: with an appendix,   containing most of the

depositions and other documents, to substantiate the statements made, and disclosing many particulars of the transactions, not included in the narrative.
Batavia [N.Y.]: Printed by D.C. Miller, under the direction of the committees. 1827.

36, xxxv p. 22cm.
"Errata": p. xxxv.
Stitched and untrimmed.

MBFM MB
NN   0022856   MH-AH CSmH ICN MiU N WHi MdBP NHi

---

narrative of the facts and circumstances relating to the kidnapping and presumed murder of William Morgan. And of the attempt to carry off David C. Miller, and to burn or destroy the printing office of the latter, for the purpose of preventing the printing and publishing of a book entitled "Illustrations of masonry." Prepared under the direction of the several committees appointed at the meetings of the citizens of the counties of Genesee, Livingston, Ontario, Monroe, and Niagara, in the state of New-York. With an appendix contain-

ing most of the depositions and other documents, to substantiate the statements made, and disclosing many particulars of the transactions, not in the narrative. To which is added, the late trials at Canandaigua. Brookfield, E. and G. Merriam, printers, 1827.
84 p. 19cm.

1. Morgan, William, 1774-ca. 1826. 2. Antimasonic party.
                                            18-22952

Library of Congress   HS527.N3 1827

NN   0022858   DLC NSchU MWA MH

A narrative of the facts and circumstances relating to the kidnapping and presumed murder of Wm. Morgan: and of the attempt to carry off David C. Miller, and to burn or destroy the printing-office of the latter, for the purpose of preventing the printing and publishing of a book entitled "Illustrations of masonry." Prepared under the direction of the several committees appointed at the meetings of the citizens of the counties of Genesee, Livingston, Ontario, Monroe, and Niagara, in the state of New-York: With an appendix containing most of the depositions and other docu-

ments, to substantiate the statements made, and disclosing many particulars of the transactions, not in the narrative. To which is added, the late trials at Canandaigua.   Rochester, N. Y.: Printed by E. Scrantom, under the direction of the committees, 1827.
88 p.   8°.

NN   0022860   NN Vi RPJCB OU IaCrM PPF MBFM

A narrative of the facts and circumstances relating to the kidnapping and presumed murder of William Morgan: and of the attempt to carry off David C. Miller, and to burn or destroy the printing-office of the latter, for the purpose of preventing the printing and publishing of a book entitled "Illustrations of masonry". Prepared under the direction of the several committees appointed at the meetings of the citizens of the counties of Genesee, Livingston, Ontario, Monroe, and Niagara in the state of New-York: with an appendix, containing most of the depositions and other

documents to substantiate the statements made, and disclosing many particulars of the transaction, not in the narrative. ⟨3d ed.⟩ Rochester, N. Y., Printed by E. Scrantom, 1828.
72 p. 20cm.
Title-page blurred.

1. Morgan, William, 1774-ca. 1826. 2. Antimasonic party.
                                            22—15042

Library of Congress   HS527.N3 1828

NN   0022862   DLC MWA CSmH PPF PHi IaGM NCanHi

A Narrative of the facts and circumstances relating to the kidnaping [!] and murder of William Morgan and of the attempt to carry off David C. Miller, and to burn or destroy the printing-office of the latter for the purpose of preventing the printing and publishing of a book, entitled "Illustrations of masonry". Prepared under the direction of the several committees appointed at meetings of the citizens of the counties of Genesee, Livingston, Ontario, Monroe and Niagara, in the state of New York: containing most of the depositions and other documents to substantiate the statements made, and disclosing many particulars of the transactions. Batavia, Printed by D. C. Miller, under the direc-

tion of the committees, 1827. Also, the supplementary report of the committee, containing the report of the coroner's inquest on the body of Wm. Morgan, etc. "Cynosure ed." Chicago, Ill., E. A. Cook & co., 1873.
iv p., 1 l., [8]-95 p. 17 cm.

Cover-title: History of the abduction and murder of Capt. William Morgan.

1. Morgan, William, 1774-ca. 1826. 2. Antimasonic party.

HS527.N3   CA 18—542 Unrev'd

NN   0022864   DLC CU NBC OClJC

A narrative of the facts, connected with, as well preceding, as subsequent to the author's with drawing from the Congregational church ...   see under   [Kellogg, John]

A NARRATIVE of the facts relative to the dismissal of Mr. Daniel Daly (late midshipman) from His Majesty's ship Lion. [Temple Bar, C. Roworth, printer, 1808?]
19 p. 20cm.

1. Daly, Daniel. 2. Naval   discipline--Gt. Br., 1807.

NN   0022866   NN

VOLUME 405

Narrative, A, of the fires which occurred in the parish of Whit-church, Shropshire, in the years 1830 and 1831; together with an account of the trials of James Lea and Joseph Grindley, etc. Whitchurch: H. Newling, 1832. 3 p.l., 69 p., 1 plan.   8°.

1. Fires. Gt. Br.: Eng.: Whitchurch.
N. Y. P. L.   December 7, 1912.

NN 0022867   NN

Narrative of the French expedition to Corea in 1866, the U.S. expedition in 1871, and the expedition of H. M.S. Ringdove in 1871.   1871

NN 0022868   DN

A narrative of the French expedition to Dantzig in 1734
  see under   [Boëncourt,   de]

Narrative of the French Revolution in 1830 ...
  see under   [Colton, Charles Caleb]
1780 ?-1832.

Narrative of the general course of history...
  see under   [Abbott, Jacob] 1803-1879.

A narrative of the grand festival at Yarmouth...
  see under   [Cory, Robert] comp.

A Narrative of the great and bloody fight between the Prince of Orange and the Duke of Orleans the king of Frances General, near the city of St. Omers, on Sunday the first of April 1677 ...   London, for T. M., 1677.
  4 p.   Folio.   Bd with: [Turnor, Tho.]
Joyful news of opening the Exchequer. 1677.

NN 0022873   CSmH

A narrative of the great success God hath been pleased to give His Highness forces in Jamaica
  see under   [Doyley, Edward]

*E065
A100
648n3

A narrative of the great victory obtained by the Lord generall in Kent. With the names of the knights, and collonels slaine, and taken prisoners. And a list of the particulars of all the fights. Also the new besieging of Dover by the Kentish-men; and the fight at Bow in Essex. And a declaration of the severall proceedings of both houses of Parliament, with those in the county of Kent ...
  Printed at London by Robert Ibbitson, in Smith-field, neer the Queenes-head tavern, 1648.
  1p.l., 6p.   18.5cm.

NN 0022875   MH MnU

A narrative of the heads of several conferences between His present Majesty ...
  see under   Gordon, Lord George, 1751-1793.

Narrative of the heroic enterprise of William Hanson, a poor fisherman, near Wexford harbour in Ireland, whose intrepid gallantry saved a mother and daughter from perishing by shipwreck, off the above place. Also, the shipwreck and sufferings of Occum Chamnan, a Siamese mandarin, at the Cape of the Needles, in the southern extremity of Africa, in the year 1674. London, Champante & Whitron [etc., 1815?]
  36 p.   fold. front. 18ᵐᵉ.
  Pages 26 and 27 do not connect.
  The shipwreck of Occum Chamnan as translated from the Voyage of Gui Tachard.
  Imperfect: p. 27–34 wanting; p. 27–34 bound between p. 24 and 25 belong to a different book.
  1. Life-saving. 2. Ship-   wrecks. 3. Hanson, William, of Bal-
  lynescar. 1. Occum Cham-   nan. 11. Tachard, Gui, 1651-1712.
  Library of Congress   G536.N23   ca 8—1767 Unrev'd

NN 0022877   DLC

The Narrative of the Honourable John Byron
  see under   Byron, John, 1723-1786.

A **narrative** of the horrid massacre by the Indians, of the wife and children of the Christian hermit, a resident of Missouri, with a full account of his life and sufferings, never before published. St. Louis, L. W. Whiting & co., 1840.
  24 p. incl. front. 23½ᶜᵐ.
  Apparently based on the "Narrative of the massacre, by the savages, of the wife and children of Thomas Baldwin ..." New-York, 1835. In the present pamphlet the name of the hermit is said to be James B. Taylor.

  1. Taylor, James B., pseud.? 2. Indians of North America—Captivities.
                                                          16-21365
  Library of Congress   E87.N23

NN 0022879   DLC ICN CSmH MoSM

A narrative of the imprisonment of two nonconformist ministers ...
  see under   Makemie, Francis, 1658-1708.

A narrative of the incidents attending the capture, detention, and ransom of Charles Johnston ...
  see under   Johnston, Charles, b. 1768.

*EC75
G95??
791?b

A **narrative** of the incidents which form the mystery, in the family of General Gunning. With biographical sketches; and strictures on the "vindication" of Mrs. Gunning. Comprising copies of all the letters, affidavits, &c. &c. The whole placed in a new point of view.
London: Printed for Taylor and co. Royal Exchange. Price one shilling and sixpence. 1791.
8°. 1p.l., [5]-45p. 21.5cm.
The "vindication" was published as A letter from Mrs. Gunning.
  No.1 in a   volume lettered on spine:
Gunningiana.

NN 0022882   MH NIC CtY IEN

A **narrative** of the Indian and civil wars in Virginia, in the years 1675 and 1676. Published from the original manuscript, in the first volume (second series) of the Collections of the Massachusetts historical society. Boston, Printed by J. Eliot, 1814. [Washington, P. Force, 1835]
  47 p. 23½ᶜᵐ. (In Force, Peter. Tracts ... Washington, 1836-46.
  v. 1, no. 11)
  Reprint.
  Moses Coit Tyler, in his History of American literature, expresses the opinion that the author was one Cotton of Aquia Creek, husband of that Mrs. Anne Cotton who wrote "An account of our late troubles". Unfortunately the printed edition followed by Force was found to contain so many errors and omissions that it was carefully compared with

manuscript and republished in Proceedings of the Massachusetts historical society, v. 9, 1867, p. 299–342, with the following note: The manuscript is evidently contemporaneous with the events described, or written not long after their occurrence ... Several leaves being destroyed at the beginning and end, there is no title, except the running-heading on each page, viz. "The Indians proseedings", "Ingram's proceedings", &c., as in the reprint. Upon the outside of the cover, in a later hand, is written "Bacons proceedings, July 27, 1764". This latter reprint was also separately issued in 1867 with title: The history of Bacon's and Ingram's rebellion.
                                                          E187.F69
—— [Reissue]
  (In American histor-   ical society. Transactions. Washington, 1839. 25½ᶜᵐ.   v. 1)
  1. Bacon's rebellion,   1676. 2. Virginia—Hist.—Colonial
period.   [826f1]
  Library of Congress   E172.A70   2—13281-1ᵃ

NN   KyU NcD ViW PU MiU-C RPJCB
0022884   DLC OClWHi NN MdBP RPB ViU NIC CU Vi

A **narrative** of the Indian and civil wars in Virginia, in the years 1675 and 1676. Published from the original manuscript, in the first volume (second series) of the Collections of the Massachusetts historical society. Boston, Printed by J. Eliot ... 1814. [Rochester, G. P. Humphrey, 1898]
  1 p.l., 51, [2] p. 24ᶜᵐ. (Added t.-p.: American colonial tracts monthly
  [v. 1] no. 10, February 1898)
  On verso of t.-p.: Colonial tracts, no. 10.
  Caption title: Colonial tracts, v. 1, no. 10.
  Reprint, without acknowledgment, from Force tracts, v. 1 (1836) no. 11.
  Moses Coit Tyler, in his History of American literature, expresses the opinion that the author was one Cotton of Aquia Creek, husband of that Mrs. Cotton who wrote "An account of our late troubles".

  1. Bacon's rebellion,   1676. 2. Virginia — Hist.— Colonial
period.

  Library of Congress   E186.A51
———— Copy 2.   F229.N23   4-15774

NN 0022885   DLC NIC Vi PBm CU ViU MiU-C PSt MB

Narrative of the Indian mutinies of 1857, compiled for the Madras Military Male Orphan Asylum. Madras, Printed at the Asylum Press by W. Thomas, 1858.
  196p. 23cm.
  Bound with Madras. Native Association.
  Memorial to the Right Honorable Lord Stanley. Madras, 1859; and Ahmad Khan, Sir Syed. An essay on the causes of the Indian revolt. Agra, 1859.

NN 0022886   WU MH

Narrative of the Indian revolt from its outbreak to the capture of Lucknow by Sir Colin Campbell. Illustrated with nearly two hundred engravings from authentic sketches. London, G. Vickers, 1858.
  1v, 452 p. illus. (incl. ports.) 27ᶜᵐ.
  Reprinted from the Illustrated times. cf. Brit. mus. Catalogue.

  1. India—Hist.—Sepoy rebellion, 1857-1858.
                                                          43—26813
  Library of Congress   DS478.N3

NN 0022887   DLC MH GEU

A narrative of the Indian wars in New England
  see under   Hubbard, William, 1621-1704.

A narrative of the insurrection which happened in the zemeedary of Banaris, Aug. 1781 ...
  see under   [Hastings, Warren] 1732-1818.

A narrative of the introduction and progress of Christianity in Scotland before the Reformation...
  see under   Reformed Dissenting
Presbyterian Church in North America.

A **NARRATIVE** of the investiture and inauguration of Oliver Cromwell, together with the speeches of His Highness and Lord Widdringtoun &c. on that solemn occasion. Edinbvrg, Printed, for A. Davidson, 1727.
  16p.   16cm.

NN 0022891   MnU

Y   **NARRATIVE** of the Irish expedition to the
145   North Pole. [By H. E.] Dublin, W. McGee, 1875.
.N 165 16p. map. 19cm.

NN 0022892   ICN

A narrative of the irruption of the Kafir hordes into the eastern province of the Cape of Good Hope, 1834-35
  see under   [Godlonton, Robert] comp.

VOLUME 405

Narrative of the journey and imprisonment of Pius vII, after his departure from Rome, until his return to that city. Paris, 1814. Reprinted, London, 1814.

(*In* The Pamphleteer. London, 1814. 22½ᶜᵐ. v. 4, p. (23)-65)

1. Pius VII, pope, 1742-1823.

Library of Congress   AP4.P2   vol. 4   CA 5—715 Unrev'd

NN   0022894   DLC ICN

Narrative of the journey of an Irish gentleman through England in the year 1752. Ed. from a contemporary manuscript, with a few illustrative notes. London, Printed at the Chiswick press, 1869.

vii, 177, (1) p.   24ᶜᵐ.

"Fifty copies only printed". This is no. 10.
Presentation copy, with autograph of W. C. Hazlitt.
Prepared for the press and annotated by W. C. Hazlitt. *cf.* Preface, signed: Henry Huth.
Binder's title: A journey through England, A.D. 1752. Privately printed, 1869.

1. England—Descr. & trav.   I. Huth, Henry, 1815-1878.   II. Hazlitt, William Carew, 1834-1913, ed.   III. Title: A journey through England.

NN   0022896   MiU CtY MH PP CSmH NcD CLU

Narrative of the journey of Col. Thomas Proctor to the Indians of the North-west
     see under   Proctor, Thomas, 1739-1806.

A NARRATIVE of the lamented death of five persons, who were drowned when they were proceeding on a fishing excursion. London, W.Kent,1815.

18 p. 14 cm.   F 2358.2*

NN   0022898   MH

A narrative of the last illness of the Right Honourable the Earl of Orford ...
     see under   Ranby, John, 1703-1773.

A narrative of the late action between the French and Confederate armies on the 1.of August, 1674—being two letters, the one from Brussels, and the other from Paris. London, Printed for P.Brooksby, 1674.

4 p.

NN   0022900   NjP

A narrative of the late dispute, between the Rev. Dr. Hughes and Mr. Forster
     see under   Forster, John, of Trinity College, Dublin.

---

*pEB65
A100
685n

A narrative of the late dreadful battels[!] between the potent Prince de l'Or, and Mendicoso the grand duke of Penuria. Giving an account of their respective forces, allies, numbers of men kill'd and taken prisoners, &c.
London,Printed for R.Rumball,in Butcher-hall-lane,near Christ church,1685.

[2]p. 34x22.5cm.
Caption title; imprint on p.[2].

NN   0022902   MH

Narrative, A, of the late engagement between His Majesties fleet, under the command of His Illustrious Highness Prince Rupert, and the Dutch, on Wednesday the 28th of May, 1673. As it was communicated in three letters: the one from an officer on board the St. Michael, to his wife... The second from a person in the Cambridge. The third from on board the French Ruby... (London:) A. Purslow, 1673.   8 p.   12°.

1. Navy (British).—History, 1673.   2. Navy (Dutch).—History, 1673.
N. Y. P. L.   March 15, 1911.

NN   0022903   NN

Narrative (A) of the late extraordinary cure wrought in an instant upon Mrs. Eliz. Savage (lame from her birth), without the using of any natural means. With the affidavits which were made before the right honorable the lord mayor; and the certificates of several credible persons, who knew her both before and since her cure. Enquired into with all its circumstances, by noted divines, both of the Church of England and others, and by eminent physicians of the college; and many persons of quality, who have expres'd their full satisfaction. With an appendix, attempting to prove, that miracles are not ceas'd. 46 pp., 1 l. 12°. London, J. Dunton & J. Harris, 1694.

NN   0022904   DNLM CtY-M CSmH

---

*E08
A100
825n

A narrative of the late fires at Miramichi, New-Brunswick; with an appendix, containing the statements of many of the sufferers, and a variety of interesting occurrences; together with a poem, entitled "The conflagration." ...
Halifax,N.S.Printed at the office of P.J. Holland.1825.

48p. 20.5cm.
The poem is not to be confused with another of the same title, by George Manners, inspired by the same disaster.

NN   0022905   MH

A narrative of the late fires at Miramichi, New-Brunswick; with an appendix... and ... a poem... 1825.

AW
5
C354:
1-1188

(Canada. Archives.
    Pamphlets in the Public Archives of Canada. Otttwa, 1968-
    sheets. 11 x 15 cm.)

Microfiche.

NN   0022906   CaBVaU

A narrative of the late massacres in Lancaster county ... 1744.
     see under   Franklin, Benjamin, 1706-1790.

Narrative of the late occurrences at the cotton mills in Glasgow, in answer to the statement of these occurrences by proprietors. Glasgow, Printed by Purvis and Aitkin, 1825.
26 p. 20½ cm.

NN   0022908   DL

A NARRATIVE of the late Parliament (so-called) their election and appearing, the seclusion of the great part of them, the sitting of the rest. With an account of the places of profit, sallaries, and advantages which they hold and receive under the present power. With some queries thereupon: and upon the most materiall acts and proceedings passed by them... By a friend to the commonwealth... n. p., [Feb.] 1658. 32 p.

NN   0022909   MnU

A **narrative** of the late Parliament (so called), their election and appearing; the seclusion of a great part of them; the sitting of the rest: with an account of the places of profit, salaries, and advantages which they hold and receive under the present power; with some queries thereupon, and upon the most material acts and proceedings passed by them. All humbly proposed to consideration, and published for information of the people; by a friend to the common-wealth, and to its dearbought rights and freedom. Anno 1657.

(*In* The Harleian miscellany. London, 1808-13. 30½ᶜᵐ. vol. III (1809) p. 449-469)

Attributed to Sir George Wharton. *cf.* Catalogus bibliothecæ Bodleianæ, 1843, v. 3, p. 40.
In editions of the Harleian miscellany in the Library of Congress: London, 1744-46. 26 x 20ᶜᵐ. vol. III (1745) p. 430-448. London, 1808-11. 22ᶜᵐ. vol. VI (1810) p. 456-481.

1. Gt. Brit. Parliament, 1640-1660. 2. Gt. Brit.—Hist.—Commonwealth and protectorate, 1649-1660.—Pamphlets.   I. Wharton, Sir George, 1st bart., 1617-1681, supposed author.
                              A 44-4972

Hamilton college. Library
for Library of Congress   DA300.H28   vol. 3
                        DA300.H29   vol. 6

NN   0022911   NCH CtY ICN NHu NjP DLC MnU DLC

N194a

A narrative of the late proceedings of some justices and others. Pretending to put in execution the late Act against Conventicles...(London?) Printed in the year 1670.

(4) 16 p. (A)A2-B4, C2. 4to.

NN   0022912   DFo

A narrative of the late proceeds at White-hall, concerning the Jevvs ...
     see under   [Jessey, Henry] 1601-1663.

A narrative of the late revivals of religion within the bounds of Geneva Presbytery
     see under   Presbyterian Church in the U.S.A. Presbyteries. Geneva.

Narrative of the late riotous proceedings against the liberty of the press, in Cincinnati, 1836
     see   Ohio anti-slavery society.

A **narrative** of the late riots at Edinburgh; and a vindication of its magistracy, against the charges advanced in the memorial for the papists of Scotland. London, 1779.   28 p.   8°.

1. Riots, Gt. Br.: Scotland: Edin-   burgh, 1779.
N. Y. P. L.   November 5, 1919.

NN   0022916   NN NcD MnU

Augustan
BX 5350
.N23

A narrative of the late treatment of the Episcopal ministers within the City of Edinburgh since March last 1708. Until their imprisonment in July thereafter, with their circumstances and defences together with some reflections upon the same. With a postscript ... London,Sold by J. Morphew,1708.
4 p.l., 33 p.

1. Episcopal church in Scotland.

NN   0022917   InU CU-A NN CtY

A narrative of the life, adventures, travels and sufferings of Henry Tufts ...
     see under   Tufts, Henry, 1748-1831.

VOLUME 405

A narrative of the life and conversion of Alexander White, æt. 23. who was executed at Cambridge, November 18, 1784, for the murder of a Captain White, at sea. Containing extracts from his manuscripts, and some letters written by him a short time before his execution. Boston, Printed and published, by Powars and Willis [1784?]

23 p. 19½ᵐ.

Subject entries: White, Alexander, 1761?-1784.

3-7419

NN 0022919 DLC MH-L MB

NARRATIVE of the life and daring exploits of James Crockett, the lion conquerer [!] Bath, J.Francis, [1862]

pp.7. Thr 1219.2

NN 0022920 MH

Biog.
C471l A NARRATIVE of the life and death of John Elliot, M.D. containing an account ... of his unhappy passion for Miss Mary Boydell ... together with an apology, written by himself ... London,Printed for J.Ridgway,1787.
46p. 26cm.
Bound with Life and memoirs of Elizabeth of Chudleigh ... London[1788]
1.Elliott, John, 1736-1786 2.Boydell, Mary 3. 4.

NN 0022921 CtY-M

A narrative of the life and death of Lieut. Joseph Morgan Willcox, who was massacred by the Creek Indians, on the Alabama river, (Miss. ter.) on the 15th of January, 1814. Compiled from various publications, and letters written by his friends and brother officers, on the occasion. ⟨Published by consent of his friends.⟩ Marietta (O.) Printed by R. Prentiss, 1816.

23 p. 20½ᵐ.

Subject entries: 1. Willcox, Joseph Morgan, 1791?-1814. 2. Indians of North American—Wars. 3. Creek Indians.

2-19300

Library of Congress, no. E83.813.N23.

NN 0022922 DLC ICN AU NN

A narrative of the life and distresses of Simon Mason, apothecary
see under Mason, Simon, b. 1701.

Narrative of the life and dying speech of John Ryer, who was executed at White-Plains, Westchester County, October 2, 1793, for the murder of Dr. Isaac Smith, deputy sheriff of that County. [Poughkeepsie?] Printed for and sold by the Flying Stationers.[1793]
24 p. 12 mo.

NN 0022924 RPJCB

Narrative of the life, and dying speech, of John Ryer: who was executed at White-Plains, in the county of Westchester, state of New-York, on the second day of October, 1793, for the murder of Dr. Isaac Smith, deputy-sheriff of that county. Printed in Danbury, by Nathan Douglas, for the publisher. — 1793. 15 p. 20½cm.

Photostatic reproduction.
See: Sabin 74542. See: Evans 26118.

57968B. I. Murder—U.S.—N.Y.— Westchester County. 2. Smith,
N.Y.P.L. Isaac, d. 1792. October 7, 1941

NN 0022925 NN

Narrative of the life & religious exercises of James Hamton ...
see under Hamton, James, 1764-1792.

A narrative of the life and sufferings of Mrs. Jane Johns, who was barbarously wounded and scalped by Seminole Indians, in East Florida ... Published exclusively for her benefit. Baltimore, Printed by J. Lucas & E. K. Deaver, 1837.

24 p. 22½ᵐ.

"Extract from the journal of Dr. Welch": p. 7-10.

1. Johns, Mrs. Jane (Hall) b. 1813. 2. Seminole war, 2d, 1835-1842.
I. Welch, Andrew.

Library of Congress E83.835.J65 2-16700
——— Copy 2.
——— Copy 3. [Mar- koe pamphlets, v. 65, no. 1;
AC901.M2 vol. 65

NN 0022927 DLC FTaSU PPL

A narrative of the life and sufferings of Mrs. Jane Johns, who was barbarously wounded and scalped by Seminole Indians, in East Florida ... Pub. exclusively for her benefit. Charleston, Printed by Burke & Giles, 1837.

29 p. 22½ᵐ.

"Extract from the Journal of Dr. Welch": p. 9-12.

1. Johns, Mrs. Jane (Hall) b. 1813. 2. Seminole war, 2d, 1835-1842.
I. Welch, Andrew.
ICN
Library of Congress E83.835.J652 20-19036

NN 0022928 DLC CtY ViU ICN

Narrative of the life and travels of John Robert Shaw, the Well Digger
see under Shaw, John Robert, b. 1761.

Narrative of the life of General Leslie Combs; embracing incidents in the early history of the North-western territory ... New-York, American Whig review office, 1852.

cover-title, 23 p. port. 24ᵐ.

First published in the American Whig review, new ser., v. 9 (1852)

1. Combs, Leslie, 1793-1881. 2. Northwest, Old—Hist.—War of 1812. 3. U. S.—Hist.—War of 1812—Personal narratives.

Library of Congress E361.C73 5—34069

KyU OC1WHi OFH OO NBuG ICU
NN 0022930 DLC PHi OHi NBu NIC MB PBL MWA FTaSU

Narrative of the life of General Leslie Combs; embracing incidents in the early history of the northwestern territory. Washington, Printed by J. T. and L. Towers, 1855.

cover-title, 24 p. 23½ᵐ.

In double columns.
First published in the American Whig review, new ser., v. 9 (1852) and reissued in pamphlet form the same year.
Cover-title mutilated.

1. Combs, Leslie, 1793-1881. 2. Northwest, Old—Hist.—War of 1812. 3. U. S.—Hist.—War of 1812—Personal narratives.

Library of Congress E361.N28 5—34798

NN 0022931 DLC CSmH MdBP

Narrative of the life of J.D. Green, a runaway slave from Kentucky
see under Green, Jacob D 1813-

Narrative of the life of James Lane, who was executed at Gallipolis, (Ohio) September 9, 1817, for the murder of William Dowell; with some observations on his behaviour under condemnation: to which is added, the address of the court, on pronouncing sentence of death upon the prisoner. Chillicothe: Printed by John Bailhache. 1817.
20 p. 17.5 cm.

NN 0022933 CSmH OC1WHi OOxM

A narrative of the life of Mr. Richard Lyde of Hereford ...
see under [Lyde, Nehemiah]

A narrative of the life of Mrs. Charlotte Clarke, daughter of Colley Cibber
see under Clarke, Charlotte (Cibber) d. 1760?

A narrative of the life of Mrs. Hamilton ...
see under Hamilton, Sarah (Beckhouse) 1745-1806.

A narrative of the life of Mrs. Mary Jemison who was taken by a party of French and Indians at Marsh Creek ...
see under [Seaver, James Everett] 1787-1827.

Narrative of the life of Moses Grandy: late a slave...
see under Grandy, Moses, b. 1786?

A narrative of the life of Sarah Shade ... Containing many well authenticated and curious facts, more particularly during her voyage to the East Indies, in the New Devonshire Indiaman, in the year 1769... Together with some extra-ordinary accounts of the ferocity of tigers, jackals... &c. Taken down by some gentlemen, and published for her benefit. London, Printed by Knight and Compton, and sold by J. Hatchard, 1801.
44 p. 21cm.
1. Shade, Sarah, 1741-

NN 0022939 MnU

A narrative of the life of Solomon Mack ...
see under [Mack, Solomon] 1735-

Nar[rative] of the life of the Reverend Mr. George Whitefield ... with the history of his travels ... To which are added, a particular account of his death and funeral ... also, his last will and testament and an exact description of his person. London, T. Robert; sold by J. Bunyon [17--]
259 p. 18 cm.
Imperfect copy: part of t. p. torn away.

1. Whitefield, George, 1714-1770.

NN 0022941 NcD

Narrative of the life of Thomas Cooper
see under Hopper, Isaac Tatem, 1771-1852.

A narrative of the life of William Beadle, of Wethersfield, in the State of Connecticut
see under [Mitchell, Stephen Mix] 1743-1835.

VOLUME 405

A narrative of the life, together with the last Speech, confession and Solem declaration, of John Lewis
see under   Lewis, John, 1727-1760.

A narrative of the lives of James Falconer, Peter Bruce, and James Dick, now under sentence of death...
see under   Falconer, James.

Narrative of the loss of the Abeona, which was destroyed by fire, on the 25th of November, 1820, in lat. 4°.30". north, 25°. west long., when one hundred and twelve individuals perished. Compiled by some of the survivors.   Glasgow: Chalmers and Collins, 1821.   40 p.   8°.

1. Shipwrecks, 1821. 2. "Abeona,"   ship.   January 22, 1916.
N. Y. P. L.

NN   0022946   NN

Narrative of the loss of the Earl of Abergavenny ...
see   An authentic narrative of the loss of the Earl of Abergavenny ...

A narrative of the loss of the Kent, by fire, in the bay of Biscay ...
see under   [McGregor, Sir Duncan] 1787-1881.

A narrative of the loss of the Royal George at Spithead, August, 1782
see under   [Slight, Julian]

Narrative of the loss of the Sceptre, man of war, of sixty-four guns, Capt. Valentine Edwards, which was wrecked in Table Bay, Cape of Good Hope, 6th November, 1799. In which is fully described every particular of the dreadful event... And an interesting description of Table Bay and the Cape of Good Hope. Written by one of the survivors...   London: W. Harris[, 182-?].   iv, 6-26 p.   front.   nar. 16°.

Bound with: Julia's journey to London.   London[, 182-?].   nar. 12°.

350449A. 1. Warships—Gt. Br.—   Sceptre.   April 12, 1928.
N. Y. P. L.

NN   0022950   NN

Narrative of the loss of the Ship Hercules
see under   Stout, Benjamin.

Spec.
G
530
.N36

A narrative of the loss of the ship Willem of Amsterdam, commanded by C. H. Roosebloom, which was wrecked on her voyage from Rio de Janiero to Antwerp, near the Port of Ilfracombe, in Devonshire, on the 21st of December, 1821. Written in French by a Dutch lady, a passenger, and translated by the Rev. Richard Frizell,1822.
21p.

1. Shipwrecks.

NN   0022952   DeU

Narrative of the loss of the steam-packet Pulaski, on the coast of North-Carolina, June 14, 1838, carefully comp. from authentic sources.   n.p. [18-]

NN   0022953   MH RPB

A narrative of the loss of the Winterton, East Indiaman... by a passenger in the ship
see under   Buchan, George, 1775-1856.

A narrative of the loss of the Winterton on her passage to India ...
see under   [Dale, John] 3d mate of the Winterton.

The narrative of the Lower House of Convocation, as to the Point of Adjournments
see under   [Hooper, George, Bp. of Bath and Wells] 1640-1727.

Narrative (The) of the magpie; or, The maid of Palaiseau founded upon the circumstance of an unfortunate female . . . unjustly sentenced to death, on strong presumptive evidence . . . iv, 5–18 pp.   *London: W. Hone*, 1815.   8°.
Bd. with : Vindication (A) of the conduct of Lady Douglas . . . London, 1814.   8°.

NN   0022957   NN PPL

A narrative of the management of the late ministry; collected from the report of the committee of secrecy
see under   Gt. Brit. Parliament. House of Commons. Committee of Secrecy.

Narrative of the manner in which the campaign against the Indians ... was conducted ...
see under   St. Clair, Arthur, 1734-1818.

Narrative of the Martyrdom, at Boston of William Robinson, Marmaduke Stevenson, Mary Dyer, and William Leddra, in the year 1659. With some particulars of the judgments which befel their persecutors and the state of New England. Taken from Besse's account of the sufferings of Friends ... Manchester, John Harrison. 1841.
viii, [3]–40 p.   18⅛ᶜᵐ.
Sabin 6552.

1. Friends, Society of—Persecutions. 2. Martyrs.
3. Persecution.

NN   0022960   ViU

Narrative of the massacre at Chicago, August 15, 1812, and some preceding events
see under   [Kinzie, Juliette Augusta (McGill) "Mrs. John H. Kinzie", 1806-1870.

Narrative of the massacre, by the savages, of the wife and children of Thomas Baldwin ...
see under   Baldwin, Thomas, b. 1750?

Narrative of the massacre of Irish protestants in 1798, and the analogy of these facts to the present position of protestants in America. Phila., 1846.

NN   0022963   PPL

A narrative of the meeting of some gentlemen, ministers and citizens, at the town-hall in Canterbury: together with their declaration presented to the mayor at the common Burghmoote. [London? 1660]

broadside.   38cm.   [Stuart tracts. Sheets 1642-1689. 45]

1. Gt. Brit. History. 1660. I. Canterbury, Eng. Citizens.

NN   0022964   MnU

E
5
.K 783

A NARRATIVE of the melancholy death of Miss Knox, &c.   [London?]T.Bailey[n.d.]
32p.   18cm.

Contents.—A narrative of the melancholly death of Miss Knox.—The history of Mr. E******n's matrimonial adventure.—The trials of Ann Francis Caroline.—The history of Amanda.

NN   0022965   ICN

A narrative of the method by which the private letters of Mr. Pope have been procur'd and publish'd by Edmund Curll
see under   [Pope, Alexander] 1688-1744, supposed author.

Narrative of the military life of Major Thompson Maxwell
see under   [Gleason, Benjamin] 1777-1847.

A narrative of the minutes of evidence respecting the claim to the Berkeley peerage ...
see under   Fitzhardinge, William Fitzhardinge Berkeley, earl, 1786-1857, petitioner.

Narrative of the miraculous cure of Anne Munnings, of Colchester. by faith, prayer. and anointing with oil, on New-year's day, 1705; Crafty Kate, of Colchester, or, The false-hearted clothier frighted into good manners, a rare and whimsical old ballad; An extraordinary love-letter, addressed to a lady of Maldon, in 1644; and The Maldon martyr's prayer, 1555. A very limited number printed. Totham, Printed by C. Clark (an amateur) at his private press, 1847.
12 l.   19⅛ᵐᵐ.
No. 3 in a volume of seven pieces lettered : Emblems [etc.]
"Miraculous cure of Anne Munnings" signed : Charles Doe.
I. Doe, Charles, fl. 1698.   II. Clark, Charles, 1806-1880.   III. Title: Anne Munnings, The   miraculous cure of.   IV. Title: Crafty Kate, of Colchester.

Library of Congress   PN6099.E6   398.5

32-6592

NN   0022969   DLC NN OO

A narrative of the miseries of New-England by reason of an arbitrary government erected there
see under   [Mather, Increase] 1639-1723.

Narratives of the mission of George Bogle to Tibet
see under   Markham, Sir Clements Robert, 1830-1916, ed.

Narrative of the mission to Otaheite, and other islands in the South Seas
see under   London Missionary Society.

VOLUME 405

A narrative of the missions to the new settlements...
see under Congregational churches in
Connecticut. General association. Committee.

A NARRATIVE of the most cruel and barbarous treatment of Miss S----h M----y,
now in the Hospital of Incurables. With
all the different letters and affidavits
published ... Dublin, 1762.
23p. 20cm.

NN 0022974   CtY-M

Narrative of the most interesting events
which preceded and accompanied the late Revolution in France... Dublin, 1789.

NN 0022975   PPL

N199.5   The narrative of the most material proceedings
at the sessions for London and Middlesex, begun
July the seventh, 1680 ... ₍London? 1680₎

4 p. A². Fo.
Caption title.

NN 0022976   DFo

Narrative of the most remarkable events which
occurred in and near Leipzig ...
see under Shoberl, Frederic, 1775-1853,
comp and tr.

Narrative of the murder of Mr. Weare, at Gill's hill, near
Aldenham, Hertfordshire, on the evening of Friday, October
24. With original letters, never before published. Compiled
from communications made by Mr. Heward, the proprietor of
the cottage where Probert resided; Mr. James Woods, the person who was decoyed into Manchester buildings for the supposed purpose of being murdered by Thurtell; and various
other authentic and original sources of information. Illustrated
with a copper plate engraving. From a drawing taken on the
spot, by Mr. Heward ... London, J. Edgerley ₍etc., 182-₎
56 p. fold. pl. 22½ᵐ.
1. Weare, William,   d. 1823. I. Thurtell, John, 1794-
1824, defendant. II. Probert,   William, d. 1825, defendant.
Library of Congress   44-16071

NN 0022978   DLC MdBP NN

Narrative of the mutiny of Bolarum in September
1855
see under MacKenzie, Colin.

KD
.N234   A narrative of the mysterious and dreadful
murder of Mr. W. Weare, containing the examination before the magistrates, the coroner's inquest, the confession of Hunt,
and other particulars previous to the trial,
collected from the best sources of intelligence, with anecdotes of Weare, Thurtell,
Hunt, Probert, and others; and a full report of the trial, and subsequent execution
at Hertford. London, Print. and published
by J. M'Gowan ₍1824₎
247 p. illus.

Continued in next column

Continued from preceding column

Cover title: Murder of Mr. Weare and trial.

1. Weare, William, d. 1823. I. Thurtell,
John, 1794-1824, defendant. II. Probert, William, d. 1825, defendant. III. Title: Murder
of Mr. Weare and trial.

NN 0022981   INS MH-L

A narrative of the negotiations occasioned by the
dispute between England and Spain in the year 1790
see under ₍Burges, Sir James Bland, bart₎
1752-1824, comp.

A narrative of the offical conduct of Anthony Stokes,
of the Inner temple London ...
see under ₍Stokes, Anthony₎ 1736-1799.

A narrative of the operations of a small British force, under
the command of Brigadier-General Sir Samuel Auchmuty,
employed in the reduction of Monte Video, on the river Plate,
A. D. 1807. By a field officer on the staff ... London, Printed
for J. J. Stockdale, 1807.
60 p. front. (plan) 27 x 22ᵐ.
Includes official dispatches, proceedings in Parliament, etc.

1. Montevideo—Capture by English, 1807.
                                                    4—15525
Library of Congress   F2845.N24

NN 0022984   DLC RPJCB

Narrative of the oppressive law proceedings...
see under ₍Humphrys-Alexander, Alexander,
calling himself earl of Stirling₎ 1783-1859.

A narrative of the origin and foundation of the Hospitals
Association
see under Hospitals Association, London.

Narrative of the pious death of the penitent
Henry Mills ...
see under Mills, Henry.

Narrative of the plans and proceedings of a
committee acting on behalf of the British civil
and military claimants on Portugal
see under ₍Blundell, Edward Straw₎

A narrative of the planting of the Massachusetts
colony anno 1628
see under ₍Scottow, Joshua₎ 1618-1698.

---

x942.069
N167   A narrative of the plot, against Her Majesty,
carried on by Captain Simon Fraser, and others,
from the first discovery thereof, by Mr. Ferguson,
on the 25th of November last, to the publishing
hereof. ₍London: Printed in the year 1704₎
8p. 23cm.

Caption title.

1. Lovat, Simon Fraser, 12th baron, 1667?-
1747.

NN 0022990   IU

Narrative of the political changes and events which
have recently taken place in the island of Terceira
see under Walton, William, 1784-1857.

Narrative (A) of the popes late fire-works in England.
n. p. ₍1680?₎ 27 pp. f°.
Bd. with: Bedloe (William). The epistle dedicatory to the sur-
viving citizens of London. n. p. ₍1680?₎ f°.

NN 0022992   NN MdBP CLU-C

A narrative of the popish-plot, shewing the
cunning contrivance thereof
see under ₍Cadbury, John₎ 1627-1704,
attributed author.

A narrative of the principal actions occurring in the
wars betwixt Sueden and Denmark ...
see under ₍Meadows, Sir Philip₎ 1626-1718.

A narrative of the proceedings against John Wilkes, esq.
from his commitment in April 1763, to his outlawry.
With a full view of the arguments used in Parliament
and out of doors, in canvassing the various important
questions that arose from his case ... London, Printed
for Richardson & Urquhart, 1768.
1 p. l., 48 p. 21ᵐ.

1. Wilkes, John, 1727-1797.

Library of Congress   DA512.W6N2   4-33521

NN 0022995   DLC ICN MiU-C PPL MWA

---

*fEC65   The narrative of the proceedings at the
A100   sessions for London and Middlesex, begun at the
679n3   Old-Bailey, on Wednesday the 10th of December,
          1679. giving an account of all the material
          tryals there, &c. With the number and names of
          the several persons condemn'd to die, and their
          particular crimes. As also how many burnt in
          the hand, &c.
          ₍London, 1679?₎
          4p. 29cm.
          Caption title.
          Narcissus Lutt-   rell's copy, priced in
          his autograph: 1d.

NN 0022996   MH

---

*fEC65   The narrative of the proceedings at the
A100   Sessions-house for London and Middlesex. Giving
680n4   an account of the tryals of divers traitors,
          clippers, coyners, highway-men, and other
          notorious offenders. The number condemned to
          dye, to be whipt, &c. with their respective
          crimes.
          London: Printed for T. Davies. 1680.
          4p. 29cm.
          Caption title; imprint on p. 4.
          Narciseus Luttrell's copy, priced & dated in
          his autograph: 1ᵈ ₍&₎ 14 Octob. 1680.

NN 0022997   MH PU

Narrative of the proceedings in America, of the
Society called Quakers, in the case of Hannah
Barnard... 1804
see under ₍Foster, Thomas₎ 1759 or 60-
1834.

A narrative of the proceedings in France, for
discovering and detecting the murderers of the
English gentlemen
see under ₍Defoe, Daniel₎ 1661?-1731.

VOLUME 405

A narrative of the proceedings in the North parish of
Hingham
   see under   [Thaxter, Thomas] 1748-1813.

E
5
.B 988804
   A NARRATIVE of the proceedings of Admiral
B---g. and of his conduct off Mahon, on the 20th
of May. By an officer of the squadron.   London,W.Owen[1756]
   24p. 20cm. (with An appeal to the people[
1756)

NN 0023001   ICN IU CtY

Z942.07
Z
1757:4
   A narrative of the proceedings of Admiral
B---g, and of his conduct off Mahon, on the
20th of May. By an officer of the squadron.
London, W. Owen [1757]
   24 p. 20cm. [Hanoverian tracts. ser.3.
1757:4]
   1.Byng, John, 1704-1757. 2. Port Mahon.
Siege, 1756.

NN 0023002   MnU

---

ar W
8298
   A narrative of the proceedings of
Admiral B---G, and of his conduct off
Mahon, on the 20th of May. By an officer
of the squadron. 2d ed. London, Printed
for W. Owen. [175-?]
   24 p. 21cm.
   No. 3 in vol. lettered: Byng--
Collection of tracts.

NN 0023003   NIC

Narrative of the proceedings of Edward Gray,
Samuel Bradford, and Robert Taylor, previous and
subsequent to the bankruptcy of C. & A. Conrad &
Co. Phila., 1813.

NN 0023004   PPL

   A narrative of the proceedings of His Majesty's fleet in
the Mediterranean, and the combined fleets of France and
Spain, from the year 1741, to March 1744. Including an accurate account of the late fight near Toulon, and the causes of our
miscarriage: the lines of battle on both sides, plans of Villa
Franca, Naples, Hieres bay, and Toulon: the French admiral's
journal in French and English, from the time he left Toulon,
until he anchored with his fleet in Alicant road. Likewise some
signals greatly wanted on the late occasion: and a list of cap-

tains and lieutenants made by Admiral Mathews in the Mediterranean, their different removes, &c. With many useful observations. By a sea-officer ... London, J. Millan, 1744.
   viii, 112 p. fold. maps, tables (part fold.) 21ᶜᵐ.
   With this is bound: Mathews, Thomas. Original letters and papers,
between Adm——l M——ws, and V. Adm——l L——k. London, 1744.
   1. Gt. Brit.—History, Naval—18th cent. 2. Austrian succession, War
of, 1740-1748.   I. A sea-officer.

   Library of Congress   DA87.N3
                          43-44745

       CtY MnU PU
NN 0023006   DLC UU MH NIC NcD DN MdAN MH MiU-C

   A NARRATIVE of the proceedings of His
Majesty's fleet in the Mediterranean, and
the combined fleets of France and Spain,
from 1741 to March 1744. By a sea-officer.
2d ed., London, J. Millan, 1744.
   112 p.
   Maps and table.

NN 0023007   MH DN ICN IU

   A narrative of the proceedings of His Majesty's fleet, under the command of Earl Howe, from
the second of May to the second of June
M.DCC.XCIV. London: Printed by T. Burton and
Cᵒ. Gate-street,Lincoln's-inn fields. Sold at Mr.
de Poggi's Exhibition room,Nᵒ.91,New Bond-street
[etc.,etc., 1796.
   2 p.ℓ.,84,85*-88*,83-91,[1],[93*]-100*,[5],
106-111,103-118 p.   front.,2 fold.plans.   28.5cm
   Folded plates engraved by A.C.de Poggi.
   "Errata" mounted on verso of t.-p.

NN 0023008   MiU-C PBL DN

F
4563
.883
v.1
   A NARRATIVE of the proceedings of Lord Geo.
Gordon, and the persons assembled under the denomination of the Protestant association, from
their last meeting at Coach-makers hall, to the
final commitment of His Lordship to the tower.
Giving a faithful detail of the riots that in-
sued... To which is added the petition presented
to His Majesty, in behalf of the Roman Catholics,
and an abstract of the late act of Parliament
passed in their favour.   London,Wallis,1780.
   66p.
   Binder's title: Tracts on the riots of
1780. vol.I.

NN 0023009   ICN ViU NcD CtY MiU CLU MiD-B

Narrative of the proceedings of Pedrarias Davila
in the provinces of Tierra Firme or Castilla del
Oro...
   see under   Andagoya, Pascual de, d. 1548.

A narrative of the proceedings of Sir Edmond
Androsse...
   see under   Stoughton, William, 1632-1701.

A narrative of the proceedings of the black people,
during the late awful calamity in Philadelphia
   see under   [Jones, Absalom]

A narrative of the proceedings of the British
fleet, commanded by Admiral Sir John Jervis
K.B.
       see under   [Bethune, John Drinkwater,
1762-1844]

A narrative of the proceedings of the commissioner
of suffering loyalists in the case of Captain Philip
Hay
   see under   Hay, Philip.

A narrative of the proceedings of the commissioners
appointed by O. Cromwell ...
   see under   [Bushnell, Walter] 1609-1667.

328.3358
N234
   Narrative of the proceedings of the contested
election for the county of Down, in the
year 1830; with the squibs, placards, songs,
etc., etc., also with the publications of
the Down elector and notes and illustrations by the same. Published by an eye-
witness. Belfast, Pr. by Henry Lanktree,
1830.
   80p. front. plate. 22cm.
   Incomplete: 80p.

NN 0023016   LNHT

   A narrative of the proceedings of the court at St. Margaret's
Hill, Southwark, in the county of Surry, against the rebel prisoners now under sentence of death for high treason. With an
account of the Lord Chief Justice Lee's speech, before he pass'd
judgment on them, and the sentence of death at large. To which
are added, the particulars of the several trials of Francis Townley, colonel of the Manchester regiment, and governor of the city
of Carlisle; Counsellor David Morgan; the captains, Thomas
Deacon, George Fletcher, Andrew Blood, and the rest of the

officers of the Manchester regiment.   London: Printed for the
proprietor [1746]   xii, 52 p.   17cm.

   1. Treason—Trials—Gt. Br.   2. Jacobite rebellion, 1745-1746.
I. Towneley, Francis, 1709-1746,   defendant. II. Morgan, Thomas
David, d. 1746, defendant.
N. Y. P. L.   July 9, 1941

NN 0023018   NN

   A narrative of the proceedings of the fleet: giving an account
of what hath passed since their arrivall at Graves End, between
...members of Parliament and Vice-admiral Lawson, and the
commissioners sent from White-hall appointed to treat on the behalf of the army. Sent in a letter of the 22. instant, from the fleet
riding at anchor at Graves-End. London, Printed by John
Streater, 1659.   8 p. 18cm. (4°.)

   Caption-title, p. 3: A letter of the 22. of December, 1659...
   Signed: M. H.

407055B. 1. Great Britain—Hist.—   PROUDFIT COLLECTION.
N. Y. P. L.   1649-1660—Pamphlets. 2. Navy,   Commonwealth and protectorate,
                                      British—Hist., 1655-1659. I. H., M.
                                            November 24, 1947

NN 0023019   NN MB CtY MH

A narrative of the proceedings of the French at
Newfoundland...
   see under   A letter from a West-India
merchant to a gentleman at Tunbridge.

   Narrative of the proceedings of the judicatories of the Reformed church in North America
relative to the Reverend David Graham...   Pittsburgh, S. Engles and co., 1811.
   198 p., 1 L.
   In letters to a friend.

NN 0023021   PMA MWA

   Narrative of the proceedings of the judicatories of
the Reformed church in North America relative to
the Rev. David Graham. [In letters to a friend]
   Pittsburgh, S. Engles & co., 1811.
   200 p.   8°.   [Miscellaneous pamphlets,
v. 381, v. 638; v. 924:1]

NN 0023022   DLC NcD

---

*EC75
A100
782n
   A narrative of the proceedings of the Lords
of Ireland. In the years 1703 and 1719, in
consequence of the attempts made at those
periods by the Lords of Great Britain, to
enforce their authority in this kingdom ... By
a friend to the constitutional rights of both
kingdoms.
   Dublin:Printed and sold by all the book-
sellers.M,DCC,LXXXII.
   8°. 52p. 20cm.
   A second edition has title: Rights of
Ireland.

NN 0023023   MH ICN CtY

941.57
N167
   A narrative of the proceedings of
the lords of Ireland in the years 1703
and 1719, in consequence of the attempts
made at those periods by the lords of
Great Britain, to enforce their authority in this kingdom ... By a friend to
the constitutional rights of both kingdoms. 2d ed. Dublin, 1782.
   52p.
   At head of title: Rights of Ireland.
Page 51 mutilated.

NN 0023025   IU

VOLUME 405

A narrative of the proceedings of the lower House
of convocation, relating to prorogations and
adjournments...
    see under   Aldrich, Henry, 1647-1710.

A narrative of the proceedings of the merchants,
traders, & others of the city of London,
concerned in the American commerce; and
the proceedings of Parliament thereupon
    see under   London. Merchants con-
cerned in the American commerce.

Narrative of the proceedings of the monthly meeting
of New York
    see under   [Hopper, Isaac Tatem]

A narrative of the proceedings of the
northern armies, under the present conduct of
Generall Monck, and the Lord Lambert ...
London,G.Horton,1659.

Bz21
5
10
        7p. 19cm. [Binder's title: Scotish history.
    v.10]
        Signed H.G.

NN   0023029   CtY

A narrative of the proceedings of the people of South
Carolina, in the year 1719
    see under   [Yonge, Francis]

A narrative of the proceedings of the Pro-
*EC7   testant dissenters of the three denominations;
A100   relating to the repeals of the corporation and
734n3   test acts, from the year 1731, to the present
        time. Addressed to the dissenters.
        London:Printed for J.Roberts,near the Oxford-
        Arms in Warwick-lane.MDCCXXXIV. 〈Price six-
        pence.〉
        8°. 43p. 20cm.

NN   0023031   MH CBPac NNUT CtY

Narrative of the proceedings of the Provincial
Council at Patna in the suit of Behader Beg
    see under   Behader, Beg.

A narrative of the proceedings of the religious
Society of the people called Quakers, in
Philadelphia, against John Evans
    see under   Evans, John, of Philadelphia.

A narrative of the proceedings of those ministers of the
county of Hampshire ...

    This work is available in this library in the Readex Micro-
print edition of Early American Imprints published by the
American Antiquarian Society.
    This collection is arranged according to the numbers in
Charles Evans' American Bibliography.

NN   0023034   DLC

A NARRATIVE of the proceedings of those
ministers of the county of Hampshire,&c., that
have disapproved of the measures taken in order to the settlement of Robert Breck, in the
first church in Springfield. With a defence
of their conduct. Written by themselves.
Boston,1736.
    ff.(2). pp.93.
    Copy A has the autographs "Sam ll Mather
hiss booke 1736" and "S.Mather his Book A.
D., 1753".
        13459.10.2*   US 134 59.10

NN   0023035   MH RPJCB InU CtHT-W MWA MBAt

A narrative of the proceedings of those ministers
of the county of Hampshire, &c. that had
disapproved of the late measures taken in
order to the settlement of Mr. Robert Breck,
in the pastoral office in the first Church in
Springfield. With a defence of their conduct
in that affair. Written by themselves...
Boston, 1736.
2p.ℓ.,93,[1]p. 18¼cm.

    Microfilm   (negative)

NN   0023036   OrU

A narrative of the proceedings relating to the bill ...
intituled an act for granting relief to pastors ...
    see under   Skinner, John, bp. of Aberdeen.

A narrative of the proceedings relative to the
discovery of the longitude at sea ...
    see under   [Harrison, John] clock maker.

A narrative of the proceedings, speeches, toasts, sentiments, and
other particulars connected with the dinner to T. W. Coke...upon
his retirement from the representation of the county. To which
is prefixed a memoir. Dedicated by permission to his Royal
Highness to Duke of Sussex...   Norwich: J. Dawson, 1833.
55 p. 8°.

1. Coke, Thomas William, 1st earl of
N. Y. P. L.   Leicester of Holkham, 1752-1842.
                                                       April 20, 1926

NN   0023039   NN CtY

A narrative of the proceedings upon the complaint
against Governor Melvill. London, Printed for T. Becket
and P. A. De Hondt, 1770.
    xlviii, 182 p. 21 cm.

1. Melville, Robert, 1723-1809. 2. West Indies, British—Pol. & govt.

F2131.N3   50-45052

NN   0023040   DLC NN CtY RPJCB MH MH-L

A narrative of the process against Madam
Brinvilliers; and of her condemnation and
execution
    see under   Brinvilliers, Marie Madeleine
(d'Aubray) Gobelin, marquise de, 1630-1676,
defendant.

A NARRATIVE of the progress of his most
Christian Majesties armes against the Dutch,
with the names of the several places taken.
Likewise a letter from his said Majesty to
the Queen of France, giving an account of his
passing the Rhine at Tolhuys: with a list of
the French nobility killed and wounded in that
action.
[London] In the Savoy:Printed by Tho.Newcomb.
1672. 11p. 27½cm.,in case 32cm.

NN   0023042   TxU CtY OU NIC N MnU CSmH ICN MH

A narrative of the pursuit of English refugees in
Germany under Queen Mary
    see under   [Brett, John] fl. 1556.

A NARRATIVE of the rebellion in the Canadas,
by A resident Canadian... Lond., Ackermann,
1838. 38 p. front. (fold. map). 21 cm.

NN   0023044   CaNSWA

Narrative of the recent voyage of Captain Ross to the
Arctic regions ...
    see under   [Williams, Edwin] 1797-1854,
comp.

A narrative of the reception of Philip, king of Castile
in England in 1506.

    (In Gairdner, James, ed. Historia regis Henrici septimi. London,
1858. 25ᶜᵐ. p. 282-303)
    Gt. Brit. Public record office. Rerum britannicarum medii ævi scriptores.
no. 10.

    1. Felipe I, king of Castile, 1478-1506.

    Library of Congress   DA25.B5 no. 10   1-6727

NN   0023046   DLC NcD OU

A narrative of the remarkable affair between Mr. Simonds,
the Polish Jew merchant, and Mr. James Ashley, merchant of
Bread-street, London. Wherein the robbery at Cranford-
bridge, the several trials at the Old-Bailey, King's-bench, and
Chelmsford, are particularly set forth. And an impartial enquiry made into the truth of the several facts, sworn on both
sides; and the whole of this intricate business set in a clear
and unprejudiced light. Interspersed with remarks on the
probability of facts not yet discovered, and the nature and
consequence of perjury. London, S. Clay, 1752.
    1 p. l., v-viii, 3-50 p. 18¼ᶜᵐ.

    The trials referred to are: the trial at the Old Bailey, at the Sep-
tember sessions, 1751, of Joseph Goddard for robbery of Henry Simons;
the trial of Simons in the Court of King's bench for perjury; and
the trial of Simons at the Chelmsford assizes, July 12, 1752, at the
prosecution of James Ashley, for assault, in putting three ducats into
Ashley's pocket with intent to charge him with robbery.
    Imperfect: p. 39-40 mutilated; p. 47-48 wanting.
    1. Ashley, James.   I. Simons, Henry, defendant. II. Goddard,
Joseph, fl. 1751, defendant. III. London. Central criminal court. IV.
Gt. Brit. Court of King's bench. V. Gt. Brit. Courts of oyer and
terminer and general gaol delivery.

                                                       31-34576

NN   0023048   DLC

Narrative of the remarkable escape and unparalleled sufferings of the gallant Captain Wilson.
To which is added the fantastical and amusing
treatise on Whimsical wives. Readers, read and
reflect.
Frederick Town, Maryland, Printed by G. S.
Keatinge, at the Office of the Republican and
general advertiser, 1814.
    144 p.   12.5 cm.

NN   0023049   MdHi

Narrative of the remarkable restoration of
Martha Howel
    see under   Howel, Martha.

A narrative of the rescue of the S. S. Danmark
by the S. S. Missouri. London, 1891.

NN   0023051   DN

A narrative of the revival of religion in the County
of Oneida ...
    see under   Presbyterian Church in the U.S.A.
Presbyteries. Oneida.

A narrative of the revival of religion, within the
bounds of the Presbytery of Albany, in the
year 1820
    see under   [McAuley, Thomas]

VOLUME 405

Narrative of the revolt and insurrection of the
  French inhabitants in the island of Grenada
    see under   [Turnbull, Gordon]

A narrative of the Rise and progress of the disputes
  subsisting between the patentees of Covent-
  Garden Theatre
    see under   [Harris, Thomas] d. 1820.

Narrative of the rise, progress and conclusion
  of the process against Mr. Maclagan ...
    see under   MacLagan, Mr.

A narrative of the royal fishing of Great Britain and
  Ireland with busses for pickled herrings and
  barrel-cod ...
    see under   [Smith, Simon]

A narrative of the Russian military expedition to
  Khiva ...
    see under   Perovskiĭ, Vasiliĭ Alekseevich,
graf.

A narrative of the seizure & confinement of
  Ann Brookhouse
    see under   Brookhouse, Ann.

Narrative of the services of the Maryland battalion in Brooklyn, on the 27th of Aug. 1776.
n.p.n.d.   8p.   Caption title.

NN 0023060   NBLiHi NN NSm

The | NARRATIVE | Of The | Sessions, | February 26, 167⅘. | With |
A Particular Account of the Tryal | of the Notorious | Coiners, | That
received Sentence for | Treason: | And | All other Malefactors Con-
demned, Burnt in the Hand, | or to be Whipt, and their respective
Crimes. | Licensed, February 27, 167⅘. |
London: Printed for L.C.1678-9. | 17.5x13.5cm. 8p.

NN 0023061   NNUT-Mc NjR

A | NARRATIVE | Of The | Sessions: | Or, | An Account of the
Notorious | High-Way-Men | And Others; | Lately Tryed and Con-
demned | At the Old-Bayly. | With all their Particular Crimes, man-
ner | of Takeing, and Behaviour since, | to the time of their Execution. |
With Allowance. |
Printed for P. Brooksby,1673. | 17.3x13.7cm. 7,(1)p. Cut on last page.

NN 0023062   NNUT-Mc

A narrative of the settlement and sale of Ireland
    see under   French, Nicholas, bp. of Fens
1604-1678.

Narrative of the shipwreck and unparalleled
  sufferings of Mrs. Sarah Allen
    see under   Allen, Sarah.

Narrative of the shipwreck of the Antelope East-India pacquet, on
the Pelew islands, situated on the western part of the Pacific
ocean; in August, 1783.   Perth: Printed by R. Morison, junr.
for R. Morison and Son; and sold by C. Elliot, T. Kay and Co.,
London, 1788.   1 p.l., viii, 268 p.   front., pl. 12°.

In original gray paper wrappers.

533543A. 1. Pelew islands—Descr.   and trav. 2. Shipwrecks, 1783.
3. Antelope (packet).
N. Y. P. L.   October 28, 1931

NN 0023065   NN NcU CtY CU InU CaBVaU DNA

A **narrative** of the siege and surrender of Maestricht, to the
most Christian king. On the 30th of June. [London, Printed
by T. Newcomb, 1673.
12 p. 30ᶜᵐ.

1. Maestricht—Siege, 1673.

                                                  44-24338
Library of Congress   D278.M3N3

NN 0023066   DLC CtY PU MB

A Narrative of the singular sufferings of John
Fillamore [sic] and others, on board the noted
pirate vessel commanded by Captain Phillips, ...
Bennington, Printed by Haswell & Smead, 1804.
23 p.   12 mo.

NN 0023067   MWA

A **narrative** of the singular sufferings of John Fillmore
and others, on board the noted pirate vessel commanded by
Captain Phillips: with an account of their daring enter-
prise, and happy escape [from the ?] tyranny of that desper-
ate crew, by capturing their vessel ... Aurora [N. Y.]
Printed by A. M. Clapp, 1837.
[13] p. 24½ cm. (*In* Buffalo historical society. Publications.
Buffalo, 1907. v. 10, p. 27–39)
Millard Fillmore papers, v. 1, p. 27-39.
Facsim. t.-p.

"The substance of the following relation was verbally delivered to
the editor, by the Hon. Increase Moseley, esq. who was intimately
acquainted with Mr. John Fillmore ... Mr. Fillmore ... being dead,
the editor has chosen to deliver the story as though it was written by
the sufferer himself ..."—Advt. in Johnstown edition of 1809.
First edition, Suffield, Conn., 1802, published under title: "A narration of the captivity of John Fillmore ..." *cf.* Gilman, Bibl. of Vermont, 1897, p. 98.

1. Fillmore, John, 1702-1777. 2. Phillips, John, d. 1724. 3. Pirates.

F129.B8B88 vol. 10   8—10421

NN 0023069   DLC NBuG NBu CU MiU-C MWA

A Narrative of the situation and treatment of the
English, arrested by order of the French
government ... with the transactions on the
arrival of the first Consul at Boulogne, Calais,
and Dunkirk ... [London, J.D. Dewick, 179-]
1 p.l., 38 p. 8°.
T.-p. mutilated.

NN 0023070   NN

Narrative of the State of Religion, presented at the meeting of
the General Convention at Royalton, September, 1833. [*n. p.*
1833.] 8vo, pp. 16.
                                          CONGREG.LIB. 99170

NN 0023071   MBC

A **narrative** of the success of the voyage of the Right Honourable Heneage Finch, earl of Winchelsea ... His Majestjes ambas-
sadour extraordinary to the High & Mighty Prince Sultan Mamet
Han, emperour of Turkey, from Smyrna to Constantinople; his
arrival there, the manner of his entertainment and audience with
the grand vizier and grand seignior.   London, Printed by I. R.,
1661.   1 p.l., 11 p., 1 l. 20cm.

Last leaf (blank?) wanting.
With armorial bookplate of Sir Joseph Copley, bart.

289393B. 1. Turkey—Court and cour-   tiers. 2. Great Britain. Legation.
Turkey.
N. Y. P. L.   July 18, 1945

NN 0023072   NN

Narrative of the sufferings and adventures of the
  Brethren Eberhard Gutsleff, Francis Helterhof,
  John Gottlob Fritsche, and David Siegmund
  Krügelstein, who for the Gospel's sake suffered
  a twelve years' imprisonment at Petersburg in
  Russia.   Phil., American Sunday school union,
  1832.
    107 p. T.
Moravians or United Brethren.

NN 0023073   NcU

Narrative of the sufferings and escape of Charles
  Jackson ...
    see under   Jackson, Charles, fl. 1798.

A narrative of the sufferings and
martyrdom of Mrs. Joice Lewis. [n.p.,
Priv.print., 1880?]
[22] p. illus. 20 ᶜᵐ.

1. Lewis, Joice (Curzon) d. 1557.

NN 0023075   NjP

A narrative of the sufferings and relief of a young
  girl [Christian Shaw] Strangely molested by
  evil spirits ...
    see under   [Cullen, Francis Grant, lord]
1658-1726.

A narrative of the sufferings and surprising
  deliverances of William and Elizabeth
  Fleming
    see under   Fleming, William, fl. 1756.

Narrative of the sufferings of Massy Harbison
    see under   Winter, John, ed.

A narrative of the sufferings of Seth Hubbell &
  family ... 1827
    see under   [Hubbell, Seth] 1759-1832.

A narrative of the sufferings of the crew of the Dee...
    see under   [Gibb, David]

Narrative of the sufferings of Thomas Delaune, for
  writing "The plea for the nonconformist"
    see under   De Laune, Thomas, d. 1685.

Narrative of the sufferings of William Moore and
  John Philly in the Inquisition of Hungary.
  Philadelphia, 1832.

NN 0023082   PSC-Hi PHi

A narrative of the suppression by Col. Burr ...
    see under   [Cheetham, James] 1772-1810.

VOLUME 405

Narrative (A) of the surprising work of God in the conversion of souls in Kilsyth, Finnieston, and Cumbernauld, and the revival of religion in Anderston and Paisley; with an account of the remarkable occurrences which took place at the dispensation of the sacrament at Kilsyth, on 22nd September, 1839. *Glasgow : D Maclure,* 1839. 32 pp. 12°.

In : ZWGF p. v. 13.

NN 0023084   NN

NARRATIVE of the Survey, by the British Commission, of the Boundary between the British Possessions in North America and the United States of America, under the Treaty of Washington of the 9th August, 1842. n. t. p.

4°. p.107-169 Map.

NN 0023085   MH-L

Narrative of the surveying voyages of His Majesty's ships Adventure and Beagle, between the years 1826-1836 ...
  see under   [Fitzroy, Robert] 1805-1865, ed.

A narrative of the tortures by the popish bloody inquisition
  see under   Lithgow, William, 1582-1645.

Narrative of the tragical death of Mr. Darius Barber, and his seven children ...
  see under   [Barber, Mrs. Eunice]

A narrative of the transactions, imprisonment, and sufferings, of John Connolly ...
  see under   Connolly, John, 1750?-1813.

A narrative of the transactions in Bengal
  see under   [Salīm Allāh, munshi]

Narrative of transactions in the South Carolina College, during the three last courses
  see under   [Blackburn, George] 1765-1823.

A narrative of the transactions of the British squadrons in the East-Indies, during the late war; comprehending, a particular account of the loss of Madaras, the operations of the squadron under the command of Admiral Griffin, in relation to which he is to be tried by a court-martial, at Chatham, on Monday, December the third; and the siege of Pontichery, by Admiral Boscawers. Together with some account of the countries ... By an officer who serv'd in those squadrons. London, D. Wilson, 1751.

1 p. l., 82 p. 20°.
1. Gt. Brit.—History, Naval—18th cent. 2. India—Hist.—European settlements, 1500-1765.

Library of Congress   DA87.N32   44-17081

NN 0023092   DLC IU CtY MH NN

Narrative of the transactions relative to the capture of the American ship, Olive Branch.
  see under   [Allen, Ira] 1751-1814.

A narrative of the travels and voyages of Bill Davis
  see under   [Taylor, Simon]

A narrative of the travels of John Vandeluer, on the Western continent. Containing an account of the conversion of an Indian chief and his family to Christianity. Being a letter written by him to his uncle in Philadelphia, in the year 1796. Hallowell [Me.] Printed by E. Goodale, 1817.

87 p. 14°°.   5-41099

NN 0023095   DLC CSmH PPRF

A narrative of the treatment Coll. Bayard received ...

This work is available in this library in the Readex Microprint edition of Early American Imprints published by the American Antiquarian Society.
This collection is arranged according to the numbers in Charles Evans' American Bibliography.

NN 0023096   DLC

A narrative of the treatment Coll. Bayard received from the time that sentence was passed against him to the time of his giving that petition which the lieut. governour & council caused to be printed and published in justification of their proceedings against him. New York, March 16, 1702. [New York, 1702] [Boston, 1940]

facsim. [6 p. 38½°°. [Photostat Americana. Second series ... Photostated at the Massachusetts historical society. No. 102]
Caption title.
Printed by William Bradford. cf. Evans, Amer. Bibl., v. 1, p. 161. One of 15 copies from the original in the Public record office, March, 1940.
1. Bayard, Nicholas,   1644?-1707.

Library of Congress   F122.N3 1702 a   41-23128

NN 0023097   DLC MiU-C ViU ViW PHi

Narrative (A) or the treatment experienced by a gentleman during a state of mental derangement: designed to explain the causes and nature of insanity, and to expose the injudicious conduct pursued towards many unfortunate sufferers under that calamity. 27° pp., 1 l. 8°.
London, E. Wilson, 1858.

NN 0023098   DNLM

A narrative of the Tungani insurrection
  see under   [Molloy, E   ]

A narrative of the uncommon sufferings and surprizing deliverance of Briton Hammon ...
  see under   Hammon, Briton, fl. 1760.

NARRATIVE OF THE U. S. EXPEDITION TO THE COREA, 1871. [Shanghai, 1871.] 8 p. 8°.
"Reprinted with additions from the Shanghai Evening courier."

NN 0023101   MSaE

Narrative of the United States' expedition to the river Jordan and the Dead Sea.
  see under   Lynch, William Francis, 1801-1865.

Narrative of the United States exploring Expedition, during the years 1838-42
  see under   Wilkes, Charles, 1798-1877.

A narrative of the very extraordinary adventures and sufferings of Mr. William Wills ...
  see under   Wills, William, surgeon.

Narrative of the visit of George IV to Scotland August 1822; by an eye-witness. Edinburgh, 1822.

NN 0023105   NjP

Narrative of the visit of His Majesty King Charles the Second to Norwich, in the September of the year 1671; as related by Blomefield and Echard, and as detailed in a private unpublished letter ... Yarmouth, 1846.

296 p. pl. 22.5 cm.

NN 0023106   MHi

Narrative of the visit to the American churches by the deputation from the Congregational Union of England and Wales
  see under   Reed, Andrew, 1787-1862.

Narrative of the volcanic eruption, or Graham island, which appeared in the Mediterranean, off Sicily, between Sciacca, and the island of Pantallaria, in the summer of 1831. Malta, Printed at the Govt. press, 1834. 32 p. 16cm.

1. Islands, Volcanic. 2. Islands   —Mediterranean sea. t. 1834.

NN 0023108   NN

Narrative of the voyage of H. M. floating dock "Bermuda," from England to Bermuda. Written in the form of a diary, by One of those on board... London, J. B. Day [1869?]

4 p. l., 85 (1) p., 1 l. 1 map. 8°.

NN 0023109   NN

Narrative of the voyage of H. M. floating dock "Bermuda," from England to Bermuda. Written in the form of a diary, by one of those on board ... London, J. B. Day [1870]

85, [1] p. 4 pl., fold. map. 15°°.   3-20009

NN 0023110   DLC DN KMK

Narrative of the voyage of H. M. S. Samarang...
  see under   Belcher, Sir Edward, 1799-1877.

A narrative of the voyage of the Argonauts in 1880
  see under   Banks, William Mitchell, 1842-1904.

Narrative of the voyages made by the schooners Sutil and Mexicana in the year 1792 to reconnoitre the Strait of Fuca...
  see under   [Espinosa y Tello, José] 1763-1815.

Narrative of the war with China in 1860
  see under   [Wolseley, Garnet J[oseph] Wolseley, viscount] 1833-1913.

VOLUME 405

PR 4334
N377
1790
A NARRATIVE of the whole process respecting some late publications of the Rev. Dr. William M'Gill. With remarks on the late conduct and decision of the Very Reverend the Synod of Glasgow and Ayr in that cause... [n.p.] 1790.
114 p. 22 cm.

On spine: McGill controversy 1790.
1. M'Gill, William. I. Title: McGill contro-   versy.

NN   0023115   CaBVaU

A narrative of the wicked plots carried on by Seignior Gondamore...
see under [Scott, Thomas] 1580?-1626.

---

*EC8
A100
802n
Narrative of the wreck of the Bangalore, Captain Lynch, on a coral bank, in the Indian Sea, April 12th, 1802. To which is added, a narrative of the loss of His Majesty's ship Litchfield, of 50 guns, on the coast of Barbary, 1758.
London: Printed for Champante & Whitrow, Jewry-street, Aldgate, Evans & son, Long-lane; Hughes, Ludgate-street, &c. &c. (Price sixpence.) [1802?]
36p. fold. front. 20cm.

Title vignette.
"Narrative of the loss of His Majesty's ship Litchfield ... November 30, 1758. By Lieutenant [James] Sutherland", with caption title: p.24-36.
Original printed blue wrappers preserved; bound in cloth.

NN   0023118   MH

Narrative of three years residence in Italy, 1819-22
see under   Martin, Selina.

A Narrative of travels on the Amazon and Rio Negro
see under   Wallace, Alfred Russel, 1823-1913.

Narrative of two wonderful cures, wrought in the Monastery of the Visitation, at Georgetown, in the District of Columbia, in the month of January, 1831. Published with the approbation of the most Rev. Archbishop of Baltimore, by James Myers. 24 pp. 8°. *Baltimore, W. A. Francis, 1831.*

NN   0023121   DNLM MdBP CtY

A Narrative of voyages and travels in the Northern and Southern Hemispheres
see under   Delano, Amasa, 1763-1823.

Case
G
681
.612
NARRATIVE of voyages to New South Wales and the East Indies, in 1840, 1841, 1842, and 1843, and to New York and the West Indies, in 1843 and 1844.   London, J. Miland, 1846.
vi, [2], 71p. 18cm.

NN   0023123   ICN

---

x954.14
N167
1764
A narrative of what happened in Bengal, in the year MDCCLX. Wherein is contained an account of the revolution, which took place at that time.   London, Printed for C. Bathurst, 1764.
51p. 21cm.

Bound with A supplement to the Narrative of what happened in Bengal, in the year 1760. London, 1764.

NN   0023124   IU MH CtY InU PHi MnU

Narrative of what has passed relative to the present dispute between England and Spain.
n.p., n.d.

NN   0023125   RPJCB

A narrative of what passed at Killalla...
see under   [Stock, Joseph, Bp. of Waterford and Lismore] 1740-1813.

A narrative of what passed at Bath, upon account of the late earthquake, which happened there on the 18th of March last, in a letter from a gentleman at Bath, to his friend at London... London: Printed for W. Owen, 1750.   1 p.l., iv, 17(1) p. 21cm. (8°.)

Publisher's advertisement, p. [18]

109044B. 1. Earthquakes—Gt. Br.,   1750. I. A gentleman at Bath.
N.Y.P.L.   May 13, 1942

NN   0023127   NN CtY

A narrative of what passed in the Common-hall of the citizens of London ...
see under   [Robins, Benjamin] 1707-1751.

Narrative of William W. Brown, a fugitive slave
see under   Brown, William Wells, 1815-1884.

---

*EC65
A100
667n
A narrative, or Journal of the proceedings of their Excellencies, the Right Honourable the Lord Holles, and the Lord Coventry, appointed by His Majesty of Great Britain to be his ambassadors extraordinary, and plenipotentiaries for the treaty held at Breda, with the ambassadors of the French King, the King of Denmark, and the States general of the United Provinces. By a person of quality, concerned in this ambassy.
[London] In the Savoy, Printed by Tho. Newcomb, and are to be sold   by Robert Pawlet at the Bible in Chancery-   lane, near Serjeants-Inne, 1667.
31p. 19.5cm.

NN   0023130   MH PHC ICN CSmH MoU

---

*EC65
A100
653n2
A narrative, or resumption of the severall proceedings in the Court of the admiralty of England, in order to the ships Sampson, St. George, and St. Salvador. With what hath been sayd and alledged for the releasing of them and their respective ladings: by the captaines of the sayd ships on the one side; and by the Advocate fiscall of this common-wealth on the other. The 24. and 27. of January, 1653. Stilo novo.
London, Printed in the year, 1653.
3p.l., 13p.   18cm.
Unofficial   transcript of suit brought to obtain release of merchants' ships.

NN   0023131   MH

Lmc73
1
The narrative or story of Mr. Jex Jex of Corpus. Done into English verse of various metres, from the original MS. in the old schools of Cambridge, by A.C.D.Barde. Cambridge, Printed by J.Palmer, 1864.
16p. 21½cm.

[I] Barde, A.C.D., pseud.

NN   0023132   CtY

Narrative or the journal of the Duke of Cumberland, Indiaman, Capt. R. Osborn, from the Time she sailed from the Downs, until she was cast away ... Written by one of the Sufferers. London, 1750.
iii, 58 p. 8°. 19 cm.

NN   0023133   CtY

A narrative or, The ordinary of Newgate's account of what passed between him and James Sheppard
see under   [Lorrain, Paul] d. 1719.

Narrative, part II. The trial and defence of Mr. Graham ...
see (in supplement)
Graham, David.
The trial and defence of Mr. Graham ...

...Narrative poems. Sohrab and Rustum, The rime of the ancient mariner, The vision of Sir Launfal. viii, 112p. Boston, New York [etc.] Houghton, Mifflin company, [c1911] (Riverside literature series

NN   0023136   OC1

Narrative poems: Sohrab and Rustum; The rime of the ancient mariner; the vision of Sir Launfal. Boston, Houghton Mifflin co., c1933.

NN   0023137   PPLas

---

*EC65
A100
647n
A narrative presented to the Right Honovrable the Lord major, aldermen, and commons of the city of London, in Common-councell assembled. London, Printed by Richard Cotes, 1647.
11, [1]p. 19cm.

NN   0023138   MH CtY NNUT-Mc CSmH

#PS283
.M6N2
The Narrative problem. v.1-2 (whole no.1-11) Oct.8,1941-Jan./Mar.1943. Minneapolis, Minneapolis Workers' Workshop.
2 v. in 1. 28cm. irregular.

No more published?

NN   0023139   MnHi

Narrative remarks [etc.] on the New England historical and genealogical society, 1874
see under   Drake, Samuel Gardner, 1798-1875.

VOLUME 405

Narrative respecting the various bills which have been framed for regulating the law of bankruptcy in Scotland; with observations connected with that subject; and a supplement, in which is considered the bill now pending in Parliament. With an appendix... Edinburgh: G. Ramsay and Co., 1813.   vi, 58, 15 p.   8°.

In: XAH p. v. 52, no. 1.

1. Bankruptcy.—Jurisprudence, Gt. Br.:   Scotland.
N. Y. P. L.   October 21, 1915.

NN   0023141   NN CtY PU

Narrative sketches of the conquest of the Mysore, effected by the British troops and their allies, in the capture of Seringapatam, and the death of Tippoo Sultaun; May 4, 1799. With notes, descriptive and explanatory. Collected from authentic materials. The 2d ed. London, Printed by W. Justins, and sold by West and Hughes [etc.], 1800.
1v, [5]-134, 2 p. front. 20ᶜᵐ.
These sketches were written from material collected to assist the design and execution of a historical painting, Storming of the Seringapatam by R. K. Porter. cf. p. [II]
"Descriptive sketch of the Storming of Seringapatam, as exhibited in the great historical picture": 2 p. at end.
1. Mysore—Hist.   2. India—Hist.—British occupation,
1765-   3. Seringapa-   tam. 4. Tipū Sulṭān, Fatḥ 'Alī,
nawab of Mysore, 1753-   1799.
Library of Congress   DS475.3.N3 1800   43-43787

NN   0023142   DLC NIC MH CU

BJ43   **Narrative** sketches of the conquest of the
525   Mysore, effected by the British troops and their allies, in the capture of Seringapatam, and the death of Tippoo Sultaun, May 4, 1799. With notes descriptive and explanatory. Collected from authentic materials. 6th ed. Newcastle, Printed for the proprietor, by J. Mitchell, 1805.
1p. l., [7]-132p. front. 15½cm.
These sketches were written from material collected to assist the design and execution of a historical painting, Storming of the Seringapatam by R.K.Porter.
"Descriptive sketch of the storming of Seringapatam, as exhibited in the great historical picture, painted by Robert Ker Porter": p.[129]-132.

NN   0023144   CtY

NARRATIVE sketches of the conquest of the Mysore, effected by the British troops and their allies in the capture of Seringapatam, and the death of Tippoo Sultaun, May 4, 1799; with notes descriptive and explanatory, collected from authentic materials. 7th ed., Worcester, printed by J. Tymbs, 1806.
nar. 12°. Front., folded colored plate.
Imperfect: pp.131-132.

NN   0023145   MH NSyU

A **narrative**, together with letters presented by
Captaine Taylor ... 1648
see under   Taylor,   , Captain.

Narrative. Visit of the Governor-General and the Countess of Dufferin to the Six Nation
Indians. August 25, 1874
see under   [Gilkison, J   T   ]

McALPIN
1654
F853   A narrative wherein is faithfully set forth
the sufferings of John Canne, Wentworth Day
[and others] ... called (as their news book saith) fift monarchy men. That is, how eight of them were taken in Coleman street, moneth second (called Aprill) day first, 1658. ... Also, of the arraignment of Wentworth Day and John Clarke, at the sessions in the Old Bailey ... Published by a friend to the prisoners; and the good old cause, they suffered for ... London,1658.
16p. 19cm. [Bound with Freedom of religious worship. [London,1654]

NN   0023148   NNUT CSmH NPV

Beinecke Library
Zd
112   A **narrative**; wherein is faithfully set forth the sufferings of John Canne, Wentworth Day, John Clarke, [and others] ... called (as their News book saith) fift monarchy men ... Also, of the arraignment of Wentworth Day and John Clarke, at the sessions in Old Bailey ... Published by a friend to the prisoners, and the good old cause they suffered for ... London, 1658.
16 p. 18 cm. [Bound with Edwards, Thomas.
Gangraena ... Lon-   don, 1646]

NN   0023149   CtY

Narratives and confessions of Lucretia P. Cannon; who was tried, convicted, and sentenced to be hung at Georgetown, Del., with two of her accomplices; containing an account of some of the most horrible and shocking murders ever committed by one of the female sex. 24 pp., 2 pl. 8°. *New York*, 1841.

NN   0023150   DNLM

[**Narratives**, field orders, annexes, administrative orders, operations reports, summaries of intelligence, etc., for the Fifth Corps and its components, the 1st, 2d, 42d, 80th, and 89th Divisions and the 6th U. S. Marines, for the period Oct. 16–Nov. 11, 1918. v. p., 1918?]
1 v. 17 maps (in pocket) 36 cm.
Binder's title: Monograph, 5th Corps.

1. European War, 1914-1918 — Regimental histories — United States—V Corps.   I. United States. Army. V Corps.

D570.27 5th.N3   72-225736

NN   0023151   DLC

Narratives for the young
see under   [Malan, César Henri Abraham]
1787-

Narratives from the Holy Scripture in Kalispel
see
[Giorda, Joseph] 1823-1882.
Smiimii lu tel kaimintis kolinzuten.

Narratives illustrating the usefulness of religious tracts
see under   American tract society.

Narratives of a late expedition against the Indians
see under   Brackenridge, Hugh Henry,
1748-1816.

Narratives of adventure and shipwreck
see under   The sea. Narratives...

Narratives of calamitous and interesting shipwrecks, &c., with authentic particulars of the sufferings of the crews ... Philadelphia: Published by Mathew Carey. Printed by A. Small. 1810.
1v, 92 p. front. 17ᶜᵐ.

1. Shipwrecks.
                                                        38-25266
Library of Congress   G525.N3
                    [2]   910.4

NN   0023157   DLC MH

Narratives of colored Americans
see under   Mott, Abigail (Field), 1766-1851, comp.

Narratives of early Virginia, 1606-1625
see under   Tyler, Lyon Gardiner,
1853-1935, ed.

Narratives of Eliza Cunningham ...
see under   American tract society.

BV3265   **Narratives** of five Christian Hindoos, one of whom was a
.N23   Brahmun, another of the writer cast, and three were Shoodrus. The narrative demonstrating that the real conversion of all the casts is practicable. Comp. by the Serampore missionaries.   Boston ed., with additions. Boston, J. Loring [*1828]
111 p. 15ᶜᵐ.
"Compiled ... under the eye of the Rev. William Ward ... from Tracts published at the Mission station."—Pref.

1. Missions—India.

NN   0023161   ICU

'F1063   **Narratives** of John Pritchard, Pierre
.N3   Chrysologue Pambrun, and Frederick Damien Heurter, respecting the aggressions of the North-West Company, against the Earl of Selkirk's settlement upon Red River. London, J. Murray, 1819.
91 p.   21cm.

Photocopy.

NN   0023162   MnHi

Narratives of Little Henry and his bearer
see under   [Sherwood, Mary Martha (Butt)]
1775-1851.

Narratives of reformations, in Canton and
Norfolk, Con.
see under   [Hallock, Jeremiah] 1758-1826.

Narratives of Revivals of Religion in Scotland,
Ireland, & Wales
see under   Glasgow Revival Tract Society.

BV
3770
.N3   **Narratives of revivals of religion in Scotland, Ireland, Wales, and America.** Philadelphia, Presbyterian Board of Publication [n.d.]
282 p. 16 cm.

1. Revivals—History. 2. Revivals—
Scotland. 3. Revivals—Ireland.
4. Revivals—Wales. 5. Revivals—
United States.

NN   0023166   MSohG

Narratives of Saskatoon, 1882-1912
see under   Historical Association of
Saskatoon.

VOLUME 405

G 02 .613

NARRATIVES of shipwrecks… London, Rivington, 1824. 123p.

Contents.-A narrative of the loss of the Lady Hobart packet on an island of ice, June 28, 1803 By Captain Fellowes.-A narrative of the loss of the honourable East India company's ship Cabalva, which was wrecked on the morning of July 7, 1818, upon the Cargados Garragos reef, in the Indian ocean. By C.W.Francken.-A narrative of the loss of the Centaur man-of-war, 1782. By Captain Inglefield.-A narrative of the loss of the Litchfield man-of-war, on the coast of Africa, November 29, 1758. By Lieutenant Sutherland.

NN 0023168   ICN CtY

---

*6267.103

Narratives of shipwrecks. Loss of the Lady Hobart packet; of the Hon. East India Company's ship Cabalva; and of the Centaur and Litchfield men-of-war.
— London. Society for Promoting Christian Knowledge. 1824. 122 pp. Sm. 8°.

G1973 — Society for Promoting Christian Knowledge, London. — Shipwrecks.

NN 0023169   MB

Narratives of South America
     see under   Empson, Charles.

Narratives of the career of Hernando de Soto in the conquest of Florida, as told by a knight of Elvas, and in a relation by Luys Hernandez de Biedma factor of the expedition. Tr. by Buckingham Smith. New York, 1866.

xxviii, 324 p. front. (port.) pl., map, illus. 26½°. (*Half-title:* Bradford club series. no. 5)

125 copies printed. Club copy. no. a.

"This book is a translation of the original Portuguese Relaçam verdadeira dos trabalhos q ho gouernador dô Fernando de souto e certos fidalgos portugueses passarom no descobrimēto da prouincia da Frolida. Agora novamēte feita per hũ fidalgo Deluas, printed at Evora in the year 1557."

CONTENTS.—The Bradford club.—Life of Soto.—Proem.—True relation of the vicissitudes that attended the governor Don Hernando de Soto and some nobles of Portugal in the discovery of the province of Florida, now just given by a fidalgo of Elvas.—Annotations made by the translator to matters in the Relaçam.—Relation of the conquest of Florida, presented by Luys Hernandez de Biedma in the year 1544 to the king of Spain in council. Tr. from the original document.—Appendix. Translations of letters, official documents and royal decrees.—Index.

1. Soto, Hernando de, ca. 1500-1542. I. Smith, Buckingham, 1810-1871, tr.

2—14279

Library of Congress   E125.S7R59

MB TxU MiU-C NjP OFH OCl OCH FSaHi
NN 0023172   DLC FMU OC GU OOxM PPULC PPL NcD FU

E125 S7R3 1904

Narratives of the career of Hernando de Soto in the conquest of Florida as told by a Knight of Elvas and in a relation by Luys Hernandez de Biedma, factor of the expedition. Translated by Buckingham Smith together with an account of De Soto's expedition based on the diary of Rodrigo Ranjel, his private secretary. Translated from Oviedo's Historia General y Natural de las Indias. Edited with an introd. by Edward Gaylord Bourne. New York, A.S. Barnes, 1904.

2 v. port., map. 18cm. (The trail makers)

Smith's earlier translation (1866) was of the original Portuguese Relaçam verdadeira dos trabalhos.

1. Soto, Hernando de, 1500?-1542. I. Smith, Buckingham, 1810-1871, tr. II. Bourne, Edward Gaylord, 1869-1908, ed.

NN 0023174   GU NN MH

Narratives of the career of Hernando de Soto in the conquest of Florida, as told by a Knight of Elvas and in a relation by Luys Hernandez de Biedma… Tr. by Buckingham Smith. Together with an account of de Soto's expedition, based on the diary of Rodrigo Ranjel… Tr. from Oviedo's Historia general y natural de las Indias. Ed., with an introduction, by E.G. Bourne. v. 1-2 London, D. Nutt, 1905.
   2 v. map., port. 12°. (Great American explorers)

NN 0023175   NN

Narratives of the career of Hernando de Soto in the conquest of Florida, as told by a Knight of Elvas and in a relation by Luys Hernandez de Biedma, factor of the expedition. Translated by Buckingham Smith, together with an account of De Soto's expedition based on the diary of Rodrigo Ranjel, his private secretary, translated from Oviedo's Historia general y natural de las Indias. Edited with an introduction, by Edward Gaylord Bourne…

New York: Allerton Book Co., 1922.   2 v. front. (port.) 12°. (American explorers.)

This book is a translation of the original Portuguese Relaçam verdadeira dos trabalhos q ho gouernador dô Fernando de souto e certos fidalgos portugueses passarom no descobrimēto da prouincia da Frolida. Agora novamēte feita per hū fidalgo Deluas, printed at Evora in the year 1557.

83039A-83040A. 1. Soto, Hernando de, ca. 1500-42. 2. Florida. — History. 3. Bourne, Edward Gaylord, 1860- 1908, editor. 4. Biedma, Luis Her- nandez de, 16th century. 5. Smith, Thomas Buckingham, 1810-71, trans- lator. 6. Fernández de Oviedo y Valdés Gonizalo. 1478-1557. 7. Elvas, Gentleman of. 8. Series. N. Y. P. L.

May 31, 1923.

NN 0023177   NN GU

BV4515 .C6 1850

Narratives of The cottager's wife [by a clergyman of the Church of England] Col. James Gardiner [by Philip Doddridge] The lost son; and The Highland maid [from Rev. T. McKenzie Fraser] New York, American Tract Society [185-?]
114 p. 16 cm.
1. Gardiner, James, 1699-1745. I. Title. II. Title: The cottager's wife. III. Doddridge, Philip, 1702-1751. The life of Col. James Gar- diner. IV. Title: The lost son. V. Fraser, T. McKenzie. The Highland maid. VI. Title: The High land maid.

NN 0023178   ViU

Narratives of the days of the Reformation
     see under   Nichols, John Gaugh, 1806-1873.

Narratives of the discovery of America
     see under   Lawrence, Arnold Walter, ed.

Narratives of the late riotous proceedings against the Liberty of the press, in Cincinnati. With remarks and historical notices, relating to emancipation. Cincinnati, 1836.
   48 p. O.

NN 0023181   RHi

Narratives of The life and conversion of the dairy-man, The old ploughman
     see under   American tract society.

DS446.5 N3

Narratives of the mutiny in the N-W provinces. [n.p., 1857-1858?] 4 v. 32cm.

Binder's title.

1. India - Politics and government, 1765-1947.

NN 0023183   GU

Narratives of The shepherd of Salisbury plain …
     see under   [More, Hannah], 1745-1833.

Narratives of The spoiled child
     see under   American tract society.

Narratives of the sufferings of Lewis and Milton Clarke …
     see under   Clark, Lewis Garrard, 1812-1897.

Narratives of the sufferings of Richard Sellar a member; of the Religious Society of Friends
     see under   Sellar, Richard.

Narratives of the Swedish nurse-maid, the Swiss peasant, Mary Eliza, the rescued brand, the bayman's wife, and Muckle Kate. New York, American tract society [185-?]

122 p. illus. 16 cm.
"The Swedish nurse-maid, by Mrs. Rev. Dr. E. Henderson."

NN 0023188   MH

Narratives of the trans-Mississippi frontier.

Princeton: Princeton Univ. Press, 1932.   19–22½cm. v.   facsims., illus., maps.

A series of reprints of Western Americana.
Editor : 1932–   C. L. Cannon.

1. No subject. I. Cannon, Carl Leslie, 1888– , editor.
N. Y. P. L.   October 21, 1932

NN 0023189   NN OO

Narratives of trapping life; stories of the trail and trap-line in the Adirondacks, Maryland marshes, Canadian wilderness, Arizona and Florida; and of the professional trapper's methods of catching fur-bearing animals in these localities. New York, The Peltries publishing company, inc. [1922]
95 p. illus. 15½cm.

1. Trapping.

Library of Congress   SK283.N3   23-9441

NN 0023190   DLC MH

Narratives of two families exposed to the great plague of London, A. D. 1665; with conversations on religious preparations for pestilence. Republished, with notes and observations, by John Scott … London, Printed for R. B. Seeley and W. Burnside, 1832.
xii, 214 p. 19½cm.

An abridged reprint of a work published anonymously in London, 1722, under title: Due preparation for the plague, as well for soul as body.

1. Plague—London. I. Scott, John, 1777-1834, ed.

7-29525†

Library of Congress   RC178.G7L77

NN 0023191   DLC

VOLUME 405

Narratives of two families exposed to the great plague of London A. D. 1665; with conversations on religious preparation for pestilence, by John Scott ... 2d ed. London, R. B. Seeley and W. Burnside, 1832.

₍iii₎-xii, 178 p. 16ᶜᵐ.

First published in 1722 under title: Due preparations for the plague.

3-28771

NN   0023192   DLC TxU

Narratives of two families exposed to the great plague of London, A. D. 1665: with conversations on religious preparation for pestilence. Republished, with notes and observations, by John Scott ... 1st American ed. New-York, Swords, Stanford and co., 1832.

xi, ₍13₎-179 p. 16ᶜᵐ.

An abridged reprint of a work published anonymously in London, 1722, under title: Due preparation for the plague, as well for soul as body.

1. Plague—London.   I. Scott, John, 1777-1834, ed.

7-29524†

Library of Congress   RC178.G7L78

NN   0023193   DLC MB

Narratori contemporanei.

₍Torino, G. Einaudi, 19

v. 19½ᶜᵐ.

44-23095

NN   0023194   DLC

NARRATORI moderni italiani.
Venezia, N. Pozza.

NN   0023195   NN

Narratori sovietici ... Traduzioni di Ettore Lo Gatto, Giovanni Bach, Svetlana Caucci Alfieri, Elena Akmentins dall'originale russo. Roma, De Carlo, 1944.

5 p. l., ₍13₎-763 p., 1 l. 24ᶜᵐ.

CONTENTS.—Leonov, Leonid. La fine di un meschino.—Zoscenko, Michail. Una notte terribile.—Nikitin, Nikolaj. La rivolta dei morti.—Erenburg, Ilja. La società per azioni "Mercure de Russie."—Sejfullina, Lidija. Giorni feriali.—Romanov, Pantelejmon. Piccole luci.—Bulgakov, Michail. La guardia bianca.—Ilf, Ilja Arnoldovic, e Petrov, E. P. Il vitellino d'oro.—Karalina, E. Scelta.—Lavrenev, Boris. Il mondo nel piccolo vetro.

1. Russian fiction—Translations into Italian. 2. Italian fiction—Translations from Russian. 3. Short stories, Russian.   I. Lo Gatto, Ettore, 1890-   tr.

45-10955

Library of Congress   PG3289.I 7N3

₍2₎   891.73082

NN   0023196   DLC

Narratori stranieri tradotti. Manduria, Lacaita

no.1 (1947): Drosinis, Giorgio. Amarillide

NN   0023197   MH OO

Narraway, Athos Maxwell. Aerial surveys of Canada.

Canada. *Forestry Branch.*
Aircraft in forestry; containing Air operations for forest fire protection, by H. I. Stevenson, district forest inspector, Forest Service, Dept. of the Interior, and Aerial surveys of Canada, by A. M. Narraway, chief aerial surveys engineer, Dept. of the Interior. Papers presented to the Third British Empire forestry conference, held in Australia and New Zealand, August to October, 1928. Ottawa, F. A. Acland, printer to the King, 1928.

SD387
.C35
1928

Narraway, Athos Maxwell.

McKinley, Ashley Chadbourne.
Applied aerial photography, by Ashley C. McKinley ... with a chapter on Oblique aerial surveys ⟨Canada⟩ by A. M. Narraway ... New York, J. Wiley & sons, inc.; London, Chapman & Hall, limited, 1929.

Narraway, Athos Maxwell.   8029.218
Oblique aerial surveys.
(*In* McKinley, Captain Ashley C. Applied aerial photography . . . Pp. 299-330. Illus. Plates. Diagrams. Maps. New York. 1929.)

N9933 — Surveying. Aerial.

NN   0023200   MB

QD305   Narraway, Frank Whitlock, 1874-
.H8N23   Ueber die reaction zwischen bibromiden und alkoholischem kali, insbesondere ueber das decylen und seine derivate.
Heidelberg, 1899.
36p.
Inaug. diss. Heidelberg.

NN   0023201   DLC PU PPC

NARRAWAY, J. R. The war in the East: the principals in the strife; and its probable issue. A lecture ... Char., Haszard, 1854. 40 p. 17 cm.

NN   0023202   CaNSWA

Narraway, James Ephraim, 1857-   071.14
                                    2   v.3
... A new American *Cybele*, by J. E. Narraway and Percy E. Raymond.
(*In* Pittsburgh. Carnegie Institute. Museum. Annals. ₍Pittsburgh₎ 1906. 25ᶜᵐ. vol. III, p. 599-604. 1 illus.)

NN   0023203   ICJ

Narrayana Menon, Thekkey Kottiejath
    see
Menon, Thekkey Kottiejath Narrayana.

NARRAZIONE completa della feste romane del di s. 9, 1846. Roma, [1846?]

24º.

NN   0023205   MH

NARRAZIONE critico-storica della reliquia preziosissima del santissimo prepuzio di N.S.Gesu' Cristo che si venera nella chiesa di Calcata. Ristampata ed accresciuta. Roma, presso V.Poggioli,1802.

pp.37.   Arc 1033.12.6

NN   0023206   MH

945.21
N167   Narrazione dei maravigliosi successi accaduti durante la memorabile lotta sostenuta dai milanesi nei cinque giorni di marzo 1848. Milano, Stamperia nazionale di M. Carrara ₍1848₎
32p.

1. Milan--Hist.

NN   0023207   IU

Narrazione del torneo fatto nella corte di Belvedere in Vaticano
    see under   [Cirni, Antonfrancesco]

Narrazione dell' Accaduto al Signor Francesco Zambeccari ed al di lui Compagno Pasquale Andreoli. Per quanto asseriscono varj Testimonj di vista ai quali si può prestare intiera fede concordando intieramente tutti nelle loro deposizioni, e da quanto raccolsero dalla voce medesima dell'Andreoli.   In Venezia, Per il Casali [1812]
iv p.   8 vo.   Black boards. Red label.

NN   0023209   CSmH

Narrazione dell' Aereobatico Esperimento tentato il 30 Agosto 1825 ...
    see under   Orlandi, Francesco.

Narrazione della battaglia di Castelfidardo e dell' assedio d'Ancona, scritta da un Romano. Italia, 1862.
pp. viii, 271. Map.
Translated from the French: Récit de la bataille de Castel-Fidardo et du siége d'Ancone par un Romain.

Castelfidardo, Italy|Ancon.₋₍₎ ₍Title:°Récit

NN   0023211   MH CU

Narrazione della battaglia di Mentana
    see under   [Leroux,   ]

Narrazione della morte di Giacomo e Beatrice Cenci, e di Lucrezia Patronia Cenci
    see also   Contemporaneous narrative of the trial and execution of the Cenci.

NARRAZIONE della solennità celebrata in Torino il dì al maggio, 1815, nella quale la Santità di Pio VII. espose la SS. Sindone. Torino, D.Pane, [1815?]

pp.14. Plate.

NN   0023214   MH

NARRAZIONE della venuta in Orvieto di S.Santita Papa Pio IX. Orvieto, presso Sperandio Pompei,1857.

pp.52.   Ital 3930.6

NN   0023215   MH

Narrazione delle geste di ... Pio II, rappresentate... dal Pinturicchio. Siena, 1771.

NN   0023216   NjP

VOLUME 405

Narrazione delle solenni reali feste fatte celebrare in Napoli da Sua Maestà il re delle Due Sicilie Carlo infante di Spagna, duca di Parma, Piacenza &c. &c. per la nascita del suo primogenito, Filippo, real principe delle Due Sicilie. Napoli, 1749.

20 p. front., xv fold. pl. (incl. plans) 58½ᶜᵐ.

Head-piece; initial.
The plates are engraved by various artists from the drawings of Vincenzo Rè.

1. Carlos III, king of Spain, 1716-1788. 2. Naples (Kingdom)—Hist. I. Rè, Vincenzo, illus.

12-17884

Library of Congress   NE1717.N2

NN   0023217   DLC NjP TxU CaOTP NNC

Narrazione delle solenni reali feste fatte celebrare in Napoli da Sua Maestà il re delle Due Sicilie Carlo infante di Spagna, duca di Parma, Piacenza &c. &c. per la nascita del suo primogenito Filippo real principe delle Due Sicilie. Napoli, 1749.

16 p. 15 fold. plates (incl. plans) 66 cm.

The plates are engraved by Giuseppi Vasi and others after designs by Vincenzo Rè.

1. Carlos III, King of Spain, 1716-1788. 2. Naples (Kingdom)—Hist. I. Rè, Vincenzo, illus.

NE1717.N2 1749a   Rosenwald Coll.   67-47796

NN   0023218   DLC NN CtY

Narrazione dettagliata e vera della battaglia data il 23 marzo 1849 sotto le mura di Novara; coll'aggiunta di due carte dove sono delineati tutti i punti strategici sui quali le due armate combatterono. [Bologna?] Societa tipografica Bolognese [1849?]

8 p. fold. map. 16.5 cm.

NN   0023219   CtY

271.811
J613n
   Narrazione di alcuni miracoli operati da Dio in varie diocesi del Belgio ad intercessione del B. Berchmans della Compagnia di Gesù. Roma, B. Morini, 1866.
   15 p. 20½ cm.

1. John Berchmans, Saint, 1599-1621, S.J.

NN   0023220   MoSU

NARRAZIONE storica della prodigiosa apparizione di Maria SSma Immacolata e istantanea conversione alla fede cattolica dell' ebreo M.A. Ratisbonne avvenuta in Roma il 20 gen. 1842. Roma,1892.

NN   0023221   MH

B
C6591n
   Narrazione storica, e componimenti, fatti in occasione, e in divota rimembranza del secondo miracolo, seguìto nell'insigne monistero di San Gio: Vangelista di Mantova, e nella persona di donna Bianca Maria Cocastella Montiglia, monaca professa nel medesimo, ad intercessione della Beatiss. Vergine immaculatamente concetta, che in una statua, fatta venire dalla città di Lucca, divotamente in detto monistero si conserva, e si venera, solennemente pubblicato nella chiesa del predetto monistero alli 21.novembre 1718, festa

della presentazione di Maria Vergine immaculatamente concetta. Mantova, Stamperia di S. Benedetto, Per A. Pazzoni [1735]
   220p. illus. 16cm.

1. Cocastella Montiglia, Bianca Maria.

NN   0023223   IU CtY

945.08
N167
   Narrazione veridica di quanto han sofferto i cento trentauno patrioti cisalpini deportati prima a Sebenico, indi a Petervaradino, con i loro nomi, cognomi, eta, patria, e professione. Si aggiungo due discorsi, recitati in occasione del loro ritorno, dal cittadino Domenico Bresciani, e dal cittadino Gio: Battista Angeli ... [Salò, Dalla stamperia Righetti, l'anno 9. repubblicano] [1800?]
   43p.

Half-title.

NN   0023224   IU

Narrazioni istoriche delle più considerevoli inondazioni dell' Arno e notizie scientifiche sul medesimo raccolte ed insieme riunite, da G. A. Firenze, Dalla tipografia Piatti, 1845.
vi, [2], 231 p. 24cm.

1. Arno River and Valley. I. A., G.

NN   0023225   NNC CtY

Narré veritable de tovt ce qvi c'est passé en la reception & ambrgade de monsieur le mareschal de Cadenet, avec la serenissime roy de la Grande Bretagne. A Paris, Chez Nicolas Rovsset, en l'Isle du Palais, vis à vis les Augustins. M. DC. XXI. [1621]
   14 p. 17 cm.
   Signatures: A-B⁴ (B⁴ blank)

1. Cadenet, Le mareschal de. 2. James I, king of Great Britain, 1566-1625.

NN   0023226   CSmH ICN

MS
q367
N16v
   Narren Club, Cincinnati.
     Versammlungen. 1872.
     1v.(unpaged) 31cm.
     MS. written in German script.
     Reports of meetings of a Narren Club, organized Jan.6, 1872, as part of the Cincinnati Orpheus. Includes a copy of the first issue (Jan.11, 1874) of the Cincinnati Kladderadatsch, humorisrisch-satirisches Wochenblatt, and a broadside: 1874! Neu-jahrs-Gruss der Träger an die Leser des Cincinnati Courier.

NN   0023227   IU

Narren, Gaukler und Volksliebblinge
    see under Wesselski, Albert, 1871-1939.

Narrenalmanach. Leipzig, 1848.

NN   0023229   NjP

Zeta
Hᴋ₄
he16
846n
   Narrenalmanach ... 4.Bd.,1846. Leipzig,Philipp Reclam,1846.
   1v. 15cm.

"Pa-tchou-ly" (p.[405]-418) is a satire on Heine's Kaiser von China. - Meyer, p.79.

NN   0023230   CtY

Die narrenbeschwerung
    see under [Murner, Thomas] 1475-1437.

Narrenbuch. 1811
    see under Hagen, Friedrich Heinrich von der, 1780-1856, ed.

HX
271
S52
2
22
   Des "Narrenkönigs" Ende; oder, Sparig's Abschlachtung vor Schweizer richtern. New York, 1885.
   8 p. 21-25cm. (Socialism in Germany; miscellaneous pamphlets, v.2, no.22)

I. Sparig, Bruno

NN   0023233   WU

Das Narrenschiff
    see under [Brant, Sebastian] 1458-1521.

---

*fGC9
R4574
LN168
   Das Narrenschiff, Blätter für fröhliche Kunst. 1.Jahrg., Nr.1-52, 2.Jahrg., Nr.1-13; Jan.1898-März 1899.
   Berlin,Carl Predeek & Co.1898-99.

     65 nos. illus.(part col.) 31cm. weekly.
     Editors: 1.Jahrg., Nr.1-3, Ludwig Abels; Nr. 4-11, Max Osborn; Nr.12-37, Max Sklarek; Nr.38-52, 2.Jahrg., Nr.1-13, Hans Hyan.
     No more published.
     Original parts, as issued, in publisher's binding of half blue morocco.

NN   0023235   MH

D426
.N27
   NARRENSPIEGEL der geschichte; Versailles und seine folgen in der weltkarikatur, zusammengestellt aus dem archiv der National-zeitung,Essen. Essen[etc.] Essener verlagsanstalt,1938.
   viii,312 p. illus. 28½cm.
   "Quellenverzeichnis":p.[305]-312.

1.World politics--Caricatures and cartoons. 2.Caricatures and cartoons.

NN   0023236   ICU InU

Der narrenthurm
    see under [Most, Johann Joseph] 1846-1906.

Narrey, Charles, 1825-1892, tr.

Dürer, Albrecht, 1471-1528.
   Albert Durer à Venise et dans les Pays-Bas; autobiographie, lettres, journal de voyages, papiers divers, tr. de l'allemand avec des notes et une introduction par Charles Narrey; ouvrage orné de 27 gravures sur papier de Chine. Paris, Vᵉ J. Renouard, 1866.

PQ2373
N6A7
   Narrey, Charles, 1825-1892.
   ... Les amours faciles. Paris, Librairie centrale,1866.

     2p.l.,273p.,1l. 18½cm.

     At head of title: Charles Narrey.

NN   0023239   NBuG NjP

NARREY, Charles,1825-1892.
   Le bal du diable. Le petit chaperon rose. Les cheveux du diable. Misère et pauvreté F., 1874.

     Vdcts. 42578.10

NN   0023240   MH PU

VOLUME 405

NARREY, Charles, 1825-1892.
Le capitaine Amadis. Comédie.
Paris. Lévy. 1879. (4), 32 pp. 8°.

NN 0023241 MB

Narrey, Charles, 1825-1892.
Ce que l'on dit pendant une contredanse.
Paris, E. Dentu, 1863. 80, 63 p. illus. 20 cm.
Catalog of the publisher's works, 63p., at end.

1. Ballroom dancing. 2. Wit and humor, French. (TITLE)

NN 0023242 NN

NARREY, Charles, 1825-1892.
Ce que l'on dit pendant une contredranse.
Nouvelle ed., P., 1873.

Front. and wdcts.

NN 0023243 MH

Narrey, Charles, 1825-1892.
Le chevrier
see under Lecocq, Alexandre Charles,
1832-1918.

Narrey, Charles, 1825-1892.
Chez elle! Comédie en un acte, par Ch. Narrey & A. Dreyfus. Paris, Calmann Lévy, 1877.
2 p. l., 31 p. 19ᵐ.

I. Dreyfus, Abraham, 1847-1926, joint author. II. Title.
12—28999
Library of Congress PQ2376.N3C4 1877

NN 0023245 DLC

Narrey, Charles, 1825-1892.
Chez elle! Comédie en un acte, par Ch. Narrey & A. Dreyfus. Paris, Calmann-Lévy, 1877.
31, 36p.
Microcard edition.
Includes catalog of the publisher.

NN 0023246 ICRL OrU

NARREY, Charles, 1825-1892.
Chez elle! Comédie.
Paris. Lévy. 1886. (4), 31 pp. 12°.

NN 0023247 MB

Narrey, Charles, 1825-1892.
A cigarette from Java, 1879
see under Meilhac, Henri, 1831-1897.

Narrey, Charles, 1825-1892.
Claudine et Frusquin ...
see under Jacobi, Georges, 1840-1906.

Narrey, Charles, 1825-1892.
Comme elles sont toutes; comedie en un acte, en prose, par Charles Narrey.
3.ed. Paris, Calmann Levy, 1875.
32 p.

Contains also: Tout pour les dames', de Henri Meilhac et Ludovic Halevy, and Le Sphinx, par Octave Feuillet.
Meilhac, Henri & Halevy, Ludovic. a.a. Feuillet, Octave.

NN 0023250 OC1W

Narrey, Charles, 1825-1892.
Comme elles sont toutes; comédie en un acte, en prose, par Charles Narrey. Nouv. éd. Paris, Calmann Lévy, 1876.
3 p. l., [3]-32 p. 19ᵐᵐ.

I. Title.
12-29426
Library of Congress PQ2376.N3C7 1876

NN 0023251 DLC NN MB

Micro-card Narrey, Charles, 1825-1892.
57-11 Comme elles sont toutes. Comédie en un acte
ser.2 en prose. Nouv. éd. Paris, Calmann Lévy,
no.904 1890. [Louisville, Ky., Falls City Press, 1959]
1 card. [Three centuries of French drama. ser.2: 17th, 18th and 19th centuries, no.904]

Microcard edition.
Collation of original: 32 p.

NN 0023252 AU NNC OrU ICRL

Narrey, Charles, 1825-1892.
Dans un coucou. Comédie-vaudeville en un acte...
[Paris, M. Lévy Frères, 1855.
39 p. 12°.
By Charles Narrey and H. Lemonier.

NN 0023253 NN CtY

NARREY, Charles, 1825-1892.
Les derniers jeunes gens. P., 1868.

Contents:- Le nid de loriots- Le but de ma vie. Le notaire en partie double.- Les solutions.- La dame au chapeau bleu.- Un moyen dangereux.

NN 0023254 MH PU

Narrey, Charles, 1825-1892.
L'éducation d'Achille. Par. Lévy, 1885.

NN 0023255 PU

PQ1222 Narrey, Charles, 1825-1892.
C6 En bonne fortune, comédie en un acte, en
v.161 prose. [Paris? 1847?]
30 p. (In Collection of French plays and librettos [v.161])

Caption title.

NN 0023256 CU NN CtW

Narrey, Charles, 1825-1892.
En bonne fortune, comédie en un acte, en prose, par Charles Narrey. Paris, Michel Lévy [1847]
2 p. l., 30 p. 18 cm.
Binder's title: Pièces de théâtre.
"Représentée pour la première fois, à Paris, sur le Théâtre royal de l'Odéon (second Théâtre Français) le 28 novembre 1847."

NN 0023257 CtY

Narrey, Charles, 1825-1892, joint author.
La femme à la broche...
see under Anicet-Bourgeois, Auguste, 1806-1871.

Narrey, Charles, 1825-1892.
Feue Brigitte. Vaudeville en un acte.
Paris, M. Lévy Frères, 1858.
31 p. 12°.
By Charles Narrey and Hippolyte Lemonier.

NN 0023259 NN CtY

Narrey, Charles, 1825-1892.
Hilda; opéra ...
see under Millet, Albert, 1863-1891.

Narrey, Charles, 1825-1892.
Ho! le vert! Bouffonnerie en un acte ...
(*In* Théâtre de campagne. Paris, 1877- 18ᵐᵐ. 5. sér., p. [1]-52)

I. Title.
CA 13-1401 Unrev'd
Library of Congress PQ1237.I 5T5 vol. 5

NN 0023261 DLC MdBP

Narrey, Charles, 1825-1892.
Ho! Le vert! Bouffonnerie en un acte.
(In Théâtre de campagne. Paris, 1877-
5. sér., 52p.)
Microcard edition.

NN 0023262 ICRL OrU

Narrey, Charles, 1825-1892. *4695-50-5
Ho! le vert! Bouffonnerie en un acte.
(In Théâtre de campagne. 5e série. 6e édition. Pp. 1-52. Paris, 1881.)

NN 0023263 MB

Narrey, Charles, 1825-1892.
Hurrah for Paris! A comedietta in one act.
New York, Happy hours co. [1879]
1 p. l., 19 p. 12°. [The acting drama, no. 118]

NN 0023264 DLC

Narrey, Charles, 1825-1892.
Laure est une chimère; vaudeville en un acte.
Paris, 1861.
35 p. 12°. [In Bibl. dram., t. 218]
By Charles Narrey and Hippolyte Lemonier.

NN 0023265 CtY

NARREY, Charles, 1825-1892.
Les marionnettes de Justin. Comédie.
Paris. Lévy. 1873. (4), 57 pp. 12°.

NN 0023266 MB PU

Narrey, Charles, 1825-1892.
Les notables de l'endroit, comédie en trois actes, en prose ... [Paris, Lacour, 1847?]
52 p. 12°.

NN 0023267 NN CtY CtW CU MB

VOLUME 405

[Narrey, Charles] 1825–1892.
Le notaire en partie double. [New York,
C. Lassalle, 1867]
p. 116–123. 4°. (Semaine littéraire. v. 167,
no. 4)

NN 0023268   NN

Narrey, Charles, 1825–1892.
O mon Adélaïde! Comédie en un acte ...
(*In* Théâtre de campagne. Paris, 1877- 18ᶜᵐ. 3. sér., p. [193]–239)

1. Title.

CA 13–1394 Unrev'd

Library of Congress   PQ1237.I 5TS vol. 3

NN 0023269   DLC

Narrey, Charles, 1825–1892.
O mon Adélaïde! Comédie en un acte.

(In Théâtre de campagne. Paris, 1877-
3. sér., p.[193]–239)

Microcard edition.

NN 0023270   ICRL OrU

NARREY, Charles, 1825–1892.
Pas de zèle! Comédie.
Paris. Lévy. 1889. (4), 45 pp. 12°.

NN 0023271   MB

841   Narrey, Charles, 1825–1892.
N168p   Les polkeuses, poème étique sur les
célébrités de la polka, par Nick Polkmall
[pseud.] Portraits et jambes d'après
nature par H. Druard. Paris, P. Masgana,
1844.
68 [3] p. illus.

NN 0023272   MiD

NARREY, Charles, 1825–1892.
Le quatrième larron [To which is appended
"Un voyage d'agrément"]. P., 1861.

NN 0023273   MH MB PU

PQ2376   Narrey, Charles, 1825–1892.
.N24S61   Sophronisba...Oh! A comedy in one act by
1901   Charles Narrey, tr. by members of the Bellevue
Atkinson dramatic club of Newport. Boston, W.H.Baker
Coll   & co., 1901.
33p. 18½ᶜᵐ. (On cover: Baker's edition of
plays)

NN 0023274   ICU PU NN IU RPB MH OU

NARREY, Charles, 1825–1892.
Le temple du célibat. Scènes de la vie de garçon.
Paris. Lévy. 1870. (4), 32 pp. 12°.

NN 0023275   MB

Narrey, Charles, 1825–1892.
Voyage autour du dictionnaire. Paris,
Clamann Lévy, 1892.
246 p.

1. French language–Dict. I. Title.

NN 0023276   DAU PU MH

Narrey, Charles, 1825–1892.
Zamore et Giroflée. Vaudeville en un acte.
Paris, M. Lévy frères, 1855.
35 p. 12°.
By Charles Narrey and Eugène Bercioux.

NN 0023277   CtY NN

Narrien, John, 1782–1860.
Analytical geometry: with the properties of conic sections, and an appendix, constituting a tract on descriptive
geometry. For the use of the Royal military college. By
John Narrien ... London, Printed for Longman, Brown,
Green, and Longmans, 1846.
xxiv, 202 p. diagr. 22ᶜᵐ. (Sandhurst. Royal military college. College
text books, v. 4)

1. Geometry, Analytic. 2. Geometry, Descriptive. 3. Conic sections.

3–24365

Library of Congress   QA551.N23

NN 0023278   DLC NWM MdBP NIC

Narrien, John, 1782–1860.
Elements of geometry: consisting of the first
four, and the sixth, books of Euclid, chiefly from
the text of Dr. Robert Simson; with the principal
theorems in proportion, and a course of practical
geometry on the ground. Also, four tracts relating to circles, planes, and solids; with one on
spherical geometry. For the use of the Royal military college. By John Narrien ... London, Printed for Longman, Brown, Green, and Longmans, 1842.
xii, 276 p. diagrs. 22ᶜᵐ. [Sandhurst. Royal military colleg   e. College text books. v.
2] 1 Euclid's ele   ments. I. Simson, Robert,
1687–1768. The   elements of Euclid. II.
Narrien, John,   1782–1860. III. Ser.

NN 0023279   ViU NWM

Narrien, John, 1782–1860.
Elements of geometry; consisting of the four
first, and the sixth books of Euclid, chiefly from
the text of Dr. Robert Simson; with the principal
theorems in proportion, and a course of practical
geometry on the ground. Also four tracts relating
to circles, planes, and solids; with one on spherical
geometry ... 2d ed.   London, Longman, Brown,
Green, and Longmans, 1849.
xi, 269 p.   diagr.   22 cm.
I. Simson, Robert, 1687–1768.

NN 0023280   OrCS

Narrien, John, 1782–1860.
Elements of geometry; consisting of the four first, and
the sixth books of Euclid, chiefly from the text of Dr.
Robert Simson; with the principal theorems in proportion, and a course of practical geometry on the ground.
Also four tracts relating to circles, planes, and solids;
with one on spherical geometry ... By John Narrien ...
3d ed. London, Longman, Brown, Green, and Longmans, 1850.
xi, 269 p. diagr. 22ᶜᵐ. (Sandhurst. Royal military college. College
text books. v. 2)
Subject entries: Euclid's elements.

8–19807†

Library of Congress, no.   QA451.N23.

NN 0023281   DLC PU

Narrien, John, 1782–1860.
An historical account of the origin and
progress of astronomy. With plates illustrating, chiefly, the ancient systems. London,
Baldwin and Cradock, 1833.
xiv, 520 p. plates. 23cm.

1. Astronomy – History.

NN 0023282   NNC MB CU CSt ViU PSC MdBP MiU WaU CtY

Narrien, John, 1782–1860.
An historical account of the origin and progress of
astronomy. With plates. By John Narrien ... London,
J. & D. A. Darling, 1850.
xiv p., 1 l., 520 p. diagrs. on v fold. pl. 23ᶜᵐ.

1. Astronomy—Hist.

5—7723

Library of Congress   QB15.N2

NN 0023283   DLC NIC OU PU

Narrien, John, 1782–1860.
Practical astronomy and geodesy: including the pro-
jections of the sphere and spherical trigonometry. For
the use of the Royal military college. By John Narrien
... London, Printed for Longman, Brown, Green and
Longmans, 1845.
xxviii, 427, [1] p. illus., diagrs. 22ᶜᵐ.

1. Astronomy, Spherical and practical. 2. Geodesy. 3. Map projection.

6—20036

Library of Congress   QB145.N2

NN 0023284   DLC ViU GU CtY DSI CU PU DN NWM

Narrigan, Daniel.
Pomology: a treatise on the culture of fruit and fruit
trees. Giving explanations how to apply certain chemicals and minerals to fruit trees to insure their health and
perfect bearing qualities. Founded on fifteen years of
observation and experiments. By Daniel Narrigan.
Columbus, Ohio state journal book and job office, 1865.
7 p. 21½ᶜᵐ.

1. Fruit-culture. I. Title.

CA 11–3268 Unrev'd

Library of Congress   SB355.N23

NN 0023285   DLC

Narro, Domingo Silva
see
Silva Narro, Domingo.

Narro, Esther, 1904– tr.

Hurlbut, Jesse Lyman, 1843–1930.
La historia de la iglesia cristiana por Jesse Lyman Hurlbut
... Nueva ed. rev. Con el prefacio por Daniel A. Poling ...
San Antonio, Tex., Casa evangelica de publicaciones [1940]

Narro, Froylán Mier
see   Mier Narro, Froylán.

Narro, Manuel, d. 1776.
Adicion al Compendio del arte de canto llano. Su autor
el r. p. f. Pedro Villasagra ... La escribia don Manuel Narro
... Valencia, Impr. de la viuda de J. de Orga, 1766.
12 p. 21ᶜᵐ. [With Villasagra, Pedro de. Arte, y compendio del canto
llano. Valencia, 1765]

1. Chant (Plain, Gregorian, etc.)

8–37428 Revised

Library of Congress   MT860.A2V6

NN 0023289   DLC

VOLUME 405

Narro, Manuel Acuña
see
Acuña, Manuel, 1849-1873.

Narro García, Ignacio.
Acto administrativo; algunos problemas que sugiere su
estudio. México, 1951.
70 p. 22 cm.
Tesis—Universidad Nacional Autónoma de México.
Bibliografía: p. 67-68.

1. Administrative law. I. Title.

53-21113

NN 0023291 DLC TxU NNC

Narro García, Ignacio.
Manifiesto que hace ante la exma. corte
suprema de justicia el ciudadano Ingacio Garcia,
como Hermano y como Fiscal de la Cofradía de
Nuestra Señora del Rosario de Peruanas de
esta Capital, en la causa que sigie contra
el ex-Mayordomo D. Jose Morales...
Lima Aranda 1862

6p.
In, Miscelanens, V.23

NN 0023292 NcD

W 4   NARRO GONZALEZ, José.
M61   Hipertensión porta; su tratamiento
1953   actual. México, 1953.
          87 p.
          Tesis - Univ. de México.
          1. Blood pressure - High - Treatment
          2. Portal vein

NN 0023293 DNLM

Narrod, Stuart Allan, 1925-
2-ketogluconic acid degradation by *Pseudomonas fluores-
cens;* a new mechanism of pyruvic acid formation. Ann
Arbor, University Microfilms ₍1955₎
  ₍University Microfilms, Ann Arbor, Mich.₎ Publication no. 13,534₎
  Microfilm copy (positive) of typescript.
  Collation of the original: vi, 71 l. diagrs., tables.
  Thesis—University of Illinois.
  Abstracted in Dissertation abstracts, v. 15 (1955) no. 11, p. 1981.
  Vita.
  Bibliography: leaves 65-70.
  1. Pseudomonas fluorescens. 2. Gluconic acid. 3. Pyruvic acid.
  Microfilm AC-1 no. 13,534   Mic 55-759

  Illinois. Univ. Library
  for Library of Congress   ₍a59b₁₎†

NN 0023294 IU DLC

Narrodon, Bartolomeo.
Du chocolate; dialogue entre un medecin un
indien, & un bourgeois, imprime à Seville l'an
1618. Tourné a present de l'espagnol & accomodé
à la francoise. In Colmenero De Ledesma,
Antonio, Du chocolate, 1643.

NN 0023295 MH-A HU

DU   Narrogin, Western Australia. Chamber of
380   Commerce.
N28   Narrogin, the garden city of the west;
1936   historical review of Narrogin and districts'
HRC   progress over the past 40 years. ₍Narrogin?,
GRA   1936?₎
          1v. (unpaged) illus. 28cm.

          Cover title.

          1. Narrogin, Western Australia - History.

NN 0023296 TxU

Narrogin Observer v.1-
  Narrogin, W.A., 1905-
    v. illus. 43cm.

  1. Australia - Period.

NN 0023297 TxU

Narron central railroad. Traffic dept.

Local freight tariff on classes and commodities between Narron central railroad stations
local freight tariff no.1... Raleigh, 1918.

NN 0023298 NcU

Narros, Gabriel, 1928-
Quiromancia y quirosofía; ensayo sobre un sector muy antiguo
y muy moderno de la psicología experimental. ₍Bilbao, 1953?₎
47 p. illus. port. 18cm. (Ediciones de conferencias y
ensayos. ₍no.₎ 68)

1. Palmistry. I. Series.

NN 0023299 NN

The narrow & wide gauges considered; also, effects of
competition and government supervision ... London,
E. Wilson, 1845.
36 p. 21ᶜᵐ.

1. Railroads—Gages. 2. Railroads—Gt. Brit.—Early works to 1850.
3. Railroads and state—Gt. Brit. 4. ₍Railroads—Competition₎
                                              A 19-868
Title from Bureau of   Railway Economics. Printed by L. C.

NN 0023300 DBRE MH-BA CtY IU

A narrow escape.
see under ₍Cudlip, Annie Hall (Thomas)₎
1838-1918.

Narrow fabric company, Reading, Pa.

Partners; a history of the development of the **Wyomissing**
industries. Reading, Pa., The Wyomissing industries ₍1936₎

TS1300   **Narrow Fabric Company, Reading, Pa.**
.Y3
         The Yarn carrier. v. 1-23, no. 6; Apr. 1931-Sept. 1953.
         ₍Wyomissing, Pa.₎

Narrow gauge railway materials ... including
complete industrial railway equipments ... of
the world. 1903.
At head of title: No.77.

NN 0023304 NN

Narrow waters
see under ₍Lieck, Albert Henry₎

Law   "Narrow waters," Author of.

       Alice in Police Court land, with some legal fictions and
other diversions, by the author of "Narrow waters." **London**
₍etc.₎ W. Hodge & company, ltd., 1936.

The narrow way, and The last ivdgement,
deliuered in two sermons
see under Bury, George, fl. 1597-1607.

XF3   The narrow way. Being a complete manual of
N234   devotion for the young. With a guide to con-
1878   firmation and communion. New York, Pott, Young,
        and co.₍1878₎
          2p.ℓ.,₍iii₎-iv,174p. 14x11cm.

NN 0023308 NNUT

The narrow way; being a complete manual
of devotion with a guide to confirmation
and holy communication. New ed. xv, 176p.
London, J. Whitaker & sons, [1883-84]

NN 0023309 OC1

The Narrow way, or, political maxims, and
considerations; respecting the present state of
affairs; tending to dissipate humourous fears
and jealousies, on all sides; perswasive of unity,
and moderation; and not unworthy the cognizance
(perhaps) of an house of commons ... London,
Printed for James Vade, at the Cock and Sugar-
Loaf near St. Dunstan's Church in Fleet-Street,
1681.
  3 p. l., 61 p Sm 4 to. (A, 3 leaves, ₍last,
  prob. blank, lacking) B, 3 leaves, B repeated,
  -H in 4s)

Bound with: ₍Kennett, W. Bishop of
Peterborough₎ A letter from a student in Oxford...

NN 0023311 CSmH

Narrows bridge-McChord field celebration.
Tacoma, Wash.
    Official opening Tacoma Narrows bridge
and McChord field June 30-July 4, 1940.
Tacoma,Johnson-Cox co., 1940. 36 p. illus.

NN 0023312 WaT

Pam   The Narrows tribune. no. 4 - 19;
74-   Dec. 29, 1949 - April 11, 1950.
334   Rock Springs, Wis.
          16 no. illus. weekly

          Ceased publication.

          1. Rock Springs, Wis.

NN 0023313 WHi

BR   Narsai, 413 (ca.)-503.
65   Die Geschichte Josefs von Mar Narses, nach
N23   einer syrischen Handschrift der Königl. Bib-
1889   liothek in Berlin hrsg., übersetzt und kri-
        tisch bearb. von Victor Grabowski. 1. Teil.
        Berlin, Druck von H. Itzkowski, 1889.
          23, 15 p. 21cm.

          Inaug.-Diss.--Leipzig.
          No more published?

          1. Creation   --Early works to 1800.
        I. Grabowski,   Victor, 1863-

NN 0023314 NIC OCH MH

Narsai, 413(ca.)-503.
Narsai; Homiliae et carmina, primo ed. cura et
studio Alphonsi Mingana. 2v. in 1. Mausilii,
Typis Fratrum praedicatorum, 1905.

Syriac text.

NN 0023315 OC1 DCU-H PPPD PU PPPCPh ICU CtY

VOLUME 405

Narsai, 413 (ca.)-503.

PJ5621
.B4
Bedjan, Paul, 1838–1920, *ed.*
... Liber superiorum, seu Historia monastica auctore Thoma, episcopo margensi. Liber fundatorum monasteriorum in regno Persarum et Arabum. Homiliæ Mar-Narsetis in Joseph. Documenta patrum de quibusdam veræ fidei dogmatibus. Edidit Paulus Bedjan ... Parisiis; Lipsiæ, O. Harrassowitz, 1901.

Narsai, 413 (*ca.*)-503.
The liturgical homilies of Narsai, translated into English with an introduction by Dom R. H. Connolly ... with an appendix by Edmund Bishop. Cambridge ₍Eng.₎ The University press, 1909.
lxxvi, 176 p. 22½ᵐ. (*Added t.-p.:* Texts and studies; contributions to Biblical and patristic literature, ed. by J. A. Robinson. vol. VIII, no. 1)
Contents.—An exposition of the mysteries.—On baptism.—On the mysteries of the church and on baptism.—On the church and on the priesthood.—Appendix: Observations on the liturgy of Narsai.

1. Nestorian church. Liturgy and ritual.   I. Connolly, Richard Hugh, 1873–   tr. II. Bishop, Edmund, 1846–1917.

                                                      25–12306 Revised
Library of Congress   BR45.T43   vol. 8, no. 1

    PPPL OC1 OO OCU NN ICU MB MH
NN   0023317   DLC NcD OKeG KyWAT MoU CtY-D PPPD PU

NARSAI, ca. 413-503.
Premier poème de Narsai sur le baptême (Memra XXI) ₍par₎ P. Brouwers. Beyrouth, Impr. catholique, 1265. [177]-207 p. 26cm. (Université Saint-Joseph, Beirut, Syria. Mélanges. t. 41, fasc. 3)

Text in French.
Bibliographical footnotes.

1. Syriac literature--Homilies   I. Brouwers, P., ed. and tr.
II. Brouwers, P.

NN   0023318   NN

Narsai, 413 (ca.)-503.
Näf, Heinrich, 1878–
Syrische Josef-gedichte, mit uebersetzung des gedichts von Narsai und proben aus Balai und Jaqob von Sarug ... Zürich, Buchdruckerei A. Schwarzenbach, 1923.

Narsai, 413(ca.)-503.
Syrische Wechsellieder von Narses. Ein Beitrag zur altchristlichen syrischen Hymnologie, nach einer Handschrift der Königlichen Bibliothek in Berlin. Hrsg., übers., und bearb. von Franz Feldmann ... Leipzig, O. Harrassowitz, 1896.
24 cm.
In Syriac and German.
Text in Syriac characters.

NN   0023320   CtY NjP OC1 O NNUT MH PU

PJ5671   Narsai, 413 (ca.)-503.
.N2J8   Das zweite Josephs-Gedicht von Narses. Nach
1901   2 Handschriften der K. Bibliothek zu Berlin.
          Berlin, 1901.
          24, 45 p.
          Max Weyl's dissertation--Giessen.

          1. Joseph, Patriarch.

NN   0023321   ICU MH

---

*FC8
N1685
820d
Narsei, ———— de.
Description d'une machine aérostatique, par le moyen de laquelle on pourra se maintenir dans l'air à la hauteur que l'on voudra, suivre toutes les directions que l'on désirera, et parcourir sept ou huit lieues par heure; par m. de Narsei, de plusieurs sociétés savantes, in-8°., avec figures. Prix: 3 fr. pour les départemens, et 4 fr. pour l'étranger.
Prospectus.
A Caen, De l'imprimerie de P.G. Le Roux. [1820?]

Continued in next column

Continued from preceding column

3, [1]p. 20cm.
Caption title; imprint on p. [4].
"Cette souscription sera fermée le premier février 1821": p. 3.
It seems that this work was never published.

NN   0023323   MH

A3A
792N
4
Narsei,   de
Description d'une machine aerostatique ... Prospectus. [Caen, Impr. de P.G. Leroux, 1821?]
4p. 20cm. [Binder's title: Mélanges sciences, 4]
Caption title.

1. Aerostatics.

NN   0023324   CtY

Narses, *of Nisibis*
see
Narsai, 413 (*ca.*)-503.

Narses, pseud.
Bahn frei für Deutschland! Von Narses.   Leipzig: Wille und Weg-Verlag, 1929.   84 p.   8°.

1. Germany—Politics, 1929.
N. Y. P. L.   April 20, 1931

NN   0023326   NN

Narseus, Saint, *of Lambron*
see Nerses, Saint, Abp. of Tarsus, 1153–1198.

Narsh, J   M.
The Narsh poultry system, by J. M. Narsh ... Big profit in raising chickens; how to get a handsome income from twenty feet square of ground ... ₍Oklahoma City, Okla.₎ J. M. Narsh ₍1910₎
46, ₍18₎ p. illus., pl. 19¼ᶜᵐ. $1.00

1. Poultry.
Library of Congress   SF487.N3   10–30739

NN   0023328   DLC

JOUR
PN
4788
.N29
Narsh, Vernon.
Education for journalism. [New York] Columbia University, 1938.
178 p.

A thesis.

#Journalism--Study and teaching.

NN   0023329   MoU

958.6
N 168.2
al-NARSHAKHĪ, MUHAMMAD IBN JAFAR, d. 959.
Description topographique et historique de Boukhara, suivie de textes relatifs à la Transoxiane, par Mohammed Nerchakhy. Texte persan publié par Charles Schefer.   Paris, E. Leroux, 1892.
290, iv p. 27cm.   (Publications de l'École des langues orientales vivantes. IIIᵉ sér., v. 13)

NN   0023330   PU CU

---

al-Narshakhī, Muḥammad ibn Ja'far, *d.* 959.
The history of Bukhara; translated from a Persian abridgment of the Arabic original by Narshakhī. ₍Edited and translated by₎ Richard N. Frye. Cambridge, Mass., Mediaeval Academy of America, 1954.
xx, 178 p. facsims. 24 cm. (Mediaeval Academy of America. Publication no. 61)

1. Bokhara—Hist.   I. Frye, Richard Nelson, 1920–   ed. and tr. (Series)

DK876.N25   *958.4   958.6   54–8493

    OrSaW CaBVaU ICIU OrPR OrStbM
    PBm OU OC1 TxU NN PSt KEmT AAP NSyU OrPS OCU PP OrU
NN   0023331   DLC CaOTP GU NBC ViU NN DDO PPT PPDrop

---

al-Narshakhī, Muḥammad ibn Ja'far, *d.* 959.
Исторія Бухары. Перевелъ съ персидскаго Н. Лыкошинъ. Подъ ред. В. В. Бартольда. Ташкентъ, Типо-лит. Θ. и Г. бр. Каменскіе, 1897.
123, II p. 24cm.
Errata (2 p.) inserted.

1. Bokhara—Hist.   I. Lykoshin, Nil Sergeevich, tr.   II. Bartol'd, Vasiliĭ Vladimirovich, 1869–1930, ed.
                                Title transliterated: Istoriîa Bukhary.
DK876.N3   52–47215

NN   0023332   DLC

---

al-Narshakhī, Muḥammad ibn Ja'far, *d.* 959.
تاريخ بخارا، تأليف ابو بكر محمد بن جعفر النرشخى. ترجمه ابو نصر احمد بن محمد بن نصر القباوى. تلخيص محمد بن زفر ابن عمر و تصحيح مدرس رضوى. ₍تهران، كتابفروشى سنائى 1320 i. e. 1940 or 41₎
8, 128 p. 22 cm.
In Persian.

1. Bokhara—History.   I. al-Qubâvî, Abû Nasr Ahmad ibn Muhammad ibn Zufar, fl. 1128, tr.   II. Muhammad ibn Zufar, fl. 1178.   III. Mudarris Ragavî, Muhammad Taqî, ed.   IV. Title.
                                Title romanized: Târîkh-i Bukhârâ.
DK876.N2   74–260906

NN   0023333   DLC MH

Narshakhi, Mukhammad
see al-Narshakhī, Muḥammad ibn Ja'far, *d.* 959.

Narsi
SEE
Narsai, 413 (Ca.)-503.

Narsinga
see
Vijayanagar, *India.*

Narsinghgarh, *India* (*State*)
, Administration report of the Narsinghgarh State.
₍Narsinghgarh? etc.₎
Ψ. 33–35 cm. annual.
Report year ends Oct. 31.
Title varies slightly.

1. Narsinghgarh, India (State)—Pol. & govt.
J601.N267R15   61–57016 rev

NN   0023337   DLC

Narsinghgarh, *India* (*State*)
see also
Madhya Bharat, *India.*

VOLUME 405

Narsinghpur, *India (State)*
Administration report.
¡Narsingpur?¡
v. 25 cm. annual.

1. Narsinghpur, India (State)—Pol. & govt.

J601.N27R15   354.54   50–56323 ‡

NN 0023339 DLC

Narsinh Mehta
see
Narasimha Mehetā, 1414–1481.

Narsinha Chintaman Kelkar
see
Kelkar, Narsinha Chintaman, 1872–1947.

Narsius, Joannes
see Naarssen, Johann van, 1580–1637.

Narsius, Johannes
see Naarssen, Johann van, 1580–1637.

Narskiĭ, Igor' Sergeevich.
Мировоззрение Э. Дембовского; из истории польской философии XIX в. Под ред. И. С. Миллера. ¡Москва¡ Изд-во Московского университета, 1954.
289 p. 23 cm.

1. Dembowski, Edward, 1822–1846.
      Title romanized: Mirovozzrenie Ė. Dembovskogo.

DK436.5.D35N3   57–47065 ‡

NN 0023344 DLC

B3305
.M74O5

Narskiĭ, Igor' Sergeevich, joint ed.

Oĭzerman, Teodor Il'ich, *ed.*
Против буржуазных и правосоциалистических фальсификаторов марксизма; сборник сокращенных переводов. Ред. и вступ. статья Т. И. Озермана и И. С. Нарского. Москва, Изд-во иностранной лит-ры, 1952.

Narsky, Igor S
see
Narskiĭ, Igor' Sergeevich.

Narssius, Johannes
see Naarssen, Johann van, 1580–1637.

NARSTUD. Nr. 1-6/7; Apr./Mai, 1924-Dez. 1924/Jan. 1925. Berlin. 7no. on 1 reel. illus. 24cm.

Film reproduction. Positive.
"Organ des Bundes der bulgerischen Volksstudentenschaften im Auslande."
Text in Bulgarian, with occasional articles in German.
No more published?

1. Periodicals--Germany, Bulgarian. I. Suyuz na bulgarskoto narodno studenstro v chuzhbina.

NN 0023348 NN

Narsy, Raoul, 1860– ed.
La France au-dessus de tout; lettres de combattants, rassemblées et précédées d'une introduction par Raoul Narsy ... Paris, Bloud et Gay, 1915.
2 p. l., 72 p. 19ᵐᵐ. (*On cover:* "Pages actuelles," 1914–1915. nᵒ 25)

1. European war, 1914–   —Personal narratives, French.   I. Title.
                                                                  15–14936

Library of Congress   D509.P2 no. 25

NN 0023349 DLC NjP MB

Narsy, Raoul, 1860–   **FR69.Nr6**
Frère Loup. Moralité en un acte en vers.
— Paris. Librairie Damby-Willemin. 1895. 31 pp. 25.5 cm.
Contains a MS. presentation inscription from the author.

E3641 — T.r. — Francesco   d'Assisi, Saint, 1182-1226. Fiction, drama, etc., relating to him. — Moralities.

NN 0023350 MB RB

Narsy, Raoul, 1860–
Journal des débats.
... La presse et la guerre. Le Journal des débats. Choix d'articles recueillis par Raoul Narsy ... Paris, Bloud & Gay, 1915.

Narsy, Raoul, 1860–
... Le supplice de Louvain; faits et documents ... Paris, Bloud & Gay, 1915.
206 p. front., plates, port., facsim. 22 cm. (*On cover:* Publications du Comité catholique de propagande française à l'étranger)

1. European war, 1914–1918—Belgium—Louvain.
                                                          18—18867
Library of Congress   D542.L7N3

NN 0023352 DLC PU NN DNW

Nart, Ignacio.
Formulario para la práctica notarial. (Redacción de documentos y escritos) Barcelona, Bosch ¡1952¡
xiv, 286 p. 23 cm.

1. Forms (Law)—Spain.   I. Title.
                                                          54–15362

NN 0023353 DLC MH–L

Narten, Ernst.
Die anmeldepflicht nach 2 des futtermittel-gesetzes vom 22. Dezember 1926.
Inaug. diss.   Leipzig, 1927
Bibl.

NN 0023354 ICRL

Narten, Georges.
...Means for preventing ice blockades, by M. Georges Narten... The Hague: Belinfante Bᵗʰˢ, late A. D. Schinkel, 1894. 13 p. incl. diagrs. plans. 4°. (International Congress of Navigation. 6th, The Hague, 1894. Question 3.)

Cover-title.
Translated by Francis A. Oliver.

1. Ice-breaking in rivers. 2. Oliver   Francis A., translator. 3. Series.
N. Y. P. L.   November 4, 1921.

NN 0023355 NN

PF3111
N37

Narten, Karl.
"Lies richtig!" Anleitung zum Richtigsprechen; deutsche Grammatik für die Oberstufe der Volks- und Bürgerschule, die Fortbildungschule, die Präparandenanstalt und die unteren Klassen (Sexta bis Quarta) der höheren Schulen.   Hannover, K. Meyer, 1890–
v.

1. German language - Grammar - 1870–

NN 0023356 CU

Narten, Perry F
Reconnaissance of radioactive rock of the Hudson Valley and Adirondack Mountains, New York, by Perry F. Narten ¡and¡ Francis A. McKeown. Prepared by the Geological Survey for the U. S. Atomic Energy Commission, Technical Information Service. Oak Ridge, Tenn., 1952.
54 p. maps (1 fold. in pocket) diagrs. 27 cm. (¡U. S. Atomic Energy Commission¡ TEI–70)
Bibliography: p. 50–52.

1. Radioactive substances—New York (State) 2. Prospecting.   I. McKeown, Francis A., joint author.   II. U. S. Geological Survey.   III. Title.   (Series)

QC770.U65 no. 70   53–60403

NN 0023357 DLC

QC770
.U65
no. 68

Narten, Perry F., joint author.

Nelson, John M *geologist.*
Reconnaissance of radioactive rocks of Maine, by John M. Nelson ¡and¡ Perry F. Narten. Prepared by the Geological Survey for the U. S. Atomic Energy Commission. Oak Ridge, Tenn., Technical Information Service, 1951.

4TJ
193

Narter, Fikret.
Buhar kazanlari. Istanbul, Kutulmus Basimevi, 1950–
v. 1. (T. C. Istanbul Teknik Universitesi Kütüphanesi. Sayi: 223)
Contents: cilt 1. Isinin elde edilmesi ve geçmesi.

NN 0023359 DLC-P4 InLP

JR56
N168d

Narthex, pseud.
Doctrinal unity; being an enquiry into the rules of interpretation. London, New York, Longmans, Green, 1919.
46 p. 23 cm.

NN 0023360 CtY

Narthex ¡by¡ H.D.
see under Doolittle, Hilda, 1886-1961.

Nárthex; la lengua por la religión y por la patria. Año 1–3, núm. 4 (agosto, 1939–abril, 1941). Montezuma, 1939–41. 3 v. facsim., illus., plates (ports.).   22–23½cm.

Monthly.
"Editada: Por la Academia literaria de Santa Teresa de Jesús" (Academia "Santa Teresa de Jesús", Aug.–Dec., 1939).
Año 1, núm. 2–año 3, núm. 2 (sept., 1939–feb., 1941) include brief summary or table of contents in English.
Subtitle varies.

Continued in next column

VOLUME 405

Continued from preceding column

Año 1, núm. 2–año 2, núm. 6 (sept., 1939–junio, 1940) include section Bibliografía (title varies).
Occasional issues include book or periodical reviews.
United with Albores to form Montezuma.

—— Suplemento escolar. Año 1, núm. 1–3 (nov., 1940–enero, 1941). Bound with the above.

1. Periodicals—U.S., Spanish.   I. Seminario de Monterrey, Monterrey, N. M. Academia literaria   de Santa Teresa de Jesús.
N.Y.P.L.   February 4, 1942

NN   0023364   NN

PQ2063
.S4G718
Rare Bk.
Coll.
Nartov, Andreĭ Andreevich, 1737–1813, tr.
⟨Saint-Foix, Germain François Poullain de⟩ 1698–1776.
Граціи; комедія въ одномъ дѣйствіи. Перевелъ Андрей Нартовъ. Въ Санктпетербургѣ въ 1. разъ представлена на Имп. Россійскомъ театрѣ 22 дек. 1757 г. ⟨Москва, Печатано при Имп. Московскомъ университетѣ ⟨1757⟩

QE709
.W317
Rare Bk.
Coll.
Nartov, Andreĭ Andreevich, 1737–1813, tr.
Walch, Johann Ernst Immanuel, 1725–1778.
Каменное царство. Перевелъ Андрей Нартовъ. Въ Санктпетербургѣ, При Имп. Академіи наукъ, 1784.

PA6639
.R9N3
Rare Bk.
Coll.
Nartov, Andreĭ Andreevich, 1737–1813, tr.
Plinius Caecilius Secundus, C.
Слово похвальное Императору Траяну. Переводъ Андрея Нартова. Печатано въ Санктпетербургѣ, 1777.

Nartow, André van, supposed author.
Antiquitez sacrées & profanes des Romains expliquées
see under Nideck, A van, supposed author.

Nartowni, Shawarsh
see
Nardowni, Shawarsh, 1898–1968.

WBB
qN236e
1901
NARTOWSKI, Mieczysław.
Elektrodiagnostyka i elektroterapia, dla użytku uczniów i lekarzy. Kraków, Krzyżanowski, 1901.
vii, 375 p. illus.

NN   0023370   DNLM

---

4 PG
Pol. 49
Nartowski, Wacław.
Stan wyościański w utworach poetyckich pisarzy polskich doby renesansowej (XVI wieku) Studyum historyczno-literackie. Lwów, Nakładem Towarzystwa Ludoznawczego, 1917.
192 p.

NN   0023371   DLC-P4

Нартский эпос; сборник статей. Дзауджикау, Гос. изд-во Северо-Осетинской АССР, 1949.
78 p. illus. 25 cm.
At head of title: Северо-Осетинский научно-исследовательский институт.

1. Folk poetry, Ossetic – Hist. & crit.
2. Ossetia—Antiq.   I. Dzaudzhikau, Russia. Nauchno-issledovatel'skiĭ institut Severo-Osetinskoĭ ASSR.
Title transliterated: Nartskiĭ ĕpos.

PK6958.N3   51–37376

NN   0023373   DLC

Narfsov, A N 1859–
Археологическая поѣздка по Темниковскому уѣзду въ августѣ 1901 года; докладъ предсѣдателя Тамбовской губернской ученой архивной коммисіи А. Н. Нарцова на засѣданіи 17-го декабря 1901 года. Тамбовъ, Тип. Губ. правленія, 1902.
53 p. illus. 25 cm.
Cover title.
"Перепечатано изъ 46 выпуска Извѣстій Тамбовской ученой архивной коммисіи."

1. Temnikovskiĭ uезd.   I. Tambovskaiā gubernskaiā uchenaiā arkhivnaiā komissiiā.   II. Title.
Title romanized: Arkheologicheskaiā poĕzdka po Temnikovskomu uĕzdu.

DK511.T38N37   73–290915

NN   0023374   DLC

Narfsov, A N 1859–
⟨Materialy dlā istorii dvorānskikh rodov Martynovykh i Slēpsovykh⟩
Матеріалы для исторіи дворянскихъ родовъ Мартыновыхъ и Слѣпцовыхъ, съ ихъ вѣтвями, А. Н. Нарцова. Тамбовъ, Типо-лит. Губ. правленія, 1904.
1 v. (various pagings) illus. 25 cm.

1. Martynov family. 2. Slepšov family.   I. Title.

CS859.M37 1904   72–223303

NN   0023375   DLC

Narfsov, A N 1859–
О каменныхъ бабахъ; ⟨рефератъ, прочитанный на годовомъ собраніи 15 дек. 1903 г.⟩ предсѣдателя Тамбовской ученой архивной коммисіи А. Н. Нарцова. Тамбовъ, Типо-лит. Губ. правленія, 1904.
16 p. illus. 26 cm.
"Оттискъ изъ 50-го выпуска Извѣстій Тамбовской ученой архивной коммисіи."
Bibliographical footnotes.

1. Megalithic monuments—Russia.   I. Title.
Title romanized: O kamennykh babakh.

GN792.R8N3   79–462103

NN   0023376   DLC

Narfsov, A N 1859–
Проектъ программы общихъ работъ на областномъ археологическомъ съѣздѣ; докладъ предсѣдателя Тамбовской губернской ученой архивной коммисіи А. Н. Нарцова на засѣданіи 12-го ноября 1901 года. Тамбовъ, Тип. Губ. правленія, 1902.
7 p. 25 cm.
Cover title.
"Перепечатано изъ 46 выпуска Извѣстій Тамбовской ученой архивной коммисіи."

1. Russia—Antiquities.   I. Tambovskaiā gubernskaiā uchenaiā arkhivnaiā komissiiā.   II. Title.
Title romanized: Proekt programmy obshchikh rabot na oblastnom arkheologicheskom s"ĕzdĕ.

GN823.N3   73–229470

NN   0023377   DLC

Narfsov, A N 1859–
⟨Stikhotvoreniiā⟩
Стихотворенія А. Н. Нарцова. Тамбовъ, Типо-лит. Н. Бердоносова и Ф. Пригорина, 1904.
ii, 80 p. port. 23 cm.
"Не для продажи."
Poems.

PG3467.N25S8   74–220711

NN   0023378   DLC

Narfsov, A N 1859–
Тамбовская и Козловская сторожевая черта; докладъ предсѣдателя Тамбовской ученой архивной коммисіи А. Н. Нарцова на засѣданіи 10 октября 1900 года. Тамбовъ, Типо-лит. Губ. правленія, 1901.
25 p. 2 fold. maps. 24 cm.
Cover title.

1. Fortification—Russia—Tambov (Government) 2. Fortification, Primitive.   I. Tambovskaiā gubernskaiā uchenaiā arkhivnaiā komissiiā.   II. Title.
Title romanized: Tambovskaiā i Kozlovskaiā storozhevaiā cherta.

UG430.T34N37   75–266831

NN   0023379   DLC

Нарты; кабардинский эпос. ⟨Перевод Веры Звягинцевой и др. Редакторы Семен Липкин и Сергей Обрадович. Москва, Гос. изд-во худож. лит-ры, 1951–
v. col. plates. 27 cm.

1. Folk literature, Kabardian.   I. Lipkin, Semen I., ed.   *Title transliterated:* Narty.

PK9201.K38N3   52–34564

NN   0023380   DLC OrU

NARTZ, Th., abbé.
Le Val de Ville. ; recherches historiques. Strasbourg, E. Bauer, 1887.
Illustr.

NN   0023381   MH

Náruč knih; výběr českých knih z let 1936–1939. ⟨Vybral se spolupracovníky Jaroslav Kunc. V Praze, Nákl. Obce pražské, 1940.
397 p. 21 cm. (32. sv. Spisů Knihovny hlavního města Prahy)

1. Czech literature—Bibl.—Catalogs.   I. Kunc, Jaroslav. (Series: Prague. Městská knihovna. Spisy Knihovny hlavního města Prahy, sv. 32)

Z926.P88 no. 32   53–53802

NN   0023382   DLC NN

Наръчник на агитатора.
⟨София⟩
v. in 11 x 15 cm.
Frequency varies.
Began publication with July 1945 issue. Cf. Български книгопис ⟨1954⟩ № 499.
Issued by Otdel "Propaganda i agitatsiiā" of Tsentralen Komitet of the Bŭlgarska Komunisticheska partiiā.
Superseded by Наръчник на агитатора: селско стопанство and Наръчник на агитатора: промышленост, строителство, транспорт и търговия.

1. Bŭlgarska Komunisticheska partiiā—Party work.   2. Bŭlgarska Komunisticheska partiiā. Tsentralen Komitet. Otdel "Propaganda i agitatsiiā."   *Title transliterated:* Narŭchnik na agitatora.

JN9609.A8K56   59–32097

NN   0023383   DLC

Наръчник по дървообработка. София, Земиздат, 1955.
388 p. illus. 21 cm.
At head of title: П. Калчев ⟨и др.⟩

1. Woodwork.   I. Kalchev, Petŭr.   *Title transliterated:* Narŭchnik po dŭrvoobrabotka.

TT180.N3   56–25652

NN   0023384   DLC

3781
S78N
Narud, Jan Arne.
Theory of nonlinear feedback systems having a multiple number of first-order operating points and its application to millimicrosecond counting techniques. ⟨Stanford, Calif.⟩ 1955.
xiii, 194 p. illus., diagrs.
Thesis (Ph.D.) - Dept. of Electrical Engineering, Stanford University.
Bibliography: p. 193–194.

3.4
N237
—— Another copy.

1. Electric cir cuits. 2.Oscillations.
I. Title: Nonlin ear feedback systems.
Brief

NN   0023385   CSt

VOLUME 405

NARUETABm UGBACE.
Lötschberg Aletschgebiet, Südrampe Lötschberg und Lötschental, Leuk und Leukerbad. Routenbeschreibungen von 35 Wanderwegen. Übers. von Helen Beyeler. Bern, Kümmerly & Frey [c1955]   127 p.   illus., maps. 18cm.   (Schweizer Wanderbücher. 15)

Bibliography, p. 116-118.

NN   0023386   NN

Naruishkin, B
  see   Naryshkin, Vasiliĭ L'vovich, 1841-1906.

Naruishkina, Ekaterina Aleksyeevna.
  see   Naryshkina, E   A

Narula, Ranjit Singh, ed.

India (*Republic*) *Supreme Court.*
  Supreme Court manual; containing Supreme Court of India rules, 1950, with an exhaustive commentary, relevant articles of the Constitution of India, relevant extracts from the Code of civil procedure, relevant ordinances, a list of Supreme Court advocates and agents and all other useful information in connection with the working practice and procedure in the Supreme Court of India, by R. S. Narula. 1st ed. Delhi, Metropolitan Book Co., 1950.

Law

Narūla, Śamaśerasiṃha
  see
Narula, Shamsher Singh, 1915-

PK 2031 .N24
Narula, Shamsher Singh, 1915-
  Scientific history of the Hindi language. Delhi, Hindi Academy [1955]
  136 p.
  Includes bibliography.

1. Hindi language—Hist.   I. Title.

NSyU CU-S
NN   0023391   MiU MoU KMK TxU CU ICU CtY DS NN WU

Narulkar, Shanta, *ed.*
  A picture and programme of adult education, edited by Shanta Narulkar and Marjorie Sykes. Sevagram, Wardha, Hindustani Talimi Sangh [1951]
  63 p. 22 cm.

1. Wardha scheme of education.   I. Sykes, Marjorie, joint ed.

LB775.G22N3   61-28732 ‡

NN   0023392   DLC CU OU NN

DS481 G35N33
Narulkar, Shanta.
  Plan and practice. Sevagram, Hindustani Talimi Sangh [1950]
  64 p. illus.

The Sevagram Pre-Basic School was formally begun in July, 1945. cf. p.[41]

1. Sevagram Pre-Basic School, Sevagram, India.   2. Education - India.

NN   0023393   CU OrU OU

Narumi, Sukeichi, 1906-
  [Tsugaru no kotoba]
  津軽のことば 鳴海助一著 [黒石] 津軽のことば刊行委員会 [昭和
  v. 21 cm.
  In colophon: 発行所 みなみ新報社

1. Japanese language—Dialects—Tsugaru Peninsula.   I. Title.
PL693.T78N28   73-816294

NN   0023394   DLC

Narumo, K
  Domestic Japan; illustrated descriptions of articles used in Japanese daily life. Yokohama, Printed by the Yokohama Seishi Bunsha, 1895.
  illus.
  Contents:- 1. Kitchen utensils.

NN   0023395   MH

Narup, Carl.
  Illustreret Norsk litteraturhistorie; siste tidsrum, 1890-1904 Kristiania Det Norske Artieforlag 1905 266 p. facim., pl., port., illus.

NN   0023396   NdU

Narup, Carl.
  Skildringer og stemninger

NN   0023397   NdU

Naruse, Jinzo, 1858-1919.
  ... The Concordia movement, by Jinzo Naruse ... New York city, American association for international conciliation [1913]
  14 p. 19½ᶜᵐ. (International conciliation [pub. by the American association for international conciliation])

1. Association Concordia of Japan.   I. Title.
                                              A 35-838
Title from Carnegie   Endow. Int. Peace. Printed by L. C.

NN   0023398   NNCE

Naruse, Jinzo, 1858-1919.
  The education of Japanese women. (In: Okuma (Shigenobu) Fifty years of New Japan. New York, 1909. 8°. v. 2. p. 192-225)

NN   0023399   NN

BV3457 .S3N2
Naruse, Jinzo, 1858-1919.
  A modern Paul in Japan; an account of the life and work of the Rev. Paul Sawayama, by Jinzo Naruse with an introduction by Rev. Alexander McKenzie ... Boston and Chicago, Congregational Sunday-school and publishing society [1893]
  [2], 178 p. front. (port.) 18ᶜᵐ.

1. Sawayama, Paul, 1851-1887.   2. Missions—Japan.

NN   0023400   ICU NjPT NIC PP OO NBC MH

Naruse, Jinzo, 1858-1919.
  A modern Paul in Japan; an account of the life and work of the Rev. Paul Sawayama, by Jinzo Naruse, with an introduction by Rev. Alexander McKenzie, D. D. and Rev. John De Forest, D. D. ... Tokyo, The Keiseisha [1910]
  1 p. l., 117 p. port. 22½ᶜᵐ.
  Added t.-p. in Japanese.

1. Sawayama, Paul, 1851-1887.   I. McKenzie, Alexander, 1830-   II. De Forest, John Hyde.   III. Title.
                                              A 12-756
Stanford univ. Library
for Library of Congress

NN   0023401   CSt DLC CtY

Bj4 2p 2
Narusé, Jinzo, 1858-1919.
  ... Montaigne et la sagesse extrême-orientale. Conférence donnée à la Faculté des lettres, par M. Narusé ... [Paris, Imprimerie J. Dumoulan] 1935.
  cover-title, 11, [1] p. 25½cm. (Université de Paris. Institut d'études japonaises. Travaux et conférences. Fasc. II)

NN   0023402   CtY CU

PL716 .S165 Orien Japan
Naruse, Masakatsu, 1906-
Saitō, Kiyoe, 1893-
  (Zuihitsu, nikki, hyōron)
  随筆・日記・評論 齋藤清衞・成瀬正勝[著 東京 至文堂 昭和26 i.e. 1951]

Naruse, Nizō
  see Naruse, Jinzō, 1858-1919.

Naruse, Sekiji.
  (Nihontō no hanashi)
  日本刀の話 成瀬関次著 [東京] 増進堂 [昭和17 i.e. 1942]
  202 p. illus. 22 cm. (小國民選書)
  List of author's works: p. 202.

1. Swords, Japanese—Juvenile literature.   I. Title.
U856.J3N37   74-815584

NN   0023405   DLC

SB235 .M54 Orien Japan
Naruse, Tōzō.
Minami Manshū Tetsudō Kabushiki Kaisha. Rinji Keizai Chōsa Iinkai.
  (Kōryankan shūshū chōsa hōkokusho)
  高梁桿蒐集調查報告書 附 製紙原料トシテノ 高梁桿 [大連] 南滿洲鐵道株式會社臨時經濟調査委員會 [1930]

Naruševiĉius, Pr
  ... Gyvenimo kova; visuomeninis romanas.

NN   0023407   OC1

Нарушение болгарского воздушного пространства турецкими самолетами. София, 1948.
  9 p. 20 cm.

1. Bulgaria—Bound.—Turkey. 2. Turkey—Bound.—Bulgaria.
  Title transliterated: Narushenie bolgarskogo vozdushnogo prostranstva turetskimi samoletami.

DR73.B8N3   51-40119

NN   0023408   DLC

Narushevich, A
  Воздушные силы наших соседей. Москва, Гос. воен. изд-во, 1931.
  111 p. illus., plans. 20 cm. (Библиотека командира)
  At head of title: А. Нарушевич.

1. Air forces.   I. Title.
  Title romanized: Vozdushnye sily nashikh sosedeĭ.

UG630.N36   75-286621

NN   0023409   DLC

VOLUME 405

Narushima, Chikuzan, 1803?–1854.
源氏物語提要　紫史吟評詳解 ｟成島筑山著｠
谷口廻瀾(爲大)述　池上秀猷題畫　東京　谷口
廻瀾先生還暦記念刊行會　昭和15｟1940｠
2, 1, 6, 242 p. illus. 23 cm.

1. Murasaki Shikibu, b. 978? Genji monogatari.   i. Taniguchi, Tametsugu, ed. ii. Title. iii. Title : Shishi gimpyō shōkai. *Title romanized: Genji monogatari teiyō Shishi gimpyō shōkai.*

J 65–1641

Harvard Univ. Chinese-   Japanese Library 5924.68
for Library of Congress   ｟1｠

NN   0023410   MH-HY

Naruszewicz, Adam Stanisław, Bp., 1733-1796.
Dyaryusz podróży Stanisława Augusta króla na
Ukraine, w roku 1787. W Warszawie, 1805.

In his: Tauryka, czyli Wiadomosci starozytne..
Appended is Głos Adama Naruszewicza... przy
zalozeniu pierwszego kamienia na kóścioł Opa-
trznóści Boskiey r.1792 [etc.]

NN   0023411   MH

Naruszewicz, Adam Stanisław, *Bp.,* 1733–1796.
Dzieła poetyczne. Nowe zupełnie wyd. W Wrocławiu,
W. B. Korn, 1826.
2 v. port. 18 cm.

PG7157.N3A6 1826   57–55668

NN   0023412   DLC

DK 430
.2
.C5N23
Naruszewicz, Adam Stanisław,
1733-1796.
Historya Jana Karola Chodkiewicza,
wojewody Wilenskiego, hetmana wielkiego
w.X.Lit. przez Adama Naruszewicza.
Edycya Tadeusza Mostowskiego. W
Warszawie, 1802.
2 v.

1. Chodkiewicz, Jan Karol, 1560-1621.

NN   0023413   ICU

Naruszewicz, Adam Stanisław, Bp., 1733–1796.
Historya Jana Karola Chodkiewicza, wojewody
wileńskiego, hetmana wielkiego W. X. Lit.
W Warszawie, T. Mostowski, 1805.
2 v. port. 21 cm. (Wybor pisarzow
polskich. Historya)
Bibliographical references included in "Noty"
at end of each volume.

NN   0023414   PU

DK430.2
C5
N37
1837
Naruszewicz, Adam Stanisław, Bp.,
1733-1796.
Historya J.K. Chodkiewicza, wojewody wileńskiego, hetmana wielkiego W. Ks. Lit., przez
A. Naruszewicza. Wyd. nowe Jana Nep. Bobrowicza z popiersiem Chodkiewicza. W Lipsku,
Breitkopf & Haertel, 1837.
2 v. port. 21 cm. (Życia sławnych polaków,
t. 1-2)
Includes bibliographical references.
1. Chodkiewicz, Jan Karol, 1560 (ca.)-1621. I. Title (1)

NN   0023415   CtY

Naruszewicz, Adam Stanisław, *Bp.,* 1733–1796.
Historya narodu polskiego. Z rękopisma Biblioteki
Puławskiej i Józefa hrabiego Sierakowskiego. W Warszawie, Nakł. Tow. Królewskiego Warszawskiego, 1803–24
｟v. 1, 1824｠
v. in   fold. maps. 21 cm.
Vols. 2– have subtitle: Od początku chrześcijaństwa, and issued
in series Wybór pisarzów polskich: Historya; published by T. Mostowski.

1. Poland—Hist.

DK414.N3   57–55686

NN   0023416   DLC

Naruszewicz, Adam Stanisław, *Bp.,* 1733–1796.
Historya narodu polskiego. Wyd. nowe Jana Nep.
Bobrowicza. W Lipsku, Breitkopf & Haertel, 1836–37.
10 v. in 5. port., fold. maps. 22 cm.

1. Poland—Hist.

DK414.N32   59–55235

NN   0023417   DLC CaBVaU OU CSt WaS CtY InU MH IU

Naruszewicz, Adam Stanisław, *Bp.,* 1733–1796.
Historya narodu polskiego przez Adama Naruszewicza.
Wyd. Kazimierza Józefa Turowskiego (wedle wyd. gröllow-
skiego) Kraków. Nakł. Wydawn. Biblioteki Polskiej, 1859–
v. in   fold. map. 21 cm.

1. Poland—Hist.   I. Title.

DK414.A2N32   65–59262

NN   0023418   DLC NN MH PU IU NNC MiU MnU NcU

PG7157
.N3A17
Naruszewicz, Adam Stanisław, Bp., 1733-1796.
Poezye. W Lipsku, Breitkopf et Haertel,
1835.
3 v. port. 15cm. (Biblioteka kieszonkowa
klassykow polskich, t.11-13)

NN   0023419   MiDW MiU MH

DK
511
.C7
N24
Naruszewicz, Adam Stanisław, Bp., 1733-1796.
Tauryka; czyli,Wiadomosci starozytne i póz-
nieysze o stanie i mieszkancach Krymu do naszych
czasow. W Warszawie, W Drukarni Nadworney
Jeego Królewskiey Mości, 1787.
129 p. 19 cm.
First edition. Cf.Estreicher,K. Bibliografia
polska XIX.stolecia,v.3,p.207.

1.Crimea—Hist. I.Title. II.Title: Wiadomości
starozytne i późniejsze ...

NN   0023420   MiU WU

Naruszewicz, Adam Stanisław, *Bp.,* 1733–1796.
Tauryka; czyli, Wiadomości starożytne i póżnieysze o
stanie i mieszkańcach Krymu do naszych czasów. W Warszawie, T. Mostowski, 1805.
540 p. 21 cm. (Wybór pisarzów polskich: Historya)
Includes Dyaryusz podróży Stanisław Augusta króla na Ukraine,
w roku 1787 (p. ｟141｠–524) with special t. p., and Głos przy założeniu
pierwszego kamienia na Kościół Opatrzności Boskiej (p. ｟525–540)
1. Crimea—Hist. 2. Stanisław II August, King of Poland, 1732–
1798. 3. Ukraine—Hist.—Sources. I. Title. II. Title: Daryusz
podróży Stanisława Augusta króla na Ukraine. III. Title. Głos przy
założeniu pierwszego kamienia na Kościół Opatrzności Boskiey.

DK511.C7N3   63–56882

NN   0023421   DLC MH

PG7157
N3A17
1804
Naruszewicz, Adam Stanisław, Bp., 1733-1796.
Wiersze różne. Edycya Tadeusza Mostowskiego.
W Warszawie, W Druk. no.646, 1804-05.
2 v. port. 20cm. (Wybór pisarzów polskich
｟15-16｠ Poezya)

I.Mostowski, Tadeusz Antoni, hrabia, 1766-
1842, ed.

NN   0023422   CSt

Naruszewicz, Adam Stanisław, Bp., 1733-1796.
Wybór poezyj z dołączeniem kilku piśm prozą oraz
listów. Wyd.popr. według druków pierwotnych i opatr-
zone słowniczkiem archaizmów. Warszawa, Nakład i
druk S.Lewentala, 1882
xxviii, 508 p. (Biblioteka Najcelniejszych utworów
literatury europejskiej. Literatura Polska)

NN   0023423   MH CtY NN

Naruszewicz, Adam Stanisław, Bp., 1733-1796.
Żywot J. K. Chodkiewicza wojewody wileńskiego. Przemyśl,
nakładem M. Dzikowskiego, etc. etc. 1857-58.
2 vol. (Biblioteka polska.)

NN   0023424   MH NN

Naruszewicz, Adam Stanisław, *Bp.,* 1733–1796.
Żywot J. K. Chodkiewicza, wojewody wileńskiego, het-
mana wielkiego W. Ks. Lit., przez Adama Naruszewicza.
Wyd. Kazimierza Józefa Turowskiego. Kraków, Nakł.
Wydawn. Biblioteki Polskiej, 1858.
2 v. in 1. 20 cm.
"Część Dyariusza wojny chocimskiej, prowadzonego przez Jakóba
Sobieskiego": v. 2, p. ｟249｠–279.

1. Chodkiewicz, Jan Karol, 1560 (ca.)–1621.   I. Title.
II. Sobieski, Jakub, 1588–1646.

DK430.2.C5N3   65–51195

NN   0023425   DLC IU OU InU

Narutowicz, Gabriel, pres. Poland, 1865–1922.
Gabrjel Narutowicz, pierwszy prezydent
Rzeczypospolitej; księga pamiątkowa
see under title

Narva ... Park college, Parkville, Missouri.
｟Parkville, Mo., 19
v. illus. (incl. ports.) col. plates. 27 cm. annual.
Published by the junior and senior classes.

I. Park college, Parkville, Mo.

ca 24–300 Unrev'd

Library of Congress   LD4471.P755

NN   0023427   DLC DHEW

Narvaez, Alejandro Mosquera
see   Mosquera Narvaez, Alejandro.

Narváez, Carlos de.
...Homenaje al sabio Caldas; su obra científica. Discurso del
dr. Carlos de Narváez... Bogotá, 1943. 11 p. illus. 24cm.
At head of title: La Sociedad colombiana de ingenieros en cooperación con la Junta
de festejos patrios.
"Bibliografía," p. 11.
Author's autographed presentation copy.

1. Caldas, Francisco José de,   1771–1816. I. Sociedad colombiana
de ingenieros, Bogotá. II. Junta   de festejos patrios, Bogotá.
N.Y.P.L.   October 3, 1944

NN   0023429   NN

Narváez, Carlos López
see
López Narváez, Carlos, 1897–

VOLUME 405

Narváez, Diego.
Palabras sinónimas inglesas. English synonyms. Con la colaboración de Mary Agnes Byrne y José García Núñez. Jerez de la Frontera, Impreso por J. Romero ₍1952₎
268 p. 15 cm.
Cover title: Diccionario de palabras sinónimas inglesas.

1. English language—Dictionaries—Spanish. 2. Spanish language—dictionaries—English. 3. English language—Synonyms.   I. Title.

PC4640.N3   54–31416

NN   0023431   DLC

Law   **Narváez, Enrique de.**

Rodríguez Piñeres, Eduardo, 1869–
... De cómo no puede ganar quien baratea lo ajeno. **Bogotá,** Tip. Voto nacional, 1938.

Narváez, Enrique de.
Juan Salvador de Narváez, 1788–1827 ; apuntes biográficos. Bogotá, Editorial Minerva, 1927.
310 p. port. 18 cm.

1. Narváez y de Castro, Juan Salvador de, 1788–1827.

F2274.N35N3   48–33344*

NN   0023433   DLC ICU NBuU CSt

G986.061
N169m   **Narváez, Enrique de.**
Los mochuelos; recuerdos de 1876–1877. Bogotá, Editorial Minerva, 1928.
144p. illus. 18cm.

1. Colombia - Hist. - 1832-1886. I. Title.

NN   0023434   TxU NBuU TNJ

Narváez, Enrique de.
... Los Mochuelos, por Enrique de Narváez. ₍Bogotá, Editorial Minerva, s. a., 1936₎
1 p. l. ₍5₎–154 p., 1 l. 20ᶜᵐ. (Biblioteca aldeana de Colombia ₍Historia y leyendas, n.° 40₎)
First published in Bogota, 1928.
CONTENTS.—Enrique de Narváez, por Guillermo Hernández de Alba.—Los Mochuelos.—Carta de Isaac Pulido J. a Enrique de Narváez.

1. Colombia—Hist.—1832–1886.   I. Hernández de Alba, Guillermo.
II. Title.

Library of Congress   F2277.N372   37–8436
—————— Copy 2.   ₍38d2₎   986

PP OOxM NIC OCU OC1W MB
NN   0023435   DLC DPU NN OrU PPT NBuU MU CSt NjP

4PQ
Span.   **Narváez, Enrique de.**
Am.   Los mochuelos. 3. ed. Bogotá, Editorial
101   Minerva ₍
            154 p.   (Selección Samper Ortega de literatura colombiana. Historia y leyendas, no. 40)

NN   0023436   DLC-P4

Narváez, Enrique L
El saneamiento por evicción con relación a la compraventa desde el punto de vista del derecho civil. **Managua, 1919.**
32 p. 22 cm.
Tesis—Facultad de Derecho y Notariado del Centro, Managua.

1. Warranty—Nicaragua.   I. Title.

65–83396

NN   0023437   DLC

Narváez, J. I. González.
See
González Narváez, J. I.

Narváez, José Joaquín Ibarra
see Ibarra Narváez, José Joaquín.

Narvaez, José Lopez
see   López Narváez, José.

Narvaez, Jose Maria.
Carta esferica de las costas de la Nueva Galicia reconocida desde el surigidero de Mazatlan asta el Cavo Corrientes. ᴺ.p. 1795.

NN   0023441   PPAmP

PQ6419
N18V3   **Narváez, Juan de**
1889   Las Valencianas Lamentaciones y El tratado de la partida del ánima. Con un prólogo de Luís Montoto y Rautenstrauch. Publícalos por primera vez María del Rosario de Massa y Candau, de Hoyos. Sevilla, Imp. de E. Rasco, 1889.
xvi, 201 p. facsim.

I. Montoto y Rautenstrauch, Luís, 1851–1929, ed.   II. Title.
III. Title: El tratado de la partida del ánima.

NN   0023442   CU NNH InU MH IU

Narvaez, Juan de, ca. 1650-1706
see   Narváez Saavedra, Juan de, d. 1706.

M
140   **Narváez, Luis de,** 16th cent.
N3   ₍El Delphin de música. Selections₎
A9   Ausgewählte Werke aus Los seys libros del Delphin de musica,1538. Hofheim am taunus, F.Hofmeister ₍n.d.₎
          20 p. 30 cm. (Die Tabulatur, Heft 11)

1.Vihuela music--To 1800. I.Title: Delphin de musica. (Series)

NN   0023444   NSyU ICN

M
140   **Narváez, Luis de,** 16th cent.
N3   ₍El Delphin de musica₎
D4   El Delphin de musica (1538). Madrid, O. Tracio S.A. ₍1923₎
          score (3 v.) (Spain. Junta para ampliación de estudios e investigaciones científicas. Centro de estudios históricos cuadernos, no.1) (Colección de vihuelistas españoles del siglo XVI)

1.Vihuela music--To 1800. I.Title.

NN   0023445   NSyU

787.6
N169s   NARVÁEZ, LUIS DE, 16th cent.
1923   ₍El delphin de musica₎ ... Composiciones escogidas de El delphin de música (1538) de Narváez, arregladas para piano y para canto y piano por Eduardo M. Torner. Madrid, Centro de estudios históricos ₍1923₎
            2p.l.,19,[1]p. 28cm. (Colección de vihuelistas españoles del siglo XVI)
            With his El delphin de música. [1923]
            At head of title: Junta para ampliación de estudios e investigaciones científicas. Centro de estudios   históricos.

NN   0023446   TxU MH-Mu NcU RPB ICN IaU MiU

M
126   Narváez,Luis de,16th cent.
.N24   ₍El delphin de música₎
D3   El delphin de música,1538. Estudio y transcripción de las ediciones originales por Eduardo M. Torner. ₍Madrid, O.Tracio 1923₎ ₍
            y. illus. 28 cm. ₍Colección de vihuelistas españoles del siglo XVI₎
            At head of title: Junta para Ampliación de Estudios e Investigaciones Científicas. Centro de Estudios Históricos.
            With cuaderno 1 is bound his El delphin de música. Selections. 1923.
            1.Vihuela music--To 1800. I.Martínez Torner, Eduardo,1888–1955,ed. II.Spain. Junta para Ampliación de Estudios e Investigaciones Científicas. III.Title.

NN   0023447   MiU ICN CU IU MH-Mu

Narvaez, Luis de, 16th cent., supposed author.
Dialogo intitulado el capon
see under El capón.

Narváez, Luis de, *16th cent.*
€ Los seys libros del Delphin de musica ‖ de cifras para tañer Vihuela. Hechos por Luys de Narbaez. Dirigi- ‖ dos al muy Illustre Señor / el Señor don Francisco delos ‖ Louos / Comēdador mayor de Leon / Adelantado ‖ de Laçoula / Señor de Sauiote / y del Lōsejo ‖ del estado de su Magestad Cesarea ₹c. ‖ y este primer libro tracta delos ᵈ₹ ‖ ocho tonos par tañer por ‖ diuersas partes en ‖ la Vihuela. ‖ ₍Valladolid₎ M.D.XXX.viij. ᵈ₹ ‖ € Con preuilegio Imperial para Castilla y Aragon y Valēcia y Cataluña por diez años. ‖
4 p. l., lxxxviij (i. e. 98) numb. l., 4 l. illus. 18¼ x 24¼ᵐ.

Colophon: € Fue impresa la presente obra delos ‖ seys libros del Delphin / Hecho por el excellente musico Luys de ‖ Narbaez enla muy noble villa de Valladolid por ‖ Diego Hernãdez de Cordoua impresor. ‖ Acabose a treynta dias del ‖ mes de Octubre. ‖ ᵈ₹ M.D.XXX.viij. ᵈ₹ ‖ ₍Printer's mark₎
Signatures : a⁴, n–e⁸, d¹⁴, e–k⁸, 2 leaves unsigned, l–m⁸. Many irregularities in numbering of leaves.
Each book, from 2 to 6, has special t.-p. as follows : € El segūdo libro del Delphin de musica ... Ay enel fantasias por algunos tonos que no son tan dificultosas de tañer como las del primer libro. € El tercero libro ... Ay enel obras cōpuestas de Josquin y canciones Frācesas de diuersos auctores. € El quarto libro ... Ay enel diferēcias de cōtrapuntos sobre el igno de nr̄a Señora. O gloriosa domina / y de Pãge

lingua y Sacris solennijs. € El quinto libro ... Ay enel romances y villancicos para tañer y cãtar y cōtrapuntos sobre algunos villãcicos. € El sexto libro ... Ay enel veynte y dos diferēcias de Cōde claros para discantar / y siete diferencias de guarda me las vacas / y vna baxa de cōtrapūto.
Each book has a full-page woodcut on verso of t.-p., showing a ship in full sail, and Amphion, astride a dolphin, playing on the vihuela. Each title and each of these cuts is surrounded by a border containing the author's cipher. All six books have the same tail-piece and 8-line poem on music on last page.
The first t.-p. is printed in red and black ; book 5 in red and black throughout (except t.-p.) the red figures in the tablature indicating the air.
Bound in full blue morocco ; inside borders, gilt edges.
1. Lute music.   I. Title: El Delphin de musica.
Library of Congress   M140.N3   29-13900

NN   0023451   IU

Film   Narváez,Luis de,16th cent.
1802   Los seys libros del Delphin de musica de cifras para tañer vihuela. Valladolid, 1538.
          98 p. illus.
          Microfilm. Rochester,N.Y., Eastman Kodak Co., n.d. 1 reel.

1. lute music. I. Title: El Delphin de musica.

NN   0023452   NSyU IU WaU

Narváez, Luis de, *16th cent.*
₍El Delphin de música₎

Los seys libros del Delphin de música de cifra para tañer vihuela (Valladolid, 1538) Transcripción y estudio por Emilio Pujol. Barcelona, Consejo Superior de Investigaciones Científicas, Instituto Español de Musicología, 1945.
59 p., 94 p. (music) facsims. 32 cm. (Monumentos de la música española, 3)

1. Vihuela music—To 1800.   I. Pujol, Emilio, 1886– ed.
(Series)

M2.M4845 vol. 3   787.6   48–40779*

PP OOxM NcD NcU PU PBm
NN   0023453   DLC CLU MoU MB OC1W MiU ICN PU MH TxU

VOLUME 405

Narváez, Luis de, 16th cent.
Tema y variaciones sobre un aire popular ¡por¡ Luis de Narváez ... Versión para piano de Eduardo M. Torner.' (In: Asociación patriótica española. Clásicos españoles de la música. Buenos Aires, 1938. v. 1, p. 35-38.)

For piano.
Biographical sketch of the composer, p. 34.

1. Piano—Arr. I. Martinez   Torner, Eduardo, 1888-1955, arr.
II. Ser.
N. Y. P. L.   September 22, 1943

NN 0023454   NN

Narvaoz, Luis Pacheco y.
see
Pacheco y Narvaez, Luis.

Narváez, Pamphilio de.
See
Narváez, Pánfilo de, 1470-1528.

Narváez, Pánfilo de, 1470-1528.
Proclamation of Pamfilo de Narvaez. To the inhabitants of the countries and provinces from Rio de Palmas to the cape of Florida, 1527. Tr. from a copy of the original in the Archives of the Indies, Seville, Spain.
(In French, Benjamin F., ed. Historical collections of Louisiana and Florida. 2d ser. New York, 1875. 26ᶜᵐ. p. ¡153¡-158)

1. Florida—Hist.—Spanish exploration to 1565.
                                                    11-6933
Library of Congress   F366.F89

NN 0023457   DLC MdBP

Narvaez, Panfilo de, 1470-1528.
Sommation à faire aux habitants des contrées et
provinces qui s'étendent depuis la rivière des Palmas.
¡Ternaux-Compans, Henri¡ 1807-1864, ed.
Recueil de pièces sur la Floride. Inédit. ¡Paris, A. Bertrand, 1841¡

Narváez, Paulino Machorro
see
Machorro Narváez, Paulino.

Narváez, Ramón María.
Paralelo entre la vida Militar de Espartero y la de Narvaez
see under   Martínez Villergas, Juan, 1817-1894.

Narváez, Ramón María, Duque de Valencia, 1800-1868.
Manifiesto del Mariscal de campo Don Ramón María Narváez, en contestacion á las acusaciones del Capitan General Conde de Luchana.
Madrid. Compañia tipográfica. 1839. 2 parts in 1 v. 18½ cm., in 8s.
The title-page to the 2d part reads. D. Ramón María Narváez ... al Congreso nacional y al público. This part was written for prior publication.

L9995 — Espartero, Joaquin Baldome.., Duke of Victoria, 1793-1879. — Spain.
Hist. Isabella, 1833-1868.

NN 0023461   MB InU NN NcD FTaSU

Narváez, Victorio de la Fuente
see   Fuente Narváez, Victorio de la.

Narváez García, Emilio.
... El buen centroamericano. Managua, Nicaragua, C. A., Editorial Nuevos horizontes, 1944.
cover-title, 1 p. l., 168 p. port. 22½ᶜᵐ.

1. Nicaragua—Pol. & govt. 2. Citizenship.   I. Title.
                                                    45-8133
Library of Congress   JL1603 1944.N3
                                                    342.7285

NN 0023463   DLC TxU LNHT MnU NIC

G917.284
N169r
1939-40   Narváez García, Emilio.
... Rutas terrestres de El Salvador, kilometraje ... 1939-40. San Salvador, El Salvador, Centro América [Tipografía comercial de N. Cabezas Duarte, 1939?]
80p. illus.,maps. 25cm.
At head of title: Orientación para el viajero.
Includes advertising matter.

1. Salvador - Descr. & trav. - Guide-books
I. Title. II. Title: Orientación para el viajero.

NN 0023464   TxU

G177
N169n   Narváez García, Emilio.
Trato social; texto de la asignatura para moral y trato social del 1er. año de secundaria, conforme el programa oficial de 14 lecciones. Managua [Editorial Nuevos Horizontes] 1944.
27p. 21cm.

1. Social ethics.

NN 0023465   TxU

G972.85
N169n   Narváez García, Rubén.
Nicaragua; las huellas del pasado; el Partido Conservador y su política en Nicaragua; el irredentismo cultural, cívico y económico; el nacionalismo defensivo. México [Imp. Zavala, 193-?]
121p. port. 23cm.

Cover title.

1. Nicaragua - Pol. & govt.

NN 0023466   TxU

G282.092
J1985n   Narváez J   , Pedro A
El muy Rvdo. padre Leonardo Jaime y Ninago, O.F.M., apóstol franciscano, "gran ecuaturiano de corazón." Quito, Editorial Ecuatoriana, 1936.
32p. port. 21cm.

Cover title.

1. Jaime y Ninago, Leonardo.

NN 0023467   TxU

Narváez López, Carlos.
Justicia internacional sometida a prueba; estudio jurídico de la controversia entre Guatemala y la Gran Bretaña por el dominio de Belice. Guatemala, 1946.
16 p. 26 cm. (Guatemala. Ministerio de Relaciones Exteriores. Publicaciones)

1. British Honduras question.   I. Title.
F1449.B7G87   56-26678 ‡

NN 0023468   DLC NNUN CU-B TxU

Narváez López, Carlos.
Los quinientos años de la Roma Republicana. ¡1. ed. nicaragüense¡ Managua, 1950.
186 p. illus. 23 cm

1. Rome—Hist.—Republic, 510-30 B. C.   I. Title.
DG231.3.N37   52-37389 ‡

NN 0023470   DLC TxU

Narváez López, Zeferino.
Los campesinos de México en sus dos épocas. México, 1949.
132 p. 20 cm.

1. Peasantry—Mexico.   I. Title.
HD325.N3   323.33   49-22757* ‡

NN 0023470-1   DLC DNAL TxU

Narváez Molina, Jorge
... Aplicación judicial de las resoluciones judiciales y recursos problemas en la práctica ... ¡por¡ Jorge Narváez Molina ... Mexico ¡Impr. moderna¡ 1952.
76 p. 23cm.
Tesis (licenciatura en derecho) - Univ. de Mexico.
Bibliography: p. 75-76.
Includes legislation.

NN 0023471   MH-L DLC-P4

Narváez Moreira, Francisco.
Del endoso. México ¡cover 1953¡
136 p. 23 cm.
Tesis profesional—Universidad Nacional Autónoma de México.

1. Indorsements—Mexico.   I. Title.
                                                    56-44864 ‡

NN 0023472   DLC MH-L

W 4
M61   NARVAEZ PEREZ, Alvaro
1950   Exploración sanitaria y breve estudio sobre bronquitis aguda y crónica del municipio de Zacualpán de Amilpas, estado de Morelos. México, Ortega, 1950.
57 p.
Tesis - Univ. de México.
1. Public health - Mexico - Morelos (State)

NN 0023473   DNLM

W 4
M61   NARVAEZ RODRIGUEZ, Alberto Javier
1952   Fiebre Q en México. México, Editorial Cultura, 1952.
72 p. illus.
Tesis - Univ. de México.
1. Q fever

NN 0023474   DNLM

VOLUME 405

Narvaez Pacheco, Jacinto.
Sitio de San Antonio de Alarache en 1689. Relacion escrita por Don Jacinto Narvaez Pacheco y continuada por Don Juan Cloquer Vargdas Machuca. (Col. de doc. inéd. para la hist. de España. T. 106, p. 319-450. Madrid, 1893)

NN 0023475 MB MH CtY

Narváez Saavedra, Juan de, d. 1706.
Sermon En La Solemnidad, Qve Se Consagrò á Christo S. N. Sacramentado, y à su Santissima Madre en su milagrosa Imagen de los Remedios por el feliz sucesso de la Flota en el viage de buelta á España. Qve discvrrio En termino de quarenta horas, y predicò en esta S. Iglesia Metropolitana de Mexico el S' D' D. Ivan De Narvaes, Y Saabedra... Sacale A Lvz El D' y M° D. Augustin De Cabañas... En Mexico, por los Herederos de la Viuda de Francisco Rodriguez Lupercio. Año de 1699. 9 p.l., 14 f. illus. (coat of arms) 20cm. (4°.)

Medina IEM 1736.

1. Sermons, Spanish-American.
N. Y. P. L.   September 10, 1935

NN 0023476 NN RPJCB

Narváez Saavedra, Juan de, d.1706.
Sermon fvnebre, manifiesto dolor de la sancta yglesia metropolitana de Mexico, en las exequias de el illustrissimo, y reverendissimo señor doctor, y maestro Don Francisco de Agviar, y Seixas su dignissimo arçobispo, celebradas presente el excellentissimo señor D. Ioseph Sarmiento de Valladares... la Real audiencia, y todos los demas tribunales de esta corte. Predicado por el D° D. Juan de Narvaez... Mexico: Herederos de la viuda de F. Rodriguez Lupercio, 1698. 16 p.l., 16 f. illus. (facsim.) 12°.

1. Aguiar Seijas y Ulloa, Francisco   de, abp., d. 1698.
N. Y. P. L.   April 30, 1925

NN 0023477 NN RPJCB

Narváez Saavedra, Juan de, d. 1706.
Sermon panegyrico, de el dia octavo de la solemne dedicacion del templo con el titulo del nombre de Maria SSma de Gvadalvpe, y S. Bernardo: dia de la visitacion de Santa Ysabel... Predicado por el Doctor D. Ivan de Narbaez... En Mexico: Por la viuda de Frācisco Rodriguez Lupercio. 1691. 1 p.l., 98-112 (really 111) f. 4°.

Medina IEM 1500.
Part of: Ramirez de Vargas, Alonso: Sagrado padron panegyricos sermons a la memoria debida al svmptvoso magnifico templo, y curiosa basilica del convento de religiosas del glorioso Abad San Bernardo... En Mexico, 1691.

1. Mary (Virgin).—Pictures and   images. Mexico: Guadalupe.
N. Y. P. L.   April 16, 1918.

NN 0023478 NN RPJCB

Narvaez Saavedra, Juan de, d.1706.
Sermon qve en la celebridad de la translacion del cuerpo del glorioso apostol de la India S. Francisco Xavier en la parrochia de la sancta Vera-Cruz de esta ciudad predico el d°°... don Ivan de Narvaez... Mexico, Viuda de F. Rodriguez Lupercio, 1694. 8 p.l.,8 numb. l.,2 l. illus. 20cm. (Sermones varios. v. 3, no. 13)

NN 0023479 CU-B RPJCB

Narváez Saavedra, Juan de, d. 1706.
Sermon Qve En La Opposicion A La Canongia Magistral de esta Santa Yglesia Cathedral Metropolitana de Mexico. Predico con termino de quarenta y ocho horas el D' D. Ivan De Narvaes Saabedra... Dedicalo Al S' D. D. Diego De Malpartida Zenteno... El D. D. Pedro Del Castillo, y Vergara... quien lo saca á luz. En Mexico, por los Herederos de la Viuda de Francisco Rodriguez Lupercio, Año de 1699. 8 p.l., 14 f. 20cm. (4°.)

Medina IEM 1737.

1. Sermons, Spanish-American.
N. Y. P. L.   September 10, 1935

NN 0023480 NN RPJCB

Narváez y Valdelomar, Gaspar de.
El doctor Gaspar de Naruaez y Valdelomar oidor de la Real audiencia de Chile siruio a los señores reyes, abuelo y padre de Su Mag. que santa gloria ayan, y lo ha cõtinuado, siruiendo a Su Mag. demas de quarenta años a esta parte... (n. p., 162-)
Microfilm copy, made in 1943, of the original in the Medina collection, Biblioteca nacional de Santiago de Chile. Positive.
Negative film in Brown university library.
Collation of the original, as determined from the film: (2) p.

Title from beginning of text.
"Y el alferez Lorēço de Naruaez, su hermano, siruio en las ciudades de Nombre de Dios, Puertobelo y Panamà mas de 28. años": p. (2)
Medina, Biblioteca hispano-chilena, 242.

1. Narváez, Lorenzo de.
Microfilm AC-2 reel 223, no. 12   Mic A 49-283

Brown Univ. Library
for Library of Congress   (1)†

NN 0023482 RPB DLC

Narvaja, Raúl López
see
López Narvaja, Raúl.

Narvaja, Ricardo, ed.
Uruguay. *Laws, statutes, etc.*
Fuentes, notas y concordancias del Código civil de la República Oriental del Uruguay, escritas por el autor del mismo código, D. Tristan Narvaja... Extraídas directamente de sus originales y pub. por el Dr. Ricardo Narvaja. Montevideo, Tipografía y litografía oriental, 1910.

HJ 9803 A16 1834 LAC-Z   Narvaja, Tristán, 1819-1877.
Administración de justicia en la Republica Oriental del Uruguay. Montevideo, Impr. del Nacional, 1841. 53p. 20cm.
Bound with Uruguay. Asamblea General. Camara de Representantes. Comisión de Cuentas. Informe. Montevideo, 1836.

anal.   1. Courts - Uruguay. I. Title. Sp.: Lucuix Collection.

NN 0023485 TxU

Narvaja, Tristán, 1819-1877.
Uruguay. *Laws, statutes, etc.*
Código civil para el estado oriental del Uruguay, promulgado por el gobierno provisorio en 23 de enero de 1868. Edicion oficial... Montevideo, Imprenta de La Tribuna, 1868.

HQ 1019 U8 N387 LAC-Z   Narvaja, Tristán, 1819-1877.
De la sociedad conyugal y las dotes. Montevideo, Impr. Liberal, 1872. 60p. 24cm.

1. Husband and wife - Uruguay. I. Title. Sp.: Lucuix Collection.

NN 0023487 TxU

Narvaja, Tristán, 1819-1877.
De la sociedad conyugal y las dotes, por d. Tristán Narvaja ... Nueva ed. Montevideo, El Anticuario, 1895. 94 p. 19™.
Cover dated 1896.

1. Husband and wife—Uruguay. 2. Dowry—Uruguay.
37-23449

NN 0023488 DLC

Narval, Edmond de.
... Notas de París ... Buenos Aires, Talleres gráficos argentinos L. J. Rosso, 1932.
277 p., 1 l. 18™.
"Es ... una recopilación de apuntes periodísticos enviados desde (París) ... de 1926 a 1928. La mayoría fueron publicados en 'Crítica' de Buenos Aires y los restantes en 'El Universal de Méjico, 'El Mundo' de la Habana, y otros periódicos hispanoamericanos."—p. (5)

1. Title.

Library of Congress   PQ7797.N35N7   34-3145
(2)   864.6

NN 0023489 DLC DPU TxU CtY

AP21 .R37   Narval, Edmond de, ed.
La Revue argentine. -6. année (no.   -31/32); -avril/août 1939. Paris (19 -39)

Narval, Louis, pseud.
see
Lesigne, Ernest.

Narvedsen, O.
Spioner på indlandsisen. (København) Gyldendal, 1954. 98p. 22 cm.

1. Title.
PZ55.N6   54-30529 ‡

NN 0023492 DLC

Narvesens kioskkompani, a/s, Oslo.
...Mange bekker små; Narvesens kioskkompani gjennem 50 år, 1894-1944. Oslo, 1951. 152 p. illus. 30cm.
At head of title: Eivind Thon.

1. News-dealers—Norway.   I. Thon, Eivind. 1889-

NN 0023493 NN

Narveson, Bert Henry, 1898-
Luther Academy; memorial history, 1868-1928. Northfield, Minn., St. Olaf College Press, 1951.
288 p. illus., ports. 22cm.
1. Luther Academy, Albert Lea, Minn.

NN 0023494 MnU

57.7 N16   Narvestad, Kjell.
Kort rettleiing i gjødsling og kalking. Kort rettleiing i silonedlegging av Knut T. Sorteberg. (Ål) Ål jordstyre (1954?) 11 p.

NN 0023495 DNAL

Narvig, William van, *pseud.*
see
Lucas, William O

Narvik sparebank.
Narvik sparebank, 1903-1953. Narvik, Fremover aksidenstrykkeri (1953) 57 p. illus. 29 cm.

(HG3170.N34N313   54-39579 ‡

NN 0023497 DLC NN

VOLUME 405

NARVIK, victoire française. [n. p., 194-] [32] p.
(chiefly illus.) 28cm.

Introduction signed: M. E. Béthouart.

1. Narvik, Battle of, 1940. I. Béthouart, Marie Émile, 1889-

NN 0023498   NN

Narwa hüdro-elektrijaama projekteerimisbüroo.
...Naroowa weejõu kasutamise kawa... Tallinn: "Waba
Maa," 1922. 13 p. diagrs., illus. maps, col'd plate. 4°.

Text on reverse of plate in Esthonian and German.

1. Water power, Russia: Narva.   2. Electricity—Power plants and
N.Y.P.L.   stations, Russia: Narva.
                                         May 13, 1925

NN 0023499   NN

Nary, Cornelius, LL. D. 1660-1738. Case of
the Roman Catholicks of Ireland. 21 pp. (Reily, H.,
Impartial hist. of Ireland, p. 112.)

NN 0023500   MdBP

Nary, Cornelius, 1660-1738.
Reily, Hugh, d. 1695?
The impartial history of Ireland. Containing, a sum-
mary account of the battles, sieges, rebellions and massa-
cres ... Together with the most remarkable transactions
both in church and state, since the reformation ... By
Hugh Reily, esq; to which is annexed, the nobility and
gentry of Ireland's remonstrance to King Charles the
Second, on his restoration ... Likewise the Case of the
Roman Catholicks of Ireland ... The latter, by the Revd.
Doĉtor Nary ... London, re-printed [17—?]

Nary, Cornelius, 1660-1738.
A letter to His Grace Edward [Synge] Lord
Arch-bishop of Tuam. In answer to his Charit-
able address. To all who are of the communion
of the Church of Rome ... Dublin, 1728.
WILLIAM
ANDREWS 235,[1] p. 19½cm.

NN 0023502   CLU-C MiU MWA

[Nary, Cornelius] 1660-1738.
A modest and true account of the chief
points in controversie between the Roman Ca-
tholics, and the Protestants: together with
WILLIAM some considerations upon the sermons of a di-
ANDREWS vine of the Church of England [i.e. John Til-
CLARK lotson]. By N.C. ... Antwerp, 1696.
MEMORIAL
LIBRARY [14],301 p. 18½cm.

Has been attributed to Nicholas Colson.

Wing C-5422

NN 0023503   CLU-C

[Nary, Cornelius] 1660-1738, supposed author.
A modest and true account of the chief points
in controversie, between the Roman Catholicks.
And the Protestants; together with some consid-
WILLIAM erations upon the sermons of a divine of the
ANDREWS Church of England. By N. C. ... Antwerp, Print-
CLARK ed in the year 1705.
MEMORIAL
LIBRARY 302 p. 18½cm.

Also attributed to Nicholas Colson.

NN 0023504   CLU-C DCU NjP DFo NNUT NNG

Nary, Cornelius, 1660-1738.
A new history of the world, containing an
historical and chronological account of the times
and transactions, from the creation to the birth
of our Lord Jesus Christ, according to the
computation of the Septuagint, which the author
manifestly shews to be that of the ancient Hebrew
copy of the Bible. Together with chronological
tables at the end of each age... Dublin, Printed
by Edward Waters, for Luke Dowling, 1720.
iv, 5-496p. 33cm.

1. World history - Early works to 1800. i.
Bible. O. T. Greek.   Selections. 1720.
Septuagint.

NN 0023505   FMU PPL

Nary, Cornelius, 1660-1738, tr.
The New Testament of Our Lord and Saviour
Jesus Christ, newly translated out of the Latin
Vulgat ...
      see under   Bible. N. T. English.
1718. Nary. (also 1719)

DA940   Nary, Cornelius, 1660-1738.
.R316   Reily, Hugh, d. 1695?
Stair fhír-cheart ar Éirinn. Mar aon le dearbhadh
chatoilicithe na h-Éireann don Dara Séarlus; Óráid Oiliféir
Plaincéad; Coinghill Luimnigh; agus Cás na gCatoilicithe
(Dr. Nary) Uilliam Ó Murchadha do chuir i nGaedhilg.
Nessa Ní Sheaghdha do chuir i n-eagar. Baile Átha Cliath,
Oifig an tSoláthair, 1941.

Narychkine, Mara de, joint author.

Máday, Andor, 1877-
La classification décimale et son application dans une bibliothèque spécialisée.

(In Revue des bibliothèques. Paris, 1928. 25cm. v. 38, p. [241]-276.
illus.)

Нарым; очерки и статьи. Новосибирск, Западно-Сибирское
краевое изд-во, 1936.

190 p. illus. 18 cm.

1. Narym, Siberia (District)—Descr. & trav.
                                  Title transliterated: Narym.

DK771.N3N35   49-39562*

NN 0023509   DLC

QH161   Naryshkin, Vasilii L'vovich.
.P23   **Pady.**
Пады; имѣніе Василія Львовича Нарышкина. Есте-
ственно-историческій очеркъ, составленный П. А.
Земятченскимъ, А. А. Силантьевымъ и В. А. Транше-
лемъ. Под общей ред. В. В. Докучаева. Изд. В. Л.
Нарышкина. С.-Петербургъ, Тип. Е. Евдокимова, 1894.

Naryshkin, Vasilii L'vovich, 1841-1906.
Catalogue des tableaux anciens et modernes composant la collection de M. B. Narischkine dont la vente aura lieu... Galerie G.
Petit... 5 avril 1883... [Paris, 1883] vi, 64 p., 17 pl.
32½cm.

Bound with: Stein, Charles. Catalogue des objets d'art de haute curiosité et
d'ameublement. [Paris, 1886]

185136B. 1. Art—Collections, Private   —Naryshkin. I. Petit, Georges.
firm, art dealers, Paris.
N.Y.P.L.   August 6, 1942

NN 0023511   NN MdBP

Naryshkina, E   A
Sur les vibrations d'un demi-espace aux conditions initiales arbitraires. Leningrad, Académie
des sciences de l'URSS, 1934.
71 p. illus. (Publications de l'Institut
séismologique, No 45)
At head of title: Académie des sciences de
l'Union des républiques soviétiques socialistes.
E. Naryškina (C. Narychkina)
In the CENTER FOR RESEARCH LIBRARIES

NN 0023512   ICRL DLC

Naryshkina, E   A
Über die Schwingungen des festen elastischen Halb-
raumes der längs der Ebene mit einer elastischen
kompressiblen Flüssigkeit grenzt. Ленинград, Изд-во
Академии наук, 1933.
40 p. illus. (Труды Сейсмологического ин-та,
№ 21)
At head of title: Академия наук Союза Советских
Социалистических Республик.
Summary in Russian.
In the CENTER FOR RESEARCH LIBRARIES

NN 0023513   ICRL

Naryshkina, Elizaveta (Kurakina)
Under three tsars; the memoirs of the lady-in-waiting,
Elizabeth Narishkin-Kurakin, edited by René Fülöp-Miller;
translated from the German by Julia E. Loesser; with fifty
illustrations. New York, E. P. Dutton & co., inc. [1931]
viii p., 2 l., 3-231 p. plates, ports. 21 cm.
"First edition."

1. Russia—Court and courtiers. 2. Romanov, House of. I. Fülöp-
Miller, René, 1891-   ed. II. Loesser, Julia (Ehrlich) 1881-   tr.
III. Title.   Full name: Elizaveta Alekseevna (Kurakina) Naryshkina.

DK188.6.N25A32   920.7   31—4288

ViU NN PP CaOTP OOxM MeB TxU CU
NN 0023514   DLC NIC MH WaSp OrP OC1 OCU ODW MB NN

Naryshkina, Elizaveta (Kurakina)
Unter drei zaren, die memoiren der hofmar-
schallin Elisabeth Narischkin-Kurakin, herausgegeben von René Fülöp-Miller. Mit 63 abbildungen.
Zürich [etc.] Amalthea-verlag [c1930]
278 p.

NN 0023515   ICN MH OC1 NN CoU NjP TxU IEN

Naryshkina, Nataliia Fedorovna (Rostopchina) 1797-1863.
1812 [i. e. Dix-huit cent douze]; le comte Rostopchine et
son temps. St.-Pétersbourg, R. Golicke et A. Willborg, 1912.
267 p. ports. 24 cm.

1. Rostopchin, Fedor Vasil'evich, graf, 1763-1826. I. Title.

DK190.6.R6N37   52-55479

NN 0023516   DLC MB

Law   Naryshkina, Rimma Leonidovna.
                FOR OTHER EDITIONS
                SEE MAIN ENTRY
Czechoslovak Republic. Laws, statutes, etc.
Конституция и основные законодательные акты Чехо-
словацкой Республики. Перевод с чешского. Под ред.
и с предисл. В. Ф. Котока. [Составители: И. С. Розенталь
и Р. Л. Нарышкина] Москва, Изд-во иностранной лите-
ры, 1955.

Naryshkina, Viera Sergieevna (Witte)
A Pétrograd pendant la Révolution; notes et souvenirs
[par] Vera Narischkina-Witte. Paris, Éditions Baudinière
[1925]
219 p. 19 cm. (Bibliothèque du lettré)

1. Russia—Hist.—Revolution, 1917-1921—Personal narratives.
I. Title.   (Series)

DK265.7.N33   67-123334

NN 0023518   DLC KyLoU NIC MH NN CSt-H ICU IU CaBVaU

VOLUME 405

Naryshkina, Vîera Sergîeevna (Witte)

...A Petrograd pendant la révolution (notes et souvenirs) Paris, Éditions Baudinière [1945]
219 p. 19 ᶜᵐ. (Bibliothèque du lettré)

1. Russia - Hist. - Revolution, 1917-1921.

NN 0023519 NjR NNC

Naryshkina, Vîera Sergîeevna (Witte)
... Souvenirs d'une fillette russe, 1890-1900. Paris, Baudinière [1925]
6 p. l., [15]-251 p., 2 l. 19ᶜᵐ. (*On cover:* Bibliothèque du lettré)
At head of title: Vera Narischkine-Witte.
On cover: Deuxième mille.

I. Title.

Library of Congress   PQ2627.A68S6 1925

26-20922

NN 0023520 DLC

Naryshkina, Vyera Sergyeyvna (Witte)

SEE

Naryshkina, Vîera Sergîeevna (Witte)

Нариси з історії техніки. вип. 1-7. Київ, Вид-во Академії наук УРСР, 1954-61.

7 v. illus., ports. 23 cm. annual.

Issued by Viddil tekhnichnykh nauk of the Akademiîâ nauk Ukraïns'koï RSR.
Superseded in 1962 by Нариси з історії техніки і природознавства.
L. C. set incomplete: v. 4-5 wanting.

1. Technology—Hist.—Ukraine.   I. Akademiîâ nauk URSR, Kiev. Viddil tekhnichnykh nauk.
Title transliterated: Narysy z istoriî tekhniky.

T26.R9N3   59-29256 rev

NN 0023522 DLC

Нариси з історії України.
Київ.
v. 22 cm.
Issued by Instytut istoriî Ukraïny of Akademiîâ nauk URSR.

1. Ukraine—Hist.—Period.   I. Akademiîâ nauk URSR, Kiev. Instytut istoriî Ukraïny.
Title transliterated: Narysy z istoriî Ukraïny.

DK508.A2A3497   52-34089

NN 0023523 DLC

Narz, F A
Figuralmelodien zu J. Johlson's deutschem Geangbuch für israelitische Schulen ... gesammelt und theils componirt von F. A. Narz. Heft 1-2. Frankfurt a. M., A. Fisher [182-?]
2 v. [bd. in one]

NN 0023524 OCH

Narzakian, Donna Dell.
Petrie finds Santa Claus, by Donna Dell [pseud.] Illustrated by Barbara Koski. New York, Comet Press Books [1955]
unpaged. illus. 15 x 22 cm.

I. Title.

PZ8.9.N3Pe   55-12200 ‡

NN 0023525 DLC

Narzanes; or, The injur'd statesman, containing the most important negotiations, and transactions of that great minister whilst he presided over the affairs of Persia... London: Printed for, and sold by T. Payne, 1755.   4 p.l., 104 p.   16°.

88352A. 1. Satire (English).
N.Y.P.L.
June 26, 1923.

NN 0023526 NN MnU MiU

Narzedzia i miejsca meki Pańskiej ...
see under [Dombrowski, Joseph] 1842-1903.

QH191.   Narzikulov, Mukhamedkul Narzikulovich, ed.
.U87   Ущелье Кондара; опыт биологической монографии. Москва, Изд-во Академии наук СССР, 1951-

---

Narzymski, Józef.
Pan prezydent w kłopotach. Obrazek sceniczny w 2 aktach, przez Józefa Narzymskiego. Lwów: B. Połoniecki, 1913. 64 p. 16°. (Teatr dla wszystkich. Nr. 38.)

1. Drama (Polish). 2. Title.
N.Y.P.L.
June 17, 1916.

NN 0023529 NN

Law   **Nas, J. H. M., ed.**   FOR OTHER EDITIONS
SEE MAIN ENTRY

Netherlands (*Kingdom, 1815-*) *Laws, statutes, etc.*
Pachtbesluit 1941; zoals, gewijzigd, gehandhaafd bij Pachtregeling 1945, Stb. F 279, Pachtvoorzieningen 1947 en 1950, Stb. H 142 en K 110, bij de Wet van 26 Maart 1952, Stb. 147, bij de Wet van 2 Januari 1953, Stb. 17 en de Wet van 12 Maart 1953, Stb. 99 en laatstelijk bij de Wet bezettingsmaatregelen IV 1955, Stb. 18, met enige uitvoeringsbesluiten en de "Pachtregeling militair gezag." Tekstuitgave 1955, bewerkt door J. H. M. Nas. Zwolle, W. E. J. Tjeenk Willink, 1955.

Nas, Johann, 1534-1590.
see Nase, Johann, 1534-1590.

Nas de Tourris, V. de.
La réforme monétaire au Siam.   Paris: E. Larose, 1911. 3 p.l., (1)4-161 p., 1 l.   4°.

1. Money, Siam, 1911.
N.Y.P.L.
October 26, 1912.

NN 0023532 NN MH

Nas Udin
see
Udin, Nas.

Nas amorosas finezas os mais constantes realces
see Comedia famosa, intitulada Nas amorosas finezas os mais constantes realces.

---

49   Náš chov. roc. 1, cislo 13/14-
N17   1941-   Praha
[Jednota Svaz Českých Zenědělcu]
Has supplement, Chovatelský pokrok (49 C452)
Begining 1954, paged and bound in main publication.
Some issues have supplement Zpravodaj, chovatelu a zootechniku.

NN 0023535 DNAL

057.86   Náš cíl; list vlasteneckého hnutí čechoslováků.
NASC   roč. 1, čís. 1-22; 1. led.-15. list. 1923.
1v. 32cm.

NN 0023536 IU

Náš dorost technický a život praktiský ...
see under Masaryková akademie práce, Prague.

Nas fronteiras do Brasil; missões salesianas do Amazonas
see under Missões Salesianas do Amazonas.

4DR   Náš državni praznik, 29. november.
Yugo-   Ljubljana [Ljudska prosveta] 1946.
41   59 p.

NN 0023539 DLC-P4

Greenlee
4504
P855   NAS faustissimas melhoras do serenissimo senhor d. Joaõ, Principe do Brazil ... Soneto. [n.p., ca.1789]
[1]p. 21cm.

NN 0023540 ICN

PG 5041   NÁS HLAS;ALMANACH SLEZSKÉHO PÍSEMNICTVÍ KRÁSNÉHO.
.S6 N24   Uspořádal Jan Strakoš. Ve Frýdku "Přítomnost", 1935.
193 p. illus.

1. Czech literature--Silesia, Czechoslovak Republic--Coll. I. Strakos, Jan, 1877- , ed.

NN 0023541 InU

NÁŠ Jadran, prirodne ljepote i umjetnost uredili Fisković Cvito, Magjer Drago, Parać Vjekoslav, Uvodie Angjeo.   Split, Izdaje Arhiv za propagandu Jadrana, Izvršnog odbora Jadranske straže, 1938.
68 p.   214 plates.   30cm.   (Biblioteka Arhiva za propagandu Jadrana)

1. Dalmatia--Civilization. 2. Dalmatia—Views. 3. Architecture—Yugoslavia--Dalmatia. 4. Painting, Dalmatian. 5. Sculpture, Dalmatian. I. Fisković, Cvito, ed. II. Jadranska straža, split, Yugoslavia. Arhiv za propaganda Jadrana.

NN 0023542 NN NNC

Наш језик. г. 1- : 1933- : нова сер., књ. 1-
1949-
Београд.
v. in   23 cm.   monthly (except July and Aug.)
Publication suspended 19
Issued by Lingvističko društvo, 1933- ; by Institut za srpski jezik of Srpska akademija nauka, 1949-

1. Serbo-Croatian language—Period.   I. Lingvističko društvo, Belgrad. II. Srpska akademija nauka, Belgrad. Institut za srpski jezik.   *Title transliterated:* Naš jezik.

PG1201.N3   38-1528 rev 2*

PPiU
NN 0023543 DLC CLSU CaBVaU CSt FTaSU NcU KU NIC

Náš kalendár.
[Budapest, L. Vállalat]
v. illus., ports. 24 cm.
Issued, 19   by Sväz demokratických Slovákov v Mad'arsku.

1. Almanacs, Slovak—Hungary.   I. Sväz demokratických Slovákov v Mad'arsku.

AY809.S5N3   61-36128

NN 0023544 DLC

VOLUME 405

057.87   Náš ľud; ľudovýchovný vestník pre Slovensko.
NAL   roč. 1-10; 23. okt. 1928-15. jún. 1938.
           Bratislava.
           10v. illus. 24cm. monthly (except during
           summer months)

NN   0023545   IU

DB 661   Náš národ. roč. 1-
.N24   sept. 1943-
           Bratislava, Slovenská liga.
           "Vydáva Vedecká spoločnosť
           pre zahraničných Slovákov."

           1. Slovaks--Period. 2. Periodicals
           (Slovak) I. Vedecka spoločnost pre
           zahraničnych Slovákov.

NN   0023546   ICU

Náš odboj; tourné výstavy "Památníku odboje" odd. M. N. O.
₍Praha: Grafia,₎ 1920.   64 p. (incl. facsim., plates.)   8°.

1. European war, 1914-1918--Czecho-   Slovakia.
N.Y.P.L.   August 31, 1926

NN   0023547   NN MB

D   Naš odboj; výstava Obecní dům hlav. mesta
558   Prahy, 28. X-31. XII, 1919. ₍V Praze, 1920₎
N3   76p. illus. 24cm.

          1. European War, 1914-1918 - Czechoslovak
          Republic

NN   0023548   WU

Naš rad. 1-   1 kol. 1953-
Zagreb.
     v. in   illus., ports., maps. 29 cm. Irregular.
     Journal of Zavod za geološka istraživanja N. R. Hrvatske, Geol-
     straživanja, and Geofizika.
     Vols. 1-2 called also no. 1-12.

     1. Prospecting—Geophysical methods—Period.   I. Zagreb.
     Zavod za geološka istraživanja.   II. Geolstraživanja, Zagreb.   III.
     Geofizika, Zagreb.
     TN269.N3   58-39188

NN   0023549   DLC

SERIAL
AP56   Naš rod. 1.-   letnik; 1929/30-
N33   ₍Ljubljana₎
          Issued by Udruženje ucitelja Jugoslavije
          (called 1929-31 Udruženje jugoslovenskih učitel-
          jstva; 1931- Jugcslovensko učiteljsko udru-
          ženje)

          I. Udruženje učitelja Jugoslavije

NN   0023550   CSt

Náš rozhlas
     see   Československý rozhlas.

Наш саобраһаj. г. 1-
1950-
Београд.
     v. illus. 24 cm. monthly.
     Issued 1950-( )1951 by Ministarstvo saobraćaja of Serbia;
     .Dec. 1951, by Glavna uprava za saobraćaj i puteve; Jan.
1952-   by Savet za saobraćaj.

     1. Automobiles—Period. 2. Motor vehicles—Period.   I. Serbia
(Federated Republic, 1945-   ) Ministarstvo saobraćaja. II. Serbia
(Federated Republic, 1945-   ) Glavna uprava za saobraćaj i
puteve. III. Serbia (Federated Republic, 1945-   ) Savet za saobra-
ćaj.   Title transliterated: Naš saobraćaj.
TL4.N3   56-28214

NN   0023552   DLC

Slavic   Náš Směr; zpravodaj strany Čs. Národních
American   socialistu v exilu. v. 1-
Imprints   1952-   New York, Strana Čs,
Coll.   Národních socialistu v exilu.
420.22
N38   no.   28 x 22 cm.

            English translation of title: Our
            direction; the reporter of Czechoslovak
            National Socialist party in exile.

NN   0023553   IEdS

Náš svet; obrázkový a spoločenský časopis slovenského ľudu.
Ročník 1

Chicago: J. Dendúr, 1930-   f°.
     v.   illus.
     Semi-monthly.
     Sub-title varies.

1. Periodicals—U. S., Slovak.
N.Y.P.L.   June 24, 1932

NN   0023554   NN

B 809.8   NAŠ SVETOVNI NAZOR; TEORIJA IN RAZVOJ
.N24   dialektičnega materializma. / Po Thalheimerju
            in drugih teoretikih socializma priredil
            Sigma ₍pseud.₎   ₍V Ljubljani₎ Cankarjeva
            družba, 1934.
            108 p.

            1. Dialectical materialism. I. Sigma, pseud.
            II. Thalheimer, August.

NN   0023555   InU MH

Náš tednik-kronika; kulturno-politično glasilo svetovnih in
domačih dogodkov.
Celovec, Narodni svet koroških Slovencev.
     v. illus., ports. 46 cm.
     Began publication in 1948.
     Title varies: 1948, Naš tednik.
     Absorbed Koroška kronika in 1949.

AP58.S55K62   64-38144

NN   0023556   DLC

015.4367
N17   Naš tisk; bibliografski katalog. let. 1-2,
           št. 3/6; jan. 1946-apr. 1947. Ljubljana
           ₍Drž. založba Slovenije₎
           2v. 21cm.

           Title varies: 1946 no. 1-2, Slovenski tisk.
           Superseded by Državna založba Slovenije.
           Objave DZS.

NN   0023557   IU

F2611   Nas vesperas de um pleito; documentos politi-
N3   cos. Rio de Janeiro, Typ. do Jornal do
             commercio de Rodrigues, 1923.
Stack   29 p. 24cm.
             Pref. signed: Manuel Duarte.
             Contents.-Defendo o tenente, by Brasilio
             Taborda.-Uma victoria da moral politica, by
             Joaquim de Mello.-Acto n.512, de 3 abril de
             1923, by Cantidiano Gomes da Rosa.

             1. Sodre, Feliciano Pires de Abreu. 2. Rio
             de Janeiro (State) - Pol. & govt. I. Duarte,
             Manuel.

NN   0023558   CSt

Nas vrt
     see   Hortikultura.

Нас вырастил Сталин; рассказы лауреатов Сталинских
премий. ₍Москва₎ Профиздат, 1950.
     317 p. ports. 23 cm.

     1. Labor and laboring classes—Russia—Biog. 2. Stalin prizes.
                                Title transliterated: Nas vyrastil Stalin.
HD8527.A1N3   51-16101

NN   0023560   DLC

Nas život; časopis Matice slov. v
Juhoslavii v. 1-   1933-
Petrovacz.
     Slovak

NN   0023561   OCl

Naš životni standard. ₍Zagreb, Izd. Komisije za agitaciju i
štampu Glavnog odbora Narodnog fronta Hrvatske, 1950₎
     1 v. (chiefly illus.) 19 x 21 cm.

     1. Croatia—Descr. & trav.—Views. 2. Croatia—Econ. condit.
3. Croatia—Soc. condit.
DB369.N37   55-30165 ‡

NN   0023562   DLC

Naša. Veselohra v jednom dejstve
     see under   Hurban, Vladimír, 1884-

Naša borba. [Srem]
     God. 2-4 (1942-44)
     Organ of Komunistička partija Jugoslavije
     za Vojvodinu
     Phototypic reproduction
     Bound with Udarnik; organ Okružnog komiteta
     Komunističke partije Jugoslavije za Srem
     At head of title: Muzej radničkog pokreta i
     narodne revolucije Vojvodine. Istorijski arhiv
     Pokrajinskog komiteta SKS za Vojvodinu. Matica
     srpska

NN   0023564   MH

NAŠA dedinka; obrázky zo sociálneho a mravné
ho života našich roľníkov. Spísal M. H. Vydal
Martin Kollár. V Trnave, tlačou A. Horovitza,
1889.

     pp. 52.

NN   0023565   MH

HS3325   Naša djeca. Glavni odbor.
Y8K67   Osnivanje društava "Naša djeca" i njihov rad sa pionirima.
           Zagreb, 1951.
           8 p. (Prilog "Biblioteke Saveza Pionira" NRH)

           Bound with Koritnik, M. Kako ćemo organizirati Pozdrav
           proljeću. 1951.

           1. Youth movement - Yugoslavia. I. Savez pionira N R
Hrvatske. /Biblioteka. Prilog. II. Title.

NN   0023566   CU

A90   Naša doba; revija za javna vprašanja.
N16   letnik 1-   1930-
           V Ljubljani, Narodna Tiskarna
           v. illus. 24 cm.

           1. Periodicals - Slovenia.

NN   0023567   CtY MH IU

VOLUME 405

DB
366
N17

Naša domovina; zbornik. Zagreb, Izd. Glavnog ustaskog stana, 1943-
v. in

Contents.- knj. 1. Nezavisna Država Hrvatska.
sv. 1. Hrvatska zemlja. Hrvatski narod. Hrvatska poviest. Hrvatska znanost.- sv. 2. Hrvatska kultura. Politička poviest Hrvata.

1. Croatia.

NN 0023568   CLU MU IU NcU

Naša fotografija; mjesečnik za stručnu i umjetničku foto-
grafiju.
Zagreb, "FOZA," nabavljačka zadruga fotografskih obrt-
nika NR Hrvatske.
v. in   illus., ports. 29 cm.
Began publication in 1947.

1. Photography—Period.

TR1.N25   58-15787

NN 0023569   DLC

"Naša izjava" i "K našoj izjavi"; stanovište hrvatskog i
slovenačkog svećenstva u Americi gledom na jugoslavensku,
bolje veliko-srpsku propagandu u Americi. New York,
Croatian Print. and Pub. Co., 1916.
32 p. 24 cm.
Signed: K.

1. European War, 1914-1918—Territorial questions—Croatia. 2.
Croatia—Relations (general) with Serbia. 3. Serbia—Relations
(general) with Croatia.   I. K.

D651.C78N3   68-38946 ‡

NN 0023570   DLC

Naša krila, nedeljni ilustrovani avijatički list, organ Aero-
kluba kralj. Jugoslavije ...
Beograd, 19
no. illus. 37 x 31¼ᶜᵐ.

1. Aeronautics—Period. 2. Aeronautics—Yugoslavia.   I. Aero-klub
kraljévine Jugoslavije.

                                   34-34127
Library of Congress   TL504.N3   629.1305

NN 0023571   DLC

Naša nada; hrvatski katolički pučki kalendar.
Chicago, Ill.
v. illus., ports. 24 cm.
Issued by the Croatian Catholic Union.

1. Almanacs, Croatian—U. S. 2. Croatians in the U. S. 3. Catholic
Church—Yearbooks.   I. Croatian Catholic Union.

AY81.R6N28   51-19130

NN 0023572   DLC

Naša nada kalendar...
19

Pittsburgh ₁19   23cm.
v. illus. (incl. ports.), tables.
"Izdala Hrvatska katolička zajednica u Sjed. Državama Amerike."
Editor : 19   , F. X. Kolander.

1. Almanacs—U. S., Croatian.   I. Hrvatska katolička zajednica u
Sjedinjenim Državama Amerike.
N. Y. L.   January 29, 1942

NN 0023573   NN

Naša nada, kalendar za Americke Katolicke
Hrvate... Cleveland, Tiskara "Americka
Domovina".

NN 0023574   OC1 InU

Naša narodna umjetnost. ₁Split, Narodna tiskara "Novo
doba," 1931₁
16 p. illus., ports., plates. 23½ᶜᵐ.

1. Art—Yugoslavia. 2. Embroidery—Yugoslavia.

Library of Congress   N7248.N3   38-25436

NN 0023575   DLC

4JN
Yugo
6

Naša partija v borbi za enakopra-
vne odnose med socialistićnimi drzava-
mi; zbornik. Ljubljana [Cankarjeva
založba] 1949.
371 p.

NN 0023576   DLC-P4 NNC

Naša poljoprivreda. ₁Zagreb, Izd. Narodne fronte Hrvatske,
1950?₁
1 v. (chiefly illus.) 19 x 20 cm.

1. Agriculture—Yugoslavia.

S267.N3   54-31832 ‡

NN 0023577   DLC

Наша пошта. Naša pošta. Revue yougoslave des postes et
télécommunications. Свеска посвећена прослави Николе
Тесле. Volume dédié au jubilé de Nicolas Tesla. Beograd
₁Штампарија "Планета," 1932₁
cover-title, 1 p. l., 275-336 p. illus. (port.) 24 cm.
Reprinted from "Наши пошта. Naša pošta," v. 100-1, 1932.
CONTENTS.—Jubilé de Nicolas Tesla.—Писма ауторитета упућена
Тесли приликом прославе његове 75-год-ишњице. Lettres des auto-
rités adressées à Tesla à l'occasion de son 75-ème anniversaire.—На-
писи. Articles.—Оцене и прикази домаће и стране штампе. Literaturberichte.—Патенти Теслини. Teslasche patente in U. S. A.—Нове
књиге.

1. Tesla, Nikola, 1856-1943.   *Title transliterated:* Naša pošta.

TK140.T4N3   926.2   48-37101

NN 0023578   DLC CU

DR 381 NAŠA POTA. 1-
.S6 N24 1919-
V Ljubljani
v.

Issued by Slovenska krščanska socialna
zveza.

1. Slovenia--Pol. & gov't--Period. I. Slovenska
krščanska socialna zveza, Ljubljana.

NN 0023579   InU

Naša praksa.
₁Beograd, Rad₁
v. in   illus., ports. 31 cm. monthly.
Ceased publication with Dec. 1951 issue.
Journal of Državna investiciona banka FNRJ.
Serbian or Croatian.

1. Finance—Yugoslavia—Period. 2. Capital investments—Yugoslavia—Period.   I. Državna investiciona banka FNRJ, Belgrad.

HG37.Y8N3   58-47428
Library of Congress   ₁3₁

NN 0023580   DLC

Naša reč. North Harrow. no.1, 1948-   d. C. 0174-24—rev. 7/69

NN 0023581   CU

Naša rědna bajkojta domownja ...
see under Mětšk, Frido, comp.

Naša serbšćina, hornjołužiska. čo. 1-
1949-   Budyšin, Domovina.
Each issue has also a distinctive title.
1. Wendic language - Period.

NN 0023583   CLU

Naša škola.
Sarajevo ₁Pedagoško društvo SRBiH₁
v. illus. 24 cm. monthly, irregular (except July and Aug.)
Began with Jan./Feb. 1950 issue. Cf. New serial titles, 1961-65.

1. Education—Yugoslavia—Period.   I. Pedagoško društvo SR
BiH.

L51.N33   68-95701

NN 0023584   DLC CaBVaU

370.943735
N178   Naša škola; časopis venovaný otázkam národnej
škoły slovenskej. roč. 2-13; 1927-1937/38.
V Bratislave, Štatne nak-vo.
v. 24cm. monthly (irregular)

Vols. for 1935-36 accompanied by separately
paged supplement.

NN 0023585   IU

Naša sloboda.
Budapesť.
v. in   illus., ports., maps. 41 cm. weekly.
Issued, 19   by Sväz demokratických Slovákov v
Maďarsku.

I. Sväz demokratických Slovákov v Maďarsku.

AP58.S53N3   64-37777

NN 0023586   DLC

Naša sloga.
Narodna borba u Istri od 1870. do 1915. godine; prema
bilješkama iz "Naše Sloge." Zagreb, Jugoslavenska akademija znanosti i umjetnosti, 1952.
200 p. 24 cm. (Građa za noviju poviest Hrvatske, knj. 1)
At head of title: Fran Barbalić.

1. Istria—Hist.   I. Barbalić, Fran, 1878-   II. Title.

DB329.N37   55-31174

              InU ICU CSt CaBVaU
NN 0023587   DLC PSt CLU WU MiU CU MH NjP CtY NNC

Naša sodobnost
see
Sodobnost.

Наша штампа.
Београд.
v. in   illus., ports. 47 cm. monthly.
Vols.   called also no.
Issued, 19   by Savez novinara Jugoslavije.
Serbian or Croatian.

1. Journalism—Yugoslavia—Period.   I. Savez novinara Jugoslavije.   *Title transliterated:* Naša štampa.

PN5355.Y8N3   61-20499

NN 0023589   DLC

VOLUME 405

4PN   Naša štampa u borbi za slobodu i
659   izgradnju socijalizma. Zagreb,
      Izd. Ureda za informacije pri
      predsjedništvu vlade Narodne Repu-
      blike Hrvatske, 1948.
      142 p.

NN 0023590   DLC-P4 NNC

Naša stručna škola.

Beograd ₍Savez pedagoških društava Jugoslavije₎
    v. in   illus., ports. 39–48 cm. monthly.
    Began publication in 1953. Cf. New serial titles, 1950–60.
    Includes legislation of Yugoslavia.

    1. Vocational education — Yugoslavia. 2. Technical education —
Yugoslavia. ɪ. Yugoslavia. Laws, statutes, etc.

    LC1047.Y8N3   64–37344

NN 0023591   DLC

AP56   **Naša stvarnost.** 1/2–   sept./okt. 1936–
N336   Beograd.
        "Časopis za književnost, nauku, umetnost i sva
Stack   društvena i kulturna pitanja."

NN 0023592   CSt CU

NAŠA stvarnost. [br.]

Beograd.   no.   illus.   25cm.

Microfilm.
   "Časopis za književnost, nauku, umetnost i sva društvena i kulturna
pitanja."
   Edited by A. Vaučo.
   Ceased publication with Apr. 1939?
1. Periodicals--Yugoslavia.   I. Vaučo, Aleksandar, ed.

NN 0023593   NN KU

HX8   **Naša stvarnost;** časopis za društvena pitanja. g. 1–17; okt.
.N25   1946–nov./dec. 1963. ₍Beograd₎
      17 v. in 24. 23 cm.
      Frequency varies.
      Vol. 1–2 called also no. 1–3.
      Organ of Savez Komunista Jugoslavije (under its earlier name:
Komunistička partija Jugoslavije), 1946–62; also of its Centralni
komitet, 1946–Jan. 1951.
      Title varies: 1946–52, Комунист.
      Absorbed by Socijalizam.

      L C set incomplete: v. 3, no. 4; v. 5, no. 6; v. 7, no. 5–12; v. 9, no.
2, 10–12 wanting.
      INDEXES:
        Author index.
        Vols. 7–17, 1953–63, with v. 17.

      1. Communism--Yugoslavia--Period. ɪ. Savez komunista Jugo-
slavije. ɪɪ. Savez komunista Jugoslavije. Centralni komitet. ɪɪɪ.
Title: Komunist₎

    HX8.N25   66–88366

NN 0023595   DLC

Naša trgovina; mjesečnik za pitanja uvoza, izvoza, otkupa,
trgovine, ugostiteljstva i turizma. god. 1–
   1950–
   ₍Zagreb, Progres₎
      v. illus. 24 cm.
      Subtitle varies.

      1. Croatia--Comm.--Period.

    HF13.N3   58–46817

NN 0023596   DLC

Naša unjetnost. Zagreb ₍Almanah Kraljevine
Yugoslavije₎ 1938.

    53 p.   illus. 26cm. (Priručna Biblioteka
Almanaha Kraljevine Jugoslavije; posebo izdanje,
glavni urednik Viktor Hanakin, sveska 7)

NN 0023597   CaBVaU

21.5   **Naša vas;** list slovenskega Kmetijskega
N17   Zadružništva. v.1, وها
       June, 1952.
       [Ljubljana] Kmetijske zadruge.

      1. Yugoslavia. Agriculture. Periodicals.
      I. Kmetijske zadruge, Ljubljana.

NN 0023598   DNAL

Naša veda
    see
Svet vedy.

Наша заједница. год. 1–
  25 sept. 1935–
  Београд.
      v. in   illus., ports., maps. 40 cm. biweekly.
      Organ of Savezni odbor of Socijalistički savez radnog naroda Jugo-
slavije.
      Serbian or Croatian.

      1. Yugoslavia—Econ. condit.—1945- —Period. ɪ. Sociali-
stički savez radnog naroda Jugoslavije.
                       Title transliterated: Naša zajednica.

    HC407.Y6A146   58–45599

NN 0023600   DLC

K   **Nasa zakonitost.** g. 1–   1947–
.N124   Zagreb.
        v. 24cm.

      "Organ Saveza drustava pravnika Hrvatske,
Udruženja za upravne nauke i praksu Hrvatske
i Republičkog zavoda za javnu upravu SR
Hrvatske."
      1. Law–Yugoslavia. I. Savez društava pravnika
Hrvatske. II. Udruženja za upravne nauke i praksu
Hrvatske. III. Republički zavod za javnu upravu
SR Hrvatske, Zagreb.

NN 0023601   ViU IU KU

Nasa zdravila in njih uporaba v domacem
zdravljenju; po izkusenih virih sestavil
A.M. [168p.] Ljubljana Zalozila Katoliska
bukvarna, 1914.

NN 0023602   OC1

Naša žena.
   ₍V Ljubljani₎
      v. illus., ports., maps. monthly.
      Issued 19   by Glavni odbor of the Antifašistična fronta
žena Slovenije.
      Vol. for 1951, no. 1 called also v. 10, no. 1; no. 2–12 called v. 9.
      Supplements accompany some issues.

      ɪ. Antifašistična fronta žena Slovenije.

    AP58.S55N32   58–48134

NN 0023603   DLC

Наша жена.
  Цетиње, 19
    و v. in 1 illus., ports. 29 cm. irregular.
    Issued by Glavni odbor of the Antifašistički front žena Crne Gore.

      1. Women in Yugoslavia—Period. ɪ. Antifašistički front žena
Crne Gore.   *Title transliterated: Naša žena.*

    HQ1715.5.A1N3   60–17935

NN 0023604   DLC

PG5441   **Naša zlata šariščina.** [Pozbiral Josif Mihaly]
P7   Perth Amboy, N.J., Printed by Vostok [1939]
N37   66 p. illus. 20 cm.

      Poems.

      1. Slovak poetry – Prešov, Czechoslovak
Republic (Region) I. Mihály, Joseph, 1907–
ed.

NN 0023605   CtY

Nasackin, Bernhard von.
   Die Stürme der Ostsee. Von Bernhard von Nasackin. (Der
Akademie vorgelegt am 11. September 1890.) St. Petersburg:
Eggers & Co., 1890. 1 p.l., 40 p. Tables. f°. (Impera-
torskaya Akademiya Nauk. Repertorium für Meteorologie. Bd.
14, no. 2.)

1. Storms, Baltic sea. 2. Series.
N. Y. P. L.   July 26, 1917.

NN 0023606   NN

BP   **al-Nasafī, ʻAbd Allāh ibn Aḥmad,** d. 1310.
167   Imami Nesefinin sözlerinden [hazırlayan]
N35   L. Lutfi. Istanbul, Selâmet Matbaası, 1931.
      14p.

      1. Islam—Addresses, essays, lectures.
      I. Lutfi, L

NN 0023607   UU

---

al-Nasafī, ʻAbd Allāh ibn Aḥmad, *d.* 1310.
   عمدة عقيدة اهل السنة والجماعة Pillar of the creed of
the Sunnites: being a brief exposition of their principal
tenets by Háfidh-uldín Abú'lbarakát Abd-ullah Alnasafi.
To which is subjoined a shorter treatise of a similar
nature by Najm-uldín Abú Hafs Umar Alnasafi. Edited
by William Cureton. London, Society for the Publication of Oriental Texts; sold by J. Madden, 1843.
    xiv, 29, 5 p.; 8 p. 27 cm.

     مقائد لنجم الدين ابي حفص النسفي: — p. 1–5 (3d group)

    ɪ. al-Nasafī, ʻUmar ibn Muḥammad, 1068?–1142. ɪɪ. al-ʻAqāʼid. ɪɪɪ.
Cureton, William, 1808–1864, ed. ɪɪɪ. Title. ɪv. Title: Pillar of the
creed of the Sunnites.
        Title transliterated: ʻUmdat ʻaqīdat ahl al-sunnah wa-al-jamāʻah.

    BP195.S8N3 1843   55–51539 rev

NN 0023609   DLC OCH MH ICU

---

al-Nasafī, ʻAbd Allāh ibn Aḥmad, *d.* 1310.
   تفسير القرآن الجليل المسمى بمدارك التنزيل وحقائق التأويل.
   تأليف ابى البركات عبد الله بن احمد بن محمود النسفي. القاهرة،
   المطبعة الاميرية، ١٩٣٩–١٩٦١، حقيقة ١٩٦٢–٦٢.
    3 v. 28 cm.
    Vol. 1 issued in 1943.
    Vol. 3 has imprint: القاهرة، الهيئة العامة لشئون المطابع الاميرية

      1. Koran—Commentaries. ɪ. Title: Madārik al-tanzīl wa-ḥaqāʼiq
al-taʼwīl.
                     Title transliterated: Tafsīr al-Qurʼān.

    BP130.4.N3   N E 63–79
    Princeton Univ. Libr.
    for Library of Congress   ₍2₎†   PL 480: UAR–809

NN 0023610   DLC NjP

BP130   **al-Nasafī, ʻAbd Allāh ibn Aḥmad,** d. 1310.
.4   Tafsīr al-Qurʼān al-jalīl.
.K35 **al-Khāzin al-Baghdādī, ʻAlī ibn Muḥammad,** 1279 *or 80*–
1883   1341.
Orien   تفسير القرآن الجليل المسمى لباب التأويل فى معانى التنزيل،
    تأليف علاء الدين على بن محمد بن ابراهيم البغدادى الصوفى
    المعروف بالخازن. وقد حلى هامش هذا الكتاب بالتفسير المسمى
    بمدارك التنزيل وحقائق التأويل، تأليف ابى البركات عبد الله بن
    احمد بن محمود النسفي. ومصر، المطبعة الازهرية، ١٣٠٠.
    ₍1883₎

---

    al-Nasafī, Abū Hafs ʻUmar, Najm al-Dīn
      see al-Nasafī, Umar ibn Muhammad,
      1068?–1142.

VOLUME 405

al-Nasafī, Ḥāfiz al-Dīn
see
al-Nasafī, 'Abd Allāh ibn Aḥmad, *d.* 1310.

Nasafi, Saïido
see 'Ubaid Allāh, *Nasafi, Saiyid Mīr, fl.* 1702–1740.

Nasafi, 'Ubaid Allāh
see 'Ubaid Allāh, *Nasafi, Saiyid Mīr, fl.* 1702–1740.

BP165
.5
.T29
1931
Orien
al-Nasafī, 'Umar ibn Muḥammad, 1068?–1142. al-'Aqā'id al-Nasafīyah.
al-Taftāzānī, Mas'ūd ibn 'Umar, 1322–1389?
شرح العقائد النسفية، لسعد الدين التفتازاني، مع الحواشي القديمة والجديدة المفيدة. وفي آخره متن عجيب وشرح غريب كلاهما للشاه عبد العزيز المحدث الدهلوى الموسوم بشرح ميزان المقائد. دهلى، المكتبة الرشيدية، 1931 or 2, 1350,

BP192
.N3
1843
al-Nasafī, 'Umar ibn Muḥammad, 1068?–1142. al-'Aqā'id.
al-Nasafī, 'Abd Allāh ibn Aḥmad, *d.* 1310. عمدة عقيدة أهل السنة والجماعة Pillar of the creed of the Sunnites: being a brief creed of their principal tenets by Ḥáfidh-uldín Abú'lbarakát Abd-ullah Alnasafí. To which is subjoined a shorter treatise of a similar nature by Najm-uldín Abú Hafs Umar Alnasafí. Edited by William Cureton. London, Society for the Publication of Oriental Texts; sold by J. Madden, 1843.

BP192
.N3
1843
al-Nasafī, 'Umar ibn Muḥammad, 1068?–1142.
al-Nasafī, 'Abd Allāh ibn Aḥmad, *d.* 1310. عمدة عقيدة أهل السنة والجماعة ... (Card 2)

al-Nasā'ī, Aḥmad ibn Shu'ayb, 830 or 31–915.
... الكتاب ... المسمى بالمجتبى، المعروف بسنن النسائي. مع شرحه زهر الربا والسندي. دهلى، المطبع المجتبائي 1916/17, 1919, ١٣٣٥
2 v. 34 cm.
المجلد الثاني من النسائي Vol. 2 has caption title only:
Reproduced from ms. copy.
1. Hadith (Collections) I. al-Suyūṭī, 1445–1505. Zahr al-rubā. II. Title: al-Mujtabā. III. Title: Sunan al-Nasā'ī.
Title transliterated: al-Kitāb al-musammā bi-al-Mujtabā.
BP135.A16 1919   N E 67–469

NN 0023619   DLC

al-Nasā'ī, Aḥmad ibn Shu'ayb, 830 or 31–915.
كتاب سنن ابي عبد الرحمن احمد بن شعيب بن علي بن بحر النسائي المسمى بالمجتبى. ومعه شرحه زهر الربا للامام جلال الدين السيوطي. وبهامشه حاشيه ابي الحسن محمد بن عبد الهادي الحنفي. مصر، المطبعة اليمنيه، 1894,
2 v. 27 cm.
1. Hadith (Collections) I. al-Suyūṭī, 1445–1505. Zahr al-rubā. II. Title. III. Title: al-Mujtabā.
Title transliterated: Kitāb sunan Abī 'Abd al-Raḥmān Aḥmad ibn Shu'ayb.
BP135.A16 1894   N E 67–470

NN 0023620   DLC

al-Nasaie, Ahmad ben Shoaib
see
al-Nasā'ī, Aḥmad ibn Shu'ayb, 830 or 31–915.

4PK
Ind.
84
Nāsaketarī Kathā
An old-Rājasthānī tale, edited with notes, a grammar and a glossary by Charlotte Krause. Lipsiae, 1925.
124 p.

NN 0023622   DLC-P4 MH CtY OC1

Nasakin, Bernhard von.
See
Nasackin, Bernhard von.

DK263
.N3
Nasakin, Nikolaĭ Vadimovich,
... Правда о Гапонѣ и 9-мъ январѣ. С.-Петербургъ, "Электропечатня" Я. Кровицкаго, 1906.
2 p. l., 3,–226 p. 21cm.
Author's pseud., II. Симбирскій. at head of title.
Title transliterated: Pravda o Gaponѣ.
1. Gapon, Georgiĭ Apollonovich, d. 1906. 2. Russia—Hist.—Revolution of 1905. I. Title.
27–1624

NN 0023624   DLC

Nasakin, S   P
Наши достижения в лесохимии. Москва, Гос. лесное техн. изд-во, 1933.
53 p. 18 cm.
At head of title: Центральный научно-исследовательский лесохимический институт Наркомлеса СССР. С. П. Насакин, А. Л. Пирятинский и Н. В. Гордон.
1. Wood—Chemistry. I. Moscow. TSentral'nyĭ nauchno-issledovatel'skiĭ lesokhimicheskiĭ institut. II. Title.
Title transliterated: Nashi dostizheniìa v lesokhimii.
TA419.N3   49–43276*

NN 0023625   DLC

TX609
.V574
Nasakin, Timofeĭ Nikitich, joint author.
Volik, Nikolaĭ Dem'ìanovich.
Ленточные конвейорные сушилки овощесушильной промышленности. Москва, Пищепромиздат, 1954.

SPECIAL COLLECTIONS
BOOK ARTS
Z
232
.B632
1816
N17
Nasalli, Girolamo.
Il giorno, xx aprile del MDCCCXVI; terzine dell'avvocato conte Girolamo Nasalli.
Parma, Dalla Stamperia Ducale, 1816.
10 p. 26cm.

NN 0023627   NNC

Nasalli (Giuseppe). Comitato centrale piacentino degli ospizi marini pei fanciulli poveri scrofulosi. Relazione sanitaria e resoconto economico amministrativo. 3, 1872. 27 pp. 8°. Piacenza. F. Solari. 1873.

NN 0023628   DNLM

BT93
1922
N2
Nasalli-Rocca, Mario, conte, 1903–
... Concordatorum Pii XI. P.M. concordantiae. Romae, Scuola tipografica missionaria domenicana, 1940.
viii, 304 p.
At head of title: Sac. doct. Marius Nasalli-Rocca de Corneliano.
1.Concordats. 2.Papacy. Treaties, etc. I. Pius XI, pope, 1922–1939. II.Title.

NN 0023629   MBtS

Nasalli-Rocca, Amedeo, *conte,* 1852–1926.
Memorie di un prefetto, compilate sull'originale e pubblicate a cura di Carlo Trionfi. Roma, Casa editrice mediterranea, 1946.
viii, 289 p. 21 cm.
1. Italy—Pol. & govt.—1870–1915. I. Trionfi, Carlo, ed.
DG556.N3A3   A F 48–3039*
California. Univ. Libr
for Library of Congress   ,1,†

NN 0023630   CU MH DLC NN

Nasalli Rocca, Angelo Maria, conte, 1897–
... Realismo nazionale: per una coscienza politica dei cattolici italiani. 1926.

NN 0023631   CSt-H

Nasalli-Rocca, Angelo Maria, *conte,* 1897–
...Il roveto; tre atti, con prefazione di Lorenzo Ruggi... Parma: Studio editoriale della stamperia bodoniana, 1928, vii, 87 p. front. (port.) 8°. (Teatro moderno. no. 1.)
459611A. 1. Drama, Italian.   2. Title.   February 19, 1930
N. Y. P. L.

NN 0023632   NN MoU NNC

Nasalli-Rocca, Angelo Maria, conte, 1897–   2799B.442
Via Mala. Romanzo. [Di, A. M. Nasalli-Rocca. — Milano. Corbaccio. 1930. 235, (3) pp. 18½ cm., in 8s.

NN 0023633   MB

Nasalli-Rocca, Angelo Maria, conte, 1897–
Via mala; romanzo. Torino, "Superga" ,1953, 227 p. 20cm.

NN 0023634   NN DLC-P4 RPB

Nasalli-Rocca, Angelo Maria, conte, 1897–
...Vita di santo Stefano, protomartire; seconda edizione con apposito capitolo sul recente scoprimento della tomba del santo. S. Benigno Canavese: Scuola tipografica D. Bosco [1923] 86 p. front. (port.) 17cm.
780988A. 1. Stephen, Saint, protomartyr.

NN 0023635   NN

Rocca, Angelo Maria Nasalli-
see Nasalli-Rocca, Angelo Maria, conte, 1897–

Nasalli-Rocca, Emilio, conte., 1901– joint ed.
Mercati, Angelo, 1870–   ed.
... Aemilia. Le decime dei secoli xiii–xiv, a cura di Angelo Mercati, Emilio Nasalli-Rocca, Pietro Sella; con carta topografica delle diocesi nei sec. xiii–xiv. Città del Vaticano, Biblioteca apostolica vaticana, 1933.

NASALLI-ROCCA, EMILIO, conte, 1901–
Atteggiamenti politici dei ducati emiliani e della città "Primogenita" nel '48. Piacenza, 1948. 27 p. port. 24cm. (Studi piacentini sul risorgimento. no. 6)
Bibliographical footnotes.
1. Emilia, Italy—Hist.   I. Series.

NN 0023638   NN

VOLUME 405

Nasalli-Rocca, Emilio, conte, 1901-
Il Card. Bessarione, legato pontificio in
Bologna (1450-1455); saggio sulla costituzione
dello Stato pontificio e sulla legislazione e
la vita giuridica del '400.   Imola, P.Galeati,
1931.

64 p.
Estratto dagli Atti e memorie della R. Deputazione di storia patria per le Romagne, 4 serie,
vol. 20, fasc. 4-6, 1931.

NN   0023639   DDO

Nasalli-Rocca, Emilio, conte, 1901-
Il conte Carlo Luigi Villa Maruffi, 1773-1852,
fondatore della Pia Casa di Ricovero e Provvidenza
Maruffi, di Piacenza. Piacenza, 1955.

NN   0023640   MH

Nasalli-Rocca, Emilio, *conte*, 1901–
Federico II° di Svevia. ₍Brescia₎ La Scuola ₍194–₎
127 p. 16 cm. (Profili della storia)
"Nota bibliografica": p. ₍121₎–127.

1. Friedrich II, Emperor of Germany, 1194–1250.
Full name: Emilio *conte* Nasalli-Rocca di Corneliano.

DD151.N3   50–18803

NN   0023641   DLC

Nasalli-Rocca, Emilio, *conte*, 1901–
Filangieri. Brescia, La Scuola ₍1950₎
155 p. 16 cm. (Maestri delle dottrine sociali)
Bibliography: p. ₍153₎–155.

1. Filangieri, Gaetano, 1752–1788.
Full name: Emilio *conte* Nasalli-Rocca di Corneliano.

JC183.F485   A 50–8053
New York. Public Libr.
for Library of Congress   ₍a₎†

NN   0023642   NN DLC

NASALLI-ROCCA, EMILIO, conte, 1901-
La letteratura legittimistica negli antichi ducati
di Parma e di Modena posteriormente al 1859.
Piacenza, 1961. 28 p. 24cm. (Studi piacentini sul risorgimento.
no. 8)

Cover title.

"Estratto da Atti e memorie della Deputazione di storia patria per le
antiche provincie modenesi, ser. viii, v. xii, anno 1960."
Bibliographical footnotes.

1. Parma and Piacenza (Duchy)--Hist. 2. Modena, Italy--Hist.
I. Series.

NN   0023644   NN

NASALLI-ROCCA, EMILIO, conte, 1901-
Magistrati dell'ottocento.   Piacenza [Soc. tip.
editoriale Porta] 1939. 41 p. illus., ports. 25cm.
(Studi piacentini sul risorgimento no. 4)

"Estratto... della Strenna dell'anno XVII dell'Istituto nazionale di cultura
fascista, sezione di Piacenza."
Bibliographical footnotes.
1. Judiciary--Italy. I. Series.

NN   0023645   NN

NASALLI-ROCCA, EMILIO, conte, 1901-   ,ed.
Panorami di Piacenza; storia, arte, pensiero, letteratura, musica, tradizioni, dialetto, geografia, economia, istituzioni culturali, benefiche e religiose.
Saggi di A. Ambrogio [et. al.] Piacenza, Associazione italiana maestri cattolici. Sezione di Piacenza,
1955. 342 p. illus. 24cm.

Bibliography at end of each chapter.
List of archaeological material and its location, p. 18-28.
1. Piacenza, Italy--Civilization. 2. Art, Italian--Collections--Italy--
Piacenza. 3. Italy--Piacenza.   I. Associazione italiana maestri
cattolici.

NN   0023646   NN

NASALLI-ROCCA, EMILIO, 1901-
...Piacenza sotto la dominazione sabauda (1744–
1749); contributo alla storia della guerra di successione
austriaca (con nuovi documenti e con illustrazioni).
Piacenza: Tipografia A. del Maino, 1929. 94 p.
illus. (incl. ports.) 4°.

Bibliographical footnotes.

625405A. 1. Piacenza, Italy—Hist. 2. Italy—Hist.

NN   0023647   NN MH

Nasalli-Rocca, Emilio, *conte*, 1901–
... Problemi religiosi e politici del duecento nell' opera di
due grandi italiani: il cardinale Giacomo da Pecorara e il pontefice beato Gregorio x. Piacenza, Libreria editrice Merlini,
1938.
3 p. l., ₍ix₎–xii, 156, ₍2₎ p. pl., port. 25ᶜᵐ.
At head of title: Emilio Nasalli Rocca di Corneliano.
"Saggio bibliografico": p. ₍139₎–153.

1. Middle ages—History. 2. Italy—Church history. 3. Pecoraria,
Iacopo, cardinal, 1170–1244. 4. Gregorius x, pope, d. 1276. I. Title.
                                    A C 39–1607
Pennsylvania. Univ. Libr.
for Library of Congress   ₍3₎

NN   0023648   PU CtY-D CLU NN IU

4K-   Nasalli-Rocca, Emilio, conte, 1901-
774   Saggio su gli statuti del comune di Castell'
Arquato (secoli XIV-XV); studi intorno alla
legislazione e alla vita giuridica del Quattrocento.
Parma, Officina graf. Fresching, 1926.
48 p.

NN   0023649   DLC-P4

Nasalli-Rocca, Emilio, *conte*, 1901–   *ed.*
Statuti di corporazioni artigiane piacentine (secoli xv–
xviii) Milano, Giuffrè, 1955.
315 p. illus. 25 cm.
At head of title: Camera di commercio, industria e agricoltura,
Piacenza.
Latin or Italian.

1. Piacenza—Gilds. I. Title.
Full name: Emilio *conte* Nasalli-Rocca di Corneliano.
HD6472.P5N3   60–37308 ‡

NN   0023650   DLC MH NIC NN

Nasalli-Rocca, Emilio, *conte*, 1901–
Studi storici sulle condizioni giuridiche del contado, con par-
ticolare riguardo alle regioni piacentina e parmigiana. Piacenza, Tip. A. del Maino, 1941.
xv, 248 p. 25 cm.
"Nota bibliografica": p. xv.

1. Parma—Pol. & govt. 2. Piacenza—Pol. & govt. 3. Parma and Pia-
cenza (Duchy)—Pol. & govt. 4. Feudal law—Parma. 5. Feudal law—
Piacenza. 6. Peasantry—Parma. 7. Peasantry—Piacenza.
Full name: Emilio *conte* Nasalli-Rocca di Corneliano.
JN5273.N3   47–41168*

NN   0023651   DLC

NASALLI-ROCCA, Emilio, conte, 1901-
Il Supremo Consiglio di Giustizia e Grazia di
Piacenza; contributo alla storia dei tribunali
supremi dell'età moderna. Piacenza, Prem. stab.
tip. A. Del-Maino, 1922.

24.5 cm. pp. 70. Plate.
"Biblioteca storica piacentina, 10."

NN   0023652   MH

DG975   Nasalli-Rocca, Emilio, conte, 1901-
.P5N2   Tracie della romanità di Piacenza; nuovi
rinvenimenti archeologici in piazza Cavilla,
agosto-ottobre 1938.   Piacenza,A.del Maino,1938.
14 p. illus.

Cover-title.
Estratto dal "Bollettino Stonco Piacentino,"
1938, a.XXXIII,facs.3.

1. Piacenza--Antiquities. I. Title

NN   0023653   InU

Nasalli-Rocca, Emilio, *conte*, 1901–
... Il trasferimento dello Studio visconteo di Pavia a Piacenza dal 1398 al 1402. Milano, Società editrice "Vita e pensiero" ₍1927₎
49 p., 2 l. 25ᶜᵐ. (Pubblicazioni della Università cattolica del Sacro
cuore. ser. 5: Scienze storiche. vol. VIII)
At head of title: Emilio Nasalli Rocca di Corneliano.

1. Pavia. Università—Hist.   I. Title.
                                        35–9605
Library of Congress   AS222.M63 ser. 5, vol. 8
                           ₍2₎   (082) 378.45

NN   0023654   DLC ICN MH NN

320.944 Nasalli Rocca, Saverio.
N17g   ... Giuseppe de Maistre nei suoi scritti ... Torino, Fratelli Bocca, 1933.
328p. front.(port.)   (On cover: Biblioteca
di storia contemporanea. n.15)

"Bibliografia": p.₍327₎-328.

1. Maistre, Joseph Marie, comte de, 1753-1821.

NN   0023655   IU

Nasalli-Rocca di Corneliano, Emilio
    see
Nasalli-Rocca, Emilio, conte, 1901-

Nasalli-Rocca di Corneliano, Mario
    see Nasalli-Rocca, Mario, *conte*, 1903–

al-Na'sānī, Muhammad Badr al-Dīn, ed.
Amālī al-Sayyid al-Murtadā
    see under   al-Sharīf al-Murtadā, 'Alam
al-Huda 'Alī ibn al-Husayn, 966-1044· or 5.

al-Na'sānī, Muhammad Badr al-Dīn, ed.
Kitāb al-ahkām al-sultāniyah
    see under   al-Māwardī, 'Alī ibn
Muhammad, 974?-1058.

al-Na'sānī, Muhammad Badr al-Dīn, ed.
Kitāb al-fiqh al-akbar
    see under   Abū, Hanīfah, d. 767 or 8.

VOLUME 405

al-Naṣānī, Muḥammad Badr al-Dīn.

كتاب نهاية الأرب من شرح معلقات العرب، تأليف محمد بدر
الدين ابي فراس النعساني الحلبي. الطبعة 1. مصر، مطبعة
السعادة، 1906.

231 p. 23 cm.

I. al-Muʻallaqāt. II. Title: Nihāyat al-arab min sharḥ Muʻallaqāt
al-ʻArab.

Title romanized: Kitāb nihāyat al-arab
min sharḥ Muʻallaqāt al-ʻArab.

PJ7642.Z5N3   77-214095

NN   0023661   DLC

Nasao Zarco y Colona, Tivisco de, *pseud.*
   see
Ataide, Manuel de Carvalho de, *d.* 1720.

Nasar ed-Dīn, shah of Persia
      see   Nasīr al-Dīn Shah, Shah of Iran,
1831-1896.

Nasarow, A   G
   see
Nazarov, Aleksandr Gavrilovich.

Nasarow, I   N
   see
   Nazarov, I   N

Nasarow, I.W.
   See
Nazarov, I.N.

Nasarre, Blas Antonio, 1689-1751, ed.

Rodriguez, Cristóbal, 1677? *ca.* 1735.
   Bibliotheca universal de la polygraphia española, compuesta
por don Christoval Rodriguez, y que de orden de Su Magestad
publica d. Blas Antonio Nassarre y Ferriz ... Madrid, A.
Marin, 1738.

Nasarre, Blas Antonio, 1689-1751, ed.

Cervantes Saavedra, Miguel de, 1547-1616.
   Comedias, y entremeses de Miguel de Cervantes Saavedra ...
divididas en dos tomos, con una dissertacion, o prologo sobre
las comedias de España ... Madrid, Impr. de A. Marin,
1749.

PQ   Nasarre, Blas Antonio, 1689-1751
6171   Funeral hecho a la gloriosa memoria de la
.A195   reyna nvestra señora doña Maria Lvisa Gabrie-
N243   la de Saboya. Por la vniversidad y estvdio
            general de la civdad de Zaragoza por Pedro
            Robinet. Zaragoça, M. Roman ¿sic?, 1714.
               88 p.   21cm.

            Bound with Pomar y Foncillas, José de, d.
            1735. Sermon en las honras funerales. Za-
            ragoza ¿1714?¿

            I. Robinet,   Pedro

NN   0023669   WU NNH

Nasarre, Higinio Ciria y
      see Ciria y Nasarre, Higinio.

Nasarre, Jose Maria.
   Figura política del hombre aragonés. Zaragoza, Insti-
tucion "Fernando el Católico" (C. S. I. C.) 1954.
   30 p. 22 cm. (Discursos de ingreso, 1)

   Publicación núm. 144 de la Institución "Fernando el Católico."
Institución Fernando el Católico. Colección monográfica núm. 64.

   1. National characteristics, Aragon.   I. Title.   (Series: Saragossa. Institución "Fernando el Católico." Publicación núm. 144.
Series: Saragossa. Institución "Fernando el Católico." Colección
monográfica, núm. 64)

DP302.A667N3   79-225313

NN   0023671   DLC

Nasarre de Letosa, Antonio.

Aragon. *Real audiencia.*
   Discurso que en la apertura del tribunal de la Real audiencia
de Aragon, leyó, el 2 de enero de 1835, d. Antonio Nasarre de
Letosa ... por indisposición del presidente el excelentísimo
señor Conde de Ezpeleta, procer del reino y capitan general
del Ejército y reino de Aragon ... Zaragoza, Imprenta real,
1835.

Nasarre y Ferriz, Blas Antonio
            see
Nasarre, Blas Antonio, 1689-1751.

Nasarre y Villelas, Blas Antonio
            see
Nasarre, Blas Antonio, 1689-1751.

Nasaruddin Latif
      see
Latif, Nasaruddin.

Nasarvanji F. Bilimoria
      see Bilimoria, Nasarvanji F.

Nasarvanji Hirjibhai Patel
   The English-Gujarati dictionary...   3d ed.
[4],373p.   Ahmedabad, Printed at the "Vijaya
Praverttak" printing press, 1895.

NN   0023677   OCl

Nasarvanji Jivanji Readymoney
      see Readymoney, Nasarvanji Jivanji.

Nasarvanji Wadia, Dosabhai
      see Wadia, Dosabhai Nasarvanji, 1883-

F   Nasatir, Abraham Phineas, 1904-
598   Anglo-Spanish rivalry on the Upper
N38   Missouri. [Cedar Rapids, Iowa, Torch
            Press, 1930-?]
               46 p. 26 cm.
               Cover title.
            "Reprinted from the Mississippi Valley
            Historical Review, XVI, No. 4, March, 1930."
            Includes bibliographical references.
            1. Missouri Valley—History.   I. Title.

NN   0023680   IEdS

Nasatir, Abraham Phineas, 1904-   *ed.*
   Before Lewis and Clark; documents illustrating the history of the Missouri, 1785-1804. St. Louis, St. Louis Historical Documents Foundation, 1952.
   2 v. (xv, 853 p.) maps (part fold.) facsims. 24 cm. (Joseph
Desloge Fund. Publication no. 3)

   Bibliographical footnotes.

   1. Missouri Valley—Hist.—Sources. 2. Missouri River. 3. Fur
trade—Missouri Valley.   I. Title.   (Series: St. Louis Historical
Documents Foundation. Joseph Desloge Fund. Publication no. 3)

F598.N3   978.0082   52—14725

         OrP OrHi WaT WaSpG Or WaSp
         IdU MtBC MtHi MtU TxU OrPS KMK CoU OrPR Wa OrU
         PPAmP N IEN ViU MB CU CaBViPA CaBVaU IdPI OrCS
NN   0023681   DLC WaU C PP OU GU OCl PU NN NcD TU

Nasatir, Abraham Phineas, 1904-
   French activities in California; an archival calendar-guide,
by Abraham P. Nasatir ... Stanford University, Calif., Stanford university press; London, H. Milford, Oxford university
press ¿1945¿
   xiii p., 1 l., 559 p. incl. facsims. 26½ᵐ.
   "Photolith."
   Includes summaries and extracts from French archives.
   Bibliography: p. 38-59, 397-457.
   CONTENTS.—pt. I. French activities in California prior to statehood.—
pt. II. Calendar guide of the materials relating to California in the archives of France.
   1. French in California. 2. California—Hist.—Sources. 3. Archives—
France.   I. Title.
                                                         A 45-2244
Stanford univ. Library
   for Library of Congress °   CD1198.U6N3
                                          ¿10¿†   979.4

         CaBVaU OrPR TU OCl ViU DLC OrHi
NN   0023682   CSt NcGU MiEM CoU CaBViPA OrU WaS WaSpG

F   Nasatir, Abraham Phineas, 1904-
864   French activities in California prior to
N24+   statehood...by Abraham P. Nasatir. [Palo
            Alto, Calif.] Stanford University Press
            [1945?]
               59 p. 26cm.
               Cover title.
            "Introductory sketch reprinted from [his]
            French activities in California; an archival
            calendar-guide."
            1. French in California. 2. California--
            Hist. I. Title.

NN   0023683   NIC

Nasatir, Abraham Phineas.
   ... The French in the California gold rush, by A. P. Nasatir
... New York ¿American society of the French legion of
honor¿ 1934.
   14 p. 22½ᵐ. (Franco-American pamphlet series. no. 3)
   Bibliographical note: p. 14.

   1. French in California. 2. California—Gold discoveries.   I. Title.

                                                         35-10148
Library of Congress   E183.8.F5F87 no. 3

NN   0023684   DLC CU ViU CtY PU

F373   Nasatir, Abraham Phineas, 1904-   ed.
.N38
1946   Government employees and salaries in
            Spanish Louisiana. ¿n. p., 1946?¿
               158 p. 27cm.
            "The originals of these documents are in the
            Archivo General de Indias, Sección, Papeles de Cuba,
            legajo 569."
            "Reprinted from the Louisiana historical quarterly,
            vol. 29, no. 4, October 1946."

            1. Louisiana (Province)—Officials and employees—
            Salaries. 2. Louisiana (Province)—Hist.—Sources.
            I. Spain. Archivo   General de Indias,
            Seville. II. Title.

NN   0023685   ViU CU-B

Nasatir, Abraham Phineas, 1904-
   Indian trade and diplomacy in the Spanish
Illinois, 1763-1792, by Abraham Phineas
Nasatir ... [Berkeley, 1926]
   v numb. l., 171 l., 373 numb. l. 29 cm.
   Thesis (Ph. D.) - Univ. of California,
May 1926.
   "Bibliographical note": p. 350-373.
   1. Missouri - Hist. 2. Fur trade - Mississippi
Valley. 3. Spain - Colonies - North America.
4. Indians of North America - Mississippi Valley.

NN   0023686   CU

VOLUME 405

Nasatir, Abraham Phineas, ed. and tr.
Moerenhout, Jacques Antoine, 1796?–1879.
The inside story of the gold rush, by Jacques Antoine Moren-
hout ... translated and edited from documents in the French
archives by Abraham P. Nasatir, in collaboration with George
Ezra Dane who wrote the introduction and conclusion ... San
Francisco, California historical society, 1935.

Nasatir, Abraham Phineas, 1904–
Jacques Clamorgan: colonial promoter of the northern
border of New Spain, by A. P. Nasatir ... ₍Santa Fe, N. M.,
1942₎
cover-title, 101–112 p. 23ᶜᵐ.
"Reprinted from New Mexico historical review, April 1942."

1. Clamorgan, Jacques Philippe. 2. Louisiana—Hist.—Colonial period.
3. Mississippi valley—Hist.—To 1803.
                                                         45–27292
Library of Congress   F352.C6N3

NN   0023688   DLC

F
352
N38
Nasatir, Abraham Phineas, 1904–
Materials relating to the history of
the Mississippi Valley ₍from the minutes of the Spanish Supreme Councils
of State, 1787–1798. A calendar guide₎
complied and edited by Abraham P. Nasatir and Ernest R. Liljegren. ₍n.p.,
193–?₎
73 p. 26 cm.
"Reprinted from the Louisiana Historical Quarterly, Vol. 21, No. 1, January,

1938.

1. Mississippi Valley—History—to
1803. I. Liljegren, Ernest R., joint
author. II. Title. mf

NN   0023690   IEdS CU

Nasavī, Moḥammad ebn Aḥmad
    see
al-Nasawī, Muḥammad ibn Aḥmad, fl. 1241.

Nasavī, Muḥammad ibn Aḥmad
    see
al-Nasawī, Muḥammad ibn Aḥmad, fl. 1241.

DK 888
.N246
al-NASAWI, MUḤAMMAD IBN AHMAD, fl. 1241.
Celâlüttin Harezemşah ₍çeviren₎ Asım
Necip. İstanbul, Devlet Matbaası, 1934.
158 p.

1. Celâleddin, Shah of Khorezm,   –1231. 2.
Turkish language—Texts. I. Asım, Necip, ed.

NN   0023693   InU MH NNC

---

al-Nasawī, Muḥammad ibn Aḥmad, fl. 1241.
Histoire du sultan Djelal ed- Dīn Mankobirti,
prince du Kharezm. Publié d'apres le ms. de la
Bibliothèque national par O. Houdas. Paris,
Leroux, 1891–95.
2 v. (Publications de l'École des langues
orientales vivantes, III ser. no. 9, 10)
v. 1 has added t.p. in Arabic.
Contents: [1] Texte arabe. - [2. Traduction
Française]

NN   0023694   MH CSt

---

al-Nasawī, Muḥammad ibn Aḥmad, fl. 1241.
Sīrat Jalāl al-Dīn
    see his
Sīrat al-Sultān Jalāl al-Dīn Mankubirtī.
Persian.

---

al-Nasawī, Muḥammad ibn Aḥmad, fl. 1241.
₍Sīrat al-Sultān Jalāl al-Dīn Mankubirtī. Persian₎
سيرة جلال الدين، يا تاريخ جلالي، نگاشته نور الدين محمد
زيدرى نسوى. ترجمه محمد على ناسح. ₍تهران، كتابفروشى
محمد على علمى ₍ديباچه 1324 ₍1945₎

4, 4, 354, 6 p. 21 cm.

1. Celâleddin, Shah of Khorezm, d. 1231.   I. Title. II. Title:
Tārīkh-i Jalālī.
                         Title romanized: Sīrat Jalāl al-Dīn.

DK888.C44N3716 1945   74–200001

NN   0023696   DLC

---

al-Nasawī, Muḥammad ibn Aḥmad, fl. 1241.
سيرة السلطان جلال الدين منكبرتى، لاحمد بن احمد النسوى،
نشر وتحقيق حافظ احمد حمدى. مصر، دار الفكر العربى،
₍1953₎ ١٩٥٣

436 p. 2 fold. maps, geneal. table. 24 cm.
Added t. p.: History of Djalâl el-Dīn Mankobirti, Shâh of
Khwârazm, by Mohammed el-Nesawi.
Bibliography: p. 389–398.

1. Celâleddin, Shah of Khorezm, d. 1231.   I. Ḥāfiẓ Aḥmad Ḥamdī,
ed. II. Title.   Title transliterated: Sīrat al-Sultān
                                                  Jalāl al-Dīn Mankubirtī.
DK888.N35 1953   59–34962

NN   0023697   DLC CU WaU MnU

---

al-Nasawī, Muḥammad ibn Aḥmad, fl. 1241.
Tārīkh-i Jalālī
    see his
Sīrat al-Sultān Jalāl al-Dīn Mankubirtī.
Persian.

Nasby, Asher Gordon, 1909–
Sunrise in the West, by A. Gordon Nasby. Great Neck,
N. Y., Pulpit digest publishing company ₍1944₎
x, 11–125, ₍1₎ p. 20ᶜᵐ.
"First edition."

1. Lutheran church—Sermons. 2. Sermons, American.   I. Title.
                                                              44–9685
Library of Congress   BX8066.N35S8
                                              ₍2₎   252.041

NN   0023699   DLC NcC NcU

Nasby, Asher Gordon, 1909–   ed.
Treasury of the Christian world; an anthology of illustrations, ideas, and expositions drawn from eighty years of sermon publication in the Christian world pulpit and from
columns of the Christian world. Foreword by George M.
Docherty. ₍1st ed.₎ New York, Harper ₍1953₎
397 p. 25 cm.

1. Homiletical illustrations.   I. Title.

BV4225.N3   251   53–5443 ‡

AU WaT KyWAT IEG MSohG InAndC–T OrStbM WaT WaS
NN   0023700   DLC IdB MBU MB OCU PPEB PP OOxM ViU

Nasby, Gordon Asher
    see
Nasby, Asher Gordon, 1909–

Nasby, Petroleum V., pseud.
    see
Locke, David Ross, 1833–1888.

The Nasby letters
    see under ₍Locke, David Ross₎ 1833–1888.

The Nasby papers. Southern humour
    see under ₍Locke, David Ross₎ 1833–1888.

WB
N244c
1887
NASCA, Giuseppe de.
Collezione de'più recenti e ricercati
opuscoli scientifico-medici; tratti dalle
più autorevoli effemeridi e dagli atti e
resoconti della R. Accademia medico-
chirurgica di Napoli. Napoli, Tocco,
1887.
vi, 306 p.
Some articles reprinted from various
medical journals.

NN   0023705   DNLM

₍Nasca, Emanuele₎
Quadro della condotta e dell'opera
del cav. Pasquale Nasca ... Aquila,
G. Mele, 1896.
28 p. 24½cm.
Signed: Emanuele Nasca ₍e₎ Narsete
Nasca.

NN   0023706   MH–L

Nasca, Pasquale, 1832–   defendant
Alle LL. Eccellenze il primo presidente e consiglieri della Corte di
cassazione di Roma. ₍Catanzaro,
1898₎
16 p. 27cm.
Caption title.
Signed at end: Pasquale Nasca.

NN   0023707   MH–L

Nasca, Pasquale, 1832–
Dottrine giuridiche, ovvero Collezione di monografie
sopra diverse tesi o quistioni di diritto. Livorno, Tip. di R.
Giusti, 1892.
xvi, 227 p. 23 cm.

1. Law—Italy—Addresses, essays, lectures.

                                              55–50404

NN   0023708   DLC

Nascantes de Azambuja
    see
Azambuja, Bernardo Augusto Nascentes de, d.1875
or 6.

NASCÉ, Francesco di Paula.
Inscriptiones Carmina et orationes. Panormi,
1833.

Port.
"Vita, a Benedicti Mondini scripta", pp.1–32.

NN   0023710   MH

Greenlee
4504
P855
NASCENDO hum novo astro na esfera portugueza,
dos augustissimos senhores d. Joao e d. Carlota,
principes do Brazil, senhores nossos. Piscatoria.
Intreluctores ... Lisboa, F.J.de França e Liz,
1793.
16p. 20cm.
Verse.

NN   0023711   ICN

Nascent phases of some basic chemical industries
    see under Chemical engineering.

VOLUME 405

Nascentes, Antenor, 1886–
... America do Sul. São Paulo, Companhia editora nacional, 1937.
219 p. plates. 18½ᵐ. (Coleção viagens, v. 13)
"Exemplar nº 0468*."

1. South America—Description and travel.

A C 39–2648
Stanford univ. Library
for Library of Congress ₍2₎

NN 0023713 CSt ICarbS CLU

Nascentes, Antenor, 1886– *comp.*
Antologia espanhola e hispano-americana, por Antenor Nascentes. Rio de Janeiro, Valverde ₍1943₎
189, ₍1₎ p. 19½ᵐ.

1. Spanish literature (Selections: Extracts, etc.) 2. Spanish-American literature (Selections: Extracts, etc.) I. Title.

44–18965
Library of Congress PQ6172.N3
₍2₎ 860.82

NN 0023714 DLC LU

PQ6172 **Nascentes, Antenor,** 1886– comp.
N3 Antologia espanhola e hispano-americana.
1945 2. ed. Rio de Janeiro, Livraria Editora Zelio Velverde, 1945.
262 p. 19cm.

1.Spanish literature (Selections: Extracts. etc. 2.Spanish-American literature (Selections: Extracts, etc.

NN 0023715 CSt

Nascentes, Antenor, 1886–
Dicionário básico do português do Brasil. 1. ed. S. Paulo, Livraria Martins ₍1949₎
777 p. 17 cm.

1. Portuguese language—Dictionaries. 2. Portuguese language—Provincialisms—Brazil. I. Title.
Full name: Antenor de Veras Nascentes.

PC5446.N3 469.79 50–14219

NN 0023716 DLC TxU MH NcU

469.7 **Nascentes, Antenor,** 1886–
N244d Dicionário básico do português do Brasil.
ed.3 3.ª ed. S. Paulo, Martins ₍1952₎
777 p. 16ᵐ.

1. Portuguese language - Dictionaries. 2. Portuguese language - Provincialisms - Brazil. I.Title.

NN 0023717 CSt

PC5327 **Nascentes, Antenor,** 1886–
N3 Dicionário da língua portuguêsa, elaborado por Antenor Nascentes a fim de ser submetido à Academia para as devidas alterações, [Rio de Janeiro?] Departamento de Imprensa Nacional, Brasil, 19
v.

At head of title: Academia Brasileira de Letras.

NN 0023718 CU

Nascentes, Antenor, 1886–
... Dicionario de dúvidas e dificuldades do idioma nacional. Rio de Janeiro, S. Paulo, Livraria editora Freitas Bastos ₍1941₎
170 p., 1 l. 18½ᵐ.

1. Portuguese language — Idioms, corrections, errors. 2. Portuguese language—Dictionaries. 3. Portuguese language—Provincialisms—Brazil. I. Title.

A 43–227
Harvard univ. Library
for Library of Congress ₍7₎

NN 0023719 MH LU NIC TxU OU OOxM PU

Nascentes, Antenor, 1886–
... Dicionario de dúvidas e dificuldades do idioma nacional. 2. ed. Rio de Janeiro, S. Paulo, Livraria editora Freitas Bastos, 1944.
220 p., 1 l. 18½ᵐ.

1. Portuguese language—Idioms, corrections, errors. 2. Portuguese language—Dictionaries. 3. Portuguese language—Provincialisms—Brazil.

45–12082
Library of Congress PC5260.N35 1944
₍3₎ 468.3

NN 0023720 DLC

G469.79 **Nascentes, Antenor,** 1886–
N17d ... Dicionário de dúvidas e dificuldades
1952 do idioma nacional. 3. ed. Rio de Janeiro [etc.] Livraria Freitas Bastos, s.a., 1952.
220p. 20cm.

1. Portuguese language - Idioms, corrections, errors. 2. Portuguese language - Dictionaries. 3. Portuguese language - Provincialisms - Brazil.

NN 0023721 TxU ICU WU

Nascentes, Antenor, 1886–
Dicionário etimológico da língua portuguesa, por Antenor Nascentes ... con prefácio de W. Meyer Lübke ... 1. e única ed. Rio de Janeiro, F. Alves ₍etc.₎ 1932–₍952₎
2 v. 28ᵐ.
"Bibliografía": v. 1, p. ₍xli₎–xliii.

1. Portuguese language—Etymology—Dictionaries. I. Title.

33–24817
Library of Congress PC5305.N3
₍a45d1₎ 469.203

OOxM OU NBC PPT
NN 0023722 DLC CU NN CtY NcD WaU TxU NIC MB PSt

469.203 **Nascentes, Antenor,** 1886–
N244d Dicionário etimológico da língua por-
1955 tuguêsa. Rio de Janeiro, Livraria Académica [etc.] 1952-55 [v.1. 1955]
2v. 27cm.

Vol.1: "Segunda tiragem da primeira edição"
Vol.2: Nomes próprios.
Contains bibliographies.

1.Portuguese language - Etymology - Dictionaries. 2.Names, Portuguese - Dictionaries. I.Title.

NN 0023723 CLSU NcD

Ayer **NASCENTES, ANTENOR,** 1886–
1453 ...Difusión de la lengua portuguesa en el Brasil
B8 Versión española y notas de Alarcón Fernández.
N24 Rio de Janeiro, Imprensa nacional, 1944.
1944 14p. 18cm. (Ministerio de relaciones exteriores. División de cooperación intelectual. Colección de monografías brasileñas. 7)

NN 0023724 ICN TNJ NjP

PC41 **Nascentes, Antenor,** 1886–
.N38 Elementos de filologia romanica. Rio ₍de₎ Janeiro₎ Ed. da Organização Simoes, 1954.
104p.

1. Romance philology. I. Title.

NN 0023725 NcU WU CoU

PC5076 **Nascentes, Antenor,** 1886–
N3 Um ensaio de phonetica differencial luso-castelhana. Dos elementos gregos que se encontram no espanhol. Trabalho apresentado em concurso para provimento da cadeira de espanhol do Collegio Pedro II. Rio de Janeiro, Typ. do Jornal do commercio, 1919.
149 p. 23cm.

1. Portuguese language - Phonology. 2. Spanish language - Phonology. 3. Spanish language - Foreign words and phrases - Greek.

NN 0023726 CU WaU ICU MH

PC **Nascentes, Antenor,** 1886–
4099 Esbozo de comparación del espanol con el
N17c português. [Santiago] Prensas de la Universidad de Chile, 1936.
18 p.

"Tirada aparte de los 'Anales de la Universidad de Chile'."

1. Spanish language - Grammar, Comparative - Portuguese. 2. Portuguese language - Grammar, Comparative - Spanish.

NN 0023727 CLU

Nascentes, Antenor, 1886–
Estudos filologicos. (1.ª serie) Por Antenor Nascentes. Rio de Janeiro, Civilização brasileira, s. a., 1939.
155 p., 2 l. 17½ᵐ.

1. Portuguese philology—Addresses, essays, lectures. 2. Portuguese language—Provincialisms—Brazil.

41–21988
Library of Congress PC5015.N3
₍2₎ 469.04

NN 0023728 DLC OCl TxU ICU WaU

G981 **NASCENTES, ANTENOR,** 1886–
B7393rT ... The expansion of the Portuguese language
no.7 in Brazil, by Antenor Nascentes ... Translated by Luiz Victor Le Cocq d'Oliveira. Rio de Janeiro, Imprenta nacional, 1944.
14p. 18cm. (Ministry of state for foreign affairs of Brazil, Division of Intellectual co-operation. Resumé n.7)

1. Portuguese language. I. Le Cocq d'Oliveira, Luiz Victor, tr. II. Title. Series (contents)

NN 0023729 TxU MiU NjP KU NNC FU

Nascentes, Antenor, 1886–
A giria brasileira. Rio de Janeiro, Livraria Académica, 1953.
xvi, 181 p. 24 cm. (Biblioteca brasileira de filologia, no. 3)
Bibliography: p. ₍ix₎–xvi.

1. Portuguese language—Provincialisms—Brazil. 2. Portuguese language—Slang—Dictionaries. I. Title.
Full name: Antenor de Veras Nascentes.

PC5446.N33 56–38359

NN 0023730 DLC CSt NIC PSt MH CU NN MiD IU

VOLUME 405

Nascentes, Antenor, 1886–
... Gramática da língua espanhola, para uso dos brasileiros.
5. ed. São Paulo ₍etc.₎ Companhia editora nacional, 1943.
2 p. l., 7–183 p. 21½ᶜᵐ.

1. Spanish language—Text-books for foreigners—Brazilians. 2. Spanish language—Grammar—1870–
                                                            44–31046
Library of Congress   PC4129.B7N3 1943
                                                            ₍2₎   468.2469

NN   0023731   DLC

Nascentes, Antenor, 1886–
O idioma nacional, por Antenor Nascentes ... Rio de Janeiro, Livraria Alves ₍etc.₎ 1930–36.
5 v. illus. (incl. ports., maps, music) 19ᶜᵐ.
Vol. 1, 4. ed., 1936; v. 2, 3. ed., 1933; v. 3, 2. ed. ₍1930₎; v. 4 (Gramática histórica) 2. ed., 7. milheiro, 1933; v. 5, 2. ed., 7. milheiro, 1935.
"Indice bibliografico": v. 5, p. ₍207₎–213.

1. Portuguese language—Grammar—1870–   2. Portuguese language—Chrestomathies and readers. I. Title.
                                                            37–36933
Library of Congress   PC5067.N3 1930

NN   0023732   DLC

PC5067   Nascentes, Antenor, 1886–
.N25   ...O idioma nacional... São Paulo₍etc.₎Companhia editora nacional, 19 –42.
           5 v. illus. 20cm.

           Vol. 1   ₍v. 2–4, 3. ed., 1942; v. 5, 2. ed., 1935.
           "Indice bibliografico": v. 5, p. ₍207₎–213.

NN   0023733   ICU

G469.5   Nascentes, Antenor, 1886–
N171   ... O idioma nacional, por Antenor Nascentes ... Rio de Janeiro
1935   Alves [etc.] 1935–42.
           5v. illus.(incl. ports.,maps, music)
           19cm.
           Vol. 1, 4. ed., 1936; v. 2–4, 3. ed., 1942;
           v. 5, 2. ed., 7. milheiro, 1935.
           Vol. 2–4 has imprint: São Paulo [etc.]
           Companhia editora nacional.
           "Indice bibliográfico": v. 5, p. [207]–213.
           1. Portuguese   language - Grammar -
           1870–   2.   Portuguese language -
           Chrestomathies   and readers. I. Ti-
           tle.

NN   0023734   TxU PU MH

PC   Nascentes, Antenor, 1886–
5067   O idioma nacional. Rio de Janeiro,
N24   Livraria Alves ₍etc.₎ 1935–42 ₍v. 1, 1936₎
1935   5 v. illus. 19–20cm.

           1. Portuguese language--Grammar--1870–
           2. Portuguese language--Readers. I. Title.

NN   0023735   NIC

Nascentes, Antenor, 1886–
... O idioma nacional. . São Paulo ₍etc.₎ Companhia editora nacional, 1937.
6 p. l., ₍9₎–302 p. illus. 20ᶜᵐ. (Biblioteca pedagogica brasileira. Ser. 2.ᵃ: Livros didaticos. v. 78)

1. Portuguese language. 2. Portuguese language—Provincialisms—Brazil. I. Title.
Library of Congress   PC5043.N3
                                                            38–32452

NN   0023736   DLC CU NcU OOcM

Nascentes, Antenor, 1886–
... O idioma nacional. 2. ed. São Paulo ₍etc.₎ Companhia editora nacional, 1941.
6 p. l., ₍9₎–312 p. illus. 20ᶜᵐ. (Biblioteca pedagógica brasileira. Ser. 2.ᵃ: Livros didáticos, v. 78)

1. Portuguese language. 2. Portuguese language—Provincialisms—Brazil. I. Title.
U. S. Dept. of state. Libr.
for Library of Congress   ₍PC5043.N   ₎
                                                            S D 44–51

NN   0023737   DS PBm OOxM NBuU MoU

PC   Nascentes, Antenor, 1886–
5067   O idioma nacional. 3. ed. São Paulo,
N3   Companhia Editora Nacional, 1942.
1942   v.

           1. Portuguese language - Grammar - 1870–
           2. Portuguese language - Chrestomathies and
           readers. I. Title.

NN   0023738   NBuU CU

Nascentes, Antenor, 1886–
... O idioma nacional, gramática para o curso ginasial. São Paulo ₍etc.₎ Companhia editora nacional, 1944.
255, ₍2₎ p., 1 l. illus., diagrs. 19½ᶜᵐ.
On cover: Para as quatro séries ginasiais.

1. Portuguese language—Grammar—1870–   I. Title.
                                                            45–21392
Library of Congress   PC5067.N32
                                                            ₍2₎   469.5

NN   0023739   DLC

Nascentes, Antenor, 1886–
O idioma nacional na escola segundaria...
S. Paulo, Cayeiras ₍etc.₎ Com. Melhoramentos de
S. Paulo ₍pref. 1935.₎

NN   0023740   PU

Nascentes, Antenor, 1886–
Lexico de nomenclatura gramatical brasileira. Rio de Janeiro ₍Edições Dois Mundos₎ 1946.
111 p. 23 cm.
Bibliography included in "Introdução."

1. Grammar, Comparative and general—Dictionaries—Portuguese.
I. Title.
                    Full name: Antenor de Veras Nascentes.
P29.N3   469.3   A 48–7949*
New York. Public Libr.
for Library of Congress   ₍1₎†

NN   0023741   NN OU NBuU DLC

Nascentes, Antenor, 1886–
O linguajar carioca. 2. ed., completamente refundida.
Rio ₍de Janeiro₎ Edição da "Organização Simões," 1953.
217 p. illus. 18 cm. (Coleção "Rex," 7)

1. Portuguese language — Dialects — Brazil. 2. Portuguese language—Provincialisms—Rio de Janeiro. I. Title.
                    Full name: Antenor de Veras Nascentes.
PC5441.N3 1953   469.79   54–17959 ‡

NN   0023742   DLC WaU TNJ ViU TxU IU FMU ICU NIC

Nascentes, Antenor, 1886–
O linguajar carioca em 1922, por Antenor Nascentes ... Rio ₍de Janeiro₎ Süssekind de Mendonça & comp. ₍1922₎
2 p. l., ₍7₎–125 p., 1 l. 18½ᶜᵐ.
"Bibliografia": p. ₍7₎–8.

1. Portuguese language—Dialects—Brazil. 2. Portuguese language—Provincialisms—Rio de Janeiro. I. Title.
                                                            43–31637
Library of Congress   PC5441.N3

NN   0023743   DLC WaU NIC IU TxU DCU–IA NN

Nascentes, Antenor, 1886–
Método prático de análise gramatical, por Antenor Nascentes ... 9. ed. 33. a 37. milheiro. Rio de Janeiro ₍etc.₎ F. Alves, 1940.
86 p., 1 l. 18ᶜᵐ.

1. Portuguese language—Grammar—1870–   2. Portuguese language—Study and teaching. I. Title.
                                                            43–21006
Library of Congress   PC5067.N33 1940

NN   0023744   DLC

Nascentes, Antenor, 1886–
Miscelânea de estudos em honra de Antenor Nascentes
    see under title

PQ9696   Nascentes, Antenor, 1886–   ed.
.B73M79
           Botelho de Oliveira, Manuel, 1636–1711.
           Música do Parnasso. Prefácio e organização do texto por Antenor Nascentes. Rio de Janeiro, 1953.

Nascentes, Antenor.
... Num paiz fabuloso. Rio de Janeiro, Calvino filho, 1934.
216 p. 19ᶜᵐ.

1. U. S.—Descr. & trav. I. Title.
                                                            34–34296
Library of Congress   E169.N27
                                                            ₍2₎   917.3

NN   0023747   DLC

Nascentes, Antenor, 1886–
... A ortografia simplificada ao alcance de todos ... 2. ed.
Rio de Janeiro, Civilização brasileira, s/a, 1940.
4 p. l., 174 p., 1 l. 19ᶜᵐ.
"Com as palavras que mudaram na ortografia simplificada e com aquelas sobre as quais há dúvidas, acentuadas todas de acordo com o decreto-lei n. 292 de 1938. Com uma grande lista de nomes proprios, históricos, geográficos e de varias naturezas."

1. Portuguese language—Orthography and spelling. 2. Portuguese language—Glossaries, vocabularies, etc. I. Title.
                                                            41–21941
Library of Congress   PC5083.N3
                                                            ₍2₎   469.81

NN   0023748   DLC CLU

Nascentes, Antenor, 1886–
... A ortografia simplificada ao alcance de todos ... 3. ed.
Rio de Janeiro, Civilização brasileira, s/a, 1941.
3 p. l., 174 p., 1 l. 19ᶜᵐ.
"Com as palavras que mudaram na ortografia simplificada e com aquelas sobre as quais há dúvidas, acentuadas todas de acordo com o Decreto-lei n. 292 de 1938. Com uma grande lista de nomes proprios, históricos, geográficos e de varias naturezas."

1. Portuguese language—Orthography and spelling. 2. Portuguese language—Glossaries, vocabularies, etc. I. Title.
                                                            43–6479
Library of Congress   PC5083.N3 1941
                                                            ₍2₎   469.81

NN   0023749   DLC IU PPT TxU NcU CtY NBuU

Nascentes, Antenor, 1886–

Lima, Hildebrando.
Pequeno dicionário brasileiro da lingua portuguesa, organizado por Hildebrando Lima e Gustavo Barroso, revisto por Manuel Bandeira e José Baptista da Luz. Redigido nas ortografias simplificada e etimológica. 2. ed., rev. e aum. por Antenor Nascentes ... C. Mello-Leitão ... Francisco Venâncio Filho ... C. Delgado de Carvalho ... José Baptista da Luz ... Rio de Janeiro–São Paulo, Civilização brasileira s/a, 1939.

VOLUME 405

PC5327
.L5
1942
Lima, Hildebrando.   FOR OTHER EDITIONS
                             SEE MAIN ENTRY

Nascentes, Antenor, 1886–

    Pequeno dicionário brasileiro da lingua portuguesa, organizado por Hildebrando Lima e Gustavo Barroso, revisto por Manuel Bandeira e José Baptista da Luz. Redigido nas ortografias simplicada e mista. 3. ed., refundida, rev. e aum. por Antenor Nascentes ... Aurelio Buarque de Hollanda Ferreira ... C. Delgado de Carvalho ... ¡e outros¡ Rio de Janeiro ¡etc.¡ Civilização brasileira, 1942.

PC
5201
N24
Nascentes, Antenor, 1886–
    O problema da regencía (regencía integral e viva)   Rio de Janeiro, F. Bastos, 1944.
    346 p. 19cm.

    1. Portuguese language--Grammar.
    2. Portuguese language--Syntax.

NN   0023752   NIC NNC TxU

Nascentes, Antenor, 1886–
    ... Tesouro da fraseologia brasileira. Rio de Janeiro, S. Paulo, Livraria editora Freitas Bastos, 1945.
    448 p. 18¡ cm.
    "Bibliografia": p. 5–6.

    1. Portuguese language—Terms and phrases.   I. Title.

    PC5347.N3   469.82   46—3901

NN   0023753   DLC FU MH WaU CU PU TxU ICU CtY

Nascentes, Célio Olimpio.
    ... Instruções gerais sôbre a aplicação da nova "tarifa de seguros incêndio do Brasil" ... see under   Instituto de resseguros do Brasil, Rio de Janeiro.

Nascentes de Azambuja, Bernardo Augusto
    see   Azambuja, Bernardo Augusto
Nascentes de.

Nascentes de Azambuja, Joaquim Marie
    see   Azambuja, Joaquim Maria Nascentes
de, 1812–1896.

492.49
N244b
Naschér, Eduard, 1853–
    Das Buch des jüdischen Jargons nebst einem Anhang: Die Gauner- oder die "Kochemersprache" mit Quellennachweis u. Erklärungen.   Wien, J. Deubler ¡1910¡
    164p. 16cm.

    1. Yiddish language - Dictionaries - German.
    2. German language - Slang.

NN   0023757   NcU MH DNLM PPDrop OCH OC1 NN ICU

Naschér, Eduard, 1853–
    Handbuch der geschichte der weltlitteratur. Nach den besten quellen bearb. von Eduard Naschér. Mit 86 bildnistafeln. Berlin, W. Werther ¡1900¡
    2 p. l., 704 p. ports. 24ᶜᵐ.

    1. Literatur—Hist. & crit.

                         1–8643
    Library of Congress   PN553.N3

NN   0023758   DLC MH MB

Naschér, Eduard, 1853–
    Handbuch der geschichte der weltlitteratur. Nach den besten quellen bearb. von Eduard Naschér. Mit 80 bildnistafeln.   Berlin, Bard, 1901.
    2 p.l., 704 p. ports. 24 cm.

NN   0023759   NcU

Nascher, Ignatz Leo, 1863–   **L610.4 N17**
    ¡Collected papers dealing chiefly with diseases and care of the
121906   aged.¡
    Extracted or reprinted from various medical serials.

NN   0023760   ICJ

Nascher, I¡gnatz¡ L¡eo¡, M.D., 1863–
    The danger of routine practice in senile cases.   n. t.-p.
¡New York, 1911¡   2 l.   8°.
    Repr.: American Journal of Clinical Medicine.

    1. Age (Old).—Diseases, etc.
  N. Y. P. L.   February 5, 1912.

NN   0023761   NN

Nascher, Ignatz Leo, 1863–
    Diagnostic hints in senile cases.   ¡Louisville, Ky., 1913.¡
5 p.   8°.
    Extracts from a course of lectures on geriatrics delivered at the College of Physicians and Surgeons, Boston, November, 1912.
    Caption-title.
    Repr.: Amer. practitioner. Feb., 1913.

    1. Age (Old).—Diseases.
  N. Y. P. L.   September 22, 1915.

NN   0023762   NN

Nascher, I¡gnatz¡ L¡eo¡, M.D., 1863–
    Dosage in old age; an important contribution to geriatric therapy.   n. t.-p.   ¡New York, 1911¡   2 l.   8°.
    Repr.: American Journal of Clinical Medicine. July, 1911.

    1. Age (Old).—Diseases, etc.
  N. Y. P. L.   February 5, 1912.

NN   0023763   NN

Nascher, Ignatz Leo, 1863–
    Errors in treatment of senile cases. Read before the Triprofessional Medical Society, New York, May 21, 1912. By I. L. Nascher... ¡New York:¡ A. R. Elliott Pub. Co., cop. 1912. 7(1) p. 8°.
    Caption-title.
    Repr.: N. Y. medical jour. Oct. 12, 1912.

    1. Age (Old).—Diseases.
  N. Y. P. L.   September 22, 1915.

NN   0023764   NN

Nascher, Ignatz Leo, 1863–
    Evidences of senile mental impairment, by I. L. Nascher... ¡Chicago, 1915.¡   4 l.   4°.
    Repr.: Amer. jour. of clinical medicine. June, 1915.

    1. Age (Old).—Diseases.
  N. Y. P. L.   September 22, 1915.

NN   0023765   NN

Nascher, Ignatz Leo, 1863–
    Functional stimulation of senile tissues. ¡By¡ I. L. Nascher. ¡New York, 1915.¡   296–298 p.   f°.
    Excerpt: Medical times. Sept., 1915.

    1. Age (Old).—Diseases.
  N. Y. P. L.   September 22, 1915.

NN   0023766   NN

Nascher, Ignatz Leo, 1863–
    El Gebir, the visionary. By I. L. Nascher...   ¡New York:¡ A. R. Elliott Pub. Co., 1915.   3(1) p.   8°.
    Caption-title.
    Repr.: N. Y. medical jour. July 10, 1915.

    1. Jābir ibn Haiyān al-Tartūsi, fl.   776.   September 22, 1915.

NN   0023767   NN

Nascher, I¡gnatz¡ L¡eo¡, M.D., 1863–
    Geriatrics.   n. t.-p.   ¡New York:¡ A. R. Elliott Pub. Company, cop. 1909.   3(1) p.   8°.
    Repr.: New York Medical Journal. August, 1909.

    1. Age (Old).—Diseases, etc.
  N. Y. P. L.   February 3, 1912.

NN   0023768   NN

Nascher, Ignatz Leo, 1863–
    Geriatrics, by I. L. Nascher...   New York: W. Wood & Co. ¡1912.¡   11 p.   12°.
    Repr.: Medical record. April 20, 1912.
    Cover-title.

    1. Age (Old).—Diseases. 2. Title.
  N. Y. P. L.   September 22, 1915.

NN   0023769   NN

Nascher, Ignatz Leo, 1863–
    Geriatrics; the diseases of old age and their treatment, including physiological old age, home and institutional care, and medico-legal relations, by I. L. Nascher, M. D. ... with an introduction by A. Jacobi, M. D. With 50 plates containing 81 illustrations. Philadelphia, P. Blakiston's son & co. ¡1914¡
    xviii, 517 p. plates. 24ᵐᵐ. $5.00

    1. Old age—Diseases.   I. Title.

    Library of Congress   RC966.N3   14–3160

    ICJ OC1W-H
NN   0023770   DLC ICRL KU-M OrU-M OrU PPT PPC DNLM

Nascher, Ignatz Leo, 1863–
    Geriatrics, the diseases of old age and their treatment, including physiological old age, home and institutional care, and medico-legal relations, by I. L. Nascher ... with an introduction by A. Jacobi, M. D. 2d ed., rev., with 50 plates containing 81 illustrations. Philadelphia, P. Blakiston's son & co. ¡*1916¡
    xx, 527 p. plates. 24 cm.

    1. Geriatrics.

    RC952.N3 1916   16—24213

NN   0023771   DLC CaBVaU PPC DNLM ICJ

Nascher, Ignatz Leo, 1863–
    Insomnia in the aged. By I. L. Nascher.   ¡Louisville, Ky., 1914.¡   181–183 p.   4°.
    Excerpt: Therapeutic record. June 15, 1914.

    1. Age (Old).—Diseases. 2. Insom-   nia.
  N. Y. P. L.

NN   0023772   NN

Nascher, Ignatz Leo, 1863–
    Lane's autointoxication complex and the manifestations of senility. By I. L. Nascher... ¡New York:¡ A. R. Elliott Pub. Co., 1914.   10 p., 1 l.   8°.
    Caption-title.
    Repr.: N. Y. medical jour. Aug. 8, 1914.

    1. Age (Old).—Diseases.
  N. Y. P. L.   September 22, 1915.

NN   0023773   NN

VOLUME 405

Nascher, Ignatz Leo, 1863–
    Longevity and rejuvenescence. By J. L. Nascher. ₍New
York, 1909.₎   795–800 p.   4°.
    Excerpt: New York medical jour. April 17, 1909.

1. Longevity.
N. Y. P. L.   September 22, 1915.

NN   0023774   NN

Nascher, I₍gnatz₎ L₍eo₎, M.D.
    Longevity and rejuvenescence. Read before the Medical
Association of the Greater City of New York, June 2, 1913.   New
York, 1913.   13(1) p.   8°.
    Repr.: New York medical jour., July 12, 1913.

1. Longevity.   2. Rejuvenescence.
N. Y. P. L.   June 6, 1914.

NN   0023775   NN

Nascher, Ignatz Leo, 1863–
    The medical care of the aged. By I. L. Nascher... ₍New
York, 1913.₎   9(1) p.   8°.
    Repr.: N. Y. medical jour. Nov. 15, 1913.
    Cover-title.

1. Age (Old).—Diseases.
N. Y. P. L.   September 22, 1915.

NN   0023776   NN OU

Nascher, Ignatz Leo, 1863–
    Medication for the senile, by I. L. Nascher. ₍Chicago, 1913.₎
2 l.   8°.
    Caption-title.
    Repr.: Amer. jour. of clinical medicine. Jan., 1913.

1. Age (Old).—Diseases.
N. Y. P. L.   September 22, 1915.

NN   0023777   NN

T112   Nascher, Ignatz Leo, 1863–
N17   [Miscellaneous articles on medical subjects
1   reprinted from various periodicals]
                                              26cm.

        1. Medicine - Collected works

NN   0023778   CtY

Nascher, Ignatz Leo, 1863–
    The neglect of the aged. By I. L. Nascher...   New York:
W. Wood & Co., 1914.   13 p.   12°.
    Repr.: Medical record. Sept. 12, 1914.
    Cover-title.

1. Aged.—Care and treatment.
N. Y. P. L.   September 22, 1915

NN   0023779   NN IU OU

Nascher, I₍gnatz₎ L₍eo₎, M.D., 1863–
    Old age in its medico-legal relations. ₍New York, 1912.₎
13(1) p.   8°.
    Repr.: New York medical jour. May, 1912.

1. Age (Old).
N. Y. P. L.   February 26, 1914.

NN   0023780   NN

Nascher, I₍gnatz₎ L₍eo₎, M.D., 1863–
    A plea for the study of geriatrics.   New York: W. Wood &
Company, 1910.   8 p.   12°.
    Repr.: Medical Record. September, 1910. Title from cover.

1. Age (Old).—Diseases, etc.
N. Y. P. L.   February 3, 1912.

NN   0023781   NN

₍Nascher, Ignatz Leo,₎ 1863–
    A project for changing the topography of New York City so
as to furnish better port facilities and encourage a more equable
distribution of the population of the city in the future.   ₍New
York, 1926?₎   7, 12 f.   4°.
    Caption-title.
    Typewritten.

1. New York (city)—Transit.   2. New York (city)—City planning.
3. Title.
N. Y. P. L.   June 22, 1927

NN   0023782   NN

Nascher, Ignatz Leo, 1863–
    Psychanalysis of criminality, by I. L. Nascher.   ₍Louisville,
Ky., 1914.₎   233–238 p.   4°.
    Excerpt: Amer. practitioner. May, 1914.

1. Criminals.—Psychology.
N. Y. P. L.   September 22, 1915.

NN   0023783   NN

Nascher, Ignatz Leo, 1863–
    Recreation as a hygienic and therapeutic agent. By I. L.
Nascher.   ₍New York, 1910.₎   209–213 p.   4°.
    Excerpt: Dietetic and hygienic gazette. April, 1910.

1. Recreation.
N. Y. P. L.   September 22, 1915.

NN   0023784   NN

Nascher, Ignatz Leo, 1863–
    Red amorphous phosphorus, by I. L. Nascher.   n. t.-p.
₍Louisville, Ky., 1913.₎   633–637 p.   4°.
    Excerpt: Amer. practitioner. Dec., 1913.

1. Phosphorus (Red).
N. Y. P. L.   September 22, 1915.

NN   0023785   NN

Nascher, I₍gnatz₎ L₍eo₎, M.D., 1863–
    The senile climacteric.   n. t.-p.   ₍New York:₎ A. R. Elliott
Pub. Company, 1911.   5(1) p.   8°.
    Repr.: New York Medical Journal. Dec. 1911.

1. Age (Old).—Diseases, etc.
N. Y. P. L.   February 5, 1912.

NN   0023786   NN

Nascher, I₍gnatz₎ L₍eo₎, M.D., 1863–
    Senile debility.   New York: W. Wood & Company, 1911.
13 p.   12°.
    Repr.: Medical Record. Jan. 1911. Title from cover.

1. Age (Old).—Diseases, etc.
N. Y. P. L.   February 5, 1912.

NN   0023787   NN

Nascher, Ignatz Leo, 1863–
    Senile mentality, by I. L. Nascher...   Philadelphia: J. B.
Lippincott Co., cop. 1911.   49–60 p.   8°.
    Repr.: Internat. clinics. v. 4, 21. series.
    Cover-title.

1. Age (Old).—Diseases.
N. Y. P. L.   September 22, 1915.

NN   0023788   NN

Nascher, Ignatz Leo, 1863–
    Some geriatric aphorisms. By I. L. Nascher...   ₍Philadel-
phia, 1914.₎   9 p.   12°.
    Repr.: Amer. medicine. New series. v. 9, no. 11.
    Caption-title.

1. Age (Old).—Diseases.
N. Y. P. L.   September 22, 1915.

NN   0023789   NN

Nascher, Ignatz Leo, 1863–
    Some remarks on arteriosclerosis, by I. L. Nascher.   ₍Phila-
delphia, 1913.₎   531–533 p.   8°.
    Excerpt: Amer. medicine. New series. v. 8, no. 8.

1. Arteries.—Diseases.
N. Y. P. L.   September 22, 1915.

NN   0023790   NN

Nascher, I₍gnatz₎ L₍eo₎, M.D., 1863–
    Sources of error in diagnosis in senile cases.   n. t.-p.   New
York, 1911.   6 p.   8°.
    Repr.: The Archives of Diagnosis. July, 1911.

1. Age (Old).—Diseases, etc.
N. Y. P. L.   February 5, 1912.

NN   0023791   NN

Nascher, I₍gnatz₎ L₍eo₎, M.D., 1863–
    The strenuous life.   New York: W. Wood & Company, 1911.
9 p.   12°.
    Repr.: Medical Record, Oct. 7, 1911. Title from cover.

1. Conduct of life.   2. Age (Old).
N. Y. P. L.   February 5, 1912.

NN   0023792   NN

Nascher, Ignatz Leo, 1863–
    Therapeutic problems in senile cases. ₍By₎ I. L. Nascher.
₍New York, 1914.₎   88–93 p.   8°.
    Excerpt: Medical review of reviews. Feb., 1914.

1. Age (Old).—Diseases.
N. Y. P. L.   September 22, 1915.

NN   0023793   NN

Nascher, I₍gnatz₎ L₍eo₎, M.D., 1863–
    Tissue cell evolution. A theory of senescence.   n. t.-p.
New York: A. R. Elliott Publishing Company, cop. 1910.   9(1) p.
8°.
    Repr.: New York Medical Journal for Nov. 5, 1910.

1. Cells.   2. Age (Old).
N. Y. P. L.   February 23, 1912.

NN   0023794   NN

VOLUME 405

Nascher, Ignatz Leo, 1863–
The treatment of bronchitis in the aged. By I. L. Nascher.
[Philadelphia, 1914.]   336–340 p.   4°.

Caption-title.
Excerpt: Medical council. Sept., 1914.

1. Age (Old).—Diseases. 2. Bron-   chitis.
N. Y. P. L.   September 22, 1915.

NN 0023795   NN

Nascher, I[gnatz] L[eo], M.D., 1863–
The treatment of diseases in senility.   New York: W. Wood
& Company, 1909.   12 p.   12°.

Repr.: Medical Record. December, 1909.

1. Age (Old).—Diseases, etc.
N. Y. P. L.   February 5, 1912.

NN 0023796   NN

Nascher, Ignatz Leo, 1863–
The wretches of Povertyville; a sociological study of
the Bowery, by I. L. Nascher, M. D.; sketches and illustrations by George Toner. Chicago, J. J. Lanzit, 1909.

4 p. l., [7]–298 p., 1 l. front., plates. 20cm.

1. New York (City)—Poor. 2. New York (City)—Soc. condit.

Library of Congress   HN80.N5N3   9-14830

NN 0023797   DLC CLU OC1 ICJ NN

Naschér, [Simon].
F. Deák. Gedaschtnissrede gehalten
am 28. Januar 1877 im Berliner Ungar-
Verein...   Berlin: W.Weber,1877.

12 p.
Repr.: Nordd. Allg. Zeitung Febr.1877

NN 0023798   OCH

4PJ   Naschér, Simon.
277   Der Gaon Haia; ein Beitrag zur
Entwickelungsgeschichte der semitischen
Sprachforschung. Berlin, Stuhr'sche
Buchhandlung, 1867.
27 p.

NN 0023799   DLC-P4 CtY OCH

Nascher, Simon.
Das Judenthum der Aufklarung. Reden fur die
Gebildeten aller Confessionen. Magdeburg,
W. Simon, 1916.
83, (1) p.   8°.

NN 0023800   NN OCH

Naschér, S[imon].
(Die) jüdische Gemeinde in Vergangenheit.
Gegenwart und Zukunft. Reden für Freunde
religiöser Cultur und Freiheit.   Berlin:
L. Gerschel, 1877.
78 p.

NN 0023801   OCH

Naschér, S[imon].
Moises Naschér. (Oberrabbiner von Baja.)
Eine exegetische Mongraphie ...   Berlin:
F. Stahn, 1879.
56 p.

NN 0023802   OCH PPDrop CtY

Naschér, Simon.
(Die) Sentenz bei Juden und Arabern.
Eine vergleichende Studie.   Berlin:
Stuhr, 1868.
19 p.

NN 0023803   OCH CU

Naschér, S[imon].
Vier Momente. Gottesdienstliche Rede
zur Feier 25jähriger Stiftung der Gemeinde
Schochare Hattob in Berlin, am 3, Januar
1880 gehalten. Berlin: F. Stahn, 1880.
16 p.

NN 0023804   OCH

Nascher, Simon, 1841-1901.
..."Wisse, was über Dir ist." Predigt zum
Neujahrstage.   [n.p., 1891]
16 p.   22.5 cm.
Caption title.
Extract from his Festpredigten, 1891?

NN 0023805   CtY

Naschér, Simon, 1841-1901.
Se8   Wissenschaftliche Vorträge ...
L4   Berlin,C.Habel,1875. 46pp. 20½cm.
875n   Contents. – Die moralische Wirkung der Kunst.
Die Faustdichtung von Goethe und Lenau. – Der
Einfluss der deutschen Philosophie auf die
deutsche Volksbildung.

NN 0023806   CtY MH

Naschér, S[imon].
Worte, gesprochen am Sarge des ...
Hirsch Nathan ... am 18. Februar 1872...
Rathenow: A. Haase, [1872].
14 p.

NN 0023807   OCH

Naschér, Sinai Simon.
see
Naschér, Simon.

Naschinetz, Vicenzo.
Concerto con corni da caccia obligati.   [17—]
parts. 23 x 31 cm.
Copyist's ms.
For 2 horns and string orchestra.

1. Orchestral music—To 1800—Parts.

M1045.N25C6   M 60-2672

NN 0023809   DLC

Naschitz, Theodor
see Nachèz, Tivadar, 1859–1930.

Naschiwin, Iwan
see
Nazhivin, Ivan Ḟedorovich, 1874–1940.

Naschke, Ernst.
Dispersion et absorption magnétique du fer entre O et 7.000
mégahertz.   [Grenoble? 1954?]   45 p.   illus.   27cm.

At head of title: No. d'ordre: 61.
Thèse—Grenoble.
Bibliography, p. 41.

1. Iron—Magnetic properties.   t. 1954.

NN 0023812   NN CtY

Der Naschmarkt-König und der Untergang seines
Reiches
see under   [Dorn, Gustav]

Naschold, Fritz, 1907–
Zur Kritik der Memoiren von August Schneegans...von
Fritz Naschold...   Schwäb. Gmünd: Rems-Zeitung, G.m.b.H.,
1932.   vii, 151 p.   21cm.

Inaugural-Dissertation — Tübingen, 1932.
Lebenslauf.
"Literatur," p. vi–vii.

626080A. 1. Schneegans, August,   1835–1898: Memoiren.
N. Y. P. L.   April 24, 1933

NN 0023814   NN ICRL OU PU CtY

HX811   Naschold, Jacob.
1894
.H4U3   Udny, Ernest.
Dr. Hertzka's Freeland colony. The Freeland colony.
(Co-operation in East Africa.) By Ernest Udny, M. A.,
arranged for publication in America by Jacob Naschold,
with preface by Dr. Hertzka ... [1st ed.—June 1894] Philadelphia, American Freeland association, ©1894.

Law   Naschold, R., ed.

Germany (Federal Republic, 1949–   ) Laws, statutes, etc.
Baupreisrecht und Baupreisbildung. Kommentar zum
neuen Baupreisrecht von Walter Daub und R. Naschold.
Wiesbaden, Bauverlag, 1951–

HD7811   Naschold, Richard, 1899–
.N17
Die stellung des schwerbeschädigten
im tarifrecht unter besonderer berücksichtigung des baugewerbes... Tübingen,
Göbel, 1933.
70 p. 21 cm.

Inaug.-diss. - Tübingen.
Lebenslauf.
"Literatur-verzeichnis": p.62–68.

NN 0023817   NjP ICRL

M   Nasci, Michele.
219   Sonate sei di cembalo con accompagna-
N244   mento di violino... [Score]. London:
Printed by Welcker, [1771?]. 33 p.
34 1/2 cm.

NN 0023818   NRU-Mus

PQ   Nascimbene, Itala.
4378   Il Convivio e la Divina Commedia;
N17c   saggio di alcuni confronti che possono
servire a stabilirne la cronologia.
Pavia, Tipografia Ponzio, 1901.
85 p.

Bibliographical footnotes.

1. Dante Alighieri. Il Convito.
2. Dante Alighieri. Divina Commedia.
3. Dante –   Chronology.

NN 0023819   CLU

VOLUME 405

Nascimbene, Luigi.
L'Italia, il suo avvenire e la sua capitale, e soluzione della questione romana.   Genova, coi topo della Gazzetta dei tribunali, 1864.
Folded map.

NN   0023820   MH

NASCIMBENE, MARIO.
[PIGMALIONE. ARR. FOR PIANO]
Pigmalione; balletto in tre quadri di Nicola Benois. Soggetto di Tamara Adrian. [Milan] 1946. 62 p. 35cm.

With superlinear descriptive text.

1. Ballets (Piano). 2. Pygmalion. I. Benois, Nicola. Pygmalion. II. Adrian, Tamara. Pygmalion.   III. Title. IV. Adrian, Tamara.

NN   0023821   NN

PA   Nascimbeni, Nascimbene.
6304   ... In M. Tullii Ciceronis De inuentione
R8   libros commentarius ... Venetijs, Apud
N3   Bologninum Zalterium, 1563.
Cage   Colophon.

[12] 128 l. 4to.

NN   0023822   DFo

PA   Nascimbeni, Nascimbene.
8555   ... Scipio minor: seu de iuuentute... libellus
N35   ... Odes...
84   Colophon: Bononiae, Bartholomaeus Bonardus et
1544   Marcus Antonius Groscius, 1544.
Cage
A-L⁴. 8vo.

NN   0023823   DFo

Nascimbene, Rinaldo.
Lezioni di ebraico e lingue semitiche comparate. Pavia, Litografia Cuochi [1945?]

141 p.

NN   0023824   MH

Nascimbene Pasio, Clelia.
... Patriottismo romantico e patriottismo classico nei prodromi del risorgimento italiano. Bologna, N. Zanichelli, 1931.

2 p. l., [vii]–xi, 177 p., 1 l. 19ᵐ.

1. Italian literature—19th cent.—Hist. & crit. 2. Italy—Hist.—1815–1870. 3. Patriotism. 4. Romanticism—Italy.   I. Title.

34–34187
Library of Congress   PQ4085.N3
[2]   850.908

NN   0023825   DLC IEN OCU MH

Nascimbeni, Giovanni.
... The cathedral of Modena; sixty-four illustrations, with text by Giovanni Nascimbeni. Milano, E. Bonomi, 1913.
xxiii p. incl. plan. 64 pl. on 32 l. 15ᵐ. (L'Italia monumentale ... [n. 29])
English and German.

1. Modena. Duomo.
A C 33–4391
Cleveland. Public library
for Library of Congress   [a37c1]

NN   0023826   OC1 OU CtY MiU NBuG NN C NIC CLSU MeB

Nascimbeni, Giovanni.
... Il duomo di Modena.   Firenze, Fratelli Alinari, 1925.   33p. 64 plates on 32 l. 16cm. (Italia monumentale... n.29)

Testo italiano, francese, inglese.

1. Modena. Duomo.   Series.

NN   0023827   MWelC MWiCA

Nascimbeni, Giovanni.
Note e ricerche intorno a Giulio Cesare Croce. Bologna, N. Zanichelli, 1914.
124 p. 24 cm. (Biblioteca de "L'Archiginnasio," ser. 2, n. 6)

1. Croce, Giulio Cesare, 1550–1609.   (Series)

PQ4621.C5M3   53–56838

NN   0023828   DLC MdBJ NN ICU ICN

Nascimbeni, Giovanni.
...Riccardo Wagner.   Genova: A. F. Formíggini, 1914. 88 p.   front. (port.)   16°.   (Profili. n. 33.)
Added t.-p.
Bibliography, p. [85–]88.

DREXEL MUSICAL FUND.
56307A. 1. Wagner, Richard,   1813–83. 2. Series.
N. Y. P. L.   October 25, 1922.

NN   0023829   NN PLatS

V   NASCIMBENI, GIOVANNI.
29   ...Riccardo Wagner. 2. edizione.   Roma,
95615 Formíggini,1923.
88p.   (Profili. n.33)

"Bibliografia": p. [85]-88.

NN   0023830   ICN NNG

Nascimbeni, Giovanni.
Riccardo Wagner. 2.ed.   Milano, Soc. An. Editr. Bietti, 1939.

88 p. port. 17 cm.
Added title-page: Profili, 33.

NN   0023831   MH-Mu

Nascimbeni, Giovanni, ed.
Un viaggio poetico nel Frignano, attribuito a Giulio Cesare Croce
see under   Croce, Giulio Cesare, 1550-1609, supposed author.

Nascimento, Abdias do, 1914–
Relações de raça no Brasil
see under   Instituto Nacional do Negro.

Nascimento, Alba Cañizares
see   Cañizares Nascimento, Alba, 1893-

Nascimento, Alfredo.
O centenario da Academia nacional de medicina do Rio de Janeiro, 1829–1929; primordios e evolução da medicina no Brasil, por Alfredo Nascimento. Rio de Janeiro, Imprensa nacional, 1929.
viii, 254 p. 27ᵐ.
Erratum slip inserted.

1. Academia nacional de medicina, Rio de Janeiro.
46–40182
Library of Congress   R25.R49

NN   0023835   DLC CU DPAHO

614.514 Nascimento, Alfredo.
N244m   O mimetismo do cholera; memoria sobre as manifestações choleriformes no Brazil como contribução ao estudo da epidemia do Valle do Parahyba em 1894-1895. Rio de Janeiro, Typ. Leite & Gomes, 1898.
496 p. 21 cm.
"Trabalho lido perante a Academia Nacional de Medicina..."
1. Cholera, Asiatic - Brazil. 2. Epidemics - Parahyba, Brazil (State) I. Title.

NN   0023836   LNHT

Nascimento, Alfredo.
HD6614   Vinte annos de labor, 1880-1900; historico da
M39N3   Associação dos Empregados no Commercio do Rio de Janeiro. Rio de Janeiro, Typ. do "Jornal do
Stack   commercio" de Rodrigues, 1900.
137 p. illus.(part fold.) 23ᵐ.

1.Associação dos Empregados no Commercio do Rio de Janeiro.   I.Title.

NN   0023837   CSt

GR 133 NASCIMENTO,ALFREDO RICARDO DO.
.B7 N24   Brasil sertanejo; historias sertanejas, curiosidades sertanejas, cantigas do sertao, mentiras e anedotas, poemas, dialeto sertanejo. [Por] Ze do Norte [pseud.] Rio de Janeiro ["ASA" Artes Graficas] 1948.
284 p. port.

1. Folk-lore--Brazil. I. Title. Folklore cds.

NN   0023838   InU NN DLC-P4

Nascimento, Augusto do.
Atlas de geografia para uso dos alunos, dos liceus, e das escolas industriais e comerciais. 3. ed. Lisboa, F. Franco, 1946.
53 p. incl. [49] col. maps (part fold.) 30 cm.

1. Atlases.
Map 48–621*

NN   0023839   DLC

Nascimento, Augusto do.
... Francês ... exercícios (resolvidos e para resolver) e curiosidades, acompanhados das necessárias notas elucidativas, graduados de harmonia com a sua sucessão lógica e dificuldade crescente e adaptados a todos os estabelecimentos de ensino secundário. Lisboa, Papelaria e livraria Fernandes & c.ª, 1.ª, 1941–
v. 17ᵐ. (*His* Biblioteca de ensino intuitivo e prático)

1. French language—Grammar—1870- 2. French language—Text-books for foreigners—Brazilians.
45–25487
Library of Congress   PC2129.B7N3
[2]   448.2469

NN   0023840   DLC

Nascimento, Carlos.
A lingua nacional (antinomias & parallelismos os factos psychologicos, acções e reacções literaria, as influencias sociaes.   Belem, Para [Brazil, Tavares Cardoso] 1917.
223 p.
1. Portuguese language. I. Title.

NN   0023841   ICarbS

VOLUME 405

Nascimento, Domingos do, 1862–
... A hulha branca no Paraná ₍por₎ major D. Nascimento. Rio de Janeiro, Turnauer & Machado, 1914.
90, ₍4₎ p., 1 l. incl. illus., pl., port. fold. map. 31½ᶜᵐ.
At head of title: Centro de letras do Paraná.

1. Water-power—Brazil—Parana.   I. Title.

22–14457

Library of Congress   TC442.P3N3

NN 0023842   DLC

Nascimento, Domingos do, 1862–
Pela fronteira. Parana, 1903.
Curytiba: 1903.   228 pp.

NN 0023843   DCU–IA

Nascimento, Faustino, 1901–
O refúgio sublime. Rio de Janeiro, Z. Valverde, 1945.
112 p. port. 26 cm.
Poems.

I. Title.

PQ9697.N216R4   50–57402

NN 0023844   DLC

Nascimento, Faustino, 1901–
Ritmos do novo continente. Rio de Janeiro, Livraria Civilização brasileira, 1933.
149 p. 22cm.

NN 0023845   NcU

Nascimento, Faustino, 1901–
...Ritmos do novo continente.   Rio de Janeiro, Livraria Civilização brasileira, 1939. 149 p. 22cm.

289979B. 1. Poetry, Brazilian.   I. Title.
N.Y.P.L.   January 18, 1945

NN 0023846   NN DPU

B869.1   **Nascimento, Faustino,** 1901.
N24lr   Ritmos do novo continente. 2. ed.
1943   revista e aumentada. Illustracoes de
            Camila Alvares de Azevedo. Rio de Janeiro,
            I. Pongetti, 1943.
               244 p. illus., port., facsim.

Includes bibliography.

NN 0023847   CaQML

4PQ   **Nascimento, Francisco Manuel do,**
Port.   1734–1819
721   Obras completas de Filinto Elysio
            [pseud.] 2. ed., emendada, e accrescentada com muitas obras inéditas, e
            com o retrato do autor. Paris, A.
            Bobée, 1817–1819.
               11 v.

DCU–IA
NN 0023848   DLC–P4 CU WaU OU InU CLU ICN MH CtY

Nascimento, Francisco Manuel do, 1734–1819.
Obras de Filinto Elysio. [pseud.] Nova
ed. Lisboa, Typographia Rollandiana, 1836–40.
22 v. in 11. 11 cm.

NN 0023849   CaBVaU NcU

Nascimiento, Francisco Manuel do, 1734–1819.
Aventures d'Arminde et de Florise; histoire veritable écrite en France en 1533 par Rodrigue Marques, l'un de leurs parens. Avec le texte portugais. Paris, 1803.

Portuguese and French on opposite pages.

NN 0023850   MH

Nascimento, Francisco Manuel do, 1734–1819, tr

Raynouard, François Juste Marie, 1761–1836.
Camoens. Ode par m. Raynouard ... avec le traduction de m. Francisco Manoel (Filinto Elysio.) Paris, Impr. de A. Bobée, 1819.

Nascimento, Francisco Manuel do, 1734–1819, tr.
FOR OTHER EDITIONS
SEE MAIN ENTRY
Raynouard, François Juste Marie, 1761–1836.
Camões, ode do cavalheiro Raynouard ... traduzida em verso portuguez por Francisco Manoel (Filinto Elisio), Vicente Pedro Nolasco, F.₍i₎ L.ᵉ Verdier; correcta e annotada, dedicada a Sua Magestade elrei o senhor d. João vi. Nosso Senhor, pelo seu humilde e fiel vassallo, Heleodoro Jacinto d'Araujo Carneiro. Lisboa, Impressão regia, 1825.

Nascimento, Francisco Manuel do, 1734–1819, tr.
₍Abailard, Pierre₎ 1079–1142.
Cartas d'Heloisa e Abailard traduzidas por Caetano Lopes de Moura ... seguidas das Cartas amorosas d'uma religiosa portugueza, restituidas á lingua materna por d. Joze Maria de Souza, morgado de Matheus, augmentadas com as imitações de Dorat e outras, e traduzidas do francez por Filinto Elysio ₍pseud.₎ e Caetano Lopes de Moura ... Paris, Livraria portugueza de J.-P. Aillaud, 1838.

DP604   Nascimento, Francisco Manuel do, 1734–1819, tr.
.O 952   FOR OTHER EDITIONS
                       SEE MAIN ENTRY
Osorio, Jeronymo, bp. of Silves, 1506–1580.
Da vida e feitos de el-rei d. Manuel; xii livros ... por d. Jerónimo Osório, bispo de Silves, vertidos em português pelo padre Francisco Manuel do Nascimento. Edição actualizada e prefaciada por Joaquim Ferreira ... ₍Pôrto₎ Livraria Civilização ₍1944₎

Nascimento, Francisco Manuel do, 1734–1819, tr.
La Fontaine, Jean de, 1621–1695.
Fabulas escolhidas entre as de J. La Fontaine. E traduzidas em portuguez, por Francisco Manoel do Nascimento ... . Londres, Typ. de H. Bryer, 1813.

869.1   Nascimento, Francisco Manuel do, 1734–1819.
N17l   Líricas e sátiras de Filinto Elísio.
          Pôrto, D. Barreira [19—]
          243p. 19cm. (Colecção Portugal, no.28)

Editor's name at head of title: Joaquim Ferreira.

1123842   I. Ferreira, Joaquim, ed. II. Title.

NN 0023856   TxU

₍Nascimento, Francisco Manuel do₎ 1734–1819.
... Poesias. Selecção, prefácio e notas do prof. José Pereira Tavares. Lisboa, Livraria Sá da Costa ₍1941₎
2 p. l., ix–xlvi p., 1 l., 267 p. front. (port.) 19ᶜᵐ. (Colecção de clássicos Sá da Costa)
Author's pseud., Filinto Elísio, at head of title.

I. Pereira Tavares, José, ed. II. Title.

46–36351

Library of Congress   PQ9261.N3A17 1941
                                 ₍2₎   869.1

NN 0023857   DLC CLU ViU TxU FU WaU ICU CU CSt CaBVaU

Nascimento, Francisco Manuel do, 1734–1819.
Poésie lyrique portugaise, ou Choix des odes de Francisco Manoel, tr. en français, avec le texte en regard. Précédées d'une notice sur l'auteur, et d'une introduction sur la littérature portugaise; avec des notes historiques, géographiques et littéraires; par A. M. Sané ... Paris, Cérioux jeune, 1808.
3 p. l., xcl, ₍1₎, 344 p. 20ᶜᵐ.

I. Sané, Alexandre Marie, 1773 (ca.)–1812, ed.
                                          22—8636
Library of Congress   PQ9261.N3A36

NN 0023858   DLC NcU OCl ViU

868N17 Nascimento, Francisco Manuel do, 1734–1819.
K1797   Versos de Filinto Elysio ₍pseud.₎ Paris,
            1797–1806.
               8v. in 4. 17cm.

Vol.7–8 have imprint: Paris, Chez Barroire, libraire.
Vol.6 includes, with special title pages, two translations by Nascimento: Voltaire's Zadig, Lisboa, 1773; and Vicq-d'Azyr's Elogio do doutor Antonio-Nunes-Ribeiro Sanchez, Paris, 1806.

NN 0023859   IU

BT 301   NASCIMENTO, FRANCISCO MANUEL DO, 1734–1819
.N244   Vida de Jesus Christo conforme os quatros
            evangelistas posta em portuguez. Lisboa,
            Impressão Regia, 1819.
               382 + 32 p.

Text followed by a list of subscribers.

1. Jesus Christ—Biog.   I. Title.

NN 0023860   InU

BS476   **Nascimento, Franklin do,** joint tr.
.B36   **Barrows, Elijah Porter,** 1807–1888.
          Principios de interpretação da Biblia, pelo Rev. E. P.
          Barrows ... vertido do inglez pelos Revs. Dr. J. M. Kyle e
          Franklin do Nascimento. New York, American tract
          society ₍1915₎

Bra   Nascimento, Gonçalo Santiago do.
SB   ... O caroá, pelo agronomo Gonçalo Santiago
261   do Nascimento ... Rio de Janeiro, 1936.
.C3N3   cover-title, 6 p. illus. 23 cm.
            At head of title: Ministerio da agricultura,
          Departamento nacional da producção vegetal.
          Serviço de plantas texteis.

NN 0023862   DPU DNLM DNAL

Nascimento, Herminio do.
...Canto coral para os liceus, escolas primarias, superiores, etc... Com um prefacio do Ex.ᵐᵒ Sr. Dr. Sá Oliveira... ₍v. 1.₎ Lisboa: Neuparth & Carneiro, 1919. v. 8°.
Portuguese words. Tunes only.
Cover-title.
Contents: ₍v. 1.₎ Livro do I e II classe.

1. School music.—Song books, etc.   2. Children.—Music for. 3. Songs
(Portuguese).
N.Y.P.L.   February 10, 1922.

NN 0023863   NN

VOLUME 405

NK2715
.P5

Nascimento, J. F. da Silva.

Pinto, Augusto Cardoso.
Cadeiras portuguesas. Texto e notas descritivas por Augusto Cardoso Pinto; documentário gráfico organizado por J. F. Da Silva Nascimento. Lisboa, 1952.

1. Beds and bedsteads. 2. Furniture, Portuguese. I. Title.

NK2713.N38   749.36   53-31451

NN 0023865   DLC

Nascimento, J F da Silva.
Leitos e camilhas portugueses; subsídios para o seu estudo. Lisboa, 1950.

113, [254] p. illus., facsim. 32 cm.

"A edição desta obra é de 500 exemplares, numerados e rubricados pelo autor ... No. 406."
Bibliography: p. [363]

1. Beds and bedsteads. 2. Furniture, Portuguese. I. Title.

NK2713.N38   749.36   53-31451

NN 0023865   DLC

Nascimento, J Marcondes do
   see   Marcondes do Nascimento, J.

Nascimento, João Cabral do
   see
Cabral do Nascimento, João, 1897–

Nascimento, José do
   see   José do Nascimento.

Map
G
5404
M3
1881
N3

Nascimento, José Maria do.
Planta hydrographica dos portos de Imbitiba e Macahe. Rio de Janeiro, Robin & Cª, 1881.
map on 2 sheets 80 x 50 cm.

Scale 1:5,000.

1. Macaé, Brazil—Maps.

NN 0023869   NIC

Nascimento, José Pereira do
   see
Pereira do Nascimento, José, 1861–1913.

NASCIMENTO, Josefa do.

See JOSEFA DO NASCIMENTO.

Nascimento, Juarez Fernandes Távora do
   see   Távora, Juarez, 1898–

G079.813
N171

Nascimento, Luiz do.
Imprensa periódica pitoresca de Pernambuco; sinopse. Recife, Edições Guararapes, 1954.
19p. 23cm.

Author's autograph presentation copy to Jordão Emerenciano.

1. Press - Pernambuco, Brazil (State) - Hist.
2. Brazilian periodicals - Pernambuco (State)
3. Brazilian newspapers - Pernambuco (State)

NN 0023873   TxU

NASCIMENTO, M. DE.
Cues and crinolines; from an old Chinese manuscript. [Peking? 1916] 98 p. (on double leaves) 27cm.

Microfiche (neg.) 3 sheets. 11 x 15cm. (NYPL FSN-02672)

NN 0023874   NN DLC-P4

W 4
P22
1928

Nascimento, Manoel França do
A prata em odontologia. Curityba, 1928.
14 p.

These - Paraná.

NN 0023875   DNLM

PQ
9261
.N32
A25

Nascimento, Manuel do, 1912–
O aço mudou de têmpera, romance. Porto, Livraria Latina Editora [1945?]
338 p. 19 cm.

NN 0023876   WU TxU NcD NcU

Nascimento, Manuel do, 1912–
Agonia. [Lisboa] Sociedade de Expansão Cultural [1954]
185 p. 19 cm. (Colecção Romance português contemporâneo)

I. Title.

PQ9261.N32A7   56-26363 ‡

NN 0023877   DLC NN MH CLU

PQ 9261
N32 E8
1943

Nascimento, Manuel do, 1912–
Eu queria viver! [Lisboa] Inquérito [1943]
219 p. 18 cm. (Biblioteca da nova geração)

NN 0023878   OU

Nascimento, Manuel do, 1912–
... Mineiros, romance. Pôrto, Livraria latina editora [1944]
3 p. l., [9]–211 p. 19 cm.

I. Title.

PQ9261.N32M5   47-27611

NN 0023879   DLC NcU RPB TxU

PQ 9261
N32
N33
1950

Nascimento, Manuel do, 1912–
Nada de importância. Lisboa, Fomento de Publicações [195 ?]
45 p. (Colecção novela, 7)

NN 0023880   CaBVaU

Nascimento, Manuel do, 1912–
Roteiro da Provincia do Algarve. [Tavira] 1951.
37 p. illus. 16 cm.

1. Algarve—Descr. & trav.—Guide-books. I. Title.

DP702.A28N3   54-36722 ‡

NN 0023881   DLC

4PQ
Port
588

Nascimento, Manuel do, 1912–
O último espectáculo. Lisboa, Distribuidores gerais: Sociedade de Expansão Cultural [1955]
148 p.

(Colecção Sec)

NN 0023882   DLC-P4 NN MH CLU WU NcU

Nascimento, Nicanor.
... Diretivas constitucionais (depois da guerra) Rio de Janeiro, A. Coelho Branco F.º, 1932.
523 p. 24ᶜᵐ.

CONTENTS.—1. pte. Diretivas constitucionais depois da guerra.—2. pte. Constituições atuais.

1. Constitutions. 2. Constitutional history. I. Title.

     43-9262

Library of Congress   JF16.N3

NN 0023883   DLC MiU

J25
+1
1952N

Nascimento, Osvaldo.
A arte moderna em face de um conceito de evolução. Ponta Grossa [Brasil, 1952]
24 p. port. 23 cm.

NN 0023884   CtY DPU

Nascimento, Osvaldo.
Planta de São Paulo. [São Paulo] Soc. Brasileira de Orientação Geobrasil, 1954.
col. map 127 x 172 cm.

Scale 1 : 20,000.
Inset : Centro da cidade ; 1 : 10,000.
——— [Indice das vias públicas. São Paulo, 1954–
1 v. (loose leaf) 24 cm.

     G5404.S24 1954.N3 Index

1. São Paulo, Brazil (City)—Maps.

G5404.S24 1954.N3   Map 60-203

NN 0023885   DLC

Nascimento, Pedro.
Algumas notas sobre Os possessos de Dostoievsky. Lisboa, Edições Ática, 1947.
63 p. port. 25 cm.

1. Dostoevskiĭ, Fedor Mikhaĭlovich, 1821–1881. Besy.

PG3325.B65N3   48-17838*

NN 0023886   DLC NN MH

4PG
Rus.
809

Nascimento, Pedro.
Algumas notas sobre Os Irmãos Karamazov de Dostoievsky. Lisboa, Portugália Editora [1949]
41 p.

NN 0023887   DLC-P4 NN

Bra
RA
824
.M6N2

Nascimento, Theodureto do.
... As estancias hydro-mineraes de Minas Geraes..., pelo Dr. Theodureto do Nascimento... Rio de Janeiro, Typ. do Serviço de informações do Ministerio da agricultura, 1929.
1 p.l., 14 p. 23 cm.
At head of title: Ministerio da agricultura, industria e commercio(Serviço de informações)

NN 0023888   DPU

Nascimento, Ulpio.
Física dos solos; estudo dos solos de Lisboa. Lisboa, 1954.
xxiii, 168 p. illus. (part col.) map, diagrs., profile, tables. 25 cm. [Portugal] Ministério das Obras Públicas. Laboratório Nacional de Engenharia Civil. Publicação no. 56)

Tinted celluloid spectacles in pocket.
"Dissertação apresentada a concurso para investigador do Laboratório Nacional de Engenharia Civil."
"Summary, conclusions and index of figures" in English.
Bibliography : p. [163]–168.

1. Soil physics. 2. Soils—Portugal—Lisbon. (Series: Portugal. Laboratorio Nacional de Engenharia Civil. Publicação no. 56)

     A 56-4066

Michigan. Univ. Libr.
for Library of Congress   [3]

NN 0023889   MiU

Nascimento, Vamireh Chacon de Albuquerque
   see
Chacon, Vamireh.

VOLUME 405

Nascimento Barbosa, Mario do
  see
  Barbosa, Mario do Nascimento.

. **Nascimento Barros** (Fabio). *Cadeira de physiologia; a dor. 94 pp., 2 l. roy. 8°. Rio de Janeiro, Carvalhaes, 1905.

NN 0023892 DNLM

Nascimento Brito, José do.
  Economia e finanças do Brasil, 1822-1940.
  Rio de Janeiro, F. Bastos, 1945.
  195 p. tables.

  Bibliography: p. 191-192.

  1. Brazil - Economic conditions. 2. Finance,
  Public - Brazil.

NN 0023893 NNC NN NcD ICU NNUN CSt-H

Nascimento Brito, José do.
  ... Estados Unidos, impressões de uma rapida viagem. Rio
  de Janeiro, Jornal do commercio, Rodrigues & cia., 1940.
  132 p. 18ᶜᵐ.

  1. U. S.—Civilization. 2. National characteristics, American.

  Library of Congress   E169.1.N36
                                              41-24323
                              ₍2₎   917.3

NN 0023894 DLC

JX4143 Nascimento Ceccatto, Gastão.
.N4   L'évolution juridique de la doctrine du
         plateau continental... Paris, Éditions A.
         Pedone, 1955.
         143 p.

         "Bibliographie": p. ₍139₎-143.

         1. Continental shelf. I. Title.

MH-L NNC-L NcD
NN 0023895   DS ICU IaU   GU IU MiU-L CtY TU

Nascimento Ceccatto, Gastão do.
  ... O pinho brasileiro, por Gastão do Nascimento Ceccatto ...
  Rio de Janeiro, Brasil, Serviço de informação agrícola, Minis-
  tério da agricultura, 1943.
  cover-title, 30, ₍1₎ p. illus. 23ᶜᵐ.
  At head of title: Ministério da agricultura. Serviço florestal.

  1. Brazilian pine. I. Brazil. Serviço florestal. II. Brazil. Serviço
  de informação agrícola.
  Library of Congress   SD397.B7N3
                                              43-50366
                              ₍3₎   634.9751

NN 0023896 DLC PPAN

Nascimento e Silva, Alfredo do.
  O mimetismo do cholera; memoria sobre as manifestações choleriformes no Brazil como contribuição ao estudo
  da epidemia do Valle do Parahyba em 1894-1895, pelo Dr.
  Alfredo Nascimento ... Trabalho lido perante a Academia nacional de medicina em sessões especiaes de maio e
  junho de 1898. Rio de Janeiro, Typ. Leite & Gomes, 1898.
  496 p., 2 l. 21ᶜᵐ.

  1. Cholera, Asiatic—Brazil.

                                              17-16818
  Library of Congress   RC132.B8N3

NN 0023897 DLC

E119 Nascimento e Silva, Alfredo do.
R55
      Instituto historico e geographico brasileiro, *Rio de Janeiro.*
        Sessão solemne do Instituto historico e geographico brazi-
      leiro, celebrada a 12 de outubro de 1892 em commemoração do
      4° centenario do descobrimento da America e homenagem á
      memoria de Christovão Colombo. Rio de Janeiro, Companhia
      typographica do Brazil; antiga Typographia Laemmert, 1892.

Nascimento e Silva, Geraldo Eulalio do
  see Silva, Geraldo Eulalio do Nascimento e.

Nascimento e Silva, Manoel Joaquim do, *b. 1837, ed.*
  Synopsis da legislação brazileira até 1878, cujo conhecimento
  mais interessa aos empregados do Ministerio da guerra; com-
  pilada da legislação impressa, do expediente dos diversos mi-
  nisterios, das ordens do dia do Exercito e de differentes obras
  publicadas no Brazil e em Portugal. (2d ed.) Por Manoel
  Joaquim do Nascimento e Silva ... Rio de Janeiro, Typ. de
  J. D. de Oliveira, 1879-₍80₎
  3 v. 23½ᶜᵐ.
  "Appendice" (v. 3, p. ₍193₎-467) : ₍1. pte.₎ Contêm as ultimas disposições
  publicadas até 31 de março de 1880.—2. pte. Artigos de guerra. Codigo
  criminal. Ordenança regulando as qualificações do crime de deserção.
  Processos militares.
    1. Law—Brazil—Indexes.   I. Brazil. Laws, statutes, etc. (In-
  dexes)   42-29271

NN 0023900 DLC

Nascimento Fernandes Tavora, Juarez do
  see Tavora, Juarez, 1898-

Nascimento Ferreira Dias, José
  see Ferreira Dias, José Nascimento.

Nascimento Ferreira e Silva, Josino do, *comp.*
  Consolidação das disposições em vigor relativas á Guarda
  nacional ou milicia civica, organizada ... pelo coronel Josino do
  Nascimento Ferreira e Silva ... Rio de Janeiro, Typ. d'O Paiz,
  1894.
  ₍254₎ p. forms (part fold.) 22½ᶜᵐ.
  Various pagings.

    1. Brazil. Guarda nacional. 2. Military law—Brazil.   I. Brazil.
  Laws, statutes, etc.
                                              44-30257
  Library of Congress   UB540.N3

NN 0023903 DLC

Nascimento Goncalves Corrêa, José do, *joint
  author.*
Paiva Manso, Levy Maria Jordão, *visconde de,* 1831-1875.
  Historia da real casa de Santo Antonio, pelos vereadores
  dr. Levy Maria Jordão e José do Nascimento Gonçalves Corrêa. Lisboa, Imprensa União-typographica, 1857.

Nascimento Guedes, Franklin do.
  Tratamento da angina diphterica. Inaugural
  dissertation. Rio de Janeiro, 1895.
  64 p

NN 0023905 PPC

Bra   Nascimento Junior, Vicente.
F   ... Gabriel de Lara (a fundação e povoamento
2651   da vila de Paranaguá) [Curitibá] Edição do
.P3N3   dr. Dicesar Plaisant, 1940]
         33 p. 18 cm.
         At head of title: Nascimento Junior da Academia
       paranaense de letras.

NN 0023906 DPU

F2551 Nascimento Junqueira, João J.
.B2
       Bahia, *Brazil (State) Departamento estadual de imprensa*
       e propaganda.
         ... A conquista da independência ... 1823. Dois de julho.
       1943. Bahia, Brasil ₍Imprensa Regina, 1943₎

Nascimento Leitão, Antonio
  see Leitão, Antonio Nascimento.

Nascimento Monteiro, Ofelia Socrates do
  see   Monteiro, Ofelia (Socrates do
  Nascimento)

Nascimento Moura, Jacinto José do
  see   Moura, Jacinto José do Nascimento.

Nascimento Pereira de Sampaio, A₍ntonio₎ do.
  ... S. João Baptista d'Ajudá. Parecer da Commissão
  africana. Relator A. do Nascimento Pereira de Sampaio
  ... Lisboa, Lallemant frères, 1883.
  12 p. 23½ᵐᵐ. (Sociedade de geographia de Lisboa)

    1. Fort Ajuda, Guinea.

  Library of Congress   DT541.N25   6-15060

NN 0023911 DLC

Nascimento Santareno, José do, 1888–
  ... Manual ilustrado do serviço de saúde militar ... **1. ed.**
  Lisboa, Tipografia Proença, 1941.
  611 p. illus., diagrs. 22½ᶜᵐ.
  Issued in 17 parts.

    1. Medicine, Military. 2. Portugal—Army—Sanit. affairs.
  I. Title.
  Library of Congress   UH395.P8N3   44-52126
                              ₍2₎   355.34

NN 0023912 DLC

FOR OTHER EDITIONS
SEE MAIN ENTRY
Nascimento Silva, Josino de, 1811-1886, ed.

Brazil. *Laws, statutes, etc.*
  Codigo criminal do imperio do Brasil, augmentado com as
  leis, decretos, avisos e portarias que desde a sua publicação
  até hoje se tem expedido, explicando, revogando ou alterando algumas de suas disposições com o calculo das penas em
  todos os gráos, por Josino do Nascimento Silva ... Nova
  edição. Rio de Janeiro, E. & H. Laemmert ₍pref. 1863₎

Nascimento Silva, Josino do, 1811-1886.

Brazil. *Laws, statutes, etc.*
  Codigo do processo criminal de primeira instancia do imperio do Brasil, augmentado com a lei de 3 de dezembro de 1841
  e seus regulamentos, disposição provisoria ácerca da administração da justiça civil, todas as leis, decretos e avisos a respeito
  até o principio do anno de 1864, explicando, revogando ou alterando algumas de suas disposições, por Josino do Nascimento Silva ... 5. ed. ... Rio de Janeiro, E. & H. Laemmert,
  1864.

VOLUME 405

Nascimento Silva, Josino do, 1811–1886, *ed.*
Novissima guia para eleitores e votantes, contendo a **Lei** regulamentar das eleições de 19 de agosto de 1846 para as camaras legislativas, assembléas provinciaes, camaras municipaes e juizes de paz do imperio do Brasil, acompanhada das resoluções do Conselho de estado, avisos, ordens e portarias até ao presente esclarecendo ou alterando os seus artigos e dos decretos e instrucções de 1855, 1856 e 1860, alterando a Lei de 1846; organisada por Josino do Nascimento Silva ... 3. ed. Rio de Janeiro, E. & H. Laemmert, 1860.
3 p. l., 315, ;2; p. 18½ᶜᵐ. *(Added t.-p.:* Manual do cidadão brasileiro, t. 7)

1. Election law—Brazil.   I. Brazil. Laws, statutes, etc.
II. Title.   42–43270

   NN   0023915   DLC

Nascimento Silva Bastos, Anadyr do, 1905–
... Flagelo dos deuses, romance. Rio de Janeiro, Editora A Noite ₁1944?₎
236 p., 1 l. front. (port.) illus. (music) 18½ᶜᵐ.

1. Title.   A 45–1932

New York. Public library
for Library of Congress   ₍2₎

   NN   0023916   NN

Greenlee
4504   Nascimento Silveira, Francisco do, 18th cent.
P855   Applauzo universal das quatro partes d
mundo na glorioza acclamaçã da rainha nossa
senhora.   Lisboa, C. Ferreira da Costa, 1777.
8p. 21cn.

   NN   0023917   ICN

NASCIMENTO SILVEIRA, Francisco do, 18th cent.
Coro das Musas junto por Venus na casa do
Sol, em obsequio dos reis fidelissimos, e de
todos os mais famosos Lusitanos antigos e modernos. Lisboa, S. T. Ferreira, 1792-96.

4 vol.

   NN   0023918   MH DLC-P4 OC1

Nascimento Veiga, Antonio de Figueiredo do
     see   Figueiredo do Nascimento Veiga,
     Antonio de.

Case
MS   NASCIMENTO di Frà Martino Luthero.
5A   ₍n.p., 17--₎
42   169-214ℓ. 30cm.

Caption title.
Manuscript on paper.
Apparently extracted from a larger work.

   NN   0023920   ICN

El Nascimiento y primeras Emprefas del Conde
Orlando. Tradvzidas por Pero Lopez Henriquez
de Calatayud.   Valladolid, n.d. [1595?]
     see under   V. Dolce, Lodovico, 1508-1568.

Nascita, studj, posizione, sociale, e
bibliografia delle principali opere e memorie
di Francesco Zantedeschi. Padova, Sicca,
1856.
9 p

   NN   0023922   PPAmP

Nascita, studj, posizione sociale, e bibliografia
delle principali opere e memorie di Francesco Zantedeschi,
Padova, Co' tipi di A.Sicca, 1857

   NN   0023923   MH

Nd6.18   Nascita, vita processo, e morte di Francesco
degli Stabili, volgarmente detto Cecco d'Ascoli. Quale per i suoi errori fu condannato ad
essergli tagliate le vene della fronte, e getato
alle fiamme ...
Firenze,1792. 31b. front. 14cm.

   NN   0023924   CtY PU

Nascius, F. C. de.
A la conquête du ciel! Contributions astronomiques.   Nantes, Guist hau, 1897.
1 v.

   NN   0023925   PU

QB502   Nascius, F. C. de.
.N24   A la conquête du ciel! Contributions astronomiques de F. C. de Nascius en quinze livres.
Nantes, 1899.

   NN   0023926   DLC NN MiU

Nascius, F. C. de.
Sur quelques particularités fort curieuses du système de l'orbite lunaire. Extrait de son ouvrage "A la conquête du ciel." Paris : F. R. de Rudeval, 1904.   3 p.l., 69 p., 2 l. illus.   8°.
In: ORG p. v. 4, no. 8.

1. Moon.—Orbit.
N. Y. P. L.   April 14, 1913.

   NN   0023927   NN

VCJ   NASCIVERA, Lodovico.
7244i   Istruzione dei mezzi conosciuti più
.814   efficaci per preservarsi dalla malattia
contagiosa chiamata tifo.   Treviso,
Paluello, 1814.
16 p.

   NN   0023928   DNLM

FILM   Nasco, Giovanni, d.1561.
M783.4   ₍Works, selections₎
N17£b   Lamentationi a voce pari di Giovan Nasco a
qvarta voci con doi passii il Benedictvs et le
sve Antiphone nouamente con ogni diligentia
stampate & date in Luce.   Venetia, Gardano,
1561.
4 part books.

Title from Cantus.
Part books: Cantus, Altus, Tenor, Bassus.
Microfilm (negative) Bologna, Biblioteca
del conservatorio, 1967. 1 reel. 35mm.

   NN   0023929   IU

Nasd news.
    see
N.A.S.D. news.

Nadal, Willy, 1902–
... Geburtenhäufigkeit und Säuglingssterblichkeit in Deutschland 1912-1925 ...   Erfurt [1926]
Inaug.-Diss. - Leipzig.
Lebenslauf.
"Literatur": p. 12.

   NN   0023931   CtY

Nase, George P.
Home songs, by George P. Nase. New Haven, Conn., Press of C. C. Treat, 1891.
31 l. 19ᶜᵐ.

1. Title.

Library of Congress   PS3527.A615H6   1891   33–39653

   NN   0023932   DLC

T113   Nase, Hans, 1906–
K8   Über die operative Behandlung der Leistenbrüche
1932   bei muskelschwachen Patienten ... Wetter(Ruhr),
1932.
Inaug.-Diss. - München.
Lebenslauf.

x. Nase, Johannes Theodor Günther, 1906-

   NN   0023933   CtY PPWI

605.7   Nase, Johann, 1534-1590.
N24.4an   Angelus Paraeneticus contra solam fidem
1588   delegatus: Das ist/ Der Warnungs Engel/ wider
den solen Glauben auszgesandt... Getruckt
zu Engelstatt/ Anno M.D.LXXXVIII.
9p.ℓ., 201, [4]p. illus. 20cm.

Colophon: Getruckt zu Ingolstatt/ durch
Wolffgang Eder. Anno M.D.LCCCVIII.
Woodcut of Baalam's ass on verso of title
page.
Head and tail   pieces.

   NN   0023934   MH-AH DHN

Summerfield
B252   Nase, Johann, 1534-1590.
Das Antipapistich eins und hundert..
Ausserlessner, gewiser Evangelischer
warhait ... Secunda-sexta centuria ...
Ingolstadt, A. Weissenhorn, 1567-70.
6v. 18cm.

Title from British Museum Catalogue.
Stamped panels of Justice and Lucrece on
front & back boards signed C K. Pigskin
binding.

1. Catholic   church. Doctrinal
and controversial   works.

   NN   0023935   KU

Nase, Johann, 1534-1590.
Das Antipapistisch eins und hundert,
Anszerlesznew gewiser Evangelischer War-
hait ... ₍Ingolstatt,Alexander Weissen
horn₎ 1568.
8 p.f.,232 f.num., 8 f.

   NN   0023936   DHN

₍Nase, Johann₎ 1534-1590.
Beinecke   Αντιγράξεις των αστρολόγων , das ist/,Die
Library   vnfelig gewisest Practica practicarum,'auff
1971   das yetzig vnd nachfolgende Jar auss Grund
1028   der grossen Coniunction, langer Erfarnuss/
vnd steter Übung/ mit Vergleichung der siben
jrrdischen Planeten/ vnd zwölff himlischen
Zaichen beschriben ... Ionas Philognysius
practicierts. [Ingolstadt, 1566]
[55] p. illus. 19 cm.
Title romanized: Antipraxeis ton astrologon.

Signatures: A-G⁴.
Illustrated t.-p.
Colophon: Anno Christi 1.5.66. A creatione
mundi uero 5.5.66. Getruckt zů Ingolstatt.

1. Prophecies. 2. Astrology - Controversial
literature. I. Title: Antipraxeis ton astrologon. II. Title: Practica practicarum.

   NN   0023938   CtY

VOLUME 405

Ex
8409
.669
Nase, Johann, 1534-1590.
ʾΑνταϞρολογοπρᾶξις ; Das ist, Die
vnfelig gewisest practica practicarum,
auff das yetzig vnd nachfolgende jar auss
grund der grossen coniunction, langer
erfarnuss vnd steter übung mit vergleichung der siben jrrdischen planeten vnd
zwölff himlischen zaichen beschriben..
Ingolstat, 1567.
63 p. illus. 18 ᶜᵐ.

NN   0023939   NjP

605.7   Nase, Johann, 1534-1590.
N24.4br   Brevis de coena dominica tractatvs, vnico
1577   sermone solidas qvinqvaginta adversariarum
obiectionvm confvtationes comprehendens, ac
perspicuè declarans verba Christi hoc
eucharistiae sacramentum sub vtraque specie
instituentis, atque dicentis...Primum
stvdiose collectus & Germanicè editus à
F. Joanne Naso S.A.C. iam vero latinitate
donatus à F. Joan. Dominico Hessio, &c.
Ingolstadii, M.D.LXXVII.

8p.ℓ., 98 numb. ℓ. [9]p. 16cm.

Colophon: Ingolstadii excvdebat Alexander
Weissenhorn cvm cohaeredibvs svis. Anno
M.D.LXXVII.
No. 1 in a volume of 16th century works.

NN   0023941   MH-AH

Z832N17
OC
Nase, Johann, 1534-1590.
Concordia alter vnnd newer guter, auch
böser Glaubensstrittiger lehren, verglichne
Beschreibung... Concordirt... F. Ioan.
Nass. [München, Adam Berg] 1583.

[10], 257, [1] ℓ.   illus.   21 cm.

NN   0023942   MnU DHN CtY NjP MH-AH

BX8068   Nase, Johann, 1534-1590.
.N25   Examen chartaceae Lutheranorum concordiae, auss-
Rare bk   musterung vnnd widerlegung dess nagelnewgeschmidten
room   concordi buchs/der nachbenandten lutherischen predig-
kanten ... mit solchem titul: Concordia, das ist/Con-
tra omnes nationes cudit odiosam reconciliationem:
Doctor Jacob Andre hat...mit papyer zusam geschweist
F.Joann.Nass. [Ingolstatt]Getruckt durch W.Eder,1581.
[1],436 p. 20½cm.
Title in red and black,with vignette.
1.Lutheran church.   Book of concord. 2.Andreae,
Jakob,1528-1590.

NN   0023943   ICU NjP MH-AH IU DHN PU

Nase, Johann, 1534-1590.
Handbüchlein Des klein Christianismi
vom rechten Glauben thůn und lassen hoff-
nen unnd förchtens kurtz und gůt leicht
und nutzlich. F.Iohan. Nase ... [Ingol-
stat durch Alexander Weissenhorn,1570]
[xiv] p., 112 f.num.

Title-page in facsimile.

NN   0023944   DHN

605.7   Nase, Johann, 1534-1590.
N24.4le   Levita catholicvs contra exodum pseud-
1589   euangelicam, oder/ Ein Schutz Predig/ von
aller Heiligen Fest vnd Feyrtag/ wider der
Secten falsche Intzicht vnd verlogne
läster Klag: Auff desz vnuerschämbsten
Georg Müllerischen Bachantischen Exodum/
zu Wittenberg aber grawsam Wiltkhumb/ &c.
Allen lieber Heiligen vnd alten Gott-
seligen längst Christlich Catholisch

Continued in next column

Continued from preceding column

verschidenen frommen Teutschen zu Ehrn/
vnnd Apostolischer Rettung/ an viler
Heiligen Tág/ in vnuerschloszen Kirchen
Gottes betracht: Auch öffentlich verbracht/
&c... Getruckt zu Ingolstatt. Anno M.D.
LXXXIX.

1p.ℓ., 188,[1]p. 20.5cm.
Colophon: Getruckt zu Ingolstatt/ durch
Wolffgang Eder. Im Jar nach der Geburt
Christi. Anno M.D.LXXXIX.

NN   0023947   MH-AH DHN

605.7   Nase, Johann, 1534-1590.
N24.4no   Nova novorum: in quibus, tvm avtores,
1581   confessio et doctrina libri, qvem patres
Bergenses concordiam vocant../Das ist/
allenthalbische newezeittung/ von der
Bergischen Vatter newangestellten Con-
cordien... [Ingolstadt] Anno. M.D.LXXXI.
[56]p. 20cm.

Colophon: Actum & impressum Anglipoli,
mense Iunio, Anno 1581.
Signatures: A-   G4
Errors in re-   gistering.

NN   0023948   MH-AH MnCS

Nase, Johann, 1534-1590.
Postilla minorum, Das ist/ Die klaines
Postill und kürtzeste Auslegung der hai-
ligen Evangelien so auff die Suntåg unnd
fürnembsten Fest vom Advent biss auff Os-
tern Catholisch gepredigt werden ...
Durch F.Iohan. Nase... [Ingolstatt,
Alexander Weissenhorn] 1573.
8 p.f., 460 f.num., 4 f.unn.

NN   0023949   MdSsW

Spec.
BR 303
.N2 P9
Nase, Johann, 1534-1590.
Praelvdivm in centurias hominum, sola
fide perditorum: das ist, Newer zeittung
vorgang und langerwarter enderung von der
grossen gloggen zu Erfurdt darmit man new-
lichst das Lutterthumb vnd sonder gross miraculum
vom weinfass aussthät leiten wol mit fünffhundert
zeügnussen zum eingang dess Schalckjars achzig
vnd acht darvon man nit vergebens gesagt dann
es schon dahin fleücht durch die welt wer es
vbersicht der hat gefehlt mit leib, leben, gut
vnd gelt ... [Ingolstatt, W. Eder, 1588.
5 p. ,   52 p.

NN   0023950   InU DHN

Nase, Johann, 1534-1590.
Qvarta centvria, das ist/ Das vierdt hunderi
der vierfach Evangelischen warheit/ in welchen
das elendt Luterthumb/ dermassen genatomiert ist/
also dass man viel hundert/ jha ein rechts Pana-
theom, allerley bösen frücht/ dess verflüchten
Evangelischen Feygenbaums/ zusamb gelesen/ und behalten findt.   Ingolstadt, Alexander Weissen-
born, 1570.
400numb. leaves, 16cm

Bound in pigskin.

NN   0023951   MnCS

xBX1780   Nase, Johann, 1534-1590.
N34   Quarta centuria; das ist, das vierdt Hundert
der vierfach evangelischen Warheit, in welchen
das elende Luterthumb dermassen geanatomiert
ist, also, dass man vil hundert, jha ein rechts
Panatheō, allerley bösen Frücht dess verflüchte
evangelischen Feigenbaums zůsamb gelesen und
behalten findt... Durch F.Ioannem Nass, dem
Joan. Friederich Scelesto edicirt. [Ingol-
statt, A.Weissenhorn, 1570]
[8],400,[7]ℓ. illus. 18cm.

Continued in next column

Continued from preceding column

Title within woodcut border.
Reply to Johann Friedrich Scelestus'
(i.e.Coelestinus) Pantheum, sive, Anatomia
et symphonia papatus. Ingolstadt, 1568-1569.

1. Coelestinus, Johann Friedrich, d.1578.
Pantheum, sive, Anatomia et symphonia papatus.
2. Catholic Church — Doctrinal and controversial
works — Catholic authors.   3. Lutheran Church
Doctrinal and   controversial works.

NN   0023953   IaU MH-AH NIC

240
099
N12
255
Nase, Johann, 1534-1590.
Qvinta centvria, das ist/ Das fünfft Hundert,
der evangelischen warheit/ darin mit fleiss beschriben wirde/ der gantz handel/ anfang/ lebens
und todts/ des thewren Manns/ D. Martin Luthers/
also/ das man gewissliche die frucht der lehr/
nach dem Baum des lehrers/ urtheilen kan. Auss
viel evangelischen Scribenten zusam bracht durch
F. Ioan Nas. Dem M. Cyriack Spangberg nachge-
folgt und zugeschriben.   [Ingolstadt, Alexander
Weissenhorn] 1570.
504 numb. leaves, 15cm Bound in pigskin.

NN   0023954   MnCS

605.7   Nase, Johann, 1534-1590.
N24.4br   Ein schöne tröstliche Kriegs vnd Sigspre-
1577   digt. Vber das Euangeliü/ wie Christus
im schifflein schlaffend/ vnd das
Jüngern/ in höchsten nöten erweckt/ vnd das
vngestüm Meer gestillt wirt/ Matth. am 8
... Anno Dñi 1571. den y. Octob...Gedruckt
zu Ingolstaat/ M.D.LXXII.
[88]p. 16cm.

Signatures: A-E8, F4
No.4 in a   volume of 16th century
works.

NN   0023955   MH-AH

Nase, Johann, 1534-1590.
Ein schöne Tröstliche Newejarspredig.
Uber das Evangelium wie Christus im Schiff-
lein schlaffend von seinen Jüngern in
höchsten nöten erweckt und das ungestüm
Meer gestilt wirt. ... F.Iohann.Nass.
Ingolstatt [Alexander Weissenhorn] 1572.
32 f.unn. (last blank).

NN   0023956   DHN

Nase, Johann, 1534-1590.
Secvnda centvria, das ist/ Das ander hundert,
der evangelischen warheit/ an welchen/ als bey der
Früchten der baum/ unserer widersacher irrige
lehr/ betrug und thorhait menigklich endecket
wirdt. [Ingolstadt, Alexander Weissenhorn]
1568.
267numb. leaves, 15cm

Bound in pigskin.

NN   0023957   MnCS DHN

605.7   Nase, Johann, 1534-1590.
N24.4e   Sextae centvriae prodromvs. Das ist/
1569   ein Vortrab vnd Morgengab/ dess sechsten
hunderts Euangelischer warheit... Durch F.
Ioan Nas. Hoschiander Lucas, D. edicirt.
[Ingolstadt] 1569.
256numb.ℓ., [31]p. 16cm.

Colophon: Gedruckt zu Ingolstaat/ durch
Alexander Weissenhon. Anno M.D.LXIX.
Title within   ornamental borders.

NN   0023958   MH-AH DHN

VOLUME 405

Nase, Johann, 1534-1590.
*pGB5 Sihe wie das ellend Lutherthumb, durch seine
N1701 aigne verfechter/ gemartert, anatomiert,
570s gemetzget, zerhackt, zerschnitten, gesotten,
gebraten, vnd letzlich gantz auffgefressen
wirdt.
[Ingolstadt,1570]
broadside. 1 illus. 42x26cm.
The woodcut illus., signed "R" over a knife,
has caption beneath it: Offenbarung der straff
vnd ausgang Lutherischer schwermerey, in Reymen
gestelt   durch F.J.N.[i.e. Frater

Johannes Nas].
Verse in 3 columns.
Imperfect? imprint cut away at foot?

NN 0023960   MH

Nase, Johann, 1534-1590.
    **Tertia centuria, Das ist/ Das dritte
Hundert der gedoppelten Evangelosen war-
hoit betreffendt. D.Luthers lehr und dol
merschung der Bibel ausz ernstlichem an-
stichen und begeren D.Andres Schmidleins
in truck geben. ... Antwort dem Thoren
nach seiner narrhait auff das er sich
nicht für klůg halt. Durch F.Ioann Nass.
(Ingolstatt, Alexander Weissenhorn,1536;
(xii) p., 260 f.num., 7 f.unn.

NN 0023961   DHN

605.7 Nase, Johann, 1534-1590.
N24.4br   Widereinwarnung/ an alle frome Teutsche
1577 ein Vermanung/ auff dass sie sich/ vor denen
vnlängst wider auffgerichten Abgöttereyen
vnnd Missbräuchen hüten... Ingolstatt/1577.
8p.l., 297p. illus. 16cm.

Colophon: Gedruckt zu Ingolstatt durch
Alexander Weyssenhorn vnd andere seine
Miterben. M.D.LXXVII.
Woodcuts on verso of p.l.8 (Crucifixion)
and on p.181 and 189.
N.2 in a volume of 16th century works.

NN 0023962   MH-AH NjP

Nase, Johann, 1534-1590.
*GC5   Zwölff Predig, von der Christling Kirchen
N1701 heiligstem Sacrament des Altars ... F. Ioan.
569z Nass ...
Getruckt zů Ingolstatt durch Alexander
Weissenhorn.M.D.LXIX.
8°. 327 numb.l.,[17]p. illus. 16cm.
Full contemporary calf (rebacked);
Virgin & Child panel, signed H A, stamped in
gilt on front cover.

NN 0023963   MH

Nase, Johann, 1534-1590.
    **Zwölff Wolgegründter Predig von der
Christling Kirchen heiligstem Sacrament
des Altars ... F.Ioan. Nass. ... Ingolstatt, Alexander Weissenhorn, 1568.
327 f.num., 1 f.

NN 0023964   DHN

Nase, Johannes Theodor Günther, 1906-
    see   Nase, Hans, 1906-

Nase, Julius.
    Das Nibelungenlied, der Runensang vom deutschen Ge-
danken. Volksausg. für das deutsche Völk besorgt von
Heinrich Lhotzky. Stuttgart, Allgeist-Verlag A. Scheuch,
1927-
    v. 26 cm.

Continued in next column

Continued from preceding column

    I. Nibelungenlied. Paraphrases, tales, etc. II. Lhotzky, Heinrich,
1859-1930.
        PZ34.1.N3   54-54540

NN 0023966   DLC IaU

830.81 Nase, Karl, ed.
N17b   ... Berlin, meine heimat im gedicht der Berliner
schule.   Berlin, L. Oehmigke (1927)
64p.

1. German poetry (Collections) 2. Poetry of
places--Berlin. I. Title.

NN 0023967   IU

4PT- Nase, Karl.
Ger.   Siebenhundert Jahre berlinischen Lebens im
352 Spiegel des Gedichts.   Berlin, L. Oehmigke
[1926]
280 p.

NN 0023968   DLC-P4 MH NN WU

Nase, William Henry.
    Nase's tonnage tables, for the use of weigh-masters,
ship-masters, boatmen and others, in converting pounds
into tons, and tons into pounds. By William Henry
Nase ... (Poughkeepsie, N. Y.) Printed for the author,
1870.
    146 p. 19½ᵐᵐ.

1. Tonnage—Tables, etc.

Library of Congress   HE738.N3   6-33346

NN 0023969   DLC NN

Naše armáda. V Praze, Svaz čs.důstojnictva [1936]
5 v. ports.
Title from spine
Contents: -1. Armáda a národ. Projevy Fr.Machník, J.
Syrový, L.Krejčí. Demokratická armáda, pacifism, a zahra-
niční politika. By E.Beneš. -2. Branná politika a demokracie. By S.Bláha. -3. Úkoly naší obrany. By S.Yester.
-4.Obrana státu. By E.Moravec. -5.Tyršova idea národní
armády. By F.A.Soukup.
    1.Czechoslovakia. Armáda   I.Svaz československého
důstojnictva

NN 0023970   MH

UA678 Naše armáda. 6. vyd. V Praze, Svaz čs. důstoj-
.C9N3   nictva, 1937.
6 v. illus, maps, ports.
Title on spine; each vol. has only special
t. p.
Edition varies: sv. 6 is 5. přepracované vyd.
Contents.--sv.1. Armáda, brannost národa a
obrana státu. E. Beneš. Armáda a národ. F. Mach-
ník, J. Syrový, L. Krejčí.--sv.2. Obrana státu.
E. Moravec.--sv.3. Úkoly naší obrany. S. Yester.
--sv.4. Idea národní armády. F. A. Soukup.--sv.
5. Protiletecká   ochrana obyvatelstva
a podniků.--sv.6.   Branná politika a
demokracie. S.   Bláha.

NN 0023971   ICU

"Naše dějiny", sestavil a vydává Národní svaz
        českých Katolíku v Texas
            see under   Narodni svaz českých katoliku
v Texas.

792.0943735
N17   Naše divadlo. 1-   1928-
    Turčiansky sv Martin, Matica slovenská.
        v. illus., ports. 26-30cm. 10 no. a year
    Issued 1928-48 by Ústredie slovenských
ochotníckych divadiel; 1949- by Matica
slovenská.

NN 0023973   IU OC1BHS

Naše doba; revue pro vědu, umění a život sociální.   r. 1-55;
    říj. 1893-ún. 1949. V Praze, J. Laichter (etc.)
    v. ports. 25 cm.
    Frequency varies.

        AP52.N35   50-33692

NIC TxU
NN 0023974   DLC CaBVaU ICU IU NN CU NcD OU GU NjP

**Naše epištoly. V Praze, Knihtiskárna národně-sociál-
niho dělnictva (J.Stolař) 1900.**
[16] p.
At head of title: Ústřední škola dělnická.
Deals with questions of education.

NN 0023975   MH

AP 56 **NAŠE GORE LIST;ZABAVNO-POUČNI ČASOPIS TEČAJ**
.N24   1-6, br.18
    5 siec.1861-25 lip.1866.
    U Zagrebu
        6 v. in 3 illus.,ports.   36 no. a year
        Editor: Mijo Krešić
        Ceased publ. with v.6, no.18 (Je.1866)

    I. Krešić,Mijo,1818-1888,ed.

NN 0023976   InU

Naše gospodarstvo.
    Maribor.
        v. illus. 28 cm. 8 no. a year.
        Began in 1955. Cf. Slovenska bibl., 1955.
        Some articles have summaries in English, French, German, or Ital-
ian.
        Vols. for   issued by Višja ekonomsko komercialna šola, Mari-
bor; Društvo ekonomistov Maribor, and Ekonomski center, Maribor.
            1. Economics—Period. 2. Yugoslavia—Econ. condit.—Period. I.
Višja ekonomsko komercialna šola, Maribor. II. Društvo ekonomistov
Maribor. III. Ekonomski center, Maribor.
        HB9.N27   68-75585

NN 0023977   DLC DNLM NSyU

Naše građevinarstvo. g. 1-   1947-
    (Beograd)
        v. in illus., tables. 29 cm. monthly.
        Organ of Ministarstvo građevina FNRJ, 1947- ; of Saves
građevinskih inženjera i tehničara Jugoslavije (called earlier Saves
građevinskih inženjera i tehničara građevinske struke FNRJ) 195
        Vols. 10-11 have tables of contents also in English, French, Ger-
man, and Russian; summaries in English or German.
        Vols. 3 bound with its supplement: Yugoslavia. Ministarstvo građe-
vina. Službeni prilog Naše građevinarstvo (v. 3, no. 2, 6-9/10)
        Supplement, Službeni vesnik Ministarstva građevina FNRJ, 1950,
no. 3-4/5, bound with v. 4, no. 3-4/5, 1950.
            1. Civil engineering—Period. I. Yugoslavia. Ministarstvo građe-
vina. II. Saves građevinskih inženjera i tehničara Jugoslavije. III.
Yugoslavia. Ministarstvo građevina. Službeni vesnik.
        TA4.N32   63-38846

NN 0023978   DLC

Naše građevinarstvo. Supplement.

TA4
.N32
g. 3   Yugoslavia. *Ministarstvo građevina.*
            Službeni prilog Naše građevinarstvo.
        (Beograd)

HC   Naše hospodářské nedostatky. Probírá A.Z.
267   V Chrudimi, Nákl.Josefa Pelcla, 1894.
D6   56 p. (Knihovna "Rozhledů",sv.3)
N37
1894
            1.Bohemia--Econ.condit.--19th cent.
            2.Austria--Econ.policy--19th cent.

NN 0023980   NSyU MH

Naše Hranice (Dříve Naše Menšiny) Neodvislý
    list hraničářů, roč
        see   Naše menšiny.

VOLUME 405

Naše Kladsko; sborník prací členů Výzkumného
Vědeckého Sboru Svazu Přátel Kladska. [Re-
dakční kruh vede Stanislav B. Polický. 1.
vyd.] Praha, Orbis, 1946.
87 p. illus., map (in pocket) 21 cm.

DD801
G5
N37

1. Glatz (Grafschaft)

NN 0023982   CtY

Naše kniha; literární a bibliografický věstník. roč. 1-
15. ún. 1920-
V Praze, A Neubert.
v. 28cm.

015.437
N17

Subtitle varies.

NN 0023983   IU NNC NIC

Naše kolo. Uredio Ljubomir Maraković
see under   Maraković, Ljubomir, 1887-
1959, comp.

Naše Kroměříz; uspořádal Ludvík Páleníček
see under   Páleníček, Ludvík.

Naše menšiny. V Úpici, Tiskem grafického
závodu V.J. Ehl.
v. illus. 27 cm.   12 no. a year.
"Organ ceských mensin."
Title varies: 1937-   Naše hranice.
Editors: 19   J.M. Vlček and Malé
Svatoňovice.

NN 0023986   IU

Naše Morava; list věnovaný veřejným otázkám.
roč. 1-   3. červen. 1897-
Brno.
v. 29cm.

057.86
NAM

NN 0023987   IU

Naše národní minulost v dokumentech; chrestomatie k dějí-
nám Československa. [1. vyd.] Praha, Nakl. Československé akademie věd, 1954-
v. facsims. 21 cm.

On half title: Československá akademie věd. Sekce filosofie a
historie.
Vol. 1-   edited by Václav Husa.
Contents.—1. díl. Do zrušení nevolnictví.

1. Bohemia—Hist.—Sources. 2. Slovakia—Hist.—Sources. I.
Husa, Václav, ed. II. Československá akademie věd. Sekce filosofie a
historie.

DB193.N37   55-36258

ICU NN InU MH
NN 0023988   DLC CaBVaU NSyU PSt NcU MiU MnU CtY

NAŠE NÁRODNI TRADICE. 1 -
V Praze, 1928-
v. in

DB 191
.N238

Issued by Svaz Národního Osvobození.

1. Czechoslovak Republic—Hist.—Period.
I. Svaz Národního Osvobození.

NN 0023989   InU MB

Naše nové občanské právo; projevy
pronesené v plenu Národního shromáždění, 25. říj. 1950. [Redigovali,
Václav Chvátal a Miloš Parma.
] Ústřední akční výbor nár.
fronty [195]
63 p.

4K
Cz
143

NN 0023990   DLC-P4

Naše novine
see
Narodne novine.

Naše noviny; deník čs. vojska ve V. Britanii.
[London] 19
v. in   illus., maps. 33ᵐ.
Caption title.
Publication began in 1940.
Subtitle varies.
——— Tělesná výchova; týdenní příloha Našich novin.
[London] 19
nos. 33ᵐ. [With Naše noviny.
Caption title.

——— Kaktus.
[London] 19
nos. 33ᵐ. [With Naše noviny.
Caption title.

1. World war, 1939–1945—Period. 2. World war, 1939–1945—Czechoslovak republic. I. Czechoslovak republic. Armáda. Československé
vojsko ve Velké Británii.

Library of Congress   D731.N25   46-41802

NN 0023993   DLC

NAŠE noviny: denník čsl. vojska ve V. Britanii.
roč. 1, čis. 75-roč. 5, čis. 221 (čis. 1-1472);
září 17, 1940 - červen. 30, 1944.
Londýn.   v.   illus.
33cm.

Microfilm
Issued by the Czechoslovak army in exile.
Ceased publication with July 30, 1944?

1. Army, Czechoslovak--Per. and soc. publ. 2. World
war, 1939-45--Gt. Br.   I. Czechoslovakia.
Armáda. 1.Brigada.

NN 0023995   NN

Naše noviny.
Naší cestou. [London] Vydaly Naše noviny v srpnu, 1943.
87 p. 21½ᵐ.

"Jsme v této knížce před vás nahrnuli kapitolky psané vojáky, většinou
novináři, tak jak jsme si je psali tady od roku 1940 pro sebe. Byly
otištěny v deníku čs. vojska ve Velké Británii, Našich novinách."—p. 5.

1. World war, 1939-   —Personal narratives, Czech.   I. Title.
45-12821
Library of Congress   D811.N28

NN 0023996   DLC InU

Naše oružje. Preveo Pravdoljub. [Chicago: Radnička straža,
1916.] 19 p. 24° (Narodna knjižnica. No. 4.)

1. Socialism—Essays and misc.   2. Pravdoljub, translator.
N. Y. P. L.   March 17, 1927

NN 0023997   NN

Naše planine.
[Zagreb, Planinarski savez Hrvatske]
v. illus., maps, ports. 24 cm. bimonthly.

Began in 1949. Cf. Union list of serials.
Journal of Planinarski savez Hrvatske (and of Planinarski savez
Bosne i Hercegovine, July/Aug. 1966-

1. Mountaineering—Period. 2. Mountains — Yugoslavia — Period.
I. Planinarski savez Hrvatske. II. Planinarski savez Bosne i Hercegovine.

G505.N34   68-77269

NN 0023998   DLC

BX 1767 NAŠE POKROKOVOST A ŘÍM. PRAHA, NÁKL. SVAZU
.N246 národního osvobození, 1925.
139 p.

At head of title: J.B.Kozák, Fr, Zelka,
Prokop Maxa, Alojs Hajn.

1. Catholic church--Doctrinal and controversial
works. I. Kozák, Jan Blahoslav, 1889-

NN 0023999   InU MB

Naše Polabí.
Brandýs n/L   1923-28.
v. I-5

NN 0024001   InU

DB 879   NAŠE PRAHA; VLASTIVĚDNÝ ČASOPIS PRO MLÁDEŽ.
.P8 A12 roč. 1 -
Praha, 1924-
v. in   illus. monthly.
Edited by Josef Keprta.

1. Prague--Description--Per. 2. Youth--Czecho-
slovak Republic--Per. I. Keprta, Josef, 1881- ed.

NN 0024002   InU

Naše řeč, listy pro vzdělávání a tříbení jazyka českého.
V Karlíně u Prahy, 19
v. 22½ᵐ. monthly (irregular)
"Vydává III. třída České akademie pro vedy a uměnf."

1. Bohemian language—Period.   I. Česká akademie věd a umění,
Prague. Třída 3. Filologická.
44-35878

Library of Congress   PG4004.N3

NIC NN CaBVaU TxU
NN 0024003   DLC CtY ICU CSt IEN RPB OU IU NcU

Naše revoluce; čtvrtletní historický sborník. roč. -14,
sv. 1/2;   -červen 1923. V Praze, Svaz národního
osvobození, 19 -38.
v. facsims. 24ᵐ.

19 -38 Issued by the Československá obec legionářská v Praze.
No more published. cf. Union list of serials.

1. Czechoslovak republic—Hist.—Period.   I. Československá obec
legionářská, Prague.
44-37039

Library of Congress   DB101.N27

NN 0024004   DLC MiU IU NcU ICU PSt OU

Naše samospráva; list Sdružení činovníků samosprávy Republikánské strany zemědělského a malorolnického lidu.
roč. 1-   1924-
V Praze, Novina.
v. 28 cm. monthly (except July and Aug.)
Editor: 1924-   Bedřich Bobek.

1. Local government—Czechoslovak Republic. 2. Local government—Period. I. Bobek, Bedřich, ed. II. Sdružení činovníků
samosprávy Republikánské strany zemědělského a malorolnického
lidu.

51-36299

NN 0024005   DLC NSyU

VOLUME 405

4PG Naše selo u pjesmi. Zagreb [Zadružna
Croat   stampa] 1951.
104   156 p.

(Zadružna knjižnica)

NN   0024006   DLC-P4

057.87 Naše Slovensko. roč. 1-3; říj. 1907-srp./září
NA   1910.   Praha.
     3v. illus., plates(part col.) 29cm.
monthly.

Cover title.
"Časopis hájící zájmy uherských Slováku."
Running title: Revue Naše Slovensko.

NN   0024007   IU NcU MiU ICU

4M 7   Naše spewy, serbski spewnik za sulu, wobzełałoj
Bjarnat Krawc a Michał Nawka. W Budysinje,
Z nakładom Zjednoćeństwa serbskich wucerjow,
1930.
    v.

NN   0024008   DLC-P4

Naše starine; godišnjak Zemaljskog zavoda za zaštitu spomenika kulture i prirodnih rijetkosti N. R. Bosne i Hercegovine. 1-
1953-
Sarajevo.
    v. illus., maps. 29 cm.

Editor: 1953-
    Š. Bešlagić.
Summaries in French.
1. Monuments—Bosnia and Herzegovina—Preservation. 2. Bosnia
and Herzegovina—Descr. & trav.   I. Bešlagić, Šefik, ed. II. Sarajevo. Zemaljski zavod za zaštitu spomenika kulture i prirodnih
rijetkosti N. R. Bosne i Hercegovine.

DB240.N3   56-27600

NN   0024009   DLC OU CU NSyU ICU

Наше стварање.

Лесковац, Новинско-издавачко предузеће Наша реч.
    v. illus. 24 cm. bimonthly (irregular)

"Часопис за друштвено-економска питања, уметност, књижев-
ност и науку."
Began in 1954. Cf. Jugoslovenski časopisi; izbor, 1955.
INDEXES:
    Vols. 1-15, 1953-68. 1 v. 24 cm.

Title romanized: Naše stvaranje.

AP56.N34   77-477298

NN   0024010   DLC

HQ 799 NAŠE TEME; ČASOPIS ZA DRUŠTVENA I OMLADINSKA
.Y8 A26 pitanja.
19 -
Zagreb.
    v. in   illus.

Frequency varies.
Subtitle varies.
Issued by Centralni komitet of the Narodna
omladina Hrvatska.
1. Youth—Yugoslavia—Period. 2. Social science
—Period. I. Narodna omladina Hrvatske—Centra
ni Komitet.

NN   0024011   InU

Naše úřední čeština; list pro očistu a tříbení české řeči úřední.
roč. 1-12, list. 1921-pros. 1933. V Praze, Vydavatelské družstvo českých úředníků železničních.
    12 v. 26 cm.

Biweekly, 1921/22; monthly, 1923-33.
Vol. 1 published in Nymburk by A. Neumann.
Subtitle varies slightly.

1. Czech language—Period.   I. Vydavatelské družstvo českých
úředníků železničních v Praze.

PG4004.N35   58-50350

NN   0024012   DLC ICU OU NNC

DB
785   Naše valašsko; sborník prací o jeho životě a
.V3   potřebách. roč.1-14. 1929-1951. ₃Brno₃
A1   v. illus.
N24   Superseded by Valašsko.
    Subtitle varies.

1.Valašsko,Moravia.

NN   0024013   MiU

057.86 Naše věda; kritický měsíčník. roč. 1
NAS
    V Praze ₃etc.₃
      v. 24-29cm.

Title varies: v.1   Věda česká.
Vols. for 1946-   issued by Odbočka v Brně
of Jednota českých filologů.

NN   0024014   IU

Naše vlast; časopis pro vlastivědnou práci.

Praha ₃Orbis₃ 195
    v. in   illus., ports., maps (part col.) 30 cm. monthly.
Began publication in 1953.
Issued, 1954-56, by Ministerstvo kultury; 1957-   by Mini-
sterstvo školství a kultury.
Supplements accompany some issues.

1. Czechoslovak Republic.   I. Czechoslovak Republic. Ministerstvo kultury. II. Czechoslovak Republic. Ministerstvo školství a
kultury.

DB191.N28   59-52564

NN   0024015   DLC

---

4 DB   Naše vlast v obrazech; sborník historických
Czesch.   památek v Československu. Slovem doprovodil
45   Miroslav Míčko.   [V Praze] Práce, 1948.
     122 p.

NN   0024016   DLC-P4 IEdS

DB 199.2
.M62   Naše vlast v obrazech; zborník historic-
       kých památek v Československu. Slovem dopro-
       vodil Miroslav Míčko. ₃V Praze₃ Práce,
       1949.
       38+122 p. illus.

       Text in Czech, Russian, English, and
French.
1. Czechoslovak Republic—Descr.—Views.
I. Title.

NN   0024017   InU

Naše vojsko.

Praha.
    no. illus., ports. 37 cm. weekly.

1. Czechoslovak Republic. Armáda—Period.

U4.N35   57-16427

NN   0024018   DLC

Naše vojsko. L'armée tchécoslovaque.

V Paříži.
    no. in   v. illus., ports., maps. 29 cm. biweekly.
Title also in French.
"Zvláštní vydání na počest 90. narozenin T. G. Masaryka": year 13,
March 7, 1940.

1. World War, 1939-1945—Period. 2. World War, 1939-1945—
Czechoslovak Republic.   I. Masaryk, Tomáš Garrigue, Pres. Czechoslovak Republic, 1850-1937. II. Title: L'armée tchécoslovaque.

D731.N254   51-17611

NN   0024019   DLC

PZ 70   NAŠE VZORY; SBÍRKA ŽIVOTOPISŮV PROSLAVENÝCH
.C9 P9   mužův i žen českých pro naši milou mládež.
     Sešit 1, 3.   V Praze, F. Bartel,1884.
     2 no. in 1 illus

     Bound with Prokeš, I.   Povídky z Krkonoš.

     1. Bohemia--Biog.

NN   0024020   InU

AP
52   Naše zahraničí. roč.1-₃11₃, ₃1919₃-31?
.N27   V Praze.
     11 v.
     Issued by Národní rada československá.
     Vols.10-₃11₃? formed by the union of Naše
     zahraničí and Československá emigrace.
     In 1932-33 combined with and published under
     the title of Čechoslovák (AP 52 .C385)
     In 1934 the union of Naše zahraničí and Čecho-
     slovák formed Národní rada (AP 52 .N24)

NN   0024021   MiU InU MH IU NNC

       Naše země, náš lid: Hlubčicko, Ratibořsko,
DD491   Kozelsko. Red.: Bohumil Sobotík s red.
S53N3   kruhem₃ V Opavě, Matice opavská, 1946.
     141 p. illus.,maps(1 fold.) 22cm.
     (Slezská knihovna, sv.2)
     Includes bibliographies.

     1.Silesia, Upper (Province) I.Sobotík,
Bohumil, ed. II.Ser.

NN   0024022   CSt CtY NN NNC

Naseby, pseud.
    Oaks and birches
       see under title

Naseby, pseud.
    The silver whistle
       see under title

Nasedkin, Filipp.
    Большая семья; роман. ₃Москва₃ Молодая гвардия,
1949.
    447 p. 21 cm.

    I. Title.   *Title transliterated:* Bol'shaîa sem'îa.
PG3476.N37B6 1949   51-17785

NN   0024025   DLC

Nasedkin, Filipp.
    Большая семья; роман. ₃Москва₃ Молодая гвардия,
1949.
    409 p. 21 cm.

    I. Title.   *Title transliterated:* Bol'shaîa sem'îa.
PG3476.N37B6 1949a   51-17788

NN   0024026   DLC

Nasedkin, Filipp.
    Большая семья; роман. ₃Изд. 4., перер.₃ Москва, Со-
ветский писатель, 1952.
    491 p. 21 cm.

    I. Title.   *Title transliterated:* Bol'shaîa sem'îa.
PG3476.N367B6 1952   52-36427

NN   0024027   DLC

VOLUME 405

Nasedkin, Filipp.
Дороги и встречи. ₍Рисунки Н. Цейтлина₎ ₍Москва₎
Молодая гвардия, 1947.
173 p. illus. 22 cm.

1. Yugoslavia—Descr. & trav.   I. Title.
Title transliterated: Dorogi i vstrechi.

DR366.N3   48-25111*

NN   0024028   DLC

Nasedkin, Filipp.
Красные Горки; роман. ₍Москва₎ Молодая гвардия,
1951.
388 p. illus. (1 col.) 21 cm.

I. Title.   *Title transliterated:* Krasnye Gorki.

PG3476.N37K7   51-32101

NN   0024029   DLC

PG3476
.N37V6
Nasedkin, Filipp.
Возвращение; роман. Ленинград, Молодая гвардия,
1945.
308 p. illus. 21 cm.

I. Title.   *Title transliterated:* Vozvrashchenie.

                                         51-32100

NN   0024030   DLC

Z5320
.M64
1955
Nasedkina, Vera Aleksandrovna.
Moscow. Publichnaîa biblioteka.
Возникновение и развитие жизни на Земле; происхож-
дение человека. ₍Указатель литературы₎ Изд. 2., доп.
Москва, 1955.

Naseeruddin Hashmi
    see   Hashmi, Nasiruddin, 1895-

Nasej starej vlasti. 121p. V Petrovci,
Kníhtlac. uc. spol. [1931] (Kniznica
národnej jednoty, 1)

Slovak

NN   0024033   OC1

Nasekin, N   A
Хлопковое волокно, его добывание и свойства. ₍Ива-
ново₎ Изд-во Ивановской промышл. области, 1933.
119 p. illus. 23 cm.
Includes bibliography.

1. Cotton growing. I. Title.
                    Title transliterated: Khlopkovoe volokno.

SB249.N3   54-50697 ‡

NN   0024034   DLC

Naselli, Carmelina.
...Domenico Cavalca.   Città di Castello: "Il Solco," 1925.
158 p.   12°.   (Biblioteca di coltura letteraria. ₍v.₎ 6.)

Bibliographical footnotes.

1. Cavalca, Domenico, d. 1342. 2. Ser.
N. Y. P. L.   April 28, 1926

NN   0024035   NN CtY MH CU NIC

Naselli, Carmelina.
Figure e scene dell "Orlando Furioso" in
un'antica pergamena catanese.   Firenze,
Centro nazionale di'studi sul rinascimento,
1941.
207-228p. plates. 24cm.

"Estratti da La Rinascita, anno quarto,
numero XVIII, marzo MCMXLI."

1. Ariosta, Lodovice, 1474-1533. Orlando
furioso.   Title.

NN   0024036   IEN

Naselli, Carmelina.
Introduzione allo studio storico della
lingua italiana. Catania, Crisafulli ₍1945₎
107 p.

1. Italian language.

NN   0024037   NNC OrU

4PQ   Naselli, Carmelina
It.   Il Petrarca nell'Ottocento.
3082 Napoli, F. Perrella, 1923.
        571 p.

(Biblioteca della "Rassegna," 7)

       MB InU OU
NN   0024038   DLC-P4 IU IEN NN IaU ICN MH PU CtY NcD

Naselli, Carmelina.
Una sacra rappresentazione siciliana ...
... Scritti vari. Torino, G. Chiantore ₍1931₎

Naselli, Carmelina.
Saggio sulle ninne-nanne siciliane. Catania, R. Pram-
polini ₍1948₎
88 p. illus. 22 cm.
Bibliographical footnotes.

1. Folk-songs, Sicilian—Hist. & crit. 2. Lullabies.   I. Title.
ML3661.N3   A 51-4231
Illinois. Univ. Library
for Library of Congress   ₍3₎†

NN   0024040   IU NN DLC

Naselli, Carmelina.
Studi di folklore; drammatica popolare, culto degli alberi,
"Tarantella," "Empanadilla." Catania, G. Crisafulli, 1953.
119 p. illus. 22 cm.

1. Folk-lore—Italy. 2. Folk-lore of trees.
                                        A 54-4771
Indiana. Univ. Libr.   GR176.N24
for Library of Congress   ₍1₎

NN   0024041   InU NN

Naselli, Carmelina.
... Studi di letteratura antica siciliana; con due facsimili ...
Catania, Vincenzo Muglia, 1935.
3 p. l., 145 p., 1 l. facsims. 18½ᶜᵐ.
Errata slip inserted after p. 145.
Bibliographical foot-notes.

1. Italian literature—Sicily.
                                        A C 36-1523
Title from Illinois Univ.   Printed by L. C.

NN   0024042   IU NcD CU

Naselli, Carmelina, ed.
PQ4201
.C7
ser. 2,
vol. 23   Vitae patrum.
... Le vite de' s. s. padri. Introduzione e note di Carmelina
Naselli. Con una tavola. Torino, Unione tipografico-editrice
torinese ₍1926₎

Naselli, Giovanni Battista, Archbishop of Palermo.   **2724.84**
Relazione dello arcivescovo di Palermo su'casi dal 15 al 22 settem-
bre 1866.
= Firenze. 1866. 23 pp. 23 cm., in 12s.

H1002 — Palermo, Sicily. Hist.

NN   0024044   MB MH

Y   NASELLI, MARIA.
712   La fortuna del Foscolo nell'ottocento.
.F 7885 Genova, F. Perrella, 1923.
        441p. 26cm.

NN   0024045   ICN NN IU MH NcD IaU CU ICU MdBJ

Naselli, Santi
L'inesplorato Monte Albura o Albuchîa, nei rinvenimenti
archeologici nella leggenda e nella storia. Castelbuono,
Tip.Le Madonie [1952]

46 p. illus.

NN   0024046   MH

Microfilm
2278   Nasem, Hossien.
        Russia and Great Britain in Iran: 1900-1914.
New York, 1954.
354 ℓ.

Thesis (Ph.D.) - Columbia University.
Bibliography: p. 343-354.
Microfilm.   Ann Arbor, Mich., University
Microfilms, 1954.   1 reel.   35mm.

1. Russia - For. rel. - Iran. 2. Iran - For.
rel. - Russia. 3. Gt. Brit. - For. rel. -
Iran. 4. Iran - For. rel. - Gt. Brit.
I. Title.

NN   0024047   CoU

Nasemann,
Die Römerzüge der beiden ersten Ottonen.
[Progr.] Königsberg in der Neumark, 1855.
18 p.   4°.
Programm - Gymnasium, Königsberg in der
Neumark.
I. Königsberg in der Neumark. Friedrich
Wilhelms-Gymnasium.

NN   0024048   MH

Nasemann, Hans, 1909-
... Die primäre Darmtuberkulose des
Jenaer Pathologischen Institutes in den Jahre
1923 bis 1935 ...   [n.p.] 1935.
Inaug.-Diss. - Jena.
Lebenslauf.
"Literaturangabe": p. 23-24.

NN   0024049   CtY MiU

Nasemann, Herwarth, 1906-
... Tetanus puerperalis (An Hand von zwei
Fällen der Jenaer Frauenklinik) 1923 und 1933 ...
Jena, 1934.
Inaug.-Diss. - Jena.
Lebenslauf.
"Literaturangabe": p. [19]-23.

NN   0024050   CtY MiU

Nasemann, Johann August Ferdinand, 1824-
Quaestiones de rhinoplastice ... auctor
Ioh. Aug. Ferd. Nasemann ...   Halis Saxonum,
Typis expressum Heynemannianis ₍1849₎
29, ₍2₎ p.

Inaug.-diss., Halle-Wittenberg, 1849.
Vita.

1. Rhinoplasty.

NN   0024051   NNC DNLM

VOLUME 405

AC 931 Nasemann, Otto, 1821–1895.
.H3   August Hermann Francke und der unterricht in
v. 136   Realgegenstaenden ...   Halle, Waisenhaus, 1863.
             39 p.
             [Haverford-Bauer pamphlets, v. 136, no. 9]

NN 0024052   DLC

NASEMANN, Otto, 1821-1895.
    Bad Lauchstädt. Halle, in comm. bei C.E.M
Pfeffer, 1885.

    pp. 52.
    (NEUJAHRSBLÄTTER, 9.)

NN 0024053   MH NjP

Nasemann, Otto, 1821-1895.
    ⊙De Horatii carminibus... Halis Saxonum, E.
Karras, 1875.
    8 p

NN 0024054   PHC NjP

Nasemann, Otto, 1821–1895.
    Friedrich der Weise, kurfürst von Sachsen ... Halle
a. S., Verein für reformationsgeschichte, 1889.
    54 p. 12°. (Schriften für das deutsche volk, 5)

                                                                1–G–131

NN 0024055   DLC NN MH MoSCS OCU NNUT

Nasemann, Otto, 1821-1895.
    Gedanken und erfahrungen über ewiges
und alltägliches; für das deutsche haus.
Hrsg. von Otto Nasemann... 2. umgearbeitete
aufl. Halle, M. Niemeyer, 1880.
    4 v. in 2. O.

NN 0024056   OO

Nasemann, Otto, 1821-1895.
    Jahresbericht des Stadtgymnasiums zu Halle
von Otto Nasemann
            see under Halle. Stadtgymnasium.
[Supplement]

AC931 Nasemann, Otto, 1821-1895.
.H3   Justinus Febronius. [Johann Nicolaus von
v. 107   Hontheim]
             p. 649-663.   [Haverford-Bauer pamphlets,
             v. 107, no. 8]
             n.t.p.

NN 0024058   DLC

Našemu Antonínu Zápotockému ⌈pozdravy a vzpomínky k
pětašedesátým narozeninám; 19. prosinec, 1949. ⌈Praha,
Ministerstvo informací, 1950⌉
    181 p. illus. 16 cm.

    1. Zápotocký, Antonín, 1884-

    DB217.Z3N3   52-31505 ‡

NN 0024059   DLC

Našemu milačku.   col'd illus.   n. p.   4°.
    Unpaged.

NN 0024060   NN

Nasenius, Gerd.
    Livshymn; dikter. ⌈Stockholm, 1949⌉
    74 p. 22 cm.

    I. Title.

                                                            A 50-5900
Minnesota. Univ. Libr.
for Library of Congress   ⌈ ⌉

NN 0024061   MnU

Nasenius, Gerd.
    ...Min skog; dikter. Stockholm: A.-b. Kungsholmens bok-
handel ⌈1938⌉ 80 p.   22cm.

    1. Poetry, Swedish. I. Title.
N. Y. P. L.   June 20, 1940

NN 0024062   NN MH

Naser, Hermann, 1905-
    ... Versuche zur Wertbestimmung bestrahlten
Ergosterins ...   Berlin, 1929.
    16 p.   8°.
    Inaug.-Diss. - Tübingen.
    Lebenslauf.

NN 0024063   CtY OU DNLM

Naser, Sayed Abdel.
    Sinai prospecting expedition: prospecting
and exploration in South Sinai, 1953-1954
            see under Egypt. Maṣlaḥat al-Manājim
wa-al-Mahājir.

Naser, Walter, 1927-
    Die Abschreibungen der Deutschen Bundespost und die
gegenwärtige Tendenz ihrer Abschreibungspolitik. ⌈n. p.⌉
1955.
    vii, 138 p. tables. 21 cm.
    Inaug.-Diss.—Munich.
    Vita.
    Bibliography : p. 125-127.

    1. Depreciation. 2. Postal service—Germany (Federal Republic,
1949-   )—Accounting.   I. Title.

    HE6999.A3N3   60-18213

NN 0024065   DLC

Nāṣer al-Dīn Shāh, *Shah of Iran*
    see
Nāṣir al-Dīn Shāh, *Shah of Iran*, 1831-1896.

Naserie, Hafisullah, 1924-
    Die afghanische Presse, ihr Werden und Sein; ein erster
Versuch. München ⌈1953?⌉
    117 l. 30 cm.
    Typescript (carbon copy)
    Inaug.-Diss.—Munich.
    Vita.
    Bibliography : leaf 117.

    1. Journalism—Afghanistan.   I. Title.

    PN5449.A3N3   58-35939

NN 0024067   DLC

Naserie, Mohammed Sarwar
    see
Sarwar Naserie, Mohammed.

834N17 Naseweis, Ernst, pseud.
Od   Des Herrn Magisters Merks seltsame An-
          sichten über literarische Zustände. Hrsg.
          von Ernst Naseweis ⌈pseud.⌉   Leipzig, O.
          Wigand, 1865.
          viii, 180p. 19cm.

NN 0024069   IU

LD   Nasgaard, Roald, 1941-
3907   Willumsen and symbolist art 1888-1910.
.G7   2v.
1973   Thesis (Ph.D.) - N.Y.U., Graduate School.
.N37

also
Film
T12110   1. Dissertations, Academic - N.Y.U. - 1973.
              2. Willumsen, Jens Ferdinand, 1863-   I.
Film   Title.

NN 0024070   NNU

Nasgaard, Sigurd
    see Naesgaard, Sigurd, 1883-

Lilly   NASH,
DA 452   The answer of the reverend and learned
.A626   Mr. Nash, to a letter sent him by his cousin,
          after the death of our late most gracious
          soveraign Lord King James. ⌈n.p., n.d.⌉
          ' broadside. 25 x 19.2 cm.

              Concerning the succession after James
          II's (?) death.

          1. James II, king of Gt. Brit., 1633-1701.
          2. Gt. Brit.--Kings and rulers--Succession.
          I. Title.

NN 0024072   InU

Nash,
    Letters of Gallowrake
            see under Gallowrake, pseud.

Nash, A.H.
    Funeral sermon [on Samuel K. Burbank]
[Pittsford, Vt., 1917]
    8p. por. 12°

NN 0024074   MWA

99.4   Nash, A   J
N17   A photoelectric planimeter. ⌈n.p.⌉ 1948.
          64-69 p.

              1. Planimeter. 2. Forest mensuration.
          I. Title.

NN 0024075   DNAL

Sch.F. Nash, A   J
634.962   Some tests on the determination of tree
C212F   heights from air photographs. Ottawa, Dept.
no.5   of Mines and Resources, Mines, Forests and
          Scientific Services Branch, Dominion Forest
          Service, 1949.
              9 l. diagrs. 28 cm. (Forest Air Survey
          publication, no. 5)

              Cover title.
              Includes bib-   -liography.

Continued in next column

VOLUME 405

Continued from preceding column

1. Forests and forestry. Mensuration. 2. Aerial photogrammetry. I. Canada. Forestry Branch.

NN 0024077 NcD

TN490
U7U62
4054

Nash, A   L
  Airborne radiometric surveying in Grand, San Juan, Emery and Wayne Counties, Utah, and Montrose County, Colorado. Oak Ridge, Tenn., Technical Information Service, 1953.
  23 p. maps, tables. 26 cm. (U.S. Atomic Energy Commission. RME-4054)
  Bibliography, p. 17.

  1. Prospecting – Radioactive substances. I. Title. (Series)

NN 0024078 DI

TN490
U7U62
1050
1954

Nash, A   L
  Results of an airborne radiometric survey in the Canon City embayment area, Colorado, by A. L. Nash [and] L. J. Brown. Oak Ridge, Tenn., Technical Information Service, 1954.
  11 p. 2 maps (1 fold.), fold. table. 27 cm. (U.S. Atomic Energy Commission. RME-1050(Rev.))

  1. Geology – Colorado. 2. Radioactivity. 3. Uranium ores – Colorado. I. Brown, L. J., jt. auth. II. Title: Radiometric survey. (Series)

NN 0024079 DI

L61
.P76

Nash, A. M.
  Progress of education in India; quinquennial review.
  Delhi.

Nash, Rev. Adam Glandinning.
  A summary of foreign marriage law: to safeguard Englishwomen engaged to foreign subjects. London, Society for Promoting Christian Knowledge, 1910.
  xii, 13–48 p.   8°.

NN 0024081 NN

GN845
.P7 N26

NASH, ADOLF.
  Zarna wczesnodziejowe. Warszawa, Nakł. Polskiego Tow. Archeologicznego, 1950.
  86 p. illus. (Studia Wczesnodziejowe. Serja archeologiczna, t.1)

  At head of title: Kazimierz Majewski.

  1. Poland--Antiq. I. Title.

NN 0024082 InU

---

*F127
N6N28

Nash, Alan.
  Under three flags. No imprint, 1934.

  14p.,1l.   27cm.in 30½cm.

  Newspaper clippings from the Buffalo times, July 30 - August 4, 1934.

NN 0024083 NBuG

Nash, Alanson.
                American hemlock (Pinus canadensis).
  [Albany. 1853.] 8°. (Assembly, no. 133.)
  Cabinet of natural history of the state of New York. Report, 1853, pp. 455–457*.*

NN 0024084 MH-A

Nash, Alanson.
  ———— The sugar maple or Acer saccharinum. [Albany. 1853.] 8°. (Assembly, no. 133.)
  Cabinet of natural history of the state of New York. Report, 1853, pp. 451–455*.*

NN 0024085 MH-A

Nash (ALBERT)
  Full salvation. 47 pp. *New York: N. Tibbals & Son* [1872]. *4°.*

NN 0024086 NN

Nash, Albert.
  Perseverance and apostasy: being an argument in proof of the Arminian doctrine on that subject.   5458.98
= New York. Tibbals. 1871. 388 pp. 12°.

E6405 — Perseverance of the Saints. — Apostasy. — Arminianism.

NN 0024087 MB KyWA ODW OO ICN

Nash, *Mrs.* Albertine A   Richards.
  The psychology of superior children, by Albertine A. Richards-Nash ... [Worcester, Mass., 1924]
  cover-title, p. [209]–246. 23cm.
  Thesis (PH. D.)—Clark university, 1922.
  "Reprinted from the Pedagogical seminary, vol. XXXI ... September, 1924."
  Bibliography: p. 245–246.

  1. Precocity. 2. Ability.   I. Title: Superior children, The psychology of.

Library of Congress   BF723.P7N3 1922   25–7298
Clark Univ. Libr.

NN 0024088 MWC DHEW OrU PPT OCU OU NcD DLC

Nash, Alden.
  And let who will be clever, a comedy in three acts, by Alden Nash ... New York, N. Y., Los Angeles, Calif., S. French, inc.; London, S. French, ltd.; [etc., etc.,] °1934.
  90 p. diagr. 19cm.

  I. Title.
                                              35–10602
Library of Congress   PS3527.A62A8 1934
Copyright D pub. 33712   [2]   812.5

NN 0024089 DLC OC1 OrCS

Nash, Alfred William, 1886–
  The principles and practice of lubrication; a manual for petroleum technologists, students, engineers, oil salesmen, etc., by Alfred W. Nash ... and A. R. Bowen ... London, Chapman & Hall, ltd., 1929.
  2 p. l., vii–xi, 315 p. illus., plates, diagrs. (2 fold.) 22 cm.
  Bibliography: p. 306–307.

  1. Lubrication and lubricants.   I. Bowen, Arthur Riley, joint author.
                                              30—16372
Library of Congress   TJ1075.N3
                             [a48d½]   621.89

NN 0024090 DLC OC1W WaS CaBVaU MiU OC1 MB NN

Nash, Alfred William, 1886–
  The principles and practice of lubrication; a manual for petroleum technologists, students, engineers, oil salesmen, etc., by Alfred W. Nash ... and A. R. Bowen ... 2d ed., rev. London, Chapman & Hall, ltd., 1937.
  2 p. l., vii–xi, 345 p. illus., plates, diagrs. (part fold.) 22cm.
  "Errata" slip attached to p. 1.
  "References" at end of each chapter except the first; "General references": p. 338.

  1. Lubrication and lubricants.   I. Bowen, Arthur Riley, joint author.

Library of Congress   TJ1075.N3 1937   38–15528
                             [3]   621.89

PPFr

NN 0024091 DLC WaS OrCS OrP MH NNC ICJ NcD OU

287.6774
D483T
N

Nash, Alice   comp.
  Golden jubilee, 1849–1899; history of the Tabernacle Methodist Episcopal Church, Detroit, Mich. [Detroit, Mich., 1899]
  90 p.

  1. Detroit, Mich. Tabernacle Methodist Episcopal Church. 2. Methodist Episcopal Church in Michigan.

NN 0024092 TxDaM-P MiD

Nash, Alfred William, 1886–
  The principles of motor fuel preparation & application, by Alfred W. Nash ... and Donald A. Howes ... London, Chapman & Hall, ltd., 1934–
  v. plates (1 fold.) tables, diagrs. 26cm.
  Includes bibliographies.

  1. Motor fuels.   I. Howes, Donald Albert, joint author. II. Title: Motor fuel preparation & application.
                                              35–3769
Library of Congress   TP692.2.N3
                             [a38n1]   665.5

NN 0024093 DLC OrP OC1W NcD NN

Nash, Alfred William, 1886–
  The principles of motor fuel preparation & application, by Alfred W. Nash ... and Donald A. Howes ... Volume I-II. New York, J. Wiley & Sons, Inc., 1935.
  2 v. plates, tables (1 fold.) diagrs. (1 fold.) 25½cm.
  Printed in Great Britain.
  "References" at end of each chapter.
  "Patent index" at end of each volume.

OKentU OCU OC1 OU MiHM PPAtR
NN 0024094   ICJ PU-Sc MB WaS Or NjR CU NcRS TU

Nash, Alfred William, 1886–
  The principles of motor fuel preparation & application, by Alfred W. Nash ... and Donald A. Howes ... 2d ed. London, Chapman & Hall ltd., 1938–
  v. illus., plates, tables, diagrs. 25¼cm.
  "References" at end of each chapter.

  1. Motor fuels.   I. Howes, Donald Albert, joint author.

Library of Congress   TP692.2.N3 1938   39–8485
                             [3]   665.5

NN 0024095 DLC MtBuM OrCS NcRS NN MiHM

Nash, Alfred William, 1886–
  The principles of motor fuel preparation & application, by Alfred W. Nash ... and Donald A. Howes ... 2d ed. New York, J. Wiley & sons, inc., 1938–
  v. illus., plates, tables, diagrs. 25¼cm.
  "References" at end of each chapter.

  1. Motor fuels.   I. Howes, Donald Albert, joint author.
                                              46–29860
Library of Congress   TP692.2.N3 1938 a
                             [2]   665.5

NN 0024096 DLC CU OC1

VOLUME 405

Nash, Alfred William, 1886-   *ed.*

Dunstan, Albert Ernest, 1878-   *ed.*
The science of petroleum; a comprehensive treatise of the principles and practice of the production, refining, transport and distribution of mineral oil. Dr. A. E. Dunstan ... managing editor, Professor A. W. Nash ... editor of contributions, Dr. Benjamin T. Brooks ... editor for the United States of America, Sir Henry Tizard ... consulting editor. London, New York ₍etc.₎, Oxford <u>university</u> press, 1938.

Nash, Alice M.
... Educational treatment of defectives, by Alice M. Nash and S. D. Porteus ... Vineland, New Jersey, The Training school ₍1919₎
cover-title, 18, ₍1₎ p.   25ᶜᵐ.   (Publications of the Training school at Vineland, New Jersey. Department of research, no. 18, November 1919)
"Reprint from the Training school bulletin, November, 1919."
"Study no. 3.—1919 series, Research laboratory, Vineland, N. J."
L. Children, Abnormal and backward--Education.   I. Porteus, Stanley David, 1883-   II. Title: Defectives, Educational treatment of.

NN   0024098   MiU NN

Nash, Andrew Jackson, 1809-1854.
Life and confessions of Andrew Jackson Nash, as related by himself, while in prison in Carlinville, Illinois, on the 19th, 20th and 21st days of June, 1854. Published for the benefit of his family. Carlinville, Ill., J. L & S. B. Dugger, printers, 1854.
24p.   24cm.

NN   0024099   IHi

Nash, Anne.
Cabbages and crime, by Anne Nash. Garden City, New York, Pub. for the Crime club by Doubleday, Doran & co., inc., 1945.
5 p. l., 9–189 p.   19ᶜᵐ.
"First edition."

I. Title.
                                          45–6550
Library of Congress *   PZ3.N17Cab

NN   0024100   DLC CaBVa WaE ViU PP OCU OEac

Nash, Anne.
... Death by design. Garden City, New York, Pub. for the Crime club by Doubleday, Doran and co., inc., 1944.
4 p. l., 180 p.   20ᶜᵐ.
"First edition."

I. Title.
                                          44–5689
Library of Congress   PZ3.N17De

NN   0024101   DLC MB PPL OEac OCU TxU

Nash, Anne.
Said with flowers, a mystery novel by Anne Nash. Garden City, New York, Pub. for the Crime club by Doubleday, Doran & co., inc., 1943.
4 p. l., 211 p.   19¼ᶜᵐ.
"First edition."

I. Title.
                                          43–6009
Library of Congress   PZ3.N17Sai

NN   0024102   DLC PP OOxM OLak WaS

Nash, Anne.
Said with flowers ... New York ₍1945₎
185 p.   16¼ᶜᵐ.   (*On cover:* Bart house mystery. ₍19₎)

I. Title.
                                          46–21108
                                          Brief cataloging
Library of Congress   PZ3.N17Sai 3

NN   0024103   DLC

Nash, Anne.
Unhappy rendezvous, by Anne Nash. Garden City, New York, Pub. for the Crime club by Doubleday & company, inc., 1946.
4 p. l., 7–215 p.   19ᶜᵐ.
"First edition."

I. Title.
PZ3.N17Un   46–7932

NN   0024104   DLC PP CaBVa

Nash, Ansel.
Memoir of Edward Dorr Griffin, D. D., president of Williams college: By Rev. Ansel Nash ... New York, S. W. Benedict & co., 1842.
72 p.   15½ᶜᵐ.
Label of J. S. Taylor & co., New York, pasted over imprint.
⟨Originally published in the Quarterly register.⟩

I. Griffin, Edward Dorr, 1770-1837.
                                          E 9–1210
Library, U. S. Bur. of   Education LD6072.7   1821

NN   0024105   DHEW MWA

Nash, Ansel.
₍Union among Christians. N. Y., 1834.
6 p

NN   0024106   PPPrHi

Nash, Arnold Samuel, *ed.*
Education for Christian marriage, its theory and practice, edited by Rev. A. S. Nash ... with a foreword by the Archbishop of York. London, Student Christian movement press ₍1939₎
2 p. l., vii–xvi, 304 p.   22ᶜᵐ.
"First published April 1939."
Bibliography : p. 301–304.

1. Marriage. 2. Family.   I. Title. II. Title: Christian marriage, Education for.
                                          40–13515
Library of Congress   HQ734.N3
                           ₍5₎   173.1

NN   0024107   DLC CtY OC1 NN CBBD MSohG

Nash, Arnold Samuel, *ed.*
Education for Christian marriage, its theory and practice, edited by Rev. A. S. Nash ... with a foreword by the Archbishop of York. New York, The Macmillan company, 1939.
2 p. l., vii–xvi, 304 p.   22ᶜᵐ.
Printed in Great Britain.
Bibliography : p. 301–304.

1. Marriage. 2. Family.   I. Title. II. Title: Christian marriage, Education for.
                                          39–27984
Library of Congress   HQ734.N3   1939
                           ₍8₎   173.1

NN   0024108   DLC NcRS OKentU IdU NBuG PP OO

Nash, Arnold Samuel, ed.
Education for Christian marriage, its theory and practice, ed. by A. S. Nash ... with a foreword by the Archbishop of York. N. Y., Macmillan, 1940.   304p.

NN   0024109   OC1W NcD PPLT

Nash, Arnold Samuel, *ed.*
Protestant thought in the twentieth century: whence & whither? New York, Macmillan, 1951.
xii, 296 p.   21 cm.
Includes bibliographies.
CONTENTS.—America at the end of the Protestant era, by A. S. Nash.—The study of the Old Testament, by G. E. Wright.—The study of the New Testament, by F. V. Filson.—The philosophy of religion, by G. F. Thomas.—Systematic theology, by W. M. Horton.—Christian ethics, by W. Beach and J. C. Bennett.—Church history, by G. H. Williams.—Pastoral theology and psychology, by S. Hiltner.—Preaching, by C. W. Gilkey.—Christian education, by H. S. Smith.—Reunion and the ecumenical movement, by H. S. Leiper.—Christianity and other religions, by J. A. Mackay.
1. Theology—20th cent. 2. Protestantism. 3. Religious thought—20th cent.   I. Title.
BR479.N3   200   51—11218

WaT MtU MtBC WaTC IdU OrCS
NBuC MsSM KyLxCB FU TU IdB Or WaS KyLxT IdPI OrP
NN   0024110   DLC WaU ICU NN MB MH TxU ViU NcU MiU

Nash, Arnold Samuel.
The university and the modern world; an essay in the philosophy of university education, by Arnold S. Nash ... New York, The Macmillan company, 1943.
xxiv, 312 p.   19¼ cm.
"Notes on bibliography" : p. 295–312.

1. Education, Higher.   I. Title.
LB2321.N35   378   43—17277

OrStbM
KEmT OrSaW Or OrCS OrU Wa WaSpG WaWW CaBVaU IEG
NN   0024111   DLC IdPI PPLT PP PV ViU OCU OU OO NIC

Nash, Arnold Samuel.
The university & the modern world; an essay in the philosophy of university education, by Arnold S. Nash ... [with a foreword by Reinhold Niebuhr]   New York, Macmillan, 1944 [c1943]
xxiv, 312 p.   19cm.

"Notes on bibliography" : p. 295–312.

OrPR MB NcRS
NN   0024112   CSaT NcD OC1W PU MH NcU MtU CaBVa OrP

Nash, Arnold Samuel.
The university & the modern world; an essay in the social philosophy of university education, by Arnold S. Nash ... with a foreword by Reinhold Niebuhr. London, S. C. M. press ltd., 1945.
228 p.   22¼ᶜᵐ.
"First published in Great Britain in January 1945."
"Notes on bibliography" : p. 206₎–217.

1. Education, Higher.   I. Title.
                                          45—4399
Library of Congress   LB2321.N35   1945
                           ₍3₎   378

NN   0024113   DLC PPLT NcU WaTC

Nash, Arthur.
Philosophy of satanology, by Rev. Arthur Nash ... Prof. I. B. Beeshy, illustrator. ₍Bluffton, O.₎ °1900.
48 p.   illus.   17ᶜᵐ.

1. Devil.   I. Title.
                                          1–30359
Library of Congress   BT980.N2

NN   0024114   DLC

QK569
C96N3   **Nash, Arthur,** writer on cyanophyceae.
The Cyanophyceae of the thermal regions of Yellowstone National Park, U.S.A., and of Rotorua and Whakarewarewa, New Zealand; with some ecological data. ₍Minneapolis₎ University of Minnesota, 1938.
1 v. (unpaged)   illus.   28cm.

Thesis - University of Minnesota, 1938.
Xeroxed photocopy.

NN   0024115   GU

VOLUME 405

QF589.8 Nash, Arthur, *writer on cyanophyceae*
N171 The cyanophyceae of the thermal regions
of Yellowstone National Park, U.S.A., and
of Rotorua and Whakarewarewa, New Zealand;
with some ecological data. [Minneapolis]
1938.
1v.(unpaged) illus.,map.

Microfilm (negative)
Thesis- University of Minnesota.
Bibliography: 15ℓ. at end.

NN   0024116   OrU

Nash, Arthur, 1870–1927.
The golden rule in business [an address]   Boston, Murray
press [1920?]   16 p.   19cm.
Cover title.

1. Employment management.

NN   0024117   NN MH

Nash, Arthur, 1870–1927.
The golden rule in business, by Arthur Nash ...   New York,
Chicago [etc.] Fleming H. Revell company [*1923]
160 p.   19½*.

1. Employment management. 2. Golden rule.   I. Title.

Library of Congress   HF5353.N3   23–11187

MB NN ViU PSC PPFr
NN   0024118   ICJ OrU NcD Or OrCS WaTC OC1 00 ODW

Nash, Arthur, 1870–1927.
The golden rule in business, by Arthur Nash ...   Enl. and
cor. ed.   New York, Chicago [etc.] Fleming H. Revell company [*1930]
3 p. l., 5–188 p. front. (port.) 21*.
Preface to the new and enlarged edition signed: Philip I. Roberts.

I. Roberts, Philip Ilott, 1872–   ed. II. Title.
Library of Congress   HF5353.N3 1930   30–24168
——— Copy 2.
Copyright A 27408   [8]   923.373

NN   0024119   DLC OC1 WaT

Nash, Arthur, 1870–1927.
An industrial miracle ...   Rev. and brought
down to date.   Cincinnati, O., The A. Nash
company [n.d.]
cover-title, 32 p.   18.5 cm.
First published in 1923.
"Excerpts from lectures delivered at the
Massachusetts institute of technology, Cambridge,
Mass."

NN   0024120   CtY

HF
5353 Nash,Arthur,1870–1927.
.N2481   An industrial miracle and how it happened, by Arthur Nash ...   Boston, Mass.,
The Murray press [1925?]
32 p.   18cm.
"Excerpts from lectures delivered at the
Massachusetts institute of technology,
Cambridge,Mass".
"A more complete story of this ... experiment by Mr.Nash himself has been published ... under the title 'The Golden rule
in business'".   Publisher's announcement.

NN   0024121   MiU DL NN

AP2
.N15   Nash, Arthur, 1870–1927, ed.
The Nash journal. v. 1; Dec. 6, 1926–Nov. 28, 1927. [Cincin-
nati, The Nash publishing company] 1926–27.

Nash, Arthur, 1870–1927.   5639-465
The organized church and organized labor.
(In Davis, Jerome, editor, 1891– . Business and the church.
Pp. 333–344. New York. [1926.])

NN   0024123   MB

Nash, Arthur Charles.
The drama of Dunquerque, by Arthur C. Nash ...   Vancouver, B. C., Printed by R. H. Storer & co. ltd., *1941.
38 p.   20½*.
Poem.

1. Dunkirk, France, Battle of, 1940—Poetry.   I. Title.
44–10917
Library of Congress   PR6027.A72D7
[2]   811.5

NN   0024124   DLC TxU NN CaBVa

Nash, Arthur Charles.
Lyrics of life, by Arthur C. Nash ...   Vancouver, Can., R. H.
Storer & co. ltd., *1941.
64 p.   25*.

I. Title.
44–33574
Library of Congress   PR6027.A73L8
[2]   811.5

NN   0024125   DLC CaBVaU CaBVa CaBViPA

Nash, Arthur Charles.
Memories in melody, by Arthur Charles Nash.   Toronto,
The Ryerson press, 1920.   86 p.   19cm.

306203B. 1. No subject. I. Title.
N.Y.P.L.   July 5, 1945

NN   0024126   NN CaOTU TxU CaBVaU CaBViPA CaBViP RPB

NASH, ARTHUR CHARLES.
Ode to Canada, and other poems.   Toronto,
W. Briggs, 1910.   60 p.   20cm.

NN   0024127   NN TxU MH RPB CaBVaU CaBViP CaBViPA

Nash, Arthur Charles.
1901
NA812ru   Ruth, and other poems.   [Vernon, B.C.]
Vernon News Ptg. & Pub. Co., 1910.
Harris   33 p.   17 cm.
Collection

1. Canadian poetry.   I. Title.

NN   0024128   RPB CaBViP

Nash, Arthur Charles.
The sojourner, by Arthur C. Nash ...   Vancouver, B. C.,
Printed by R. H. Storer & co., ltd., *1943.
64 p.   23½*.

I. Title.
44–33559
Library of Congress   PR6027.A73S6
[2]   811.5

NN   0024129   DLC CaBViPA CaBVa

Nash, Arthur Charles.
Songs of the seasons, by Arthur C. Nash.   Vancouver, B. C.,
Dunsmuir printing company, *1944.
40 p.   24*.

I. Title.
45–14963
Library of Congress   PR6027.A73S7
[2]   811.5

NN   0024130   DLC CaBVaU CaBVa

Nash, Augustus.
Jesus' life; discussions for men's Bible classes, by
Augustus Nash ...   Cleveland, 1912.
[52] p.   19½*. $0.50

12–26696

NN   0024131   DLC OC1 00 PP

17
1891   Nash, Rev. B. W.
Baptist harmony, a new collection of hymns and
spiritual songs.   La Grange, N. C., author, 1876.
3 p.l., 312 p.   24°.

NN   0024132   DLC

Nash, Rev. B.W.
245.206
N248B   Baptist harmony; a collection of hymns
and spiritual songs ... 2d ed.   Goldsboro,
N. C., Baptist Review Job Office, 1884.
312 p.   12 cm.

1. Baptists.   Hymns.   2. Hymns, English.
I. Title

NN   0024133   Nc)

Nash, Beau.
See
Nash, Richard, 1674–1762.

Nash, Ben.
Developing marketable products and their packagings, by
Ben Nash ...   1st ed.   New York and London, McGraw-Hill
book company, inc., 1945.
xii, 404 p. incl. illus. (incl. facsims.) forms, diagrs. (1 col.) fold.
col. pl. 23*.
Bibliography: p. 385–387.

1. Marketing.   I. Title.
45–0207
Library of Congress *   HF5415.N23
[10]   658.8

ODW MB ICJ PP CaBVaU IdPI IdU OrCS OrU Wa WaS
NN   0024135   DLC DAU CoU CaBVa NcGU NcC NcD CU OC1

Nash, Ben.
The manufacturer and the development of the design project, by Ben Nash ...   New York, National
alliance of art and industry, inc. [c1932]
[17] p.   18 cm.   (National alliance of art and
industry. Monograph no, 2)

1. Advertising, Art in.   I. Title: Design project.

NN   0024136   NNC

Nash, Ben.
An outline of package requirements.   4099.09-101
—   New York. [1931.] 11 pp. [Industrial Institute of the Art Center,
New York. Talk no. 1.] 23 cm.

D649 — S.r. — Packages.

NN   0024137   MB NN

VOLUME 405

Nash, Ben.
American management association.
Profitable packaging, by Ben Nash ... Katharine Fisher ...
Arthur S. Allen ₍and others₎ ... New York, N. Y., American
management association, ᶜ1932.

*K
.M48875 Nash, Benjamin H   , 1833–
v.1
no.8   Seaboard & Roanoke Railroad Co., vs.
            Joyner's administrator. Note of argument
            of counsel for appellee. ₍Richmond? 189–?₎
            16 p. 23cm. ₍Miscellaneous law briefs₎
            Caption title.
            "In the Supreme Court of Appeals of Virginia."

            1. Railroads—Va. I. Seaboard & Roanoke Rail-
            road Co., appellee. II. Joyner's (Sinclair)
            administrator, appellant. III. Virginia.
            Supreme Court of Appeals.

NN   0024139   ViU

Nash, Bennett H.
Notice of George Perkins Marsh, by Bennett H.
Nash and Francis P. Nash.   Cambridge,
J. Wilson, 1883.
p. [447]–457. 24 cm.
From Proceedings of the American Academy of
Arts and Sciences, Vol. XVIII. p. 447."
1. Marsh, George Perkins, 1801–1882.
I. Nash, Francis P.

NN   0024140   MdBP

[NASH, Bennett Hubbard.]
Prose scelte. [Camb., 1871?]

pp. 92.

NN   0024141   MH

PS635
.Z9N2   Nash, Mrs. Bernard F.
         Honesty is the best policy; a play...
         Des Moines, Ia.[c1936].
         16 p.   18 1/2 cm.

NN   0024142   DLC

Nash, Bert, 1895–
Hot Springs national park, the valley of vapors. Illustrated
by Walter McDonald. Texarkana ₍1947₎
48 p. illus. 20ᶜᵐ.

1. Hot Springs national park.
F419.H8N3   917.67411   47–21358
                                       Brief cataloging

NN   0024143   DLC

Nash, Bert, 1895–
My Texas, 'tis of thee; a collection of facts, fun and figures
by Bert Nash, illustrated by the author. Texarkana, Tex.,
Hussman-Nash ₍1946₎
48 p. illus. 19½ᶜᵐ.

1. Texas. I. Title.
F387.N3   917.64   47–3769

NN   0024144   DLC

Nash, Bert Allen, 1898–
Mental hygiene and education ₍by₎ Bert A. Nash.
(*In* National education association of the United States. Addresses
and proceedings, 1935. p. 492–493)

1. Mental physiology and hygiene. I. Title.
                                            E 36–388
U. S. Off. of educ. Library   L13.N212 1935
for Library of Congress   [L13.N4 1935]

NN   0024145   DHEW DLC

Nash, Bert Allen, 1898–   joint author.

Kansas. *Legislative council. Research dept.*
Receiving home for children. Dependent, neglected, delinquent, and defective children as institutional problems; possible receiving home for diagnosis, preliminary treatment, and
placement; experience of other states. Prepared jointly for
Legislative council Committee on public welfare and Governor's advisory committee on children's institutions ... ₍Topeka₎
Research dept., Kansas Legislative council ₍1942₎

Nash, Bert Allen, 1898–
A statistical study of the development
of standardized tests during the past twenty
years ... by Bert Allen Nash ...
[Columbus] The Ohio state university, 1928.
6 p.

NN   0024147   OU

Nash, Bert Allen, 1898–
A statistical study of the development of standardized tests
during the past twenty years ... by Bert Allen Nash ...
₍Columbus, O., H. L. Hedrick₎ 1932.
14 p. 24ᵐᵐ.

Abstract of thesis (PH. D.)—Ohio state university, 1928.
Biography.
Mimeographed.

1. Mental tests.

Library of Congress   BF431.N35 1928   32–4099
Ohio State Univ. Libr.
———— Copy 2.   ₍2₎   [151.2] 371.26

NN   0024148   OU DLC

PR2297   Nash, Berta (Sturman) 1917–
f.L8839   Renaissance prompt copies: A looking glasse
            for London and England. 1947.
            95 l.

            Typewritten.
            Thesis—Univ. of Chicago.

            1. Lodge, Thomas, 1558?–1625. A looking glass
            for London and England.

NN   0024149   ICU

[Nash, Berta (Sturman)] 1917–
The second quarto of A king and no king, 1625.
(*In* Virginia. University. Bibliographical Society. Studies in
bibliography. Charlottesville. 26cm. v.4 (1951–52) p.166–170)
Signed: Berta Sturman.
Bibliographical footnotes.

1. Beaumont, Francis, 1584–1616. A king and no king. 2. Fletcher,
John, 1579–1625, joint author. A king and no king.

NN   0024150   ViU WaSpG

Nash, Bradley De Lamater, 1900–
A hook in Leviathan; a critical interpretation of the
Hoover Commission report, by Bradley D. Nash and Cor-
nelius Lynde. With an introd. by Arthur Krock. New
York, Macmillan, 1950.
xix, 284 p. diagrs. 22 cm.

1. U. S. Commission on Organization of the Executive Branch
of the Government. 2. U. S.—Executive departments. I. Lynde,
Cornelius, joint author. II. Title.

JK643.C47A588   353   50–6744

          Wa WaS WaU–L WaT
          IdPI WaSpG OU ODW CaBViP CaBVaU MtU OrP Or OrU
          MiU PP PPGi PPT OCl CoU PSt OU IdU IaU NcRS OrPS
NN   0024151   DLC ICU LU NcGU ViU NcU MB TxU NNUN

Nash, Bradley De Lamater, 1900–
Investment banking in England, by Bradley D. Nash ...
Chicago & New York, A. W. Shaw company; ₍etc., etc.₎ 1924.
x, 114 p. diagrs. 21½ᶜᵐ.

"Prize monograph, Chicago trust company prizes for research relating to business development and the modern trust company (1924
award—first prize)"
Bibliography: p. 107–108.

1. Banks and banking—Gt. Brit. 2. Investments—Gt. Brit. I. Chicago trust company. II. Title.
                                            24–22559 Revised
Library of Congress   HG2992.N3

     PPT OCl ICJ NN ODW OCU OrU WaU–L WaTC WaS CaBVaU
NN   0024152   DLC MtU CoU FMU NcD NcRS ICRL CU TU

Nash, Bradley De Lamater, 1900–
Staffing the Presidency, prepared for the National Planning Association. ₍Washington₎ 1952.
xiii, 78 p. diagr. 20 cm. (Planning pamphlets, no. 80)

1. U. S. Executive Office of the Presidency. I. Title.
(Series)
HC101.N352 no. 80   353   53–9

     ViU NIC TxU LU FTaSU MH–L CaBVaU OrCS OrPR MtU WaS
NN   0024153   DLC MiU AAP NN PSC PPT PSt MH–BA NcD

Nash, C. W.
Narrative of Hatch's battalion of
cavalry. n.p. n.d.
pp.594–611.

Palmer coll.
Reg't. histories.
Minnesota.

NN   0024154   OClWHi

Nash, Carroll Blue, 1914–
Effects of starvation and thirst on the chemical composition
of rats of various ages, by Carroll Blue Nash ... ₍College
Park, Md.₎ 1939.
1 p. l., iii, 35 (f. e. 36) numb. l., 1 l. incl. tables, diagrs. 29 x 24½ᶜᵐ.
Thesis (PH. D.)—University of Maryland, 1939.
Type-written (carbon copy)
"Literature cited": leaf at end.

1. Rats. 2. Starvation. 3. Thirst.
Library of Congress   QP88.N3   43–31898

NN   0024155   DLC

Byzh   Nash, Charles.
76   The Goodrich-court guide ... a new enl. & rev.
         ed.: with three illustrations from sketches taken
         by the late Sir Samuel Meyrick ... Hereford,
         Printed by E.Weymss,1867.
         42p. front.,plates. 18cm.

NN   0024156   CtY

Nash, Charles Barnes, 1815–1892, ed.

History of the war in Affghanistan, from its commencement to its close; including a general sketch of the
policy, and the various circumstances which induced the
British government to interfere in the affairs of Affghanistan. From the journal and letters of an officer high in
rank, and who has served many years in the Indian army.
Edited by Charles Nash, esq., with an introductory description of the country, and its political state previous to
the war. London, T. Brooks, 1843.

SPECIAL COLLECTIONS
SELIGMAN
1844E   ₍Nash, Charles Barnes, 1815–1892.
N17   Railway and land taxation, shewing the origin,
         progress, law, operation, and statistics, of the
         poor and other rates, and their injustice and
         impolicy with reference railways, with a digest
         of all the legal decisions, and a glance at the
         local rates and general taxation of railways and
         land. By the author of "Indian letters," "Legal
         and genealogical researches," "Contributions to
         daily and other literature", &c. &c. London,
         Brown's Library, 1844.
         21 p. 24cm.

NN   0024158   NNC MH–BA IU

VOLUME 405

⌈Nash, Charles Barnes, 1815-1892.
The railway robberies ... London ⌈W.Lake,
printer⌉ 1846.
21 p. 17 cm.

"From the Railway record."

NN 0024159 MH-BA

⌈Nash, Charles Barnes, 1815-1892.
Railways and shareholders; with glances at
railway transactions - shareholders' powers -
accounts and audits - railway meetings - defective legislation - &c. &c. By an Edinbro'
reviewer ... London, P.Richardson ⌈etc.⌉
1849.
20 p. 20.5 cm.

NN 0024160 MH-BA

Nash, Charles Edgar.
The lure of Long Beach, by Charles Edgar Nash; being a
detailed account of the traditions, history and growth of a
grand little island off the New Jersey coast; with a foreword
by the Hon. Walter E. Edge ... ⌈Long Beach, N. J.⌉ The Long
Beach board of trade, 1936.
4 p. l., 170 p. plates (1 col.) ports. 22½ᶜᵐ.

1. Long Beach, N. J. I. Title.

Library of Congress   F142.O2N3   36-16897
————— Copy 2.
Copyright A 96597   ⌈3⌉   974.948

NN 0024161 DLC FMU FU NIC PHC PP

Nash, Charles Edgar.
The magic of Miami Beach, by Charles Edgar Nash. A
detailed account of the traditions, history and phenomenal
growth of a wonder city built with the touch of Aladdin upon
the sands of the semi-tropical lower east coast of Florida.
Philadelphia, David McKay company ⌈*1938⌉
4 p. l., 143 p. illus., plates, ports. 25¼ᶜᵐ.

"First edition."

1. Miami Beach, Fla.—Descr. 2. Miami Beach, Fla.—Descr.—Views.
3. Miami Beach, Fla.—Hist. I. Title.

Library of Congress   F319.M6N3   38-18743
————— Copy 2.
Copyright A 119818   ⌈5⌉   917.5938

NN 0024162 DLC NcD ViU OCl OEac OLak

Nash, Charles Edgar.
Trailer ahoy! By Charles Edgar Nash ... Lancaster, Pa.,
Intelligencer printing company, 1937.
6 p. l., ⌈15⌉–261 p. incl. illus., plates, ports. 22ᶜᵐ.

"An Intell pictorial."

1. Automobiles—Trailers. 2. U. S.—Descr. & trav.—Views. I. Title.
                                                        37-20410
Library of Congress   TL297.N3
————— Copy 2.
Copyright A 103123   ⌈5-3⌉   629.2262

NN 0024163 DLC MB NIC Or NN PU PHC OU

Nash, Charles Edward.
Biographical sketches of Gen. Pat Cleburne and Gen.
T. C. Hindman; together with humorous anecdotes and
reminiscences of the late civil war. By Charles Edward
Nash ... Little Rock, Ark., Tunnah & Pittard, printers,
1898.
300 p. front., illus. 19¾ᵐ.
"Malthus' theory": p. ⌈289⌉–300.

1. Arkansas—Hist.—Civil war. 2. Cleburne, Patrick Ronayne, 1828–
1864. 3. Hindman, Thomas Carmichael, 1818–1868.
                                                        98–1609
Library of Congress   E496.N24

NN 0024164 DLC OkU MWA ArU CaBVaU NcD OClWHi

Nash, Charles Edward.
"Bottom rail on top;" or, Thirty years ago. By Dr. C. E.
Nash... Little Rock, Arkansas Democrat Co. ⌈189–?⌉ 16 p.
16°.

Cover-title.

1. United States.—History : Civil   war : Personalia. 2. Title.
N. Y. P. L.   July 13, 1924

NN 0024165 NN

NASH, C⌈harles⌉ E⌈dward⌉.
Granny's grave; laughter in tears and tears
in laughter. Little Rock, [Ark], Thompson
litho. and ptg.co., [19-?].

pp. 28.

NN 0024166 MH

Nash, Charles Edward.
Historical and humorous sketches of the donkey, horse and
bicycle. The bicycle viewed from four standpoints: anatomical, phisiological ⌈!⌉, sociological, and financially. Also an al-
legory on the bicycle road to hell ... By Dr. C. E. Nash ...
Little Rock, Ark., Press of Tunnah & Pittard, 1896.
246 p., 1 l. illus. 19½ᵐ.

1. Cycling. I. Title.
                                                        7–25797
Library of Congress   PZ3.N171H

NN 0024167 DLC ArU MiU DSI

Nash, Charles Edward.
813.08   Southern stories, by C. E. Nash. 2d ed.
B264s   ⌈Little Rock, Ark., 1900?⌉
        28, 28, 30, 32 p. illus. 18 cm.
        Cover title.
        Contents.–A wild boar chase.–Common sense
on saloons; extracts from Hon. Peter Sterling.–
Granny's grave.–Eight hours in the fresh water
deep.–The status of the Negro.–A thrilling
tragedy.–Anniversary of my seventy-sixth
birthday.
        1. Short   stories, American.
Southern states.   I. Title.

NN 0024168 NcD

Nash, Charles Edward.
The status of the Negro, from a Negro's standpoint, in his
own dialect. A thrilling tragedy in the days of reconstruction. Anniversary of my seventy-sixth birthday. Read before the Little Rock medical society. ⌈By⌉ Dr. Charles E.
Nash ... Little Rock, Ark., Press of Tunnah & Pittard, 1900.
32 p. illus. 18½ᵐ.

1. Negroes. 2. Crime and criminals—Arkansas. I. Title. II. Title:
The Negro, Status of.
                                                        0–2550 Revised
Library of Congress   E185.6.N24

NN 0024169 DLC CtY

Nash, Charles Edward.
A wild boar chase, for men and boys.
Little Rock, The author, n. d.
28 p.
The sketches of Cleburne and Himdman are
concerned mostly with their private lives.
"Historical and humorous sketches" is an attack
on the bicycle, partly in the form of a dialogue
between the devil and a cyclist.

NN 0024170 ArU

Nash, Charles Ellwood.
The business before us. By Rev. C.
Ellwood Nash, An address delivered before
the General conference of the Universalist
church at Rochester, N.Y., October 22,1890.
Akron,Ohio, G.C.Jackson,printer, n.d.
23 p.

NN 0024171 OClWHi

Nash, Charles Elventon.
The history of Augusta; first settlements and early days
as a town, including the diary of Mrs. Martha Moore Ballard, 1785 to 1812. Augusta, Me., Charles E. Nash & Son,
1904 ⌈i. e. 1961⌉
vii, 612 p. port. 25 cm.

Signatures printed in 1904, first published in 1961.
"Mrs. Ballard's diary": p. ⌈229⌉–~~171~~464 ⌈⌉

1. Augusta, Me.—Hist. I. Ballard, Martha Moore, 1785–1812.

F29.A9N3   974.16   62–27118

NN 0024172 DLC MiU NN

Nash, Charles Elventon.
In memory of William Berry Lapham,
Born August 21, 1828. Died February 22,
1894. Portland, Brown Thurston co. 1894.
15 p.

NN 0024173 OClWHi

E78
.M2N3   **Nash, Charles Elventon.**
            The Indians of the Kennebec. New
            York, H. W. Blake, 1892.
            65 p. illus., facsims. 28 cm.
            "126 copies reprinted from The
            history of Kennebec County, Maine."
            Bibliographical footnotes.

            1. Abnaki Indians. 2. Indians of
            North America—Maine. I. Title.

NN 0024174 MB NN

Nash, Charles Elventon.
William Berry Lapham ... Read before the ... society,
May 3, 1894.
(*In* Collections and proceedings of the Maine historical society. Port-
land, 1894. 23½ᶜᵐ. 2d ser., v. 5, p. 337–344. port.)

1. Lapham, William Berry, 1828–1894.
                                                        A 15–1167
Title from Bangor Pub.   Libr. Library of Congress F16.M33

NN 0024175 MeBa

Nash, Charles Elwood.
A genealogy of the descendants of Thomas Wildman, 1613–
1689, of Bedford, N. Y. (formerly a township under Connecticut jurisdiction) with an account of the ancient Wildman family
in England, 1085–1634 A. D. Compiled by Charles Elwood
Nash. Southington, Conn., C. E. Nash & co., 1946–
pts. geneal. tab. 23ᵐ.
Bibliographical foot-notes.

1. Wildman family (Thomas Wildman, 1613–1689)
                                                        46–6719
Library of Congress   CS71.W673 1946

NN 0024176 DLC

Nash, Charles Ellwood, 1855–1932.
... The Saviour of the world. By Charles Ellwood Nash ...
Boston, Universalist publishing house, 1895.
3 p. l., ⌈5⌉–105 p. 17ᵐ. (*Added t.-p.:* Manuals of faith and duty, ed. by
J. S. Cantwell. no. VII)
Series in part at head of t.-p.

1. Redemption. I. Title.
                                                        38–33139
Library of Congress   BT775.N3

NN 0024177 DLC MH-AH

VOLUME 405

E78
.T3L4

Nash, Charles H.

Lewis, Thomas McDowell Nelson, 1896–
Hiwassee island, an archaeological account of four Tennessee Indian peoples, by Thomas M. N. Lewis and Madeline Kneberg, partially based on field reports by Charles H. Nash. Knoxville, Tenn., The University of Tennessee press, 1946.

Nash, Charles Patterson, 1897–   comp.

Virginia. *Laws, statutes, etc.*
The Code of Virginia (pleading and practice) An abridgment of the Virginia Code of 1936 for the student of Virginia pleading and practice, selected by Charles P. Nash, jr. ... Charlottesville, Va., The Michie company, 1936.

Nash, Charles Patterson, 1897–   ed.

American law institute.
Virginia annotations to the Restatement of the law of conflict of laws, as adopted and promulgated by the American law institute, prepared by Gordon Lewis and Richard Burwell Persinger, under the supervision of Charles Patterson Nash ... under the auspices of the Virginia bar association. St. Paul, Minn., American law institute publishers, 1940.

Nash, Charles R
The effect of class size upon pupil achievement in written composition in three low ability groups inthe Frankford high school, Phila., Penn. 1937.
92 p

NN 0024181   PPT

Nash, Charles R
The history of legislative and administrative changes affecting the Philadelphia public schools (1869-1921), by Charles R.Nash. ₍Philadelphia₎Teachers college,Temple university, 1943.
ix,169p. tables. 23cm.

Thesis(Ed.D.) - Teachers college, Temple university, 1943.
"Bibliography": p.155-169.

NN 0024182   PSt PPPL NN

Nash, Charles R
The history of legislative and administrative changes affecting the Philadelphia public schools, 1869-1921. ₍Philadelphia?₎ 1946₎
ix, 169 p. 23 cm.

Thesis—Temple University.
Bibliography: p. 155-169.

1. Philadelphia—Public schools.

LA357.P5N3   379.748   50-3693

NN 0024183   DLC InU CU OrU PPT OU NNU-W PP NcD

Nash, Charles Sumner, 1856-1926.
Association and council as factors in Congregationalism; a paper read before the Congregationalist ministers of San Francisco and vicinity by Charles Sumner Nash... ₍San Francisco: The Murdock press, 1903₎ 18 p. 19½cm. (Pacific theological seminary. Publications. no. 4.)

1. Congregational Churches—school of religion, Berkeley, Cal.   Govt. and discipline. I. Pacific
N.Y.P.L.   December 23, 1937

NN 0024184   NN CU-B CtY-D OO

Nash, Charles Sumner, 1856-1926.
Congregational administration; the Carew lectures before the Hartford theological seminary 1908-1909, by Charles Sumner Nash ... Boston, New York ₍etc.₎ The Pilgrim press, 1909.
5 p. l., 3-179 p. 19cm. $0.75

10-3020

NN 0024185   DLC PPEB MWA PPPD OO WHi

BT
175
N3   Nash, Charles Sumner, 1856-1926.
Our changed conception of God. ₍Lincoln, Pantagraph printery₎ 1915.
15 p. 16 cm.

1. God - Addresses, essays, lectures.
I. Title.

NN 0024186   NRCR

Nash, Charles Sumner, 1856-1926.
Our widening thought of God ... By Charles Sumner Nash ... San Francisco, P. Elder and company ₍*1914₎
v, 20 p., 1 l. 20cm $0.25

I. Title.

15-533

NN 0024187   DLC CU-B

Nash, Charles Sumner, 1856-1926, ed.

Religious progress on the Pacific slope; addresses and papers at the celebration of the semi-centennial anniversary of Pacific school of religion, Berkeley, California. Boston, Chicago, The Pilgrim press ₍*1917₎

Nash, Charles William, 1848-1926.
The birds of Ontario in relation to agriculture
see under Ontario. Dept. of Agriculture.

Nash, Charles William, 1848–
Check list of the birds of Ontario and catalogue of birds in the biological section of the museum
see under Ontario. Education Dept.

Nash, Charles William, 1848-1926.
Check list of the vertebrates of Ontario and catalogue of specumens in the biological section of the Provincial Museum
see under Ontario. Education Dept.

Nash, Charles William, 1848-1926.
Vertebrates of Ontario ...
see under Ontario. Education Dept.

NASH,Charlotte Gregory.
The moon and the crow. [Hanover? 1938].

33 x 25 cm. p.(1). 1 colored plate.
"This poem was composed on March 15,1938 while the author painted the accompanying picture. Grig's friends have printed it for her birthday guests at Hanover,April 21,1938."
With author's autograph dedication.
In original red wrappers.

NN 0024193   MH

Nash, Chauncey Cushing.
John Warner Barber and his books, by Chauncey Cushing Nash. Milton, Mass., 1934. 35 p. facsim., plates, 2 ports. (incl. front.) 24cm.

"Twenty-five copies reprinted from the Note book of the Walpole Society, 1934."
Bibliography of books "written for the most part by John Warner Barber," p. 18-33; "Books illustrated by Barber," p. 34-35.

778743A. 1. Barber, John Warner,   1798-1885. 2. Barber, John Warner,
1798-1885.—Bibl.
N. Y. P. L.   November 8, 1935

NN 0024194   NN NNC MH CtY

368.3
N171   Nash, Chester C
The contribution of life insurance to social security in the United States. Geneva, International Labour Office, 1955.
19p. tables. 26cm.

Cover title.
Reprinted from the International labour review, v.72, no.1.

1. Insurance, Life. I. Title.

NN 0024195   OrU

LD
3907
.G7
1970
.N3
also
Film
T6557   Nash, Christopher, 1936–
A modern bestiary; representative animal motifs in the encounter between nature and culture in the English, American, French and Italian novel, 1900-1950.
370p.
Thesis (Ph.D.) - N.Y.U., Graduate School.

1. Dissertations, Academic - N.Y.U. - 1970.
2. Animals in literature. I. Title.

NN 0024196   NNU

Nash, Clara *i. e.* Clarissa Hosmer (Hapgood) 1839–
Verses, by Clara Hapgood Nash, selections from poems published from time to time in various periodicals. Cambridge ₍The University press₎ 1909.
viii p., 1 l., 98 p. front. (port.) 22cm.

9-27413

NN 0024197   DLC

Nash, Clarence Ward.
Alfalfa in Maryland. ₍College Park, 1907₎ 291-314 p. illus. 8°. (Maryland. Agricultural experiment station. Bulletin 118.)

1. Alfalfa, U. S.: Maryland.
N. Y. P. L.   June 14, 1911.

NN 0024198   NN MBH PP

Nash, Clarence Ward.
Corn. Variety tests, seed breeding, selection and testing. ₍Baltimore: Thomas & Evans Prtg. Co., 1910₎ (1)104-134 p. illus. 8°. (Maryland. Agricultural experiment station. Bulletin. 141.)

1. Corn.
N. Y. P. L.   February 23, 1911.

NN 0024199   NN

Nash, Mrs. Clarissa Hosmer (Hapgood)
see Nash, Clara Hosmer (Hapgood)
1839–

Nash, Claude Witten.
An analysis of the educational opportunities offered by the colleges and universities, separate professional and technical schools, and teacher training institutions in Pennsylvania, Maryland,New Jersey,Delaware, and the District of Columbia ... by Claude Witten Nash ... [Columbus] The Ohio state university, 1934.
3 p.

NN 0024201   OU

VOLUME 405

Nash, Cleve Crumby, 1912–
 The input impedance of a rectangular aperture antenna.
Ann Arbor, University Microfilms, 1949 ₁i. e. 1950₎

(₁University Microfilms, Ann Arbor, Mich.₎ Publication no. 1556)

Microfilm copy of typewritten ms. Positive.
Collation of the original: iii, 51 l. diagrs.
Thesis—University of Illinois.
Abstracted in Microfilm abstracts, v. 10 (1950) no. 1, p. 71–72.
Vita.
Bibliography: leaf 51.

1. Radio—Antennas. 2. Impedance (Electricity)
Microfilm AC-1 no. 1556   Mic A 50-30

Michigan. Univ. Libr.
fo. Library of Congress   ₍2₎†

NN 0024202   MiU DLC IU

Nash, Clifford Harris.
 Christ interpreted: Paul's letter to Romans ...
see under   Bible. N. T. Romans. English. 1954. Nash.

QL795
.D6N3   **Nash, Cyril,** 1886–
 Yours faithfully; the autobiography of a
schnauzer. Illus. by John Nicolson. London,
New York, Toronto, Longmans, Green [1938]
 xii, 180 p. illus. 19 1/2cm.

1. Dogs—Legends and stories.   I. Title.

NN 0024204   MB

Nash, D. H., joint author.

Bataille, Louis.
 ... Le langage maritime commercial en français et en anglais.
Nautical and commercial conversation in French and in English ₁par₎ Louis Bataille ... ₁et₎ D. H. Nash ... 3. ed. rev. et
augm. Paris, Société d'éditions géographiques, maritimes et
coloniales, 1929.

PS593   **Nash, Dan.**
.L9   ... Ireland and American songster ....
N14   N.Y., c1880.

NN 0024206   DLC RPB PP

PR   **Nash, Daniel.**
6027   My son is in the mountains, a novel.
A81M9   London, J. Cape ₁1955₎
 222 p. 20cm.

NN 0024207   NIC PU MH NN

A
974.77   **Nash, Daniel,** 1763–1836.
qN248   Baptismal records of Father Daniel
Nash in central New York State, 1797-
1827. Being a copy of the "Record of
births, baptisms and marriages" performed by Rev. Daniel Nash. "Baptisms
&c. 1797-1827" filed at Fenimore House,
Cooperstown, New York. Copied, typed,
and indexed by Mrs. Gertrude H. Smith.
Sherburne, N.Y., 1955.
 ₍19₎, 45, ₍13₎, 21 l. port. 29 cm.

Includes "Father Daniel Nash" from
"The story of Cooperstown, N.Y.," by R.
Birdsall, and "The Father Daniel Nash, A.
B." from "Descendants of Thomas Nash," by
S. Nash.

1. Registers of births, etc. New York
(State) H1. New   York (State) 2.
Registers of   births, etc.
Chenango County, N.Y.

NN 0024209   NN

Nash, David William, 1809 or 10–1876.
 XIV. - On the Gaulish inscriptions. Read
May 3rd, 1865.   [London, 1865]
 p. 326–360. 8°.
 n. t. p.
 Fragment of Jour. of Royal Soc. of Literature,
London, 1865? v. 8, p. 326–360.

NN 0024210   NN

PR1119   **Nash, David William,** 1809 or 10–1876.
.A2
no. 10 a Merlin.   FOR OTHER EDITIONS
                         SEE MAIN ENTRY
 ... Merlin; or, The early history of King Arthur: a prose
romance (about 1450–1460 A. D.) edited from the unique ms.
in the University library, Cambridge, by Henry B. Wheatley.
With an introduction by D. W. Nash, esq., F. S. A. ... (2d ed.,
rev., 1875) London, Pub. for the Early English text society,
by N. Trübner & co., 1865 (i. e. 1875)–

Nash, David William, 1809 or 10–1876.
 Merlin the enchanter and Merlin the bard.
[In Early English text society. Publications.
Original series, no. 10. London, 1865]

40

NN 0024212   DLC MdBP

Nash, David William, 1809 or 10–1876.   *4608.10.1
 Merlin the enchanter and Merlin the bard.
(In Merlin. Merlin, or the early history of King Arthur. Pp. i*–
xvi*. London. 1899.)

NN 0024213   MB

Nash, David William, 1809 or 10–1876.
 On the antiquity of the Egyptian calendar.
By D.W. Nash ... Read before the Syro-Egyptian
society of London, December 11, 1849 ... [no
imprint]
 1 p.l., [29]–57 p. fold. facsim. 21.5 cm.

NN 0024214   MiU

NASH, David William, 1809 or 10–1876.
 On the antiquity of the Egyptian calendar. Plate.
 (*In* Syro-Egyptian society. Original papers. Vol. 1,
pp. 27–57. London, 1850.)

NN 0024215   MB

Nash, David William, 1809 *or* 10–1876.
 The Pharaoh of the exodus. An examination of the
modern systems of Egyptian chronology. By D. W.
Nash ... London, J. R. Smith, 1863.
 viii, 319 p. front. 23ᵐᵐ.

1. Chronology, Egyptian.   1. Title.

                                     22-5656
Library of Congress   CE29.N3

NN 0024216   DLC CaBViP MdBP NcD PPAmP NBB NcU

Nash, David William, 1809 *or* 10–1876.
 Taliesin; or, The bards and druids of Britain. A translation of the remains of the earliest Welsh bards, and an
examination of the bardic mysteries. By D. W. Nash ...
London, J. R. Smith, 1858.
 xii, 344 p. 22ᵐᵐ.
 The translations are accompanied by "the originals as they are found in
the Myvyrian archæology". *cf.* Pref.
 1. Welsh poetry—Hist. & crit. 2. Welsh poetry—Translations into English. 3. English poetry—Translations from Welsh. 4. Bards and bardism.
5. Druids and druidism. 6. Taliesin.

                                     20-4861
Library of Congress   PR8920.N3

NcU PPDrop
NN 0024217   DLC CU OC1 MiU IU MB OOxM CtY PHi MdBP

Nash, Denis Frederic Ellison.
 The principles and practice of surgical nursing. London,
E. Arnold ₁1955₎
 vii, 1007 p. illus. 22 cm.

1. Surgical nursing.
                                     A 57-5723
Wayne Univ. Library
for Library of Congress   ₍2₎

CaBVaU
NN 0024218   MiDW NcU-H MoSU OC1W DNLM NBC N OrU-M

Nash, Dennison J.
 The American composer; a study in social-
psychology. [Philadelphia] 1954.
 xiii, 235 numb. l. tables. 29 cm.
 Thesis (Ph. D.) - University of Pennsylvania,
1954.
 Typewritten.
 Bibliography: l. i-vii.

NN 0024219   PU

Nash, Dennison.
 The American composer: a study in social-psychology.
Ann Arbor, University Microfilms ₁1954₎
 (₁University Microfilms, Ann Arbor, Mich.₎ Publication no. 7807)
 Microfilm copy (positive) of typescript.
 Collation of the original, as determined from the film: xiii, 235 l.
tables.
 Thesis—University of Pennsylvania.
 Abstracted in Dissertation abstracts, v. 14 (1954) no. 5, p. 879–
880.
 Bibliography : leaves i-vii.
 1. Music—Psychology. 2. Music—U. S.   I. Title.
Microfilm AC-1 no. 7807   Mic 58-6726

NN 0024220   DLC NN MiDW

796.02   **Nash, Dick.**
N248s   Sports chronicle; a tabulation of
1946   University of Southern California major
sports results from January 1, 1922 to
July 1, 1946 [by Dick Nash and Dean B.
Cromwell] 2d ed. [Los Angeles, 1946]
 32p. tables. 19cm.

1.University of Southern California -
Athletics. I.Cromwell, Dean B., joint
author. II.   Title.

NN 0024221   CLSU

Nash, Mrs. Donna (MacLachlan) 1878–   comp.

Michigan. *Century of progress commission.*
 Report of the Michigan Century of progress commission on
the Michigan exhibit, a Century of progress exposition, Chicago, 1933. Compiled by Mrs. Donna M. Nash. ₁Chicago,
1933₎

Nash, Doris Louise

Chapuzet, M   L.
 Mes premiers pas en français, por M. L. Chapuzet ... y W. M.
Daniels ... Ed. francesa-española por Doris L. Nash ... Bos-
ton, Nueva York ₁etc.₎ D. C. Heath y compañía ₁ᶜ1918₎

Nash, Dorothy.
 Family records from 48 Bibles copied in
a prize contest. These records presented to
the Ohio society Daughters of the American
Revolution...[Mariemont,O., 1935-36.]
 4p.l., 137,39 p.

 "Presented by Mrs. George Eggleston Malone,
state director, Children of the American
Revolution in Ohio 1930-1937"
 Typescript

NN 0024224   OC1WHi

VOLUME 405

Nash, E   Gee
    see   Nash, Elizabeth Gee.

Nash, Edgar Smiley, 1872–
    George William Curtis. [Manuscript]
[Providence, 1894]
    [10 f.]   sq. O.
    Commencement oration, 1894.

NN   0024226   RPB

Nash, Edgar Smiley, 1872–
Boy scouts of America. *Delaware and Montgomery
counties federated councils.*
    Year book.
    Philadelphia, Pa.

Nash, Edmund.
    Government controls of dried fruits during
World war I, prepared in the Historical price
research section, by Edmund Nash. [Washing-
ton] 1941.
    [a]–d, 16 p.

    Bibliography: p. 16.

NN   0024228   NNC DFT MB MH-BA

[Nash, Edmund]
    ... Labor conditions in Poland ... [Washington, U. S. Govt.
print. off., 1944]
    20 p. 23ᶜᵐ. ([U. S. Bureau of labor statistics] Serial no. R. 1671)
    "Prepared by Edmund Nash."–p. 1.
    "From the Monthly labor review (July 1944) of the Bureau of labor
statistics, United States Department of labor."

    1. Labor [and laboring classes,—Poland. 2. Insurance, State and
compulsory—Poland.   I. Title.
                                 L 44–182
    U. S. Dept. of labor. Libr.
    for Library of Congress   [2]

NN   0024229   DL

HD8526
.U5
1955

Nash, Edmund.
    U. S. *Bureau of Labor Statistics.*
    Labor conditions in the Soviet Union, selected studies [by
Edmund Nash. Rev. and enl. ed. Washington] 1955.

Nash, Edmund, joint author.
    Purchasing power of Soviet workers, 1954

    see under

    U.S. Bureau of Labor Statistics.

Nash, Edmund.   *9385.973A408
    Transportation, freight rates, and marine war
risk insurance, 1914–1920; prepared in the Historical Price Research Section. [Washington]
1941.
    36 p. 27cm. (U. S. Bureau of Labor Sta-
tistics. [Historical price survey])
    "Sources referred to by notes": p. [37]
    1. European War, 1914–1918—Economic aspects—
U. S. 2. Railroads—U. S. 3. Shipping—U. S.
I. Title. II. Series.

NN   0024232   MB NNC DFT

Nash, Edmund Strudwick, et al., *petitioners.*
    (United States, *respondent*)
    Action brought under the Sherman antitrust law of
1890.
    Briefs and other records in this case, 1912–
    not separately listed or cataloged are to be found on shelf:
    HD2780.N3N3

    1. Trusts, Industrial—Law. 2. Naval stores. I. American naval stores
co., petitioner. II. National transportation & terminal co., petitioner. III.
United States, respondent.

                                    CA 16–292 Unrev'd
    Library of Congress   HD2780.N3N3

NN   0024233   DLC

Nash, Edmund Strudwick.
    An open letter to Senator Jas. P. Taliaferro [of
Florida] [Savannah, Ga., 1909]
    13 p. 8vo.
    Signed, "E. S. Nash, President American Naval
Stores Company, Savannah, March 22, 1909."
    Covers included.
    Note: Relates to the controversy connecred with
the Federal prosecution of the so-called Turpentine
and Naval Stores Trust under the Anti-Trust laws.

NN   0024234   GU-De

Nash, Edward, 1851–
    Jackson's strategy; a lecture delivered by Captain
E. Nash, late R. A. ... October 21, 1904 ... London, Ke-
gan Paul, Trench, Trübner & co., ltd., 1904.
    32 p. 18½ᶜᵐ.

    1. Jackson, Thomas Jonathan (Stonewall) 1824–1863. 2. Strategy.
                                     War 8–171
    Library, Military   Information Division

NN   0024235   DNW ICJ

Nash, Edward, 1851–
    The principles of strategy, by Captain Edward Nash
... London, K. Paul, Trench, Trübner & co., ltd., 1905.
    viii p., 1 l., 93 p. 10 maps. 17ᶜᵐ. (Military handbooks for officers and
non-commissioned officers. vol. xv)

    1. Strategy.
                                      War 10–57
    Library, Second Section,   General Staff U163.N24

NN   0024236   DNLM DN NjP ICJ NN DNW

Nash, Edward Barrington.
    Robert Burns; an address upon the portraiture of the
poet delivered in the Royal Glasgow institute of the fine
arts, 29th September 1896, by Edward Barrington Nash
... Andrew J. Kirkpatrick, esq. in the chair. Paisley,
A. Gardner, 1896.
    36 p. 22 x 17½ᶜᵐ.

                                    7–30233
NN   0024237   DLC

Nash, Edward Barrington.
    The Raeburn-Burns controversy; visualizing
the obvious. [London] 1925.

    [4] p. 22 cm.

    Cover title.

    1. Burns, Robert, 1759–1796 – Iconography,
portraits. 2. Raeburn, Sir Henry, 1756–1823.
I. Title.

NN   0024238   CaBVaU

Nash, Edward W., 1838–1899, comp.

O'Callaghan, Edmund Bailey, 1797–1880.
    Catalogue of the library of the late E. B. O'Callaghan,
M. D., LL. D., historian of New York. Comp. by E. W. Nash.
New York, D. Taylor, printer, 1882.

Nash, Edward W., 1838–1899.

Kings county genealogical club.
    Kings county genealogical club. Collections. v. 1, no. I–VI.
[New York, E. W. Nash, 1882–94.]

Nash, Edwin.
    A lecture on pre-Adamite London, given
in the theatre of Merchant Taylor's
school, Charterhouse square, London,
13th February, 1879... London, Blades,
East and Blades, 1879.
    1 p.l., v p., 1 l., 51 p. illus.,
fold. map, diagrs. (1 fold.) 23cm.
    Manuscript letter from the author to
Charles J. Shoppee inserted.
    With this is bound: Darling, C. W.
Anthropophagy. 1886.
    1. Geology of England. London. I.Title
Pre-Adamite   London.

NN   0024241   MnU MH IEdS

Nash, Edwin Adelbert, 1916–
    A study of selected cases of litigation in two Iowa district
courts with particular reference to the content of the business
law course. Ann Arbor, University Microfilms [1955]
    ([University Microfilms, Ann Arbor, Mich.] Publication no. 12,912)
    Microfilm copy of typescript. Positive.
    Collation of the original: 2 v. (viii, 490 l.) illus., tables.
    Thesis—State University of Iowa.
    Abstracted in Dissertation abstracts, v. 15 (1955) no. 9, p. 1516.
    Bibliography: leaves 487–490.

    1. Commercial law—Iowa—Cases. 2. Business education. 3. Edu-
cation, Secondary—Curricula. I. Title: Selected cases of litigation
in two Iowa district courts.

    Microfilm AC–1   no. 12,912   Mic A 55–2011
    Iowa. Univ. Library
    for Library of Congress   [1]†

NN   0024242   IaU DLC

Nash, Edwin Anderson, 1875–
    Random rhymes and poems for home folks, by Edwin
A. Nash ... Chicago, Ill., Stearns brothers & company,
1924.
    126 p. front., illus., port. 18ᶜᵐ.
    Second edition.

    I. Title.
                                      24–30331
    Library of Congress   PS3527.A633R3 1924

NN   0024243   DLC

Nash, Eleanor Arnett.
    ... Bachelors are made. New York and London, D. Apple-
ton-Century company, inc. [1946]
    5 p. l., 272 p. 20ᶜᵐ.

    I. Title.
                                      46–1250
    Library of Congress °   PZ3.N172Bac

NN   0024244   DLC CoU PP

Nash, Eleanor Arnett.
    Beauty is not an age. [1st ed.] New York, Harper [1953]
    225 p. 22 cm.

    1. Fashion. 2. Clothing and dress. 3. Beauty, Personal. I. Title.
    TT507.N27   646   52—11693 ‡

    WaS Wa CaBVa CaBViP WaSp WaE
NN   0024245   DLC Or OrP NcU PJA PP TU OO IU FTaSU

VOLUME 405

Nash, Eleanor Arnett.
... Footnote to life. New York, London, D. Appleton-Century company, incorporated ₁1944₎
3 p. l., 229, ₁1₎ p. 20ᶜᵐ.

I. Title.

Library of Congress   PZ3.N172Fo   44–7587

NN   0024246   DLC OU PP CaBVa

Nash, Eleanor Arnett.
It was Mary. New York, D. Appleton-Century Co. ₁1947₎
273 p. 21 cm.

I. Title.
PZ3.N172 It   47–31372*

NN   0024247   DLC PP ViU WaE

Nash, Eleanor Arnett.
Kit Corelli; TV stylist. New York, J. Messner ₁1955₎
182 p. 21 cm. (A Romance for young moderns)

I. Title.
PZ7.N167Ki   55–6926 ‡

NN   0024248   DLC CaBVa WaSp WaT

Nash, Eleanor Arnett.
Lucky Miss Spaulding. New York, Messner ₁1952₎
182 p. 21 cm. (A Romance for young moderns)

I. Title.
PZ3.N172Lu   52–8896 ‡

NN   0024249   DLC WaT CaBVa OC1

Nash, Elizabeth Gee, tr.

Fleuron, Svend, 1874–
Flax: police dog, by Svend Fleuron; translated from the Danish by E. Gee Nash; illustrated by Cecil Aldin. New York, H. Holt and company ₁1931₎

Nash, Elizabeth Gee, tr.

Siwertz, Sigfrid, 1882–
... Goldman's, translated from the Swedish by E. Gee Nash. New York, Cosmopolitan book corporation, 1930.

Nash, Elizabeth Gee.
The Hansa: its history and romance, by E. Gee Nash. With eighty illustrations from original sources and a sketch-map. London, John Lane; New York, Dodd, Mead and company ₁1929₎
2 p. l., vii–xiii p., 1 l., 279 p. front., illus., plates, ports., maps, plans, facsim. 22ᶜᵐ.
Bibliography: p. 263.

1. Hanseatic league.   I. Title.
30–1269 Revised
Library of Congress   HF455.N3

CaBVaU
OO OC1 MB MH ViU NBuU WaU OrU IdU WaSpG MtU WaS
NN   0024252   DLC CU NcD AAP PSt ICarbS PPL PU MiU

Nash, Elizabeth Gee, tr.

Hedin, Sven Anders, 1865–
Jehol, city of emperors, by Sven Hedin ... translated from the Swedish by E. G. Nash. New York, E. P. Dutton & company, inc., 1933.

Nash, Elizabeth Gee, tr.
Nordström, Ester Blenda Elisabeth, 1891–
Tent folk of the far North, by Ester Blenda Nordström; translated from the Swedish by E. Gee Nash. London, H. Jenkins limited ₁1930₎

Nash, Elizabeth Gee, tr

Turi, Johan Olafsson.
Turi's book of Lappland, by Johan Turi; edited and translated into Danish by Emilie Demant Hatt, translated from the Danish by E. Gee Nash. Original title: "Muittalus samid birra." New York and London, Harper & brothers ₁1931₎

Nash, Elizabeth Gee, tr.

Fleuron, Svend, 1874–
The wild horses of Iceland, by Svend Fleuron; translated from the Danish by E. Gee Nash. New York, H. Holt and company ₁1933₎

Nash, Elizabeth Todd.
Fifty Puritan ancestors, 1628–1660; genealogical notes, 1560–1900, by their lineal descendant, Elizabeth Todd Nash. New Haven, The Tuttle, Morehouse & Taylor company, 1902.
xii, 182, ₁8₎ p. plates, ports., facsims., fold. geneal. tables. 27ᶜᵐ.
Blank pages for "Descendants record" (₁8₎ at end)

1. Nash family (Thomas Nash, d. 1658) 2. New England — Geneal.
I. Title.
2–8223
Library of Congress   CS71.N25 1902

NN   0024257   DLC CaBVaU NIC PHi MWA OC1WHi OC1 NN

Nash, Elizabeth Todd.
One hundred and one legends of flowers, by Elizabeth Todd Nash ... Boston, The Christopher publishing house ₁ᶜ1927₎
340 p. plates. 20½ᶜᵐ.
Each plate accompanied by guard sheet with descriptive letterpress.
Bibliography: p. 338–340.

1. Plant lore. 2. Flowers in poetry.   I. Title.
27–8498
Library of Congress   QK83.N3

NN   0024258   DLC MB FU PPL PP OC1 OC1h MBH

Nash, Ellison D   F
see
Nash, Denis Frederic Ellison.

NASH, ELWIN HARRAL THOMAS.
Dr. Nash's cookery book. London: Simpkin, Marshall, ltd. [1937] ix, 11–183 p. 21½cm.

1. Cookery, English.

NN   0024260   NN DNAL OC1

F499
.W46N3 Nash, Emily, 1806?–1888.
The diary of Emily Nash, 1812–1888.
Vital records only ... The Puritan manuscripts [edited by] Vernon S. Phillips ...
Akron, O. [1936?–
v. 28½x22½ cm.

Caption title.
Mimeographed.

1. Welshfield, O.—Geneal.—Sources. (I, Phillips, Vernon Sirvilian, 1871– ed. II. The Puritan manuscripts.

NN   0024261   DLC ICN MB

Nash, Ephraim.
... The farmer's practical horse farriery ... To which is prefixed an account of the breeds in the United States ... 14th thousand rev. Auburn & Buffalo [N. Y., 1857]
197 p. 8°. 18.5 cm.
At head of title: A book for every farmer.

NN   0024262   CtY DNLM

Nash, Ephraim.
... The farmer's practical horse farriery. Containing practical rules on buying, breeding, breaking, lameness, vicious habits, management ... treatment and cure of diseases ... &c. ... Comp. by E. Nash ... Auburn ₁N. Y.₎ E. Nash, 1858.
vi, ₁13₎–197, ₁1₎ p. illus. 18ᶜᵐ.
At head of title: A book for every farmer.

1. Horse. 2. Horse—Diseases.
12–19924
Library of Congress   SF951.N25

NN   0024263   DLC MiEM PSt MnHi NN OO OC1

42
N17
1859
Nash, Ephraim.
The farmer's practical horse farriery.
Auburn, N.Y., Saxton, 1859.
197 p.

1. Horses. 2. Horses. Diseases.

NN   0024264   DNAL

42
N17
Nash, Ephraim.
The farmer's pratical horse farriery.
Auburn [N.Y.] Yates, 1860.
197 p.

1. Horses. 2. Horses. Diseases.

NN   0024265   DNAL

Nash, Eric Francis, 1904–
Machines and purchasing power, by E. F. Nash. London G. Routledge & sons, ltd., 1935.
vii, 229 p. diagrs. 19 cm.

1. Consumption (Economics) 2. Credit. 3. Currency question. 4. Machinery in industry. 5. Business cycles.   I. Title.
HB771.N3   330.1   35–38097 rev

NN   0024266   DLC WaT NN OCU ViU MiU OU TxU

Nash, Ernest
[Photographs of ancient cities of Italy]
New York, E. Nash, [n.d.]
378 photographs, boxed, 26-1/2 x 22 cm. (Size of photographs varies.)

Contents.– [Box 1–2] Rome, 171 photographs. –[Box 3] Ostia, 57 photographs –[Box 4] Pompeji, 8 photographs. –[Box 5] Herculaneum, 37 photographs. Paestum, 13 photographs. Tivoli, 9 photographs. Cerveteri, 5 photographs. Fiesole, 2 photographs.

[Photographs of the Laocoon group]
New York, E. Nash [n.d.]

15 photographs mounted on 13 sheets of heavy card board. In portfolio. 45 x 33cm.

1. Photographs. 2. Laocoon. 3. Human figure in art.

NN   0024268   OCU

VOLUME 405

Nash, Ernest.
Roman towns; photographs and text by Ernest Nash. New York, J. J. Augustin ₁1944₎
3 p. l., 201, ₁1₎ p. incl. mounted front., 188 pl. (incl. plans) 25ᶜᵐ.
Bibliography: p. ₁191₎–198.

1. Cities and towns, Ancient. 2. Italy—Antiq. 3. Architecture, Roman.
I. Title.
Library of Congress　　NA310.N3　　　　　　44—5712
　　　　　　　　　　　　₍44x10₎　　　　　　　　722.7

MoU KyU CaBVaU CaBVa IdB
OCU MtU Or OrP WaS MiU OO OC1 MdBWA NBuC TxU OrU
NN　0024269　　DLC IdU NcD TU PSC PSt PP DDO ViU OU

Nash, Ernest, joint ed.

DG806
.B55
Bittner, Herbert, *ed.*
Rome, edited by Herbert Bittner and Ernest Nash; introd. by Giuseppe Prezzolini. Chicago, H. Regnery Co., 1950.

Nash, Ethel Miller.
With this ring, by Ethel Miller Nash. New York, Association press, 1942.
x, 112 p. 21ᶜᵐ.
Bibliography: p. 111–112.

1. Marriage. 2. Family. I. Title.
　　　　　　　　　　　　　　　　　　42—20163
Library of Congress　　HQ734.N32
　　　　　　　　　　　　₍8₎　　　　　　　173.1

NN　0024271　　DLC NcGU NcRS CU OC1

Nash, Eugene Arus, 1837–1911.
A history of the Forty-fourth regiment, New York volunteer infantry, in the civil war, 1861–1865, by Captain Eugene Arus Nash. Chicago, R. R. Donnelley & sons company, 1911.
xiv, 484 p. front., plates, ports., 4 maps. 24ᶜᵐ.

1. New York infantry. 44th regt., 1861–1864. 2. U. S.—Hist—Civil ʳar—Regimental histories—N. Y. inf—44th.
Library of Congress　　E523.5.44thN　　　11—29619

NcD PPL NN OC1WHi
NN　0024272　　DLC ViU DNW CaBVaU OrStbM IU NcU TxU

Nash, Eugene Arus, 1837–1911.
History of Cattaraugus Co., New York
see under ₍Ellis, Franklin₎ 1828–1885.

H615.1
N25r
Q9
Nash, Eugene Beauharnais, 1838–
...Caracteristicos regionales por E.B. Nash...Traducidos por el Dr.Juan N.Arrisga...Mexico, A.Carranza e Hijos, 1909,
xii,247 p,　　　20cm. (Biblioteca de "La homeopatia")

NN　0024274　　MiU

H616.07
N25
Q8
Nash,Eugene Beauharnais,1838–
...Como se debe repertoriar un caso para encontrar el similimum,por E.B.Nash... Traduccion do L.Arringa. Mexico, A.Carranza y comp., 1908.
54,[1] p.　13½ cm.
At head of title:Biblioteca de "La Homeopatia."

NN　0024275　　MiU

Nash, Eugene Beauharnais, 1838–
Directions for the domestic use of important homeopathic remedies, by E. B. Nash ... ₁Cortland↑ N. Y., ᶜ1874₎
cover-title, ₍2₎–22 p. 14½ x 8ᶜᵐ.

1. Homeopathy—Popular works.
　　　　　　　　　　　　　　　　　7–13824†
Library of Congress　　RX76.N24

NN　0024276　　DLC

Nash, Eugene Beauharnais, 1838–
How to take the case and to find the similimum, by E. B. Nash ... Philadelphia, Boericke & Tafel, 1907.
54 p., 1 l. 17ᶜᵐ.

1. Homeopathy. I. Title.
　　　　　　　　　　　　　　　　8—306
Library of Congress　　RX74.N3

NN　0024277　　DLC PPHa MiU

Nash, Eugene Beauharnais, 1838–
How to take the case and to find the simillimum. 2d ed. By E. B. Nash ... Philadelphia, Boericke & Tafel, 1914.
54 p., 1 l. 17ᶜᵐ. $0.50

1. Homeopathy. I. Title.
　　　　　　　　　　　　　　　　15–1636
Library of Congress　　RX74.N3 1914

NN　0024278　　DLC DNLM OU ICJ

Nash, Eugene Beauharnais, 1838–
... Indicaciones caracteristicas de terapeutica homeopatica, por el Dr. E.B.Nash... Traducción hecha por el Doctor Juan Antiga... de la 2d ed. corrigida y aumentada. Mexico, C. Bouret, 1905.
522 p. (Biblioteca de La homeopatia)

NN　0024279　　MiU

Nash, Eugene Beauharnais, 1838–
Leaders for the use of sulphur, with comparisons, by E. B. Nash ... Philadelphia, Boericke & Tafel, 1907.
vi, 159 p. 17ᶜᵐ.

1. Sulphur—Therapeutic use.
　　　　　　　　　　　　　　　　7–12885
Library of Congress　　RX615.S9N2

NN　0024280　　DLC PBa PPHa MiU OC1W-H DNLM ICJ

Nash, Eugene Beauharnais, 1838–
Leaders in homœopathic therapeutics. By E. B. Nash, M. D. Philadelphia, Boericke & Tafel, 1899.
6, 5–381 p. 21ᶜᵐ.

1. Homeopathy—Materia medica and therapeutics.
　　　　　　　　　　　　　　　　99–295 Revised
Library of Congress　　RX601.N2

NN　0024281　　DLC ICRL PU-D MiU ICJ

WB
930
N248L
1901
Nash, Eugene Beauharnais, 1838–
Leaders in homœopathic therapeutics. 2d ed., rev. and enl. Philadelphia, Boericke & Tafel, 1901.
420 p. 21 cm.

1. Formularies, Homeopathic I. Title

NN　0024282　　WU-M

Nash, Eugene Beauharnais, 1838–
Leaders in homœopathic therapeutics, by E. B. Nash ... 4th ed. Philadelphia, Boericke & Tafel, 1913.
493 p. 20ᶜᵐ. $2.50

1. Homeopathy—Materia medica and therapeutics. I. Title.
　　　　　　　　　　　　　　　　14–4509
Library of Congress　　RX601.N2 1913

NN　0024283　　DLC DNLM OU ICJ

RX601
N38
1950
NASH, Eugene Beauharnais, 1838–
Leaders in homoeopathic therapeutics, by E.B. Nash. 6th ed. Philadelphia, Boericke & Tafel, 1950 [c1926]
493p. 21cm.

1. Materia medica 2. Homeopathy I. Title

NN　0024284　　CtY-M OU

Nash, Eugene Beauharnais, 1838–
Leaders in respiratory organs, by E. B. Nash ... Philadelphia, Boericke & Tafel, 1909.
vi p., 1 l., 188 p. 20ᶜᵐ. $1.50

1. Respiratory organs—Diseases—Homeopathic treatment.
　　　　　　　　　　　　　　　　9—12903
Library of Congress　　RX321.N3

NN　0024285　　DLC PPHa MiU ICJ

Nash, Eugene Beauharnais, 1838–
Leaders in typhoid fever, by E. B. Nash ... Philadelphia, Boericke & Tafel, 1900.
135 p. 16½ᶜᵐ.

1. Typhoid fever—Homeopathic treatment.
　　　　　　　　　　　　　　　　May 16, 1901–69
Library of Congress　　RX226.T8N2

NN　0024286　　DLC PPC DNLM MiU PPHa

Nash, Eugene Beauharnais, 1838–　　　　615.1 R307
Leitsymptome in der homöopathischen Therapie, von E. B. Nash, M.D. Uebersetzt von Dr. Paul Klien, ... Leipzig, W. Schwabe, [1917–1919].
356 p. 23ᶜᵐ.
"Beilage zur Allgemeinen homöopathischen Zeitung."

NN　0024287　　ICJ

Nash, Eugene Beauharnais, 1838–
Leitsymptome in der homöopathischen therapie. 2. aufl. übersetzt und überarb. in der wissenschaftlich-literarischen abteilung der dirma Dr. Willmar Schwabe, Leipzig. Leipzig, Schwabe, 1935.
x, 366 p.

NN　0024288　　NNC

WB
930
N248L
1950
NASH, Eugene Beauharnais, 1838–
Principes de thérapeutique homéopathique. Tr. de l'anglais par Léo Borliachon. Paris, Doin, 1950.
xiv, 416 p.
Translation of Leaders in homéopathic therapeutics.
1. Formularies - Homeopathic

NN　0024289　　DNLM

VOLUME 405

Nash, Eugene Beauharnais, 1838 -
Regional leaders, by E. B. Nash ... Philadelphia, Boericke & Tafel, 1901.
282 p. 17ᶜᵐ.

1. Homeopathy—Materia medica and therapeutics.   ɪ. Title.
1-11886

Library of Congress   RX631.N24

NN   0024290   DLC PBa MiU LU

Nash, Eugene Beauharnais, 1838-
Regional leaders, by E. B. Nash ... 2d ed., rev. and enl. Philadelphia, Boericke & Tafel, 1908.
315 p. 17½ᶜᵐ.

1. Homeopathy—Materia medica and therapeutics.
8-21508

Library of Congress   RX631.N26 Copyright

NN   0024291   DLC PPHa OU

Nash, Eugene Beauharnais, 1838–
The testimony of the clinic, by E. B. Nash ... Philadelphia, Boericke & Tafel, 1911.
2 p. l., ₉₎-209 p., 1 l. front. (port.) 19ᶜᵐ. $1.50

1. Homeopathy—Materia medica and therapeutics.
11-1043

Library of Congress   RX601.N3

NN   0024292   DLC DNLM PPHa MiU ICJ

Nash, Eveleigh, 1873–
I liked the life I lived; some reminiscences, by Eveleigh Nash. London, J. Murray ₍1941₎
vii, 180 p. front., pl., ports. 20½ᶜᵐ.
"First edition 1941."

1. Authors and publishers.   ɪ. Title.
A 41-4301

Harvard univ. Library
for Library of Congress   Z325.N8A3
₍4₎   926.55

NN   0024293   MH MoSW CtY

Nash, *Mrs.* **F   B.**
Lessons on the gentle art of cookery, by Mrs. F. B. Nash. Fargo, N. D., Commonwealth pub. co., printers, 1892.
1 p. l., 5-79, ₍2₎ p. 18½ᶜᵐ.

1. Cookery, American.
8-23706†

Library of Congress   . TX715.N251

NN   0024294   DLC MU

Nash, F. K.
Circumcision and baptism, sacrements of the covenant of grace, being a candid consideration of the points at issue between Presbyterians and Baptists ...   Fayetteville, Presbyterian office, pr. 1859.
79 p.   D.

NN   0024295   NcU

Nash, Florence.
June dusk, and other poems, by Florence Nash. New York, George H. Doran company ₍°1918₎
x p., 1 l., 13-104 p. front. (port.) 19½ᶜᵐ. $1.25

ɪ. Title.
18-18111

Library of Congress   PS3527.A635J9 1918

NN   0024296   DLC WaSp NNC MU NN MB

F27
L7N3   **Nash, Florence Walton Ryder.**
"What one should see in Lincoln County;" a paper read before the Woman's Club of Wiscasset. ₍n. p., 192-?₎
22 p. illus. 23 cm.

Bibliography: p. 22.

1. Lincoln Co., Me. - Description and travel. 2. Lincoln Co., Me. - History. I. Title.

NN   0024297   MeB

Nash, Frances Olivia Hartopp, 1887–
Kattie of the Balkans, by F. O. H. Nash ... illustrated by J. M. Pollock. London and New York, F. Warne & co., ltd. ₍1931₎
4 p. l., 152 p. col. front., illus. 21ᶜᵐ.

ɪ. Title.
36-1433

Library of Congress   PZ7.N168Kat

NN   0024298   DLC PPGi

Nash, Francis, 1850-
Abner Nash; an address...in New Bern, N.C., June 7th, 1923.

NN   0024299   NcU

Nash, Francis, 1850-
Borough towns of North Carolina.

(In N.C. booklet.   1906.   v.6, no.2.)

NN   0024300   NcU

Nash, Francis, 1850-
Continental line of North Carolina.

(In N.C. booklet.   Jan. 1918.   v.17, no.3.)

NN   0024301   NcU

Nash, Francis, 1850-
County records as sources of local history.

(In N.C. Literary and historical association Minutes.   1912.)

NN   0024302   NcU

Nash, Francis, 1850-
Edmund Fanning.

(In Ashe, S.A.   Biographical history of N.C.   1905-   v.1.)

NN   0024303   NcU

Pam.
Coll.   **Nash, Francis,** 1850-
22803   Edmund Strudwick, man and country doctor; an address delivered on the occasion of the presentation of a portrait of Dr. Strudwick to the State hospital at Raleigh, December 14, 1926. Raleigh, N. C., Edwards and Broughton, 1927.
10 p. 23 cm.

1. Strudwick, Edmund, 1802-1879.

NN   0024304   NcD NcWsW NcU

Nash, Francis, 1850-
Governor Abner Nash.

(In N.C. booklet.   1922-3.   v.22, nos 1-4.)

NN   0024305   NcU

Nash, Francis, 1850-
Governor Alexander Martin...1908...

NN   0024306   NcU

Nash, Francis, 1850-
Herman Husbands.

(In Ashe, S.A.   ed.   Biographical history of N.C.   1905-   v.2.)

NN   0024307   NcU

Nash, Francis, 1850–
Hillsboro, colonial and revolutionary, by Francis Nash ... Raleigh, Edwards & Broughton, printers, 1903.
100 p. 23ᶜᵐ.

1. Hillsboro, N. C.—Hist.

Library of Congress   F264.H7N2   4—3644

MB NcU NN
NN   0024308   DLC TU C NIC TKL PHi Nc MWA MiU OO

975.6565 **Nash, Francis.** 1850-
H655n   Hillsboro, colonial and revolutionary. With a biographical sketch by John J. Parker. Chapel Hill, N.C., Orange Printshop, 1953.
xii, 96 p. 23 cm.

¶Reprint of a 1903 ed., with the addition of the index and the biographical sketch of the author.™

1. Hillsboro, N.C. Hist. H.1. North Carolina. Hills-   boro. I. Title.

NN   0024309   N TxU NcU-L NcRS NN NcGU

Nash, Francis, 1850–
... Historic Hillsboro, by Francis Nash. ₍Raleigh, E. M. Uzzell & co., printers, 1903₎
cover-title, 18 p., 1 l. 18½ x 14ᶜᵐ. (The North Carolina booklet; great events in North Carolina history, vol. ɪɪɪ, no. 4, August, 1903)
The t.-p. reads: ... The North Carolina booklet ...

1. Hillsboro, N. C.—Hist.

Library of Congress   F251.N86   5-1254

NN   0024310   DLC NcU

Nash, Francis, 1850–
The history of Orange county, part I. ₍Raleigh, N. C., 1910₎
₍55₎-113 p. (The North Carolina booklet; great events in North Carolina history, vol. X, no. 2, October, 1910)

1. Orange co., N. C. - History.

NN   0024311   NNC NcU

VOLUME 405

Nash, Francis, 1850–
James Few.

(In Ashe, S.A.   ed.   Biographical
history of N.C.   1905–   v.2.)

NN   0024312   NcU

Nash, Francis, 1850–
James Hunter.

(In Ashe, S.A.   ed.   Biographical
history of N.C.   1905–   v.2.)

NN   0024313   NcU

Nash, Francis, 1850–
Presentation of portrait of Governor Alexander Martin to
the state of North Carolina, in the hall of the House of representatives, at Raleigh, November 16, 1908, by the North Carolina society of the Sons of the revolution. Address by Francis
Nash, esq., a member of the society. ₁n. p., 1908₁
19 p.   22½ᶜᵐ.

1. Martin, Alexander, 1740–1807.   I. Sons of the revolution. North
Carolina society.

Library of Congress   E203.N8N2   9–14739

NN   0024314   DLC NcD NN Nc

Nash, Francis, 1850–
The relation of the clerk of the Superior
Court to appeals to the Supreme Court.   [Raleigh,
n.d.]
17 p.   O.

NN   0024315   NcU

Nash, Francis, 1850–
Revaluation and taxation in North Carolina.

(In South Atlantic quarterly.   Oct.1920.
v.19,no.4.)

NN   0024316   NcU

Nash, Francis, 1850–   Raleigh, 1926.
The special tax bonds of North Carolina and
their repudiation.

NN   0024317   NcU

Nash, Francis, 1850–
Thomas Ruffin.

(In N.C. bar association   Report.   1911.
v.13.)

NN   0024318   NcU

Nash, Francis Henry, ed.
The cantara, being a choice selection of solos,
duets ... from the best masters for the use of
seminaries and schools ... ed. and arranged by
Francis H. Nash & Geo. F. Bristow.   New York,
1870.
228 p.   22 cm.

NN   0024319   RPB

Nash, Francis Henry, ed.
The cantara, being a choice selection of solos,
duets, trios, and quartetts, from the best masters
For the use of seminaries and schools in city and
country.   Edited and arranged by Francis H. Nash
and Geo. F. Bristow.   New York and Chicago.
A. S. Barnes and company, 1873, [c. 1868,
pref. 1869]
288 p.   21 cm.
Pieces not numbered.

NN   0024320   NNUT

Nash, Francis Henry,   ed.
The cantara, no. 2. Being a choice selection of solos, duets,
trios, and quartetts, from the best masters. For the use of seminaries and schools in city and country. Ed. and arr. by Francis H.
Nash and Geo. F. Bristow...   New York, A. S. Barnes & co.,
1868.   288 p.   22cm.

Most of the songs with piano accompaniment.
Imperfect: t.-p. mutilated.

549703B. 1. Schools—Music.   I. Bristow, George Frederick, 1825–
1898, jt. ed. II. Title.
N.Y.P.L.   January 15, 1951

NN   0024321   NN

Nash, Francis Henry, ed. & arr.
₁The cantara, acc. piano₁
The cantara, ₁no.2₁ being a choice selection
of solos, duets,trios,and quartetts, from the
best masters. For the use of seminaries and
schools in city and country. Ed. and arr. by
Francis H.Nash and Geo.F. Bristow.   New York,
A.S.Barnes, 1873.
268 p.   21ᶜᵐ.

1.School song books. 2.Part-songs, Secular.
I.Bristow, George   Frederick, 1825–1898,
ed. & arr.

M1994
N24C22

NN   0024322   CSt NN ICN

Nash, Francis Henry, joint comp.

Curtis, George Henry, comp.

The school vocalist: a new musical manual; for the use of
academies, female seminaries, grammar schools, high schools,
and adult classes. By George Henry Curtis ... and Francis
Henry Nash ... Words of the historical subjects by William
Oland Bourne. New York, A. S. Barnes & co.; Boston, O.
Ditson; ₁etc.,etc.₁ 1857.

M1994
.C975S4
1857

NASH, Francis Philip.
The mission of American colleges and the relations of the Phi Beta Kappa Society to that
subject; an address delivered before the Phi
Beta Kappa Society in Hobart College, Geneva,
N.Y., June 22, 1880. Geneva, N.Y., College
press print., 1880.

Pamphlet.

NN   0024324   MH

Nash, Francis Philip, 1836–1911.

₁Coxe, Arthur Cleveland, bp.₁ 1818–1896.
The ladye chace: a ballad. By the author of "Christian ballads". Ed. by Francis Philip Nash ... ⟨Cabinet
ed.⟩ Philadelphia, Lippincott & co., 1877.

NASH, Francis Smith.
Instruction for army, navy, marine,hospital,
state and hospital med. exam. boards.
[Washington?] n.d.

NN   0024326   MH

Nash (Francis Smith). Reminiscences, medical
and hygienic, of the Arctic. 12 pp. 12°. *Richmond, 1897.*
Repr. from: Virginia M.Semi-Month.,Richmond,1897,ii.

NN   0024327   DNLM

Nash, Frank, 1855–

North Carolina. *State dept. of archives and history.*
Addresses at the unveiling of the bust of William A. Graham
by the North Carolina Historical commission in the rotunda of
the state capitol. Delivered in the hall of the House of representatives, January 12, 1910. Raleigh, Edwards & Broughton
printing co., 1910.

F251
.N83
no. 7

Nash, Frank, 1855–
... Drainage assessments: their imposition and their col-
lection under the North Carolina drainage laws, by Frank
Nash, assistant attorney-general. Chapel Hill, N. C., 1922.
11 p. 23 cm. (North Carolina. Geological survey, 1891–
Circular no. 4)
At head of title: ... Drainage and reclamation division.

1. Drainage laws—North Carolina.   I. Title.
HD1683.U5N87   G S 22–324 rev

U. S. Geol. Survey. Libr.
for Library of Congress   ₁r49e1₁†

NN   0024329   DI-GS PPAmP NN NcU DLC

Nash, Frank, 1855–
The North Carolina constitution of 1776 and its makers,
by Frank Nash.

(*In* North Carolina. University. The James Sprunt historical
publications, pub. under the direction of the North Carolina historical
society. Chapel Hill, N. C., 1912. 22½ cm. v. 11, no. 2, p. ₁5₁–23)
A paper read before the North Carolina historical society, February 5, 1912.

1. North Carolina. Constitution.

F251.J28   vol. 11   13—33017

NcU
NN   0024330   DLC MsSM CU MiU OClW NN ViU PSC-Hi

NASH,Frank, 1855–
Recent Decisions of the Supreme Court of
North Carolina on the State Constitution (151–
178 N.C.Rep.) [1909–19]. Raleigh, n.d.

32 p.

NN   0024331   MH-L NcU

Nash, Frank, 1912–
The house cried murder. ₁New York₁ Phoenix Press ₁1952₁
223 p. 21 cm.

I. Title.

PZ4.N249Ho   52–8535 ‡

NN   0024332   DLC

Nash, Frank L
Our heavenly Father. A course of lectures on the Lord's
Prayer. San Francisco, 1885.
159 p. 18cm.

F857
N18

NN   0024333   CU-B

Nash, Frederick.

Laus Deo. Poetry by Alonzo G. Shears. New Haven,
C. H. Loomis, ᶜ1867.
score (3 p.) 36 cm.

Caption title: The morning light.
For chorus (SATB) and keyboard instrument.

1. Choruses, Sacred (Mixed voices, 4 pts.) with piano.   I. Title.
II. Title: The morning light.

M2072.4.N   52–55132

NN   0024334   DLC

Nash, Frederick, judge.
An address delivered before the members of
Eagle lodge, no. 71, on the anniversary of St. John,
the evangelist, December 27, 1838. Hillsborough,
Dennis Heartt, 1839.
17 p.   D.

NN   0024335   NcU

VOLUME 405

LF509
.C7
Rare Bk
Coll
Nash, Frederick, 1782-1856, illus.
[Combe, William] 1742-1823.
A history of the University of Oxford, its colleges, halls, and public buildings ... London. R. Ackermann, 1814.

Nash, Frederick, 1782-1856.

Panorama of Paris, a series of thirty-eight views of its most interesting public buildings, monuments, etc. engraved by eminent artists from original drawings by Frederick Nash. London, Tilt [182-]
38 pl. 33 cm.

1.Paris-Descr.-Views.

NN 0024337 NjP

Nash, Frederick, 1782-1856, illus.

Scott, John, 1783-1821.
Picturesque views of the city of Paris and its environs; consisting of views on the Seine, public buildings, characteristic scenery, etc. The original drawings by Mr. Frederick Nash; the literary department by Mr. John Scott, and M. P. B. de La Boissière ... London, Printed for Longman, Hurst, Rees, Orme, and Brown, by J. Moyes, 1823.

M920
N24f
Nash, Frederick C
Faces you have saw; caricatures of familiar people seen about Detroit, by Fred. Nash. Detroit [Winn & Hammond? ca. 1900]
1v.(unpaged) illus 17cm.

Drawings and text on facing pages.

1.Caricatures and cartoons-Detroit, Mich.
2.Detroit, Mich.-Biog.-Portraits. I.Title.

NN 0024339 Mi MiU MiD

Nash, Frederick C.
The family album. [Detroit] 1907.
356 p. ports.

NN 0024340 MiD-B

Nash, Frederick C.
More faces you have saw. [Detroit, Richmond & Backus] n. d.
unp. ports.

NN 0024341 MiD-B

Nash, Frederick H   comp.
Ye names & ages of all ye old folks in every hamlet, city and town in ye state of Connecticut, now living, with ye sketches of twenty living centenarians. Comp. by Frederick H. Nash ... New Haven, Printed by Price, Lee & co., 1884.
52 p. 22½ cm.
Includes names of more than 6,000 people 80 years of age and over.

1. Connecticut—Biog. 2. Connecticut—Geneal.

F93.N24   3—15619

NN 0024342 DLC PHi MWA OClWHi OKentU

Nash, Frederick Hapgood, 1874-
A comedy of jurisprudence in Georgia; paper read before the Association of life insurance counsel, December 10, 1915, by Frederick H. Nash ... [New York, Metropolitan life press, 1916]
9 p. 23½ cm.

Continued in next column

Continued from preceding column

. Insurance law—Georgia.   I. Title.

17-7167

Library of Congress   HG8907.G6N3

NN 0024343 DLC NcD-L WaU-L

NASH, Frederick Hapgood, 1874-
The commedia dell'arte. Thesis for French XX. a [at Harvard University], 1895.

4°. ff. 40. Type-written.
Includes a detailed study of the influence of the commedia dell'arte Molière.
"Bibliography," pp. 39-40.

NN 0024344 MH

Nash, Frederick Hapgood, 1874-
Federal supervision of insurance companies. An address to the National convention of state insurance commissioners, at Bretton Woods, N. H., Sept. 27, 1905, by Frederick H. Nash. [Boston, 1905]
28 p. 25 cm.
Half-title.

1. Insurance—U. S.—State supervision.

6-28525

Library of Congress   HG8917.N2

NN 0024345 DLC MB

Nash, Frederick Hapgood, 1874-
The measure of damages upon breach of a life insurance contract; paper read before the Association of life insurance counsel, December 2, 1936, at New York city, by Frederick H. Nash ... [n. p., 1937?]
cover-title, p. 697-724. 23 cm.

1. Insurance, Life—U. S. 2. Insurance law—U. S. 3. Damages—U. S. I. Title.
37-35634
Library of Congress
———— Copy 2.   [3]   368.30973

NN 0024346 DLC WaU-L

Nash, Frederick Ogden
see Nash, Ogden, 1902-1971.

Nash, G.H.

Breckenridge, J   E.
The manufacture and chemistry of fertilizers. Addresses by J. E. Breckenridge, G. H. Nash. Chicago, Baltimore, Soil improvement committee of the National fertilizer association [1918]

Nash, G.H., engineer.

Steps in long distance telephone connections, by G. H. Nash...
(In International communications review, New York. March, 1930, vol. vi, no. 2, p. 1-8)

NN 0024349 NcD

Nash, G   T   A
Ratepayers and appeals. Hadleigh, Essex, Tower Bridge Publications [1951]
60 p. 19 cm. (The Everyman's guide series)

1. Local taxation—Gt. Brit. 2. Land—Taxation—Gt. Brit. I. Title.
352.1   52-15026 ‡

NN 0024350 DLC

Atlas
coll'n
Nash, G   V
Atlas of Pierce County, Wisconsin; drawn and comp. from personal surveys of Nash & Morgan. Appleton, Wis., G. V. Nash; Oshkosh, Wis., F. B. Morgan, 1877-78.
53, [2] p. incl. illus., col. maps (1 double) 43cm.
Map of Wisconsin (col., fold.) inserted at end.
Pages 7-8   wanting.
————   Copy 2.

NN 0024351 MnHi NIC DLC NN

Nash, G. V.
Atlas of Pierce county, Wisconsin. Milwaukee, 1877-78.
53 p.

Microfilmed as publication no. 116, in "County Histories of the 'Old Northwest,' Series I: Wisconsin" New Haven, Conn.: Research Publications, Inc., 1972. Reel 34.

NN 0024352 ICRL

Atlas
coll'n
Nash, G   V
An illustrated historical atlas of Manitowoc County, Wisconsin. Manitowac, Wis., 1878.
80 p. incl. illus., col. maps (part double) 47cm.

NN 0024353 MnHi DLC

Nash, G. V.
An illustrated historical atlas of Manitowoc county, Wisconsin. Manitowoc, 1878.
80 p.

Microfilmed as publication no. 117, in "County Histories of the 'Old Northwest,' Series I: Wisconsin" New Haven, Conn.: Research Publications, Inc., 1972. Reel 34.

NN 0024354 ICRL

Nash, Garrita Barry.
"The full penalty" (a play in three acts) by Garrita B. Nash and Maud Tarleton Winchester. New York [Binghamton, N. Y., Printed by Vail-Ballou co.] 1913.
168 p. 18½ cm. $0.50

I. Winchester, Maud Tarleton, joint author. II. Title.
Library of Congress   PS635.Z9N252   13-16878

NN 0024355 DLC

NASH, Garrita Barry.
The Spanish gypsy; an opera in four acts; adopted from George Eliot's "Spanish Gypsy", by Garrita Barry Nash and Lily A.Long.

4°. Typewritten.
Libretto. Words only.

NN 0024356 MH

NASH, GEOFFREY DALRYMPLE.
"Miniaturoj." London, Esperanto pub. co.,1931.
57 p. 19cm.

Poems.

1. Esperanto--Books in.

NN 0024357 NN

VOLUME 405

ar W Nash, George.
7153   The drama, a treatise on poetry and
         verse, dramatic composition, dramatic
         authors, and the effects of dramatic amuse-
         ments. To which is annexed, The poet's
         death, a ballad.   London, Saunders and
         Otley, 1839.
           27 p. 22cm.

             1. Drama--Hist. and crit.

NN   0024358   NIC MH

Nash, George.
     The French prisoners; a history.   Calcutta,
William Rushton, 1843.
     226 p.   18 cm.
     1. Prisoners of war. I. Title.

NN   0024359   NcU

---

822   Nash, George.
N17m   Man and his mistress; or, Woman's revolt.
       A mock-heroic melo-drama.   Calcutta, S.
       Smith, 1842.
          66p. 20cm.

NN   0024360   IU MH

Nash, George, Co.
     The Nash patent salt-bath furnace for hardening.   New
York ₍1911₎. 20 p. 8°.

1. Steel.—Hardening.
N.Y.P.L.   February 24, 1912.

NN   0024361   NN

NASH, GEORGE C.
     General Forcursue and Co. More letters to the secretar
of a golf club, by George C.Nash; illustrated by Christopher Millett & the author.   London: Chatto & Windus,
1936. viii, 212 p. incl. front. illus. 19½cm.

     "Nearly all of these letters have previously appeared
in Punch."

873880A. 1. Golf. 2. Wit and humor, English. I. Title.

NN   0024362   NN

NASH, GEORGE C.
     Letters to the secretary of a golf club, by George C.Nash;
illustrated by Christopher Millett.   London: Chatto & Windus, 1935. x, 195 p. incl. front. illus. 20cm.

     Illustrated end papers.
     Reprinted in part from Punch.

821906A. 1. Golf. 2. Wit and humor, English. I. Title.

NN   0024363   NN MiD

Nash, George C
     The LMS at war, by George C. Nash (G. C. N. of Punch)
Euston, The London Midland and Scottish railway ₍1946₎
     3 p. l., 87, ₍1₎ p. col. front., plates (part col.) 25½ x 19½cm.

     Map on lining-papers.
     "First published 1946."

     1. London Midland and Scottish railway. 2. World war, 1939-1945—
Transportation.
          HE3020.L75N3   385   47-16614

NN   0024364   DLC ICU MiU GU

Nash, George C.
     The Ulster bridgehead "Operation Sirocco," 1939–1945. Bel-
fast, Davidson and co., ltd. Sirocco engineering works ₍194–₎
₍36₎ p. illus. 25cm.

     1. World war, 1939–1945—Busi-   ness histories₎—Gt. Br. I. David-
son & company, ltd., Belfast.

NN   0024365   NN

Nash, George James.
     ... Plumbing and hot-water fitting, by G. J. Nash ... Lon-
don, G. Allen & Unwin ltd ₍1946₎
     128 p. illus., diagrs. 19ᶜᵐ. (The New builders' handbook, no. 3)
     "First published in 1946."

     1. Plumbing. 2. Sanitation, Household.

          TH6123.N3   696.1   47-20654

NN   0024366   DLC NcC

F486   Nash, George Kilbon, 1842-1904.
0514   A century of statehood.   Address by George
v.12   K. Nash.
p.25-
29   (In Ohio archaeological and historical
       publications.   Columbus, 1903.   23½cm.
       v. 12, p. 25-29.   illus.,port.)

          1. Ohio.-History.-Addresses, essays, lectures.
       I. Title.

NN   0024367   NBuG

Nash, George Kilbon, 1842-1904.
     Magnificent record of Republican admin-
istration. Full text of the masterly and
convincing speech of Judge George K. Nash,
Republican candidate for governor, at the
Akron meeting, Saturday, September 23rd,
1899. Akron, n.d.
     15 p.

NN   0024368   OClWHi

Nash, George Kilbon, 1842-1904.
     Speech of Hon. George K. Nash, accept-
ing a renomination for Governor, June 25,
1901. n.p.n.d.
     [4] p.

     P.16, 005

NN   0024369   OClWHi

Nash, George Kilbon, 1842-1904
     see also Ohio. Governor. 1900-
1904 (G.K. Nash)

Nash, George Valentine, 1864–1921.
     ... American ginseng: its commercial history, protection and
cultivation. By George V. Nash ... Washington, Govt. print.
off., 1895.
     22 p. illus. 23ᶜᵐ. (U. S. Dept. of agriculture. Division of botany.
Bulletin no. 16)

     1. Ginseng.   Agr 9–703 Revised
U. S. Dept. of agr. Librar
for Library of Congress   QK1.U4 no. 16
—— Copy 2.   SB295.G5N3 1895

          DLC
NN   0024371   DNAL MBH MB MiU OO OCl PU PPHor MH-A

Nash, George Valentine, 1864–1921.
     ... American ginseng: its commercial history, protection, and
cultivation. By George V. Nash. Revised and extended by
Maurice G. Kains. Washington, Govt. print. off., 1898.
     32 p. incl. illus. (incl. map) tables. 23ᶜᵐ. (U. S. Dept. of agricul-
ture. Division of botany. Bulletin no. 16. Rev. ed.)

     1. Ginseng. ɪ. Kains, Maurice Grenville, 1868-
                                                   43-22933
Library of Congress   QK1.U4 no. 16 1898
—— Copy 2.   SB295.G5N3 1898

NN   0024372   DLC MB

Nash, George Valentine, 1864–1921.
     ... Costa Rican orchids ... by George Valentine Nash.
New York, 1907–
     v. plates. 24ᶜᵐ. (Contributions from the New York botanical
garden. no. 91   )
     From the Bulletin of the Torrey botanical club.

     1. Orchids—Costa Rica.

                                        CA 9—69 Unrev'd
Library of Congress   QK1.N515 no. 91

NN   0024373   DLC MiU OU OO

Nash, George Valentine, 1864–1921.
     ... The dichotomous panicums; some new species ...
By Geo. V. Nash.
New York, 1899–
     v. 24ᶜᵐ. (Contributions from the New York botanical garden.
no. 3)
     Reprinted from the Bulletin of the Torrey botanical club.

     1. Panicum.

                                        CA 9—43 Unrev'd
Library of Congress   QK1.N515 no. 3

NN   0024374   DLC OU OO MiU

Nash, George Valentine, 1864-1921.
     Hardy woody plants in the New York botanical
garden, by George V. Nash ... ₍n.p.₎, 1920?₎
     cover-title, ₍138₎ p. 23½ᶜᵐ.
     Various pagings.
     "Reprinted ... from the Journal of the New York botanical
garden, 1917-1920."

     1. Shrubs. 2. Trees. I. New York botanical garden.
II. Title.

NN   0024375   ViU

Nash, George Valentine, 1864-1921.
                    The Letchworth park arboretum. ₍Lan-
caster.₎ 1912.₎ 8°.
Journal of the New York botanical garden, 1912, xiii, 39-52.

NN   0024376   MH-A

Nash, George Valentine, 1864-1921.
     Notes on some Florida plants. 2 pt.
[New York, 1895–96]
     (In Columbia University - Department of
botany. Contributions, 74, 89)
     "Reprinted from the Bulletin of the Torrey
botanical club, vol. xxii, no. 4," and vol. xxiii,
no. 3.

NN   0024377   MH-A

Nash, George Valentine, 1864–1921.
     ... A preliminary enumeration of the grasses of Porto
Rico, by George V. Nash. New York, 1903.
     cover-title, p. 369–389. 24ᶜᵐ. (Contributions from the New York bo-
tanical garden. no. 39)
     Reprinted from the Bulletin of the Torrey botanical club, 30. Jl, 1903.

     1. Grasses—Porto Rico.

                                        CA 9—464 Unrev'd
Library of Congress   QK1.N515 no. 39

NN   0024378   DLC OU MiU OO

Nash, George Valentine, 1864–1921.
     ... A revision of the family *Fouquieriaceae*, by George
V. Nash. New York, 1903.
     cover-title, p. 449–459. 24ᶜᵐ. (Contributions from the New York bo-
tanical garden. no. 42)
     Reprinted from the Bulletin of the Torrey botanical club, 30. Aug.,
1903.

     1. Fouquieriaceae.

                                        CA 9—462 Unrev'd
Library of Congress   QK1.N515 no. 42

NN   0024379   DLC OU MiU OO

VOLUME 405

Nash, George Valentine, 1864-1921.
Revision of the genus Asimina.   [New York, 1896]
(In Columbia University - Department of botany. Contributions, 95)
"Reprinted from the Bulletin of the Torrey botanical club, vol. xxiii, no. 6."

NN 0024380   MH-A

Nash, George William, 1856–
... Excursion planned for the City history club of New York, by George W. Nash, M. D. No. x—Historic Richmond, comp. from the "Memorial history of Staten Island," by Ira K. Morris, and from information given by many friends on the island ... [New York] ʻ1908.
24 p. illus. (maps) 19ᶜᵐ. [City history club of New York. Excursions, no. 10]

1. Staten Island, N. Y.—Historic houses, etc.
17-19484

Library of Congress   F128.37.C5 no. 10

NN 0024381   DLC

Nash, George William, 1856–
City history club of New York.
Excursion[s] planned for the City history club of New York ... [New York] ʻ1897-1916.

Nash, George William, 1856–   **joint author.**
Kelley, Frank Bergen.
... Excursions planned for the City history club of New York by Frank Bergen Kelley ... Historic Brooklyn ... [New York, 1909]

Nash, George William, 1856–
City history club of New York.
... The milestones and the old Post road, by George W. Nash, M. D., and Hopper Striker Mott. Reprinted from the Historical guide to the city of New York ... Revised, 1915 ... [New York, 1915]

Nash, George Williston, 1868–
Other forms of compensation for teachers.
(In National education association of the United States. Journal of proceedings and addresses, 1907. p. 108–111)

1. Teaching.
E 8-106
Library, U. S. Office of   Education L13.N212 1907
Library of Congress   [L13.N4 1907]

NN 0024385   DHEW OU WaS

Nash, George Williston, 1868–
The responsibility of the normal school for training teachers for all lines of school work.
(In National education association of the United States. Addresses and proceedings, 1917. p. 388)

1. Normal schools.   I. Title.
E 18-749
Library, U. S. Bur. of   Education

NN 0024386   DHEW OU OO WaS

Nash, Gilbert, 1825-1888.
Bay leaves, and other poems, by Gilbert Nash. Boston, 1870.
12 p.

NN 0024387   OCH NjP

Nash, Gilbert, 1825-1888.
Bay leaves, and other poems. By Gilbert Nash. Boston, Nichols and Noyes, 1870.
viii, 295 p. 18ᶜᵐ.

I. Title.

Library of Congress   PS2459.N26   22-15159

NN 0024388   DLC ICN ViU NcD CtY OO OCH OU NBuG

Nash, Gilbert, 1825-1888.
Christmas: a poem. 1 p. (*Mag. Am. Hist.* v. 18, 1887. p. 535.)—

NN 0024389   MdBP

Nash, Gilbert, 1825-1888, *comp.*
... Historical sketch of the town of Weymouth, Massachusetts, from 1622 to 1884. Comp. by Gilbert Nash ... Pub. by the town of Weymouth, under the auspices of the Weymouth historical society. [Boston, A. Mudge & son, printers] 1885.
x, 346 p. 26½ᶜᵐ. (⟨no. 2⟩ Weymouth historical society. [Publications])
The larger portion of the text was originally published in Duane H. Hurd's History of Norfolk county, Massachusetts, published at Philadelphia, 1884.

1. Weymouth, Mass.—Hist.   I. Weymouth, Mass.
6—2147
Library of Congress   F74.W77W7 no. 2

PHi
NN 0024390   DLC NN MH WaE MeB MU OCl OU MiU MWA

Nash, Gilbert, 1825-1898
The Dorchester and Weymouth families of Humphrey.
Humphreys, Frederick, 1816-1900.
The Humphreys family in America. By Frederick Humphreys, M. D., assisted by Otis M. Humphreys, M. D., Henry R. Stiles, M. D., Mrs. Sarah M. Churchill. New York, Humphreys print, 1883.

Nash, Gilbert, 1825-1888.
... The original journal of General Solomon Lovell, kept during the Penobscot expedition, 1779: with a sketch of his life by Gilbert Nash. Together with the Proceedings of the society for 1879-80. [Boston] The Weymouth historical society, 1881.
127 p. 2 pl., map. 25ᶜᵐ. (⟨no. 1.⟩ Weymouth historical society. [Publications])
"A sketch of the history and proceedings of the ... society": p. [5]–10.
"List of donors from the organization to January 1, 1881": p. 11–13.
"General Lovell's Journal": p. [93]–105.
"Robert Lovell genealogy": p. [109]–116.

1. Penobscot expedition, 1779. 2. Lovell, Solomon, 1732-1801. 3. Lovell family.
6—2146
Library of Congress   F74.W77W7 no. 1

MWA ViU
NN 0024392   DLC MU TxU MeB MnU NcD OU MiU OClWHi

Nash, Gilbert, 1825-1888.
Adams, Charles Francis, 1835-1915.
... Wessagusset and Weymouth, an historical address by Charles Francis Adams, jr., delivered at Weymouth, July 4, 1874, on the occasion of the celebration of the two hundred and fiftieth anniversary of the permanent settlement of the town. Weymouth in its first twenty years, a paper read before the society by Gilbert Nash, November 1, 1882. Weymouth thirty years later, a paper read by Charles Francis Adams, before the Weymouth historical society, September 23, 1904. [Weymouth, Mass.] The Weymouth historical society [Boston, T. R. Marvin & son, printers] 1905.

TH1715
G3
Nash, Gordon Douglas.
Garston, Eng. Building Research Station.
The thermal insulation of buildings; design data and how to use them. London, H. M. Stationery Off., 1955.

F
74
.W54
N24
Nash, Gilbert, 1825-1888.
Weymouth in its first twenty years, with some facts and queries concerning its first church and ministers. By Gilbert Nash, recording secretary of the Weymouth historical society. [Weymouth, 1883]
[22] p. 18 x 18 cm.
Mounted clipping from Weymouth gazette supplement, February 23, 1883.

NN 0024395   MiU MH MA

BX5107
.L8A3
Nash, Glendinning, ed.
London diocese book ...
London [etc.] Society for promoting Christian knowledge

Nash, Gr
Коротка історія земель Чехословацької Республіки. Прага [Вид. Укр. громадського ком-ту] 1923.
171 p. illus. 19 cm.

1. Czechoslovak Republic—Hist. 2. Bohemia—Hist.   I. Title.
Title transliterated: Korotka istoriîa zemel' Chekhoslovats'koï Respubliky.
DB205.N3   53–53620 †

NN 0024397   DLC

Nash, Grace Helen.
Andalucia
see under   Lecuona y Casado, Ernesto, 1895–

Nash, Grace Helen, arr.
La comparsa; carnival procession
see under   Lecuona y Casado, Ernesto, 1895–

Nash, Grace Helen.   8050A.918
Finding; a book for beginners at the piano. Illustrated by Lillian Stout.
— New York. G. Schirmer (Inc.). [1932.] vii, 70 pp. Illus. Music. 30½ cm.

D2918 — T.r. — Pianoforte. Instruction books.

NN 0024400   MB OrSaW NN

Nash, Grace Helen.
...Music study course for the piano; specially designed for the adult beginner and for piano classes in high school and college, by Grace Helen Nash. New York: G. Schirmer, Inc. [cop. 1928.] Publ. pl. no. 33433. x, 102 p. illus. f°. (Schirmer's scholastic ser. v. 204.)

"Supplementary reading for the student," p. viii–ix. "Supplementary material for the teacher," p. ix–x.

514954A. 1. Piano—Methods.   JUILLIARD FOUNDATION FUND.
N. Y. P. L.   I. Title.
                                        February 20, 1931

NN 0024401   NN OCl

Nash, H   A.
A synthetic grammar of the English language, adapted to the instruction of private students, containing rules and observations well illustrated for assisting the student to write with perspicuity and accuracy. By H. A. Nash ... Charleston [W. Va.] Gibbens, Atkinson & co., printers, 1876.
vi, 95 p. 23ᶜᵐ.

1. English language—Grammar—1870–
11-17991
Library of Congress   PE1111.N3

NN 0024402   DLC

VOLUME 405

Nash, H. Alden
The student's compendium of the book of common prayer: being notes historicaland... by Rev. H.Alden Nash,...London, Longmans, Green,and Co.,1880.
XI,116p.   17cm.

DLC: YA 26993

NN   0024403   DLC

Nash, H.H. Ashley.
Palestine exhibition, Town hall, Oxford, November 16, 17, 18, 19, 1897. Guide book and programme
      see under   London society for promoting Christianity amongst the Jews.

Nash, Harold L   1892–
The dawn of a conviction, by Harold L. Nash. Boston, The Christopher publishing house [1942]
5 p. l., 5–80, [1] p. front. (port.) 23½ᵐ.

1. Spiritualism.   I. Title.   43–698

Library of Congress   BF1301.N3
                         [2]   133.98

NN   0024405   DLC

Nash, Harold Siegrist.
... Talk no.1–5 of University series no.13 -- "The Art and Science of the Potter" WLW, November 22°December 2–,1929 [by] Harold S. Nash... [Cincinnati, 1929]
5 nos. in 1 v. 28cm.

Mimeographed.

NN   0024406   OCU

Nash, Harriet A.
Polly's secret; a story of the Kennebec, by Harriet A. Nash; illustrated by Harry C. Edwards. Boston, Little, Brown, and company, 1902.
4 p. l., 291 p. front., plates. 19 x 15ᶜᵐ.

I. Title.
                                        2—23904
Library of Congress   PZ7.N173P

NN   0024407   DLC Or OEac OLak

Nash, Harriet A.
Polly's secret; a story of the Kennebec.
Boston, Little, 1914.
291 p

NN   0024408   PP

Nash, Harriet A.
... Polly's secret, by Harriet A. Nash; with illustrations in color by Hattie Longstreet Price. Boston, Little, Brown and company, 1926.
4 p. l., 292 p. col. front., col. plates. 22½ᶜᵐ. (The Beacon Hill bookshelf)

I. Title.
                                        26—15065
Library of Congress   PZ7.N173P 4

NN   0024409   DLC PP PHatU MB NN WaS WaSp

Nash, Harriet A.
... Polly's secret... With illustrations in color by Hattie Longstreet Price. Boston, Little, Brown, and company, 1933 [1926]
4 p.l., 292 p.col. plates (incl.front.)
O   (At head of title: The Beacon Hill bookshelf)

NN   0024410   OO OClh OCl

LB1140   Nash, Harriet C
N25   How is our school growing? A growth instrument designed to help teachers of 3-6 year old children to study their group programs and plans.   [Hartford, Conn.] Connecticut State Board of Education, c1955.
          86 p. forms.   (Connecticut. State Dept. of Education. Bulletin 67)

          Bibliography: p. [81]–86.

          1. Nursery schools. 2. Kindergarten.

NN   0024411   CU OCU

Nash, Harry B
Industrial-arts tests for junior and senior high school. Test II by Harry B.Nash ... and Roy R.Van Duzee ... Mechanical drawing ... Milwaukee, Wis., The Bruce publishing company, c1929-30.
6pts. tables,diagrs. 28½cm.

In portfolio.

NN   0024412   MoU

Nash, Harry B
Key Nash-Van Duzee instructional review tests in mechanical drawing. New York, Chicago [etc]. The Bruce publishing company [c1931]
17 p.
On verso of title-page: Harry B. Nash and Roy R. Van Duzee.

NN   0024413   OU

Nash, Harry B
Nash-Van Duzee industrial arts tests ... by Harry B. Nash ... and Roy R. Van Duzee ... Milwaukee, Wis., The Bruce publishing company, ©1927-1928.
1 v. illus.,tables, fold. form. diagrs. 24c.
Caption title.
Various paging.
Contents.-Test I: Woodwork: Scale A: Manual of directions.-Test I: Woodwork: Scale A: Technical and related information.-Scale A: Key.-Scale A: Class record.-Test I: Woodwork: Scale B.-Test I: Woodwork: Scale B: Performance.

NN   0024414   OrCS

---

q744   Nash, Harry B
N171   Nash-Van Duzee industrial arts tests, by Harry B. Nash and Roy R. Van Duzee. New York [c1930]
         6 pieces in portfolio.

         Test II- Mechanical drawing.

NN   0024415   IU

Nash, Harry B
Nash-Van Dezee instructional review tests. Mechanical drawing, by Harry B. Nash... and Roy R. Van Duzee ... New York [etc.] The Bruce publishing co. [1930]
96 p.

Printed in part on one side of the leaf only, on perforated, detached sheets.

NN   0024416   OU

BF441   Nash, Harvey, 1923-
N3   The estimation of body size in relation to actual body size, personal ethos, and developmental status. [Berkeley, 1951]
          x,157 l. diagrs.,tables.

          Thesis (Ph.D.) - Univ. of California, June 1951.
          Bibliography: p.150-153.

NN   0024417   CU

MANN
Film   Nash, Harvey, 1923-
1481   The estimation of body size in relation to actual body size, personal ethos, and developmental status. [Berkeley, Calif.] 1951.
          x, 157 p.

          Thesis - University of California.
          Microfilm copy of typescript. Berkeley, Library Photo Service, University of California, 1969. 1 reel. 35 mm.

          1. Mind and body. 2. Body size. 3. Puberty. 4. Self-perception. I. Title.

NN   0024419   NIC

Nash, Henry.
Barerock; or, The island of pearls ... illustrated by L. Speed. London, E. Arnold [1891]
viii p., 1 l., 411 p. incl. front., illus, pl. map. 12°.   1-18916—M 4

NN   0024420   DLC OU NN PPL MB

Nash, Henry John, 1816–1896.
Bible studies...and other papers, by Henry John Nash... ser. 2-   Putney: A. W. Patching & co., ltd., 19   v. 19cm.

1. Bible—Essays and misc.   I. Title.   July 31, 1942
N. Y. P. L.

NN   0024421   NN

NASH, HENRY JOHN, 1816-1896.
Essays on mining and kindred subjects, by Henry John Nash. London: Search Pub. Co., 1933. 80 p. 19cm.

"Thexarticles by my father were originally issued some years ago and have not been substantially altered."—Note, signed: A.C.N.

696779A. 1. Mines and mining.

NN   0024422   NN

Nash, Henry John, 1816–1896.
Lecture on life, and other papers, by Henry John Nash... Putney: A. W. Patching & co., 1935. 88 p. incl. front. (mounted port.) 19cm. (On half-title: Our reader, vol. 5, p. 24–25.)

59262B. 1. Life.
N. Y. P. L.   August 19, 1942

NN   0024423   NN

[Nash, Henry John] 1816–1896.
Our reader ... v. 1–   Putney: Patching, printers, 1937-   20½cm.

Author's name from caption-titles.

1. Mines and mining.
N. Y. P. L.   August 19, 1942

NN   0024424   NN

VOLUME 405

Nash, Henry S   1832–1901.
Loosening teeth, or chronic alveolitis ... Its causes,
clinical history and treatment ... By Dr. Henry S. Nash
... New York, B. F. Welles, 1897

v. 19ᶜᵐ.

1. Gums—Diseases.

7–7073

Library of Congress   RK381.N24

NN   0024425   DLC PU-D MiU DNLM ICJ NN ICRL

Nash, Henry S   1832–1901.
Chronic alveolitis (pyerrhoea alveolaris
phagedenic pericementitis, Rigg's diseases, etc.)
its causes, clinical history and treatment, with
general directions for the care of the teeth.   New
and rev. ed.   By Dr. Henry S. Nash ...   New
York, F. Schleuning, 1899.
v. 1.   20.5 cm.
Only vol. 1 published.
The first edition was published under the title
Loosening teeth, or chronic alveolitis.

NN   0024426   MiU PPWD

Nash, Henry Sylvester, 1854–1912.
The atoning life, by Henry Sylvester Nash ...   New York,
The Macmillan company, 1908.

ix, 148 p. 19¼ᵐ.

1. Atonement.   I. Title.

8—12601

Library of Congress   BT265.N2
Copyright A 204382   ⟨a39b1⟩   232.3

NN   0024427   DLC NRCR NN MB PPL

Nash, Henry Sylvester, 1854–1912.
The atoning life.   New York, Harper ₍1950₎

xii, 112 p. 20 cm.   (The Presiding Bishop's book for Lent ₍1950₎)

1. Atonement.   I. Title.   (Series)

BT265.N2 1950   232.3   50–5313

NN   0024428   DLC Or AU PPPD PPLT MB NcD

Nash,Henry Sylvester,1854–1912.
239   The belief in democracy & justification
S63   by faith...(In Slocum lectures for 1903–04)
        p.77–94.   19½ cm.

NN   0024429   MiU

Nash, Henry Sylvester, 1854–1912.
Ethics and revelation.   By Henry S. Nash ...   New
York, The Macmillan company; London, Macmillan & co.,
ltd., 1899.

vii, 277 p. 19¼ᶜᵐ.

1. Christian ethics.   2. Revelation.   I. Title.

99—2676

Library of Congress   BJ47.N3

OCl OO OCU CtY
NN   0024430   DLC NNUT ICRL CSaT MB IEG NcD PPL PHC

Nash, Henry Sylvester, 1854–1912.
Genesis of the social conscience; the relation between the
establishment of Christianity in Europe and the social question, by H. S. Nash ...   New York, The Macmillan company;
London, Macmillan & co., ltd., 1897.

viii, 309 p.   19½ cm.

"Notes": p. 305–309.

Continued in next column

Continued from preceding column

1. Social history.   2. Church and social problems.   3. Sociology,
Christian—Hist.   4. Social ethics—Hist.

HN31.N2   8–31808 rev

WaTC OrU
ODW OO OU ICJ NjP NIC MB OCH CoU InU FMU NBuU
NN   0024431   DLC NcD TU NjNbS MH PPPD PPD PU PSC

Nash, Henry Sylvester, 1854–1912.
Genesis of the social conscience; the relation between
the establishment of Christianity in Europe and the
social question, by H. S. Nash ...   New York, London,
The Macmillan co., 1910.

viii, 309 p. 19½ᵐ.

"Notes": p. 305–309.

NN   0024432   CU

Nash, Henry Sylvester, 1854–1912.
The history of the higher criticism of the New Testa-
ment; being the history of the process whereby the Word of
God has won the right to be understood, by Henry S. Nash
...   New York, The Macmillan company; London, Macmil-
lan & co., ltd., 1900.

xi, 192 p. 19 cm.   (Half-title: New Testament handbooks, ed. by
S. Mathews)

1. Bible.   N. T.—Criticism, interpretations, etc.—Hist.   I. Title.

BS2350.N3 1900   0—5249

MiU MdBP NNUT MB TU NjPT
NN   0024433   DLC OrU NjNbS ICRL NcD PPT PP PV OCl

Nash, Henry Sylvester, 1854–1912.
The history of the higher criticism of the New Testament;
being the history of the process whereby the Word of God
has won the right to be understood, by Henry S. Nash ...
New York, The Macmillan company; London, Macmillan &
co., ltd., 1901 ₍c1900₎

xi, 192 p. 19 cm.   (Half-title: New Testament handbooks, ed. by S.
Mathews)

NN   0024434   FTaSU WaTC ODW MH

Nash, Henry Sylvester, 1854–1912.
The history of the higher criticism of the New Testa-
ment; being the history of the process whereby the word
of God has won the right to be understood, by Henry S.
Nash ...   New ed., with a new preface.   New York, The
Macmillan company; London, Macmillan & co., ltd., 1906.

xvii, 192 p. 19 cm.   (Half-title: New Testament handbook, ed.
by Shailer Mathews)

1. Bible.   N. T.—Criticism, interpretation, etc.—Hist.

BS2350.N3 1906   6—8752

OO NcU OrU NjPT MU
NN   0024435   DLC OKentU CoU MeB WaSp PPPD NNUT OU

NASH, Henry Sylvester, 1854–1912.
Is there a social question – for America?
Boston, 1896.

NN   0024436   MH Nh

Nash, Henry Sylvester, 1854–1912.   3485.130
Literature and life in the Apostolic Age. Syllabus of eight lectures
to be given in the rooms of the Twentieth Century Club, ...
beginning Nov. 3, 1903. Arranged by the Biblical Lectures Committee of the Twentieth Century Club of Boston.
= ₍Boston, 1903.₎ ⟨7⟩ pp. 8°.

F2746 — Christianity. — Apostles. — ₍T₎wentieth Century Club. Boston. Biblical Lectures Committee.

NN   0024437   MB

Nash, Henry Sylvester, 1854–1912.
Prayers and meditations, by Henry Sylvester Nash.
New York ₍etc.₎ Longmans, Green, and co., 1915.

2 p. l., 35, ₍1₎ p. 17ᵐᵐ. $0.40

I. Title.

15–25966

NN   0024438   DLC NcU

NASH,Henry Sylvester,1854–1912.
Prayers and meditations. New impression.
New York,etc.,Longmans,Green and Co.,1916.

17 cm. pp.₍4₎,35,₍1₎.
"1st ed.,Nov.1915;re-printed,April 1916."

NN   0024439   MH

Nash, Henry ₍Sylvester₎, 1854–1912.
Protestant Episcopal; a plea for the constitutional study of
the Church's name.   ₍New York;₎ Protestant Episcopal Soc. for
the Promotion of Evangelical Knowledge, 1912.   23⟨1⟩ p. 12°.

1. Protestant Episcopal Church in   the U. S. of America.—Name.
2. Protestant Episcopal Society for   the Promotion of Evangelical
Knowledge.
N. Y. P. L.   March 26, 1913.

NN   0024440   NN

NASH, Henry Sylvester, 1854–1912.
The Rt. Rev. Phillips Brooks.   Sermon.
        Bost.   Damrell & U.   [1893.]   12 pp. 8°.

NN   0024441   MB

Z4011   Nash, Herbert Charles, 1857–1902, comp
.S8
Stanford University. *Libraries.*
Australiana in Leland Stanford Junior University Li-
brary.   The gift of Thomas Welton Stanford.   ₍Stanford
University, Calif., 1901?₎

₍Nash, Herbert Charles₎ 1857–1902, comp.
In memoriam.   Leland Stanford, jr.   ₍San Francisco?
1884?₎
249 p. 2 port. (incl. front.) 22½ᶜᵐ.
Biographical sketch signed : H. C. N. ₍i. e. Herbert Charles Nash₎
Inserted are newspaper clippings concerning Leland Stanford junior
university and also concerning the death of Senator Stanford.

1. Stanford, Leland, jr., 1868–1884.   2. Stanford, Leland, 1824–1893.
I. Title.

Library of Congress   CT275.S66 I 6   10—6475

NN   0024443   DLC

Nash, Herbert Charles, 1857–1902.
A Klondike diamond; a farce in one act ...
Stanford University, California, 1901.
32 p.   16 cm.

NN   0024444   RPB

Nash, Herbert Charles, 1857–1902.   4076.239
The Leland Stanford, Jr. Museum. Origin and description.
= ₍San Francisco.₎ 1886. ⟨23⟩ pp. 22½ cm.

H1580—Leland Stanford Junior Unive. y, Palo Alto, California. Leland Stanford, Jr. Museum.

NN   0024445   MB

VOLUME 405

Rare Books Dept.
Nash, Herbert Charles, 1857-1902.
The train robber. A farce in one act ... As performed by a company of amateurs at Deer Park Inn, California, August 6, 1895. San Francisco, C.A. Murdock & Co., 1895.
39 p. 18cm.

NN   0024446   CU RPB

HS537
.N7A5
1947
Nash, Howard Prevear, 1871-

Freemasons. *New York (State) Grand lodge.*
Collated constitutions of the Grand lodge of Free and accepted masons of the state of New York, by R∴W∴Howard P. Nash ... New York, The Grand lodge, 1947.

HS445
.N7A32
Nash, Howard Pervear, 1871-   comp.

Freemasons. *New York (State) Grand lodge.*
Compilation & digest of decisions and relevant matter contained in proceedings of the Grand lodge of Free and accepted masons of the state of New York, with topical index, by R∴ W∴ Abel Crook ... New York, The Grand lodge, 1929-

---

Nash, Howard Pervear, 1871-   ed.

Cyclopedia of law and procedure ... New York, The American law book company ₁etc., etc.₁ 1901-12.

Nash, Howard Pervear, 1871-   joint ed.

Encyclopædia of forms and precedents for pleading and practice, at common law, in equity, and under the various codes and practice acts. Ed. ... under the supervision of James Cockcroft ... Northport, N. Y., J. Cockcroft, 1896-1904.

HS445
.N7A3
1952
Nash, Howard Pervear, 1871-   ed.
FOR OTHER EDITIONS
SEE MAIN ENTRY
Freemasons. *New York (State) Grand Lodge.*
Handbook of masonic law of New York, by Howard P. Nash. Rev. ed. New York, Grand Lodge, F. & A. M., 1952.

Nash, Howard Pervear, 1871-   comp.

Freemasons. *New York (State) Grand lodge.*
Handbook of masonic law of New York and index-digest to the two volumes of "Compilation and digest of masonic law" published in 1929 and 1932. New York, The Grand lodge, F. & A. M., 1935.

Nash, Howard Pervear, 1871-   comp.
Sigma alpha epsilon.
The sixth general catalogue of Sigma alpha epsilon, comp. during the terms of the following eminent supreme recorders: Howard P. Nash, Edward H. Virgin, William C. Levere. Evanston, Ill. ₁The Evanston index co.₁ 1904.

Nash, I   E
Cold flame; a drama...by I. E. Nash and Joseph Kaye. ₁n. p.₁ c1932. 42, 30, 45 f. 28cm.

Typescript.

1. Drama, American. I. Kaye, Joseph. it au. II. Title.

NN   0024454   NN

Nash, Ide D   1872-
My prison experience in Oklahoma; bootlegging a failure and a lecture to young men, by Ide D. Nash ... ₁Hugo, Okla., The Husonian₁ 1918.
92 p. 18ᶜᵐ.

1. Prisons—Oklahoma. ₁. Title.

Library of Congress   HV9475.O6N3   18-16235

NN   0024455   DLC

NASH, INGBERT, father, 1885-1935.
Die Brüder Kommunisten. München, Verlag Zeichenring [1933] 8, 31 p. 23cm.

Film reproduction. Negative.
Cover-title.
Imperfect: p. 9-24 wanting.

1. Bolshevism--Germany.

NN   0024456   NN

Nash, Irene.
Following a star ₁by₁ Irene Nash. London: A. Gray (books) ltd. ₁193-?₁ 249 p. 19cm.

77963B. 1. Moving pictures—   Fiction. 2. Fiction, English. I. Title.
N.Y.P.L.   November 22, 1940

NN   0024457   NN

Nash, Irene (Lande)
see
Lande-Nash, Irene, 1914-1961.

Nash, J.
Brothers Maris.
1907.

NN   0024459   NjP

Nash, J
Royal institute of painters in water colours.

NN   0024460   NjP

Nash, J.A.
see Nash, John Adams, 1798-1877.

Nash, J. Eveleigh
see Nash, James Eveleigh.

Nash, J   Frank, 1924-
Esters of gentisic acid and their toxicities. 1952.
112 l.
Thesis - Ohio State University.

NN   0024463   OU

Nash, J. Kirke
see Nash, John Kirke.

Nash, J.O.
see Nash, James Okey.

[Nash, J.P.]
see Nash, James Powell.

Nash, J.T.C.
see Nash, James Thomas Charles, 1865-

Nash, J.V.
see Nash, James Vincent, 1886-

FILM
5983
HF
Nash, Jacob
₁General labor account book, 1705-1710.₁
Boston, 1705-10₁
1 v. On film.
Microfilm copy of original manuscript in Baker library, Harvard university Graduate school of business administration.

1. Accounting - To 1800.

NN   0024469   CU

Nash, James of Limerick.
Several informations of John MacNamarra ... relating to the horrid popish plot in Ireland
see under MacNamarra, John, of Cratelagh

Nash, James of Nice.
Guide to Nice. Lond., 1884.

NN   0024471   DN

Nash, James, of Nice.
History of Nice and its neighbourhood. Lond. Kirby, 1882.
283 p. T.

NN   0024472   NRU

Nash, James Addison.
The southern family physician. By James Addison Nash ... 2d ed. Philadelphia, Pile & M'Elroy, printers, 1860.
52 p. front. (port.) 14½ᶜᵐ.

1. Medicine, Popular.

Library of Congress   RC81.N288   7-10380†

NN   0024473   DLC

Nash, James Addison.
The third edition of Dr. Nash's practice, containing all the practical matter of the two former editions of the "Southern family physician." Rev. and improved. Dallas, Tex., Texas Baptist publishing house, 1878.
220 p. 17½ᶜᵐ.

1. Medicine, Popular.

Library of Congress   RC81.N29   7-10379†

NN   0024474   DLC DNLM

Nash, James Eveleigh, ed.
The Ladysmith treasury. London, Sands, 1900.
343 p.

NN   0024475   PP

VOLUME 405

Nash, James J
Institutiones philosophicae. Bruxellis,
Goemaers, 1868.
v.

NN   0024476   PPCCH

Nash, James Meyndert William.
De geologie der Grande-Chartreuseketens ... door James
Meyndert William Nash ... Delft, Gedrukt bij de Technische
boekhandel en drukkerij, J. Waltman, jr., 1926.
5 p. l., ₍vii₎-x p., 1 l., 240 p. illus., plates (part fold.)
3 fold. col. maps, 4 fold. profiles. 27ᶜᵐ.
Proefschrift—Delft.
"Literatuurlijsten": p. ₍213₎-240.
"Stellingen" and "Errata" on loose leaves.

1. Geology—France.   I. Title.   II. Title: Grande-Chartreuseketen.

——— Copy 2.   G S 27-15
Library, U. S. Geological   Survey 203(540) N17g

NN   0024477   DI-GS PU CU IU DLC PPF

NASH, James Okey.
S.Ignatius of Antioch;was he an obsessed
neurotic? A comment on Dr.Streeter's
"Primitive church." ₍London,Mowbray,1930₎.

NN   0024478   MH

Nash, James Okey
The victory of faith, by J. O. Nash ... with
foreword by the Archbishop of York ... West-
minister, National society; ₍London₎ Society for
promoting christian knowledge ₍1942₎
xxvi, 244 p. 18½cm. (Church education
publications)
"First published in 1933."

NN   0024479   NcD

Nash, James Philip.
Roberts, John R.
... The geology of Val Verde county, by John R. Roberts
and James P. Nash ... Austin, Tex., The University ₍1918₎

Nash, James Philip.
... Road-building materials in Texas, by James P. Nash
in cooperation with C. L. Baker, E. L. Porch, jr., and R. G.
Tyler ... Austin, Tex., The University ₍1918₎
159 p. 10 pl. on 8 l. 23½ cm. (University of Texas bulletin.
no. 1839; July 10, 1918)
"Bureau of economic geology and technology. Division of economic
geology."

1. Road materials.   I. Baker, Charles Laurence, 1887-   II.
Porch, Edwin Leight, jr.   III. Tyler, Richard Gaines, 1885-   IV.
Texas. University. Bureau of economic geology and technology.
Division of economic geology.   v. Title.
                                    20—27030
Library of Congress   TE200.N3 1918

MtBC OrCS OU OrU NSyU
NN   0024481   DLC CU GU CoU PU MiU OU OCU ICJ MtBuM

Nash, James Philip.
... Road materials of Texas, by James P. Nash ... Austin, Tex., The University ₍1915₎
70 p. front., plates, map. 23ᶜᵐ. (Bulletin of the University of Texas.
1915: no. 62. Nov. 5, 1915)
At head of title: Bureau of economic geology and technology. J. A.
Udden, director.

1. Road materials.   I. Texas. University. Bureau of economic geology and technology.

Library of Congress   TE200.N3   16—27081

ICJ NN
NN   0024482   DLC NSyU MtBuM OrU PU MiU OU OCl OCU

Nash, James Philip.
... **Roads** and pavements. Austin, Tex., The University
₍1917₎

Nash, James Philip.
... Tests of concrete aggregates used in Texas, by J. P. Nash
... Austin, Tex., The University ₍1917₎
80 p.   illus. diagrs. 23½ᶜᵐ.   (University of Texas bulletin. no. 1771:
Dec. 20, 1917)
"Bureau of economic geology and technology ... Division of engineer-
ing ..."

1. Concrete—Testing.   I. Texas. University. Bureau of economic
geology and technology. Division of engineering.   II. Title.

Library of Congress   TA440.N3   19—27341
——— Copy 2.   AS36.T4 no. 1771

NN   0024484   DLC TxU OrU OU PU MiU ICJ ICU NN

Nash, James Philip.
... Texas granites, by J. P. Nash ... Austin, Tex., The
University ₍1917₎
8 p. 5 pl. on 3 l. (incl. front.) 23½ᶜᵐ. (University of Texas bulletin.
no. 1725: May 1, 1917)
At head of title: ... Bureau of economic geology and technology. J. A.
Udden, director.

1. Granite—Texas.   I. Texas. University. Bureau of economic
geology and technology.

Library of Congress   TN970.N3   18—27067

OCl MtBC ICJ NN OrCS MiEM MU OrU
NN   0024485   DLC KMK IU CoU MtBuM PP PU OU MiU OCU

Nash, James Powell.
Observations on the public right of fishing by
angle or nets ...
see under   Hughes, William, 1803-1861.

RB151   Nash, James Thomas Charles, 1865-
.N3   Evolution and disease. Bristol,
1915   John Wright, 1915.
viii, 73 p. 22 cm.

1. Diseases--Causes and theories of
causation. I. Title.

NN   0024487   ViU-M DNLM

614.49   Nash,James Thomas Charles,1865-
N251e   Evolution and disease,by J.T.C.Nash ... New
1915   York, W.Wood and company, 1915.
viii,73 p. 22ᶜᵐ.
Founded on the author's Chadwick public lectures
on The evolution of epidemics,delivered in April,
1913. cf.Pref.
"Printed in England."
"References": p.72-73.

1.Epidemics--Hist. I.Title.

NcD
NN   0024488   MiU PPC OU DNLM IU-M ICJ CtY-M NcU

Nash, James Vincent, 1886-
... Exploring the world of men, by J. V. Nash, Elizabeth L.
Hayes and Franklin Barnes. Chicago, Follett publishing
company ₍°1935₎
320, ₍4₎ p. incl. illus., pl. 21ᶜᵐ. (Follett social science readers.
book 6)
Maps on lining-papers.
Published separately under the following titles: pt. 1, Races of men
by J. V. Nash.—pt. 2, The tongues of man, by Elizabeth L. Hayes.—
pt. 3, Man and his records, by F. Barnes.

1. Ethnology—Juvenile literature. 2. Language and languages—Ju-
venile literature. 3. Writing—Hist. 4. Paleography—Juvenile litera-
ture.   I. Hayes, Elizabeth Le May.   II. Barnes, Franklin.   III. Title.
                                    36—3520
Library of Congress   PE1127.S6F6 bk. 6
——— Copy 2.
Copyright A 90240   ₍3₎   (308.2) 572

NN   0024489   DLC OrMonO WaSp MH

RH   Nash, James Vincent, 1886-
H-J   Great fighters for freedom ₍by₎ J.V. Nash.
1266   Girard, Kan., Haldeman-Julius co. ₍°1928₎
Little   64p. 13ᶜᵐ. (Little blue book no.1266,
KANSAS   ed. by E. Haldeman-Julius)
COLLECTION   Contents.- Giordano Bruno.- Desiderius Eras-
Kenneth Spencer   mus.- Nicholas Copernicus.- Thomas Paine.
Research Library   1. Free thought. 2. Liberty. I. Haldeman-
Julius Publishing co. II. Title. III.
YA 27742   Series.

NN   0024490   KU-RH DLC

Nash, James Vincent, 1886-
... Homosexuality in lives of the great.
J.V. Nash. Girard, Kansas, Haldeman-Julius
publications ₍°1930₎
64 p. 13 cm. (Little blue book, no. 1564,
ed. by E. Haldeman-Julius)
Reference to Walt Whitman, p. 59-60.

NN   0024491   RPB

YA   Nash, James Vincent.
28083   How Galileo was gagged by the inquisition.
(Little Blue Book No. 1383.)

NN   0024492   DLC

Nash, James Vincent, 1886-
How the world lives, by J. V. Nash, drawings by Richard S.
Rodgers. Chicago, Thomas S. Rockwell company, 1931.
112 p. incl. front., illus. 20½ᶜᵐ.

1. Sociology—Juvenile literature.   I. Title.
Library of Congress   H95.N3   31-25996
——— Copy 2.
Copyright A 40591   ₍5₎   301

NN   0024493   DLC MB WaS OO ODW OCl

J301   Nash, James Vincent, 1886-
N174   How the world lives, by J. V. Nash, drawings by Richard S.
Rodgers. Chicago, Follett pub. co. ₍°1931₎.
112 p. incl. front., illus. 20½ᶜᵐ.

NN   0024494   OrMonO WaSp

Nash, James Vincent, 1886-
How the world lives, by J.V.Nash. Man and his
customs, by Margaret Fry. Chicago, Follett
publishing co. ₍c.1934₎
"Follett social science readers, 5."

NN   0024495   MH

YA   Nash, James Vincent, 1886-
27994   Huxley: Who advanced human progress 100 Years.
(Little Blue Book No. 1328.)

NN   0024496   DLC

YA   Nash, James Vincent, 1886-
27962   Isaac Newton: Superman of science.
(Little Blue Book No. 1368.)

NN   0024497   DLC

VOLUME 405

RH
H-J
1368
Little

KANSAS
COLLECTION
*Kenneth Spencer
Research Library*

Nash, James Vincent, 1886–
Isaac Newton: superman of science ₍by₎
J.V. Nash.   Girard, Kan., Haldeman-Julius
co. ₍c1929₎
64p. 13ᶜᵐ. (Little blue book no.1368,
ed. by E. Haldeman-Julius)

1. Newton, Sir Isaac, 1642-1727.
I. Haldeman-Julius Publishing co. II.
Title. III. Series.

NN 0024498   KU-RH

Nash, James Vincent, 1886–
... Living and working together, by J. V. Nash and Margaret Fry. Chicago, Follett publishing company ₍*1935₎
218, ₍2₎ p. illus. 21ᶜᵐ. (Follett social science readers. book 5)
Illustrated lining-papers.
Published separately under the following titles: pt. 1, How the world
lives, by J. V. Nash.—pt. 2, Man and his customs, by Margaret Fry.

1. Sociology—Juvenile literature. 2. Manners and customs—Juvenile
literature. I. Fry, Margaret. II. Title.
36-3518
Library of Congress   PE1127.S6F6 bk. 5
——— Copy 2.
Copyright A 90239   ₍3₎   (308.2) 301

NN 0024499   DLC OrMonO

Nash, James Vincent, 1886–
Living and working together, by J.V. Nash and
Margaret Fry. Chicago, Follett [1936]

218 p. (Follett Social science readers, 5)

NN 0024500   MH

Nash, James Vincent, 1886–
... Making life secure, by James V. Nash ... ₍and₎ Harley W.
Mitchell ... Chicago, Follett publishing company ₍*1935₎
355, ₍3₎ p. incl. illus., plates. 21ᶜᵐ. (Follett social science readers.
book 7)
Illustrated lining-papers.
Parts 1 and 2, published separately under the following titles: This
man-made world, by A. R. Fisher and Man and his riches, by Mary B.
Ambler.
CONTENTS.—pt. 1. This man-made world.—pt. 2. Man and his riches.—
pt. 3. Man and his government.
1. Inventions—Juvenile literature. 2. Economics—Juvenile literature.
3. Political science—Juvenile literature. I. Mitchell, Harley W. II.
Fisher, Anthony R. This man-made world. III. Ambler, Mary B. Man
and his riches. IV. Title.
36-3517
Library of Congress   PE1127.S6F6 bk. 7
——— Copy 2.
Copyright A 90241   ₍3₎   (308.2) 608

NN 0024501   DLC OC1 OrMonO

Nash, James Vincent, 1886–
Races of men, by J. V. Nash; drawings by Don Nelson.
Chicago, Thomas S. Rockwell company, 1931.
110 p. incl. front., illus. 20½ᶜᵐ.

1. Ethnology—Juvenile literature. I. Title.
31-15324
Library of Congress   GN330.N3
——— Copy 2.
Copyright A 38364   ₍5₎   572

NN 0024502   DLC GU OrMonO PPGi ODW OLak MB

Nash, James Vincent, 1886–
Races of men, by J.V. Nash. The tongues of
man, by Elizabeth L. Hayes. Man and his records,
by Franklin Barnes
see his Exploring the world of men.

RH
H-J
1593
Little

KANSAS
COLLECTION
*Kenneth Spencer
Research Library*

Nash, James Vincent, 1886–
Romantic heroes of the Confederacy ₍by₎
J.V. Nash.   Girard, Kan., Haldeman-Julius
co. ₍c1931₎
64p. 13ᶜᵐ (Little blue book no.1593,
ed. by E. Haldeman-Julius)

Continued in next column

Continued from preceding column

1. Confederate States of America. Biography. I. Haldeman-Julius Publishing co.
II. Title.   III. Series.

NN 0024504   KU-RH

Case
3A
1261

YA
28103

NASH, JAMES VINCENT, 1886–
Voltaire's weapon – the smile! Girard,
Kan., Haldeman-Julius publications[194-?]
62p. 13cm.   (Little blue book 1406)
Includes Floyd Dell, "Upton Sinclair in
America," p.58-62.
Tan wrappers with union label; copyright
date removed. For date of issue, see P.B.S.A.
64 (1970), 50-52. Originally issued 1929.

NN 0024505   ICN DLC

Nash, Jay Bryan, 1886–1965.
The administration of physical education, with special refer-
ence to public schools, by Jay B. Nash ... New York, A. S.
Barnes and company, incorporated, 1931.
xiii, 491 p. incl. illus., maps, plans, diagrs., forms. 23½ᶜᵐ.
Bibliography at end of each chapter except chapters I and IX;
"General bibliographies": p. 477.

1. Physical education and training. 2. Playgrounds. I. Title.
31-30241
Library of Congress   GV361.N3
——— Copy 2.
Copyright A 44138   ₍5₎   371.73

OCU ODW OO OC1 MiU MB PPT OrU CaBVaU OrAshS
NN 0024506   DLC KEmT WU OrSaW OrCS NcGU NcRS ViU

Nash, Jay Bryan, 1886–1965.
The administration of physical education,
with special reference to public schools.
New York, Barnes, 1932.
xiii, 491 p. incl. illus., maps, plans,
diagrs., forms. 24 cm.

NN 0024507   TU IdU-SB

Nash, Jay Bryan,   1886–1965.
The administration of play and recreation activities in a city, by Jay B. Nash ... ₍New York,
Playground and recreation association of America,
1922₎
7, ₍1₎ p. 18½cm.

Caption title.
"Address given at Recreation congress, Atlantic
City, N. J., October 9-12, 1922."

unacc.

NN 0024508   IdU-SB

Nash, Jay Bryan, 1886–1965.
Building morale, by Jay B. Nash ... New York, A. S.
Barnes and company ₍1942₎
vi, 154 p. 21½ᶜᵐ.

1. Morale. 2. Democracy. 3. Totalitarianism. I. Title.
42-12059
Library of Congress   HM291.N3
₍18₎   301.15

OC1 OU OrCS OrU MtU Wa
NN 0024509   DLC NcD DNLM OrSaW CU TU PP PPD OO OLak

GV
345
N37

Nash, Jay Bryan, 1886–1965, ed.
Character education through physical
education. New York, Barnes, c1932.
x, 315 p. (Interpretations of physical
education, v.3)

Bibliography: p.291-315.

1. Physical education and training.
2. Moral education. I. Title. II. Series.

NN 0024510   WaU NcC OC1 OU NcRS PP CaBVaU

Nash, Jay Bryan, 1886–1965.
Contributions of physical education to general education.
(*In* National education association of the United States. Addresses
and proceedings, 1928. p. 563-567)

1. Physical education ₍and training₎ I. Title.
E 31-174
Library, U. S. Office of   Education L13.N212 1928

NN 0024511   DHEW OU

Nash, Jay Bryan, 1886–1965
The contribution of physical education to mental morality—
abstract ₍by₎ Jay B. Nash.
(*In* National education association of the United States. Addresses
and proceedings, 1931. p. 543)

1. Physical education ₍and training₎ I. Title.
E 33-544
Library, U. S. Office of   Education L13.N212 1931
Library of Congress   [L13.N4 1931]
₍2₎

NN 0024512   DHEW

Nash, Jay Bryan, 1886-1965.
The Fremont plan of athletics [by] J.B. Nash,...
[n.p., n.d.]
6 l.   26 cm.
Typewritten.
1. Physical education and training. I. Title.

NN 0024513   CU

GV341
N28

Nash, Jay Bryan, 1886–1965, ed.
Interpretations of physical education ... edited by Jay B.
Nash ... New York, A. S. Barnes and company, incorporated, 1931-35.
5 v. illus., diagrs. 19½ cm. (School of education series, New York
university)
Vol. I published 1930 under title: Symposium on physical education
and health.
Includes bibliographies.
CONTENTS.—I. Mind-body relationships.—II. Nature and scope of examinations.—III. Character education through physical education.—
IV. Physiological health.—v. Professional preparation.
1. Physical education and training. 2. Hygiene. I. Title.

GV341.N28   371.73   31—22051

MtU WaWW OrCS OrLgE OrU Or
NN 0024514   DLC WaTC PWcS OU MiU OOxM OCU KEmT MeB

Nash, Jay Bryan, 1886–1965, ed.
Interpretations of physical education ... edited by Jay B.
Nash ... New York, A. S. Barnes and company, incorporated,
₍1931₎-38.
5 v. illus., diagrs. 19½ᶜᵐ. (School of education series, New York
university.
Vol. I published 1930 under title: Symposium on physical education
and health.
Includes bibliographies.
Ordinary edition (limited)
CONTENTS.—I. Mind-body relationships.—II. Nature and scope of ex-
aminations.—III. Character education through physical education.—IV.
Physiological health.—v. Professional preparation.
1. Physical education and training. 2. Hygiene. I. Title.

NN 0024515   DHEW ViU

Nash, Jay Bryan, 1886–1965.
... Leisure for what? From the thirteenth Iowa conference
on child development and parent education, by Jay B. Nash ...
Iowa City, Ia., The University ₍1940₎
12 p. 23½ᶜᵐ. (₍Iowa. University₎ Child welfare pamphlets, no. 75)
University of Iowa publication. New series, no. 1111, Feb. 28, 1940.

1. Leisure. I. Title.
E 40-181
U. S. Off. of educ. Library
for Library of Congress   [LB1103.I 6 no. 75]
₍2₎   ([159.9227]) (136.7)

NN 0024516   DHEW OU

Nash, Jay Bryan, 1886–1965, ed.
Mind-body relationships, edited by Jay
B. Nash. New York, A.S. Barnes and company,
incorporated, 1931. 276 pp.
(Interpretations of physical education
series, vol.I.)

NN 0024517   OU

VOLUME 405

Nash, Jay Bryan, 1886–*1965.*
A modern public school physical education program—Abstract.
(*In* National education association of the United States. Addresses and proceedings, 1930. p. 512–515)

1. Physical education (and training)

E 33–239

Library, U. S. Office of   Education L13.N212 1930
Library of Congress   [L13.N4 1930]
(3)

NN 0024518   DHEW

Nash, Jay Bryan,   *1886–1965, ed.*   3767.**220**
— Nature and scope of examinations.
New York. Barnes & Co. 1931. viii, 307 pp. Charts. [New York University. School of Education Series. Interpretations of physical education. Vol. 2] 19 cm.
Articles by various writers.

D587 — S.r. — Examinations.

NN 0024519   MB CU

(Nash, Jay Bryan) 1886–*1965, ed.*
The new day for the Indians; a survey of the working of the Indian reorganization act of 1934. (New York, Academy press) 1938.
47, (1) p. illus. (incl. maps) diagr. 21ᶜᵐ.

"This pamphlet ... has been put together under the editorial supervision of Prof. Jay B. Nash ... Oliver La Farge ... and W. Carson Ryan."—p. 2.

1. Indians of North America—Government relations.   I. La Farge, Oliver, 1901–   joint ed.   II. Ryan, Will Carson, 1885–   joint ed.   III. Title.   IV. Title: Indian reorganization act of 1934.

39—20662

Library of Congress   E93.N23
(41c1)   970.5

NN 0024520   DLC Or NjP PHC NN NNC PPT

Nash, Jay Bryan, 1886–*1965.*
Opportunities in physical education, health and recreation. New York, Vocational Guidance Manuals (1950)
80 p. 22 cm. (Vocational guidance manuals)
Bibliography: p. 52–53. "Selected list of professional magazines": p. 54.

1. Physical education as a profession. 2. Recreation leadership. 3. Health education.   I. Title.

GV224.A1N78   371.73069   50–7523

OEac TxU MiD
NN 0024521   DLC OrCS OrPS OCl PU-Penn PPCCH LU

Nash, Jay Bryan, 1886–*1965.*
Opportunities in physical education, health, and recreation. (Rev. ed.) New York, Vocational Guidance Manuals (1953)
128 p. 21 cm. (Vocational guidance manuals)

1. Physical education as a profession. 2. Recreation leadership. 3. Health education.   I. Title.
GV224.A1N78 1953   371.73069   53–6761 ‡

NN 0024522   DLC PPT NcC OCl OEac

Nash, Jay Bryan, 1886–*1965.*
The organization and administration of playgrounds and recreation, by Jay B. Nash ... New York, A. S. Barnes & company, 1927.
xii, 547 p. incl. front., illus., plans, diagrs. 23½ᶜᵐ.
Bibliography at end of each chapter.

1. Playgrounds. 2. Community centers. 3. Play. 4. Games. 5. Amusements. 6. Sports.   I. Title.
Library of Congress   GV423.N3
27–22470 Revised

PU–W ODW OCU OO WaU MB NN MH MtU WaT IdU WaS OrU Or
NN 0024523   DLC PHC PPT KMK PPSJ WU DHEW NcD PP

GV423
.N3
1931
Nash, Jay Bryan, 1886–*1965.*
The organization and administration of playgrounds and recreation, by Jay B. Nash ... New York, A. S. Barnes & company, 1931.
xii, 547 p. incl. front., illus., plans, diagrs. 23½ᶜᵐ.
Bibliography at end of each chapter.

1. Playgrounds. 2. Community centers. 3. Play. 4. Games. 5. Recreation. 6. Sports. I. Title.

NN 0024524   PSt CaBVaU

GV423
.N3
1938
Nash, Jay Bryan, 1886–*1965.*
The organization and administration of playgrounds and recreation. New York, Barnes, 1938 [c1927]
xii, 547 p. illus. 24 cm.
Includes bibliographies.

1. Playgrounds. 2. Recreation.

NN 0024525   MB OC1W

Nash, Jay Bryan, 1886–*1965*
Philosophy of recreation and leisure. St. Louis, Mosby, 1953.
222 p. illus. 23 cm.

1. Recreation.   I. Title.

GV14.N25   790   53–5924 ‡

WaS WaT CaBVaU
NN MB OU NcRS CaBVa IdU PPT MiU MtBC OrCS OrPE
NN 0024526   DLC OrU OC1W PPEB PSt TU TxU OOxM ViU

Nash, Jay Bryan, 1886–*1965*
Physical education: interpretations and objectives. New York, A. S. Barnes (1948)
288 p. diagrs. 22 cm.
Includes bibliographies.

1. Physical education and training.

GV342.N3   371.732   48–7233*

NcGU WaT IdPI OrPS WaWW WaChenE ICRL CtY-M
NN 0024527   DLC OrU CaBVaU MtU Or OrCS OO MB OU

Nash, Jay Bryan, 1886–*1965.*
Physical education: organization and administration, by J. B. Nash, Francis J. Moench, and Jeannette B. Saurborn. New York, A. S. Barnes, 1951.
viii, 498 p. illus. 22 cm.
Includes bibliographies.

1. Physical education and training.

GV361.N315   371.732   51–3755

MtBC
OrP OrU WaS TxU ViU ICRL OrMonO OrPR OrPS IdPI
NN 0024528   DLC TU NcU MiU CaBVa CaBVaU Or OrCS

Nash, Jay Bryan, 1886–*1965.*
Physical education: organization and administration, by J. B. Nash, Francis J. Moench, and Jeannette B. Saurborn New York, Ronald Press (c1951)
viii, 498 p. illus. 22 cm.
Includes bibliographies.

1. Physical education and training.

NN 0024529   MtU

Nash, Jay Bryan, 1886–*1965, ed.*
... Physiological health. School of education series, New York university. xi, 308p. diagrs. New York, A. S. Barnes and company, incorporated, 1933 (Interpretations of physical education: Jay B. Nash, editor, v.4)

Bibliography: p. (285)–308

NN 0024530   OCl PP

Nash, Jay Bryan, 1886–*1965.*
... Professional preparation. School of education series, New Yorkuniversity. x,423p. tables (some fold.) New York, A.S.Barnes and company, incorporated, 1935. (Interpretations of physical education... Jay B. Nash, ed., v.5)

NN 0024531   OCl

Nash, Jay Bryan, 1886–*1965.*
The relation of public playgrounds and recreation centers to our national ideals of democracy.
(*In* National education association of the United States. Addresses and proceedings, 1921. p. 519–521)

1. Physical education (and training). 2. Play.   I. Title.

E 22–162

U. S. Off. of educ.   Library
for Library of Congress   (41d1)

NN 0024532   DHEW OO OU

98.5
N17
Nash, Jay Bryan, 1886–1965.
Report to Recreation advisory committee, Arlington county, Virginia. [n.p., 1944]
25 numb. l.
1. Arlington co., Va. Parks. 2. Planning, Community. 3. Playgrounds. I. Arlington co., Va. Recreational advisory committee.

NN 0024533   DNAL

Nash, Jay Bryan, 1886–*1965.*
Spectatoritis, by Jay B. Nash ... New York, Holston house, Sears publishing company, inc. (c1932)
4 p. L, 284 p. diagr. 21ᶜᵐ.

1. Leisure. 2. Conduct of life. 3. Mental physiology and hygiene. I. Title.

Library of Congress   BJ1498.N3   32–14186

OOxM DHEW WaU
NN 0024534   DLC WaT IdU OrPR OrCS OrU PPT OO ODW

Nash, Jay Bryan, *1886–1965.*

Spectatoritis. N.Y., Barnes, 1937.
284p.

NN 0024535   OC1W PPT

170
N17s
1938
Nash, Jay Bryan, 1886–*1965.*
Spectatoritis ...   New York, A. S. Barnes and company, 1938.
284p.

1. Leisure. 2. Conduct of life. 3. Mental physiology and hygiene. I. Title.

NN 0024536   IU Mi CU MU

Nash, Jay Bryan, 1886–1965.
Standards of play and recreation administration.
see under   National Municipal League.
Committee on play and recreation administration.

Nash, Jay Bryan, 1886–1965.
Syllabus. Organization of playground activities arranged by Jay B. Nash ... and Ruth M. Findlay... School of directed activities University of California 1917.
1 p.l., 41 p. fold. outline. 29 cm.
Typewritten.
1. Playgrounds. I. Title: Organization of playground activities. II. Findlay, Ruth M. jt. author.

NN 0024538   CU

VOLUME 405

Nash, Jay Bryan, 1886-1965, ed.

New York university. *School of education.*
... Symposium on physical education and health, compiled
and edited by Jay B. Nash ... assisted by Emma R. Frazier
and Marguerite Vollmer; February 27, 28, March 1, 1930.
New York, N. Y., New York university press book store [*1930]

RA420
.N28
Nash, Jay Bryan, 1886- 1965.
Teachable moments, a new approach to health, by Jay B.
Nash ... New York, A. S. Barnes and company, 1938.
x p., 2 l., 3-243 p. diagr. 19½ cm.
"This edition was printed in the one hundredth anniversary year
of A. S. Barnes and company."—p. [IV]

     1. Hygiene. 2. Hygiene—Study and teaching. I. Title.
                         38—36000

   Library of Congress   RA420.N28
                [48z2]   613.07

         OrU-M OrStbM TU
         WaTC OrSaW MtU IdU Or OrCS OrLgE OrMonO CaBVaU OrU
NN   0024540   DLC KEmT WaE ICRL PPT OO OC1 OC1W OU

Nash, Jean, 1912–
The student editor's manual ... Illustrations by Hugh Troy.
New York, 1947.
[3]–82 p. illus., diagr. 28ᶜᵐ.
Caption title.
"First edition, March 1947."
Bibliography: p. 67.

     1. College and school journalism. I. Title.
   LB3621.N3   371.805   47–4523
                                      Brief cataloging

NN   0024541   DLC CaBVa MtU Or WaS PSt PU-Penn TxU

Nash, Jessie Pinning.
Road-building materials in Texas
     see under   Nash, James Philip.

Nash, Jessie Pinning.
Tests of concrete aggregates used in Texas
     see under   Nash, James Philip.

TD1954
N174
Nash, Joe Bert, 1921–
Metabolic studies of some 5-substituted-5-
phenylhydantoins.   [Austin, Tex., 1954]
73,[2] l. illus. 28cm.
Thesis (Ph.D.) - University of Texas, 1954.
Vita.
Bibliography: l.68-73.

     1. Hydantoins. 2. Metabolism. Dept.:
Pharmacy.

NN   0024544   TxU

HS
397
N25
Nash, Joel.
Lebanon; or, A 'light' from the Lebanon
Lodge at Gloucester; being explanatory
lectures on the spirituality of freemasonry.
Colchester, S. Haddon [pref. 1836]
vii, 96 p. 21cm.

     1. Freemasons—Addresses, essays, lec-
tures. 2. Freemasons. Gloucester. Lebanon
Lodge. I. Title. II. Title: A light from
the Lebanon Lodge at Gloucester.

NN   0024545   NIC

PT8175
.N27A7
Nash, Jørgen, 1930-
Af en studedrivers erindringer; småprosa. Illustrationer
af Jørgen Rytter. København, Borgen, 1951.
55 p. illus. 21 cm.
CONTENTS.—Af en studedrivers erindringer.—Den første vårfest.—
November-da capo.—Geder og godtfolk.—Omar Khairat.—Om gøgl og
illusion.

     I. Title.

                                   A 52–1194

   Minnesota. Univ. Libr.
   for Library of Congress   [2]

NN   0024546   MnU DLC NN CU

Nash, Jørgen, 1920–
Atom-elegien, af Jørgen Nash.   Fredericia, Nordiske landes
bogforlag, 1946.   34 p.   22cm.
"1. oplag. 500 eksemplarer."

NN   0024547   NN

PT8175
.N27G3
Nash, Jørgen, 1920-
Galgenfuglen; et romaneksperiment. København, Tha-
ning & Appel, 1949.
183 p. 20 cm.

     I. Title.

                                   A 50–5901

   Minnesota. Univ. Libr.
   for Library of Congress   [2]

NN   0024548   MnU NcU NN CU

Nash, Jørgen, 1920-
Leve livet.   Med tegninger af Asger Jorn.   [København]
Thaning & Appel, c1948.
45 p. illus.

NN   0024549   CU DLC-P4

4PT
Dan.-
32
Nash, Jörgen, 1920-
Salvi dylvo.   [Af] Jorgen Nash og Asger
Jorgensen.   København, Helhesten [   ]

NN   0024550   DLC-P4

Dan
N251s
Nash, Jørgen, 1920-
Salvi Dylvo; [digte af] Jørgen Nash og
[litografi af] Asger Jørgensen.   København,
Helhestens Forlag [1945?]
[46] p. illus. 22cm.

     300 copies. No.171, signed by the author
& illustrator.

     I. Jorn, Asger Oluf, 1914-   illus. II.
Title.

NN   0024551   IEN

Nash, Jørgen, 1920–
...Sindets underjord; digte.   Kjøbenhavn, Nyt nordisk for-
lag, 1943.   110 p.   20cm.
One of 550 copies.

NN   0024552   NN IEN

839.811
N251u
Nash, Jørgen, 1920-
Udvalgte digte.   København, Borgens
forlag, 1954.
108p.   20cm.

NN   0024553   IEN KU CU DLC-P4 MH MnU

Nash, Jørgen, 1920-
Vredens sange; digte. København, Borgen [c1951]
57 p. 21 cm.

     I. Title.

                                 A 52–784

   Minnesota. Univ. Libr.
   for Library of Congress   [2]

NN   0024554   MnU

PS593
.L9N45
Nash, John i.e. "Jolly Nash.
Jolly John Nash's Our boys songster, containing
the largest collection of new and original songs
heretofore placed before the public, by the above
humorous and witty vocalist ...   New York,
A.J. Fisher [c1876]
60, [1] p.   16 cm.
Colored portrait on cover.
With music.

NN   0024555   RPB DLC NN

QA270
N34
Nash, John, *mathematician*.
n-Person games. 4 June 1951.   Santa
Monica, Calif., Rand Corp., c1951.
3 l.   table.   (Project Rand research
memorandum, RM-615)

     On cover: U.S. Air Force, Project Rand.
Copyright date stamped on t.p.

NN   0024556   CU

Nash, John, of Grays-Inn.
A poem, condoling the death of K. Charles II.
of blessed memory: and contratulating His present
Majesty. By John Nash of Grays-Inn, esq; ...
London: Printed for Randal Taylor ... 168⅝
1 p.l., 2 p.   35x23½ᶜᵐ. fold.to 28x19ᶜᵐ.
[Poetry longwaies. London, 1683-85. no.144]
WILLIAM
ANDREWS
CLARK   Signatures: 1 leaf unsigned, A¹.
MEMORIAL   Title within heavy line border.
LIBRARY   In double columns.
     Narcissus Luttrell's copy, dated 14. March.

—— —— Microfilm   copy (negative)

NN   0024557   CLU-C CtY CSmH

Nash, John, *playwright*.
Backwoods Romeo, a comedy in three acts. Rev. by J. C.
McMullen. Boston [1947]
85 p. 19 cm. (Baker's edition of plays)

     I. McMullen, Joseph Carl, 1882–   II. Title.
   PS3527.A6355B3   812.5   47–26044*

NN   0024558   DLC

Nash, John.
The customer's nightmare; a barber shop burlesque for men,
by John Nash and Adam Pflieger. Philadelphia, The Penn
play company [c1941]
34 p. diagr. 18½ᶜᵐ.

     I. Pflieger, Adam, joint author. II. Title.
                                          41–11869
   Library of Congress   PS3527.A6355C8 1941
                        [2]   812.5

NN   0024559   DLC

---

p1926
NA813he
Nash, John
Hero in distress, a farce in three acts.
Boston, Baker's Plays [1950]
85p.   19 cm.
Harris
Collection

NN   0024560   RPB NN

VOLUME 405

Nash, John.
High, Wyde and handsome, a comedy in three acts, by John Nash ... Boston, Mass. and Los Angeles, Cal., Baker's plays [°1941]
73 p. diagr. 18½ᶜᵐ. (*On cover:* Baker's edition of plays)

ɪ. Title.
41-7377
Library of Congress   PS3527.A6355H5 1941
[2]   812.5

NN   0024561   DLC

Nash, John, *playwright.*
The hot water hero, a delightful farce comedy in three acts, by John Nash ... Boston, Mass., and Los Angeles, Calif., Baker's plays [1942]
94 p. illus. (plan) 18½ᶜᵐ. (*On cover:* Baker's edition of plays)

ɪ. Title.
42-11206
Library of Congress   PS3527.A6355H6
[2]   812.5

NN   0024562   DLC

PN6111B
.N32H6 **Nash, John.**
How green was her boy-friend, a farce in three acts. (Revised and rewritten by J. C. McMullen) Franklin, Ohio, Eldridge Entertainment House, 1949.
81 p. diagr. 19cm. (An Eldridge 3-act play)

I. McMullen, Joseph Carl, 1882–
II. Title.

NN   0024563   ViU RPB

Nash, John.
Little Nell, a burlesque melodrama; mortgage, tears and everything, by John Nash ... Franklin, O., Denver, Colo., Eldridge entertainment house [°1940]
37 p. diagr. 19ᶜᵐ. (*On cover:* Eldridge popular one act plays)

ɪ. Title.
41-7112
Library of Congress   PS3527.A6355L5 1940
———— Copy 2.
Copyright D pub. 73127   [2]   812.5

NN   0024564   DLC

p1926
NA813ℓ **Nash, John,** *playwright.*
Harris   Love begins at sixty-five, a comedy in three
Collection   acts. Boston, Baker's Plays [1951]
93p. diagr. 19 cm.

NN   0024565   RPB NN

Nash, John.
Moonlight and applesauce, a three-act comedy, by John Nash ... Franklin, O., Denver, Colo., Eldridge entertainment house, inc. [1942]
78 p. diagr. 19ᶜᵐ. (*On cover:* Eldridge hi-test non-royalty plays)

ɪ. Title.
43-6081
Library of Congress   PS3527.A6355M65

NN   0024566   DLC

Nash, John.
Pardon my millions, a comedy in three acts. Boston, Baker's Plays [1948]
85 p. 19 cm. (Baker's royalty plays)

ɪ. Title.
PS3527.A6355P3   812.5   49-18118*

NN   0024567   DLC NN ViU

Nash, John.
Redheaded royalty from Arkansas, a comedy of college life and youth, by John Nash. Boston, Mass. and Los Angeles, Cal. [Walter H. Baker co., °1940]
104 p. 19ᶜᵐ. (*On cover:* Baker's edition of plays)

ɪ. Title.
40-23624
Library of Congress   PN6120.C6N3
———— Copy 2.
Copyright D pub. 70657   [2]   812.5

NN   0024568   DLC

PN6111B
.N32S33 **Nash, John.**
"Scootin' Grandma", a farce in three acts. Boston, W. H. Baker Co. [1949]
91 p. 19cm. (Baker's edition of plays)

NN   0024569   ViU RPB NN

Nash, John, *playwright.*
The sheriff gets his man, a comedy in one act, by John Nash. Philadelphia, The Penn publishing company [°1938]
29 p. diagr. 18½ᶜᵐ.

ɪ. Title.
39-8284
Library of Congress   PS3527.A6355S5 1938
———— Copy 2.
Copyright D pub. 60050   [2]   812.5

NN   0024570   DLC

p1926
NA813sm **Nash, John**
Harris   Smart idiot, a comedy in three acts, by
Collection   John Nash. Boston [Walter H. Baker, c1952]
91p. 19 cm. (On cover: Baker's edition of plays)

NN   0024571   RPB NN

Nash, John.
The sweetheart of U Baka Pi, a three act comedy. Boston, Baker's Plays [1948]
83 p. 19 cm. (Baker's edition of plays)

ɪ. Title.
PS3527.A6355S9   812.5   49-18121*

NN   0024572   DLC ViU NN

Nash, John.
There ain't no mystery, a mystery-comedy in three acts, by John Nash ... Boston, Mass., and Los Angeles, Cal., Baker's plays [°1941]
91 p. diagr. 18½ᶜᵐ. (*On cover:* Baker's edition of plays)

ɪ. Title.
41-19085
Library of Congress   PS3527.A6355T5 1941
[2]   812.5

NN   0024573   DLC

Nash, John, *playwright.*
They gave him a co-ed, a comedy of college life and youth, by John Nash ... Boston, Mass., and Los Angeles, Cal., Baker's plays [1943]
112 p. diagrs. 19ᶜᵐ.

ɪ. Title.
43-8333
Library of Congress   PS3527.A6355T33
[3]

NN   0024574   DLC

Nash, John, *writer on temperance.*
Napoleon of Temperance. Sketches of the life and character of Neal Dow...N.Y., 1852.

NN   0024575   NRAB

Nash, John, 1752-1835.
Brayley, Edward Wedlake, 1773–1854.
Illustrations of Her Majesty's palace at Brighton; formerly the pavilion: executed by the command of King George the Fourth, under the superintendence of John Nash ... To which is prefixed a history of the palace, by Edward Wedlake Brayley ... London, J. B. Nichols and son; [etc., etc.], 1838.

f728.8 **Nash, John, 1752-1835.**
N174r The Royal Pavilion at Brighton, published by command of & dedicated by permission to the King. [London, John Nash, c1825]
[4] p. 28 mounted col. illus.

Plates colored by hand.

1. Brighton, Eng. Pavilion.

NN   0024577   MiDA

Nash, John, 1893-

see   **Nash, John Northcote, 1893-**

Nash, John Adams, 1798-1877, ed.
The **Connecticut Valley** farmer. A monthly journal of agriculture, horticulture, and rural economy. v. 1, v. 2, no. 1-8;   Dec. 1854.
Springfield [Mass.] S. Bowles & co., 18 -54.

Nash, John Adams, 1798-1877, ed.
The **Farmer.** A monthly journal, scientific and practical, devoted to agriculture, horticulture, and rural economy. v. 1,   v. 2, no. 1-8,   -Dec. 1854; new ser., v. 1, Jan.-Dec. 1855. Springfield [Mass.] S. Bowles & co., 18 -54; Amherst, Mass., J. A. Nash. 1855.

Nash, John Adams, 1798-1877.
Memoir of Seth Burroughs, of Williamsburgh, Mass., who died May 10, 1828. By J. A. Nash, A. M. Revised by the Publishing committee. Boston, Printed by T. R. Marvin, for the Massachusetts Sabbath school union, 1829.
108 p. 15½ᶜᵐ.

1. Burroughs, Seth, 1800–1828.   ɪ. Massachusetts Sabbath school society.
35-37062
Library of Congress   BX7260.B88N3
[a45b1]   922.573

NN   0024581   DLC RHi RPB

VOLUME 405

Nash, John Adams, 1798–1877.
The progressive farmer: a scientific treatise on agricultural chemistry, the geology of agriculture; on plants, animals, manures, and soils. Applied to practical agriculture. By J. A. Nash ... New York, C. M. Saxton, 1853.

x, [11]–254 p. 19½ᶜᵐ.

1. Agricultural chemistry. 2. Agriculture. I. Title.

Library of Congress   S493.N3

17—20282

NN   0024582   DLC OOxM KyU PU-V NcD

Nash, John Adams, 1798–1877.
The progressive farmer: a scientific treatise on agricultural chemistry, the geology of agriculture; on plants, animals, manures, and soils. Applied to practical agriculture. By J. A. Nash ... New York, C. M. Saxon, 1854.

x, [11]–254 p. 20ᶜᵐ.

1. Agricultural chemistry. 2. Agriculture.   I. Title.

41–34711

Library of Congress   S493.N3 1854

NN   0024583   DLC OU TU IEN DNAL ViU MH

MANN
S   Nash, John Adams, 1798-1877.
499   The progressive farmer: a scientific
N25   treatise on agricultural chemistry, the geology
1857   of agriculture; on plants, animals, manures,
       and soils. Applied to practical agriculture.
       New York, A. O. Moore, 1857.
       x, 254 p. 20 cm.

"Catechism of scientific and practical agriculture": p. [233]–254.

1. Agricultur   al chemistry.
2. Agriculture.   I. Title.

NN   0024584   NIC

Nash, John Adams, 1798-1877.
The progressive farmer; a scientific treatise on agricultural chemistry, the geology of agriculture, on plants, animals, manures, and soils. Applied to practical agriculture. 12°. pp. 254. New York, 1859.

NN   0024585   MBH

Nash, John Blake.
An investigation of some problems of ecology of the beaver, Castor canadensis canadensis Kuhl, in northern Manitoba. [Winnipeg] 1951.

64 l. illus. 28cm.
"Sponsored by Province of Manitoba Department of Mines and Natural Resources, Game and Fisheries Branch."
Thesis – Univ   ersity of Manitoba.
Bibliography: leaves 63–64.

NN   0024586   CaBVaU

Nash, John F., 1868–
Syracuse, N. Y. *Grade crossing commission.*
Report of Syracuse Grade crossing commission to Syracuse Common council of plan adopted for changes in streets and in the location and use of existing tracks, switches, and railroad facilities, of railroads owned and operated by the New York central railroad company, in the city of Syracuse, N. Y. [Syracuse, 1930?]

Continued in next column

Nash, John Fiske, b. 1824.
Abraham Lincoln; an address delivered by Mr. John F. Nash at Ottawa, Illinois, February twelfth, one thousand, nine hundred and seven. [Ottawa, Free trader press, 1907]

26 p. 18½ x 14½ᶜᵐ.

Continued from preceding column

1. Lincoln, Abraham, pres. U. S.—Addresses, sermons, etc.

8–17981 Revised

Library of Congress   E457.8.N25

NN   0024588   DLC OC1WHi

[Nash, John Henry] 1871–1947.
[An announcement of the publication of a new edition of The heathen Chinee ...]
see his   The Heathen Chinee.

Nash, John Henry, 1871–1947.
An anthology of effort. [San Francisco,] 1926

NN   0024590   PSC

fZ239   Nash, John Henry, 1871–1947.
N3N28   Archbishop Hanna on The Vatican Library.   [San Francisco,
x   1929]
           sheet 65x48cm. fold. to 33x24cm.

A broadside, with text within an ornamental border, announcing "... a luncheon meeting of the San Francisco Advertising Club at the Palace Hotel ... Wednesday, seventeenth of April MDCCCCXXIX."
A mounted photograph, with title, The vestibule of the Library at The Vatican, laid in.

I. Title.

NN   0024591   CU-B

fZ239   Nash, John Henry, 1871–1947.
N3N3   A bad case of jitters.   [San Francisco] 1932.
x   folder ([2] l.) 40cm.

Cover title.
Poem, with title: A printer dreams a terrible dance of death.

1. Printing - Poetry. I. Title.   II. Title: A printer dreams a terrible dance of death.

NN   0024592   CU-B IEN

Nash, John Henry, 1871–1947.
Books distinguished in English and American literature, with facsimiles of first editions privately printed for William Andrews Clark, jr., by John Henry Nash, collated by Cora Edgerton Sanders of the Clark library, as shown in the typographic library and museum of John Henry Nash ... San Francisco, from April the second to April the thirteenth. San Francisco, 1934.

1 p. l., 10 p. 22ᶜᵐ.
On cover: A catalogue of books printed for William Andrews Clark, jr. by John Henry Nash, of San Francisco.
1. Privately printed books—Bibl. I. Clark, William Andrews, 1877–1934. II. Sanders, Cora Edgerton. III. Title.

34–17629

Library of Congress   Z232.N25
——— Copy 2.   [2]   015.79461

NN   0024593   DLC IEN TxU ViU

Nash, John Henry, 1871-1947.
Books distinguished in English & American literature, with facsimiles of first editions, privately printed for William Andrews Clark, jr. by John Henry Nash ... to be shown in the Typographic library and museum of John Henry Nash ... San Francisco, from April the second to April the thirteenth, both dates inclusive, 1934.
San Francisco: Printed by John Henry Nash, [1934].
2 l. col. illus. 43cm., in cover 44cm.
Printed on outside of double leaf; imprint on verso of 2d leaf.
The illustration re   produces Rowlandson's
caricature of Thomas Gray.
Unbound; in orig. mailing wrapper addressed to Philip Rosenbach.
I. Clark, William Andrews, 1877–1934.

NN   0024595   PPRF CLU-C DLC

Nash, John Henry, 1871–1947.
Books, pamphlets and broadsides by or about John Henry Nash
see under   Maxwell, William Black, collector.

Nash, John Henry, 1871–1947.
Crocker, Templeton.
Catalogue of an exhibition of the Templeton Crocker collection of exquisite bookbindings, arranged by Nell O'Day, from March second to April third, nineteen thirty-six, in the Nash typographic library and museum. San Francisco, Printed by J. H. Nash, 1936.

Nash, John Henry, 1871–1947, ed.
Cobden-Sanderson and the Doves press; the history of the press and the story of its types, told by Alfred W. Pollard; the character of the man set forth by his faithful scribe, Edward Johnston; with The ideal book; or, Book beautiful, by Thomas James Cobden-Sanderson; and a list of the Doves press printing. San Francisco, Printed by J. H. Nash, 1929.

xviii, 35 p., 1 l. 32 cm.
"An edition of 339 numbered copies ... Inserted in each copy is a leaf of Doves press printing, twenty-seven of which are vellum. This copy is no. 161."

"A list of the Doves press printing": p. 30–35.

1. Doves press. 2. Golden-Sanderson, Thomas James, 1840–1922. 3. Books. I. Cobden-Sanderson, Thomas James, 1840–1922. The ideal book. II. Pollard, Alfred William, 1859–1944. III. Johnston, Edward, 1872–1944.

30—11742

Library of Congress   Z232.C65N

[a48g½]   [094.1] 655.142

WaSp CaBVa OrU CaBVaU
NjN ViU NcU NRU MiU NBuU OKentU NBu CLSU WaU NSyU
NN   0024599   DLC ICU NNC CSt PSC NjP MH OC1 OO OCU

Nash, John Henry, 1871–1947.
Cobden-Sanderson and the Doves Press; the history of the press and the story of its types, told by Alfred W. Pollard; the character of the man set forth by his faithful scribe, Edward Johnston; with The ideal book; or, Book beautiful, by Thomas James Cobden-Sanderson; and a list of the Doves Press printings. San Francisco, Printed by J.H. Nash, 1929.
xi p. 33 cm.
A prospectus, issued in blue wrappers.
"A note by the printer" (p. [vii]–xi) is also included in the work advertised (p. [v]–ix)

NN   0024600   ICN ViU MH

AAy
X174   Nash, John Henry, 1871–1947.
+929c   [A collection of folio pieces printed by
Rare   John Henry Nash for advertising purposes
Books   and for private circulation. San Fran-
Col   cisco, 1929-1936]
           17 pieces in portfolio. 52 x 37cm.

1. Printers - San Francisco. 2. Printing - Specimens.

NN   0024601   TxU

Nash, John Henry, 1871–1947. ed.
Bible. O. T. Ecclesiastes. English. 1920.
Ecclesiastes; or, The preacher. [San Francisco, Printed by J. H. Nash, 1920]

Nash, John Henry, 1871–1947.
Emendatio mechanica plagularum; an announcement of importance to advertisers, printers, authors & poets from John Henry Nash. [San Francisco, J.H. Nash, 19—?]

NN   0024603   PSC

VOLUME 405

Nash, John Henry, 1871-1947
[Eight examples of the printing of John Henry Nash.] San Francisco, John Henry Nash, 1924-[1938]
[19]p. incl. illus.(incl. port.) 28x35cm - 32x56cm.
In portfolio case; part folded; part colored. Decorative borders and initials used.

NN 0024604 OrCS

F868
F24R3
N3
Nash, John Henry, 1871-1947, printer.
The Farallones, The painted world and other poems of California ... by Milton S. Ray in two volumes. [Printer's announcement] San Francisco, Printed by J.H. Nash, 1934.
5 p. 28cm.

Contents: The making of the books by J.H. Nash, printer.-Milton S. Ray: a Californian poet, by B.P. Kurtz.- Milton S. Ray: a Californian ornithologist, by H.S. Swarth.
"Comments on the Farallones, The painted world and other poems of California": [4] p. inserted at end.

NN 0024605 CU-B

---

f Z1261
C65
1933
N3
Nash, John Henry, 1871-1947, printer.
[John Henry Nash announces] A bibliography of the history of California, 1510-1930, by Robert Ernest Cowan and Robert Granniss Cowan. San Francisco, Printed by J.H. Nash, 1932.
v.12-13 p. 30cm.

The work, proposed for the fall of 1932, was published in 2 v. in 1933.

NN 0024606 CU-B

Typ
970N
34.598F
Nash, John Henry, 1871-1947
The heathen Chinee, Plain language from truthful James, by Bret Harte. With an introduction by Ina Coolbrith and a bibliography by Robert Ernest Cowan. Illustrated by Phil Little, printed by John Henry Nash ...
[San Francisco,1934?]
[2]p. front.,pl. 36cm.
Printed on double leaves, Chinese style.
Original rose wrappers.
Prospectus.

NN 0024607 MH OrCS

WILLIAM ANDREWS CLARK MEMORIAL LIBRARY
Nash, John Henry, 1871-1947.
John Henry Nash announces the publication in four folio volumes of the Vulgate or St. Jerome version of the Holy Bible. [San Francisco, J. H. Nash, 1932]
1 p.l.,vii,[2] p. 47ᵐ.
Contains specimen title-page and two pages of text of the forthcoming publication.
250 copies printed for direct sale.
"The Bible itself has not been printed, due to the changes en-   gendered by the late

depression."-- O'Day, Nell. A catalogue of books printed by John Henry Nash ... San Francisco, 1937. p.78-79.
Bound in blue marbled boards; in slip case.
cop.2 ___   2d copy.
Bound in gold marbled boards; in slip case.

NN 0024609 CLU-C NNC

Nash, John Henry, 1871-1947.
John Henry Nash, printer
see under title

Nash, John Henry, 1871-1947, ed.

Yeats, William Butler, 1865-
The lake isle of Innisfree, by William Butler Yeats, with a facsimile of the poem in the poet's handwriting, also an appreciative note by George Sterling. The manuscript is in the Bender collection at Mills college. [San Francisco, Printed by J. H. Nash] 1924.

PQ4338
.B6E48
1922
Rare bk.
Coll.
Nash, John Henry, 1871- 1947
FOR OTHER EDITIONS SEE MAIN ENTRY
Boccaccio, Giovanni, 1313-1375.
Life of Dante; Giovanni Boccaccio's encomium on Dante or "Trattatello in laude di Dante" ⟨commonly known as the Life of Dante⟩. Translated from the Italian by Philip Henry Wicksteed, M. A. San Francisco, Printed by J. H. Nash for his friends, 1922.

Nash, John Henry, 1871- 1947
The Max John Kuhl memorial collection of fine books ...
see under title

Nash, John Henry, 1871-1947.
The nineteenth Psalm of Israel's great poet David.   San Francisco, 1930
see under   Bible. O.T. Psalms. XIX. English. 1930.

Nash, John Henry, 1871-1947.
A printer dreams a terrible dance of death
see his   A bad case of jitters.

Nash, John Henry, 1871-1947.
The Psalms of the singer David.   San Francisco, 1929
see under   Bible. O. T. Psalms. English. 1929. Authorized.

WILLIAM ANDREWS CLARK MEMORIAL LIBRARY
Nash, John Henry, 1871-1947.
The renaissance of good health ... [San Francisco, J. H. Nash, 1928?]
2 l. 34ᵐ.
Colored head-piece; title within line border.
"To William Andrews Clark, jr. ... John Nash and Mary Nash wish a merry Christmas and a happy New Year."
"One copy only was printed."

NN 0024617 CLU-C

Nash, John Henry, 1871-1947.
Samples of printing of John Henry Nash.
v.p.,1926-32.
5 loose sheets in portfolio. 42cm.

Contents.-1. John Henry Nash announces a bibliography of California.-2. The cool grey city of love.-3. In memoriam: P.L.Campbell.-4. League of western writers.-5. A bad case of jitters.

NN 0024618 OrU

L Nash
Na
Nash, John Henry, 1871-1947
San Francisco, where type glorifies letters. [San Francisco, Printed by J.H. Nash, 1927?]
[8]l. illus. 39cm.

1. Printing. Hist. San Francisco. I. Title.

NN 0024619 IEN PSC

Nash, John Henry, 1871-1947.

Crocker, Templeton.
The Templeton Crocker collection of seventy books from the famous Aldine press (1494-1595) with a foreword by John Eugene Hasty ... San Francisco, Printed by J. H. Nash, 1935.

Nash, John Henry, 1871-1947.
This book announces the publication in four folio volumes of the Comedy of Dante Alighieri of Florence, commonly called The divine comedy. A line-for-line translation in the rime-form of the original by Melville Best Anderson. San Francisco, Printed by John Henry Nash, 1929.
[13] p. 35½ᵐ.
Title and text within double line border.
Excerpts from the text.
Notification that Mr. Edward L. Stone's "copy of The comedy of Dante Alighieri will be number 34" pasted on front lining-paper.
I. Dante Alighieri.   Divina commedia.

OrU CLU PPRF
NN 0024621 ViU NcU WaU CtY CSmH MeWC MH ICarbS

V
094.24
N251t
Nash, John Henry, 1871-1947
To our friends, whom we find more precious every year. From John Henry and Mary Henrietta Nash, Berkeley, California. [San Francisco, Printed by J.H.Nash, 193-]
2 l. 1 illus. 43½cm.
Rare Book Room
Caption title; ornamental border.
A Christmas greeting.
I.Nash, Mrs. Mary Henrietta (Ford)

NN 0024622 CSt

Nash, John Henry, 1871-1947.
To William Andrews Clark, jr., friend ... [by] John Henry Nash. [San Francisco, J. H. Nash, n.d.]
1 leaf. 49ᵐ.
WILLIAM ANDREWS CLARK MEMORIAL LIBRARY
Broadside.
Colored headpiece.
Unbound, in half-leather folder; in slip case.
I. Clark, William Andrews, 1877-1934.

NN 0024623 CLU-C

Nash, John J
Doctrine explanations. Confession. Sin and the sacrament of penance explained in simple language for children. With questions for teachers. Edited by Rev. J. J. Nash, D. D. New York, Cincinnati [etc.] Benziger bros., 1900.
cover-title, 80 p. 15½ᵐ.

1. Catholic church—Catechisms and creeds—English. 2. Penance. 3. Confession.

Library of Congress   BX2265.N3   0-6944 Revised

NN 0024624 DLC

Nash, John J   ed.
Practical explanation and application of Bible history. Edited by Rev. John J. Nash, D. D. New York, Cincinnati [etc.] Benziger bros., 1902.
518 p. 20ᵐ.

1. Catholic church — Catechisms and creeds. 2. Bible — Catechisms, question books. I. Title.

Library of Congress   BS606.N3   2—11638

NN 0024625 DLC PV OC1ND OC1JC OC1StM

Sy13
Q8
935N
Nash, John Kirke
The birds of Midlothian. London, H. F. & G. Witherby [1935]
xxiv, 303 p. illus., fold. map. 22 cm.

Bibliography: p.297-298.

1. Birds - Edinburghshire, Scotland.

NN 0024626 CtY

VOLUME 405

Nash, John Northcote, 1893–
Bucks Shell guide, by John Nash, with notes on monuments by Katherine A. Esdaile. London, B. T. Batsford, limited ₁1936₎
1 p. l., 5–46 p. illus., plates, 2 maps. 23 x 18ᶜᵐ. (*On cover:* Shell guide₁s₎)
Illustrated lining-papers and covers.

1. Buckinghamshire, Eng.—Descr. & trav.—Guide-books.   ɪ. Esdaile, Mrs. Katharine Ada (McDowall)

Library of Congress   DA670.B9N3   37–23221
                                ₃₎   914.2575

NN   0024627   DLC

PR6037
.I4D8
Sieveking, Lancelot de Giberne, 1896–
... Dressing gowns and glue, by Capt. L. de G. Sieveking ᴅ.ꜱ.ᴄ. ... With illustrations by John Nash, with an introduction about the verses by G. K. Chesterton, and an introduction about the drawings by Max Beerbohm, and something about all concerned by Cecil Palmer; ed. by Paul Nash. ₁London₎ C. Palmer ₁1920₎

Nash, John *Northcote,* 1893– illus.

NN   (above entry)

Nash, John Northcote, 1893–
English garden flowers. London, Duckworth, 1948.
30 p. col. illus. 29 cm.

1. Flowers—Pictorial works. 2. Plants, Ornamental—Gt. Brit. ɪ. Title.
SB407.N3   635.9084   49–21205*

NN   0024629   DLC MiD MB PSt WaS

PR6003
.A965F5
Rare bk.
coll.
Nash, John Northcote, 1893– illus.
Bates, Herbert Ernest, 1905–
Flowers and faces. Engravings by John Nash. ₁London₎ Golden Cockerel Press ₁1935₎

Nash, John Northcote, 1893– ed.
Unwin, Francis Sydney, 1885–1925.
Francis Unwin, etcher and draughtsman; with a memoir by Campbell Dodgson ... seventeen collotype plates; edited by John Nash. London, The Fleuron limited, 1928.

Nash, John Northcote, 1893–
... John Nash.   London: The Fleuron, 1925.   3 p. l., 17 pl.   15½cm.   (British artists of to-day. no. 2.)
Preface signed: Sidney Schiff.

231149A. 1. Paintings, British.   ɪ. Schiff, Sidney. ɪɪ. Ser.
Card revised

NN   0024632   NN

Nash, John Northcote, 1893–
Poisonous plants, deadly, dangerous and suspect, engraved on wood and with an introduction by John Nash, with brief descriptions by W. Dallimore, edited by Dr. A. W. Hill, ꜰ. ʀ. ꜱ. London, F. Etchells & H. Macdonald, 1927.
xii, 85 p., 1 l. incl. 1 illus., plates. 31¼ᶜᵐ. (*Half-title:* The Haslewood books)
Printed on one side of leaf only.
"Of this edition printed in England, on Renker's Ingres paper, at the Curwen press, 350 numbered copies have been issued. This is number 7."

1. Poisonous plants. 2. Botany—Gt. Brit.   ɪ. Dallimore, William. ɪɪ. Hill, Arthur William, 1875– ed.
27–18013
Library of Congress   QK100.G7N3

NN   0024633   DLC MB ICU MH-A ViU WaU

PR6007
.E3S4
Rare bk.
Coll.
Nash, John Northcote, 1893– illus.
De La Mare, Walter John, 1873–
Seven short stories, by Walter De La Mare, chosen from The connoisseur and other stories, Broomsticks and other tales, The riddle and other stories. With illustrations by John Nash. London, Faber and Faber limited, 1931.

Nash, Jo. Northcote, 1893– illus.
Gathorne-Hardy, Robert, 1902–
... Wild flowers in Britain, by Robert Gathorne-Hardy. Illustrated from drawings and lithographs by John Nash and from photographs. London, B. T. Batsford ltd. ₁1938₎

LD4711
R35
v. 40
Nash, John *Purcell,* 1915–
Uniform convergence of Fourier series, by John P. Nash. ₁Houston, Tex.₎ Rice Institute₎ 1953.
31–57 p. (The Rice Institute pamphlet, special issue, Nov. 1953) (Studies in mathematics)
Title from table of contents.

1. Fourier series - Addresses, essays, lectures.   ɪ. Title.
(Ser. B™)

NN   0024635   CU

NASH, JOHN TULLOCH.
Volunteering in India; or, An authentic narrative of the military services of the Bengal yeomanry cavalry during the Indian mutiny, and Sepoy war. London, G. Philip, 1893. viii, 136 p. front. 20cm.

1. Army, Indian—Regt. hist.—Bengal yeomanry cavalry.   2. India—Hist.—Mutiny, 1809.   3. India—Hist.—Sepoy rebellion, 1857–1858.

NN   0024636   NN PPL OC1 MH WU CU

E
5
.B 29
NASH, JONATHAN.
A sermon, delivered in Chester, May 21, 1814, at the funeral of the Rev. Aaron Bascom. Springfield₁Mass.₎Dickman, 1814.
19p.

NN   0024637   ICN RPB MH

Nash, Jonathan.
A sermon, delivered in Middlefield, October 31, 1813. Occasioned by this occurrence in Providence, viz:– the Sabbath on which it was delivered completed twenty-one years of his ministry. Springfield, T. Dickman, 1815.
23 p.   21 cm.

NN   0024638   MWA MWiW

Nash, Joseph.
The relations between capital and labor in the United States. By Joseph Nash. The first-prize essay awarded by the Boston Young men's Christian union, 1878. Boston, Lee and Shepard, 1878.
60 p. 23ᶜᵐ.

1. Labor and laboring classes—U. S.
7–33063†
Library of Congress   HD8072.N25

NN   0024639   DLC NcD FU PPL Nh MH MB

Nash, Joseph, *bird fancier*
1872. **British song birds:** | A Practical Treatise | on their | habits, nidification, and incubation; | the mode of rearing young birds, | and their treatment in sickness and in health. | By Joseph Nash. | [Vignette.] | With Illustrations on Steel by Newton Fielding. | London: William Tegg. | 1872.
1 vol. 12mo, pp. 1–96, 8 pll. (col.), 16 text-figs. London.
A treatise on the rearing of cage-birds. First published in 1824 under the title, "A Practical Treatise on British Song Birds." etc. (q.v.). The present edition is essentially the same as the original; the text is slightly altered in places and the plates are poorly-colored copies.

NN   0024640   ICF-A PPAN NN

Nash, Joseph, ₁Bird fancier₎
British song birds: the mode of rearing them, and their treatment in sickness and in health ... London, 1876.
96 p. col. front., illus., col. plates. 18.5 cm.
1. Cage - birds.

NN   0024641   CtY

Nash, Joseph, *bird fancier*
A practical treatise on British song birds; in which is given every information relative to their natural history, incubation, &c. ... By Joseph Nash...   London: Sherwood, Jones, and co., 1824.   vi, 102 p.   col'd illus.   19cm.

220968B. 1. Birds—Care.   2. Birds, Song—Gt. Br.
N. Y. P. L.   May 13, 1943

NN   0024642   NN CtY ICF-A

Nash, Joseph, of Boston, Mass.
Josephine; an historical drama, in four acts ... with list of characters, scenes, stage appointments ...   Boston, F. *Wood,* 1874.
₃₎–60 p.   18 cm.

NN   0024643   RPB DLC MH PPL NN

Nash, Joseph, of Hadley, 1663–1740.   No. 8 in **H.90.470
An elegy occasioned by the death of the much lamented Doct. Thomas Hastings, of Hatfield, who died April 14th, 1728 ... *Broadside.* [Hadley? 1728.] Size, 14½ × 9 inches.

M4572 — Broadsides. — Hastings, Thomas, 1680–1728.

NN   0024644   MB

Nash, Joseph, of Hadley, 1663–1740.   No. 5 in **H.90.470
An elegy upon the much lamented decease of the reverend & excellent Mr. Solomon Stoddard, late faithful pastor of the Church of Christ in North Hampton, N. E. ... February 11th ... 1729. *Broadside.* [Hadley? 1729.] Size, 12¾ × 8½ inches.

L7318 — Broadsides. — Stoddard, Solomon, 1643–1729.

NN   0024645   MB

Nash, Joseph, 1809–1878.
Altenenglische Herrensitze; Façaden und Innenräume in englischer gothik und renaissance gezeichnet von Joseph Nash. Facsimiledrucke des unter dem Titel "Mansions of England in the olden time" in den Jahren 1839–1849 in London erschienenen Werkes. 104 Lichtdruck-Tafeln.   Berlin, New York, Bruno Hessling, n. d.
[12] p.   plates, in portfolio.

NN   0024646   OC1W

Nash, Joseph, 1809–1878.
Altenglische herrensitze.   Berlin, E. Wasmuth [1900?]
4 p. l., 104 pl.   (part col. mounted)   34 cm.

NN   0024647   OCU

ART
LIBRARY
NA
+7328
+N3215
Nash, Joseph, 1809–1878
Altenglische Herrensitze. Mit einer Einleitung von L. MacLean. Berlin, Kunstwissenschaft, 1911.
3p. 104 pl. (32 col.) 36cm.
Translation of The mansions of England in the olden time.

1. Architecture, Domestic - England
2. England - Historic houses I. Title

NN   0024648   WU

VOLUME 405

Nash, Joseph, 1809-1878
Altenglische herrensitze... Berlin, E. Wasmuth
₍1925₎.
₍7₎ p.

NN   0024649   OU

**NA360   Nash, Joseph, 1809-1878.
N2   Architecture of the Middle ages.   Drawn
from nature and on stone by Joseph Nash.
₍London₎ T. S. MacLean, 1838.

3p.ℓ.,25 plates.   55½cm.

1. Architecture, Medieval.
I. Title.

RP CLSU IEN
NN   0024650   NBuG MB OC RPB LNHT ICU CU MdBP PBm

›NK4743   Nash, Joseph, 1809-1878.
N2   Characteristics of British palaces, in the
olden time; the letter-press descriptions by
Mrs. S. C. Hall, the plates drawn on stone by
Joseph Nash ...   [London] M. A. Nattali [1838]

2 p. l.₍5₎-42p.,1 l.   13 col.plates(incl.
front.)   35½cm.

Consists of scenes from British history.
Plates dated 1836-1838.

NN   0024651   NBuG CtY

Wing
W   NASH, JOSEPH, 1809-1878.
3945   Descriptions of the plates of the mansions
.611   of England in the olden time.   London, T.
M'Lean, 1849.
iv,63p.   24cm.

Covers first through fourth series of plates
Bookplate: John M. Wing.

NN   0024652   ICN

Nash, Joseph, 1809-1878, illus.

Price, Lake.
Interiors and exteriors in Venice, by Lake Price; litho-
graphed by Joseph Nash from the original drawings. London,
T. McLean, 1843.

Nash, Joseph, 1809-1878.
Interiors of old English mansions, reproduced in colours
after the orig. coloured drawings by Joseph Nash ... The
Hague, S. Blok ₍n.d.₎
₍4₎ p., 32 mounted col. pl. 45 x 34½ᵐ.
In portfolio.

1. House decoration—England. 2. Architecture, Domestic—England.
3. England—Historic houses.   I. Title.
44-36937
Library of Congress   NK2043.N3

NN   0024654   DLC CU PP OOxM OC1MA MtBC

**RARE BOOK
DEPT.**
*K.407
.1   Nash, Joseph, 1809-1878.
The mansions of England in the olden time.
London, T. M'Lean, 1838-49.
4 v. in 2 plates. 55cm.
Engraved title pages.

1. Architecture, Domestic—England.
2. England—Historic houses, etc. I. Title.

NN   0024655   MB

Nash, Joseph, 1809-1878
The mansions of England in the olden time;
first, second, and third series. Lond. 1839-41.
3 v. f.

NN   0024656   NN

Nash, Joseph, Architect, 1809-1878.   *8100.15=**K.407.1
The mansions of England in the olden time.
[London.] M'Lean. 1839. 4 v. 104 plates. Elephant f°.

G927 — Interiors. — Country and seas. ₂ houses. — England. Fine arts. Arch.
— T.r. — Castles.

NN   0024657   MB

Nash, Joseph, 1809-1878.
The mansions of England in the olden time, by Joseph Nash.
London, T. M'Lean, 1839-49.
4 v. plates. 55ᵐ.
Engraved title-pages.
On t.-p. of v. 2, 4: Second, fourth series respectively.

1. Architecture, Domestic—England. 2. England—Historic houses, etc.
I. Title.
12—20506
Library of Congress   NA7328.N25

NN   0024658   DLC DeU NjP ICU NcD MH WaSp MB InU

Nash, Joseph, 1809-1878.
The mansions of England in the olden time.
Re-edited by J. Corbet Anderson. With the
original one hundred and four illustrations,
carefully reduced and executed in lithography,
by Samuel Stanesby. London, Sotheran, 1869.

4v. in 2. col. plates. 38cm.

Added colored title-pages.

NN   0024659   NBuG PPMoI OC1SA DDO

Nash, Joseph, 1809-1878
Mansions of England in the olden time...with
the original 104 illustrations... London, Sotheran
and co., 1869.
5 v. 104 col. pl.

NN   0024660   OC1MA

Nash, Joseph, 1809-1878.
The mansions of England in the olden time.
Re-edited by J.Corbet Anderson. With the
original one hundred and four illustrations,
carefully reduced and executed in lithography
by Samuel Stanesby. London, Sotheran, 1869-7
2 v. plates. 39 cm.

1.Architecture, Domestic - England. 2.Eng-
land - Historic houses. I.Anderson, John
Cobret,   ed.

NN   0024661   NjP MH

Nash, Joseph, 1809-1878.
The mansions of England in the olden time; by Joseph Nash.
Re-edited by J. Corbet Anderson. With the original one hundred and four illustrations, carefully reduced and executed in
lithography, by Samuel Stanesby ... London, H. Sotheran &
co., 1869-72.
4 v. plates. 38ᵐ.
Added title-page, engraved.

1. Architecture, Domestic—England. 2. England—Historic houses, etc.
I. Anderson, John Corbet, 1827-1907, ed. II. Title.
43-47639
Library of Congress   NA7328.N255

MH CtY IU KMK CLSU OC1 OCU PP
NN   0024662   DLC TU CU-I FU CU ICU PU-FA Vi MiD

---

f728.83   Nash, Joseph, 1809-1878.
N17m.a1   The mansions of England in the olden time ...
Re-edited by J. Corbet Anderson. With the original one hundred and four illustrations, carefully reduced and executed in lithography, by
Samuel Stanesby ...   London, H. Sotheran & co.
1869-72.
5v. 104 col.pl.

Added title-pages, illus.
Plates bound in 4 v. Title-pages of these
volumes bound with text in v.₍5₎

NN   0024663   IU PP

Rare
728.8   Nash, Joseph, 1809-1878.
N17m   The mansions of England in the olden time;
by Joseph Nash. Re-edited by J. Corbet
Anderson. With the original one hundred and
four illustrations, carefully reduced and
executed in lithography.   London, H.
Sotheran, 1874.
74 p. 104 plates. 39 cm.

1. Architecture, Domestic--England. 2. Eng
land--Historic houses, etc. I. Anderson, John
Corbet, 1827-1907, ed. II. Title.

NN   0024664   LU CaBVa MiU OC1W

Fine Arts Dept.
*Cab.60
.166.10 Nash, Joseph, 1809-1878.
Mansions of England in the olden time.
Facades and interiors in English Gothic and Ren-
aissance. New York, B. Hessling [190-?]
4 v. in 1. plates. 48cm.
Engraved t. p. to each v.

1. Architecture, Domestic—England. 2. England—Historic houses, etc. I. Title.

NN   0024665   MB

Nash, Joseph, 1809-1878.
Mansions of England in the olden time, façades
and interiors in English gothic and renaissance, by
Joseph Nash ...   New York, B. Hessling [1900]
[14] p., 104 pl. 49 cm.
In portfolio.
In 4 sections (A-D) each with brief descriptive
text and group of 26 plates.
Plates A3-4,9,15,23,25; B4, 19; C2,7,9,20;
D, D18, 21 missing.
1. Architecture, Domestic - Gt. Brit. 2. Gt.
Brit. - Historic houses, etc.

NN   0024666   CU

Nash, Joseph, 1809-1878.
The mansions of England in the olden time, by Joseph
Nash. New ed., edited by Charles Holme, with an introduc-
tion by C. Harrison Townsend. London, New York ₍etc.₎
Offices of 'The Stvdio', 1906.
4 p. l., vii p. civ pl. 29ᶜᵐ.
On cover: Special winter number of "The Studio", 1905-6.

1. Architecture, Domestic—England. 2. England—Historic houses,
etc. I. Holme, Charles, 1848-1923, ed. II. The Studio.
6-4712
Library of Congress   NA7328.N3

WaT IdU CU ICJ NN NjP CU-S
CaBViP MtBC OrStbM CaBVa WaSp WaS OrCS CaBVaU
PP OO NcRS NcD GU MsU AU CoU MU ViU MH MB OrU
NN   0024667   DLC CU NSyU FU NcU MiU OC1 OC1SA OU

Nash, Joseph, 1809-1878.
The mansions of England in the olden time, by Joseph
Nash. New ed., containing 104 plates, including 32 plates
in colour; with an introduction by Reginald Blomfield,
A. R. A. London, W. Heinemann, 1912.
3 p. l., 104 pl. (32 col.), ₍2₎ p. 35½ cm.

1. Architecture, Domestic—England. 2. England—Historic houses,
etc.
12—14135
Library of Congress   NA7328.N32

MdBP
NN   0024668   DLC PSt NᴺC TxU CoU OrCS OrU ViU NN

VOLUME 405

f
NA
7328   Nash, Joseph, 1809-1878.
N3   The mansions of England in the olden
191?   time. New ed. New York, B. Hessling,
          1912.
            104 plates.

1. Architecture, Domestic--England. 2.
England--Historic houses, etc. I. Title.

NN 0024669   UU

q723.542
P96e1   Nash, Joseph, 1809-1878.
           A series of views, illustrative of Pugin's
         Examples of Gothic architecture; sketched from
         nature, and drawn on stone. With letter-press
         descriptions, by W. H. Leeds. London, A.
         Pugin, 1830.
           20p. ₂22₃ plates. 34cm.

NN 0024670   IU CtY NjP

Nash, Joseph, 1809-1878.
  Thirty illustrations to Bunyan's Pilgrim's progress in
fac-simile of the original drawings. By Joseph Nash. In
the possession of William Leaf, esq. (of Park Hill, Streat-
ham). ₂Streatham, 184-?₃
  1 p. l., 30 mounted col. pl. 55½ x 45ᶜᵐ.
  Only 75 copies printed.

1. Bunyan, John, 1628-1688. Pilgrim's progress—Illustrations.
                                                    11-33640
Library of Congress   NC1115.N3

NN 0024671   DLC MB

Nash, Joseph, 1809-1878.
  Views of the interior and exterior of Windsor castle,
by Joseph Nash. London, T. M'Lean, 1848.
  29 l. 25 mounted col. pl. 72ᶜᵐ.
  In portfolio.
  Illus. t.-p., in colors.

1. Windsor castle.
                                                    14-21832
Library of Congress   NA7746.W5N3

NN 0024672   DLC NIC TxU MB

Spec. Coll.
f728.81 Nash, Joseph, 1809-1878.
W766n   Views of the interior and exterior of
         Windsor castle. London, T. M'Lean, 1848.
           13l. 12 mounted col. plates. 63cm.

           Illustrated t.-p., in colors.

         ₍1.Windsor castle. ✓LC.

NN 0024673   CLSU

NA7746
q.W5N3 Nash, Joseph, 1809-1878.
1852   Views of the interior and exterior of
         Windsor Castle. London, T. M'Lean, 1852.
           1 l., 26 plates(part col.) 57x38 cm.

1. Windsor Castle.

NN 0024674   T ViU

FINE ART
NA
7746   Nash, Joseph, 1809-1878.
W7   Views of the interior and exterior of
N25   Windsor Castle, forming a supplemental
1852   volume to the Mansions of England, by Jos-
         eph Nash. London, T. McLean, 1852.
           ₂4₃ p., 26 plates. 56cm.

         1. Windsor Castle. I. Title. II. His
       Mansions of   England.

NN 0024675   NIC

Nash, Joseph, 1902-194-/
  Surgical physiology, by Joseph Nash ... Springfield, Ill.,
Baltimore, Md., C. C. Thomas ₂1942₃
  xxii, 406 p., 1 l. incl. illus., tables. diagrs. (1 fold.) 26 cm.
  "References": p. 445-470.

1. Physiology.   I. Title.

QP34.N3   612   42—15567

OrCS CaBVaU MtU OrU-D NNU CU
NN 0024676   DLC DNLM ICJ OU OOxM OrU-M ViU PPC PPJ

Nash, Joseph, 1902-1944
  Surgical physiology... Springfield, Ill.,
Thomas, 1945.

NN 0024677   PU-V

Nash, Joseph, 1902-1944
  Surgical physiology... Springfield, Ill.
Thomas, ₂1946₃

NN 0024678   PU-Med

Nash, Joseph, 1902-1944.
  Surgical physiology ... Springfield, Ill.,
C. C. Thomas ₂1942, 1947₃
  496 p. 25cm.

  "References": p. 445-470.

NN 0024679   Mi

Nash, Joseph, 1902-1944.
  Surgical physiology, by Joseph Nash ... Springfield, Ill.,
Baltimore, Md., C. C. Thomas ₂1950₃
  xxii, 496 p., 1 l. incl. illus., tables. diagrs. (1 fold.) 25cm.
  "References": p. 445-470.

1. Physiology.   I. Title.

NN 0024680   ViU

Nash, Joseph, 1902-1944.
  Surgical physiology; 2d ed., rev. and edited by Brian
Blades with the collaboration of Edward J. Beattie, Jr. ₂and
others₃ Springfield, Ill., Thomas ₂1953₃
  xxxi, 686 p. illus. 25 cm.
  Includes bibliographies.

1. Physiology. 2. Surgery, Operative.   I. Blades, Brian Brewer,
1906-   ed. II. Title.

QP34.N3 1953   612   53—8662

PU-Med-TS PPJ IU CaBVaU
PPC NcU NcD DNLM ViU IParkA TU PPT-M PU-V PPHa
NN 0024681   DLC OrU-M PU PPPH OU OClW-H ICJ PPWM

Nash, Judah, 1728-1805.
  Works by this author printed in America before 1801 are available
in this library in the Readex Microprint edition of Early American
Imprints published by the American Antiquarian Society.
  This collection is arranged according to the numbers in Charles
Evans' American Bibliography.

NN 0024682   DLC

Nash, Judah, 1728-1805.
  A discourse, delivered at the funeral of Mrs. Anna Kendall,
consort of the Rev. Samuel Kendall, of New-Salem, on the 22d
day of April, 1790, in the eightieth year of her age. By Judah
Nash... Springfield ₂Mass.₃: Printed by Ezra Waldo Weld.
1792. 13 p. 19cm. (4°.)

  See: Sabin 51848, note. Evans 24567.
  Signatures: ₂A⁴₃ B⁴.
  With this was presumably issued: Foster, Joel. A discourse, occasioned by the
death, and delivered at the interment, of Rev. Samuel Kendall... Springfield ₂Mass.₃
1792. (q. v.).

56R0358. 1. Kendall, Anna, d. 1790.

NN 0024683   NN CtY MWA MA

Nash, Kathleen M.
  Royal visit; a play for six women, by Kathleen M. Nash.
London, S. French, limited ₂1939₃
  22 p. 18¼ᶜᵐ. (On cover: French's acting edition. no. 1538)

  I. Title.
                                                    39-17631
Library of Congress   PR6027.A66R6 1939
Copyright D pub. 63006   ₂2₃   822.91

NN 0024684   DLC

Nash, Kevin Ll
  The elements of soil mechanics in theory and practice;
four lectures delivered at King's College, London. London,
Constable ₂1951₃
  112 p. illus. 21 cm.

  1. Soil mechanics.   I. Title.

TA710.N3   620.19   51-6687 †

NN 0024685   DLC NN CaBVaU CU DNAL

Nash, L.L.
          see Nash, Leonidas Lydwell, 1846-1917.

NASH, L. R.

    See NASH, Luther Roberts, 1871-

Nash, L.S.

Logansport and northern Indiana railroad company.
  Report of the chief engineer, exhibiting the character
and prospects of the road, and also a statement of the
secretary, showing the condition of the affairs, of the
Logansport and northern Indiana railroad company, pre-
sented to the board of directors at their meeting at
Logansport, May 1, 1854. New York, Railroad journal
job printing office, 1854.
  36 p. fold. map. 23½ᶜᵐ.
  L. S. Nash, chief engineer.
  I. Nash, L. S.
                                                    A21-1170
NN 0024688   DBRE

MANN
Thesis
SB   Nash, Lee Blanton, 1914-
324   The effect of light and mineral nutrition on
1940   composition and cooking quality of potatoes.
N251   ₂Ithaca, N. Y.₃ 1940.
           84 l. illus. 27 cm.

           Thesis (Ph. D.) - Cornell Univ., June 1940.
Thesis --- ----- Archival copy.
1940   1. Potatoes. 2. Cookery (Potatoes)
N253.   3. Plants, Effect of light on. 4. Plants -
         Nutrition. I. Title.

NN 0024689   NIC

VOLUME 405

Nash, Leonard Kollender, 1918–
The atomic-molecular theory. Cambridge, Harvard University Press, 1950.
v, 115 p. 23 cm. (Harvard case histories in experimental science, case 4)
Bibliography: p. 114–115.

1. Atomic theory. 2. Molecular theory. I. Title. (Series)

QD461.N3   541.2   50–12355 rev

IdU OrPR OrPS MtBC Wa OrCS NNCU-G
OKentU IdPI OrU NcGU MoU KU-M NN WaS CaBVaU OrMonO
NN 0024690   DLC FU TxU ViU MB MH NNC ICJ CU PHC NIC

Nash, Leonard Kollender, 1918–
[The gases in meteorites]

Thesis, Ph.D.– Harvard university, 1944.
Typewritten.

NN 0024691   MH

Nash, Leonard Kollender, 1918–
Method for continuous fluorine analysis in mixtures of fluorine and nitrogen. Oak Ridge, Tenn., Technical Information Branch, Tennessee AEC, 1949.
5 p. diagrs. 27 cm.
At head of title: United States Atomic Energy Commission. AECD-2158.
"Declassified: July 15, 1948."

1. Fluorine. I. Title. II. Ser.

NN 0024692   ViU

Nash, Leonard Kollender, 1918–
Plants and the atmosphere. Cambridge, Harvard University Press, 1952.
ix, 122 p. illus. 23 cm. (Harvard case histories in experimental science, case 5)
Bibliography: p. [121]–122.

1. Plants—Assimilation. I. Title. (Series)

QK882.N3   581.133   52—5401

OrU KU-M OrLgE OrMonO MtBC Wa
MoU FMU MtBuM OrCS PP ScU CaBVaU IdPI OrAshS
NN MB ICJ TxU ViU MiU WaS NNC NIC NN CU MU KEmT OU
    0024693   DLC PWcS DNAL PPD PIm PPT OOxM OC1GC

Nash, Leonidas Lydwell, 1846-1917.
Assurance of Immortality. n.d.

NN 0024694   Nc

Nash, Leonidas Lydwell, 1846-1917.
Baptism, the nature, mode, and subjects ... Greensboro, Christian advocate, n.d.
16 p. S.

NN 0024695   NcU Nc

Nash, Leonidas Lydwell, 1846-1917.
Christian Family. n.p., n.d.

NN 0024696   Nc

Nash, Leonidas Lydwell, 1846–1917.
Early morning scenes in the Bible, by L. L. Nash ... New York, Chicago [etc.] Fleming H. Revell company [1910]
209 p. 19½ cm. $1.00

10-21642

NN 0024697   DLC NcD Nc

Nash, Leonidas Lydwell, 1846–1917.
Recollections and observations during a ministry in the North Carolina conference, Methodist Episcopal church, South, of forty-three years, by L. L. Nash, D. D. Introduction by Rev. R. H. Bennett ... Raleigh, Mutual publishing company, printers. 1916.
142 p. front. (port.) 22½ cm.

33–35168

Library of Congress   BX8495.N32A3   922.773

NN 0024698   DLC NcC NcD NcRS NcU Nc

Cp252
N252r   Nash, Leonidas Lydwell, 1846-1917.
Regeneration. By Rev. L. L. Nash, D.D., pastor of Hay Street M. E. Church, South, Fayetteville, N.C. Fayetteville, N.C., Fayetteville Printing and Publishing Co., 1897.
13 p. 20cm.

NN 0024699   NcU

Nash, Leonidas Lydwell, 1846–1917.
Spiritual life. By Rev. L. L. Nash ... With an introduction by Bishop O. P. Fitzgerald, D. D. Nashville, Tenn., Publishing house Methodist Episcopal Church, South, Barbee & Smith, agents, 1808.
203 p. 19 cm.

1. Christian life. I. Title.

98–1055 Revised

Library of Congress   BV4501.N25

NN 0024700   DLC NcD Nc NcU

E158
.T765   Nash, Leslie, ed.
Travelguide. Vacation & recreation without humiliation.
New York.

Nash, *Mrs.* **Letitia Morse.**
Adventuring, by Letitia Morse Nash. Dallas, Tex., American poetry association, inc. [*1938]
5 p. l., 68 p. front. (port.) 20 cm.
Poems.

I. Title.

39–4686

Library of Congress   PS3527.A636A7 1938
———— Copy 2.
Copyright A 126103   [2]   811.5

NN 0024702   DLC

Nash, Letitia Morse.
Singing words. [Poems] Dallas, Story Book Press [1949]
79 p. port. 20 cm.

I. Title.

PS3527.A636S5   811.5   49–5325*

NN 0024703   DLC

Engineering
K
TD
499
T97   Nash, Lewis H
        The "Crown meter" as a positive displacing piston measuring device; a demonstration of the displacing action of the "Crown" piston meter, by Lewis H. Nash. [n.p.] Crown [189 ?]
        3 p. illus. 22 x 20cm.
        Caption title.
        No. 8 in vol. lettered: 12 papers on water meters.

        1. Water-meters. I. Title.

NN 0024704   NIC

ND673
.R9S37   Nash, Lili M.
Schaeffer & Brandt, inc., *New York.*
Peter Paul Rubens; loan exhibition for the benefit of the United hospital fund of New York. Foreword by Gustav Gluck; introduction by Julius Held; catalogue by Lili M. Nash. November 23–December 19, 1942. New York, Schaeffer & Brandt, inc. [1942]

Nash, Louis P.
... First reader. Æsop and Mother Goose, by Louis P. Nash ... Boston, Chicago, Thompson, Brown & co., 1897.
96 p. illus. (part col.) 19½ cm. (Literature readers)

1. Readers and speakers—1870–

12–8051

Library of Congress   PE1119.N3

NN 0024706   DLC PBa

Nash, Louis P
First reader. Aesop and Mother Goose. Boston, etc., Thompson, Brown & co., 1902.

At head of title: Literature readers.

NN 0024707   MH

Nash, Luther Roberts, 1871–
Anatomy of depreciation, a discussion of utility accounting methods from time to time in effect or proposed by regulatory or utility representatives, with particular reference to recent controversies, by Luther R. Nash ... Washington, D. C., Public utilities reports, inc., 1947.
x, 214 p. port. diagrs. 21 cm.

1. Depreciation. 2. Public utilities—Accounting. I. Title.

HD2765.N3   380.16826   47—3138

PSt OrU-L OrCS OrP WaS WaT WaTC CaBVa NBuU-L
NN 0024708   DLC NcD ICU ICJ PU-L TxU ViU-L CU CoU

HD2766
.N23   **Nash, Luther Roberts,** 1871–
The economics of public utilities; a reference book for executives, investors, engineers, and students, by L. R. Nash ... 1st ed. New York [etc.] McGraw-Hill book company, inc., 1925.
xii, 430 p. diagrs. 23½ cm.
"References to supplementary reading" at end of most of the chapters.

1. Public utilities—U. S. I. Title.

25—17724

Library of Congress   HD2766.N23
[42u2]   380.16

TU
MiU ViU-L ICJ NN NcRS IdU-SB OrPR WaS CaBVaU CaBVa
NN 0024709   DLC CU CoU OrCS MB PU PHC OC1 OU OO

NASH, L[uther] R[oberts], 1871–
The economics of public utilities; a reference book for executives, investors, engineers, and students. First ed., 3d impression. New York, etc., McGraw-Hill Book Co.,Inc.,1925.

Diagrs.

NN 0024710   MH

VOLUME 405

Nash, Luther Roberts, 1871–
The economics of public utilities; a reference book for executives, investors, engineers, and students, by L. R. Nash ... 2d ed. New York and London, McGraw-Hill book company, inc., 1931.
xvii, 508 p. diagrs. 23½ᶜᵐ. $4.00
"References to supplementary reading" at end of most of the chapters.

1. Public utilities—U. S.   I. Title.
Library of Congress   HD2766.N23 1931   31–35277
——— Copy 2.
Copyright A 45524   ₍₃₎   380.16

WaU–L
MH ViU CU MiHM TU FMU NIC CoU WaE MtU IdU WaWW Or
NN   0024711   DLC NN PPD OU OCl OO MiU ViU–L PU–L NcD

NASH, **Luther Roberts**, 1871–
Financial problems of electric railways. n p. [1916].
1.8°. pp. 16.
"Reprinted from Stone & Webster journal, June, 1916".

NN   0024712   MH

NASH, **Luther Roberts**, 1871–
History and economics of the jitney. n.p. [1916].
1.8°. pp. 17..
"Reprinted from Stone & Webster journal, May, 1916."

NN   0024713   MH

NASH, **Luther Roberts** 1871–
Public utility depreciation accounting... [Chicago, Ill.], The journal of land and public utility economics, 1926.
16 p.   charts.
Cover title.
Reprinted from The journal of land & public utility economics, v.2, no.4, October 1926.

NN   0024714   MH–BA

Nash, Luther Roberts, 1871–
Public utility economics, with special reference to electric railways; notes on lectures by L. R. Nash ... abstracted by Henry H. Norris. ₍Boston₎ Printed for private distribution by Boston elevated railway, 1925.
2 p. l., iii–v, 96 p. diagrs. 18ᶜᵐ.

1. Public utilities. 2. Electric railroads.   I. Norris, Henry Hutchinson, 1873–   ed.   II. Title.
Library of Congress   HD2763.N3   25–20483

NN   0024715   DLC MB

Nash, Luther Roberts, 1871–
Public utility rate structures; a reference book for rate designers, executives, and students, by L. R. Nash ... 1st ed. New York and London, McGraw-Hill book company, inc., 1933.
xi, 379 p. diagrs. 23½ᶜᵐ.
"References to supplementary reading" at end of each chapter except chapter xiv.

1. Public utilities—Rates. 2. Public utilities—U. S.   I. Title.
Library of Congress   HD2763.N32   33–12639
——— Copy 2.
Copyright A 62277   ₍₅₎   380.16826

Or
WaU TU MiHM CoU DNAL WaTC PSC PPT MtU IdU MtBC OrCS
NN   0024716   DLC CU PU–L MiU OCl OU OCU NN ViU NcD

NASH, **Luther Roberts,** 1871–
Recent developments in service-at-cost franchises for utilities. n.p. [1919]
1.8°. pp. 48.
"Reprinted from Electric Railway Journal, Jan.4, 1919."

NN   0024717   MH–BA

NASH, **Luther Roberts,** 1871–
Some commercial considerations in central station rate making; an address, Harvard university, 1915.
1.8°. pp. 14.

NN   0024718   MH–BA

Nash, Luther   Roberts, 1871–
Valuation of public service properties. 2d ed.   ₍Bost₎ 1912.
20p.
Reprint from the Stone and Webster Public service journal, Oct. 1912.

NN   0024719   IU MiU OO WaS MH–L PPD

NASH, **Luther Roberts,** 1871–
Valuation of public service properties. 3d ed. [Boston, 1912?]
1.8°. pp. 20.
Reprinted from the Stone & Webster public service journal for October, 1912"

NN   0024720   MH–BA

Nash, Lydia.
A table book and introductory arithmetic, by Lydia Nash. New York, Press of T. Hart & co. ₍ᶜ1877₎
68 p. 16½ᶜᵐ.

1. Arithmetic—Problems, exercises, etc.
                                            2–27878
Library of Congress   QA103.N2512

NN   0024721   DLC OO

Nash, Lydia.
A table book and introductory arithmetic. By L. Nash. New York, Cincinnati ₍etc.₎ Benziger brothers ₍ᶜ1878₎
90 p. 16½ᶜᵐ.

1. Arithmetic—Problems, exercises, etc.
                                            2–27879
Library of Congress   QA103.N2514

NN   0024722   DLC MH DAU

Nash, Lyman Junius, 1845–1930.
Wisconsin. *Supreme court.*
In memoriam, Justice Roujet DeLisle Marshall. ₍Madison?₎ 1923₎

Law   **Nash, Lyman Junius, 1845–1930.**
Wisconsin. *Laws, statutes, etc.*
Table of laws amended, repealed or created by laws of 1911. Issued by revisor of statutes. Madison, Wis., Democrat printing company, state printers, 1911.

Nash, Lyman Junius, 1845–1930, ed.
Wisconsin annotations, 1914, embracing all annotations of the constitution and statutes of Wisconsin contained in the Statutes of 1898 and in Sanborn and Sanborn's Supplement of 1906, together with continuations thereof down to the present time; also the text of the constitutions of the United States and of Wisconsin, a table of all private, local and special acts arranged under descriptive heads and some of the historic legal documents through which Wisconsin derived its territorial and political sovereignty. Prepared and ed. by Lyman J. Nash, revisor, and Arthur F. Belitz, assistant revisor. Pub. by the state of Wisconsin. Madison, 1914.

Law   Nash, Lyman Junius, 1845–1930, ed.
Wisconsin. *Laws, statutes, etc.*
Wisconsin statutes. ₍1st₎— ed.; 1911–12—Chicago ₍etc.₎ Callaghan.

Nash, Lyman Junius, 1845–1930.
Wisconsin. *Laws, statutes, etc.* ⌐FOR OTHER EDITIONS SEE MAIN ENTRY
Wisconsin town laws 1917 with forms. Comp. pursuant to section 35.20 of the statutes. By Lyman J. Nash, revisor and Arthur F. Belitz, assistant revisor. Pub. by the state of Wisconsin. Madison, 1917.

Nash, M.,   ed.
Treeby, S.
The elements of astronomy; with methods for determining the longitudes, aspects, &c. of the planets for any future time ... By S. Treeby ... Rev. and cor. by M. Nash ... New York, S. Wood & sons; Baltimore, S. S. Woods & co., 1823.

F9999   Nash, Manning.
Cantel; the industrialization of a Guatemalan Indian community. 1955.
267 l.

Thesis—Univ. of Chicago.

1. Cantel, Guatemala.   2. Indians of Central America—Guatemala.

NN   0024729   ICU

Nash, Manning.
Cantel; the industrialization of a Guatemalan Indian community. Chicago ₍Library, Dept. of Photographic Reproduction, University of Chicago₎ 1955.
Microfilm copy (positive) of typescript.
Collation of the original, as determined from the film: vi, 267 l. maps (part fold.) plans, tables.
Thesis—University of Chicago.
Bibliography: leaves 241–248.

1. Cantel, Guatemala.   2. Industrialization—Case studies.
Microfilm 4553 HC   Mic 57–5416

NN   0024730   DLC NN NIC NNC

HC148   Nash, Manning.
.C3N3   Cantel; the industrialization of a Guatemalan Indian community. Chicago ₍Library, Dept. of Photographic Reproduction₎University of Chicago, 1955.
1955   vi, 267 l. illus., maps, plans (part fold. 20cm.
Thesis—University of Chicago.
Bibliography: leaves 241–243.
Photocopy of microfilm.

NN   0024731   FMU

Nash, Margaret.
Municipal employment bureau in the United States.
From National municipal review, July 1915, v.4: 429–436

NN   0024732   DL

VOLUME 405

Nash, Mrs. Margaret A. (Moger), tr.

₍Elisabeth, *queen consort of Charles 1, king of Rumania*₎ 1843–1916.
Suffering's journey on the earth, by Carmen Sylva ₍pseud.₎ queen of Roumania; tr. from "Leidens erdengang," by Margaret A. Nash, illustrated by Percy A. Nash. 2d ed. London, Jarrold & sons ₍1906?₎

★★
cF
593
N29

Nash, Marie.
Diary. Michigan to California, April 29, 1861-May 31, 1861.
₍56₎ p. 15cm.

1. Nash, Marie. 2. Overland journeys to the Pacific. 3. Diaries. 4. Manuscripts.

NN 0024734 C

F835
N17

Nash, Marie K.
The earth renewed as paradise. [n.p., n.d.]
11 p. illus. 20cm.

Cover title.

NN 0024735 CU-B

Nash, Marvin W.
John Paisley Cameron.

(In N.C. bar association Report. 1917 v.19.)

NN 0024736 NcU

₍Nash, Mary E₎
Everybody's letter writer: containing all necessary instructions in the art of letter writing, together with numerous models of all kinds of letters. By the author of "Good manners." Chicago, T. S. Denison ₍°1888₎
83 p. 19½ᵐ.

1. Letter-writing. I. Title

Library of Congress   PE1483.N3

11—6210

NN 0024737 DLC

Nash, Mary E.
Everybody's letter writer: containing all necessary instructions in the art of letter writing.

With her Good manners, 1889.₎

36

NN 0024738 DLC

Nash, Mary E.
Good manners; a guide to good behaviour, embracing the usages of the best society ... By Mary E. Nash ... Chicago, T. S. Denison ₍°1886₎
103 p. 19ᵐ.

1. Etiquette.

Library of Congress   BJ1852.N3
(Copyright 1886: 29095)

9–30983†

NN 0024739 DLC OkU

AC5
.N3.

Nash, Mary E.
Good manners; a guide to good behavior... Chicago, 1889.

NN 0024740 ICRL DLC

Nash, Mary Eleanor, 1889-   joint ed.
Martínez Sierra, Gregorio, 1881–
Three one-act plays: La suerte de Isabelita, Rosina es frágil, Cada uno y su vida, by Gregorio Martínez Sierra; edited with introduction, notes, exercises and vocabulary by Lawrence A. Wilkins ... and Mary E. Nash ... New York, H. Holt and company ₍°1930₎

Nash, Mary Rooker
see Nash, Mrs. Vernon.

Nash, Marygold V.

Alice Meynell, by Marygold V. Nash. ₍In Archives of the Letters club of the University of British Columbia, v. 23, 1941-1942.₎

NN 0024743 CaBVaU

₍Nash, Maude Cushing₎
Children's occupations. Boston, New York, Houghton Mifflin company ₍°1920₎
xi, ₍1₎ p., 1 l., 341, ₍1₎ p. col. front., illus., plates (part col.) diagrs. 19¼ᵐ. (*Half-title:* The kindergarten children's hour, ed. by Lucy Wheelock ... V. 2)

Illustrated t.-p. and lining-papers in colors.

1. Kindergarten—Methods and manuals.   I. Title.

21—1044

Library of Congress   LB1143.K45 vol. 2

NN 0024744 DLC MB ViU PP WaS OClBE OCU OCl OClh

Nash, Melaliah.
The Columbian ephemeris and astronomical diary for the year 1812... New York: Largin & Thompson, 1812. 112 p. incl. diagrs., tables. 4°.

On cover:

154848A.   1. Nautical almanacs and   ephemerides—U. S.   May 19, 1925
N.Y.P.L.

NN 0024745 NN NNC

Nash, Melatiah, tr.
Louvet de Couvrai, Jean Baptiste, 1760–1797.
Emilia de Varmont, or, The necessary divorce; and Memoirs of Curate Sevin. A moral and political tale. Founded on facts. Translated from the French of M. Louvet, by Melatiah Nash. Three volumes in one ... New-York, Printed by T. & J. Swords, no. 99 Pearl-street, 1799.

Nash, Melatiah, ed.
Ladies and gentleman's diary, 1820-22
see under title

Nash, Michael.
Stenography; or, The most easy and concise method of writing shorthand on an entire new plan, adapted to every capacity, and to the use of schools. By M. Nash. Norwich, Printed by W. Chase and co., for the author; ₍etc., etc.₎ 1783.
xx, ₍48₎ p. 20 x 16ᵐ.

1. Shorthand.   I. Title.

11—12016

Library of Congress   Z56.N25

NN 0024748 DLC CtY PU NN

Nash, Michael, Methodist.
Gideon's Cake of Barley Meal. A letter to the Rev. William Romaine, on his preaching for the emigrant popish clergy; with some strictures on Mrs. Hannah More's remarks, published for their benefit, 1793. London, printed for J.S. Jordon, 1793.
55 p.
1. Church of England - Doctrinal and controversial works. I. Romaine, William. II. More, Hannah. III. Title.

NN 0024749 TNJ-R

252
L99o

[Nash, Michael] Methodist.
Gideon's cake of barley meal. A letter to the Rev. William Romaine, on his preaching for the emigrant popish clergy; with some strictures on Mrs. Hannah More's remarks, published for their benefit, 1793. 2d ed. With another letter sent to Mr. Romaine prior to this, and sundry notes and remarks; wherein all the objections and replies of the opponents that have come to the author's knowledge are fully answered... London, J. S. Jordan, 1793.
117 p. 21 cm.

Bound with:- Lyttelton, George. Observations on the conversion and apostleship of St. Paul.- Whitefield, George. The Rev. Mr. Whitefield's answer to the Bishop of London's last pastoral letter.- Moody, Robert. The Moabite's horn cut off.- Townsend, William. Remarks on the charge of the Bishop of St. David's.- Bryson, T. A serious address to youth of both sexes.- Parker, D. A charitable morsel of unleavened bread.- Williams, W. B. The good Samaritan.- La Marche, J. F. Letter of the Right Rev. John Francis de la Marche.- Moad, F. An account of the manner in which the persons confined in the prisons of Paris were tried and put to death.- Witherly. To the great and learned among Christians... Joseph Priestley.- A word in season to the traders and manufacturers of Great Britain.- Law, William. The spirit of prayer.

NN 0024752 LU

Nash (M₍ichael₎) Methodist.
The ignis fatuus; or will o' the wisp at Providence Chapel, detected and exposed: with a seasonable caution ... to avoid the bogs of his ambiguous watch-word and lying warning. *London: W. Treppass,* 1798. viii, 9–68 pp. 4°.

NN 0024753 NN

B
73
.6474

NASH, MICHAEL, Methodist.
Paine's Age of reason measured by the standard of truth. Wakefield's Examination of, and a layman's answer to The age of reason, both weighed in the balance, and found wanting... London, Printed for the author, 1794.
84p.

"A layman's answer" refers to "The age of infidelity" by Thomas Williams.

NN 0024754 ICN

Nash, Mildred Archer, joint illus.
Borglum, Solon Hannibal, 1868–1922.
Sovnd constrvction; a comparative analysis of natvral forms and their relation to the hvman figvre, by Solon H. Borglvm ... six hvndred plates drawn by the avthor and Mildred Archer Nash. New York, Priv. print. for the Committee of the Solon Borglum memorial fund ₍1923₎

Nash, Myrtle Corliss, 1915–
A quantitative study of effects of past experience on adaptation-level. Ann Arbor, University Microfilms ₍1952₎
(₍University Microfilms, Ann Arbor, Mich.₎ Publication no. 3632)
Microfilm copy of typescript. Positive.
Collation of the original, as determined from the film: 1 v. (various pagings) illus., tables.
Thesis—Bryn Mawr College.
Vita.
Abstracted in Dissertation abstracts, v. 12 (1952) no. 3, p. 335.
Bibliography: leaves 114–117.

1. Adaptability (Psychology)   I. Title. II. Title: Adaptation-level.

Microfilm AC-1   no. 3632   Mic 54 683

NN 0024756 DLC PBm OrU

VOLUME 405

Nash, N. Richard.
Incognito, a mystery comedy in three acts, by N. Richard Nusbaum ... New York, N. Y., Los Angeles, Calif., S. French; ₍etc., etc.₎ 1941.
128 p. plates, diagr. 18 cm. (*On cover:* French's standard library edition)

I. Title.

PS3527.A6365 I 5 1941   812.5   41–24204 rev

NN   0024757   DLC

Nash, N. Richard.
Parting at Imsdorf, a one-act drama, by N. Richard Nusbaum ... New York, N. Y., Los Angeles, Calif., S. French; London, S. French, ltd.; ₍etc., etc.₎ 1941.
48 p. diagr. 19 cm.

I. Title.

PS3527.A6365P3 1941   812.5   41–8562

NN   0024758   DLC NRCR

812.54
N248r   Nash, N.   Richard
The rainmaker: a romantic comedy, by ... N.Y. Bantam Books, 1955.
ix, 115p. illus. 16cm.

NN   0024759   OWorP

Nash, N. Richard.
The rainmaker, a romantic comedy in three acts. ₍Acting ed.₎ New York, French ₍1955₎
102 p. illus. 19 cm.

I. Title.   *Name originally:* Nathan Richard Nusbaum.

PS3527.A6365R3 1955a   812.5   55–33708 ‡

IU LN KU MtBuM OrCS
NN   0024760   DLC ViU OU NN MoU OrPS MtU UU WaU MB

Nash, N   Richard.
The rainmaker; a romantic comedy. New York, Random House ₍*1955₎
182 p. 21 cm.

I. Title.

PS3527.A6365R3   812.5   55–7125 ‡

OrP WaS WaSp MtBC OrLgE OrPS WaT ScU MtU
PP PU NcC PPLas Or LU NcD OOxM TxU CaBVa CaBVaU
NN   0024761   DLC WaU NBuU ViU MB TU NN NcD OC1 OC1W

Nash, N. Richard
Rouge atomique; an exercise on one act. ₍New York₎ Dramatists Play Service [1955]
18p. 20cm.

NN   0024762   AAP NN NNC

812.4
N25sb   Nash, N   Richard.
Second best bed; comedy in three acts, by N. Richard Nusbaum. Philadelphia, Pa., c1941.
114 ℓ. 27ᵐ.
Unpublished typescript.

NN   0024763   CSt

NASH, N. RICHARD.
Second best bed; comedy in three acts. ₍New York, Rialto mimeographing and typing service bureau, 1946₎ 46, 57, 51 ℓ. 29cm.

Typescript.
Produced at the Ethel Barrymore theatre, New York, June 3, 1946.

1. Drama, American. 2. Shakespeare, William, in drama. 3. Shakespeare Anne (Hathaway), 1556-1623-- Drama. I. Title.

NN   0024764   NN

Nash, N   Richard.
See the jaguar; play in three acts. Acting ed. ₍New York₎ Dramatists Play Service ₍1953₎
133 p. 20 cm.

I. Title.

PS3527.A6365S4 1953   812.5   53–31512 ‡

NN   0024765   DLC CaOTP LU ViU MtBC WaT PU OC1

Nash, N. Richard.
Sky road, a comedy of the airways in three acts, by N. Richard Nusbaum ... Evanston, Ill., New York ₍etc.₎ Row, Peterson & company ₍1941₎
127, xi p. front., plates. 20 cm.

I. Title.   *Name originally:* Nathan Richard Nusbaum.

PS3527.A6365S5   812.5   41–22166 rev

NN   0024766   DLC OC1

Nash, N. Richard.
So wonderful! (In white) A play in one act, by N. Richard Nusbaum ... New York, N. Y., Los Angeles, Calif., S. French; London, S. French, ltd.; ₍etc., etc.₎ 1937.
38 p., 1 ℓ. diagr. 18½ cm.

I. Title.   *Name originally:* Nathan Richard Nusbaum.

PS3527.A6365S6 193⁷   812.5   37–38175 rev
₍r57d‡₎

NN   0024767   DLC CaBVaU WaT Or OC1

Nash, N   Richard.
The young and fair; a play. New York, Dramatists Play Service ₍1949₎
115 p. port. 20 cm.

I. Title.

PS3527.A6365Ye   812.5   49–7986*

CaBVa
NN   0024768   DLC FMU MoU WaU CaBVaU OrU WaT PJB

Nash, N. Richard.
The young and fair. Acting ed. ₍New York, Dramatist play service ₍c1949₎ 94 p. plan. 19cm.

1. Drama, American. I. Title.

NN   0024769   NN MtU

Nash, Nathan Richard
see Nash, N. Richard.

US   Nash, Nathaniel C
978MAS   The Sunday law, unconstitutional and
NAS   unscriptural; an argument presented in committee of the whole in the Massachusetts legislature, by Nathaniel C. Nash. Boston, Printed for the author, 1868.
23 p. 23cm.

NN   0024771   MH-L ICN MB

NASH, Nathaniel C.
The Sunday law unconstitutional and unscriptural; an argument presented in Committee of the Whole in the Massachusetts Legislature. 2d ed. Boston, printed for the author, 1868.
pp. 23.

NN   0024772   MH CtY NN

Nash, Nathaniel C
The Sunday law, unconstitutional and unscriptural. An argument presented in committee of the whole in the Massachusetts legislature. 3d ed. By Nathaniel C. Nash. Boston, The author, 1868.
23 p. 21½ᵐ.

1. Sunday legislation—Massachusetts.   I. Title.

Library of Congress   BV133.N3 1868   44–27120

NN   0024773   DLC MH OC1WHi

Nash, Nellie Clayton.
Cape Split chickens, and other stories, by Nellie Clayton Nash; illustrations by Mabel Rollins Harris. Boston: The Cornhill Co. ₍cop. 1918₎ 6 p.l., 64 p. incl. front. illus. 8°.

Contents: Cape Split chickens. A family misunderstanding. Banty Hen takes a swim. Yellow legs and black boots. Mr. Black Drake, bachelor.

1. Poultry.—Legends and stories. (American). 3. Harris, Mabel Rollins, illustrator. 4. Title.   2. Juvenile literature.—Fiction   N. Y. P. L.   April 11, 1919.

NN   0024774   NN

Nash, Nellie Clayton.
Cape Split ducklings, by Nellie Clayton Nash; illustrations by Stanley F. Leland. Boston, The Cornhill company ₍*1918₎
4 p. l., ₍3₎–86 p. front., illus. 21ᵐ.

1. Ducks.   I. Title.

Library of Congress   PZ10.3.N175C   19–15083

NN   0024775   DLC MiU

U85   Nash, Norman   comp.
810n   The artist's assistant, containing a choice selection of receipts from various authors, principally from the Valuable secrets of arts and trades; to which is prefixed a chymical treatise on the metals ... Springfield, 1810.
72p. 15½cm.

NN   0024776   CtY MH-BA MH

39   Nash, Norman.
10964   A new system of orthography, containing the elementary sounds of human language, represented by 42 simple characters, adapted and arranged in pairs and families, according to the analogy of the sounds, and of the forms, of the letters. Also, their syllabic combinations. Philadelphia 1836.
24 p. 24°.

NN   0024777   DLC PPL

Nash, Norman
Scripture references on some of the most important doctrines revealed in the New Testament... Winchester, Davis, 1821.
20 p

NN   0024778   PPPrHi

VOLUME 405

Rel.Pams. Nash, Norman, 1790-1870.
v. 69   A letter to the Executive committee of
3   the Domestic and Foreign Missionary Society
of the Protestant Episcopal Church in the
United States of America... Philadelphia,
Printed by William Stavely, 1827.
8 p. 22cm.

Concerns his actions at the Indian
Mission School, Green Bay, Wis.

NN 0024779 WHi ICN

Nash, Norman Burdett, 1888–
Henry A. Coit (1830-1895) : educator, leader, pioneer—
a great American schoolmaster. New York, Newcomen
Society in North America, 1950.
24 p. illus., mounted port. 23 cm.
"Newcomen address ... delivered during the '1946 Massachusetts
dinner' of the Newcomen Society of England, held ... at Boston ... on
June 20, 1946."

1. Coit, Henry Augustus, 1830-1895.
LD7501.C8217 1956   922.373   51–1478

OrCS IdU AAP
NN 0024780 DLC TxU NcRS MB ViU FTaSU WaPS OU NN

Nash, Norman Burdett, 1888–   3458.303
Honesty and the creeds.
(In Creeds and loyalty ... Pp. 123-150. New York. 1924.)
Bibliography, p. 150.

M9011 — T.r. — Creeds.

NN 0024781 MB

Nash, Norman Burdett, 1888–
The parish as a social instrument, by the Rev. Norman B.
Nash, s. t. d. New York, N. Y., The National council, Department of Christian social service, 1935.
12 p. 18½ᵐ.
"An address, slightly abridged, delivered ... at the Episcopal social
work conference, held at Montreal, Canada, on June 13, 1935."—p. ₍2₎

1. Church and social problems—Anglican communion. 2. Parishes.
I. Protestant Episcopal church in the U. S. A. National council. Dept. of
Christian social service. II. Title.
38–10687

Library of Congress   HN37.A6N3
₍a44d1₎   261

NN 0024782 DLC

Nash, Ogden, 1902-1971.
The bad parents' garden of verse, by Ogden Nash; illustrated by Reginald Birch. New York, Simon and Schuster,
1936.
x p., 1 l., 13-132 p. incl. front., illus. 20½ᵐ.

I. Birch, Reginald Bathurst, 1856–   illus. II. Title.
36–21491
Library of Congress   PS3527.A63B3 1936
———— Copy 2.
Copyright A 93723   ₍5–2₎   817.5

OC1 OO NN MB OrAshS Or WaS IdB CoU ViU
NN 0024783 DLC FU MU OrU NcU NcRS PP PSt OU ICN

Nash, Ogden, 1902-1971.
Morley, Christopher Darlington, 1890–
Born in a beer garden; or, She troupes to conquer: sundry
ejaculations by Christopher Morley, Cleon Throckmorton and
Ogden Nash, and certain of the Hoboken ads, with a commentary on them by Earnest Elmo Calkins. Embellishments
by Edward A. Wilson, George Illian, Cleon Throckmorton,
August William Hutaf and Jay. New York, The Foundry
press: R. C. Rimington, 1930.

Nash, Ogden, 1902-1971, joint author.
Alger, Joseph.
The cricket of Carador, by Joseph Alger & Ogden
Nash; illustrations by Christopher Rule. Garden City,
N. Y., Doubleday, Page & co., 1925.

Nash, Ogden, 1902-1971.
The face is familiar; the selected verse of Ogden Nash. Boston, Little, Brown and company, 1940.
xxii, 352 p. 22ᵐ.
"First edition."

I. Title.
₍Full name: Frederic Ogden Nash₎
40–35057
Library of Congress   PS3527.A637F3 1940
₍a46x5₎

OrAshS OrMonO WaE MtBC NIC TU
PU NcRS NcC OYesA OEac Or WaS CaBVa IdPI IdU OrSaW
NN 0024786 DLC MB TU CoU IEN OC1 OLaK OU ViU PPT

Nash, Ogden, 1902-1971.
The face is familiar; the selected verse of Ogden Nash.
Garden City, N. Y., Garden City publishing company, inc.
₍1941₎
xxii, 352 p. 21ᵐ.

I. Title.
A 43–2686
Joint university libraries,   Nashville
for Library of Congress   ₍PS3527.A ₎
₍2₎   817.5

ViU OC1W MB IU LU OrU
NN 0024787 TNJ MsU OU CoU NBuC NBuU TxU NcD FU MiU

RARE BOOK
DEPT.
20th   Nash, Ogden, 1902-1971.
Century   The face is familiar. London, J. M. Dent
₍1942₎
xxi, 294p. 14cm.
"First published in the United States ...
1940; Great Britain, 1942."

NN 0024788 WU

1926   Nash, Ogden, 1902-1971.
N2523fa   The face is familiar. London, J. M. Dent
1954   ₍1954₎
Harris   xi, 174 p. 19 cm.
Collection
"First published in Great Britain 1942."
"Revised and rearranged by the author 1954."
Poems.

NN 0024789 RPB WaSpG INS IaU KU

Nash, Ogden, 1902-1971.
Family reunion. ₍1st ed.₎ Boston, Little, Brown, 1950.
xiii, 146 p. 21 cm.

I. Title.
Full name: Frederic Ogden Nash.
PS3527.A637F34   817.5   50–10762

OrCS OrP Wa WaE WaS WaSp WaT CaBVaU OrSshS ICU NBuU
OC1U FMU PPL PPD NcGU TU CoU OC1W ICN CaBVa IdB Or
NN 0024790 DLC MB NcRS ViU TxU NN MiU TU PSt PP

811.5
N252fa Nash, Ogden, 1902-1971.
1951   Family reunion. London, J. M. Dent.
₍1951₎
xiii,146p. 19cm.

NN 0024791 IEN

817   Nash, Ogden, 1902-1971.
N25fa   Family reunion. ₍1st ed. ₎ Boston, Little,
Brown, 1950 ₍1953₎
146 p.

Verse.

Family reunion.

NN 0024792 KMK

SPECIAL COLLECTIONS
B812N175
Q53   Nash, Ogden, 1902-1971.
1954   Family reunion. Boston, Little, Brown
₍1954₎
xiii, 146 p. 21 cm.

Inscribed by the author to Mrs. Daniel
Longwell.

NN 0024793 NNC

Nash, Ogden, 1902-1971.
Four prominent So and So's
see under Armbruster, Robert.

Nash, Ogden, 1902-1971.
... Free wheeling, illustrated by Soglow. New York, Simon
and Schuster, 1931.
100 p. illus. 19ᵐ.
Verses.

I. Title.
Library of Congress   PS3527.A637F7 1931
———— Copy 2.
31–32452
Copyright A 43930   ₍3₎   817.5

OC1 OC1U MB NN MH ViU PP PPGi WaS Or
NN 0024795 DLC OU CoU TU TxU GU ViU NcD OO OEac

811.52
N252g   Nash, Ogden, 1902-1971.
Good intentions. Boston, Little,
Brown and company, 1942.
xiv, 180 p. 21 cm.

NN 0024796 OWorP PSt CoD NBuU CaOTP MB ViU AU NcU

Nash, Ogden, 1902-1971.
... Good intentions. Boston, Little, Brown and company,
1942.
xiv, 180 p. 21 cm.
Verse.
"First edition."

I. Title.
PS3527.A637G6   817.5   42–25547

MtU WaE WaS WaT WaSp WaSpG OrStbM OkU
NcD NNC ScU WU MU KEmT KyLxCB CoU OrP Or CaBVa
NN 0024797 DLC MiU OO OC1 OLaK NcRS NcC PPA PP PU

*
AC8   Nash, Ogden, 1902-1971.
.A6
no.A-5   Good intentions. New York, Editions
1942   for the Armed Services, ₍1942₎
121 p. 10 X 14cm. (Armed Services
ed. A-5)

NN 0024798 ViU

811.5
N252g   Nash, Ogden, 1902-1971.
1942   Good intentions. ₍Verses₎ ₍New York₎
Grosset & Dunlap ₍c1942₎
180 p. (Universal Library, 89)

NN 0024799 ICarbS

VOLUME 405

Nash, Ogden, 1902-1971.
 ... Good intentions. Boston, Little, Brown and company, 1943 ₍c1942₎
  xiv, 180 p. 21 cm.
  Verse.

   i. Title.

         Full name: Frederic Ogden Nash.

 NN 0024800 OrU

Nash, Ogden, 1902-1971.
 Good intentions, by Ogden Nash. London, J. M. Dent & sons ltd. ₍1943₎
  xii, 228 p. 18½ᵐ.
  Verse.
  "First published in the United States ... 1942. First published in Great Britain 1943."

   i. Title.   44-4632

   Library of Congress PS3527.A637G6 1943
          ₍3₎   817.5

 NN 0024801 DLC

Nash, Ogden, 1902-1971.
 ...Good intentions. Boston, Little, Brown & do. 1944 ₍c1942₎
  180 p

 NN 0024802 PU CoU

Nash, Ogden, 1902-1971.
 Good intentions. Boston, Little... 1945.

 NN 0024803 PPT

Nash, Ogden, 1902-1971.
 Good intentions. ₍Verses₎ Garden City, N. Y., Blue Ribbon Books ₍1947₎
  xiv, 180 p. 20 cm.

   i. Title.

   PS3527.A637G6 1947 817.5 47—6021*

 NN 0024804 DLC MiU MB OrStbM

818
N175g **Nash, Ogden,** 1902-1971.
 ... Good intentions. Boston, Little, Brown and company, ₍1955, c1942₎
  xiv, 180 p. 20 cm.
  Verse.

 NN 0024805 LU

NASH, OGDEN, 1902-1971.
 Grin and bear left: poem.

 NN 0024806 PPULC

Nash, Ogden, 1902-1971.
 ... Happy days; illustrated by Soglow. New York, Simon and Schuster, 1933.
  161 p. illus. 20½ᵐ.
  Verses.
  Music: p. ₍77₎-₍91₎

   i. Title.   33-30714

   Library of Congress PS3527.A637H2 1933
   —— Copy 2.
   Copyright A 68695   ₍5₎   817.5

  OCl OO OEac MB NN CaOTP NcRS
 NN 0024807 DLC CU GU NjP WaS WaE ICU PP PU OOxM

Nash, Ogden, 1902-1971.
 ... Hard lines, illustrated by Soglow. New York, Simon and Schuster, 1931.
  xi, ₍1₎, 13-99 p., 1 l. illus. 19ᵐ.
  Verse.

   i. Title.
   Library of Congress PS3527.A637H3 1931 31-26364
   —— —— Copy 2.
   Copyright A 34131   ₍3-4₎   817.5

  CoFS NcD PP PPL CaOTP CaBVaU OrU WaE WaS OrP
  OOxM ViU MB TxU NN MH CaBVaU WU NcGU LU ViU NSyU
 NN 0024808 DLC InU MB CoU CU TU CSt-H OEac OCl OO

SPECIAL COLLECTIONS
B812N175
R43 Nash, Ogden, 1902-1971.
1932 Hard lines, and others. Illustrated by O. Soglow. ₍London₎ Duckworth ₍1932₎
  72 p. illus. 22 cm.

  "These verses were selected from two volumes, Hard Lines and Free Wheeling, both published by Simon & Schuster in the U. S. A. in 1931."
  "Sample copy. Not for sale."

 NN 0024809 NNC PSt NNU-W

PS
3527 Nash, Ogden, 1902-1971.
A637 I'm a stranger here myself. Boston,
I.5 Little, Brown ₍c1938₎
   xiv, 283 p. 20cm.
   Verse.

  FTaSU KEmT KyLxCB KyBB KyLx KyU NcD
 NN 0024810 CoD GU NBuU CaOTP OU CoU MB NBuC PSt

Nash, Ogden, 1902-1971.
 ... I'm a stranger here myself. Boston, Little, Brown and company, 1938.
  5 p. l., ix-xiv, 283 p. 21ᶜᵐ.
  Verse.
  "First edition."

   i. Title.   38-27466

   Library of Congress PS3527.A637 I5 1938
   Copyright A 117909 ₍10-2₎   817.5

  WaS OrU OrStbM WaTC OrMonO CaBVa CaBVaU
  OOxM ViU MtU KyU-H AU ScU OClW WaE WaSp OrAshS Or
 NN 0024811 DLC OU NjR MsSM NcC NcD NN MH ICU OCl

---

*
AC8
.A6 Nash, Ogden, 1902-1971.
no.981 I'm a stranger here myself. New York,
1938 Editions for the Armed Services, ᶜ1938.

  222 p. 10 x 14cm. (Armed Services ed. 981)

 NN 0024812 ViU

PS3527
.A637I5 Nash, Ogden, 1902-1971.
1939 I'm a stranger here myself. Boston, Little, Brown, 1939.
   xiv, 283 p. 21cm.
   Verse.

 NN 0024813 ViU MiU OO

Nash, Ogden, 1902-1971.
 ... I'm a stranger here myself. Boston, Little, Brown and company, 1941.
  5 p. l., ix-xiv, 283 p. 21 cm.
  Verse.

 NN 0024814 ViU

817
N1751
1938r NASH, OGDEN, 1902-1971.
  I'm a stranger here myself. Boston, Little, 1945 ₍c1938₎
   xiv, 283p. 20cm.

   Verse.
   "Published June 1938. Reprinted July 1945."

 NN 0024815 TxU PJA

PS3527
.A637M3 Nash, Ogden, 1902-1971.
1945 Many long years ago. Boston, Little, Brown ₍1945₎
   xvii, 333 p. 20cm.
   Poems.

   I. Title.
   Full name: Frederic Ogden Nash.

 NN 0024816 ViU LU KEmT NBuU CoU MB

Nash, Ogden, 1902-1971.
 ... Many long years ago. Boston, Little, Brown and company, 1945.
  xvii, 333 p. 20ᵐ.
  Poems.
  "First edition."

   i. Title.   ₍*Full name: Frederic Ogden Nash*₎

   Library of Congress ° PS3527.A637M3 45-8449
          ₍15₎   817.5

  CaBVaU OClJC Wa WaS IdPI
  OOxM OEac MB OCl AU KyMDC MsU NNC WaT Or CaBVa
 NN 0024817 DLC NcGU NcD NcC MiU TxU PV PP PU OU

Rare Books
20th Cent.
 Nash, Ogden, 1902-1971.
  Many long years ago. London, J. M. Dent ₍1954₎
  198p. 19cm.

 NN 0024818 WU KU WaSpG RPB NcU

PN6110 Nash, Ogden, 1902-1971, ed.
.C1N25 The moon is shining bright as day; an anthology
MoPo of good-humored verse, selected, with an introd. ₍1st ed.₎ New York, J. B. Lippincott Co. ₍1953₎
   x, 177 p. illus.

  1. Children's poetry. I. Title.

 NN 0024819 ICU

PZ
8.3 Nash, Ogden, 1902-1971, ed.
N3 The moon is shining bright as day; an
Mo anthology of good-humored verse selected, with an introd., by Ogden Nash. Philadelphia, J. B. Lippincott ₍c1953₎
   177p. illus. 22cm.

  1. Children's poetry I. Title

 NN 0024820 WU WaU DLC CoU NBuU

Nash, Ogden, 1902-1971, ed.
 The moon is shining bright as day; an anthology of good-humored verse. ₍1st ed.₎ Philadelphia, Lippincott ₍1953₎
  177 p. illus. 22 cm.

  1. Children's poetry. i. Title.

         Full name: Frederic Ogden Nash.

   PZ8.3.N3Mo   53—7143 ‡

  OrMonO WaE OrCS OrP WaS WaSp OrLgE OrU WaT
  IU MsU TU TxU GU IaU NcD MB OU PPT Wa KU MoU Or Wa
 NN 0024821 DLC WaU NN PP OCl PRosC OEac OOxM NcGU

VOLUME 405

Nash, Ogden, 1902–1971, ed.
         FOR OTHER EDITIONS
         SEE MAIN ENTRY
Wodehouse, Pelham Grenville, 1881–
   ... Nothing but Wodehouse, edited by Ogden Nash. Garden City, N. Y., Garden City publishing company, inc. ₍*1936₎

Nash, Ogden, 1902–1971.
   The Ogden Nash pocket book; introduction by Louis Untermeyer. Philadelphia, The Blakiston company, distributed by Pocket books inc., New York, N. Y. ₍1944₎
   viii, 147, ₍1₎ p. 16½ᵐ.
   Humorous verse.
   "1st printing November 1943."

   I. Title.
                  ₍*Full name:* Frederic Ogden Nash₎
                              44–6452
   Library of Congress   PS3527.A637A6 1944
            ₍5₎   817.5

NN 0024823   DLC WU GU NBuU NN OClW

M1621
.D
   Nash, Ogden, 1902–1971.

   Duke, Vernon, 1903–
     ₍Ogden Nash's musical zoo₎

     Ogden Nash's musical zoo; with illus. by Frank Owen. ₍1st ed.₎ Boston, Little, Brown, 1947.

   Nash, Ogden, 1902–1971, joint author.
PS3531
.E676 O5
   Perelman, Sidney Joseph, 1904–
     ... One touch of Venus. Boston, Little, Brown and company, 1944.

Rare Book
Collection
PS3527 Nash, Ogden, 1902–
.A637   Parents keep out; elderly poems for young-
P3   erly readers ₍by₎ Ogden Nash, drawings by Barbara Corrigan. Boston, Little, Brown and co., 1951.
    xiii, 1 l., 3–137 p. illus. 21 cm.

    Inscribed by Nash on flyleaf.

    I. Corrigan, Barbara, illus. II. Title.

NN 0024826   NcU ViU MoU WaU

Nash, Ogden, 1902–1971.
   Parents keep out, elderly poems for youngerly readers. Drawings by Barbara Corrigan. ₍1st ed.₎ Boston, Little, Brown, 1951.
   137 p. illus. 21 cm.

   I. Title.
                  Full name: **Frederic Ogden Nash.**
   PZ8.3.N3Par   51–18805 ‡

OrP OrU WaS WaSp WaT OrLgE Wa ICN IU
NN 0024827   DLC MH MB MiU TxU CoU ViU OU CaBVa Or

Nash, Ogden, 1902–1971.
   Parents keep out, elderly poems for youngerly readers. Drawings by Barbara Corrigan. Boston, Little, Brown₎1902, c1951₎
   137 p. illus. 21 cm.

NN 0024828   OU

Nash, Ogden, 1902–1971.
   The pocket book of Ogden Nash. Introd. by Louis Untermeyer. New York, Pocket Books ₍1954₎
   256 p. illus. 17 cm. (A Cardinal edition, C-158)
   Verse.

   I. Title.
                   Full name: **Frederic Ogden Nash.**
   PS3527.A637A6 1954   817.5   55–22792 ‡

NN 0024829   DLC MiU IEN

Nash, Ogden, 1902–1971.
   ... The primrose path; illustrated by Soglow. New York, Simon and Schuster, 1935.
   354 p. illus. 20½ cm.
   Verses.

   I. Title.
   PS3527.A637P7 1935   817.5   35–2750

CU MB WU
NN NcRS NBuU IdU WaS OrCS OrU UU NcRS NSyU ViU
NN 0024830   DLC ICU PP PU PPD OCl OClW OU OOxM MB

RARE BOOK
DEPT
20th   Nash, Ogden, 1902–1971.
Century   The primrose path; illustrated by Soglow. London, J. Lane ₍1936₎
    xvi, 218p. illus. 23cm.
    Poems.
    "First published in England 1936."

NN 0024831   WU

PS3527
A637P73
1953a   Nash, Ogden, 1902–1971.
     The private dining room, and other new verses. Boston, Little, Brown and company ₍1953₎
     169 p. 20 cm.

NBuC ICU
NN 0024832   MB KMK NBuU KyLx KyLxCB CaOTP KEmT KU

Nash, Ogden, 1902–1971.
   The private dining room, and other new verses. ₍1st ed.₎ Boston, Little, Brown ₍1953₎
   169 p. 20 cm.

   I. Title.
                   Full name: **Frederic Ogden Nash.**
   PS3527.A637P73   817.5   52–12647 ‡

NcU CaBVa CaBVaU IdB Or WaSp WaT Wa MtU OrVS
OrP OrU WaE WaS PPFr PLF PPC PPGi OOxM TxU MiU
OCl OO OU PPD PWcS CoD MU KyU-N KMK OrMonO OrCS
NN 0024833   DLC TU OkU CoU PU PBm PPL MB ViU NN

1926
N2523pr Nash, Ogden, 1902–1971.
1953   Private dining room, and other new verses. London, J.M. Dent ₍1953₎
Harris   xi, 146 p. 19 cm.
Collection
    "First published in Great Britain 1953."

NN 0024834   RPB TU ViU WU

Rare   Nash, Ogden, 1902–1971.
Books   Quartet for prosperous bastards ... ₍n.p., n.d.₎
Dept.   ₍3₎ p. 1 col. illus. 28cm.
    Illustrated by Rockwell Kent.

    *I. Kent, Rockwell, 1882–   illus.

NN 0024835   CU

PS3527
.A637 Nash, Ogden, 1902–1971.
A6   The selected verse of Ogden Nash. New York,
1945 Modern Library ₍1945₎
    xi, 246 p. 19cm. (The Modern library of the world's best books)

CtY WaSp CaBVa CaBVaU WaT PP
NN 0024836   ViU WaU TU GU ScU IaU LU MeB NcU ICU

817.5
N175S Nash, Ogden, 1902–1971.
    The selected verse of Ogden Nash. New York, ₍Random House, 1946₎
    xi, 246 p. 19 cm. (The Modern library of the world's best books)

NN 0024837   OO

Nash, Ogden, 1902–1971.
   The selected verse of Ogden Nash. ₍1st ed.₎ New York, Modern Library ₍1946₎
   xi, 246 p. 19 cm. (The Modern library of the world's best books)

   PS3527.A637A6 1946   817.5   46–25186*

OrU OrLgE WaSp
NN 0024838   DLC MiU MiD RPB AU KyU-H MtBC Or OrP

M1508 Nash, Ogden, 1902–1971. Sweet bye and bye.

   Duke, Vernon, 1903–
    ₍Sweet bye and bye. Selections; arr.₎

    Sweet bye and bye. Lyrics by Ogden Nash. Book by S. J. Perelman ₍and₎ Al Hirschfeld. New York, Harms ₍1946₎

Rare
PS
3527 Nash, Ogden, 1902–1971.
A81T5   Three little Christmas carols. New
1936 York, William Bradford Press, 1936.
    ₍12₎ p. illus. 16cm.

    Number 314 of an edition of 400 presented to Larry Spivak. This is the second of a series of keepsakes printed in the spirit of Christmas ... for the friends of the William Bradford Press ... Designed by Eugene M. Ettenberg typographer to the William Bradford Press." Signed: Gene Ettenberg.

NN 0024840   NIC NNC NN

812N175
L31
   Nash, Ogden, 1902–1971.
    Verses from 1929 on. New York, Modern Library ₍1952₎
    xxxii, 522 p. (The modern library)

NN 0024841   NNC

Nash, Ogden, 1902–1971.
   Versus. Boston, Little, Brown, 1949.

   Clipping of a review by John K. Hutchens laid in.

NBuU KEmT OrU NBuC
NN 0024842   ViU OU CoU CaOTP MB NBuU ICU ViU GU KU

Nash, Ogden, 1902–1971.
   Versus. ₍1st ed.₎ Boston, Little, Brown, 1949.
   xiii, 169 p. 20 cm.

   I. Title.
                   Full name: **Frederic Ogden Nash.**
   PS3527.A637V4   817.5   49–7579*

WaSp WaT OrMonO OrCS MtU MsSM
CaBViP WaE CaBVaU IdB OClJC IdPI Or OrCS OrP WaS
MiU PLF PU PHC PP PPD KyMdC NBuU NIC AAP CaBVa
NN 0024843   DLC AU PPFr NNC TxU MB OCl MH NcU TU

VOLUME 405

RARE BOOK
DEPT.
20th   Nash, Ogden, 1902-1971.
Century   Versus. London, J. M. Dent [1949]
            xiii, 169p. 20cm.
            "First published in U.S.A. ... Great Britain
            1949."

NN   0024844   WU

Nash, P.A., defendant.
    The charges, specification and evidence in case
of Capt. P.A. Nash, pro. marshall, 18th dist. O.
before general court-martial, Cleveland, O., 1865.
Cleveland, 1865.
    116p.

NN   0024845   OClWHi

Nash, Paul.
    Municipal markets and slaughterhouses in Europe. Washington: Gov. Prtg. Off., 1910. 117 p. illus. 8°. (United
States. Manufactures bureau. Special consular reports. v. 42,
part 3.)

1. Markets, Europe. 2. Abattoirs,   Europe.
N. Y. P. L.   February 15, 1912.

NN   0024846   NN

759.2
N176
    Nash, Paul, 1889-1946.
        Aerial flowers by Paul Nash. Oxford,
    Counterpoint publications, 1947.

        8 p. 1 col. pl., 5 illus. in text. 29.5
    cm.
    "This brochure was designed by Paul Nash shortly
    before he died, July 11th, 1946, and is now
    published by his friends, one year later, as a
    small tribute to his memory. The édition is
    limited to one thousand copies of which this is
    number 434. The production is the work of the
    Chiswick press,   London."
    1. Flowers, Aerial.

NN   0024847   CLCM

Nash, Paul, 1889-1946, illus.

British artists at the front ...
London, Published from the offices of "Country life," ltd.
[etc.] 1918-

Nash, Paul, 1889-1946, illus.

Drinkwater, John, 1882-
    Cotswold characters, by John Drinkwater, with five engravings on wood by Paul Nash. New Haven, Yale university
press; [etc., etc.] 1921.

Nash, Paul, 1889-1946.
    Dorset Shell guide, compiled and written by Paul Nash.
London, Architectural press [1936]
    46 p. illus., plates, maps. 23 x 18ᶜᵐ. (On cover: Shell guide[s])
    Illustrated lining-papers and covers.

    1. Dorset, Eng.—Descr. & trav.—Guide-books.
                                                    36-23278
    Library of Congress   DA670.D7N3
                                    [3]   914.233

NN   0024850   DLC

PR6037
.I 4D8   Nash, Paul, 1889-1946, ed.

        Sieveking, Lancelot de Giberne, 1896-
            ... Dressing gowns and glue, by Capt. L. de G. Sieveking,
        D. S. C. ... With illustrations by John Nash, with an introduction about the verses by G. K. Chesterton, and an introduction about the drawings by Max Beerbohm, and something about all concerned by Cecil Palmer; ed. by Paul Nash.
        [London] C. Palmer [1920]

Nash, Paul, 1889-1946.
    Fertile image; edited by Margaret Nash, with an introd.
by James Laver. London, Faber & Faber [1951]
    32 p. illus. 26 cm.

    1. Photography, Artistic. 2. Photography—Landscapes.   I. Title.

    TR660.N28 1951   779.3   51-8983 ‡

NN   0024852   DLC NN MH CSt IU KEmT CaBVa Or WaS

Typ   Nash, Paul, 1889-1946.
905   [Genesis]
24.5983PF   Signed proofs of the 12 woodcuts prepared
             for the Nonesuch press edition of the first
             chapter of Genesis]
             [London, 1924]
                 12ℓ. 19.5x26.5cm., mounted to 56x40.5cm., in
             portfolio 56.5x41cm.
                 Proofs on india paper, each signed, numbered
             and dated by the artist.
                 Laid in in an envelope are an autograph note,
             signed (Paul Nash) and dated July 31, 1931,
             stating "Only   four complete sets of

             the series of 'Genesis' engravings were issued.
             This is the 4th & last set ..."; and a T.L.s.
             (A. Knyvett Lee) to John Carter, dated 21st
             July 1931, transmitting the set.
                 Each proof mounted in a folder, the set in a
             portfolio of decorated boards designed by Nash.

NN   0024854   MH

Nash, Paul, 1889-1946.
    Genesis; twelve woodcuts by Paul Nash, with
the first chapter of Genesis in the authorized
version
        see under Bible. O.T. Genesis. I. English. 1924. Authorized.

Nash, Paul, 1889-1946, illus.

Ford, Ford Madox, 1873-1939.
    Mister Bosphorus and the muses; or, A short history of
poetry in Britain, variety entertainment in four acts; words by
Ford Madox Ford, music by several popular composers; with
harlequinade, transformation scene, cinematograph effects, and
many other novelties, as well as old and tried favourites; decorated with designs engraved on wood by Paul Nash. London,
Duckworth & co. [1923]

Nash, Paul, 1889-1946.
    Monster Field; a discovery. Oxford, Counterpoint Publications, 1946.
    [8] p. illus. (1 mounted col., on cover) 28 cm.
    The text of the essay ([5] p.) is a photocopy (positive) from ms.

    I. Title.
                                                    A 49-6945*
    Harvard Univ. Library
    for Library of Congress   [1]

NN   0024857   MH CtY InU

Nash, Paul, 1889-1946.
    Outline, an autobiography, and other writings. With a
pref. by Herbert Read. London, Faber and Faber [1949]
    271 p. illus. (part col.) ports. 25 cm.

    I. Title.
    ND497.N3A3 1949   927.5   50-2644

         NcD DSI NcU NNC MB KU MoU NjP OrP OrU WaS LU
NN   0024858   DLC UU OCl CtY MH ICU PSt CU-S NBuU

Nash, Paul, 1889-1946.
    Paintings, drawings and illustrations. Ed. by Margot
Eates, with essays by Herbert Read [and others. 1st ed.
Memorial vol.] London, Lund, Humphries [1948]
    xii, 80 p. 132 plates (part col.) port. 30 cm.
    "Books Illustrated by Paul Nash": p. 41. "Select bibliography":
p. [75]

    I. Eates, Margot, ed.

    ND497.N3E2   [759.2] 927.5   49-18613*

                        CaBVaU OrU WaS
NN   0024859   DLC IEN CSt MB TxU MH OU CaBVa CaBViP

759.93   Nash, Paul, 1889-1946.
N176b   Paul Nash, with introductions by John
            Salis and C. E. Montague. New York,
            G. H. Doran [1918]
                [9]p., 15 col. plates (British artists
            at the front, 3)

                1. European war, 1914-1918 - Pictorial
            works. I. Series. II. Salis, John.

NN   0024860   MiDA

            Nash, Paul, 1889-1946.
                Paul Nash. London, 1923; New York, 1923; London, 1955
                see under [Bertram, Anthony] 1897-

ND497   NASH, PAUL, 1889-1946.
.N3R42
            Read, Herbert Edward, 1893-
                ... Paul Nash. [Harmondsworth, Middlesex, Eng.] Penguin
            books [1944]

ND497   NASH, PAUL, 1889-1946.
.N3T3
            Tate Gallery, *London.*
                Paul Nash, 1889-1946. Memorial exhibition: paintings,
            watercolours, and drawings. At the Tate Gallery, Mar.
            17th-May 2nd, 1948. Arr. by the Tate Gallery and the
            Arts Council of Great Britain. [London] 1948.

Nash, Paul, 1889-1946.
    Paul Nash; ten coloured plates and a critical appreciation
by Herbert Read; also, a biographical note with a portrait
and two half-tone reproductions in the text. [London] Soho
gallery limited [1937]
    [12] p. illus. (incl. port.) 8 col. mounted pl. 38 x 30ᶜᵐ. (Half-title:
Contemporary British painters ... 1)
    Colored illustration mounted on p. [1] and [3] of cover.
    Bibliography: p. [7]

    I. Read, Herbert Edward, 1893-
                                                    38-25077
    Library of Congress   ND497.N3R4
                                    [5]   759.2

NN   0024864   DLC CSmH WaS CaOTP

Nash, Paul, 1889-1946.
    Places; 7 prints reproduced from woodblocks designed
& engraved by Paul Nash. With illustrations in prose.
London, W. Heinemann, ltd., 1922.
    4 p. l., front., 6 pl. 28ᶜᵐ.
    Descriptive letterpress on versos facing the plates.
    "Of this edition ... two hundred and ten copies have been printed, of
which numbers one to two hundred are for sale. This is number 194."

    I. Title.
                                                    24-28350
    Library of Congress   NE1217.N3A3

NN   0024865   DLC WaU

VOLUME 405

Spec.
NE
642,
N3
A4

C1951

Nash, Paul, 1889-1946.
Places; 7 prints reproduced from wood-blocks designed & engraved by Paul Nash. With illustrations in prose. London, W. Heinemann, 1922.
[22] p. illus. 28.5 cm.
"This edition ... consists of fifty-five copies on Japon paper with the designs printed direct from the wood-blocks ... each is numbered and signed by the artist. This is number 21."

Armorial bookplate, engraved, of Ralph Woodford Saint Hill.
Illustrated covers.

1. Wood-engravings, English - Specimens. 2. Nash, Paul, 1889-1946. I. Title.

NN   0024867   CtU IEN

PR6003
.O67Z55

Bottomley, Gordon, 1874-1948.
Poet & painter; being the correspondence between Gordon Bottomley and Paul Nash, 1910-1946, edited by Claude Colleer Abbott and Anthony Bertram. London, New York, Oxford University Press, 1955.

Nash, Paul, 1889-1946.

NK2110   Room and book, by Paul Nash.   London, The
N3   Soncino press ltd. [1932]
xix, 98 p., 2 l.   illus. (part col., part mounted) plates (part col.)   22 cm.   Cream cloth.

Contents.--Room: The modern aesthetic. Modern English furniture. The room equipped.--Book: Foreword to cover. The cover. The page. Modern processes in illustration.

1. House decor   ation. 2. Books. I. Title.

NN   0024869   CSmH OrU CaOTP NNC ICN WU MH KU LU

Nash, Paul, 1889-1946.
Room and book, by Paul Nash.   London: The Soncino Press, Ltd. [1932.]   xix, 98 p.   illus. (part col'd mounted), plates. 22cm.

First edition.
Contents: Introduction. Room: The modern aesthetic. Modern English furniture. The room equipped. Book: Foreword to cover. The cover. The page. Modern processes in illustration. Index.

646348A.   1. Interior decoration.   2. Books--Decoration. I. Title.
N. Y. P. L.   June 9, 1933

NN   0024870   NN CaBVa WaS

Nash, Paul, 1889-1946.
Room and book, by Paul Nash.   New York, C. Scribner's sons, 1932.
xix, 98 p., 2 l.   illus. (part col., part mounted) plates (part col.) 22 cm.
Printed in England.
Contents.--Room: The modern aesthetic. Modern English furniture. The room equipped.--Book: Foreword to cover. The cover. The page. Modern processes in illustration.

1. House decoration. 2. Books.   I. Title.

                                                                      32-26659
Library of Congress   NK2110.N3
                                    [3]   747

NN   0024871   DLC CtY MB NcU NN OCl

Nash, Paul, 1889-1946, illus.

PR6001
.R75S3

Rare Bk   Armstrong, Martin Donisthorpe, 1882-
Coll.   Saint Hercules, and other stories, by Martin Armstrong, with drawings by Paul Nash. London, Printed by O. Simon at the Curwen press, and published by the Fleuron ltd. [1927]

Nash, Paul, 1889-1946.   *4095.08-91.3
[Sketches illustrating the European War.] With introductions by John Salis and C. E. Montague.
= New York. George H. Doran Co. [192-?] (24) pp. Illus. Portrait. 15 colored plates. [British artists at the front. No. 3.] 30 cm.

N1977 — European War, 1914-1919.   ws and illustrations. — S.rc. — Salis, John, pref. — Montague, Charles Edward, pref., 1867-

NN   0024873   MB

Nash, Paul, 1889-1946.
A specimen book of pattern papers designed for and in use at the Curwen press; with an introd. by Paul Nash.   London, Fleuron ltd., 1928.
xiv p.   col. papers.   F.

NN   0024874   NcD

Nash, Paul, 1889-1946, illus.
Leroy, L   Archier.
Wagner's music drama of the Ring, by L. Archier Leroy; with wood engravings by Paul Nash. London, N. Douglas [1925]

PR6013
.R35W4
Rare bk.
Coll.

Nash, Paul, 1889-1946, illus.
Graves, Robert, 1895-
Welchman's hose, by Robert Graves; wood engravings by Paul Nash. London, The Fleuron, 1925.

thesis
B
N374

Nash, Peter Whitwell, 1913-
Esse actuale; the problem of existence and individuality in Giles of Rome. [Toronto] 1948.
ii, 308, iv, 90 leaves.

Thesis - University of Toronto.
"Selection of texts from Giles' Commentary on the first book of the Sentences, edition of 1521, Venice," leaves 1-82 (2d group)
Bibliography: leaves 83-90 (2d group)

NN   0024877   CaOTU

JV5
W6
1924
no.366

Nash, Sir Philip A   M
The economics of world power. [Bradford, England, 1924?]
17 l.   diagr., tables.   24 cm. (World Power Conference, 1st, London, 1924. [Paper] no.366)
Conference proof.

1.Power resources. I.Title.   II.Title: World power, The econom-   ics of.   (Series)

NN   0024878   DI

Nash, Philip Curtis, 1890-1947.
An adventure in world order, by Philip Curtis Nash. Boston, The Beacon press, 1944.
x, 189 p. 20½ cm.
"Copyright ... [by] the American Unitarian association."

1. International organization.   I. American Unitarian association. II. Title.
                                                                      44-2497
Library of Congress   JC362.N3
                                    [a44k5]   321.021

WaSpG MoU MH-AH
OCU OO OCl PP Or CaBVa OrCS OrP OrU WaS
NN   0024879   DLC MeB MB PSt IdU NcD ViU ViU-L OU

Nash, Philip Curtis, 1890-1947.
Dumbarton Oaks and the League covenant; a comparison and an evaluation. [Toledo, Toledo Blade, 1944]
cover-title, [16] p.   22 x 10cm.

"A reprint of articles that appeared on the 'Pages of opinion' in the Blade of November 13, 14 and 15."

NN   0024880   ViU-L

Nash, Philip Curtis, 1890-1947.
... The educator views democracy [by] Philip C. Nash ... Commencement, Henry J. Doermann theatre, February 6, 1939. [Toledo, O., 1939]
12 p. 23cm.   (Bulletin of the University of Toledo. [Vol. xvi, no. 6. February 1939])

1. Democracy. 2. Education--Addresses, essays, lectures [etc.] 3. U. S.--Politics and government.   I. Title.
                                                                      E 40-631
U. S. Off. of educ.   Library   JC428.N3
   for Library of Congress   [2]

NN   0024881   DHEW OrCS

Nash, Philleo, 1909-
... The excavation of Ross mound group I, by Philleo Nash. Milwaukee, Wis., Pub. by order of the Board of trustees [1933]
46 p.   diagrs., 9 pl. 27cm.   (Bulletin of the Public museum of the city of Milwaukee. v. 16, no. 1. ... Dec. 20, 1933)
Each plate accompanied by guard sheet with descriptive letterpress (included in paging)
Bibliographical foot-notes.

1. Mounds--Wisconsin. 2. Indians of North America--Wisconsin.
                                                                      34-31838
Library of Congress   QH1.M63   vol. 16, no. 1
-------- Copy 2.   E74.W8N3
                          [3]   (507.4) 913.77552

NN   0024882   DLC GU OrPR OrU OCU PU OU OCl MiU NN

Nash, Philleo, 1909-
The place of religious revivalism in the formation of the intercultural community on Klamath Reservation. 1937.
ii, 113 l.   29 cm.
Typescript (carbon copy)
Thesis--University of Chicago.
Bibliography: leaves 112-113.

1. Klamath Indian Reservation, Or. 2. Indians of North America--Religion and mythology. 3. Ghost dance.   I. Title.
E99.K7N3 1937b   299.7   74-154219
                                                    MARC

NN   0024883   DLC ICN

Historical
Library

Micro-
form
Room

Nash, Philleo, 1909-
The place of religious revivalism in the formation of the intercultural community on Klamath Reservation. 1937.
ii, 113 l.   29 cm.
Typescript (carbon copy)
Thesis--University of Chicago.
Bibliography: leaves 112-113.
Microfilm of typescript.   Chicago, Dept. of Photoduplication, University of Chicago Library [n. d.]   1 reel.   35 mm.
   1. Klamath Indian Reservation, Or. 2. Indians of North America--Religion and mythology. 3. Ghost dance.   I. Title.
E99.K7N3 1937b   299.7   74-154219
                                                    MARC

NN   0024884   WHi

Nash, Philleo, 1909-
... The place of religious revivalism in the formation of the intercultural community on Klamath reservation ... by Philleo Nash ... [Chicago, 1937]
1 p. l., p. 377-442, 445-449. 20½ cm.
Part of thesis (PH. D.)--University of Chicago, 1937.
"Private edition, distributed by the University of Chicago libraries, Chicago, Illinois."
"Reprinted from Social anthropology of North American tribes, University of Chicago press, 1937."
Bibliography: p. 445-449.
1. Klamath Indian reservation, Or. 2. Indians of North America--Religion and mythology.   I. Title.
                                                                      38-11219
Library of Congress   E99.K7N3
Univ. of Chicago Libr.
-------- Copy 2.   [2]   [299.7] 970.62

NN   0024885   ICU NcD OCU DLC

VOLUME 405

76
NA819

Harris
Collection

Nash, Polly
  [Manuscript book of poems. [Cumming-
ton, Mass., 180-?]
  [24] p. 17 cm.

NN 0024886 RPB

Nash, Priscilla.
  Rhythmical aspects of the lute songs of
Thomas Campian.

  68 numb. l. Music. 29 cm.
  Typewritten.
  Thesis - Radcliffe college, 1944.

NN 0024887 MH

Nash, Preston Garland, 1849-1901.
  In memoriam. Rev. Joshua Peterkin, D. D. Born
August 2d, 1814. Died March 7th, 1892. Address by
Rev. Preston Nash, rector of Christ church, Rich-
mond, Virginia. [Richmond, Va., 1901]
  cover-title, 16 p. illus. 23 cm.

  "Delivered in Holy Trinity church, Richmond, Virginia, January 31, 1901, upon the occasion of the
unveiling of a ... tablet to the memory of Rev.
Joshua Peterkin ..." cf. p. [3]

  1. Peterkin, Jos-   hua, 1814-1892.

NN 0024888 Vi ViN CSmH

Nash, R.L.
      see Nash, Robert Lucas, 1846-

Nash, Ralph Lee
Edward Fairfax's translation of the Gerusalemme libera-
ta

Thesis - Harvard, 1951

NN 0024890 MH

Nash, Ray.
  Five years creating the international mind in the younger
generation, by Ray Nash. 1923-1928. New York, Brooks-
Bright foundation [1929] 128 p. illus. 26cm.

  "Of this edition there have been printed one hundred numbered copies each signed
by the founder...Florence Brooks-Aten." This copy unnumbered.

282709B. 1. No subject. I. Brooks-   Bright foundation.
N. Y. P. L.   December 12, 1944.

NN 0024891 NN CtY PU MH

Nash, Ray, 1905- ed. and tr.

Plantin, Christophe, 1514-1589, *supposed author.*
  An account of calligraphy & printing in the sixteenth century from dialogues attributed to Christopher Plantin, printed
and published by him at Antwerp, in 1567. French and Flemish text in facsimile, English translation and notes by Ray Nash
and foreword by Stanley Morison. Cambridge, Mass., Department of printing and graphic arts, Harvard college library,
1940.

Typ
970
54.5983

[Nash, Ray, 1905-   ]
  C.P.R. [i.e. Carl Purington Rollins] keeper
of the human scale.
  The Dyke Mill,Montague,Massachusetts,20
August 1954.
  9,[1]p. ports. 23cm.,in folder 24cm.
  Caption title; imprint on p.[10].
  Signed at end: Ray Nash.
  "Two hundred and fifty copies have been
printed at the printing-office of the Yale
university press."
  Original print   ed red wrappers; in
cloth folder.

NN 0024893 MH NN CtU OrU NjP ICN KyU

Nash, Ray, 1905-
  Dürer's 1511 drawing of a press and printer. Cambridge,
Dept. of Printing and Graphic Arts, Harvard College Library, 1947.
  [12] p. plate. 24 x 31 cm.

  1. Printing-press. 2. Dürer, Albrecht, 1471-1528. 3. Printing—
Hist. I. Title.
  Z249.N3   655.1   47-12066*

NN 0024894 DLC NcU MeB OrU PP PU-FA KyU MH NNGr

655.1
N252d

Nash, Ray, 1905-
  Dürer's 1511 drawing of a press and printer. Cambridge,
Dept. of Printing and Graphic Arts, Harvard College Library, 1947.
  [12] p. plate. 24 x 31 cm.
  "550 copies printed in Sept. 1947 at the
Anthoensen Press, Portland, Maine, in Janson
types, on Oxbow paper."

  1. Printing-press. 2. Dürer, Albrecht, 1471-1528. 3. Printing—
Hist. I. Title.

NN 0024895 FU MU

Z8317
.78
.D3

Nash, Ray, 1905- ed.

Dartmouth college. *Library.*
  Fifty years of Robert Frost; a catalogue of the exhibition
held in Baker library in the autumn of 1943, edited by Ray
Nash. Hanover, N. H., Dartmouth college library, 1944.

RARE BOOK
DEPARTMENT

Z
.239
G68
N25
1946F

Nash,Ray,1905-
  Fifty years of type designer; [a review of
A half-century of type design and typography,
by Frederic W.Goudy]
  (In: Print. Woodstock,Vt. 25cm. v.4,no.3
(1946),p.[82]-83)
  Chronological list of Goudy types: p.[82]

  1.Goudy,Frederic William,1865-1947. A
half-century of type design and typography.
2.Book industries and trade--Period. I.Print;
a quarterly journal of the graphic arts.

NN 0024897 NSyU

Nash, Ray, 1905-
  Navy at Dartmouth, by Ray Nash. Hanover, Dartmouth
publications, 1946.
  6 p. l., 96 p. plates, ports., diagrs. 24cm.

  1. Dartmouth college. 2. Naval education—U. S. I. Title.
                                        46-20371
  Library of Congress   LD1438.N3
                                        [3]   359.071173

NN 0024898 DLC MU PU-Penn MB

Nash, Ray, 1905-
  Pioneer printing at Dartmouth, by Ray Nash, with A checklist of Dresden imprints by Harold Goddard Rugg. Hanover,
Printed by G. T. Bailey, 1941.
  40 p., 1 l. fold. front., facsims. 20½cm.
  "This is number 122 of two hundred copies printed ... the first thirty
copies constituting Keepsake no. 46 of the Columbiad club of Connecticut,
fifty copies for the Dartmouth college library, and one hundred copies for
sale."
  History of a press operated by Alden Spooner, 1778-1779, in Dresden,
Vermont, the part of Hanover in which Dartmouth college was located.
In February, 1779, Dresden became a part of New Hampshire.
  1. Printing—Hist.—Hanover, N. H. 2. Spooner, Alden, 1757-1827.
  I. Rugg, Harold Goddard, 1883-   II. Title.

  Library of Congress   Z209.H3N3
                                        41-9980
  ———— Copy 2.   [3]   655.17423

   NNC NN RPJCB LU NjP OrU
NN 0024899 DLC MoSW ViU MiU NjN KyU ICU PSC OCl MnU

Nash, Ray, 1905-
  The poet and the pirate.
  (In The New colophon. New York. 28 cm. v. 2, pt. 3 (1949)
p. 311-321)

  1. Frost, Robert, 1875-
  [Z1007.C72 vol. 2, pt. 3]   A 52-4096

Grosvenor Library
for Library of Congress   [2]

NN 0024900 NBuG

Wing
fZW
35
.613

NASH, RAY, 1905-
  A preliminary checklist of American writing
manuals and copybooks to 1850. Chicago, The
Newberry Library [194-?]
  72p. 28cm.

  Typescript.
  Additions tipped in.

NN 0024901 ICN

Z119
.P0534

Nash, Ray, 1905-   ed.

Printing & graphic arts. v. 1-
  Feb. 1953-
  Lunenburg, Vt., Stinehour Press.

Nash, Ray, 1905-
  Printing as an art. [A history of the Society of Printers,
Boston, 1905-1955.] Cambridge, Published for the Society
of Printers by Harvard University Press, 1955.
  xi, 141 p. illus. 25 cm.
  Bibliographical footnotes.

  1. Society of Printers, Boston. I. Title.

  Z120.S728   655.062744   55—7446

        MtU WaSp
  OO OCl OCU OOxM PPD PP KyU PU OU OClSA TU Or OrP
  CtY-M TxU NcD PPDrop OrMonO NSyU MU AAP CaBVaU MdBP
NN 0024903   DLC CU-B NcGU PSC PSt MH NBuG MB ViU

Nash, Ray, 1905-
  Rastell fragments at Dartmouth, by Ray Nash.
  (In The Library. London, 1943. 22½cm. Fourth ser., vol. XXIV,
no. 1, 2, June, September, 1943, p. [66]-73. facsims.)
  "Transactions of the Bibliographical society. New ser., vol. XXIV, nos.
1, 2."

  1. Rastell, John, d. 1536. 2. Printing—Specimens—Facsimiles.
  I. Dartmouth college. Library. II. Title.
Cleveland. Public library
for Library of Congress   [Z871.L69 4th ser., vol. 24, no. 1, 2]
                                        A 44-8117
                                        [5]   (010.5)

NN 0024904 OCl OCU

1901
F9396xna

Harris
Collection

Nash, Ray, 1905-
  Robert Frost and his printers. [Chicago,
Black Cat Press, 1946]
  p.10-12, illus. 25 cm.

  Article in The Book collector's packet,
vol. 4, no. 5.

  Includes the "too long unprinted" poem,
One step backward taken, by Robert Frost.

NN 0024905 RPB

VOLUME 405

Nash, Ray, 1905-
... Some early American writing books and masters, by Ray Nash. ₍Hanover, N. H.₎ °1943.
24, ₍2₎ p. illus. 21 x 16¼ᵐ.
"225 copies printed."
A paper prepared for the November 1942 meeting of the Club of odd volumes. *cf.* Pref.
"Books shown at the Club of odd volumes meeting": p. ₍25₎

1. Penmanship—Copy-books—Bibl. 2. Penmanship.
43–13364
Library of Congress   Z43.A2N3
₍3₎   016.652

PPCS
NN   0024906   DLC FU MoSW OrU TxU NcD MB PU KyU PHi

Nash, Ray, 1905-
... Some early American writing books and masters, by Ray Nash. ₍Hanover, N. H.₎ °1943.
24, ₍2₎ p. illus. 21 x 16¼ᵐ.
A paper prepared for the November 1942 meeting of the Club of odd volumes. *cf.* Pref.
"Books shown at the Club of odd volumes meeting": p. ₍25₎
"Published by H₍ofer, Philip₎ & N₍ash, Ray₎ Second edition."
1. Penmanship—Copy-books—Bibl. 2. Penmanship.
43–13364

NN   0024907   RPJCB

Nash, Ray, 1905-
Thoreau MacDonald's drawings for Dartmouth
see under   MacDonald, Thoreau, 1901-

Nash, Ray, 1905-
Writing: some early American writing books and masters. ₍Cambridge, Mass., Harvard college library...₎ c1943.
24 ₍2₎ p.

NN   0024909   OC1 PSC

NASH, RAY, 1905-
₍... Writing; some early American writing books and masters ...
[Hanover, N.H., Printed April 1943, published by H & N.]
24,[2]p. illus. 21cm.
Title within calligraphic border.
225 copies printed.
"Books shown at the Club of odd volumes meeting": p. [25].
Orig. printed gray-blue wrappers.

NN   0024910   PPRF

Nash, Richard, 1674-1762.
₍In his Eccentric personages, p. 79.₎ ₎Beau Nash. 8 pp.
By Richard Nash and W. Russell.

NN   0024911   MdBP

Nash, Richard, 1674-1762.
Epitaphium Richardi Nash, armigeri
see under   ₍King, William₎ 1685-1763.

*EC7
N1765
763j
Nash, Richard, 1674-1762.
The jests of Beau Nash, late master of the ceremonies at Bath. Consisting of a variety of humorous sallies of wit, smart repartees, and bons mots; which passed between him and personages of the first distinction, and the most celebrated for true wit and humour. Dedicated to the Right Honourable the Earl of Chesterfield ...
London:Printed for W.Bristow,in St.Paul's church-yard;and sold by the booksellers at Bath. M DCC LXIII. <Price one shilling.>
₍1p.l.,₎iv,1,[1],   iii,[1],83p. front. (port.)
16.5cm.
Errata: [1]p.   preceding p.[1].

NN   0024913   MH IU CtY ICN MnU CLU-C

Nash, Richard, 1674-1762.
Life, extracted principally from his original papers
see under   [Goldsmith, Oliver] 1728-1774.
The life of Richard Nash.

BX
269
T47
1948
Nash, Robert, 1902-
A Day with Christ. How it's done. Pass it on... [New York, Spiritual book associates, 1948?].
24, 48, 36 p.   21 cm.   [With, as issued: Thomas de Saint-Laurent, Raymond de. Confidence... New York, 1948?]

1.Jesus Christ – Devotional. 2.Spiritual life.
48–325.

NN   0024915   IMunS

Nash, Robert, 1902-
Everyman at his Prie-dieu. Dublin, Gill, 1954

NN   0024916   MH

Nash, Robert, 1902-
Everyman at his prie-dieu. Westminster, Md., Newman Press, 1954.
309 p. 22 cm.

1. Meditations.   I. Title.
BX2182.N27   242   54–5660 ‡

NN   0024917   DLC PRosC

Nash, Robert, 1902-
In the news, by Robert Nash, s. j. Dublin, Browne and Nolan limited, 1944.
51, ₍1₎ p. 18¼ᵐ.

1. Catholic church—Doctrinal and controversial works, Popular. I. Title.
45–20787
Library of Congress   BX1755.N27
₍2₎   230.2

NN   0024918   DLC

BS
1545
V28
Nash, Robert, 1902-
In the news. [New York] Spiritual Book Associates [1946].
51p.   20cm.
No. 3 in a vol. with binder's title: Ezechiel.
A selection of the Spiritual Book Associates with the permission of Browne & Nolan.
1. Theology, Doctrinal – Popular works.

NN   0024919   IMunS

Nash, Robert, 1902-
Is life worthwhile? Dublin, Browne and Nolan ₍1949₎
296 p. 20 cm.

1. Christian life—Catholic authors.   I. Title.
BX2350.N28 1949   248   51–29520

NN   0024920   DLC OrStbM DCU IMunS MH

Nash, Robert, 1902-
Label your luggage, by Robert Nash, s. j. Dublin, Browne and Nolan limited ₍1944₎
39 p. 18ᵐ.
"First impression July, 1943 ... Fourth impression March, 1944."

1. Christian life—Catholic authors.   I. Title.
A 45–918
Harvard univ. Library
for Library of Congress °   BX2350.N3
₍4₎†   248

NN   0024921   MH DLC

Nash, Robert, 1902-
Label your luggage, by Robert Nash, s. j. ₍New York₎ The Spiritual book associates ₍1945?₎
39 p. 19ᵐ. ₍*With, as issued:* Ryan, Mary. Our Lady's hours ... ₍New York, 1945?₎
First published in Dublin, 1943.

1. Christian life—Catholic authors.   I. Title.
46–14872
Library of Congress   BX2025.R9
₍2₎   248

NN   0024922   DLC

BX2350
.N28
1951
Nash, Robert, 1902-
Living your faith. ₍1st American ed.₎ New York, Prentice-Hall ₍1951₎
311 p. 22 cm.
"Originally published ₍1949₎ in Ireland under the title: Is life worthwhile?"

1. Christian life—Catholic authors.   I. Title.
BX2350.N28 1951   248   51–1977

NN   0024923   DLC MBtS OrP WaE WaS WaSpG WaT MB

Nash, Robert, 1902-
Marriage before & after. Dublin, Brown & Nolan, Limited, The Richview Press, [n. d.]
214 p.
First published March, 1947.

NN   0024924   MiDP WaSpG Or IMunS

Nash, Robert, 1902-
Marriage: before and after. New York, Didier ₍1952₎
214 p. 19 cm.

1. Marriage—Catholic Church.   I. Title.
HQ734.N34   *301.426 173.1   54–1959 ‡

NN   0024925   DLC

Nash, Robert, 1902-
The nun at her prie-dieu. Westminster, Md., Newman Press, 1950.
298 p. 23 cm.

1. Monasticism and religious orders for women.   I. Title.
BX4210.N3   271.9   50–10406

NN   0024926   DLC WaSpG

Nash, Robert, 1902-
The nun at her prie-dieu. Westminster, Md., Newman Press, 1953.
298 p. 23 cm.

1. Monasticism and religious orders for women.   I. Title.

NN   0024927   PRosC

Nash, Robert, 1902-
A pamphlet tells its tale. Dublin, Irish messenger office [1946]

20 p. 18 cm.

NN   0024928   MH

VOLUME 405

Nash, Robert, 1902–
Pass it on, by Robert Nash, s. j. ... Dublin, Browne and Nolan limited, 1943.
36 p. 18ᶜᵐ.

1. Catholic church—Doctrinal and controversial works—Catholic authors.   I. Title.

Harvard univ. Library   A 45–805
for Library of Congress °   BX1755.N3
[2]†   230.2

NN   0024929   MH DLC

Nash, Robert, 1902–
The priest at his prie-dieu. Westminster, Md., Newman Press, 1949.
300 p. 23 cm.

1. Meditations. 2. Clergy—Religious life.   I. Title.

BX2182.N28   242   49–9771*

NN   0024930   DLC OrStbM

BS   NASH, Robert, 1902–
2551   The priest at his prie-dieu. Westminster,
N2   Maryland, The Newman Press, 1952.

300 p. 21 cm.

1. Priests—Meditations. I. Title.

NN   0024931   MBtS

Nash, Robert, 1902–
The priest at his prie-dieu. Westminster, Md., Newman Press, 1954.
300 p. 23 cm.

1. Meditations. 2. Clergy—Religious life.   I. Title.

NN   0024932   PRosC

Nash, Robert, 1902–
Saint of the displaced: St. Joseph Pignatelli, S.J. Dublin, M. M. Gill, 1955.

43 p. 18cm.

1. Pignatelli, Jose Maria, Saint, 1737-1811
I. Title.

NN   0024933   InReS

Nash, Robert, 1902–
The seminarian at his prie-dieu. Westminster, Md., Newman Press, 1951.
312 p. 23 cm.

1. Seminarians—Religious life.   I. Title.

BX903.N3   242   52–6323 ‡

NN   0024934   DLC

240.4   Nash, Robert, 1902–
2295   The seminarian at his prie-dieu, by ...
N252s   Westminster, Md., Newman, 1954.

312p. 22cm.

I. Title. 1. SEMINARIANS - MEDITATIONS

NN   0024935   OWorP PRosC

Nash, Robert, 1902–
Send forth thy light, by Rev. Robert Nash, s. j. Westminster, Md., The Newman bookshop, 1946.
199 p. 19ᶜᵐ.

1. Meditations.   I. Title.
BX2182.N3   248   47–52
Pub. 1Nov46; publisher; A8415.

NN   0024936   DLC OrStbM WaSpG

Nash, Robert, 1902–
Standing on holy ground. Westminster, Md., Newman Press, 1955.
178 p. illus. 21 cm.

1. Israel—Descr. & trav. 2. Jordan—Descr. & trav.   I. Title.
DS107.4.N3   *915.694   55–12010 ‡

NN   0024937   DLC PSt WaSpG PRosC PP

---

247   Nash, Robert, 1902–
N25t   That they be one. Dublin, Clonmore & Reynolds [1954]

136 p. 19cm.

1. Charity. 2. Prayer. 3. Priesthood.
I. Title.

NN   0024938   InRenS IMunS

Nash, Robert, 1902–
This is Christianity. Dublin, M. H. Gill, 1952.
174 p. 19 cm.

1. Catholic Church—Apologetic works. 2. Christian life—Catholic authors.   I. Title.
A 55–579 ‡

St. Mary's College,   St. Marys, Kan. Libr.
for Library of Congress   [2]

NN   0024939   KXSM

Nash, Robert, 1902–
Thy light and Thy truth, a companion to Send forth Thy light. Westminster, Md., Newman Press, 1948.
197 p. 20 cm.

1. Meditations.   I. Title.

BX2182.N32   248   48–8609*

NN   0024940   DLC OrStbM OCIND

---

247   Nash, Robert., 1902–
N25w   We Catholics, a collection of spiritual essays. Dublin, M H. Gill, 1953.

viii, 136 p. 18cm.

1. Spiritual life. 2. Catholic Church - Addresses, essays, lectures. I. Title.

NN   0024941   InRenS WaSpG

Nash, Robert Lewis
A guidance program for West junior high school, Columbus, Ohio... [Columbus] Ohio state university, 1938.
7 p.l., 7-115 numb. l.
Thesis.

NN   0024942   OU

Nash, Robert Lucas, 1846–   *3562.148.1902
Australasia as a contributor to the world's supplies.
(In Co-operative Wholesale Societies, Limited, England and Scotland. Annual for 1902. Pp. 301–315. Manchester, 1902.)

E6762 — Australasia. Stat.

NN   0024943   MB

Nash, Robert Lucas, 1846–
The banking institutions of Australasia. .... By Robert Lucas Nash. London, The "British Australasian" Company, ltd.; Melbourne, McCarron, Bird and Co., [1890?].
[94] p. incl. tables. 3 pl., 13 port. 21ᶜᵐ.
"A reprint of articles published in the British Australasian, Australian Times and Anglo-New-Zealander."

NN   0024944   ICJ ICU NcD FU

Microfilm   Nash, Robert Lucas, 1846–   FOR OTHER EDITIONS
18094   SEE MAIN ENTRY
HG   Fenn, Charles.
Fenn's compendium of the English and foreign funds, debts and revenues of all nations; together with statistics relating to national resources & liabilities, imports, exports, population, area, railway guarantees, municipal finance & indebtedness, banks of all nations, and all descriptions of government, provincial, and corporate securities held and dealt in by investors at home and abroad ... 13th ed., entirely re-written and brought down to the latest date. By Robert Lucas Nash ... London, E. Wilson, 1883.

---

q332.6   Nash, Robert Lucas, 1846–
N17613   The investor's sinking-fund and redemption tables. Showing investors the return offered by securities in the shape of interest, drawings, redemptions, terminable annuities. 3d ed. ... Sydney [19--?]
unp. tables.

NN   0024946   IU

Nash, Robert Lucas, 1846–
Money market events, and the value of securities dealt in on the stock exchange in the year 1868. With extracts from the "Investors' monthly manual." London, Wilson, 1869.
20 p. illus. 21½ ᶜᵐ.

NN   0024947   NjP

Nash, Robert Lucas, 1846–
New South Wales. The railways and tramways of the colony. Reprint from a work entitled: "New South Wales, 'The mother colony of the Australias.'" 1896.
[Sydney, C. Potter, government printer, 1896]
cover-title, 11 p. fold. diagr. 25ᶜᵐ.

1. Railroads—New South Wales.   I. Title.
A 13–2342

Title from Bureau of   Railway Economics. Printed by L. C.

NN   0024948   DBRE ICJ

Nash, Robert Lucas, 1846–
A short inquiry into the profitable nature of our investments. With a record of more than five hundred of our most important public securities during the ten years 1870 to 1880...by Robert Lucas Nash... London: E. Wilson, 1880.   108 p. incl. tables. 12°.

482665A. 1. Securities—Gt. Br.
N. Y. P. L.   August 22, 1930

NN   0024949   NN OCl

Nash, Robert Lucas, 1846–
A short inquiry into the profitable nature of our investments. With a record of more than five hundred of our most important public securities during the ten years 1870 to 1880 ... 2d ed. By Robert Lucas Nash ... London, E. Wilson, 1881.
[4], 115, [1] p. 18½ᶜᵐ.
Partly reprinted from the Economist.

1. Securities. 2. Investments.

NN   0024950   ICU MH-BA MiU

VOLUME 405

Ng832
880nc

Nash, Robert Lucas, 1846–
A short inquiry into the profitable nature of our investments. With a record of more than five hundred of our most important public securities during the twelve years, 1870–1881 ... 3d ed. (rev. and enl.) ... London, E.Wilson,1881.
2p.ℓ.,133,[1]p. 18½cm.
"Partly reprinted from the 'Economist' and 'Investor's manual.'"

NN 0024951 CtY

Nash, Robley Wilson, 1908– joint author.

Peirson, Henry Byron, 1894–
The planting and care of shade trees, by H. B. Peirson and R. W. Nash. Augusta, Me., 1936.

Nash, Rodney M., joint ed.

Baldwin, William Edward, 1883– ed.
Ohio township officers manual with forms, annotated, containing all Ohio law relating to townships with complete annotations to January 1, 1939 (by) William Edward Baldwin ... text and comment by Charles P. Baker, jr. ... Cleveland, Banks-Baldwin company (°1939)

Nash, Mrs. Rosalind Frances Mary Shore Nightingale
see
Nash, Mrs. Rosalind (Nightingale)

Nash, Rosalind (Nightingale)
The co-operative housewife.
(In Massingham. Labour and protection. Pp. 169–204. London, 1903.)   9337.242

F3537 — Cooperation.

NN 0024955 MB

Nash, Mrs. Rosalind (Nightingale) ed.

Nightingale, Florence, 1820–1910.
Florence Nightingale to her nurses; a selection from Miss Nightingale's addresses to probationers and nurses of the Nightingale school at St. Thomas's hospital. London, Macmillan and co., limited, 1914.

Nash, Rosalind (Nightingale).
... The law relating to health in factories and workshops. By Rosalind Nash. (London) Women's co-operative guild, 1897.
20 p. 18 cm. (Public health papers. vii)
Bound with Ravenhill, Alice: The health of the community ... 1897.

NN 0024957 CaBVaU

Nash, Mrs. Rosalind (Nightingale)
... Life and death in the potteries. By Rosalind Nash ... Manchester, The Labor press limited, co-operative printers, 1898.
cover-title, 12 p. 18½cm.
At head of title: Women's co-operative guild.

Continued in next column

Continued from preceding column

1. Potters—Gt. Brit. 2. Lead-poisoning. I. Women's co-operative guild. II. Title.
24–32281

Library of Congress   HD7269.P8G7 1898

NN 0024958 DLC

Nash, *Mrs.* Rosalind (Nightingale)
... The position of married women. By R. Nash. Annual congress, 1907 ... (n. p., 1907)
15 p. 18½cm.
At head of title: Women's co-operative guild.

1. Women in England. I. Women's cooperative guild. II. Title.
24–32280

Library of Congress   HQ1597.N3

NN 0024959 DLC

Nash, Mrs. Rosalind (Nightingale)

Cook, *Sir* Edward Tyas, 1857–1919.
A short life of Florence Nightingale, abridged from The life, by Sir Edward Cook, with additional matter, by Rosalind Nash. New York, The Macmillan company, 1925.

RT37.N6
N17

Nash, Mrs. Rosalind (Nightingale)
A sketch of the life of Florence Nightingale, by Rosalind Nash ... London, Society for promoting Christian knowledge (1937)
32 p. 21½cm.

1. Nightingale, Florence, 1820–1910.

NN 0024961 NNC

F118
.N28

Nash, Mrs. Rosalyn S.
Genealogical information from tables of contents of the Vosburgh collection at the Library of Congress, indexed by (1) Counties (2) Towns and villages (3) Towns and churches [by] Rosalyn S. Nash. Washington, D.C. 1933.
1 p.l., 75 numb l., 1 l., 76–79 numb, 1., 1 l., 80–88 numb. l. 28.5 cm.
In Manuscript.

NN 0024962 DLC

F118
.N282

Nash, *Mrs.* Rosalyn S   *comp.*
Genealogical information from tables of contents of the Vosburgh collection at the Library of Congress. Indexed by (1) counties (2) towns and villages (3) towns and churches [by] Rosalyn S. Nash. Washington, D.C., 1933.
1 p.l., 54 numb. l., 1 l., 7 numb. 1., 1 l., 6 numb. 1., 1 l., 11 numb. 1. 26½cm.
Typewritten.
1. Registers of births, etc.--New York(State) 2. New York--Geneal.--Sources. I. Vosburgh, Royden Woodward. II. Title. III. Title: Vosburgh collec tion.

NN 0024963 DLC

E98
.E2N2

Nash, Roy, fl. 1926–
The American Indian today; his economic life. San Francisco, Community Chest of San Francisco, 1934.
4 l. 30 cm.
Caption title.
Address delivered over station KPO Feb. 18, 1934.

1. Indians of North America – Econ. condit. I. Title.

NN 0024964 DI

Nash, Roy, fl. 1926–
O Brasil em 2044; uma tarefa para a mocidade brasileira. Conferência lida no Salão de Conferências da Biblioteca do Ministério das Relações Exteriores do Brasil, no dia 16 de Agosto de 1944. Rio de Janeiro, CEB, 1944.
72 p. 16 cm. (C. E. B. Conferencias, 16. Série Itamarati)

1. Brazil. I. Title.

F2508.N23
50–46506

NN 0024965 DLC IU MH CU

Nash, Roy, fl. 1926–
The conquest of Brazil, by Roy Nash, with eight maps and seventy-seven illustrations. New York, Harcourt, Brace and company (1926)
xvi, 438 p. front., plates, maps. 22½ cm.
"About books on Brazil": p. 399–401.

1. Brazil. I. Title.

F2508.N25 1926
26–12472

WaS WaE WaTC IdU Or OrU CaBViP ViU MiHM PPUnC CU MB DN PPT NcD NcU MsSM WU CoU
NN 0024966 DLC NjN NIC PU PPFr MiU OClW OU OCl NN

F2508
.N25
1927

Nash, Roy, fl. 1926–
The conquest of Brazil. London, J. Cape (1927)
xvi, 438 p. plates, maps. 22cm.
"About books on Brazil": p. 399–401.

1. Brazil. I. Title.

NN 0024967 ViU

Nash, Roy, fl. 1926–
... A conquista do Brasil ... Tradução de Moacyr N. Vasconcellos. São Paulo (etc.) Companhia editora nacional, 1939.
501 p. incl. front., illus. (maps) plates. 18½ cm. (Biblioteca pedagogica brasileira. Ser. 5.ª: Brasiliana v. 150)
"Do original norte-americano: The conquest of Brazil." Bibliographical footnotes.

1. Brazil. I. Vasconcellos, Moacyr Nascimento, 1908– II. Title.

F2508.N2518
41–2541

NN 0024968 DLC NcD OU WU IaU CSt MB

E93
.N32

Nash, Roy, fl. 1926–
The government service program – it's objectives, by Roy Nash, superintendent, Sacramento Indian Agency. Address to the Western Regional Conference of the National Fellowship of Indian Workers, Galilee, Lake Tahoe, Nevada, August 14, 1940. [n.p., 1940?]
29 l. 29 cm.

1. Indians of North America – Government relations. I. Title.

NN 0024969 DI

E78
.L8N3

Nash, Roy, fl. 1926–
The Indians of Louisiana in 1931.
[n.p.] 1931?
10 l. 27 cm.

1. Indians of North America – Louisiana.

NN 0024970 DI

E78
.T4N3

Nash, Roy, fl. 1926–
The Indians of Texas. [Washington] 1931.
[4] 17 l. 29 cm.

1. Indians of North America – Texas.

NN 0024971 DI

VOLUME 405

E99
.S28U46

Nash, Roy, fl. 1926–

United States. Bureau of Indian Affairs.
... Seminole Indians. Survey of the Seminole Indians of
Florida ... Washington, U. S. Govt. print. off., 1931.

NN   0024973   DI

E99
S28N2
Nash, Roy, fl. 1926–
Seminole survey of 1930. ‹n.p., 1930›
91 ℓ.
Cover title: The Florida Seminole and
his environment.

1. Seminole Indians. 2. Indians of
North America - Florida. I. Title: The
Florida Seminole and his environment.

Nash, Roy, 1929–
And the angels sing; a story of Giovanni Pierluigi da
Palestrina. Illus. by Brother Harold Ruplinger. Notre
Dame, Ind., Dujarie Press ‹1955›
95 p. illus. 24 cm.

1. Palestrina, Giovanni Pierluigi da, 1525?–1594—Fiction. 2. Musical fiction.   I. Title.
ML3925.P15N3   780.881   55–42164 ‡

NN   0024974   DLC NN

Nash, Roy, 1929–
I'll bow sadly; a story of Giuseppe Verdi. Illus. by
Brother Harold Ruplinger. Notre Dame, Ind., Dujarie
Press ‹1955›
96 p. illus. 24 cm.

1. Verdi, Giuseppe, 1813–1901—Fiction. 2. Music—Juvenile literature.   I. Title.
ML3930.V4N3   [813.5] 780.881   56–15677 ‡

NN   0024975   DLC FMU

Nash, Roy, 1929–
Sing, my poor heart, sing; a story of Franz Peter Schubert. Illus. by Brother Harold Ruplinger. Notre Dame,
Ind., Dujarie Press ‹1955›
96 p. illus. 24 cm.

1. Schubert, Franz Peter, 1797–1828—Fiction. 2. Musical fiction.
I. Title.
ML3925.S3N3   780.881   55–3364 ‡

NN   0024976   DLC

Nash, Roy, 1929–
The thundering silence; a story of Ludwig van Beethoven.
Illus. by Brother Harold Ruplinger. Notre Dame, Ind.,
Dujarie Press ‹1954›
102 p. illus. 24 cm.

1. Beethoven, Ludwig van, 1770–1827. 2. Music—Juvenile literature.   I. Title.
ML3930.B4N3   927.8   55–672 ‡

NN   0024977   DLC DCU

Nash, Roy, 1929–
The wandering minstrel; a story of Antonín Dvořák.
Illus. by Brother Harold Ruplinger. Notre Dame, Ind.,
Dujarie Press ‹1955›
101 p. illus. 24 cm.

1. Dvořák, Antonín, 1841–1904—Fiction. 2. Music—Juvenile literature.   I. Title.
ML3930.D9N3   [813.5] 780.881   56–15328 ‡

NN   0024978   DLC NN

Nash, Ruth Cutter.
... Calendrical interpretation of a golden breastplate from
Peru, by Ruth Cutter Nash. New York, Museum of the Amer-
ican Indian, Heye foundation, 1939.
2 p. l., 12 p. fold. front. 16½ᶜᵐ. (Indian notes and monographs ...
‹Miscellaneous› no. 52)
Bibliography: p. 12.

1. Peru—Antiq. 2. Indians of South America—Costume and adorn-
ment. 3. Indians of South America—Calendar.   I. Title.
                                                    40–8439
Library of Congress   F3429.3.C8N3
                              ‹5›   913.85

NN   0024979   DLC NN GU PP ViU DPU PSt MU LNHT OrU
          MtU NcD DI PU–Mu

Nash, S. Elizabeth
            SEE
Nash, Susannah Elizabeth

Nash, S. S. On the right footing. 6 pp.
‹Harper's Mag. v. 29, 1864, p. 37 L.›

NN   0024981   MdBP

Nash, Samuel John.
An address to the Board of agriculture, on
the subject of enclosures and tithes ... Oxford, Printed and sold by R. Slatter ‹1801?›
1 p. l., 22 p. 22 x 17 cm.

NN   0024982   MH–BA

Nash, Simeon, 1804–1879.
Code pleading, practice and forms, adapted to Ohio
laws, but applicable to all code states, by Simeon Nash.
5th ed., enl. and improved by Judge Hiram L. Sibley ...
Cincinnati, Robert Clarke company, 1906–07.
2 v. 23ᶜᵐ.
Paged continuously.

1. Code pleading—Ohio. 2. Code pleading.   I. Sibley, Hiram Luther,
1836–   ed.
Library of Congress   6–27287

NN   0024983   DLC OU OClW MtU

Nash, Simeon, 1804–1879.
Crime and the family. By Simeon Nash ... Cincinnati,
R. Clarke & co., 1876.
iv p., 1 l., 156 p. 20ᶜᵐ.

1. Crime and criminals. 2. Domestic education.
                                                    10–17419†
Library of Congress   HV6157.N3

NN   0024984   DLC OC MH–L NcD OCU OClWHi OO

Nash, Simeon, 1804–1879.
A digest of decisions of the Supreme court of Ohio, contained in the first twenty volumes of the Ohio reports. ‹1821–
1851› By Simeon Nash. Cincinnati, H. W. Derby, 1853.
xii, 753 p., 1 l. 24½ᶜᵐ.

1. Law reports, digests, etc.—Ohio.   I. Ohio. Supreme court.
                                                    32–31833
Library of Congress

NN   0024985   DLC PPB OClJC OClW NN IU

Nash, Simeon, 1804–1879.
A digest of the decisions of the Supreme Court of Ohio, con-
tained in the first twenty volumes of the Ohio reports ‹1821–51›.
Cincinnati: H. W. Derby, 1853.   xii, 753 p., 1 l.   8°.

———— A supplement to Nash's digest. A digest of the
decisions ... contained in the ten first volumes of the Ohio state
reports ‹1852–60›.   Columbus: Follett, Foster & Co, 1861
viii, 487 p.   8°.

1. Law reports, U. S.: Ohio.—Digests.
N. Y. P. L.   September 23, 1912.

NN   0024986   NN

---

k771
.N261.
Nash, Simeon, 1804–1879.
A digest of the decisions of the Supreme
Court of Ohio, contained in the first ten
volumes of the Ohio State Reports. By
Simeon Nash. Cincinnati, Robert Clarke,
1862.
vii, 487 p.
at head of title: A supplement to Nash's
Digest.

1. Ohio—Law reports, digests, etc.
I. Ohio. Supreme Court.

NN   0024987   ICU

Nash, Simeon, 1804–1879.
Morality and the state. By Simeon Nash ... Columbus, O., Follett, Foster & co., 1859.
xviii, 442 p. 20ᶜᵐ.

1. Ethics. 2. Political ethics. 3. Social ethics.   I. Title.
                                                    10–2425
Library of Congress   BJ55.N2

NN   0024988   DLC PSt ScU PPL PU OOxM OC1 OO OClWHi NN

Nash, Simeon, 1804–1879.
Ohio Digest, Supreme Court Decisions
see his   A digest of decisions ...

Nash, Simeon, 1804–1879.
Pleading and practice under the Civil code. By Simeon
Nash. Cincinnati, H. W. Derby, 1856.
2 p. l., iii–v, 820 p. 25ᶜᵐ.

1. Code pleading—Ohio.
                                                    36–29716

NN   0024990   DLC WaU–L OClW

Nash, Simeon, 1804–1879.
Pleading and practice under the civil code. By Simeon
Nash. 2d ed., rev. and enl. Cincinnati, R. Clarke & co.,
1859.
vii, 844 p. 24ᶜᵐ.

1. Code pleading—Ohio. 2. Code pleading.
                                                    16–18725

NN   0024991   DLC

Nash, Simeon, 1804–1879.
Pleading and practice under the Civil code. 3d ed., rev.
and enl. Cincinnati, R. Clarke, 1864.
xii, 844 p. 24 cm.

1. Code pleading—Ohio.
                                                    49–30181*

NN   0024992   DLC OU OClW ViU–L

Nash, Simeon, 1804–1879.
Pleading and practice under the codes of Ohio, New
York, Kansas and Nebraska, and applicable, also, to the
practice in other states in which a code has been adopted,
with appropriate forms, by Simeon Nash. 4th ed.,
greatly enl. ... Cincinnati, R. Clarke & co., 1874.
2 v. 23½ᶜᵐ.
Paged continuously.

1. Code pleading—Ohio. 2. Code pleading.
Library of Congress   16–18724

NN   0024993   DLC NcU NcD PPB OO OClW OU WaU–L

VOLUME 405

Nash, Simeon, 1804–1879
The principle of protection vindicated. Lecture
...January 27 and February 3, 1844, Gallipolis,
Wm. Nash, 1844.
24 p.

NN 0024994 OClWHi

Nash, Solomon.
Journal of Solomon Nash, a soldier of the revolution.
1776–1777. Now first printed from the original manuscript. With an introduction and notes, by Charles I.
Bushnell. New York, Priv. prin., 1861.
iv, [5]–65 pp. front., pl., port. 2° .
Subject entries: U. S.—Hist.—Revolution—Personal narratives.
2–4025

Library of Congress, no. E275.N28.

NN 0024995 DLC TxU OFH MB PBL

Nash, Solomon.
Journal of Solomon Nash, a soldier of the revolution
1776–1777. Now first printed from the original manuscript. With an introduction and notes, by Charles I.
Bushnell. New York, Priv. print., 1861.
iv, [5]–65 p. front., pl., port. 25¼ᶜᵐ. [Crumbs for antiquarians, by C. I.
Bushnell, v. 1, no. 3]

1. U. S.—Hist.—Revolution—Personal narratives. I. Bushnell, Charles
Ira, 1826–1883, ed.
10–13075

E203.B97

NN 0024996 DLC NBuHi MiU-C ViU MB

QA276 **Nash, Stanley William,** 1915–
N3 I. Contribution to the theory of experiments with many treatments. II. On the law
of the iterated logarithm for dependent random variables. [Berkeley, 1950]
58 l.

Thesis (Ph.D.) - Univ. of California, June
1950.
Includes bibliographies.

NN 0024997 CU

Nash, Stephen Gordon.
Original poems written previous to 1860.
n.p., 1860.
224 p. 20 cm.

NN 0024998 RPB

Nash, Stephen P[ayne] 1821–1898.
Anneke Jans Bogardus; her farm, and how it became
the property of Trinity church, New York. An historic
inquiry, by Stephen P. Nash, LL.D. New York, Prepared
and printed for the use of the church, 1896.
vii, 105 p. 22ᶜᵐ.

1. Bogardus, Annetje Jansen, 1600?–1663. 2. New York (City)—Hist.
I. New York. Trinity church.
4–20143

Library of Congress F128.4.N24

NN 0024999 DLC NN

Film **Nash, Stephen Payne,** 1821–1898.
10095 Anneke Jans Boagrdus; her farm, and how
it became the property of Trinity church.
New York, Prepared and printed for the use
of the church, 1896.
100p.

Microfilm copy made by the New York State
Library in 1966. 1 reel.

NN 0025000 IaU

Nash, Stephen Payne, 1821–1898.
[Haight, Benjamin Isaacs] 1809–1879, ed.
Correspondence touching the action of the American church
union in the case of the Rev. Colin C. Tate, of Ohio. New
York, Pott & Amery, 1869.

16 **Nash, Stephen Payne,** 1821–1898.
1242 Speech for the prosecution, in the trial of the
Rev. S.H. Tyng, jr. [New York, Pott & Amery,
1868]
37 p. 8°. [American church union. Publications. no. 2]

NN 0025002 DLC MH

Nash, Stephen P[ayne], 1821–1898.
The standing committees: their province in
connection with the ordering of deacons and priests,
and the consecration of bishops. New York,
Pott, Young & Co., 1875.
21 p. 8°.
In: ZRM p.v.

NN 0025003 NN MH NBuG

Nash, Mrs. Susan Higginson.
The Architectural record.
The restoration of colonial Williamsburg in Virginia ...
New York, F. W. Dodge corporation, [1935.

Nash, Susannah Elizabeth.
Cooking craft; a practical handbook for students in training
for cookery and for the homeworker, by S. Elizabeth Nash...
London: Sir I. Pitman & Sons, Ltd., 1926. xvi, 345 p. illus.
(incl. plans.) 8°.

267253A. 1. Cookery, English.
N. Y. P. L. November 23, 1926

NN 0025005 NN MB

TX651 **Nash, Susannah Elizabeth**
N35 Cooking craft, a practical handbook for
1939 students in training for cookery and for the
homeworker. 4th ed. London, I. Pitman
[1939]
xvi,351 p. illus.

1. Cookery. I. Title.

NN 0025006 CU

929.2 **Nash, Sylvester,** 1795–1862.
N253 The Nash family, in part, traced down
1850 from Thomas Nash, an emigrant from England
in 1638. With additions by Herman S.
Noble – Watertown, N.Y., from the "Northern
New-York Journal" Press, 1850.
15 p. 23 cm.

1. Nash family (Thomas Nash, d. 1658)
H 1. Genealogy. Nash family (Thomas Nash,
d. 1658) I. Noble, Herman S

NN 0025007 WaS

Nash, Sylvester, 1795–1862.
The Nash family; or, Records of the descendants of
Thomas Nash, of New Haven, Connecticut. Collected
and comp. by the Rev. Sylvester Nash, A. M. ... 1640.
Hartford, Press of Case, Tiffany & company, 1853.
iv, [5]–304 p. front., ports. 23½ᶜᵐ.
Blank leaves at end for "Family record."

1. Nash family (Thomas Nash, d. 1658)
9–12552
Library of Congress CS71.N25 1853

NN 0025008 DLC MWA PHi NN MB

Nash, T.A.M.
see Nash, Thomas Arthur Manly, 1905–

qM788.66 **Nash, Ted,** 1922–
N177s Studies in high harmonics, for tenor and alto
saxophone. New York, Leeds Music Corp., c1946.
24p. illus. 31cm.

1. Saxophone—Studies and exercises. I.
Title.

NN 0025010 IU IEN PP

q **Nash, Ted,** 1922–
MT Ted Nash's studies in high harmonics for
505 tenor and alto saxophone. New York, MCA
N3 Music [c1946]
MUSIC score (22p.) 31cm.

1. Saxophone - Instruction and study. 2.
Saxophone - Studies and exercises (Jazz) I.
Title.

NN 0025011 TxU

Nash, T[heodore] E[dward] D[elafayette] 1881–
Love and vengeance; or, Little Viola's victory; a story
of love and romance in the South; also society and its
effects. By T. E. D. Nash. [Portsmouth, Va., T. E. D.
Nash, *1903] .
1 p. l, 171, [1] p. front. (port.) 23ᶜᵐ.
4–35722

NN 0025012 DLC

NASH, THIRZA.
The ex-gentleman. Colonial ed. London,

NN 0025013 NN

Nash, Thirza.
For passion is darkness. London, Cassell [1951]
347 p. 20 cm.

I. Title.

PZ3.N1773Fo 51–27023

NN 0025014 DLC

Nash, Thirza.
The Geyer brood. London, Cassell [1946]
243 p. 19 cm.

I. Title.
A 48–8337*
New York. Public Libr.
for Library of Congress [1]

NN 0025015 NN PU

Nash, Thirza.
Witchweed; a novel. London, etc., Cassell and
co. [1947]
284 p. 19 cm.

NN 0025016 MH

VOLUME 405

[Nash, Thomas]
A plea for the poor in which (1) their inexpressible hardships and sufferings are verified from facts; (2) their maintenance shewn an intolerable burthen upon the public; (3) methods for making beggars and vagabonds useful, and providing for the impotent; (4) summary of the schemes of Judge Hale, Sir Josiah Child, Mr. Fielding, submitted to the consideration of Parliament by a merchant of the city of London.　London, 1759.
viii, 59 p.　8°.

NN　0025017　　MH-BA

Nash, Thomas, 1567-1601.
... The complete works of Thomas Nashe. In six volumes. For the first time collected and edited with memorial-introduction, notes and illustrations, etc., by the Rev. Alexander B. Grossart ... ₍London and Aylesbury₎ Printed for private circulation only, 1883-85.
6 v.　26ᶜᵐ.　(The Huth library)
"50 copies."
Title-pages prefixed to v. 1-3 read "in four volumes"; corrected titles are bound at end of v. 4.
With reproductions of original title-pages.

CONTENTS.—v. 1. Memorial-introduction.　1. Biographical. Anatomie of absurditie, 1589.　Martin-Mar-prelate tractates, 1589.—v. 2. Pierce Penilesse his svpplication to the divell, 1592.　Harvey-Greene tractates, 1591-2.—v. 3. Haue with you to Saffron-Walden, 1596.　Terrors of the night, 1594.—v. 4. Christ's teares ouer Ierusalem, 1593.—v. 5. The vnfortvnate traveller, 1594.—v. 6. ₍Memorial-introduction—Critical₎. The tragedie of Dido, 1594.　Summers last will and testament, 1600.　Glossarial-index, etc.
Added engraved series title in each volume.
I. Grosart, Alexander Balloch, 1827-1899, ed.

Library of Congress　　　　PR2721.G7
19—8038

OCU OU CtY MdBP MH RPB InU KEmT NIC MU OU MiU
NN　0025019　　DLC TxU MB NcD PSC PPT PU PBm OCl OClW

Nash, Thomas. 1567-1601.　　　　　*4602.56
The works of Thomas Nashe, edited from the original texts by Ronald B. McKerrow. Text: vol. 1, 2.
London, Bullen, 1904.　v. 8°.
No. 135 of an edition of 750 copies.
Contains fac-simile title-pages.
Contents.— Text.— 1. The anatomie of absurditie.— A countercuffe giuen to Martin Iunior.— The returne of ... Pasquill.— The first parte of Pasquils apologie.— Pierce Penilesse his svpplication to the Diuell.— Strange newes, of the intercepting certaine letters.— The terrors of the night.　2. Christs teares over Ierusalem.— Th vnfortvnate traveller.— The tragedie of Dido.

F7206 — MacKerrow [McKerrow], Ronald Brunlees, ed.

NN　0025020　　MB

Nash, Thomas, 1567-1601.
The works of Thomas Nashe. Edited from the original texts by Ronald B. McKerrow. Text: 7.
v.1-3.　London, A.H. Bullen, 1904-5.
3 v.　8°.
No. 744 of 750 copies printed.

NN　0025021　　NN

Nash, Thomas, 1567-1601.
The works of Thomas Nashe; ed. from the original texts, by Ronald B. McKerrow ...　London, A. H. Bullen ₍etc.₎, 1904-10.
5 v.　front. (v. 5, fold. facsim.)　22½ᶜᵐ.
With reproductions of original title-pages.
CONTENTS.—v. 1. The anatomie of absurditie.　A covntercvffe given to Martin Ivnior.　The retvrne of Pasqvill.　The first parte of Pasqvils apologie.　Pierce Penilesse his svpplication to the divell.　Strange newes of the intercepting certaine letters.　The terrors of the night.—v. 2. Christs teares ouer Ierusalem.　The vnfortvnate traveller.　The tragedie of Dido.—v. 3. Have with yov to Saffron-Walden.　Nashes lenten stvffe.　Svmmers last will and testament.　Shorter pieces.　Doubtful works.—v. 4. Notes.—v. 5. Introduction and index.
I. McKerrow, Ronald Brunlees, 1872-1940, ed.

Library of Congress　　　　PR2721.M3
5—34975

OCU OCl ViU OrPR MtU NcD LU TxU CaBVaU
NN　0025022　　DLC CtY InU MH TU PBm PU PSC OO OU

Nash, Thomas, 1567-1601.
The works of Thomas Nashe, edited from the original texts, by Ronald B.McKerrow ... London,Sidwick & Jackson,ltd.,1910.
5v.　front.(v.5,fold.facsim.)　22½cm.
With reproductions of original title-pages.
"Seven hundred and fifty copies printed. No.328."

NN　0025023　　CtY NjP MH OOxM OClW ODW PPL PU-F MiU

PR
2721
M15
1910
Nash, Thomas, 1567-1601.
Works.　Edited from the original texts, by Ronald B. McKerrow...　London, Sidgwick & Jackson, 1910.
5 v.　illus.　23cm.
With reproductions of original title-pages.
Contents.—v.1. The anatomie of absurditie. A covntercvffe given to Martin Ivnior.　The retvrne of Pasqvill.　The first parte of Pasqvils apologie.　Pierce Penilesse his svpplication to the divell.　Strange newes, of the intercepting certaine letters.　The terrors of the night.—v. 2. Christs teares over Ierusalem.　The vnfortvnate traveller.　The tragedle of Dido.—v. 3. Have with yov to Saffron-Walden.　Nashes lenten stvffe.　Svmmers last will and testament.　Shorter pieces.　Doubtful works.—v.4. Notes.—v. 5. Introduction and index.

NN　0025025　　NIC DeU OrU

Nash, Thomas, 1567-1601.
Works; edited from the original texts by Ronald B. McKerrow.　London, Sidgwick & Jackson, 1920.
5 v.　O.

NN　0025026　　NcD

BR757
.A6
1846
Nash, Thomas, 1567-1601, supposed author.

An **almond** for a parrot; being a reply to Martin Marprelate.　Re-printed from the Black letter ed., with an introd. and notes.　London, J. Petheram, 1846.

NN　0025028　　DFo CSmH

Nash, Thomas, 1567-1601.
The anatomie of absurditie: contayning a breefe confutation of the slender imputed prayses to feminine perfection, with a short description of the seuerall practises of youth, and sundray follies of our licentious times.　No lesse ₍pleasant to be read, then profitable to be remei ₎ered, especially of those, two liue more licentiously, or addicted to a more nyce stoycall austeritie. Compiled by T.Nash ...　London, by I. Charlewood for Thomas Hacket, ... 1589.
sm. 4to.　Red morocco.

¶⁴, A-E⁴.

NN　0025029　　MiU ViU WaPS

Humanities
Library
Microfilm
AC
4
E5
Reel
no.
387
Nash, Thomas, 1567-1601.
The anatomie of absurditie: contayning a breefe confutation of the slender imputed prayses to feminine perfection, with a short description of the seuerall practises of youth, and sundry follies of our licentious times ... Compiled by T.Nashe ... At London, Printed by I. Charlewood for Thomas Hacket ... 1589.
University microfilms no. 15022 (case 65, carton 387)
Short-title catalogue no. 18364.
1.England — Soc. life & cust.　2. Poetry - Early works to 1800.　I. Title.

NN　0025031　　MiU CtY OU

PR
1121
.C69
v.3
Nash, Thomas, 1567-1601.
The anatomie of absurditie: contayning a breefe confutation of the slender imputed prayses to feminine perfection, with a short description of the severall practises of youth, and sundry follies of our licentious times.　No lesse pleasant to be read, then profitable to be remembered ... Compiled by T.Nashe ...　London, Printed by I.Charlewood for Thomas Hacket, 1589. ₍Reprinted, London, 1866₎
ii p., reprint: ₍2₎,v.₍6₎-54.　21 cm.　(In

Collier,J.P.,ed. Illustrations of old English literature. London,1866. v.3)
ii p. (editor's Introd.) follow the t.p. which is part of the reprint.

1.England—Soc.life & cust.　2.Poetry—Early works to 1800.　I.Collier,John Payne,1789-1883, ed.　II.Title.

NN　0025031　　MiU CtY OU

NASH, Tho[mas], 1567-1601.
The apologie of Pierce Pennilesse or Strange newes of the intercepting of certaine letters, and a convoy of verses, as they were going privilie to victuall the Lowe Countries. By Tho. Nashe. London, printed by John Danter, dwelling in Hoffes Lane neere Holburne conduit,1593.

4°.　A in 2, B-L in 4's,M in 2.　Unpaged.
Printer's mark on title-page.
Published in 1592 with title: Strange newes of the intercepting　certaine letters,etc.

Imperfect:　First 2 leaves too closely trimmed at head.
Huntington: 2 ll, B-L in 4's,M in 2.

NN　0025033　　MH CSmH

Humanities
Library
Microfilm
AC
4
E5
Reel
no.
325
Nash, Thomas, 1567-1601.
The apologie of Pierce Pennilesse: or Strange newes, of the intercepting certaine letters, and a conuoy of verses, as they were going priuilie to victuall the Lowe Countries ... By Tho. Nashe ... Printed at London by Iohn Danter, and are to be solde by William Barley ... 1593.
A reply to Gabriel Harvey's "Fovre letters and certaine sonnets", an answer to Greene's "A qvip for an vpstart courtier".
Published in 1592 with title: Strange newes, of the intercepting certaine letters, and a convoy of verses.
Running title: Foure letters confuted.
University microfilms no. 15031 (case 55, carton 325)
Short-title catalogue no. 18378a.

1. Harvey, Gabriel, 1550?-1631.　I. Title.

NN　0025035　　MiU ViU CaBVaU WaPS

Nash, Thomas, 1567-1601.
The choise of valentines; or, The merie ballad of Nash his dildo.　₍By Thomas Nash₎ ...　Ed. by John S. Farmer.　London, Priv. print. for subscribers only, 1899.
2 p. l., ₍viii₎-xiii, 23 p., 1 l.　22ᶜᵐ.
"From mss. copies in the Inner Temple ... and Bodleian ... libraries."

I. Farmer, John Stephen, ed.　II. Title.

Library of Congress　　　　PR2326.N3C5
24-8186
₍32b1₎

ViU IEdS OrU IEN TxU OrPS
NN　0025036　　DLC CtY PSt OClW MiU ICU NjP MnU NcD

NASH, THOMAS, 1567-1601.
The choise of valentines; or, The merie ballad of Nash, his dildo.　Edited by John S. Farmer.　London, Privately printed for subscribers only, 1899.　xiii, 23 p. 23cm.

Microfiche (neg.) 1 sheet. 11 x15cm. (NYPL FSN 11, 683)

NN　0025037　　NN

Nash, Thomas, 1597-1601.
Christ's tears over Jerusalem.　n.p., 87 p.　8°.
n.t.p.

NN　0025038　　MWA

Nash, Thomas, 1567-1601.
Christ tears over Jerusalem. Wherunto is annexed, a comparative admonition to London ... London, J. Roberts, 1593.

NN　0025039　　PU CSmH NHu

VOLUME 405

FILM

Nash, Thomas, 1567-1601.
Christs teares over Ierusalem. Wherunto is
annexed, a comparatiue admonition to London ...
By Tho.Nashe. At London, Printed by Iames
Roberts ... 1593.
University microfilms no.15023 (case 45,carton 259)
Short-title catalogue no.18366.

NN   0025040   MiU WaPS

STC
18367

[Nash, Thomas, 1567-1601]
[Christs teares over Iervsalem. VVhereunto is
annexed, a comparatiue admonition to London ...
By Tho. Nashe.]
[London.Printed [by R.Field] for Andrew VVise,
and are to be sold at his shop in Pauls church-
yard,at the signe of the Angell.1594.]
6p.ℓ.,92 numb.ℓ. 18cm.
Printer's mark (McK.222) on t.-p.
A reissue of sheets of the 1593 edition, with
new preliminaries and cancel leaf [83].
Imperfect: all   before leaf 5, leaves
38-40 & 87-92   wanting; title and collation from McKerr-   ow's edition of Nash.

NN   0025041   MH MiU WaPS NHu CSmH

FILM

Nash,Thomas,1567-1601.
Christs teares over Iervsalem. VVherevnto is
annexed,a comparatiue admonition to London ...
By Tho.Nashe. London. Printed for Andrew
VVise ... 1594.
University microfilms no.15024 (case 55,carton 325)
Short-title catalogue no.18367.

NN   0025042   MiU

Ig
N177
593c

Nash, Thomas, 1567-1601.
Christs Teares Over Iervsalem. Whereunto is
annexed a comparatiue admonition to London. A
Ioue Mvsa. By Tho. Nash. [Fleur de lis device]
London,Printed for Thomas Thorp.1613.
4p.ℓ.,190p. 18cm.
Title within woodcut border (McKerrow 248);
headpieces, tailpiece, initials.
Signatures: α⁴A-Z⁴Aa⁴(last ℓ. blank)
Pages 60-21, 64, 66, 97, 104, misnumbered
62-63, 66, 69, 197, 140 respectively.

NN   0025043   CtY DFo ICN MH

Nash, Thomas, 1567-1601.
Christ's tears over Jerusalem: whereunto is annexed A
comparative admonition to London ... By Tho. Nash.
Reprinted from the ed. of 1613. London, From the private press of Longman, Hurst, Rees, Orme, and Brown,
printed by T. Davison, 1815.
xi, 168 p. 28ᶜᵐ. (Brydges, Sir S. E. Archaica. London, 1815. pt. vii
(v. 1, no. 5))
With reproduction of t.-p. of 1613 ed.
First published 1593.

I. Title.

16-7279

Library of Congress   PR1121.B7 vol. 1

NN   0025044   DLC MdBP TU OU MiU MB NN NjP

[Nash, Thomas, 1567-1601, supposed author.
A] [C]ountercuffe giuen to|| Martin Iunior: by the venturous,||
hardie, and renowned Pasquill of Eng-||lande [pseud.], Caualiero.||
Not of olde Martins making...|| [4 lines]|| Printed between the
skye and the|| grounde, wythin a myle of an Oake, and not manie||
Fieldes off, from the vnpriuiledged Presse of|| the Ass-ignes of
Martin|| Iunior.|| [London: John Charlewood?, Anno Dom.
1589.]|| ·4 ℓ. 18cm. (4°.)

STC 19456.   Union theological seminary: McAlpin collection, v. 1, p. 123.
Leaf 4 signed Aᵢᵢᵢ.

Catchwords: l. 2ᵃ, hold; l. 2ᵇ, Maugre; l. 3ᵃ, grounded; l. 3ᵇ, as; l. 4ᵃ, In.
Leaf 4ᵇ, lines 6-7: ...From Graues-ende Barge the|| eyght of August..
Formerly attributed to Thomas Nash.
For description and discussion, cf. Nash, Thomas. The works...edited...by
Ronald B. McKerrow. London, 1904-10. v. 1, p. 51-56 and v. 5, p. 49-58.

1. Marprelate controversy.   I. Nash, Thomas, 1567-1601,
supposed au. II. Title.   *Card revised*
N.Y.P.L.   *November 8, 1943*

NN   0025046   NN CSmH MH NNUT-Mc MWiW-C

Nash, Thomas, 1567-1601, supposed author.
A countercuffe giuen to Martin Iunior: by the
venturous, hardie, and renowned Pasquill of Eng-
lande, caualiero ... Printed between the skye
and the grounde ... [London, John Charlewood]
1589.

STC
19456

A⁴. 4to.
Sometimes, probably erroneously, attributed to
Thomas Nash; see *The works of Thomas Nashe* (1958),
edited by McKerrow, and Pforzheimer, v.2, no.650.
There are two editions which fit the description of STC 19456; STC numbers arbitrarily
assigned.

Sig. A1r., 1.2 ends "giuen to"; A3r. begins
"Maugre".
Frank Brewer Bemis copy.

NN   0025048   DFo MiU WaPS

Nash, Thomas, 1567-1601, supposed author.
A countercuffe giuen to Martin Iunior: by the
venturous, hardie, and renowned Pasquill of England, caualiero ... Printed betweene the skye
and the grounde ... [London, John Charlewood]
1589.

STC
19456.2

A⁴. 4to.
Sometimes, probably erroneously, attributed to
Thomas Nash; see *The works of Thomas Nashe* (1958),
edited by McKerrow, and Pforzheimer, v.2, no.650.
There are two editions which fit the description
of STC 19456; STC numbers arbitrarily assigned.

Sig. A1r., 1.2 ends "Martin Iu-"; A3r. begins
"who beeing".
Harmsworth copy.

NN   0025050   DFo

FILM

Nash, Thomas,1567-1601.
A countercuffe giuen to Martin Iunior: by
the venturous,hardie,and renowned Pasquill
of England ... Printed, betweene the skye
and the grounde ... [London?, J.Charlewood]
1589.
University microfilms no.15173 (case 86,carton 516)
Short-title catalogue no.19456.

1.Marprelate controversy. I.Title.

NN   0025051   MiU DLC

Nash, Thomas, 1567-1601.

Marlowe, Christopher, 1564-1593.
Dido, queen of Carthage. A tragedy; by Christopher
Marlowe, and Thomas Nash. London, Hurst, Robinson,
and co.; Edinburgh, A. Constable and co., 1825.

Ig
N177
590

[Nash, Thomas] 1567-1601.
The first parte of Pasquils apologie.
Wherein he renders a reason to his friends
of his long silence; and gallops the fielde
with the Treatise of Reformation ... written
by ... Iohn Penrie. Printed where I was,and
where I will bee readie ... to send you the
May-game of Martinisme ... Anno.Dom.1590.
[London,Printed by John Charlewood,1590]
[32]p. 20cm.
Signatures: A-D⁴(A₁[blank?]wanting)E²(E₂,
blank, wanting)
Uncut.

NN   0025053   CtY MWiW-C MiU WaPS

Wg
N177
A590f

Nash, Thomas, 1567-1601.
The FIRST parte of Pasquils apologie. Wherein
he renders a reason to his friendes of his long
silence: and gallops the fielde with the treatise of reformation lately written by a fugitive, Iohn Penrie.
[London] Printed where I was, and where I will
bee readie by the helpe of God and my Muse,to
send you the May-game of Martinisme for an intermedium,betweene the first and seconde part
of the apologie [i.e. by J.Charlewood].Anno.
Dom.1590. [54]p. 17½cm.

Printer's device (McKerrow 112) on t.-p.
Signatures: A-D⁴, E²(A1 is blank except for
register; E2 blank).
Attributed to Nash.

NN   0025055   TxU MH CSmH CtY

FILM

Nash,Thomas,1567-1601.
The first parte of Pasquils apologie. Wherein
he renders a reason to his long
silence: and gallops the fielde with the treatise of reformation lately written by a fugi-
tiue,Iohn Penrie. Printed where I was,and where
I will bee readie by the helpe of God and my
muse,to send you the May-game of Martinisme for
an intermedium,betweene the first and seconde
part of the Apologie [London? James Roberts]
... 1590.
By Thomas Nash. cf.Brit.mus. Catalogue.

An answer to Penry's "A treatise wherein is manifest-
lie proved,that reformation and those that sincerely
fauor the same,are vnjustly charged to be enemies,vnto
hir Maiestie,and the state."
University microfilms no.15171 (case 58,carton 348)
Short-title catalogue no.19450.
1.Penry,John,1559-1593. A treatise wherein is manifest
lie proved that reformation and those that ... fauor the
same,are vnjustly charged to be enemies. I.Title. II.
Title: Pasquils   apologie.

NN   0025057   MiU

Nash, Thomas. 1567-1601.   2558.131.2
[Extracts] From Strange newes, or Foure letters confuted.
(In Smith. Elizabethan critical essays. Vol. 2, pp. 239-244. Ox-
ford. 1904.)
Answers passages in Harvey's Fovre letters ... The passages are re-
printed in this volume.

F7526 — Harvey, Gabriel. 1545?-1630?

NN   0025058   MB

Wg
N177
596h

NASH, THOMAS, 1567-1601.
Haue vvith you to Saffron-vvalden. Or,
Gabriell Harueys hunt is vp. Containing a full
answere to the eldest sonne of the halter-
maker. Or, Nashe his confutation of the sinfull doctor. Tho mott or posie, in stead of
Omne tulit punctum: Pacis fiducia nunquam. As
much to say, as I sayd I would speake with him.
Printed at London by Iohn Danter.1596.
[166]p. illus. 17½cm.
Signatures: A-X⁴(X4 prob. blank, wanting)
Imperfect: top and outer margins of sheet A
restored, with headlines in facsimile.

NN   0025059   TxU CtY DFo

FILM

Nash,Thomas,1567-1601.
Haue vvith you to Saffron-VValden. Or,Gabriell
Harueys hunt is vp ... Or,Nashe his confutation
of the sinfull doctor ... Printed at London by
Iohn Danter 1596.
By Thomas Nash. cf.Brit.mus. Catalogue.
One of the tracts in a literary controversy between
Thomas Nash and Gabriel Harvey.
University microfilms no.15025 (case 58,carton 347)
Short-title catalogue no.18369.

1.Harvey,Gabriel,1550?-1631. I.Title.

NN   0025060   MiU WaPS

VOLUME 405

PR
2287
.P62
N25
1870
Nash,Thomas,1567-1601.
　　　Have with you to Saffron-Walden: or,Gabriell
Harveys hunt is up. Containing a full answere to the eldest sonne of the halter-maker:
or,Nashe his confutation of the sinfull doctor ... Printed at London by John Danter.
1596. ⌊Reprinted⌊London, 1870⌋
　　　ii p.,⌊reprint: 155 p. 22 cm. ⌊Miscel-
laneous tracts. Temp.Eliz.& Jac.I. no.9⌋
　　　ii p.bound after the t.p.which is part of
the reprint.
　　　An answer to Pierce's supererogation by
Gabriel Harvey.

　　　Editor's Introd.signed: J.P.C⌊ollier⌋
　　　Autograph of J.D.Coleridge on front fly-
leaf.

　　　1.Harvey,Gabriel,1550?-1631.
I.Collier,John Payne,1789-1883,ed.
II.Title.

NN　0025062　　MiU OU ICarbS IU NjP MH

Nash, Thomas, *1567-1601, supposed a.r.*
　　The hospitall of incvrable fooles
　　　see under　Garzoni, Tommaso.

Nash, Thomas, 1567-1601.
　　　Nashes Lenten stuffe, containing the description and first
procreation and increase of the towne of Great Yarmouth
in Norffolke: with a new play neuer played, before, of
The praise of the red herring. Fitte of all clearkes of
noblemens kitchins to be read: and not vnnecessary by all
seruing men that haue short boord-wages, to be remembered
... London, Printed for N. L. and C. B.,1599.
　　　4 p. l., 75 p. 17¼ x 18½ cm.

　　　1. Herring.

　　　　　　　　　　　　　　　　　　　　A 18—1594

Harvard Univ. Library
for Library of Congress　　　⌊a55c⌋

DFo
NN　0025064　　MH CLU-C CtY ICN MWiW-C TxU CaBVaU

FILM
Nash,Thomas,1567-1601.
　　　Nashes Lenten stuffe,containing,the description and first procreation and increase of the
towne of Great Yarmouth in Norffolke: with a
new play neuer played before,of The praise of
the red herring ... London Printed ⌊by T.Jud-
son and V.Sims⌋ for N.L.⌊ing⌋ and C.B.⌊urbie⌋
... 1599.
　　　"A comically burlesque panegyric of the red herring."
--Dict.nat.biog.
　　　University microfilms no.15026 (case 55,carton 325)
　　　Short-title catalogue no.18570.
　　　1.Herring. I.　　　Title: Lenten stuffe. II.
Title: The praise　　　of the red herring.

NN　0025065　　MiU WaPS

PR2326
.N3L5
1871
Manly
Nash,Thomas,1567-1601.
　　　Nash's Lenten stuff:containing the description
and first procreation and increase of the town
of Great Yarmouth,in Norfolk:with a new play,
never played before,of The praise of the red-
herring. Fit for all clerks of noblemen's kitch-
en's to be read;and not unnecessary by all
serving-men,who have short board-wages,and to
be remembered... Edited by Charles Hindley.
London,Reeves and Turner,1871.
　　　xix,113,⌊1⌋ p. 25cm.
　　　With reproduc-　　　tion of original t.-p.,
1599.

　　　OCl PU MiU
NN　0025066　　ICU CLSU NcU NIC CtY NBuG MdBP NNC

Nash, Thomas, 1567-1601.

⌊Marlowe, Christopher⌋ 1564-1593.
　　　The life of Marlowe and The tragedy of Dido, queen of
Carthage ⌊by⌋ C. F. Tucker Brooke ... New York, L. Mac-
Veagh, The Dial press, 1930.

Nash, Thomas, 1567-1601, supposed author.
　　Mar-Martine
　　　see under title

Nash, Thomas, 1567-1601, supposed author.
　　Martins Months minde
　　　see under　Marphoreus, pseud.

Case
Y
14 5
.N 18
Nash, Thomas,　1588-1648.
　　　Miscelanea; or, A fourefold vvay
to a happie life; set forth in a dia-
logue betweene a countryman, a citizen,
a divine, and a lawyer.　By T.N. ...
London,1639.

　　　Running title: Qvaternio; or, A
foure-fold way to liue well.

NN　0025070　　CSmH ICN

Nash, Thomas, 1567-1601, supposed author.

BR757
.P32
1844
　　　Pap with a hatchet; being a reply to Martin Marprelate.
Re-printed from the original quarto ed. with an introd. and
notes. London, J. Petheram, 1844.

STC
18371
Nash, Thomas, 1567-1601.
　　　Pierce Penilesse his supplication to the diuell.
Describing the ouer-spreading of vice, and
suppression of vertue ... London, Imprinted
by Richard Ihones, 1592.

　　　A², B-L⁴. 4to.
　　　J. O. Halliwell-Phillipps - M. J. Perry copy.

NN　0025072　　DFo MH

Case
3A
643
NASH, THOMAS, 1567-1601.
　　　Pierce Penilesse his svpplication to the
diuell. Barbaria grandis habere nihil. Written by Tho. Nash, gent.　London, Printed by
A.Ieffes, for I.Busbie, 1592.
　　　40ℓ.　18cm.
　　　Signatures: ❡³,A-C⁴,D&E¹ (a single leaf
so signed),F-L⁴. The first 16 leaves not
numbered.
　　　Second edition.

　　　Bound by Riviere.
　　　Bookplates: Frederick Locker; Louis H.
Silver.
　　　In pencil on front flyleaf: W. A. White
27 Apl 1905.
　　　STC 18372.

NN　0025074　　ICN CSmH DFo NHu MWiW-C

Humanities
Library
Microfilm
AC
4
E5
Reel
no.
549
Nash, Thomas, 1567-1601.
　　　Pierce Penilesse his svpplication to the
diuell ... Written by Tho. Nash ... London,
Printed by Abell Ieffes, for I. B.⌊usbie⌋
1592.
　　　University microfilms no.15027 (carton
549)
　　　Short-title catalogue no.18373.
　　　1. England - Social life and customs.
2. Theater - Moral and religous aspects. 3.
Poetry - Early　　　works to 1800.
I. Title.

NN　0025075　　MiU WaPS

Humanities
Library
Microfilm
AC
4
E5
Reel
no.
574
Nash, Thomas, 1567-1601.
　　　Pierce Penilesse his svpplication to the
diuell ... Written by Tho.Nash ... London,
Printed by Abell Ieffes, for I.B.⌊usbie⌋
1593.
　　　University microfilms no. 16664 (carton
574)
　　　Short-title catalogue no. 18374.
　　　1. England - Social life & customs. 2.
Theater - Moral and religious aspects. 3.
Poetry - Early　　　works to 1800. I.
Title.

NN　0025076　　MiU WaPS

Nash, Thomas, 1567-1601.
Ig
M77
592e
　　　Pierce Penilesse his supplication to the
Diuell ... Written by Tho. Nash, gent.
London Printed⌊by T.C.⌋for Nicholas Ling,and
are to be sold at his shop,at the Northwest
doore of S.Paules.1595.
　　　⌊72⌋p.　18cm.
　　　Signatures: A-I⁴.
　　　Imperfect: some leaves slightly bled at
top.

NN　0025077　　CtY CSmH DFo

Humanities
Library
Microfilm
AC
4
E5
Reel
no.
387
Nash, Thomas, 1567-1601.
　　　Pierce Pennilesse his supplication to
the diuell ... Written by Tho. Nash ...
London Printed for Nicholas Ling ... 1595.
　　　Colophon: London Imprinted by T.C.
⌊reed⌋ for Nicholas Ling.
　　　University microfilms no. 15028 (case
65, carton 387)
　　　Short-title catalogue no. 18375.
　　　1. England - Soc. life & cust. 2.
Theater - Moral　　　and religious aspects.
3. Poetry - Early　　　works to 1800.

NN　0025078　　MiU ViU WaPS

Nash, Thomas, 1567-1601.
　　　Pierce Pennilesse's supplication to the Devil. By Thomas
Nash.　From the first edition of 1592, compared with later
impressions.　With an introduction and notes, by J. Payne
Collier ... London, Reprinted for the Shakespeare society,
1842.
　　　xxxii, 108 p.　22 cm. ⌊Shakespeare society. Publications, no. 12⌋
　　　Vol. IX, no. 2, in the L. C. set.
　　　With reproduction of original t.p.: Pierce Pennilesse his supplication
to the deuill. Describing the ouer-spreading of Vice, and the suppression of Vertue.　Pleasantly interlac'd with variable delights: and
pathetically intermixt with concepted reproofes. Written by Thomas
Nash, Gentleman.　London, Imprinted by Richard Ihones ... 1592.

　　　1. England—Soc. life & cust.　2. Theater—Moral and religious
aspects.　3. Poetry—Early works, to 1800.　I. Collier, John Payne,
1789-1883, ed. II. Title.

PR2888.L5　vol.9　　　　　　　16—13787
――― Copy 2. In original cloth binding. PR2724.P6 1842

OrU OrCS
NN　0025080　　DLC TxHU GU OOxM NN NIC WU NcU CaBVaU

PR
2326
.N3
P6
1870
Nash,Thomas,1576-1601.
　　　Pierce Penilesse his svpplication to the
diuell ... Written by Tho.Nash,gent. London,
Printed by Abell Ieffes,for Iohn Busbie.1592.
⌊Reprinted, London, 1870⌋
　　　ii p.,⌊reprint: v.⌋ ⌊1⌋ 101 p. 22 cm. ⌊Mis-
cellaneous tracts. Temp.Eliz.& Jac. no.6⌋
　　　ii p. (Introd.) follow the t.p.which is part
of ⌊the reprint.
　　　"Our reproduction ... is from the second ed.,
which the author revised and corrected ..."--
Editor's Introd.signed: J.P.C⌊ollier⌋
　　　Autograph of J.D.Coleridge on flyleaf.
　　　I.Collier,John Payne,1789-1883,ed.　II.Title.

NN　0025081　　MiU IU MH NjP MB　OU

VOLUME 405

Nash, Thomas, 1567-1601.
...Pierce Penilesse, his svpplication to the Divell (1592).
London: J. Lane[, 1924]. xii, 127 p. 12°. (Bodley head quartos. no. 11.)

With facsim. t.-p. of the 2. ed. of 1592.

182907A. 1. Satire, English.   2. England—Social life, 16th
cent. 3. Title. 4. Ser.
N. Y. P. L.   June 30, 1925

NN   0025082   NN IU

Nash, Thomas, 1567-1601.
... Pierce Penilesse, his svpplication to the divell (1592)
London, John Lane; New York, E. P. Dutton & company
[1924]
   xii, 137, [1] p. facsim. 19ᶜᵐ. (The Bodley head quartos, ed. by G. B.
Harrison. [no. xi])
   "The text ... is that of the third edition of 1592."—p. ix.
   With facsimile of original t.-p.
   Satire on the vices of the time; includes a defense of poetry, and of
stage plays.
   1. England—Soc. life & cust. 2. Theater—Moral and religious aspects.
3. Poetry—Early works to 1800.   I. Harrison, George Bagshawe, ed.
II. Title.
                                              25—6264

Library of Congress   PR2326]

MiU OrPS OOxM KMK ViU NN TxU KEmT
OC1W OOxM MiU ViU CaBVaU OrU PBm NcD NIC PU-F WaU
NN   0025083   DLC MdBP MB PSC OU PBm PU PHC TxU OU

PR1125
.H5
   Nash, Thomas, 1567-1601. Pierce Penilesse, his
   supplication to the Devil.

Hibbard, George Richard, ed.
   Three Elizabethan pamphlets. London, Harrap [1951]

Nash, Thomas, 1567-1601, supposed author.
Plaine Percevall the peace-maker of England
see under   [Harvey, Richard] 1560-1623?

Case
3A
642
   NASH, THOMAS, 1567-1601.
   A pleasant comedie, called Summers last
will and testament. Written by Thomas Nash.
Imprinted at London, By Simon Stafford for
Water [sic] Burre, 1600.
   [29]ℓ. 18cm.
     Signatures: [A]² ([A]₁ blank, wanting),
B⁴,C⁴⁻²,D-H⁴,I². C₃₋₄ cancelled. B₃ not
signed. Signature F missigned D throughout,

but signature on F₁ almost completely obli-
terated and replaced by an "F" stamped in by
hand.
   Greg 173. Clawson 608 (the present copy)
   Bound by F. Bedford.
   Bookplates: John L. Clawson; Ex Musaeo
Huthii; Louis H. Silver.
   STC 18376.

NN   0025087   ICN MH CtY CSmH NNCoCi DFo TxU

STC
18376
   Nash, Thomas, 1567-1601.
   A pleasant comedie, called Summers last
will and testament ... Imprinted at London by Simon
Stafford, for Walter Burre, 1600.

     [A]², B-H⁴, I². ([A]1, blank, and gathering
G lacking; C3-4 cancelled; [A]2, title-page, from
another copy; gathering F signed D1-4.) 4to.
   Greg, v. 1, no. 173. Pforzheimer, v. 2, no.765.
   William Sommers was jester to Henry VIII.
   Kemble-Devonshire-Huntington library duplicate
copy.

NN   0025088   DFo

MP
2
   Nash, Thomas, 1567-1601.
   A pleasant comedie, called Summers last will
and testament. London, Imprinted by Simon
Stafford for Water Burre, 1600.
   [56]p.

   William Summer, or Sommers, was court fool
or jester to Henry VIII.
   Micro-opaque. New York, Readex Microprint,
1953. 1 card. 23 x 15cm. (Wells, H. W., ed.
Three centuries of drama: English)
   1. Sommers, William, d. 1560.   i. Title:
Summer's last   will and testament.

NN   0025089   FMU

Humanities
Library
Microfilm
AC   Nash, Thomas, 1567-1601.
4   A pleasant comedie, called Summers last
E5   will and testament. Written by Thomas Nash.
Reel   Imprinted at London by Simon Stafford for
no.   Water[!] Burre. 1600.
387   University microfilms no.15029 (case 65,
        carton 387)
       Short-title catalogue no.18376.
       1. Sommers, William, d.1560. I. Title.
       II. Title: Summers last will and testament.

NN   0025090   MiU ViU WaPS

Nash, Thomas, 1567-1601.
A pleasant comedie, called Summers last will and testament.
   London. Imprinted by Simon Stafford for Walter Burre. 1600.
   [29] ff. Sm. 4°.   **G.3975.9
Same. (In Dodsley, R., editor. A select collection of old plays.
   New edition. Vol. 9, pp. 1-80. London, 1825.)
                      2588.1.9=**G.3961.2.9
Same. (In Same. 4th edition. Vol. 8, pp. 1-92. 1874.) 2574.53.8

E7603 — "Summer's last will and testament."

NN   0025091   MB

Nash, Thomas. 1567-1601.   2558.131.1
   Preface to Greene's Menaphon: To the gentlemen students of both
   vniuersities. [Extracts] From The anatomie of absurditie. 1589.
   (In Smith. Elizabethan critical essays. Vol. 1, pp. 307-337. Oxford. 1904.)
     The running title of the whole is A general censure. The work relates
   to Elizabethan verse.
     An edition of Menaphon is on shelf-number *6606.20; of An anatomie of
   absurditie, on shelf-number *4601.10.1.

F7527 — Elizabethan literature.

NN   0025092   MB OC1W

Nash, Thomas. 1567-1601.   2558.131.2
   The preface to Sidney's Astrophel and Stella. 1591.
   (In Smith. Elizabethan critical essays. Vol. 2, pp. 223-228. Ox-
   ford.)
     Reprinted from a copy of the 1st quarto edition in the British Museum.
   Another edition is on shelf-number *4557.66.1.

F7527 — Sidney, Sir Philip. 1554-1586.

NN   0025093   MB

[Nash, Thomas] 1567-1601, attributed author.
The returne of the knight of the poste from hell
see under title

Wg   [Nash, Thomas] 1567-1601.
N177
A589r   The RETURNE of the renowned Caualiero Pasquill
   of England, from the other side of the seas, and
   his meeting with Marforius at London vpon the
   Royall Exchange. VVhere they encounter with a
   little houshold talke of Martin and Martinisme,
   discouering the scabbe that is bredde in England: and conferring together about the speedie
   dispersing of the golden legende of the liues
   of the saints.
   [London] If my breath be so hote that I burne

   my mouth, suppose I was printed by Pepper Allie
   [1, e. J.Charlewood] Anno.Dom.1589.   [31]p.
   17½cm.
     Printer's device (McKerrow 112) on t.-p.
     Signatures: A-D⁴.
     Attributed to Nash.

NN   0025096   TxU CSmH MH CtY MWiW-C

FILM
   Nash, Thomas, 1567-1601, supposed author.
     The returne of the renowned caualiero Pas-
   quill of England, from the other side the seas,
   and his meeting with Marsorius at London vpon
   the Royal Exchange. VVhere they encounter with
   a little houshold talke of Martin and Martinisme ... and conferring together about the
   speedie dispersing of the golden legende of
   the liues of the saints ... [London, J.
   Charlewood. 1589.
     Generally attributed to Thomas Nash.
     University microfilms no.15174 (case 56,carton 331)
   Short-title   catalogue no.19457.
   1.Marprelate   controversy. I.Title. II.
   Title: Pasquill   of England.

NN   0025097   MiU WaPS MiU

Nash, Thomas, 1567-1601.
   Songs from the dramatists
     see his   Thomas Nashe.

Nash, Thomas, 1567-1601.
   Strange newes, of the intercepting certaine
   letters, and a conuoy of verses, as they were going
   priuilie to victuall the low countries ... By
   Tho. Nashe ...   Printed at London and Iohn
   Danter, ... 1592.
     sm. 4to. Tree calf.

NN   0025099   CSmH MiU

FILM
   Nash, Thomas, 1567-1601.
     Strange newes, of the intercepting certaine
   letters, and a conuoy of verses, as they were
   going priuilie to victuall the Low countries
   ... By Tho.Nashe ... Printed at London by Iohn
   Danter ... 1592.
     A reply to Gabriel Harvey's "Fovre letters and cer-
   taine sonnets",an answer to Greene's "A qvip for an
   vpstart courtier".
     Published in 1593 with title: The apologie of Pierce
   Pennilesse: or Strange newes.
     Running title: Foure letters confuted.
     University microfilms no.15050 (case 43,carton 258)
     Short-title catalogue no.18377a.
     1.Harvey,Gabriel,   1545?-1630. I.Title.

NN   0025100   MiU WaPS

STC   Nash, Thomas, 1567-1601.
18377v.2   Strange newes, of the intercepting certaine
   letters, and a conuoy of verses, as they were
   going pruilie to victuall the Low Countries ...
   Printed at London by Iohn Danter, 1593.

     [A]¹, B-L⁴, M². 8vo.
     Running title reads: Foure letters confuted.
   Another issue of STC 18377b. Differs in the
   cancelling of gathering A.--see photostats
   shelved with book.
   W. H. Crawford-W. A. White copy.

NN   0025101   DFo MWiW-C

Microfilm
R4388/2 Nash, Thomas, 1567-1601.
     Strange newes, of the intercepting of
   certaine letters, and a convoy of verses,
   as they were going privilie to victuall
   the Low Countries. London, J. Danter,
   1593.
     [88] p.
     Short-title catalogue no. 18377b.
     Microfilm. 1 reel. 35 mm.
     I. Title.

NN   0025102   CaBVaU ViU NNC MiU

Nash, Thomas, 1567-1601.
   Strange Newes, Of the intercepting certaine Letters
   and a Convoy of Verses, as they were going Privilie the
   [i. e. to] victuale the Lowe Countries ... By Tho. Nashe,
   Gentleman. Printed at London by Iohn Danter ... 1592.
   [London reprinted, 1870]
     ii p., reprint: xiv, [15]-94 p. 21 x 16ᵐᵐ. (Cover-title: Miscellaneous
   tracts. Temp. Eliz. & Jac. i. [no. 2])
     Introduction signed: J. Payne Collier.

Continued in next column

VOLUME 405

Continued from preceding column

A reply to Gabriel Harvey's "Fovre letters and certaine sonnets, London, 1592" (no. 5 of Collier's reprints) which was published after Greene's death in answer to Greene's "A qvip for an vpstart courtier, London, 1592" (no. 3 of Collier's reprints) in the original edition of which was a satirical notice of Harvey that incited the controversy.
Published in 1593 with title: The apologie of Pierce Pennilesse: or, Strange newes.
Running title: Foure letters confuted.

1. Harvey, Gabriel, 1545?–1630. 2. Greene, Robert, 1558–1592. I. Collier, John Payne, 1789–1883, ed. II. Title.

17–25568

Library of Congress   PR1125.C6 no. 2

NN   0025104   DLC NcD OU NjP MB

MICPT
822.08
Nash, Thomas, 1567–1601.
Summer's last will and testament. London, 1600.
(In Three centuries of drama: English, 1512–1641)

Microprint.

NN   0025105   MoU

[Nash, Thomas] 1567–1601.
SUMMER'S last will and testament. 1825.
By Thomas NASH.

NN   0025106   MH

[Nash, Thomas] 1567–1601.
Summer's last will and testament.
(In [Dodsley, Robert] A select collection of old plays. London, 1825–27. 19½cm. v. 9, p. [1]–80)
William Summer, or Sommers, was court fool or jester to Henry VIII.

1. Sommers, William, d. 1560.   I. Title.

Library of Congress   PR1263.D6 vol. 9   12–3026

NN   0025107   DLC

[Nash, Thomas] 1567–1601.
Summer's last will and testament.
(In Dodsley, Robert, ed. A select collection of old English plays. 4th ed. by W. C. Hazlitt. London, 1874–76. 21½cm. v. 8, p. [1]–92)

1. Sommers, William, d. 1560.   I. Title.

14–21866

Library of Congress   PR1263.D7 vol. 8

NN   0025108   DLC NIC

MIC–7
PR
1263
D6
no. 633,
634
Nash, Thomas, 1567–1601.
Summer's last will and testament.
(In Dodsley, Robert, ed. A select collection of old English plays. 4th ed... London, 1874–76. v. 8)

Microfiche (negative) Microcard Editions Inc.
2 cards   7.5 x 12.5 cm.

NN   0025109   NBuU

M1528
L2225S82
Nashe, Thomas, 1567–1601. Summer's last will and testament.
Lambert, Constant, 1905–1951. [Summer's last will and testament. Piano-vocal score. English]

Summer's last will and testament; a masque for orchestra, chorus, and baritone solo. Words taken from the pleasant comedy of that name written in 1593 by Thomas Nashe. [London] Oxford University Press [*1937]

M1523
L2225S82
1946
Case
Nash, Thomas, 1567–1601. Summer's last will and testament.
Lambert, Constant, 1905–1951. [Summer's last will and testament. Piano-vocal score. English]

Summer's last will & testament; a masque for orchestra, chorus, and baritone solo, to words taken from the pleasant comedy of that name written in 1593 by Thomas Nashe. The drawings by Michael Ayrton. [Arranger, Archibald Jacob. London] Oxford University Press, 1946 [*1937]

STC
18379
Nash, Thomas, 1567–1601.
The terrors of the night. Or, A discourse of apparitions ... London, Printed by Iohn Danter for William Iones, 1594.

A–H⁴. (H4, probably blank, lacking.) 4to.
Thomas Rawlinson–Richard Heber–Britwell Court copy.

NN   0025112   DFo CSmH PU

Humanities
Library
Microfilm
AC
4
E5
Reel
no.
258
WaPS
Nash, Thomas, 1567–1601.
The terrors of the night or, A discourse of apparitions ... Tho: Nashe. London, Printed by Iohn Danter for William Iones ... 1594.
University microfilms no. 15032 (case 43, carton 258)
Short-title catalogue no. 18379.

NN   0025113   MiU WaPS

PR
2722
1929
Nash, Thomas, 1567–1601.
... Thomas Nashe. Norwich, Printed and published by Martin Kinder at the Walpole press, 1929.
20 p. incl. front. (port.)   23 cm.   (Songs from the dramatists)

"This edition is limited to two hundred and fifty copies, of which this is no. 98."

Autograph presentation copy from A. L. Long?

NN   0025114   MiU NcD MH

Nash, Thomas, 1567–1601.
Tom Nash his ghost ...
see under title

PR2670
.D5
1914
Nash, Thomas, 1567–1601, joint author.
Marlowe, Christopher, 1564–1593.
... The tragedy of Dido, queen of Carthage, written by Christopher Marlowe and Thomas Nash. 1594. [Amersham, Eng.] Issued for subscribers by the editor of the Tudor facsimile texts, 1914.

Nash, Thomas, 1567–1601.
The trimming of Thomas Nash
see under   [Harvey, Gabriel] 1550?–1631.

STC
18380
Nash, Thomas, 1567–1601.
The vnfortunate traueller. Or, The life of Iacke Wilton ... London, Printed by T. Scarlet for C. Burby, 1594.

A–O⁴. (O2–3 in facsimile; O4 from another copy.) 4to.
Some margins trimmed affecting some running titles and signatures.
W. A. White–F. J. Hogan copy.

NN   0025118   DFo MH

Humanities
Library
Microfilm
AC
4
E5
Reel
no.
549
Nash, Thomas, 1567–1601.
The vnfortvnate traueller. Or, The life of Iacke Wilton ... [By] Tho. Nashe. London, Printed by R. Scarlet for C. Burby ... 1594.
University microfilms no. 15033 (carton 549)
Short-title catalogue no. 18380.

NN   0025119   MiU WaPS

Humanities
Library
Microfilm
AC
4
E5
Reel
no.
557
Nash, Thomas, 1567–1601.
The vnfortvnate traueller. Or, The life of Iacke Wilton. Newly corrected and augmented ... [By] Tho. Nashe. London, Imprinted by Thomas Scarlet for Cuthbert Burby. 1594.
University microfilms no. 16669 (carton 557)
Short-title catalogue no. 18381.

NN   0025120   MiU WaPS

328
N253u
P2
Nash, Thomas, 1567–1601.
The unfortunate traveller; or, The life of Jack Wilton: with an essay on the life & writings of Thomas Nash by Edmund Gosse. London, C. Whittingham & co., 1892.
xiii, 216 p.   front. (port), facsim. 20cm.
Chiswick press editions.
No. 263 of limited edition of 500 copies.

CaBVaU PU PPL PBm ICN IdU CU–S MeB MWiW–C OrU NIC
NN   0025121   MiU ViW IaU MA MB MH NN WU ICarbS TxU

Nash, Thomas, 1567–1601.
The vnfortvnate traueller; or, The life of Jack Wilton, by Thomas Nashe; edited by H. F. B. Brett-Smith.   Boston: Houghton Mifflin Co., 1920.   1 p. l., xx, 132 p.   12°.   (Percy reprints.   no. 1.)
Printed in Great Britain.
Facsimile of original title-page reads: The vnfortvnate Traueller. or, The life of Jacke Wilton. Newly corrected and augmented... Tho. Nashe. London, Imprinted by Thomas Scarlet for Cuthbert Burby. 1594.

1. Fiction (English). 2. Brett-editor. 3. Title. 4. Series.   Smith, Herbert Francis Brett,
N. Y. P. L.   December 22, 1920.

NN   0025122   NN PU MB ICU ViU OrCS

823
N17u
1920a
Nash, Thomas, 1567–1601.
The vnfortvnate traveller; or, The life of Jacke Wilton, by Thomas Nashe. Ed. by H. F. B. Brett-Smith.   Boston and New York, Houghton Mifflin company, 1920.
xx, 132 p.   20cm.   (Half-title: The Percy reprints, no. 1)
With reproduction of original t.-p., dated 1594.
I. Brett-Smith, Herbert Francis Brett, ed. II. Title.

NN   0025123   IU

Nash, Thomas, 1567–1601
The unfortunate traveller; or, The life of Jacke Wilton... New York, Houghton Mifflin co., 1920.
3 p. l., v–xx, 132 p.

NN   0025124   OCU

Nash, Thomas, 1567–1601.
The vnfortvnate traveller; or, The life of Jacke Wilton, by Thomas Nashe; ed. by H. F. B. Brett-Smith. Oxford, B. Blackwell, 1920.
3 p. l., v–xx, 132 p.   facsim.   20cm.   (Half-title: The Percy reprints, no. 1)
Reprint of the edition of 1594, with facsimile of original t.-p.
"Bibliographical note": p. xvii–xx.

I. Brett-Smith, Herbert Francis Brett, ed. II. Title.

Library of Congress   PR2724.U5 1594 a   21–2382

OC1W KEmT WaTC CaBVa WU WaU
NN   0025125   DLC NIC NBC NcD PJB PBm PHC MiU OU NN

VOLUME 405

Nash, Thomas, 1567-1601
...The unfortunate traveler; or, The life of
Jack Wilton...introduction by S.C. Chew. c1925.
(Rogues' bookshelf)

NN 0025126 OCl

Nash, Thomas, 1567-1601.
... The unfortunate traveler; or, The life of Jack Wilton, by
Thomas Nashe; with an introduction by Samuel C. Chew. New
York, Greenberg, 1926.
xxviii, 194 p. 20ᶜᵐ. (The rogues' bookshelf)

"The text followed here is that of the first editions of 1594, word for
word. The spelling and punctuation, however, have been modernized as
far as possible. A few necessary explanatory footnotes have been added,
and the work has been divided into chapters."

I. Title.   26-9703
Library of Congress   PR2724.U5 1926
——— Copy 2.   PN6071.P5RG vol. 5

NN 0025127 DLC MiU PPL PU PSC OCX ODW OClW ViU

PR   Nash, Thomas, 1567-1601
2326   The unfortunate traveller, edited by H. F. B
N3   Brett-Smith. Oxford, Blackwell, 1927.
U5   132p. 20cm. (Percy reprints, no. 1)
1594a

NN 0025128 WU OO ViU OCU PBm MH NcRS CaBVaU OrU

Nash, Thomas, 1567-1601.
The vnfortvnate traveller. Or, The life of Iacke Wilton...
(In: Shorter novels. London₁, 1929₁. 16°. v. 1, p. ₁261-₁
356.)
Includes reproduction of title-page of original edition with imprint: London,
1594.

516653A. 1. Fiction, English.   I. Title.
N. Y. P. L.   June 16, 1911

NN 0025129 NN

Nash, Thomas, 1567-1601.
The unfortunate traveller, by Thomas Nash; edited by Philip
Henderson, illustrated by Haydn Mackey. London: The Verona
Soc., 1930. xxvi, 161 p. illus. 23cm.

"One thousand copies of this edition have been printed at the Alcuin Press, Chipping
Campden, Gloucestershire."
"The...text has been taken from the earliest edition of The unfortunate traveller
in the British Museum."
With reproduction of the t.-p. of the first edition, London, 1594.
Bibliography, p. viii.

657993A. 1. Fiction, English.   I. Henderson, Philip, editor.
II. Mackey, Haydn, illustrator.   III. Title.
N. Y. P. L.   January 27, 1934

         NNCoCi RPB OOxM
         PPL PSC NcD PU ICN ICU NcGU MiU LU NRU PSC MiU IaU
NN 0025130 NN RPB CLSU OU TxU ICarbS FU KMK OKentU

Nash, Thomas, 1567-1601.
The unfortunate traveller; or, The life of Jack Wilton.
Illustrated by Michael Ayrton; with an introd. ₁London₁
J. Lehmann, 1948.
121 p. plates. 23 cm.

"The present text follows that of the second edition printed in
London by T. Scarlet for C. Bury in 1594 as amended by H. F. B.
Brett-Smith in his edition for the Percy reprints."

I. Title.
[PR2724.U]   A 50-5020
Stanford Univ. Library
for Library of Congress   ₍2₎

NN 0025131 CSt TU MiU NN MH NRU IU CtY

823.39 Nash, Thomas, 1567-1601.
N177u   The unfortunate traveller; or, The life
1948   of Jacke Wilton. Edited by H.F.B. Brett-
        Smith, Oxford, Basil Blackwell, 1948.
        132p. 20cm. (The Percy reprints, no.1)

        Corrections: p.124.

        I. Brett-Smith, Herbert Francis Brett,
        ed. II. Title.

NN 0025132 KU

PR   Nash, Thomas, 1567-1601.
2326   The unfortunate traveller; or, The life of Jack Wilton.
N3   Illustrated by Michael Ayrton; with an introd. ₁London₁
U5   J. Lehmann, 1950.
1950   121 p. plates. 23 cm.

"The present text follows that of the second edition printed in
London by T. Scarlet for C. Bury in 1594 as amended by H. F. B.
Brett-Smith in his edition for the Percy reprints."
"First published in this edition in 1948...
reprinted in 1950."

NN 0025133 WU MtBC OU NBuC

Nash, Thomas, 1567-1601. 1953
The unfortunate traveller. 1953
see in Shorter Elizabethan novels.

PR 2724 NASH, THOMAS, 1567-1601
.U5 F5   Le voyageur malchanceux; ou, La vie de Jack
         Wilton (The unfortunate traveller; or, The life
         of Jack Wilton) Traduction, introduction et
         notes par Charles Chassé. Paris, Aubier ₁1954₎
         315 p. (Collection bilingue des classiques
         etrangers)

         With reproduction of original title page,
         London, 1594.
         English and French texts on opposite pages.

NN 0025135 InU ICN

PO 2724 [Nash, Thomas] 1567-1601, supposed author.
.W 87   A wonderfull, strange and miraculous, astro-
1591 p   logicall prognostication for this yeer of Our
         Lord God. 1591. Discouering such wonders to
         happen this yeere, as neuer chaunced since Noes
         floud. Wherein if there be found one lye, the
         author will loose his credit for euer. By Adam
         Fouleweather... London, T.Scarlet [1591]

         Photostat (negative) of the copy in the
         Bodleian library.

NN 0025136 MdBJ

FILM   Nash,Thomas,1567-1601.
       A wonderfull,strange and miraculous,astro-
       logicall prognostication for ... 1591 ... By
       Adam Fouleweather ₁pseud.₎ ... ... Imprinted at
       London by Thomas Scarlet ₁1592₎
       By Thomas Nash. cf.Halkett & Laing.
       University microfilms no.15875 (case 85,carton 509)
       Short-title catalogue no.11209.

       1.Marprelate controversy.

NN 0025137 MiU DLC WaPS

Y   Nash, Thomas,   1567-1601.
1095   A wonderfull, strange and miracu-
.78   lous, astrologicall prognostication
       for this yeer of our Lord God, 1591.
       Discouering such wonders to happen
       this yeere, as neuer chaunced since
       Noes floud. Wherein if there be found
       one lye, the author will loose his cred-
       it for euer. By Adam Foulewather...
       [pseud.]   Lond.1591 [repr.1892]
       sq.T.   (in   Saintsbury, G.E.B..

       ed. Elizabethan and Jacobean pampnlets.
       1892. p.[185]-208)

       Written at the time of the Martin
       Marprelate controversy in reply to at-
       tacks made by Richard Harvey in his
       "Theological discourse of the Lamb of
       God" and in   his "Plaine Percevall"
       cf. Dict. nat.   biog.

NN 0025139 ICN MB

x 828   Nash, Thomas, 1588-16₊ᵈ.
N177q   Miscelanea, or, A fourefold vvay to a happie
1639   life. Set forth in a dialogue betweene a
        countryman, a citizen, a divine, and a lawyer.
        By T. N. of the Inner Temple.   London, Print-
        ed by I. Dawson, and are to bee sold by T.
        Slater, 1639.
        ₁16₎, 280p. 22cm.

        "The epistle dedicatorie" signed: Tho₃Nash.
        Running title: Qvaternio, or A foure-fold way
        to liue well. Published in 1633 and 1636 with
        that title.

NN 0025140 IU

AW   Nash,Thomas,1588-1648.
1   Miscelanea; or, A fourefold way to a happie life.
R475   Set forth in a dialogue, betweene a countryman,a
       citizen,a divine,and a lawyer. By T.N. ... London,
       Printed by I.Dawson, 1639.
       Dedication signed: Tho.Nash.
       Running title: Quaternio,or a foure-fold way to
       liue well.
       Earlier ed.issued,1633,under: Quaternio; or,A
       foure-fold way to a happie life.

       Microfilm of original in the Huntington
       Library. Ann Arbor, Mich., University
       Microfilms, 1973. (Early English books,
       1475-1640, reel 1321)
       STC no.18384.

NN 0025142 MiU CaBVaU

Nash, Thomas, 1588-1648.
Qvaternio or A Fovrefold Way To A Happie Life; set forth
in a Dialogue betweene a Countryman and a Citizen, a Divine
and a Lawyer. Per Tho: Nash Philopolitem. ₁Four Latin quo-
tations₎ London, Printed by Iohn Davvson. 1633.
8 p. l., 280 p. 20¹/₄ᶜᵐ.
Imperfect: p. 195-198 wanting.

I. Title.   24—28741
Library of Congress   PR2826.N31Q8

NN 0025143 DLC WU MiDW CtY CSmH NNUT-Mc

STC   Nash, Thomas, 1588-1648.
18382   Quaternio or A fourefold way to a happie
copy 1 life; set forth in a dialogue betweene a
        countryman and a citizen, a divine and a
        lawyer ... London, Printed by Iohn Dawson, 1633.
        A⁴,)(⁴, B-2N⁴. 4to.
        Pforzheimer, v. 2, no. 766.
        Harmsworth copy.

STC   ---- ---- Another issue.
18383   Differs from STC 18382 in that A1, title-page,

        is a cancel with imprint reading: London, Printed
        by Nicholas Okes and are to be sold by Iohn
        Benson, 1636.
        Cf. Pforzheimer, v. 2, no. 766.

NN 0025145 DFo

AW   Nash,Thomas,1588-1648.
1   Quaternio; or,A fourefold way to a happie life; set
R475: forth in a dialogue betweene a countryman a divine and a citi-
1250   zen,a divine and a lawyer. Per Tho: Nash ... London,
       Printed by I.Dawson, 1633.
       Microfilm of original in the Union Theological Sem-
       inary Library,McAlpin Collection. Ann Arbor,Mich.,
       University Microfilms, 1971. (Early English books,
       1475-1640,reel 1250)
       STC no.18382.
       Microfilm.
       I.Title.

NN 0025146 MiU WaPS CaBVaU

VOLUME 405

N[ash], Tho[mas], 1588-1648.
Quaternio, or A fourefold way to a happy life, set forth in a discourse betweene a country-man, a citizen, a divine, and a lawyer; wherein the commodities of the country and the city, together with the excellency of divinity and the law are set forth. By Tho. N. London, N. Okes, 1636.
4°. pp. (16), 280.

NN   0025147   MH CtY IU

Nash, Thomas, 1845-1885, ed. and tr.
The speech of Aeschines against Ctesiphon
see under   Aeschines.

Nash, Thomas Arthur, 1850-
The life of Richard lord Westbury, formerly lord high chancellor, with selections from his correspondence, by Thomas Arthur Nash ... London, R. Bentley and son, 1888.
2 v. fronts. (ports.) 23ᶜᵐ

1. Westbury, Richard Bethell, 1st baron, 1800-1873. 2. Law—Gt. Brit. 3. Gt. Brit.—Pol. & govt.—1837-1901.

Library of Congress   DA565.W53N3
                                                        20—11281

OCl MH NjP CaBVaU WaU-L MdBP NcD MiEM
NN   0025149   DLC CaBVaU PP NBC LU CtY PBm PPB PPL

Mu614.0966 NASH, Thomas Arthur Manly, 1905-
N 174   ...Advice on tsetse surveys and clearings [by] T.A.M.Nash... Rev.ed.,July 1937. Kaduna,The Govt.printer,1937.
2ℓ.,9p. 24cm.

At head of title: Nigeria.

NN 0025150   PU PU-Mu

Nash, Thomas Arthur Manly, 1905-
The Anchau rural development and settlement scheme. [Prepared for the Tsetse Fly and Trypanosomiasis Committee. London, Pub. for the Colonial Office by H. M. Stationery Off., 1948.
22 p. illus. maps (part fold.) plans. 34 cm.
"References": p. 22.

1. Agriculture—Nigeria—Anchau.   I. Gt. Brit. Colonial Office. Tsetse Fly and Trypanosomiasis Committee. II. Title.

S471.N7N3   56—16675

IEN DNAL
NN   0025151   DLC NcD MH CtY NNC CU IU NNU-W NIC

Nash, Thomas Arthur Manly, 1905-
Tsetse flies in British West Africa. [Prepared for the Tsetse Fly and Trypanosomiasis Committee. London, Published for the Colonial Office by H. M. Stationery Off., 1948.
77 p. plates, 15 fold. col. maps (in pocket) 34 cm.
"Corrections": slip inserted.
Includes bibliographies.

1. Tsetse-flies. 2. Trypanosomiasis.   I. Gt. Brit. Colonial Office. Tsetse Fly and Trypanosomiasis Committee.

SF807.N3   632.772   50—15828

NN   0025152   DLC CU DNAL DNLM NN NIC

Nash, Thomas H., tr.

Klarwill, Victor, 1873-   ed.
Queen Elizabeth and some foreigners; being a series of hitherto unpublished letters from the archives of the Hapsburg family. Edited, with introductions, by Victor von Klarwill. Authorized translation by Professor T. H. Nash. With 36 illustrations from contemporary sources. London, John Lane [1928]

Nash, Thomas Palmer, 1890-
The ammonia content of the blood, and its bearing on the mechanism of acid neutralization in the animal organism ... by Thomas Palmer Nash, jr. ... [Baltimore, 1921]
1 p. l., p. 463-488. 1 illus. 25ᶜᵐ.
Thesis (PH. D.)—Cornell university, 1922.
On cover: By Thomas P. Nash, jr., and Stanley R. Benedict.
"Reprinted from the Journal of biological chemistry, vol. XLVIII, no. 2, October, 1921."
Bibliography: p. 487-488.
1. Blood—Analysis and chemistry. 2. Ammonia.   I. Benedict, Stanley Rossiter, 1884-   joint author.
                                                        22—20442

Library of Congress   RB145.N3
Cornell Univ. Libr.   [2]

NN   0025154   NNC OU DLC

Nash, Thomas Palmer, 1890.   Chapel Hill,1911
Composition of the resene of Pinus Heterophyll -la.
      By Thomas P. Nash, Jr.

NN   0025155   NcU

Nash, Treadway Russell, 1725-1811, ed.
Collections for the history of Worcestershire. London, Ptd. by J. Nichols, 1781-82.
2v. illus.,plates,ports.,fold.map,plans, geneal.tables. 44cm.

Paging irregular in v.2, p.255 and 259 numbered 235 and 159 respectively.
The thirteen facsimiles from the Domesday book, with their two engraved dedications are bound at end of v.2 with "Observations on Domesday for Worcestershire". They are preceded by an appendix of 168p.
This history was founded on ms. collections made by Thomas Habington (1560-1647) in the possession of the Society of Antiquaries of London; in 1774 they were entrusted to Nash for the purpose of revising and publishing. At different time, additions to the original mss. has been made by William Habington (1605-1654) William Thomas, and Charles Lyttelton, Bishop of Carlisle. cf. Introd.

DA
670   ___ ___. Index, compiled by John Amphlett,
.W9A2
no.3

of Clent. Oxford, Printed for the Worcestershire Historical Society by J. Parker, 1894-95.
2v. in 1.(xliv,358p.) 29cm. (Worcestershire Historical Society. [Publications, no.3]

1. Worcestershire, Eng.   (Series)

NN   0025159   ScU PPL

DA
670   [Nash, Treadway Russell] 1725-1811.
W9   Collections for the history of Worcester-
N2   shire.   London, Printed by J. Nichols, 1781-82.
2 v. illus., ports., maps (1 fold.) facsims., geneal. tables (part fold.) 43 cm.
Engraved half-title, v. 1: The history and antiquities of Worcestershire.
Error in binding, v. 1: p. 473-474 reversed, and bound in following p. 478.
Errors in paging, v. 2: 255 and 259 numbered 235 and 159 respectively.
Founded on manuscript collections made by Thomas Habington (1560-1647) in the possession of the Society of Antiquaries of London; in 1774 they were entrusted to Nash, for the purpose of revising and publishing.

Cf. Introd.
Vol. 2 contains 13 facsimiles from Domesday book relating to Worcestershire, with "Observations on Domesday."
Supplement containing corrections and additions (104 p. at end of v. 2) has special t. p. and imprint: [London] Printed for J. White, 1799.

1. Worcestershire – Hist. I. Domesday book. II. Title.

NN   0025161   Vi CtY CU PHi PPL MH ViU MiU MdBP

---

xf942.47   Nash, Treadway Russell, 1725-1811.
N17c   Collections for the history of Worcestershire.   London, Printed by J. Nichols, sold by T. Payne and Son ... Fletcher at Oxford, and Lewis at Worcester, 1781-82.
2v. illus., facsims., geneal.tables, fold. map, plans, plates, ports. 46cm.

Dedication signed: T. Nash.
This history was founded on the manuscript collections made by Thomas Habington. In 1774 the Society of Antiquaries, to whom they had been bequeathed, entrusted them to Nash for revision and publication. Cf. Introd. Except for minor differences in placing of the plates and other variations noted below, this copy agrees with the description given in A bibliographical account of ... English topography, by W. Upcott (N.Y., B. Franklin, 1968) v.3, p.1330-1337.
Both volumes have added t.p., engr.: The history and antiquities of Worcestershire.
Imperfect: lacks plan of Nash's plantation on p.256, v.2.

Includes extra plates: port. of James Johnstone Junior, M.D. (facing p.301, v.1) and an additional port. of Sir Edwyn Sandys (facing p.224, v.2)
Inserted inside front cover of v.1 are a small pencil sketch of Hallow Park and a fold. original water-color sketch: The view of Hanbury Church & schoole. Grainger's script. Thomas's sculpt.
Large paper copy, bound in original boards.

I. Habington, Thomas, 1560-1647.

---- ---- Supplement. [London] Printed for J. White, 1799.
104p. illus.

Bound with v.2 of the main work.

NN   0025167   IU NcD

DA670   Nash, Treadway Russell, 1725-1811.
W9N2   Collections for the history of Worcester-
f   shire. [London] Printed by J.Nichols; sold by T.Payne, 1781-99.
Locked   2 v. illus.(part.fold.),13 col.facsims.
stack   46cm.
Dedication signed: T.Nash.
Paging irregular in v.2: p.255 and 259 are numbered 235 and 159 respectively.
The 13 facsims., from the Domesday book, with their 2 engraved dedications are bound at end of v.2, with "Observations upon Domesday"; they are preceded by a Supplement of 104 pages having special   t.p.

This history was founded on manuscript collections made by Thomas Habington (1560-1647) in the possession of the Society of Antiquaries of London; in 1774 they were entrusted to Nash, for the purpose of revising and publishing. At different times, additions to the original manuscripts had been made by William Habington (1605-1654), William Thomas and Charles Lyttelton, Bishop of Carlisle.

An index to Dr.Nash's Collections for a history of Worcestershire, compiled by John Amphlett. Oxford, Printed for the Worcestershire Historical Society by J.Parker, 1894-95. 2 v.(xliv,358 p.) 29cm. [Worcestershire Historical Society. Publications]
Pages [i]-xliv bound at front of v.2.
Contents.—pt.1.Names of persons.—pt.[2.] Index of names of places.
1.Worcestershire, Eng. - Hist. I.Amphlett, John, 1845-1918. II.Title. III.Ser.

NN   0025170   CSt MiU

VOLUME 405

ₜNash, Treadway Russellₗ 1725–1811.
Collections for the history of Worcestershire ... 2d ed., with additions. ₜLondonₗ Printed for J. White, 1799.
2 v. illus., 75 pl. incl. front., port., fold. map, plans. 13 facsim., geneal. tab. 45½ᵐ.

Title vignette.
In double columns.
Dedication signed: T. Nash.
Paging irregular in v. 2: p. 255 and 259 numbered 235 and 159 respectively.
Most of the plates drawn and engr. by J. Ross.
Upcott gives in his collation a Plan of the city of Worcester, not given in list of plates in this copy; also a port. of John Hough, which Lowndes says, "was not published with the work, and does not belong to it."

The 13 facsim. from the Domesday book, with their two engr. dedications are bound at end of v. 2, with "Observations upon Domesday": they are preceded by a Supplement of 104 p. having special t.-p.
This history was founded on ms. collections made by Thomas Habington (1560–1647) in the possession of the Society of antiquaries of London; in 1774 they were entrusted to Nash, for the purpose of revising and publishing. At different times, additions to the original mss. had been made by William Habington (1605–1654) William Thomas and Charles Lyttelton, bp. of Carlisle. *cf.* Introd.

Subject entries: Worcestershire, Eng.

S-6176

Library of Congress, no.   DA670.W9N2.

NN   0025172   DLC LNHT DFo OCl NjP MB NN MWA

Nash, T₍readway₎ Russell, 1725–1811.
Copy of the original death-warrant of Humphrey Littleton, with observations on it. Communicated.. to the Secretary of the Society of Antiquaries ... ₜLondon, 1803ₗ
10 p., 1 pl,. 4°.
n.t.-p.
In: CBA p. v. 8.

NN   0025173   NN

Nash, Treadway Russell, 1725–1811.

Butler, Samuel, 1612–1680.
Hudibras, by Samuel Butler; with notes by the Rev. Treadway Russel Nash, D. D. A new ed., in two volumes ... London, J. Murray, printed by W. Nicol, 1835.

Nash, Treadway Russell, 1725–1811.
An index to Dr. Nash's Collections for a history of Worcestershire. Comp. by John Amphlett ... Oxford, Printed for the Worcestershire historical society, 1894-1895.
xliv, 358 p. 28½ᵐ. ₜWorcestershire historical society. Publicationsₗ

1. Worcestershire, Eng.—Hist.—Sources.   I. Amphlett, John, 1845–1918, comp.

NN   0025175   MiU OCl

Nash, Treadway Russell, 1725–1811.
An index to Dr. Nash's Collections for a history of Worcestershire. Comp. by John Amphlett ... Oxford, Printed for the Worcestershire historical society, 1894–1895.
xliv, 358 p 29cm. ₜWorcestershire historical society. Publications 1ₗ

I. Amphlett, John, 1845–1918, comp. .

NN   0025176   MnU NIC ICU ICN TxU

Nash, Treadway Russell, 1725–1811.
Observation on the time of the death and place of burial of Queen Katharine Parr. Read at the Society of Antiquaries, June 14, 1787. ₜLondon, 1787ₗ
9 p., 1 pl. 4°.
n.t.-p.

NN   0025177   NN

Nash, Vaughan, 1861–1932.
La cooperazione in rapporto col commercio internazionele
Traduzione del U.Rabbeno. Milano, 1889

NN   0025178   MH

330.954   Nash, Vaughan, 1861–1932.
N178g   The great famine and its causes. With eight photographs by the author and a map of India showing the famine area. London, Longmans, Green, 1900.
viii, 261 p. plates, map.

Reprinted from the "Manchester guardian." cf. Pref.

1. India – Famines.   I. Title.

NN   0025179   WaU MdBP DL

Nash, Vaughan, 1861– 1932.
The great famine and its causes, by Vaughan Nash; with eight photographs by the author and a map of India showing the famine area. London, New York ₜetc.ₗ Longmans, Green, and co., 1900.
viii p., 1 l., 261, ₍1₎ p. front., 7 pl., fold. map. 20ᶜᵐ.
Reprinted from the "Manchester guardian." cf. Pref.

1. India—Famines.

2-26547

Library of Congress   DS413.N25

NN   0025180   DLC CU PPGi PPL MiU

Nash, Vaughan, 1861–1932.
The great famine and its causes. New York, 1900.

NN   0025181   Nh MB

Nash, Vaughan. 1861–1932   *3562.148(1901)
The Indian famine and its lessons.
(In Co-operative Wholesale Societies Limited, England and Scotland. Annual for 1901. Pp. 163–184. Manchester. 1901.)

K1821 — Famines. India.

NN   0025182   MB

---

334   Nash, Vaughan, 1861–1932.
N178r   The relation of co-operative to competitive trading.   Manchester, Eng. ₜ1887?ₗ
11p.
YA 20177   Specially recommended by the Adjudicators of prize papers in connection with Carlisle congress, 1887.

NN   0025183   IU DLC MH

Nash, Vaughan, 1861–1932.

Gt. Brit. *Board of trade. Committee on retail coal prices.*
... Report of the committee appointed by the Board of trade to inquire into the causes of the present rise in the retail price of coal sold for domestic use ... London, H. M. Stationery off., Eyre and Spottiswoode, printers, 1915.

NASH, Vaughan, 1861–1932.   *3562.148 (1894)
Some aspects of industrial mortality.
(In Co-operative wholesale societies limited. England and Scotland. Annual for 1894. Pp. 314–348. London. ₜ1894.ₗ)

NN   0025185   MB

Nash, Vera Mae
A self study of Anderson township high school... ₜCincinnati, 1941ₗ
3 p.l., ii-iii, 100 numb. l. incl. tables, forms.
Thesis – University of Cincinnati.

NN   0025186   OCU

D070
N17   Nash, Vernon
Educating for journalism, by Vernon Nash ... 1938.
x, 178 p. 27½ᶜᵐ.

Thesis, Doctor of education, Teachers college, Columbia university, 1938.
Reproduction of typewritten copy.
"Annotated references": p. 171-178.

1. Journalism - Study and teaching.

NN   0025187   NNC IU OrU ICN

Nash, Vernon.
...Exit empire, by Vernon Nash. Illus. by William Huntington... New York, Fellowship publ., 1943. 47 p. illus. 19cm. (Fellowship studybook. no. 2.)

1. Colonies and colonization.   2. World war, 1939– —Reconstruction. I. Ser.
N. Y. P. L.   September 14, 1945

NN   0025188   NN NRCR CSt-H

Nash, Vernon.
... Exit empire, by Vernon Nash; illustrations by William Huntington ... New York, N. Y., Fellowship publications, 1943.
48 p. illus. (incl. map) 19ᵐ. (Forerunners studybook, no. 3)
"For further reading" at end of each chapter except one.

1. Imperialism. 2. World politics.   I. Title.
                                46-2014
Library of Congress   JC359.N3
                    ₍3₎   321.03

NN   0025189   DLC Mi MiHM NN OBiC-M

Nash, Vernon.
It must be done again; the case for a world federal union, by Vernon Nash; illustrated by excerpts from John Fiske's "Critical period of American history" ... New York, N. Y., Federal union, inc., 1940.
1 p. l., ₍1₎, 45 p. 19½ᵐ.
"First printing, October, 1940."
"Concerning the compiler": p. 45.

1. International organization. 2. U. S.—Hist.—Confederation, 1783–1780.   I. Fiske, John, 1842–1901. The critical period of American history, 1783–1789. II. Title.
                                41–10808
Library of Congress   JC362.N36 1940
                    ₍44d1₎   321.021

NN   0025190   DLC CSt-H Or OrCS

Nash, Vernon.
It must be done again; the case for a world federal union, by Vernon Nash; with an edited abridged version of John Fiske's "Critical period of American history". New York, N.Y., Federal union, inc., 1941.
48p. 20cm.
"Second printing, June 1941."
"Concerning the compiler": p.₍2₎ of cover.

NN   0025191   MoU

VOLUME 405

940.933144
P191
v.5
no.11
   Nash, Vernon
      Organized efforts for a governed world.
⌈New York, National Peace Conference, 1942⌉
⌈4⌉p. 28cm. (In Pamphlets on post-war
planning. v.5, no.11)

      Caption title.

      1. International cooperation. I. Title.

NN   0025192   OrU

   Nash, Vernon.
      It must be done again; in the 1780's, American
federal union; in the 1940's, federal world government. Chiefly an edited, abridged version of
John Fiske's "Critical period of American history".
New York, World federalists, inc., c1946.
      48 p.

NN   0025193   OCl

JC362
N54
1946
   Nash, Vernon
      It must be done again - in the 1780's Ameri-
can federal union - in the 1940's federal world
government. Chiefly an edited, abridged version
of John Fiske's "Critical period of American
history". New York, World Federalists, 1946.
48 p. 21cm.

      "First printing, October 1940 ... third
printing, May 1946."
      "Concering the compiler": p.⌈2⌉ of cover.

NN   0025194   CU

   Nash, Vernon.

      It must be done again—in the 1780's
American Federal Union—in the 1940's Federal
World Government; chiefly an edited, abridged
version of John Fiske's "Critical period of
American history". New York, United World
Federalists, 1948.
      48 p. 20cm.
      1. International cooperation. 2. U. S.—Hist.—
Confederation, 1783-1789. I. Fiske, John,1842-
1901. The critical   period of American
history, 1783-1789.   II. Title.

NN   0025195   ViU

Nash, Vernon, *comp.*
      Trindex; an index to three dictionaries: Giles' Chinese-
English dictionary, K'ang Hsi tzu tien, P'ei wen yun fu; in
which are listed the 13,848 characters of Giles' dictionary,
arranged in numerical sequence according to the Kuei hsieh
system of converting characters into numerals devised by the
editors of the Harvard-Yenching institute Sinological index
series ... Compiled by Vernon Nash. Peiping, China, Printed
by Index press, Yenching university ⌈1936⌉
      2 p. l., lxx, 584, ⌈2⌉ p. 16ᶜᵐ.

      Cover-title also in Chinese.
      Two tables of the Kuei hsieh system (1 leaf) laid in.

      1. Chinese language—Dictionaries—English. 2. Chinese language—
Writing. I. Giles, Herbert Allen, 1845-1935. Chinese-English diction-
ary. II. K'ang Hsi, emperor of China, 1655-1723. K'ang Hsi tzŭ tien.
III. P'ei wen yun fu. IV. Title.

                                    38–13192

Library of Congress   PL1455.G622

                  ⌈2⌉   495.132

NN   0025197   DLC CaBVaU CtY NN NjP

Nash, Vernon.
      ... What is taught in schools of journalism; an analysis of
the curricula of the members of the American association of
schools and departments of journalism, by Vernon Nash ...
⌈Columbia, Mo.⌉ 1928.
      77 p. 23ᶜᵐ. (University of Missouri bulletin. v. 29, no. 45 ⌈i. e. 47⌉
Journalism series, no. 54)

      "Condensed from a thesis submitted ... in partial fulfillment of the
requirements for a master's degree from the University of Missouri."

      1. Journalism—Study and teaching. I. Title. II. Title: Schools of
journalism.

                                    29–27202

Library of Congress   PN4788.N3

NN   0025198   DLC MoU OrU ViU OCU OCl OU

JX
1954
.N25
   Nash, Vernon.
      The world must be governed. New
York, Harper [1949]
      206 p.
      #International organization.
      (A)The world must be governed.

NN   0025199   MoU PP

   Nash, Vernon.
      The world must be governed. ⌈1st ed.⌉ New York, Har-
per ⌈1949⌉
      xvi, 206 p. 21 cm.

      1. International organization. I. Title.

      JX1954.N3   341.1   49–8579*

           CLSU NN ViU MB NcD ICU WaSpG MtBC WaT KEmT OKentU
NN 0025200   DLC OOxM CaBVaU OrP OrU Wa WaS WaSp

   NASH, VERNON
      The world must be governed. 2d ed.
Harper c1949.
      206 p.

NN   0025201   Or

JX
1954
N3
1950
   Nash, Vernon.
      The world must be governed. 2d ed.
New York, Harper [pref.1950]
      xvi,206p. 21cm.

      1.International organization. I.Title.

NN   0025202   CLSU

   Nash, Vernon.
      Yes, but - questions and answers about a
federal world government. New York, World
Federalists, U.S.A., inc. c1946⌉
      32 p. 21 cm.

      1. International organization. I. Title.

NN   0025203   NcU-L

JX1954
N37
1947
   Nash, Vernon
      "Yes, but--" Questions and answers about
a federal world government. ⌈3d. rev. printing. New York, United World Federalists,
1947⌉
      32 p. 22cm. ⌈United World Federalists.
Pamphlets⌉

      Cover title.

      1. International organization.

NN   0025204   CU

   Nash, Vernon.
      "Yes, but—" Questions and answers about a
federal world government... [New York, United
world federalists, 1948] 32 p. 21cm.

      6. (rev.) printing.

      1. Federation, International, 1939-

NN   0025205   NN

   Nash, Mrs. Vernon.
      Educational materials on the orient. New
York, Progressive education assn., 1943.
      36 p.

NN   0025206   WaS

X851
+943n
   Nash, Mrs. Vernon   comp.
      Educational materials on the orient ...
New York, Progressive education association
[1943]
      cover-title,36 numb l. 27cm.
      Mimeographed.
      Includes lists of films and phonograph
records.

NN   0025207   CtY

*
M1
.S444
v.45
no.6
   Nash, W
      Canton march, for the piano forte.
Composed for, and dedicated to Miss E. A.
Gedney. N. York, Engraved, Printed and
Sold by E. Riley, 29 Chatham St., °1827.
      ⌈1⌉ p. 35cm. ⌈Sheet music collection, v. 45,
no. 6⌉
      Caption title.

      1. Marches (Piano) I. Title.

NN   0025208   ViU

⌈NASH, W.   8051.454
      General Harrison's grand march at the battle of Tippecanoe. [For
pianoforte.]
      New York. Bancroft. 1835. (2) pp. F°.

NN   0025209   MB

MT224
.N3
   Nash, W
      The musical student's class book. Containing
the elementary principles of music, completely
explained with major and minor scales, chords
and exercises for the voice; and introductory
lessons for the piano forte or organ. Also a
number of the popular songs, duetts, glees and
catches. The whole selected from the most
eminent authors and arranged by W. Nash. Nashville, W. Hasell Hunt & Co., 1837.
      68+ p. 25 cm.
      1. Piano instruction and study. 2. Music-
instruction and   study. I. Title.

NN   0025210   T

   Nash, W., 1882-
      see Nash, Walter, 1882-

   Nash, W.E.
      see Nash, William Edward.

   Nash, W. Gifford, 1867-1920
      see Nash, Wallis Gifford, 1867-1920.

   Nash, W. H. Howard.
      The sun myth mania; a witness to the credulity of the incredu-
lous, by W. H. Howard Nash... ⌈London⌉ Christian Evidence
Soc. ⌈1918?⌉ 8 p. 8°.

      1. Bible.—Mythology. 2. Sun in   mythology.
      N. Y. P. L.   August 23, 1920.

NN   0025214   NN

VOLUME 405

Nash, Wallis.
  The farm, ranch and range in Oregon, by Wallis Nash...
₍Portland, Ore.?₎ The Lewis and Clark Centennial Exposition
Commission for the State of Oregon, 1904.   32 p. incl. tables.
illus.   12°.
  Cover-title.
          YA. 25426   YA. 28630

1. Agriculture—U. S.—Oregon.   2. Portland, Ore. Lewis and Clark
Centennial Exposition, 1905.
N. Y. P. L.   September 13, 1927

NN   0025215   NN OrHi Or WaU DLC

Nash, Wallis.
  The farm, ranch and range in Oregon.
Lewis & Clark Centennial Exposition ... Portland,
Oregon, 1905.   Salem, 1904.
  32 p.   plates.
  Micro-opaque. Louisville, Ky., Lost Cause
Press, 1969. 3 cards.   7.5 x 12.5 cm.
(Travels in the West and Southwest [no. 324])
  1. Oregon. Descr. & trav. I. Portland, Ore.
Lewis and Clark Centennial Exposition, 1905.
II. Title.

NN   0025216   ViU UU OOxM MsU OrU

Nash, Wallis
  The farm, ranch and range in Oregon... Lewis
& Clark centennial exposition, celebrating the
100th anniversary of the exploration of the
Oregon country by Captains Meriwether Lewis
and William Clark...   Portland, Ore., 1905.
          32p.
  Printed by direction of the Lewis & Clark
centennial commission for the state of Oregon,
1904.
  cover title·

NN   0025217   InU KMK

Nash, Wallis.
  A lawyer's life on two continents, by Wallis Nash.
Boston, R. G. Badger ₍1919₎
  212 p. front., plates, ports. 20½ᵐ.

  I. Title.
  Library of Congress   CT275.N3A3   19–15642

CaBViPA WaU Or
NN   0025218   DLC CU-AL OrCS OrHi WaS Or OrU MB NN

Nash, Wallis.
  Oregon: there and back in 1877, by Wallis Nash ...
London, Macmillan and co., 1878.
  xviii p., 2 l., 285 p. incl. front., illus. plates, double map. 19½ᵐᵐ.

  1. Oregon—Descr. & trav. 2. U. S.—Descr. & trav.   I. Title
  Library of Congress   F881.N24   Rc–400

CaBVaU IdU CaBVa WaWW OrHi CaBViPA WaS
PPFr WaT NBuG OC1 WaU WaTC Or MtU OrU MtBuM Wa
NN   0025219   DLC CtY WaSp OrP OrHi OrU PPGi PSC

Nash, Wallis.
  Oregon: there and back in 1877.   London,
Macmillan, 1878.
  xviii, 285 p.   illus., plates, double map.
20 cm.
  Micro-opaque. Louisville, Ky., Lost Cause
Press, 1969. 10 cards. 7.5 x 12.5 cm.
(Travels in the West and Southwest [no. 325])ˆ
  1. Oregon. Descr. & trav. 2. U.S. Descr. &
trav. I. Title.

NN   0025220   ViU MsU OOxM OrU

NASH, Wallis
  ... Selected chapters from the settler's
handbook to Oregon ... "The settler's capital"
and "various crops". Portland, Ore., Dunham
printing co., 1905.
  p. ₍57₎ –86.

NN   0025221   WaU WaS

Nash, Wallis.
  Selected chapters from "The settler's handbook to Oregon;"   "The six districts of
Oregon" and "The farm and its industries."
  167p   Portland, Or.,Gill 1905   8   264C

NN   0025222   WaS

Nash, Wallis.
  The settler's handbook to Oregon, by Wallis Nash ...
Portland, Or., The J. K. Gill co., 1904.
  1 p. l., ₍5₎–190 p., 1 l. 21ᶜᵐ.

  1. Oregon
  Library of Congress   F876.N25   5–9041

OrSaW NN WaU
NN   0025223   DLC OrU OrHi Or OrP WaS WaSp IdU ICJ

Nash, Wallis.
  Two years in Oregon. By Wallis Nash ... New York,
D. Appleton and company, 1882.
  311 p. front., plates. 19½ᵐ.
  "Sequel to the sketch pub. three years ago ₍Oregon: there and back in
1877₎"

  1. Oregon—Descr. & trav.   I. Title.
  Library of Congress   F881.N25   Rc–401

IdB CoU OrU Or OrP WaS WaSp Wa WaWW WaT
OrPS MtU CaBVa CaBViPA WaTC OrStbM CaBVaU OrHi
OC1 OO OC1W MiU NBuG ICJ NN MH NjP MWA WaU NcC
NN   0025224   DLC IEN OU GU DI–GS CtY PSC PHi PPL

Nash, Wallis.
  Two years in Oregon.   New York, Appelton,
1882.
  311 p.   plates. 20 cm.
  "Sequel to the sketch published three years ago
[Oregon; there and back in 1877]"
  Micro-opaque. Louisville, Ky., Lost Cause
Press, 1969. 9 cards. 7.5. x 12.5 cm.
(Travels in the West and Southwest [no. 326])
  1. Oregon. Descr. & trav. I. Title.

NN   0025225   ViU MsU UU OOxM

Nash, Wallis.
  Two years in Oregon. By Wallis Nash ... New York,
D. Appleton and company, 1882.
  311 p. front., plates. 19½ᵐ.
  "Sequel to the sketch pub. three years ago ₍Oregon: there and back in
1877₎"
  "Second edition."

  1. Oregon—Descr. & trav.
  ——— copy 2   1–Rc–401

NN   0025226   DLC NcD MH–Z NcD

Nash, Wallis Gifford, 1867-1920.
  Night wish; song for voice and piano. [Words
by] Jacob Trapp. [Music by] W. Gifford Nash.
New York, G. Schirmer [c1942]
  I. Title. (Series: Vocal music)

NN   0025227   FTaSU

Nash, Wallis   Gifford, 1867-1920.
  Night wish. Song for voice and piano, by W.
Gifford Nash.   New York, G. Schirmer inc. [c1942]
  First line: Dream, my love, of lovely things.
  Words by Jacob Trapp.
——Edition for low voice.
  1. Songs, U. S.   Printed for the Music Division.
II. Song index (2).   I. Trapp, Jacob.

NN   0025228   NN

Nash, W₍allis₎ Gifford, 1867-1920.
  Night wish. Song for voice and piano.
New York, G. Schirmer, inc. c1942.
  6p. 30cm.
  High voice.

NN   0025229   OrU

Nash, Wallis Gifford, 1867-1920.
  The student's technique; modern method for
piano, by W. Gifford Nash.   Portland, Ore.
[1904]
  18 p. music. 31 cm.
  1. Piano. Instruction and study. 2. Piano.
Studies and exercises. I. Title. II. Title:
Modern method for piano.

NN   0025230   OrU

MT755.3   Nash, Wallis Gifford, 1867-1920.
N 178   Technique, theory and memorizing;
          modern method for piano students. Rev.ed.
          Bozeman, Mont.,W.G.Nash, 1918.
          33p. 30cm.

NN   0025231   OrU

Nash, Walter, 1882-
  ... The Australian-New Zealand agreement;address ... at a meeting of the
Study committees of the Empire parliamentary association, held at the House of
Commons, Westminster, on 29th February,
1944; the Rt. Hon. C.R. Attlee ... in the
chair.   Lond.Empire parliamentary assoc.
1944.
  0.

NN   0025232   CaBViP

Nash, Walter, 1882-

Canadian institute of international affairs.
  ... Canada and the United nations; report of the proceedings
of the fifth ₍i. e. ninth₎ annual conference of the Canadian institute of international affairs. Toronto, May 23–24, 1942.
By W. E. C. Harrison and A. N. Reid, with an address by
the Hon. Walter Nash ... Toronto, The Ryerson press ₍1942₎

HB   Nash, Walter, 1882-
236   Guaranteed prices — a successful reality,
N58   by the Hon. Walter Nash, Minister of Marketing.
N28   [Wellington, N.Z., Standard Press, 1938]
HRC   [12]p. tables. 25cm.
GRA
          Cover title.

          1. Price regulation - New Zealand. I. Title.

NN   0025234   TxU

VOLUME 405

HB 236 N58 N27 HRC GRA

Nash, Walter, 1882-
Guaranteed prices, why and how, by Walter Nash, M.P. [Wellington, N.Z.] Standard Print [1935]
24p. 22cm.

Author's stamped copy.
Cover title.

1. Price regulation - New Zealand. I. Title. A.F.: Nash, Walter, 1882-

NN   0025235   TxU NcD

HF 1629 N3 HRC GRA

Nash, Walter, 1882-
Import control regulations; questions to and answers by, the Minister of Customs and Finance, W. Nash, and subsequent statements issued by the Conference. Wellington, Importers' National Conference, 1939.
28p. 25cm.

Cover title.

1. Import quotas - New Zealand. I. Importers National Conference.

NN   0025236   TxU

Nash, Walter, 1882-
... International and inter-empire problems from a New Zealand standpoint; address ... Lond. Empire parliamentary assoc. 1939?
O.

NN   0025237   CaBViP

HJ1774 N3

Nash, Walter, 1882-
Nash replies to the critics. [Wellington?] New Zealand Labour Party [194-?]
28p. 21cm.

Cover title.

1. World War, 1939-1945 - Finance - New Zealand. I. Title. S Australiana

NN   0025238   PSt

HJ 1774 N37 HRC GRA

Nash, Walter, 1882-
Nash replies to the critics. [Wellington, New Zealand, New Zealand Labour Party, 1940]
31p. 20cm.

Ms. notes.

1. Finance, Public - New Zealand. I. Labour Party (New Zealand). II. Title.

NN   0025239   TxU

Nash, Walter, 1882-
New Zealand, a working democracy, by Walter Nash, with an introduction by Eric Estorick. New York, Duell, Sloan and Pearce [1943]
ix, 385 p. illus. (map) 21cm.

1. New Zealand. 2. World war, 1939-   —New Zealand. 3. World war, 1939-   —Peace.
Library of Congress   D742.N4N3   43-17694

WaSpG WaTC KEmT TxU PSt ScU
WaPS MtBC Wa OrU OrSaW OrPR OrP WaE WaS WaT
ViU OClW OClW OU CaBVa CaBViP CaBVaU Or OrCS
NN   0025240   DLC NcD NcC PPT PSC PPD OO MiHM

Nash, Walter, 1882-
New Zealand, a working democracy, by Walter Nash. London, J. M. Dent & sons ltd. [1944]
vii, [2], 290 p. front. (port.) illus. (map) 22cm.
"First published in Great Britain, 1944."

1. New Zealand. 2. World war, 1939-   —New Zealand. 3. World war, 1939-   —Peace.
                                                        44-47820
Library of Congress   D742.N4N3 1944
                         [5]   940.53931

NN   0025241   DLC CSt-H FU NIC CaBVaU

D 742 N4 N3 1944a HRC GRA

Nash, Walter, 1882-
New Zealand, a working democracy, by Walter Nash. Melbourne, George Jabor [etc., etc., 1944, c1943]
310p.

1. New Zealand. 2. World war, 1939-   - New Zealand. 3. World war, 1939-   - Peace.

NN   0025242   TxU

940.93931 N178n 1944r

NASH, WALTER, 1882-
New Zealand, a working democracy, by Walter Nash. London, J.M. Dent & sons ltd. [1945]
vii, [2], 290p. front. (port.) illus. (map) 22cm.

"First published in Great Britain, 1944. Reprinted 1945."

1. New Zealand. 2. World war, 1939-1945 - New Zealand. 3. World war, 1939-1945 - Peace.

NN   0025243   TxU

Nash, Walter, 1882-
New Zealand's experience with land-value taxation and how that nation is planning for improved public and private housing in the post-war years, by the Honorable Walter Nash, minister of New Zealand to the United States. An address before a joint meeting held in New York on January 23, 1943, by the American institute of planners and the Citizens' housing council of New York. [New York, Citizens' housing council of New York, incorporated, 1943]
22 p., 1 l. 23cm.

1. Land—Taxation—New Zealand. I. Citizens' housing council of New York.
                                                      43-17938
Library of Congress   HJ4444.N3
                         [6]   336.226

NN   0025244   DLC MB NN IU OU DNAL CaBViP

336.211 (931) N18

Nash, Walter, 1882-
New Zealand's experience with land-value taxation and how that Nation is planning for improved public and private housing in the post-war years, by the Minister of New Zealand to the United States. Washington, New Zealand Legation, 1943.
22p.

An address before a Joint Meeting held in New York on Jan. 23, 1943 by the American Institute of Planners and the Citizens' Housing Council of New York.

1. Real property - Taxation - New Zealand.
2. Land economics. 3. Housing - New Zealand.
I. American Institute of Planners.
II. Citizens' Housing Council of New York.

NN   0025246   DHUD

Nash, Walter, 1882-
Postwar planning for peace and full employment
    see under Laidler, Harry Wellington, 1884-

Nash, Walter, 1882-
Social progress in New Zealand, by the Hon. Walter Nash, M.P. London, The Labour party [1944]
18, [2] p. illus. (port.) 21½cm.

1. New Zealand—Soc. condit. 2. Veterans—New Zealand. 3. Labor party (New Zealand) I. Labor party (Gt. Brit.) II. Title.
                                                      45-18485
Library of Congress   HN866.N3
                         [3]   309.1931

NN   0025248   DLC CtY NNC NN

Nash, Walter, 1882-
... The South Pacific and world affairs ... Lond. Empire parliamentary assoc. 1946.
26 p. nar. O.

NN   0025249   CaBViP

Nash, Walter H
Reverie. G. Schirmer. c1928.
9 p.

Organ.

NN   0025250   OrP

---

891 .A6 rev. no. 1749 a

Nash, Walter Howard, 1896-   joint author.
[Ashby, Wallace] 1890-   FOR OTHER EDITIONS SEE MAIN ENTRY
Modernizing farmhouses ... [Washington, U. S. Govt. print. off., 1944]

Zn48 118

Nash, Walter L
An account of the English coins of Charles I., preceded by a sketch of the early history of the English mint. [Reading, E.J. and F.Blackwell, printers, pref. 1881]
58, [1]p. plates. 23cm.

NN   0025252   CtY

Nash, Walter L.

Reading, Eng. St. Giles (*Parish*)
The church-wardens' account book for the parish of St. Giles, Reading. Transcribed from the manuscript by W. L. Nash. Part I (1518-46) Containing the accounts for the last twenty-nine years of the reign of King Henry the Eighth. [Reading, Eng., 1881]

Nash, Walter Llewellyn.
Ancient Egyptian draughts-boards and draughts-men. [London, 1902]
341-348 p. pl.

NN   0025254   OCl

913.32 N178g

Nash, Walter Llewellyn.
A general index to the Archaeological reports, Vols. I-XVIII, 1890-1-1908-9. London, Egypt Exploration Fund [1910?]
99p.

1. Egypt—Antiq.—Period. 2. Archaeological reports—Indexes. I. Egypt Exploration Society.

NN   0025255   TxFTC

VOLUME 405

Nash, Walter Llewellyn.
A general index to the Archaeological reports, vol. I-XVIII
see also Egypt Exploration Society. Archaeological reports 1890/1-1912/13 A general index.

Nash, W[alter] Llewellyn.
A general index to the Transactions of the Society of Biblical archaeology
see in Society of Biblical Archaeology, London.
Transactions.

Nash, Walter Llewellyn.
...The totemic origin of the Egyptian gods, by W. L. Nash... [London] Privately printed, 1918. 12 p. 3 pl. 22cm. (The "Scarab club" papers. 3.)

1. Totemism—Egypt. 2. Religion —Egypt.
N. Y. P. L. April 3, 1942

NN 0025258 NN PU-Mu OCl

Nash, Willard Glover.
... A century of gossip: or, The real and the seeming. By Willard G. Nash. Chicago, W. B. Keen, Cooke & co., 1876.
334 p. front., plates. 19ᵐ.
At head of title: New England life.

I. Title.
7—25796

Library of Congress PZ3.N178C

NN 0025259 DLC CoU ICU OFH MB

MICROFILM
F 5200 Nash, Willard Glover
A century of gossip; or, The real and the seeming. By Willard G. Nash. Chicago, W. B. Keen, Cook & Co., 1876.
334 p. illus. (Wright American fiction, v.III, 1876-1900, no.3936, Research Publications, Inc. Microfilm, Reel N-1)

At head of title: New England life.

NN 0025260 NNC CU

Nash, Willard Glover. 1806.7
New England life. A century of gossip; or, the real and the seeming. Chicago. Keen, Cooke & Co. 1876. Illus. 16°.

△1260 — New England. Hist. Fict

NN 0025261 MB PPL

Nash, Willard Lee, 1898-
A study of the stated aims and purposes of the departments of military science and tactics, and of physical education in the land-grant colleges of the United States, by Willard Lee Nash ... New York city, Teachers college, Columbia university, 1934.
3 p. l., 129 p., 1 l. 22½ᵐ.
Thesis (PH. D.)—Columbia university, 1934.
Vita.
Published also as Teachers college, Columbia university, Contributions to education, no. 614.
Bibliography: p. 109-114.
1. Military education—U. S. 2. Physical education and training—U. S. 3. Universities and colleges—U. S.—Curricula. 4. Agricultural colleges—U. S. I. Title: Military science and tactics, and ... physical education in the land-grant colleges of the United States. II. Title: The lan... grant colleges of the United States.
Library of Congress U429.A1N3 1934 34-34064
Columbia Univ. Libr. [2] 355.071173

OCU OC1W OO DNW DHEW MB ViU CLSU DLC
NN 0025262 NNC OrCS MtU OrU PU-Penn PSC PPT OCl

355.07 W17m
Nash, Willard Lee, 1898-
A study of the stated aims and purposes of the departments of military science and tactics and physical education in the land-grant colleges of the United States, by Willard L. Nash ... New York city, Teachers college, Columbia university, 1934.
3 p. l., 129 p. 23½ᵐ. (Teachers college, Columbia university. Contributions to education, no. 614)
Issued also as thesis (PH. D.) Columbia university.
Bibliography: p. 109-114.
1. Military education—U. S. 2. Physical education and training—U. S. 3. Universities and colleges—U. S.—Curricula. 4. Agricultural colleges—U. S. I. Title: Military science and tactics and physical education in the land-grant colleges of the United States. II. Title: The land-grant colleges of the United States.
Library of Congress U429.A1N3 1934 a 34-34063
——— Copy 2. LB5.C8 no. 614
Copyright A 77007 [19] 355.071173

NN 0025263 DLC PSt DAU NcU CU KEmT

Nash, William.
I have song of war for knight. Words from Rokeby, by Sir Walter Scott. New York, M. Bancroft [1829?]
[8] p. 34 cm.
Caption title.
For voice and piano.

1. Songs (Medium voice) with piano. I. Title.
M1.A13N M 60–1850

NN 0025264 DLC

Nash, William.
My native vale; a song. Boston, J. L. Hewitt [182-]
[2] l. 34 cm.
Caption title.

1. Songs (High voice) with piano. I. Title.
M1.A13N M 60–2497

NN 0025265 DLC

Nash, William, comp.
Sacred harmony; or, Elegant extracts of sacred music; being a collection of the most approved chants, arranged in regular order, for the full Episcopal church service ... also, a selection of the most beautiful psalm and hymn tunes ... The whole arranged for the organ or pianoforte. Cincinnati, 1836.
24 x 28 cm.

NN 0025266 CtY

Nash, William Alexander, 1840-1922.
Address of William A. Nash ... Address of Alfred H. Curtis ... Recommendations of Hon. Fred[eric]k D. Kilburn ... [On banking. New York, 1906]
12 l. 12°.

NN 0025267 NN

Nash, William Alexander, 1840-1922.
Credit and currency for an emergency, by William A. Nash ... New York [1910?]
cover-title, 8 p. 23ᵐ.

1. Banks and banking—U. S. 2. Clearing-house—U. S. 3. Currency question—U. S.—1901-
Library of Congress HG538.N3 11—7937

NN 0025268 DLC

Nash, William Alexander, 1840-1922.
The currency problem and the present financial situation; a series of addresses delivered at Columbia university, 1907-1908. New York, The Columbia university press, 1908.

Nash, William A[lexander], 1840-1922.
The New York Clearing House. New York, Columbia University Press, 1908.
1 p.l., p. 91-94. 8°.
Repr.: "The currency problem and the present financial situation".

NN 0025270 NN OO

Nash, William A[lexander], 1840-1922.
Practical suggestions versus financial theories. Delivered before the sub-committee of the Committee on Banking and Currency, House of Representatives, January 16, 1913. n. p., 1913. 8 p. 8°.

Title from cover.

1. Clearing houses, U. S.
N. Y. P. L. February 20, 1914.

NN 0025271 NN MiU

Nash, William Arthur, 1922-
Bending of an elliptical plate by edge loading. Ann Arbor, University Microfilms, 1948 [i. e. 1949]
([University Microfilms, Ann Arbor, Mich.] Publication no. 1174)
Microfilm copy of typewritten ms. Positive.
Collation of the original: v, 60 l. diagrs.
Thesis—University of Michigan.
Abstracted in Microfilm abstracts, v. 9 (1949) no. 2, p. 90-91.
Bibliography: leaf 60.
1. Elastic plates and shells. 2. Strains and stresses. I. Title.
Microfilm AC–1 no. 1174 Mic A 48–383*

Michigan. Univ. Libr.
for Library of Congress [2]†

NN 0025272 MiU DLC

Nash, William Arthur, 1922-
Bibliography on shells and shell-like structures. Washington, U. S. Navy Dept., David Taylor Model Basin, 1954.
xii, 63 p. 27 cm. (TMB report 863)

1. Elastic plates and shells—Bibl. (Series: U. S. David W. Taylor Model Basin, Carderock, Md. Report 863)
Z5851.N3 016.62011282 56–61171

NN 0025273 DLC CLU CSt CaBVaU WaS AAP KU

016.6208023 N253 suppl.
Nash, William Arthur, 1922-
Bibliography on shells and shell-like structures. Washington, U.S. Navy Dept., David Taylor Model Basin, 1954.
xii, 63 p. 27. (TMB Report 863)
"The listing is believed to be current through December 1953."
—[Supplement] (1954-1956)
Gainesville, Fla., Dept. of Engineering Mechanics Engineering and Industrial Experiment Station, University of Florida, 1957-
v. 27.
1.Elastic plate s and shells - Bibl.

NN 0025274 CSt

TA1 .F63 no.107– 108 1955
Nash, William Arthur, 1922-
General instability of ring-reinforced cylindrical shells subject to hydrostatic pressure. Effect of large deflections and initial imperfections on the buckling of cylindrical shells subject to hydrostatic pressure. Gainesville, Florida Engineering and Industrial Experiment Station, 1955.
[16] p. diagrs. 28cm. (Florida. University. Engineering and Industrial Experiment Station. Technical paper ser ies, no. 107-108).

Engineering progress at the University of Florida, v. 9, no. 5.
"Reprinted from the Proceedings of the second U. S. National Congress of Applied Mechanics."
Includes bibliographies.

1. Strains and stresses. I. Ser. II. Ser. III. Florida. University, Gainesville. Engineering and Industrial Experiment Station.

NN 0025276 ViU

VOLUME 405

Nash, William C
On the observations of rainfall made at the Royal Observatory, Greenwich, in the years 1841 to 1879. 7 pp. 8°. [n. p., 1879, rel subseq.] [P., v. 2031.]

NN 0025277 DNLM

Nash, William Edward.
DA690 B78N3 W. E. Nash's illustrated guide to Brighton, with large and complete map of the town, and seventeen illustrations ... Brighton, Printed and pub. by W. E. Nash [1886?]

cover-title, 32 p. illus., fold. map. 21.8cm. 1|2 blue morocco.

Includes advertising.

1. Brighton, Eng.--Descr.--Guide-books. I. Title.

NN 0025278 CSmH

Nash, William Giles.
America, the true history of its discovery, by William Giles Nash ... London, G. Richards, ltd., 1924.
xiii, [2], 291, [1] p. front., illus. 24½cm.
"The argument of this case is ... that ... Alonso Sanchez of Huelva, and not Cristobal Colón, was the actual discoverer of America, as far as modern times are concerned ... and that the person who was really instrumental, after him, in enabling Cristobal Colón ... to make the voyage at all was Martin Alonso Pinzón, of Palos."—p. 4-5.
"Names of those who accompanied Cristobal Colón on the expedition which sailed ... the 3rd of August, 1492, and returned ... the 15th of March, 1493": p. 257-260.
1. Sánchez de Huelva, Alonso. 2. Colombo, Cristoforo. 3. Pinzón, Martin Alonso, 1440?-1493. 4. America — Disc. & explor. — Spanish. I. Title.
Library of Congress E109.S7N2 25-5467

CaBViP CaBVaU TxU
TxU AU MiU PPL NN MChB OKentU MtU CaBViPA OrCS CU
NN 0025279 DLC CLSU CSt KMK FTaSU OCl MB FMU NIC

Nash, William Giles.
The Rio Tinto mine; its history and romance. By William Giles Nash ... London, Simpkin, Marshall, Hamilton, Kent & co., ltd., 1904.
xi, 235 p. front., plates. 22½cm.
"Works and authorities quoted": p. ix.

1. Rio Tinto mines. 2. Copper mines and mining—Spain.

Library, U. S. Geol. G S 6-1260

NN 0025280 DI-GS CtY OU IEN OkU IdU ICU NjP ICJ

Nash, William Gill, 1899–
The training and placement of beginning teachers in the public schools of Kentucky, for the school years 1935–36 through 1939–40 ... by William Gill Nash ... [Frankfort, Ky., 1940]
2 p. l., 727–811 p. incl. tables. 22½ cm. (*On cover:* Kentucky. Dept. of education. Educational bulletin, vol. VIII, no. 8, October, 1940)
Thesis (PH. D.)—University of Kentucky, 1940.
Bibliography: p. 809–811.
1. Teachers [Training of]—Kentucky. 2. [Teachers—Appointment—Kentucky] 3. [Teachers—Certificates—Kentucky]
L152.B35 vol. 8, no. 8 371.109769 E 40—834
——— Copy 2. LB1715.N35 1940
U. S. Office of Education. Library for Library of Congress [a58d½]†

NN 0025281 DHEW PPT OU DLC MH NcU OrCS MsSM

[**Nash,** *Mrs.* **William H**]
Cloud City cook-book. Leadville, Col., Herald Democrat steam book and job printing house, 1889.
48, [2] p. 20½cm.
Advertising interspersed.

1. Cookery, American. I. Leadville, Col. Congregational church.

Library of Congress TX715.N258 8-23705†
(Copyright 1889: 14733)

NN 0025282 DLC

Nash, William T.
How to build business; a series of leaflets designed to interest and secure prospects; encourage and retain policyholders; prevent lapsation and facilitate the work of agents, by William T. Nash ... Chicago, New York, The Spectator company, 1924.
3 p. l., 3–336 p. illus. 20cm.

1. Insurance, Life. I. Title.

Library of Congress HG8876.N25 24-7501

NN 0025283 DLC OU WaS ICJ

Nash, William T.
The monthly income policy: its advantages and how to present them, by William T. Nash ... New York, Chicago, The Spectator co. [c1912]
vi, 40 p. 16cm. $0.30

1. Insurance, Life. I. Title.

Library of Congress HG8830.N3 12-24929

NN 0025284 DLC ICJ

Nash, William T.
Multiplying your income; or, How to sell life insurance, by William T. Nash ... Chicago, New York, The Spectator company, 1914.
v, 115 p. front., illus. 18cm. $1.00

1. Insurance, Life—Agents. I. Title. II. Title: How to sell life insurance.

Library of Congress HG8876.N3 14—10318

NN 0025285 DLC MB ICJ

Nash, Winifred H., joint author.

Blankenship, Russell.
Learning activities and tests to accompany Literature we like [by] Russell Blankenship ... and Winifred H. Nash ... New York, Chicago [etc.] C. Scribner's sons [c1941]

Nash, Winifred H., joint ed.

FOR OTHER EDITIONS SEE MAIN ENTRY

Blankenship, Russell, *ed.*
... Literature we appreciate [edited by] Russell Blankenship ... Winifred H. Nash ... [and] Pauline Warner ... Illustrations by George Wright. New York, Chicago [etc.] C. Scribner's sons [c1941]

Nash, Winifred H., joint ed.

Blankenship, Russell, *ed.*
... Literature we like [edited by] Russell Blankenship ... [and] Winifred H. Nash ... illustrations by George Wright. New York. Chicago [etc.] C. Scribner's sons [c1939]

Nash-Williams, Alvah Harry, ed.
Hannibal at bay; selections from Livy XXIII-XXVI see under Livius, Titus. Selections. Latin.

Nash-Williams, Alvah Harry, ed.
Hannibal in defeat.
see under Livius, Titus. Selections. Latin.

937.04 N178h Classics Lib'y
Nash-Williams, Alvah Harry, ed.
Hannibal triumphant: selections from Nepos' Hannibal and Livy XXI-XXIII. Edited with introd., notes and vocabulary. London, Macmillan, 1946.
xxvii, 123p. illus. 18cm. (Modern school classics)

1. Latin literature - Chrestomathies and readers. 2. Punic war, 2d, 218-201 B.C. I. Title. I. Nepos, Cornelius

NN 0025291 TxU

PA 258 N25
Nash-Williams, Alvah Harry
Introduction to continuous Greek prose composition, by A. H. Nash-Williams. London, Macmillan; New York, St. Martin's Press [1948]
vii, iii p. 18cm.

1. Greek language--Composition and exercises I. Title: Continuous Greek prose composition.

NN 0025292 NIC IU WaU LU CU

Nash-Williams, Alvah Harry
Introduction to continuous Greek prose composition. London, Macmillan, 1955.
111p. 18cm.
"First edition 1948"

1. Greek language - composition and exercises
PA258.N3I6

NN 0025293 KAS

488.2 N178i
Nash-Williams, Alvah Harry.
Introduction to continuous Greek prose composition. London, Macmillan; New York, St. Martin's Press, 1955.
vii, 111p. 18cm.

"First edition 1948."

1. Greek language - Composition and exercises. I. Title. II. Title: Continuous Greek prose composition.

NN 0025294 TxU

Nash-Williams, Victor Erle, 1897-
Catalogue of the Roman inscribed and sculptured stones found at Caerleon, Monmouthshire, by V.E.Nash-Williams and A.H.Nash-Williams. Cardiff, Pub.by the National Museum of Wales and by the Press Board of the University of Wales, 1935

At head of title: Amgueddfa Genedlaethol Cymru. National Museum of Wales

NN 0025295 MH

Nash-Williams, Victor Erle, 1897-
...The Roman legionary fortress at Caerleon in Monmouthshire... [no. 2- Cardiff: National Museum of Wales and Press Board of the Univ. of Wales, 1930- v. in illus., plans, tables. 24cm.

"Exploration...inaugurated by the National Museum of Wales in 1926, and since continued by [the] Caerleon Excavation Committee, acting in conjunction with the National Museum."—*Pref.* [no. 2]

1. Great Britain—Archæology—Roman remains. 2. Caerleon, Eng.—Archæology. 3. Pottery, Roman. I. Caerleon Excavation Committee. II. Title.
N. Y. P. L. April 26, 1937

Reprinted from Archæologia Cambrensis, 1929-19
[No. 1] The amphitheatre, by R. E. M. Wheeler and Mrs. Wheeler, was issued in Archæologia, v. 78, p. 111-218.
CONTENTS.—[no. 2] Report on the excavations carried out in Jenkins's field in 1926. By V. E. Nash-Williams.—[no. 3] Report on...the Prysg field, 1927-9. By V. E. Nash-Williams.—
[no. 5] Report on...the eastern corner in 1929. By Christopher Hawkes.—
[no. 7] Report on...the Town Hall field in 1930. By W. F. Grimes.

NN 0025297 NN

VOLUME 405

DA690
C12N54   Nash-Williams, Victor Erle, 1897-
     The Roman legionary fortress at Caerleon
in Monmouthshire; report on the excavations
carried out in the Prysg Field, 1927-9.
Cardiff, Published by the National museum
of Wales and by the Press Board of the
University of Wales, 1931-33.
     3 pts. in 1 v.   illus., plans (part fold.)

     At head of title: Amgueddfa genedlaethol
Cymru. National museum of Wales.

NN   0025298   CU NjP

     Nash-Williams, Victor Erle, 1897-
     The early Christian monuments of Wales. Cardiff, University of Wales Press, 1950.
     xxiii, 258 p. illus., 71 plates, maps. 30 cm.
     "Published on behalf of the National Museum of Wales and the Board of Celtic Studies of the University of Wales."
     Bibliography: p. [xxi]-xxiii.

     1. Monuments—Wales. 2. Wales—Antiq. 3. Christian art and symbolism. I. Title.

     NB1593.N3   731.76   51-17929

     DDO MB MH NIC CU CaBVaU CaOTP OOxM
NN   0025299   DLC CLU GU IaU ScU ICU NcD CtY NjPT

Nash-Williams, Victor Erle, *1897–*   Per. Room *3311.1.80
   Further excavations at Caerwent, Monmouthshire, 1923-5.
— (*In* Society of Antiquaries, London. Archaeologia. Vol. 80, pp.
229–288. Illus. Plates. Plans. Oxford. 1930.)

D1720 — Monmouthshire, England. Antiq. — Roman antiquities in Great Britain.

NN   0025300   MB

     Nash-Williams, Victor Erle, 1897–
     The Roman frontier in Wales. Cardiff, University of Wales Press, 1954.
     xviii, 161 p. illus., maps (1 fold. col.) plans. 26 cm.
     "Published on behalf of the Board of Celtic Studies of the University of Wales."
     "Early documentary authorities relating to Roman Wales": p. [144]-146. Bibliographical footnotes.

     1. Wales—Hist.—To 1536. 2. Wales—Antiq. I. Title.

     DA715.N37   942.9   55-25849

     NNC CU IU ViU TU OCU PBm TxU
NN   0025301   DLC OrU OU NcD ODW IEN NN CtY MH ICU

877.17
N178

     Nash-Williams, Victor Erle, 1897-
     The Roman inscribed and sculptured stones found at Caerwent (Venta Silurum) With notes on Mars-Lenus-Ocelus and the Caerwent temple. Cardiff, Published by the University of Wales Press and the National Museum of Wales [1954]
     cover-title, 18 p. illus., plates, plans (1 fold.)
     "Reprinted from the Bulletin of the Board of Celtic Studies, vol. XV, part I, pages 81-98." Bibliography: p. 17-18.

NN   0025302   NNC

DA147
.C2N3   Nash-Williams, Victor Erle, 1897-
     ... The Roman legionary fortress at Caerleon in Monmouthshire; report on the excavations carried out in the Prysg field, 1927-9 ... by V.E. Nash-Williams ... [Cardiff, The National museum of Wales and the Press board of the University of Wales 193
     v. illus., fold. tab. 24.5 cm. S.
     At head of title: Amgueddfa genedlaethol Cymru. National museum of wales.

NN   0025303   DLC DSI

Nash-Williams, Victor Erle, 1897-
     ... The Roman legionary fortress at Caerleon, Monmouthshire, by V. E. Nash-Williams ... Cardiff, National museum of Wales, 1940.
     33 p., 1 l. front., illus., XIV pl., 3 fold. maps. 24½ cm.

     At head of title: Amgueddfa genedlaethol cymru. National museum of Wales.
     Maps in pocket on inside of back cover.

     CU CtY
NN   0025304   NNC MoU IU ICU RPB MiU OU OO OClW OCU

     Nash-Williams, Victor Erle, 1897-
     The Roman legionary fortress at Caerleon, Monmouthshire. [2d ed.] Cardiff, National Museum of Wales, 1946.
     33 p. illus., 3 fold. maps (in pocket) 25 cm.
     At head of title: National Museum of Wales.

     1. Caerleon, Eng.—Antiq. 2. Gt. Brit.—Antiquities, Roman.
     I. Cardiff, Wales. National Museum of Wales. II. Title.

     DA147.C2N32   913.4243   49-42909*

NN   0025305   DLC NcU

Byz
C12
940Nc   Nash-Williams, Victor Erle, 189[?-
     The Roman legionary fortress at Caerleon, Monmouthshire.   Cardiff, National Museum of Wales, 1952.
     33 p. illus., 3 fold. maps (in pocket) 25 cm.
     At head of title: National Museum of Wales.

NN   0025306   CtY

Nash and Kollock School, Hillsboro, N.C.
     Soiree musicale
     Hillsboro, 18-
     D.
     Library has:
     June 10. 1891.

NN   0025307   NcD

NASH & SWEET
     Reduction sale, registered Jerseys ... June 12, 1946.   Author, 1946.
     72 p. illus.

NN   0025308   Or

R   Nash airflyte magazine. Detroit, Nash Motors Division of Nash-Kelvinator Corporation.
     Library has
     v.1–   Early Fall 1949–
     Issued ten times a year.
     1. Automobiles – Period. I. Nash-Kelvinator Corporation. Detroit. Nash Motors Division

NN   0025309   MiD

Nash county, N.C. Board of education.
     Rocky Mount, [1927?]
     Nash county teachers handbook, 1927-1938.

NN   0025311   NcU

Nash Co., N.C. Treasurer.
     Statement for Nash County. [Nashville, 19-   ]
     v. D.
     Library has:
     1920/21,
     Annual.
     Report year ends December 1st
     Includes Report of the Clerk of the Superior Court.

NN   0025312   NcU

Nash directory service...Ravenna-Kent directory ...1936-37- Cleveland Heights, O., Nash directory service.

NN   0025313   OCl

Nash engineering company.
     Vicario, Carlo.
     Priming centrifugal pumps aboard ship, a manual compiled by Carlo Vicario ... South Norwalk, Conn., Nash engineering company [1942]

Nash engineering company.
     Compressors, ejectors, pumps. [South, Norwalk, Conn., Nash engineering co., 1927-40]
     23 v. in 1. illus. (part col.) tables, diagrs. 28 cm.
     Binder's title.
     1. Air-compressors. 2. Pumping machinery.

NN   0025315   CU

Nash engineering company
     Pump installation [and] operation. [South Norwalk, Conn., Nash engineering co., 1926-39]
     22 v. in 1. illus., diagrs. 23 cm.
     Binder's title.
     1. Pumping machinery.

NN   0025316   CU

(Nash holos)
     Наш голос. Our voice.
     Trenton, Асоціяцїя українцїв Америки.
     v. 22 cm. monthly (irregular).
     Continues Бюлетень of Asotsiåtsiå ukraïntsiv v Amerytsi. In Ukrainian.

     1. Ukrainians in the United States—Periodicals. I. Asotsiåtsiå ukraïntsiv v Amerytsi. II. Title: Our voice.

     E184.U5N35   73-640967

NN   0025317   DLC

Nash Jezik
     see under   Lingvističko društvo, Belgrad.

The Nash journal. v. 1; Dec. 6, 1926-Nov. 28, 1927. [Cincinnati, The Nash publishing company, 1926-27.
     1 v. illus. 30½ cm. weekly.
     Arthur Nash, editor.
     No more published.

     I. Nash, Arthur, 1870-1927, ed.

     Library of Congress   AP2.N3   28-8208

NN   0025319   DLC NN

Nash junior college
     Annalis; annual of Nash junior college. c1934.
     1 v.
     Nash jr. coll. later became part of Fenn College.

NN   0025320   OFH

VOLUME 405

Nash-Kelvinator Corporation
see also
American Motors Corporation.
Nash Motors Company, *Kenosha, Wis.*

NASH-KELVINATOR CORPORATION.
Annual report. 1917-53. [Detroit.] etc.   37 no. in 2 v.
tables. 21-28cm.

Report year for 1917-36 ends Nov. 30; for 1937-53, Sept. 30.
Reports for 1917-36 issued by the company under its earlier name, the
Nash motors company.
Reports for 1917-18 lack title.
In 1954, the Nash-Kelvinator company merged with the Hudson motor
company to form the American   motors corporation. For later
years, see: American motors   corporation. Report.

NN 0025322   NN

Nash-Kelvinator Corporation.
Annual report to stockholders.
₍Detroit₎
    v. illus. 23-28 cm.

Title varies slightly.

HD9710.U54N33   49-21516*‡

NN 0025323   DLC

₍Nash-Kelvinator corporation₎
    The national salesmen's crusade. ₍n.p.,
1939₎
    17 numb.ℓ.

Manifold copy.

NN 0025324   MH-BA

621.56
N178sTS
Engin   NASH-KELVINATOR CORPORATION.
Lib'y   Curso simplificado de preparacion para mecanicos de servicio de refrigeradores. Detroit
          ₍c1947₎
          5pℓ.,236p. illus. 28cm.

    "Primera edicion espanola, 1947."
    English edition has title: Simplified training course for refrigerator servicemen.

    1. Refrigeration and refrigerating machinery.

NN 0025325   TxU OC1 NN MiD

Nash-Kelvinator corporation.
    Simplified training course for refrigerator servicemen. Detroit, Nash-Kelvinator corporation ₍1942₎
    2 p. L., 236 p. incl. illus., tables, diagrs. 20½ᵐ.
                               TP492.N24
    —— —— Instructor's manual. Detroit, Nash-Kelvinator
corporation ₍1942₎
    2 p. L., 48 p. 20½ᵐ.

    1. Refrigeration and refrigerating machinery.   I. Title.
                                         42-51956
Library of Congress   TP492.N24 Manual
                               ₍3₎   621.56

NN 0025326   DLC WaS

ＨＥＡＵ   Nash-Kelvinator Corporation.
+ＮＡ   Souvenir, Citizen's banquet commemorating
          Nash Motors Golden Anniversary, April 3,
          1952. Kenosha, Wis. [1952]
          70 p.   illus.   28 cm.

    Cover title.
    "Great cars for fifty years, golden anniersary, 1902-1952."

    1. Wisconsin - Industries.

NN 0025327   WHi

Nash-Kelvinator Corporation. Kelvinator Division.
    Displaying appliances of tomorrow. ₍Detroit,
Kelvinator division of Nash-Kelvinator corporation
n.d.₎
    28 p.   illus. (part col.) blue prints.
49.5 x 65.5 cm.

NN 0025328   Mi OrP

Nash-Kelvinator corporation - Kelvinator division
    Displaying appliances of Tomorrow... ₍Detroit...
1945?₎.
    28, XII (i.e. XI) ₍1₎ p. col. illus.

NN 0025329   OC1

Nash-Kelvinator Corporation. Nash Motors
Division.
    Nash airflyte magazine
        see under title

Nash-Kelvinator corporation. Nash Motors Division.
    Nash family album; a pictorial roll call of the
passenger cars manufactured by Nash motors and its
predecessor companies since 1902. [Detroit, Nash
motors, 1951] 60 p. illus. 28cm.

1. Automobiles—Type—   Nash. 2. Automobiles—
Type—Rambler.   3. *Automobiles - Type—*
Jeffery. I. Title.

NN 0025331   NN MB

Nash-Kelvinator Corporation, Detroit. Nash
Motors Division
    Nash Motors Division dealers standard accounting system manual. Rev. June, 1950. Celina,
Ohio, Reynolds & Reynolds, 1950, ᶜ1938.
    1 v. (loose-leaf) forms.

NN 0025332   MiD

Nash-Kelvinator Corporation. *Nash Motors Div.*
    Nash technical handbook. ₍Milwaukee, Wis.,
Nash Motors, Div. ₍of₎ Nash-Kelvinator Corp.
₍1942?₎
    ii,115 p. illus.,diagrs.

    Cover-title.
    "A supplement to the Nash technical manual
and contains specifications, wiring diagrams,
frame charts and drawings, applicable to Nash
cars built from 1937 through 1942."

NN 0025333   CU

Nash-Kelvinator Corporation. Nash Motors
Division.
    Nash technical handbook. [Milwaukee, Wis.?
1945?]
    113 p. illus. 22cm.
    Cover title.
    A supplement to the Nash technical manual,
applicable to Nash cars built from 1937 through
1942.

    1. Nash automobile. 2. Automobiles—Handbooks,
manuals, etc.

NN 0025334   MB

Nash-Kelvinator Corporation. Nash Motors.
    Nash technical handbook. Milwaukee, Wis.
[1946-47]
    3 v. in 1. illus. 21cm. (Nash craftsman
service)
    Vol. 3 has imprint: Detroit, Mich.
    CONTENTS.—[v.1] Tune-up.—[v.2] Body repair.
—[v.3] Wheel alignment.

    1. Nash automobile. 2. Automobiles—Handbooks, manuals, etc.

NN 0025335   MB

TL215   Nash-Kelvinator Corporation. *Nash Motors Div.*
N3A37   Nash technical handbook on tune-up.
          Milwaukee, Wis., Nash Motors, Div. of Nash-
          Kelvinator Corp. ₍1946?₎
          66 p. illus.,diagrs.

    1. Automobiles - Handbooks, manuals, etc.
    2. Nash automobile. I. Title.

NN 0025336   CU

TL215   Nash-Kelvinator Corporation. *Nash Motors Div.*
N3A38   Nash technical handbook on wheel alignment.
          Detroit, Mich., Nash Motors, Div. of Nash-
          Kelvinator Corp. ₍1947?₎
          111 p. illus.,diagrs.

    1. Automobiles - Handbooks, manuals, etc.
    2. Nash automobile. 3. Automobiles - Wheels.
    I. Title.

NN 0025337   CU OC1

TL215   Nash-Kelvinator Corporation. Nash Motors Di
.N2   vision.
N2   Nash technical service manual.
19
          Detroit, 19
              v. illus. 28cm.

    Title change: 1941-48, Nash technical
manual.- 1949-   , Nash technical service
manual.

    1.Automobiles - Handbooks, manuals, etc. 2.
Automobiles -   Maintenance and repair.
3.Nash automobi   le. I.Title.
                               G-1773

NN 0025338   OrCS OC1 OrP

Nash-Kelvinator Corporation. Nash Motors Div. Ｔ2
                                                709
Nash technical service manual. 19 -1957. Detroit,
    Nash-Kelvinator Corporation, 1950-57.
    8 v. in 6. illus.
    Crerar has 1950-1957.
    Includes supplements.

    I. Nash-Kelvinator Corporation, Detroit.
629.287051 629.2886105

NN 0025339   ICJ

Nash-Kelvinator Corporation. Nash Motors Division.
    ₍Nash₎.Technical service manuals.

    Library has
1940/41;
1940 ₍pt.1₎; 1941 ₍pt.2-3₎; 1942 ₍pt.3₎

NN 0025340   MiD

NASH-KELVINATOR CORPORATION. Temperature research
    foundation, New York.
    Yesterday and today in refrigeration. New York:
Temperature research foundation of Nash-Kelvinator
corporation [1938?] 13 p. incl. diagr. 23cm.

    1. Refrigeration and cold storage—Hist.

NN 0025341   NN

M/1025   Nash-Kelvinator Corporation, New York, N.Y.
N253   Librarians stress value of air conditioning in
          preserving books. Indicate importance of humidity
          and temperature control in survey conducted by the
          Temperature research foundation. New York,
          [n.d.]
          6 p. 30.5 cm.
          [Typewritten]

NN 0025342   DAS

VOLUME 405

DK651 Nash Krai.
.A7A2

Наш край. г. 1-
1922-
Астрахань.
v. illus., maps (part fold.) 26 cm
Frequency varies.
Organ of Astrakhanskoe ėkonomicheskoe soveshchanie,
1922- (with Astrakhanskaia gubernskaia planovaia komissiia,
19- of Astrakhanskaia gubernskaia planovaia komissiia, 19-
Aug. 1928; of Astrakhanskaia okruzhnaia planovaia komissiia, Sept.
1928-

1. Astrakhan, Russia (Government)—Econ. condit.—Period. I.
Astrakhan, Russia (Government) Gubernskoe ėkonomicheskoe soveshchanie. II. Astrakhan, Russia (Government) Gubernskaia planovaia komissiia. III. Astrakhan, Russia (District) Okruzhnaia planovaia komissiia. *Title transliterated:* Nash krai.

DK651.A7A2
51-35397

NN 0025343 DLC

Nash kraĭ (Minsk)
see Savetskaia kraina.

Nash Motors Company, *Kenosha, Wis.*
see also
Nash-Kelvinator Corporation.

Nash Motors Company, *Kenosha, Wis*
Annual report.

[Kenosha, Wis.,]
nos. tables. 4°.

1. Automobiles—Companies.
N. Y. P. L. June 29, 1927

NN 0025346 NN

338.7 Nash motors company, Kenosha, Wis.
N172 Annual report of the Nash motors company (Maryland corporation) fiscal year ended November 30
[1917-]1936. [Kenosha, 1918-37]
20v. illus.

Title varies: 1916/17-1917/18, The Nash motor
company.
Other slight variations in title.
On Jan. 4, 1937 merged with the Kelvinator corporation to form the Nash-Kelvinator corporation.

NN 0025347 IU

NASH MOTORS COMPANY, *Kenosha, Wis.*
In memoriam, James Jackson Storrow.

Broadside. 20 3/4 x 14 1/4 inches. Port.
Engraved by Tiffany & Co., New York.

NN 0025348 MH

Nash motors company, Kenosha, Wis.
Instruction book, Nash one-ton truck, model
2018 and Nash two-ton truck, model 3018... n.d.
149 p. illus. diagrs.

Includes Price list of parts, p. 74-149.

NN 0025349 MiD

Nash motors company, Kenosha, Wis.
Instruction book, Nash quad, model 4017.
n. d.
213 p. illus. diagrs.

Includes Price list of parts, p. 77-213.

NN 0025350 MiD

Nash motors company, *Kenosha, Wis.*
Instruction book, Nash Quad ... model 4017A, Ordnance department, U. S. army ... Kenosha, Wis., The
Nash motors company [1918?]
66 p. illus. (incl. chart) 23cm.

1. Automobile trucks. I. Title: Nash Quad.

18-14748
Library of Congress UG683.N3

NN 0025351 DLC Or ICJ

Nash Motors Company, *Kenosha, Wis.* 4035B.112
LaFayette owner's manual. 3510 series.
[Kenosha, Wis., Nash Motors Co., 1935]
32 p. illus. 23cm.

1. LaFayette automobile. 2. Automobiles—
Repairing.

NN 0025352 MB

The Nash motors company, Kenosha, Wis.
Nash instruction book pertaining to Nash
quad, model 4017. Kenosha, Wis., Nash motors
co. n. d.
74 p., illus diagrs 23 cm.

NN 0025353 DNW

Nash Motors Company, Kenosha, Wis.
Nash technical service manual
see under Nash-Kelvinator Corporation.
Nash Motors Div.

Nash Motors Company, *Kenosha, Wis.*
Owner's manual. 1938-39, 41-42, 46-
[Kenosha, Wis.,] Nash Motors (Division of Nash-
Kelvinator Corp.) 1938-
v. in illus. 23cm.
Cover title.
Title and imprint vary slightly.
1938-39, English export ed.; 1941, 4th ed.;
1942, 2d ed.

1. Automobiles—Repairing. 2. Nash automobile.

NN 0025355 MB

[Nash motors company, Kenosha, Wis.]
Specifications, Nash automobiles (all models)
1918-1946. [The Author, 1946?]
26 ℓ.

Cover-title.

NN 0025356 MiD

(Nash opyt prigotovleniia pishchi)
Наш опыт приготовления пищи отличного качества. Москва, Гос. торговое изд-во, 1953.
50 p. illus. 20 cm.

1. Moscow—Restaurants, lunch rooms, etc.—Addresses, essays, lectures. *Title transliterated:* Nash opyt prigotovleniia pishchi otlichnogo kachestva.

TX945.N29 63-47351

NN 0025357 DLC

TN808 (Nash opyt raboty.)
R9N3 Наш опыт работы. Москва, Углетехиздат, 1953.
81 p. illus 20 cm. (Библиотечка шахтера-новатора)

1. Coal mines and mining—Russia.
Title transliterated: Nash opyt raboty.

54-23716 ‡

NN 0025358 DLC

(Nash opyt raboty po okhrane truda.)

Наш опыт работы по охране труда. [Москва] Профиздат,
1958.
47 p. 20 cm.

1. Industrial hygiene—Russia.
Title transliterated: Nash opyt raboty po okhrane truda.

TD895.N3 65-38040 ‡

NN 0025359 DLC

Нашъ остзейскій вопросъ. Leipzig, F. A. Brockhaus.
С.-Петербургъ, Р. Шмицдорфъ (К. К. Реттеръ) [188-?]
2 p. l., [3]-86 p. 24½ cm.

States.
1. Baltic provinces. 2. Germans in the Baltic states.
Title transliterated: Nash ostzeĭskiĭ vopros.

DK511.B3N23 48-40365

NN 0025360 DLC

PG3227 (Nash prazdnik.)
.N3 Наш праздник; сборник произведений для эстрады. Ленинград, "Искусство"; [etc.] 1938.
243, [1] p. 16 x 12 cm.

1. Russian literature—20th cent. *Title transliterated:* Nash prazdnik.

PG3227.N3 49-32347

NN 0025361 DLC

BX496 (Nash put')
.A1O55 Наш путь. Our way.
[Chicago]
v. in illus., ports. 27 cm. monthly (irregular)
Began publication in 1927. Cf. Union list of serials.
Issued by Tikhonovskoe pravoslavnoe russkoe obshchestvo.

1. Orthodox Eastern Church, Russian, in the U. S.—Period.
I. St. Tichon's Russian Orthodox Society, Chicago. II. Title: Our way.
Title transliterated: Nash put'.

BX496.A1O55 67-34567

NN 0025362 DLC

(Nash put')
Наш път; месечно списание. Notre route; revue mensuelle
bulgare. г. 1- 1952-
Paris [D. Naidenov]
v. in illus., ports. 27 cm.

I. Naĭdenov, Dantcho, ed.
Title transliterated: Nash pŭt.

AP58.B8N26 62-26572

NN 0025363 DLC

(Nash put')
Наш путь; журнал литературы и современной жизни. Our
way. № 1-6; ноябрь 1953-май/июнь 1954. Лос-Анжелос.
6 no. in 1 v. 28 cm.
Edited by S. Korsuneĭs.

I. Korsuneĭs, S. V., ed. II. Title: Our way.
Title transliterated: Nash put'.

AP51.N33 67-122332

NN 0025364 DLC

Nash technical service manual
see under Nash-Kelvinator Corporation.
Nash Motors Div.

VOLUME 405

PG3228
.A72N32
(Nasha ėstrada.)
Наша эстрада; репертуарный сборник для армейской и флотской художественной самодеятельности.
Москва, Воен. изд-во министерства обороны СССР, 19

    v. illus. music. 21 cm.

    1. Russian literature—20th cent.—Period.   *Title transliterated:* Nasha ėstrada.

PG3228.A72N32   67–37197

NN   0025366   DLC

(Nasha fabrichnaia marka.)
Наша фабричная марка; (сборник. Москва, Московский рабочий, 1954.
    59 p. 20 cm.

    1. Commercial products—Russia.   *Title transliterated:* Nasha fabrichnaia marka.

HF1041.N26   56–22063

NN   0025367   DLC

PG3450
.A1N3
(Nasha mat' priroda.)
Наша мать природа. Москва, Тип. Об-ва распространения полезных книгъ, 1896.
    288 p. 19 cm. (Новая книга.)

         Title transliterated: Nasha mat' priroda.

PG3450.A1N3   55–46410

NN   0025368   DLC

Наша періодическая печать (*transliterated:* Nasha periodicheskaia pechat')
    see
Алфавитный список періодических изданій Россійской Имперіи (*transliterated:* Alfavitnyĭ spisok periodicheskikh izdaniĭ Rossiĭskoĭ Imperii)

(Nasha pravda.)
Наша правда.
Львів. Комуністична партія західної України.
    v. in   22 cm. monthly.

    1. Communism—Period. 2. Communism—Ukraine.   I. Komunistychna partiia zakhidnoi Ukrainy.   *Title transliterated:* Nasha pravda.

HX8.N3   48–40379

NN   0025370   DLC

JN6583
.N3
(Nasha propagandistskaia robota.)
Наша пропагандистская работа; опыт пропагандистов комсомольских кружков Москвы. (Москва) Молодая гвардия, 1936.
    77 p. illus. 20 cm.

    1. Civics, Russian.   *Title transliterated:* Nasha propagandistskaia robota.

JN6583.N3   54–45459

NN   0025371   DLC

DK267
.N278
(Nasha rodina.)
Наша родина. Под ред. А. Стецкого, С. Ингулова и Н. Баранского. (Москва) Партиздат, 1937.
    85 p. illus. 23 cm.

    1. Russia—Soc. condit.—1917-   2. Russia—Econ. condit.—1918-   I. Stetskiĭ, Aleksei Ivanovich, ed.   II. Baranskiĭ, Nikolaĭ Nikolaevich, 1881-   ed.   *Title transliterated:* Nasha rodina.

DK267.N278   57–52911

NN   0025372   DLC ICU

AP58
.B8N28
(Nasha rodina.)
Наша родина; общественно-политическо и литературно-художествено списание.
София, Българска Комунистическа партия.
    v. in   illus., ports. 33 cm. monthly.
    Vols.   called also no.

    I. Bŭlgarska Komunisticheska partiia.   *Title transliterated:* Nasha rodina.

AP58.B8N28   60–24717

NN   0025373   DLC

AP50
.N345
(Nasha strana.)
Наша страна. Nuestro pais. año 1-   (no. 1- set. 18, 1948-
Buenos Aires.
    v. in   illus., ports. 42 cm. weekly.

         Title transliterated: Nasha strana.

AP50.N345   56–44178

NN   0025374   DLC

DK1
.N3
(Nasha strana)
Наша страна. (г. 1-5) № 7; апр. 1937-июль 1941. Москва, Известия Советов депутатов трудящихся СССР (etc.)
    5 v. illus. (part col.) ports., maps (part fold. col.) 31 cm. monthly.
    Edited by F. IA. Kon.
    No more published?
    L. C. set incomplete: v. 4, no. 1-2, v. 5, no. 2, wanting.

    1. Russia.   I. Kon, Feliks IAkovlevich, 1864-1941, ed.   *Title transliterated:* Nasha strana.

DK1.N3   51–52538

NN   0025375   DLC

Nasha strana; istoricheskii sbornik.
Наша страна; историческій сборникъ. № 1; 1907. С.-Петербургъ.
    400 p. 26 cm.
    Supersedes Былое upon its suppression in Oct. 1907.

    1. Russia—Hist.—Addresses, essays, lectures.   *Title transliterated:* Nasha strana; istoricheskiĭ sbornik.

DK188.3.N3   54–54736

NN   0025376   DLC MH

(Nasha tsel-kommunizm.)
Наша цель—коммунизм; материалы по тринадцатой теме. Москва, Правда, 1949.
    37 p. 22 cm. (В помощь слушателям политшкол)

    1. Communism—Russia.   (Series: V pomoshch' slushateliam politshkol)   *Title transliterated:* Nasha tsel'—kommunizm.

DK267.N28   50–56543

NN   0025377   DLC

DK18
.N3
(Nasha velikaia rodina.)
Наша великая родина. (В работе ... принимали участие Н. Н. Михайлов и др. Москва, Гос. изд-во полит. лит-ры, 1949.
    565 p. illus., ports. 23 cm.

    1. Russia.   *Title transliterated:* Nasha velikaia rodina.

DK18.N3   49–52322*

NN   0025378   DLC

(Nasha velikaia rodina.)
Наша великая родина. (Москва) Гос. изд-во полит. лит-ры, 1953.
    515 p. illus. 23 cm.
    By N. N. Mikhailov and others.

    1. Russia.   I. Mikhailov, Nikolai Nikolaevich, 1905-   *Title transliterated:* Nasha velikaia rodina.

DK18.N3 1953   55–16546

NN   0025379   DLC NNC ViU CaBVaU

DK18
N3
1954
(Nasha velikaia rodina.)
Наша великая родина. Изд. 2. Москва, Гос. изд-во полит. лит-ры, 1954.
    503 p. illus. 23 cm.
    By N. N. Mikhailov and others.

    1. Russia.   I. Mikhailov, Nikolai Nikolaevich, 1905-   *Title transliterated:* Nasha velikaia rodina.

DK18.N3 1954   55–28373

NN   0025380   DLC

DK18
.N3
1955
(Nasha velikaia rodina)
Наша великая родина. Изд. 3., перер. и доп. Москва, Гос. изд-во полит. лит-ры, 1955.
    495 p. illus., group port., fold. col. map (in pocket) 23 cm.
    By N. N. Mikhailov and others.

Microfilm
Slavic
785
DK
    — — — Microfilm copy (negative)
    Made in 1957 by the Library of Congress.
    1. Russia.   I. Mikhailov, Nikolai Nikolaevich, 1905-   *Title transliterated:* Nasha velikaia rodina.

DK18.N3 1955   56–41256

NN   0025381   DLC

DK18
.N32
(Nasha velyka bat'kivshchyna)   укр.
Наша велика батьківщина. (В роботі ... брали участь М. М. Михайлов и др.) Київ, Держ. вид-во політ. літ-ри УРСР, 1950.
    542 p. illus., ports. 23 cm.

    1. Russia.   *Title transliterated:* Nasha velyka bat'kivshchyna.   (I. Title: Nasha velikaia rodina.)

DK18.N32   51–24949

NN   0025382   DLC

Наша внешняя торговля (*transliterated:* Nasha vneshniaia torgovlia)
    see
Внешняя торговля (*transliterated:* Vneshniaia torgovlia)

VOLUME 405

H8
.N35
Nasha zarìà.

Нама заря. г. i–
1910–
Омскъ.

v. 25 cm. monthly.

Published 1910–17 in St. Petersburg (Petrograd) ; ceased publication in 1919? Cf. Union list of serials.

1. Social sciences—Period. *Title transliterated:* Nasha zarìà.

H8.N35 52–51242

NN 0025384 DLC InU

Nāshād, *pseud.*
see
Sen, N B

---

el-Nashar, Ali Sami
see al-Nashshār, 'Alī Sāmī.

---

al-Nashāshībī, Anwar.
من ميونخ الى وارسو، او السياسة العالمية فى عام. مجموعة
احاديث سياسية اذيعت من محطة مصلحة الاذاعة الفلسطينية،
بقلم انور النشاشيبى. القدس، المطبعة التجارية المقدمة 1939،
157 p. 19 cm.

1. World politics—1933–1945—Addresses, essays, lectures.
I. Title.
Title romanized: Min Myūnikh ilā Wārsū.

D725.N36 N E 68–3417

NN 0025387 DLC

---

al-Nashāshībī, Anwar.
معالجات فى الحقل القومى، بقلم انور النشاشيبى. القدس،
مكتبة الاندلس 1950؟،
70 p. 17 cm.

1. Palestine—Politics and government—1948– I. Title.
Title romanized: Mu'ālajāt fī al-ḥaql al-qawmī.

DS126.5.N28 73–257236

NN 0025388 DLC

---

al-Nashāshībī, 'Azmī.
من القدس الى لندن، بقلم عزمى النشاشيبى. القدس،
المطبعة التجارية، 1946.
90 p. 23 cm.

1. England—Description and travel—1946– 2. London—Description—1901–1950. I. Title.
Title romanized: Min al-Quds ilā Landan.

DA631.N37 74–212897

NN 0025389 DLC

---

al-Nashāshībī, Muḥammad Is'āf, comp.
(Nuql al-adīb)
نقل الاديب، لمحمد اسعاف النشاشيبى. قدم له وترجم
لمؤلفه اسحق موسى الحسينى. بيروت، دار ريحانى للطباعة
والنشر 195–؟،
147 p. 20 cm.

دفعلارات منقولة من هنا وهناك،
Includes bibliographical references.

1. Quotations, Arabic. I. Title.

PN6095.A7N3 74–219893

NN 0025390 DLC

Nash'at, Aḥmad.
رسالة الاثبات فى التعهدات، تأليف احمد نشأت. الطبعة 6.
مصر، دار الفكر العربى، 1955.
2 v. 24 cm.
Bibliographical footnotes.

1. Evidence (Law)—Egypt. I. Title.
Title transliterated: Risālat al-ithbāt fī al-ta'ahhudāt.

N E 65–2393

NN 0025391 DLC

Nash'at, Muḥammad 'Alī.
الفكر الاقتصادى فى مقدمة ابن خلدون، تأليف محمد على
نشأت. القاهرة، مطبعة دار الكتب المصرية، 1944.
228 p. 24 cm.
رسالة الدكتوراه — جامعة فؤاد الاول
Bibliography: p. 213–214.

1. Economics—Hist. 2. Ibn Khaldūn, 1337–1406. Kitāb al-'Ibar. al-Muqaddimah. I. Title.
Title transliterated: al-Fikr al-iqtiṣādī fī Muqaddimat Ibn Khaldūn.

HB125.A2N3 N E 65–792

NN 0025392 DLC

Nashat, Muḥammad Alī.
Ibn Khaldoun, pioneer economist. Cairo,
Government press, 1945.

Thesis – Fouad I university.
"Extrait de 'L'Egypte contemporaine', revue
de la Société Fouad Ier d'économie politique,
de statistique et de législation, t.XXXV, pp.
375 à 490."

NN 0025393 MH CtY

330.1
N253
Nashat, Muḥammad Alī.
Ibn Khaldoun pioneer economist. Cairo,
Government Press, 1945.
114 p.

1. Economics 2. Ibn Khaldoun

NN 0025394 NNUN

893.71b56
DN3
Nashat, Muḥammad 'Alī.
Ibn Khaldoun, pioneer economist. (Cairo,
Société Fouad Ier d'économie politique,
1945?)
(377)–490 p.

Reprinted from the periodical L'Egypte contemporaine.
Abridged English version of the author's
Arabic volume Rā'id al-iqtiṣād, Ibn Khaldūn.
Bibliography: p. 483.

NN 0025395 NNC

Nash'at, Muḥammad Ṣādiq, 1898–
(Mu'allim-i jadīd)
معلم جديد، عربيرا بايرانيان و فارسى را يعرب مىآموزد.
تأليف سيد محمد صادق نشأت. چاپ 1. (تهران، كتابفرشى
محمد على علمى 1948؟،
v. 23 cm.

«باين جلد كتابى در محاورات عربى و فارسى مشتمل بر كلمات كتاب و كلمات
ديكر ملحق ميشود.»

1. Arabic language—Text-books for foreigners—Persian. 2. Persian language—Text-books for foreigners—Arabic. I. Title.

PJ6111.N37 74–205074

NN 0025396 DLC

Nash'at, Ṣādiq
see
Nash'at, Muḥammad Ṣādiq, 1898–

Nash'at Mīrdāmād, Ṣādiq
see
Nash'at, Muḥammad Ṣādiq, 1898–

(Nashata duma)

Нашата дума; възражения на бившите министри Ив. Ев.
Гешовъ, д-ръ Ст. Даневъ, Т. Теодоровъ, М. Ив. Маджаровъ, Ив. Пѣевъ и П. Арбашевъ срѣщу обвиненията на
Държавния съдъ 1923 година. София, Миръ, (1925)
329 p. 24 cm.
Includes bibliographical references.

1. Bulgaria—History—1878–1944—Sources. 2. Balkan Peninsula—History—War of 1912–1913. I. Geshov, Ivan Evstratiev, 1849–1925.
Title romanized: Nashata duma.

DR87.7.N37 70–264021

NN 0025399 DLC

UE1
.N3
(Nashata konnitsa)

Нашата конница. г. 1–
1918–
София, Фондъть "Нашата конница" (etc.)
v. in illus., ports. 31 cm.
Frequency varies.

1. Cavalry—Period. 2. Bulgaria. Armìfà. Konnitsa.
Title transliterated: Nashata konnitsa.

UE1.N3 48–43069*

NN 0025400 DLC

Nashaway woman's club, Nashua, N. H.
Calendar, 1896–7. Nashua, 1896.

NN 0025401 Nh

Nashby, Petroleum V. pseud.
see
Locke, David Ross, 1833–88

Nashchinskiĭ, David, d. 1793.
Prokopovicz, Feofan, abp., 1681–1736.
Theophanis Procopowicz Liber in qvo historia de certamine sanctorvm apostolorvm Pavli et Barnabae cvm ivdaizantibvs, itemqve difficvltas oraevli, a Petro apostolo editi, de ivgo legis intolerabili, vberivs in conspectv proponitvr, operoseqve examinatvr, concinnatvs Kiouiae anno Domini MDCCXII. Lipsiae, ex officina Breitkopfia, 1782.

DK
127
.5
N25
Nashchokin, Vasilĭi Aleksandrovich, 1707–1760.
Записки Василія Александровича Нащокина. Санктпетербургъ, Тип. П. Академіи наукъ. 1842.
2 p. l., iiii)–vi p., 1 l., 384 p., 1 l. 22½ cm.
Edited by D. I. fAzykov.

1. Russia—Hist.—1689–1800—Sources. I. fAzykov, Dmitriĭ Ivanovich, 1773–1845, ed.
Title romanized: Zapiski.

NN 0025404 DLC WU NIC

Nashe, Thomas
see
Nash, Thomas, 1567–1601.

VOLUME 405

HF3626
.N3

(Nashe kupechestvo i torgovlīā)

Наше купечество и торговля съ серьезной и каррика-
турной стороны. Сборникъ, изданный подъ ред. русскаго
купца. Москва, въ Тип. Грачева и комп., 1865–67.

3 v. in 2. port. 23½ cm.

1. Russia—Comm.   *Title transliterated:* Nashe kupechestvo i torgovlīā.

HF3626.N3   20–9107 rev

NN   0025406   DLC

(Nashe pokolenīe)

Наше поколение; сборник молодых писателей журнала
Октябрь. Под ред. и с предисл. Ф. Панферова. ₁Мо-
сква₎ Гос. изд-во худож. лит-ры, 1933.

491 p. 20 cm.

1. Russian literature—20th century.   I. Panferov, Fedor Ivanovich, 1896–1960, ed.   II. Oktīabr'.
             Title romanized: Nashe pokolenie.

PG3227.N325   71–257379

NN   0025407   DLC

(Nashe polozhennīā i nashi zavdannīā)

Наше положення і наші завдання; реферат виголоше-
ния на III крайовому з'їзді Спілки укр. молоді В. Британії 10 березня 1951 року. Лондон, Вид. Крайового ком-ту
Спілки укр. молоді у В. Британії, 1951.

30 p. 18 cm.

At head of title: M. M.

1. Ukraine—Pol. & govt.—1917——Addresses, essays, lectures.
I. M., M.   II. M. M.
           Title transliterated: Nashe polozhen-
nīā i nashi zavdannīā.

DK508.8.N39   68–53665

NN   0025408   DLC

PG3226
.N3

(Nashe vremīā)

Наше время; литературный сборник. Казань ₁Изд. А. А.
Дубровина₎ 1869.

312 p. 19 cm.

1. Russian literature—19th cent.   *Title transliterated:* Nashe vremīā

PG3226.N3   54–50350

NN   0025409   DLC

Nashed, Wilson, 1919–
Development of medicinal membranes
containing ion exchange adsorbates.
Purdue University, 1954.

66 p. xxiv (iii)
Thesis (PhD)–Purdue University

1. Ion exchange   I. Title: Medicinal membranes
containing ion exchange adsorbates.

NN   0025410   PPSKF

Nashed, Wilson, 1919–
The development of medicinal membranes containing ion
exchange adsorbates. Ann Arbor, University Microfilms
₁1954₎

(₁University Microfilms, Ann Arbor, Mich.₎ Publication 8054)
Microfilm copy of typescript. Positive.
Collation of the original: iii, 66, xxiv l. illus.
Thesis—Purdue University.
Abstracted in Dissertation abstracts, v. 14 (1954) no. 6, p. 966–967.
Vita.
Bibliography: leaves 62–66.
1. Ion exchange.   I. Title: Medicinal membranes containing ion
exchange adsorbates.
Microfilm AC-1   no. 8054   Mic A 54–1448

Purdue Univ. Library
for Library of Congress   ₁1₎†

NN   0025411   InPU DLC

TR890
.N36

Nashel'skiĭ, A   IU
Организация и эксплуатация сельских киноустановок.
Москва, Искусство, 1955.

161 p. illus. 23 cm.

1. Moving-picture projection.   I. Title.
          Title transliterated: Organizatsīīā i ėks-
pluatatsīīā sel'skikh kinoustanovok.

TR890.N36   56–16133

NN   0025412   DLC

PN1993
.5
.R9N3

Nashel'skiĭ, A   IU
Организация работы сельской киносети. Москва, Госкиноиздат, 1949.

199 p. illus. 22 cm.

At head of title: А. Ю. Нашельский, М. М. Зайонц.

1. Moving-pictures—Russia.   I. Zaĭonts, M. M., joint author.
          Title transliterated: Organizatsīīā
raboty sel'skoĭ kinoseti.

PN1993.5.R9N3   50–20766

NN   0025413   DLC

HD
9715
.O4N3

Nashert, Walter.
Tepees to towers; the story of building the
Sooner state. ₁Oklahoma City?₎ n.d.₎
iii, 240 p. illus., ports. 23 cm.

1. Construction industry--Oklahoma.
I. Title.

NN   0025414   OkU

DK32
.N3
(Rare Bk
Coll)

(Nashi, spisannye s natury russkimi)

Наши, списанные с натуры русскими. вып. 1–14. Санктпетербургъ, Изд. Я. А. Исакова, 1841.

14 no. in 1 v. (177 p.) illus. 28 cm.

Issued in pts.
No more published. Cf. N. Berezin. Русскія книжныя рѣдкости,
1902, № 373.

1. Russia—Soc. life & cust.
         Title transliterated: Nashi, spisannye s natury russkimi.

DK32.N3   60–58590

NN   0025415   DLC InU

CT1212
.N3

(Nashi dīeīāteli)

Наши дѣятели; галлерея замѣчательныхъ людей Россіи въ
портретахъ и біографіяхъ. С.-Петербургъ, Изд. А. О.
Баумана, 18

v. ports. 24 cm.

1. Russia—Biog.   *Title transliterated:* Nashi dīeīāteli.

CT1212.N3   65–42975

NN   0025416   DLC CaBVaU

PG3227
.N33

(Nashi dni; al'manakh)

Наши дни; альманах. .–5. Москва, Гос. изд-во, 19 –25.

v. 24–27 cm.

Subtitle varies slightly.
Began publication in 1922. Cf. Каталог изданий Гос. изд-ва, 1927.

1. Russian literature—20th cent.—Period.   *Title transliterated:* Nashi dni.

PG3227.N33   56–52296

NN   0025417   DLC CSt-H WU InU

AP50
.N35

(Nashi dostizhenīā)

Наши достижения. г. ₁1₎–₁9₎; янв. 1929–май 1937. Москва.

v. in illus., plates, ports., maps. 25–27 cm.

Bimonthly, 1929; monthly, 1930–May 1937.
Editor: Jan. 1929–June 1936, M. Gor'kiĭ

I. Gor'kiĭ, Maksim, 1868–1936, ed.
          Title transliterated: Nashi dostizhenīā.

AP50.N35   52–45840

NN   0025418   DLC

(Nashi dumy, nashi pīesnīe)
Наші думи, наші пѣснѣ. Львовъ, Нью-Іоркъ, 1922.

54 p. 16 cm. (Народна библіотека, ч. 13)

1. Folk-song, Ukrainian.   2. Dumy, Ukrainian.

PG3926.N33   73–222742

NN   0025419   DLC MH

The NASHI He Jhi P'i. ₍Cambridge, Mass., 1939₎

facsim. of 24 ₁i.e. 1–7, 1–17₎ℓ. 13 x 27 cm.
Photographic reproduction by the Harvard film
service of both front and back of scroll.
Original scroll: 22 x 1195 cm.
In port-folio.
Typewritten explanation of 2 ℓ. by Quentin
Roosevelt.

NN   0025420   MH-P

M1756
.N387

(Nashi pesni)

Наши песни; песенник. Москва, Музыка, 19

v. 14 cm.

1. Songs, Russian—Texts.   *Title romanized:* Nashi pesni.

M1756.N387   75–205940

NN   0025421   DLC

(Nashi pīātnitsy)
Наши пятницы. ₁n. p.₎ 1861.

₁16₎ plates. 24 x 31 cm.

1. Drawings, Russian.

NC267.N37   74–220684

NN   0025422   DLC

HD9710
.R92N3

(Nashi podarki rodine)

Наши подарки родине; подарки молодых патриотов автоза-
вода имени Сталина социалистической родине в честь
двадцатилетия ленинско-сталинского комсомола. ₁Мо-
сква₎ Молодая гвардия, 1938.

44 p. 17 cm.

1. Avtomobil'nyĭ zavod
leninskiĭ kommunisticheskiĭ sofūz molodezhi.   2. Vsesofūznyĭ
          Title transliterated: Nashi podarki rodine.

HD9710.R92N3   51–47198

NN   0025423   DLC

VOLUME 405

(Nashi pozytsii.)
Наші позиції. число 1-
1948-
₍Neu-Ulm₎
no. in   v. ports. 21-31 cm.
Organ of Tsentral'nyĭ komitet of Ukraïns'ka revoliŭtsiĭno-demokratychna partiĭa.

1. Ukraïns'ka revoliŭtsiĭno-demokratychna partiĭa.   i. Ukraïn-
s'ka revoliŭtsiĭno-demokratychna partiĭa.   Tsentral'nyĭ komitet.
Title transliterated: Nashi pozytsiĭ.

DK508.44.N3   67-42018

NN   0025424   DLC NSyU

PZ64
.N27   (Nashi skazki.)
Наши сказки.   Составители М. Боголюбская и А. Табен-
кина.   Рисунки И. Кузнецова.   Москва, Детская лит-ра,
19-
v. illus. (part col.) 23 cm. (Библиотечка детского сада
"Для дошкольного возраста."
CONTENTS.—
кн. 2. Сказки и песенки народов СССР.
кн. 3. Сказки и песенки народов разных
стран.
1. Tales. 2. Children's songs.   i. Bogoliubskaia, M. K., comp.
ii. Tabenkina, Anna L'vovna, comp.   iii. Kuznetsov, I., illus.
Title romanized: Nashi skazki.

PZ64.N27   68-39566

NN   0025425   DLC

(Nashi sosĕdi v Srednĕĭ Azīi.)
Наши сосѣди въ Средней Азіи. С.-Петербургъ, Изд. ред.
журнала "Всемірный путешественникъ," 1873-
v. fold. col. maps, port. 24 cm.
CONTENTS: 1. Хива и Туркменія.

1. Turkmenistan—History. 2. Khiva—History.
Title romanized: Nashi sosĕdi v Srednĕĭ Azīi.

DK938.N37   71-289141

NN   0025426   DLC

DK269
.N33   (Nashi vesti.)
Наши вести.
New York.
v. in   illus., ports. 28 cm. semimonthly.
Issued by Soiŭz chinov Russkogo korpusa.

1. Russians in foreign countries—Period.   i. Soiŭz chinov Russkogo korpusa.
Title transliterated: Nashi vesti.

DK269.N33   65-51344

NN   0025427   DLC KU

HC240
.N27   (Nashi zapadnye sosedi.)
Наши западные соседи; краткий политико-экономический
справочник по Польше, Румынии, Литве, Латвии, Эсто-
нии и Финляндии. Москва, Издательство "Военный
вестник," 1928 ₍i. e. 1927₎
253 p. 21ᶜᵐ.
"В составлении справочника приняли участие тт. Зейферт, Ф. Н.,
Колесинский, В. А., Мазалов, А. А., Узар, Я. Д."—р. ₍4₎
"Использованные источники": p. ₍252₎-253.

1. Poland—Econ. condit.—1918-   2. Rumania—Econ. condit.—
1918-   3. Finland.—Econ. condit.—1918-   4. Baltic states—
Econ. condit.   *Title transliterated:* Nashi zapadnye sosedi.

                                                   44-21817
Library of Congress   HC240.N27

NN   0025428   DLC

Nashimoto, Yūhei, 1900-
(Shinsei Shina keiei ron)
新生支那經營論 梨本祐平著 ₍東京₎ 改造社
₍昭和13 i. e. 1938₎
3, 3, 329 p. 20 cm.

1. China—Economic policy. 2. China—Politics and government—
1937-1949. 3. Japan—Foreign economic relations—China. 4. China—
Foreign economic relations—Japan.   I. Title.

HC427.8.N38   74-816690

NN   0025429   DLC

Nashimura ₍Yasuji₎ ₍1876-   ₎ Ueber
Schenkelhalsfrakturen beim kindlichen Alter
mit besonderer Rücksicht auf deren Entste-
hungsmechanismus. 30 pp. 8°. München,
Kastner & Callwey. 1907

NN   0025430   DNLM

S623
.N33
Nashivanko, M   S
Укрепление и облесение песков. Москва, Гослесбум-
издат, 1949.
47, ₍1₎ p. illus. 22 cm.
Bibliography: p. ₍48₎

1. Sand-dunes. *Russia* 2. Soil conservation—Russia.
Title transliterated: Ukreplenie i oblesenie peskov.

S623.N33   50-56599

NN   0025431   DLC

Nashkovskiĭ, Marian
see
Naszkowski, Marian.

Nashold, Blaine Sanders, 1923-
The isolation of actinomycetes from natural
sources and the influence of various materials
on the production of antibiotic substances...
1945.
Thesis - Ohio state university.
By Blaine Sanders Nashold, jr.

NN   0025433   OU

Nashorn, Henry.
Turn to the index
see under   New York (City) Board of Education.

Nashotah alumni bulletin
see   Nashotah news.

NASHOTAH HOUSE, Delafield, Wis.
See NASHOTAH HOUSE, Nashotah, Wis.

Nashotah house, *Nashotah, Wis.*
Founded 1842 as a mission, under Jackson Kemper, first missionary bishop of the Protestant Episcopal church in the United States
of America, by the Rev. James Lloyd Breck and the Rev. William Adams; incorporated 1847 as Nashotah house; unofficially
called Nashotah theological seminary, on the title-pages of its
earlier catalogs.

NASHOTAH HOUSE, Nashotah, Wis.
An appeal for Nashotah. 1881-82.
[Beaver Dam, Wis., printed by Burleson Bros.],
n. d.
pp.16.
Cover serves as title-page.

NN   0025438   MH

BV
4070
.N232   Nashotah House, Nashotah, Wis.
Catalogue...
Nashotah, Wis.,
v. 19cm.

.. *Nashotah House, Nashotah, Wis.-Registers*

NN   0025439   NNC WHi DLC

Nashotah *House, Nashotah Wis*
Catalogue of the officers and students of the
Nashotah theological seminary ...
Delafield, N. C. Hawks, printer for Nashotah
house, 18
v. front. 23 cm.
Catalogue for   includes a Catalogue of
the alumni.

NN   0025440   CSmH Nh DLC MnHi MB PHi PPL OC1WHi

Nashotah house, Nashotah, Wisconsin
Report of the jubilee ceremonies of Nashotah
house... ₍Milwaukee, Wisconsin...₎1892.
92 p. front.

NN   0025441   OC1

Nashotah mission, *Nashotah, Wis.*
see
Nashotah house, *Nashotah, Wis.*

YARC
N253   The Nashotah manual. Delafield, 1865.

NN   0025443   DLC

F9029
N25   Nashotah news.
N   v. 1-24, no. 3; 1926/27-May 1960.
Nashotah House, Nashotah, Wis.
Microfilm copy (negative) made by the Wis-
consin State Historical Society.
Not published July 1936-Nov. 1943.
Publication discontinued. Succeeded by
Nashotah Quarterly Review.
Title varies: Nashotah alumni bulletin,
Nashotah news and alumni bulletin.
Collation of original: 24+ v., illus.,
ports., 30 cm.,   irregular.

v. 2-3(no. 7-12); Dec. 1927-June 1929.
v. 4 (no. 13-15, 17-18); Nov. 1929-May 1931.
v. 5 (no. 20-21); Feb.-June, 1932.
v. 7 (no. 23-24); Feb. 1934-Feb. 1935.
v. 9-24, no. 3; Dec. 1943-May 1960.

1. Nashotah House, Nashotah, Wis.
2. Protestant Episcopal Church in the U.S.A. -
   Periodicals.   3. Protestant Episcopal
Church in the U.S. A. - Wisconsin.

NN   0025445   WHi

VOLUME 405

Period. The Nashotah Quarterly Review. Nashotah
1295   House, Nashotah, Wisconsin.
       v. 21cm.

NN   0025446   MH-AH

Nashotah scholiast
     see   The Church scholiast.

Nashotah theological seminary, *Nashotah, Wis.*
   see
Nashotah house, *Nashotah, Wis.*

(al-Nashrah al-Ifrīqīyah al-Asyawīyah.)

النشرة الافريقية الآسيوية .

,القاهرة, السكرتارية الدائمة لتضامن الشعوب الافريقية الآسيوية .

v. in   27 cm. monthly (irregular)
Issued also in English under title: The Afro-Asian bulletin.
Supplements accompany some issues.
1. Asia—Politics—Period. 2. Africa—Politics—Period. I. Permanent Organization for Afro-Asian Peoples' Solidarity. Permanent Secretariat.
     Title transliterated: al-Nashrah al-Ifrīqīyah al-Asyawīyah.

DS35.N26   N E 65–1286

NN   0025449   DLC NSyU

(al-Nashrah al-ihṣā'īyah al-zirā'īyah wa-dirāsat al-'ayyinah al-zirā'īyah)

النشرة الاحصائية الزراعية ودراسة العينة الزراعية .

,عمان, دائرة الاحصاءات العامة .

v. illus. 28 cm. annual.
Added title   : Agriculture statistical yearbook
and agricultural sample survey.
Arabic and English.
1. Agriculture—Jordan—Statistics—Periodicals.   I. Jordan.
Dā'irat al-Ihṣā'āt al-'Āmmah. II. Title: Agriculture statistical yearbook and agricultural sample survey.

S322.J6N37   74–644623
                               MARC-S

NN   0025450   DLC

(al-Nashrah al-Miṣrīyah)

النشرة المصرية المطبوعات . السنة الاولى –

,القاهرة, مطبعة دار الكتب المصرية .

v. 24 cm.
Three no. a year, with sexennial accumulations, 1955–60; biennial, 1960–.
Added t. p.: Egyptian publications bulletin.
Issued by دار الكتب المصرية، شعبة الابداع القانوني
Arabic or English.
1. Egypt—Imprint—Period. I. Cairo. Dār al-Kutub al-Miṣrīyah. Shu'bat al-Idā' al-Qānūnī. II. Title: Egyptian publications bulletin.
     Title transliterated: al-Nashrah al-Miṣrīyah lil-maṭbū'āt.

Z3651.C3   N E 63–1777 rev

NN   0025451   DLC NSyU OrPS UU

---

al-Nashrah al-qaḍā'īyah...

النشرة القضائية اللبنانية .

بيروت، وزارة العدل .

v. in   27–29 cm. monthly.
Began in 1944. Cf. M. al-Mahdī. Dalīl al-dawrīyāt al-'Arabīyah al-Jārīyah, 1965.
Added title: Revue judiciaire libanaise.
Some contributions in French.
1. Law—Period—Lebanon. I. Lebanon. Wizārat al-'Adl.
II. Title: Revue judiciaire libanaise.
     Title romanized: al-Nashrah al-qaḍā'īyah al-Lubnānīyah.

K14.A8   N E 68–705

NN   0025452   DLC NNC

---

al-Nashrah al-tashrī'īyah.

النشرة التشريعية .

القاهرة، الهيئة العامة لشؤون المطابع الاميرية .

v. in   24 cm. monthly.
Began publication in 1952. Cf. Cairo. Dār al-Kutub al-Miṣrīyah. Qism al-Fahāris al-'Arabīyah wa-al-Ifranjīyah. Fihris al-dawrīyāt al-'Arabīyah, v. 1, 1961.
Issued   وزارة العدل ، قسم المجموعة الرسمية   by
of Egypt;   وزارة العدل ، قسم المجموعة الرسمية —June 1962 by
of United Arab Republic; July 1962–   وزارة العدل، المكتب by
       الفني بمحكمة النقض .

   I. Egypt. Wizārat al-'Adl. II. United Arab Republic. Wizārat al-'Adl. III. United Arab Republic. Maḥkamat al-Naqḍ. IV. Egypt. Laws, statutes, etc. V. United Arab Republic. Laws, statutes, etc.
     Title transliterated: al-Nashrah al-tashrī'īyah.

                   N E 65–2424
                   PL 480: UAR-C-88
Library of Congress   (2₄,

NN   0025454   DLC CLL

(Nashrat al-buḥūth al siyāḥiyah)

نشرة البحوث السياحية .

,القاهرة, وزارة السياحة ، وكالة الوزارة للتخطيط ، ادارة البحوث .

no. 29 cm. quarterly.

1. Tourist trade—Periodicals. 2. Tourist trade—Egypt—Periodicals. I. United Arab Republic. Wizārat al-Siyāḥah. Wakālat al-Wizārah lil-Takhṭīṭ. Idārat al-Buḥūth.
     Title romanized: Nashrat al-buḥūth al-siyāḥīyah.

G155.A1N38   74–212658

NN   0025455   DLC

Nashrat al-'īdā' al-shahrīyah
     see under   al-Nashrah al-Miṣrīyah lil-maṭbū'āt.

Nashrī, Muḥammad
   see
Neṣrī, Mehmet, *d. ca.* 1520.

Nash's and Pall Mall magazine
     see   Nash's-Pall magazine.

Nash's first novel library.
London, E. Nash and Grayson, Ltd., 1925.

[Analyzed]

NN   0025458   DLC

AP4
.N12   ... Nash's illustrated weekly.

     [London, The Periodical publishing co., ltd.,
         v.   illus. (incl. ports.)   35½cm.

     I. Nash, Eveleigh, 1873–, ed.

NN   0025459   DLC

AP4
.N14   Nash's magazine. [London, The National
     Magazine Co., Ltd., 19   ]
     United with Pall Mall magazine Oct. 1914–
to form Nash's and Pall Mall magazine.

NN   0025460   DLC

Nash's Merchant and seamen's expeditious measurer; containing a set of tables, which show at one view. The solid contents of all kinds of packages and casks, according to their several lengths, breadths, and depths; also, rules for determining the contents of all sorts of casks in wine and beer measure. Stereotype ed., corr. New York, Baker & Taylor company, 1942.
     1 p. l., 195, (1) p.   24½ x 11½ᵐᵐ.
     Cover-title: Expeditious measurer.
     Earlier edition published under title: The merchant and seaman's expeditious measurer ... New York, A. L. Nash, 1904.
     1. Mensuration. 2. Freight and freightage—Tables and ready-reckoners. I. Title: Expeditious measurer.

                          43–1801.
Library of Congress   T51.M55 1942
                   (2,   511.8

NN   0025461   DLC

Nash's new corporation report; published monthly covering charter and permits filed by organizations active in all phases of the petroleum industry... Texas, September, 1931.
Dallas, Lloyd N.Nash, publisher, 1931–
v. 28 cm. monthly.

NN   0025462   DI-GS

Nash's officers of petroleum companies in the United States; and alphabetical list of the officers of companies active in all phases of the petroleum industry, showing addresses and positions... Dallas, Tex., Lloyd N. Nash, publisher, c1931.
166 p. 27½ cm. semi-annual.

NN   0025463   DI-GS

Nashshabah, 'Adnan, ed.
   al-Mu'ahadat al-duwaliyah al-Suriyah al-thuna'iyah.
     see under   Syria. Treaties, etc.

---

al-Nashshar, 'Ali Sami, ed.
   I'tiqadat firaq al-Muslimin wa-'al-mushrikin
     see under   al-Razi, Fakhr al-Din Muhammad ibn 'Umar. 1149 or 50–1210.

NASH'S Pall Mall magazine. v. 1–99 (no. 1–532) May 1893–Sept. 1937. London.

     99 v. in   illus. 25 cm. monthly.

     Title varies: v. 1–54 no. 257, Pall Mall magazine; v. 54 no. 258–v. 79 no. 407, Nash's and Pall Mall magazine (after the merger of these two publications); v. 79 no. 408–v. 432, Nash's magazine; v. 96 no. 509–510; New Nash's Pall Mall magazine.
     Vol. 54 no. 258–259 incorrectly numbered v. 53
     Merged into   Good housekeeping.

NN   0025466   CaBVaU CtH GU OCl TNJ OU

---

x8   Nash's   Pall Mall magazine.
M441   ₍Stories by W. Somerset Maugham and an article
no.144   about Maugham by Desmond MacCarthy, in Nash's
     and Pall Mall magazine.   London, 1923–35₎
     38 pts. illus. 30cm. ₍Maugham collection no
   144₎

NN   0025467   IU

Nash's petroleum directory, (1931
Dallas,Tex., L.N. Nash, c1931–
v. 29 cm. annual
Lloyd N. Nash, publisher.

NN   0025468   DI-GS

VOLUME 405

Nash's war manual. London, E. Nash, 1914.

350 p. 19½ᶜᵐ.

On cover: Nash's war manual, facts about the causes of the war: the armies and navies engaged: descriptive information about the countries involved, etc.

1. European war, 1914–

War 15–81

Library, War College Div.   General Staff

NN   0025469   DNW CtY NjP CaBViP NN CSt–H

Nash's war manual. / London, E. Nash, 1914.

350 p. 19½ᶜᵐ.   2d impression.

On cover: Nash's war manual, facts about the causes of the war: the armies and navies engaged: descriptive information about the countries involved, etc.

1. European war, 1914–1918.

NN   0025470   ViU

---

al-Nashshār, 'Alī Sāmī.

مناهج البحث عند مفكري الاسلام ونقد المسلمين للمنطق الارسطاطاليسي، تأليف على سامى النشار. الطبعة 1. القاهرة، دار الفكر العربي، 1947.

263, 8 p. 24 cm.

Cover title: Les méthodes chez les penseurs musulmans et leur critique de la logique Aristotelicienne, par Ali Sami el Nashar.
Bibliography: p. [246]–257.
1. Logic—Hist.—Islamic countries. 2. Logic, Medieval.   I. Title.
Title romanised: Manāhij al-baḥth 'inda mufakkirī al-Islām wa-naqd al-Muslimīn.

BC34.N3   N E 67–1906

NN   0025471   DLC ICU

---

al-Nashshār, 'Alī Sāmī.

نشأة الدين: النظريات التطورية والمؤلهة. تأليف على سامى النشار. الاسكندرية، دار نشر الثقافة، 1949.

231 p. 23 cm.
Includes bibliographies.

1. Religion.   I. Title.
Title romanised: Nash'at al-dīn.

BL48.N3   N E 68–1758

NN   0025472   DLC

---

al-Nashshār, 'Alī Sāmī.

نشأة الفكر الفلسفى فى الاسلام، تأليف على سامى النشار. القاهرة، مكتبة النهضة المصرية، 1954،

16, 228 p. 24 cm.
Bibliography: p. [211]–[218]

1. Mohammedanism—Origin.   I. Title.
Title transliterated: Nash'at al-fikr al-falsafī fī al-Islām.

BP173.2.N3   N E 62–470

NN   0025473   DLC

---

al-Nashshār, 'Alī Sāmī.

شهداء الاسلام فى عهد النبوة، تأليف، على سامى النشار. القاهرة، مطبعة دار الكتاب العربي، 1952.

174 p. 24 cm.

1. Muslim martyrs.   I. Title.
Title romanised: Shuhadā' al-Islām fī 'ahd al-nubūwah.

BP72.N3   N E 68–2583

NN   0025474   DLC

HF5681
.P8N3

al-Nashshār, Muḥammad Ḥamdī.

قواعد تحديد الأرباح التجارية والصناعية من الناحيتين العملية والفنية، تأليف محمد حمدى النشار. [195–؟]

822 p. 24 cm.
Bibliography: p. 321–822.

1. Profit—Accounting.   I. Title.
Title transliterated: Qawā'id taḥdīd al-arbāḥ.

HF5681.P8N3   NE 68–2566

NN   0025475   DLC

Nashtar, Abdul Karim, 1878–

Hand book of commercial Hindustani, by Abdul Karim 'Nashtar' ... Revised by Lt.-Col. C. L. Peart ... Ballygunge, Calcutta, The author, 1924.

4 p. l., 156 (i. e. 158) p. front. (port.) 18ᶜᵐ.
Error in paging: numbers 137–138 repeated.

1. Hindustani language—Conversation and phrase books.   I. Peart, Charles Lubé, 1876–   ed.   II. Title.   III. Title: Commercial Hindustani.

Library of Congress   PK1985.N3   33–35863 Revised
                           [r37b2]   491.43

NN   0025476   DLC

PK
1985
.N25

Nashtar, Abdul Karim, 1878–

Hindustani colloquial manual. Calcutta, 1918.

vi, 69 p. 18cm.

NN   0025477   NIC

PK
1983
.N3

Nashtar, Abdul Karim, 1878–

Simple colloquial Hindustani. For use in Jute Mills. Calcutta, Author, 1929.

ii, 56 p.

1. Hindustani language – Grammar.
I. Title.

NN   0025478   NNC

Nashua, *N. H.*

An account of the Soldiers' and sailors' monument, erected by the people of the city of Nashua, N. H., in the year eighteen hundred eighty-nine, in honor of the men of Nashua who served their country during the war of the rebellion, A. D. 1861–65. Published by order of the city councils, November, 1889. Nashua, N. H., J. H. Barker, printer, 1889.

124 p., 1 l. front., 2 pl. 23½ᶜᵐ.
Compiled by F. G. Noyes.
1. Nashua, N. H. Soldiers' and sailors' monument.   I. Noyes, Frank Gardner, 1833–   comp.

Library of Congress   F74.N2N22   4–11986

NN   0025479   DLC DNW NhDo MH NN Nh OCH

Nashua, N. H.

Annual report of the municipal government see its   Report of the municipal government of the city of Nashua.

Nashua, N. H.

Charter, rules and orders of the city council, with a list of the members of the city government ...Nashua, 1854.

NN   0025481   Nh

Nashua, N. H.

The charter with its amendments and the reordained ordinances of the city of Nashua see under   Nashua, N. H. Charters.

Nashua, N. H.

Compte rendu officiel de la XVIIeme convention nationale des Canadiens-Français des Etats Unis

see under   Convention nationale des Canadiens-Français des Etats Unis. [Supplement]

Nashua, N. H.

Memorial service for William McKinley. ...Nashua, N.H., Sept. 19, 1901. n.p., n.d.

18 p.

NN   0025484   OClWHi

Nashua, *N. H.*

The official report of the semi-centennial celebration of the city of Nashua, New Hampshire, June 28, 29 and 30, 1903, including illustrations and descriptions of leading industries and residences.   Comp. and published by the Telegraph publishing co., Nashua, New Hampshire.   Nashua, N. H., Telegraph publishing co. [1903]

215 p. incl. illus., plates. front. 17 x 25½ᶜᵐ.

Subject entries: Nashua, N. H.—Hist.

3–28994

Library of Congress, no.   F44.N2N25.   Copyright.

NN   0025485   DLC

Nashua, *N. H.*

Report of the municipal government of the city of Nashua.

Nashua.
    v. in   illus. 24 cm.   annual.
    Report year for   –1877/78 ends Jan. 31; for 1878–Dec. 31.
    1. Nashua, N. H.—Pol. & govt.

    JS13.N145   352.0742   50–32287

NN   0025486   DLC DNAL NhDo Nh MB

Nashua, N. H.

Reports of the selectmen.

Nashua,   23½ – 24cm.
    include the report of the Superintending School Committee.
    Continued, 1853/54, as the Annual report of the municipal government.

1. Municipal govt.—U. S.—N. H.—   Nashua.
N. Y. P. L.   December 13, 1935

NN   0025487   NN

Nashua, N. H.

Soldiers' and sailors' monument see under   Nashua, N. H.
An account of the Soldiers' and sailors' monument ...

[Nashua, N. H. Baptist churches]

Murder of Caroline H. Cutter by the Baptist ministers and Baptist Churches
see under   [Cutter, Calvin] 1807–1872.

Nashua, *N. H. Board of education.*

Annual report.

Nashua, N. H., 18
    v. 21½ᶜᵐ.

E 14–1028

Library, U. S. Office of   Education L177.N4A2

NN   0025490   DHEW DLC CtY OCU MiU Nh MB

VOLUME 405

Nashua, N. H. Board of education
Manual; list of members, committee and teachers.
Nashua, 1899.

NN 0025491   Nh

Nashua, N. H. Board of health.
Annual report of the city marshal and of
Board of health for the year 1885. Nashua, 1886.

NN 0025492   Nh

W 2   NASHUA, N. H. Board of Health
AN3.2   Mortuary report.
N2B6m
       ₁Nashua? 18--₁-
              v.

NN 0025493   DNLM

Nashua, N.H. Board of Trade.
Nashua, the gate city of New Hampshire.   Nashua, N. H.
₁191-₁   6 l.   24°.
   Cover-title.

1. Nashua, N.H. 2. Economic his-   tory, U.S.: N.H.: Nashua.
N.Y.P.L.   December 18, 1916.

NN 0025494   NN

Nashua, N.H. Charters.
Charter, amendments and general laws relating to the govern-
ment of cities, with the revised ordinances of the city of Nashua...
Nashua, N. H.: Gazette Press Co., 1892.   212 p.   8°.
   "Ordinances passed and amended since January 1, 1892:" blank pages, p. 171-
212.

115819A. 1. Municipal charters and   ordinances, U. S.: N. H.: Nashua.
2. Nashua (N.H.). Ordinances.
N.Y.P.L.   April 10, 1924.

NN 0025495   NN

Nashua, N.H. Ordinances, etc.
Charter and ordinances of the city of Nashua;
with the rules and orders of the city council, and
the names of the officers and members of the city
government for 1862-63.   Nashua, New Hampshire telegraph office, 1862.
       111 p.   8°.

NN 0025496   MB

Nashua, N.H. Charters.
The charter with its amendments and the reordained ordinances of the City of Nashua.   Nashua: Moore & Langley, 1878.
112 p.   lea.   8°.

1. Municipal charters and ordinances,   U. S.: N. H.: Nashua.
N.Y.P.L.   January 12, 1915

NN 0025497   NN MB

KFX1909   Nashua, N. H. Charters.
N27A35
1916   Nashua. *N. H.* Ordinances, etc.
       Revised ordinances of the city of Nashua. With the old
and new charter and amendments now in force. Published
by order of the Board of aldermen in accordance with section
111. of the new charter. 1915. Nashua, N. H., The Marquis
press, printers, 1916.

Nashua (N.H.)   City Council.
An account of the soldiers' and sailors'
monument
       see under   Nashua, N.H.

Nashua, N. H. Committee on finance.
... Annual report of the Finance committee
of the city of Nashua. Also, reports of city
treasurer, city marshal, and chief engineer of
fire department, and schedule of city debt and
city property ... 13rd 1856/66
Nashua, N. H., 1866

/ v. 22 cm.

1. Finance--Nashua, N. H.

NN 0025500   VSmH

Nashua, N.H. Committee to investigate town
accounts.
       Report for the year 1838-40 ...   Nashua,
1838-53.

NN 0025501   Nh

Nashua, N.H. City library.

       see

Nashua, N.H. Public library.

Nashua, N.H. Common council.
Account of the Soldiers' and sailors' monument.
Nashua, 1889.
       see under   Nashua, N.H.

NASHUA, N.H. - Crown Hill Baptist Church.
Directory, Crown Hill Baptist Church, Nashua,
N.H. [Nashua, N.H.], 1919.

nar. 8°. pp. [12]. Ports. and illustr.

NN 0025504   MH

Nashua, N.H. Edgewood Cemetery

       see   Edgewood cemetery, Nashua,
N.H.

Nashua, N. H. First congregational church.

       Manual. 1872.

NN 0025506   NhDo

Nashua, N. H. First Congregational church.
Manual. Nashua, 1888.

NN 0025507   Nh

Nashua, N. H. First Congregational church
New church; issued in commemoration of the
dedication of the First Congregational church
of Nashua, N. H., on May 17, 1894. n.p., n.d.

NN 0025508   Nh

Nashua, N. H. First congregational church.

The two hundredth anniversary of the First congregational
church, in Nashua, N. H., Wednesday, Dec. 15, 1885. Published
by vote of the church.

NN 0025509   NhDo Nh

                                No. 14 in *4335.8a
Nashua, N. H.   First Unitarian Congregational Society.
A church memorial, consisting of the history . . . with articles,
covenant, and statement of faith, to which are added letters from
past and present pastors.
Nashua. Beard. 1859. 39 pp. 18½ cm., in 6s.

NN 0025510   MB CtY-D CtY MWA NN Nh MH

Nashua, N. H. Fire department.
City ordinance, extracts from the statutes and
the rules and regulations. Nashua, 1854.

NN 0025511   Nh

26.6   Nashua, *N.H. High School.*
Catalogue of the instructors and students of
Nashua High School, for the year ending November,
1837. Press of Israel Hunt, Jr. - Nashua.
O.D. Murray, Printer, 1837.
[3] 4-7 p. 17 cm.

NN 0025512   DLC

Nashua, N.H. Highland Spring Sanatorium
       see   Highland Spring Sanatorium, Nashua,
N.H.

Nashua, N.H. Nashua Literary Institution
       see   Nashua Literary Institution, Nashua,
N.H.

Nashua, N.H. Ordinances, etc.
Charter, amendments and general laws relating
to the government of cities, with the revised
ordinances of the city of Nashua
       see under   Nashua, N.H. Charters.

Nashua, N.H. Ordinances, etc.
The charter with its amendments and the
reordained ordinances of the City of Nashua
       see under   Nashua, N.H. Charters.

TH225   NASHUA, N.H. Ordinances, etc.
.N25A5   City of Nashua zoning ordinance...approved June
1930   11, 1930... [Nashua, N.H., 1930]
       31 p. 22½ cm.

1. Building laws--Nashua, N.H.

NN 0025517   ICU

NASHUA, N.H. Ordinances.
Ordinances of the City of Nashua, to which is
appended the names of the members of the city
government, and the officers of the city for the
year 1854. Nashua, A. Beard, 1854.

nar. 8°. pp. 32.

NN 0025518   MH

VOLUME 405

Nashua, N. H. Ordinances, etc.
Ordinances of the city of Nashua, with a
compilation of the public statutes relating to
the government of cities and special acts
relating to the city of Nashua. ₍Nashua₎
The Marquis press, 1910.
254 p.   21 cm.

Cover-title: Laws and ordinances, Nashua,
N. H., 1910.

1. Municipal corporations - Nashua, N. H.
I. New Hampshire.   Laws, statutes, etc.

NN 0025519   NNC

Nashua, *N. H.* Ordinances, etc.
Revised ordinances of the city of Nashua. With the old
and new charter and amendments now in force. Published
by order of the Board of aldermen in accordance with section
111, of the new charter. 1915. Nashua, N. H., The Marquis
press, printers, 1916.
270 p. 22½ᵐ.
On cover: Laws and ordinances, Nashua, N. H.

I. New Hampshire. Laws, statutes, etc. II. Nashua, N. H. Charters.
III. Title.

Library of Congress   JS1159.N35A5 1915   33—3022

NN 0025520   DLC IU NN

Nashua, N. H. Ordinances.
Revised ordinances of the city of Nashua, with the charter and
special acts in amendment and supplement thereto. 1927.
Nashua, N. H.: The Phaneuf press, 1928.   272 p.   23cm.

190569B. 1. No subject. I. Nashua,   N. H. Charters.
N. Y. P. L.   September 9, 1942

NN 0025521   NN IU ICU

D   NASHUA, N.H. PILGRIM CHURCH.
284261   Manual of the Pilgrim church, of Nashua.
.6   The confession of faith, covenant, forms of
            admission, and rules of government.   Nashua,
            H.R.Wheeler, 1879.
            14p. 20cm.

NN 0025522   ICN

Nashua, N. H. Public library.
Annual report of the library trustees, 18
Nashua, 18
v.

NN 0025523   Nh MB

Nashua, N. H. Public library.
Bulletin of the Public library, Nashua, N. H.
18

NN 0025524   Nh NhDo MB

Nashua, N. H. Public library.
Catalogue of the public library of the city of Nashua.
Manchester ₍N. H.₎ J. B. Clarke, 1868.
138 p. 20½ᵐ.
—— Supplement to the Catalogue of the Nashua city library,
containing the books added ... since the first catalogue was
printed ... ₍with₎ Index ... by the name of the author. Nashua,
1874.
1 p. l., p. ₍141₎–320. 22ᵐ. ₍With its Catalogue. 1868₎

                                          1–9074–5 Revised
Library of Congress   Z881.N25

NN 0025525   DLC Nh

Nashua, N. H. Public library.
Catalogue of the public library of Nashua, N. H. ...
1891. ₍Boston, A. Mudge & son, printers, 1891₎
1 p. l., 290 p. 27ᵐ.
Dictionary catalog; Dewey class nos. added.

1. Catalogs, Dictionary.   2. Catalogs, classified (Dewey decimal)
                                          4–12618
Library of Congress   Z881.N25'91

NN 0025526   DLC

Nashua, N. H. Public Library
Finding list of the fiction added to the
library since 1891. Nashua, 1898.

NN 0025527   Nh

Nashua, N. H. Public library
Historical fiction. Nashua, 1897.

NN 0025528   Nh

Nashua, N. H. Public library.
Quarterly bulletin. v. 1–
Jan. 1903–
Nashua, 1903–
v. in   23½ᵐ.
No issue for Oct. 1903.
Irregular volume numbering as follows: Jan. 1903–Jan. 1904: v. 1, no. 1–
4.—Apr. 1904–Jan. 1906: v. 2, no. 1–8.—Apr.–Oct. 1906: v. 3, no. 9–11.—Jan.
1907–Oct. 1912: v. 3, no. 2–24 (no. 23 incorrectly numbered 22)—Jan. 1913–
Apr. 1914: v. 4, no. 25–30.—July 1914–Oct. 1914: v. 4, no. 3–4.—Jan. 1915–
v. 5, no. 1–
                                          8–25032 (rev. '15)
Library of Congress   Z881.N25B

NN 0025529   DLC MB OC1 NhDo

027.22   Nashua, N.H. Public Library.
N253s   Semi-centennial report, 1867–1917.   Nashua,
           ₍Public Library₎ Board of Trustees ₍1917?₎
           17p. illus. 23cm.
           "John M. Hunt Memorial."

NN 0025530   IU NN

WX   NASHUA, N. H. St. Joseph's Hospital
2   Report.
AN3   1st-   1908/09-
N2SJ2r   Nashua.
               v. illus.
               Period covered by reports is irregular.
               Issued 1908/09-1915/16 with title:
           Annual report.

NN 0025531   DNLM

Nashua (N.H.) Soldiers' and Sailors' Monument
Building Committee.
An account of the Soldiers' and sailors'
monument
see under   Nashua, N.H.

Nashua, N. H. Souvenir booklet committee.
Nashua's 75 years of progress. 1853...1928...
Nashua, N. H., Printed by The Phaneuf press,
1928.
92 p. illus., ports., map.

NN 0025533   MiD-B RWoU MiDW

Z   NASHUA, N.H. UNION ATHENÆUM LIBRARY.
79   Catalogue of the Union athenæum library,
.N 17   Nashua, N.H.   Nashua, A.Beard, 1860.
           32p.

NN 0025534   ICN Nh

Nashua, N.H. Union Saint-Jean Baptiste de
Nashua
    see   Union Saint-Jean-Baptiste, Nashua,
N.H.

Nashua and Lowell railroad corporation
Agreement between the Concord, Nashua and Lowell,
Manchester and Lawrence, Boston and Lowell, and
Boston and Maine railroads. ₍Boston? 1852₎

NASHUA AND LOWELL RAIL-ROAD CORPORA-
TION. An act to establish the Nashua and
Lowell Rail-Road Corporation. [Boston: Dutton and Wentworth, 1836.] 7 p. 8°. (Massachusetts. Senate. 1836, document no. 50.)

NN 0025537   NN DLC M MB MBAt MH MH-BA

Nashua and Lowell Railroad Corporation.
...Annual report of the Nashua & Lowell Railroad Company.
₍no.₎
₍Boston? 18   23cm.
no.
18   at head of title: Nashua and Lowell Railroad.

1. Railways—U. S.—Indiv.—   Nashua and Lowell.
N. Y. P. L.   June 27, 1933

NN 0025538   NN DLC ICJ Nh MB MH-BA MiU-T

HE2791   Nashua and Lowell railroad corporation.
N222   Answer to the attack of Geo. Stark, on the manage-
1879a   ment of the Nashua & Lowell R. R. Nashua, N. H., Press
           of O. C. Moore, 1879.
           13 p. 23ᵐ.

1. Stark, George, 1823–1892. The Nashua and Lowell railroad.
MB   A 16–1022 Revised
Title from Bureau of   Railway Economics. Printed by L. C.

NN 0025539   DBRE DLC

Nashua and Lowell railroad corporation.
The charters granted to the Nashua & Lowell rail road corporation, and the general provisions concerning corporations
and rail roads referred to in the Massachusetts charter; together
with the by-laws of said corporation. Nashua, N. H., Printed
by A. and A. Beard, 1836.
32 p. 24ᵐ.

1. Railroad law—Massachusetts.   I. New Hampshire. Laws, statutes, etc. II. Massachusetts. Laws, statute, etc.
                                          A 19—1810
Bur. of railway econ. Libr.
for Library of Congress   ₍a41b1₎

NN 0025540   DBRE MH-BA MWA MiU-T NN

Nashua and Lowell railroad corporation.
Concord railroad corporation.
Contract. Concord, Manchester and Lawrence rail-
road. December 27, 1860. ₍n. p., 1865?₎

Nashua and Lowell railroad corporation.
Boston and Lowell railroad corporation.
Contract between the Boston & Lowell and Nashua &
Lowell railroad corporations, February 1, 1857. Lowell,
Mass., Stone, Huse & co., printers, 1877.

VOLUME 405

Nashua and Lowell railroad corporation.
₍Contract of lease between the Nashua and Lowell and Boston and Lowell railroad corporations for ninety-nine years, after October 1, 1880₎

(*In* Boston, Concord and Montreal railroad company. Testimony. Boston, Concord and Montreal railroad vs. Boston and Maine railroad, Boston and Lowell railroad. Consolidated case. ₍n. p., 1888₎ 23ᶜᵐ. v. 1, p. 187–198)

Dated November 10, 1880.

1. ₍Leases₎ i. Boston and Lowell railroad corporation.

A 24–935

Title from Bureau of   Railway Economics. Printed by L. C.

NN   0025543   DBRE

Nashua and Lowell railroad corporation.

Peterborough railroad company.
₍Contract of lease between the Peterborough railroad and the Nashua and Lowell railroad corporation for twenty years from April 1, 1873₎

(*In* Boston, Concord and Montreal railroad company. Testimony. Boston, Concord and Montreal railroad vs. Boston and Maine railroad, Boston and Lowell railroad. Consolidated case. ₍n. p., 1888₎ 23ᶜᵐ. v. 1, p. 199–209)

Nashua and Lowell railroad corporation.

Wilton railroad company.
₍Contract of lease between the Wilton railroad and the Nashua and Lowell railroad corporation for twenty years from April 1, 1873₎

(*In* Boston, Concord and Montreal railroad company. Testimony. Boston, Concord and Montreal railroad vs. Boston and Maine railroad, Boston and Lowell railroad. Consolidated case. ₍n. p., 1888₎ 23ᶜᵐ. v. 1, p. 209–211)

Nashua and Lowell railroad corporation.
Evidence in behalf of the Nashua & Lowell railroad company, petitioners for leave to extend their road through the ledge at Lowell, before the joint railroad committee of the Mass. legislature, February 16, 1880. J. H. Benton, jr., Chas. R. Train, counsel for petitioners. Boston, Press of Rockwell and Churchill, 1880.

75 p. 23 cm.

1. Benton, Josiah Henry, 1843–1917. ii. Train, Charles Russell, 1817–1885.

A 15–1769 rev

Bureau of Railway   Economics. Library
for Library of Congress   ₍r58c₂₎

NN   0025546   DBRE ICJ MB

Nashua and Lowell railroad corporation.

Boston and Lowell railroad corporation.
Operating rules and regulations of the Boston & Lowell and Nashua & Lowell railroads, and branches. April, 1872. Boston, J. McIntire, printer, 1872.

Nashua and Lowell railroad corporation.

Boston and Maine railroad.
Railroad controversy: containing a copy of the contract between the Boston & Maine, and Boston & Lowell, and Nashua and Lowell railroads, with correspondence and documents relating thereto. Concord, Steam printing works of McFarland & Jenks, 1859.

Nashua and Lowell railroad corporation.
Report of the committee of investigation of the Nashua and Lowell railroad company; appointed by a vote of the stockholders, May 29, 1850. Boston, Eastburn's press, 1851.

xii, ₍13₎–128, 61 p. 24 cm.

A 17–285 rev

Bureau of Railway   Economics. Library
for Library of Congress   ₍r58c₂₎

NN   0025549   DBRE MB Nh

NASHUA AND LOWELL RAILROAD CORPORATION.
Report of the grantees, oe [sic] the Nashua and Lowell Rail-Road Corporation, with the report of the engineer. May 21, 1836. Nashua: Printed by A. Beard, 1836. 20 p. incl. tables. 23cm.
Engineer's report signed: Joshua Barney.

828955A. 1. Railways—U.S.—Indiv.—Nashua and Lowell.

MiU-T
NN   0025550   NN CtY Nh DLC CSmH MBAt MCM MH-BA

Nashua and Lowell railroad corporation.

Boston and Lowell railroad corporation.
Rules of the Boston & Lowell and Nashua & Lowell railroad companies, for the government of the executive service. Rev. and adopted by the boards of directors. Boston, J. McIntire, printer, 1872.

Nashua & Nashville [N.H.] directory, almanac and memorandum, 1850
    see under   Kimball & Dodge, comp.

Nashua and Rochester railroad.
Nashua and Rochester railroad, from the city of Nashua to Rochester in the state of New Hampshire, six per cent. first mortgage bonds, guaranteed by the Worcester and Nashua railroad company, in denominations of $500, $1,000 and $5,000 ... Twenty years to run ... Worcester, Printed by C. Hamilton, 1874.

16 p. 23ᶜᵐ.

"Mortgage, or deed of trust": p. ₍5₎–12.
"Lease ₍of the Nashua and Rochester railroad to the Worcester and Nashua railroad company₎": p. ₍13₎–16.

i. Worcester and Nashua railroad company.

A 21–1309

Title from Bureau of   Railway Economics. Printed by L. C.

NN   0025553   DBRE CtY OO

Nashua and Rochester Railroad.
Prospectus of the Nashua & Rochester Rail Road; an air line route between Portland and New York. Nashua: Moore & Berry, 1868. 9 p. 8°.

Cover-title.

1. Railways, U. S. (Indiv.): Nashua   and Rochester Railroad.
N. Y. P. L.   April 25, 1921.

NN   0025554   NN

Nashua annual advertiser, prefixed to the Nashua directory, 1841. Nashua, 1841.

NN   0025555   Nh

Nashua Board of Trade, Nashua, N.H.
    see   Nashua, N.H. Board of Trade.

The Nashua directory. 18
    see   Gill's Nashua and Nashville directory.

The Nashua directory. 1845
    see under   Murray and Dodge. [supplement]

The Nashua directory. 1850
    see   Kimball and Dodge, comp.
The Nashua and Nashville [N.H.] directory, almanac, and memorandum. 1850.

The Nashua directory ...
Greenough co., W. A., Boston.
W. A. Greenough co.'s ... Nashua directory including Hudson, N. H. ... no. ₍1₎
₍1861/5₎–1874/5, 1877/8–1883/4, 1885, 1887/8, 1889
19
Boston, Mass., W. A. Greenough co., 1864–¹19

The Nashua directory for the year 1856. Embracing names of the citizens, residences, professions, occupations, etc. ... Nashua, L. Waterman, 1856.

1 p. l., 11–175 p. illus. 15ᶜᵐ.
p. 150–175, advertising matter.

1. Nashua, N. H.—Direct. i. Waterman, Lewis, pub.

9–30709

Library of Congress   F44.N2A18

NN   0025561   DLC MWA

Nashua High School
    see   Nashua, N.H. High School.

NASHUA LITERARY INSTITUTION, Nashua, N.H.
Catalogue of the officers and students...
18

Nashua [N.H.] Gazette Press [etc.] 18   17½–18½ cm.
nos.

Title varies slightly.

NN   0025563   NN CSmH Nh

---

683   **Nashua Lock Co.**
N253   Illustrated catalogue. Manufactory, Nashua, N.H. Boston, 1879.
      vi, 180 p. illus. 27 cm.

      1. Locks and keys. Catalogs.

NN   0025564   N

Nashua Manufacturing Company
   see Textron, inc.

Nashua Public Library
    see   Nashua, N.H. Public Library.

Nashua River Paper Company.   *7695.86
Nashua River Paper Company (petitioner) v. Commonwealth of Massachusetts ... [Testimony and arguments.] May 25, 1900, to May 31, 1902.
= Boston, 1901–02. 4 v. [Commonwealth of Massachusetts. Worcester, ss. Supreme Judicial Court.] 8°.
The company claimed damages for injury to their water supply from takings by the Metropolitan Water Board. The closing argument for the Commonwealth was by J. M. Hallowell.

E7266 — Massachusetts. Supreme Jud Court. — Damages. Law. — Water. Law.

NN   0025567   MB

VOLUME 405

Nashua river valley survey
  see   Nashua valley survey.

Nashua suburban directory for Milford, Mount
  Vernon, Amherst, Merrimack and Hollis,
  N. H. ...
    see   Directory for Milford, Mount
  Vernon, Amherst ...

Nashua valley survey.
  Report on sources of pollution, Nashua river valley, Massachusetts. WPA state planning projects, Nashua valley survey
project 65-14-7603. Sponsored by Massachusetts Department
of public health. Boston, Mass., 1936.
  xi, 89 numb. l. incl. illus., maps, tables, diagrs. (part fold.) pl. 27½cm.
  On cover: Sources of pollution, Nashua river valley ...
Mimeographed.

  1. Water—Pollution. 2. Water-supply—Massachusetts. 3. Sewage
disposal. 4. Nashua river. I. Title. II. Title: Sources of pollution,
Nashua river valley.

  Library of Congress   TD425.N25   37-27758
                               [5]   628.16097444

  NN   0025570   DLC IU NN MB

Nashua valley survey project
  see   Nashua valley survey.

Nashua valley water supply and sewerage project
  see   Nashua valley survey.

Nashville.
  Annual report of the departments ...
    see   Nashville.
  Reports of departments.

Nashville.
  Annual reports of the treasurer and recorder
  chief of Fire department, and other officers

    see

  Nashville.
  Reports of departments.

Nashville.
  Historical hand-book and official guide to
  Nashville
    see under title

Nashville,   defendant.
  Laminated-pole case
    see under   U.S. Circuit Court (6th Circuit)

NASHVILLE.
  Municipal bonds for sale [trunk sewer bonds and
street improvement bonds]. Special notice. Nashville
[Ambrose & Bostelman] 1903. [7], [7] p. 15cm.

  Film reproduction. Positive.

  1. Sewerage--Finance--U.S.--Tenn.--Nashville. 2. Highway finance--
U.S.--Tenn.--Nashville.   t. 1903.

  NN   0025577   NN

Nashville.
  Recorder's report.
  [Nashville,
    v.   23cm.

  1. Finance—Nashville, Tenn.
                                              11-6538
  Library of Congress   HJ9013.N15 c

  NN   0025578   DLC

Nashville.
  Reports of departments ...   Nashville, 18
     v.
    Title varies: Communication from ... the
  mayor ... with accompanying documents. Annual
  reports of the treasurer and recorder, chief of
  fire department and other officers ...; Annual
  exhibit showing the financial operations and
  other work of the various departments ...
  Reports of departments.

  NN   0025579   DLC CtY NN NjP T

Nashville.   Agricultural and industrial
                  state normal school.
    see

  Tennessee agricultural and industrial state normal
              school, Nashville.

Nashville. American Baptist Theological Seminary
    see
American Baptist Theological Seminary, *Nashville.*

Nashville.   Audit division.
  ...Annual audit report.

  Nashville   28cm.

  1. Finance—U. S.—Tenn.—
N. Y. P. L.   Nashville.
                                   March 11, 1947

  NN   0025582   NN

Nashville. Audit division.
HD4606
.N3A5
  Nashville. *City planning and zoning commission.*
    Six-year program for municipal improvements, 1939-40.
  Prepared for the Mayor and Board of public works and the
  City council by the City planning and zoning commission ...
  and the Audit division, C. P. Moore, city auditor, with the
  cooperation of National resources planning board ... [Nash-
  ville, 1939]

Nashville. Bank of Tennessee
    see
Bank of Tennessee, Nashville.

Nashville. Bar
    see   Nashville Bar Association.

Nashville.   Board of Aldermen.
  Report upon a proposed system of public edu-
  cation, for the city of Nashville...
    see under   Ingraham, J W   of
  Tennessee.

L203
.N3A3 Nashville. Board of Education.
       Annual report of the public schools.
       1854/55-
       Nashville, 1855-
          v. 23 cm.

       Report year ends June 30; 1854/55, 1870/71,
       irregular.
          Title varies slightly.
          Reports for 1876/77-1877/78 contain a
       History of the Nashville public schools.
          Reports for 1873/74, 1878/79-1883/84,

       1888/89-1889/90, 1897/98 include Rules for the
       organization and government of the public
       schools, Courses of study, Examination
       questions, City school laws, etc.
          Reports for 1920/21-   are statistical
       in nature.

          1. Nashville--Public schools. 2. Public
       schools--Tenn.

  NN   0025588   T TU DHEW RPB CtY

Nashville. Board of education.
  Course of study, hand-book in Arithmetic for
  grammer grades.   Nashville, Board, 1917.
       153 p.

  NN   0025589   PU

Nashville.   *Board of education.*
  Course of study, handbook in arithmetic, music, writing,
  drawing, for grammar grades, Nashville public schools,
  1911. Nashville, Williams printing company, 1911.
       140 p. 19½cm.

  1. Education—Tennessee—Nashville. 2. Education—Curricula. [1. 2.
Course of study—Elementary schools—Nashville, Tenn.]
                                              E 15-893
  Library, U. S. Bur. of   Education LB1563.N2

  NN   0025590   DHEW

372.4   Nashville. *Board of education.*
N178c   Course of study: handbook in English, read-
        ing, spelling, composition, language, grammar
        and literature. For grammar grades, Nashville
        Public Schools, 1906-07.   Nashville, Tenn.,
        Ambrose & Bostelman, printers and binders,
        1908.
           70p. 20cm.

           1. Reading (Elementary) 2. English language
        - Study and teaching. Sp.: Littlefield Fund.

  NN   0025591   TxU

375   Nashville.   Board of education.
N17cp   Course of study, Nashville public schools, pri-
1928   mary grades ...   Nashville, Ambrose [1928]
           107p.

           Includes bibliographies.

           1. Education--Nashville, Tenn.--Curricula.

  NN   0025592   IU

VOLUME 405

Nashville. *Board of education.*
Course of study of the Nashville public schools, with directions to teachers. Nashville, J. T. S. Fall & sons, printers, 1869.
2 p. l., 87 p. 20½ᶜᵐ.

1. Nashville—Public schools. 2. Education—Tennessee—Nashville. 8. Education—Tennessee—Curricula.

33–38961

Library of Congress   LB1563.N3 1869   379.768

NN 0025593   DLC NN

Nashville. Board of Education.
A history of the colored schools of Nashville, Tenn.
see under Hubbard, G. W., comp.

Nashville. Board of education.
Hume-Fogg high school, September, 1912. Floor plans, general introduction, courses of study in detail. ₍Nashville. 1912.₎
48 p. 12°.

1. Education (Secondary), U. S.:   Tenn.: Nashville.
N. Y. P. L.   December 8, 1915.

NN 0025595   NN

Pam
LB2826.5
.N2N3 **Nashville. Board of Education.**
Information concerning Nashville public schools. Comparative rates of taxation, school costs, etc. compiled from government reports and other official and educational records available, January, 1927. Building needs and prospective relief. ₍Nashville, Printed, issued, and distributed by direction of the city Board of Education, 1927.₎
11 p. 23 cm.

NN 0025596   T

Nashville. Board of education.
Outline of course of study. Changes in various subjects, advance directions, typical programs. Nashville public schools, 1911. Nashville: Ambrose Prtg. Co., 1911. 43 p. 12°.

1. Education, U. S.: Tenn.: Nashville.
N. Y. P. L.   December 8, 1915.

NN 0025597   NN

Nashville. Board of education.
Rules and regulations of the city public schools of Nashville. Nashville: Amer. Steam Book and Job Off., 1879. 15 p. 8°.

Bound with: Same. Annual reports, 1870/71–1879/80.

1. Schools.—Regulations, etc., U. S.:   Tenn.: Nashville.
N. Y. P. L.   June 22, 1916.

NN 0025598   NN

Pam
L203
.N3B2 **Nashville. Board of Education.**
1855   Rules for the government of the free schools of the City of Nashville. Nashville, W. F. Bang & Co., 1855.
8 p. 18 cm.

1. Nashville--Public schools. 2. Education--Tenn.--Nashville.

NN 0025599   T

Nashville. *Board of education.*
Rules for the organization and government of the public schools, city of Nashville, Tennessee. 1928. Adopted by the Board of education, November 26, 1928. ₍Nashville? 1928₎
28 p. 23ᶜᵐ.

1. School management and organization—Tennessee—Nashville.

E 34–9

Library, U. S. Office of   Education LB2802.N2A2

NN 0025600   DHEW

Pam
LC144
.T4N3 **Nashville. Board of Education. Instruction Committee.**
All-year schools. Report of Instruction Committee to Nashville (Tenn.) Board of Education. Printed by authority of Instruction Committee. ₍Nashville, 1922₎
cover-title, 8 p. 23 cm.

1. School attendance--Tenn.--Nashville.
I. Title.

NN 0025601   T DHEW

Nashville. Board of Health.
Annual report of the city health officer
see its Report.

Nashville. Board of Health.
The care of babies in hot weather. n. t.-p. ₍Nashville: Remy-Nance Prtg. Co., 1912.₎ 7(1) p. 16°.

Title from cover.

1. Infants.—Care, etc.
N. Y. P. L.   December 24, 1914.

NN 0025603   NN

W 2
AT2.2
N2D4o **NASHVILLE. Board of Health**
Condensed monthly statement of mortality.
Nashville, 187 -98.
v.
Continued by the Board's Official report.

NN 0025604   DNLM

NASHVILLE. Board of health.
Hot-weather care of infants and young children.
₍Nashville.₎ 1898. (8) pp. 16°.

NN 0025605   MB DNLM

W 2
AT2.2
N2D4o **NASHVILLE. Board of Health**
Official report. Jan. 1899-Aug. 1913.
Nashville.
15 v. in
Continues the board's Condensed monthly statement of mortality.
Continued by Official report issued by the Dept. of Health.

NN 0025606   DNLM MB

Nashville. *Board of health.*
Report.
Nashville, Tenn., 18   –19
v. plans (part fold.) 23½ᶜᵐ.

1. Nashville, Tenn.--Sanit. affairs.

8–12987

Library of Congress   RA155.N25

NN 0025607   DLC ICJ MB NcD DNLM DL NjP KyU TU

Nashville. *Board of park commissioners.*
Annual report.
₍Nashville,
v. plates. 23ᶜᵐ.

1. Nashville—Parks.

11–28513

Library of Congress   SB483.N25A3

NN 0025608   DLC

Nashville. Board of park commissioners.
An exhibition of Italian paintings lent by Mr. Samuel H. Kress ... to Board of park commissioners, Nashville, Tennessee ...
see under Kress, Samuel Henry, 1863–

HD4606
.N3A5 **Nashville. Board of public works.**

Nashville. *City planning and zoning commission.*
Six-year program for municipal improvements, 1939–40. Prepared for the Mayor and Board of public works and the City council by the City planning and zoning commission ... and the Audit division, C. P. Moore, city auditor, with the cooperation of National resources planning board ... ₍Nashville, 1939₎

Nashville. Board of Trade.
Nashville its advantages and opportunities ...
[Nashville, Tenn., Keelin-Williams Print. Co.] 1906.
95 p. 8°.

NN 0025611   NN

Nashville.   Board of Trade.
Year book of Nashville Board of Trade, Nashville, Tennessee.
[Nashville], 1907–.
Continued from 1907/8. illus. 23ᶜᵐ.

NN 0025612   ICJ

Nashville   Buford college.
see
Buford college, Nashville.

Nashville. Carnegie Library
see Nashville. Public Library.

917.68
N248n **Nashville.**   Centennial commission.
Nashville city guide book, issued under authority of the Board of directors, Centennial commission. First edition ... Edited by Charles Edwin Robert. Nashville, Pub. by Wheeler brothers, 1880.
112p. incl. illus., map. 23cm.

Advertising matter interspersed.

1. Nashville – Descr. – Guide-books.

NN 0025615   LNHT NcD

Nashville,   Central Tennessee college.
see
Walden university, Nashville.

VOLUME 405

HC108
.N2N16   Nashville. Chamber of Commerce.
         Economic survey of essential facts about
         Nashville, Tennessee as a location for defense
         projects. Prepared for General Lytle Brown.
         Nashville, 1941.
         1 v.(loose-leaf) illus.,maps(part fold.)
         30 cm.
         One map in pocket.
         Part typewritten and part reproduced from
         typewritten copy.

   NN   0025617   T

F444
.N2N19   [Nashville. Chamber of commerce]
         In and around Nashville, Tennessee ...
         [Nashville, Brandau-Craig-Dickerson co., 1925?]
         cover-title, [20] p. illus. 14 x 20.5 cm.
         "Compliments, Chamber of commerce,
         Nashville, Tenn."

   NN   0025618   DLC

Nashville   Chamber of commerce.
         Letter and documents in relation to the location of the
         railroad bridge across the Cumberland River at Nash-
         ville. Printed by order of the Nashville Chamber of
         commerce. Nashville, W. F. Bang & co., printers, 1856.
         32 p. 22½cm.

         1. Nashville, Tenn.--Bridges.

   Library of Congress   TG25.N25A3 1856   6-43804†

   NN   0025619   DLC ViU

Nashville. Chamber of commerce.
   Manual.
   Nashville,
         v. 21½cm. annual.

                                              7—33359
   Library of Congress   HF296.N27

   NN   0025620   DLC

Nashville.   Chamber of commerce.
   Nashville, Davidson County, Tennessee. The progressive city of the south. Climate, water, altitude, agricultural, mineral and forest surroundings
   unequaled.
   [Nashville, 1901]

F444
.N2N2

   NN   0025621   DLC

F444
q.N2N4   Nashville. Chamber of Commerce.
         Nashville in the 20th century. Pictorial ed.
         Nashville, Foster & Webb [1900?]
         cover-title, 44 [4] p. illus.(incl.ports.,
         maps) 49x35 cm.
         Colored illustrations on covers.
         "Issued by the direction of the Chamber of
         Commerce."
         Includes advertising matter.

   NN   0025622   T

HF296
.N272   Nashville. Chamber of Commerce.
         One hundred years; Nashville and its Chamber
         of Commerce, 1847-1947.   [Nashville, 1948]
         [16] p. illus.(incl.ports.,map,facsim.)
         28 cm.
         On cover: 100th anniversary, Nashville
         Chamber of Commerce, 1947.

         1. Nashville. Chamber of Commerce. 2. Nash-
         ville--Econ. condit.

   NN   0025623   T

Nashville.   Chamber of commerce.
   Special committee.
         Report of the special committee for the
         chamber of commerce on the advantages of
         Nashville as a suitable place for a
         permanent army post and encampment.
         Nashville, Marshall, 1898.
         24 p. 25cm.

   NN   0025624   DNW

Nashville .   Charters.
         Amended charter of the city of Nashville. 1899.   Nashville:
   Marshall & Bruce Co., 1899.   22 p.   8°.

   1. Municipal charters and ordinances,   U. S.: Tenn.: Nashville, 1899.
   N. Y. P. L.   February 24, 1920.

   NN   0025625   NN I

Nashville.   *Charters.*
   Charter of the city of Nashville. [Nashville? 1883]
   8 p. 22cm.

                                              CA 25-1400 Unrev'd
   Library of Congress   JS1161.A8 1883

   NN   0025626   DLC

Nashville. *Charters.*
   The charter of the city of Nashville, as amended by various acts of the General assembly of Tennessee, including all
   amendatory acts passed by the General assembly of 1909, to
   which all such acts of 1909 are prefixed. Nashville, Tenn.,
   McQuiddy printing company, 1909.
         146 p. 22½ cm.

         1. Tennessee. Laws, statutes, etc.

         JS1161.A8 1909   11-10495 rev

   NN   0025627   DLC NN

Nashville .   Charters.
   The charter of the city of Nashville. The commission form
   of government act of 1913, and various amendments during the
   same session, and sidewalk acts, 1907 and 1911. Compiled by
   A. G. Ewing, jr., city attorney, and F. M. Garard, assistant city
   attorney. Nashville: McQuiddy Prtg. Co., 1913. 107 p. 8°.

   1. Municipal charters and ordinances,   U. S.: Tenn.: Nashville.
   N. Y. P. L.   March 20, 1920.

   NN   0025628   NN IU T

352.0768 Nashville.   Charters.
N172c   The charter of the city of Nashville;
1917   the commission form of government ori-
         ginal act of 1913, and all subsequent
         amendments, including acts of 1917;
         sidewalk assessment acts of 1907, 1911;
         police and fire pension acts of 1913,
         1915 and 1917; gutter act of 1917; and
         transportation trustees acts of 1917.
         Comp. by A. G. Ewing, Jr. ... and J.
         Washington Moore ...   [Nashville,
         1917]
         173p.

   NN   0025629   IU U NNC

JS1161
.A8   Nashville. Charters.
1915   The charter of the city of Nashville. The
         commission form of government act of 1913, and
         subsequent amendments, and sidewalk acts 1907
         and 1911. Compiled by A.G. Ewing, Jr., City
         attorney and F.M. Garard, Assistant City
         attorney. Nashville. McQuiddy Printing
         Company, 1915.
         121 p. 24cm.

         I. Ewing, A.G. II. Garard, F.M.

   NN   0025630   T NjP NN IU

JS1161
.A8   Nashville. Charters.
1921   The charter of the city of Nashville.
         Mayor and City council form of government.
         Compiled by Morton B. Adams, City Attorney,
         and J. Washington Moore, assistant city
         attorney.   Nashville, Ambrose Printing Co.,
         1921.
         121 p. 23cm.

         I. Adams, Morton B. II. Moore, J.
         Washington.

   NN   0025631   T

Nashville.   Charters.
         The charter of the City of Nashville, as
         contained in chapter 125 of the Private acts of
         1923, and all acts amendatory thereto. Also
         chapter 3, Private acts of 1923, repealing for-
         mer charter of 1921. Compiled by Morton B.
         Adams, J. Washington Moore and Norman R.
         Minick. Nashville, Baird-Ward Printing Co.,
         1923.
         159 p.

   NN   0025632   NNC IU T

Nashville. *Charters.*
   The charter of the city of Nashville, as contained in chapter
   125 of the private acts of 1923, and all acts amendatory thereto.
   Also chapter 39 Private acts of 1923, repealing former charter
   of 1921. Compiled and revised by J. Washington Moore, city
   attorney, Jack Keefe ... [and others] assistant city attorneys.
   Nashville, Tenn., Bramblett printing co., inc., 1932.
         280 p. 23cm.

         1. Nashville. Law dept.
                                                       45-41693
   Library of Congress   JS1161.A9A3 1932
                             [2]   352.0768

   NN   0025633   DLC

Nashville. Charters.

         Charter, city of Nashville, passed by
   Seventy-third General assembly, state of
   Tennessee, 1943. Nashville, Rich print-
   ing co. [1943]
         254p. 22½cm.

   NN   0025634   NcD

VOLUME 405

Nashville. *Charters.*
Charter of the city of Nashville, Tennessee. Chapter no. 47, Private acts of the General assembly of the state of Tennessee for the year 1943 as amended. Charlottesville, Va., Michie city publications company, 1945.

2 p. l., 296 p. 22½ᶜᵐ.

"Prepared ... by Michie city publications company."—Pref.

I. Michie city publications company.

45–18537
Library of Congress   JS1161.A9A3 1945
                             ₍2₎   352.0768

NN 0025635   DLC

Nashville. *Charters.*
Charter of the city of Nashville, Tennessee. Chapter no. 246, Private acts of the General Assembly of the State of Tennessee for the year 1947 as amended through the legislative session of 1949. Charlottesville, Va., Michie City Publications Co., 1949.

342 p. 24 cm.

"Prepared ... by Michie City Publications Company."

I. Michie City Publications Company, Charlottesville, Va.

JS1161.A8 1949   352.0768   49–27569*

NN 0025636   DLC

Nashville. *Charters.*
Charter of the city of Nashville, Tennessee. Chapter no. 246, Private acts of the General Assembly of the State of Tennessee for the year 1947, as amended through the legislative session of 1951. Charlottesville, Va., Michie City Publications Co., 1952.

318 p. 24 cm.

I. Michie City Publications Company, Charlottesville, Va.

352.0768   52–22886

NN 0025637   DLC TNJ NN

Nashville. *Charters.*
A digest of the charter, amendments and acts of the General Assembly pertaining to the City of Nashville: with the ordinances of the city in force June, 1868
see under Lovering, Amos, comp.

Nashville. Charters.

Nashville. *Ordinances, etc.*
A digest of the general laws of the corporation of Nashville. Prepared by Wm. A. Glenn, under an act of City council, approved March 11, 1865. Nashville, Printed by Bell, Jones & co., 1865.

Nashville. *Charters.*
... Nashville charter bill, 1921 ... Nashville, Tenn., Baird-Ward printing company ₍1921₎
63 p. 23 cm.

I. Tennessee. Laws, statutes, etc.

NN 0025640   NNC

Nashville. Children's Museum.
Report. 1st–
1944/47–
₍Nashville₎
v. illus. 23 cm.

AM101.N273   51–36091 ‡

NN 0025641   DLC OClWHi

Nashville. Christ church.
Christ church, Nashville, 1829–1929 ... Nashville, Tenn., Marshall & Bruce co. ₍ᶜ1929₎
297 p. front., plates, ports., map, facsim. 23½ᶜᵐ.

"History publication committee: Mrs. Anne Rankin, editor-in-chief."

1. Protestant Episcopal church in the U. S. A.—Tennessee. 2. Tennessee—Church history. I. Rankin, Mrs. Anne, ed.

Library of Congress   BX5980.N25C5   29–11490

NN 0025642   DLC NcD TNJ–R ViU IEG TxU NN TU

Film
R–31   **Nashville. Christ Church.**
Records: 1829–1939; Parish register: 1895–1917.
Microfilm (Positive and negative)
2 reels.

1. Protestant Episcopal Church in the U. S. A. - Tennessee 2. Tennessee - Church history.

NN 0025643   TNJ–R

BR55
?T4   **Nashville. Christian Church.**
Address and correspondence delivered in the... Dec. 30, 1855.
16 p. (Theological pamphlets, 89:9)

NN 0025644   DLC

Nashville. Citizens.
Credit of the west
see under Nashville. Committee appointed at a meeting of merchants and other citizens.

Nashville. Citizens.
Improvements for the creation of water power by means of a dam and lock in the Cumberland River ...
see under title

Pam
Coll   **Nashville. Citizens.**
Nashville's greeting to the Confederate veterans, Richmond, 1896. ₍Nashville, Tenn., Press of Brandon Printing co., 1896₎
₍2₎p. illus. 19½ x 20cm

Cover-title.

NN 0025647   NcD CSmH

F436
.L47   **Nashville. Citizens.**
Presentation of loving cup. From the people of Nashville to Major Eugene Castner Lewis. Sunday afternoon, July 7, 1913. ₍Nashville, 1913₎
1 v. (unpaged) front. (col.), illus., plates, ports. 28 cm.

1. Lewis, Eugene Castner. 2. Nashville. Tennessee Centennial and International Exposition, 1897. 3. Nashville—Parks. 4. Nashville—Monuments.

NN 0025648   T

F
390
.N28
1836b   **Nashville. Citizens.**
Proceedings of a meeting of the citizens of Nashville, Tenn., in favor of recognising the Independence of Texas. [Washington] Gales & Seaton [1836]
6 p. 24cm. (U. S. 24th Congress, 1st Session. [Senate Doc. No.] 418)
Caption title.
"June 27, 1836. Read, and ordered to be printed."
"Signed: J. Catron, Chairman."
First published as a broadside, Nashville, 1836. cf. Streeter no. 1223. Not in Streeter.

NN 0025649   TxDaDF TxU

Nashville. *City attorney*
see
Nashville. *Law dept.*

Nashville. City council, defendant.

Tennessee. *Supreme court.*
C. E. Rust et al. *vs.* Mayor and City council of Nashville. Decision of the Supreme court of Tennessee in the case of C. E. Rust et al. *vs.* Mayor and City council of Nashville, relative to the Nashville special assessment or front foot assessment act. Nashville, 1913.

Nashville. *City council.*
Report of the committee of the City council of Nashville upon the affairs of the Nashville and northwestern railroad company. ₍Nashville? 1859?₎
16 p. 22ᶜᵐ.

1. Nashville and northwestern railroad company. I. Title.

A 23–123 Revised
Bur. of railway econ. Libr.
for Library of Congress   ₍r41b2₎

NN 0025652   DBRE DHEW NcD IU ViU

Nashville. City Council.
Rules and regulations governing the City Council, and amended charter ...
= Nashville, Tenn. 1905. 86 pp. 15 cm.
The amended charter is catalogued separately.

H2208

NN 0025653   MB T Or

HD4606
.N3A5   **Nashville.** *City planning and zoning commission.*
Six-year program for municipal improvements, 1939–40. Prepared for the Mayor and Board of public works and the City council by the City planning and zoning commission ... and the Audit division, C. P. Moore, city auditor, with the cooperation of National resources planning board ... ₍Nashville, 1939₎

711.40973   **Nashville—City Planning and Zoning Commission.**
N178n2   Capital improvements budget and program.
Nashville.
v. tables. 23cm.
Each report covers a six year period ending in June or July.
Prepared by the Advance Planning Division.

NN 0025655   IU

VOLUME 405

Nashville. City Planning and Zoning Commission
Financial structure: Nashville and Davidson
County; informational report about the financial
capacities of our community, by the Advance
planning and research division of the Nashville
city and Davidson County planning commissions.
[Nashville?] 1955.
70 p. charts. 36 cm.
1. Finance – Davidson Co., Tenn.
I. Davidson County, Tennessee. Planning
Commission.

NN 0025656 TU MiU PU-FA NN IU T PPCPC

Nashville. City planning and zoning commission.
Low standard housing in Nashville, Tennessee.
Nashville City planning and zoning commission.
1937.
iv, 38 numb. l. incl. tables., 24 maps.
27.5 cm.
Bibliography: 1 iv.
1. Housing – Nashville, Tenn.

NN 0025657 NNC IaU

Nashville. City planning and zoning commission.
Tennessee. *Railroad and public utilities commission.*
Nashville transportation survey. Findings. Prepared for
the Railroad and public utilities commission of the state of
Tennessee. Under the direction of Chas. W. Hawkins, engineer. With the cooperation of the City planning and zoning
commission, city of Nashville. 1937. [Nashville, 1937]

NA9127
.N18N35 Nashville. City Planning and Zoning Commis-
sion.
Planning activities, 1954. [Nashville]
Nashville City Planning Commission and
Davidson County Planning Commission [1955]
cover-title, 30 [i.e.42] p. incl.maps.
24x35 cm.

Reproduced from typewritten copy.

NN 0025659 T IU DHUD PPCPC

Nashville. City Planning and Zoning Commission.
Project outline for street and highway study
of City of Nashville and Davidson County, Tennessee, prepared by Nashville City Planning Commission and Davidson Planning Commission.
Nashville, Jan. 4, 1955.
17 p.

NN 0025660 PPCPC

Nashville. *City planning and zoning commission.*
Six-year program for municipal improvements, 1939–40.
Prepared for the Mayor and Board of public works and the
City council by the City planning and zoning commission ...
and the Audit division, C. P. Moore, city auditor, with the
cooperation of National resources planning board ... [Nash-
ville, 1939]
5 p. l., 64 numb. l. incl. tables, diagrs. 28ᶜᵐ.

1. Nashville—Public works. I. Nashville. Audit division. II.
U. S. National resources planning board. Region 3. III. Nashville.
Mayor. IV. Nashville. Board of public works. V. Nashville. City
council.
Library of Congress HD4606.N3A5 44–44247
[2] 352.5

NN 0025661 DLC OrU IU

Nashville. City Planning and Zoning Commission
Study and recommendations for the
location of a municipal auditorium.
[Nashville] City Planning Commission,
Advance Planning Division [1954]
28 p. (chiefly illus., maps) 32x44 cm.

Cover title.
Part of illustrative matter in pocket.

1. Auditoriums.

NN 0025662 NIC PU-FA MiD NNC NcU PPCPC

289.6 Nashville. City planning and zoning com-
N182 mission.
A traffic safety survey of the city of Nashville,Tennessee. Sponsored and directed by the
City planning and zoning commission;conducted
under the auspices of the Tennessee emergency
relief administration... report prepared under
the direction of Chas.W.Hawkins,assistant city
planning engineer. [Nashville] 1934.
220 numb.l plates,maps. 29cm.

Mimeographed.

NN 0025663 DNAL

Nashville. City Planning Commission
see
Nashville. City Planning and Zoning Commission.

Nashville. Cokesbury Press
see Cokesbury Press, Nashville.

Pam
HG2529 Nashville. Committee appointed at a meeting of
1833 merchants and other citizens.
.N3 Credit of the west. Report of a committee
appointed at a meeting of merchants and other
citizens of Nashville, Tennessee, April 2,
1833, in regard to the business, resources,
and credit of the State of Tennessee. Nashville, Printed at the office of the National
Banner, 1833.
[9] p. 19 cm.

Submitted in reply to "Report made by the

minority of the Committee of Ways and Means
in the House of Representatives of the United
States."

1. Bank of the United States, 1816-1836.
2. Tenn.--Econ. condit. 3. U.S. Congress.
House. Committee on Ways and Means. Bank of
the United States. Title.

NN 0025667 T NcD TxU TKL PPAmP

Nashville. Committee of '98.
Historical hand-book and official guide to
Nashville
see under title

Nashville. Committee on First annual convention, U. C. V.
First annual convention, United Confederate veterans.
Chattanooga, Tenn. July 3d, 4th, 5th, 1890. [Chatta-
nooga? 1890]
cover-title, 36 p. 22ᶜᵐ.

1. United Confederate veterans.
6-7467†* Cancel
Library of Congress E485.3.A122

NN 0025669 DLC

Nashville. Committee on Leisure-Time
Problems of Housing Project Areas
see Council of Community Agencies of
Nashville and Davidson County. Committee on
Leisure-Time Problems of Housing Project Areas.

Nashville. Community chest
see
Community chest of Nashville.

Nashville. Community Services Commission.
A future for Nashville
see under Tennessee. Community
Services Commission for Davidson county and the
city of Nashville.

Nashville. Confederate soldiers' home
see
Tennessee. Confederate soldiers' home, Nashville.

Nashville, Tenn. Conference of federal and
state representatives to consider plans for
the eradication of the cattle tick.
see Conference of federal and state
representatives to consider plans for the
eradication of the cattle tick, Nashville, Tenn.,
1906.

Nashville. Conference of state supervisors and Negro
teacher trainers in agricultural education. *19th*, 1940.
see
Conference of state supervisors and Negro teacher trainers
in agricultural education. *19th, Nashville,* 1940.

Nashville. Conference on education and
race relations. 1st, 1931
see Conference on education and
race relations. 1st, Nashville, 1931.

Nashville. Convention, 1850.
see
Southern convention, Nashville, Tenn., 1850.

Nashville. Council of community agencies
see
Council of community agencies, *Nashville.*

Nashville. Council of social agencies
see
Council of community agencies, *Nashville.*

Nashville. Cumberland college
see Nashville. University.

Nashville. Dargan-Carver Library
see Dargan-Carver Library, Nashville,
Tenn.

VOLUME 405

W 2
AT2. 2
N2D4o
NASHVILLE. Dept. of Health
    Official report.
    Oct. 1913-
    Nashville.
        v.
    Continues Official report issued by the
    Board of Health.

NN   0025682   DNLM TNF TU

Nashville.   Education, Board of
    see   Nashville. Board of Education.

Nashville.   First American National Bank.
    see   First American National Bank.

Nashville.   First Baptist Church.
    Church records, 1820 - 1916.
    3 reels.
    Microfilm (Negative)

NN   0025685   TNSB

286.1768
N178fbco
Nashville.   First Baptist Church.
    The constitution, declaration of faith, and
covenant of the Nashville Baptist Church,
adopted July 9th, 1836. Together with the
names of the members of the church, the board
of trustees, the building committee, and the
committee of supervision of the church. Nashville, Tenn., Printed by W. Hasell Hunt & Co.,
1836.
    16p. 14½cm.
    Xeroxed from the original found in the 1884
cornerstone of   First *Baptist Church,*
Nashville.

NN   0025686   KyLoS

Nashville. First Christian Church.
    Correspondence between the Christian Church at
Nashville and New Orleans and the Rev. Jesse B.
Ferguson
        see under   Ferguson, Jesse Babcock, 1819-
1870.

Nashville. First Edgefield Presbyterian Church.
    Manual of The First Edgefield Presbyterian
Church, Nashville, Tennessee. Nashville,
Brandon Printing and Lithograph Co., May, 1888
    16 mo.   Tan paper covers.

NN   0025688   CSmH

BX9211
.N25F5
Nashville. First Presbyterian Church.
    The First Presbyterian Church, Nashville,
Tennessee. The addresses delivered in con-
nection with the observance of the one hundredth
anniversary, November 8-15, 1914. Nashville,
Foster & Parkes, 1915.
    231 p. port. 24cm.

    1. Nashville, Tenn. First Presbyterian
Church. 2. Presbyterians in Tennessee. I.Title.

NN   0025689   T NN NcD TxU TU

Pam
BX9225
.M63N2
Nashville. First Presbyterian Church.
    In loving memory of our dear pastor, T. V.
Moore, D.D., by the session of the First
Presbyterian Church, Nashville, Tennessee.
Nashville, Printed at the "Union and American"
1871.
    24 p. 61 cm.

NN   0025690   T ViU CSaT

Film
R-51
Nashville. First Presbyterian church.
    The John M. Hill fund of First
Presbyterian church.
    Unnumbered MSS pages.
    Microfilm (Negative)

    1. Hill, John M. 2. Manuscripts, English -
Facsimilies. 3. Presbyterian Church -
Manuscripts - Facsimilies.

NN   0025691   TNJ-R

Nashville. First Presbyterian church.
    Manual of the First Presbyterian church, Nashville,
Tenn.: with a brief history from its organization, November,
1814, to November, 1868. Prepared by the pastor, the Rev.
Robert F. Bunting, D. D., for the use of the congregation.
Approved by the Session, published by the deacons, November, 1868. Nashville, Tenn., Printed at the Southern Methodist publishing house, 1868.
    102 p. front. 22 cm.

    I. Bunting, Robert Franklin, 1828-1891.

    BX9211.N3F5   48-30289

NN   0025692   DLC CSmH

Nashville. First Presbyterian Church.
    Manual. Nashville, 1872.
    26 p. 4°.

NN   0025693   MWA

Film
R-52
Nashville. First Presbyterian Church.
    Papers pertaining to the sale of First
Presbyterian church building. 1955
    Unnumbered leaves. Typescript.
    Microfilm (Negative)

    1. Manuscripts, English - Facsimilies.
2. Presbyterian church - Manuscripts -
Facsimilies.

NN   0025694   TNJ-R

Film
R-167
Nashville. First Presbyterian Church.
    Records of the boards of Deacons.
    Unnumbered pages.
    Microfilm (Negative)

    1. Manuscripts, English - Facsimilies.
2. Presbyterian church - Manuscripts -
Facsimilies.

NN   0025695   TNJ-R

Nashville. First Presbyterian church.
    Tribute of respect to the memory of Rev. John Todd Edgar,
D. D., pastor of the First Presbyterian church, Nashville, Ten-
nessee. Published by the church. Nashville, Tenn., J. T. S.
Fall, printer, 1860.
    36 p. 23½ᵐ.
    "Funeral discourse, preached at the obsequies of Rev. John T. Edgar,
D. D., by Rev. Joseph Bardwell, November 15th, 1860": p. [10]-26.

    1. Edgar, John Todd, 1792-1860. 2. Funeral sermons. I. Bardwell,
Joseph, 1828-1893. II. Title.
                                      36-23699

    Library of Congress   BX9225.E4N3   922.573

NN   0025696   DLC GU T MnHi MWA

Film
R-166
Nashville. First Presbyterian Church.
    Various papers.
    Unnumbered pages.
    Microfilm (Negative)

    1. Manuscripts, English - Facsimilies.
2. Presbyterian church - Manuscripts -
Facsimilies.

NN   0025697   TNJ-R

[Nashville. First Presbyterian church. *Master's workers*]
    Old time Tennessee receipts. [Nashville, 1943]
    cover-title, 299 p. illus. 22ᵐ.
    "Prepared and published by members of the Master's workers, one
of the leading organizations of ladies within the First Presbyterian
church of Nashville."—Foreword.

    1. Cookery, American.   I. Title. II. Title: Tennessee receipts.
                                      43-18300

    Library of Congress   TX715.N26
                        [2]   641.5

NN   0025698   DLC ViU WU

Nashville. Fisk university
    see
Fisk university, Nashville.

Nashville. Garden Study Club
    see
Garden Study Club of Nashville.

Nashville. George Peabody College
    see
George Peabody College for Teachers, *Nashville.*

Nashville. Grain exchange.
    Code of by-laws and rules of the Nashville grain ex-
change. Nashville, McQuiddy [19—]
    30 p. 15ᵐ.

                                  CA 19-1 Unrev'd

    Library of Congress   HD9038.N2N3

NN   0025702   DLC

Nashville. Health board
    see   Nashville. Board of health.

VOLUME 405

Nashville. *Housing authority*
see
Nashville housing authority.

Nashville.   Immanuel Baptist Church.
  Church records, v. 1-8, 1887 - 1952.
  2 reels.
  Microfilm (negative)

NN 0025705   TNSB

Nashville. Institute for Brazilian Studies
see **Vanderbilt University,** *Nashville. Institute for Brazilian Studies.*

Nashville. Institute of research and training in the social sciences.
  Papers. no. 1–
  Nashville, Tenn., Vanderbilt university press, 1941–
    nos. 25ᶜᵐ.
    Cover-title.

  1. Southern states—Econ. condit.—1918– 2. Southern states—Soc. condit. 3. Social sciences—Collections.
                                        42-10964 Revised
  Library of Congress   HC107.A13N27
                              [r44c2]   330.975

NN 0025707   DLC OrCS OrU NcD CU MsU GEU

HC107 Nashville. Institute of research and training
.A13V38   in the social sciences.
  Van Sickle, John Valentine, 1892–
    Planning for the South, an inquiry into the economics of regionalism, by John V. Van Sickle. Nashville, Tenn., Vanderbilt university press, 1943.

Nashville. Institute of research and training in the social sciences.
  Studies sponsored by the Institute ...
  Nashville, Tenn.

NN 0025709   CtY

Nashville. Jackson committee.
      see
Jackson committee of Nashville.

Nashville. Joint health education committee
      see
Joint health education committee, Nashville.

Z   Nashville. Joint University Libraries.
733   Annual report.
.N3
    Began publication with report for 1951/52.
    Report year ends April 30.

NN 0025712   OrU

Nashville. Joint university libraries.
    The development of library resources and graduate work
      see under Conference of graduate deans and librarians, joint university libraries, Nashville, 1944.

Nashville. Joint university libraries.
    The development of university centers in the South; papers presented at the dedication of the Joint university library, December fifth and sixth, 1941, Nashville, Tennessee. Edited with an introduction by A. F. Kuhlman. Nashville, Tenn., Pub. by the Peabody press and the Vanderbilt university press for the Joint university libraries, 1942.
    128 p. incl. front., illus. (plans) 24½ cm.

    1. Libraries, University and college. 2. Library cooperation. 3. Universities and colleges—Southern states. I. Kuhlman, Augustus Frederick, 1889– ed. II. Title. III. Title: University centers in the South.
  Joint University   Libraries, Nashville   A 42—2051
  for Library of Congress   Z675.U5N3
                                [a50k1]†   027.775

    WaWW OrP OrCS OrPR OrU OrSaW OrStbM IdU
    NcRS PPT PV MeWC PU PBm OClW TxU ViU DLC MtU WaTC
NN 0025714   TNJ AAP AU NIC KEmT NBuU ICJ IaAS NcD

---

027   Nashville. Joint university libraries.
N2538H The Joint university libraries. A handbook of
1943   their facilites and services. Nashville, Tenn., 1943.
      22p.

NN 0025716   IU

Film Nashville, Joint University Libraries.
1659   [Manuscript collection]
      1 reel.
      Microfilm copy (negative) of nos. 5-15, 17, 18, and 20 in the JUL Manuscript Collection.
      Contents.- no.5. Origin and history of Bristol-Goodson, 1852, by Joe R. Anderson.- no.6. 21 letters describing service with Tenn. Volunteers in Confederate Army, 1861-1884.

NN 0025717   TNJ

Z   Nashville. Joint University Libraries.
733   Miscellaneous publications, no.1–
N2452 Nashville, 1942–
      v.
      Each issue has distinctive title.
      1. Nashville. Joint University Libraries.

NN 0025718   UU OrU NNC IU CU CLU FU TxDaM MiU OrCS

Z   Nashville. Joint University Libraries.
733   Report.
N2451 Nashville.
      v. in 28cm. annual.
      Period covered by report ends April 30.

NN 0025719   UU MBU IU LU OU

027.7 Nashville. Joint University Libraries.
N17s   A survey of resources needed and their estimated cost. Made by the staff of the libraries and the faculties of George Peabody College, Scarritt College, Vanderbilt University, under the direction of A.F. Kuhlman. Nashville, 1948.
      vi, I-46, II-53 l. tables (part fold.) 28 cm.
      I. Kuhlman, Augustus Frederick, 1889– II. Title.

NN 0025720   LU CU

Nashville. Joint university libraries. Conference of graduate deans and librarians, 1944
  see
Conference of graduate deans and librarians, *Joint university libraries. Nashville, 1944.*

Nashville. Joint university libraries. Conference on the development of library research resources and graduate work in the cooperative university centers of the South
  see
Conference of graduate deans and librarians, *Joint university libraries, Nashville, 1944.*

TX715 Nashville. Jordonia Methodist Church.
.N24   Woman's Society of Christian Service.
      Cook book, comp. by [the] Woman's Society of Christian Service, Jordonia Methodist Church. Nashville, 1955.
      1 v. (unpaged) illus. 21 cm.
      Cover title.
      Blank pages interspersed.
      Contains sketch of Jordonia Methodist Church.

NN 0025723   T

JS1161 Nashville. Law dept.
.A9A3   Nashville. *Charters.*
1932   The charter of the city of Nashville, as contained in chapter 125 of the private acts of 1923, and all acts amendatory thereto. Also chapter 39 Private acts of 1923, repealing former charter of 1921. Compiled and revised by J. Washington Moore, city attorney, Jack Keefe ... [and others] assistant city attorneys. Nashville, Tenn., Bramblett printing co., inc., 1932.

Nashville. Liberty and union convention, 1865.
    Proceedings of the Liberty and union convention, which assembled at the capitol, in Nashville, Tennessee, on the 9th of January, 1865. Five hundred and thirty delegates. Nashville, Tenn., B. C. Mercer, printer, 1865.
    13 p. 20½ᶜᵐ.

    1. Tennessee—Pol. & govt.—Civil war. I. Title.
                                        13-15515
  Library of Congress   JK5225.1865.A2

NN 0025725   DLC T

---

a   Nashville. Lockeland Baptist Church.
    Church records, 1903 - 1952.
    1 reel.
    Microfilm (negative)

NN 0025726   TNSB

Pam Nashville. McKendree Methodist Church.
BX8481 Historical synopsis and annual exhibit of
.N2M3 McKendree Station, Nashville District, Tennessee Conference, M. E. C. S., for conference year ending October, 1872 ... Nashville, Roberts & Purvis, 1872.
      28 p. 24 cm.
      1. Church membership.

NN 0025727   T

Nashville, Tenn. McKendree Methodist church.
  History of McKendree Methodist church, 1933.
  Nashville, McKendree M.E. church, 1933.
  [16] p. illus. 21 cm.

NN 0025728   NcD ViU

VOLUME 405

Pam
HS537
.T23N2   **Nashville. Masonic Widows' and Orphans' Home.**
Charter, by-laws and rules of the Masonic
Widows' and Orphans' Home, Nashville, Tennessee.
Nashville, Tenn.: Brandon Print. Co., 1887.
17 [2] p. 15 cm.

I. Title: Masonic Widows' and Orphans' Home
of Tennessee, Charters, by-laws and rules of the.

NN   0025729   T

Nashville. Mayor, defendant.

Tennessee. *Supreme court.*
C. E. Rust et al. *vs.* Mayor and City council of Nashville.
Decision of the Supreme court of Tennessee in the case of C. E.
Rust et al. *vs.* Mayor and City council of Nashville, relative
to the Nashville special assessment or front foot assessment
act. Nashville, 1913.

Nashville. Mayor.
Communication from the mayor ... with
accompanying documents
    see Nashville.
Reports of departments.

HD4606
.N3A5   **Nashville. Mayor.**

Nashville. *City planning and zoning commission.*
Six-year program for municipal improvements, 1939-40.
Prepared for the Mayor and Board of public works and the
City council by the City planning and zoning commission ...
and the Audit division, C. P. Moore, city auditor, with the
cooperation of National resources planning board ... [Nash-
ville, 1939]

**Nashville. Mechanics' institute and library asso-
ciation of Tennessee.**
Report of the ... annual exhibition.
Nashville, 1855-
    v.   22-22½ᶜᵐ.
Report of 1st exhibition has title: Report of the first annual exhibition
of the Mechanics' institute of Tennessee, held in Nashville, from the 1st
to the 8th of October, 1855. Embracing also, the charter, constitution, and
general memoranda relating to the institute.
Title varies slightly.

1. Nashville, Tenn.—Exhibitions.

Library of Congress   T180.N25   5-40318†

NN   0025733   DLC T

**Nashville. Medical convention of the state of
Tennessee**
    see Medical convention of the state of
Tennessee, Nashville.

Nashville. Meharry Medical College
    see
Meharry Medical College, Nashville.

Nashville. Merchants.
Credit of the west
    see under Nashville. Committee
appointed at a meeting of merchants and
other citizens.

Nashville. Merchants exchange.
Annual report.
Nashville, 18
    v. fold. plan. 23ᶜᵐ.
Report year ends Aug. 31.
Report for 1888 has title: Annual report of the Merchants exchange ...
with list of officers and standing committees for 1888-89.

1. Nashville—Comm. 2. Nashville—Descr. & trav. 3. Tennessee—
Descr. & trav.

Library of Congress   HF296.N25   7-22470 Revised

NN   0025737   DLC

Nashville. Montgomery Bell Academy
    see
Montgomery Bell Academy, *Nashville.*

TX153
.N2   **Nashville. Moore Memorial Presbyterian Church.**
The housekeeper's manual: a collection of
valuable receipts, carefully selected and
arranged. By the ladies of Moore Memorial
Presbyterian Church, Nashville, Tenn.
Nashville, Publishing House of the Methodist
Episcopal Church, South, 1875.
274 p. 19 cm.

Blank pages inserted between p.120-121, 240-
241 for personal recipes.

NN   0025739   T

Nashville. Mount Olivet Cemetery Company
    see   Mount Olivet Cemetery Company,
Nashville.

**Nashville. National conference of colored men of
the U.S., 1879**
    see   National conference of colored men of
the U.S., Nashville, Tenn., 1879.

**Nashville. National league on urban conditions
among Negroes.**
    see
National league on urban conditions among Negroes.

Nashville. Old Oak Club
    see
Old Oak Club, *Nashville.*

Nashville. Open letter club.
    see
Open letter club, Nashville.

Nashville. Ordinances, etc.
An act concerning the Water Works of the Town
of Nashville, passed 6th November, 1833.
Nashville, 1833.
8 p.

NN   0025745   THi

Nashville. Ordinances.
Building laws of Nashville, Tennessee. Handbook for architects, engineers, contractors, builders, plumbers, and all who are
engaged in the erection of buildings. Compiled by Baxter J.
Hodge. 1909. Nashville: McQuiddy Prtg. Co., 1909. 234 p.
12°.

1. Building laws, U. S.: Tenn.:   Nashville. 2. Hodge, Baxter J.,
compiler.   April 6, 1920.
N. Y. P. L.

NN   0025746   NN

614.85   **Nashville. Ordinances, etc.**
N17b   Building laws ... An ordinance provid-
1917   ing for fire limits and regulations
governing the construction, alteration,
equipment, repair or renewal of buildings or structures within the corporate
limits, 1917. Commission government ...
Nashville, Tenn., 1917.
250p.

NN   0025747   IU

Nashville. Ordinances.
Building ordinance.
1906. In effect October 13, 1906.   Nashville: McQuiddy Prtg.
Co., 1906. 126 p. 8°.

1. Building laws, U. S.: Tenn.:   Nashville.
N. Y. P. L.   April 12, 1920.

NN   0025748   NN

Nashville. Ordinances, etc.
Building zone ordinance, city of Nashville,
Tennessee. Passed on third reading by City
council, July 19, 1933, approved by the mayor,
July 20, 1933, all amendments as of August 1,
1936. Prepared by City planning and zoning
commission. [Nashville 193-?]
13 p. 17 pages of maps. 31cm.

NN   0025749   NNC

710.1   **Nashville. Ordinances, etc.**
N17b   Building zone ordinance, city of Nashville,
Tennessee. Passed on third reading by City council, July 19,1933. Approved by the mayor, July
20,1933. All amendments as of March 1,1940
[Nashville] City planning and zoning commission
[1940]
29p. 18 maps.
Reproduced from typewritten copy.
1. Cities and towns--Planning--Zone system. I
Nashville, Tenn.--City planning and zoning commission. II. Title.

NN   0025750   IU

Nashville. Ordinances, etc.
By-laws of the town of Nashville. [Nashville]
Bradford, 1814.
36 p.

NN   0025751   THi T

Nashville. Ordinances.
The code of Nashville. Prepared and edited by J. C. Bradford...   Nashville: A. B. Tavel, 1885. 2 p.l., 288 p. 8°.

1. Municipal charters and ordinances,   U. S.: Tenn.: Nashville, 1885.
2. Bradford, J. C., editor.
N. Y. P. L.   April 12, 1920.

NN   0025752   NN MB T NcD

VOLUME 405

Nashville.   Ordinances, etc.
The Code of the city of Nashville, Tennessee. The charter as amended and the general ordinances of the city. Enacted as a whole November 4, 1941. Effective November 10, 1941. Published by order of the Council. Charlottesville, The Michie Company, 1941.
988 p. 22½cm.

NN   0025753   ViU-L T TU

Nashville. *Ordinances, etc.*
The Code of the city of Nashville, 1947; containing the general ordinances of the city assembled for the editorial staff of the publishers by E. C. Yokley. Charlottesville, Va., Michie City Publications Co., 1948.
vii, 726 p. 24 cm.

To be kept up to date by annual pocket supplements.

I. Yokley, Emmett C., 1909–   II. Michie City Publications
Company, Charlottesville, Va.

JS1161.A9A3 1947   352.0768   48–16432*

NN   0025754   DLC

Nashville.   Ordinances, etc.
A compilation of the general laws of the city of Nashville: together with the charters of the city, granted by the states of North Carolina and Tennessee, and a list of the chief officers of the municipal government of Nashville ... from 1806 to 1860. Comp. by James E. Rains. Nashville, Tenn., J. O. Griffith and company, printers, 1860.
xiv p., 1 l., 280 p. 22½ᶜᵐ.

I. North Carolina. Laws, statutes, etc. II. Tennessee. Laws, statutes, etc. III. Rains, James Edward, 1833–1862.

11–13190

Library of Congress   JS1161.A9A3 ©1860

NN   0025755   DLC NcD-L PP NN

Nashville. *Ordinances.*
A copy of the acts of the corporation of Nashville and legislature of Tennessee, authorizing the subscription of $500,000 of stock in the Nashville and Chattanooga rail road company, with the opinion of the Supreme court of Tennessee, confirming said subscription. Nashville, Printed by W. F. Bang & co., 1849.
cover-title, ₃₁–20 p. 22½ᶜᵐ.

1. Nashville and Chattanooga railroad company.   I. Tennessee. Laws, statutes, etc. II. Tennessee. Supreme court.

A 21—1175

Bur. of railway econ. Libr.
for Library of Congress   ₍a41b1₎

NN   0025756   DBRE

Nashville. Ordinances, etc.
A digest of the charter, amendments and acts of the General Assembly pertaining to the City of Nashville: with the ordinances of the city in force June, 1868
see under Lovering, Amos, comp.

352.0768 Nashville.   Ordinances, etc.
N172o   Digest of the city of Nashville, to
1908   which are prefixed the state laws incorporating and relating to said city,
with an appendix containing various
grants, contracts and franchises;
comp. by Hill McAlister, city attorney
and Edward J. Smith, assistant city
attorney, 1908.   Nashville, 1908.
1284p.

NN   0025758   IU

Nashville. *Ordinances, etc.*
A digest of the general laws of the corporation of Nashville. Prepared by Wm. A. Glenn, under an act of City council, approved March 11, 1865. Nashville, Printed by Bell, Jones & co., 1865.
186 p. 22ᶜᵐ.

"Charter of the city of Nashville with the amendments thereto since January 31, 1848": p. 5–18.

I. Nashville. Charters. II. Glenn, William A.

42–34694

Library of Congress   JS1161.A9A3 1865

NN   0025759   DLC NN

Nashville.   Ordinances, etc.
A digest of the ordinances and resolutions enacted and adopted by the city of Nashville for the issuance of bonds, granting of franchises, licenses, and rights of way, and making certain contracts, up to the 1st of Juanuary 1916, ...
Nashville, 1916.

JS1161
.A9A3

NN   0025760   DLC

Nashville. Ordinances, etc.
...Digest of the ordinances and resolutions of the city of Nashville. Compiled by Albert G. Ewing, jr. ... and Frank M. Garard ... 1917, [¹16] Nashville, Tenn., Marshall & Bruce co., 1917, '16.
2 v. 25 cm.
Imprint varies: v. 2, Nashville, Tenn., Baird-Ward printing co., 1916.
Vol. 2 has title: A digest of the ordinances and resolutions enacted and adopted by the city of Nashville for the issuance of bonds, granting

of franchises, licenses and rights of way, and making certain contracts, up to the 1st of January, 1916, also a complete list of the city officials to date.

NN   0025762   NcD-L

Nashville. *Ordinances, etc.*
Digest of the ordinances of the city of Nashville, to which are prefixed the state laws incorporating, and relating to, the city, with an appendix containing various grants and franchises. Comp. by Claude Waller ... and Frank Slemons ... Nashville, Tenn., Marshall & Bruce co., 1893.
viii, 812 p. 23 cm.

I. Tennessee. Laws, statutes, etc. II. Waller, Claude. III. Slemons, Frank.

JS1161.A9A3 1893   11—13189

NN   0025763   DLC NN NcD-L

Nashville. *Ordinances, etc.*
Digest of the ordinances of the city of Nashville, to which are prefixed the state laws incorporating, and relating to the city, with an appendix containing various grants and franchises. Comp. by Edwin A. Price ... and K. T. McConnico ... Nashville, Tenn., Boylin printing co., 1901.
x p., 1 l., 1107 p. 23½ᶜᵐ.

I. Tennessee. Laws, statutes, etc. II. Price, Edwin A. III. McConnico, K. T.

11—13188

Library of Congress   JS1161.A9A3 1901

NN   0025764   DLC NN

Nashville   Ordinances, etc.
Laws of Nashville. Prepared by Lytton Taylor, city attorney, by the authority of the mayor and city council. Nashville, Tenn.: A. B. Tavel, 1888. 4 p.l., 421 p. 8°.

1. Municipal charters and ordinances, Lytton.   U. S.: Tenn.: Nashville. 2. Taylor, Lytton.
N. Y. P. L.   March 17, 1920.

NN   0025765   NN NcD-L T NcD

Pam
JS1161
.A9A3
1827   Nashville. Ordinances, etc.
The laws of the corporation of Nashville, as revised, re-enacted and passed 20th December, 1827. To which are added The acts of North Carolina and Tennessee, relating to the town of Nashville.   Nashville, John S. Simpson, 1828.
70 p. 19 cm.

I. Tennessee. Laws, statutes, etc. II. North Carolina. Laws, statutes, etc.

NN   0025766   T

Pam
JS1161
.A9A3
1830   Nashville. Ordinances, etc.
Laws of the corporation of Nashville, passed from the 20th December, 1827, to the 4th November, 1830.   Nashville: printed by Hunt, Tradiff & Co., 1830.
26 p. 19 cm.

Index in ms. on flv leaf at end.

I. Tennessee. Laws, statutes, etc.

NN   0025767   T THi

JS1161
.A9A3
1837   Nashville. Ordinances, etc.
Laws of the corporation of Nashville, to which are prefixed the laws of North Carolina and Tennessee relating to the town of Nashville. Published by authority.   Nashville, Wm. E. Matthews, 1837.
iv p., 1 l., 93, viii p. 23 cm.

"Errata": leaf preceding p.₍1₎

I. Tennessee. Laws, statutes, etc. II. North Carolina. Laws, statutes, etc.

NN   0025768   T TxDW TKL

Nashville.   Ordinances, etc.
Ordinances and regulations governing sale of milk and ice cream in the city of Nashville. Issued by the city board of health. n. t.-p. Nashville: Davie Prtg. Co. ₍1912.₎   15 p. 16°.

Title from cover.

1. Ice cream.—Jurisprudence, U. S.:   Tenn.: Nashville. 2. Milk supply.—
Jurisprudence, U. S.: Tenn.: Nash-   ville. 3. Nashville (Tenn.).
Health Board.
N. Y. P. L.   April 3, 1914.

NN   0025769   NN

Nashville.   Ordinances, etc.
Ordinances of the City of Nashville, of a public nature, in force August 1st, 1872. To which is prefixed a compilation of the state laws chartering and relating to the city and other laws relating to city corporations in general and with an appendix containing rules of the City Council, and an historical record of the chief officers of the city, from its incorporation in 1806, to those elected in 1871, inclusive. Compiled...by J. Lellyett.   Nashville: Robert & Purvis, 1872. xxxviii p., 1 l., 315 p. lea. 8°.

1. Municipal charters and ordinances, John.   U. S.: Tenn.: Nashville. 2. Lellyett, John.
N. Y. P. L.   January 25, 1915.

NN   0025770   NN T PU

JS1161
.A9A3
1875   Nashville. Ordinances, etc.
Ordinances of the City of Nashville, to which are prefixed the state laws chartering and relating to the city. With an appendix. Compiled by William K. McAlister, Jr. Nashville, Republican Banner Book and Job Print., 1875.
3 p. l., 336 p. 23 cm.

Continued in next column

VOLUME 405

Continued from preceding column

——— Ordinances enacted by the Mayor and City Council of Nashville since October 1, 1875. Intended as a supplement to McAlister's city digest. Nashville, Tavel, Eastman & Howell, 1878.
    cover-title, 32, 3 p. 21 cm.
    I. Nashville. Charters. I. Tennessee. Laws statutes, etc. II. McAlister, William K comp.

NN 0025772 T NN

Nashville.   Ordinances, *etc.*
    Ordinances of the City of Nashville, to which are prefixed the state laws chartering and relating to the city. With an appendix. Compiled by W. K. McAlister, Jr.   Nashville: Marshall & Bruce, 1881.   3 p.l., 486 p. 8°.

1. Municipal charters and ordinances,   U. S.: Tenn.: Nashville. 2. Mc-
McAlister, William K., the younger.
N. Y. P. L.   January 25, 1915.

NN 0025773 NN T NcD-L PPL

JS1161
.A9A3
1850   Nashville. Ordinances, etc.
    The revised laws of the City of Nashville, with the various acts of incorporation and laws applicable to the town and City of Nashville, and a list of the different boards of mayor and aldermen ... from the year 1806 to 1850, inclusive. Compiled by John Hugh Smith and John M. Lea. Nashville, Harvey M. Watterson, 1850
      192 p. 23 cm.

NN 0025774 T NcD

Nashville   Ordinances, *etc.*
    Revised laws of the City of Nashville; with the laws of North Carolina and Tennessee, relating to the Town and City of Nashville, and a list of the different boards of mayor and aldermen, and other officers of said city, from the year 1806 to 1855, inclusive. Compiled by W. A. Glenn.   Nashville: Union and American Steam Press, 1854. 237 p. 8°.

1. Municipal charters and ordinances,   U. S.: Tenn.: Nashville. 2. Glenn,
W. A.
N. Y. P. L.   January 25, 1915.

NN 0025775 NN TNDC T

Nashville   Ordinances, *etc.*
    Traffic law ordinance of the City of Nashville regulating traffic upon streets and rates of fare that may be charged by taxicabs and automobiles. Nashville: Higginbotham [1914]. 22 p. 16°.

1. Streets.—Jurisprudence, U. S.:   Tenn.: Nashville. 2. Streets.—
Traffic, U. S.: Tenn.: Nashville. 3.   Automobiles.—Jurisprudence,
U. S.: Tenn.: Nashville. 4. Cab   service.—Jurisprudence, U. S.:
Tenn.: Nashville.
N. Y. P. L.   April 15, 1916.

NN 0025776 NN IU

Nashville.   Ordinances, etc.
    Zoning regulations.   Nashville, City planning commission.

NN 0025777 PPCPC

Nashville. Peabody College for Teachers
    see
    George Peabody College for Teachers, *Nashville.*

Nashville. Planning commission
    see   Nashville. City planning and zoning commission.

Nashville. Planters' bank of Tennessee.
    see
    Planters' bank of Tennessee, Nashville.

SSPF
Tenn1 Nashville. Police Dept.
N17   Rules and regulations ... Sept.1, 1955.
A4   [Nashville? 1955?]
1955   53p. 16cm.

    1.Police - Nashville.

NN 0025781 CtY-L

Nashville. Public Library.
    Classified catalogue of the accessions to Carnegie Library of Nashville for the year 1906. Nashville [1906]
    45 p. 23 cm.
    Cover title.

    Z881.N254   8-32521 rev*

NN 0025782 DLC

Nashville. Public Library.
    [Descriptive folder.]   [Nashville: Foster, Webb & Parkes, 1911.] 2 l. 16°.

1. Libraries, U. S.: Tenn.: Nashville.
N. Y. P. L.   February 10, 1913.

NN 0025783 NN

Nashville. Public Library.
    Nashville Library exhibit. Small model library exhibited by the Carnegie Library of Nashville at the Tennessee State Fair, September 19–24, 1910. [Nashville, 1910]
    [4] p. 17 cm.
    160 children's books listed.

    1. Children's literature—Bibl.
    Z1037.N25   10-32645 rev*

NN 0025784 DLC

Nashville. Public Library.
    Nashville Public Library. [Report of the librarian] 1st-
    Nashville.
    v. in   23–28 cm. annual.
    Title varies: 1902–   Report.
    Issues for 1902–   published by the library under an earlier
name: Carnegie Library of Nashville.

    Z733.N24   027.4768   8–25033 rev*

NN 0025785 DLC IU LU NN PPDrop ICJ MB TU

028.431 Nashville. Public library.
N253n   Novels too good to miss; additions thru 1941. [Nashville, 1943]
    [18]p.

    At head of title: "Nashville public library, February 1943."
    Caption title.
    Various pagings.
    Mimeographed.

    1. Fiction--Bibl   2. Bibliography--Best books. I. Title.

NN 0025786 IU NNC

Nashville. Public Library. Report
    see its Nashville Public Library. [Report of the librarian]

Nashville. Public Schools.
    Course of study ...
       see under Nashville. Board of education.

321.8 Nashville--Public Schools.
N17d   Democracy's hope, a manual for teaching democracy -- prepared by the teachers of the city public schools, Nashville, Tennessee. [Nashville] 1951-52.
    2v. illus., ports. 28cm.

    Contents.- [v.1] Elementary grades.- [v.2] Secondary grades.

    1. Democracy--Study and teaching. I. Title.

NN 0025789 IU

Nashville. *Public Schools.*
    Tennessee through the printed page; a classified list of materials relating to Tennessee for school libraries.
    Nashville.
    v. 23–28 cm.
    First published in 1940.
    Issued by Nashville Public Schools, School Library Division.

    1. Tennessee—Bibl. I. Title.

    Z1337.N32   015.768   44-42258 rev*

NN 0025790 DLC TU

TX715
.N2   Nashville. Public Schools. Home Economics Dept.
    Nashville City schools, 1852-1952. Centennial cook book. [Nashville, 1952?]
    cover-title, 4 p. l., 81 l. illus. 28 cm.

    Reproduced from typewritten copy.

    1. Cookery, American. 2. Receipts. I. Title: Centennial cook book.

NN 0025791 T

Nashville. *Public works, Board of*
    see
    Nashville. *Board of public works.*

Nashville. Publishing house of the Methodist episcopal church, South
    see
    Publishing house of the Methodist episcopal church, South, Nashville.

VOLUME 405

Nashville. Regional conference on teacher training in home economics for Negroes, *9th,* 1940
see
Regional conference on teacher training in home economics for Negroes. *9th, Nashville,* 1940.

Nashville, Tenn. Robertson association.
see
Robertson association, Nashville, Tenn.

Nashville.   Roger Williams university.
see
Roger Williams university, Nashville, Tenn.

BX4603
.N2S3 Nashville. St. Mary's Church.
Old St. Mary's; an historical sketch of St. Mary's Church, Nashville, Tenn., 1847-1947. Souvenir booklet published on the occasion of the celebration of the Centennial of the dedication of the Church. Sponsored by the Parish Holy Name Society and the Parish Council of Catholic Women.   Nashville, Cullom & Ghertner, 1947.
52 p. illus.,ports. 28 cm.
Pages 33-52, advertising matter.

NN 0025797   T

Nashville. Scarritt college for Christian workers
see
Scarritt college for Christian workers, *Nashville.*

WA
1253.1 Nashville. School Health Service
qN2r   Report
.Nashville, 19
v.
Report year for   -1942 ends Dec. 31;
for 1943/44-   ends June 30.
Report for 1943/44 covers the period
Jan. 1, 1943-June 30, 1944.

NN 0025799   DNLM

Nashville. Southern convention
see
Southern convention, *Nashville, Tenn.,* 1850.

Nashville. Southern rural life conference
see
Southern rural life conference, *Nashville,* 1943.

Nashville. Southern rural life council
see
Southern rural life council, *Nashville.*

Nashville.   Southern sociological congress 1912.
see
Southern sociological congress. Nashville, Tenn., 1912.

Nashville.   State convention of the colored citizens of Tennessee, 1871.
see
State convention of the colored citizens of Tennessee, Nashville, 1871.

Nashville. State hospital
see
Tennessee. State hospital, Nashville.

Nashville.   State library.
see
Tennessee. State library, *Nashville.*

Nashville.   State Library and Archives
see
Tennessee. State Library and Archives, *Nashville.*

Nashville. State Normal College
see
George Peabody College for Teachers, *Nashville.*

Nashville.   State penitentiary
see
Tennessee. State penitentiary, Nashville.

Nashville. State Training and Agricultural School for Boys
see
Tennessee. State Vocational Training School for Boys, *Nashville.*

Nashville. State Vocational Training School for Boys
see
Tennessee. State Vocational Training School for Boys, *Nashville.*

Nashville. Tennessee Agricultural and Industrial State University
see
Tennessee. Agricultural and Industrial State University, *Nashville.*

N4775
.A6A5 Nashville. Tennessee Centennial and International Exposition, 1897.
1898b   Art album of the Tennessee Centennial and International Exposition, held at Nashville, May 1 to October 31, 1897. Photographs by W. G. and A. J. Thuss.   Nashville, Marshall & Bruce, 1898.
1 v.(unpaged, chiefly illus., front.(map)) 24x31 cm.
Illustrations in copies essentially the same but not in the same sequence.

"Compliments of Nashville, Chattanooga and St. Louis R'y."

1. Art--Exhibitions. I. Thuss, William Gustav. II. Thuss, Andrew Joseph, 1866-1956.

NN 0025814   T NN MB

Nashville. Tennessee centennial and international exposition, 1897.
Catalogue (illustrated) Fine arts department, Tennessee centennial ... Nashville, Press of the Brandon company [1897]
80, 266 p. incl. illus., ports., plans. 19½ᵐ.

1. Art—Exhibitions.

Library of Congress   N4775.A6   9-18278†

NN 0025815   DLC ViU CtY

Nashville. Tennessee centennial exposition, 1897.
Catalogue of books, library woman's building, Nashville, 1897.   Nashville, Brandon printing co. 1897.
126 p.

NN 0025816   NN PP

Nashville. Tennessee Centennial and International Exposition, 1897.
From Cherokee to Tennessee, 1796-1896
see under title

Nashville.Tennessee Centennial and International Exposition, 1897.
Major Eugene Castner Lewis
see under title

R
1882 NASHVILLE. TENNESSEE CENTENNIAL AND INTERNATIONAL EXPOSITION, 1897.
.61   Official guide to the Tennessee centennial and international exposition and city of Nashville.   Nashville,Tenn.,Marshall & Bruce co., 1897.
183p. 21½cm.
Includes advertising.
Contents.—pt.1. Guide to exposition.—pt.2. Guide to Nashville.

NN 0025819   ICN TU T ViU TKL

Nashville. Tennessee centennial and international exposition, 1897.
Official history of the Tennessee centennial exposition, opened May 1, and closed October 30, 1897. Published under the direction of Dr. W. L. Dudley and G. H. Baskette of the Committee on publication. Herman Justi, editor. Nashville, Tenn. [Press of the Brandon printing company] 1898.
495 p. col. front., illus. (incl. map, plan) ports. 35ᵐ.

I. Justi, Herman, ed.

Library of Congress   T775.B1A2   6-3768

NN 0025820   DLC NcD ICRL TKL ICJ ICN DSI

VOLUME 405

Nashville¿   Tennessee Centennial exposition,
1897.
    The opening of the United States government
building. [Nashville, Tenn., 1897].
    9p. YA16327.

NN 0025821   DLC OClW

T775
.C1A2 Nashville. Tennessee Centennial and International
       Exposition, 1897.
           Programme from May 1st '97 to Oct. 31st '97,
       Tennessee Centennial.   ₍Nashville, Marshall &
       Bruce Co., 1897₎
           1 v.(unpaged) 22 cm.
           Binder's title.
           Programs arranged chronologically; original
       covers bound in.
           Includes advertising matter.

NN 0025822   T

Nashville. Tennessee centennial and international
     exposition, 1897.
     U.S. *Board of management of government exhibit, Tennessee
     centennial exposition*, 1897.
         ... Report on the United States government exhibit at the
     Tennessee centennial exposition, Nashville, 1897. Washington,
     Govt. print. off., 1901.

Nashville. Tennessee centennial and international
     exposition, 1897.
     New York (*State*) *Commission, Tennessee centennial and
     industrial exposition, Nashville*, 1897.
         The Tennessee centennial. A souvenir of the trip taken by
     the Brooklyn party and the New York state commissioners to
     attend the "Brooklyn day" and the "New York state day"
     exercises at the Nashville exposition, October eighth to Oc-
     tober fifteenth, eighteen hundred and ninety-seven. ₍Brook-
     lyn₎ The New York state & Brooklyn commissioners, 1898.

T775
.B2A2 Nashville. Tennessee Centennial and International
       Exposition, 1897.
           Tennessee Centennial Exposition, Nashville.
       Nashville, Brandon ₍Print. Co., 1897₎
           ₍2₎ 48 ₍2₎ p. illus.,ports. 23 cm.
           Irish-American Day, Tennessee Centennial
       Exposition, Tuesday, September 21st, 1897.
       Irish-American Centennial Association of Tennes-
       see, 1897: p.₍1₎ of cover.
           "Preamble and resolutions adopted by the
       Irish-American Centennial Association of

Tennessee": p.₍2₎ and ₍3₎ of cover.
           "Distinguished Irish-Americans": p.₍4₎ of
       cover.
           Letter from Thomas W. Wrenne, President of
       Irish-American Centennial Association of Tennes-
       see dated August 10, 1897: in pocket.

           ₍1.₎ Irish-American Centennial Association of
       Tennessee.

NN 0025826   T TU TKL PPL RPB PBL

T775
.B1A4 Nashville. Tennessee Centennial and International
       Exposition, 1897.
           Tennessee. Her illustrious history, marvelous
       resources, wonderful capabilities. Developed by
       the Tennessee Centennial Exposition.   ₍Nash-
       ville, Foster & Webb, 1897₎
           192 p. illus.,ports.,maps. fold.map.
       18x27 cm.

           Colored illustration inserted between p.72-73

           1. Tennessee.

NN 0025827   T TU

T775
.D7A1 Nashville. Tennessee Centennial and International
       Exposition, 1897. Woman's Department.
           Catalogue woman's department, Tennessee Cen-
       tennial and International Exposition, May 1 to
       October 31, 1897.   Nashville, Burch, Hinton
       ₍1897?₎
           59 p. illus.,ports. 20 cm.
           Includes advertising matter.

NN 0025828   T

Nashville. Tennessee, industrial school
    see
Tennessee. Industrial school, Nashville.

Nashville₁   Tennessee school for the
                                           blind.
    see
Tennessee school for the blind, Nashville.

Nashville. Tennessee Taxpayers Association
    see **Tennessee Taxpayers Association**, *Nashville*.

Nashville. Trade, Board of
    see Nashville. Board of Trade.

Nashville. Trevecca Nazarene College
    see **Trevecca Nazarene College**, *Nashville*.

Nashville. Typographical Union
    see International Typographical Union of
North America. Union no. 20. Nashville.

Nashville. Union Bank
    see Union Bank of Tennessee.

Nashville, Tenn. University.
    Annual announcement of the law, literary, and medical
departments ...
Nashville, Tenn., 18
    ₁ v. 21½ᶜᵐ. ⅀

                              CA 7-2111 Unrev'd
    Library of Congress   LD3607.A2

NN 0025836   DLC

Nashville. University.
    Bulletin of information. Vol. I (no. 3), 2 (no. 3), 3 (no. 2, 4), 4 (no.
    I, 2), 5 (no. 4), 6 (no. 4, 6), 7 (no. 2), 8 (no. 4), 9 (no. 3).
    Nashville, Tenn. 1902-11. v. Plate. 20 cm.

H8092

NN 0025837   MB

NASHVILLE. University

    Catalogs, announcements of courses,
requirements for admission and other
publications relating to the academic
program will be found under the above
call number. Included also are similar
publications of individual schools or
departments of instruction of the
institution.

NN 0025838   DNLM

Nashville.   **University.**
    Catalogue of the literary and medical departments.
Nashville, 18
    v. 22½ᶜᵐ.

                              CA 9-171 Unrev'd
    Library of Congress   LD3607 A35

NN 0025839   DLC NjP NN

Nashville.   **University.**
    Catalogue of the officers and graduates of the Univer-
sity of Nashville. With an appendix, containing sundry
historical notices, etc. Nashville, A. Nelson & co., printers, 1850.
    35 p. 22ᶜᵐ.

                              7-26590†
    Library of Congress   LD3612.5 1850

NN 0025840   DLC DNLM TKL T

Nashville.   **University.**
    Catalogue of the officers and students of the literary
department ... with the announcements of the medical,
law and literary departments.
Nashville, Tenn., 18
    v. 23ᶜᵐ.

                              CA 7-2083 Unrev'd
    Library of Congress   LD3607.A4

NN 0025841   DLC

LD3613
.N3   Nashville. University.
           Charters and historical data. Nashville,
       1911.
           cover-title ₍32₎ p. illus.(incl.ports.)
       15x24 cm. (On cover: University of Nashville.
       Bulletin of information. v.9, no.3 ₍i.e. 2₎
       June, 1911)
           Includes advertising matter.

           1. Nashville. University--Hist.

NN 0025842   T

Nashville   **University.**
    Laws of Cumberland college, in Nashville, Tennessee:
enacted by the Board of trustees, November 5, 1825.
Nashville, Printed at the office of the Whig ₍1825₎
    2 p. l., ₍3₎-32 p., 1 l. 22ᶜᵐ.

                                              7-25816
    Library of Congress   LD3600.5 1825

NN 0025843   DLC NIC T MB MH TxU

VOLUME 405

Nashville. University.
Laws of the University of Nashville, in
Tennessee. New edition. Nashville, T.: S. Nye and
co., 1835.
₃₃, 4-28 p.

NN 0025844   M MB MH MHi TKL PPPrHi PPAmP T

Nashville. University.
Laws of the University of Nashville, in Tennessee. New
ed. Nashville, Printed by B. R. M'Kennie, 1840.
81, ₄₁ p. 21 cm.

LD3600.5 1840   9-8675 rev

NN 0025845   DLC MB MH

LD3617.7
1908   Nashville. University.
Memorial exercises held by the University
of Nashville, Peabody College for Teachers,
November 23, 1908, in commemoration of the
life and services of John Meredith Bass, together with resolutions adopted by the institutions with which he was connected, and
tributes from the members of Peabody faculty
and other friends. ₃Nashville, 1908₃
61 p. front.(port.) 28 cm.

NN 0025846   T

Pam
LB2827
.N38   Nashville. University.
Memorial of the president and trustees of
the University of Nashville, to the Congress
of the United States. Nashville, Printed
at the Republican and Gazette Office, 1834.
12 p. ₈ cm.

1. School lands--Tenn. 2. U.S.--Public
lands.

NN 0025847   T

Nashville. University.

Lindsley, John Berrien, 1822-1897.
On medical colleges. An introductory lecture, to the course
of 1858-59, in the medical department of the University of
Nashville, by J. Berrien Lindsley ... Pub. by the class. Nashville, Printed by J. T. Bell & co., 1858.

Nashville. University.
Organization of the university senate.
Nashville, 1897.

NN 0025849   NjP

Nashville. University.
... Proceedings at the inauguration of William H. Payne
as chancellor of the University of Nashville, and as president
of the Normal college, Nashville, Tenn. 5 October, 1887.
Cambridge, J. Wilson and son, 1887.
16 p. 22ᶜᵐ.
At head of title: Peabody education fund.

1. Payne, William Harold, 1836-1907.
                              E 15-2605 Rev[.el]
U.S. Off. of educ. Library   LD3617.4 1887
for Library of Congress   ₃37b2₃

NN 0025850   DHEW NcD

I
78   NASHVILLE. UNIVERSITY.
.5539   Regulations of the military and literary
departments of the University of Nashville.
<Revised copy>   Nashville,Tenn.,Leroi,1871.
22p.

Binder's title: Nashville. University.

NN 0025851   ICN MB

Nashville. University.
Reports of the board of trustees of the University of Nashville, East Tennessee University, at Knoxville, and West Tennessee College, at Jackson.   Nashville: G. C. Torbett and Co.,
1858.   p. ₃403-₃408. 8°.

1. No subject. 2. Tennessee. Uni-   versity. 3. West Tennessee College,
Jackson, Tenn.   June 15, 1925
N.Y.P.L.

NN 0025852   NN

Nashville. University.
Scientific department ... ₃Nashville, 1855₃
₄₁ p. 23¼ᶜᵐ.

                                   CA 9-5981 Unrev'd
Library of Congress   LD3607.A25

NN 0025853   DLC

Nashville, Tenn. University.
University of Nashville, collegiate department. Western military institute. Register of cadets ... 1855/56-
and announcement of officers ... 1856/57-

Nashville, 1856-
v. 23ᶜᵐ.

                                   CA 7-2266 Unrev'd
Library of Congress   LD3607.A3

NN 0025854   DLC

Nashville. University. Alumni society.
Cross, Nathaniel.
An address delivered before the Alumni society of the
University of Nashville, October 7, 1846, by Nathaniel
Cross ... With an appendix, containing a catalogue of
the alumni and certain proceedings of the society. Nash-
ville, Burton & Billings, printers, 1846.

Nashville. University. Alumni society.
Shelton, William, 1824-
American universities. An address before the Alumni soci-
ety of the University of Nahsville ₄₁ by William Shelton ...
With an appendix, containing proceedings of the Society, etc.
Nashville, Tenn., Wheeler, Marshall & Bruce, printers and sta-
tioners, 1874.

Nashville. University. Alumni society.
The general principles of organization and the
evolution of organic forms
see under   Cochran, Jerome.

Nashville. University. Alumni Society.
Tennessee; and the duty of her educated sons
see under   Stephens, William Henry.

I
78   NASHVILLE. UNIVERSITY. Board of trustees.
.5539   O Davidson academy, 1785 to 1806. Cumberland
college, 1806 to 1826. The University of Nashville, 1826. Laws of North Carolina and Tennessee relating thereto. List of trustees. History. Compiled by order of the Board of trustees
of the University of Nashville. 1892. Nashville,Tenn.,Marshall,1892.
44p.

Binder's title: Nashville. University.

NN 0025859   ICN PPUnC T

Nashville. University. Medical Dept.
Announcement of lectures; Medical Departments of the University of Nashville and of
Vanderbilt University,
                              Nashville, Tenn.,
v. 22-24cm.

Vol. for 1887 includes "Catalogue of alumni
... 1850 to 1887 inclusive".
Title varies: Annual announcement.

NN 0025860   NcD-MC DNLM DLC

Nashville. University. Medical dept.
R746   Catalogue for the session 1856-7, and
N25   announcement for the session 1857-8. Nashville,
857   Tenn., 1857.
25p. plate. 22cm.

1. Medical colleges.   24119

NN 0025861   CtY-M

Nashville. University. Medical dept.
Eve, Paul Fitzsimmons, 1806-1877.
The claims of medicine to be regarded a science. An introductory lecture delivered at the opening of the third session
in the Medical department of the University of Nashville,
(31st October, 1853.) By Paul F. Eve ... Published by the
class. Nashville, Tenn., Printed at the office of the Nashville
med. journal, 1853.

Nashville. University. Medical department.
Lecture introductory to the second course in
the medical department of the University of Nashville
see under   Bowling, William King, 1808-
1885.

Nashville. University. Medical dept.
Jennings, Thomas Reed, 1805-1874.
Valedictory address to the graduates of the Medical department of the University of Nashville, delivered February 28,
1857, by Thomas R. Jennings ... Published by request of the
faculty and the class. Nashville, Tenn., 1857.

Nashville. University. Medical Dept.
Alumni Association.
Bulletin
see   The Medical and surgical bulletin.

Nashville. University. *Montgomery Bell Academy*
see
Montgomery Bell Academy, *Nashville.*

VOLUME 405

Nashville. University. *Peabody Normal College*
see
George Peabody College for Teachers, *Nashville.*

Nashville. University. *Western Military Institute*
see
Western Military Institute, *Nashville.*

Nashville. Vanderbilt southern history society.
see
Vanderbilt southern history society, Nashville, Tenn.

Nashville. Vanderbilt University
see Vanderbilt University, *Nashville.*

Nashville. Vine Street Temple.
Memorial service. Lee J. Loventhal
see under title

Nashville. Vocational school for colored girls
see Tennessee. Vocational school for
colored girls, Nashville.

Nashville   Walden university.
see
Walden university. Nashville.

Nashville. Ward–Belmont School
see Ward–Belmont School, Nashville.

Nashville. Work shop for the blind
see Tennessee. Work shop for the blind, N
Nashville.

Nashville .   Watkins Institute.
See
Tennessee. Watkins Institute, Nashville.

Nashville. Western Military Institute
see
Western Military Institute, *Nashville.*

Pam
HQ316
.N2N3   Nashville. Woman's Mission Home.
History of Woman's Mission Home and annual
reports for the year 1893.   Nashville,
Marshall & Bruce Co., 1894.
cover-title, 16 p. 15 cm.

1. Charities--Nashville. 2. Unmarried
mothers--Nashville. 3. Delinquent girls.

NN 0025879   T

Nashville. Woodmont Baptist Church.
Church records, 1941 - 1952.
1 reel.
Microfilm (negative)

NN 0025880   TNSB

BV
800
.A   Nashville   (Diocese) Synod, 1st, 1905.
reel 4   Synodus dioecesana nashvillensis prima,
bk. 72   habita in urbe nashvillensi, die decima Febru-
arii, 1905, in ecclesia cathedrali Sanctae
Mariae sub titulo Deptem Dolorum a Thoma
Sebastiano Byrne, D.D., episcopo nashvillensi.
[n.p., n.d.]

Film reproduction. Positive.
Collation of the original: ix, 162 p., 1 l.

NN 0025881   DCU

BV
800   Nashville (Diocese) Synod, 2nd, 1937.
.A   The second synod of the diocese of Nashville
reel   celebrated June eleventh 1937 in the pro-
20   cathedral of the Incarnation, Nashville ...
book   William L. Adrian [bp.] presiding. [n.p., n.d.]
331
Film reproduction. Positive.
Collation of the original: 116 p.

NN 0025882   DCU

BV
800   Nashville   (Diocese) Synod, 3rd, 1947.
.N25   The third synod of the diocese of Nashville,
1947   convoked September sixteenth, Nineteen hundred
and forty-seven, in the church of St.Mary of
the Seven Dolors, Nashville, His Excellency,
the Most Reverend William L. Adrian, D.D.,
Bishop of Nashville, presiding. [n.p., n.d.]
120 p. 20cm.

NN 0025883   DCU

BV
800   Nashville, (Diocese) Synod, 3rd, 1947.
.A   The third synod of the diocese of Nashville
reel   convoked September 16, 1947 in the church of St.
20   Mary of the Seven Dolors, Nashville, William L.
book   Adrian [bp.] presiding. [n.p., n.d.]
332
Film reproduction. Positive.
Collation of the original: 120 p.

NN 0025884   DCU

Nashville, Ill., Board of education.
Catalogue of the Nashville public schools,
1902/03

(Nashville. Ill., 1903.
1 v.

NN 0025885   DHEW

Nashville, Me.
see Nashville Plantation, Me.

Nashville, Mich. Baptist church. Ladies' aid society
What to eat and how to cook it; a book of tested recipes
prepared by the ladies of the Baptist church. Nashville,
Mich., 1929. 53 p. 19½cm.

Advertising matter interspersed.

1. Cookery, American. I. Title.

NN 0025887   NN

Nashville Agricultural Normal Institute, *Madison, Tenn.*
see Madison College, *Madison College, Tenn.*

AY67
.N2C8   Nashville American Cumberland Almanac.
18 -   Nashville, The American
Company, 18 -
v. tables. 22cm.

Includes information about Nashville and
the State of Tennessee as well as general
information.

1. Almanacs, American. 2. Statistics--
Yearbooks. I. Nashville American

NN 0025889   T

AY306
.N2N3   Nashville American Cumberland Almanac.
1896–   Nashville, The American
Company, 1895–
v. tables. 22 cm.

1. Almanacs, American. 2. Statistics--Year-
books. I. Nashville American. II. Title: Cumberland Almanac.

NN 0025890   T

The **Nashville** American, Nashville, Tenn. Celebrating the
98th anniversary of Tennessee's oldest daily newspaper. v.
35, no. 12717; June 26, 1910. [Nashville, 1910]
[180] p. illus. 58ᶜᵐ.
Various pagings.

1. Nashville.

Library of Congress   F444.N2N32   10—23252

NN 0025891   DLC

Nashville and Chattanooga Railroad Company
see Nashville, Chattanooga and St. Louis Railway.

Nashville and Decatur railroad company.
Organization and charter of the Nashville and Decatur
railroad company, and by-laws, as amended prior to 1872,
and first mortgage and contract of lease. Nashville,
A. B. Tavel, printer, 1887.
62 p. 22¼ᵐ.

A 22-803

Title from Bureau of   Railway Economics. Printed by L. C.

NN 0025893   DBRE

VOLUME 405

Nashville and Decatur railroad company.
Organization, charter and by-laws of the Nashville and Decatur railroad company. January, 1867. Nashville, F. M. Paul, printer, 1867.
32 p. 22½ᶜᵐ.

A 18-620

Title from Bureau of   Railway Economics. Printed by L. C.

NN 0025894   DBRE

Nashville and Edgefield directory...
see   Polk's Nashville (Davidson county, Tenn.) city directory...

Pam.
Coll.   **Nashville and Knoxville Railroad Company.**
30270   Charter of the Nashville and Knoxville Railroad Company, passed December 22, 1853. Nashville, Nashville Union and American Steam Press, 1854.
17 p. 23 cm.

Supplementary matter (1 l.) inserted.

I. Tennessee. Laws, statutes, etc.

NN 0025896   NcD

Nashville and Memphis Railroad Company
see
Memphis and Ohio Railroad Company.

Nashville & St. Louis railway, petitioner.
U. S. *Dept. of justice.*
... Louisville & Nashville railroad company and Nashville, Chattanooga & St. Louis railway, petitioners, v. United States of America, respondent, and Interstate commerce commission, intervening respondent. Brief of the United States in opposition to the motion of the petitioners for a preliminary injunction. [Washington, Govt. print. off., 1911]

Nashville & Tennessee centennial and international exposition. [Columbus, O., Ward brothers, ᵉ1897]
cover-title, 8 p. 23½ᶜᵐ.

Photographs on strip folded seven times.

1. Nashville, Tenn. Tennessee centennial and international exposition, 1897.

Library of Congress   T775.C1N2

5-28685†

NN 0025899   DLC

Nashville at Christmas-tide
see under   Nashville Job Printing Company.

The Nashville banner.
The Nashville banner book of type. [Nashville, n. d.]
cover-title, 20 l. illus. 46½ᶜᵐ.

Running title : The Banner book of type.

1. Printing—Specimens. 2. Type and type-founding. 3. Advertising
36-25367

Library of Congress   Z250.N25

[2]   655.24

NN 0025900   DLC

Nashville Baptist association
see
Baptists. *Tennessee. Nashville Baptist association.*

---

*A
1823-27 **Nashville Bar Association.**
.D63
no.10   Memorial of the members. January 4, 1825. Washington: Gales & Seaton, 1825.
8 p. 22cm. ([U.S., 18th Cong., 2d sess., 1824-1825. [Senate. Ex. Doc., 29]
Documents relating to the Judiciary, no. 10.

NN 0025902   ViU

F436
.C353N3 **Nashville Bar Association.**
Proceedings of the Nashville Bar, in relation to the death of Hon. G. W. Campbell. Nashville, W. F. Bang, 1848.
32 p. 24 cm.

1. Campbell, George Washington, 1769-1848.

NN 0025903   T

Pam
HG2526
.N2A2   **Nashville Building Association.**
Constitution of the Nashville Building Association. Together with the act of incorporation. Adopted August 2, 1854. Nashville, Union and American Steam Press [1855]
15 p. 18 cm.

The act of incorporation created also the Memphis Building and Loan Association.

1. Building and loan associations. 2. Memphis Building and Loan Association Company.

NN 0025904   T

Nashville business directory
see   Nashville city and business directory.

F444
.N2N23 Nashville Centennial trade guide and business directory. [Milwaukee] Milwaukee Lithographing & Engraving Co. [1880?]
cover-title [35] p. illus. 25 cm.

Includes advertising.

1. Nashville—Hist. 2. Nashville—Indus. 3. Nashville. Centennial Exposition, 1880.

NN 0025906   T

Nashville, Chattanooga & St. Louis Railway.
385.065   Annual report to the stockholders.
N253A
[Nashville?]
v. in   maps. 23-25 cm.

Report year ends June 30, 18   -1915/16;
Dec. 31, 1916.
Reports for 18   -187 / issued under an earlier name of the company: Nashville and Chattanooga   Railroad Company.
Title varies   slightly.

NN 0025907   NcD T NjP TxU RPB CU NN ICJ MB DLC

FILM
H18   **Nashville, Chattanooga & St. Louis Railway.**
Annual report. 1st-   1848-
[v. p.]

Microfilm copy (negative) of originals in the Tennessee State Library, Nashville.
1848-1871/72 reports issued under earlier name of railroad: Nashville and Chattanooga Railroad Company.

1. Railroads—Southern States. I. Nashville and Chattanooga Railroad Company.

NN 0025908   AU

Nashville, Chattanooga & St. Louis railway.
Battlefields in Dixie land and Chickamauga national military park, with description of the important battles fought along these lines and the story of the engine "General." [Nashville; Nashville, Chattanooga & St. Louis Ry., and Western & Atlantic R. R. [1906?]
63, [1] p. front., illus.

1. Chickamauga and Chattanooga national military park. I. Western and Atlantic railroad. II. Title: Battlefields in Dixie land.

NN 0025909   NNC

Ga
E470
N3   **Nashville, Chattanooga & St. Louis Railway.**
Battlefields in Dixie land and Chickamauga National Military Park with description of the important battles fought along these lines and the story of the engine, "General", [by] Nashville, Chattanooga and St. Louis Railway and Western and Atlantic Railroad. [Nashville, 1917]
63 p. illus. maps. 21cm.

NN 0025910   GU

E470
.N38   **Nashville, Chattanooga & St. Louis Railway.**
Battlefields in Dixie land and Chickamauga National Military Park. With description of the important battles fought along these lines, and the story of the engine "General". [Issued by the] Nashville, Chattanooga & St. Louis Ry. and Western & Atlantic R. R. [Chicago, Poole Bros., 1928]
63 [1] p. incl. illus., ports., maps (part col., 1 double) 21 cm.

NN 0025911   T IU TxU

Nashville, Chattanooga and St. Louis railway.
Before railroads. A contemporary view of the agriculture, industry and commerce of the South in the 'forties ... [Nashville, 1929]
cover-title, 16 p. incl. plan. 23 cm.

CONTENTS.—Letter from V. K. Stevenson to Hon. J. C. Calhoun. Dec. 12, 1846.—Extracts from an address of V. K. Stevenson to the Tennessee Legislature. Jan. 11, 1847.—Extracts from a report to the commissioners of the Nashville & Chattanooga railroad, made by J. E. Thomson. Feb., 1847.

1. Southern states—Econ. condit. I. Stevenson, Vernon K. II. Thomson, John Edgar, 1808-1874. III. Title.

A 30-137 rev

Bureau of Railway   Economics. Library
for Library of Congress   [r53c1]

NN 0025912   DBRE IU NN

Nashville, Chattanooga & St. Louis Ry.
The capture of a locomotive, a brilliant exploit of the war. Atlanta, Ga., 1895.
20p. (Cover-title: The general story of Andrews' Raiders, April 12, 1862) YA 21046

NN 0025913   DLC TKL

VOLUME 405

Nashville, Chattanooga and St. Louis railway.
　　Charter of the Nashville and Chattanooga railroad company and the various acts amending the same; together with the acts of the legislatures of the states of Alabama and Georgia, granting right of way, etc., to said railroad ... Comp. by order of the Board of directors. Nashville, Tenn., Union and dispatch job rooms, 1868.
　　109 p. 23 cm.

　　ɪ. Tennessee. Laws, statutes, etc.

A 17–478 rev

Bureau of Railway　　　Economics. Library
for Library of Congress　　ₜᵣ53b⅟₂ₗ

NN　0025914　　DBRE

Nashville, Chattanooga and St. Louis railway.
　　Charter of the Nashville and Chattanooga railroad company, and the various acts amending the same ... Comp. by order of the Board of directors. Nashville, Tenn., Paul & Tavel, 1872.
　　2 p. l., 233 p. 24 cm.
　　Contents.— pt. ɪ. ₜCharters₎—pt. ɪɪ. Special acts of Tennessee, Alabama and Georgia relating to the Nashville and Chattanooga railroad, from 1865 to 1872, inclusive, together with the general laws of Alabama and Georgia upon the subject of railroads, and the charter of the Nashville & northwestern railroad company, with the special acts of Tennessee and Kentucky relating to the same, from 1852 to 1872, inclusive.

A 17–330 rev

Bureau of Railway　　　Economics. Library
for Library of Congress　　ₜᵣ53b⅟₂ₗ

NN　0025915　　DBRE T

Nashville, Chattanooga & St. Louis railway.
　　Chickamauga and Chattanooga national park. [Nashville, 1903]

E481
.C5N3

NN　0025916　　DLC

Pam
F436
.N25
　　Nashville, Chattanooga & St. Louis Railway.
　　Excellent situation in Tennessee for intelligent northern farmers, along the line of The Nashville, Chattanooga & St. Louis Railway. ₜByₗ J. B. Killebrew, Immigration agent. Nashville ₜ1898?ₗ
　　cover-title, 8 p. 15 cm.

　　1. Tennessee—Emig. & immig. 2. Tennessee—Descr. & trav. I. Killebrew, Joseph Buckner, 1831–1906.

NN　0025917　　T

Pam
F442.1
.N2
　　Nashville, Chattanooga & St. Louis Railway.
　　Facts about the Cumberland table-land of Tennessee, and Sand Mountain of Alabama. By J. B. Killebrew, A. M., PH. D., former Commissioner of Agriculture, and now in charge of Immigration for Nashville, Chattanooga & St. Louis Railway. Nashville, Marshall & Bruce Co., 1897.
　　cover-title, 16 p. 19 cm.

NN　0025918　　T

F217
.T3N3
　　Nashville, Chattanooga & St. Louis Railway.
　　Facts and figures concerning the region traversed by the system of railroads controlled and operated by the Nashville, Chattanooga & St. Louis Railway. Issued by Passenger Department. Nashville, 1895.
　　32 p. 24 cm.

　　Includes land reached by Western & Atlantic Railroad, leased by N. C. & St. L. Railroad.

NN　0025919　　T

　　...First consolidated five per cent mortgage ₍dated April 2, 1888, due April 1, 1928. United States Trust Co. of New York, trustee. [New York, 1888] 26 p. 23cm.

　　Cover-title.

763516A. 1. No subject. I. United States Trust Company of New York.

NN　0025920　　NN

Nashville, Chattanooga & St. Louis railway.
　　Information for immigrants concerning middle Tennessee and the counties in that division traversed by or tributary to the Nashville, Chattanooga & St. Louis Ry. ... By J. B. Killebrew ... Issued by the Passenger department ... Nashville, Tenn., Marshall & Bruce co., printers, 1898.
　　148 p. illus. (incl. double map) 19ᵐᵐ.

　　1. Tennessee—Emig. & immig. 2. Tennessee, Middle—Descr. & trav. ɪ. Killebrew, Joseph Buckner, 1831–1906.

Rc–1294

Library of Congress　　F442.2.N25

NN　0025921　　DLC CLSU

Nashville, Chattanooga & St. Louis railway.
　　Baker, George Henry, 1859–
　　　... Instructions for locomotive fuel economy ... by George H. Baker ... Economical firing. Economical boiler-feeding. Economical use of steam. ₜNew York, Printed by Macy & co.₎ 1916.

Nashville, Chattanooga & St. Louis railway.
　　John W. Thomas. A memorial. ₜNashville, Tenn., Press of Ambrose & Bostelman co., 1906₎
　　179, ₍1₎ p. port. 24⅟₂ᵐᵐ.

　　1. Thomas, John W., 1830–1906.

15–28119

Library of Congress　　HE2754.T5N3

NN　0025923　　DLC TxU TU ViU

Nashville, Chattanooga and St. Louis railway.
　　Georgia.
　　　Lease contract, Western & Atlantic railroad, December 27, 1919, to December 27, 1969. Nashville, Ambrose print ₜ1919?₎

Pam
S643
.N25
　　Nashville, Chattanooga & St. Louis Railway.
　　Lime in agriculture. Nashville, Agricultural Division, Traffic Department, Nashville, Chattanooga & St. Louis Railway, 1915.
　　cover-title, 20 p. illus. 24 cm.

　　1. Lime. 2. Fertilizers and manures. I. Title.

NN　0025925　　T

Pam
HE2791
.N293b
1869
　　Nashville, Chattanooga & St. Louis railway.
　　List of stockholders in Nashville & Chattanooga Railroad. May 14th, 1869. Nashville, John T. S. Fall & Sons, 1869.
　　36 p. 22 cm.

NN　0025926　　T

FOR OTHER EDITIONS
SEE MAIN ENTRY
Nashville, Chattanooga & St. Louis railway, petitioner.
U. S. *Interstate commerce commission, intervening respondent.*
　　... Louisville & Nashville railroad company and Nashville, Chattanooga & St. Louis railway, petitioners, v. United States of America, respondent, and Interstate commerce commission, intervening respondent. Answer of the Interstate commerce commission. Charles W. Needham, solicitor. ₜWashington, Govt. print. off., 1911₎

385.13
N253M
　　Nashville, Chattanooga & St. Louis Railway.
　　₍Mortgages of Nashville, Chattanooga and St. Louis railway. [Nashville, Tenn.? Hasslock & Ambrose, printers, 19—?]
　　[231] p. 22cm.

　　Each part has special title-page and separate paging.

NN　0025928　　NcD

Pam
HE1049
.N3
　　Nashville, Chattanooga & St. Louis Railway.
　　Motor carriers for hire and the railroads. A statement by the Nashville, Chattanooga & St. Louis Railway, January 20, 1931. ₜNashville?₎ 1931.
　　15 p. 23 cm.

　　Cover title.

　　1. Railroads—Freight. 2. Transportation, Automotive—Freight. I. Title.

NN　0025929　　T

Nashville, Chattanooga & St. Louis Railway.
　　Peach growing along the line of the Nashville, Chattanooga & St. Louis R'y ... J. B. Killebrew, Industrial and Immigration agent. Nashville [Marshall & Bruce Co., 1901?]
　　48 p. incl. illus., fold. map. 18 cm. (Along the line of the Nashville, Chattanooga & St. Louis Ry. Pamphlet no. 7, 2d ed.)
　　1. Peach. I. Killebrew, Joseph Buckner, 1831–1906. II. Title.

NN　0025930　　T

Nashville, Chattanooga and St. Louis railway.
　　Reclaiming the gullied lands of West Tennessee. Nashville, Tenn., 1915.
　　20 p. il. 22.5 cm.

NN　0025931　　DNAL

Nashville, Chattanooga and St. Louis railway.
　　Report of a committee appointed by the Board of directors showing the business and financial condition of the Nashville & Chattanooga R. R. co., from December 1, 1860, to June 30, 1865 ... Nashville, Tenn., J. T. S. Fall & sons, printers, 1866.
　　32 p. 22 cm.
　　James H. Grant, W. S. Huggins, Thos. C. Whiteside, committee.

　　ɪ. Grant, James H.

A 19–105 rev

Bureau of Railway　　　Economics. Library
for Library of Congress　　ₜᵣ53b⅟₂ₗ

NN　0025932　　DBRE T NcD ViU

---

*
TF25
.S68
1868
v.21,
no.10
　　Nashville, Chattanooga and St. Louis Railway.
　　Report of a Committee appointed by the Board of Directors showing the condition and value of the rolling stock, road bed and superstructure, depots, machine shops, tools, and all other assets, as well as the liabilities, of the Nashville & Chattanooga R. R. Co., on September 1st, 1868. W₍S. Huggins, E.L. Jordan, John Fizzell, A.L. Landis, committee. Nashville, John T. S. Fall, 1868.
　　4 p. 21 cm. (Streeter pamphlets. S.E.R.R.)
　　1. Railroads—Southeastern States. I. ads. Southeastern railro

NN　0025933　　ViU T

VOLUME 405

Nashville, Chattanooga and St. Louis railway.
The seventy-fifth anniversary of the Nashville, Chattanooga & St. Louis railway. 1848. 1923. ₍Nashville? Tenn., 1923₎
32 p. illus. (incl. facsims.) 21ᶜᵐ.

1. Railroads—Anniversaries.

A 23–1726

Title from Bureau of   Railway Economics.   Printed by L. C.

NN   0025934   DBRE

F436   Nahhville, Chattanooga & St. Louis railway co.
.N29   Side trips from Nashville via the Nashville, Chattanooga & St. Louis railway during the U.S.U. reunion...
Nashville, 1904.

NN   0025935   DLC

Nashville, Chattanooga and St. Louis railway.
Soil and geological map of Tennessee, issued by J. B. Killebrew, industrial and immigration agent of the Nashville, Chattanooga & St. Louis Ry. J. M. Safford, state geologist. Chicago, Ill., Rand, McNally & co., 1899.
map.   57 x 104½ᶜᵐ.
Scale: 12 miles = 1 inch.
Lower part of sheet contains county and railroad map of Tennessee and descriptive matter.

1. Agriculture—Tennessee—Maps. 2. Geology—Tennessee—Maps. I. Killebrew, Joseph Buckner, 1831–1906. II. Safford, James Merrill, 1822–

Library, U. S. Geol.   survey

G S 7–785

NN   0025936   DI-GS

G3960
1906   **Nashville, Chattanooga and St. Louis Railway.**
.N3   Soil and geological map of Tennessee.
Nashville, 1906.
63 x 98 cm. (folded 22 cm.)

Scale: 12 miles-1 inch.

1. Maps—Tennessee. 2. Geology—Tenn.

NN   0025937   TU

973.73   **Nashville, Chattanooga & St. Louis railway.**
N248s   "Southern battlefields", a list of battlefields on and near the lines of the Nashville, Chattanooga & St. Louis railway and Western & Atlantic railroad,/ and a brief description of the more important battles fought along these lines, also information about Lookout Mountain, Chickamauga park and the famous engine "General." Chicago, Poole bros., n.d.
47p. incl. illus., maps. 20cm.

NN   0025938   LNHT RPB

E470.5   Nashville, Chattanooga & St. Louis rail-
.N25   way.
"Southern battlefields"; a list of battlefields on and near the lines of the Nashville, Chattanooga & St. Louis railway and Western & Atlantic railroad and a brief description of the more important battles fought along these lines, also information about Lookout Mountain, Chickamauga Park and the famous engine "General". Nashville, Tenn. ₍n. d.₎
41 p. illus. maps. 19cm.

NN   0025939   MnHi ViU NcU MoKU WaSp

Nashville, Chattanooga and St. Louis railway company.
"Southern battlefields". A list of battlefields on and near the lines of the Nashville, Chattanooga & St. Louis railway and Western & Atlantic railroad, and a brief description of the more important battles fought along these lines; also, information about Lookout mountain, Chickamauga park, and the famous engine "General." Nashville, Tenn., The Nashville, Chattanooga & St. Louis railway ₍189–?₎

47, ₍1₎ p. illus. (incl. ports., maps) 20 cm.

Maps on p. ₍2₎–₍3₎ of cover.
"Standard publications of the Nashville, Chattanooga & St. Louis railway": p. ₍48₎

1. U. S. – Hist. – Civil war – Campaigns and battles. 2. Tennessee – Hist. – Civil war. 3. Georgia – Hist. – Civil war. 4. Chickamauga and Chattanooga national military park. I. Western and Atlantic railroad company. II. Title. III. Title: Battlefields on and near the lines of the Nashville, Chattanooga & St. Louis railway.

E470.5.N25

NN   0025942   Vi MiD-B

Nashville, Chattanooga & St. Louis Railway.
The story of the "General," 1862... Issued by the passenger departments of the Nashville, Chattanooga & St Louis Railway and the Western & Atlantic Railroad... ₍Nashville: Brandon, 1906₎ 20 p. illus. (incl. map, ports.) 21½ x 9cm.

588131. 1. United States—Hist.—   Civil war—Military, 1862, Apr. 7 –
Nov. 10—Chattanooga railroad expedi-   tion. 2. Andrews, James J
1829?–1862. I. Western & Atlantic   Railway. II. Title: The "General,"
The story of.   *Revised*
N. Y. P. L.   April 30, 1935

NN   0025943   NN DNW GU CSmH DI

E470
.55
.N37
1909   Nashville, Chattanooga and St. Louis Railway.
The story of the "General", 1862. Issued by the Passenger Departments of the Nashville, Chattanooga & St. Louis Railway and the Western & Atlantic Railroad. ₍Nashville, Tenn., Marshall & Bruce Co., 1909₎
24 p. illus.   23 x 10cm.
"Revised edition."

1. Chattanooga Railroad Expedition, 1862.
I. Title. II. Title: Andrews raiders.

NN   0025944   ViU

Pam
E473.55
.N2   Nashville, Chattanooga & St. Louis Railway.

The story of the "General" 1862. Issued by the passenger departments of the Nashville, Chattanooga & St. Louis Railway and the Western & Atlantic Railroad. ₍Chicago, Poole Bros., c1917₎
32 p. incl. illus., ports., double map. 18x10 cm.

Title vignette.

NN   0025945   T GU

Nashville, Chattanooga and St. Louis Railway
see also
St. Louis and Southeastern Railway Company.

---

*
TF173
.N374
1942   Nashville, Chattanooga and St. Louis Railway. Employes Educational Service.

Lesson no. 1–₍18₎ Nashville, Tenn., 1942.
18 pts. in 20 v. fold. map. 23cm.

1. Railroads—Education and training

NN   0025947   ViU

Z881
.N3   Nashville, Chattanooga and St. Louis Railway. Library.
Catalogue of the Nashville, Chattanooga and St. Louis Railway library. Alphabetical list of books, giving case, shelf, and book number. ₍Nashville?₎ 1911.
150 p. 20 cm.

1. Catalogs, Library.

NN   0025948   T

Nashville, Chattanooga & St. Louis Railway.
Traffic Department. Industrial, Agricultural and Immigration Division.
.... Sweet potato recipes supplied by housewives throughout the South who have local reputations for preparing the most toothsome dishes from the southern tuber. .... Compiled and published for distribution by the Industrial, Agricultural and Immigration Division, Traffic Department [of the] Nashville, Chattanooga & St. Louis Railway. Nashville, Tennessee, 1921.
cover-title, 16 p. 24ᶜᵐ.   (A. C. no. 8.)

NN   0025949   ICJ

Nashville children's museum
     see   Nashville. Children's Museum.

Nashville city and business directory ... v. 1–
₍1853₎   Nashville, L. P. Williams & co., 1853–
      v. fold. map. 19½–23ᶜᵐ.
The issue for 1853, v. 1, includes a second part: ... the post offices, address and business reference of the principal dealers and professional men in the state of Tennessee; also a third part: ... the cards and business reference of the ... merchants of ... Charleston, S. C. ... Savanah, Augusta, Macon, Atlanta, and Rome, Ga. And reference to the principal dealers in ... a part of south Kentucky, and a part of north Alabama ...
Title varies: ₍1853₎ The Nashville, state of Tennessee, and general commercial directory.
1855/6–1857, Nashville business directory.
1859–   Nashville city and business directory.
Compilers and publishers: ₍1853₎–1859, J. P. Campbell;–18   L. P. Williams & co.
1. Nashville, Tenn.—Di-   rect. 2. Tennessee—Direct. 3. Southern states—Direct. I. The   Nashville, state of Tennessee, and
general commercial direc-   tory. II. Nashville business directory.
Library of Congress   F444.N2A184   9–6116 (rev '23)

NN   0025951   DLC NcD MH TKL PHi PPULC

Nashville city directory ...
     see
Polk's Nashville (Davidson county, Tenn.) city directory ...

Nashville colored directory.

₍Nashville₎
     v. illus., ports. 31 cm.
Compiler: R. C. Grant.

1. Negroes—Nashville. I. Grant, R. C.

F444.N2A1845   48–34894*‡

NN   0025953   DLC

VOLUME 405

Pam
TE324
.T2N2   Nashville Commercial Club. Highway Reform
     Committee.
     Proposed Tennessee highway law. A bill pre-
     pared by the Highway reform committee of the
     Nashville Commercial Club, and submitted, by
     order of the club, to the General Assembly of
     1891, being a revision of, and containing the
     essential features of the State Road Congress
     bill, of August, 1890. Nashville, Tenn.,
     Hasslock & Ambrose, 1891.
     23 p. 24cm.

NN   0025954   T NcU

280.28
N17   Nashville cooperative dairyman.

     Nashville, Tenn., Nashville Milk Producers.

NN   0025955   DNAL

                Nashville, 1862.
Nashville Daily Gazette.

NN   0025956   MABt

     Nashville daily news.
       Carrier's address to the patrons of the Nashville
     daily news
       see under title

Pam
E435
.N3   Nashville daily patriot.
     Buchanan's record. ₍Nashville₎ Nahsville(!)
     Patriot Office, 1856.
     16 p. 22 cm.

     Caption title.
     At head of title: Campaign document, no.1.
     Second edition.

     1. Campaign literature, 1856--Republican.
     2. Buchanan, James, Pres. U.S., 1791-1868.

NN   0025958   T

Beinecke
Library
Folio   The Nashville daily Union.
AN43
N17   Nashville, Tenn.,
N179   65½-73cm.

NN   0025959   CtY

Nashville democrat. 1888-?
Nashville, Tenn. 1888-?
   v. 59cm. daily.

NN   0025960   NcU

GB1225
.T2N2   The Nashville flood of December and
     January, 1926-27 ... ₍Nashville₎ C. J.
     Burnell ₍1927?₎
     ₍32₎ p. illus. 24x32 cm.

     "This booklet is prepared and presented
     to the public as more than a memento of the
     worst flood in the history of Nashville. It
     has been conceived and published as an his-
     toric document, revealing by a remarkable
     collection of photographs and an accurative
     narrative, the complete story of the flood".

     Continued in next column

Continued from preceding column

     12 photographs mounted in front; photo-
graphed by Nashville Aeronautic Corp. December 30, 1926.

     1. Nashville--Floods. 2. Floods--Tenn.
3. Cumberland River.

NN   0025962   T

Nashville - Gallatin Interurban Railway.
     The historic Blue grass line
       see under   Anderson, James Douglas,
     1868-1948.

Nashville greets confederates! Programme.
     Nashville reunion, 1904 ... [Nashville,
     Tenn.]
     p. 337-352   4°.
     Taken from the advance of July Veteran.

NN   0025964   NN

Nashville Homestead-Building association.
     Constitution. n.d.

NN   0025965   OWibfU

Nashville Housing Authority.
     Capitol Hill redevelopment project. Nashville ₍1952₎
     46 p. illus. 29 cm.

     1. Cities and towns—Planning--Nashville.   ɪ. Title.

     NA9127.N18N38   711.09768   53-16854 ‡

NN   0025966   DLC NIC TU

Nashville housing authority.

HD7304
.N3M3
Marks, Eli Samplin, 1911–
     Housing survey; low income housing areas of Nashville,
Tennessee, 1940. Prepared for the Nashville housing authority
by Eli S. Marks ... John H. Brandon, survey director. ₍Nash-
ville, 1940₎

HD7304
.N3N2   **Nashville Housing Authority.**
     Housing survey; low income housing areas of
Nashville, Tennessee, 1949. ₍Conducted by₎ The
Nashville Housing Authority in cooperation with
Parent-Teacher Associations and the Department
of Social Science, Fisk University. Report pre-
pared by Preston Valien, Dept. of Social Science,
Fisk University. ₍Nashville, 1949₎
     3 p. ℓ., 36(i.e.37) p. 62 p. of tables.
17 maps(1 fold.) 28 cm.

     Page 20a a continuation of table on p.20.

     Reproduced from typewritten copy.
     On cover: 1949 housing survey of the low
income housing areas, Nashville, Tennessee.

     1. Housing--Nashville.

NN   0025969   T TU IU NN

Nashville housing authority.
   Report.

     ₍Nashville₎
     v.   tables. 29cm. annual.

     1. Housing - Nashville.

NN   0025970   NNC NN

Nashville illustrated in colors
     see under   [Boylin, Gerald]   comp.

Map
G
3964   Nashville in 1804 from notes of one then
N4   resident. ₍n.p., n.d.₎
1804   mss. map 26 x 35 cm.

     No scale indicated.
     Photostat.
     Signed W. A. E.

     1. Nashville, Tenn.--Maps.

NN   0025972   NIC

Map
G
3964   Nashville in 1804 from notes of one then
N3   resident (Mrs. Temple, daughter of Dunc:
1804a   Robertson) ₍n.p., n.d.₎
     map 16 x 22 cm.

     No scale given.
     Photostat.

     1. Nashville, Tenn.--Maps.

NN   0025973   NIC

Map
G
3964   Nashville in 1854. ₍n.p. 1854?₎
N3   map 18 x 24 cm
1854   Scale not indicated.
     Photostat.

     1. Nashville, Tenn.--Maps.

NN   0025974   NIC

F444
.04N2   Nashville Industrial Corporation, Old Hickory,
     Tenn.
     Old Hickory. ₍Nashville, Brandon Print.
Co. ₍192-?₎
     31 p. illus.,map,plans. fold.plate(in
pocket) 31 cm.

     Illustrated cover.

     1. Old Hickory, Tenn.

NN   0025975   T

The Nashville Jewish community
     see under   Nashville Y.M.H.A. news.

Nashville Jewish Community council.
     Study of Jewish population, Nashville, Tennes-
see. 1949.

NN   0025977   PU-PSW

VOLUME 405

GT4985
.N2   Nashville Job Printing Company.
        Nashville at Christmas-tide.   ₍Nashville,
1891₎
        ₍24₎ p. illus. 30 cm.

        Stories and poems about Christmas with
        additional miscellaneous information.
        Includes advertising matter.

        1. Christmas. I. Title.

NN   0025978   T

W 1
NA182   NASHVILLE journal of medicine and surgery.
        v. 1-114, no. 3; Feb. 1851-Mar. 1920.
        Nashville.
        114 v. in
        Publication suspended Jan. 1862-May
1866.
        Issues for July 1866-Dec. 1890 called
        new ser., v. 1-46, but constitute v. 22-68.
        Issues for July 1870-Dec. 1890 called
        also whole vols. 27-62.
        Merged into Medical life in Jan. 1921.

NN   0025979   DNLM ICJ MBCo NcD DLC

F444
.N2N3   Nashville Land Improvement Company.
        West Nashville. The new manufacturing
        city of the South. Development of an in-
        dustrial town three miles from the State
        House at Nashville, Tenn. A center of the
        charcoal-iron business.   Nashville, Bran-
        don Printing Co., 1887.
        13 ₍2₎ p. fold.map..diagr. 22 cm.

        1. Nashville--Indus. 2. Nashville--Manuf.
        ₍I.₎ Title.

NN   0025980   T NcU

F444
.N2N32   Nashville Land Improvement Company.
        West Nashville, founded by the Nashville Land
        Improvement Company, Nashville, Tennessee.
        ₍Nashville, Marshall & Bruce, 1900?₎
        28 ₍4₎ p. illus.,plan. 20x27 cm.

        On cover: West Nashville; the brightest and
        cleanest town in fair Tennessee.

        1. Nashville--Hist. 2. Nashville--Descr.
        I. Title.

NN   0025981   T

The **Nashville** medical news, a semi-monthly journal. .... Vol. I,
107991 no. 1-9, April–August 1, 1887. [Nashville, Tenn., 1887.]
        1 vol. 25ᶜᵐ.
        Cover-title; no index.
        Editors: Richard Douglas, J. W. McAlister.
        Ceased publication Aug. 1, 1887.

NN   0025982   ICJ ICRL NcD DNLM

W 1
NA182J   The NASHVILLE medical record. v. 1-3,
        no. 3; Sept. 1858-Jan. 1861. Nashville.
        3 v. illus.
        Issues for Nov. 1860-Jan. 1861 called
        new ser.
        Issued Sept. 1858-Sept. 1859 with
        title: Nashville monthly record of
        medical and physical science.

NN   0025983   DNLM InU NIC

Nashville men. (Young Men's Christian Assn.)
        Nashville, Tenn. v1-5 no 40? Ap 25 1901-
        Je 23 1905//?

NN   0025984   T

Nashville monthly record of medical and physical
        science
        see   Nashville medical record.

Nashville News. w. 1873-1966//
        v.
        microfilm.

Continued as Maple Valley News.

        1.Nashville, Mich.-Newspapers. I.Nashville,
        Mich. Newspapers (Microfilm)

NN   0025986   Mi

A Nashville pen, pseud.

        see

Reno, Mrs. Itti (Kinney) 1862-

Nashville Plantation, *Me.*
        Annual report of the municipal officers ...

Fort Fairfield, Me.
        v. tables. 23½ᶜᵐ.

                                                  CA 35-896 Unrev'd
        Library of Congress   JS13.N164   352.07411

NN   0025988   DLC

Nashville population handbook: 1950

        see under

Reiss, Albert J

SF483
.N3   **Nashville Pure-bred Poultry Association.**
        Premium list, lst-   annual
        greater Nashville poultry show. 1920-
        Nashville, 1920-
        nos. 23 cm.

        1. Poultry.

NN   0025990   TU

G3964
.N2
1954   **Naive, William Thomas**, 1879-
.N3   Greater Nashville. ₍Nashville₎ Nashville Pure Milk Co.,
        °1954.

Nashville Real Estate Board.
        Yearbook.

        ₍Nashville₎
        v. illus. (part col.) ports. 30 cm.
        Each vol. has also a distinctive title: Cumberland country of
        middle Tennessee.

        1. Tennessee.   r. Title: Cumberland country of middle Tennessee.
        F436.N32   917.68   49-26679*‡

NN   0025992   DLC T Or

Nashville Real Estate Exchange
        see Nashville Real Estate Board.

Nashville Retail Merchants Association.
        The city of Nashville
        see under   Halley, Robert Ambrose.

HC108
.N2N19   Nashville, "Rock City", "The Gibraltar of
        Commerce". A compendium of firms and insti-
        tutions contributing to the city's rapid
        growth. Nashville, Brandon ₍1907₎
        27 ₍1₎ p. illus. 24x32 cm.

        On cover: Nashville 1907.
        Running title: Nashville-A Southern city
        worth while.

        1. Nashville--Indus. 2. Nashville--Manuf.

NN   0025995   T

Pam
HG2613
.N2N2   Nashville Savings Institution.
        Charter and by-laws of the Nashville Savings
        Institution. Incorporated 1850. Nashville,
        John T. S. Fall, 1850.
        cover-title, 16 p. 14 cm.

        1. Savings-banks--Nashville. 2. Banks and
        banking--Nashville.

NN   0025996   T

Nashville section, Engineering association of
        the South
        see   Engineering association of the
        South. Nashville section.

The Nashville, state of Tennessee, and general
        commercial directory
        see   Nashville city and business directory.

Nashville student. (Cumberland Presbyterial
        Publishing House) Nashville, Tenn. v1-2
        no1? S 25 1894-O 9 1895//?

NN   0025999   T

Nashville, Tenn. In photo gravure from recent
        negatives
        see under   Albertype Company.

NASHVILLE Tennessean.
        Nashville.   v.   illus., ports.
        Microfilm.
        Daily.

        t. U.S.--Tennessee--Nash-   ville.

NN   0026002   NN

Nashville Tennessean.
        Members of Gaines family organize
        see under title

VOLUME 405

The Nashville Tennessean.
Style book. ₍Nashville₎ 1947.
72 p. 19 cm.

1. Printing, Practical—Style manuals. 2. Journalism.
Z253.N26   655.25   47–29397*

NN   0026004   DLC

F444
.N2A1865 Nashville Tennessean and the Nashville American
1918 classified directory; containing the
names, addresses and phone numbers of
representative manufacturing, business and
professional interests of Nashville, Tennessee and vicinity. ₍Nashville? 1918?₎
63 p. 23 cm.

Running title: Tennessean and American
directory.

1. Nashville—Direct. I. Title: Tennessean
and American classified directory.

NN   0026005   T

Nashville. The decisive battle of the rebellion
see under   [De Peyster, John Watts]

Nashville; the gateway of the South
see under   [Kress, S. H. & Co.]

The Nashville True Whig, Nashville, Tenn.
Nashville, Tenn., Printed and published by
B. R. McKennie & Co., 1853.
1 vol. Lg. folio. Unbound.
Published tri-weekly?
Library has:

NN   0026008   CSmH

Nashville Typographical Union
    see   International Typographical Union of
North America. Union no. 20, Nashville.

Nashville union.

Polk, James Knox, *pres. U. S.*, 1795–1849.
... Speech of the Hon. James K. Polk, delivered at a
public dinner at Mooresville, Maury County, Tennessee,
on the 22d. day of October, 1835. ₍Nashville, 1835₎

Nashville Union
    see also   Nashville Union and American.

Nashville Union and American.
Reflections and suggestions on the present state of par-
ties. By an old Clay Whig. Nashville, Printed by G. C.
Torbett and company, 1856.

Film   Nashville union and American.
14-34   Mar. 30, 1835-Aug.? 1875.
     ₍Nashville, Tenn.₎
     v. illus.   cm.

Formed by the union of Nashville American and
Daily union.
Title varies: Mar. 30, 1835-Aug.? 1837, Union.
Sent.? 1837-May 17, 1853, Nashville union.
Nov. 1866-Aug. 1868, Nashville union and dis-
patch.

NN   0026013   OU NcU

Nashville union and American
    see also   Nashville union.

Nashville union and dispatch
     see   Nashville union and American.

Nashville woman's literary club.
Votes for men, a comedy by the Nashville
woman's literary club, Maude Glasner, President.
Michigan, c1913.
23 p. 21 cm.
Cover title.

NN   0026016   RPB

Nashville's greeting to the Confederate veterans,
Richmond, 1896
    see under   Nashville. Citizens.

BM21
.N2Y72 Nashville Y. M. H. A. news.
The Nashville Jewish community. ₍Nash-
ville Cullom & Ghertner₎ 1933.
91 p. ports. 26 cm.

Special edition of the Y. M. H. A. news,
September, 1933.
Includes advertising.

1.) Young Men's Hebrew Association, Nashville. I. Title.

NN   0026017   T

Nashwān ibn Saʿīd al-Ḥimyarī, *d.* 1178?
Die auf Südarabien bezüglichen angaben Našwān's im
Šams al-ʿulūm, gesammelt, alphabetisch geordnet und hrsg.
von ʿAẓīmuddīn Aḥmad, PH. D. Leyden, E. J. Brill; London, Luzac & co., 1916.
xxiii, ₍1₎, 44 p.; 1 L, 163 p. 23½ cm. (*Half-title:* E. J. W. Gibb
memorial series, vol. xxiv)

Added t. p.: متنخبات في اخبار اليمن من كتاب شمس العلوم ودواه كلام
العرب من الكلوم، لنشوان بن سعيد الحميري. وقد اعتني بتنسقها وتصحيحها
عظيم الدين احمد.

Vita (on verso of p. xxiii)
"In the press for several years," but publication delayed.

1. Arabic language—Dictionaries. 2. Arabia, Southern—Kings and
rulers. 3. Names, Arabic. 4. Arabic language—Dialects—Arabia,
South. I. Ahmad, Azimuddin, maulavi, 1882– ed. II. Title:
Shams al-ʿulūm. III. Title: Muntakhabāt fi akhbār al-Yaman.

PJ709.G6   vol. 24   20–22950 rev
—— Copy 2.   PJ6963.N3

NN   0026019   DLC NcD NIC PU MiU MB NN OCl

Nashwān ibn Saʿīd al-Ḥimyarī, *d.* 1178?
Die himjarische Kasideh. Hrsg. und übersetzt von Alfred
von Kremer. Leipzig, F. A. Brockhaus, 1865.
vii, 32 p. 24 cm.

Arabic text has title: القصيدة الحميرية

1. Arabia, Southern—Hist.—Poetry. I. Kremer, Alfred, Freiherr
von, 1828–1889, ed. and tr. II. Title. III. Title: al-Qaṣīdah al-Ḥimya-
rīyah.

PJ7755.N3Q3   1865   N E 62–93

NN   0026020   DLC OCl PU NjP

Nashwān ibn Saʿīd al-Ḥimyarī, *d.* 1178?
الحور العين، للامير ابو سعيد نشوان الحميري. حققه وضبطه
وعلق حواشيه ووضع فهارسه كمال مصطفى. مصر، مكتبة
الخانجي، ١٩٤٨ ₍1948₎

50, 375 p. diagrs. 26 cm.
CONTENTS.—رسالة الحور العين ولنبيه السامعين — تفسير رسالة الحور
العين.

1. God (Mohammedanism) I. Title.
      Title transliterated: al-Ḥūr al-ʿayn wa-tanbīh al-sāmiʿīn.

BP166.2.N3   1948   60–35210

NN   0026021   DLC InU

Nashwan ibn Saʿid, al-Himyari, d. 1178?
... The lay of the Himyarites, by Neshwan ibn
Saʿid; tr. and ed. by W. F. Prideaux. Sehore,
[India] Printed at the High school press, 1879.
xx, (2), 66 p. 10 [i. e. 8] fold. geneal. tab.

This poem deals with "the vanity of human
power," and is also "a terse epitome of the
ancient history of El-Yemen."
"Impression limited to twenty-five copies.
No. 11."
Title in red and black, with Arabic title at
head of title-page.

NN   0026022   OCl ICU

Nashwān ibn Saʿīd al-Ḥimyarī, *d.* 1178?
Šams al-ʿulūm wa-dawāʾ kalām al-ʿArab min al-kulūm
₍von₎ Našwān bin Saʿid al-Ḥimjarī. Hrsg. von K. V. Zetterstéen. Leiden, E. J. Brill, 1951–
v. 27 cm.

Added t. p.: كتاب شمس العلوم ودواه كلام العرب من الكلوم، تأليف
نشوان بن سعيد الحميري. عني بتحقيقه ونشره ك. ف. ستريستين.

CONTENTS.—T. 1. Heft 1. ١–٥٠. Heft 2. ٥١–

1. Arabic language—Dictionaries. I. Zetterstéen, Karl Vilhelm,
1866–1953, ed. II. Title. III. Title: Shams al-ʿulūm.

PJ6620.N3   59–34975

NN   0026023   DLC OU CU NN

4K-807   **Nasi, Carlo.**
Abuso dei bisogni o delle passioni del minorenne
(Art. 415 Codice penale) Strozzini e strozzati
(Da uma memoria legale presentata alla Corte
d'appello di Brescia. Torino, Fratelli Bocca,
1899.
71 p.

NN   0026024   DLC-P4 MH-L

Nasi, Carlo
... Memoriale in difesa di Diamilla
Muller Ing. Demetrio ricorrente
contro sentenza della Corte d'appello
di Torino (novembre 1893) Torino,
Tip. Cugini Baravalle e Falconieri
₍1893?₎
cover-title, 29 p. 30cm.
At head of title: Ecc.ᵐᵃ Corte
suprema di Roma (Sezione penale).

Società anonime - Responsabilità
penali di non amministratori -
Questioni diverse.
Signed at end: Avv. Carlo Pa-
lomba; Avv. Carlo Nasi, estensore.

NN   0026026   MH-L

Nasi, Carlo.
... Omicidio - causa di morte -
cosa giudicata - motivazione. Alla
Corte suprema di Torino. Memoria di-
fensiva per Garavetti Margherita, ricorrente contro la sentenza della
Sezione d'accusa 28 gennaio 1886.
Torino, Speirani, 1886.
35 p. 24½cm.

Signed: Filippo Rossi ₍e₎ Carlo Nasi.

NN   0026027   MH-L

VOLUME 405

Nasi, Carlo.
    ... Reati di stampa. Ricerca del
direttore questioni diverse. Torino,
Festa e Tarizzo, 1889.
    ccover-title, 39 p. 24cm.
    "Nell'interesse del notaio Adamo
Fassini (parte civile contro Soldano
Stefano, Castellino Delfino, avv. cav.
Andrea Ferrero-Gola e il giornale L'Eco
della Macra, condannati al carcere e

accessorii per ingiurie e diffamazioni
con sentenza 9 maggio 1889 del Tribunale di Saluzzo."

NN   0026029   MH-L

Nasi, Carlo.
    ... La responsabilità civile del tipografo nei reati di diffama-
zione ed ingiuria commessi col mezzo della stampa periodica.
Appendice: Giurisprudenza sul tema: responsabilità del direttore, del proprietario, dell'editore di un periodico. **Torino,**
Fratelli Bocca ; etc., etc., 1901.
    1 p. L., v–vi p., 1 L., 231 p. 24ᵐ.

    1. Libel and slander—Italy. 2. Legal responsibility—Italy. 3. **Press**
law—Italy.
                                                            44–16072

NN   0026030   DLC MH-L CtY

Nasi, Carlo, appellant
    ... Il sottoscritto ¿Carlo Nasi¿ nella
sua qualità di parte civile nel processo elettorale per frodi, iniziatosi,
in seguito a sua denunzia del 23 dicembre 1889, crede dover suo e suo diritto
rispondere brevi osservazioni alle re-
quisitorie del Procuratore Generale, in
data 30 dicembre 1889, notificategli il
12 gennaio 1890. ¿Torino? Tip. Cugini
Baravalle e Falconieri, 1890?¿
    12 p. 31cm.

    Title from text.
    At head of title: Ecc.ᵐᵃ Sezione
d'accusa presso la Corte d'Appello
di Torino.
    Signed at end: Avv. Carlo Nasi,
Parte Civile.

NN   0026032   MH-L

Nasi, Carlo.
    Tavole dei delitti e contravvenzioni secondo il **Codice**
penale per il Regno d'Italia e le disposizioni per **la sua**
attuazione con confronti e tavole di computo **per gli aumenti**
e le diminuzioni delle pene. Torino, Unione tipografico-
editrice, 1890.
    1 v. (unpaged) 30 cm.

    1. Criminal law—Italy.   I. Italy. Laws, statutes, etc. **Codice**
penale. II. Title.
                                                            53–50837

NN   0026033   DLC MH

Nasi, Carlo, *novelist.*
    Controdestino; romanzo. Torino, A. Viglongo, 1946.
    302 p. 22 cm.

    I. Title.
    PQ4831.A8C6   853.91   A 49–3717*
    Yale Univ. Library
    for Library of Congress   ¿1¿†

NN   0026034   CtY IU NjP IEN DLC

Nasi, David Isaac Cohen
    see Nassy, David de Isaac Cohen,
    1747–1806.

¿NASI, GIACOMO¿
    Endecasyllabi di Essione Partico ¿pseud.¿
    Callifilo archiludimagistro. Venegia, A.
    spese di A. Bulison, 1684.
    115p. 16cm.

    Attributed to Giacomo Nasi.---cf. Croce,
Nuovi saggi sulla letteratura italiana.

NN   0026036   ICN

Nasi, Giambattista
    see Nasi, Giovanni Battista.

Nasi, Gian'Agostino
    Le granlezze di Maria Vergine esprèsso in
settantadue considerazioni che contengono la
vita, le cirtu', ed i titoli piu' singolari della
stessa. Livorno, tip. Egisto Vignozzi, 1854.
    x, 12–50¿ p. 14 cm.

NN   0026038   PLatS

NASI, Giovanni Battista.
    Cinque lettere sulle cagioni dell'
dierno decadimento del teatro comico
italiano, indiritte ad un erudito rispettabile
amico da Giambattista Nasi. Milano, Tip.d'
Omobono Manini, 1824.

NN   0026039   MH

B
G861ln   Nasi, Giovanni Battista.
    Elogio funebre della fu n. d. contessa Teresa
Grimaldi, nata Guaita patrizia comense, consacra-
to alla di lei memoria da Giambattista Nasi.
Como, Presso P. Ostinelli, 1819.
    31p.

    1. Grimaldi, Teresa (Guaita), contessa, 1787–
1819.

NN   0026040   IU

Nasi, Gracia Mendesia
    see **Mendesia, Gracia,** 1510 (*ca.*)–1569†

Nasi, Kaarlo W
Report on visit to the Philippines

    see under

U.S. Operations Mission to the Philippines.

WO
N254a
1895   NASI, Luigi
    Appunti di medicina operativa presi
    alle lezioni del prof. L. Nasi, anno
    accademico 1894-95. ¿Modena, 1895¿
    224 p. illus.

NN   0026043   DNLM

Nasi (Luigi). Dell' ernia cieeale acistica, considerazioni e nota clinica. Dell' erniotomia, suoi
accidenti e relative indicazioni. 25 pp. 8°.
Modena, Moneti & Namias, 1883.

NN   0026044   DNLM

Nasi (Luigi). Ovariotomia eseguita in Modena
il 28 giugno 1883 dal prof. Giovanni Bezzi. 7
pp. 8°. ¿*Modena, Vincenzi,* 1883¿.
Repr. from: Spallanzani, Modena, 1883, 2. s., xii.

NN   0026045   DNLM

NASI, LUIGI, *writer on military art and science.*
    ... Preparémonos para la victoria; traduci-
do al español, por el teniente coronel
Schemoni L. Asunción, Talleres gráficos del
estado, 1915.
    70p. 20cm.

    Translation of Prepariamoci alla vittoria!

    1. Military art and science. I. Schenoni
Lugo, Manlio, 1879- tr. II. Title.

NN   0026046   TxU

Nasi, Nunzio, 1850–1935.
    ... Il diritto e la guerra.   Campobasso: G. Colitti e figlio,
1919.   1 p.l., (1)6–26 p. 8°.   (Collana Colitti di conferenze
e discorsi. no. 54.)

    1. Law (International),   1914- . 2. European war,
    1914- . 3. Series.   October 14, 1920.
    N. Y. P. L.

NN   0026047   NN MH NjP DLC-P4

Nasi, Nunzio, 1850–1935
    ... Discorsi pronunziati da S. E.
il Ministro Nunzio Nasi alla Camera
dei deputati sul riordinamento del-
l'amministrazione postale e tele-
grafica con i Decreti del nuovo
organico, le Relazioni a S.M. e le
Tabelle comparative del personale.
Roma, Unione cooperativa editrice,
1899.
    78 p. incl. tables. 23½cm.

    At head of title: Ministero delle
poste e dei telegrafi.

NN   0026049   MH-L

Nasi, Nunzio, 1850–1935.
    ... Discorso di s.e. il Ministro dell'istruzione
pubblica (Nasi) pronunziato alla Camera dei
deputati nella tornata del 17 aprile 1902
    see under   Italy. Ministero dell'educazione
nazionale.

Nasi, Nunzio, 1850–1935.
    ... E ammissibile il ricorso in Cassazione
avverso la sentenza dell'Alta Corte ? (Il caso Nasi)
    see under   Marino-Lucca, Mario.

Nasi, Nunzio, 1850–1935.
    Memorie, storia di un dramma parlamentare. Roma, F.
Ciuni ¿1943¿
    478 p. plates, ports., facsims., music. 22 cm.
    L. C. copy imperfect : p. 17–32 wanting.

    1. Italy—Pol. & govt.—1870–1915.

    DG556.N33A3   48–36066*

NN   0026052   DLC MH

Nasi, Nunzio, 1850–1935.
    ... Memorie; storia di un dramma parlamentare.
Mazara, Società editrice siciliana [1951]
    478 p. port. 23cm.

    Preface signed: Virgilio Nasi.
    "Le onoranze a Nunzio Nasi nel primo centenario
della nascita," 23 p. inserted.
    1. Italy—Politics, 1890–1930. 2. Sicily—Hist.,
1860- . I. Nasi,   Virgilio, ed.

NN   0026053   NN

Nasi, Nunzio, 1850–1935.
    Sul bilancio della pubblica istruzione
    see under   Italy. Ministero dell'educazione
nazionale

VOLUME 405

Nasi, Nunzio, *1850-1935.*　　　　**L379.1 Q100**
49497　Per la pubblica educazione. Discorsi pronunziati dal ministro
On. Nunzio Nasi.　Roma, tipografia ditta L. Cecchini, 1901.
143 p.　25½ᵗᵐ.
Contents.— Per l'unione magistrale. — Per la cultura scientifica — Per l'arte.— Per
il riordinamento degli studi.— Per la riforma scolastica.

NN　0026055　ICJ

Nasi, Nunzio, 1850-1935
La teoria del progresso legislativo.
Saggio dell'avv. Nunzio Nasi Virgilio ...
Trapani, P.A. Rizzi, 1875.
　203 p.　21½cm.
　Bibliographical footnotes.

NN　0026056　MH-L

｢Nasi, Virgilio｣
Ricorso per l'incompetenza dell'autori-
tà giudiziaria a procedere contro
l'ex-ministro on. Nunzio Nasi.　｢Roma,
Tip. Forense, 1904｣
　cover title, 8 p.　24cm.
　Signed: Virgilio Nasi; Francesco
Faranda.

NN　0026057　MH-L

Nasi kraji.　n.p., n.d.
　₍8₎ p. of pl.
　Cover-title.

NN　0026058　OC1

Nasi noviji humoristi; zbirka humoreska i satira
mladih hrvatskih pisaca.　Vol. 1-　Zagreb, Huro-
risticna knjiznica ₍n.d.₎

NN　0026059　OC1

Naši pjesnici.　Zagreb, Izd. Narodne knjižnice

4　(1922)　-　Nazor, Vladimir, 1876-1949
　　　　Carmen vitae

NN　0026060　MH

Naši pogledi; sestajali so se zastopniki nar-
odov načinu razdeljevli evropo...　Ljubljana, Slovenski klub na univerzi, 1937.

Collection of seven articles.

1. Yugoslavia.

NN　0026061　KU

Naši dan₎.

Sarajevo ｢Izvršni odbor Saveza studenata BiH｣
₍1 v. illus., ports. 39 cm. weekly (irregular)
"List studenata SR Bosne i Hercegovine."

1. Students—Periodicals. 2. Students—Bosnia and Herzegovina.
i. Savez studenata BiH. Izvršni odbor.

LH5.S33N3　　　　70-432878

NN　0026062　DLC

Naši gradovi na moru.　Split. Zagreb ｢"Tipografija" d. d.｣
1927.
　cover-title, 64 p.　24ᵐ.
　"Preštampano iz Nove Evrope (knj. xv)"

1. Spalato.
Library of Congress　　　DR396.S65N3　　38-23085
　　　　　　　　　　　　　　₍2₎　　　　　　914.369

NN　0026063　DLC IU

Naši obmejni problemi
　　see under　Družba sv. Cirila in Metoda,
Ljubljana.

AP58
.S55N33

Naši razgledi; štirinajstdnevnik za politična, gospodarska in
kulturna vprašanja.　leto 1-　8 mar. 1952-
　Ljubljana ｢Naš tisk, etc.｣
　v. illus., ports., maps.　35 cm.
　Vols. 3, no. 11-　　　called also no. 58-

　AP58.S55N33　　　　　　58-43874

NN　0026065　DLC

Naši v poušti.　Praha, Naše vojsko, 1946.　1 v. of illus.　26cm.

399489B. 1. World war, 1939-1945　—Campaigns—Near East. 2. World
war, 1939-1945—Pictorial works.
N. Y. P. L.　　　　　　　　　　　　　May 26, 1948

NN　0026066　NN InU

Naši zapiski; socialistična revija.
letnik 1-
jul. 1902-
Ljubljana ₍etc.₎ Slovenska socialna matica
₍etc.₎ 1902-
v.　24cm.

Frequency varies.
Subtitle varies: letnik 1-9, socialna revija.
Not published 1915-1919.

NN　0026067　NNC MH

Naši zbori; dvomesečnik slovenskih zborovskih skladb z
glasbeno-knjižno prilogo.
Ljubljana, Državna založba Slovenije, 19
　v. in　　illus., ports. 34 cm.
　Each issue consists of vocal music.

1. Choruses, Secular (Mixed voices), Unaccompanied. 2. Music,
Slovenian. 3. Music—Period.

M1579.N37　　　　　　　　M 59-639

NN　0026068　DLC

Nasi Zydzi w miasteczkach ...
　　see under　₍Szaniawski, Klemens₎ 1849-
1898.

Nasīb al-Ikhtiyār
　see
al-Ikhtiyār, Nasīb.

Nasīb Arslān, *amīr*
　see
Arslān, Nasīb, *amīr*, 1867 or 8-1927.

Nasib Khan
　see　Khan, Nasib.

Nasib Khan, Rana
　see　Khan, Rana Nasib.

TN871
.2
.T34

Nasibov, Aleksandr Ashotovich.

Temirkhanov, Gadzhi.
Нефть идет! ｢Литературная запись А. Насибова.
Москва｣ Профиздат, 1953.

Nasica, *pseud.*
　see Majani, Augusto, 1867-

Nasica, Scipion, 1906-
... Contribution à l'étude et au traitement de
l'épilepsie des moignons ...　Lyon, 1933.
Thèse - Univ. de Lyon.
"Bibliographie": p. [68]-70.

NN　0026076　CtY

Nasica, T　　*d.* 1850.
Mémoires sur l'enfance et la jeunesse de Napoléon jusqu'à
l'âge de vingt-trois ans; précédés d'une notice historique sur
son père, par T. Nasica ... dédiés à S. A. I. le prince-président,
par l'abbé Nasica ...　Paris, Ledoyen, 1852.
xv, 406 p. fold. geneal. tab. 22½ᵐ.
Preface dated Ajaccio, 1829.

1. Bonaparte, Carlo Maria, 1746-1785. 2. Napoléon I, emperor of the
French, 1769-1821.
Library of Congress　　　DC205.N25　　　2-13057

NN　0026077　DLC NIC MB MH

Nasica, T　　*d.* 1850.
... Mémoires sur l'enfance et la jeunesse de
Napoléon jusqu'à l'âge de vingt-trois ans;
précédés d'une notice historique sur son père ...
Paris, P. Dupont, 1865.
xii, 288 p. fold. geneal. tab.　18 cm.
(Bibliothèques populaires)

NN　0026078　RPB NjP CtY

Nasica, T.　　*d.* 1850.
Notice sur la vie de Charles Bonaparte, père de Napoléon.
(In his Mémoires sur l'enfance et la jeunesse de Napoléon ...
Pp. 1-49.　Paris.　1852.)

H1084 — Bonaparte, Charles Marie. 1746-1784.

NN　0026079　MB

Nasielski, Adam.
As pik. n.d.

NN　0026080　OC1

Nasielski, Adam
Awantura w Chicago.　₍1938₎

NN　0026081　OC1

Nasielski, Adam
Centrala1 1 1

NN　0026082　OC1

VOLUME 405

Nasielski, Adam
Dyktator zwariował. ‹cl938›.

NN 0026083 OCl

Nasielski, Adam
Eksperyment Doktora Visconta. ‹cl937›.

NN 0026084 OCl

Nasielski, Adam
Grobowiec Ozyrysa; wielka gra Bernada Zbika.
1936.

NN 0026085 OCl

Nasielski, Adam
Kapitan Irena. 1936.

NN 0026086 OCl

Nasielski, Adam
Mecz o kobiete. n.d.

NN 0026087 OCl

Nasielski, Adam
Minus trzy. ‹n.d.›

NN 0026088 OCl

Nasielski, Adam
Piaty temat. n.d.

NN 0026089 OCl

Nasielski, Adam
Porwano kobiete; powiesc kryminalna. n.d.

NN 0026090 OCl

Nasielski, Adam
R.

NN 0026091 OCl

Nasielski, Adam
Skarb z Fernando Poo. ‹1934›.

NN 0026092 OCl

Nasielski, Adam
Skok w Otchlan; wielka gra Bernarda Zbika. ‹n.d.›

NN 0026093 OCl

Nasielski, Adam
Zielony lont. ‹2 v. in 1›

NN 0026094 OCl

Nasielski, Adam
Znak kwadratu. ‹2 v. in 1›

NN 0026095 OCl

Nasier, Alcofribas, the later [pseud.]
De tribus impostoribus, A. D. 1230
see De tribus impostoribus.

Nāṣif, 'Iṣām al-Dīn Ḥifnī.
اخفاق الفاشية، بقلم عصام الدين حفني ناصف. الطبعة 1.
القاهرة، مطبعة لجنة التاليف والترجمة والنشر، 1943.
56 p. 23 cm.

1. Fascism. I. Title.
Title romanized: Ikhfāq al-fāshīyah.

JC481.N27 N E 68-2640

NN 0026097 DLC

Nāṣif, Malak Ḥifnī, 1886–1918.
(al-Nisā'īyāt)
النسائيات، مجموعة مقالات نشرت فى الجريدة فى موضوع
المراة المصرية. بقلم باحثة البادية. ‹وبها مقدمة بقلم احمد لطفى
السيد. الطبعة 2. مصر، يطلب من المكتبة التجارية الكبرى
‹1925›
2 v. in 1. port. 24 cm.

1. Women in Egypt—Addresses, essays, lectures. I. Title.

HQ1793.N37 1925 73-221267

NN 0026098 DLC

Nāṣif, Mālak Hifnī, 1886-1918.
Ueber die ägyptische Frauenfrage; Aufsätze von Melek Hifni
Nâçif; aus dem Arabischen übersetzt. Konstantinopel: Abajoli,
1926. 126 p. 8°.

"In 80 Exemplaren als Manuskript gedruckt."
Preface signed: O. Rescher.

1. Woman—Egypt. 2. Arabic litera-   ture—Woman. 3. Rescher, Oskar,
1883- , translator.   1883- , translator.
N. Y. P. L.   March 8, 1927

NN 0026099 NN NjP OCl

Nāṣif, Manṣūr 'Alī, comp.
(al-Tāj al-jāmi' lil-uṣūl)
التاج الجامع للأصول فى احاديث الرسول، تاليف منصور على
ناصف. وعليه غاية المأمول، شرح التاج الجامع للأصول.
الطبعة 2. القاهرة، دار احياء الكتب العربية، 1932.
5 v. 28 cm.
Vocalized.

1. Hadith (Collections) I. Nāṣif, Manṣūr 'Alī. Ghāyat al
-ma'mūl, sharh al-Tāj al-jāmi' lil-uṣūl. 1932. II. Title.

BP135.A2N28 1932 74-214868

NN 0026100 DLC

Nāṣif al-Yāzijī
see
al-Yāzijī, Nāṣif, 1800–1871.

Nāṣif Buṭrus
see
Buṭrus, Nāṣif.

Nāsif Ma'lūf
see
Mallouf, Nassif, 1823-1868 or 9.

Nasik, Philip Henry Loyd, *Bp. of*
see
Loyd, Philip Henry, *Bp.*, 1884–1952.

Nasilov, V   M
Грамматика уйгурского языка. Москва, 1940.
151, ‹1› p. 22 cm.
At head of title: Московский институт востоковедения.

1. Uigur language—Grammar. I. Moscow. Institut vostokove-
deniῐᾶ. *Title transliterated:* Grammatika uigurskogo ῐāzyka.

PL49.N3 49-32353

NN 0026104 DLC

Nasilowski, Karl, 1891-
Ein Beitrag zur Kenntnis der Harnröhrensteine.
Berlin [1918]
22, [2] p. 23 cm.
Inaug.-diss. – Berlin.
Lebenslauf.

NN 0026105 CtY

Nasim, Mohammad, 1908-
كشور. دصصف ء نسيم انهونى. لاهور، شعاع
ادب ‹1950›
184 p. 18 cm.
In Urdu.
Text partially vocalized.
A novel.

I. Title. *Title transliterated:* Kishvir.

PK2200.N352K5 S A 65-1873

NN 0026106 DLC

Nasīm, Raḥīm Shāh.
تربور، د پښتنو د معاشرے په حقله يوه اصلاحى درامه.
ليکونکے: رحيم شاه نسيم. پيښور، جديد دار الکتاب ‹؟-195›
240 p. 19 cm.

I. Title. *Title transliterated:* Tarbūr.

PK6820.N35T3 S A 66-513
PL 480: P-Pushto-36

NN 0026107 DLC ICU

Nasīm Ḥijāzī
see
Ḥijāzī, Nasīm.

Nasīm Nawfal
see
Nawfal, Nasīm, 1846–1899.

Slavic-   Našim dětem; učebnice pro I. třídu českých
American   svobodomyslných škol v Americe. Uspořadal
Imprints   Výbor učitelského sboru českých svobodo-
Coll.   myslných škol v Chicagu. Chicago, Sdružení
420.29   českých svobodomyslných škol v Chicagu, 1935.
N373   122 p. illus. 22 cm.
English translation of title: To our
children; the textbook for the first grade
of Czech liberal-minded schools in America.
Compiled by the Committee of teachers staff
of Czech liberal-minded schools in Chicago,
Ill.
rw

NN 0026110 IEdS

VOLUME 405

QL1　Nasimovich, A　　　A
E8　　The biology of the weasel in Kola Peninsula
no. 257　in connection with its competitive relations with
　　　the ermine.　[n.p., n.d.]
　　　12 l.　tables.　27 cm.　(English transla-
　　　tions of Russian zoological literature.
　　　Trans. 257)
　　　From Zoologicheskii zhurnal, v. 28, p. 177–82,
　　　1949.
　　　Typewritten (carbon copy)
　　　Translated by J. D. Jackson, 1955.
　　　1. Weasels. I. Jackson, J. D., tr. II. Title.

NN　0026111　DI

Nasimovich, A　　　A　　　ed.
　　Преобразование фауны позвоночных нашей страны;
биотехнические мероприятия. Москва, Изд. Московского об-ва испытателей природы, 1953.
　　234 p.　illus.　26 cm.
　　Includes bibliographies.

　　1. Animal industry—Russia. 2. Vertebrates—Russia.　ι. Moskov-
skoe obshchestvo ispytatelei prirody.　ιι. Title.
　　　　Title transliterated: Preobrazovanie fauny
　　　　pozvonochnykh nashel strany.

SF55.R95N3　　　　54–43477

NN　0026112　DLC

Nasimovich, A　　　A
　　Роль режима снежного покрова в жизни копытных животных на территории СССР. Москва, Изд-во Академии
наук СССР, 1955.
　　401 p.　illus.　21 cm.
　　At head of title: Академия наук СССР. Институт географии.
　　Includes bibliography.

　　1. Snow. 2. Ungulata. 3. Mammals—Russia.　ι. Title.
　　　　Title transliterated: Rol' rezhima snezhnogo
　　　　pokrova v zhizni kopytnykh zhivotnykh.

QH543.N3　　　　56–57654 ‡

NN　0026113　DLC CaBVaU

Nasimovich, A　　　A
　　В Забайкалье; записки натуралиста. Рисунки В. В.
Трофимова. Москва, 1951.
　　102 p.　illus.　22 cm.　(Московское общество испытателей при-
роды. Среди природы, вып. 39)
　　Includes bibliography.

　　1. Natural history—Transbaikalia.　ι. Title.
　　　　Title transliterated: V Zabaĭkal'e.

QH191.N3　　　　61–41118 ‡

NN　0026114　DLC MiU

Nasimovich, Aleksandr Fedorovich, 1880–1947.
　　... Бурелом; сборник рассказов. Москва, "Земля и фа-
брика," 1923.
　　156 p., 1 l.　18½ cm.
　　At head of title: А. Насимович.
　　CONTENTS.—Мараказия.—В чистую.—Омрачный Вернада.—
Топор.—Около смерти.—Собственность.—Какая ни на есть.—Херу-
вимская.

　　ι. Title.　　　Title transliterated: Burelom.
　　Library of Congress　PG3476.N42B8
　　　　　　44–21732

NN　0026115　DLC

Nasimovich, Aleksandr Fedorovich, 1880–1947.
　　(Gorod premoguchii)
　　Город премогучий; роман. Москва, Московский ра-
бочий 1928.
　　383 p.　20 cm.
　　At head of title: А. Насимович.

　　ι. Title.

PG3476.N374G6　1928　　73–216509

NN　0026116　DLC

Nasimovich, Aleksandr Fedorovich, 1880–1947.
　　(Grekh)
　　Грех; повести и рассказы. Москва, Московское т-во
писателей, 1928.
　　196 p.　20 cm.
　　At head of title: А. Насимович.
　　CONTENTS: Детство Ратнера.—Грех.—Записки приказчика.—
Деревянные ножки.—За кулисами.

　　ι. Title.

PG3476.N374G7　1928　　73–216693

NN　0026117　DLC

PG3476
.N374B35　Nasimovich, Aleksandr Fedorovich, 1880–
　　... Гул шагов; семь сцен из пьесы "Барометр показывает
бурю"; для клубных постановок. Репертуар Театра рево-
люции. (Москва) Московское театральное издательство,
1927.
　　62 p.　17 x 13 cm.
　　At head of title: А. Насимович.

　　ι. Title.　　Title transliterated: Gul shagov.

　　　　　　　　43–43453

NN　0026118　DLC

Nasimovich, Nikolaĭ Fedorovich, 1876–　　ed.
Chemodanov, Gennadiĭ Nikolaevich, d. 1929.
　　Нерчинская каторга; воспоминания бывшего началь-
ника конвойной команды. 2. изд. под редакцией Н. Чужака (псевд.) и В. Плескова. Москва, Изд-во Всесоюз-
ного об-ва политкаторжан и сс.-поселенцев, 1930.

PG3476
.A88P8　Nasimovich, Nikolaĭ Fedorovich, 1876–
Auslender, Sergeĭ Abramovich, 1886–
　　Пугачевщина. Роман, с послесловием Н. Ф. Чужака
(псевд.) Москва, Молодая гвардия, 1928.

B　　Nasini, Giuseppe.
N254n　　Della vita e delle opere del ... Giu-
　　seppe Nasini, pittore del secolo XVII;
　　notizie raccolte ed ordinate, con brevi
　　biografie degli altri pittori della me-
　　desima famiglia.　Prato, 1872.
　　103 p.　front. (port.)

　　Bibliographical foot-notes.

NN　0026121　IU NjP

QD71　Nasini, Raffaello, 1854–1931, ed.
.R7
　　Rome (City)　Laboratorio chimico centrale delle gabelle.
　　Annali del Laboratorio chimico centrale delle gabelle ...
　　Roma, Tipografia cooperativa sociale (etc.) 1891–1914.

Nasini, Raffaello, 1854–1931.
　　La cattedra di chimica nella Università di Pisa. Prolusione al corso
di chimica generale letta il giorno 17 gennaio 1907 nell' aula dell'
Istituto di chimica generale.　28 pp.
　　(In Annali delle università toscane. Tomo 27. Pisa. 1907.)

K3007 — Reale università di Pisa. I…uto di chimica generale. — Chemistry.
Hist.

NN　0026123　MB PU

Nasini, R(affaello), and U. Bresciani.
　　La materia allo stato sovraffuso e discontinuità in alcune sue
proprietà fisiche in vicinanza del punto di fusione.　(Reale
Accad. dei Lincei.　Mem. Classe di scienze fisiche, matematiche
e naturali.　Roma, 1912.　4°.　Serie 5, v. 9, p. 341–401, 735–
750, 9 pl.)

1. Surfusion. 2. Melting point. 3.　　Bresciani, U., jt. au.
N. Y. P. L.　　　　　　　　　　　　　　　　　June 2, 1914.

NN　0026124　NN

Nasini, Raffaello, 1854–1931.
　　Relazione sulle analisi e sulle ricerche
eseguite durante il triennio 1886–89 nel
laboratoria chimica centrale delle vecchia ...
Rome Botta, 1890.
　　496 p.

NN　0026125　PPF

Nasini, Raffaello, 1854–1931.
　　I soffioni boraciferi e la industria dell' acido borico in
Toscana, relazione del prof. Raffaello Nasini ... Roma,
Tip. della R. Accademia dei lincei, 1906.
　　109 p., 1 l.　illus. (incl. port.)　30½ cm.
　　Pubblicata in occasione del vi Congresso internazionale di chimica appli-
cata che si terrà in Roma nell' aprile del 1906.
　　"Bibliografia": p. 105–109.

　　1. Borax. 2. Boric acid.
　　　　　　　　　　　　　　　　　　　G S 19–158
　　Library, U. S. Geological　　　Survey　403(550) qN17

NN　0026126　DI-GS

Nasini, Raffaello, 1854–1931.
　　... I soffioni boraciferi e la industria dell' acido borico
in Toscana ... Roma, Tipografia nazionale di G. Bertero
e c., 1907.
　　124 p.　illus. 26 cm.
　　"vi Congresso internazionale di chimica applicata—Roma 1906. Comu-
nicazione fatta nella sezione ιι (Chimica inorganica e industrie relative)"
　　"Bibliografia": p. 119–124.

　　1. Borax—Italy—Tuscany.
　　　　　　　　　　　　　　　　　　G S 10–601
　　Library, U. S. Geol.　　　survey　403(550) qN18

NN　0026127　DI-GS

Nasini, Raffaello, 1854–1931.
　　... I soffioni e i lagoni della Toscana e la industria boracifera;
storia, studi, ricerche chimiche e chimico-fisiche eseguite prin-
cipalmente nell' ultimo venticinquennio. Roma, Tipografia
editrice Italia, 1930.
　　xl, 658 p.　incl. illus., tables, diagrs. plates (incl. ports., facsims.)
31½ cm.
　　At head of title: Raffaello Nasini, senatore del regno.

　　1. Borax—Italy—Tuscany. 2. Boric acid.　ι. Title.
　　　　　　　　　　　　　　　　　　G S 30–246
　　Library, U. S. Geological　　　Survey　403(550) qN19

NN　0026128　DI-GS CU MH ICU NcD PU

Nasini, Raffaello, 1854–1931.
　　... Sul peso normale pei saccarimetri.　Roma, Tipografia nazionale di G. Bertero, 1891.
　　54 p.　double pl.　31½ cm.
　　At head of title: Pubblicazione del Laboratorio chimico centrale delle
gabelle. R. Nasini e V. Villavecchia.

　　1. Saccharimeter.　ι. Italy—Laboratorio chimico centrale delle ga-
belle.　ιι. Villavecchia, V., joint author.
　　　　　　　　　　　　　　　　　　Agr 9–862
　　Library, U. S. Dept. of　　　Agriculture　386N17

NN　0026129　DNAL

Nasino, Pablo Bartolomé.
　　Tratado de economía social y mutualismo argentino; estudio
de las instituciones mutuales de la República argentina, y de
diversas cuestiones económico-sociales que figuran en los pro-
gramas de economía política vigentes en la Facultad de derecho
y ciencias sociales y en la Facultad de ciencias económicas de la
Universidad nacional de Buenos Aires, por Pablo Bartolomé
Nasino. Buenos Aires, Est. gráf. "Franco," 1919.
　　619 p.　incl. tables.　23 cm.

　　1. Cooperation—Argentine republic. 2. Insurance—Argentine republic. 3. Labor and laboring classes—Argentine republic. 4. Caja internacional mutua de pensiones, Buenos Aires.　ι. Buenos Aires. Universidad nacional.
　　Library of Congress　HD3468.N3　　42–49272

NN　0026130　DLC MB MH NcU TxU PPB

VOLUME 405

Nasio, Juan.
    Ramón y Cajal, maestro de generaciones. Prólogo del
profesor Dr. Gregorio Marañón. ₍Buenos Aires, Unión de
Editores Latinos, 1955₎
    144 p. 25 cm.
    Includes bibliography.

    1. Ramón y Cajal, Santiago, 1852-1934.

R483.R23N3   57-18973 ‡

NN   0026131   DLC MH CU NcU NN PPJ

Nasio, Juan.
    Sulfanilamidoterápia local, por ... Juan Nasio ...
Buenos Aires, A. López, 1942.
    150, 3 p. illus., tables, diagrs. 23ᶜᵐ.
    Cover-title.
    Includes bibliographies.

NN   0026132   ICJ DNLM NNC

615.2
N254s   Nasio, Juan.
    Sulfanilamidoterápia local; experiencias
realizadas en el Instituto de Farmacología de
la Facultad de Medicina del Litoral. Estudio
clínico efectuado en el Hospital Rosario y en
especial en la Sala VII. ₍Buenos Aires, A.Ló-
pez, 1943₎
    150 p. illus.,diagrs.,tables. 24 cm.
    "Trabajos del autor sobre el tema": p.150.
    Includes bibliographies.

    1.Sulphanila-   mide.

NN   0026133   MiU

Nasio, Juan.
    Tratamiento médico de la úlcera gastroduodenal
experimental. Prologo por A. C. Ivy. Buenos
Aires ₍Talleres Gráficos "La Prensa Médica Argentina"₎ 1946.
    151 p. illus.
    At head of title: Instituto de Farmacología de
la Facultad de Ciencias Médicas del Litoral.
    Includes bibliographies.

    1 Stomach (Diseases) 2. Ulcers. 616.33

NN   0026134   ICJ DNLM MH

WI   NASIO, Juan
350   Tratamiento médico de la úlcera
N254tr   gástrica y duodenal, acción de la
1953   bantina. Buenos Aires, El Ateneo,
              1953.
              140 p. illus.
              1. Peptic ulcer - Treatment

NN   0026135   DNLM MiU ICJ PPC

Nasionale boekhandel beperk.
    Ons skry wers.   Kaapstad, 1955.   30 p.   ports.   22cm.

    1. Authors, Afrikaans—Dictionaries.

NN   0026136   NN

Nasionale Bounavorsingsinstituut
    see South African Council for Scientific and Industrial
Research. *National Building Research Institute.*

Nasionale Finansiekorporasie van Suid-Afrika
    see
National Finance Corporation of South Africa.

Nasionale Instituut vir Personeelnavorsing
    see National Institute for Personnel Research.

HQ799   Nasionale Jeugbond van Transvaal.
S7N22   Gedenkalbum oor die eerste tien jaar van
bestaan; uitgegee deur die Hoofraad van
Transvaal. ₍Pretoria, 1950₎
        40 p. illus., ports. 24cm.

    1. Youth movement - Transvaal. I. Title.

NN   0026140   CSt-H

Nasionale Konferensie insake Maatskaplike Werk
    see
    National Conference on Social Work.

Nasionale Konferensie oor Alkoholisme, *Pretoria, 1961*
    see
    National Conference on Alcoholism, *Pretoria, 1951.*

Nasionale museum, *Bloemfontein*
    see
Bloemfontein. Nasionale museum.

Nasionale Party van Transvaal.
    ...Notule van die kongres...
₍no.₎

₍Pretoria, 19   21½ - 24½cm.
nos.

    No. 22 (1935) title adds: en Opgaaf van ampsdraers van afdelings- en taksbesture.

NN   0026144   NN

Nasionale spaarsaamheidsbeweging
    see
National thrift organisation (*South Africa*)

NASIONALE VROUEMONUMENTEKOMMISSIE.
    Christiaan Rudolph de Wet, 1854-1922. Saamgestel
deur M. C. E. van Schoor, S. I. Malan en J. J. Ober-
holster, en uitgegee deur die Nasionale vrouemonumentekommissie in opdrag van die Genl. de Wet-standbeeld-
onthullingskomitee. Bloemfontein, 1954. 176 p.
illus., ports. 18x26cm.

    1. DE WET,CHRISTIAAN RUDOLPH, 1854-1922
I. Generaal de Wet-standbeeld-onthul-
    lingskomitee   II. Schoor,C.E.van,ed.

NN   0026146   NN

Nasionale vroueraad van Suid-Afrika
    see
National council of women of South Africa.

Nasionalisme bring oorwinning
        see under ₍Nel, M   D   C
de W   ₎

Nasir, Ahmad, 1836-1912
        see Nazir Ahmad, 1836-1912.

---

al-Nāṣir, 'Alī.
    (Qiṣṣat qalb)
قصة قلب، مقطوعات شعرية. بقلم على الناصر. حلب،
مطبعة الشهباء، 1928.
    8, 44 p. 17 cm.
    Cover title.

    I. Title.

PJ7852.A675Q5   73-206554

NN   0026150   DLC

---

al-Nāṣir, 'Alī.
سريال ₍تاليف₎ على الناصر ₍و₎اورخان ميسر. ₍حلب₎ 1947.
    77 p. 20 cm.

    I. Muyassar, Ürkhān, joint author. II. Title.
                        Title transliterated: Siryāl.

PJ7852.A675S5   N E 65-547

NN   0026151   DLC

Nasir, Eugene.
    The *bupleura* (Umbelliferae) of north-west Himalaya.
Berkeley, University of California Press, 1955.
    417-444 p. illus., map. 26 cm. (University of California publica-
tions in botany, v. 27, no. 7)
    Bibliography: p. 444.

    1. Bupleurum. 2. Botany—Himalaya Mountains. (Series: Cali-
fornia. University. University of California publications in botany,
v. 27, no. 7)

QK1.C2 vol. 27, no. 7   A 55-9520
——— Copy 2.   QK495.U48N3

California. Univ. Libr.
for Library of Congress   ₍5₎†

DLC
NN   0026152   CU MoU NNBG IdPI PU PSt OCU TxU OU

Nasir, Gamal Abdul
    see
Nasser, Gamal Abdel, *Pres. United Arab Republic*, 1918–

Nasir, George.
    Fifteen poems. [Winnipeg, 1948]
    15 p.

    Cover title.

    1. Canadian poetry, English.
    I. Title.

NN   0026154   CaOTP RPB MH

Nasir, George.
    New poems. Winnipeg, Manitoba [1949]   [8] p.
23cm.

NN   0026155   NN

Nāṣir, Jamāl Abd al-
        see Nasser, Gamal Abdel, Pres.
United Arab Republic, 1918–

297.5
N178s   Nasir, Khalil Ahmad.
    The status of women in Islam. Washington,
The Ahmadiyya Movement in Islam ₍n.d.₎
    18 p. 22cm.

    1. Women, Mohammedan. I. T.

NN   0026157   MiDW

VOLUME 405

al-Nāṣir, al-Malik
see
al-Malik al-Nāṣir Muḥammad ibn Qalāwūn, *Sultan of Egypt and Syria*, 1285–1341.

W 4   NASIR, Mohammed, 1911–
M96   Über die biologische Bedeutung der
1954   Katalasen. München, 1954.
       23 *l*. illus.
       Inaug.-Diss. - Munich.
       1. Catalase

   NN   0026159   DNLM

Nasir, Shaikh Mahmud, 1890–
     ... Some observations on barren soils of lower Bari
Doab colony in the Punjab, by S. M. Nasir ... Calcutta,
Superintendent government printing, India, 1923.
     1 p. l., 11 p. 25ᶜᵐ. (Pusa. Agricultural research institute. Bulletin
no. 145)

     1. Soils—India—Punjab. ₍1. India—Punjab—Soils₎
                      Agr 23–1149 Revised
   Library, U. S. Dept. of   Agriculture 22P97 no. 145

   NN   0026160   DNAL

Nasir Ahmad Farooki
see
Farooki, Nasir Ahmad.

Nasir Ahmad Khan
see
Khan, Nasir Ahmad.

Nāṣir al-Dīn Abū al-Ma'ālī Muhammad ibn
al-Malik al-'Ādil
     see   al-Malik al-Kāmil, Muhammad,
sultan of Egypt and Syria, 1180?–1238.

Nāṣir al-Dīn, 'Alī.
قضية العرب ₍تأليف₎ علي ناصر الدين. بيروت، دار العلم
للملايين، 1946.

     136 p. illus., map. 20 cm.
     Bibliographical footnotes.

     1. Panarabism.   I. Title.
           Title romanized: Qaḍīyat al-'Arab.

   DS63.7.N3 1946   N E 68–3455

   NN   0026163   DLC

Nāṣir al-Dīn, 'Alī.
قضية العرب ₍تأليف₎ علي ناصر الدين. ₍الطبعة 2، بيروت₎
دار الحكمة، 1955.

     153 p. illus., map. 22 cm.
     Bibliographical footnotes.

     1. Panarabism.   I. Title.
           Title romanized: Qaḍīyat al-'Arab.

   DS63.7.N3 1955   N E 68–3429

   NN   0026164   DLC

Nasir al-Din Abu Said 'Abd Allah ibn 'Umar, al-
Baidawi
     see   al-Baydāwi, 'Abd Allah ibn 'Umar,
d. 1286?

Nasir al-Dīn al-Ṭūsī
see
al-Ṭūsī, Nasir al-Dīn Muḥammad ibn Muḥammad, 1201–1274.

Nāṣir al-Dīn ibn Burhān al-Dīn, *al-Rabghūsī.*
     Narrationes de prophetis. Cod. Mus. Brit. Add. 7851.
Reproduced in facsim. with an introd. by K. Grønbech.
Copenhagen, E. Munksgaard, 1948.
     14 p., facsim.: 252 p. 31 cm. (Monumenta linguarum Asiæ
Maioris, edidit K. Grønbech, 4)

     1. Manuscripts, Turkish—Facsimiles. 2. Manuscripts. Gt. Brit.—
Facsimiles.   I. Grønbech, Kaare, 1901–   II. Title.   (Series)

   Z115Z.N3   51–28811

   NN   0026167   DLC NN OC1 NcD TxU CU OU InU MH NjP

Nasīr al-dīn Mughultā'ī
     see   Mughultā'ī, 1290–1361.

Nāṣir al-Dīn Muḥammad ibn 'Abd al-Raḥīm ibn al-Furāt
see
Ibn al-Furāt, Muḥammad ibn 'Abd al-Raḥīm, 1334 *or* 5–1405.

Nāṣir al-Dīn Muḥammad ibn 'Izz al-Dīn 'Abd al-Raḥīm,
known as Ibn al-Furāt
see
Ibn al-Furāt, Muḥammad ibn 'Abd al-Raḥīm, 1334 *or* 5–1405.

Nāṣir al-Dīn Muḥammad ibn Muḥammad al-Ṭūsī
see
al-Ṭūsī, Naṣir al-Dīn Muḥammad ibn Muḥammad, 1201–1274.

Nāṣir al-Dīn Shāh, *Shah of Iran*, 1831–1896.
     A diary kept by His Majesty the Shah of Persia, during
his journey to Europe in 1878. From the Persian, by
especial permission of His Majesty, by Albert Houtum
Schindler and Baron Louis de Norman. London, R. Bentley
& son, 1879.
     3 p. l., 306, ₍1₎ p. 22½ cm.
     Colophon: Year of the Leopard, 1295. Printed by order, at the
special printing office of His Majesty, under the direction of Sanī'a
ud Dowleh, and published at Teheran on the 6th Safer, 1296, the
anniversary of the birth of the shah.
     Translation of سفرنامه بفرنگ (romanized: Safarnāmah bi-Farang)
     1. Europe—Descr. & trav.—1800–1918.   I. Schindler, Sir Albert
Houtum-, 1846–1916, tr.   II. Norman, Louis, baron de, tr.   III. Title.

   D919.N323   3–16796 rev 2

   NN   0026172   DLC OC1 PU CU NIC NcU

Nāṣir al-Dīn Shāh, *Shah of Iran*, 1831–1896.
     The diary of H. M. the Shah of Persia, during his tour
through Europe in A. D. 1873. By J. W. Redhouse ... A
verbatim translation ... 3d thousand. London, J. Murray,
1874.
     1 p. l., xx, 427 p. front. (port.) illus., facsim. 20½ cm.
     Added t.-p. in colors.
     Translation of روزنامه سفر اول فرنگستان (romanized: Rūznāmah-i
safar-i avval-i Farangistān)
     1. Europe—Descr. & trav.—1800–1918.   I. Redhouse, Sir James
William, 1811–1892, tr.   II. Title.

   D919.N313   3–16797 rev 2

   NN   0026173   ICU DNW NN OC1W MB PPL PPWa
                     DLC OrU CU PU CtY MdBP CLU UU NSyU

Nāṣir al-Dīn Shāh, Shah of Iran, 1831–1896,
comp.
     Dictionnarie manuel; français-persan. ₍Tihran,
1296–₎   1878–   ₎

     Title-page lacking; caption title.

     1. French language - Dictionaries - Persian.

   NN   0026174   NNC

Nāṣir al-Dīn Shāh, Shah of Iran, 1831–1896.
Bahā Ullāh, 1817–1892.   FOR OTHER EDITIONS
                        SEE MAIN ENTRY
     Epistle to the Son of the Wolf ₍by₎ Bahá'u'lláh, translated
by Shoghi effendi. Wilmette, Ill., Bahá'í publishing committee, 1941.

Nāṣir al-Dīn Shah, shah of Iran, 1831–1896.
     Ganjina-i-muhawarat. The Wazir-i-Lankuran;
and, Selections from the diary of His Majesty
Nasiru-D-Din Shah
     see under title

D
919   Nāṣir Al-Dīn Shāh, Shah of Iran, 1831–1896.
.N268   Reisentagebuch des Nasreddin-Schah; nach
     der persischen Handschrift. Leipzig, E. J.
     Günther, 1874.
     271p. 18cm.

     1. Europe - Descr. & trav. - 1800–1918.
     I. Title.

   NN   0026177   TNJ

Nāṣir al-Dīn Shāh, Shah of Iran, 1831–1896.
     (Safarnāmah-i Nāṣirī)
سفرنامه ناصری. ₍تهران₎ در کارخانه باقر طهرانی مطبوع
گردید ₍1869₎

     485 p. illus. 26 cm.
     Title from spine.
     Reproduced from ms. copy.

     1. Khorasan—Description and travel.   I. Title.

   DS324.K47N37 1869   74–214759

   NN   0026178   DLC CLU

Nasir-al-Dīn Shah, Shah of Iran, 1831–1896.
     Selections from the diary of the first journey
of His Majesty Nasiruddin, Shah Qajar, Shahin-
shah of Persia, to Europe ... 1200 A. H.
     (In: Ganjina-i-muhawarat ... Calcutta, 1905.
8°.   p. 49–67)

   NN   0026179   NN

Nāṣir al-Dīn Yaḥya, *called* Ibn al-Bībī
see
Ebn Bībī, Nāṣer al-Dīn al-Ḥoseyn ebn Moḥammad, *fl.*
1281.

Nāṣir al-Ḥānī
see
al-Ḥānī, Nāṣir.

Nāṣir al-Sharī'ah, Muḥammad Ḥusayn.
تاريخ قم موسوم بمختار البلاد؛ تأليف محمد حسين بن محمد
حسن قمی مدعو ناصر ₍ناصر الشريعة₎ رقم أ، احمد و محمود
اخوان کتابچی؛ جايگاه فروش: کتابفروشی و چاپخانه اسلاميه،
تهران ₍1945₎

     278 p. 20 cm.

     1. Qom.   I. Title.   II. Title: Mukhtār al-bilād.
           Title romanized: Tārīkh-i Qum.

   DS325.Q6N35 1945   78–251741

   NN   0026182   DLC NNC

Nāṣir è Ḥosraw
see
Nāṣir-i Khusraw, 1004–*ca.* 1088.

VOLUME 405

Nasir Ed-Din
see Nāṣir al-Dīn Shāh, Shah of Iran,
1831-1896.

Nasir Hosrau
see Nāṣir-i Khusraw, 1004-ca. 1088.

Nasir-i Khosrov
see
Nāṣir-i Khusraw, 1004-*ca.* 1088.

Nāṣir-i Khusraw, 1004-*ca.* 1088.
... Diary of a journey through Syria and Palestine. By
Nāsir-i-Khusrau, in 1047 A. D. Translated from the Persian
and annotated by Guy Le Strange. London, 1888.
xiv p., 1 l., 72 p. front. (fold. map) illus., plan. 23 cm. (*Is*
Palestine pilgrims' text society. ⟨Library. vol. IV, no. 1⟩)

1. Syria—Description and travel. 2. Palestine—Description and
travel.   I. Le Strange, Guy, 1854-1933, ed. and tr.
[DS102.P2 vol. 4]   A C 33-4077
Union Theol. Sem. Libr.
for Library of Congress   ⟨r69d2⟩ rev 2

NjNbS
NN   0026187   NNUT TxU MH MiU OCU ViU OCl MdBP CU

Nāṣir-i Khusraw, 1004-*ca.* 1088.
گشایش و رهایش، تألیـف شاه سیـد خسرو مـروزی
قبادیانی. با تصحیح و مقدمه سعید نفیسی. بمبئی، مطبعه
قادری پریس، 1950.
8, 125, xix p. 23 cm.
(انتشارات انجمن اسمیلی) (The Ismaili Society series, A. no. 5.)
Added t. p.: Kitab-i gushā'ish wa raha'ish (The book of unfettering and liberation) by Nasir-i Khusraw.
Introductory matter and index in English.
Reproduced from MS. copy.
1. Ismailites.   I. Title.   II. Series: Ismaili Society, Bombay.
The Ismaili Society series, A. no. 5.
Title romanized: Gushāyish va rahāyish.

BP195.I 8N34   72-284688

NN   0026188   DLC

Nāṣir-i Khusraw, 1004-*ca.* 1088.
خوان الاخوان، تألیف ناصر خسرو علوی. بسعی و اهتمام
و تصحیح یحیی الخشاب، بانضمام مقدمه و چهار فهرست.
القاهرة، مطبعة المعهد العلمی الفرنسی للآثار الشرقیة، 1940.
xxvi, 6, 265 p. facsims. 25 cm.
Cover title: Ḫuān al-Iḫwān, text persan inédit de Nāṣir è Ḫosraw.
Introd. in French.
1. Islamic theology—Early works to 1800.   I. el-Khachab, Yahya,
ed.   II. Title.
Title transliterated: Khvān al-ikhvān.

BP88.N3K5   1940   N E 67-1425

NN   0026189   DLC MH

Nasir i Khusraw, 1004-ca. 1088.
Избранное. ⟨Переводы А. Адалис и др. Вступ. очерк
Л. Бузург-Зода. Составление, комментарии и ред. И. С.
Брагинского⟩ Сталинабад, Гос. изд-во Таджикской ССР,
1949.
228 p. illus., fold. map. 18 cm. (Классики таджикской литера-
туры)
At head of title: Носир Хисроу.
Added t. p., Tajik in Russian transliteration.
In prose and verse.
(Series: Klassiki tadzhikskoĭ literatury)
Title transliterated: Izbrannoe.

PK6978.9.N3A6   50-37309

NN   0026190   DLC

Nāṣir-i Khusraw, 1004-ca. 1088, supposed author.
Kalami pir, a treatise on Ismaili doctrine
see Kalami Pir.

PK
6495
.N25
K4
1950
Nasir-i Khusraw, 1004-ca. 1088.
Kitab-i Gusha'ish wa Raha'ish (The book of
unfettering and liberation) Edited in the
original Persian by Sa'id Nafisi. Leiden,
Brill, 1950.
125 p. (Ismaili Society ser.A,no.5)

I.Nafisi,Sa'id,1897-1966,ed. II.Title.

NN   0026192   MiU

BP
166.2
N375
MAIN
Nasir-i Khusraw, 1004-ca.1088.
Nasir-e Khosraw Kitâb-e Jâmi'al-Hikmatain.
Le livre réunissant les deux sagesses; ou,
Harmonie de la philosophie grecque et de la
théosophie ismaélienne. Texte persan édité
avec une double étude préliminaire en français et en persan par Henry Corbin et Moh.
Mo'in. Teheran, Département d'iranologie de
l'Institut franco-iranien, 1953.
144, 348p. 25cm. (Bibliothèque iranienne,
3)

Added t.p. in Persian.

1. Theosophy. 2. Philosophy, Islamic -
Greek influences. I. Corbin, Henry, ed.
II. Mu'in, Muhammad, ed. III. Title: Jami'
'al-hikmatain. IV. Series.

PPT CtY
NN   0026194   TxU NN NNC NIC MH DLC-P4 ICU PU OU

Nāṣir-i Khusraw, 1004-ca.1088.
Safar-nāmah. Berlin, "Kaviani", 1340 ⟨A. D.
1921⟩
144, ⟨11⟩ p.

NN   0026195   NNC

Nāṣir-i Khusraw, 1004-ca. 1088.
(Safar-namè)
Сафар-намэ; книга путешествия. Перевод и вступ.
статья Е. Э. Бертельса. Москва, Academia, 1933.
206 p. illus. 18 cm. (Восточные литературы)
At head of title: Насир-и Хусрау.
Translation of Safarnāmah.

1. Syria—Description and travel. 2. Palestine—Description and
travel.   I. Title.

DS105.N317   73-206197

NN   0026196   DLC CaBVaU

Nāṣir-i Khusraw, 1004-ca. 1088.
⟨Safarnāmah. Arabic⟩
سفرنامه / كتبه باللغة الفارسية ناصر خسرو علوی؛ نقله الى
العربية وقدم له وعلق عليه يحيى الخشاب. ــ الطبعة 1. ــ
⟨القاهرة : معهد اللغات الشرقية، كلية الآداب، جامعة فؤاد
الأول، 1945.
24, 134 p. : ill. ; 27 cm. ــ (جامعة
فؤاد الأول ؛ 1)

⟨Safarnāmah. Arabic⟩

Bibliography: p. ⟨127⟩-130.
Includes indexes.

1. Near East—Description and travel.   I. al-Khashshāb, Yaḥyā,
ed. II. Title. III. Series: Cairo. Jāmi'at al-Qāhirah. Ma'had al
-Lughat al-Sharqīyah. Maṭbū'āt Ma'had al-Lughāt al-Sharqīyah ; 1.
Title romanized: Safarnāmah.

DS46.N312   1945   74-228683

NN   0026198   DLC

Nāṣir-i Khusraw, 1004-ca. 1088.
Sefer nameh; relation du voyage de Nassiri Khosrau en
Syrie, en Palestine, en Égypte, en Arabie et en Perse, pendant les années de l'hégire 437-444 (1035-1042) Publié,
traduit et annoté par Charles Schefer. Paris, E. Leroux,
1881.
lviii, 348, 97 p. col. plates. 28 cm. (Publications de l'école des
langues orientales vivantes, 2. sér., v. 1)
1. Levant—Descr. & trav. 2. Asia, Western—Descr. & trav. I.
Schefer, Charles Henri Auguste, 1820-1898, ed. and tr.   (Series:
Paris. École des langues orientales vivantes. Publications, 2. sér.,
v. 1)

DS46.N316   50-46512 rev

NN   0026199   DLC MH OCl CtY NjP DDO MB CU UU

Nāṣir-i Khusraw, 1004-ca.1088.
Sefername. İstanbul, Millî eğitim basǐmevi,
1950.
xxviii, 268 p. (Dünya edebiyatǐndan tercü-
meler. Şark-İslâm klâsikleri: 22)

Tr. by Abdülvehap Tarzi.
Notes: p. 160-268.

NN   0026200   NNC

PK
6495
.N25
S563
1949
Nasir-i Khusraw,1004-ca.1088.
Six chapters of Shish Fasl,also called
Rawshana'i-nama. Persian text,edited and
translated into English,by W.Ivanow. Leiden,
Brill,1949.
111,47 p. (Ismaili Society,ser.B,no.6)

I.Ivanov,Vladimir Alekseevich,ed. II.Title:
Shish Fasl. III.Title: Rawshana'i-nama.

NN   0026201   MiU NNC CtY MH PPT

Nāṣir ibn Burhān Rabghūzī
see Nāṣir al-Dīn ibn Burhān al-Dīn, *al-Rabghūzī.*

Nāṣir ibn Khusrau, Abū Mu'īn, *'Alavī Ḳubādiyānī Marvazī*
see
Nāṣir-i Khusraw, 1004-*ca.* 1088.

Nasir Khosrew
see Nāṣir-i Khusraw, 1004-ca. 1088.

Nāṣir Maḥmūd al-Naqshabandī
see
al-Naqshabandī, Nāṣir Maḥmūd.

Nāṣir Rabghūzī
see Nāṣir al-Dīn ibn Burhān al-Dīn, *al-Rabghūzī.*

Nasir-ud-Dīn, *mullah*
see
Nasreddin Hoca.

Nāṣir-ud-Dīn Hāshimī
see
Hashmi, Nasiruddin, 1895-

Nasir Uddin Hasan
see Hasan, Nazir-ud-din, *nawab nazir yar jung bahadur.*

Nasireddin, or Nasir-Eddin, d. 1286
see   al-Baydāwī, 'Add Allāh ibn 'Umar,
d. 1286?

Nasireddinus, Tusensis.

woo

al-Tūsī, Nasīr al-Dīn Muhammad ibn Muhammad,
1201-1274.

VOLUME 405

al-Nāṣirī, Abū Rās Muhammad ibn Ahmad ibn
'Abd al-Qādir
    see   al Nāṣirī, Muhammad Abū Ra's ibn
Ahmad, 1751-1823.

---

al-Nāṣirī, Aḥmad ibn Khālid
    see
al-Salāwī, Aḥmad ibn Khālid, 1835-1897.

DT
268
J4N17
Al-Nasiri, Muhammad Abu Ra's ibn Ahmad,
1751-1823.
    Description & histoire de l'île de Djerba.
Traduite du manuscrit du Chikhr Mohammed Abou
Rasse Ahmed en-Naceur, par Exiga, dit Kayser.
Tunis, Imprimerie franco-tunisienne, 1884.
    29, 26 p.

    1. Jerba. 2. Tunis - Descr. & trav. I. Title
Exiga, dit Kayser. II. Title.

NN 0026214   CLU

---

al-Nāṣirī, Muhammad al-Makkī.
    (al-Abḥās al-Islāmīyah fī al-Mamlakah al-Maghribīyah)
    الاحباس الاسلامية في الملكة المغربية، تقرير مقدم بقلم محمد
    المكي الناصري. فيه ملحقات عن احباس الجزائر وتونس
    الاوقاف السورية، وقف السكة الحديدية الحجازية، الاوقاف
    المصرية، اوقاف المسلمين في آسيا وأوربا، امتيازات بني
    اسرائيل في مناطق المملكة المغربية، وفيه وثائق خزينية عن
    الاحباس من عهد الاستقلال. ﴿طوان﴾ أ المقدمة 1935
    15, 174 p. 25 cm.
    Bibliography : p. 9-10 (1st group)
    1. Charitable uses, trusts and foundations (Islamic law) — Morocco. I. Title.

                                             74-228100

NN 0026215   DLC

DT324
.L33
1930z
Orien
Arab
al-Nāṣirī, Muhammad al-Makkī.
al-Lajnah al-Sharqīyah lil-Difā' 'an al-Maghrib.
    (Faransā wa-siyāsatuhā al-Barbarīyah fī al-Maghrib al-Aqṣā)
    فرنسا وسياستها البربرية في المغرب الاقصى. تقرير مقدم
    الى المؤتمر الاسلامي العام وجميع مسلمي العالم من اللجنة
    الشرقية للدفاع عن المغرب. مصدر بكلمة لمحمد المكي الناصري.
    ﴿n. p., 193-﴾

Nasiridinus, Tusinus.
    see
al-Tūsī, Naṣīr al-Dīn Muhammad ibn Muhammad,
1201-1274.

Naṣīriyān, 'Alī Aṣghar.
    شراره، بقلم علي اصغر نصیریان (ن - شمعان) با مقدمة
    سعید نفیسی. ﴿تهران ابوالحسن حدادی﴾ (1950) ﴿pref. 1329﴾
    80 p. 21 cm.
    Short stories.

    I. Title.
                        Title romanized: Sharārah.

PK6561.N36S5   75-264924

NN 0026218   DLC NNC

Nasiru 'd-Din Rubguzi
    see   Naṣīr al-Dīn ibn Burhān al-Dīn,
al-Rabghūzī.

Nāṣiru'd-Dīn Šah
    see   Nāṣir al-Dīn Shāh, Shah of Iran,
1831-1896.

Nasiruddin, el-Toussy.
    see
al-Tūsī, Naṣīr al-Dīn Muhammad ibn Muhammad,
1201-1274.

Nasiruddin, Shah Qajar.
    see   Nāṣir-al-Dīn Shāh, Shah of Iran,
1831-1896.

Nasiruddin Hashmi
    see
Hashmi, Nasiruddin, 1895-

Nāṣiruddīna Hojjā
    see
Nasreddin Hoca.

Naṣit, Galip.
    ... Destan, 1 perdelik piyes ﴿yazan﴾ muallim Galip Naṣit ...
İstanbul, Devlet matbaasi, 1933.
    23 p. 19½ᶜᵐ.   (Mektep temsilleri, n° 2)

    I. Title.
                                             40-24665

Library of Congress   PL248.N25D4

NN 0026225   DLC NNC

Wason
Pamphlet
N
234+
Nasjah.
    Hang Tuah, untuk anak-anak.   Djakarta,
Balai Pustaka, 1951.
    38 p. (chiefly illus) 27cm.

    1. Hang   Tuah, d. 1477--Cari-
    catures and   cartoons. I. Title.

NN 0026226   NIC

Fybl8
Nl73
75
Nasjah
    Tjerita si Pai Bengal, dan tjerita-tjerita
lain. Djakarta, Balai Pustaka, 1952.
    136 p. illus. 19 cm.

NN 0026227   CtY

Nasjonal samling.
    Fritt folk; riksorgan for Nasjonal samling
    see under title

Nasjonal samling.
    NS årbok.
    ﴿Oslo﴾ Blix, 19
    v. illus. 21½ᶜᵐ.
    "Utgitt av Rikspropagandaledelsen."

    1. Norway—Pol. & govt.—Year-books. 2. Norway—Pol. & govt.—
    1905-   3. Norway—Hist.—German occupation, 1940—

                                             44-1675
    Library of Congress   JN7601.N3
                           ﴿2﴾   329.9481

NN 0026229   DLC

Nasjonal samling.
JA26
.N2
    NS månedshefte. 1.-   årg.;
    15. juni 1941-
    Oslo, Nasjonal samlings rikstrykkeri.

Nasjonal samling.
    ...Oplysningsskrifter.
    nr.
    Oslo, 193   23½cm.
    no. illus.

    1. Fascism—Norway.
N. Y. P. L.   July 31, 1936

NN 0026231   NN

Nasjonal Samling. Frontkjemperkonteret.
    Legionsminner; trekk av den Norske Legions
historie . ﴿Redaksjon E. Jul Christiansen
Furum, med velvillig assistanse av Rikspro-
pagandaledelsen﴾   Oslo, I kommission Hos
Viking Forlag, 1943.
    1 v. (unpaged) illus. 25 cm.
    Contributions by various authors.
    1. Nationalsozialistische Deutsche Arbeiter-
Partei. Waffenschutzstaffel Norwegen. Norske
Legion. 2. World War, 1939-1945. Campaigns -

    Eastern. 3. World War, 1939-1945. - Pictorial
works. I. Furum, E. Jul Christiansen, ed.
II. Nasjonal Samling. Rikspropagandaledelsen.
III. Title.

NN 0026233   CSt-H DLC-P4

Nasjonal samling. *Presse- og propagandaavdelingen.*
    Quisling saken, dokumentasjon og referater fra sakens
behandling i Stortinget 1932 ... Ansvarlig redaksjon: H. N.
Østbye. Oslo, Blix forlag, 1941.
    194 p. port. 22 cm.

    1. Quisling, Vidkun, 1887-1945.   I. Østbye, H. N., ed.

DL529.Q5N38   52-55188

NN 0026234   DLC WU

Nasjonal Samling. Rikshirden. Hirdstaben.
    Bolsjevismen. Ansvarlig: Orvar Saether-
Hirdstaben.   [Oslo? Nasjonal Samlings Riks-
trykkeri, 1941]
    97, [1] p.   23 cm.   (Ideologisk månedshefte
for Hirden)
    "Litteratur": p. 95-[98]
    1. Communism 2. Communism - Anti-
communist literature. I. Saether, Orvar,
1904-   ed. II. Title.

NN 0026235   CSt-H

Nasjonal samling. *Riksmøte.* 8th, Oslo, 1942.
    Der VIII. ﴿i. e., Achte﴾ Parteitag der Nasjonal samling,
25.-27. Sept. 1942 in Oslo. Reden und Bilder. ﴿Oslo, 1942﴾
    98 p. illus. 26 cm.

    1. Norway—Hist.—German occupation, 1940-1945. 2. World War,
1939-1945—Norway.   I. Title.

JN7691.N35   49-37896*

NN 0026236   DLC

JN7691
N258
1942
Nasjonal Samling. Riksmøte. 8th, Oslo, 1942.
    N.S. 8. Riksmøte ﴿25.-27. September, 1942.
Oslo﴾ Rikspropagandaledelsen ﴿1942﴾
    157 p. illus., ports. 30cm.
    Includes speeches by Vidkun Quisling, R.J.
Fuglesang, Gulbrand Lunde and others.

    1. Fascism - Norway. I. Nasjonal Samling.
Rikspropagandaledelsen. II. Quisling, Vidkun,
1887-1945. III. Fuglesang, Rolf Jørgen, 1909-
IV. Lunde, Gul-   brand, 1901-1942.
V. Title.

NN 0026237   CSt-H

VOLUME 405

Nasjonal Samling. Rikspropagandaledelsen.
Nasjonalverket Det nye Norge; tilegnet Vidkun
Quisling. Redaktør H.N. Østbye. Oslo, Blix
[1941-45]
3 v. illus., ports., maps. 26cm.

DL532
N255

1. Fascism - Norway. 2. Norway - Pol. & govt. -
1905-1945. I.Østbye, Halldis Neegård, 1886-
ed. II. Title.

NN 0026238   CSt-H

Nasjonalforeningen mot tuberkulosen for folkehelsen.
Årbok.
Oslo, Indremisjonstrykkeriet.
v. 20 cm.

1. Tuberculosis—Yearbooks. 2. Hygiene, Public—Norway.

RC306.N28   55-43282 ‡

NN 0026239   DLC DNLM

W 1   NASJONALFORENINGEN mot tuberkulosen
NA198G   for folkehelsen
            Årsmelding. Oslo, 19
            v.   W1 NA198G
            1. Tuberculosis societies

NN 0026240   DNLM

Nasjonalforeningen mot tuberkulosen for folkehelsen.
Catalogue of Norwegian Christmas seals, 1906-1955. Oslo,
Nasjonalforeningen mot tuberkulosen for folkehelsen and Norske
kvinners sanitetsforening, 1955. 36 p. illus. 19cm.

1. Seals and poster stamps—Norway.   I. Norske kvinners sanitetsforening.

NN 0026241   NN

Nasjonalforeningen mot tuberkulosen for
folkehelsen.
[Meddelelser]
see Helse nytt.

Nasjonalforeningen mot tuberkulosen for folkehelsen.
Sangbok. Sandnes, I. Dahles boktr., 1952.
244 p. 12 cm.
Without the music.

1. Song-books, Norwegian.

M1772.N3S3   M 54-2571 ‡

NN 0026243   DLC

Nasjonalforlagets billedserie.
nr.

Oslo, 194   no. illus.   29cm.
Monthly?

1. News periodicals, Pictorial   —Norway.
N.Y.P.L.   September 21, 1951

NN 0026244   NN

Nasjonalforlagets ordbøker; engelsk-
norsk...

[Oslo? Aas & Wahls boktr., 1936_

v. 24cm.

Editor: 1_ hft., Carl Knap.

1.English language. Dictionaries.
Norwegian. I.Knap, Carl Stefanus, 1867-
ed.

NN 0026245   MnU

Nasjonalgalleriet, *Oslo*
see Oslo. Nasjonalgalleriet.

Nasjonalgalleriet, den retrospektive utstilling av skulptur
og maleri. [Oslo] Cammermeyer [1940]
47, xvi p. illus. 24 cm.
At head of title: Utstillingsplanen av 1940.
Bibliography : p. [i]-xvi.

1. Paintings, Norwegian—Exhibitions. 2. Painting, Modern—20th
century—Norway. 3. Sculpture, Norwegian—Exhibitions. 4. Sculpture, Modern—20th century—Norway.   I. Oslo. Nasjonalgalleriet.

ND768.N37 1940   74-216216

NN 0026247   DLC

Naskah dan lampiran bagian pokok dari ...
see under Komisi Gabungan Irian
(Indonesia and the Netherlands)

[Naske, Adolph Carl, 1814-1864]
*GB8   Glück und Ende der Liguorianer in Wien. Eine
V6755R   kurzgefasste Darstellung des Lebens und Wirkens
4.8.48   dieser am 6. April 1848 förmlich ausgewiesenen
          Congregation, nebst einigen historischen Daten
          über die nunmehr in das National-Eigenthum
          übergegangene Kirche zu St. Maria am Gestade
          (Maria Stiegen) in Wien.
          [Wien]Zu haben bei dem Buchhändler Jakob Bader,
          Stadt,Strobelgasse.Gedruckt bei Anton Benko.
          [1848]

          folder(4p.) 24.5x19.5cm.
          Caption title; imprint on p.4.
          Dated & signed at end: Wien am 8. April 1848.
          Adolph Carl Naske.

NN 0026250   MH

[Naske, Adolph Carl, 1814-1864]
*pGB8   Pia desideria der subalternen Staatsbeamten.
V6755R   Veröffentlicht von Einem aus ihrer Mitte.
3.22.48   [Wien]Zu haben bei dem Buchhändler Jakob Bader,
          Stroblgasse.Gedruckt bei Anton Benko.[1848]

          folder([4]p.) 38x25cm.
          Caption title; imprint on p.[4].
          Dated & signed at end: Wien, am 22. März 1848.
          Adolph Carl Naske.

NN 0026251   MH

[Naske, Adolph Carl, 1814-1864]
*GB8   Das Todtenlied für die Polizei-Spione.
V6755R   Zeitgemässe Reflexion über die alte und die neue
3.31.48   Polizei.
          [Wien]Zu haben bei dem Buchhändler Jakob Bader,
          Stadt,Strobelgasse.Gedruckt bei Anton Benko.
          [1848]

          folder(4p.) 24.5x19cm.
          Caption title; imprint on p.4.
          Dated & signed at end: Wien am 31. März 1848.
          Adolph Carl Naske.

NN 0026252   MH

[Naske, Adolph Carl, 1814-1864]
*GB8   Die Wucher-Pest in Wien. Zeitgemässe
V6755R   Darstellung des in Wien seit einigen Jahren
4.13.48   gleich einer Pestseuche grassirenden Wucher-
          Unfuges und der hieraus entspringenden, immer
          allgemeiner werdenden Verarmung unserer
          Mitbürger.
          [Wien]Zu haben bei dem Buchhändler Jakob Bader,
          Stadt,Strobelgasse.Gedruckt bei Anton Benko.
          [1848]
          folder(4p.) 24x19.5cm.

          Caption title; imprint on p.4.
          Dated & signed at end: Wien am 13. April
          1848. Adolph Carl Naske.

NN 0026254   MH

Naske, Carl, 1863-

TP155
.E8   Eucken, Arnold, 1884-   *ed.*
bd. 1,   Elektrische und magnetische materialtrennung, materialver-
t. 4   einigung, herausgegeben von A. Eucken ... Bearbeitet von
         A. Eucken ... E. Kirschbaum ... R. Ladenburg ... F. Merkel †
         ... C. Naske ... P. H. Prausnitz ... J. Reitstötter ... G. Stein ...
         P. A. Thiessen ... Mit 180 figuren im text. Leipzig, Aka-
         demische verlagsgesellschaft m. b. h., 1934.

Naske, Carl, 1863-
Integraltafeln für ingenieure und verwandte berufe sowie
für studierende technischer hoch- und fachschulen, aufgestellt
von Carl Naske ... Leipzig, O. Spamer, 1935.
iv, 48 p. 20cm.
"Benütztes schrifttum": p. iv.

1. Integrals.

Library of Congress   QA310.N3   36-6905
Copyright A—Foreign   30014
                          [2]   517.39

NN 0026256   DLC

Naske, Carl, 1863-
Mechanische materialtrennung, herausgegeben von A.
Eucken ... bearbeitet von C. Naske ... H. Madel ... W. Siegel
... Mit 246 figuren im text. Leipzig, Akademische verlagsgesellschaft m. b. h., 1933.
x, 385 p. illus., diagrs. 25cm. (*Added t-p.:* Der chemie-ingenieur ...
hrsg. von A. Eucken ... und M. Jakob ... bd. 1. [Physikalische arbeits-
prozesse des betriebes] 2. t.)

1. Chemical engineering.   I. Madel, Hans, 1887-   joint author.
II. Siegel, Wilhelm, 1885-   joint author. III. Eucken, Arnold, 1884-
ed. IV. Title.
                                             A C 33-1011
Title from Columbia   Univ. Printed by L. C.

NN 0026257   NNC NN OU OCI PU

Naske, Carl, 1863-
... Mischen fester Stoffe, von C. Naske.
(*In* Der Chemie-Ingenieur. Bd. 1, Teil 4, p. 137-156. diagrs. 1934)

NN 0026258   ICJ

Naske, Carl, 1863-
Die Portland-cement-fabrikation. Ein handbuch für
ingenieure und cementfabrikanten, von oberingenieur
Carl Naske ... Mit 183 abbildungen im text und 3
tafeln. Leipzig, T. Thomas, 1903.
vii, 302 p. illus., diagrs., 3 fold. pl. 27cm.

1. Portland cement.

Library of Congress   TP883.N25   4-9240

NN 0026259   DLC NIC CU NN MH ICJ

Naske, Carl, 1863-
Portland- zement-fabrikation. Ein handbuch fur
ingenieure und zement-fabrikation. Leipzig
Thomas. 1909.
410 p.

NN 0026260   PPF

Naske, Carl, 1863-
Die Portland-Zement-Fabrikation; ein Handbuch für Ingenieure und Zementfabrikanten, von Carl Naske... Leipzig: T.
Thomas [pref. 1914]. 496 p. incl. diagrs., illus., tables. 3. ed.,
rev. and enl. 4°.

59578A. 1. Cement, etc. (Portland).   —Manufacture.
N.Y.P.L.   October 25, 1922.

NN 0026261   NN

VOLUME 405

4TP   **Naske, Carl,** 1863–
88   Die Portlandzementfabrikation; ein
    Handbuch für Ingenieure und Zement-
    fabrikanten. 4. vollständig umgearb.
    und verm. Aufl. Leipzig, T. Thomas
    [c1922]
    469 p.

NN   0026262   DLC-P4 DBS

Naske, Carl, 1863–
    ... Zerkleinerung fester Materialien (Brechen und Mahlen)
von C. Naske.
    (*In* Der Chemie-Ingenieur. Bd. 1, Teil 2, p. 1–80. illus., tables, diagrs.
1933)

NN   0026263   ICJ

Naske, Carl, 1863 –
    Zerkleinerungsvorrichtungen und mahlanlagen, von
Carl Naske ... mit 257 figuren im text. Leipzig, O. Spamer, 1911.
    x, 235 p. illus., diagrs. 24ᶜᵐ. (*Half-title:* Chemische technologie in
einzeldarstellungen, herausgeber: F. Fischer) M. 13.50

    1. Crushing machinery. 2. Milling machinery.

    Library of Congress   TJ1345.N3   11–6044

NN   0026264   DLC MiU OU OCl ICJ NN OClW

Naske, Carl, 1863–
    Zerkleinerungsvorrichtungen und Mahlanlagen, von Carl Naske,
    ... Zweite, erweiterte Auflage, mit 316 Figuren im Text.
Leipzig, O. Spamer, 1918.
    x, 278 p. incl. illus., tables, diagrs. 24ᶜᵐ. (*Half-title:* Chemische Technologie
in Einzeldarstellungen. Allgemeine chemische Technologie.)
    Bibliographical foot-notes.

NN   0026265   ICJ CtY

Naske, Carl, 1863–
    Zerkleinerungsvorrichtungen und mahlanlagen, **von**
Carl Naske ... 3., erweiterte aufl. mit 415 figuren im text.
Leipzig, O. Spamer, 1921.
    xii, 339 p. illus., diagrs. 24ᶜᵐ. (*Half-title:* Chemische technologie in
einzeldarstellungen, herausgeber: prof. dr. Arthur Binz ... Allgemeine chemische technologie)

    1. Crushing machinery. 2. Milling machinery.
    Library of Congress   TJ1345.N3 1921   22–23065

NN   0026266   DLC ICJ

Naske, Carl, 1863–
    Zerkleinerungsvorrichtungen und mahlanlagen, von Carl
Naske ... 4., erweiterte aufl. Mit 471 figuren im text. Leipzig, O. Spamer, 1926.
    x, 375 p. illus., diagrs. 24ᶜᵐ. (*Half-title:* Chemische technologie in
einzeldarstellungen ... Allgemeine chemische technologie)

    1. Crushing machinery. 2. Milling machinery.
    Library of Congress   TJ1345.N3 1926   27–5301

NN   0026267   DLC MiU NN

Naske, Emilie, 1866–
    ... Nur noch ein jahr! Roman. Wien und Leipzig, Frau
und mutter-verlag [ᶜ1937]
    307, [1] p. 19ᵐ.

    I. Title.
                                       38–21901
    Library of Congress   PT2627.A62N7 1937
    Copyright A—Foreign   38712

NN   0026268   DLC

[Naske, Emilie] 1866–
    ... Thea liebt und schweigt. roman. Wien und Leipzig,
Frau und mutter-verlag [ᶜ1937]
    318, [1] p. 19ᵐ.
    Author's pseud., Emmy Leitner, at head of title.

    I. Title.
                                       38–13885
    Library of Congress   PT2627.A62T5 1937
    Copyright A—Foreign   38763

NN   0026269   DLC

Naskov, Peder Zachariæsen, 1635–1695.
    The articles of faith, of the Holy Evangelical Church, accord-
ing to the word of God, and the Ausburg Confession. Set forth
in forty sermons. By Magist. Petrus Sachariæ Nakskow...
Translated from the original into English, by Jochum Melchior
Magens. New-York: Printed and sold, by J. Parker and W.
Weyman...1754[–55]. 1 p.l., ii, ii p., 1 l., 314 (really 416], 30 p.,
1 l. 4°.

    "First issued serially in monthly numbers in this year."—*Evans* 7262.
    Two blank versos disregarded in paging; p. 211–414 wrongly numbered 111–
314.
    With two copies of a half-title: "Numb. IV. Articles of faith, of the Evangelical
Church, in forty sermons," inserted at end.
    "The whole system of the XXVIII articles of the evangelical unvaried con-
fession. Presented at Ausbourgh... New-York: Printed by J. Parker and W.
Weyman, 1755," 30 p., 1 l., has separate registration.

                       LENOX COLLECTION.
    1. Lutheran, Evangelical, Church—   Doctrine. 2. Sermons. 3. Magens,
Joachim Melchior, ca, 1715–1783,   translator.
N. Y. P. L.   May 7, 1930

NN   0026271   NN WHi DLC ICU PPiPT CtY N MWiW-C PPLT

Micro-
film   Naskov, Peder Zachariaesen, 1635–1695.
    The articles of faith of the holy ev. church, according to
the Word of God and the Augsburg Confession, set forth in
forty sermons ... [Trans. J. Magens] New York, Parker &
Weyman, 1754.
    314 p.

    Microfilm. Chicago, University of Chicago Library, Depart-
ment of Photographic Reproduction, 1960. 1 reel. 35mm.
(Microfilm corpus of American Lutheranism, reel 1, part 2)

    1. Augsburg Confession. 2. Lutheran Church--Sermons.
I. Magens, Jochum Melchior, 1715–1783. II. Title.   (Series)

NN   0026272   CBPL NcD ICRL ICU

PN2859   Nasková, Růžena (Nosková), 1884–
.C9   Jak šel život: pamětí a zápisky. Praha,
N3   Družstevní práce, 1952.
    263p. plates (part col.), ports.

    1. Actors - Correspondence, reminiscences,
etc. I. Title.

NN   0026273   NcU

Nasková, Růžena (Nosková) 1884–
    Jak šel život; pamětí i zápisky. [7 vyd.] Praha, Orbis,
1954
    314 p. ports.

NN   0026274   MH

Nasková, Růžena (Nosková) 1884–   *ed.*
    Jeden život; hrst vzpomínek na Helenu Malířovou. [Za
red. Růženy Naskové a Boženy Paškové. 1. vyd.] Praha,
Svoboda, 1948.
    123 p. ports. 22 cm.

    1. Malířová, Helena (Nosková) 1877–1940. I. Pašková, Božena,
joint ed. II. Title.
    PG5038.M37Z75   55–56196

NN   0026275   DLC MH

Nasková, Růžena (Nosková) 1884–
    ...Malá kronika dnů, 1934–1946. V Praze, Československý
kompas, 1947. 120 p. illus. 21cm. ("Umělci o sobě a
o všem." sv. 15)
    1. vyd.

    1. Actors and acting, Czecho-   Slovakian.

NN   0026276   NN MH InU

PG   Naslaitis, A. J.
8715   Skambancois stygos (eiliu
.N32   rinkinelis) Sutaise A. J. Naslaitis.
    Worcester, Mass., Spaustuveje M.
    Paltanaviciaus, 1915.
    vᵖ 22 cm.
    Stamped on cover: Knygu rinkinys J.
K. Karazija. Worcester, Mass.

    1. Lithuanian poetry (Collections)
    2. Lithuanian collection. I. Title

NN   0026277   OKentU

Наследие Белинского; сборник статей. Москва, Советский
писатель, 1952.
    369 p. 21 cm.
    Errata slip inserted.

    1. Belinskiĭ, Vissarion Grigor'evich, 1811–1848.
                     Title transliterated: Nasledie Belinskogo.

    PG2947.B5N3   53–26823

NN   0026278   DLC OrU CaBVaU

Nasledov, Dmitriĭ Nikolaevich, 1903–
    ... Физика ионных и электронных процессов ... Ленин-
град, Москва, ОНТИ НКТП СССР, Главная редакция тех-
нико-теоретической литературы, 1937.
    313, [1] p. illus., diagrs. 22ᵖᵐ.
    At head of title: Проф. Д. Н. Наследов.
    "Допущено в качестве учебного пособия для втузов и вузов 2
изданию 1937 г. Всесоюзным комитетом по высшей школе при СНК
СССР."
    "Материалом для составления настоящей книги явились стено-
граммы моих лекций, читанных в 1933–34 гг. в 6. Ленинградском фи-
зико-математическом институте на физических специализациях."—
p. [6]
    1. Physics. 2. Ions. 3. Electrons.   *Title transliterated:* Fizika
ionnykh i ėlektronnykh   protsessov.

    Library of Congress   QC173.N3   43–30129

NN   0026279   DLC

Naslén, P
    see
    Naslin, Pierre.

Naslian, Jean, *Abp.,* 1875–
    Les mémoires de Mgr. Jean Naslian, évêque de Trébizonde,
sur les événements politico-religieux en Proche-Orient de
1914 à 1928. Beyrouth [pref. 1955]
    2 v. 25 cm.

    1. Catholic Church. Armenian rite—Hist. 2. Armenia—Hist.
    3. Armenian question.
    BX1622.N3   57–38235 ‡

NN   0026281   DLC NIC NN MH TU ICU OCU MoSW TU OU CU

Naslin, P., joint author.
TR591
.F3
    Fayolle, P
    Photographie instantanée et cinématographie ultra-
rapide, par P. Fayolle et P. Naslin. [Paris, Revue d'optique, 1950]

Naslin, Pierre.
    Les systèmes asservis. Préf. de l'ingénieur général Nico-
lau. Paris, Revue d'optique, 1951.
    333 p. diagrs. 25 cm. (Bibliothèque de l'ingénieur, mécanicien,
constructeur, 1)
    Bibliography: p. [329]–333.

    1. Servomechanisms. I. Title.

    TJ213.N3   53–19054

NN   0026283   DLC NN MiU PPF CU

VOLUME 405

Naslin, Pierre.
Technologie et calcul des systèmes asservis
see Journées des servo-mécanismes,
Brussels, 1953. Tournées des servo-mécanismes..

Naslin, Pierre.
Vocabulaire technique trilingue. 19 glossaires techniques
français-anglais-allemand suivis de 3 répertoires alphabéti-
ques. Paris, Revue d'optique théorique et instrumentale,
1951.
xvii, 398 p. 23 cm.

Added t. p.'s in English and German.

1. Technology—Dictionaries—Polyglot. 2. Dictionaries, Polyglot.
I. Title.

T10.N3   603   51–12296

ICJ
NN 0026285   DLC DI ICU NN OC1 IU DPU MB CU PU–E1

Naslin, Mme Victor.
Nouvelle méthode de lecture ou l'art d'enseigner aux enfants à lire
tout de suite couramment.
= Paris. Truchy. [1862.] xii, 109, (1) pp. Illus. 18°.

E6873 — France. Lang. Read.

NN 0026286   MB ViU

M1690   Naslund, Bertil
N255w   Winter construction. Translated by
H. A. G. Nathan. Ottawa, 1955.
64 l. illus. 28 cm. (National Research
Council, Canada. Technical translation TT–583)

Cover title.
"From Stat. Komm. Byggnadsforsk. Broschyr
5, 1952."

1. Climate. Human relations. 2. Building.
Meteorological relations. I. t. ser.

NN 0026287   DAS

Naslund, Elmer.
The voice of Verdun, by Elmer Naslund. St. Louis, Mo.,
The Elm publishing co. [1935]
4 p. l., 11–346, [1] p. 19¼ᶜᵐ.

1. European war, 1914–1918—Fiction. I. Title.

Library of Congress   PZ3.N179Vo   35–5818

NN 0026288   DLC

Naslund, O. J.
Flottningsmaterial och flottledsbyggnader...
Stockholm...[1915].
2 p.1., [2, 6] p.

NN 0026289   MiU

BV3427   Nasmith, Augustus I
N25A32   The interesting life of the ordinary
missionary - China - 1912–1949. [n.p.,
n.d.]
100 p.   front.   28 cm.
Cover title.
Processed.

1. Missions - China. 2. Missionaries,
American - Correspondence, reminiscences,
etc. I. Title.

NN 0026290   CSt–H

Nasmith, David, 1829–1894.
The chronometrical chart of the history of England, civil and
military; religious, intellectual and social, from B. C. 55 to A.D.
1860. Together with table of the contemporary sovereigns of
Europe, from William the Conqueror to Queen Victoria. By
David Nasmith.   London: G. Philip & Son [1863]. vi, 14 p.
tables. f°.

142047A. 1. Great Britain.—History: Chronology.
N. Y. P. L.   August 25, 1924

NN 0026291   NN ICN

Nasmith, David, 1829–1894.
The institutes of English adjective law. (Procedure in
court.) Embracing an outline of the law of evidence and
measure of damages.   By David Nasmith ...   London,
Butterworths, 1879.
xxii p., 1 l., 355 p. 18½ᶜᵐ.

1. Civil procedure—Gt. Brit. 2. Evidence (Law)—Gt. Brit. 3. Damages—
Gt. Brit.   I. Title.   II. Title: English adjective law.

22–15292

PU–L ViU–L WaU–L
NN 0026292   DLC NjP MdBP CtY CU–AL NN ICRL PPB

Nasmith, David, 1829–1894.
The institutes of English private law: embracing an
outline of the substantive branch of the law of persons
and things.   By David Nasmith ...   London, Butterworths, 1875.
2 v. xv tab. 18½ᶜᵐ.
Paged continuously.

1. Law—Gt. Brit. [1. English law]   I. Title.   II. Title: English private
law.

22–15293

MdBP
NN 0026293   DLC PPB PU–B MH ViU–L WaU–L NjP CU–AL

Nasmith, David, 1829–1894.
The institutes of English public law: embracing an outline
of general jurisprudence: the development of the British constitution; public international law; and the public municipal
law of England.   By David Nasmith ...   London, Butterworths, 1873.
vi p., 2 l., 455 p. VII tab. 18ᶜᵐ.

1. Jurisprudence. - 2. Gt. Brit.—Constitutional history. 3. International law. 4. Law—Gt. Brit.   I. Title.   II. Title: English public law.

22–15294

WaU–L ViU–L
NN 0026294   DLC CSt–Law MH CtY NN PPB PU MdBP NjP

920.02   Nasmith, David, 1829–1894.
N17m   Makers of modern thought; or, Five hundred years
struggle (1200 A.D. to 1699 A.D.) between science,
ignorance, and superstition …   London, G.
Philip & son; [etc., etc.] 1892.
2 v.

PPD MiD NNC
NN 0026295   IU WaS CaBVaU OrCS NNUT MB OC1W PPL

Nasmith, David, 1829–1894.
Outline of Roman history from Romulus to Justinian,
(including translations of the Twelve tables, the Institutes of Gaius, and the Institutes of Justinian), with special reference to the growth, development and decay of
Roman jurisprudence.   By David Nasmith ...   London,
Butterworth; [etc., etc.] 1890.
1 p. l., xix, 618 p. map, diagr. 21½ᶜᵐ.

1. Roman law. 2. Roman law—Hist. 3. Rome—Hist.   I. Leges XII
tabularum. II. Gaius. Institutiones. III. Corpus juris civilis. Institutiones.

1–1440 Revised

PPDrop OCU MiU WaU–L WaSpG
NN 0026296   DLC CtY GU–L MH–L NjP ICU KU PPB OC1

Nasmith, David, 1829–1894.
Popular errors concerning education, and their
influence ...   London, G. Philip & Son [1863?]
24 p.   8°.
Repr.: Educational Times.

NN 0026297   NN

Nasmith, David, 1829–1894.
The practical linguist; being a system based entirely upon
natural principles of learning to speak, read, and write the German
language. By David Nasmith...   London: D. Nutt, 1870.
2 v.   8°.

1. German language—Exercises and   readers. 2. Title.
N. Y. P. L.   April 7, 1925

NN 0026298   NN MB ICN

Nasmith, David, 1829–1894.
The practical linguist: being a system
based entirely upon natural principles of
learning to speak, read and write the English
language ... In two parts. Part I. London,
D. Nutt, 1871.
viii, 160 p. 18 cm.

No more published.
"Elementary lessons on grammar": p. 127–50.

1. English language - Grammar - 1870–1930.

NN 0026299   NNC

Nasmith, Frank, editor.
The artificial silk handbook. Compiled and edited by Frank
Nasmith...   Manchester: J. Heywood, Ltd. [, 1926?] 135 p.
incl. diagrs., tables. illus. 12°.

Advertising matter included in paging.

294287A. 1. Silk, Artificial.   2. Silk, Artificial—Trade and
stat.—Directories. 3. Silk,   Artificial—Terminology.
N. Y. P. L.   May 20, 1927

NN 0026300   NN

Nasmith, George Gallie, 1877–
Canada's sons and Great Britain in the world war; a com-
plete and authentic history of the commanding part played by
Canada and the British empire in the world's greatest war, by
Col. George G. Nasmith ... with an introduction by Gen. Sir
Arthur W. Currie ... illustrated with reproductions from the
official photographs of the Canadian and British governments.
Toronto, The John C. Winston co., limited [*1919]
xx, 21–607 p. incl. illus. (maps) plates, ports. front. 24ᶜᵐ.
Plates printed on both sides.
1. European war, 1914–1918—Canada. 2. European war, 1914–1918—
Gt. Brit.   I. Title.
Library of Congress   D547.C2N3   19—15625

OC1 PP MiU OC1W CtY NN MB
NN 0026301   DLC CaBVa CaNSWA CaOTU OrU NcD CaBVaU

Nasmith, G[eorge] G[allie] [8]77–
... The chemistry of wheat gluten. By G. G. Nasmith.
[Toronto] The University library, published by the librarian, 1903.
cover-title, 22 p. 26½ᶜᵐ. (University of Toronto studies. Physiological series. no. 4)
"Reprinted by permission from the Transactions of the Canadian institute, vol. VII."
Bibliography: p. 22.

1. Gluten.
                                         4–7863

Library of Congress   QP1.T7
——— Copy 2.   Library of Congress QD431.N25

NN 0026302   DLC DNLM CaOTU PBm MiU OCU OO OU NN

Nasmith, George Gallie, 1877–
On the Fringe of the Great Fight.
N. Y., n.d.

NN 0026303   DN

VOLUME 405

Nasmith, George Gallie, 1877–
    On the fringe of the great fight, by Colonel George G. Nasmith, C. M. G.   New York, G. H. Doran [1917?]
    xiii p., 1 l., 263, [1] p.   6 pl., 2 port. (incl. front.) 22 cm.

NN   0026304   IU PU PP OC1

Nasmith, George Gallie, 1877–
    On the fringe of the great fight, by Colonel George G. Nasmith, c. m. g. Toronto, McClelland, Goodchild & Stewart [1917]
    xiii p., 1 l., 263, [1] p. 6 pl., 2 port. (incl. front.) 22ᶜᵐ.

    1. European war, 1914–1918—Personal narratives, Canadian.
    I. Title.

Library of Congress   D640.N3   18–18473

NN   0026305   DLC CSf Or CaBViPA CaBVa IdB NN MB

Nasmith, George Gallie, 1877–   , and H. P. Eddy.
    Report to R. C. Harris, esq., commissioner of works, Toronto, Ontario, Canada, upon the sewage disposal problem of North Toronto [by] George G. Nasmith [and] Harrison P. Eddy... April 3rd, 1926. [Toronto: The Carswell Co. Ltd., 1926] 38 f. incl. diagrs., plans, tables. 27½cm.

    "Memorandum accompanying report," f. 8–38.

785161A. 1. Sewage disposal—
Harrison Prescott, 1870– , jt. au.
N. Y. P. L.
                Canada—Toronto. I. Eddy,
                II. Toronto. Works Department.
                          October 22, 1935

NN   0026306   NN CaOTU

Nasmith, George Gallie, 1877–
    Smiths of a better quality, by George G. Nasmith. [Toronto:] National Council of Education[, cop. 1925]. 138 p. 12°.

204581A. 1. Children—Care and hy-   giene.
N. Y. P. L.   October 16, 1925

NN   0026307   NN TxU CaBVaU

Nasmith, George Gallie, 1877–
    Timothy Eaton, by George G. Nasmith. Toronto, McClelland & Stewart [1923].
    xl, 312 p., 1 l. incl. plates. 2 port. (incl. front.) 24ᶜᵐ.

    "This special edition is limited to four hundred copies of which this is no. 5."

    1. Eaton, Timothy, 1834–1907. 2. Retail trade—Toronto.
                                      45–46552

Library of Congress   HF5465.C6E35

        OU ICU CaBVaU CaBVa DLC
NN   0026308   NN WaU CaOTU MH CtY WHi NcD TxU OC1

Nasmith, James, C. E.
    Remarks on the introduction of the slide principle in tools and machines employed in the production of machinery.
    (In Baker, Thomas. Elements of mechanism. Pp. 227–243. London, 1858–9.)

F2563 — Slide. In mechanics.

NN   0026309   MB

Nasmith, James, 1740–1808, ed.

Dallaway, James, 1763–1834.
    Antiquities of Bristow in the middle centuries; including the topography by William Wyrcestre, and the life of William Canynges. By the Rev. James Dallaway. Bristol, Mirror office, 1834.

Nasmith, James, 1740–1808.

Cambridge. University. *Corpus Christi college. Library.*
    Catalogus librorum manuscriptorum quos Collegio corporis Christi et B. Mariæ Virginis in Academia Cantabrigiensi legavit reverendissimus ... Matthæus Parker, archiepiscopus cantuariensis. Edidit Jacobus Nasmith ... Cantabrigiæ, typis Academicis, excudebat J. Archdeacon[, etc., etc.] 1777.

Law   Nasmith, James, 1740–1808.

    Gt. Brit. *Court of Quarter Sessions of the Peace (Isle of Ely)*
    The duties of overseers of the poor, and the sufficiency of the present system of poor laws considered, in a charge delivered to the Grand Jury at the general Quarter Sessions of the Peace for the Isle of Ely, holden on 2 April, 1799, by James Nasmith, chairman. To which are annexed, remarks on a late publication, entitled, "Observations on the present state and influence of the poor laws, founded on experience, by Robert Saunders, Esq." Wisbech, J. White [1799]

Nasmith, James, 1740–1808.
    An examination of the statutes now in force relating to the assize of bread; with remarks on the bill intended to be brought into Parliament by the country bakers ... Wisbech, Printed and sold by J.White [etc., etc.] 1800.
    2 p. l., 85 p., 1 l. incl. tables. 21.5 cm.

NN   0026313   MH–BA NSyU CtY

Nasmith, James, 1740–1808, ed.

Symon Simeonis, *fl.* 1322.
    Itineraria Symonis Simeonis, et Willelmi de Worcestre. Quibus accedit Tractatus de metro, in quo traduntur regulæ a scriptoribus medii ævi in versibus leoninis observatæ. E codicibus mss. in bibliotheca Coll. Corp. Christi Cantab. asservatis primus eruit ediditque, Jacobus Nasmith ... Cantabrigiæ, J. Archdeacon, 1778.

Nasmith, Joseph.
    Modern cotton spinning machinery, its principles and construction. By Joseph Nasmith ... With two hundred and thirty-two illustrations. Manchester, J. Nasmith; [etc., etc.] 1890.
    322 p. incl. illus., plates. 28 x 22½ᶜᵐ.
    Glossary: p. [308]

    1. Cotton spinning. 2. Cotton machinery.   3–31712
Library of Congress   TS1583.N25

NN   0026315   DLC PPF MB

Nasmith, Joseph.
    Recent cotton mill construction and engineering. Manchester [Eng.] J. Heywood, n.d.
    275 p. illus., fold. tables. 18cm.

NN   0026316   NcRS NcC

Nasmith, Joseph.
    Recent cotton mill construction and engineering. By Joseph Nasmith... Manchester [etc.] J. Heywood [1894?]
    284 p. incl. illus., tables, diagrs. fold. plates. 18 1/2cm.

    1. Textile factories. 2. Cotton growing and manufacture.

NN   0026317   DP MiU ICJ ICRL NcC CtY

Nasmith, Joseph.
    Recent cotton mill construction and engineering. 2d edition.
— Manchester. Heywood. [190–?] 288 pp. Illus. Plates. Plans. Diagrams. Sm. 8°.

G4101 — Cotton manufacture.

NN   0026318   MB

NASMITH, JOSEPH, 1850–1905.
    Recent cotton mill construction and engineering. By the late Joseph Nasmith...and Frank Nasmith... Third edition. Manchester [etc.] J.Heywood ltd. [1909] 382 p. incl. diagrs., tables. illus., plans, plates. 18½cm.

843026A. 1. Cotton—Manufacture—Machinery and mill works. I. Nasmith, Frank, ed.

NN   0026319   NN

Nasmith, Joseph,
    Students' cotton spinning. Manchester, Nasmith; pref. 1892.
    445 p.

NN   0026320   PPD

Nasmith, Joseph.
    The students' cotton spinning. 2d edition, revised and enlarged. Manchester. Nasmith. [1893.] 510 pp. Illus. 17½ cm., in 8s.

K8042 — T.r. — Cotton manufacture.

NN   0026321   MB

Nasmith, Joseph.
    The students' cotton spinning. By Joseph Nasmith ... 3d ed. rev. and enl. Manchester, J. Nasmith; [etc., etc., 1896]
    622 p. illus. 18½ᶜᵐ.

    "The present edition has been in great part rewritten ... that portion of it which appeared in the preceding editions and dealt with the construction and engineering of mills has been omitted."—Pref.

    1. Cotton—Spinning.
                                3–31710
Library of Congress   TS1577.N25

        PP PPF OCU OU ____
NN   0026322   DLC ICJ ICRL CtY NcC NN PPWI MiU OrCS

Nasmith, Joseph.
    The students' cotton spinning. Manchester, J. Nasmith [1899?]
    622 p. illus. 12°.
    6. ed.

NN   0026323   NN

Nasmith, Joseph.
    The students' cotton spinning. By Joseph Nasmith ... Manchester, Haywood, [1922]
    622 p.

NN   0026324   NcRS

Nasmith, Robert.
    A treatise upon the entail of the covenant of grace ... Glasgow, Printed by R. Sanders for the author, 1725.
    [40], 294, [1] p. 16ᶜᵐ.

    Commendatory letters by Thomas Lining and W. Hamilton.

NN   0026325   CLU–C

Nasmyth, Alexander, 1758–1840, illus.

PR4327
.I55
Rare bk.
coll.
    Illustrations to the works of Robert Burns from original drawings by Alex. Nasmyth, Sam Bough, R. S. A., Wm. E. Lockhart, R. S. A., Clark Stanton, A. R. S. A. Engraved by William Forrest, H. R. S. A., & Robert Anderson, A. R. S. A. Edinburgh, W. Paterson, 1880.

VOLUME 405

₍Nasmyth, Alexander₎ 1758-1840.
Sixteen engravings from real scenes supposed to be described in the novels and tales of the author of Waverley. Edinburgh, Archibald Constables and Co.; London, Hurst, Robinson and Co., 1821.
1 p. l., 16 plates. 25cm.

Engraved title-page.
From cover-title: "Engraved by W. H. Lizars, from drawings by Alexander Nasmyth."

NN 0026327   NNC

Nasmyth, Alexander, 1789-1849.
On the human mouth. Read before the Ethnological society, April 23, 1845. Extracted from the Edinburgh New Philosophical journal, January, 1846. London, John Churchill, 1846.
23 p.   21 cm.

NN 0026328   PPiU-D PU-D

Nasmyth, A₍lexander₎ 1789-1849.
Report of a paper on the cellular structure of the ivory, enamel, and pulp of the teeth as well as of the epithelium ... read at the ninth meeting of the British association for the advancement of science, held at Birmingham, in August 1839. By A. Nasmyth ... London, R. and J. E. Taylor ₍1839₎
25 p. 9 pl. (5 col.) 22ᶜᵐ.
Reprinted from vol. VIII. of the Transactions of the association.

1. Teeth.

Library of Congress   QL858.N25   6-25540†

NN 0026329   DLC NN

WU   NASMYTH, Alexander, 1789-1849.
N258r   Researches on the developement,
1839   structure, and diseases of the teeth.
London, Churchill, 1839.
xvi, 165, 4, 3 p. illus.

NN 0026330   DNLM KyU OU

Nasmyth, Alexander, 1789-1849.
Researches on the development, structure and diseases of the teeth. By Alexander Nasmyth ... Baltimore, The American society of dental surgeons, 1842.
xii, ₍13₎-116 p. front. (port.) 22ᶜᵐ. (Lettered on cover: American library of dental science)

1. Teeth.

16-5106

Library of Congress   QM311.N3

NN 0026331   DLC CaBVaU ICRL DNLM ICJ MiU

Nasmyth, Alexander, 1789-1849.
Researches on the development, structure and diseases of the teeth. By Alexander Nasmyth ... London, J. Churchill, 1849.
viii, 230 p. front. (port.) illus., x pl. 23ᶜᵐ.

PPC NIC
NN 0026332   ICJ DNLM PPiU-D MdBP MnU CaBVaU PPD

Nasmyth, Alexander, 1789-1849
Researches on the development, structure and diseases of the teeth. London, J. Churchill, 1899.

NN 0026333   OClW

Nasmyth, Alexander, 1789-1849.
Three memoirs on the developement ₍!₎ and structure of the teeth and epithelium ... with diagrams exhibited in illustration of them. By Alexander Nasmyth ... London, J. Churchill, 1841.
2 p. l., ₍i₎i₎-xvi, ₍2₎, 47 p.   9 pl. (part col.) 23ᶜᵐ.
"Read at the ninth annual meeting of the British association for the encouragement of science, held at Birmingham, in August, 1839."
Withheld from publication in the society's Transactions. cf. Introd.
1. Teeth. 2. Epithelium. 3. British association for the advancement of science.

OU
NN 0026334   MiU PPiU ICU MBCo PPC PPiU-D MnU DNLM

Nasmyth, Alexander, 1789-1849.
Three memoirs on the development and structure of the teeth and epithelium, read at the 9th annual meeting of the British Association for the Encouragement of Science held at Birmingham in August, 1839... 2d ed., to which is added a letter to the Right Hon. Lord Francis Egerton London, Churchill, 1842.

67 + 58 p. plates. 22.5 cm.

NN 0026335   MH PPC

NASMYTH Arthur.
Divine poems, in three parts, viz. Poeticall applications, Jobs adversity, Poeticall prayers. With Mans looking-glasse. Edinburgh, printed for James M₄ller, 1665.

24°. pp. (8), 88. Woodcuts.
"The Christian's example or Job's adversity" and "Poetical prayers" mingled with spirit-ejaculations have separate title-page.
"Speculum hominis,   Mans looking-glasse" pp. 86-88.

NN 0026336   MH

Nasmyth, Charles J.
Audit procedure and reports by C. Nasmyth... Scranton, Pa., Institute of business sci., ₍c1921-1922₎.
39, 39, 56 p.

NN 0026337   OCl

HF5567   Nasmyth, Charles J.
.N3   Audit procedure... Introduction by Ernest W. Lovejoy... Scranton, Pa., 1924.
iv, 38, [1] p. 20ᶜᵐ.

Bibliography: 1 p. at end.

NN 0026338   ICU

Nasmyth, Charles J., and Stuart Chase, 1888-
Audit procedure and reports.
— Scranton. 1928. iv, 55, (2) pp. Chart. Tables. [International Textbook Company. Commercial blue book. No. 54.] 19 cm.
Contains examination questions.

N6963 — S.r. — Jt. auth. — Auditors.

NN 0026339   MB WaS

HF5667   Nasmyth, Charles J., joint author.
.B387
Bennett, Robert Joseph, 1871-
... Curso completo de auditoría; intervención y fiscalización de contabilidades; versión castellana de Oliverio I. López-Hidalgo. La Habana, Cuba, Cultural, s. a., 1942.

Nasmyth, Charles J
A message to Congress. What price democracy? By Charles J. Nasmyth ... Private ed. ... Brockton, Mass., Distributed by the author ₍1943₎
79 p. 21ᶜᵐ.
"A substantial part of this booklet consists of excerpts from a 600-page work ... being withheld ... from publication for the 'duration'."—Author's note.

1. Railroads—U. S.—Finance. 2. Bankruptcy—U. S. I. Title.
44-38879

Library of Congress   HE2251.N3
₍3₎   385.13

NN 0026341   DLC NNC

Nasmyth, Mrs. Florence G., ed.

Wentworth, Lydia G   1858-
Selected writings of Lydia G. Wentworth; with introduction and editorial notes by Ralph Westlake; edited by Florence G. Nasmyth and Ralph Westlake. ₍Boston₎ The Norwood press, 1936.

NASMYTH George William, 1882-1920.
Armenia; a touchstone of victory. Boston, 1918.

Pamphlet.

NN 0026343   MH

NASMYTH, George William, 1882-1920.
What I saw in Germany. [London, 1914.]
pp. 8.
"Reprinted from 'War and Peace', Oct. 1914."

NN 0026344   MH

NASMYTH, George William, 1882-1920.
Constructive mediation, an interpretation of the ten foremost proposals. n.p., [1915].
pp. 7. Illustr. and tables.
"Reprinted from The Survey, March 6, 1915."
Presentation copy with author's autograph contains E. A. Filene's Melting pot. pp. 6-7.

NN 0026345   MH

Nasmyth, George William, 1882-1920.
Experiments in impact excitation ... ₍New York? 1911₎
1 p. l., p. ₍69₎-177 incl. illus., tables, diagrs. 25½ᶜᵐ.
Thesis (PH. D.)—Cornell university.
"Reprinted from the Physical review, vol. XXXII, no. 1 and no. 2, 1911."

1. Electric waves. I. Title: Impact excitation, Experiments in.
12-1177

Library of Congress   QC665.N3

NN 0026346   DLC MiU

Nasmyth, George William, 1882-1920.
The frequency of the singing arc. By George W. Nasmyth. ₍New York, The Macmillan co., 1908₎
cover-title, p. ₍117₎-140 incl. tables, diagrs. 25½ᶜᵐ.
"Reprinted from the Physical review, vol. XXVII, no. 2, August, 1908."

1. Electric arc.
12-10132

Library of Congress   QC705.N2

NN 0026347   DLC MiU

VOLUME 405

Nasmyth, George William, 1882–*1920.*
"Organized insanity"; or, The Hague, a reply to Admiral Mahan, by George W. Nasmyth. **Washington,** D. C., American peace society, 1914.
12 p. 22ᶜᵐ.

1. Mahan, Alfred Thayer, 1840–   2. Militarism.   ɪ. Title.

Library of Congress   JX1974.N2   14–17741

NN   0026348   DLC

Nasmyth, George William, 1882–1920.
... The Roman Catholic church and the League of nations, by George Nasmyth, ᴘʜ. ᴅ.; report to the International committee. The Hague, Holland, 1919.
cover-title, 16 p. 23ᶜᵐ.
At head of title: The World alliance for promoting international friendship through the churches.
Report in English and French.
Bibliography: p. 16.

1. League of nations. 2. Catholic church.   ɪ. World alliance for promoting international friendship through the churches. ɪɪ. Title.

Library of Congress   JX1975.N25 .   19–18452 Revised

NN   0026349   DLC NIC

Nasmyth, George William, 1882–1920.
Social progress and the Darwinian theory; a study of force as a factor in human relations, by George Nasmyth, ᴘʜ. ᴅ., with an introduction by Norman Angell. New York and London, G. P. Putnam's sons, 1916.
xxiii, 417 p. diagr. 19½ᶜᵐ.

1. Sociology. 2. Evolution. 3. War.   ɪ. Title.
                       16—6087
Library of Congress   HM106.N3

    OrCS OrSaW
    PU MiU OC1 OC1W OO ViU NN ICJ MB WaTC WaWW MtU Or
NN   0026350   DLC KEmT MoU AAP CBDP CU PSC PHC PPFr

Nasmyth, George William, 1882–*1920.*
... Universal military service and democracy, by George W. Nasmyth... Washington, D. C.: Amer. Union against Militarism ₁1917₁. 14 p., 1 l. 8°.
Repr.: Jour. of race development. Oct., 1916.

1. Military service (Compulsory).   U. S. 2. American Union against Militarism.
N. Y. P. L.   June 28, 1917.

NN   0026351   NN DNW MH–L MH

Nasmyth, George William, 1882–*1920.*
... Universal military training and democracy, by George Nasmyth ... Washington, D. C., American union against militarism ₁1919₁
14, ₁2₁ p. 1 illus. 23ᶜᵐ.

1. Military service, Compulsory.   ɪ. Title.
                    19–3989
Library of Congress   UB343.N3

NN   0026352   DLC OO OU PSC DHEW

Nasmyth, George William, 1882–*1920.*
The universities and American international relations, by George W. Nasmyth... (In: Clark University, Worcester, Mass. Latin America. New York. 1914. 8°. p. 321–327.)

1. Colleges, etc. 2. Pan-American-   ism.
N. Y. P. L.   February 11, 1915.

NN   0026353   NN

QC
71
P57+
v.40
no.12

Nasmyth, George William, 1882–1920.
Ein weiterer Ausbau der Formel für die Frequenz der Lichtbogenschwingungen. Leipzig, J. A. Barth, 1911–12.
2 v. illus. 24cm.

Reprinted from Jahrbuch der drahtlosen Telegraphie und Telephonie.

1. Oscillators, Electric.

NN   0026354   NIC

Nasmyth, George William, 1882–1920.
Pasdermadjian, Garegin, 1873–
Why Armenia should be free; Armenia's rôle in the present war, by Dr. G. Pasdermadjian (Armen Garo) ... With an introduction by George Nasmyth ... Boston, Hairenik publishing company, 1918.

Nasmyth, George William, 1882–1920.
... The World alliance and international reconstruction, by George Nasmyth, ᴘʜ. ᴅ.; report to the International committee. The Hague, Holland, 1919.
cover-title, 23 p. 23ᶜᵐ.
At head of title: The World alliance for promoting international friendship through the churches.

1. International cooperation. 2. Peace.   ɪ. World alliance for promoting international friendship through the churches. ɪɪ. Title.
               19–18451 Revised
Library of Congress   JX1907.N2

NN   0026356   DLC

Nasmyth, James Hall, 1808–1890.
The autobiography of James Nasmyth, engineer; passages selected to form a continuous narrative from the original edition of Samuel Smiles...edited by A. F. Collins... Cambridge, Eng.₁: Univ. Press, 1931. xv, 104 p. front. (port.), illus., plates. 12°. (The Craftsman ser.)

554300A. 1. No subject. I. Collins,   Archie Frederick, 1869–   , editor.
II. Smiles, Samuel, 1812–1904.
N. Y. P. L.   December 7, 1931

NN   0026357   NN

Nasmyth, James Hall, 1808–1890.
Baker, Thomas, *d.* 1871.
The elements of practical mechanism and machine tools, by T. Baker, ᴄ. ᴇ. With remarks on tools and machinery by James Nasmyth, ᴄ. ᴇ. With numerous illustrations. 5th éd. London, Lockwood & co., 1873.

B
N258n
1883

Nasmyth, James Hall, 1808–1890.
James Nasmyth, engineer. An autobiography edited by Samuel Smiles. With a portrait by George Reid, etched by Paul Rajon. London, J. Murray, 1883.
xviii, 456p. illus., ports., diagrs. 21cm.

1. Nasmyth, James Hall, 1808–1890. I. Smiles, Samuel, 1812–1904.

    ScU NIC MeB CtY MiU InU
NN   0026359   IU CaBVaU IEdS PHC ICN ICJ RPB NRU ICU

NASMYTH, JAMES HALL, 1808–1890.
James Nasmyth, engineer; an autobiography, edited by Samuel Smiles... New York: Harper & Bros., 1883. xvii, 461 p. incl. front. illus., plates, ports. 19cm.

3'44561. 1. No subject. I. Smiles, Samuel, 1812–1904, ed.

    OC1W MH I ViU PBL
NN   0026360   NN DNW LU MdBP Vi WU NjP OCU MWA WaS

Nasmyth, James Hall, 1808–1890.
James Nasmyth engineer; an autobiography, ed. by Samuel Smiles ... New ed., rev. and cor. for American readers, by James Nasmyth. New York, Harper & brothers, 1884.
xvii. 461 p. incl. front., illus., plates, ports. 9 pl. 19ᶜᵐ.

ɪ. Smiles, Samuel, 1812–1904, ed.   4—11

Library of Congress   TJ140.N25A3
                 ₁a36b1₁   926.2

NN   0026361   DLC NcD OKentU PPD PPL PPGi PPLas

B
N258n
1885

Nasmyth, James Hall, 1808–1890.
James Nasmyth, engineer. An autobiography edited by Samuel Smiles. With a portrait by George Reid, etched by Paul Rajon. 3d ed. London, J. Murray, 1885.
xviii, 458p. illus., port. 22cm.

1. Nasmyth, James Hall, 1808–1890. I. Smiles, Samuel, 1812–1904.

NN   0026362   IU   NN DSI PU

Ub66
N17
912n

Nasmyth, James Hall, 1808–1890.
James Nasmyth engineer; an autobiography, ed. by Samuel Smiles ... Popular ed. ... London, J. Murray, 1912.
xx,450p. incl. front., illus., ports. plates. 19cm.

I. Smiles, Samuel, 1812–1904, ed.

NN   0026363   CtY IdU MU

620.92
N258A
1944

Nasmyth, James Hall, 1808–1890.
James Nasmyth engineer; an autobiography, ed. by Samuel Smiles. ₁Milwaukee, Lee Engineering Research Corp., 1944₁
461p. facsim., illus.
First published by Harper & Brothers, 1883

I. Smiles, Samuel, 1812–1904, ed.

NN   0026364   FTaSU

Nasmyth, James Hall, 1808–1890.
Der Mond als Planet, Welt und Trabant von J. Nasmyth und J. Carpenter. Vierte Auflage. Zweite, völlig veränderte, verbesserte und vermehrte deutsche Umarbeitung des englischen Originaltextes von Prof. Dr. Hermann J. Klein. Mit zahlreichen Holzschnitten, zwei lithographierten und neunzehn Tafeln in Lichtdruck. Hamburg und Leipzig, L. Voss, 1906.
vi, ₁2₁, 214 p. 46 illus. incl. diagrs., XXI pl. (incl. col. front., map). 23½ᶜᵐ.

NN   0026365   ICJ DN–Ob

Nasmyth, James, 1808–1890.
Mond betrachtet als planet, welt und trabant, by James Carpenter. Leipzig, Voss, 1876.
165 p.

NN   0026366   PPF

Nasmyth, James Hall, 1808–1890.
The moon: considered as a planet, a world, and a satellite. By James Nasmyth, ᴄ. ᴇ., and James Carpenter, ꜰ.ʀ.ᴀ.s. ... With twenty-four illustrative plates of lunar objects, phenomena, and scenery; numerous woodcuts, &c. 2d ed. London, J. Murray, 1874.
xvi, 189 p. front., illus, 23 pl. (incl. mounted photos.) 28½ x 22½ᶜᵐ.

1. Moon.   ɪ. Carpenter, James, 1840–1899, joint author.

Library of Congress   QB581.N2   2–18052

    PPL PPWa PSC MiU OU ODW NN NjP
NN   0026367   DLC OO CtY DSI FMU MH

VOLUME 405

Nasmyth, James Hall, 1808–1890.
The moon : considered as a planet, a world, and a satellite. By James Nasmyth, c. e., and James Carpenter, f. r. a. s. ... With twenty-six illustrative plates ... ₍3d ed.₎ New York, Scribner & Welford, 1885.
xv, ₍1₎, 213 p. front., illus., 25 pl. (incl. mounted photos.) 23½ᵐ.

1. Moon.   i. Carpenter, James, 1840–1899, joint author.

Library of Congress   QB581.N21   2—18053

MiHM MH PPA PPGi I
NN 0026368   DLC ICJ PU NBuG ViU PSC MiU OClW CU IU

Nasmyth, James Hall, 1808–1890.
The moon: considered as a planet, a world, and a satellite. By James Nasmyth ... and James Carpenter ... London, J. Murry, 1916.

NN 0026369   PSC

Nasmyth, James Hall, 1808–1890.

Buchanan, Robertson, 1770–1816.
Practical essays on mill work and other machinery. By Robertson Buchanan, engineer. With notes and additional articles, containing new researches on various mechanical subjects, by Thomas Tredgold ... And now rev. into a third edition with additions, by George Rennie ... Illustrated by upwards of seventy plates, and numerous figures. London, J. Weale, 1841–50.

Nasmyth, James Hall, 1808–1890.
Remarks on the introduction of the slide principle in tools and machines employed in the production of machinery. (In Buchanan, Robertson. Practical essays on mill work. Appendix B. Pp. 393–418. Illus. Diagrams. London. 1841.)   4012.22
Same. (In Baker, Thomas. Elements of mechanism. Pp. 227–243. London. 1858, 59.)   8019.706

L3216 — Slide. In mechanics.

NN 0026371   MB

Nasmyth (Robert). *On tic douloureux. 2 p. l., 31 pp. 8°. Edinburgh, Abernethy & Walker, 1823. ₍Also in: P., v. 1272.₎

NN 0026372   DNLM

W 4 NASMYTH, Thomas
E23   Disputatio medica inauguralis, de rachitide ... Edinburgi,
1777   Balfour et Smellie, 1777.
N. 1   44 p. 19 cm.
          Diss. – Edinburgh.

NN 0026373   DNLM

Naso, *bp. of Autun*
        see
Modoin, *bp. of Autun, d. ca. 840.*

Naso, Eckart von, 1888–
... Die begegnung; novelle. Bielefeld und Leipzig, Velhagen & Klasing ₍1936₎.
90, ₍1₎ p. 19ᶜᵐ.

1. Luise, queen consort of Frederick William iii, king of Prussia, 1776–1810—Fiction. 2. Napoléon i—Fiction. i. Title.

Library of Congress   PT2627.A65B4 1936   37–11808
Copyright A—Foreign   35013
                            ₍2₎   833.91

NN 0026375   DLC CtY CU NN WU MH NNC MB IaU

188
Naso, Eckart von, 1888–
Die Begegnung; Novelle. ₍Feldpost-Ausg. 2. Aufl.₎ Bielefeld, Velhagen & Klasing ₍1944₎

NN 0026376   IU PU

Naso, Eckart von, 1888–
... Die chronik der giftmischerin. Potsdam, G. Kiepenheuer, 1926.
150, ₍1₎ p. 16½ᶜᵐ. (*Half-title:* Die liebhaberbibliothek)

1. Brinvilliers, Marie Madeleine Marguerite (d'Aubray) Gobelin, marquise de, 1630?–1676—Fiction. i. Title.
Library of Congress   PT2627.A65C5 1926   28–25673

NN 0026377   DLC PPG

Naso, Eckart von, 1888–
Der Feldherr; aus dem Roman "Moltke - Mensch und Feldherr". Berlin-Grunewald, etc., H.Hillger ₍1942₎
79 p. (Hillgers deutsche Bücherei, 687-88)

NN 0026378   MH DLC

Naso, Eckart von, 1888–
Die grosse Liebende; ein Roman um Ninon de Lenclos. Frankfurt am Main, H. Scheffler ₍1950₎
366 p. 20 cm.

1. Lenclos, Anne, called Ninon de, 1620–1705—Fiction. i. Title.
                            A 51–7220
New York. Public Libr.
for Library of Congress   ₍3₎

NN 0026379   NN CU MB

Naso, Eckart von, 1888–
... Der Halbgott; ein Roman um Alkibiades.   Frankfurt am Main, H. Scheffler ₍c1949₎   413 p.   map.   21cm.

547575B. 1. Alcibiades—Fiction.   i. Title.
N. Y. P. L.   September 11, 1950

NN 0026380   NN C PSt

Naso, Eckart von, 1888–
Ich liebe das Leben; Erinnerungen aus fünf Jahrzehnten. Hamburg, W. Krüger ₍1953₎
728 p. illus. 21 cm.

1. Theater—Berlin. i. Title.

PN2658.N3A3   56–26318 ‡

NcD PPGi MiU
NN 0026381   DLC NBuU NSyU CU CaBVaU OCl NN CtY MH

PN2656 Naso, Eckart von, 1888–
.B4B4   Köpfe und gestalten...
Berlin. Staatliches schauspielhaus.
150 jahre Schauspielhaus am Gendarmenmarkt, 5. dezember 1786–5. dezember 1936; herausgegeben von der intendanz der Staatlichen schauspiele, Berlin. ₍Berlin, S. Bayer, inh. E. Thieme, 1936₎

Naso, Eckart von, 1888–
Menschen unter glas, roman von Eckart von Naso. Berlin, A. Scherl g. m. b. h. ₍1930₎
290, ₍1₎ p. 19ᶜᵐ.

i. Title.
Library of Congress   PT2627.A65M4 1930   31–3288
Copyright A—Foreign   9861
                            ₍2₎   833.91

NN 0026383   DLC OCl NN

Naso, Eckart von, 1888–
Moltke, Mensch und Feldherr. Berlin, Büchergilde Gutenberg ₍°1937₎
298 p. port. 21 cm.

1. Moltke, Helmuth Karl Bernhard, Graf von, 1800–1891.
DD219.M7N3 1937   50–50436

CU DAL N
NN 0026384   DLC OCl MB NcD NN CtY NRU MH UU CoD

Naso, Eckart von, 1888–
... Moltke, mensch und feldherr. Berlin, Wolfgang Krüger verlag ₍°1937₎
460, ₍4₎ p. front., illus. (incl. map) plates, ports. 21ᶜᵐ.

1. Moltke, Helmuth Karl Bernhard, graf von, 1800–1891.
                            A C 38–1318
New York. Public library
for Library of Congress   ₍2₎

PPG FTaSU NcD IaU GU
NN 0026385   NN MH CaBVaU DAL MB IEN WU ICU NNC

Naso, Eckart von, 1888–
Moltke, Mensch und Feldherr. ₍Berlin, W. Krüger, 1943₎
445 p. plates, ports., fold. maps. 20 cm. (Die Bücher des Frontarbeiters, Bd. 29)

1. Moltke, Helmuth Karl Bernhard, Graf von, 1800–1891. (Series)

DD219.M7N3 1943?   48–41907*

NN 0026386   DLC MH CtY IU

Naso, Eckart von, 1888–
Moltke, Mensch und Feldherr. Hamburg, W. Krüger ₍1951, °1937₎
476 p. illus., ports. 21 cm.

1. Moltke, Helmuth Karl Bernhard, Graf von, 1800–1891.
DD219.M7N3 1951   55–25832

NN 0026387   DLC

Naso, Eckart von, 1888–
Pariser Nokturno; Chronik der Marquise von Brinvilliers. Frankfurt am Main, H. Scheffler ₍1952₎
170 p. 20 cm.
First published in 1926 under title: Die Chronik der Giftmischerin.

1. Brinvilliers, Marie Madeleine (d'Aubray) Gobelin, marquise de, 1630–1676—Fiction. i. Title.
PT2627.A65C5 1952   833.91   53–16083 ‡

NN 0026388   DLC CU OCU NN

Naso, Eckart von, 1888–
Preussische Legende; Geschichte einer Liebe. Berlin, Krüger ₍c1959₎
218 p.

NN 0026389   NNC PPG

Naso, Eckart von, 1888–
... Preussische legende, geschichte einer liebe. Berlin, W. Krüger ₍1943₎
218, ₍2₎ p. 19½ᵐ.

i. Title.
Library of Congress   PT2627.A65P7   46–12138
                            ₍2₎   833.91

NN 0026390   DLC CtY CU IU NN WU MH

VOLUME 405

Naso, Eckart von, 1888–
Preussische Legende; Geschichte einer Liebe. Hamburg,
W. Krüger ₁1952, *1939₎
217 p. 20 cm.

1. Title.
PT2627.A65P7 1952   55–45714 ‡

NN   0026391   DLC NN

Naso, Eckart von, 1888–
... Der rittmeister. Berlin, W. Krüger ₁1942₎
162, ₁1₎ p. 19¼ᵐᵐ.
A novel.

1. European war, 1914–1918—Fiction.   ɪ. Title.
PT2627.A65R5 1942   833.91   A F 46–1301
Yale univ. Library
for Library of Congress   ₍4₎†

MiD PU DLC PPF
NN   0026392   CtY NcU PPG CU NN NNC PU MB IaU MnU

Naso, Eckart von, 1888–
... Der rittmeister. Berlin, W. Krüger ₁1943₎
133, ₁1₎ p. 19ᵐ.
A novel.

1. Title.
Library of Congress   PT2627.A65R5
                        ₍2₎   45–20259
                                            833.91

NN   0026393   DLC CaBVa IU WU NjP MH IEN CLSU

Naso, Eckart von, 1888–
Rossbach und Zorndorf. Bielefeld, Velhagen & Klasing
₁1943₎
20 p. 17 cm. (Velhagen & Klasings deutsche Lesebogen, Nr. 175)
"Alleinberechtigte Ausgabe aus Seydlitz, ein Reiterroman."

1. Seydlitz, Friedrich Wilhelm, Freiherr von, 1721–1773—Fiction.
ɪ. Title.
PT2627.A65S45   49–34074*

NN   0026394   DLC MB

Naso, Eckart von, 1888–
... Scharffenberg, roman eines schauspielers. Berlin, Universitas ₁1935₎
300, ₁1₎ p. 19¼ᵐ.

1. Title.
Library of Congress   PT2627.A65S35 1935   35–19437
                                                833.91

NN   0026395   DLC CtY CU NN OC1

Naso, Eckart von, 1888–
Seydlitz; Roman eines Reiters. Bielefeld, Velhagen &
Klasing ₁*1932₎
334 p. 20 cm.

1. Seydlitz, Friedrich Wilhelm, Freiherr von, 1721–1773—Fiction.
ɪ. Title.
PT2627.A65S4 1932   833.91   33–4480 rev*

IEN MB IaU MiD PPG OC1
NN   0026396   DLC NcU PPT GEU CtY CU NN WU MH NNC

---

*PT2627
.A65S4
1942

Naso, Eckart von, 1888–
Seydlitz: Roman eines Reiters. 73. bis 92. Tsd.
Bielefeld, Velhagen & Klasing [1942]
334 p., port. 20cm.

1. Seydlitz, Friedrich Wilhelm von, 1721–1773—
Fiction. 2. Cooperative acquisitions project
(Library of Congress)—German texts, 1938–1945.
I. Title.

NN   0026397   RPB PPG DLC

NASO, ECKART VON, 1888–
Spannungen; Orléans, Worms, Jena.   Hamburg, W. Krüger
[1952?]   140 p.   19cm.

1. Jeanne d'Arc, Saint, 1412–1431. 2. Luther, Martin. 3. Goethe
and Schiller. I. Title.

NN   0026398   NN CtY InU MH

1888 –
Naso, Eckart von, ₖReferendar: Die Unterscheidung von
Mord und Totschlag mit Berücksichtigung der modernen
Gesetzesentwürfe. Breslau 1916: Breslauer Genossensch.-
Buchdr. VIII, 52 S. 8°
Breslau, Jur. Diss. v. 9. Okt. 1916, Ref. Gretener, Heilborn
₍Geb. 2. Juni 88 Darmstadt; Wohnort: Breslau; Staatsangeh.: Preußen; Vorbildung: Friedrichs-G. Breslau Reife 07; Studium: Göttingen 3. Kiel 3.
Halle 1, Breslau 1 S.; Rig. 2. Aug. 12.₎   [U 16. 200

NN   0026399   ICRL

[Naso, Ephraim Ignaz, d.1680?]
Monimentum historico-panegyricum, tam antiqui quam
gloriosi stemmatis equitum, baronum, comitum & Sacri
Romani Imperii principis ab Herberstein. Wratislaviae,
In heredum Baumannianorum typ., 1680

203 p. plates

1. Herberstein family. I. Title. X ref: Loewenfels,
Ephraim Ignaz Naso von, d.1680? (To main entry)

NN   0026400   MH

Berk   **Naso, Joseph,** d. after 1595 (J, Js)
Bericht von der geistlichen Gegenwart
dess Leibs Christi im Abentmale. Bremen,
₁15₎88. Unpaged.

NN   0026401   OSW

Berk   **Naso, Joseph,** d. after 1595 (J,Js).
Historia des Abendtmals. ₁N.p., n.d.₎
65 leaves.

NN   0026402   OSW

WU   **NASO, Olindo**
400   Lezioni di ortognatodonzia. Catania,
N261L   Reina, 1954–
            v. illus.
            1. Orthodontia

NN   0026403   DNLM IEN–D

Naso, Ovidius, junior, pseud.
see Lockhart, John Ingram.

Naso, Publius Ovidius

see

Ovidius Naso, Publius

Naso–Albanese (Francesco). Alcune considerazioni di clinica sifilopatica e di sifiloterapia, a proposito d'un caso di sifilide ad evoluzione rapida con affezione gommosa del palato e
perforazione della volta. Uranoplastia; protesi
meccanica. 28 pp. 8°. Napoli, Pontieri, 1894.

NN   0026406   DNLM

Nasoetion, A   Diapari
see
Nasution, A   Diapari.

Nasoetion, B
see
Nasution, B

Nasoetion, Basir
see
Nasution, Basir.

Nasoetion, M   Yoenan
see
Nasution, M   Yunan.

Nasoetion, Masdoelhak Hamonangan.
De plaats van de vrouw in de Bataksche maatschappij.
Utrecht, Kemink ₁1943₎
118 p. fold. map. 24 cm.
Proefschrift—Utrecht.
"Stellingen" : ₍2₎ p. inserted.
Bibliography: p. ₍109₎–113.

1. Women in Sumatra. 2. Batak.
HQ1754.S8N3   55–54845

NN   0026411   DLC CtY–L PU MH NNC ICU CaBVaU

Nasoetion, Moechtar
see
Nasution, Muchtar.

Nasolini, Sebastiano, 1768–1816?
₁Adriano in Siria. Libretto. Italian₎

Adriano in Siria; dramma per musica, da rappresentarsi
nel Teatro alla scala, il carnevale 1790. Milano, G. B.
Bianchi ₁1790₎
58, ₁10₎ 17 cm.
Vol. 9, no. 3, of a collection with binder's title: Drammi per
musica.
Libretto by Metastasio. Cf. L. C. Cat. opera librettos.
"Programmi dei due balli ... composti dal Francesco Clerico":
10 p. at end.
1. Operas—To 1800—Librettos. ɪ. Metastasio, Pietro Antonio
Domenico Buonaventura, 1698–1782. Adriano in Siria. ɪɪ. Title.

ML48.A5 vol. 9,   no. 3   77–207967

NN   0026413   DLC

ML48   **Nasolini, Sebastiano,** 1768–1816?
I8   ₁Andromaca. Libretto₎
Andromaca, a new serious opera, in two acts,
as performed at the Theatre royal in the Hay
market. The music by Signor Nasolini, under
the direction of Signor Federici. London,
Printed by Hammond and Cane ₁18––₎
35 p. ₁Italian operas₎

Libretto only (by Salvi)

ɪ. Salvi, Antonio. ɪɪ. Title.

NN   0026414   CU

VOLUME 405

VM 1613.3 N 26a
NASOLINI, SEBASTIANO, 1768-ca.1816.
...Aria (Deh se mirate il pianto). Arrangé pour le piano forté par L.Adam... Paris,Erard₍n.d.₎ 6p. and 9 pt. 35½cm. (Ariettes italiennes. no.451)

Caption title.
Parts for 1st and 2d violin, 1st and 2d viola, bass, 1st and 2d oboe, bassoon and 1st and 2d horn bound in.
French and Italian words. French translation by Desriaux.
Plate no.: 449.

NN 0026415 ICN

M1505 .A2N26
Nasolini, ₍Sebastiano₎ 1768-1816.?
Aria /oh Cara imagine/ Del Sigᵗᵉ Nasolini. Ms., 18th Cent., ₍18₎p. obl.fol.

For alto and orchestra.
Full score.
Number at bottom of t.-p.:436.

NN 0026416 DLC

Nasolini, Sebastiano, 1768-1816?
₍La Calliroe. Libretto. Italian₎

La Calliroe; dramma per musica. Firenze, Albizziniana, 1792.
₍44 p. 17 cm₎
Vol. 22, no. 1, of a collection with binder's title: Drammi per musica.
Libretto by Mattia Verazi. Cf. LC Cat. opera librettos.
1. Operas—To 1800—Librettos. I. Verazi, Mattia. La Calliroe. II. Title.

ML48.A5 vol. 22, no. 1 72-222284

NN 0026417 DLC

M 1500 .N26C3
Nasolini, Sebastiano, ca. 1768-1816?
... Il Catone in Utica. Drama per musica da rappresentarsi nel nobmo. Teatro di S. Samuele di Sebastiano Nasolini l'anno 1791 Venezia. 1791 6 giugno...

343p. obl. 4°.
Full score. Transcript of copy at the British Museum, 1910.
At head of title: "L'originale del maestro."

NN 0026418 DLC

M1505 .A2N25
Nasolini, Sebastiano, 1768-1816.?
Duetto. Deh calma quel core. Del Sigᵗᵉ Sebastiano Nasolini. MS., 18th Cent., 11ℓ. obl. fol.

Duet of Eugenia (Soprano) and il Conte (Tenor)
Full Score

NN 0026419 DLC

ML50 N3M6 1805 Music Library
Nasolini, Sebastiano, 1768-1816?
[La morte di Cleopatra. Libretto]
Cleopatra; dramma per musica da rappresentarsi nel Regio Teatro degli Intrepidi detto della palla a corda la primavera del 1805. Firenze, Stamp. Luchi, 1805.
32 p.

Text by A. S. Sografi. Cf. Loewenberg. Annals of opera.

I. Sografi, Antonio Simeone, 1759-1818. II. Title. III. Title: La morte di Cleopatra.

NN 0026420 CU

Nasolini, Sebastiano, 1768-1816?
₍Eugenia. Libretto. German & Italian₎

Eugenie; ein Singspiel für das Kurfürstliche Theater. Dresden, 1794.
151 p. 17 cm.
Libretto by G. M. Foppa. Cf. Loewenberg. Annals of opera.

1. Operas—To 1800—Librettos. I. Foppa, Giuseppe Maria, fl. 1792-1813. Eugenia. II. Title.

ML50.2.E8N38 1794 63-47626 rev/M

NN 0026421 DLC

Nasolini, Sebastiano, 1768-1816?
[Il tuo destino ingrata] the favorite duett ... in the opera of Mitridate ..., written by Daponti, and composed by Nasolini. [London] M. Kelly, [18]
6 p. f°.

NN 0026422 NN

NASOLINI, SEBASTIANO, 1768-1816?
Idol mio, mio bene amato; notturno for two voices. London, Birchall [182-] Pl.no.1113 score (4 p.) 34cm.

Caption title.
With piano acc.

1. Vocal duos, Secular (Women) --Keyboard acc.

NN 0026423 NN MH

Nasolini, Sebastiano, 1768-1816?
₍La Merope. Libretto. Italian₎

La Merope; dramma serio per musica. Firenze, P. Fantosini, 1803.
31 p. 17 cm.
Vol. 20, no. 4, of a collection with binder's title: Drammi per musica.
Libretto by M. Butturini. Cf. Loewenberg. Annals of opera.
1. Operas—To 1800—Librettos. I. Butturini, Mattia, 1752-1817. La Merope. II. Title.

ML48.A5 vol. 20, no. 4 78-221685

NN 0026424 DLC

Nasolini, Sebastiano, 1768-1816?
₍La Merope. Libretto. Italian₎

La Merope; dramma serio per musica. Firenze, G. Fantosini, 1806.
35 p. 17 cm.
Vol. 20, no. 7, of a collection with binder's title: Drammi per musica.
Libretto by M. Butturini. Cf. Loewenberg. Annals of opera.
1. Operas—To 1800—Librettos. I. Butturini, Mattia, 1752-1817. La Merope. II. Title.

ML48.A5 vol. 20, no. 7 79-221688

NN 0026425 DLC

---

ar V 5762
Nasolini, Sebastiano, 1768?-1806?
₍Merope. Libretto. English₎
Merope e Polifonte, a serious opera in two acts. As performed at the King's Theatre, in the Hay-Market, for the benefit of Madame Banti. London, Bastie and Brettell, 1802.
55 p. 18cm.
Italian and English on opposite pages.
Libretto attributed to Metastasio. Cf. Brit. Mus. Cat.

NN 0026426 NIC

Nasolini, Sebastiano, 1768-1816?
₍La morte di Cleopatra. Libretto. Italian₎

La morte di Cleopatra; tragedia per musica del A. S. Sografi. ₍La musica è del Sebastiano Nasolini₎ Venezia, Stamperia Valvasense, 1794.
62 p. 19 cm.
Scenario of "Adelaide di Guesclino: ballo tragico-pantomino in 5 atti. Composto e diretto dall Carlo Augusto Favier.": p. ₍31₎-42. Composer not named.
Includes the casts of both the opera and the ballet.
1. Operas—To 1800—Librettos. 2. Ballets—To 1800—Scenarios. I. Sografi, Antonio Simeone, 1759-1818. La morte di Cleopatra. II. Favier, Charles Auguste. Adelaide di Guesclino. III. Title. IV. Title: Adelaide di Guesclino.

ML50.2.M786N4 62-66433

NN 0026427 DLC

Nasolini, Sebastiano, 1768-1816?
₍La morte di Mitridate. Libretto. Italian₎

La morte di Mitridate; dramma serio per musica. Firenze, G. Fantosini, 1804.
20 p. 17 cm.
Vol. 20, no. 6, of a collection with binder's title: Drammi per musica.

1. Operas—Librettos. I. Title.

ML48.A5 vol. 20, no. 6 75-221687

NN 0026428 DLC

[NASOLINI, Sebastiano] 1768-1816?
La morte di Semiramide; dramma per musica rappresentato la prima volta in Napoli nel real teatro di S. Carlo nell'estate del 1815. Napoli, Angioli, [18- ?]

pp. 30.
Libretto. Words only.

NN 0026429 MH

Nasolini, Sebastiano, 1768-1816?
₍La morte di Semiramide. Libretto. Italian₎

La morte di Semiramide; dramma serio per musica. Firenze, G. Fantosini, 1810.
41 p. 17 cm.
Vol. 21, no. 1, of a collection with binder's title: Drammi per musica.
"Antonio Simone Sografi ... the author or rather arranger of the text."—LC Cat. opera librettos.
1. Operas—Librettos. I. Sografi, Antonio Simeone, 1759-1818. La morte di Semiramide. II. Title.

ML48.A5 vol. 21, no. 1 71-222273

NN 0026430 DLC

VM 1613.3 N 26a
NASOLINI, SEBASTIANO, 1768-ca.1816.
...Prière et air... Paris,P.Porro₍n.d.₎ 5p. and 6 pt. 35½cm. (Répertoire italien; ou Choix d'airs... no.11)

Bound with his Aria... ₍n.d.₎
Parts for 1st and 2d violin, viola, bass, 1st and 2d horn and 1st and 2d oboe bound in.
Piano accompaniment by Dietrick.
French and Italian words. French translation by P.Porro.

NN 0026431 ICN

Nasolini, Sebastiano, 1768-1816?
₍Il trionfo di Clelia. Libretto. Italian₎

Il trionfo di Clelia; nuovo dramma del Antonio Simone Sografi, da rappresentarsi in musica nel Teatro grande alla scala di Milano, il carnevale del 1799. Milano, G. B. Bianchi ₍1799₎
53, ₍2₎ p. 17 cm.
Vol. 1, no. 5, of a collection with binder's title: Drammi per musica.
Includes the synopsis of 2 ballets by Urbano Garzia: Il bruto milanese (p. ₍27₎-36) and L'oracolo (2 unnumb. p. at end)
1. Operas—To 1800—Librettos. I. Sografi, Antonio Simeone, 1759-1818. Il trionfo di Clelia. II. Title.

ML48.A5 vol. 1, no. 5 72-207955

NN 0026432 DLC

ML50 N3V4 1803 Music Library
Nasolini, Sebastiano, 1768-1816?
₍La vendetta di Nino. Libretto₎
La vendetta di Nino; dramma serio per musica, da rappresentarsi in Bologna nel Teatro della comune la primavera del corrente anno 1803, secondo della Rep. italiana. Bologna, Stampe del Sassi [1803?]
40, 13 p.

Scenario of "Il sotterraneo, ossia Caterina di Coluga; ballo tragico in cinque atti. Composto da Lorenzo Panzieri": 2d group of paging.

I. Panzieri, Lorenzo /Il sotterraneo. II. Title.

NN 0026433 CU

Nason, Alvin.
The distribution and biosynthesis of niacin in germinating corn. ₍n. p.,1950₎
612-623 p. diagrs. 27 cm.

Thesis—Columbia University.
"Reprinted from the American journal of botany, vol. 37, no. 8 ... October, 1950."
Bibliography: p. 622-623.

1. Nicotinic acid. 2. Germination. 3. Corn. I. Title.

QK898.N5N3 A 52-178

Columbia Univ. Libraries
for Library of Congress ₍1₎†

NN 0026434 NNC DLC

VOLUME 405

Nason, Arthur Huntington, 1877–
American poetry and prose; a syllabus designed for a study of American thought and its development, cultural, political & religious, by Arthur Huntington Nason... New York: The author, 1928. 24 p. 8°.

Published as "What is American 'literature'?" in The Sewanee review, April, 1927.

409328A. 1. American literature—   Outlines, syllabi, etc.   April 23, 1929
N. Y. P. L.

NN   0026435   NN N MB NcD MH NNU-W CSmH

Nason, Arthur Huntington, 1877–
De profundis heraldicis; or, Diplings from the depths, by Arthur Huntington Nason. New York city, A. H. Nason, 1913.

15, [1] p. illus. (coats of arms) 18½ᶜᵐ. $0.50

CONTENTS.—A ballade of dead scholarship; reprinted from the Colonnade.—The (Mont) joys of heraldry; reprinted from the Evening post.—Heraldry as it is written; reprinted from the Nation.—The "Handmaid of history"; or, An artist's model—which? Reprinted from the Nation.

1. Heraldry.   I. Title.

Library of Congress   CR27.N3   14–1348

NN   0026436   DLC MB

Nason, Arthur Huntington, 1877–
Efficient composition; a college rhetoric, by Arthur Huntington Nason... New York city, The New York university press, 1917.

xvii, 517 p. III pl., diagrs. 21ᶜᵐ.

1. English language—Rhetoric.   I. Title.

Library of Congress   PE1408.N25   18–11300

NN   0026437   DLC OrCS PHC PU MiU OC1W OC1

Nason, Arthur Huntington, 1877–
Heralds and heraldry in Ben Jonson's plays, masques and entertainments, by Arthur Huntington Nason... University Heights, New York city, 1907.

3 p. l., [ix]–xviii, 164 p. incl. front., illus. 25ᶜᵐ.

"Select bibliography": p. [139]–142.

1. Jonson, Ben, 1573?–1637.   2. Heraldry—Gt. Brit.   I. Title.

Library of Congress   PR2642.H4N3   7—29874

        PU OCU MiU ViU NjP MB NN
NN   0026438   DLC DAU KU MsU PSt NcD GU MsSM OrU

Nason, Arthur Huntington, 1877–
James Shirley, dramatist; a biographical and critical study, by Arthur Huntington Nason... New York city, A. H. Nason, 1915.

xv p., 2 l., 3–473, [1] p. front., ports., facsims. 24½ᶜᵐ.

Thesis (PH. D.)—Columbia university, 1915.
Vita.
Published also without thesis note.
"Annotated bibliography": p. [399]–459.

1. Shirley, James, 1596–1666.

Library of Congress   PR3146.N3 1915 a   15—16408
Columbia Univ. Libr.   [s21c1]

NN   0026439   NNC DLC OrU

Nason, Arthur Huntington, 1877–
James Shirley, dramatist; a biographical and critical study, by Arthur Huntington Nason... New York, A. H. Nason, 1915.

xv p., 2 l., 3–471, [1] p. front., ports., facsims. 24½ᶜᵐ.

"Annotated bibliography": p. [399]–459.
Issued also as thesis (PH. D.) Columbia university.

1. Shirley, James, 1596–1666.

Library of Congress   PR3146.N3   15—12634

        PBm OU MiU OCU ODW MB NN WaSpG WaS CaBVaU
NN   0026440   DLC OKentU DAU ViU NIC NcD TU DFo PU

Nason, Arthur Huntington, 1877–
Questions on Shakespeare's development as a dramatist. n.p., 1901.

16 p. 15.5 cm.

NN   0026441   MH

Nason, Arthur Huntington, 1877–
Short themes; a freshman manual for the first semester, by Arthur Huntington Nason... New York city, The author, 1909.

viii p., 1 l., 133 p. 19¼ᶜᵐ. $1.00   9–25757

NN   0026442   DLC ViU

Nason, Arthur Huntington, 1877–
Short themes; a freshman manual for the first semester, by Arthur Huntington Nason... 2d ed. New York city, The author, 1910.

viii p., 1 l., 187 p. III pl. 19ᶜᵐ. $1.25

1. English language—Rhetoric.   10–15872

Library of Congress   PE1413.N25

NN   0026443   DLC NjP WaS OrCS OC1W PHC OC1 MiU

Nason, Arthur Huntington, 1877–
Short themes and long ... by Arthur Huntington Nason... New York, A. H. Nason, 1914–

v. 18½ᶜᵐ.

1. English language—Rhetoric.   I. Title.   II. Title: Themes.

Library of Congress   PE1413.N27   14–18554

NN   0026444   DLC

Nason, Arthur Huntington, 1877–
Talks on theme writing and kindred topics, by Arthur Huntington Nason... New York city, The author, 1909.

xv, 321 p. 19¼ᶜᵐ.

        9–6860

NN   0026445   DLC ViU

Nason, Arthur Huntington, 1877–
Yule-tide song, and other verse. [Augusta, Me.] 1911.
27 p. D.

NN   0026446   RPB

Nason, Arthur L.

Massachusetts. *Commission on cold storage of food.*
... Report of the Commission to investigate the subject of the cold storage of food and of food products kept in cold storage. January, 1912. Boston, Wright & Potter printing co., state printers, 1912.

Nason, Charles D.
Schools of the society for the propagation of Christian knowledge among the Germans of Penn. n. p. 1899...
115 p.

NN   0026448   PU

NASON, Charles Pinckney Holbrook.
Anniversary thoughts. Discourse, May 8, 1892.
Phila. Allen, L., & S. 1893. 22 pp. 12°.
Title on cover Way-marks.

NN   0026449   MB

Nason, Charles Pinckney Holbrook.
Jeanne d'Arc, heroine of France ⟨A. D. 1412–1431⟩ her origin, mission, triumph, martyrdom, rehabilitation; a lecture by Charles Pinckney Holbrook Nason... Boston, The Stratford company [c1928].
36 p. front. 25ᶜᵐ. (*On cover:* The Stratford booklets)

1. Jeanne d'Arc, Saint, 1412–1431.

Library of Congress   DC103.N3   28–29639

NN   0026450   DLC MB

Nason, Charles Pinckney Holbrook
Self-sacrifice; a discourse delivered in the Central Congregational church, Chelsea, Mass., Sunday morning, June 2nd, 1878, by Rev. C. P. H. Nason... Chelsea [Mass.] H. Mason & son, printers... 1878.

19 p. pl. 22 cm. Orig. tan paper covers.

1. Altruism.   I. Title.

NN   0026451   CSmH

Nason, Charles Pinckney Holbrook.
Thanksgiving discourse, delivered at a union service in the First Presbyterian Church, Germantown, Philadelphia... November 29, 1888. [Philadelphia, 1888.] 22 p. 8°.
Title on cover: The habit of praise.

1. Thanksgiving day.—Sermons.   June 10, 1913
N. Y. P. L.

NN   0026452   NN

[Nason, Daniel]
A journal of a tour from Boston to Savannah, thence to Havana, in the island of Cuba ... thence to New Orleans and several western cities ... by a citizen of Cambridgeport. Cambridge, Printed for the author, 1849.
114 p. 16ᶜᵐ.
Cover-title: Tour South and West in 1848.

1. U. S.—Descr. & trav.   2. Havana—Descr.   I. Title.

Library of Congress   E166.N26   1–21523

        MsU NcD MoU MWA ICN CSt
NN   0026453   DLC MWiW-C NN ICRL GU-De OC1WHi TxU

Nason, Edith Holloway, 1895–   *Joint author.*
                  FOR OTHER EDITIONS
                  SEE MAIN ENTRY
Macleod, Annie Louise, 1883–
Chemistry and cookery; some theories of chemistry and applications to cookery processes, by Annie Louise Macleod ... and Edith H. Nason ... 2d ed. New York and London, McGraw-Hill book company, inc., 1937.

Nason, Edith Holloway, 1895–
Introduction to experimental cookery, by Edith H. Nason ... 1st ed. New York and London, McGraw-Hill book company, inc., 1939.

ix, 317 p. incl. illus., tables, diagrs. 21ᶜᵐ. (*Half-title:* McGraw-Hill home economics series, Annie L. Macleod ... consulting editor)

Chapter v, "Introduction to statistical measurements", by Alice E. Ebersold.
"References" at end of each chapter except the first and last.

1. Cookery.   I. Ebersold, Alice Emily, 1913–   II. Title: Experimental cookery. Introduction to.

Library of Congress   TX663.N25   39–33982

———— Copy 2.

Copyright A 132710   [8]   641.072

        KEmT PPB OU OC1 OCU OC1W
NN   0026455   DLC PPT OrCS IdPI MtBC NcRS CU TU MU

VOLUME 405

Nason, Edith Holloway, joint author.

Hill, Arthur Joseph, 1888–
... The utilization of cassia oil for the synthesis of cinnamyl alcohol, by Arthur J. Hill and Edith H. Nason. [Easton, Pa., 1924]

Nason, *Mrs.* Edna (Selover)
Cavalcade, by Edna Selover Nason. [New York, A. H. Nason] 1930.
4 p. l., 26 p. 21ᶜᵐ.

I. Title.
                    [Full name: Mrs. Edna Walton (Selover) Nason]
                                                    31–5550
Library of Congress   PS3527.A66C3 1930
Copyright A 33001   [2]   811.5

NN   0026457   DLC

Nason, Edna (Selover)
Chimes in the rain, by Edna Selover Nason. Los Angeles, Calif., The Ward Ritchie press [1946]
viii p., 1 l., 20 p. 22ᶜᵐ.
Poems.

I. Title.
                    [Full name: Edna Walton (Selover) Nason]
                                                    46–15600
Library of Congress   PS3527.A66C5
                              [2]   811.5

NN   0026458   DLC

Nason, Edward S.
A centennial history of Morning star lodge, A. F. and A. M. A. D. 1793 ... A. D. 1893. By Bro. Edward S. Nason ... Worcester, Mass., The Lodge, 1894.
236 p. front., illus., plates, ports., facsim. 23½ᶜᵐ.

1. Freemasons. Worcester, Mass. Morning star lodge.
                                                    13–16274
Library of Congress   HS539.W9M6

NN   0026459   DLC MWA

Nason, Edward S
Poem, written by Bro. E.S. Nason, and read at the banquet given by Morning star lodge, F. and A.M., Worcester, Mass ... April 2, A.D. 1878 at the presentation of a Past Master's jewel to Bro. Clark Earle, Past Master. Worcester, Tyler & Seagrave, 1878.
cover-title, 8, [2] p. 24 cm.
Includes a Song, written, and music composed by Bro. E.S. Nason. (Without music)

NN   0026460   RPB

Nason, Edward S.
Nason's vocal class book; containing a thorough and systematic course of instruction in the art of singing; together with a choice collection of music, original and selected, adapted to the use of high schools ... Boston, 1847.
viii, [9]-168 p. 15 x 22 cm.

NN   0026461   RPB MWA

Nason, Edward S
Nason's vocal class book: containing a thorough and systematic course of instruction in the art of singing: together with a choice collection of music, original and selected, adapted to the use of high schools, common schools, the social circle and juvenile singing schools. Boston, Wm. J. Reynolds & co., 1850.
193 p.

NN   0026462   MiD-B

-VM
1994
N 26v
1853
NASON, EDWARD S   comp.
Vocal class book: containing a thorough and systematic course of instruction in the art of singing, together with a choice collection of music, original and selected, adapted to the use of high school, common school, the social circle, and juvenile singing schools.   Boston, W.J.Reynolds, 1853.
193p. 14x20cm.

"Elements of   vocal music": p.[9]-94.

NN   0026463   ICN

NASON, Edward S.
Vocal class book. B.,1856[cop.1847].

obl. 8°

NN   0026464   RPB

-VM
1994
N 26v
NASON, EDWARD S   comp.
Nason's vocal class book: containing a thorough and systematic course of instruction in the art of singing together with a choice collection of music, original and selected, adapted to the use of high schools, common schools, the social circle, and juvenile singing schools…   Boston, O.Ditson & co.,1859.
193p. 14x19½cm.

NN   0026465   ICN NNUT MH

Nason, Elias, 1811–1887.
The American evangelists, Dwight L. Moody and Ira D. Sankey, with an account of their work in England and America; and a sketch of the lives of P. P. Bliss and Dr. Eben Tourjée. By the Rev. Elias Nason. Boston, D. Lothrop & co. [1877]
360 p. front., illus., ports. 19ᶜᵐ.

1. Moody, Dwight Lyman, 1837–1899. 2. Sankey, Ira David, 1840–1908. 3. Bliss, Philip Paul, 1838–1876. 4. Tourjée, Eben, 1834–1891. I. Title.
                                                    37–37663
Library of Congress   BV3785.M7N35
Copyright 1877: 7307   [3]   922

NN   0026466   DLC MB MH

Nason, Elias, 1811–1887.
Billerica. A centennial oration, by the Rev. Elias Nason, July 4, 1876 ... Lowell, Printed by Marden and Rowell, 1876.
25 p. 24ᶜᵐ.

1. Billerica, Mass.—Hist. 2. Fourth of July orations.
                                                    1–16868
Library of Congress   F74.B4N2

NN   0026467   DLC PHi OClWHi

Nason, Elias, 1811–1887.
A brief record of events in Exeter, N. H. during the year 1861, together with the names of the soldiers of this town in the war. By Rev. Elias Nason ... Exeter, Printed by S. Hall, 1862.
16 p. 19¼ᶜᵐ.

1. Exeter, N. H.—Hist. 2. U. S.—Hist.—Civil war—Registers, lists, etc.
                                                    3–21056
Library of Congress   F44.E9N19

NN   0026468   DLC MWA PHi PPL NjP Nh NIC OClWHi NN

Nason, Elias, 1811–1887.
A brief record of events in Exeter, N. H. during the year 1862; together with the names of the soldiers of this town in the war. By Rev. Elias Nason ... Exeter, Fogg & Fellowes, 1863.
20 p. 18¼ᶜᵐ.

Subject entries: Exeter, N. H.—Hist.
                                                    3–699
Library of Congress, no.   F44.E9N2

NN   0026469   DLC NIC MnHi PHi OClWHi NN

E
464
C585
v.63
no.3
Nason, Elias, 1811–1887.
A brief record of current events in Exeter, N. H., during the year 1863: together with the names of the soldiers of this town in the war. By the Rev. Elias Nason ... No. 3. Exeter [N. H.] Fogg & Fellowes, 1864.
24 p. 17cm. (bound in 25cm. vol.)

1. Exeter, N. H.—Hist. 2. U. S.—Hist.—Civil War—Registers, lists, etc.

NN   0026470   NIC OClWHi CSmH NN MH

Nason, Elias, 1811–1887, ed.
Carmina cœli; or, Songs on heaven. Boston, H. Hoyt [*1870]

Nason, Elias, 1811–1887.
Centennial Oration, Billerica, Mass. Lowell, 1876
25p. 8°

NN   0026472   MWA

Nason, Elias, 1811–1887.
Howe, Nathanael, 1764–1837.
A century sermon, delivered in Hopkinton, Mass., on Lord's day. December 24, 1815. By Nathanael Howe ... 4th ed. With a memoir of the author and explanatory notes by Elias Nason, A. M. Boston, J. P. Jewett & co., 1851.

Nason, Elias, 1811–1887.
Chapin's hand-book of St. Augustine, by Elias Nason... St. Augustine: G. H. Chapin, 1884.   48 p.   illus., map.   12°.

1. St. Augustine, Fla.—Guide-   books, 1884.
N. Y. P. L.   August 26, 1926

NN   0026474   NN MWA FTaSU PLatS OClWHi MB MH NcD

Nason, Elias, 1811–1887.
Chrestomathis française ...
    see his   Nason's French reading book.

[Nason, Elias] 1811–1887, comp.
The Congregational hymn book, for the service of the sanctuary ... Boston, J. P. Jewett and company; Cleveland, O., H. P. B. Jewett, 1857.
58, 752 p. 18½ᶜᵐ.
Preface signed: Elias Nason.

1. Congregational churches—Hymns. 2. Hymns, English. I. Title.
                                                    35–33521
Library of Congress   BV395.N3 1857
——— Copy 2.   245.2058

NN   0026476   DLC CtY NjNbS PPLT MB NNUT NN

---

hMusic
N263
1858
[Nason, Elias] 1811–1887, comp.
The Congregational tune book: being a selection from the standard choral music of the church, together with some other ancient and modern compositions, adapted to the hymns of the "Congregational hymn book," "Vestry hymn book," and to congregational singing generally. Boston, J. P. Jewett and Co., 1858.
208 p. 13 x 16 cm.
Preface signed by Elias Nason.

NN   0026477   RPB CtY MH OCl NNUT

VOLUME 405

Nason, Elias, 1811–1887.
Discourse delivered before the New-England historic-genealogical society, Boston, April 2, 1868, on the life and character of the Hon. John Albion Andrew, late president of the society. With proceedings and appendix. By the Rev. Elias Nason ... Boston, New-England historic-genealogical society, 1868.

76 p. front. (port.) 26ᶜᵐ.

Reprinted from the New England historic genealogical register.

1. Andrew, John Albion, 1818–1867.   1. New England historic genealogical society.

6–46428

Library of Congress   E513.A64

NN   0026478   DLC

Nason, Elias, 1811–1887.
A discourse on the death of James Abram Garfield, president of the United States. Delivered in Pawtucket Church, Lowell, and also in the Centre Church, Dracut, Mass., September 25, 1881. By the Rev. Elias Nason... Boston: M. H. Sargent & Sons, 1881.
16 p.   8°.

1. Garfield, James Abram, 20th pres.   U.S.
N. Y. P. L.   August 26, 1919.

NN   0026479   NN MWA MiD-B OC1WHi OO MH

Nason, Elias, 1811–1887.
Eulogy on Abraham Lincoln, late president of the United States, delivered before the New England historic-genealogical society, Boston, May 3, 1865, by Rev. Elias Nason ... Boston, W. V. Spencer, 1865.

28 p. 24ᶜᵐ.

1. Lincoln, Abraham, pres. U. S., 1809–1865 — Addresses, sermons, etc.

12–4546

Library of Congress   E457.8.N26

MB MiU-C
NN   0026480   DLC NIC MWA PP OC1WHi PHi PPL NN NjP

Nason, Elias, 1811–1887.
A gazetteer of the state of Massachusetts; with numerous illustrations on wood and steel. By the Rev. Elias Nason ... Boston, B. B. Russell, 1874.

576 p. front., illus., pl., ports., fold. map. 23½ᶜᵐ.

1. Massachusetts—Descr. & trav.—Gazetteers.

1—12005

Library of Congress   F62.N26

PV OO OC1 Nh MB I MWA DI-GS WaS
NN   0026481   DLC MnHi MHi GU IaU CU NcD MH PHi

*F62
.N26   Nason, Elias, 1811–1887.
1876   A gazetteer of the state of
            Massachusetts; with numerous illus-
            trations on wood and steel. Boston,
            B. B. Russell, 1876.
            576 p. illus., fold. map., plates,
            ports. 24cm.

        1. Massachusetts—Descr. & trav.—
        Gazetteers.

NN   0026482   MB MdBP CoU

G
844   NASON, ELIAS, 1811–1887.
.612   A gazetteer of the state of Massachusetts;
           with numerous illustrations on wood and steel.
           Boston, B.B.Russell, 1878.
           576p. 24p.

NN   0026483   ICN DI-GS

Nason, Elias, 1811–1887.
A gazetteer of the state of Massachusetts. With numerous illustrations. By the Rev. Elias Nason ... Rev. and enl. by George J. Varney ... Boston, B. B. Russell, 1890.

724 p. front., illus., pl. 23½ᶜᵐ.

CONTENTS.—The state. —The counties of the commonwealth. —The cities, towns, and villages.

1. Massachusetts—Descr. & trav.—Gazetteers. 2. Massachusetts.
1. Varney, George Jones, 1836–1901, ed.

1—12006

Library of Congress   F62.N27

NN   0026484   DLC MeB NIC OO MH

Nason, Elias, 1811–1887.
A history of the town of Dunstable, Massachusetts, form its earliest settlement to the year of Our Lord 1873. By the Rev. Elias Nason ... Boston, A. Mudge & son, printers, 1877.

316 p. front. (port.) illus. 24ᶜᵐ.

Inscriptions from the various cemeteries: p. 228–268.
Lists of deaths and births from Dunstable records: p. 268–277.
Bicentennial oration of G. B. Loring: p. 279–298.

1. Dunstable, Mass.—Hist. 2. Epitaphs—Dunstable, Mass. 3. Registers of births, etc.—Dunstable, Mass.   1. Loring, George Bailey, 1817–1891.

1—11354

Library of Congress   F74.D9N2

OC1WHi MH MB Nh
NN   0026485   DLC MdBP InU VtU ViU CU MWA PHi OC1W

Nason, Elias, 1811–1887.
The Howe family gathering, at Harmony Grove, South Framingham, Thursday, August 31, 1871. By Rev. Elias Nason ... Boston, E. Howe, 1871.

46 p. col. front. (coats of arms) illus. 25½ᶜᵐ.

1. Howe family.

9—11225

Library of Congress   CS71.H855 1871

NN   0026486   DLC MWA ICN OC1WHi Nh MH

Nason, Elias, 1811–1887.
Joshua Coffin, esq. ⟨Communicated for the New England historical and genealogical register for July, 1866, by Rev. Elias Nason⟩ ₍Boston? Printed by D. Clapp & son?₎ 1866.

4 p. 24½ᶜᵐ.

Caption title.

1. Coffin, Joshua, 1792–1864.

4–25063†

NN   0026487   DLC MBAt

Nason, Elias, 1811–1887, ed.

Baxter, Joseph, 1676–1745.
Journal of several visits to the Indians on the Kennebec River, by the Rev. Joseph Baxter ... 1717. With notes by the Rev. Elias Nason ... Boston, D. Clapp & son, printers, 1867.

Nason, Elias, 1811–1887.
The life and public services of Hon. Henry Wilson. By Hon. Thomas Russell ... and Rev. Elias Nason ... Boston, B. B. Russell; Portland, Me., J. Russell; ₍etc., etc.₎ 1872.

419 p. front. (port.) pl. 19ᶜᵐ.

Principally the work of Mr. Nason. cf. New England hist. and geneal. register, v. 26, p. 451; v. 30, p. 272; v. 32, p. 268.
Title-page of Boston edition of 1876 reads: By Rev. Elias Nason ... and Hon. Thomas Russell. Title-page of Boston edition of 1881 attributes the work to Nason alone.

1. Wilson, Henry, 1812–1875.   1. Russell, Thomas, 1825–1887, joint author.

14–15946

Library of Congress   E415.9.W6N18

NN   0026489   DLC OOxM KMK MiD NNC MHi MiU OO

Nason, Elias, 1811–1887.
The life and public services of Henry Wilson, late vice-president of the United States. By Rev. Elias Nason ... and Hon. Thomas Russell ... Boston, B. B. Russell; Philadelphia, Quaker city publishing house; ₍etc., etc.₎ 1876.

452 p. front. (port.) illus., pl. 19ᶜᵐ.

1. Wilson, Henry, 1812–1875.   1. Russell, Thomas, 1825–1887, joint author.

13–26816

Library of Congress   E415.9.W6N2

ViU MeB OFH ViHaI MB MdBP MiD NNC
OC1WHi OU MiU PPL PPGi PP OCU NIC NcD GU MoU MnHi
NN   0026490   DLC PPDrop WaS I MB OFH Nh ODW OC1

Nason, Elias, 1811–1887.
The life and public services of Henry Wilson, by Rev. Elias Nason ... Boston, D. Lothrop & company ₍*1881₎

452 p. front. (port.) illus., pl. 19½ᶜᵐ.

Title-page of Boston edition of 1876 reads: By Elias Nason ... and Hon. Thomas Russell.
First edition, Boston, 1872.

1. Wilson, Henry, 1812–1875.   1. Russell, Thomas, 1825–1887, joint author.

13—26817

Library of Congress   E415.9.W6N22

NN   0026491   DLC NjP OrU IEN PPGi OO

Nason, Elias, 1811–1887.
The life and times of Charles Sumner. His boyhood, education, and public career. By Elias Nason ... Boston, B. B. Russell; Philadelphia, Quaker-city publishing-house; ₍etc., etc.₎ 1874.

356 p. front. (port.) plates. 19ᶜᵐ.

1. Sumner, Charles, 1811–1874.

13–19832

Library of Congress   E415.9.S9N2

TNJ MoU NjP KyLx AAP ICarbS TU MoSU CaBVa OrU WaTC
OC1W OU MiU PV PSC PPT OFH NcD CoU LU MeB OKentU
NN   0026492   DLC MB NIC MiDW Ok TNF I MB NN Nh ODW

NASON, Elias, *1811–1887.*
A literary history of the Bible.
Bost. Lothrop & co. [1881.] 32 pp. Portrs. 12°.

NN   0026493   MB NN MWA

4BR
1024   Nason, Elias, 1811–1887.
        Lives and labors of eminent divines:
        Charles H. Parkhurst [and others]
        accounts of their labors of reform
        and evangelization and sketches of their
        their lives, by Elias Nason and J.
        Frank Beale, Jr. Philadelphia, J. E.
        Potter, 1895.
        360 p.

NN   0026494   DLC-P4 NRCR ViU NjPT

922
N182L   NASON, Elias, 1811–1887.
         The lives of the eminent American evangelists
         Dwight Lyman Moody and Ira David Sankey, together
         with an account of their labors in Great Britain
         and America; and also a sketch of the lives of
         Philip P. Bliss and Eben Tourjée ... Boston,
         B. B. Russell ₍c1877₎
         360 p. front., illus., ports.

         Also published under title: The American
         evangelists.

NN   0026495   WaU PP IaU MH-AH OOxM MWA CtY

VOLUME 405

Nason, Elias, 1811–1887.
A memoir of Mrs. Susanna Rowson, with elegant and illustrative extracts from her writings in prose and poetry. By Elias Nason ... Albany, N. Y., J. Munsell, 1870.
212 p. front. (port.) 24ᶜᵐ.
Extracts interspersed in memoir.
"Mrs. Rowson's pupils ₍list₎": p. ₍208₎–206.

1. Rowson, Mrs. Susanna (Haswell) 1762–1824.
₍33b1₎ 29–30626
Library of Congress PS2736.R3Z7

MtU
NcU PPL PPT CSmH ICU MH Nh MiD OU MiU-C CaBVaU
NN 0026496 DLC PPRF TU KyLx MsU NcD ViU MWA NjP

[Nason, Elias] 1811–1887.
Memoir of the Rev. Nathanael Howe, of Hopkinton, Mass. [Boston, J.P. Jewett & co., 1851]
[3]–18 p. 20 cm.
Title-page wanting. Caption-title.
Forms introduction to Howe, Nathaniel, 1764–1837. A century sermon ... 4th ed. with a memoir of the author ... by Elias Nason.

NN 0026497 RPB

Nason, Elias, 1811–1887.
A monogram on our national song. By the Rev. Elias Nason ... Albany, J. Munsell, 1869.
69 p. 22ᶜᵐ.

1. National songs, American. I. Title.
18–13425
Library of Congress PS310.P3N3

CSmH CU PP MnHi NjP MdBP NcD NIC PSt
NN 0026498 DLC CtY MWA OU PHi OO OClWHi MB Nh GU

Nason, Elias, 1811–1887.
... Nason's French reading-book. Chrestomathie française; or, A course of lessons in French literature, designed as an introduction to the study of the French language ... By Elias Nason ... Portland, Sanborn & Carter; Newburyport, M. H. Sargent ₍etc.₎ 1849.
xvi, ₍17₎–127 p. 21ᶜᵐ.
At head of title: 2d edition.

1. French language—Chrestomathies and readers.
10–27178†
Library of Congress PC2115.N3

NN 0026499 DLC MH

₍Nason, Elias₎ 1811–1887, comp.
The new congregational hymn and tune book, for public, social, and private worship ... Boston, J. P. Jewett and company; Cleveland, O., H. P. B. Jewett, 1859.
viii, 218, xi–xii p. 24ᶜᵐ.
Preface signed: Elias Nason.

1. Hymns, English. I. Title.
45–47994
Library of Congress M2117.N25N4 1859

NN 0026500 DLC MBU-T MWA NBuG RPB

Nason, Elias, 1811–1887, ed.
The New-England historical and genealogical register. v. 1–
Jan. 1847–
Boston, S. G. Drake; ₍etc., etc.₎ 1847–

Nason, Elias, 1811–1887.
Originality. By Rev. Elias Nason ... Boston, D. Lothrop and company, 1882.
59 p. 18ᶜᵐ.
"An address, delivered before the Shakespearean club of the Massachusetts agricultural college, at Amherst, June 21, 1881."

I. Title.

Library of Congress PS2459.N265O7 24–21735

NN 0026502 DLC TxU OFH OU

Nason, Elias, 1811–1887.
Our obligations to defend the government of our country, a discourse on the war, by Rev. Elias Nason, delivered at Exeter, N. H., April 21, 1861. ₍n. p., 1861₎
6 p. 21ᶜᵐ.
No. 7 in a volume of pamphlets with binder's title: Civil war discourses. 23ᶜᵐ.
Caption title.

1. U. S.—Hist.—Civil war—Addresses, sermons, etc. I. Title.
27–17709
Library of Congress E649.C543

NN 0026503 DLC NIC TxU NjP PHi OClWHi NN MB Nh

E
5
.B 21 NASON, ELIAS, 1811–1887.
An outline of the remarks made at the funeral of Mrs. Rhoda Ball, who died at Natick, Dec. 11, 1852, aged 25 years. n.p.₍1852?₎
7p.

NN 0026504 ICN

Nason, Elias, 1811–1887.
A selection of sacred songs, for the use of schools and academies. By Elias Nason ... Boston, Saxton and Pierce, 1842.
86, 4 p. 16ᶜᵐ.
On cover: Sacred songs.

1. Hymns, English. I. Title: Sacred songs.
6—18376
Library of Congress BV525.N3
₍a37b1₎ 245.2

NN 0026505 DLC MB

Nason, Elias, 1811–1887.
A selection of sacred songs; for the use of schools, academies, and the social circle. By Elias Nason... Newburyport: M. H. Sargent, 1850. 111 p. 2. ed. 16°.
Tunes indicated.

JUILLIARD FOUNDATION FUND.
372965A. 1. Hymns.
N. Y. P. L. January 7, 1929

NN 0026506 NN RPB

Nason, Elias, 1811–1887.
A sermon on the war, by the Rev. Elias Nason, preached to the soldiers at Exeter, N. H., May 19, 1861. ₍n. p., 1861₎
4 p. 24ᶜᵐ.
No. 4 in a volume of pamphlets with binder's title: Civil war sermons.
Caption title.

1. U. S.—Hist.—Civil war—Addresses, sermons, etc.
27–17691
Library of Congress E649.C547

NN 0026507 DLC MB TU NjP OClWHi NN Nh

Nason, Elias, 1811–1887.
Sir Charles Henry Frankland, baronet: or, Boston in the colonial times. By Elias Nason ... Albany, J. Munsell, 1865.
v, ₍7₎–129 p. 22ᶜᵐ. ₍Munsell's series of local American history, no. 2₎
"300 copies printed, of which 50 are on large paper."—Sabin, Bibl. amer.

1. Frankland, Sir Charles Henry, 1716–1768. 2. Boston—Hist.—Colonial period.
3–11690
Library of Congress F67.F84

NcA-S OO PHi MB MiU-C OCl ICU Nh ViU I PPL
NN 0026508 DLC AU MWA NNUT ViU NIC MiU IaU PP

Nason, Elias, 1811–1887, comp.
Songs for the school room; a selection of sacred and secular songs for the use of schools, academies, and the social circle, by Elias Nason, M.D. Newburyport, John G. Tilton and company ₍c. 1855₎
126 p. 16 cm.
147 sacred songs; 23 secular songs; [2] doxologies numbered 143–144] Ridiculous but true.
Ms. annotations by Prof. Bird.

NN 0026509 NNUT RPB

Nason, Elias, 1811–1887.
The strength and beauty of the sanctuary. A sermon preached at the dedication of the first congregational church in Natick, Mass., Nov. 15, 1854. Boston, 1855. YA. 11862
24p.

NN 0026510 DLC PPPrHi ICN WHi PHi RPB

AC901
W3 Nason, Elias, 1811–1887.
Thou shalt not steal. A sermon ... Boston, Whipple & co., 1853.
16 p. (Waterman pamphlets, 139:20)

NN 0026511 DLC RPB

Case
C
89 ₍NASON, ELIAS₎ 1811–1887, comp.
613 The vestry hymn book; a choice collection of psalms and hymns for social and private worship. Boston, J.P.Jewett and company, 1858.
574p. 12½cm.

Without music. Tunes indicated by title.
Preface signed: Elias Nason.
To be used in connection with Congregational tune book.

NN 0026512 ICN CtY NNUT

Nason, Elias, 1811–1887.
William Bentley Fowle. By Rev. Elias Nason ... (In New England historic genealogical society. Memoirs of several deceased members ... Boston, 1878. 25ᶜᵐ. p. ₍97₎–107)

Subject entries: Fowle, William Bentley, 1795–1865.
8–14075
Library of Congress, no. F1.N495.

NN 0026513 DLC

W.C.L. Nason, Elias S.
M780.88
A512P Isador waltz; composed and arr. for one or two performers on the piano forte, by E. S.
no.13 Nason. Boston, Oliver Ditson, c1847.
3 p. 33 cm.
Caption title.
₍No. 13₎ in a vol. of piano music collected by H. H. Alexander.

1. Waltzes (Piano, 4 hands) I. Title.

NN 0026514 NcD IaU RPB NNUT MB

VOLUME 405

Nason, Emma C..
Rev. Edward Taylor
see under   Terry, John Taylor.

Nason, Mrs. Emma (Huntington) 1845–
The loves of Goethe ...
(In The Cosmopolitan. Irvington, N.Y., 1897.
25 cm.   v. XXIV, no. 2, p. [172]–181. illus.)

NN   0026516   CtY

Nason, *Mrs.* Emma (Huntington) 1845–
Old colonial houses in Maine built prior to 1776, by Emma
Huntington Nason ... Augusta, Me. [Press of the Kennebec
journal] 1908.
x p., 1 l., 106 p. incl. front. 22 pl. 24½ᵐ.

1. Maine—Historic houses, etc.   I. Title.
8–15274
Library of Congress   F20.N26

NN   0026517   DLC MWA OC1 OC MeB CU ICU OO NN MB

Nason, *Mrs.* Emma (Huntington) 1845–
Old Hallowell on the Kennebec, by Emma Huntington
Nason ... Augusta, Me. [Press of Burleigh & Flynt] 1909.
7 p. l., 359 p. front., plates, ports. 25ᶜᵐ. $2.50

1. Hallowell, Me.—Hist.
9–31504
Library of Congress   F29.H15N3

PPL PHi OC1WHi NN MB CaBVaU PPAmP
NN   0026518   DLC NcU NcD OO FTaSU MWA MeB CoU CU

Nason, Mrs. Emma (Huntington) 1845–
Poem, Ancient Koussinoc.
(In Augusta centennial souvenir issued by the
Daily Kennebec Journal, June 8, 1897.
28 x 35 cm.   p. 58–60)

NN   0026519   RPB

1845–
Nason, Emma Huntington. The tower. 2
pp. (Atlant. Monthly, v. 33, 1874, p. 541.)

NN   0026520   MdBP

Nason, *Mrs.* Emma (Huntington) 1845–
The tower with legends and lyrics, by Emma Huntington Nason. Boston and New York, Houghton, Mifflin and
company, 1895.
vi, 141 p. 19½ᵐ.
Poems.

I. Title.
[Full name: Emma Caroline (Huntington) Nason]
24–21740
Library of Congress   PS2459.N27

NN   0026521   DLC NcD PP MB NN

Nason, Emma Huntington. 1845–. Two faces:
[poem.] 3 pp. (Atlant. Monthly, v. 71, 1893, p. 801.)

NN   0026522   MdBP

Nason, Emma (Huntington) 1845–
White sails, by Emma Huntington Nason. Boston,
D. Lothrop company [°1888]
162 p. incl. front., 12 pl. illus. 23 cm.
Verse.

I. Title.
[Full name: Emma Caroline (Huntington) Nason]
24—21741
Library of Congress   PS2459.N272

NN   0026523   DLC MB OC1 NBuG

Nason, Frank Lewis, 1856–1928.
The Blue Goose, by Frank Lewis Nason ... New York,
McClure, Phillips & co., 1903.
viii, 295 p. 20ᵐᵐ.

I. Title.
3–7161
Library of Congress   PZ3.N182B1

NN   0026524   DLC IU PPL PPYH OC1 OC1W NN

Nason, Frank L[ewis] 1856–1928
... Geological studies of the archæan rocks. By Frank
L. Nason, A. M. (*In* New Jersey. Geological survey,
1863–   Annual report ... Trenton, 1864–
23ᶜᵐ. 1889 (1890) p. 12–65. illus.)

1. Geology—New Jersey. 2. Geology, Stratigraphic—Archean.

Library, U. S. Geol.   survey   G S 5–128

NN   0026525   DI-GS

Nason, Frank L[ewis] 1856–1928.
Iron mines. Notes on the active iron mines. Frank
L. Nason. (*In* New Jersey. Geological survey, 1863–
Annual report ... Trenton, 1864–   23ᵐ.
1890 (1891) p. 51–127. fold. map)

1. Iron mines and mining—New Jersey.

Library, U. S. Geol.   survey   G S 5–133

NN   0026526   DI-GS OU

Nason, Frank L[ewis] 1856–1928
The post-archean age of the white limestones of Sussex County, N. J. Frank L. Nason. (*In* New Jersey.
Geological survey, 1863–   Annual report ... Trenton, 1864–   23ᵐ. 1890 (1891) p. 25–50. fold. plates)

1. Geology—New Jersey. 2. Geology, Stratigraphic—Post-Archean.

Library, U. S. Geol.   survey   G S 5–132

NN   0026527   DI-GS

Nason, Frank Lewis, 1856–1928.

Winslow, Arthur, 1860–
... A report on the Iron Mountain sheet, including
portions of Iron, St. Francois and Madison counties.
By Arthur Winslow... Erasmus Haworth ... Frank L.
Nason ... Jefferson City [Tribune printing co.] 1894.

NASON, Frank Lewis, 1856 – 1928.
A report on the iron ores of Missouri, from
field work prosecuted during 1891 and 1892.
Jefferson City, 1892.

1.8°. Maps, plates, and wdcts.
(Missouri – Geological survey. [Subject
reports], 2.)

NN   0026529   MH PPAN OC1 OU

Nason, Frank Lewis, 1856–1928.
Missouri. *Geological survey.*
[Reports, vol. I–XIII] Jefferson City, 1891–1900.

Nason, Frank Lewis, 1856–1928.
... Some New York minerals and their localities, prepared
for the New York state museum of natural history, by Frank
L. Nason ... Albany, C. Van Benthuysen & sons, 1888.
19, [1] p. pl. 23ᵐ. (New York state museum. Bulletin no. 4)

1. Mineralogy—New York (State)
G S 7–451
U. S. Geol. survey. Library   [221] N45b no. 4
for Library of Congress   [Q11.N82 no. 4]
[a40b1]   (507.4)

OC1 OCU OU DLC NN MH CaBVaU
NN   0026531   DI-GS MiU MU MoU MdBP NcU WU PPWa PU

Nason, Frank Lewis, 1856–1928.
To the end of the trail, by Frank Lewis Nason. Boston and New York, Houghton, Mifflin and company, 1902.
4 p. l., 302 p., 1 l. 19½ᵐ.
2–18267

NN   0026532   DLC OU

[Nason, Frank Lewis] 1856–1928
The triassic rocks, or the red sandstones of New Jersey. (*In* New Jersey. Geological survey, 1863–
Annual report ... Trenton, 1864–   23ᵐ. 1888
(1889) p. 16–44. illus., fold. map)

1. Geology—New Jersey. 2. Geology, Stratigraphic—Triassic.

Library, U. S. Geol.   survey   G S 5–127

NN   0026533   DI-GS

Nason, Frank Lewis, 1856–1928
The vision of Elijah Berl, by Frank Lewis Nason ... Boston, Little, Brown, and company, 1905.
vii, 290 p., 1 l. 20ᵐ.

I. Title.
5–9276
Library of Congress   PZ3.N182Vi

NN   0026534   DLC TNJ OU IU PU

NASON, George W., jr.
[New-Berne illustrated almanac and general
household informant, for 1872. New Berne, N.C.,
[1871].

Wdcts.

NN   0026535   MH

Nason, George Warren, 1834–1913.
History and complete roster of the Massachusetts regiments, minute men of '61 who responded to the first call
of President Abraham Lincoln, April 15, 1861, to defend
the flag and Constitution of the United States ... and biographical sketches of minute men of Massachusetts, by
George W. Nason. Boston, Mass., Smith & McCance,
1910.
413, [1], iv, iv p., 1 l. incl illus., plates. front. 23½ᵐ.
Includes the Third, Fourth, Fifth, Sixth and Eighth regiments, M. V. M.,
the Third battalion of rifles and the Boston light artillery.
1. U. S.—Hist.—Civil war—Regimental histories—Mass. 2. Massachusetts—Militia. 3. Massachusetts—Hist.—Civil war.
10–27627
Library of Congress   E513.4.N27

ViU MtHi WaS IaU MB DNW I
NN   0026536   DLC OC1WHi CaBVaU Or MWA TxU ViN NcD

VOLUME 405

C
676
N18m
Nason, H   K
    Microbiology of pulp and white-water systems
[by] H.K. Nason and R.S. Shumard...   St. Louis,
Mo., Monsanto chemical company, 1939.
    caption-title, 11 numb. 1., 11 plates. 29½cm.

    Mimeographed.
    Bibliographies: p.5, 8-9.

    1. Paper making and trade. I. Shumard, R
S   , joint author. II. Title.

NN   0026537   LU

Nason, Henry Bradford, 1831-1895, ed.

Rensselaer polytechnic institute, *Troy. N. Y.*
    Biographical record of the officers and graduates of the
Rensselaer polytechnic institute. 1824-1886. Ed. by Henry B.
Nason ... With an introduction by Benjamin H. Hall. Troy,
N. Y., W. H. Young, 1887.

                            FOR OTHER EDITIONS
                            SEE MAIN ENTRY.
Mason, Henry Bradford, 1831-1895, ed.
Elderhorst, William, 1828-1861.
    Elderhorst's manual of qualitative blow-pipe analysis and
determinative mineralogy. Edited by Henry B. Nason ... and
Charles F. Chandler ... 4th ed., rev. and enl. Philadelphia
and London, T. E. Zell, 1874.

Nason, Henry Bradford, 1831-1895, ed.
Wöhler, Friedrich, 1800-1882.
    Hand-book of mineral analysis. By Friedrich Wöhler
... Ed. by Henry B. Nason ... Philadelphia, H. C. Baird,
1871.

Nason, Henry Bradford, 1831-1895.
    On the formation of ether ... Göttingen, 1857.
    32 p.   22.5 cm.
    Inaug.-diss. - Göttingen.

NN   0026541   CtY

Nason, Henry Bradford, 1831-1895, ed.

Rensselaer polytechnic institute, *Troy, N. Y.*
    Proceedings of the semi-centennial celebration of the
Rensselaer polytechnic institute, Troy, N. Y., held June
14-18, 1874, with catalogue of officers and students, 1824-
1874. Troy, N. Y., W. H. Young, 1875.

[Nason, Henry Bradford] 1831-1895
    Systematic method of qualitative
blowpipe analysis, printed for the class
of 1880. R.P.I.   Troy, Young, 1879.

NN   0026543   MA

Nason, Henry Bradford, 1831-1895.
    Table of reactions for qualitative
chemical analysis.   Troy, Rensselaer
polytechnic institute, n.d.

NN   0026544   MA

Nason, Jerry.
    Famous American athletes of today
    see under title

Nason (John James). On some of the responsibilities of the medical profession in regard to
sanitation, moral as well as general. The presidential address, delivered at the annual meeting
of the Birmingham and Midland Counties Branch
of the British Medical Association, June 19, 1884.
32 pp. 8°. *London, J. & A. Churchill,* [1884].

NN   0026546   DNLM

Nason, John Marshall.
    A history of public high school development in Virginia
and North Carolina. Chicago, 1928.
    x, 392 l. maps, diagrs. tables. 29 cm.
    Thesis—University of Chicago.
    Typescript (carbon copy)
    Bibliography: leaves 385-392.

    1. High schools—Virginia—Hist. 2. High schools—North Caro-
lina—Hist.

    LA379.N3   53-52551

NN   0026547   DLC ICU

B2580
.N3
1946
    Nason, John William, 1905—
        Leibnitz's attack of the Cartesian
doctrine of extension. [n. p., 1946]
    447-483 p.   26cm.
    Reprinted from Journal of the History of ideas,
October, 1946, vol. VII, No. 4, College of the
City of New York.
    1. Leibnitz. Gottfried Wilhelm, Freiherr von,
1646-1716. 2. Descartes, René, 1596-1650.

NN   0026548   ViU

TF7
N183p
    Nason, John William, 1905-
        The program of faculty consultations on
religion in higher education. Being an
account of a program sponsored jointly by
the American council on education, the Edward
W. Hazen foundation, and the National council
on religion in higher education and reported
in the Educational record for October 1946.
    [n.p., 1946?]
    12 p.   23 cm.

NN   0026549   CtY-D

    Nason, John William, 1905-
        Religion in higher education, by John W.
Nason. Reprinted from "The Educational
Record" for October 1946. Washington,D.C.,
The American Council on Education [1946?]
    p.422-432.   23cm.

NN   0026550   PSC-Hi MH-AH

Nason, Joseph, joint author.

Cruickshank, Frederick David.
    History of Weston, by F. D. Cruickshank, M. D., and J. Nason
... With introduction by J. C. Boylen ... [Weston, Ont., The
Times & guide, 1937]

    Nason, K   D
        The dog with a bad name, by K. D. Nason.
With illustrations by C. G. C. Foster.
London, Country Life Limited [1936]
    vii, 9-107 p. illus.   21½cm.

NN   0026552   ViW

LC1045
.A23
no. 3581
    Nason, Leigh M.
    [Averill, Felix E   ]
    ... Composite report of regional conferences on the improve-
ment of instruction in war production training. Washington,
D. C., Federal security agency, U. S. Office of education, Vocational training for war production workers, 1942.

Nason, Leonard Hastings, 1895–
    Among the trumpets; stories of war horses and others, by
Leonard Nason. Boston and New York, Houghton Mifflin
company, 1932.
    4 p. l., [3]-309 p. 19¼[cm].

    1. European war, 1914-1918—Fiction. I. Title.
    Library of Congress   PZ3.N185Am   32-9035

                                    WaS OrU
NN   0026554   DLC MeB NN MB ViU PP PPGi PV MiU OEac

Nason, Leonard Hastings, 1895–
    ... Approach to battle. New York, Doubleday, Doran & co.,
inc., 1941.
    4 p. l., 113 p. 28[cm].
    At head of title: Major Leonard H. Nason.
    "First edition."

    1. U. S.—Defenses. 2. U. S.—Army. I. Title.
    Library of Congress   UA23.N22   41-3055
    ——— Copy 2.
    Copyright   [15]   355.450973

NN   0026555   DLC NcD WaS WaE PP PPD OCl OU ViU

Nason, Leonard Hastings, 1895–
    Chevrons, by Leonard H. Nason. New York, George H.
Doran company [1926]
    339 p. 19¼[cm].

    1. European war, 1914-1918—Fiction. I. Title.
    Library of Congress   PZ3.N180Ch   26-17804 Revised

                LU OU MiEM NcD
                OCl OCX OO OEac MiU PPL PU MeB OrU NBuU CU-I TxU
NN   0026556   DLC WaE OrCS WaTC WaSp IdPI WaS MH MB

Nason, Leonard Hastings, 1895–
    Chevrons, by Leonard H. Nason. New York, Grosset
& Dunlap [1927]
    339 p. 19¼ cm.

NN   0026557   ViU

Nason, Leonard Hastings, 1895–
    Contact Mercury, by Leonard H. Nason. Garden City, New
York, Doubleday & company, inc., 1946.
    4 p. l., 247 p. 20¼[cm].
    "First edition."

    I. Title.
    Library of Congress   PZ3.N185Cl   46-2154

                OCl
NN   0026558   DLC OU MB OrP WaS CaBVa KEmT PP PPGi

Nason, Leonard Hastings, 1895–
    A corporal once, by Leonard H. Nason ... Garden City,
N. Y., Doubleday, Doran & company, inc., 1930.
    4 p. l., 312 p. 19¼[cm].
    "First edition."

    1. European war, 1914-1918—Fiction. I. Title.
    Library of Congress   PZ3.N185Co   30-25290 Revised

NN   0026559   DLC MB CU-I OU WaE PP PU OO OCl OClh

Nason, Leonard Hastings, 1895–
    The fighting Livingstons, by Leonard H. Nason ... Garden
City, N. Y., Doubleday, Doran & company, inc., 1931.
    3 p. l., 332 p. 20[cm].
    "First edition."

    1. European war, 1914-1918—Fiction. I. Title.
    Library of Congress   PZ3.N185Fi   31-4811

NN   0026560   DLC OU WaS MeB PPL OO MiU

VOLUME 405

Nason, Leonard Hastings, 1895–
The incomplete mariner, by Leonard H. Nason. Garden City, N. Y., Doubleday, Doran & company, inc., 1929.
4 p. l., 3–315 p. 19½ᵐ.
Contents.—The incomplete mariner.—Hunger.—Narrow waters.

i. Title.

Library of Congress   PZ3.N185 In   29–22804 Revised

NN   0026561   DLC FMU FTaSU MB CU

PZ   Nason, Leonard Hastings, 1895–
3   The man in the white slicker, by
N185   Leonard H. Nason. New York, Grosset &
Man   Dunlap [c1920]
            290p. 20cm.

1. European War, 1914–1918 – Fiction
I. Title

NN   0026562   WU

Nason, Leonard Hastings, 1895–
The man in the white slicker, by Leonard H. Nason. Garden City, N. Y., Doubleday, Doran & company, inc., 1929.
3 p. l., 290 p. 19½ᵐ.

1. European war, 1914–1918—Fiction.   i. Title.
Library of Congress   PZ3.N185Man   29–10954
——— Copy 2.

OC1h
NN   0026563   DLC IEdS PPL PU NN MB ViU PU OO OC1

Nason, Leonard Hastings, 1895–
Sergeant Eadie, by Leonard H. Nason. Garden City, N. Y., Doubleday, Doran & company, inc., 1928.
2 p. l., 374 p. 19½ cm.

1. European war, 1914–1918—Fiction.   i. Title.

PZ3.N180Se   28–8412

LU OrU MeB OU IdPI
NN   0026564   DLC IEdS OC1 OO OLak OC1h CSt-H PU

Nason, Leonard Hastings, 1895–
Three lights from a match, by Leonard H. Nason ... New York, George H. Doran company [c1927]
308 p. 19½ᵐ.
Contents.—Three lights from a match.—Eye-wash.—Rockets at daybreak.

1. European war, 1914–1918—Fiction.   i. Title.
Library of Congress   PZ3.N180Th   27–11488 Revised

PU PPL MB ViU
NN   0026565   DLC WaS WaT PSt NcD MB OU FTaSU LU

Nason, Leonard Hastings, 1895–
Three lights from a match, by Leonard H. Nason ... New York, Grosset & Dunlap [1927]
308 p. 19½ᵐ.
Contents.—Three lights from a match.—Eye-wash.—Rockets at daybreak.

NN   0026566   OrU KEmT

Nason, Leonard Hastings, 1895–
Three lights from a match, by Leonard H. Nason. Garden City, N. Y., The Sun dial press, inc. [1937]
308 p. 20ᵐ.
Contents.—Three lights from a match.—Eye-wash.—Rockets at daybreak.

1. European war, 1914–1918—Fiction.   i. Title.
Library of Congress   PZ3.N185Th 8   37–14405

NN   0026567   DLC

Nason, Leonard Hastings, 1895–
The top kick, by Leonard H. Nason. Garden City, N. Y., Doubleday, Doran and company, inc., 1928.
4 p. l., 3–309 p. 19½ cm.
Contents.—A sergeant of cavalry.—The roofs of Verdillot.—A matter of business.

1. European war, 1914–1918—Fiction.   i. Title.

PZ3.N185To   28—23048

NIC OU ViU MeB IEdS NcD OCX OO TxU WaS
NN   0026568   DLC CtY MB NN OC1h PPL GU TNJ FTaSU

PS3527
.A668T6 Nason, Leonard Hastings, 1895–
1930
            The top kick. New York, Grosset & Dunlap [1930]
            309 p   20cm
            Contents.—A sergeant of cavalry.—The roofs of Verdillot.—A matter of business.

1. European War, 1914–1918—Fiction.   I. Title.

NN   0026569   ViU

Nason, Leonard Herbert.
History of the prehistoric ages: written by the ancient historic band of spirits. Translated by James Cooper. Chicago, C. E. Southard, 1880.
pp. x, 390.   Port.

NN   0026570   MH ICU IU DLC OFH MiU

Ed.D   Nason, Leslie James.
'54   Patterns of circumstances related to
N263   educational achievement of high school
            pupils of superior ability.   June 1954.
            xv,191f.   illus.   29cm.

Thesis (Ed.D) – Univ. of Southern California.   Typewritten.

1. Prediction of scholastic success.
2. Precocity.
FILM 300
no.1 r.286e

NN   0026571   CLSU

Nason, Marshall Rutherford, 1917–
Charlar repasando [by] Marshall Rutherford Nason [and] Rosalyn Thelma Campbell. Illus. by M. J. Davis. New York, Oxford University Press, 1951.
ix, 359 p. illus. 21 cm.

1. Spanish language—Conversation and phrase books.   i. Campbell, Rosalyn Thelma, joint author.   ii. Title.

PC4121.N35   468.242   51–2844 rev

NN   0026572   DLC FTaSU WaS

PC4121
.N35   Nason, Marshall Rutherford, 1915–
1953   Charlar repasando [by] Marshall Rutherford
            Nason [and] Rosalyn Thelma Campbell. Illus.
            by M. J. Davis. New York, Oxford University
            Press [1953]
            ix, 360 p. illus. 21cm.

1. Spanish language—Conversation and phrase books.   I. Campbell, Rosalyn Thelma, joint author.   II. Title.

NN   0026573   MB

Nason, Philip Stephen.
The Messianic hope in the book of Isaiah ... by Philip Stephen Nason ... [Boston] 1942.
[4] p.   23ᵐ.
Abstract of thesis (ph. d.)—Boston university.

1. Bible. O. T. Isaiah—Prophecies. 2. Messiah—Prophecies. 3. Bible—Prophecies—O. T. Isaiah.   i. Title.

Library of Congress   BS1515.N3   43–195

NN   0026574   DLC

Nason, R   B.
Elements of strength and weakness in physical education as taught in preparatory schools.
(In National education association of the United States. Journal of proceedings and addresses, 1908. p. 1019–1024)

1. Physical education.

Library, U. S. Bur. of   Education   E 9–289

NN   0026575   DHEW WaS OU

NASON, Reuben, 1778–1835.
An address delivered at Gorham on opening the academy in that place, September 8, 1806. Portland, J. M'Kown, 1806.

pp. 15.

NN   0026576   MH MHi RPB NHi

NASON, Reuben, 1778–1835.
A valedictory address on relinquishing the charge of Gorham Academy, August 19, 1834. Portland, printed at the Mirror office, 1834.

1. 8°.   pp. 14.

NN   0026577   MH

Nason, Robert W.
[Collection of Briefs, Bills, etc. in Cases, 1894–1927] [Boston, etc., 1894–1927]
7 vol.   4°.
1. Proctor, Thomas William.

NN   0026578   MH–L

Nason, Rosalyn Thelma Campbell
see
Nason, Thelma Campbell.

PC4121
.N35   Nason, Thelma Campbell, joint author.
            Nason, Marshall Rutherford, 1917–
            Charlar repasando [by] Marshall Rutherford Nason [and] Rosalyn Thelma Campbell. Illus. by M. J. Davis. New York, Oxford University Press, 1951.

PS1151
.U5   Nason, Thomas Willoughby, 1889–   illus.
            Bryant, William Cullen, 1794–1878.
            The poems of William Cullen Bryant, selected and edited with a commentary by Louis Untermeyer, and illustrated with engravings on wood by Thomas W. Nason. New York, The Limited editions club, 1947.

Nason, Thomas Willoughby, 1889–
[Sunday in Marblehead; wood engraving]
(In The Colophon. New York, 1930–40. 27 cm. pt. 7 [no. 3] (1931) 1 l.)

[Z1007.C71 pt. 7, no. 3]   A 53–2158

Grosvenor Library
for Library of Congress   [2]

NN   0026582   NBuG

Nason, Thomas Willoughby, 1889–   illus.
Thoreau, Henry David, 1817–1862.
Walden; or, Life in the woods, by Henry David Thoreau; with wood-engravings by Thomas W. Nason. New York, For the Heritage club [1939]

VOLUME 405

Nason, Wayne Crocker, 1874-1934.
H. Leslie Perry memorial library, Henderson,
N.C.

(In Nason, W.C. Rural libraries. ₁1928₎

NN 0026584 NcU

₁Nason, Wayne Crocker,₎ 1874-1934.
...Hospitales rurales... Washington, D. C.: La Unión
panamericana, 1926. ii, 17 p. illus. 8°. (Pan American
Union. Salud pública y puericultura. no. 24.)

"Por Wayne C. Nason," p. 1.
A translation of his article issued as Farmers bull., no. 1485 of the United States
Agriculture Dept.
Repr.: Pan American Union. Boletín.

1. Hospitals—Construction, descrip-   tion and plans.—U. S. 2. Ser.
N. Y. P. L.   April 17, 1928

NN 0026585 NN

Nason, Wayne Crocker, 1874-1934.
... Organization of rural community buildings. ₁By W. C.
Nason. Washington, Govt. print. off., 1921₎

42 p. illus. 23ᶜᵐ. (U. S. Dept. of agriculture. Farmers' bulletin
1192)
Contribution from the Office of farm management and farm economics.
Superseded by Farmers' bulletin no. 1622, Rural buildings for business and social uses, by W. C. Nason.

1. Community centers. 2. Architecture—Designs and plans.
₁1, 2. Community buildings₎ I. Title.
                                                        Agr 21-701
U. S. Dept. of agr. Library   1Ag84F no. 1192
for Library of Congress   [S21.A6 no. 1192]

                                  ₁a37g1₎   (630.6173)

NN 0026586 DNAL WaWW CaBVaU DHEW OU OCl OO MB

Nason, Wayne Crocker, 1874-1934
... Plans of rural community buildings. ₁By W. C. Nason.
Washington, Govt. print. off.,₎ 1921₎

38 p. incl. illus., plans. 23ᶜᵐ. (U. S. Dept. of agriculture. Farmers'
bulletin 1173)
Contributions from the Office of farm management and farm economics.

1. Community centers. 2. Architecture—Designs and plans. ₁1, 2.
Community buildings₎ I. Title.
                                                        Agr 21-228
Library, U. S. Dept. of   Agriculture 1Ag84F no. 1173
Library of Congress   [S21.A6 no. 1173]

CaBVaU
NN 0026587 DNAL DHEW MB OO OCl OU WaWW WaS

Nason, Wayne Crocker, 1874-1934
... Rural buildings for business and social uses. ₁By Wayne
C. Nason. Washington, U. S. Govt. print. off.,₎ 1930₎

ii, 38 p. illus., plans. 23½ᶜᵐ. (U. S. Dept. of agriculture. Farmers' bulletin no. 1622)
Contribution from Bureau of agricultural economics.
Supersedes Department bulletin no. 825, Rural community buildings
in the United States; Farmers' bulletin no. 1192, Organization of rural
community buildings; and Farmers' bulletin no. 1274, Uses of rural
community buildings.

1. ₁Community buildings₎ I. Title.
                                                        Agr 30-538
                                  [S21.A6 no. 1622]
Library, U. S. Dept. of   Agriculture 1Ag84F no. 1622

NN 0026588 DNAL MB CaBVaU OU OCl WaWW

Nason, Wayne Crocker, 1874-1934.
... Rural community buildings in the United States.
By W. C. Nason ... and C. W. Thompson ... Washing-
ton ₁Govt. print. off.₎ 1920.

36 p. illus. 23ᶜᵐ. (U. S. Dept. of agriculture. Bulletin no. 825)
Contribution from the Bureau of markets.

1. Community centers. I. Thompson, Carl William, 1879-1920, joint
author. II. Title.
                                                        Agr 20-296
Library, U. S. Dept. of   Agriculture 1Ag84B no. 825

NN 0026589 DNAL WaWW OO OU OCl DHEW

Nason, Wayne Crocker, 1874-1934
... Rural community fire departments. ₁By Wayne C. Nason. Washington, U. S. Govt. print. off.,₎ 1931₎

ii, 46 p. illus. 23ᶜᵐ. (U. S. Dept. of agriculture. Farmers' bulletin no. 1667)
Contribution from Bureau of agricultural economics.

1. Fire-departments. ₁Rural₎ I. Title.
                                                        Agr 31-876
Library, U. S. Dept. of   Agriculture 1Ag84F no. 1667
Library of Congress   [S21.A6 no. 1667]

NN 0026590 DNAL CaBVaU OU OCl WaWW

Nason, Wayne Crocker, 1874-1934, joint
author.
Manny, Theodore Bergen, 1897-
... Rural factory industries. By T. B. Manny ... and Wayne
C. Nason ... Washington ₁U. S. Govt. print. off.₎ 1934.

Nason, Wayne Crocker, 1874-1934.
... Rural hospitals. By Wayne C. Nason ... ₁Washington, Govt. print. off., 1926₎

ii, 46 p. illus. 23ᶜᵐ. (U. S. Dept. of agriculture. Farmers' bulletin
no. 1485)
Contribution from Bureau of agricultural economics.

1. Hospitals. I. Title.
                                                        Agr 26-415
Library, U. S. Dept. of   Agriculture 1Ag84F no. 1485

NN 0026592 DNAL WaWW CaBVaU OU OO OCl

Nason, Wayne Crocker, 1874-1934
...Rural industries in Knott county,
Kentucky. A preliminary report. Washington,
D.C., 1932. 1 p. l., 24p. illus., map. 27 cm.
At head of title: United States Department
of agriculture. Bureau of agriculture
economics. In cooperation with Kentucky
agricultural experiment station.

NN 0026593 DL

Nason, Wayne Crocker, 1874-1934
... Rural libraries. ₁By Wayne C. Nason₎ ₁Washington,
U. S. Govt. print. off.,₎ 1928₎

ii, 50 p. illus. 23½ᶜᵐ. · (U. S. Dept. of agriculture. Farmers' bulletin no. 1559)
Contribution from Bureau of agricultural economics.

1. ₁Rural₎ libraries.
                                                        Agr 28-399
Library, U. S. Dept. of   Agriculture 1Ag84F no. 1559

MiU
NN 0026594 DNAL CaBVaU MoU WaWW WaS OClW OU OO

Nason, Wayne Crocker, 1874-1934.
... Rural planning—the social aspects. ₁By Wayne C.
Nason₎ ₁Washington, Govt. print. off.,₎ 1923₎

ii, 30 p. illus. 23ᶜᵐ. (U. S. Dept. of agriculture. Farmers' bulletin
1325)
Contribution from Bureau of agricultural economics.

1. Cities and towns—Civic improvement. 2. Community centers.
I. Title.
                                                        Agr 23-802
U. S. Dept. of agr. Library   1Ag84F no. 1325
for Library of Congress   [S21.A6   ]

MB MiU
NN 0026595 DNAL CaBVaU Or WaWW DHEW OU OCl OO

Nason, Wayne Crocker, 1874-1934.
... Rural planning: the social aspects of recreation places.
₁By Wayne C. Nason₎ ₁Washington, Govt. print. off.,₎ 1924₎

ii, 30 p. illus. 23 cm. (U. S. Dept. of agriculture. Farmers'
bulletin no. 1388)
Contribution from Bureau of agricultural economics.

1. Cities and towns—Civic improvement. 2. Community centers.
I. Title.
                                                        Agr 24-281
U. S. Dept. of Agr. Libr.   1Ag84F no. 1388
for Library of Congress   ₁a48g1₎

NN 0026596 DNAL WaWW OO OU DHEW MB Or CaBVaU

Nason, Wayne Crocker, 1874-1934.
... Rural planning—the village. ₁By Wayne C. Nason₎
₁Washington, Govt. print. off., 1925₎

ii, 46 p. illus. 23ᶜᵐ. (U. S. Dept. of agriculture. Farmers' bulletin
no. 1441)
Contribution from Bureau of agricultural economics.

1. Cities and towns—Civic improvement. I. Title.
                                                        Agr 25-625
Library, U. S. Dept. of   Agriculture 1Ag84F no. 1441

NN 0026597 DNAL CaBVaU Or OO OU OCl MB

Nason, Wayne Crocker, 1874-1934.
... Rural planning—the village. ₁By Wayne C. Nason ...
Issued March 1925; slightly revised August 1935. Washing-
ton, U. S. Govt. print. off., 1935₎

ii, 41 p. illus., plans. 23ᶜᵐ. (U. S. Dept. of agriculture. Farmers'
bulletin no. 1441)
Contribution from Bureau of agricultural economics.

1. Cities and towns—Civic improvement. I. Title.
                                                        Agr 35-416
Library, U. S. Dept. of   Agriculture 1Ag84F no. 1441 rev.
Library of Congress   [S21.A6 no. 1441]

NN 0026598 DNAL WaWW OU

Nason, Wayne Crocker, 1874-1934.
... Uses of rural community buildings. ₁By W. C. Na-
son₎ ₁Washington, Govt. print. off., 1922₎

32 p. illus. 23ᶜᵐ. (U. S. Dept. of agriculture. Farmers' bulletin 1274)
Contribution from the Bureau of agricultural economics.

1. Community centers. ₁I. Community buildings₎ I. Title.
                                                        Agr 22-799
Library, U. S. Dept. of   Agriculture 1Ag84F no. 1274

MB
NN 0026599 DNAL CaBVaU Or DHEW WaWW OU OCl OO

Nason, William A
With the Ninth Army corps in East Tennessee. By First
Sergeant W. A. Nason, late adjutant Eleventh New Hamp-
shire volunteers. Providence, The Society, 1891.

70 p. 21 cm. (Added t.-p.: Personal narratives of events in the war
of the rebellion, being papers read before the Rhode Island soldiers
and sailors historical society. 4th ser.—no. 15)
"Edition limited to two hundred and fifty copies."

1. New Hampshire infantry. 11th regt., 1862-1865. 2. Tennessee—
Hist.—Civil war. 3. U. S.—Hist.—Civil war—Regimental histories—
9th corps.
E464.R47 4th ser.
———— Copy 2.   E470.6.N26   10—32773

NN 0026600 DLC NIC MB MH OClWHi NNC

B610.24
Ed4   Nason, William W.
1816-17   De pertussi ... Edinburgi, Excudebat
           R. Allan, 1817.

           [4], 25 p. 22 cm. (In Edinburgh.
         University. Dissertationes medicae, 1816-17)

           Inaug. Diss. - Edinburgh.

NN 0026601 MnU-B

711.40973
M767n   Nason, Law, Wehrman & Knight, inc.
         The comprehensive plan, Montevideo, Minnesota;
         report₍s₎ Minneapolis, 19 -
           v. fold.col.plan. 28cm.

NN 0026602 IU

Nason Manufacturing Co., New York.
Catalogue and list of prices for ... all varieties of
wrought iron pipe, boiler flues ... etc., also illustrated supplement of specialties. *New York*, 1877.
136 pp. 12°.
Gift of Dr. J. S. Billings.

NN 0026603 NN

VOLUME 405

Nason manufacturing co., New York.
Illustrated lists of prices for...pipe...
N. Y., 1866, 1900-1902.
4 v. 8° & 4°

NN   0026604   DLC

Nason manufacturiug company, *New York.*
. . . Illustrated lists of prices for wrought and cast
iron pipe, etc. . . . April, 1901. ₍New York, Nason
m'f'g co., 1901₎

illus. 8°.

Copyright by Nason manufacturing company, New York, N. Y. Class A,
XXc, no. 7619, Apr. 20, 1901; 2 copies rec'd Apr. 20, 1901.

May 23, 1901-74

NN   0026605   DLC

Nason Manufacturing Company, *New York.*
Reference book for the engineer, architect and mechanic.

New York: Nason Manufacturing Co., 1907.   illus.   v.   4°.

1. Machinery—Catalogues.   2. Hardware—Catalogues.
3. Plumbing—Catalogues.
N. Y. P. L.   October 28, 1927

NN   0026606   NN

Nasone, P. Ovidio
    see   Ovidius Naso, Publius.

BT190   **Nasoni, Angelo.**
N2   Juris canonici compendium, biennali scholae
1903   accommodatum; auctore sac. Angelo Nasoni ...
Ed. 2. ad recentissima decreta regesta. **Medio-**
lani, J. Palma, 1903.

xl, 456 p.   22cm.

Bibliographical footnotes.

1.Canon law-Commentaries-Pre-code.

NN   0026608   MBtS IMunS

Nasonis, Publius Ovidius

    see

Ovidius Naso, Publius.

Nasonov, Arsenii Nikolaevich.
Монголы и Русь; история татарской политики на Руси.
Москва, Изд-во Академии наук СССР, 1940.

177 p.   23 cm.

At head of title: Академия наук СССР. Институт истории.
Bibliography: p. 154-₍159₎

1. Russia—Hist.—1237-1480.   2. Mongols in Russia.   I. Title.
                Title transliterated: Mongoly i Rus'.

DK90.N3   52-54668

NN   0026610   DLC WU WaU

DK511   **Nasonov, Arsenii Nikolaevich,** ed.
.N7N62   **Novgorodskaîa letopisʹ.**
Новгородская первая летопись старшего и младшего
изводов. ₍Под ред. и с предисл. А. Н. Насонова₎ Москва, Изд-во Академии наук СССР, 1950.

DK100   **Nasonov, Arsenii Nikolaevich,** ed.
.O3   Очерки истории СССР: Период феодализма, конец XV в.—
начало XVII в. Укрепление русского централизованного
государства (конец XV–XVI вв.) Крестьянская война и
борьба русского народа против иностранной интервенции
в начале XVII в. Под ред. А. Н. Насонова, Л. В. Череп-
нина, А. А. Зимина. Москва, Изд-во Академии наук
СССР, 1955.

Nasonov, Arsenii Nikolaevich.
"Русская земля" и образование территории древнерус-
ского государства; историко-географическое исследова-
ние. Москва, Изд-во Академии наук СССР, 1951.

259 p.   fold. maps.   27 cm.

At head of title: Академия наук СССР. Институт истории.
Errata slip inserted.
Bibliographical footnotes.

1. Russia—Hist.—To 1533.   I. Title.
              Title transliterated: "Russkaîa zemlîa."

DK71.N3   52-25403

NN   0026612   DLC LU OrU CSt FMU NSyU

Nasonov, Dmitrii Nikolaevich.
О природе возбуждения; стенограмма публичной лекции, прочитанной 1 апреля 1948 года ... в Москве. Москва ₍Правда₎ 1948.

15 p.   illus.   22 cm.

At head of title: Всесоюзное общество по распространению политических и научных знаний.

1. Protoplasm.   I. Title.
         Title transliterated: O prirode vozbuzhdenîîa.

QH591.N28   50-18941 ‡

NN   0026613   DLC

QH591   **Nasonov, Dmitrii Nikolaevich.**
.N3   ... Реакция живого вещества на внешние воздействия;
денатурационная теория повреждения и раздражения. Москва, Ленинград, Издательство Академии наук СССР, 1940.

251, ₍1₎ p.   illus., plates (1 col.) diagrs.   26½ᶜᵐ.

At head of title: Академия наук Союза ССР. Д. Н. Насонов и В. Я.
Александров.
Errata slip mounted on p. ₍252₎
"Литература": p. 226-₍247₎

1. Protoplasm.   I. Aleksandrov, V. îA., joint author.   II. Akademîîa
nauk SSSR.   III. Title.
         Title transliterated: Reakßiîa zhivogo veshchestva.

                           44-10365

Library of Congress

NN   0026614   DLC

Nasonov, I
Iсторія КIM (у короткому викладі) Переклад з російсь-
кої. Харків, Молодий більшовик, 1931.
(Підручники для комсомольського політнавчання)

Microfilm copy   (positive)
Collation of the original : 99 p.

Negative film in the Library of Congress.

1. Young Communist International.
          Title transliterated: Istorîîa KIM.

                     Mic 53-674

NN   0026615   DLC

Nasonov, I
История КИМ (в кратком изложении) Москва, Молодая гвардия, 1930.

149 p.   18 cm.

1. Young Communist International.
          Title transliterated: Istorîîa KIM.

HX11.Y6N3   59-55382 ‡

NN   0026616   DLC

Nasonov, Nikolai Viktorovich, 1855-1939, ed.

QL281   Фауна СССР. Москва, 1911–
.F3
A–Z   v. in   illus., plates, maps (part fold. col.) 24-27 cm.
      At head of title, 1865-   : Зоологический институт Академии
наук СССР.

570.6   **Nasonov, Nikolai Viktorovich, 1855- 1939.**
Ak132   ... Zur morphologie der Turbellaria rhabdo-
v.2   coelida des Japanischen meeres. Teile I und II.
Ленинград, Издательство Академии наук СССР., 1932.
4 p. l., 115 p., VIII pl. (part fold.)   25½ᶜᵐ.
(Академия наук Союза Советских Социалистических
Республик. Труды лаборатории экспериментальной
зоологии и морфологии животных. Том 2)

At head of title: N. Nasonov (N. Nassonov)
Added t-p.: Académie des sciences de l'Union
des Républiques Soviétiques Socialistes. Travaux

du laboratoire de zoologie expérimentale et de
morphologie des animaux ... Sur la morphologie
des Turbellaria rhabdocoelida de la mer du Japon.
Resumé in Russian: "К морфологии ... Японского
моря", p. 113-115.
Bibliographical footnotes.

NN   0026619   NNC

Nasmyth, James Hall, 1808–1890.
The moon, considered as a planet, a world, and a satel-
lite, by James Nasmyth, C. E. and James Carpenter ...
With twenty-six illustrative plates of lunar objects, phe-
nomena, and scenery, numerous diagrams, etc. New
York, J. Pott & co.; London, J. Murray, 1903.

xix, 315, ₍1₎ p. col. front., illus., plates. 21ᶜᵐ.

"Fourth edition."

1. Moon.   I. Carpenter, James, F. R. A. S., joint author.

Library of Congress   QB581.N22   4-14172/3

NN   0026620   DLC OU OrSaW WaS PP PU OC1 OC1W NN WaU

Nasonov, Nikolaĭ Viktorovich, 1855-1939.
... Добавочные образования, развивающиеся при вложе-
нии хряща под кожу взрослых хвостатых амфибий. Москва,
Ленинград, Издательство Академии наук СССР, 1941.
90, ₍2₎ p. incl. illus. (facsim.) tables. port. 27ᶜᵐ.
At head of title: Академия наук Союза ССР. Акад. Н. В. Насонов.
"Литература": p. ₍90₎ Bibliographical foot-notes.
Contents.—Зелинский, Н. Д. и Федотов, Д. М. О работах акад.
Н. В. Насонова по проблеме организаторов.—Насонов, Н. В. Доба-
вочные образования, развивающиеся при вложении хряща под кожу
взрослых хвостатых амфибий (followed by summary in English by
А. А. Передельский)—Передельский, А. А. Сводка исследований акад.
Н. В. Насонова над проблемой организатора и некоторые выводы.

1. Embryology—Batrachia.   2. Morphology.   3. Urodela.   I. Akademîîa nauk SSSR.   II. Title.
      Title transliter-   *ated:* Dobavochnye obrazovanîîa ...
Library of Congress   QL959.N3   44-10359
                           ₍2₎

NN   0026621   DLC

Nasonov, V
    Complete self instructor for the balalaïka ...
    see under   Andree, Vasiliĭ Vasil'evich,
     1861-1918.

NASONVILLE, R. I.—Dixième anniversaire du Sanctuaire Sainte-Thérèse (1923-
1933.)—Fêtes commémoratives du dimanche 24 septembre 1933. Illustrations.
Woonsocket, 1933. 72 p.
Historique du sanctuaire.

NN   0026623   RWoU

NASORAEANS.

See MANDAEANS.

---

ar W   **Nasos, N   A.**
31281   Ἀπολογία τοῦ Ἑλληνικοῦ
ἕενους, ἤ, Σύντομος ἔκθεσις τῶν
διατρεξάντων καὶ ὀλίγαι λέξεις
πρὸς ἀπάντησιν. Apologie de la nation
grecque...The Greek nation's apology...
Ἀθήνησιν, 1855.
32 p. 21cm.

Greek, French and English.

     Title transliterated:
     Apologia tou Hellēnikou
     ethnous.

NN   0026625   NIC

VOLUME 405

Насосы; каталог-справочник. ₁Составитель Д. Н. Азарх₎ Москва, Гос. научно-техн. изд-во машиностроит. лит-ры, 1950.

207 p. illus. 27 cm.

At head of title: Министерство машиностроения и приборостроения СССР. Главхиммаш. Всесоюзный научно-исследовательский институт гидромашиностроения.

1. Pumping machinery—Catalogs. I. Azarkh, David Naumovich. II. Russia (1923– U. S. S. R.) Ministerstvo mashinostroeniíà i priborostroeníà.
Title transliterated: Nasosy ; katalog-spravochnik.

TJ902.N25 1950   52–31292 rev ‡

NN   0026626   DLC

DF 901
S56 N38   Nasoulēs, Dēmosthenēs G
1950   Σκόπελος (ἡ ἀρχαία Πεπάρηθος) ἱστορικὴ μονογραφία. Ἀθῆναι, 1950.
              82 p. illus.

1. Skopelos (Island) *Title romanized:* Skopelos (hē archaia Peparēthos)

NN   0026627   CaBVaU DLC MiD OCU

Naspo Bizaro
    see under ₁Caravia, Alessandro₎ 1503–1568.

Nasporing van de beswaarnissen nevens de redenen der zelve, welke zeer veele van de burgers en schutters en verdere ingezetenen der stadt Leyden, vermeinen te hebben. ₁Leyden?₎ de auteurs, 1748. 16 pp. sq. 8°.

NN   0026629   NN

Nasr, A   H
    The chorography of the marine algae inhabiting the northern part of the Red Sea coast. 1940.
    (In Bulletin, Institut d'Egypte, v. 22, no. 2; p. 193–219. maps, tables, diagrs.)

Bibliography: p. 217–219.

NN   0026630   PPAN

Nasr, A. H.
    The marine algae of Alexandria. I. A report on some marine algae
        see under   Hurghada, Egypt. Marine Biological Station.

Nasr, A. H.
    The marine algae of Alexandria. II. A study of the occurrence of some marine algae
        see under   Hurghada, Egypt. Marine Biological Station.

Nasr, A   H
    Some new and little known algae from the Red Sea.   Paris, Publications de la Revue algologique, 1939.
    cover-title, 20 p.   illus., pl.   25½ cm.

This copy received and date stamped, Nov. 6, 1939. Republished in Revue algologique, v. 12, p. 57–76, 1941.
Bibliography: p. 20.

NN   0026633   PPAN

Nasr, Anis.
    النبوغ اللبناني في القرن العشرين ₁تأليف₎ انيس نصر.
    ₁حلب، يطلب من مكتبة العصر الجديد
    –1938.
    v. illus., facsims., ports. 26 cm.

1. Lebanon—Biog.   I. Title.
Title romanized: al-Nubūgh al-Lubnānī.

CT1919.LAN37   N E 68–2805

NN   0026635   DLC

Nasr, Asad Y
    Income arising in the government sector
        see under   Badre, Albirt Yūsuf, 1912–

Nasr, Asad Y.
    Income arising in the industrial sector
        see under   Badre, Albirt Yūsuf, 1912–

Nasr, Asad Y.
    Income arising in the services sector
        see under   Badre, Albirt Yūsuf, 1912–

619.4   Nasr, Hamed.
N18n   The nutritional significance of microbial synthesis in the pig caecum.   Cairo, Fouad I University Press, 1952.
            ix, 138p. illus., diagrs., tables. 24cm.

"This book covers the subject matter of a Ph.D. thesis accepted in Aberdeen University in March 1950."
Bibliography: p.131–138.

NN   0026639   IU NIC IaAS

711.3   Nasr, Iman, 1896–
L5   ... Ueber das Synthalin ... ₁Zeulenroda i.
1928   Thür.,1928₎
             Inaug.-Diss. – Leipzig.
             Lebenslauf.
             "Literatur": p.42–46.

NN   0026640   CtY ICRL

Nasr, Mohammed Abdul-Muizz
    see
Nasr, Muhammad 'Abd al-Mu'izz.

610.932 Nasr, Moustafa Hamed.
N18i   ... Innere medizin bei den alten Aegypten ...   Tübingen ₁1928?₎
              37p.

At head of title: Aus der medizinischen klinik der universität Tübingen ...
Inaug.-diss.--Tübingen.
Lebenslauf.
"Literaturverzeichnis": p.35–36.

NN   0026642   IU ICRL CtY DNLM

Nasr, Muhammad 'Abd al-Mu'izz.
الدولة والمواطن، بحث فى نظرية السيادة. ₁تأليف₎ محمد عبد
المز نصر. الاسكندرية، مطابع رمسيس، 1952.
100 p. 24 cm.
Bibliography: p. 99–100.

1. Political science—Hist.   I. Title.
Title transliterated: al-Dawlah wa-al-muwāṭin.

JA81.N36   N E 64–3439

NN   0026643   DLC

Nasr, Muhammad Makkī
    see
al-Jarīsī, Muhammad Makkī Nasr.

Nasr, Mustafā Ḥāmid
    see   Nasr, Moustafa Hamed.

Nasr, Nasīm.
    (al-Shi'r al-'Arabī fī balāṭāt al-mulūk)
الشعر العربي في بلاطات الملوك ₁تأليف₎ نسيم نصر. ₁بيروت₎
دار مجلة الأديب، 1950.
120 p. 22 cm.

1. Arabic poetry—History and criticism. 2. Authors and patrons. I. Title.

PJ7519.P33N3   74–220405

NN   0026646   DLC

Nasr, Raja Tewfik, 1929–
    The phonological problems involved in the teaching of American English to native speakers of Lebanese Arabic. Ann Arbor, University Microfilms ₁1955₎
    ₁University Microfilms, Ann Arbor, Mich.₎ Publication no. 12,628)
    Microfilm copy of typescript. Positive.
    Collation of the original, as determined from the film: 3, v, 163 l.
    Thesis—University of Michigan.
    Abstracted in Dissertation abstracts, v. 15 (1955) no. 9, p. 1617.
    Bibliography: leaves 162–163.

1. English language—Study and teaching—Lebanese students. 2. English language—Phonetics. 3. Arabic language—Dialects—Lebanon.

Microfilm AC-1   no. 12,628   Mic A 55–2152

Michigan. Univ. Libr.
for Library of Congress   ₁1₎

NN   0026647   MiU DLC LU TxU

PE 1130 Nasr, Raja Tewfik, 1929–
A8 N3   The phonological problems involved in the teaching of American English to native speakers of Lebanese Arabic, by Raja T. Nasr, 1955.
1955a   163 l.

Thesis - University of Michigan.
Bibliography: leaves 162–163.
Photocopy of typescript. Ann Arbor, Mich., University Microfilms, 1967. 25 cm. (Doctoral dissertation series, Publication no. 12,628)

NN   0026648   OU FU CLU InU

Nasr, Sayyid Taki
    see   Nasr, Taqi, 1907–

Nasr, Taghi, seyyed
    see   Nasr, Taqī, 1907–

VOLUME 405

Naṣr, Taqī, 1907–
  Essai sur l'histoire du droit persan à l'époque des Sassanides ... par Seyyed Taghi Nasr. Paris, A. Mechelinck, 1932.

  4 p., 1, 386 p., 1 l.   25 cm.
  Thèse–Paris.
  Bibliography: p. ₍367₎–375.

  1. Law—Iran—History and criticism.   2. Iran—Politics and government.   I. Title.

                                                      37–18179

NN   0026651   DLC CtY

Naṣr, Taqī, 1907–
  Essai sur l'histoire du droit persan dès l'origine à l'invasion arabe, par Seyyed Taghi Nasr. Paris, A. Mechelinck, 1933.

  4 p., 1, 386 p., 1 l.   maps.   26 cm.
  Errata slip inserted.
  Bibliography: p. ₍367₎–375.

  1. Law—Iran—History and criticism.   2. Iran—Politics and government.   I. Title.

                                                      A C 34–494

  New York. Public Libr.   rev 2
  for Library of Congress   ₍r73e2₎†

NN   0026652   NN IEN-L CU DLC NNC PBm

Naṣr, Zakarīyā Aḥmad.
  العلاقات الاقتصادية الدولية، تأليف زكريا أحمد نصر.
  ₍القاهرة، مطبعة نهضة مصر، ١٩٥٣ ؛تاريخ خاتمة الطبع: ١٩٥٤؛
  ₍1954₎

  477 p.   diagrs.   25 cm.
  Bibliographical footnotes.

  1. Commerce.   I. Title.
            Title transliterated: al-ʻAlāqāt al-iqtiṣādīyah al-duwalīyah.

  HF1007.N34   60–29000

NN   0026653   DLC

Nasr ad-Dīn, Hōja, 14th cent.
    see   Nasreddin Hoca.

Nasr al-Dīn, khodja, 14th cent.
    see   Nasreddin Hoca.

Naṣr al-Dīn, *khwājah*
      see
      Nasreddin Hoca.

Naṣr al-Dīn, Muhammad ibn Muhammad, al-Ṭūsī,
    1201?–1274
      see   al-Ṭūsī, Naṣīr al-Dīn Muhammad
      ibn Muhammad, 1201–1274.

Naṣr al-Dīn, Mullā
      see
      Nasreddin Hoca.

Naṣr Allāh, ʻAzīz.
  الرحلة العراقية، تأليف عزيز نصر الله. مصر، مطبعة التقدم،
  .1916

  128 p.   18 cm.

  1. Mesopotamia—Descr. & trav.   I. Title.
            Title romanized: al-Riḥlah al-ʻIrāqīyah.

  DS70.6.N3   N E 68–986

NN   0026659   DLC

Nasr- Allah, Feylessouf
    see   Nassrollah, Feylessouf.

Nasr Allāh Khān Fidāʼī, *d.* 1896 *or* 7.
  ... داستان ترکتازان هند ... گردآوردهٔ خامهٔ میرزا نصر الله
  خان فدائی فرخوانده به دولت یار جنگ بهادر در
  چابخانهٔ خالقی نواب نامه نگار و بنگرانی خودشان بزیور چاپ
  آراسته گردید.

  ₍Bombay, Published for the author Nawab Dowlut Yar
  Jang Bahadoor by J. B. Marzban & Co., 1309 i. e. 1892₎
    5 v.   port.   25 cm.
    Vols. 2–5 have cover title only; v. 3–5 lack imprint.
    Vol. 5: ₍فرهنگ هر چهار كاخ داستان ترکتازان هنده₎
    Reproduced from ms. copy.
    1. India—History.   2. Muslims in India—History.   I. Title.
            Title romanized: Dāstān-i
            turktāzān-i Hind.

  DS452.N37   71–264931

NN   0026661   DLC

Nasr Askar, Ibrahim, 1901–
  ... Der Einfluss C-vitaminarmer Ernährung
  auf das Netzgewebe der Nager ...   Würzburg,
  1929.
  Inaug.-diss. – Würzburg.
  Lebenslauf.
  "Literatur": p. 27–28.

NN   0026662   CtY

Nasr-ed-Dīn, *mullah*
      see
      Nasreddin Hoca.

Nasr ed-Din, Shah af Iran
      see under   Nāṣir al-Dīn Shāh, Shah of
      Iran, 1831–1896.

Nasr-eddin, *hoja*
      see
      Nasreddin Hoca.

Nasr Efendi, khodja, 14th cent.
      see   Nasreddin Hoca.

  ... The Nasr i Be–Nazir; or, Story of Prince
  Be–Nazir
      see under   ₍Hasan, Mīr₎ fl. 1786.

Naṣr ibn Muḥammad, Abū al-Layth
      see
      Abū al-Layth al-Samarqandī, Naṣr ibn Muḥammad, *d.*
      983?

Naṣr ibn Muzāḥim, *d.* 827 *or* 8.
  نخبة المحدثين في كتاب صفين كما توقع الى الامام امير المؤمنين
  علي بن أبي طالب، تأليف نصر بن مزاحم التميمي الكوفي. اعتنى
  بضبطه ركلام، وتصحيحه حسين قصفه. ديتروت مشئن، على
  نفقة عبد اللطيف حمود والمصحح، ١٩٢٥/١٣٤٣ ؛1925₎

  251 p.   29 cm.

  1. Siffin, Battle of, 657.   I. Title.
            Title transliterated: Nukhabat al-
            muḥaddithīn fī kitāb Ṣiffīn.

  DS97.N28   N E 62–452

NN   0026669   DLC

Naṣr ibn Muzāḥim, *d.* 827 or 8.
  وقعة صفين. بيروت، تطلب من المكتبة العاملية، 1921.

  400 p.   23 cm.
  Author named on p. 3: نصر بن مزاحم.
  Abridged by the publisher, Maḥmūd ʻAbbās al-ʻĀmilī.

  1. Siffin, Battle of, 657.   I. al-ʻĀmilī, Maḥmūd ʻAbbās, ed.
  II. Title.
            Title romanized: Waqʻat Ṣiffīn.

  DS97.N32   72–210943

NN   0026670   DLC

Naṣr ibn Muzāḥim, *d.* 827 or 8.
  وقعة صفين، لنصر بن مزاحم المنقري. تحقيق وشرح عبد
  السلام محمد هارون. الطبعة الأولى. ₍القاهرة، عيسى البابي
  الحلبي، ١٣٦٥ ₍1945/46₎

  15, 766 p.   map.   21 cm.
  Bibliographical footnotes.

  1. Siffin, Battle of, 657.   I. Title.
            Title transliterated: Waqʻat Ṣiffīn.

  DS97.N3   N E 61–16

NN   0026671   DLC

Nasra (Alexandre) ₍1868–   ₎.   *Contribution
  à l'étude clinique des névroses post-infectieuses
  (hystérie, neurasthénie, hystéro-neurasthénie).
  153 pp.   4°.   Paris, 1896. No. 149.

NN   0026672   DNLM

Nasra, G., Bey
    see   Jibrāʼil Nasrah Bey.

Nasralla, Zakaria Habib
    see   Habib Nasralla, Zakaria.

Z470   **Nasrallah, Joseph**
L4N38   L'imprimerie au Liban. Gravure sur bois
Library   de Zaher.   Beyrouth ₍1948?₎
School   xxiv,160 p.   illus.,facsims.

             At head of title: Troisième conférence
             générale de l'UNESCO.
             "Sous le patronage de la Commission
             libanaise du mois de l'UNESCO, novembre–
             décembre 1948."
             Slips mounted on t.p. and cover: Paris,
             Office des Éditions universitaires.

NN   0026675   CU ICU NN

Nasrallah, Joseph.
  L'imprimerie au Liban.   Gravure sur bois de Zaher.
  Harissa, 1948 ₍cover 1949₎

  xxiv, 160 p.   illus., facsims.   24 cm.

  1. Printing—Hist.—Lebanon.   2. Printers—Lebanon.

  Z186.L4N38   52–44880

NN   0026676   DLC NIC IU CSt-H MH MiU NcD

PJ
5601   **Nasrallah, Joseph.**
.N26   Les manuscrits de Maʻloula.   ₍n.p., 194–
             v.
             Cover title.
             "Extraits du Bulletin d'études orientales de
             l'Institut franqais de Damas,année 1942–1943."

NN   0026677   MiU

VOLUME 405

Nasrallah, Joseph.
Marie dans la sainte et divine liturgie byzantine. Paris, Nouvelles Éditions latines (1955)
107 p. illus. 19 cm. (Collection Le Monde catholique)
Bibliographical footnotes.

1. Mary, Virgin. 2. Orthodox Eastern Church. Liturgy and ritual.
A 57-1058

Harvard Univ. Library
for Library of Congress (1)

DDO DCU
NN 0026678   MH CBGTU MiU NjP InStme NjPT ODaU-H

281.1
zJ57n Nasrallah, Joseph.
Saint Jean de Damas, son époque, sa vie, son oeuvre. Harissa (Lebanon) (Imp. Saint Paul) 1950.
xv, 200 p. illus. 25 cm. (Les Souvenirs chrétiens de Damas, 2)
On label over imprint: Paris, Office des Éditions universitaires.
"Bibliographie": p. (viii)-xv.

1. Joannes, of Damascus, Saint.
52-15

DDO MH CtY-D NcD PPT MiU IEG NBuU KyTrA
NN 0026679   MoSU-D InStme CU TxFTC DGU ICU IMunS

Nasrallah, Joseph.
Saint Julien le Pauvre. (Paris, Nouvelles Éditions latines, 1955)
32 p. illus. 19 cm.

1. Paris. Saint Julien le Pauvre (Church)
A 55-5015

Catholic Univ. of   America. Library
for Library of Congress (1)

NN 0026680   DCU

Nasrallah, Joseph.
Souvenirs de St Paul. Harissa, 1944.
xx, 71 p. illus. 26 cm. (Les Souvenirs chrétiens de Damas, 1)
"Bibliographie": p. (xi)-xvii. "Sources": p. (xviii)-xx.

1. Paul, Saint, apostle. 2. Damascus. I. Title. (Series)
BS2505.N3   [922.1] 225.92   48-41781*

NN 0026681   DLC MiU

KG35
N186v Nasrallah, Joseph
Vie de la Chrétienté melkite sous la domination turque. Paris, P. Geuthner, 1949.
(95)-107 p. 24 cm.

Cover title.
"Extrait de la Revue des études islamiques, année 1948."
Bibliographical footnotes.

1. Melchites.   2. Syria - Church history.

NN 0026682   CtY-D

Nasrallah, Mourtada.
La forme des actes en droit international privé, spéciale-ment selon le droit français. Ambilly, 1952.
190 p. 25 cm.
Thèse—Geneva.
Bibliography: p. (175)-183.

1. Conflict of laws—Formalities. 2. Conflict of laws—Formali-ties—France.
56-21245

NN 0026683   DLC CU-L MH-L NNC PU-L

Nasrallah, Yusuf
see Nasrallah, Joseph.

Nasrallah Haddad, E., joint author.
Arabiasch wie des in Palastine gesprochen wird. Ein Leitfaden für Anfänger. Jerusalem, 1927.
96 p.

NN 0026685   PPDrop

Nasrallah Haddad, E., joint author.
Manual of Palestinean Arabic for self-instruc-tion
see under Spoer, Hans Henry, 1873-

Nasrallah Haddad, E., joint author.
Standard colloquial Arabic, by Elias N. Haddad and Jalil Z. Irany. 3d ed.   Jerusalem, 1955.
48 p.: 144 p.
Added title page in Arabic.
Earlier editions published under title: The spoken Arabic of Palestine.
"Prepared in such a way as to meet the need of a student in any Arabic-speaking country, with special reference to the Hashemite Kingdom of Jordan, Syria, and Lebanon". - Pref.
1.Arabic language - Grammar. 2. Arabic language - Chrestomathies and readers.

I. Irany, Jalil Z   joint author.

NN 0026688   CU UU NN MiD InU NcD

Nasreddin, hoca
see Nasreddin Hoca.

Nasreddin, Hodscha
see Nasreddin Hoca.

Nasreddin, Khodzha
see Nasreddin Hoca.

Nasreddin Hoca.
Cuentos de Yehá, recogidos, ordenados y publicados por Tomás García Figueras; los que han sido traducidos del árabe, lo fueron por el intérprete Antonio Ortiz Antiñolo. Ilustrados con maderas y litografías de Teodoro N. Miciano. Jerez de la Frontera (Prensas de la Nueva litografía jerezana s. a.) 1934.
3 p. l., ix-xxiii p., 1 l., 300, (1) p., 1 l. incl. illus., plates. 3 pl. 23½ cm.
"1.ª edición: 500 ejemplares."
"Bibliografía": p. xxiii.
I. García Figueras, Tomás, 1892-   ed. II. Title.
A 40-3075 rev

Michigan. Univ. Libr.   GR245
for Library of Congress   (r68c2)

NN 0026692   MiU

894.35
N186 Nasreddin Hoca.
Cuentos de Yeha, recogidos, ordenados y publicados por Tomás García Figueras. Los que han sido traducidos del Árabe, le fueron por los intérpretes Antonio Ortiz Antiñolo y José Linares Rubio. 2. ed. aum. Tetuán, Editora Marroquí, 1950.
274 p. 24cm.
I. Ortiz Antiñolo, Antonio,   tr. II. García   Figueras, Tomás, 1892-   ed.   III, Title. IV. Title: Yehá.

NN 0026693   MnU MH ScU

PL
248 Nasreddin Hoca.
N3 Fjörutíu og fimm tyrkneskar kými-sögur.
A54 Thorsteinn Gíslason thýddi. Reykjavík,
1904 Prentsmidja "Fraekarna", 1904.
100 p.

NN 0026694   WaU MH NIC

Nasreddin Hoca.
Hodscha Nasreddin; ein türkischer Eulenspiegel. Übersetzt und eingeleitet, von Dr. Otto Spies.   Berlin: Weltgeist-Bücher(, 1928). 54 p. 12°. (Weltgeist-Bücher, umfassen den Geist der ganzen Welt. Nr. 285.)

421374A. 1. Turkish literature—   Fiction. 2. Spies, Otto, 1901-
N. Y. P. L.   translator. 3. Title.   August 13, 1929

NN 0026695   NN

Nasreddin Hoca.
Der hodscha Nasreddin; türkische, arabische, berberische, maltesische, sizilianische, kalabrische, kroatische, serbische und griechische märlein und schwänke, gesammelt und her-ausgegeben von Albert Wesselski ... Weimar, A. Duncker, 1911.
2 v. 20½ cm. (Half-title: Narren, gaukler und volksliebinge, hrsg. von Albert Wesselski. 3.-4. bd.)
Bibliography: v. 1, p. xxxii-liii.

I. Wesselski, Albert, 1871-1939, ed. and tr. II. Title.
PL248.N3A48   894.357   36-12896 rev

NN 0026696   DLC MiU NIC InU ICarbS RPB ICN MH NN

Nasreddin Hoca.
The Khoja; tales of Nasr-ed-Din, translated from the Turkish text by Henry D. Barnham, c. m. g., with a foreword by Sir Valentine Chirol. New York, D. Appleton and company, 1924.
xxviii p., 1 l., 259, (1) p. illus. 21 cm.
London edition (Nisbet & co., ltd.) has title: Tales of Nasr-ed-Din Khoja.

I. Barnham, Henry Dudley, 1854-   tr. II. Title.
PL248.N3A23 1924   24-15895

NN 0026697   DLC PU CoU NcD PPAmP OCl MiU NN OrU

Nasreddin Hoca.
لطایف ملا نصر الدین ... بسعی و اهتمام مدیر کتابخانه و چاپخانه اقبال تنظیم و چاپ شده است. تهران، چاپخانه اقبال، 7 or 1946، 1325.
112 p. 23 cm.

I. Iqbāl, Javād, ed. II. Title.
Title romanized: Laṭāyif.
PK6495.N33L3   77-282372

NN 0026698   DLC

PL
248 Nasreddin Hoca
N18m Manzum Nasreddin Hoca fıkra ve hikâyeleri. [Ha-
1950 zırlayan] Sami Ergun. Ankara, Millî Eğitim Bası-mevi, 1950.
xi, 143 p. col. illus.

I. Ergun, Sami

NN 0026699   CLU

Nasreddin Hoca.
Moslygo napkelet, Hodza-strófák
see under Kunos, Ignácz, 1862-1945.

VOLUME 405

Nasreddin Hoca.
　Nasreddin Hoca.　Istanbul, Kanaat Matbaa
ve Kütüphanesi, 1918.
　238 p.　plates.

　I. Köprülü, Mehmet Fuat, 1890-　　ed.

NN　0026701　NNC

Nasreddin Hoca.
　Nasreddin Hoca fıkraları, toplayan: Tasvir
Neşriyatı ₍önsöz: İsmail Hami Danişmend₎
İstanbul, Tasvir₍ Neşriyatı ₎195-?₎
　103 p.　illus.　(Tasvir Nesriyati: 5.　Halk
kitapları serisi: 2)

NN　0026702　NNC

Nasreddin Hoca.
　Nasreddin Khodjas schwänke und streiche.　Türkische geschichten aus Timurlenks tagen erzählt von Ali Nouri.　Breslau, Schlesische verlags-anstalt v. S. Schottlaender, etc. etc. 1904.
　pp. 234.　Illus.

　‖Ali Nouri°

NN　0026703　MH OC1 NN NIC

Nasreddin Hoca .
　Nasradin-hodza, njegove sale, dosetke i lakridje
... Belgrade...n.d.
　192 p.

NN　0026704　OC1

Nasreddin Hoca.
　Nasreddin, der Schelm;' Fahrten, Meinungen und Taten des
lachenden Philosophen Nasreddin Hodscha, des türkischen Eu-
lenspiegels, erzählt von Herm. Siegfried Rehm...　Berlin: £
Schuster & Loeffler, 1916.　144 p.　16°.

　"Erste bis dritte Auflage."

526782A. 1. Turkish literature—　　Fiction. I. Rehm, Hermann
Siegfried, 1859-　, editor.
N. Y. P. L.　　　　　　　　　　　June 27, 1931

NN　0026705　NN

Nasreddin Hoca .
　Nasreddin, der schelm; fahrten, meinungen und
taten des lachenden philosophen Nasreddin Hodscha
... Berlin und Leipzig...1918.
　166 p.

NN　0026706　OC1

PL248　Nasreddin Hoca.
N3　　Nasreddin hoca lâtifeleri külliyati.
1943　Ankara, Akba kitabevi ₍1943₎
　88 p.　illus.

　At head of title: Derleyip toplanan
Zaparta.

　I. Zaparta.　II. Title.

NN　0026707　CU

Nasreddin Hoca.
　Nasreddin Hodscha; turkiska sagor och
skämthistorier, återgivna och inledda av
Fredrik Böök. Stockholm, P. A. Norstedt
₍1928₎
　96 p.　illus., col. plates.

　I. Böök, Fredrik, 1883-　　ed.

NN　0026708　NNC

Nasreddin Hoca.
　Naszreddin hodsa tréfái...török (kisázsiai)
szövegét gyüjtötte, forditással és jegyzetekkel
ellátta Kunos Ignácz.　96,[2],46p.　Budapest,
Magyar tudományos akadémia, 1899.　(Magyar tudományos akadémia, Budapest - Nyelv és széptudományi
osztály, v.27, no. 2)

NN　0026709　OC1 NNC

Nasreddin Hoca.
　Les plaisanteries de Nasr-Eddin Hodja, traduites du turc par J.-A.
Decourdemanche.
　Paris.　Leroux.　1876.　108 pp.　[Bibliothèque orientale elzévi-
rienne. 5.] 18°.
　Bibliographie, pp. 107, 108.

G4124 — S.r. — T.r. — Wit and humor. — Decourdemanche, Jean Adolphe, tr.

NN　0026710　MB ICN RPB OC1W MH

Nasreddin Hoca.
　Les plaisanteries de Nasr-Eddin Hodja, tr. du
turc par J.-A. Decourdemanche.　2. éd. augm. des
Naivetés de Karacouch.　[4],154p.　Paris, E.
Leroux, 1908.　(Bibliothèque orientale elzévi-
rienne, v.5)

NN　0026711　OC1

Nasreddin Hoca.
　The pleasantries of Cogia Nasr Eddin Effendi; translated from
the Turkish by George Borrow.　　Cleveland, The Clerk's press,
1916.　39 p.　14cm.　(The folk humour series.　no. 2.)
　No. 29 of 32 copies printed.
　"Typography and presswork done by Charles C. Bubb, clerk in holy orders."
　"Taken from the translation of 'The Turkish jester' made by George Borrow some
time about 1854, and published posthumously in 1884."
　Printer's presentation copy to Mrs. E. W. Worthington.

52R0724. 1. Turkish literature—　　Fiction. I. Borrow, George, 1803-
1881, tr.　II. Title.

NN　0026712　NN

Nasreddin Hoca.
　Priče i dosjetke.　Sakupio: Ahmet Halit-Jašaroglu.
₍Preveo: Ismail Čaušević₎　Sarajevo, Svjetlost, 1952.
　123 p.　illus.　20 cm.
　At head of title: Nasrudin-hodža.
　Translation of Nasreddin Hoca fıkraları.

　I. Yaşaroğlu, Ahmet Halit, comp.　II. Title.

PL248.N3N37　　　　　　　55-32465 rev

NN　0026713　DLC

Nasreddin Hoca.
　Die Schwänke des Nassr-ed-din und Buadem von Mehemed Tewfik.
Mit Genehmigung des Verlegers aus dem Türkischen übersetzt
und stellenweise erläutert von E. Müllendorff.
　Leipzig.　Reclam.　[1890.] 93 pp.　[Universal-Bibliothek. 2735.]
16°.
　Buadem is catalogued separately.

G3930 — T.r. — Wit and humor. — Muellendorff, Eugen, tr. 1855-

NN　0026714　MB MH NjP

Nasreddin Hoca.
　Tales of Nasr-ed-Din Khoja, translated from the Turkish text by Henry D. Barnham ... with a foreword by Sir
Valentine Chirol. London, Nisbet & co., ltd. ₍1923₎
　255, ₍1₎ p.　front., plates.　19½ cm.

　American edition (D. Appleton and company, New York) has title:
The Khoja; tales of Nasr-ed-Din.

　I. Barnham, Henry Dudley, 1854-　tr.　II. Title.

PL248.N3A23　1923　　　　　　24-20874

CaBVaU
NN　0026715　DLC CtY NIC FMU MU WaBeN NN PP OrStbM

Nasreddin Hoca.
　Sottisier de Nasr-Eddin-Hodja, bouffon de
Tamerlan; suivi d'autres faceties turques, traduits
sur des manuscrits inédits par
J.-A. Decourdemanche.　Bruxelles, Gay et Doucé,
1878.
　xii, 314 p.　21 cm.
　I. Decourdemanche, Jean Adolphe, 1844-1914?,
tr. II. Title.

NN　0026716　ICU ICN OC1 MH NIC

PL248　Nasreddin Hoca.
N3F7　Trente-trois plaisanteries de Khodja Nasr-ed Din, traduites
1847　du turc en français et suivies de quelques proverbes et d'une
lettre turque.　Smyrne, 1847.
　15, 14 p.

　With an appendix of exercises in Turkish characters.
　Photocopy.

NN　0026717　CU MH

Nasreddin Hoca.
　Turkish gems; or, The tales of my childhood.　Being the
funny sayings and doings of Nassr-ed-Din Hodja, the Turkish Aesop.　By S. V. Bedickian.　₍Alleghany, Pa., Press of
T. A. M'Nary₎ 1896.
　90 p.　16 cm.

　I. Bedickian, S. V., ed.　II. Title.

PL248.N3T8　　　　　　　53-48943 rev 2

NN　0026718　DLC

Nasreddin Hoca.
　The Turkish jester; or, The pleasantries of Cogia Nasr
Eddin Effendi.　Translated from the Turkish by George
Borrow.　Ipswich, W. Webber, 1884.
　52 p.　20 cm.
　Edition of 150 copies.

　I. Borrow, George Henry, 1803-1881, tr.　II. Title.

PL248.N3E5　1884　　　-894.357　　　1-28225 rev 2

NSyU InU
NN　0026719　DLC OKentU TxU OC1W CtY CSmH NjP OC1

Nasreddin Hoca.
　Vie de Nasreddin Hodja.　₍Édité par₎ Kemaleddine
Chukru.　₍Istanbul₎ Librairie Kaanat ₍1932?₎
　184 p.　illus., port. 20 cm.

　I. Kalelizade, Kemalettin Şükrü, ed.

PL248.N3A33　　　　　　　N E 64-851

NN　0026720　DLC

Nasreddin Hoca.
　Wybór tekstów tureckich.　Opowiadania
Chodży Nasreddina.　Opracował i opatrzył
komentarzem językowym Władysław Zimnicki.
Warszawa, Państwowe wydawnictwo naukowe,
1951.
　52 p.　24½ cm.

NN　0026721　NjP

Nasreddin-Schah
　see　Naṣir al-Dīn Shāh, shah of Iran,
1831-1906.

Nasreddin-shakh, Shah of Iran
　see　Naṣir al-Dīn Shāh, Shah of Iran,
1831-1896.

The National Union Catalog Pre-1956 Imprints 501

VOLUME 405

Nasretdin Afandi
see   Nasreddin Hoca.

al-Naṣrī, Abū al-Walīd Ismāʿīl ibn Yūsuf
see
Ibn al-Aḥmar, Ismāʿīl ibn Yūsuf, *d.* 1404 *or* 5.

Nasri, Aida Riad.
The cooperative movement in Egypt, its present condition
and future prospects. Cairo, 1948.
38, ₁11₁ l. diagrs., maps. 26 cm.
Thesis (M. A.)—American University at Cairo.
Photocopy (positive)
Bibliography : leaves ₁39₁–₁40₁

1. Agriculture, Cooperative—Egypt. 2. Cooperation—Egypt.
ɪ. Title.
HD1491.E3N3 1948a   334.683   50–28476

NN   0026726   DLC

PK1976   Nasri, M   H
N3   The royal practical Urdu- English dictionary, with pronunciation
1950   and English- Urdu proverbs & idioms in Urdu clear nastaliq. Edited
          by M. H. Nasri and Syed Zulfaqar Husain, Muqbil, Dehlvi.   3d ed.
          Lahore, Malik House, 1950.
          955 p.

          Imperfect copy? Preliminary matter between title page and p.
          [1] wanting?

          1. Urdu language - Dictionaries - English. I. Husain,
          Syed Zulfaqar, joint author. II. Title.

NN   0026727   CU

Naṣrī Ḥannā Qaṣīr.
التحفة الادبية في الامثال العربية، تأليف نصري قصير. ₁مصر₁
مطبعة المصر التاسع عشر ₁1894. ١٨٩٤₁
181 (i. e. 183) p. 24 cm.

1. Proverbs, Arabic.   ɪ. Title.
                          Title transliterated: al-Tuḥfah al-adabīyah
                          fī al-amthāl al-ʿArabīyah.
PN6519.A7N3   59–36680

NN   0026728   DLC

Nasroddin, Mula
   see
   Nasreddin Hoca.

Nasroen A   S
Indonesia pertama kali dalam pameran internasional
₁oleh₁ Nasroen A. S. ₁Djakarta, Bulan Bintang, sepatah
kata, 1952₁
unpaged. illus., ports. 18 cm.
Cover title.

1. Colombo, Ceylon. Colombo Exhibition, 1952. ɪ. Title.
T523 1952.N3   S A 68–5328 rev

NN   0026730   DLC WU MiU CU NIC CtY

Wason   Nasroen, M.
PL5089   Ada-ada sadja, oleh M. Nasroen. Djakarta,
N26   "Endang" ₁195 ₁
            71 p. illus. 23cm.

NN   0026731   NIC

Wason   Nasroen, M.
Pamphlet   Bunga rumput ditepi djalan, oleh M.
B   Nasroen. Djakarta, J.B. Wolters, 1952.
327   80 p. 19 cm.

1. Ethics, Indonesian. I. Title.

NN   0026732   NIC

JQ778   Nasroen, M.
.N3   Daerah otonomi tingkat terbawah.
          ₁Djakarta₁ Beringin trading company ₁1955?₁
            84 p.

1. Autonomy. 2. Indonesia - Pol. and govt.

NN   0026733   DS

Nasroen, M.
Keamanan dan masalah hukum. Oleh:
mr. M. Nasroen. Djakarta, "Endang"
₁1954₁
33 p. 23cm.

NN   0026734   MH-L NIC

Nasroen, M
Kebudajaan Indonesia, oleh M. Nasroen. Djakarta, Bulan
Bintang, 1951.
20 p. 20 cm.

1. Indonesia—Civilization.   ɪ. Title.
DS625.N35   S A 65–10490
                                   PL 480: Indo-1877

NN   0026735   DLC CU IU WU CtY MiU NIC

Otd22   Nasroen, M
951N   Masalah sekitar otonomi. Groningen, J.B.
          Wolters, 1951.
            126 p. 23 cm.

1. Indonesia - Pol. & govt.

NN   0026736   CtY NNC MH-L NIC

Nasroen, M
Pantjasila, pusaka lama. Djakarta, Endang, 1954.
40 p. 23 cm.

1. Indonesia—Pol. & govt.—1950-   ɪ. Title.
JQ763 1954.N3   S A 62–850

NN   0026737   DLC MH-L NIC

Nasroen, M
Soal pembentukan daerah otonom dan tingkatan daerah
otonom. Djakarta, Endang, 1954.
36 p. 23 cm.

1. Local government—Indonesia.   ɪ. Title.
                                   S A 62–589

NN   0026738   DLC NIC CU

Nasruddin, Ahmad Murad bin
   see
   Ahmad Murad bin Nasruddin.

Nasrudin, *hodža*
   see
   Nasreddin Hoca.

Nasrudin, Mulla
   see
   Nasreddin Hoca.

Nasrullah Khan, Nawabzada.
The ruling chiefs of western India and the Rajkumar
College. Bombay, Thacker, 1898.
vii, 200 p. ports. 20 cm.

1. India—Kings and rulers. 2. Rajkumar College.   ɪ. Title.
DS434.N32   73–221794

NN   0026742   DLC

LC   Nasrullah Khan, Nawabzada.
4946   The ruling chiefs of western India and the
.I4   Rajkumar College. 2d ed. Bombay, G.Claridge,
K45   1904.
1904   200 p. illus.

          1.Education of princes. 2.Rajkumar College,
          Rajkote,India. I.Title.

NN   0026743   MiU

Nasrullāh Khān Fidāʾī
   see
   Nasr Allāh Khān Fidāʾī, d. 1896 or 7.

Nasrun, M
   see
   Nasroen, M

Nass, Fritz, 1893–
Der Detektor-Empfänger, gestern und morgen; Ausblick
auf Möglichkeiten zur Leistungssteigerung unter Berücksichtigung des Selbstbaus von Detektor-Empfängern.
₁Frankfurt am Main-Fechenheim, Druck und Verlag: Main-
druck, 1948₁
23 p. illus. 21 cm.

1. Radio—Amateurs' manuals.   ɪ. Title.
TK9956.N3   57–34505

NN   0026746   DLC

Nass, Georg
Ueber die oxydation alkylierter benzoesäuren zu
mehrbasischen säuren.
Inaug. Diss.   Freiburg, 1889.

NN   0026747   ICRL

Nass, Gustav, 1901–
Beiträge zur experimentellen religions-
psychologie ... Kiel, 1932.   60 p.
Inaug. Diss. -Bonn, 1932.
Lebenslauf.

NN   0026748   ICRL PU CtY

Nass, Herbert, 1892–
... Über Demodex folliculorum ... Bonn,
1920.
24 p. 1 plate. 21.5 cm.
Inaug.-diss. - Bonn.
Lebenslauf.

NN   0026749   CtY ICRL DNLM

VOLUME 405

G630.6
Int8
1945cv
no.14
Nass, Hermann, 1913–
El crédito agrícola en Venezuela. Caracas,
Editorial Crisol, 1945.
42p. charts, tables. 23cm. (Cuadernos verdes
[Serie nacional] 14)

At head of title: Comité Organizador, Tercera
Conferencia Interamericana de Agricultura.

1. Agricultural credit – Venezuela. I. Title.
Series (contents)

NN   0026750   TxU NN

Nass, Hugo.   385.9436 Q900
Der Verzollungsdienst der Eisenbahnen. Eine eisenbahnpoli-
109271 tische Studie, von Hugo Nass und Hugo Reik, ... Wien,
J. Bettenhausen, 1909.
64 p. 22½ᶜᵐ.

NN   0026751   ICJ CU

Nass, Ida S
Chains of industrial slavery and the remedy. By Mrs. Ida
S. Nass ... Fairhaven [Wash.] Imperial city news print, 1894.
68 p. 18ᶜᵐ.

1. Social problems—Miscellanea. 2. Paper money—U. S.   I. Title.
Library of Congress   HD8072.N28
                                                  7—33062

NN   0026752   DLC

---

al-Naṣṣ, ‘Izzat
see
al-Nuṣṣ, ‘Izzat.

Nass, Jack, 1907–
... Les bois en Pologne; préface de M. H. Truchy ... Paris,
A. Pedone, 1933.
3 p. l., iv, 169, [1] p. maps (2 fold.) diagr. 24ᶜᵐ.
At head of title: Dr. J. Nass.
"Bibliographie": p. [163]–165.

1. Lumber trade—Poland. 2. Forests and forestry—Poland.
[2. Poland—Forestry] 3. [Wood industries]
                                                  Agr 33–961
[Library, U. S. Dept. of   Agriculture 99.66N18
                                         [HD9765.P   ]

NN4   0026754   DNAL MH CU NN

Nass, Johann
see Nase, Johann, 1534–1590.

Nass, Karl, 1897–1945.
Die Nordgrenze der Urnenfelderkultur in Hessen. Mar-
burg/Lahn, Kommissionsverlag N. G. Elwert, 1952.
2 v. (85 p.) illus., port. 24 cm. (Kurhessische Bodenaltertümer,
Heft II, 1–2)
Bibliographical footnotes.

1. Pottery—Hesse. 2. Hesse—Antiq.   I. Title.   (Series)
GN814.K8K84 Heft 2, etc.   54–35873

NN   0026756   DLC MoU MH-P

Nass, Lucien, 1862–1928.
see Cabanès, Augustin, 1862–1928.

Nass, Lucien, 1874–   610.4 N181
... Curiosités médico-artistiques. [Première]-troisième série ...
133009 Clichés du "Correspondant médical." Paris, Le François,
* [1870]–1914.
3 vol. in 2. illus. 21ᶜᵐ.
At head of title: Docteur Lucien Nass.
Ser. 1 published by Librairie mondiale; ser. 2, by A. Michel.

NN   0026758   ICJ PPC

N
8223
.N3
Nass, Lucien, 1874–
Curiosités médico-artistiques.   Paris, La
Librairie mondiale [1907–
v. illus. 22 cm.

Vol. 2 has imprint: Paris, A. Michel.

1. Medicine and art. I. Title.

NN   0026759   WU NRU ICRL MnU-B DNLM TNJ CU CtY MiU

R705
910N
Nass, Lucien, 1874–
Curiosités médico-artistiques. Paris, Librairie
Mondiale [1910?]
4 p. l., [3]–308p. illus. 22cm.

1. Medicine – Caricatures and cartoons.
2. Medicine – Anecdotes, facetiae, satire, etc.

NN   0026760   CtY-M

N
72
.N372
Nass, Lucien, 1874–
Curiosités medico-artistiques; deuxième
série. (300 dessins à la plume); clichés du
"Correspondant medical". Paris, A. Michel
[1909?]
346p. illus. 21cm.

1. Art and science. I. Title.

NN   0026761   TNJ

Nass, Lucien, 1874–
Curiosités medico-artistiques. Troisième série.
Paris, Librairie le François, 1914.
303 p. illus. 21 cm.

NN   0026762   PPiU-D OClW-H PPJ MH

Nass (Lucien). *Les empoisonnements sous
Louis XIV, d'après les documents inédits de l'af-
faire des poisons, 1679–82. 204 pp., 1 pl. 8°.
Paris, 1898, No. 458.

NN   0026763   DNLM

Nass, Lucien, 1874–
Essais de pathologie historique. Le siège de Paris
et la commune, par le docteur Lucien Nass. Paris, Plon-
Nourrit et cⁱᵉ, 1914.
2 p. l., ii, 360 p. 19ᶜᵐ. fr. 3.50

1. Paris—Hist.—Commune, 1871. 2. Paris—Siege, 1870–1871. 3. Social
psychology.
Library of Congress   DC311.N3
                                                  14–3980

NN   0026764   DLC CaBVaU NN MB NcD IaU GU CtY IEN

Nass, Lucien, 1874–   joint author.
Cabanès, Augustin, 1862–1928.
... La névrose révolutionnaire; édition refondue et notable-
ment augmentée ... Paris, Albin Michel [1924]

Nass, Lucien, 1874–
... Les névrosés de l'histoire. Paris, Librairie univer-
selle, 1908.
2 p. l., 328 p., 1 l. 10 pl. 19½ᶜᵐ.
CONTENTS.—La névrose des races royales.—La névrose mythomanique.—
Les névroses sociales.—La névrose religieuse.—La névrose coloniale.

1. Hysteria, Epidemic. 2. Kings and rulers. 3. Degeneration.
Library of Congress   HV4962.N3
                                                  8–6069

NN   0026766   DLC ICJ PU ICRL DNLM

PN
2051
N3
Nass, Lucien, 1874–
Le nu au théâtre depuis l'antiquité [par]
L. Nass & G. J. Witkowski. Nouv. éd.
refonduc. Paris, Librairie le François, 1914.
308p. illus. 21cm.
Bibliographical footnotes.

1. Theater – Moral and religious aspects
I. Witkowski, Gustave Joseph, 1844–   joint
author II. Title

NN   0026767   WU GU

PN
2622
N84
N387
MAIN
Nass, Lucien, 1874–
The nude in the French theatre [by] L. Nass
& G.J. Witkowski. With an introd. by Anatole
France. [New York, S. Roth, c1953]
160p. illus. 25cm. (Boar'shead books)

1. Theater – France – History. 2. Nudity in
the performing arts. I. Witkowski, Gustave
Joseph, 1844–   joint author. II. Title.

NN   0026768   TxU NNC IEN NIC

Nass, Lucien, 1874–
Pauvres docteurs! Moeurs médicales.
Préface de Pinard. Paris, A. Michel [1906]
xii, 315 p. 12°.

NN   0026769   DNLM PU

HV6549
.C3
Nass, Lucien, 1874–   joint author.

Cabanès, Augustin, 1862–1928.
... Poisons et sortilèges ... Paris, Plon-Nourrit et cⁱᵉ,
1903.

Nass, Lucien, joint author.

Baudin, Pierre, 1863–
... La rançon du progrès. Paris, F. Juven [1909]

Nass, Lucien, 1874–
Le siège de Paris et la Commune; essais de
pathologie historique
see his   Essais de pathologie historique.

LD3907
.G7
1954
.N3
Nass, Martin L., 1926–
The effects of three variables on
children's concepts of physical
causality.
103p. tables, diagrs.
Thesis (Ph.D.) – N.Y.U., Graduate
School, 1954.
Bibliography: p.100–103.

NN   0026773   NNU-W

VOLUME 405

Nass, Otto.
Das recht der feiertagsheiligung, von dr. jur. Otto Nass ...
Berlin, C. Heymann, 1929.
vii, 90 p. 22ᶜᵐ.

"Literaturverzeichnis": p. ₍vi₎–vii.

—————— Nachtrag ... Berlin, C. Heymann, 1933.
6 p. 22ᶜᵐ.

1. Holidays—Germany.   i. Title.

36–6701

NN   0026774   DLC CtY

Nass, Otto.
Verwaltungsreform durch Erneuerung der Verwaltungs-
wissenschaft. Tübingen, Mohr, 1950.
xi, 158 p. 24 cm.

1. Administrative law—Germany (Federal Republic, 1949-   )
2. Germany (Federal Republic, 1949-   )—Pol. & govt. 3. Public
administration.   i. Title.

55–29703

NN   0026775   DLC NNC ICU GU

1890–
Naß, Otto, Referendar, a. Aschersleben: Die Bereicherungs-
haftung des Gläubigers in der Zwangsvollstreckung bei
Versteigerung fremder im Gewahrsam des Schuldners sich
befindender Sachen. Halle a. S. 1913: Hohmann. 60 S. 8°
Rostock, Jur. Diss. v. 25. Jan. 1914, Ref. Matthiaß, Wachenfeld
[Geb. 17. Aug. 90 Hettstedt; Wohnort: Halle a. S.; Staatsangeh.: Preußen;
Vorbildung: G. Aschersleben Reife 09; Studium: Grenoble 1, München 2,
Berlin 1, Halle 2 S.; Rig. 26. Nov. 13.]   [U 14. 1120

NN   0026776   ICRL MH-L MiU

Nass (Paul). * Ueber den Gerbstoff der Castanea
vesca. 39 pp. 8°. *Dorpat, W. Just,* 1884.

NN   0026777   DNLM

Nass, Raoul B
Two popular philosophic-scientific essays in the spirit of
faith and religion: i. The idea of God and of the notion of
reality. ii. The world—all of our Creator (an astronomic-
Biblical universal outlook of God's kingdom.) By: Dr. Raoul
B. Nass. Brooklyn, N. Y. ₍Printed by Twersky bros.₎ 1943₎
4 p. l., 70 p. 22ᶜᵐ.

1. Religion—Philosophy. 2. Religion and science.   i. Title: The idea
of God and of the notion of reality. ii. Title: The world—all of our
Creator.

A 44–5356

Harvard univ. Library
for Library of Congress   ₍3₎

NN   0026778   MH OCH NN

Nass, Raoul B
... Ueber die Bedeutung des Verhaltens der
elastischen Fasern in den Lungen Neugeborener...
Basel, 1935.
Inaug.-diss. - Basel.
"Literaturverzeichnis": p. 20.

NN   0026779   CtY MiU

Nass, Wilhelm, 1888–
Thoracoplastik...
Inaug. Diss. Bonn, 1919
Bibl.

NN   0026780   ICRL DNLM CtY

334N187   Nass, Rudolf.
Os   Sturm und sonne, gedichte ...   Berlin-Charlot-
tenburg, Vita, 1915.
140p.

NN   0026781   IU

Nassagaweya (Township) Council
Nassagaweya centennial 1850–1950, an historical volume of Nassagaweya Township in
Halton County, pub. by the Township Council
and including the early history of Nassagawey-
a as written by the late Joshua Norrish, an
early settler. Acton, ₍1950₎.
90p. illus., ports.
Fold. sheet in pocket: "One hundred years of
progress...reprint from issues of Acton Free
Press and   Canadian Champion of
Aug. 4, 1949"

NN   0026782   CaOTU CaBViP

NASSAGAWEYA (Township) Ontario.   _ ORDINANCES, etc.
TOWNSHIP OF₎ Nassagaweya/ BY-LAW No. 16./ For the Guidance
and Instruction of Inspectors/ of Houses of Public Entertainment, &c./
₍Text of the by-law, signed:₎/ ALEX. MCNAUGHTON./ JAMES
MCNAIR, Reeve./ Township Clerk./ Nassagaweya, 6th February, 1851.
Printed by Jones & Harris, Dundas./ [1851].
Broadside. 5 lines. 36 lines in 2 col. 4 lines.   42.5 x 29.6-30.3 cm.

NN   0026783   CaOTP

Nassagaweya (Township) Ontario. Presbyterian Church.
One hundred years at Nassagaweya Presbyterian church, 1836-
1936. ₍Guelph? Ont.₎ Published for the Historical committee,
1936. 24 p. illus. (incl. ports.) 23½cm.

Cover-title.
"Author's preface" signed: A. E. Byerly, D.O.

1. Nassagaweya, Ont.—Churches,   Presbyterian. I. ₍Byerly, Alpheus
Edward, 1894–   December 5, 1938₎
N. Y. P. L.

NN   0026784   NN

1881–
Nassal, Franz₎ Aesthetisch-rhetorische Beziehungen zwischen
Dionysius von Halicarnass und Cicero. Tübingen 1910:
Laupp. x, 169 S. 8°
Tübingen, Phil. Diss. v. 3. Mai 1910, Ref. Schmid
[Geb. 16. Mai 81 Hoßkirch; Wohnort: Tübingen; Staatsangeh.: Württem-
berg; Vorbildung: Gymn. Ehingen Reife M. 01; Studium: Tübingen 12 S.;
Coll. 24. Febr. 10.]   [U 10. 4190

NN   0026785   ICRL NjP InU CtY MH NN

NASSALL, HANS.
Der Vorläufige Reichswirtschaftsrat und die Wirtschaftsvertretungen
in den einzelnen Ländern zur Zeit der Weimarer Republik.
[Freiburg₎ 195–?₎   xxii, 244 l.   28cm.

Inaug.-Diss. — Albert-Ludwigs-Universität zu Freiburg.
Bibliography, l. iv–xiv.

1. Germany. Reichs wirtschaftsrat. 2. Representation, Functional—
Germany.

NN   0026786   NN

Nassall (Léo Laurentius). * De sectione legali.
32 pp. 12°. *Wirceburgi, F. E. Nitribitt,* [1798].

NN   0026787   DNLM

Nassalski, Marjan, 1860–
Formularium legale practicum in parochorum, vicariorum
foraneorum nec non curiarum episcopalium usum compositum
cui binae documentorum appendices accedunt. Edidit Marianus Nassalski ... Ed. 2., aucta et emendata. Wladislaviae
₍Druk H. Neumana w Włocławku₎ 1905.
4 p. L., ₍vii₎–xlviii, 500, 214 p., 1 L., lIII, ₍1₎ p. 23½ᶜᵐ.
"Lexicon ₍latino-polonicum, polonico-latinum₎": 1 L., p. ₍i₎–xxxxix at
end.
"Conspectus operum in hoc libro adhibitorum": verso of 4th prelim.
leaf.

1. Forms (Canon law) 2. Catholic church—Government.   I. Title.

40–12260

NN   0026788   DLC MBtS

Brown
M28
.N35   Nassann, William
The Connecticut march. Waterbury, Conn.,
Johnson and Nassann ₍c1911₎
5 p. 35 cm.
Cover title.
For piano.

1. Marches (Piano). 2. Connecticut—Songs
and music. I. Title.

NN   0026789   MB

Nassans (Alexandre). * Du traitement du ca-
tarrhe vésical, principalement par les injections
de nitrate d'argent. 34 pp. 4°. *Paris,* 1857,
No. 276, v. 608.

NN   0026790   DNLM

BT192   Nassans, Auguste de.
L2N3   Les droits des curés d'après le droit cano-
nique, par m. le dr. Aug. de Nassans ... Paris,
P. Téqui, 1903.
xii, 212 p. 23cm.

1. Parishes (Canon law) 2. Clergy (Canon law)
3. Pastors (Canon law) I. Title.

NN   0026791   MBtS

Nassār, Jamāl al-Dīn.
مجموعة طب الاسنان وامراض الفم ، لجمال الدين نصار.
₍دمشق₎ مطبعة الجامعة السورية 1940–.
v. 25 cm.
CONTENTS:— كتاب 1. علم اللغة الطبية . مفردات الطب —

1. Mouth—Diseases. 2. Therapeutics, Dental.   I. Title.
                    Title romanized: Majmū'at ṭibb
                    al-asnān wa-amrāḍ al-fam.

RC815.N34   72–218327

NN   0026792   DLC

Nassār, Maḥmūd.
الاحسان العام في مصر، لمحمود نصار. القاهرة، مطبعة
لجنة التاليف والترجمة والنشر ، 1941.
208 p. 24 cm.
Bibliography: p. ₍198₎–203.

1. Public welfare—Egypt. 2. Public welfare.   I. Title.
                    Title romanized: al-Iḥsān al-'āmm fī Miṣr.

HV443.N37   74–224980

NN   0026793   DLC

Nassar, Salwa Chuckri, 1913–
A cloud-chamber study of cascade showers and
knock-on electrons in lead, by Salwa Chuckri
Nassar ... [Berkeley, Calif., 1945]
2 p.l., 24 numb. l. incl. diagrs. (1 mounted)
mounted pl. 29 cm.
Thesis (Ph. D.) - Univ. of California, Oct. 1945₎
Bibliography: p. 24.

NN   0026795   CU

VOLUME 405

Nassar, Seraphim, comp.

Orthodox Eastern church. *Liturgy and ritual. English.*
Book of divine prayers and services of the Catholic Orthodox
church of Christ, comprising the most important of the private
and public prayers; services of the dominical feasts of the distinguished saints; and of all Sundays of the year; in the order
ordained by the Holy Orthodox church of Christ; to which
are appended an index and a table for finding Easter, covering
a period of twenty years, 1938 to 1958, compiled and arranged
by the Reverend Seraphim Nassar ... ₁New York, The Black-
shaw press, inc., 1938₁

Nassar, Seraphim.
Christianity, a fulfillment of Judaism; a refutation of the
Zionist claim for the possession of Palestine, the restoration
of the glories of David and the pomp of Solomon, based on
texts of the Scripture. Spring Valley, Ill., 1944.

82 p. 19 cm.

1. Judaism—Controversial literature. 2. Jews—Restoration.
3. Zionism. I. Title.

BM585.N3   55–46292 ‡

NN   0026797   DLC IaU PPiPT NN

Nassar Zacarías, Ricardo.
El derecho internacional ante la bomba atómica. México,
1954.

101 p. 23 cm.

Tesis (licenciatura en derecho)—Universidad Nacional Autónoma
de México.
Includes bibliography.

1. Atomic bomb. 2. International relations. I. Title.

JX5133.A7N3   58–20650 ‡

NN   0026798   DLC MH-L

DT515   Nassarawa province, Nigeria.
.N3   Notes on Nassarawa province, Nigeria.
London, Wunstable & Watford, Printed by Waterlow & sons limited, 1920.
cover-title, 32 p. incl. tables. 24.5 cm.

NN   0026799   DLC

Nassarre, Pablo, *b.* 1664.
Escvela mvsica, segvn la practica moderna, dividida en
primera, y segvnda parte. Esta primera contiene qvatro
libros, el primero trata del sonido armonico, de svs divi-
siones, y de sus efectos. El segvndo, del canto llano, de sv
vso en la iglesia, y del provecho espiritual que produce. El
tercero, del canto de organo, y del fin, porqve se introduxo en
la iglesia, con otras advertencias necessarias. El qvarto, de
las proporciones qve se contraen de sonido à sonido; de las
que ha de llevar cada instrumento musico; y las observan-
cias, que han de tener los artifices de ellos. Sv avtor el padre

Fr. Pablo Nassarre ... Zaragoza, Los herederos de Diego
de Larvmbe, 1723–24.
2 v. 30½ cm.
Vol. 2 has title: Segvnda parte de la Escvela mvsica, que contiene
qvatro libros. El primero, trata de todas las especies, consonantes, y
disonantes; de sus qualidades, y como se deven usar en la musica. El
segvndo, de variedad de contrapuntos, assi sobre canto llano, como de
canto de organo, conciertos, sobre baxo, sobre tiple, à tres, a quatro,
y à cinco. El tercero, de todo genero de composicion, à qualquier
numero de voxes. El qvarto, trata de la glossa, y de otras advertea-
cias necessarias a los compositores. Compuesto por fray Pablo Nassarre ... Zaragoza, Los herederos de M. Roman, impressor de la
Vniversidad, 1723.
1. Music. 2. Composition (Music)

MT40.A2N2   5–27490

      NcU IaU OO ViU TxU NcD
NN   0026801   DLC OU IU DHN NN CU MiU CU-B ICN NNC

MC781.6   Nassarre, Pablo, b. 1664.
      Escuela musica... Zaragoza, Los herederos
de Diego de Larumbe, 1723–24.
2 v. 30 cm.

Microcard copy on 37 cards.

1. Composition (Music) 2. Music.
Removal card.

NN   0026802   OrU CaBVaU ICRL

Nassarre, Pablo, *b.* 1664.
Fragmentos mvsicos. Reglas generales, y muy necessarias para canto llano, canto de organo, contrapunto, y
composicion. Compvestos por Fr. Pablo Nassarre ...
Zaragoça, Por T. G. Martinez, 1683.

8 p. l., 142 p. 15½ᶜᵐ.

1. Music—Theory—16th and 17th cent. 2. Composition (Music)

Library of Congress   MT6.A2N25   7–13024

NN   0026803   DLC NNH

Nassarre, Pablo, *b.* 1664.
Fragmentos musicos, repartidos en quatro tratados. En que
se hallan reglas generales, y muy necessarias para canto llano,
canto de organo, contrapunto, y composicion. Compuestos por
Fr. Pablo Nassarre ... Y aora nuevamente añadido el vltimo
tratado por el mismo autor; y juntamente exemplificados con
los caractères musicos de que carecia. Sacalos a luz ... D.
Joseph de Torres. Madrid, En su imprenta de musica, 1700.

8 p. l., 288 p. 21ᶜᵐ.

1. Composition (Music) 2. Music—Theory—16th-17th cent.
I. Torres Martínez Bravo, José de, 1665-1738, ed.

Library of Congress   MT40.A2N26   6–8811

NN   0026804   DLC OO NNH TxU NcU MiU CU DHN

NASSARRE, PABLO, b. 1664.
Fragmentos musicos, repartidos en quatro tratados.
En que se hallan reglas generales, y muy necessarias
para canto llano, canto de organo, contrapunto, y
composicion. Compuestos por Fr. Pablo Nassarre... Y
aora nuevamente añadido el vltimo tratado por el mismo
autor; y juntamente exemplificados con los caractères
musicos de que carecia. Sacalos a luz...D. Joseph de
Torres... Madrid, En   su imprenta de musica,
1700.

[Rochester, N.Y., University of Rochester press, 1956]
7 cards. 7.5 x 12.5cm.
Microprint copy reproduced from the original in the Sibley music
library, Eastman school of music.
Collation of the original: 8 p. l., 288 p. 21cm.

1. Composition (Music) 2. Music—Theory, 1601-1700. 3. Composition,
to 1800. 4. Theory, 1601-1700.
I. Torres Martínez Bravo, José de, 1665-1738, ed.

     CaBVaU ViU
NN   0026806   NN OU NNC NcU CoU ICRL CU-B ICN OrU

Nassarre y Ferriz, Blas Antonio, 1689-1751, ed.

Rodriguez, Cristóbal, 1677?–ca. 1735.
Bibliotheca universal de la polygraphia española, compuesta
por don Christoval Rodriguez, y que de orden de Su Magestad
publica d. Blas Antonio Nassarre y Ferriz ... Madrid, A.
Marin, 1738.

Nassarre y Ferriz, Blas Antonio, 1689-1751.

Castillo Sotomayor, Joannes del, 1563-1640.
D. Joannis del Castillo Sotomayor ... Quotidianarum con-
troversiarum juris tomus primus₁-octavus₁ ... Opus revera
pragmaticis forensibus utilissimum, cum summariis, & indicibus, ad sublevandum lectoris laborem, opportunis. Nova
editio, ab innumeris veteris preli mendis expurgata, & cha-
racterum varietate distinctis allegationibus non mediocri
labore adornata. Coloniae Allobrogum, sumptibus Perachon &
Cramer, 1727, (v. 2-8) 1726.

Nassart, Jean.
⁶Comment les Belges resistent à la
domination allemande... Lausanne, Paris,
Payot et cie., 1916.
xvi, 473 p. plates, facsims. 23 cm.

NN   0026809   DHN

Nassau, Charles Francis,
Decompression in cranial fractures. Phila.,1911.
17 p.

NN   0026810   PPC

Nassau, Charles William.
In memoriam; Charles W. Nassau ...
see under   Nassau, Joseph Eastburn,
1827-1894.

Nassau, Erich, 1888- ; Aus d. med. Klinik zu Heidelberg. Das Blut-
bild beim Hunde mit Eckscher Fistel. Leipzig: Vogel 1914.
20 S. 8° ¶ Aus: Archiv. f. experim. Pathol. u. Pharmakol.
Bd 75.
Heidelberg, Med. Diss. v. 25. Sept. 1914, Ref. Krehl
[Geb. 25. Juli 88 Reichenbach i. Schl.; Wohnort: Heidelberg; Staatsangeh.:
Preußen; Vorbildung: G. Reichenbach Reife 09; Studium: Freiburg 1, Berlin 3,
Heidelberg 6 S.; Coll. 14. Mai 14; Approb. 12. Aug. 14.] [U 14. 1982

NN   0026812   ICRL DNLM MBCo CtY

Nassau, Erich, 1888-
Enuresis, von Dr. Erich Nassau ...
(*In* Neue deutsche Klinik. Berlin, 1929. 26ᶜᵐ. Bd. 3, p. 211-222. diagrs.)
"Literatur": p. 222.

NN   0026813   ICJ

.N2   Nassau, Erich, 1888-
Hebraic   נדחל בנים. מדריך כללי לאם ולמטפלת מאת א. נסאו וי. רותם.
Sect.   ₁Merhavya, 1951₁ מרחביה, ספרית פועלים (לבל)

205 p. illus. 21 cm.

1. Children—Care and hygiene. 2. Children—Diseases. I.
Rotem, Jacob, joint author. *Title transliterated:* Gidul banim.

RJ61.N2   53–40608

NN   0026814   DLC

Nassau, Erich, 1888-
המטפלת. מורה־דרך לעובדות בתי־הילדים ולאמהות, מאת
ד"ר א. נסאו ... הקיבוץ הארצי השמר הצעיר.
₁Merhavya, 1944₁
175, ₁1₁ p. illus. 17ᵐ.
"רשימת לועזית": p. 173.

1. Infants—Diseases. 2. Infants—Care and hygiene. I. Title.
Title transliterated: Ha-metapeleth.

Library of Congress   RJ17.N3   45–13195

NN   0026815   DLC

RJ216   Nassau, Erich, 1888-   joint author.
.M5473
   Meyer, Ludwig Ferdinand, 1879-
     Physiology and pathology of infant nutrition, by L. F.
Meyer ₁and₁ Erich Nassau. Translated by Kurt Glaser and
Susanne Glaser. Completely rev. 2d ed. Springfield, Ill.,
Thomas (ᶜ1955₁

RJ216   Nassau, Erich, 1888-   joint author.
.M55
   Meyer, Ludwig Ferdinand, 1879-
     Die säuglingsernährung; eine anleitung für ärzte und
studierende, von L. F. Meyer ... und E. Nassau ... mit 85
abbildungen im text. München, J. F. Bergmann, 1930.

Nassau, Flandrine de, abbess of Sainte-
Croix de Poitiers
see   Charlotte Flandrina, gravin
van Nassau, 1579-1640.

VOLUME 405

Nassau, George Richard Savage, 1756-1823.

Z997 Catalogue of the choice, curious, and extensive
N26   library of the late George Nassau, esq. ...
      which will be sold by auction, by Mr. Evans ...
      [London, Printed by W. Nicol, 1824]

      2 pt. in 1 v. 22.5 cm. 3|4 brown roan.
      Sale of pt. 1 "Monday, February 16, and eleven
      following days, (Sunday excepted.) 1824." Pt. 2,
      "Monday, March 8, and seven following days,
      (Sunday excepted.) 1824."
      Prices and purchasers in ms. on margins.
      With ex-libris   of Peter Hardy.
      In the library,   Oct. 24, 1930.
      1. Bibliography   --Rare books. 2. Books
                         39-557-5

NN 0026819   CSmH NNC MWiW-C MH NN PU

Nassau, George Richard Savage, 1756-1823.
      Pictures, water-colour drawings, engraved
      British portraits, prints, &c. Catalogue of the
      valuable collection of George Nassau ... Which
      will be sold by auction, by Mr. [R.H.] Evans ...
      On Thursday, March 25 ... 1824. [London,
      Printed by W. Nicol, 1824]
      1 p.l., 19 p. 8°.
      Priced copy.

NN 0026820   NN

Nassau, George Richard Savage, 1756-1823.
      Madonna and child ("The little Cowper Madonna")
      by Raphael (1483-1520)
          see under   Duveen Brothers.

Nassau, Hendrik Jan, 1791-1873.
      Adnotationum nonnullarum in librum Ciceronis
      de Senectute ... Fasciculus I. Groningae, 1829.

NN 0026822   PU

Nassau (Hendrik] J[an])
      Bedenkingen over de wet op denturfaceijns en hare toe-
      passing, inzonderheid over hagen invloed op de vervde-
      rijen; naar aanleiding van 'twerkje: Conclusie over den
      turfaceijns, genomen in de teregtzitting der Arrondisse-
      ments-Regtbank te Assen, 2. Jan. 1843, door Mr. E. J.
      Thomassen à Thuessink van der Hoop,.. Tevens een
      paar woorden over 'tvergraven der hoogeveenen, de
      latere wetgeving op dit punt, en over de wijze, hoe de
      Groninger veenkolonien in blcei zijn gebrazt. Assen: T.
      J. van Tricht, 1843. 2 p.l., iv, 36 pp. 8°.
      In: TB p. v. 32.

NN 0026823   NN

Nassau, Hendrik Jan, 1791-1873.
      Eenige aanteekeningen betrekkelijk 't ontwerp van
      wet op 't lageronderwijs. 19 pp. Assen: van Gorcum
      en Comp, 1856. 8°.

NN 0026824   NN

Nassau, Hendrik Jan, 1791-1873.
      Geschriften van d'. H. J. Nassau, Verzameld en uitge-
      geven onder toezigt van m. H. J. Smidt, dr. H. J. Nas-
      sau Noordewier, J. Brals en A. W. Stellwagen. ... Gro-
      ningen, J. B. Wolters, 1876-79.
      3 v. front. (port.) 25½cm.
      "Lijst der bekende gedrukte geschriften van wijlen d'. H. J. Nassau": v. 3,
      p. [417]-424.
      Contents.—1. deel. Letterkunde, geschiedenis, wijsbegeerte, enz.—2. deel.
      Opvording, onderwijs, schoolwezen.—3. deel. De levende taal, vergelijkende
      taal-studie, historische taalkunde.
      1. Dutch philology—Collected works. 2. Education—Netherlands.

NN 0026825   MiU CU LU

4LB   Nassau, Hendrik Jan
663   Lager-onderwijs in ons Vaderland
      en deszelfs regeling van staatswege;
      hoofdzakelijk historisch beschouwd, in
      verband tot godsdienst en burgerstaat.
      Assen, T. J. van Tricht, 1841-
          v. 1-

NN 0026826   DLC-P4

Nassau, H[endrik] J[an] 1791-1873.
      Mr. Petrus Hofstede ... in zijn leven en
      werken. Koevorden, D.H. van der Scheer, 1839.
      8 p.l., 64 p. 1 port. 8°.

NN 0026827   NN

PF74 Nassau, Hendrik Jan, 1791-1873.
N3   De Nederlandsche taal en Grimm's Deutsches Wörterbuch;
      aanteekeningen en bedenkingen, door H.J. Nassau. Te Groningen,
      C. M. van Bolhuis Hoitsema, 1858.
      119 p.

      1. Dutch language. 2. Grimm, Jakob Ludwig Karl, 1785-1863.
      /Deutsches Wörterbuch. I. Title.

NN 0026828   CU

Nassau, Hendrik Jan, 1791-1873.
      Vlugtige gedachten over 't koninklijk besluit . . .
      2. Jan. 1842, betrekkelijk 't lageronderwijs, en eenige
      bedenkingen over 't onderrigt in de kerkgeschiedenis
      en die van 't vaderland. 3 p.l., 31 pp. Assen: T. J.
      van Tricht, 1842. 8°.

NN 0026829   NN

Nassau, Isabella Ann, 1829-1906.
      Malango ma Bokenaka ma Tyatyi ya Jisu
      Kraist... Tyatyi ya Anyambe, by Miss Isabella
      A. Nassau. N.Y., Amer. Tract Soc. [c1902]
      156p. 19cm.

      "Church history"-- Benga.

NN 0026830   PPPrHi

Nassau, Jason John, 1893-
      Ambrose Swasey; builder of machines, tele-
      scopes and men... [1937]
      12p.

      Cover-title.
      Reprinted from Popular astronomy, v. 45, no.
      8, Oct. 1937.

NN 0026831   OCl

Nassau, Jason John, 1893-
      ... Elusive eclipses, by Jason John Nassau
      ... (Cleveland, Ohio, 1933)
      15 p. illus., diagrs. 23½ cm.
      At head of title: The Worcester R. Warner
      memorial lecture.
      "Presented under the auspices of the Cleve-
      land engineering society at Severance hall,
      February 15, 1933, Cleveland, Ohio."

NN 0026832   DN-Ob OCl

Nassau, Jason John, 1893-
      A friend to Case, to science, to mankind, by Dr. J. J.
      Nassau ... A tribute to Dr. Dayton C. Miller ... [Cleve-
      land? 1936]
      cover-title, [8] p. illus. (incl. ports., music) diagr. 30 x 22½cm.
      "Reprinted from the May-June issue of the Case alumnus, 1936."

      1. Miller, Dayton Clarence, 1866-1941.

      Library of Congress   QC16.M6N3   41-38754
                                                        [2]   925.3

NN 0026833   DLC OCl

Nassau, Jason John, 1893-
      Geodetic astronomy...   Cleveland, The
      University book store, 1924.
      82p. mimeo.

NN 0026834   OClW

QB525 Nassau, Jason John, 1893-
.N35
1933   Lake Erie levels and sun-spots, by J. J.
      Nassau and William Koski. Northfield,
      Minn. Popular Astronomy, 1933.
      4 p. illus., graphs. 26cm.
      Reprinted from Popular Astronomy, vol. XLI.
      No. 4, April, 1933.

      1. Sun-spots. I. Koski, William,
      II. Title.

NN 0026835   ViU

Nassau, Jason John, 1893-
      ... Magnitudes and colors in the globular
      cluster Messier 12 and selected area 108 [by]
      J.J. Nassau and J.A. Hynek. [Deleware, O.,
      1941]
      18p. (Contributions from the Perkins observa-
      tory, no. 17, v. 2)

      "Reprinted from the Astrophysical journal, v.
      96, p. 37-54, 1942"

NN 0026836   OU

Nassau, Jason John, 1893-
      Practical astronomy. 2d ed. New York, McGraw-Hill
      Book Co., 1948.
      xii, 311 p. illus., map. 24 cm. (McGraw-Hill astronomical series)
      First ed. pub. in 1932 under title: A textbook of practical astron-
      omy.

      1. Astronomy, Spherical and practical. I. Title.

      QB145.N3 1948   522   48—7632*

      MtBC CaBVa WaS OrSaW
      ICU MiHM MB ViU CU MiU TU PSC TNJ LU OrP CaBVaU
NN 0026837   DLC MtU CoU AU TxU GU FTaSU OCU KEmT

523.24 Nassau, Jason John, 1893-
N187s   A study of solar motion by harmonic analysis
Physics [by] J.J. Nassau and P.M. Morse. [n.p.] 1927.
Lib'y   73-85p. illus. 24cm.

      Cover title.
      "Reprinted ... from the Astrophysical jour-
      nal, vol. LXV, no.2."

      1. Solar system - Motion in space. 2. Har-
      monic analysis. I. Morse, Philip McCord,
      1903-   joint author.

NN 0026838   TxU

Nassau, Jason John, 1893-
      A textbook of practical astronomy, primarily for engineer-
      ing students, by Jason John Nassau ... 1st ed. New York
      and London, McGraw-Hill book company, inc., 1932.
      x, 226 p. illus., diagrs. 24cm. (Half-title: McGraw-Hill astronom-
      ical series) $3.00

      1. Astronomy, Spherical and practical.

      Library of Congress   QB145.N3   32-2650
      Copyright A 45974   [5]   522

      PSC PU ODW OU OCl MiU MiHM DHEW
NN 0026839   DLC FMU MH CaBVaU OrCS NcD CU PPT PV

Nassau, Johan Maurits, vorst van

          see

Johan Maurits, prince of Nassau-Siegen, 1604-1679

*EC75 Nassau, John, fl.1792.
N1873   The cause of the Roman Catholics pleaded, in
792c   an address to the Protestants of Ireland. By
      the Rev. John Nassau ...
          Dublin:Printed by H.Fitzpatrick, for J.Moore,
      45,College-green.MDCCXCII.
      8°. 2p.l.,60p. 19.5cm.

NN 0026841   MH IU MWA KU

VOLUME 405

Nassau, Joseph Eastburn, 1827-1894.
"Liberia, a piller to Johovah", sermon preached
on behalf of African colonization, July 3, 1859.
12 p.

NN   0026842   PHi

Nassau, Joseph Eastburn, 1827-1894.
In memoriam. Joseph Eastburn Nassau, D. D.
Born, March 12th, 1827. Died, February, 21st,
1894
see under [Miller, George D   ]

[Nassau, Joseph Eastburn] 1827-1894.
In memoriam. Rev. Charles W. Nassau, D. D., died August
6th, 1878, and Mrs. Hannah H. Nassau, died June 21st, 1878.
New York, Trow's printing company, 1879.
44 p. 23½ᶜᵐ.

1. Nassau, Charles William, 1804-1878. 2. Nassau, Mrs. Hannah
(Hamill) 1807-1878. I. Title.

                                                      36-22131
Library of Congress   BX9225.N35N3   922.573

NN   0026844   DLC PPPrHi

Nassau, Joseph Eastburn, 1827-1894.
A sermon preached at the funeral of Mrs. Jane
O. Comstock. ... Warsaw, N.Y., Dudley, 1859.

NN   0026845   PPPrHi PPL

Nassau, Lodewijk van.
see Lodewijk, graaf van Nassau, 1538-
1574.

Nassau, Mabel Louise.
... Old age poverty in Greenwich village; a neighborhood
study, by Mabel Louise Nassau; introduction by Henry R.
Seager ... New York, Chicago [etc.] Fleming H. Revell company [¹1915]
105 p. 19ᶜᵐ. (Greenwich house series, no. 6)
"Studies made while in residence at Greenwich house settlement during the winter of 1913-14."—Pref.

1. Old age pensions. 2. Poor—New York (City) 3. Greenwich village, New York (City) I. Title.

                                                      15-15584
Library of Congress   HD7106.U6N7

OC1W OOxM NN NjP
NN   0026847   DLC OrPR KEmT CU ViU PHC PP MiU OC1

Nassau, Mrs. Mary Brunette (Foster) 1849-1884.
The path she trod, a memorial of Mary
Burnette (Foster) Nassau, by her husband
see under [Nassau, Robert Hamill]
1835-1921.

Nassau, Mary Cloyd (Latta) 1837-1870.
Crowned in Palmland
see under Nassau, Robert Hamill,
1835-1921.

Nassau, Mrs. Mary Cloyd (Latta) 1837-1870, tr.

Lembo la Benga. Hymns in the Benga language. By the
Corisco mission, West Africa. [New York?] Printed by the
American tract society, 1873.

Nassau, Maurits, vorst van

see

Johan Maurits, prince of Nassau-Siegen, 1604-1679

Nassau, Robert Hamill, 1835-1921.
Africa, an essay, by Rev. Robert Hamill Nassau, M. D.
Philadelphia, Allen, Lane & Scott, 1911.
35 p. illus. 23ᶜᵐ.
"These verses were written ... in March, 1872."—Pref.

                                                      11-13535

NN   0026852   DLC PPPrHi NjP

GN657   Nassau, Robert Hamill, 1835-1921.
.B2N2   Bantu sociology... [Philadelphia, Allen, Lane &
         Scott] 1914.
         40 p. 23cm.

         1. Bantus.

NN   0026853   ICU NjP PU PPAN

Nassau, Robert Hamill, 1835-
Corisco days; the first thirty years of the West Africa
mission, by Rev. Robert Hamill Nassau ... Philadelphia,
Allen, Lane & Scott [1910]
192 p. 20½ᶜᵐ.

                                                      11-13536

NN   0026854   DLC PPPrHi NjP

[Nassau, Robert Hamill] 1835-1921.
Crowned in palm-land. A story of African mission life ...
Philadelphia, J. B. Lippincott & co., 1874.
390 p. front. (port.) plates, map. 19ᶜᵐ.
A memoir of Mrs. Mary Cloyd Nassau.
Genealogy of Latta family: p. 13-14.

1. Nassau, Mrs. Mary Cloyd (Latta) 1831-1870. 2. Missions—Africa.
3. Latta family. I. Title.

                                                      33-18572
Library of Congress   BV3542.N3N3

NN   0026855   DLC PPL IEN PPPrHi PHatU NjP MB

Nassau, Robert Hamill, 1835-
Fañwe primer and vocabulary.   199 p.
New York, Printed by E.O.Jenkins, 1881.

NN   0026856   OC1 NN

Nassau, Robert Hamill, 1835-1921.
Fetichism in West Africa; forty years' observation of
native customs and superstitions, by the Rev. Robert
Hamill Nassau ... With twelve illustrations. London,
Duckworth & co., 1904.
xvii p., 1 l., 389 p. 12 pl. (incl. front.) map. 21½ᶜᵐ.

1. Fetichism. 2. Ethnology—Africa, West.
                                                      5—17304
Library of Congress   BL2465.N3 1904

NN   0026857   DLC CtY ODW OC1 CU ICJ ViU

Nassau, Robert Hamill, 1835-1921.
Fetichism in West Africa; forty years' observation of
native customs and superstitions, by the Rev. Robert
Hamill Nassau ... With twelve illustrations. New
York, C. Scribner's sons, 1904.
xvii p., 1 l., 389 p. 12 pl. (incl. front.) map. 22ᶜᵐ.

1. Fetichism. 2. Ethnology—Africa, West.
Library of Congress   BL2465.N3 1904   4-24535

MB NN ICN NNUT MH PU OU WaWW WaSp OrU
NcD FU NRU ViHaI NjNbS PP PHC PPL OO OC1CC OC1 MiU
NN   0026858   DLC NIC InAndC-T   OOxM GU NBuU ICU

BL   NASSAU, Robert Hamill, 1835-1921
2465   Fetichism in West Africa. Forty years'
N18   observation of native customs and super-
        stitions. By the Rev. Robert Hamill Nassau,
        M.D., S.T.D., for forty years a missionary
        in the Gaubin district of Kongo-française ...
        With twelve illustrations. New York,
        Charles Scribner's Sons, 1907.
        xvii, 1 l., 389 p. 12 plates (incl.
        front.) map 21 cm.

NN   0026859   MBCo OC1W PPL PSC

Nassau, Robert Hamill, 1835-1921.
The Gaboon and Corisco Mission. New York,
Board of Foreign Missions, 1873.
11p. map, 26cm.

NN   0026860   OKentU

Nassau, Robert Hamill, 1835-1921, ed.

Mackey, James Love, 1820-1867.
Mackey's Grammar of the Benga-Bantu language. Revised
by Rev. R. H. Nassau ... New York, American tract society,
1892.

Nassau, Robert Hamill, 1835-1921.
Historical sketch of the Missions in Africa
under the care of the Board of Foreign Missions
of the Presbyterian Church. Philadelphia,
W.F.M/S. Presbyterian church, 1881.
24p. (In Hist. Sketches of missions... care
of Bd. of For. Miss. of the Presb. Church)

NN   0026862   OO PPPrHi

Nassau, Robert Hamill, 1835-
History of the presbytery of Corisco, Africa.
Trenton, N. J., Brandt, 1869.
(pam)

NN   0026863   PPPrHi OO

BV3625 Nassau, Robert Hamill, 1835-
.C6N37   A history of the presbytery of Corisco.
        Ogove river, west coast of Africa, February,
        1888. Trenton, N.J., U.S.A., From the press
        of Albert Brandt, jr., 1888.
        28 p. 23½ cm.

        1. Missions - Corisco. I. Title: Corisco,
        Presbytery of.

NN   0026864   NjR NjP

Nassau, Robert Hamill, 1835-
In an elephant corral; and other tales of West African
experiences, by Robert Hamill Nassau ... New York,
The Neale publishing company, 1912.
180 p. 19ᶜᵐ. $1.00
CONTENTS.—The transformed matricide.—Nguva's chain.—In an elephant corral.—Upset by a hippopotamus.—My fight with Nyare—Gorilla-
hunting.—Uvengwa: a vampire.—A psychic mystery.—Voices of an African tropic night.

1. Africa, West—Descr. & trav. 2. Hunting—Africa, West. 3. Animals, Legends and stories of. I. Title.

Library of Congress   DT639.N3   13-1062

NjP
NN   0026865   DLC DAU CLU NcD NNC NcU MB CU OC1W PU

VOLUME 405

Nassau, Robert Hamill, 1835–1921, ed.

Lembo la Benga. Hymns in the Benga language. By the Corisco mission, West Africa. ₁New York₇ Printed by the American tract society, 1873.

NN 0026867   NN ICN NjP

Nassau, Robert Hamill, 1835–1921.
Mawedo; the palm-land maiden, by Rev. R. H. Nassau ... New York, American tract society ₍c1882₎ 206 p. front., plates. 18cm.

NEGRO DIVISION

1. Missions — Gabun — Fiction
N.Y.P.L.   **REPRINT**   I. Title. II. American tract society.   *Revised*   September 6, 1940

NN 0026868   DLC OrU NIC FU InU NcD PP PU PBm OC1
OC1W MB NN NjP PPPrHi CU FTaSU

Nassau, Robert Hamill, 1835–1921.
My Ogowe; being a narrative of daily incidents during sixteen years in equatorial West Africa, by Robert Hamill Nassau ... New York, The Neale publishing company, 1914.
708 p. front., plates, ports., maps. 23cm.

1. Africa, French equatorial—Descr. & trav. 2. Missions—Africa, French equatorial.   I. Title.

Library of Congress   DT546.N3   14–9085

NN 0026868   DLC OrU NIC FU InU NcD PP PU PBm OC1

₁Nassau, Robert Hamill₎ 1835–1921.
The path she trod, a memorial of Mary Brunette (Foster) Nassau, by her husband. Philadelphia, Press of Allen, Lane & Scott, 1909.
204 p., 1 l. ports. 23½cm.

1. Nassau, Mrs. Mary Brunette (Foster) 1849–1884.   I. Title.

Library of Congress   BV3542.N28N3   11–18347 Revised

NN 0026870   DLC NjP PPPrHi

Nassau, Robert Hamill, 1835–
Spiritual beings in West Africa; their classes & functions. n.p. [1903]

NN 0026871   NjP

Nassau, Robert Hamill, 1835–
Tales out of school, by Robert Hamill Nassau ... Philadelphia, Allen, Lane & Scott, 1911.
153 p. front. 20½cm.

Schoolgirl tales of a Presbyterian mission at Libreville, West Africa, 1850–1880.

11–13753

NN 0026872   DLC PPPrHi PU NjP

Nassau, Robert Hamill, 1835–1921.
Tanwe primer and vocabulary. New York, 1881.

NN 0026873   NjP

Nassau, Robert Hamill, 1835–1921.
Where animals talk; west African folk lore tales, by Robert H. Nassau ... Boston, R. G. Badger ₍c1912₎
250 p. 19cm.

1. Animals, Legends and stories of.   I. Title.

Library of Congress   GR350.N3   12–3830

NN 0026874   DLC WaS IaU NBuC CU PU OC1 OCU NN ViU
NjP InAndC-T KEmT

Nassau, Robert Hamill, 1835– 1921.
Where animals talk: west African folk lore tales, by Robert H. Nassau .. London, Duckworth ₍1914₎
250 p. 19cm. $1.50

GR 350 N26 1914

NN 0026875   NIC OC1 MiU CtY ICarbS CaBVaU

Nassau, Robert H₍amill₎.
Where animals talk; West African folk lore tales. Boston: The Four Seas Co., 1919.   250 p.   12°.

398-N

1. Africa (West).—Folk-lore.
N.Y.P.L.   2. Title.   CENTRAL CIRCULATION.   February 28, 1920.

NN 0026876   NN NcD ICN PPT OU

Nassau, Robert Hamill, 1835–1921.
The youngest king; a story of the Magi, by Robert Hamill Nassau ... Philadelphia, The Westminster press, 1911.
95 p. front. 19½cm. $0.50

11–24146

NN 0026877   DLC OrU NN NjP PU-Mu

Nassau, Willem Lodewijk, graaf van
SEE
Willem Lodewijk, graaf van Nassau, 1560–1620.

Nassau-Dillenburg, Johan VI, Count of
see   Johan VI, Count of Nassau-Dillenburg, 1536–1606.

Nassau la Leck, Lodewijk Theodorus, *graaf van₍ 1697?–1781.*
Briev van Jonkheer Lodewyk Theodorus grave van Nassau la Leck. &c. &c. aan den Heer advocaat Linguet, schryver der Annales politiques, civiles & litteraires onzer achtiende eeuw. Dienende om zyn vaderland de Republiek der Vereenigde Neederlanden en zyne medeburgeren te verdedigen, tegen de verkeerde en teffens beledigende uitdrukkingen van dien schryver, te vinden in het xxxiiste stukie dier Annales op het artikel over Holland ... Utrecht, G. T. van Paddenburg, 1779.
46 p. 22½cm. ₍With his Brieven over de Noord-Americaansche onlusten Utrecht, 1777–79₎
1. Netherlands—Pol. &   govt. 2. Netherlands—For. rel.   7–6485

Library of Congress   E208.N26

NN 0026880   DLC MiU-C

Nassau la Leck, Lodewijk Theodorus, *graaf van₍ 1697?–1781.*
Brieven over de Noord-Americaansche onlusten, den waarschijnlijken uitslag dier oorlog, en den invloed die deeze gebeurtenisse zoude kunnen hebben, zo op de belangens van Europa in 't algemeen, als van deezen staat in 't bijzonder. Door Jonkheer Lodewijk Theodorus grave van Nassau la Leck ... Utrecht, G. T. van Paddenburg, 1777–79.
6 v. in 1. 22½cm.
Parts 3–6 paged continuously: pt. 3: 47, ₍1₎ p.; pt. 4: ₍49₎–96 p.; pt. 5: ₍97₎–143 (i. e. 151) p.; pt. 6: ₍153₎–208 p.
1. U. S.—Hist.—Revolution—Foreign public opinion. 2. U. S.—For. rel.—Netherlands.   3. Netherlands—For. rel.—U. S.
     7–6484
Library of Congress   E208.N26

NN 0026881   DLC RPJCB NBu CtY ICU PU MiU MiU-C NN

₍Nassau la Leck, Lodewijk Theodorus, *graaf van₎ fl. 1780.*
Het Engelsch nieuwe-jaars compliment. Of, Samensprack tusschen een zee-officer, geeweeze ₍₎ koopman, Noordhollandsche boer en een Duitscher. Over de rencontre voorgevallen op den laatsten december en eerste januarij, tuchen ₍!₎ het Engelsch esquader onder de commodore Fielding en het Hollands esquader onder den schoutbijnagt graaf van Bijland: als mede over eenige zaken, betrekkelijk tot de tegenwoordige tijdsomstandigheden ... Amsterdam, J. Stanhoffius, 1780.
64 p. 19cm.
1. Anglo-Dutch war, 1780–1784.   I. Title.   6—45597
Library of Congress   DJ205.N3

NN 0026882   DLC NN

NASSAU LA LECK, Lodewijk Theodorus, graaf van.
Lettre à monsieur Linguet, servant à defendre sa patrie, la république des Provinces-Unies & ses concitoyens contre les assertions hasardées même offensantes, inserées, dans le numero XXXIIme de ses Annales, à l'article sur la Hollande. Utrecht, G.T. van Paddenburg, 1779.
pp. 42†.

NN 0026883   MH

Nassau la Leck, Lodewyk Theodorus, grave van
Missive aan den wel ecdelen heer en meester Lambertus Julius Vitringa, advocaat voor de hoven van justitie in Holland; betreklyk tot zeeker zedeelte zyner wel eedelens verhandelinge over belangens en plichten der onzyddge mogentheeden en hunne onderdanen &c. Door jonkheer Lodewyk Theodorus grave van Nassau la Leck. Te Utrecht by G. T. van Paddenburg, MDCCLXXVIII. (1778)
16 p. 22 cm.
Authenticating signature of the author on vo of t.-p.

NN 0026884   MiU-C

N₍assau la₎ L₍eck, Lodewijk Theodorus₎ graaf van, 1697?–1781.
De Noord Amerikaan in Holland, of De bedrogen hoogmoed, in vijf bedrijven, door N. L. ... Utrecht, G. T. van Paddenburg, 1778.
v, ₍1₎, 56 p. 21½cm.
1. U. S.—Hist.—Revolution—Drama.
Library of Congress   E295.N26   7–5214

NN 0026885   DLC RPJCB NN

Nassau la Leck, Lodewijk Theodorus, graaf van, 1697?–1781.
Politike brieven, over verscheide gewichtige onderwerpen, betreklyk, zo tot het staatkundig als huishoudelyk bestier der republiek, wordende in dit eerste stukie onderzogt, in hoe veere de cumulatie of ophoping van veele ampten op een persoon nuttig of schadelyk zy... Stukie 1. *Utrecht: G. J. van Paddenburg*, 1780. ₍ pmp. 8°.

NN 0026886   NN

Nassau la Leck, Lodewijk Theodorus, graaf van, 1697?–1781
Staatkundige verhandeling... Amsterdam, 1780.
In pam. case: A la guerre de la Hollande avec l'Angleterre v.I

NN 0026887   RPJCB

Nassau Noordewier, Hendrik Jan.
Commentatio literaria continens quaestiones duas ad Plutarcheam Periclis vitam pertinentes. Dordraci, P.K. Braat, 1869.
40 p. 23cm.

PA4369 .P4N3

Thesis - Utrecht.

1. Plutarchus. Vitae parallelae. Pericles.

NN 0026888   OCU NjP

VOLUME 405

Nassau Noordewier, Hendrik Jan, ed.
Isocratis Aegineticus (XIX), et Isaei Oratio de
Cironis hereditate (VIII)
see under   Isocrates.

PT1682
.W8N3   Nassau Noordewier, Johanna Maria

Bijdrage tot de beoordeeling van den
Willehalm.   Delft, P.J. Koumans, 1901.
128 p. 23 cm.

Proefschrift--Groningen.
"Stellingen": p. ₍123₎-128.
Bibliographical footnotes.

1. Wolfram von Eschenbach, 12th cent.
Willehalm. (x) Noordewier, Johanna Maria
Nassau.

NN   0026890   TU KU PU OCl

Nassau. Noordewier, Michael.
Metaphorae Aristophaeneae. Specimen littera-
rium inauguralis. [Leyden] Delphis-Batavorum,
1891.

NN   0026891   MH CU MB

Nassau-Saarbruck, Sophia Christina Charlotte, princess
of
see
Sophia Christina Charlotte, princess of Nassau-Saarbruck.

Nassau-Saarbrücken, Elisabeth, graefin von
see
Elisabeth, countess of Nassau-Saarbrücken, d.1456.

Nassau-Siegen, Charles, prince de
see
Nassau-Siegen, Karl Heinrich Nikolas Otto, Prinz, 1745-
1808.

Nassau-Siegen, Johan de Middelste, graaf van
see Johan de Middelste, graaf van Nassau-Siegen, 1561-
1623.

Nassau-Siegen, Johan Maurits, vorst van
see
Johan Maurits, prince of Nassau-Siegen, 1604-1679

DL766
.N37
₍Rare Bk
₍oll   Nassau-Siegen, Karl Heinrich Nikolas Otto, Prinz, 1745-
1808.
Письмо Его Величеству Королю Шведскому, и Опровер-
жение реляціи, которая была напечатана въ "Гамбургскихъ
газетахъ," о морскомъ сраженіи, бывшемъ 13 августа по
старому стилю 1789 года между галерными флотами швед-
скимъ и флотомъ россійскимъ. Въ Санктпетербургѣ, Въ
Имп. тип., 1789.
14 p. 22 cm.
A translation of the author's letter in French, issued also in St.
Petersbourg in 1789. Cf. Bib. nat. Cat.
1. Russo-Swedish War, 1788-1790—Sources.   I. Gustaf III, King
of Sweden, 1746-1792. II. Title.
Title transliterated: Pis'mo Ego Ve-
lichestvu Korolîu Shvedskomu.
DL766.N37   56-52235

NN   0026897   DLC

Nassau-Siegen, Karl Heinrich Nikolas Otto, Prinz,
1745-1808.
Un paladin au XVIIIe siècle
see under   Aragon,
Marquis, de.

Nassau-Siegen, Maurits, vorst van
see
Johan Maurits, prince of Nassau-Siegen, 1604-1679

Nassau-Zigen, Karl Genrikh Nikolaí Otton, prints
see
Nassau-Siegen, Karl Heinrich Nikolas Otto, Prinz, 1745-
1808.

Nassau (Duchy)
Herzoglich nassauisches allgemeines intelligenzblatt. 1.-60.
jahrg.; 1809-1868. Wiesbaden, Gedruckt in der Herzoglichen
hofbuchdruckerei ₍etc., 1809-68₎
v.   tables (part fold.) 24-25½ᶜᵐ. weekly.
1866-1868 have title: Intelligenzblatt für Nassau. Caption titles for
the issues from Jan. 4 to Oct. 4, 1866 (approximate date of Nassau's an-
nexation by Prussia) retain original form.
Includes Beilagen.
1867-1868 continue in part the Verordnungsblatt für das herzogthum
Nassau which in 1809 (first year) was a Beilage to the "Intelligenzblatt".
cf. 1867, no. 3, p. 25 and Verordnungsblatt, 1809.
1. Nassau (Duchy)—Pol. & govt. I. Nassau (Duchy) Laws, statutes, etc. II. Title. III. Title: Intelligenzblatt, Herzoglich nassauisches
allgemeines. IV. Title: Intelligenzblatt für Nassau.

Library of Congress   J7.G365   39-8789

NN   0026901   DLC

DD491
.H61C6   Nassau (Duchy)
Nassauisches urkundenbuch ... Die urkunden
des ehemals Kurmainzischen gebiets, einschliess-
lich der herrschaften Eppenstein, Koenigstein und
Falkenstein; ... Bearbeitet von dr. W. Sauer.
Wiesbaden & Niedner, 1885-
v. 27 cm. (Codex diplomaticus nassoicus)
I. Title.

NN   0026902   DLC

4-Serials
Nassau (Duchy)
Staats-Adress-Handbuch.

NN   0026903   DLC-P4 NN

Nassau (Duchy)
Verordnungsblatt des herzogthums Nassau
see under   Nassau (Duchy) Laws, statutes,
etc.

Nassau (Duchy) Commission über die prüfung der cassen-
trennung.
Verhandlungen der durch beschluss der Landesdeputirten-
versammlung vom 19. januar 1835 gewählten Commission über
die prüfung der cassen-trennung von den jahren 1835 und 1836.
Wiesbaden, L. Schellenberg ₍1836₎
1 p. l., 135 p., 1 l. 25 x 21ᶜᵐ.
HJ49.N3A15
—— Anlagen zu den Verhandlungen ... Wiesbaden, Gedruckt
bei L. Riedel, 1836.
2 v. tables. 24½ x 20½—25 x 22ᶜᵐ.
CONTENTS.—1. bd. Anlage 1-18 nebst unteranlagen. Enthält die ein-
nahme.—2. bd. Anlage 19-46 nebst unteranlagen. Enthält die ausgaben.
1. Finance—Nassau (Duchy)   I. Title.
Library of Congress   HJ49.N3A15 Anlagen
39-8790

NN   0026905   DLC MiU

Nassau (Duchy) Constitution.

Nassau (Duchy) Laws, statutes, etc.
Sammlung der landesherrlichen edicte und anderer verordnungen, welchen vom 1. julius 1816 an, im ganzen umfange
des herzogthums Nassau gesetzeskraft beigelegt worden ist ...
Wiesbaden, Herzoglich nassauische hofbuchdruckerei, 1817-
46.

Nassau, Ger. Evangelische blaettervereinigung
fuer soldaten und kriegsgefangene Deutsche
see
Evangelische blaettervereinigung fuer soldaten und
kriegsgefangene Deutsche, Nassau, Ger.

Nassau. Gewerbeverein.
see
Gewerbeverein fuer Nassau.

Law   Nassau (Duchy) Hofgericht, Wiesbaden.

Haas, Robert, of Wiesbaden, ed.
Ausführliche und unparteiische Darstellung der ersten
Quartalverhandlungen in den öffentlichen und mündlichen
Schwurgerichten des Hofgerichtsbezirks Wiesbaden. Wies-
baden, C. W. Kreidel, 1850.

Nassau (Duchy) Landesdeputirten-
versammlung
see
Nassau (Duchy) Ständesversammlung, 1818-
1848
Deputirtenversammlung.

Nassau (Duchy) Landtag
see
Nassau (Duchy) Ständeversammlung, 1818-
1848.
Nassau (Duchy) Ständeversammlung, 1848-
1851.
Nassau (Duchy) Ständeversammlung, 1852-
1866.

Nassau. Laws, statutes, etc.
Bau-Polizei-Verordnung vom 26.Dezember 1873,
nebst den Polizei-Verordnungen über die
Errichtung von Gebäuden in der Nähe von Eisenbahnen und die Anlage der Schornsteine. Idstein
1874.

16 p. 16°.

NN   0026912   MH-L

DD   Nassau (Duchy) Laws, statutes, etc.
491   ₍Collection of edicts of princes of Nassau-
H688Al++ Saarbrücken. Saarbrücken, etc., 1748-80₎
₍501₎ p. 31cm.

Pages numbered in mss.

1. Nassau (Duchy)--Hist.--Sources.

NN   0026913   NIC

4K   Nassau (Duchy) Laws, statutes, etc.
Ger. Entwurf einer Civil-Process-Ordnung
1885 für das Herzogthum Nassau. Mit den
Motiven. Wiesbaden, Druck der C.
Ritter'schen Buchdr., 1849.
339 p.

NN   0026914   DLC-P4 MH-L

Nassau (Duchy) Laws, statutes, etc.

Nassau (Duchy)
Herzoglich nassauisches allgemeines intelligenzblatt. 1.-60.
jahrg.; 1809-1868. Wiesbaden, Gedruckt in der Herzoglichen
hofbuchdruckerei ₍etc., 1809-68₎

VOLUME 405

4K
Ger.
2278

Nassau (Duchy) Laws, statutes, etc.
Die im vormaligen Herzogthum Nassau
neben dem Reichsstrafgesetzbuche
geltenden Straf-Gesetze und Verordnungen, zusammengestellt von E.
Preusser. Wiesbaden, C. Limbarth,
1876.
464 p.
I. Preusser, E   ed.

NN 0026916   DLC-P4 MH-L

Nassau (Duchy) Laws, statutes, etc.
Die in vormaligen herzogthum Nassau neben
dem reichsstrafgesetzbuche geltenden straf-
gesetze und verordnungen, zusammengestellt von
E. Preusser. Ergänzungsband. Wiesbaden, 1881.

NN 0026917   MH-L

Nassau (Duchy) Laws, statutes, etc.
Kirchengesang Teutsch vnd Lateinisch, Dauon
in Newburgischer vnd Zweybruckischer gleich-
förmiger Kirchenordnung meldung geschicht
see under   Evangelische Landeskirche
in Neuburg (Duchy)

Nassau (Duchy) Laws, statutes, etc.
Kirchen-ordnung, wie es mit der christlichen
lehre und ceremonien &c. in weyland des Herrn
Ludewigs, grafens zu Nassau, zu Saarbrücken und
zu Saarwerden &c. graf-und herrschafften zu
halten ist ...
see under   Evangelische Landeskirche in
Nassau. Kirchenordnung.

Nassau (Duchy) Laws, statutes, etc.
Nassau-Catzenelnbogische Gerichts und
Landordnung
see under   Nassau-Katzenelnbogen. Laws,
statutes, etc.

4K
Ger.
1777

Nassau (Duchy) Laws, statutes etc.
Das Nassauische Familien- und
Vormundschaftsrecht zusammengestellt
von Phil. Bertram. Wiesbaden, Chr.
Limbarth, 1876.
350 p.
I. Bertram, Phil   ed.

NN 0026921   DLC-P4

4K
Ger.
1772

Nassau (Duchy) Laws, statutes, etc.
Die Nassauische Gemeindegesetzge-
bung, zusammengestellt von Phil.
Bertram. Wiesbaden, Chr. Limbarth,
1887.
287 p.
I. Bertram, Phil   ed.

NN 0026922   DLC-P4 MH-L

Nassau (Duchy) Laws, statutes, etc.
Das nassauische Privatrecht, zusammengestellt
von Dr. Phil. Bertram. Wiesbaden, C. Limbarth
1873.
768 p.
I. Bertram, Phil   ed.

NN 0026923   DLC-P4

4K
Ger.
1894

Nassau (Duchy) Laws, statutes, etc.
Das nassauische Privatrecht, zusammengestellt von Dr. Phil. Bertram.
2. neu bearb. Aufl. Wiesbaden, C.
Limbarth, 1878.
848 p.

NN 0026924   DLC-P4

Nassau (Duchy) Laws, statutes, etc.
Nassauisches Bürgerbuch; Sammlung
der Landesgesetze, die Gesetze aus
den Jahren 1848 und 1849 enthaltend.
2. Aufl. Wiesbaden, C. W. Kreidel,
1850.
624 p.

4K
Ger.
2477

NN 0026925   DLC-P4

Nassau (Duchy) Laws, statutes, etc.
Reglement, oder Kleine berg-ordnung im
hochfürstenthum Nassau-Sigen, zu Dillenburg
publicirt den 22.May 1592. Wetzlar, G.E.Winck-
ler 1712.

f°. pp.8.

NN 0026926   MH

Nassau (Duchy) Laws, statutes, etc.
Sammlung der landesherrlichen edicte und anderer verordnungen, welchen vom 1. julius 1816 an, im ganzen umfange
des herzogthums Nassau gesetzeskraft beigelegt worden ist ...
Wiesbaden, Herzoglich nassauische hofbuchdruckerei, 1817-
46.
4 v. fold. tables, fold. plans. 24 x 27ᶜᵐ.
Title varies slightly.
Imprint varies: v. 3, Gedruckt bei L. Schellenberg.—v. 4, Druck von
L. Niedel.
CONTENTS.—bd. 1. Enthaltend die bis zum ende des jahres 1815
erschienenen edicte und verordnungen.—bd. 2. Die im laufe des jahres
1816 erschienenen edicte und verordnungen.—bd. 3. Die in den jahren
1817 bis 1823 einschliesslich erschienenen verordnungen und edicte.—
bd. 4. Die edicte und verord-   nungen aus den jahren 1824 bis 1845
einschliesslich.
    CONTENTS.—bd. 1. Nassau (Duchy) Con-   stitution. II. Title.
                                                    30-16183

NN 0026927   DLC MH NN

Nassau (Duchy) Laws, statutes, etc.
Verordnungsblatt des herzogthums Nassau.   -58. jahrgang. Wiesbaden, Herzogliche hofbuchdr. [etc.] 18   -66.
v. fold. tables. 24½-26½ᶜᵐ.
Imprint varies.
Issued irregularly.
26. jahrgang misnumbered : 27. jahrgang.
"Beilage des Herzoglich nassauischen allgemeinen intelligenzblatts,
1825. Wiesbaden, Gedruckt bei L. Schellenberg [1825]" (2 p. l., 51 p.)
appended to jahrgang 1825.

1. Law—Nassau (Duchy) 2. Administrative law—Nassau (Duchy)
I. Title. II. Title : Herzoglich nassauische allgemeine intelligenzblatt.
                                                    15-8319 Revised

NN 0026928   DLC PU MH-L

Nassau (Duchy) Laws, statutes, etc.

[Rühle von Lilienstern, Johann August Friedemann] 1744?-
1829?
Weisthum der gesetze, ordnungen und vorschriften, welche
in die nassauische teutsche länder, ottoischer linie, von den
ältesten zeiten bis hierhin ergangen sind. Aufgestellt nach
der zeit- und buchstabenfolge ... Hadamar, Gedruckt mit den
schriften der Neuen gelehrten-buchhandlung, auf kosten der
Intelligenz-ausfertigung zu Dillenburg, 1802-03.

Nassau (Duchy) Laws, statutes, etc. (Indexes)
Alphabetisches register der für das herzogthum Nassau bis
ende 1831 erlassenen, sowohl älteren, noch gültigen, als neueren landesherrlichen edicte und verordnungen; mit besonderer
hinweisung auf die drei bände der Verordnungssammlung und
Verordnungsblätter, worin solche abgedruckt sind, hrsg. von
R. J. A. v. Meex. Wiesbaden, H. W. Ritter, 1832.
2 p. l., 122 p. 26ᶜᵐ.
—— Copy 2.
—— Erster nachtrag zum Alphabetischen register der für das
herzogthum Nassau vom anfange 1832 bis ende 1838 erlassenen
landesherrlichen edicte und verordnungen, hrsg. von R. J. A.
v. Meex. Wiesbaden,   A. Scholz, 1839.
39 p. 26ᶜᵐ.

—— Zweiter nachtrag zum Alphabetischen register der für das
herzogthum Nassau vom anfange 1839 bis ende 1846 erlassenen
landesherrlichen edicte und verordnungen, hrsg. von R. J. A.
v. Meex ... Wiesbaden, H. W. Ritter, 1848.
50 p. 26ᶜᵐ.

1. Law—Nassau (Duchy) I. Nassau (Duchy) Laws, statutes, etc.
Sammlung der ... edicte und verordnungen. II. Nassau (Duchy) Laws,
statutes, etc. Verordnungsblatt. III. Meex, R. J. A. von, comp. IV.
Title.
                                                    30-1191

NN 0026931   DLC MH-L MH

Nassau (Duchy) Oberappellationsgericht.
Entscheidungen des herzoglich
Nassauischen Oberappellations-Gerichts
zu Wiesbaden über wichtigere Streitfragen des Civilrechts. Hrsg von
Christoph Flach. Giessen, B. C.
Ferber, 1842-53.
3 v. in 1

4K
Ger.
2543

NN 0026932   DLC-P4 MH-L

Nassau (Duchy) Oberappellationsgericht.
Sammlung der merkwürdigeren Entscheidungen des Herzoglich Nassauischen Oberappellations-Gerichts zu Wiesbaden, hrsg. von Wilhelm von der Nahmer. Frankfurt am
Main, Verlag der Hermannschen Buchhandlung, 182
v. 21 cm.

1. Law reports, digests, etc.—Nassau (Duchy)   I. Nahmer, Wilhelm von der, ed. II. Title.
                                                    65-58559

NN 0026933   DLC MH-L

Nassau (Duchy) Stände

see

Nassau (Duchy) Ständeversammlung.

Nassau (Duchy) Ständeversammlung, 1818-1848. Deputirtenversammlung.
Verhandlungen der Landes-deputirten-versammlung des herzogthums Nassau von dem jahre [5. märz 1818-5. april] 1848.
Wiesbaden, L. Schellenberg [etc., 1818-48]
27 v. tables (part fold.) forms. 24½ x 21½-32½ᶜᵐ.
Title varies: 1818-1824, Sitzungs-protocolle der ersten[-siebenten]
Landständischen deputirten-versammlung des herzogthums Nassau.
1825-1832 Sitzungs-protocolle der Landständischen deputirtenversammlung [etc.]
1832 -1848, Verhandlungen der Landes-deputirten-versammlung [etc.]
(1848 has subtitle : Den entwurf eines neuen wahlgesetzes betreffend)

—— Register zu den Verhandlungen der Landes-deputirten
in den versammlungen der Landstände des herzogthums Nassau während der ersten und zweiten wahlperiode von 1818 bis
1831. Wiesbaden, Druck der L. Schellenberg'schen hofbuchdruckerei, 1835.
48 p. 20½ x 25½ᶜᵐ.
                    J353.N3K3 Register 1818-1831

—— Verhandlungen der Landes-deputirten-versammlung des
herzogthums Nassau über die prüfung der cassen-trennung.
1836. Wiesbaden, L. Schellenberg [1836]
2 p. l., 258 p., 1 l. incl. tables. 24½ x 20½ᶜᵐ.

1. Nassau (Duchy)—Pol. & govt.   I. Title. II. Title: Sitzungs-protocolle der ... Landständischen deputirtenversammlung.
Library of Congress   HJ49.N3A14   39-8792

NN 0026937   DLC MiU

Nassau (Regierungsbezirk) Historische kommission
see   Verein für Nassauische Altertumskunde
und Geschichtsforschung, Wiesbaden. Historische
Kommission für Nassau.

J353
.N3J3

Nassau (Duchy) Ständeversammlung, 1818-1848.
Herrenbank.
Sitzungs-protocoll der Herrenbank bei
der Stände-versammlung des herzogthums Nassau
in jahr [1818-]1847 nebst dessen anlagen.
Wiesbaden, Gedruckt E.F.C. Enders [etc.],
[1818-47]
v. tables (part fold.) 31½x20cm.

1. Nassau—Pol. & govt. I. Title. II.
Title: Protokoll der Herrenbank.

NN 0026939   DLC MiU

VOLUME 405

Nassau (*Duchy*) *Ständeversammlung*, 1848–1851.
Verhandlungen der Stände-versammlung des herzogthums Nassau von dem jahre 1848[–1850/51] Wiesbaden, Druck der L. Schellenberg'schen hof-buch-druckerei [1848–51]

3 v. in 10. tables (part fold.) 25½ x 22cm.
Vol. 4, 1848, has imprint: Druck der Wiesbadener druckereien.

1. Nassau (Duchy)—Pol. & govt.   i. Title.
39–8791

Library of Congress   J353.N3K32

NN   0026940   DLC

J353
.N3K33   Nassau (*Duchy*) *Ständeversammlung*, 1852–1866.
Verhandlungen der ... Ständeversammlung des herzogthums Nassau im jahre 1852 [–1866] Wiesbaden [1852–66]
45 v. in 16   tables (part fold.)   24x20½–30x23cm.
Included in this entry and bound in original bindings without respect to order are the following: Verhandlungen der Stände-versammlung (joint sessions) Verhandlungen der Ersten kammer der Ständeversammlung, Verhandlungen der Zweiten kammer der Ständeversammlung.

Each of the Verhandlungen includes its Anlagen.
————Vertrauliche verhandlungen der Ständeversammlung des herzogthums Nassau über die eisenbahnangelegenheit aus den jahren 1855, 1856, 1857, 1858. Wiesbaden, Druck von Ph. Müller & comp. [1859?]

1. Nassau—Pol. & govt.   2. Railroads—Nassau.   I. Title.   II. Title: Nassau (Duchy) Ständeversammlung, 1852–1866. 1. Kammer. verhandlungen.   III. Title: Nassau (Duchy) Ständeversammlung, 1852–1866. 2. Kammer. Verhandlungen.

NN   0026943   DLC

Nassau (Duchy) Ständeversammlung Deputirtenversammlung. Commission über die prüfung der cassen-trennung

see

Nassau (Duchy) Commission über die prüfung der cassen-trennung.

Nassau, Bahamas. Bahama society for the diffusion of knowledge.

see

Bahama society for the diffusion of knowledge, Nassau.

Nassau, Bahamas. Boys' Industrial School.
Report.
[Nassau?]
v. 36cm. annual.

HV9120.5.N3   55–39208 ‡

NN   0026946   DLC

Nassau, Bahamas. Development Board.
The "treasure islands" of the Bahamas; prepared for yachtsmen, sportsmen and lovers of scenes and legends of an older day.   Nassau [1948?]
26p. illus. 24cm.

1. Bahamas - Descr.   i. Title.

NN   0026947   FMU

HV8404
.5   Nassau, Bahamas. Prison.
.N3A3   Report.   1929-1931.   [Nassau, 1930-1932]
3 v.   27-33 cm.

NN   0026948   DLC

Nassau, N. Y. Reformed Protestant Dutch church.
Records of the Reformed Protestant Dutch church in the town of Nassau, Rensselaer County, N. Y. Transcribed by the New York genealogical and biographical society; ed. by Royden Woodward Vosburgh.   New York city, 1919.
2 p. L, iii, 144 numb. l. 36 x 28½cm.
Autographed from type-written copy.
CONTENTS.—Introduction.—Pastors of the church.—Births and baptisms, 1804-1880.—Marriages, 1805-1880.—Members received, 1806-1841.—Dismissions, 1834-1840.
1. Registers of births, etc.—Nassau, N. Y.   i. Vosburgh, Royden Woodward, ed. II. New York genealogical and biographical society. III. Title.

Library of Congress   F129.N2N5
19–14063

NN   0026949   DLC

Nassau. v. 1-
Jan. 1939-
[Tottenville, N. Y., Nassau smelting & refining co., inc., 1939-
v. illus, diagrs. 21cm. monthly.

1. Founding—Period. 2. Smelting—Period.   i. Nassau smelting & refining co., inc., Tottenville, N. Y.

Library of Congress   TS200.N224   43–27171
[2]   669.805

NN   0026950   DLC

The Nassau. Published by the Sophomore Class.
Princeton, N. J. June 30, 1852 Vol. 1 No. 1 4p.
DLC Rare Book Div.—Broadside Coll.

NN   0026951   DLC

Nassau, magazine of international life in the Bahamas.
[Nassau, Nassau Magazine Ltd.]
v. illus, ports. 30 cm. 5 no. a year.
Began with Dec. 1933 issue. Cf. Union list of serials.
Subtitle varies slightly.
Superseded by Nassau, Freeport and the Bahama Islands.

1. Bahamas. 2. Nassau.

F1650.N36   77–439696

NN   0026952   DLC NN CtY

Nassau an der Lahn, Ger. Anstalt für Blödsinnige.
Jahresberichte. 1874-75.   Limburg.

NN   0026953   DNLM

NASSAU and resort islands of the Bahamas.

Nassau, Bahamas.   v.   illus., ports.
31cm.

Five issues a year.

Supersedes: Nassau, magazine of international life in the Bahamas.
Title varies: v. 3, no. 4-v. 4, no. 1, spring-fall, 1951, Nassau; magazine of life and times in the enchanted Bahamas; v. 4, no. 2-v. 6, no. 2, winter, 1951/52-winter, 1953/54, Nassau and the "out islands" of the Bahamas.
For later file, which continues its numbering, see Nassau and the Bahamas.
1. Nassau, Bahama Islands--Per. and soc. publ. 2. Bahama Islands--Per. and soc. publ. I. Title: Nassau; :magazine of life and times in the enchanted Bahamas;   II. Title: Nassau and the "out islands" of the Bahamas.

NN   0026955   NN

NASSAU and the Bahama Islands.

Nassau, Bahamas.   v.   illus. (part col.),
ports.   31cm.

Five issues a year.
For earlier file, whose numbering it continues, see Nassau and resort islands of the Bahamas.
HRG
+
1. Nassau, Bahama Islands--Per.   and soc. publ. 2. Bahama Islands--Per. and soc. publ.

NN   0026956   NN

Nassau archeological society.
Bulletin.
v. 1-
summer 1955-
Sea Cliff, N. Y., 1955-
v. illus., plates. 28cm.

·1 New York - Antiq. - Period.

NN   0026957   NNM

T976.411
N187Dt Nassau Bay Telephone Company.
Nassau Bay, Texas. Telephone directory.

[Nassau Bay? Tex.]
v. 24cm.

1. Nassau Bay, Tex. - Direct. - Telephone.

NN   0026958   TxU

Nassau boat club of the city of New York.
Constitution, by-laws. rules and list of members, etc.
[New York] 19
v. 14¼cm.

CA 18-344 Unrev'd

Library of Congress   GV793.N24

NN   0026959   DLC

Nassau building & accumulating fund association.
Articles of association.   B'klyn, Van Anden, 1851.
24 p.

NN   0026960   NN

Nassau cable railway company, Brooklyn.
Cable railway. Fare 5 cents. Including a transfer to any of the lines. It will benefit your property. Read it. [Brooklyn? N. Y., 1884?] 22 p.   25½cm.

Caption-title: For five cents. The citizens of Brooklyn can ride crosswise, lengthwise, transfer, and to New York, for five cents.
Two letters to the mayor of Brooklyn and a letter to the Board of aldermen (p. 3-7) dated "The Nassau cable railway co., office of the secretary...Brooklyn, N. Y., July 22, Aug. 13, and July 30, 1884," and signed "Charles H. Swan, secretary."
"Opening of the Highgate hill tramway by the lord mayor, M.P. (Highgate 'Express,' England, May 31, 1884.)," p. 7–22.

906157A. 1. Railways, Street—   U. S.—N. Y.—Brooklyn. 2. Railways, Cable. i. Swan, Charles H.   II. Highgate Express.
III. Title.
N. Y. P. L.   July 14, 1938

NN   0026961   NN

Nassau club of Princeton, N.J.
...Constitution, by-laws and list of members.
[Princeton, N.J.]

nS2725
.P85N31

NN   0026962   DLC NjP

Nassau Club of Princeton, N.J.
Report of special committee on club house.
[n.p., 1903]

NN   0026963   NjP

VOLUME 405

Nassau country club, *Glen Cove, N. Y.*
... Club book.
[Brooklyn,
v. pl. 17½ cm.
At head of title: Nassau country club, Glen Cove, Long Island,
N. Y.

Library of Congress   HS2725.G5N3   CA 15-412 Unrev'd

NN   0026964   DLC NN

F.2
N26
N2665r   **Nassau County, Fla.** *Board of Health.*
VAULT   Rules and regulations in relation to
           quarantine. Adopted by the Board of Health
           for Nassau County, Fla., Feb. 12, 1890.
           [Fernandina, Fla.?, 1890?]
           4 p. 24cm.

           Caption title.

           1. Quarantine - Nassau Co., Fla.   2. Public
Health laws -   Nassau Co., Fla.
I. Title.

NN   0026965   FU

Nassau co., N. Y.
... Land map of the county of Nassau, state of New York
... Designed and compiled ... by Ferdinand W. Wisner,
deputy county clerk. Mineola, N. Y., '1938.
1 p. l., 67 (i. e. 68) numb. l. incl. 69 maps.   68½ x 73½ cm.
Title from map sheets.
Maps on the scale of 1 : 9,600 or 1 inch to 800 feet.
——Changes to the Land map of the county of Nassau for
the year[s] 1938-[1944. Mineola, N. Y., '1939-45.
7 sheets. maps. 67½ x 73½ cm. (1 sheet, 130½ x 130½ cm.)
Sheet for 1944, blue line print.
                                    G1254.N3N28 1938 Suppl.
1. Nassau Co., N. Y.—Maps.   I. Title.

G1253.N3N28   1938   Map 43-81 rev

NN   0026966   DLC

Nassau county, N. Y.
GB1025
.N7A3
GW-6   **U. S.** *Geological survey.*
           ... Record of wells in Queens county, N. Y., exclusive of
those published in U. S. Geological survey Professional
paper 44. Prepared by the United States Geological survey
in cooperation with the Water power and control commission and with Nassau and Suffolk counties ... Albany, 1938.

Nassau co., N. Y.

Thompson, David Grosh, 1888-
... Withdrawal of ground water on Long island, N. Y. [by
David G. Thompson and R. M. Leggette] Prepared in co-
operation with the United States Geological survey, and with
Nassau and Suffolk counties, N. Y. ... Albany, J. B. Lyon
company, printers, 1936.

Nassau co., *N. Y.* *Board of statutory consolidation and revision.*
... Codification and revision of the laws relating to Nassau
county. First report of the Board of statutory consolidation
and revision of Nassau county. Submitted May, 1939. Albany, J. B. Lyon company, printers, 1939.
195 p. incl. tables, forms. 23 cm.
At head of title: Legislative document (1939) no. 104. State of New
York.

1. Law—Nassau co., N. Y.—Codification.
                                                   39-28543
Library of Congress   JS451.N79N33 1939
————— Copy 2.   [2]   352.0747245

NN   0026969   DLC NNC NN

JS3
.N 7N3   **Nassau county. N. Y. Board of supervisors.**
           Proceedings...1904/05--1916/17,--
1918/19,--1919-1927.
           Oyster Bay, 1905-[28] 23 v.   8°

NN   0026970   DLC MtU MnU NNC-L N

Nassau County (N. Y.). *Charters.*
...An act providing a form of government for the county of
Nassau, in conformity with section twenty-six of article three
of the constitution. [Albany, 1923.] 252 p. 4°.

Caption-title.
At head of title: State of New York... In Assembly, March 6, 1923.

NN   0026971   NN

NASSAU COUNTY, N.Y. *Charters.*
County government law of Nassau county; otherwise
known as the Nassau county charter (Ch. 879, L. 1936
as amended by Ch. 618, L. 1937). Nassau county
administrative code (Ch. 272, L. 1939). Nassau county
civil divisions act (Ch. 273, L. 1939). Nassau county
district court act (Ch. 274, L. 1939). Including all
amendments to such county government law, administrative code, civil   divisions act, and

district court act, to September 3rd 1945.
[Mineola, N.Y., [1945?] 587 p.   23cm.

t.1945.

NN   0026973   NN NBuG NNC

Law lib. Nassau County, N. Y. *Charters.*
           County government law of Nassau County;
Nassau County administrative code; Nassau
County civil divisions act; Nassau County
district court act. [Including all amendments to such county government law, administrative code, civil divisions act, and district court act, to December 1, 1952.
Mineola?, N.Y., 1953?]
           702 p. 24 cm.
           1. Nassau County, N.Y. Pol. & govt. Lw 1.
Charters.

NN   0026974   N NNC-L

NASSAU COUNTY (N. Y.) *Charters.*
Proposed charter for Nassau County, New
York; being chapter 863 of the laws of 1923.
Subject to adoption by the voters of the
county at the general election in the year
1925. With a summary. Dated August 1, 1923.
Albany, J.B. Lyon Co., printers, 1923.

NN   0026975   MH NN N

S336.747245 Nassau Co., N. Y. *Comptroller's Office.*
qN266   Budget.
           [Mineola]
               v. in   tables. 28 cm.

           1. Budget. Nassau Co., N. Y.

NN   0026976   N

S
352.109747 Nassau Co., N. Y. *Comptroller's Office.*
qN266   Five year cumulative report of County of Nassau, New
York and all municipal subdivisions, showing: indebtedness,
assessed values, tax levies, tax rates. [1st]-
1938-42—   Mineola,
               v. in   tables. 23 x 29 cm. annual.

           Compiled by the County Comptroller.

           1. Finance, Public. Nassau County, N.Y. 2. Municipal
finance. New York (State) Nassau County.

NN   0026977   N

308
Z
Box 687 **Nassau county, N. Y.** *Comptroller's office.*
           Five year cumulative report of county of
Nassau, New York and all municipal subdivisions, showing: indebtedness, assessed values,
tax levies, tax rates. Issue as of December
31, 1943. Compiled by Theodore Bedell, jr.
... [1944]
           cover-title, 64 p. tables. 22 x 28 cm.

           1. Finance - Nassau county, N. Y. I. Bedell,
Theodore   jt. au.

NN   0026978   NNC

S
336.747245 Nassau Co., N. Y. *Comptroller's Office.*
qN2663   Report of County of Nassau, New York.

           [Mineola]
               v. in   tables. 29 cm. annual.

           1. Finance. Public. Nassau Co., N.Y.

NN   0026979   N PP NN

Nassau County, N. Y. *Comptroller's office.*
Statement showing indebtedness of the county...and all
municipal subdivisions.

Mineola, N. Y.   23cm.
Annual.
Statement as of Dec. 31st.

1. Debt, Public—U. S.—N. Y.—   Nassau County.
N. Y. P. L.   January 15, 1942

NN   0026980   NN

Nassau co., N. Y. *County Attorney.*
           First interim report by James L. Dowsey,
County Attorney, to the Board of Statutory
Consolidation and Revision of Nassau County.
February 25, 1939. [Mineola, N. Y., 1939,
cover-title, 8 p.

           1. Law—Nassau co., N. Y.—Codification.
I. Nassau co., N. Y. Board of statutory consolidation and revision.

NN   0026981   NNC

S
336.22
N266   Nassau County, N. Y. *County Executive.*
               The draft of a proposed amendment to the tax law;
to which is added a short account of the experience of Nassau
County in liquidating taxes on real property. Prepared under
the direction of J. Russel Sprague, county executive.
[Mineola? N. Y., 1938?]
           23 p. 27 cm.

           Cover title.
           1. Real property tax. Nassau Co., N. Y. Lw. L Tax
sales and tax titles.   New York (State) 2. Tax
collection. Nassau   Co., N. Y. Lw. 2. Tax collection.
New York (State)   w. 3. Tax liens. New York (State)
L Sprague, John   Russel, 1886-

NN   0026982   N

Nassau county, N. Y. *County Executive.*
Your county, Nassau. [Mineola? 1947] 32 p.   illus.
28cm.

Issued by the Office of county executive.

NN   0026983   NN

NASSAU COUNTY, N. Y. *County Executive.*
Your county, Nassau. [Mineola, 1955?]   [64] p.
illus., col. maps. 26cm.

1. Nassau county, N. Y. —Govt.   t.1955.

NN   0026984   NN

WA
199.N3   **Nassau Co., N. Y.** *Dept. of Health*
qB1   Nassau health; annual report. 1st-
1939-

           Mineola,
               v. illus.

           4th report, 1942 incorrectly called 3d.

           1. Public health - Nassau Co., N. Y.
I. Title

NN   0026985   DNLM

VOLUME 405

Nassau co., *N. Y. Dept. of public welfare.*
Manual of medical care; rules and regulations governing medical care provided to recipients of public assistance by the Nassau county Department of public welfare. Edwin W. Wallace, commissioner.   Mineola, Long island, N. Y., 1942.

cover-title, xiii, 131 (i. e. 133) p. incl. tables.   forms.   28^{cm}.

Includes extra numbered pages 108a–108b.
Reproduced from type-written copy.

1. Charities, Medical.   2. Charities—New York (State)—Nassau co.
                                              43–13553
Library of Congress   HV688.U55N76
                                      [2]   361.1

NN   0026986   DLC IU NN

Nassau co., *N. Y. Dept. of public welfare.*
Public assistance ... Annual report of the Nassau county Department of public welfare ...
[Mineola?] 19

v. in   tables, diagrs. 27½ x 22¼^{cm}.

1. Public welfare—New York (State)—Nassau co.
HV86.N79N32   361.6   46–44997

NN   0026987   DLC N Wa NN NNC

Nassau County, N.Y. Dept. of Public Welfare.
Report of the committee to study the job of case supervisor. Mineola, N.Y., Nassau County Department of Public Welfare [1949?]
27ℓ., 27 charts.

Mimeographed.

NN   0026988   ScU Wa

361.06   Nassau co.,N.Y. Dept.of public welfare.
N266s   Social data on home relief case loads in Nassau county,New York, as of February 1,1938 – July 1, 1938. Compiled and tabulated by Section of research & statistics, Department of public welfare, Nassau county,New York.   Garden city, N.Y.[1938]

4 p.l., 9 numb.l.   28^{cm}.

Mimeographed.

1.Nassau co.,N.Y. --Charities. I.Title.

NN   0026989   CSt

GB1025   Nassau Co., N. Y. Dept. of Public Works.
.N7A3   De Laguna, Wallace, 1910–
GW-13   The configuration of the rock floor in western Long Island, N. Y., by Wallace de Laguna and M. L. Brashears, jr. [Washington?] 1946.

GB1025   Nassau Co., N. Y. Dept. of Public Works.
.N7A3   Roberts, Claude Martin, 1903–
GW-10   Record of wells in Nassau County, N. Y. Supplement 1. In addition to those published in U. S. Geological Survey Professional paper 44 and N. Y. Water Power and Control Commission Bulletin GW-5. By C. M. Roberts and M. L. Brashears, Jr. Prepared by the U. S. Geological Survey in cooperation with the Water Power and Control Commission, and the Nassau County Dept. of Public Works. Albany, 1946.

                                     351.8649
                                     154
Nassau County, *N. Y. Emergency Work Bureau.*
... Report of activities for the period[s, Nov./Dec. 1931–1933/34] Mineola (L. I.) N. Y. [1931–1934]

4 v. in 1. illus., plates, tables, diagrs. 21^{cm}.

At head of title: Nassau County Emergency Work Bureau. Established under the Temporary emergency relief act, chapter 798, Laws of 1931, as amended.
No. 1 covers period from organization, Nov. 2–Dec. 15, 1931; no. 2, Nov. 1931–May 1932; no. 3, June 1932–May 1933; no. 4, June 1933–June 17, 1934.
Superseded by Nassau County Emergency Relief Bureau.

NN   0026992   ICJ NN Wa DL

355.23   Nassau county, N.Y. Fire commission.
N1Af   The fire service in national defense. County fire commission, Nassau county, N.Y., June 16th, 1941. n.p., County fire commission, 1941.
cover-title, [8]p. tables. 27½cm.

1. U.S.--Civilian defense.   2. Fire departments. I. Title.

NN   0026993   LU

Nassau Co., N.Y. Health, Dept. of
          see Nassau Co., N.Y. Dept. of Health.

Nassau Co., N.Y. Joint Committee on
      Conduit Boulevard
          see Joint Committee on Conduit
Boulevard.

N
          Nassau county, N. Y. Meadowbrook hospital.

      Annual report ...

      [Hempstead, N. Y.?]
              v. illus. 23^{cm}.

      1. Hospital reports.

NN   0026996   NNC

Nassau Co., N.Y. Mosquito Extermination
      Commission
          see Nassau county extermination
Commission, Freeport, N.Y.

Nassau County, N.Y. Office of County Executive
      see Nassau Co., N.Y. County Executive.

Nassau County, N.Y. Office of the county
      comptroller
          see Nassau Co., N.Y. Comptroller's
Office.

Avery

      Nassau County, N. Y. Planning Commission.
      Land use, Mineola school district no. 10, Town of North Hempstead. [Mineola, N. Y., 1954?]
      cover-title, 7 p. tables. 28cm.

NN   0027000   NNC-A

312
(747245) Nassau County, N.Y. Planning Commission.
N17   Population estimates; a report for the Nassau County Planning Commission. Mineola, N.Y., 1947.
      72p.

      1. Population - Nassau Co., N.Y.

NN   0027001   DHUD

S
71L3   Nassau Co., N. Y. Planning Commission.
qN265r   Report of progress.
      [Mineola, L. I., N. Y.]
              v.   29 cm. annual.

              1. Regional planning. Nassau County, N. Y.

NN   0027002   N IU

NASSAU COUNTY, N.Y. Police dept.
      Report.
Mineola.   no.   28cm.

      Annual.

1. Police--U.S.--N.Y.--Nassau   county.

NN   0027003   NN N

Nassau County, N.Y. Public welfare department
      see Nassau County, N.Y. Dept. of
public welfare.

Nassau County, N.Y. Sanitation commission.
      Sanitary sewers, Nassau County; a report...
      see under MacCallum, Clarence.

Nassau County, N. Y. Sanitation commission.
      Summary report; comprehensive drainage plan for Nassau County, New York, prepared under the direction of W. Fred Welsch... December twenty-three, nineteen hundred thirty-five. [Mineola, 1935] 23 p. charts, plans. 28cm.

      Cover-title.
      Printed in double columns.
      "Prepared by W. Fred Welsch, assistant engineer, Nassau County Sanitation commission, in collaboration with Clarence MacCallum, consulting engineer, and the Department of county engineer."—p. 4.

859960A. 1. Drainage—U. S.—   N. Y.—Nassau County. I. MacCallum, Clarence. II. Nassau County,   N. Y. Engineer.
N. Y. P. L.   August 19, 1937

NN   0027006   NN

Nassau county, N. Y. Transit commission.
      ...Report[s] to Hon. J. Russel Sprague, county executive... [1st – [Mineola, 1949]   parts.   27cm.

      First report is a photostatic reproduction of the original in the Municipal reference library of New York city.
      Report on the Long island railroad. Second report is a compendium of the salient points of the report made by the J. G. White engineering corporation.

      1. Long island railroad company.   I. White, J. G., engineering corporation.
N. Y. P. L.   January 22, 1951

NN   0027007   NN

Nassau County, N.Y. Statutory consolidation
      and revision board
          see Nassau co., N.Y. Board of Statutory
consolidation and revision.

Nassau Co., N.Y. Supervisors, Board of.
          see Nassau Co., N.Y. Board of Supervisors.

371.42   Nassau County, N. Y. Vocational Education
qN268   and Extension Board.
              Nassau County needs vocational education now! [Mineola, N. Y., 1955]
              2 v. illus. (part col.) col. maps, ports. 27 cm.

              Contents.--v. 1. Survey report.--v. 2. Statistics. Summary reports.

              1. Vocational   education. New York (State)   Nassau County.   *

NN   0027010   N

NASSAU county agricultural news. v. 42, no. 1-9; 11-v. 43, no. 8, 10-date; Jan.-Sept., Nov. 1956-Aug., Oct. 1957-date
Mineola, N.Y.   v.   illus.   31cm.

      Monthly.
      Published by the Agricultural dept. of the Nassau county extension service association.

      For earlier file, whose numbering it continues, see the Nassau county farm and home bureau news.

1. Agriculture--Per. and soc. publ. 2. Agriculture--U.S.--N.Y.--Nassau county. I. Nassau   county extension service association. Agricultural dept.

NN   0027012   NN

VOLUME 405

Nassau county agricultural society premium list of the first annual fair of Nassau county agricultural society; together with a sketch of the county, its accessibility, soil, clime ... Fernandina; published by the Fernandina Observer, 1875.

NN 0027013 FHi

43.9
N18 Nassau County (N.Y.) Artificial Breeding
Co-operative, inc.
Annual report. 1st-
1947-
[n.p., 1948']-

1. Impregnation, Artificial. Societies.
2. Cattle breeders' societies, Cooperative.

NN 0027014 DNAL

Nassau County Association, Mineola, N.Y.
Annual report.
[no.] 1-
[Mineola, L.I., 1914-   nar. 16°.
v.

1. Nassau county, N.Y. 2. Gov-   ernment (Local), U.S.: N.Y.: Nassau county. 3. Charters, U.S.: N.Y.:   Nassau county.
N.Y.P.L.   June 26, 1918.

NN 0027015 NN

Nassau County Association, Mineola, N.Y.
...Report to Board of Supervisors of Nassau County. Dated, December 2nd, 1918. [New York]; Repr. and distributed by the Nassau County Assoc., Inc.[, 1918.] 135 p.   8°.

Cover-title.

1. Nassau County, N.Y.—Govt.   2. Nassau County Association,
Mineola, N.Y.   Mineola, N.Y.
N.Y.P.L.   October 6, 1928

NN 0027016 NN

Nassau County Committee.
The Nassau County Committee and state parks on Long Island, with a note on the proposed transfer of Hempstead's town lands to the state.   Glen Head, L.I.: The Nassau County Committee, 1925.   7 p.   illus. (maps.)   4°.

1. Parks—U.S.—N.Y.—Long Island.
N.Y.P.L.   August 24, 1927

NN 0027017 NN

NA9127 Nassau County committee.
.N28N3   ...Report no.[1]-
Glen Head, L.I., 1925-
v. maps (part fold.) 23½-28 ᵐᵐ.

NN 0027018 ICU NN

Nassau County (N.Y.) Committee Opposing Mandatory Centralization of Rural Schools.
A protest against mandatory centralization of rural schools in the State of New York.
[Brookville? N.Y.] 1939.
20 p.   26 cm.
Signed: Francis T. Nichols, chairman.
1. Schools. Centralization. New York (State) I. Title.

NN 0027019 N

Nassau County Council of Social Agencies. Division of Services for the Aging. Committee on Leisure Time Activities.
Suggested standards and practice for organizing and operating activity programs for older adults. [New York, 1955]
cover-title, 14 p.   22 cm.

NN 0027020 NcD

NASSAU COUNTY DENTAL SOCIETY, WOODMERE, NEW YORK. BULLETIN

NN 0027021 LNL

Nassau county (N.Y.) elementary principals' association.
Democratic education in Nassau county elementary schools; a county-wide survey, what Nassau county elementary schools are doing in training youth for civic responsibility ... [Garden City, N.Y., Country life press corporation, 1941]
vi, 21 p. 19½ᵐ. (*Its* Research bulletin, 1940-41)
"Helpful references": p. 21.

1. Citizenship. 2. Education of children. 3. Education—New York—
Nassau co.   i. Title.

                                        42-10139
Library of Congress   LA338.N3N3 1940-41
[2]   (370.62747245) 372.83

NN 0027022 DLC

Nassau county (N.Y.) elementary principals' association.
... Research bulletin[s] ... 1940/41-
[Garden City, N.Y., Country life press corporation, 1941-
v. 19½ᵐ.

1. Education—Societies.
                                        42-10140
Library of Congress   LA338.N3N3
[2]   370.62747245

NN 0027023 DLC

W 2   Nassau county extermination commission,
AN6.1   Freeport, N.Y.
N2M9a   Annual report.

[Rockville Centre? N.Y., 19—]-
v.

NN 0027024 DNLM NN

---

428   Nassau county extermination commission, Free-
N18   port, N.Y.
Mosquitoes; their life history and control.
Freeport, N.Y. Nassau county extermination commission, 1937.
31 p.   illus.   28cm.

NN 0027025 DLC DNLM IU

S   Nassau County Farm and Home Bureau
96   news. v. 1-   Apr. 1915-
N26   Mineola, N.Y.
v.   25-31 cm.

Through v.5, no.4, April 1919 as Nassau County Farm Bureau news.

I. Nassau   County Farm Bureau news.

NN 0027026 NIC DNAL NN

S   Nassau County Farm Bureau Association.
96   Circular no. 1-   August 1915-
N261   [Mineola, N.Y.]
nos.   24 cm.

"Cooperative Extension Work in Agriculture and HOme Economics - Nassau County Farm Bureau Association, United States Dept. of Agriculture, New York State Dept. of Agriculture, New York State College of Agriculture."

NN 0027027 NIC

G1441   [Nassau County, Long Island, N.Y. atlas, Brook-
f.N2   lyn, 1914.

NN 0027028 ICU

Nassau County firemen's association. Constitution and by-laws, rules and regulations. [Mineola]

NN 0027029 NJQ

_____ Nassau County firemen's association.
Official souvenir program, annual parade and tournament, v.1,1903- Mineola,1903-

NN 0027030 NJQ

275.28   Nassau County 4-H news. v.
N18
Mineola. Nassau County Farm and Home Bureau and 4-H Club Association, 4-H Club Department.

NN 0027031 DNAL

F127   Nassau County Historical and Genealogical
.N2N3   Society.
The Nassau County historical journal.

[Uniondale, etc., N.Y., Nassau County Historical and Genealogical Society]

The Nassau County historical journal.

[Uniondale, etc., N.Y., Nassau County Historical and Genealogical Society]
v. in illus., ports. 23-27 cm.
Semiannual   ; quarterly
Began publication in 1937. Cf. Union list of serials.

1. Nassau Co., N.Y.—Hist.—Period. i. Nassau County Historical and Genealogical Society.

F127.N2N3   58-30748

NN 0027033 DLC ICN WHi N NBHi NNQ NHuHi NN

Nassau County Historical Society.
The Nassau County Historical Society journal.

[Garden City, N.Y.]
v. illus. 23 cm.
Continues the Nassau County historical journal.
ISSN 0004-9450

1. Nassau Co., N.Y.—History—Periodicals. i. Nassau County Historical Society. Journal.

F127.N2N3   974.7'245'005   74-646808

NN 0027034 DLC

Nassau county kennel club.
Catalogue of the annual show...
[no.]

[Belmont Park, L.I.? 19   no.   23cm.

1. Dog shows—U.S.—N.Y.
N.Y.P.L.   April 11, 1944

NN 0027035 NN

Nassay county (N.Y.) Library Association.
Directory of libraries in Nassau county
see under   Baldwin, N.Y. Public Library.

Nassau County (N.Y.) Library Association.
NCLA odds and book ends
see under title

VOLUME 405

... Nassau county pictorial. ₁Vol. 1, no. 1,
April, 1938. New York, Nassau division of
the Long Island association, 1938₎
cover-title, 88, ₁2₎ p. illus., diagr.
35½cm.

1. Nassau co., N. Y. - Description and travel.
I. Long Island association, inc. Nassau
    county division.

NN   0027038   NNC MBHi

370.9747
qN26   Nassau County ₍ N. Y.₎ School Study Com-
            mittee.
        Minutes of meetings, 1950 ₁i.e. 1951₎-
        date ₁52₎ Reports I, II, III ₁Jan. 14-
        Apr. 28, 1952 and₎ other reports. ₁n.p.,
        1952?₎
            1 v.   maps, diagrs., tables. 29 cm.
            Title from label mounted on cover.
            Imperfect: Minutes for September meeting
        wanting.
            1. Education. New York (State) Nassau
        County.

NN   0027039   N

S352.074724S
qN268   Nassau County Village Officials Association.
        Eighteen years of progress, 1925-1943.
        New York, Bruce Ellis Associates ₁1943?₎
        95 p. illus., ports., facsims.
        24 x 31 cm.

        Includes advertising.

            1. Nassau County. I. Title.

NN   0027040   N

        Nassau County Young Woman's Christian
            Association
                see   Young Women's Christian Associations.
        Nassau Co., N.Y.

Nassau daily review.
    The Nassau daily review's 1930 manual, for the guidance
of its employees and to inform the public. ₁Albany, N. Y.,
°1930₎
        46 p. 23¼ᵐ.

        1. Newspapers.

        Library of Congress   PN4899.F8N3   30-5810

NN   0027042   DLC

        Nassau daily review.

Hall, Harry G   comp.
    1930 commercial survey of metropolitan Long Island, com-
piled expressly for the Nassau daily review, Rockville Centre,
New York, by Harry G. Hall ... ₁Mineola, L. I., Printed by
the Davenport press, °1930₎

        Nassau Daily Review.
        1936 facts and figures, Metropolitan Long
Island ... ₁Long Island City₎ Nassau Daily
Review and Nassau Daily Star ₁1936₎
        1 v.(unpaged) charts.

        Cover-title.

NN   0027044   MH-BA

        Nassau daily review-star.
        The newspaper after "V" day... ₁Hempstead? N. Y.,1944₎
        cover-title, 32 p. illus. (incl. ports.) 28 x 21¼ᵐ.
        "Answers to post-war newspaper survey, the Nassau daily review-
star."—p. 5.

        1. American newspapers. I. Title.

                                                45-17286
        Library of Congress   PN4867.N3
                                ₁2₎   071

NN   0027045   DLC IU

Nassau daily review-star.

Writers' program, *New York.*
    The story of the five towns: Inwood, Lawrence, Cedarhurst,
Woodmere, and Hewlett, Nassau county, Long island. Compiled by workers of the Writers' program of the Work projects
administration in the state of New York ... Co-sponsor, Law-
rence-Cedarhurst chamber of commerce ₁Rockville Centre,
N. Y.₎ The Nassau daily review-star ₁°1941₎

        Die Nassau-Dillenburger auswanderung nach
            Amerika im 18. jahrhundert
            see under   Gerber, Adolf.

Nassau Electric Railroad. Company
        ... Adee vs. Nassau Electric Railroad...
        see under
    Adee.

NASSAU ELECTRIC RAILROAD COMPANY.
    Atlantic avenue franchise application. History of the
efforts of the Nassau electric railroad company to meet the
public demand for trolley transportation on that tho-
roughfare. August 11, 1913.   [Brooklyn? 1913]   31 p.
20½cm.

    Cover-title.

    1. Railways, Street—Franchises—U.S.—N.Y.—New
York. I. Title.

NN   0027049   NN

Nassau Electric Railroad Company.
    Consolidated mortgage four per cent. gold bonds. Nassau
Electric Railroad Company to Guaranty Trust Company of New
York. Consolidated mortgage. Dated June 30, 1898. Due Janu-
ary 1, 1951...   ₁New York, 1899.₎   60, 5 p.   4°.

    1. Railways—Mortgages.
N. Y. P. L.   August 11, 1928

NN   0027050   NN

Nassau Fire Insurance Company.
    Act of incorporation, charter and by-laws.
B'klyn, 1852.
    46 p.

NN   0027051   NN

Nassau, Freeport and the Bahama Islands.

₁Nassau, Nassau Magazine Ltd.₎
        v. in.   illus., ports. 31 cm. 5 no. a year.
    Supersedes Nassau; magazine of international life in the Bahamas.
    Title varies: Nassau; magazine of life and times
in the enchanted Bahamas.—   -midseason 1960, Nassau
and resort islands of the Bahamas.—spring 1960—.
Nassau and the Bahama Islands.
        1. Bahamas. 2. Nassau, Bahamas.   I. Title: Nassau, magazine
of life and times in the enchanted Bahamas. II. Title: Nassau and
resort islands of the Bahamas. III. Title: Nassau and the Bahama
Islands.

F1650.N37   68-1148

NN   0027052   DLC NN

        Nassau golden fleece news gleaner
            see   Golden fleece news gleaner.

Nassau gun club, Princeton, N. J.

Browne, Charles, 1875–
    The Gun club cook book; or, A culinary code for apprecia-
tive epicures; being a discussion of the methods and procedures
of cooking, together with observations on kitchen usages, and
including many receipts from many lands, by Charles Browne
... illustrations by Leonard Holton. Rev. ed. New York,
London, C. Scribner's sons, 1931.

Nassau gun club, Princeton, N. J.

Browne, Charles, 1875–
    The Gun club drink book, being a more or less discursive
account of alcoholic beverages, their formulae and uses, together with some observations on the mixing of drinks, by
Charles Browne ... illustrated by Leonard Holton. New York,
C. Scribner's sons; London, C. Scribner's sons, ltd., 1939.

        Nassau Hall

            see

        Princeton University. Nassau Hall.

W 2   NASSAU health ₁monthly₎
AN6.1
N2D4h   Mineola, N. Y., Nassau Co. Dept. of
               Health ₁1938?₎ -
                   v. illus.
               1. Public health - Nassau Co., N. Y.
               I. Nassau Co., N. Y. Dept. of Health

NN   0027057   DNLM

    The Nassau herald ... of Princeton university ... ₁Balti-
more, Williams & Wilkins co. press, 1901₎-
        v. fronts. (ports.) illus., plates. 24ᵐ.

    1. Princeton university. Senior class.

    Library of Congress   LD4627.N3   1-12750

NN   0027058   DLC DHEW NN

Nassau Herald, Class Day, May 13th, 1869. No. 5.
    Princeton, N. J. Stelle & Smith. 1869. 48 pp. 8°.

G7276 — Princeton University. Classes. Class of 1869. — College periodicals.

NN   0027059   MB RPB

        Nassau herald. Class day ...
            no. 7, June 26, 1871.
        I v.   22 cm.
        Unbound in box.
        Includes poetry.

NN   0027060   RPB

        The Nassau herald, no. 22 Pub. by the Class of
        1886, Princeton college, Class Day. Monday
        June 21, 1886.   Trenton, N.J., 1886.
            77 p.   19 cm.
            Bd. with [Paton, Stewart] A historical
        drama in four acts. Princeton, N. J., 1886.

NN   0027061   RPB

        The Nassau Herald of the class of '94 of
        Princeton university... ₁Trenton, N.J., The
        John L. Murphy pub. co.₎ 1894.
        121p.

NN   0027062   OClW

        The Nassau herald. Class of nineteen hundred and fif-
teen, Princeton university. v. 1–
    1915–
        New York, Printed for the class by Burr printing
    house ₁1915₎
        v. illus., ports. 23¼ᵐ.
        To be published at five year intervals.

        I. Princeton university. Class of 1915.

                                                15-20175
        Library of Congress   LD4604 1915

NN   0027063   DLC OClWHi

VOLUME 405

Spec.
PS 3545 The Nassau Herald. Class of nineteen hundred
I 6245   and sixteen, Princeton University. Vol. 1,
Z 82   June 1916. Princeton, N. J., Printed for
1916   the class by the Princeton University
           Press, 1916.
           383 p. illus. 24 cm.
           Black cloth; gold lettering on front cover
      and spine.
           Includes brief article on Edmund Wilson
      (p. 261)
           1. Wilson, Edmund, 1895-1972. I. Princeton
      University. Class   of 1916.

NN 0027064   MoSW

---

*
PS3511
.I 9Z753 The Nassau herald. Class of nineteen
1917   hundred and seventeen, Princeton Univer-
           sity. v. 1, June. Printed for the
           class by the Princeton University Press.
           Princeton, N. J., 1917.
           363 p. illus., ports. 24cm.
           Francis Scott Key Fitzgerald portrait and
      short biographical sketch p. 99-100.
           Ms. checklist of J.F.B. from Princeton University
      Chronicle, v.7, no.2, containing the names
      and cause of death of twenty-one members of the
      Class of 1917 laid in.
           1. Fitzgerald, Francis Scott Key, 1896-1940.
      I. Princeton Univ   ersity. The Nassau
      herald.

NN 0027065   ViU

Nassau hospital association. Certificate of
incorporation and by-laws of the Nassau hospital association of Hempstead, North Hempstead and Oyster Bay, Queens County, New
York, with list of officers, committees and
staff, and donors and donations, 1896-1897.
N.Y.1897. 24p.

NN 0027066   N

   Nassau hospital association.
      Year book.   [Mineola]
      -1920, Report year ends March 31.

NN 0027067   NN NNC NJQ

Nassau-Katzenellenbogen. Laws, statutes, etc.
   Nassau-catzenelnbogische Berg-Ordnung.
2te Auf. Wetzlar, 1711.

   80 p. f°.

NN 0027068   MH-L

Nassau-Katzenelnbogen. Laws, statutes, etc.
   Nassau-Catzenelnbogische Gerichts
   und Landordnung. Nassaw Catzenelnbogen
   u., Gedruckt zu Herborn in der Graf-
   schafft. 1616.

      67, 188 p.

      Alternate leaves blank.

4K
11157

NN 0027069   DLC-P4 MH-L

Nassau-Katzenellenbogen. Laws, statutes, etc.
   Nassau-catzenelnbogische Gerichts- und
Land-Ordnung. 2te Auf. Wetzlar, 1711.

   (10), 68 p.

NN 0027070   MH-L MH

Nassau-Katzenelnbogen. Laws, statutes, etc.
   Nassau-catzenelnbogischer land-ordnung. 2e
aufl. Wetzlar,G.E.Winckler,1711.

   6 pt. (paged contin.) f°. pp.188. Coat-of-
arms and geneal. tables.

NN 0027071   MH MH-L

Nassau-Katzenelnbogen. Laws, statutes, etc.
   Nassau-catzenelnbogische policey-ordnung.
2e aufl. Wetzlar,G.E.Winckler,1711.

   f°. pp.202. Coat-of-arms.

NN 0027072   MH MH-L

   Nassau laboratories, Hackensack, N.J.
      Graphite lubrication handbook; a guide to
   increased war production for plant engineers.
   2d ed.   Hackensack, N.J. [1942?]
      28 p.
      Cover-title.

NN 0027073   WaS

D621.89
N18   Nassau laboratories, Hackensack, N. J.
      Plant engineer's handbook; a guide to in-
      creased war production. Hackensack, N. J.,
      Nassau laboratories [1942]
      cover-title, [16] p. 19cm.

      About the lubrication uses of Cograph, natu-
   ral colloidal graphite.

      1. Lubrication and lubricants. I. Title.

NN 0027074   NNC

   Nassau lawyer. v.1-
   1953†-
   Mineola, N.Y.,
      v. monthly (except July-Sept.)
      Published by the Bar Association of Nassau
   County, N.Y.

NN 0027075   NcD-L NNC-L

The Nassau literary magazine. v. 1-   . Feb. 1842-
   Princeton, N. J., 1842-
      v.   map. 21½-24cm.
   Monthly during the college year.
   Conducted by the senior class of Princeton university.
   Title varies: Feb. 1842-   The Nassau monthly.
                                     The Nassau literary magazine.

   1. Princeton university.

   Library of Congress   CA 7—2,y4 Unrev'd
                              LH1.P8N3

NN 0027076   DLC OU DHEW NN CU MdBJ   NcD NjP

Rare
PS
2972   The Nassau literary magazine.
.1   [Four issues of the magazine contain-
N26+   ing contributions from Booth Tarkington]
       [Princeton, N.J., 1891-93]
       4 pts. in 1 v. 26cm.

       I. Tarkington, Booth, 1869-1946.

NN 0027077   NIC

Nassau literary magazine.
   A Princeton anthology, 1921-1925, selected by Edward
Steese, Neilson Abeel and C. H. D. Robbins, jr., from poems
published in the Nassau literary magazine. Princeton, Princeton university press, 1925.
   4 p. l., 104 p. 21½cm.

   1. College verse—Princeton. I. Steese, Edward, ed. II. Abeel, Neilson, 1902-   joint ed. III. Robbins, Charles Henry Darlington, joint
ed. IV. Title.
                                              27—15249
   Library of Congress   PN6110.C7N3

NN 0027078   DLC MB NN UU ViU

Nassau literary magazine.
   [Princeton men of letters, from the Nassau Lit. 1912. Princeton, 1912. 67 p. illus. 8°. (Nassau literary mag. Graduate number, 1912.)

   Title from cover.

I. Colleges, etc., U. S.: Princeton   Bequest of Hon. J. L. Cadwalader.
Authors (American).   University.—Graduates. 2.
N. Y. P. L.   April 7, 1915.

NN 0027079   NN

Nassau mail steamship line.
   Nassau, island of New Providence, Bahamas, a
guide to the great sanitarium of the western hemisphere. N. Y., 1879.

NN 0027080   Nh

W 1   NASSAU medical news.
NA207   v. 1-   Dec. 1927-
      Garden City, N. Y. [etc.] Nassau County
      Medical Society.
         v. in   illus., ports.

         Vol. numbers irregular.
         1. Medicine - period. I. Nassau
      County (N. Y.) Medical Society

NN 0027081   DNLM PPC

   The Nassau Monthly
         see   The Nassau literary magazine.

   Nassau, N. P., Bahamas, with meteorological
   tables and other statistics of interest to invalids
   and travelers. 16 pp. 8°. [Montreal, n. d.]

NN 0027083   DNLM

The Nassau rake, ed. and pub. by the Sophomore class of
   the College of New Jersey.
   Princeton, N. J., 18
      v. 22½cm.

   1. Princeton university.
                              CA 9-4020 Unrev'd
   Library of Congress   LD4627.N5

NN 0027084   DLC CtY PU

Nassau Services Company, *East Williston, N. Y.*
   Levittown; indexed street map. East Williston, ©1948.
   map 46 x 36 cm.
   Scale not given.

   1. Levittown, N. Y.—Maps.

   G3804.L666 1948.N3   Map 49-928*

NN 0027085   DLC

Nassau-Siegen (*Grafschaft*)
   see also
Nassau (*Duchy*)

Nassau smelting & refining co., inc., Tottenville, N. Y.

Nassau. v. 1-
Jan. 1939-
   [Tottenville, N. Y., Nassau smelting & refining co., inc., 1939-

---

NASSAU SMELTING AND REFINING WORKS, New York.
   Guide to the use of standard linotype metal in the Mergenthaler lino
type machines.
      N. Y., 1896. 29 pp. 8°.

NN 0027088   MB

Special
Collections   Nassau Stamp Co. Ltd., New York.
×SCG   Auction catalogue of postage stamps, sale 1-
.P907   New York, Nassau Stamp Co. Ltd., 1907-
.N18A   nos. 22cm.
           Incomplete: nos.1-2, 5, 7, 21 & 30 only.

           1. Postage-stamps—Catalogs.

NN 0027089   MB

VOLUME 405

Nassau station
    see   Case Institute of Technology, Cleveland. Nassau Astronomical Station. [Supplement]

Nassau Street Theatre, New York.
    The First American Play-Bill
      see under   Winship, George Parker.

Nassau-Suffolk business. conditions
    see   Long Island business.

Nassau-Suffolk labor news...
    v. 1

Hempstead, N. Y.: Nassau-Suffolk labor news, inc., 1938–
    v.   illus. (incl. ports.)   55½cm.

Weekly.
Slight irregularities in numbering.
"Official newspaper: American federation of labor affiliates — Nassau and Suffolk counties; sponsored by Central trades and labor council of Nassau and Suffolk counties."

1. Trade unions—U.S.—N.Y.—   Nassau County. 2. Trade unions
—U.S.—N.Y.—Suffolk County.   3. Trade unions—Per. and soc.
publ.—U.S.
N.Y.P.L.   October 8, 1940

NN 0027094 NN

Nassau water company, Brooklyn
    see   Brooklyn. Board of water commission
Nassau water dept.

NASSAUER, Erich.
    Die notwendige vorbedingung in der lehre vom ursachen-zusammenhang. Marburg (Lahn), J. Hamel, 1934.

    pp. 67+(1). 8⁰.
    Inaug.-diss. --- Marburg.

NN 0027096 MH-L

Nassauer, Hans, 1884–
    Besitzerwerb durch Mittelspersonen nach gemeinem Recht und dem Recht des Bürgerlichen Gesetzbuchs ... von Hans Nassauer ... Neumünster, R. Hieronymus, 1910.

    2 p.l., [7]–37 p., 1 l. 23cm.

    Inaug.-Diss. - Heidelberg.
    "Lebenslauf": leaf at end.
    "Literatur-Verzeichnis": p. [7]–8.

NN 0027097 MH-L ICRL

AC   Nassauer, Kurt
831   Die vermengung des geldes nach bürgerlichem recht. ... Düren, 1935. 61 p.
    Inaug. Diss. - Erlangen, 1935.
    Literatur-Verzeichnis.

NN 0027098 ICRL

Nassauer, Kurt, 1911–
    Denker der hellenischen Frühzeit; eine Monographie von Kurt Nassauer, mit auszugsweiser Wiedergabe der Quellen zusammengestellt von Carl Huber. Frankfurt am Main, G. K. Schauer, 1948.

    273 p. 18 cm. (Civitas Gentium; Quellenschriften und Monographien zur Soziologie und Kulturphilosophie, 5)

    Bibliography: p. 259–261.

    1. Greek literature—Hist. & crit. 2. Philosophy, Ancient.   i.
Huber, Carl.   (Series: Civitas gentium; Quellenschriften zur Soziologie und Kulturphilosophie, 5)

    PA3057.N3   A 54–466

    Harvard Univ. Library
    for Library of Congress   [1]†

DLC
NN 0027099   MH NNC LU CU CtY OU DDO MoKU MoU ICU

Nassauer, Kurt, 1911–
    Die rechtsphilosophie William James' ... von Kurt Nassauer ... Bern, Buchdruckerei G. Grunau & cie., 1943.

    xxiii, 101 p. 23ᶜᵐ.

    Inaug.-diss.—Basel.
    "Erscheint in den Berner wirtschaftswissenschaftlichen abhandlungen als heft nr. 36."
    Curriculum vitae.
    "Quellen- und literaturverzeichnis": p. [95]–99.

    1. James, William, 1842–1910. 2. Law—Philosophy.

                                 46–16216

NN 0027100   DLC CtY-L CtY

Nassauer, Kurt, 1911–
    ... Die rechtsphilosophie William James', von dr. Kurt Nassauer. Bern, P. Haupt [etc.] 1943.

    xxiii, 99 p. 23ᶜᵐ. (Berner wirtschaftswissenschaftliche abhandlungen, hrsg. von prof. dr. Alfred Amonn [u. a.] ... Hft. 36)

    Issued also as inaugural dissertation, Basel.
    "Quellen- und literaturverzeichnis": p. [vii]–viii, [95]–99.

    1. James, William, 1842–1910. 2. Law—Philosophy.

                                 46–43487

NN 0027101   DLC ICU NN

QD305 Nassauer, Max.
.A2N23 Beitraeg zur kenntnis des oxalbernsteinsäure-esters und des oxalessigesters.
    Wuerzburg, 1894.
    46p.
    Inaug. diss.- Wuerzburg.

NN 0027102 DLC

Z997   Nassauer, Max, Frankfurt a. M.
.E27
    Eeden, Frederik Willem van, 1860–1932.
    Bibliothek van wijlen dr. Frederik van Eeden en enkele andere kleinere bijvoegingen waaronder de bibl. entomologie dr. M. Nassauer, Frankfurt a. M. Verkooping 9 en 10 januari 1934 in ... Amsterdam door boekhandel en antiquariaat P. A. Hemeryck (A. T. Kleerekoper) Amsterdam [1934]

Nassauer, Max, 1869–1931.   610.4 N18
⁰⁰⁷¹ Der Arzt der grossen und der kleinen Welt. Aerztliche Skizzen von Dʳ Max Nassauer. Zweite vermehrte Auflage. München, O. Gmelin, 1909.

    48, xxxix, [49]–81 p. 23ᶜᵐ.
    Contents.—Die Praxis.—Der Fronarbeiter.—Der Arzt der feinen Welt (Der Faiseur).—Der Märtyrer.—Der soziale Arzt.—Kurierfreiheit.—Das Testament.—Intermezzo (Die Kündigung).

NN 0027104 ICJ DNLM

Nassauer, Max, 1869–
    Des weibes leib und leben in gesundheit und krankheit, von frauenarzt dr. Max Nassauer ... Völlig neu bearb., mit vielen neuen medizinischen wie künstlerischen abbildungen. Stuttgart, E. H. Moritz, 1923.

    xvi, 316 p. illus., 8 pl. (incl. front.) 18¹ᶜᵐ. (Half-title: Bücherei der gesundheitspflege. bd. 16)

    1. Woman—Health and hygiene. 2. Obstetrics. i. Title.

    Library of Congress   RG121.N3   24–8299

NN 0027105   DLC DNLM

618.1   Nassauer, Max, 1869–1931.
N266w3 Das Weibes Leib und Leben in Gesundheit und Krankheit. 3. verb. und erweiterte Aufl. Stuttgart, E. H. Moritz [c1926]
    xv, 270 p. illus. 21cm. (Bücherei der Gesundheitspflege, Bd. 16)

    1. Woman - Health and hygiene. 2. Obstetrics. I. Title.

NN 0027106 FU

WZ   NASSAUER, Max, 1869-1931
350   Doktorsfahrten; Ärztliches und
N266do Menschliches. Stuttgart, Enke, 1902.
1902   139 p.

NN 0027107 DNLM PPC

WZ   NASSAUER, Max, 1869-1931
350   Die Doktorschule. Das ist der Arzt
N266d   der grossen und der kleinen Welt und
1922   die hohe Schule für Aerzte und Kranke.
    3. Aufl. München, Gmelin, 1922.
    93 p.
    Title

NN 0027108 DNLM

R707.1 Nassauer, Max, 1869–
N18   Die doktorschule; das ist, Der arzt der grossen
1925   und der kleinen welt und Die hohe schule für aerzte und kranke, in 4. auflage. Von Max Nassauer. München, Gmelin, 1925.
    122 p. 22ᶜᵐ.

    I. Title. II. Title: Der arzt der grossen und der kleinen welt.   III. Title: Die hohe schule für aerzte   und kranke.

NN 0027109 NNC

Nassauer, Max, 1869–1931.
    Doktorsfahrten von gestern und von heute. Ärztliches und Menschliches. 3. verm. Aufl. Stuttgart, F. Enke, 1926.
    169 p. 23 cm.

    1. Physicians—Correspondence, reminiscences, etc. i. Title.

    R512.N25A3 1926   50–46820

NN 0027110   DLC DNLM ICJ ICRL

Nassauer, Max, 1869–1931.
    Ein fall beginnender tuberculose der gebärmutterschleimhaut...
    Inaug. diss. Wuerzburg, 1894.

NN 0027111 ICRL DNLM

Nassauer, Max.
    —— Gebirge und Gesundheit. Hygienische Winke, besonders für die Frauen. 42 pp. 8⁰. München & Wien, G. Lammers, 1908.

NN 0027112 DNLM

f   NASSAUER, Max
PZ   Der gute Doktor. Ein nützlich Bilderbuch
34.7   für Kinder und Eltern von Max Nassauer.
N18   Bilder von Hellmut Maison ... München, Braun & Schneider [19—]
    31, [1] p. illus. (col.) 35 1/2 cm.

    Colophon: Meisenbach Riffarth & Co., München.
    In original printed, paper-covered boards.

    1. Physicians--   Juvenile literature.
    I. Maison,   Hellmut.

NN 0027113 MBCo DNLM

VOLUME 405

Nassauer, Max, 1869-1931.
Die hohe Schule für Aerzte und Kranke. 2.
Auflage. Munchen, Verlag der Aerztlichen
Rundschau Otto Gmelin ₁n.d.₂
88p. 22cm.

NN 0027114   OKentU

NASSAUER, Max.
Der moderne kindermord und seine bekämpfung
durch findelhäuser. Leipzig,Würzburg,1919.

(4)+72 p.

NN 0027115   MH-L

Nassauer, Max.   3-N
Das Nessushemd. Dresden: Carl Reissner, 1913. 2 p.l.,
312 p. 12°.

1. Title.   CENTRAL CIRCULATION.
N.Y.P.L.   April 20, 1914.

NN 0027116   NN

Nassauer, Max, 1869-1931.
Pasmis, Novellen von Max Nassauer. Dresden, C. Reissner
₁1909₂ 191 p. 20cm.

328563B. 1. No subject. I. Title.
N.Y.P.L.   July 10, 1946

NN 0027117   NN

Nassauer (Max) [1860-   ]. *Ueber bösartige
Blasengeschwülste bei Arbeitern der organisch-
chemischen Grossindustrie. [Frankfurt.] 53
pp., 1 l. 8°. Wiesbaden, J. F. Bergmann,
1919.

NN 0027118   DNLM

1884-
Nassauer, Richard, Referendar: Welche Rechtsfolgen ent-
stehen, wenn der Eigentümer aneinandergrenzender Grund-
stücke auf diesen ein einheitliches Gebäude errichtet?
Frankfurt a. M. 1911: Knauer. VI, 39 S. 8°
Marburg, Jur. Diss. v. 11. Sept. 1911, Ref. Leonhard
[Geb. 18. Febr. 84 Frankfurt a. M.; Wohnort: Frankfurt; Staatsangeh.:
Preußen; Vorbildung: Goethe-Gymn. Frankfurt Reife O. 03; Studium:
Freiburg i. B. 1, München 2, Berlin 1, Marburg 3 S.; Rig. 4. Juli 11.]
                                        [U 12. 3457]

NN 0027119   ICRL

Nassauer, Rudolf.
Poems. London, Methuen ₁1947₂
48 p. 21 cm.

PR6027.A75P6   821.91   48-25709*

NN 0027120   DLC MH IEN NNC

Nassauer, Siegfried, 1868-
Burgen und befestigte Gutshöfe um Frankfurt a.M.,
ihre Geschichte und Kriege. 3.Aufl. Frankfurt a.M.,
Verlag der Goldsteinschen Buchhandlung [1916]

367 p. illus.

NN 0027121   MH NjP

NASSAUER, SIEGFRIED, 1868-
Josef Stern; Lebensbild eines Journalisten, von Siegfried Nassauer. [Frankfurt a.M., 1931.] 43 p. illus.
(facsims., ports.) 2.ed. 12°.

644635A. 1. Stern, Josef, 1839-1902.

NN 0027122   NN NNC

Nassauer, Siegfried, 1868-
Kleine erlebnisse ₁von₂ Siegfried Nassauer. ₁Frankfurt a.
M., Voigt & Gleiber, 1930₂
135, ₁1₂ p. plates, facsim. 20½cm.

I. Title.

                                        32-15045

Library of Congress   PT2627.A66K6 1930   928.3

NN 0027123   DLC

923.14   Nassauer, Siegfried, 1868-
N266V   Von Kronen und Thronen ... Frankfurt
          am Main, Goldsteinsche Buchhandlung. 1922.
          251 p. plates, ports., facsims. 21½cm.

          *Literatur-Nachweis: p. ₁249₂-251.

          1. Europe. Kings and rulers. I. Title.

NN 0027124   NcD

914.358 Nassauer, Siegfried, 1868-
N187w   Was die Frankfurter Brunnen erzählen;
          eine illustrierte Chronik. Frankfurt a.
          M., Goldsteinschen Buchhandlung, 1921.
          756 p. illus.

          Bibliography: p.754-756.

          1. Frankfurt am Main - Description.
          I. Title.

NN 0027125   WaU MH CtY

Nassauische annalen
        see Verein für Nassauische Altertumskunde
und Geschichtsforschung, Wiesbaden.
Annalen.

DD491   Nassauische Heimatblätter. 1.-   Jahrg.₂
H6   1897/98-
N38   Wiesbaden, Verein für Nassauische Altertums-
          kunde und Geschichtsforschung.
          illus. 21 cm. 2 no. a year.

          1951-1960 includes Bodenaltertümer in
          Nassau, I.-X.
          Title varies: 1897-1913, Mitteilungen des
          Vereins für Nassauische Altertumskunde und
          Geschichtsforschung.

NN 0027127   CtY NN

Nassauische Landesbank, Wiesbaden.
110 ₁i. e. Hundertzehn₂ Jahre Nassauische Landesbank,
1840-1950. Wiesbaden, 1950.
97 p. illus. 25 cm.

HG3060.W54N34   59-44508 ‡

NN 0027128   DLC

Nassauische landesbibliothek, Wiesbaden
        see
Wiesbaden. Nassauische landesbibliothek.

Nassauische Landescreditcasse
        see
Nassauische Landesbank, Wiesbaden.

Nassauische Lebensbilder.. Wiesbaden ₁Historische Kommission für Nassau, 19

     v. ports. 25 cm. (Veröffentlichungen der Historischen Kom-
mission für Nassau, 10)

Vol. ₁ -6 edited by Karl Wolf.
Includes bibliographies.

     1. Nassau (Duchy)—Biography. I. Wolf, Karl, 1885-   ed.
(Series: Verein für Nassauische Altertumskunde und Geschichtsforschung, Wiesbaden. Historische Kommission für Nassau. Veröffentlichungen, 10)

DD491.H6V57 bd. 10   70-245173

NN 0027131   DLC CaBVaU MH NIC OU CU

---

q332.2   Nassauische Sparkasse, Wiesbaden.
N18   Geschäftsbericht.

          Wiesbaden.
              v. illus.(part col.) maps, diagrs.,
          tables. 30cm.
          Period covered by report varies.
          Supersedes in part Nassauische Landesbank,
          Wiesbaden. Bericht über das Geschäftsjahr
          Nassauische Landesbank, Nassauische Sparkasse.
          Some issues are   combined reports.

NN 0027132   IU NN

Nassauische Union.
    Hundertjahrfeier der Nassauischen Union ...
    see under title

Nassauische volkskunde
    see under [Diener, Walter] ed.

Die Nassauischen heilquellen; Soden, Cronthal, Weilbach,
Wiesbaden, Schlangenbad, Schwalbach und Ems, beschrieben durch einen verein von aerzten, nebst geognostischer
skizze und karte des Taunus. Wiesbaden, C. W. Kreidel,
1851.
v p., 1 l., 330 p., 1 l. fold. map. 22cm.
"Vorwort" signed: Dr. v. Ibell.
"Literatur" at head of most of the parts.

    1. Health resorts, watering-places, etc.—Hesse-Nassau. 2. Mineral
waters—Hesse-Nassau. 3. Taunus. I. Ibell, R. von.

                                        29-3128

Library of Congress   RA865.5.N3

NN 0027135   DLC ICJ CtY-M DNLM

Nassauischer Verein für Naturkunde.
    Jahrbücher. Bd. 1-
    1844-19
    Wiesbaden.
        v. in   illus., ports., maps. 21-23 cm.
    Vols. 1-18 (1844-63) issued by the society under its earlier name:
Verein für Naturkunde im Herzogthum Nassau.
    Some no. in combined issues.
    Supplements accompany some issues.
    INDEXES:
    Vols. 1-20, 1844-66, in v. 19-20.
    Vols. 1-35, 1844-82, in v. 35.
    Vols. 36-53, 1883-1900, in v. 54.
    Vols. 1-80, 1884-1929, in v. 80.
    1. Science—Societies, etc.

    Q49.W5   6-34484 rev*

NN 0027136   DLC ICRL DNLM ICJ MiU N IaAS GU CU

Nassauischer Verein für Naturkunde. Jahrbücher (Index)
    Inhaltsübersicht der ersten 20 Hefte der Jahrbücher .... x p.
    [In NASSAUISCHER VEREIN FÜR NATURKUNDE. Jahrbücher,
    vol. 19-20. Wiesbaden 1864-1866.]

NN 0027137   ICJ

Nassauischer Verein für Naturkunde.
    Katalog der Bibliothek des Nassauischen Vereins für
Naturkunde. Im Auftrage des Vorstandes herausgegeben von Aug. Römer.
    [Wiesbaden, J. Niedner, 1882.]
    iv, 89 p. 1 pl. (In its Jahrbücher. Jahrgang 35. 24cm.)
    ——— Nachtrag zu dem Kataloge. Von Aug. Römer.
    No. 1-, 1883-. (In its Jahrbücher. Jahrgang 36-.)

NN 0027138   ICJ

Z929   Nassauischer Verein für Naturkunde.
.W53
       Wiesbaden. Nassauische Landesbibliothek.
          Verzeichnis der Tauschschriften (Zeitschriften, Serien,
       Sammelwerke und Einzelschriften) des Nassauischen Vereins
       für Naturkunde.
          Wiesbaden.

---

                                        *2839A.75-49
Nassauisches Geschlechterbuch, herausgegeben von Bernhard Koerner, bearbeitet in Gemeinschaft mit Carl Welcker. Band I.
— Görlitz. Starke. [1926.] I v. Portraits. Plates. Genealogical charts. Coats of arms, mostly colored. [Deutsches Geschlechterbuch (genealogisches Handbuch bürgerlicher Fami-
lien). Band 49.] 14 cm., in 8s.

N9522 — S.r.c. — Genealogy. Nassau, Germany. — Nassau, Germany, Biog. &
geneal. — Koerner, Gustav Bernhard, 1875-

NN 0027140   MB

VOLUME 405

Nassauisches gewerbeblatt. Mitteilungen fuer
den Gewerbeverein fuer Nassau.

soo

Geverbeverein fuer Nassau.
Mittheilungen.

Nassauisches Heimatbuch, Regierungsbezirk
Wiesbaden
see under Jacobi, Karl, ed.

Nassauisches Landesmuseum, *Wiesbaden*
see
Wiesbaden. Städtisches Museum.

Nassauisches urkundenbuch
see under Nassau (Duchy)

Nassauisches urkundenbuch
see also in Codex diplomaticus Nassoicus.

Nassausche Domeinraad
see Orange-Nassau, House of. *Domeinraad.*

Nassauw, Maurits van
see Johan Maurits, Prince of Nassau-
Siegen, 1604-1679.

WB   NASSE, Christian Friedrich, 1778-1851
N267a   Anleitung zur Uebung angehender
1834   Aerzte in Krankheits-Beobachtung und
         Beurtheilung. Bonn, Habicht, 1834.
         142 p.

NN 0027148   DNLM CtY MiU

Nasse, Christian Friedrich,
1778-1851.
Archiv für den thierischen magnetismus ... 1.- bd.;
1817-
Altenburg und Leipzig, F. A. Brockhaus; [etc., etc.]
1817-

GN   Nasse, Christian Friedrich, 1778-1851
23   Die Aufgabe der Anthropologie   [Leipzig, 1823]
N38   128 p. 22cm. (Nasse's Zeitschrift Heft 1,
         Jahrg.1823)

NN 0027150   PPT

Nasse, Christian Friedrich, 1778-1851.
Die behandlung der Gemüthskranken und Irren
durch Nichtärzte, Bonn, E. Weber, 1844.
1 p.l., 65 pp., 1 l. 8°

NN 0027151   DNLM

Nasse (Christian Friedrich) [1778-1851]. "De
neuritide. 67 pp. 8°. Halа, in off. Batheana,
[1800].

NN 0027152   DNLM

WB   NASSE, Christian Friedrich, 1778-1851
N267h   Handbuch der allgemeinen Therapie.
1845   Bonn, Habicht, 1840-45.
         2 v.

NN 0027153   DNLM

Nasse, Christian Friedrich, 1778-1851.
Jahrbücher für Anthropologie und zur Pathologie
und Therapie des Irrseyns
see under title

QZ   NASSE, Christian Friedrich, 1778-1851
N267L   Leichenöffnungen; zur Diagnostik
1821   und pathologischen Anatomie. Reihe 1.
         Bonn, Marcus, 1821.
         194 p.
         No more published?

NN 0027155   DNLM

WX   Nasse, Christian Friedrich, 1778-1851.
N267m   Das Medicinische Klinikum zu Bonn. Coblenz,
1825   Hölscher, 1825.
         36 p.

            1. Bonn. Universität. Medicinisches Klinikum.
         I. Title

NN 0027156   DNLM

Nasse, Christian Friedrich, 1778-1851.
Die Untersuchung des Scheintodes vom wirklichen Tode; zur Beruhigung über die Gefahr,
lebendig begraben zu werden.   Bonn, T. Habicht,
1851.
1 p.l., 66 p. 12°.

NN 0027157   DNLM

WL   NASSE, Christian Friedrich, 1778-1851
N267u   Untersuchungen zur Lebensnaturlehre
1818   und Heilkunde. Bd. 1, Abth. 1. Halle,
         Curt, 1818.
         196 p.
         No more published?

NN 0027158   DNLM

QZ   NASSE, Christian Friedrich, 1778-1851
N267u   Untersuchungen zur Physiologie und
1839   Pathologie, von Friedrich Nasse und
         Hermann Nasse. Bonn, Habicht,
         1835-39.
         2 v. in 1.
         I. Nasse, Hermann, 1807-1892

NN 0027159   DNLM ICJ

QU   NASSE, Christian Friedrich, 1778-1851
N267v   Verbrennung und Athmen,
1846   chemische Thätigkeit und organisches
         Leben. Bonn, Weber, 1846.
         vi, 154 p.

NN 0027160   DNLM

Nasse, Christian Friedrich, 1778-1851.
Vermischte Schriften psychologischen und
physiologischen Inhalts.   Bonn, Eduard Weber, '50.

NN 0027161   PPWI

W   NASSE, Christian Friedrich, 1778-1851
N267v   Von der Stellung der Aerzte im
1823   Staate. Leipzig, Cnobloch, 1823.
         iv, 408 p.

NN 0027162   DNLM CtY ICJ

NASSE, Dietrich, 1860-1898.
Beitrage zur anatomie der tubificiden.
Inaug.-diss. Bonn, 1882.

4°. pp.30 . Plates.
"Aus dem anatomischen labor[at]orium zu Bonn".
"Vita", after p.30.

NN 0027163   MH-Z

Nasse, Dietrich   1860-1898.
— & von Brunn (Max R. F.) Chirurgische
Krankheiten der unteren Extremitäten. 3 v.
roy. 8°. Stuttgart, F. Enke, 1897-1910.

NN 0027164   DNLM OCIW-H

Nasse, Dietrich, 1860-1898.
Chirurgische Krankheiten der unteren Extremitäten. Von D. Nasse und M. von Brunn.   Stuttgart, F. Enke [1907]-10.
cclxv, 833p. illus. 25cm. (Deutsche Chirurgie. Lfg.66)

"Literatur": p.[xxiii]-cclxv.

1. Leg--Surgery. I. Brunn, Max von, 1875-1924.

NN 0027165   IU-M CtY ICJ ViU

Nasse (D[ietrich]) [1860-98.] Die Exstirpation
der Schulter und ihre Bedeutung für die Behandlung der Sarkome des Humerus.
In: Samml. klin. Vortr., n. F., Leipz., 1899, No. 96 (Chir.,
No. 23, 507-518).

NN 0027166   DNLM

Nasse (Dietrich   [1860-1898] &
Borchardt (M.). Malformations, injuries,
and diseases of the ankle and foot.
In Syst. Pract. Surg. (Bergmann, et al.), 8°. N. Y. &
Phila 1904. III, 717-887.

NN 0027167   DNLM

Nasse , Ernst
Die Bedeutung der Eviktion einer ver-
kauften und übergebenen beweglichen
Sache nach gemeinem Recht und nach dem
bürgerlichen Gesetzbuch ... von Ernst
Nasse ... Bonn, K. Drobnig, 1899.

43 p. 22cm.

Inaug.-Diss. - Erlangen.
Bibliographical footnotes.

NN 0027168   MH-L ICRL MH

Nasse, Erwin, 1829-1890.
Adolf Held. [Nekrolog.]
(In Verein fuer Socialpolitik. Schriften. 19. Pp. i-xv. Leipzig,
1880.)
Verzeichniss der Schriften welche Dr. Held veröffentlicht hat, pp. xiii-xv.

E2515 — Held, Adolf.

NN 0027169   MB OU

Nasse, Erwin, 1829-1890.
Armenpflege und Selbsthülfe. Ein Vortrag ...
Bonn, A. Marcus, 1868.
24 p. 12°.

NN 0027170   NN

Nasse, Erwin, 1829-1890.
Bemerkungen über das preussische steuersystem, von dr.
Erwin Nasse ... Bonn, A. Marcus, 1861.
2 p. l., [iii]-vi, 112 p. incl. tables. 21cm.

1. Taxation—Prussia.

Library of Congress   HJ2711.N2   7—40435

NN 0027171   DLC ICJ NIC

VOLUME 405

Nasse, Erwin, Siemens, Georg *and* **Schmidt, H.**
Bericht der Enquete-kommission über die Raiffeisen'-schen darlehnskassen-vereine.
Landw. jahrb. bd. 4, p. 549–581.   Berlin, 1875.

1. Cooperative banks. 2. Raiffeisen banks.

Library, U. S. Dept. of   Agriculture   Agr 4-1467

NN 0027172   DNAL

Nasse, Erwin.
Der bericht der untersuchungskommission über die Raiffeisen'schen darlehnskassenvereine und die kritik des Herrn Regierungsrath Nöll.
Landw. jahrb. bd. 5, p. 557–596.   Berlin, 1876.

1. Cooperative banks. 2. Credit. 3. Raiffeisen banks.

Library, U. S. Dept. of   Agriculture   Agr 4-1445

NN 0027173   DNAL

NASSE, Erwin.
Ein blick auf die kommerzielle und industrielle lage Englands. Jena, 1887.

NN 0027174   MH

Nasse, Erwin.
Einkommen- und Ertragbesteurung im Haushalt preussischer Gemeinden.
(In Verein fuer Socialpolitik. Schriften. 12. Pp. 269–302. Leipzig, 1877.)

E2494 — Income tax. — Prussia. Towns.

NN 0027175   MB

NASSE, Erwin, 1829–1890.
Das geld- und münzwesen. [Tübingen, 189–?]
1. 8°.   pp. (48).
pp. [237]–284 of a volume of the Handbuch der politischen oekonomie.

NN 0027176   MH

NASSE, Erwin.
F. C. Dahlmann; rede, gehalten am 13. mai 1885.
Bonn, M. Cohen & sohn, (F. Cohen), 1885.
pp. 34.

NN 0027177   MH

Nasse, Erwin, 1829–1890.
Meletemata de publica cura ahnonae apud Romanos...   Bonnae, Formis. F. P. Lechneri, 1851.
40p.

NN 0027178   MiU NBuU PU

Nasse, Erwin, 1829–1890.
... Металлическия деньги и валюта. Статьи Э. Нассе и В. Лексиса изъ Schönberg's Handbuch der politischen oekonomie. Москва, Типо-лит. Высоч. утв. Т-ва И. Н. Кушнеревъ и ко., 1897.
1 p. l., 192, [4] p. 19¼ᶜᵐ. (Научно-популярная библиотека "Русской мысли.") 1)
"Переводъ сдѣланъ съ послѣдняго 4-го изданія 1896 г.... не вездѣ буквально и дословно."—р. 2.
"Литература": p. [193]–[195].
1. Money.   I. Lexis, Wilhelm Hector Richard Albrecht, 1837–1914.
II. Title.   *Translation of Das geld und münzwesen.*
       Title transliterated: Metallicheskiîa den'gi i valîuta.
                    41-28753
Library of Congress   HG221.N33

NN 0027179   DLC

Nasse (Erwin)
Die Niederlande und Preussen. Eine Antwort an Herrn Groen van Prinsterer. *Bonn: M. Cohen & Sohn, 1867.*
34 pp. 8°.

NN 0027180   NN

Nasse, Erwin, 1829–1890.
On the agricultural community of the middle ages, and inclosures of the sixteenth century in England. Tr. from the German of E. Nasse, by Colonel H. A. Ouvry ... London, Macmillan & co., 1871.
2 p. l., 100 p. 23ᶜᵐ.
Published under the sanction of the Cobden club.

1. Village communities—England. 2. Land tenure—England—Hist.
I. Ouvry, Henry Aimé, tr. II. Cobden club.

Library of Congress   HD1289.G7N2   7–39455

MiU OC1 OC1W OU NN WaU ViU OKentU NIC I
NN 0027181   DLC WaU-L OrU NcD CtY CU PU PBm PPT

---

333   Nasse, Erwin, 1829–1890.
N18   On the agricultural community of the
     middle ages and inclosures of the sixteenth
     century in England; tr. from the German...
     by H. A. Ouvry. 2d ed.   London, Williams
     & Norgate, 1872.
     100p. 23cm.

     Publication sponsored by the Cobden Club.

     1. Village communities. Gt. Brit.
     2. Land tenure. England. History.
     I. Cobden Club.   II. Title.

     DFo NN ICJ MdBP NjP
NN 0027182   KU NIC ICarbS TxDaM TU CtY PU PPPD PPL

Nasse, Erwin, 1829–1890.
Die Preussische bank und die ausdehnung ihres geschäftskreises in Deutschland. Von dr. Erwin Nasse ... Bonn, A. Marcus, 1866.
vi, 98 p. 23ᵐᵐ.

1. Preussische bank, Berlin. 2. Banks and banking—Germany.
                    16–11381
Library of Congress   HG3060.B54P74

NN 0027183   DLC MiU NN

NASSE, Erwin.
Die richtung der deutschen warenausfuhr.
[n.p., 1882?]

NN 0027184   MH

NASSE, Erwin.
Das sinken der warenpreise während der letzten fünfzehn jahre. Jena, G. Fischer, 1888.
pp. (2), 70.
"Sonderabdruck aus den Jahrbüchern für Nationalökonomie und Statistik, n.f., xvii."

NN 0027185   MH IU

Nasse, Erwin, 1829–1890.
Ueber die mittelalterliche feldgemeinschaft und die einhegungen des sechszehnten jahrhunderts in England, von Erwin Nasse. Bonn, Druck von C. Georgi, 1869.
1 p. l., 71, [1] p. 27 x 21ᵐᵐ.
Bibliographical foot-notes.

1. Village communities—England. 2. Land tenure—England—Hist.
I. Title.
                    42–49327
Library of Congress   HD1289.G7N17

NN 0027186   DLC MoU CSmH MiU-L

Nasse, Erwin.
Ueber die Reform der Personalbesteurung.
(In Verein fuer Socialpolitik. Schriften. 3. Pp. 1–21. Leipzig, 1873.)

E2505 — Taxation. Personal property.

NN 0027187   MB

Nasse, Erwin, 1829–1890.
Ueber die universitätsstudien und staatsprüfungen der preussischen verwaltungsbeamten, von dr. Erwin Nasse ... Bonn, A. Marcus, 1868.
37, [1] p. 21¼ᵐ.

1. Education—Germany. 2. Citizenship—Germany. [1, 2. Education and citizenship—Germany]
                    E 15–1632
Library, U. S. Bur. of   Education   LC1092.P8N2

NN 0027188   DHEW

Nasse, Erwin.
Die Universitätsstudien der preussischen Verwaltungsbeamten und die Gesetze vom 9. Mai 1869 und 11. März 1879.
(In Verein fuer Socialpolitik. Schriften. 34. Pp. 159–184. Leipzig, 1887.)

E2487 — Prussia. Educ. — Political science. Study.

NN 0027189   MB

Nasse, Erwin, 1829–1890.
Die Währungsfrage in Deutschland. [Bonn, 1885.]
p. [295–]345 incl. tables. 8°.
Caption-title.
Signed: Erwin Nasse.
Excerpt: Preussische Jahrbücher. Bd. 55, Heft 3.

28237A. 1. Bimetallism, Germany.   1885. 2. Title.
N. Y. P. L.   January 12, 1922.

NN 0027190   NN

Nasse, Erwin, 1829–1890.
Die wirthschaftliche bedeutung von erbzins- und erbpachtverhältnissen.
Landw. jahrb. bd. 7, p. 41–83.   Berlin, 1878.

1. Land tenure. 2. Rent.
                    Agr 4-1446
Library, U. S. Dept. of   Agriculture

NN 0027191   DNAL

Nasse, Friedrich
see
Nasse, Christian Friedrich, 1778–1851.

Nasse (Gaston). • Du traitement des rétrécissements spasmodiques de l'œsophage, la dilatation brusque à l'aide de la pince de M. le professeur Broca. 34 pp., 1 l., 1 pl. 4°. *Paris, 1878, No. 425.*

NN 0027193   DNLM

Nasse, Gilbert.
Le circuit de régulation. Préf. de P. Ailleret. Paris, Hermann, 1949 [*1948]
119 p. diagrs. 25 cm. (Actualités scientifiques et industrielles, 1071)
Issued also as thesis, Paris, under title: Contribution à l'étude du circuit de régulation.
Bibliography: p. [117]

1. Automatic control. 2. Servomechanisms. (Series)
Q111.A3 no. 1071   621.3174   A 50–1525
Brown Univ. Library
for Library of Congress   [3]†

NN 0027194   RPB LU MoSW NcD PU MU CtY IEN DLC

R10   Nasse, Gilbert
Pa947.   Contribution à l'étude du circuit de
     régulation. Paris, 1949.
     Thèse - Paris.

NN 0027195   CtY

TK168   Nasse, Gilbert.
.J3
1953   Janet, Paul André Marie, 1863–1937.
     Problèmes et exercices d'électricité générale et de machines électriques. Nouv. éd. rev. et mise à jour par G. Nasse. Paris, Gauthier-Villars, 1953.

VOLUME 405

Nasse, Gilbert.
Le réglage automatique ou régulation; principes généraux: application au réglage de la fréquence et de la puissance dans les réseaux électriques. ₁Paris₎ Rédaction des élèves, 1955   95 p. illus.   27cm.   (École supérieure d'électricité, Paris. ₁Publication₎ no. 268)

Cover title; at head of title: Société française des électriciens…

Paris.

1. Electric generators—Control. control. I. École supérieure d'électriciens, Paris. t. 1955.   2. Electric controllers. 3. Automatic tricité. ~~Paris~~. II. Société française

NN 0027197   NN

Nasse, Hermann.
Deutsche Maler der Frühromantik, von Hermann Nasse… München: H. Schmidt₁ 1924₎.   134 p.   front., illus.   8°. (Hugo Schmidts Kunstbreviere.)

Bibliography, p. 132.

160171A. 1. Painting, German, 19th   cent.
N. Y. P. L.   May 7, 1925

NN 0027198   NN NjP MnU OU PSC

Nasse, Hermann.
Gemälde aus der Sammlung des Univ.-Professors Dr. Freih. Fr. W. von Bissing zu München. Illus. Portrait. Plates.   *4072.168.5
(In Münchner Jahrbuch der bildenden Kunst. Band 5, pp. 94–114. Münich. 1910.)

H6573 — Germany. Fine arts. Paint. Bissing, Friedrich Wilhelm, Freiherr von. 1873-. — Fine arts. Colls.

NN 0027199   MB

Nasse, Hermann.
Jacques Callot, von Hermann Nasse; mit einem titelbild & 104 abbildungen auf 50 tafeln in lichtdruck. Leipzig, Klinkhardt & Biermann₁1901₎
6 p. l., 78 p. front. (port.) 49 pl. (Half-title: Meister der graphik, bd.1)
Series title also at head of t.p.
"Aus der literatur": p.76–78

NN 0027200   WaTC

Nasse, Hermann.
… Jacques Callot, von Hermann Nasse; mit einem titelbild & 98 abbildungen auf 45 tafeln in lichtdruck. Leipzig, Klinkhardt & Biermann₁1909₎
6 p. l., 100 p. front. (port.) 44 pl. 30ᶜᵐ. (Half-title: Meister der graphik, bd. 1)
Series title also at head of t.p.
"Aus der literatur": p. 98–100.

1. Callot, Jacques, 1592?–1635.
                                                    11—28757
Library of Congress   NE650.C3N4

      OClMA OU MB NN NBB
NN 0027201   DLC PP TxU GU NBuU TU MdBWA NcU CtY

Wing
fZ   **NASSE, HERMANN.**
4123   …Jacques Callot. Mit einem titelbild & 104
.C 137   abbildungen auf 50 tafeln in lichtdruck. Leipzig, Klinkhardt & Biermann₁1919₎
             ₁9₎,77,₁2₎p. front. (port.)49 pl. 31cm. (Meister der graphik bd.1)

             "Aus der literatur": p.76–₁78₎

      IU CU PPT NjP WU CLU PJB N
NN 0027202   ICN IaU OU OO OCl MH PBm NBuG PSt NcD

---

q769.945
B414n **Nasse, Hermann.**
         Stefano della Bella; ein Maler-Radierer des Spätbarocks; Studie von Hermann Nasse. Mit 25 Lichtdrucktafeln. Strassburg, J. H. Ed. Heitz (Heitz & Mündel), 1913.
         82p. 25 plates. 29cm. (Zur Kunstgeschichte des Auslandes, Heft 104)

         Bibliography: p.₁70₎–72.

         1. Bella, Stefano della, 1610–1664. ✓(Series)

         IaU MWiCA CSt CU MiDA NjP
NN 0027203   IU CtY NN NIC NNU OClMA MU NcD DSI-GA

Nassé, Hermann, 1873–
Wilhelm Leibl. München, H. Schmidt ₁c.1923₎

85 p. illus. 19 cm. (Hugo Schmidts Kunstbreviere)

NN 0027204   MH CaBVaU NSyU

Nasse, Hermann, 1807–1892.   S612.11
Das Blut in mehrfacher Beziehung physiologisch und patholo-   J600
gisch untersucht, von Dr. Hermann Nasse. Bonn, T. Habicht, 1836.
₄, viii, 379, ₁₎ p. 21½ᶜᵐ.
"Verzeichniss der angeführten Schriften": p. ₁373₎–379.

NN 0027205   ICJ DNLM KU-M

Nasse, Hermann, 1807–
——. Commentatio de bilis quotidie e sanguine secreta copia et indole. 24 pp. 4°. Marburgi, typ. Bimrkofteri Academica, ₁1851₎

NN 0027206   DNLM

Nasse (Hermann) [1807–]. *De insania commentatio secundum libros Hippocraticos. 3 p. l., 81 pp., 1 l. 4°. Bonnæ, typ. Thormannianis, ₁1851₎

NN 0027207   DNLM IEN

Nasse (Hermann) [1807–92]. Ueber den Einfluss der Nahrung auf das Blut. 99 pp. 8°. Marburg, Elwert, 1850. [P., v. 1891.]

NN 0027208   DNLM

WH   **NASSE, Hermann, 1807–1892**
qN272u   Untersuchungen über die Einflüsse, welche
1871   die Lymphbildung beherrschen. ₁Zur Erinnerung … Carl Friedrich Heusinger … bei der Feier des fünfzigsten Jahrestages seines Antritts der Professur an der Universität Jena dargebrachten Glückwünsche₎ Marburg, Elwert, 1871.
             72 p.
             1. Heusinger, Karl Friedrich von, 1792–1883

NN 0027209   DNLM MH ICJ CtY-M

Nasse, Hermann, 1807–1892.
——. Vorstudien zur Lehre von der Lymphbildung. Untersuchungen über die Verschiedenheiten und Schwankungen in der Absonderung und Zusammensetzung der Lymphe. 40 pp. 4°. Marburg, N. G. Elwert, ₁1862₎.

NN 0027210   DNLM

Nasse, Hermine, 1904–
… Über das Vorkommen von Arginase in menschlichen Hoden und Ovarien; ein Beitrag zur Frage nach den Beziehungen zwischen intermediärem Arginin-Stoffwechsel und Geschlechtsfunktion… Berlin, 1931.
Inaug.-diss. – Göttingen.
Lebenslauf.
"Sonderabdruck aus 'Archiv für Gynäkologie', Bd. 143, H.3".
Bibliographical foot-notes.

NN 0027211   CtY MiU

Nasse (Jn.-Julien). *Sur l'opération de la boutonnière appliquée au traitement des fistules urinaires urétrales. 23 pp. 4°. Montpellier, J. Martel ainé, 1822.

NN 0027212   DNLM

Nasse (Joannes Christianus). *Diss. sistens mechanicam obstructionis theoriam. 35 pp., 2 l. 4°. Halæ Magdeb., typ. J. C. Hilligeri, ₁1747₎

NN 0027213   DNLM

Nasse ([Karl Friedrich] Werner), ₁1822– ₎. *De singularum cerebri partium functionibus ex morborum percrutatione indagatis. 1 p. l., 62 pp., 1 l. 4°. Bonnæ, typ. Lechnerianis, 1845.

NN 0027214   DNLM OClW-H

Nasse, Karl Friedrich Werner, 1822–
—— . Statistische Mittheilungen über die grossherzogl. Irrenanstalt [Heilanstalt Sachsenberg und Pflege-Anstalt zu Dömitz] aus dem sechsjährigen Zeitraume von 1855–61, incl. (vom Herrn Dr. Nasse dem statistischen Bureau mitgetheilt). 12 pp. roy. 8°. [Schwerin, 1862.]

NN 0027215   DNLM

WM   **NASSE, Karl Friedrich Werner, 1822–**
N267v   Vorschläge zur Irrengesetzgebung, mit besonderer
1850   Rücksicht auf Preussen. Marburg, Elwert, 1850.
             48 p.

NN 0027216   DNLM

Nasse, Leo.
… Krieg und metallindustrie, von L. Nasse … Berlin, L. Simion nf., 1915.
32 p. 24ᶜᵐ. (Krieg und volkswirtschaft, hft. 3)
On cover: Volkswirtschaftliche zeitfragen … nr. 286, jahrg. 36, hft. 6.

1. Metal trade—Germany. 2. European war, 1914–1918—Economic aspects—Germany. I. Title.

Library of Congress   HC286.2.K67 hft. 3
                                                    22-1615

NN 0027217   DLC NN

Nasse, Leopold.
Über die cession der klagen in den fällen der litisæstimationsleistung … von Leopold Nasse … Bonn, Univ.-buchdr. von C. Georgi, 1894.
3 p. l., 46 p. 21½ᶜᵐ.
Inaug.-diss.—Göttingen.

1. Civil procedure (Roman law)   I. Title.
                                                    34-7916

NN 0027218   DLC MH

---

*XF   **Nasse, Maria Anna.**
.2504   Gedichte. Soest, Selbstverlag des Verfasserin,
.S9R4   1860.
no.2   67 p. 17cm.
             No.[2] in volume lettered on spine: German poems.

NN 0027219   MB

Nasse, Max.
Amerikas pelzindustrie, ergebnisse einer studienreise deutscher kürschner und pelzwarenfabrikanten im auftrage der Studienkommission zusammengestellt und bearb. von syndikus Max Nasse. Berlin, Druck von C. Oeckler, 1925.
146 p. illus. 24½ᶜᵐ.
Advertising matter: p. 137–146.

1. Fur. 2. Fur trade.
                                                    Agr 26-643
Library, U. S. Dept. of   Agriculture 412.62N18

NN 0027220   DNAL

Nasse, Max.
Berufsverhältnisse und Berufserziehung in der Fahrzeugindustrie. Leipzig, B. G. Teubner, 1943.
57 p. illus. 21 cm. (Berufskundliche Schriften für die Fahrzeugindustrie, Heft 1)

1. Automobile industry and trade—Germany. I. Title. (Series)
TL73.N3   49–34002*

NN 0027221   DLC

VOLUME 405

QP 156 N26 — Nasse, Otto. *Johann Friedrich, 1839-1903.*
Beiträge zur Physiologie der Darmbewegung.
Leipzig, W. Engelmann, 1866.
70 p. 24 cm.

Includes bibliographical references.

1. Intestines - Innervation. 2. Intestines -
Physiology. I. Title. II. Title: Der Darmbewegung.

NN 0027222 NIC MiU DNLM

Nasse, Otto Johann Friedrich, 1839-1903.
[Collected papers on physiology.]

NN 0027223 ICJ

---

q543 N18uEb — Nasse, Otto *Johann Friedrich, 1839-1903.*
Concerning the application of Millon's
reagent. Extract from Archiv für die
gesammte physiologie des menschen und
thiere. Hrsg. von dr. E. F. Pflüger,
b.83, s.361, 1901. Tr. from German by
Alexis Matthew Bagusin. [Urbana, 1914]
10 leaves.

Typewritten copy.

NN 0027224 IU

Nasse, Otto Joh. Friedrich, 1839-1903.
. . . De materiis amylaceis num in sanguine
mammalium inveniantur disquisitio. Socio ad
respondendum assumpto M. Vogel. 35 pp. 8°.
Halis, typ. orphanotrophei. 1866.   c.

NN 0027225 DNLM ICRL

Nasse, Otto Johann Friedrich, 1839-1903.

Hermann, Ludimar, 1838-1914, ed.
Handbuch der physiologie, bearb. von prof. H. Aubert ...
prof. C. Eckhard [u. a.] ... Hrsg. von dr. L. Hermann ...
Leipzig, F. C. W. Vogel. 1879-83.

Nasse (Otto [Joh. Friedrich]) [1839-1903]. *Die
Schleimhaut der inneren weiblichen Geschlechts-
theile im Wirbelthierreich. 39 pp. 8°. Marburg, C. L. Pfeil, [1-69]. [P., v. 1894.]

NN 0027227 DNLM ICRL

Nasse, Otto Johann Friedrich, 1839-1903.   591.473 0200
Zur Anatomie und Physiologie der quergestreiften Muskelsubstanz,
von Dr. Otto Nasse, ... Mit einer Tafel. Leipzig, F. C. W.
Vogel, 1882.
vi, 106 p. 1 pl. 24cm.

NN 0027228 DNLM ICJ CtY

Nasse, Rudolf, 1837-1899.
Die bergarbeiter-verhältnisse in Grossbritan-
nine. Saarbrücken, Klingebeil, 1891.
v. p. O. [In, Economics pamphlets,
v.17]

NN 0027229 NcD

Nasse, Rudolf, 1837-1899.
Die kohlenvorräthe der europäischen staaten, insbesondere Deutschlands, und deren erschöpfung, von R.
Nasse ... 2. aufl. Berlin, Puttkammer & Mühlbrecht,
1893.
55, [1] p. incl. tables. 23½cm.

1. Coal mines and mining—Germany. 2. Coal mines and mining.

CA 17-3666 Unrev'd

Library of Congress   HD9553.5.N3

NN 0027230 DLC

Nasse, Rudolf, 1837-1899.
Prussia. *Ministerium der öffentlichen arbeiten.*
Der steinkohlenbergbau des Preussischen staates in der
umgebung von Saarbrücken. Im auftrage des herrn ministers der öffentlichen arbeiten dargestellt von A. Hass-
lacher ... B. Jordan ... R. Nasse ... und O. Taeglichsbeck
... Berlin, Ernst & Korn, 1884-90.

NASSÉ, Sotir G.
Histoire du droit public sanctionnateur et de
la juridiction administrative en Roumanie.
Paris, 1924.

Thèse --- Univ. de Paris.

NN 0027232 MH-L CtY

Nassé, Sotir G.
... Histoire du droit public sanctionnateur et
de la juridiction administrative en Roumaine.
Paris, H. d'Arthez, 1924.
286 p. 26 cm.

NN 0027233 CtY

Nasse, Walther

Verein für socialpolitik, *Berlin, ed.*
Die schiffahrt der deutschen ströme. Untersuchungen über
deren abgabenwesen, regulierungskosten und verkehrsverhält-
nisse ... Vom Verein für socialpolitik hrsg. Leipzig, Duncker
& Humblot, 1903-05.

Nasse, Walther.
Zur verkehrsbedeutung des Rheins ... Rostock, C.
Boldt'sche hof-buchdruckerei, 1901.
96 p. 22½cm.

Inaug.-dis.—Rostock.
"Litteratur": p. 7-8.

NN 0027235 DLC

Nasse, Wernerus
see Nasse, Karl Friedrich Werner, 1822-

Nassef, Essameddine Hefni
see
Nāṣif, 'Iṣām al-Din Ḥifnī.

---

838 H468Bn — Nassen, Josef, 1861-1903.
Heinrich Heine's familienleben.
1.t.: Heine's beziehungen zu mutter,
schwester und gattin. Zum ersten male
nach sämtlichen vom dichter selbst
vorliegenden nachrichten und mit
berücksichtigung aller dem verfasser
über diesen gegenstand bekannt
gewordenen schriften kritisch dargestellt.   Fulda, Fuldaer actien-
druckerei, 1895.

Bibliography: p.[139]-167.
No more published?

NN 0027239 IaU OClW MtU CtY NIC OCH PPL PU MiU

Nassen, Josef, 1861-1903.
Neue Heine-Funde
see under Heine, Heinrich, 1797-1856.

Nassen, Paul.
Kapital und arbeit im dritten reich; Hitlers mai-pro-
gramm und seine durchführung, von Paul Nassen. Berlin,
E. S. Mittler & sohn, 1933.
vii, [1], 90, [1] p. 21 cm.

———— Microfilm copy (negative).
Made in 1943 by the Library of Congress.
Microfilm 441 reel 42, no. 4 DD

1. Germany—Economic policy. 2. Labor and laboring classes—
Germany. 3. Germany—Soc. condit. 4. Hitler, Adolf, 1889-
I. Title.
HC286.3.N23   330.943   35—15506

CU IEN NNC
NN 0027241 DLC IaU ICU WU MiU NcD NN TxU CtY MH

Nassen, Paul.
Kapital und Arbeit im Dritten Reich.
Berlin, F. S. Mittler & Sohn, 1935.

NN 0027242 NN

Nassen, Paul, joint author.

Heilfron, Eduard, 1860-
Der neue plan; Young-plan und Haager vereinbarungen
nebst den deutschen ausführungsvorschriften, herausgegeben
und erläutert von prof. dr. Ed. Heilfron und dr. Paul Nassen
... Berlin, C. Heymann, 1931.

Nassenheide, graf Arnim-Schlagenthin-
see
Arnim, Henning August, graf von, 1851-1910.

Nasser-ed-Din, *shah of Persia*
see
Nāṣir al-Dīn, *shah of Persia, d. 1896.*

Nasser Gholi Rahimi
see
Qājār Raḥīmī, Nāṣer Qolī.

Nasser (Alfred) & c[ie].
... Marques de fabriques et brevets; groupement des disposi-
tions amalgamées, complétées et revisées jusqu'à la date du 1er
mars 1933 d'après les divers arrêtés organisant la protection de
la propriété commerciale, industrielle, littéraire, artistique,
musicale, etc., dans les états sous mandat français: Syrie, Liban,
Alaouites, Alexandrette, Jebel Druze. Publié par: Alfred
Nasser & c[ie] ... Beyrouth, Rép. libanaise [Imprimerie Khalifé,
1933]
cover-title, 1 p. l., 33 p. 22cm.
At head of title: Mars 1933. Syrie & Liban.

"Tarif confidentiel pour correspondants" (1 leaf) and "Modification
des taxes officielles" (1 leaf) inserted.

1. Patent laws and legislation—Syria. 2. Patent laws and legislation—Lebanon. 3. Copyright—Syria. 4. Copyright—Lebanon. 5. Trade-
marks—Syria. 6. Trade-marks—Lebanon. 7. Competition, Unfair—
Syria. 8. Competition, Unfair—Lebanon. I. Syria. Laws, statutes,
etc. II. Lebanon. Laws, statutes, etc.
44-23716

NN 0027248 DLC

Nasser (Alfred) & c[ie].
... Marques de fabriques et brevets; groupement des disposi-
tions amalgamées, complétées et revisées jusqu'à la date du 1er
mars (1) 1933 d'après les divers arrêtés organisant la protection de la propriété commerciale, industrielle, littéraire, artistique, musicale, etc., dans les états sous mandat français:
Syrie, Liban, Alaouites, Alexandrette, Djebel Druze. Publié
par: Alfred Nasser & c[ie] ... Beyrouth [Imprimerie Khalifé,
1937]
cover-title, 2 p. l., 35 p. 24½cm.

At head of title: Syrie & Liban.
"La présente édition est revisée et mise à jour jusqu'au 30 septembre
1937."

1. Patent laws and legislation—Syria. 2. Patent laws and legislation—Lebanon. 3. Copyright—Syria. 4. Copyright—Lebanon. 5. Trade-
marks—Syria. 6. Trade-marks—Lebanon. 7. Competition, Unfair—
Syria. 8. Competition, Unfair—Lebanon. I. Syria. Laws, statutes,
etc. II. Lebanon. Laws, statutes, etc.   38-36828 Revised

NN 0027250 DLC

VOLUME 405

WI
380
N267f
1953

NASSER, Américo
Fechamento do côto duodenal nas gastro-
duodenectomias; estudo experimental. São
Paulo, 1953.
99 p. illus.
Tese para concurso - Univ. de São
Paulo.
1. Gastroenterostomy

NN   0027251   DNLM

Nasser, Bartholomaus, 1560-1614.

Bible. *German, 1614.*
Biblia, das ist: Die gantze Heylige Schrifft teutsch.
D. Martin Luther. Nicht allein in gewisse verss abgetheilt
sondern auch mit newen lehrhafften summarien vnd schönen
figuren gezieret. Getruckt zu Strassburg, M.DC.XIV.

Nasser (Constantin). * Recherches sur les modifications de la température par les onctions générales. 50 pp. 4°. *Lyon,* 1884, l. s., No. 201.

NN   0027253   DNLM PPC

Nasser, David.
A cruz de Jerusalém. Rio de Janeiro, Seção de Lívros,
Emprêsa Gráfica O Cruzeiro, 1948.
202 p. 22 cm.

1. Levant—Descr. & trav. 2. Palestine—Pol. & govt.   I. Title.

DS49.N3   50-17659

NN   0027254   DLC

Nasser, David.
Falta alguem em Nuremberg; torturas da polícia de
Filinto Strubling Muller. Rio de Janeiro, Edições do Povo,
1947.
206, [8] p. 25 cm.
"Apêndice. Cinco cartas de Luiz Carlos Prestes": p. [189]-[207]

1. Secret service—Brazil. 2. Political crimes and offenses—Brazil.
I. Prestes, Luis Carlos, 1898-   II. Title.
                    A 51-6363

New York. Public Libr.
for Library of Congress   [1]

NN   0027255   NN LNHT

Nasser, David.
Para Dutra ler na cama. Rio de Janeiro, Seção de Lívros
da Emprêsa Gráfica "O Cruzeiro," 1947.
218 p. 22 cm.

1. Brazil—Pol. & govt.—1930-   2. Brazil—Soc. condit.
I. Title.

F2538.N3   981   48-19480*

NN   0027256   DLC

Nasser, David
A revolução dos covardes; diário secreto de Severo
Fournier, reportagens políticas e ordens da censura
do ditador. Rio de Janeiro, Empresa Grafica O
Cruzeiro, 1947
268 p.
1. Brazil - Hist. - 1930-54. I. Fournier, Severo

NN   0027257   MH

904
N267v
1961

Nasser, David
O Velho capitão, e outras histórias reais.
2.ª ed. [Rio de Janeiro] Edições O Cruzeiro
[1911]
2 v.(674p.) 23cm.

NN   0027258   TxDaM

Nasser, Friedrich, respondent.
...De differentiis regnorvm...
see under   Conring, Hermann, 1606-
1681, praeses.

Nasser, Gabriel C
... Salpingite et grossesse ...   Paris,
A. Legrand & J. Bertrand, 1941.
35 p.
Thèse.

NN   0027260   DNLM MnU NNC IU

Von
KleinSmid
HX
442
N334

[Nasser, Gamal Abdel, Pres. United Arab
Republic] 1918-
The charter.   Cairo, Information Dept.,
U.A.R. [n.d.]
103p. 24cm.

✓1.Socialism in the United Arab Republic.
I.United Arab Republic.   Maṣlahat al-
Isti'lāmāt.

NN   0027261   CLSU

DT107.82
.N221

Nasser, Gamal Abdel, Pres., United Arab
Republic, 1918-
Egypt's liberation; the philosophy of the
revolution. Introduction by Dorothy
Thompson. Cairo, Govt. print. offices
[1957]
73 p. port. 19½cm.

1. Egypt - History. 2. Egypt - Polit. &
govt. I. Title.

NN   0027262   DS MH-L InU ICU

Nasser, Gamal Abdel, *Pres. United Arab Republic,* 1918-
Egypt's liberation; the philosophy of the revolution [by]
Gamal Abdul Nasser. Introd. by Dorothy Thompson.
Washington, Public Affairs Press [1955]
119 p. 20 cm.

1. Egypt—Hist.—Philosophy. 2. Egypt—Pol. & govt.—1952-
I. Title.

DT107.83.N323   1955   962   55-7692 rev ‡

     OrCS MtBC OrU WaSpG Wa WaS WaWW NRCR NIC
     MoU RP WU UU CaBVaU CaBVa IdB MtU IdPI OrPS Or OrP
     ODW NjP FTaSU MH KU CLSU NNC NBuU InAndC-T OkU TNJ
     OC1 OCU OU OOxM NcC NcD ViU MiU MnU AAP NN IEN
NN   0027263   DLC MB CU OO LU TxU PP TU CSt PPT DS

Pamphlet
D
1800

Nasser, Gamal Abdul, Pres. United Arab
Republic, 1918-
Die Philosophie der Revolution [von] Gamal
Abd el-Nasser. Cairo, "Mondiale" Press
[1952]
78 p. port. 20cm.

NN   0027265   NIC

DT
365
A1
F53
v.2
no.1

Nasser, Gamal Abdel, 1918-
The philosophy of the Egyptian revolution;
translated by Richard H. Nolte. N.Y.,
American Universities Field Staff, 1954.
43 p. (Its Reports Service, North Africa
series, v.2, no.1)

I. Nolte, Richard H., tr. II. Title.

NN   0027266   MBU

.83
.N333
Rare Bk
Coll

Nasser, Gamal Abdel, *Pres. United Arab Republic,* 1918-
The philosophy of the revolution [by] Gamal Abd el-
Nasser. [n. p., 195-]
73 p. illus. 20 cm.

1. Egypt—Hist.—Philosophy. 2. Egypt—Pol. & govt.—1952-
I. Title.

Shelf
DT107.83.N333   962   56-45238 rev ‡

NN   0027267   DLC MH KyU PP WaU

DT107.83
Z9
1952A

Nasser, Gamal Abdel, Pres. United Arab
Republic, 1918-
The philosophy of the revolution. [n.p.,
1952?]
64 p. 20 cm.

1. Egypt - Hist. - Philosophy.

NN   0027268   CtY

DT
107.83
N333
1954

Nasser, Gamal Abdel, Pres. United Arab Republic,
1918-
The philosophy of the revolution. Introduction
by Dorothy Thompson [Cairo?, The National
Publication House, 1954]
75p. 19cm.

1. Egypt - Hist. - Philosophy   2. Egypt -
Pol. & govt. - 1952-   I. Title

NN   0027269   WU

Nasser, Gamal Abdel, *Pres. United Arab Republic,* 1918-
Speeches and press-interviews.
[Cairo, Information Dept.]
v. illus. 25 cm. quarterly.

1. Egypt—Pol. & govt.—1952-   I. United Arab Republic.
Maṣlahat al-Isti'lāmāt.

DT107.83.N39   N E 63-857 ‡

NN   0027270   DLC IEdS OrPS CU PPiU KU MH

Nasser, Johann Adolph.   46524-3
Vorlesungen über die geschichte der deutschen poesie. Altona,
etc. J. H. Kaven, 1798-1800.
2 vol.

Germ. poetry

NN   0027271   MH TxU OCU

Nasser (Sélim-Ragheb). *Sur un cas de tumeur
cérébrale d'évolution pseudo-méningitique.
23 pp. 8°. Genève, 1924.

NN   0027272   DNLM

Nasset, Edmund Sigurd.
Food and you. Springfield, Ill., Thomas [1951]
92 p. 23 cm.

1. Food. 2. Nutrition.   I. Title.

TX551.N3   1951   612.39   51-6896 ‡

    MiU MsU   OrSaW WaS IdPI DNLM DNAL TU OrCS
NN   0027273   DLC CaBViP MtBC NN ICJ TxU MB MU OrPS

Nasset, *Mrs.* **Elizabeth (Custer)** 1905-
The effects of radium and radium in combination with me-
tallic sensitizers on *Endamoeba dysenteriae* in vitro, by Eliza-
beth Custer Nasset and Charles A. Kofoid ... Berkeley,
Calif., University of California press, 1928.
cover-title, 1 p. l., p. [387]-416. illus., pl. 16-17, tables, diagrs. 28ᵐ.
(University of California publications in zoology. v. 31. no. 17)
"Literature cited": p. 410-412.

1. Radium—Physiological effect. 2. [Endamoeba dysenteriae]   I. Kofoid, Charles Atwood, 1865-   joint author. II. Title.
                    A 28-2265

California. Univ. Libr.
for Library of Congress   [a41g1]

    ViU OO OU MU CoU
NN   0027274   CU OrSaW CaBVaU OrU PPC PPAmP MiU OC1W

WE
200
N267f
1920

NASSETTI, Francesco
Fistole conseguenti a lesioni esposte
delle ossa. Bologna, Cappelli, 1920.
133 p. illus.
Extracted from Archivio italiano
di chirurgia, v. 1, fasc. 4, 1920.

NN   0027275   DNLM

VOLUME 405

4PQ
It
1977
Nassi, Giulio
Letteratura italiana del
medioevo. Firenze, Editrice
universitaria "Marzocco" ₁1955₎
478 p.

ICN MH IU NjR FTaSU OrU
NN 0027276 DLC-P4 PU NIC RPB CU CtY OCU OClJC IaU

Nassi, Jacques, 1909-
... L'infiltration anesthèsique de la chaine
sympathique lombaire par voie para-vertébrale;
indications et résultats ... Lyon, 1935.
Thèse - Univ. de Lyon.
"Bibliographie": p. [193]-199.

NN 0027277 CtY

Nassi, Robert J
Reviewing Spanish, first year, by Robert Nassi ... New
York, N. Y., Amsco school publications, inc. ₁1942₎
3 p. l., 165, ₁21₎ p. illus. (maps) 17 cm.

1. Spanish language—Grammar—1870-   2. Spain. 3. Spanish America.

PC4111.N3   468.242   42-18217 rev

NN 0027278 DLC

Nassi, Robert J
Reviewing Spanish, two years, by Robert Nassi ... New
York, N. Y., Amsco school publications, inc. ₁1942₎
3 p. l., 171, ₁27₎ p. illus. (maps) 17½ cm.

1. Spanish language—Grammar—1870-   2. Spain. 3. Spanish America.

PC4111.N32   468.242   42-18218 rev

NN 0027279 DLC

Nassi, Robert J
Reviewing Spanish, three years, by Robert Nassi ... New
York, N. Y., Amsco school publications, inc. ₁1942₎
3 p. l., 170, ₁27₎ p. illus. (maps) 17½ cm.

1. Spanish language—Grammar—1870-   2. Spain. 3. Spanish America.

PC4111.N33   468.242   42-18219 rev

NN 0027280 DLC

PC4121
.G5
Nassi, Robert, joint author.

Ginsburg, Ruth R
Speaking Spanish, an introductory course ₁by₎ Ruth R.
Ginsburg ₁and₎ Robert J. Nassi. Boston, Allyn and Bacon,
1955.

Nassian.
Le miral moundi, pouemo en bint
see under Hillet,

NASSIBIAN, Archak.
Contribution à l'étude de la pleurésie
syphilitique. Paris, 1912.

[58 p.]

NN 0027283 MBCo DNLM

Nassiboff (Julie) ₁née Malujenko₎ [1877-   ].
*Contribution à l'étude du traitement de la
méningite cérébro-spinale épidémique par
le sérum de Dopter. 63 pp. 8°. Montpellier,
1911. No. 11.

NN 0027284 DNLM CtY

Nassif, Albert
... La détermination de la monnaie de
paiement dans les obligations contract-
uelles en Egypte et au Liban ... par me.
Albert Nassif ... Alexandrie, Journal
des tribunaux mixtes, 1943.

75 p.   27½cm.
Thèse - École française de droit du Caire.
At head of title: Université de Paris.
Faculté de droit.
"Bibliographie":   p. ₁69₎-72.

NN 0027285 MH-L NNC

Nassif, Albert
Évolution de la politique britannique aux
Indes. [Beyrouth, 1946]
p.[237]-327.

Cover title.
Contains author's autograph.
Extract from Annales, 1946, no. 3-4, of Beirut,
Université Saint-Joseph, Faculté de droit.

NN 0027286 OCl

Nassif, Élie.
Capitalisme ou collectivisme, l'alternative présenté. ₁Le
Caire₎ Les Lettres françaises ₁ᶜ1946₎
190 p.   24 cm.
"Index bibliographique": p. 183-186.

1. Capitalism. 2. Socialism. 3. Russia—Economic policy.   I. Title.

HB501.N28   47-26278*

NN 0027287 DLC

Nbp97
E3
943n
Nassif, Elie
L'Egypte est-elle surpeuplée? Le Caire,
1943.
614-773p. tables. 24cm.
Thèse - Paris.
Bibliography: p.769-772.

1. Egypt - Population. 2. Agriculture -
Economic aspects - Egypt. I. Title.

NN 0027288 CtY MH NNC

Nassif, Nikoula
see Niqūlā ibn Yūsuf al-Turk, 1763-1828.

Nassim (Amīn Ḥanna). *Ueber Leberfunk-
tionsprüfung bei Zirkulations-Störungen und
eigentlichen Lebererkrankungen. (Zwei neue
Substanzen im Harn von Leberkranken.)
Eine neue Methode zur Leberfunktionsprü-
fung. 49 pp. 8°. Zürich, Leemann & Co., 1916.

NN 0027290 DNLM

HD5723
.A53
1937 j
Nassimbene, R.
U.S. *Work projects administration.*
... Age of WPA workers, November 1937. By R. Nassim-
bene, under the supervision of John N. Webb, coordinator of
urban research, Division of social research. Washington, U. S.
Govt. print. off., 1938.

Nassimbene, R.

U.S. *Works progress administration.*
... Changing aspects of urban relief, by F. L. Carmichael
and R. Nassimbene, under the supervision of John N. Webb,
chief, Urban surveys section, Division of research. Washington, U. S. Govt. print. off., 1939.

NASSIO, Cleonege, pseud.

See VOLPE, Francesco Maria della.

Nässir ed Dīn, *shah of Persia*
see
Nāṣir al-Dīn, *shah of Persia, d.* 1896.

Nassir Eddin
see
al-Ṭūsī, Naṣīr al-Dīn Muḥammad ibn Muḥammad, 1201-
1274.

Nassir Eddin Yahia
see Ebn Bībī, Nāṣer al-Dīn al-Ḥoseyn ibn
Mohammad, fl. 1281.

Nassiri Khosrau
see
Nāṣir-i Khusraw, 1004-ca. 1088.

Nassiri, Mohammad.
... La donation en droit iranien ... par Mohammad Nassiri
... Paris, M. Lavergne, imprimeur, 1937.
1 p. l., ₁5₎-174 p. 25½ᵐ.
Thèse—Univ. de Paris.
"Bibliographie": p. ₁167₎-169.

1. Gifts—Persia.   I. Title.

                                   41-40691

NN 0027298 DLC CtY

Nassiruddin-el-Toussey
see al-Tusi, Nasir al-Din, Muhammad ibn
Muhammad, 1201?-1274.

PQ4831
A776
V5
Nassisi, Tommaso
La voce del cuore. Milano, Gastaldi
₁1952₎
43p. 19cm.   (Poeti d'oggi)

Poems.

NN 0027300 RPB

PF5399
T3N3
Nassl, Johann.
Die laute der Tepler mundart von Johann Nassl ...
Prag, K. K. Hofbuchdr. von G. Haase söhne, 1863.
16 p. 24ᵐ. (Beiträge zur geschichte Böhmens, hrsg. vom Vereine für
geschichte der Deutschen in Böhmen. abth. II, bd. I, nr. 1)

1. German language—Dialects—Tepl.   I. Verein für geschichte der
Deutschen in Böhmen, Prague.

                                   11-3161

Library of Congress   PF5399.T3N3

NN 0027301 DLC MdBP NIC

PF5399
T3N34
Nassl, Johann
Über den mit der Dehnung und der Schärfung
der Stammsilben verbundenen Lautwechsel in
der Conjugation des Verba der Tepler Mundart.
Pilsen, Druck von C. Maasch, 1877.
5 p.

Accompanies "Programm" - K.K. Staats-
Real- und Obergymnasium in Mies.

1. German language - Dialects - Tepl.

NN 0027302 CU

Nasso, Celina E   Rodríguez
see
Rodríguez de Martínez Paiva, Celina E

VOLUME 405

Nasso, Enzo.
I mostri di stoppa: sabotaggi, menzogne e pregiudizi dei comunisti contro l'Opera Sila. 2. ed. Roma, Porfiri ₁195-₎
70 p. 10 cm. (Collezione di inchieste sulla realtà. n. 1)

1. Opera per la valorizzazione della Sila. 2. Reclamation of land—Sila, Italy. ɪ. Title₁
HD1975.S54N3 1950z   60-21253

NN 0027304 DLC

WS   NASSO, Ivo
200   Manuale di pediatria. Milano,
N268m   Wassermann, 1937.
1937   784 p.
                1. Children - Diseases
                2. Infants - Diseases

NN 0027305 DNLM

WS   NASSO, Ivo
200   Manuale di pediatria. ₁2. ed.₁
N268m   Milano, Principato ₁1940₁
1940   xvi, 778 p. (Biblioteca di medicina, 1)
                1. Children - Diseases
                2. Infants - Diseases   Series

NN 0027306 DNLM DLC

WS   NASSO, Ivo
200   Manuale di pediatria. 4. ed. riv.
N268m   Milano, Principato ₁1953₁
1953   xii, 530 p.
                1. Children - Diseases

NN 0027307 DNLM

Nasso, Marco
... Algebra elementare ad uso dei licei e degli instituti tecnici (Io biennio) secondo i programmi governativi... Torino, Tipografia e libreria Salesiana, 1898.
426p.

NN 0027308 MiU

NASSÓ, Marco.
Algebra elementare ad uso della la classe liceale secondo il programma governativo dell' 11 Nov.1904. Torino, Salesiana, 1909.

NN 0027309 MH

Nasso, Marco
... Aritmetica generale ed algebra ad uso dei licei, secondo il programma governativo dell' 11 Novembre 1904 ... 9ᵃ ed. riveduta. Torino, Libreria editrice internazionale, 1918.
2 p.l., 530 p.   diagrs., tables. 24 cm.

NN 0027310 RPB

Nasso, Marco
... Elementi di calcolo algebrico ad uso delle scuole normali... Torino, Tipografia e libreria Salesiana, 1899.
106p.

NN 0027311 MiU

Nasso, Roberto di.
Guida del sistemista. Sintesi di studi sul gioco a sistema per i concorsi pronostici. ₁Roma? 1950?₁
v. 24 cm.

1. Probabilities.   ɪ. Title.
GV1302.N3   65-37923 ‡

NN 0027312 DLC

W 4   Nasso, Saúl Guillermo
B92   Cesárea vaginal. Buenos Aires, Bossio
No.3537   & Bigliani, 1918.
                64 p. (Buenos Aires. Universidad Nacional. Facultad de Ciencias Médicas. Tesis. no. 3537)

Series

NN 0027313 DNLM

Nasso, Sergio.
La malattia emolitica del neonato

see under

Ceppellini, Ruggero.

Nassoin, Cafetan, ed.
Dictionnaire françois-italien de M. l'abbé François Alberti de Villeneuve
see under   Alberti di Villanova, Francesco
d', 1737-1800.

Nassokin (Casimir). *Om ros. [Erysipelas.]
54pp. 8°. Helsingfors, J. C. Frenckell & Son, 1862.

NN 0027316 DNLM

Nassonov, M.
see Nasonov, Nikolaĭ Viktorovich, 1855-1939.

Nassonov, P.
Sel'skokhozĭaĭstvennoe raĭonirovanie
see under Chernomorskiy okrug, Russia. Zemel'noe upravlenie.

336.24   Nassos, Ernest John.
N188t   Tax minimization by noncorporate taxpayers.
                Urbana ₁1952₁
                119ℓ. 28cm.

                Thesis—University of Illinois.
                Typewritten (carbon copy)
                Bibliography: leaves 116-119.
1952   ----- ----- Thesis copy.
N188

                1. Income tax--U.S. I. Title.

NN 0027318 IU

HA1916   Nassos, G   K
.N36   Symbolē eis tēn diereunēsin tōn hypó
                tēs Tourkias parechomenōn stoicheiōn epi
                tēs dēmographikēs katastaseōs autēs
                (basei tēs genomenēs ten 23.10.55 en
                Tourkia, genikēs apographēs). Athēnai,
                1955.
                23 p. illus., map.

                1. Turkey - Census. I. Title.

NN 0027319 DS OCU

Nassouhi, Essad.
...Textes divers relatifs à l'histoire de l'Assyrie, par Essad Nassouhi. Leipzig: E. Pfeiffer, 1927. 38 p. illus. (incl. facsims.) 24½cm. (Altorientalische Gesellschaft. Mitteilungen. Bd. 3, Heft 1–2.)

1. Assyrian and Babylonian literature   —Collections. 2. Assyrian and Babylonian inscriptions. I. Ser.
N. Y. P. L.   August 25, 1933

NN 0027320 NN PU CtY OCH OCl NIC ICU

Nassoupnis (Anastase). *L'hydarthrose syphilitique double des genoux. 68 pp. 8°. Paris, 1922. No. 191.

NN 0027321 DNLM CtY

Nassour, Sarah A.
Skin of gods (Hycette) by Sarah A. Nassour. Los Angeles, New York ₁etc.₁ Suttonhouse ₁1938₁
5 p. l., 3–225 p. 21¼ᵐ.

1. Jemez Indians—Fiction.   ɪ. Title.   40-51185
Library of Congress   PZ3.N188Sk

NN 0027322 DLC OkU WaE

Nassovia. Zeitschrift für nassauische Geschichte und Heimatkunde.
Jahrg. 1-
Wiesbaden: P. Plaum ₁1900-   4°.
v. illus.
Semi-monthly.
Editors: 1900-19 , C. Spielmann.

1. Nassau, Germany.—Per. and soc.   publ.
N. Y. P. L.   November 24, 1916.

NN 0027323 NN

Nassovischen Oraignien-boom
see under [Buchell, Arend van] 1565-1641.

Nassoy, H.
...L'enfant maudit! Drame en 3 actes pour jeunes gens...
Orléans: H. Moutier₁, 1929?₁. 64 p. 2. ed. 12°.

474132A. 1. Drama, French.   2. Title.
N. Y. P. L.   May 15, 1930

NN 0027325 NN

Nassoy, H.
...La folle! Comédie en 2 actes, pour jeunes filles... Orléans: H. Moutier₁, 1925?₁. 59 p. 12°.

1. Juvenile literature—Drama, French.   2. Title.
N. Y. P. L.   February 9, 1927

NN 0027326 NN

Nassoy, H.
...L'homme noir; drame en 3 actes et 7 tableaux pour jeunes gens... Orléans: H. Moutier₁, 1929?₁. 83 p. 12°.

485465A. 1. Drama, French.   I. Title.
N. Y. P. L.   July 21, 1930

NN 0027327 NN

Nassoy, H.
...La piccola Miss; dramma in tre atti. Versione di A. Marescalchi... Roma: Libreria Salesiana, 1939. 54 p. 17cm.

1. Drama, French—Translations   into Italian. I. Marescalchi, Amilcare. II. Title.
N. Y. P. L.   February 19, 1941

NN 0027328 NN

Nassoy, H.
... M. Pouitte détective; comédie en 1 acte. Suivie de Baoum!!! sketch sportif en 5 round. Pour jeunes gens. Orléans: H. Moutier ₁1936₁ 66 p. 19cm.
Cover-title.

909268A. 1. Drama, French.   I. Title. II. Title: Baoum!!!
N. Y. P. L.   October 29, 1937

NN 0027329 NN

Nassoy, H., and E. Ritter.
...Le neveu de M. Pascal; comédie en 3 actes pour jeunes gens... Orléans: H. Moutier₁, 1929?₁. 119 p. 12°.

513070A. 1. Drama, French.   I. Ritter, E., jt. au. II. Title.
N. Y. P. L.   February 3, 1931

NN 0027330 NN

VOLUME 405

Nassoy, H.
...Niquedouille caporal; comédie bouffe en 3 actes pour jeunes gens. Orléans: H. Moutier [1936] 84 p. 19cm.

Includes incidental songs (words and music).

909268A. 1. Drama, French.   I. Title.
N.Y.P.L.   October 29, 1937

NN   0027331   NN

Nassoy, H.
...Niquedouille chez l'colon! Bouffonnerie militaire en trois actes... Orléans: H. Moutier[, 192-]. 70 p. 16°.

513076A. 1. Drama, French. I. Title.
N.Y.P.L.   February 26, 1931

NN   0027332   NN

Nassoy, H.
...Niquedouille malade! Comédie militaire en trois actes ... Orléans: H. Moutier[, 1929?]. 86 p. 12°.

513070A. 1. Drama, French.   I. Title.
N.Y.P.L.   February 26, 1931

NN   0027333   NN

Nassoy, H.
..."Petite Miss;" drame en 3 actes pour jeunes filles... Orléans: H. Moutier[, 1929?]. 78 p. 12°.

485465A. 1. Juvenile literature—   Drama, French. I. Title.
N.Y.P.L.   July 21, 1930

NN   0027334   NN

Nassoy, H.
...Sœurette; drame en 3 actes, avec chants et musique, pour jeunes filles... Orléans: H. Moutier[, 1922]. 51 p. 12°.

Contains music of 2 incidental songs.

1. Juvenile literature—Drama, French.   2. Title.
N.Y.P.L.   January 19, 1927

NN   0027335   NN

Nassoy, H.
...La valise! Comédie en 1 acte, pour jeunes gens... Orléans: H. Moutier[, 1925?]. 40 p. 12°.

1. Juvenile literature—Drama,   French. 2. Title.
N.Y.P.L.   February 15, 1927

NN   0027336   NN

Nassr-ed-din, hodja
    see   Nasreddin Hoca.

Nassr, 'Adel Abou.
    La Cécidomie de l'olivier au Liban
    Perrisia oleae
       see under   Lebanon. Service des
    recherches agricoles.

Nassr, 'Adel Abou.
    La Cécidomie de la vigne
       see under   Lebanon. Service des
    recherches agricoles.

Nassr, 'Adel Abou.
    Histoire de l'olivier
       see under   Lebanon. Service des
    recherches agricoles.

Nassr, 'Adel Abou.
    Liste des insectes nuisibles aux cultures
    au Liban
       see under   Lebanon. Service des
    recherches agricoles.

Nassr, 'Adel Abou.
    Nouvelles études sur divers insectes
    nuisibles aux cultures
       see under   Lebanon. Service des recherches
    agricoles.

Nassr, 'Adel Abou.
    Rapport sur l'etude biologique du dacus oleae
       see under   Lebanon. Service des
    recherches agricole.

Nassr, Taghi
    see
    Nasr, Taqī, 1907-

Nassr ed-Dīn, Shah of Iran
    see   Nāṣir al-Dīn Shāh, Shah of Iran,
    1831-1896.

Nassri, Kiamil.
    ... Tests d'intelligence et rendement scolaire; recherches sur deux types de tests d'intelligence et sur leur signification à l'école. Par Kiamil Nassri ... Paris, Les Presses universitaires de France, 1930.

viii, 246 p. diagrs. 24ᶜᵐ.

At head of title: Faculté des lettres de l'Université de Paris.
Thèse—Univ. de Paris.
"Bibliographie": p. [235]-241.

1. Mental tests.   I. Title.
                                          40-20608
                                          Provisional
Library of Congress   LB1131.N17
                     [2]   [159.928]   151.2

NN   0027346   DLC CtY MH

Nassrollah, Feylessouf, 1897-
Lactotherapie 1) per injectionen, 2) per os, 3) per us. ext. *Berlin - Frieden aug 1929* 48p.
Inaug.-diss.—Berlin, 1929

NN   0027347   ICRL CtY OU

Nassūr, Adīb.
قبل فوات الأوان، دراسات ومطالعات حول الأحداث السورية
١٩٤٨ — ١٩٥٥ [تأليف] أديب نصور. [الطبعة ١]. بيروت، دار
العلم للملايين [1965]

223 p. 21 cm.
Bibliographical footnotes.

1. Syria—Pol. & govt.   I. Title.
                     Title romanized: Qabla fawāt al-awān.
DS98.2.N36   N E 68-2895

NN   0027348   DLC

Nassūr, Adīb.
وطنيون وأوطان، الوطنية كما فهمها أنبل رجال الفكر والعمل
فى التاريخ [تأليف] أديب نصور. [الطبعة ١]. بيروت، دار
العلم للملايين ، 1952.

152 p. 25 cm.

1. Nationalism.   I. Title.
                     Title romanized: Waṭanīyūn wa-awṭān.
JC311.N27   74-204031

NN   0027349   DLC

Nassy, David de Isaac Cohen, 1747-1806.
Works by this author printed in America before 1801 are available in this library in the Readex Microprint edition of Early American Imprints published by the American Antiquarian Society.
This collection is arranged according to the numbers in Charles Evans' American Bibliography.

NN   0027350   DLC

J
009
.8   NASSY, DAVID DE ISAAC COHEN, 1747-1806.
          Observations on the cause, nature, and treatment of the epidemic disorder, prevalent in Philadelphia. Translated from the French. Philadelphia, Printed by Parker & co. for M. Carey, 1793.
          26p.   (in Select pamphlets. 1796)

          RPJCB
NN   0027351   ICN NCH MH MHi IEN-M MWA DLC NNNAM

Nassy, David de Isaac Cohen, 1747-1806.
Observations sur la cause, la nature, et le traitement de la maladie epidemique, qui regne à Philadelphie. Par D. Nassy ... Philadelphie: Imprimé par Parker & cⁱᵉ. pour M. Carey. 26 Nov.—1793.

48 p., 1 l. 20½ᶜᵐ.

Added t.-p.: Observations on the cause, nature, and treatment of the epidemic disorder, prevalent in Philadelphia. By D. Nassy ... Philadelphia, Printed by Parker & cᵒ. for M. Carey. Nov. 26,—1793.
English and French on opposite pages.

1. Yellow fever—Philadelphia, 1793.

Library of Congress   RC211.P5N3   35-37097
—— Copy 2. [Mis-   cellaneous pamphlets, v. 118, no. 6]
                     AC901.A5   vol. 118, no. 6
                     [2]

          PPC PHi MWA DS NN PPL RPJCB NNNAM
NN   0027352   DLC DNLM NcD-MC N MH CtY-M CtHT-W PP

W 4
A52
1952   NASSY, Evert Aron
          Gehoorafwijkingen bij verhemeltespleet.
          Amsterdam, 1952.
          75 p. illus.
          Academisch proefschrift - Amsterdam.
          Summary in Dutch, English, and
          French.
          1. Palate - Cleft

NN   0027353   DNLM

W 4
A52
1918   NASSY, Jacques George
          Verduurzaming van virus fixe in
          verband met de bestrijding der
          hondsdolheid in de tropen. Amsterdam,
          1918.
          76 p.
          Proefschrift - Amsterdam.

NN   0027354   DNLM

Nassyf, Nikoula
    see   Niqūlā ibn Yūsuf al-Turk, 1763-1828.

Nast, Albert André, 1884-
    Aux soldats de la France
       see his   La vie morale et la guerre.

Nast, Albert André, 1884-
    ... L'enfant dans la lumière; illustrations de Guy Arnoux, musique d'Andrée Fœgeli. Paris, G. Crès & cⁱᵉ, 1919.

2 p. l., 184 p., 1 l. col. illus. 24½ x 19½ᶜᵐ.
Includes songs with music.

I. Arnoux, Guy, illus.   II. Fœgeli, Andrée.   III. Title.
                                          43-29771
Library of Congress   PZ23.N3E56

NN   0027357   DLC NjN

VOLUME 405

Nast, Albert André, 1884–
... L'enfant de la nuit; pièce en prose, en cinq actes, avec un avant-propos Le drame de la cécité et un poème Au-delà des ténèbres. ₁Paris₁ OCIA éditions ₁1944₁

226 p. 18ᶜᵐ.

At head of title: Albert Nast.
"Chérie-Grace, ou, La leçon de Molière; pièce en prose, en quatre tableaux": p. ₁115₁–226.

ɪ. Title. ɪɪ. Title: Chérie-Grace.

45–19680

Library of Congress   PQ2627.A69E5
(2)   842.91

NN   0027358   DLC NN ICU CtY CU ICRL

RC178
.G7L715
Nast, Albert André, 1884–   tr.

Defoe, Daniel, 1661?–1731.
... Journal de l'année de la peste. Traduction ₁par₁ Albert et Andrée Nast. ₁Paris, De Noël ₁194–₁

W
61
N269m
1955
NAST, Albert André, 1884–
Le malade, la mort et le médecin.
Paris, SEGEP ₁1955₁
188 p.
1. Medicine - Philosophy   Title

NN   0027360   DNLM

WL
344
N269m
1921
NAST, Albert André, 1884–
La migraine; la peptonothérapie pré-
prandiale. Paris, Crès ₁1921?₁
110 p.

NN   0027361   DNLM CtY

4HQ
614
Nast, Albert André, 1884–
La répression de l'adultère chez
les peuples chrétiens; étude critique.
Préf. de M. Émile Chenon. Paris,
A. Rousseau, 1908.
256 p.

NN   0027362   DLC-P4 CU-L MH

W 9
N269s
1948
NAST, Albert André, 1884–
Sous le regard d'Hygie. Pauvres
médecins, pauvres malades! Chelles,
Face à la vie ₁1948₁
323 p.
1. Medicine - Addresses, essays,
lectures

NN   0027363   DNLM OrU

Nast, Albert André, 1884–
... La statue en délire; pièce en quatre actes. Chelles: La Guette ₁1926₁. 152 p. 12°.

1. Drama, French. 2. Title.
N. Y. P. L.   May 7, 1928

NN   0027364   NN

Nast, Albert André, 1884–
La vie morale et la guerre; discours prononcé au Palmarium de Bourges, le 27 avril 1916, avec l'autorisation de MM. les Géné-raux commandants les 5ᵉ et 8ᵉ régions territoriales, par Albert Nast...lettre de M. Justin Godart... Paris: Fédération aboli-tionniste, branche française ₁1916₁. 23(1) p. 12°.

At head of title: Aux soldats de la France!

1. Sex.—Ethics. 2. Venereal dis-   eases. 3. European war, 1914– —
Addresses, sermons, etc.
N. Y. P. L.   December 4, 1917.

NN   0027365   NN

Nast, Alfred.
... Code de la coopération; étude sur le régime légal· et réglementaire de la coopération en France. Textes (lois, dé-crets, arrêtés, etc.) classés et annotés ... **Paris, Recueil Sirey,** 1928.

2 p. l., vi p., 1 l., 703 p., 2 l. 22½ᶜᵐ.

1. Cooperation—France. 2. Cooperation—₁Legislation₁ ɪ. Title.
Agr 29–1705

Library, U. S. Dept. of   Agriculture 280.2N18

NN   0027366   DNAL MH CU CtY

NAST, Alfred.
Étude juridique sur les sociétés coopératives de consommation, etc. Paris, 1904.

NN   0027367   MH

Nast, Alfred, editor.
Juris-classeur commercial. Traité des sociétés. Alfred Nast ... rédacteur en chef, Jean Michel ... secrétaire général ... ₁t.₁ ɪ–   Paris, Administration des Juris-classeurs ₁1913–

Nast, Alfred.
Recueil de lois, décrets, arrêtés et circulaires concer-nant les sociétés de secours mutuels publié sous le con-trôle du Ministère du travail et de la prévoyance sociale (Direction de la mutualité) ... ₁par₁ Alfred Nast ... ₁et₁ Jean Michel ... Paris, Administration des Juris-clas-seurs ₁1913₁

128 p. 29ᶜᵐ.

"Extrait du 'Juris-classeur des sociétés.'"

1. Insurance, Industrial—France. 2. Friendly societies—France. ɪ. Mi-chel, Jean, joint ed. ɪɪ. France. Laws, statutes, etc. ɪɪɪ. France. Direc-tion de la mutualité. ɪv. Title.
18–1958

Library of Congress   HD7174.N3

NN   0027369   DLC

Nast, Alfred.
... Le régime juridique des coopératives; principes co-opératifs et exposé synthétique de la législation ... Paris, Jouve & cⁱᵉ, 1919.

296 p. 25½ᶜᵐ.

Thèse.—Univ. de Paris.

1. Cooperation. ɪ. Title.
22–1130

Library of Congress   HD2968.N3

NN   0027370   DLC CtY MH

Nast, Alfred.
Le régime juridique des coopératives. Principes co-opératifs et exposé synthétique de la législation, par Al-fred Nast ... Paris, M. Rivière & cie, 1919.

2 p. l., 330 p., 1 l. 25ᶜᵐ.

"Liste des ouvrages cités dans ce volume": p. ₁287₁–295.

1. Cooperation. 2. Cooperation—France. 3. Cooperation—Bibliography.
ɪ. Title.
L 22–66

Library, U. S. Dept. of   Labor

NN   0027371   DL

Nast, Alfred.
Les syndicats agricoles. Étude critique sur la récente jurisprudence de la Cour de cassation et les projets légis-latifs actuels, par Alfred Nast ... Paris, F. Pichon et Durand-Auzias, 1909.

45 p., 1 l. 24½ᶜᵐ.

"Extrait du Bulletin de la Société de législation comparée."

1. Agricultural societies—France. 2. Agriculture, Cooperative—France.
ɪ. Title.
18–13940

Library of Congress   HD1486.F8N3

NN   0027372   DLC

HE6187
.S73
Nast, Charles A., ed.

The Stamp journal. v. 1–   (no. 1–   );
Jan. 1908–
Florida, N. Y. ₁etc.₁

Nast, Charles A

The stamp publications of the state of Colo-rado, by Chas. A. Nast. Reprinted from The Stamp Collector. Columbus, Ohio, George W. Linn Co., 1912.

₁20₁p. 23cm. (Bound with: Anderson, Peter John. Early English philatelic literature. 1912)
No. 32 of 125 copies.

NN   0027374   NBu MiU

QK643
W353
BIOLOGY
LIBRARY
G
Nast, Charlotte Georgia, 1905–
The embryogeny and seedling morphology of Jug-lans regia, by Charlotte Georgia Nast ... ₁Berke-ley, Calif., 1938?₁
2 p.l., 58 numb. l. mounted plates, diagrs.
29cm.

Part of plates preceded by guard sheets with descriptive letterpress.
Thesis (Ph.D.) – Univ. of California, May 1938.
"Literature cited": p.53–58.

308t
N269
MB25
-- --- Another copy.
1. Botany - Morphology   2. Botany - Embryology
3. Walnut   Ref.t.1.

NN   0027375   CU

Nast, Charlotte Georgia, 1905–
... Morphological development of the fruit of *Juglans regia* ₁by₁ Charlotte G. Nast.
(*In* Hilgardia. Berkeley, Calif., 1935. 24ᶜᵐ. v. 9, no. 7, p. 345–381 incl. plates)

"Literature cited": p. 362.

1. Pecan. ɪ. Title.
A 35–1290

Title from Univ. of Calif.
Library of Congress   ₁81.H5 vol. 9, no. 7₁

NN   0027376   CU

Nast, Clara (Seyffert), 1866–
Csöppike, a pajkos kis leany; Gasparne David
Margit forditasa. ₁Budapest, Nova iordalmi
intezet, 1924₁
₁125p.₁

NN   0027377   OCl

Nast, Clara (Seyffert), 1866–
Csöppike az iskolaban, Gasparne David Margit,
forditasa; Galambos Margit es Mühlbeck Karoly,
erediti rajzaival.

NN   0027378   OCl

Nast, Clara (Seyffert) 1866–
Erlkönigs Töchter. Novelle von Herbert Fohrbach ₁Pseud.₁.
(In Deutsche Roman-Bibliothek. Jahrgang 25, Band 2. Stutt-gart, 1897.)

F5615 — Tr.

NN   0027379   MB

PT
2627
A67
H4
Nast, Clara (Seuffert) 1866–
Die Herren von Krischacken; Roman aus
Preussisch-Litauen von Cl. Nast. Breslau,
Schlesische Verlags-Anstalt, 1907.
354p. 19cm.

NN   0027380   WU

Nast, Frau Clara (Seyffert) 1866–
Die hexe; Arme Anna Feodorowna! Zwei dorf-
geschichten von Herbert Fohrbach ₁pseud.₁
Stuttgart, C. Krabbe ₁n.d.₁
94p. illus.

NN   0027381   ScU

VOLUME 405

Nast, Clara (Seyffert) 1866–
Hummelchen, eine Erzaehlung fuer Maedchen.
Berlin, Weichert, 1917.
255 p.

NN 0027382 PPG

Nast, Clara (Seyffert) 1866–
Hummelchen geht in die Schule... Berlin, Weichert,
[n. d.]
223 p.

NN 0027383 PPG

Nast, Frau Clara (Seyffert)
Hummelchen will studieren; eine erzaehlung fuer
junge maedchen. Berlin, A. Weichert[n. d.]
224 p.

NN 0027384 PP

Nast, Clara (Seyffert), 1866–
Kein Recht auf Glück; Roman von Clara Nast. Berlin: A.
Weichert [1930] 254 p. 16½cm.

760700A. 1. Fiction, German. I. Title.
N.Y.P.L. September 10, 1935

NN 0027385 NN

PT
2627
A67
M5
Nast, Clara (Seyffert) 1866–
Mit Waffen der Nächstenliebe; zeitgeschicht-
liche Erzählung. Berlin, R. Bachmann [c1915]
239p. illus. 22cm.

NN 0027386 WU

Nast, Clara (Seyffert) 1866–
Lydia Antonowna Obolenski's Festfahrt. Skizze aus Russisch-Polen.
(In Deutsche Roman-Zeitung. Jahrgang 1912. Band 3, pp.
353-357. Berlin. 1912.)

NN 0027387 MB

PZ
33
N28
Pe
Nast, Clara (Seyffert) 1866–
Pension Lustig; eine Erzählung für junge
Mädchen. Berlin, A. Wiechert [1910]
238p. illus. 22cm. (Clara Nasts Mäd-
chenschriften, 12)

NN 0027388 WU

Nast, Frau Clara (Seyffert) 1866–
Platon Kiritschenko und die seinen; humoristische erzählung von Klara Nast. Leipzig, P. Reclam jun. [1922]
152 p. 15½cm. (On cover: Reclams universal bibliothek, nr. 6289, 6290)

I. Title.
Library of Congress PT2627.A67P6 1922 23-3376

NN 0027389 DLC MB

Nast, Clara (Seyffert), 1866–
Unseres Aennchens Schuljahre; Erzählungen für jüngere Mädchen, von Clara Nast. Mit Aquarell- und Federzeichnungen von
Heinrich Susemihl. Grosse Ausgabe. Berlin: A. Weichert
[1907] 248 p. col'd front., col'd plates. 22½cm.

58626B. 1. Juvenile literature— Fiction, German. I. Title.
N.Y.P.L. September 3, 1940

NN 0027390 NN

PZ
33
N28
U5
Nast, Clara (Seyffert) 1866–
Unseres Aennchens Schuljahre; eine
Erzählung für Mädchen, von Clara Nast.
Berlin, A. Weichert [c1919]
248p. illus. 22cm.

NN 0027391 WU

Nast, Colette, 1913–
Karine. Précédé d'une lettre à Karine par Robert Garric.
Paris, Éditions sociales françaises, *1946.
180 p. illus. (part col.) 21 cm.

I. Title.
PZ23.N34K3 47-29170*

NN 0027392 DLC

4PZ-
Fr-
5070
Nast, Colette, 1913–
Le tuteur de Caracas. Illus. de Manon Iessel.
Paris, Editions Gautier-Languereau, 1950.
128 p. (Bibliothèque de Suzette)

NN 0027393 DLC-P4

Nast, Colette, 1913–
Vingt petites filles sous le soleil. Illustrations de Claire
Marchal. Paris, Gautier-Languereau, 1953.
125 p. illus. 22 cm. (Bibliothèque de Suzette)

I. Title.
PZ21.B45N38 54-16198 ‡

NN 0027394 DLC

Nast, Condé.
Class publications. Baltimore, 1913. 12 p. 8°.
Repr.: Merchants' and manufacturers' jour. of Baltimore. June, 1913.

1. Advertisement and advertising.
N.Y.P.L. January 16, 1914.

NN 0027395 NN

Nast, Condé, 1874-1942.
The Condé Nast collection; French and English
furniture, paintings of the French school, including works by Watteau, Schall, Huet and others,
Georgian silver, porcelains, oriental and French
rugs, removed from the apartment of the late Condé
Nast. Public auction sale, Jan. 7, 8 and 9.
Parke-Bernet Galleries, inc., New York, 1943.
155p. illus. 28cm.

Sale no. 418.

NN 0027396 FMU

PS3519
.A323
L63
Nast, Denise, tr.

Jackson, Charles Reginald, 1903–
Le poison (The lost week-end) Roman, tr. de l'américain par
Denise Nast. Paris, R. Julliard [1946]

NN 0027397 CtY

Nast, Eberhard. Über den Eiweissgehalt des Blutes im
Kindesalter mit besonderer Berücksichtigung der Tuber-
kulose. Berlin: Springer 1914. 21 S. 8° ¶ Aus: Zeit-
schrift f. Kinderheilk. Orig. Bd 11.
Straßburg, Med. Diss. v. 28. Juli 1914, Ref. Salge
[Geb. 14. Mai 88 Kannstatt; Wohnort: Frankfurt a. M.; Staatsangeh.: Württemberg;
Vorbildung: OR. Kannstatt Reife 07, Erg. G. Kannstatt 07; Studium: Tübingen 5,
Freiburg 2, Berlin 1, Freiburg 2 S.; Coll. 15. Mai 14; Approb. 10. Juni 14]
[U 14. 2833]

NN 0027398 ICRL DNLM CtY MH-M

Nast, Elsa Ruth, *pseud.*
see
Watson, Jane (Werner) 1915–

Nast, Ernst, 1896–
Wehrpflicht, Militärpflicht, Landsturmpflicht.
Greifswald, 1919. 22½cm.
Inaug.-Diss. - Greifswald
Lebenslauf.
"Literatur": pp.[5]-6.

NN 0027400 CtY

Nast, F A.
A tentative price list of entire U. S. envelopes arrang-
ing to J. W. Scott's system, with the corresponding numbers according to Prof. Horner, by F. A. Nast... New York: The
J. W. Scott co. [1887?] 51 p. illus. 21cm.

1. Envelopes, Stamped—Catalogues. I. Horner, W. E. V. II. Scott stamp
and coin company, ltd., New York.
N.Y.P.L. February 16, 1944

NN 0027401 NN MB RPB

Nast, Franz
Arbeitszeit und arbeitslohn in deutschen baugewerbe.
werbe.
Frankfurt am Main, 1928. (Diss.)

NN 0027402 MiU ICU

ML
89
N26++
Nast, Frederick.
Music and musicians in New York.
Illustrated by Geo. P. Elder. New York,
1881.
1 v. 34cm.

Work consists of mounted text from Harper's
new monthly magazine, v. 62, no. 372, May,
1881, p. 803-818, and mounted illustrations.

1. Music-- New York (City)
2. Musicians-- New York (City)

NN 0027403 NIC

Nast, Hans. Über proteinogene Amine, die Synthese des
[β-p-Oxyphenyl-äthyl]- [β-4(5)-Imidazolyl-äthyl]- amins und
anderer Phenylalkyl-Imidazolylalkyl-amine. Weida i. Thür.
1920: Thomas & Hubert. 59 S. 8° ¶ Auch in: Berichte
der Dtsch. Chem. Gesellschaft (nur d. exper. Teil zus. mit
Gerngross).
Berlin, Phil. Diss. v. 12. Okt. 1920, Ref. Beckmann, Nernst
[Geb. 2. Sept. 91 Pr. Stargard, Westpr.; Wohnort: Berlin; Staatsangeh.: Preußen;
Vorbildung: RfG. Hohenzollernsch. Schöneberg Reife 10; Studium: Freiburg 6,
Berlin 7 S.; Rig. 29. Aug. 20.] [U 20. 3377]

NN 0027404 ICRL CtY MH

NAST, Hans-Albert, 1900–
Über die reaktionsfähigkeit ungesättigter
und gesättigter kohlenwasserstoffe der fettreihe. Inaug.-diss., Jena. Borna-Leipzig,
R. Noske, 1927.
pp.(6),51 .
"Lebenslauf", at end.

NN 0027405 MH-C ICRL CtY

QL1
P7
v.15
no. 1
Nast, Janusz
Cztery nowe gatunki z rodzaju Idiotettix
Osb. (Homoptera, Jassidae). Warsaw, 1952.
6, [2] p. illus. 25 cm. (Warsaw.
Panstwowe Museum Zoologiczne. Annales, Tom
XV, Nr. 1)
"Four new species of the genus Idiotettix
Osb. (Homoptera, Jassidae)."
In English. Russian summary.

1. Leaf-hoppers. (Series)

NN 0027406 DI

QL1
P7
v.14
no.14
Nast, Janusz
Notatki homopterologiczne VI-IX. Homoptero-
gical notes VI-IX. Warszawa, 1951.
[193]-198 p. illus. 25 cm. (Warsaw.
Panstwowe Museum Zoologiczne. Annales Musei
Zoologici Polonici, t. 14, nr. 14)

1. Homoptera. I. Title. (Series)

NN 0027407 DI

QL1
.P7
v.14
no.11
Nast, Janusz.
Nowe rodzaje i gatunki neotropikalnych Fulgoridae w zbiorach British Museum (Homoptera).
New genera and species of neotropical Fulgoridae
in the collection of the British Museum (Homoptera). Warszawa, 1950.
[167]-175 p. illus. 25 cm. (Warsaw.
Panstwowe Museum Zoologiczne. Annales Musei
Zoologici Polonici, v. 14, no. 11)

1. Homoptera. I. Title. II. Title: Fulgoridae in the collection of the British
Museum (Homoptera) (Series)

NN 0027408 DI

VOLUME 405

QL1
P7
v.15
no.4
Nast, Janusz
Uwagi o niektórych Ledrinae (Homoptera, Jassidae). Warsaw, 1952.
[33]–42 p. [4] p. illus. 25 cm.
(Warsaw. Panstwowe Museum Zoologicsne. Annales, Tom XV, Nr. 4)
"Notes on some Ledrinae (Homoptera, Jassidae)."
In English.
Bibliography: p. 40.

1. Leaf-hopper (Series)

NN 0027409 DI

Nast, Johann, 1722–1807.
Historisch-critische-nachrichten von den sechs ersten teutschen Bibel-ausgaben, die zu Maynz, Strasburg und Augspurg vom jahr 1462. bis zum jahr 1477. sind gedrukt worden; aus der Herzoglich-würtembergischen consistorial-bibliothek zu Stuttgard, und aus schriftlichen beyträgen, nebst einer critischen anzeige aller übrigen vor Luthero theils wirklichen theils vermeintlichen Bibelausgaben, ans licht gestellt von M. Johannes Nast. Stuttgard, C. F. Cotta, 1767.
6 p. l., 100 p. 17ᶜᵐ.
1. Bible—Versions, German—Bibl. I. Stuttgart. K. Öffentliche bibliothek.

Library of Congress Z7770.N25
6–25039

NN 0027410 DLC

CF72
N269
Nast, Johann, 1722–1807.
Litterarische Nachricht von der hochteutschen Bibelübersezung welche vor mehr als 500. Jahren in den KlösternTeutschlands üblich war, auch von Erfindung der Buchdruckerkunst biss zum Jahr 1518. vierzehnmal gedruckt worden. Samt einer charakteristischen Beschreibung dieser vierzehn Ausgaben, verfasset von M.Johannes Nast ... Stuttgart,C.F.Cotta,1779.
1p.£.,xlvi,128p. 18cm.

NN C027411 NNUT PPeSchw

Bonaparte
Collection
No. 9618
[Nast, Johann] 1722–1807.
Der teütsche sprachforscher./ Allen liebhabern ihrer mutersprache zur prüfung vorgelegt... Stutgart,1777–78.
2v.in 1.

"Eine schwäbische antwort auf Domitors...rechtschreibung...von Fulda": v.1, p.137–146.
"Vom stummen h und e und dem teutschen accent," von Fulda: v.1, p.147–294.

NN 0027412 ICN MH ICU NjP CLU

4DF-
12
Nast, Johann Jakob Heinrich, 1751–1822.
Einleitung in die griechischen Kriegs- Alterthümer zum Gebrauch seiner Vorlesungen. Stuttgart, J.B. Mezler, 1780.
416 p.

NN 0027413 DLC-P4 ICU ICN

Z355.093
N189
Nast, Johann Jakob Heinrich, 1751–1822.
Römische Kriegsalterthümer aus ächten Quellen geschöpft. Ein Beitrag zur Aufklärung der römischen Taktik. Halle, J.J. Gebauer, 1782.
xxii, 456 p. fold. plates. 20cm.

By J.J. Heinrich and J.F. Hösch. cf. Holzmann Deut. Anon. Lex.
1. Military art and science. Early works to 1800. 2. Rome. Army. I. Hösch, Jakob Friedrich, ritter von, 1743–1841, jt. author. II. Title.

NN 0027414 MnU InU

Nast, Johann Jakob Heinrich, 1751–1822.
Ueber Homers sprache aus dem gesichtspunkt ihrer analogie mit der allgemeinen kinder- und volkssprache. Von Joh. Jak. Heinrich Nast ... Stuttgart, Johann Benedikt Metzler, 1801.
1 p.l., 84 p. 20ᶜᵐ.
"Kurzgefaster lebenslauf des jubel-greisen von ihm selbst aufgesezt": p.[59]–84.

1. Homerus—Language. 2. Nast family.

NN 0027415 ViU PU MH

NAST,Leo.
Das chikaneverbot im B.G.B. Rostock,1903.
85 p.
Inaug.-diss. - Rostock.

NN 0027416 MH-L ICRL

NAST,Leo,1885-
Die Berliner brauindustrie. Inaug.-diss., Heidelberg. Berlin,R.Trenkel,1916.
"Lebenslauf",at end.

NN 0027417 MH CtY NNU-W

Nast, G.L. Louis
see Nast, Louis.

308
Z
Box 679
Nast, Louis
... über die ἅπαξ λεγόμενα und seltenen poetischen wörter bei Äschylus, soweit ihre überlieferung in den handschriften nicht feststeht ... Gumbinnen, Krauseneck, 1882.
1 p. l., 22 p.

Programm, Königl. Friedrichsgymnasiums zu Gumbinnen.

1. Aeschylus.

NN 0027419 NNC MH ViU

GR203
.L5N2
NAST,LOUIS
Die volkslieder der Litauer,inhaltlich und musikalisch. Tilsit,O.v.Mauderode,1893. 52p.
Scores.

At head of title: Wissenschaftliche beilage zum bericht des K. Gymnasiums zu Tilsit,Ostern, 1893.
Programm nr. 16.

NN 0027420 InU OCl MH

Nast, Marcel Henri, 1882–
Code manuel des tribunaux pour enfants (commentaire de la Loi du 22 juillet 1912) par Marcel Nast ... et Marcel Kleine ... Paris, Librairie générale de droit et de jurisprudence, 1913.
2 p. l., 354 p., 1 l. 18½ᶜᵐ.
"Index bibliographique": p. [1]–6.
"Texte de la Loi du 22 juillet 1912": p. [303]–314.
"Appendice": p. [325]–354.

1. Juvenile courts—France. I. Kleine, Marcel, joint author. II. France. Laws, statutes, etc. III. Title.
31–31054

NN 0027421 DLC MH-L

Nast, Marcel Henri, 1882–
... La fonction de la jurisprudence dans la vie juridique française. (Conférence publique fait à l'Université de Strasbourg le 9 décembre 1921) Strasbourg, Imprimerie alsacienne, 1922.
13 p. 24ᶜᵐ.
Imprint covered by label of F. Pichon et Durand-Auzias, Paris.
23–5665

NN 0027422 DLC CtY-L

Nast, Marcel Henri, 1882-   L331.11 Q701
... Législation industrielle. Des conventions collectives relatives à l'organisation du travail. ... Par Marcel Nast, ... Paris, A. Rousseau, 1907.
[4], 360 p. 25½ᶜᵐ.
Thèse — Univ. de Paris.
"Bibliographie," p. 1–6.

NN 0027423 ICJ

DD801
.A397N3
Nast, Marcel Henri, 1882–
... Le malaise alsacien-lorrain. Paris, G. Crès, 1920.
64 p.

1. Alsace-Lorraine—Hist. 2. Alsace-Lorraine question.

NN 0027424 ICU MH

1865 -
Nast, Otto, Prakt. an d. Klinik: Aus d. Univ.-Ohrenkl. zu Tübingen. Die Behandlung der Kehlkopftuberkulose mit Hochfrequenzströmen speziell mit der sogenannten kalten Kaustik. Tübingen 1911: Laupp. 17 S. 8°
Tübingen, Med. Diss. v. 7. Sept. 1911, Ref. Perthes
[Geb. 19. Febr. 85 Kannstatt; Wohnort: Berlin; Staatsangeh.: Württemberg; Vorbildung: Gymn. Kannstatt Reife Juli 04; Studium: Tübingen 5, Freiburg i. B. 2, Berlin 1, Tübingen 2 S.; Coll. 28. Juli 11; Approb. 2. Aug. 11.]
[U 12. 4416]

NN 0027425 ICRL CtY DNLM

Nast, Paul H   comp. and ed.
Drillers handbook on rock

see under

Davey Compressor Company, Kent, Ohio.
Rock Drill Division.

NAST, ROBERT.
...Goldpsychose; oder, Ein Radikalmittel zur Behebung der Wirtschaftskrise... Zürich: C. Huber[, 1931]. 30 p. 22½cm.

640243A. 1. Gold [money], 1931.

NN 0027427 NN

Nast, Robert.
... Kosmische hypothesen; biologie des weltalls, mit einleitung über die relativität der logik. Leipzig, Bonanza aktien gesellschaft [°1928]
146 p., 1 l. 17½ᶜᵐ.

1. Cosmology—Curiosa and miscellany. I. Title.
29–4604
Library of Congress BD701.N3

NN 0027428 DLC

ML3925
.B17B7
1941
Nast, Roderich, 1894–   ed.
Brachvogel, Albert Emil, 1824–1878.
Friedemann Bach, ein roman aus der zeit Friedrichs des Grossen, von A. E. Brachvogel. Berlin, A. Weichert [1941]

Nast, Thomas, 1840–1902.
Catalogue of the art collection of the late Thomas Nast, consisting of arms and armor; Indian and oriental implements; brasses and bronzes; carved ivory and other cabinet objects; an important collection of European and oriental ceramics; medals; tapestries; buffalo and elk antlers; a few choice pieces of antique furniture, etc., etc. Also a beautiful set of the "Treasure of Hildesheim." To be sold at auction ... April 16, 17 and 18, 1907 ... by the Merwin-Clayton sales company ... [New York] 1907]
30 p. 22½ᶜᵐ.
489 items.
1. Art objects—Private collections. I. Merwin sales company, New York.
42–49006
Library of Congress NK530.N3

NN 0027430 DLC

VOLUME 405

NC
1429
.N27
A5

Nast, Thomas, 1840–1902.
Catalogue of the library, correspondence, and original cartoons of the late Thomas Nast ... to be sold at auction ... by the Merwin-Clayton Sales Company ... ₍New York, 1906?-07?₎
2 v. in 1. illus., port. 25 cm.
Vol.2 has title: Catalogue of original drawings and cartoons of the late Thomas Nast, and a collection of photographic portraits.
First portion sold Apr.2-3,1906; 2d,Feb.19-20,1907.
I.Merwin Sales Company,New York.

NN 0027431   MiU OrU MH

Nast, Thomas, 1840–1902.
Thomas Nast's Christmas drawings for the human race. New York, Harper & brothers, 1890.
3 p. l., front., illus., 60 pl. 29ᵐᵐ.
Illus. t.-p.

1. Drawings, Reproductions of. 2. Christmas.

Library of Congress   NC1075.N3
                                      11-20965

NN 0027432   DLC WaS NcD MWA CLU MsU OC1 MH

Nast, Thomas, 1840–1902, comp.
The Civil war scrapbook of Thomas Nast containing 234 pencil sketches, 32 wash drawings, 638 photographs, 10 woodcut proofs of his work. New York, 186-?
1 v. illus. 46 cm.
"Several plates and sketches were removed & not replaced for illustrations in Life of Nast by Paine".

NN 0027433   RPB

Nast, Thomas, 1840–1902.
₍A collection of specimens of the work of Thomas Nast. New York, 1871-72₎
33 pieces in 1 v. plates (mostly mounted) 45 1/2 x 33 1/2cm.
Detached from Harper's weekly, 1871-72.
Includes a portrait and biographical sketch of the artist, detached from Harper's weekly, May 11, 1867.

1. Etchings. 2. Caricatures and cartoons—U. S. I. Harper's   weekly.

NN 0027434   MB

Nast, Thomas, 1840–1902, illus.
₍Locke, David Ross₎ 1833-1888.
Ekkoes from Kentucky. By Petroleum V. Nasby ₍pseud.₎ ... Bein a perfect record uv the ups, downs, and experiences uv the Dimocrisy, doorin the eventful year 1867, ez seen by a naturalized Kentuckian. Illustrated by Thomas Nast. Boston, Lee and Shepard, 1868.

Nast, Thomas, 1840–1902, illus.
₍Pullen, Henry William₎ 1836-1903.
The fight at Dame Europa's school: showing how the German boy thrashed the French boy; and how the English boy looked on. With 33 illustrations by Thomas Nast. New York, F. B. Felt & co. ₍1871₎

Nast, Thomas, 1840–1902, illus.
Shaw, Henry Wheeler, 1818-1885.
Josh Billings: his works, complete. (Four volumes in one.) With one hundred illustrations, by Thomas Nast and others and a biographical introduction. New York, G. W. Dillingham; London, S. Low, son & co., 1888.

Nast, Thomas, 1840–1902.
Lincoln entering Richmond
see under title

Nast, Thomas, 1840–1902.
Little Mac: how he captured Manassas
see under title

Nast, Thomas, 1840–1902, illus.
₍Pullen, Charles Henry₎
Miss Columbia's public school; or, Will it blow over? By a cosmopolitan. With 72 illustrations by Thomas Nast ... New York, F. B. Felt & co., 1871.

Nast, Thomas, 1840–1902, illus.
Locke, David Ross, 1833-1888.
The moral history of America's life-struggle. By D. R. Locke (Petroleum V. Nasby) Illustrated by Th. Nast. Introductory chapter by Hon. Charles Sumner ... Boston, I. N. Richardson and company; ₍etc., etc.,₎ ʼ1874₎

Nast, Thomas, 1840–1902, illus.
Nast's illustrated almanac. 1871-
New York, McLoughlin bros., ʼ1870; Harper & brothers, ʼ1871-

Microfilm
36629
PZ

Nast, Thomas, 1840–1902, illus.
Dickens, Charles, 1812-1870.
Pictures from Italy. Sketches by Boz. and American notes. By Charles Dickens. Illustrated by Thomas Nast and Arthur B. Frost. New York, Harper & brothers. 1877.

Nast, Thomas, 1840–1902, illus.
U. S. President, 1885-1889 (Cleveland)
The President's message, 1887, with illustrations by Thomas Nast. New York and London, G. P. Putnam's sons, 1888.

Nast, Thomas, 1840–1902, illus.
FOR OTHER EDITIONS
SEE MAIN ENTRY
Wells, David Ames, 1828-1898.
Robinson Crusoe's money; or, The remarkable financial fortunes and misfortunes of a remote island community. By David A. Wells ... With illustrations by Thomas Nast ... New York, P. Smith, 1931.

₍Nast, Thomas₎ 1840–1902.
₍Scrapbook of caricatures attacking Tammany₎ clipped from periodicals and mounted. New York? 1900?₎
1 v. 39cm.

1. Caricatures and cartoons. 2. Tammany hall. 3. Tammany society, or Columbian order.

NN 0027446   NNC

Nast, Thomas, 1840–1902, illus.
₍Shaw, Henry Wheeler₎ 1818-1885.
Selections from the writings of Josh Billings ₍pseud.₎ or; Proverbial philosophy of wit and humor; introduction by Carl Purlington ₍!₎ Rollins ... illustrations by Thomas Nast ... Athens, Ga., K. DeRenne, 1940.

Nast, Thomas, 1840–1902, illus.
Shapley, Rufus Edmonds, 1840-
Solid for Mulhooly; a political satire by Rufus E. Shapley ... New ed. with original illustrations by Thomas Nast. Philadelphia, Gebbie & co., 1889.

Nast, Thomas, 1840-1902.
The struggles of Petroleum V. Nasby
see under Locke, David Ross, 1833-1888.

Nast, Thomas, 1840–1902, illus.
₍Locke, David Ross₎ 1833-1888.
"Swingin round the cirkle", by Petroleum V. Nasby ₍pseud.₎ ... His ideas of men, politics, and things as set forth in his letters to the public press. Illustrated by Thomas Nast. Boston, Lee and Shepard, 1888.

Lilly
NC 1075
.N3 T58

NAST,THOMAS,1840-1902
Time, merry christmas for all nations. [n.p.,1889?]
broadside. illus. 53.5 x 34.1 cm.

Illus. engraved "Th: Nast. 1889."

NN 0027451   InU

Nast, Thomas, 1840–1902, illus.
Franklin, Allan.
The trail of the tiger, being an account of Tammany from 1789; the society of St. Tammany, or Columbian order; Tammany hall; the organization; and the sway of the bosses. ₍By₎ Allan Franklin. ₍New York?₎ 1928.

q741
N18t

Nast, Thomas, 1840–1902.
₍Two original pen and ink drawings₎
Both are signed by the artist: Th: Nast.
One has title "Tweed, foreman of Big six"; the other (in a frame with label "Th. Nast") has, as part of its composition, the legend "'Home rule.' (Far off.) What he said and what he did not say. Portland, Maine".
Presented, in 1937, to the University of Illinois Library, by John N. Chester, class of 1891.

1. Tweed, William Marcey, 1823-1878. I. Chester, John Needels,   1864-

NN 0027453   IU

PZ8
.3
.Y33
1880z
Rare Bk

Nast, Thomas, 1840–1902, illus.
FOR OTHER EDITIONS
SEE MAIN ENTRY
Yankee Doodle. ₍New York, McLoughlin Bros., 188-?₎

226.2
N269a

Nast, William, 1807-1899.
Allgemeine Einleitung über die Echtheit und göttliche Autorität des neutestamentlichen kanons, das Verhältniss des Neuen Testaments zum Alten Testament und die richtigen Grundsätze richtiger Schriftauslegung. Cincinnati, Jennings and Graham, 1860.
158 p.
1. Gospels--Evidences, authority, etc. I. Title.

NN 0027455   TxDaM

Nast, William, 1807-1899.
Das biblische Christenthum und seine gegensätze, nebst betrachtungen ueber einige zu wenig beachtete schriftwahrheiten... Cincinnati, 1883.

NN 0027456   ODW

BT201
.N269c

Nast, William, 1807-1899.
Christologische Betrachtungen nach Dr. van Oosterzee's "Bild Christi." Cincinnati, Hitchcock & Walden [1866?]
275p.

1. Jesus Christ. I. Title.

NN 0027457   TNJ-R

VOLUME 405

232
N2
Nast, William, 1807–1899.
    Christologische Betrachtungen nach Dr. van Oosterzee's "Bild Christi." Cincinnati, Poe & Hitchcock, 1867.
    275 p.

    I. Oosterzee, Johannes Jacobus van, 1817–1882. Bild Christi.

NN   0027458   TxDaM-P   ODW

Nast, William, 1807–1899.
    A commentary of the Gospels of Matthew and Mark, critical, doctrinal, and homiletical, embodying for popular use and edification the results of German and English exegetical literature, and designed to meet the difficulties of modern skepticism. With a general introduction, treating of the genuineness, authenticity, historic verity, and inspiration of the gospel records, and of the harmony and chronology of the Gospel history. By William Nast, D. D. Cincinnati, Poe & Hitchcock, 1864.
    760 p. front. (port.) 27½ cm.

    The author's revision of the original German edition, published in "lieferungen," 1860–61, under title: Kritisch-praktischer commentar über das Neue Testament.
    The "general introduction" also published separately in 1866, under title: The Gospel records.
    No more published.

    1. Bible. N. T. Gospels—Evidences, authority, etc. 2. Bible. N. T. Matthew—Commentaries. 3. Bible. N. T. Mark—Commentaries.

    BS2555.N27   226.2   39—18077

NN   0027460   DLC PPPD ODW P

Nast, William, 1807–1899.
    A commentary on the Gospels of Matthew and Mark, critical, doctrinal, and homiletical, embodying for popular use and edification the results of German and English exegetical literature, and assigned to meet the difficulties of modern skepticism with a general introduction... Cincinnati, Poe, 1865.
    760 p.

NN   0027461   OO

Nast, William, 1807–1899.
    A commentary on the Gospels of Matthew and Mark, critical, doctrinal, and homiletical, embodying for popular use and edification the results of German and English exegetical literature, and designed to meet the difficulties of modern skepticism. With a general introduction, treating of the genuineness, authenticity, historic verity, and inspiration of the gospel records, and of the harmony and chronology of the gospel history. By William Nast, D. D. Cincinnati, Poe & Hitchcock, 1867.
    760 p. front. (port.) 27½".

    The author's revision of the original German edition, published in "lieferungen," 1860–61, under title: Kritisch-praktischer commentar über das Neue Testament.
    The "general introduction" also published separately in 1866, under title: The Gospel records.
    No more published.

NN   0027463   NRCR

Nast, William, 1807–1899.
    Deutsches gesangbuch der Bisch. Methodisten-kirche
      see under   Methodist Episcopal church.

Nast, William, 1807–1899.
    The Gospel records: their genuineness, authenticity, historic verity, and inspiration, with some preliminary remarks on the Gospel history. By William Nast, D. D. A rev. ed. of the author's general introduction to the first volume of his Commentary on the New Testament. Cincinnati, Poe & Hitchcock, 1866.
    373 p. 19½".

NN   0027465   MiU KyWA WaTC OrU NIC OO ODW MiAlbC

Nast, William, 1807–1899.
    The Gospel records: their genuineness, authenticity, historic verity, and inspiration, with some preliminary remarks on the Gospel history. By William Nast, D. D. A rev. ed. of the author's general introduction to the first volume of his Commentary on the New Testament. Cincinnati, Hitchcock & Walden, 1868.
    373 p. 19½".

    1. Bible. N. T. Gospels—Evidences, authority, etc. 2. Bible—Evidences, authority, etc.—N. T. Gospels. I. Title.

    Library of Congress   BS2555.N3   20–16827 Revised

NN   0027466   DLC NcD

NAST, William, 1807–1899.
    The Greek verb taught in a simple and fundamental manner according to the Greek tables of Friederich Thiersch. With alterations, additions and selections from Buttman. Larger grammar. Gambier, Ohio, 1835.

    pp. 46.

NN   0027467   MH KyLx PBL

Nast, William, 1807–1899.
    Der grössere Katechismus für die deutschen Gemeinden der Bisch. Methodisten-Kirche
      see under   Methodist Episcopal Church.

F
83941
.6128
NAST, WILLIAM, 1807–1899.
    Der hundertjährige Bestand des amerikanischen Methodismus. Ein Vortrag, gehalten bei der Eröffnung des Jubiläumsjahres. Nebst einer Abhandlung über die Stellung des Methodismus in geistiger Ausbildung und höheren Lehranstalten von Rev. H. Liebhart. Cincinnati, Poe & Hitchcock, 1866.
    128p. 18cm.

NN   0027469   ICN

Nast, William, 1807–1899.
    Der kleinere Katechismus für die deutschen gemeinden der Bisch. Methodisten-Kirche ...
      see under   Methodist Episcopal church.

226.2
N269k
Nast, William, 1807–1899.
    Kritisch-praktischer Commentar über das Neue Testament für die Bedürfnisse unserer zeit... Cincinnati, L. Swormstedt & A. Poe, 1860.
    1 v. (664 p.)
    CONTENTS. --Bd. 1. Die Evangelien von Matthäus und Markus. No more published.
    1. Gospels—Evidences, authority, etc. 2. Matthew—Commentaries. 3. Mark—Commentaries.

NN   0027471   TxDaM IEG ODW CtY NcD

F
83941
.6129
NAST, WILLIAM, 1807–1899.
    Kritisch-praktischer Kommentar über das Neue Testament für die Bedürfnisse unserer Zeit. Nach den neueren exegetischen Werken deutscher englischer Theologen bearbeitet. Cincinnati, Hitchcock & Walden, 1872.
    2v. in 1. port. 27cm.

    Originally published in parts, 1860–61.
    Contents.--1. Bd. Die Evangelien von Matthäus und Markus.--2. Bd. Das Evangelium nach Lukas.

NN   0027472   ICN KyWAT

Nast, William, 1807–1899.
    The larger catechism ...
      see under   Methodist Episcopal Church.

Nast, William, 1807–1899.
    Das leben und wirken des Johannes Wesley und seiner haupt-mitarbeiter. Bearbeitet nach den besten englischen quellen von Wilhelm Nast ... Cincinnati, L. Swormstedt & J. H. Power, 1852.
    300 p. front. (port.) 18½".

    1. Wesley, John, 1703–1791. 2. Methodism.

                                  37–12960
    Library of Congress   BX8495.W5N3
                            [2]   922.742

NN   0027474   DLC OC KyWAT CtY-D ODW

287.111
N269l
Nast, William, 1807–1899.
    Das Leben und Wirken des Johannes Wesley und seiner Haupt-Mitarbeiter. Cincinnati, L. Swormstedt & Poe, 1855.
    300 p.

    1. Wesley, John, 1703–1791. 2. Methodism.

NN   0027475   TxDaM

BY88
.S9N26
Nast, William   1807–1899.
    Mindre katekesen. Lärobok för religions-undervisningen. Öfversättning. Göteborg, Boktryckeriet Wesleyana [1874]
    63p. 16cm.

    1. Catechisms--Swedish. 2. Methodist church--Catechisms and creeds--Swedish. 3. Methodists, Swedish. I. Title.

NN   0027476   IEG

RS
N189pG
Nast, William, 1807–1899.
    Philosophie des erlösungsplanes. Ein buch für unsere zeit von einem amerikanischen burger. Für das deutsche publikum bearb. nach der neuesten englischen ausg., und mit analysirenden fragen über jedes kapitel versehen, von W. Nast. Cincinnati, Poe & Hitchcock [vorwort 1858]
    226 p. 20 cm.

NN   0027477   CtY-D PU

Nast, William, 1807–1899.
    Wurst, Raimund Jakob.
    R. J. Wurst's deutsche sprachdenklehre. Zum selbstunterricht in der muttersprache eingerichtet und mit einer erklärung der gebrauchs-methode versehen von Wilhelm Nast. Cincinnati, L. Swormstedt & A. Poe, 1852.

Nast, William, 1807–1899.
    Sammlung von geistlichen Liedern für kirchlichen und häuslichen Gottesdienst
      see under   Methodist Episcopal Church.

Nast, William, 1807–1899.
    The smaller catechism
      see under   Methodist Episcopal Church.

BX
8335
.N3
Nast, William, 1807–1899.
    Större katekesen, af W. Nast. Lärobok för religions-undervisning. Bearbetad af Albert Ericson. Chicago, Swedish M.E. Book Concerns förlag [förord 1869]
    vii, 120 p. 13 cm.

    1. Methodist Episcopal Church--Catechisms and creeds. I. Ericson, Albert, 1840–1910, tr. II. Title.

NN   0027481   MnHi

VOLUME 405

BT720
.F65

Nast, William, 1807–1899.

Fletcher, John William, 1729–1785.
Der verdorbene und verlorene zustand des menschen, bewiesen in einer appellation an thatsachen u. die gesunde vernunft. Nebst einer antwort an diejenigen, welche fragen: was sollen wir thun, um selig zu werden? Verfasst von Johannes Fletscher ... und aus dem englischen übersetzt von Wilh. Nast ... Cincinnati, J. F. Wright und L. Swormstedt, 1841.

Nast, William, 1807–1899, *ed.*
Was ist und will der methodismus? Beantwortet in einer sammlung von abhandlungen und gesprächen. Herausgegeben von Wilhelm Nast. Cincinnati, L. Swormstedt & A. Poe, 1853.
[224] p. 19[cm].
Various pagings.
On cover: Traktat ausgabe.

1. Methodist church—Doctrinal and controversial works. I. Title.
38-23454

Library of Congress   BX8331.N3

NN   0027483   DLC ODW CtY IEG PPLT

Nast, William H
Original drawings by American artists from the collection of William H. Nast of Denver, Colo., with additions. To be sold at public auction, Thursday and Friday evenings, April 26th and 27th, 1934, at 8 o'clock. Exhibition from Monday, April 16th, 1934, until time of sale. New York city, Plaza book auction corp. [1934]
43 p. illus. 24[cm].
314 items; priced in manuscript.

1. Drawings, American. 2. Drawings—Private collections.
44-15519

Library of Congress   NC105.N3
[2]   741.9

NN   0027484   DLC PPPM

NAST-KOLB, Adolf.
Das recht auf ergänzung des pflichtteils nach bürgerlichem gesetzbuch verglichen mit der gemeinrechtlichen querela inofficiosae donationis. Rostock, 1902.

Inaug.-diss.- Rostock.

NN   0027485   MH-L ICRL

Nast-Kolb, Alban.
Zwei faelle von retrouterinem subperitonealem tumor. Tuebingen, 1899.
Inaug.-diss. - Tuebingen.

NN   0027486   ICRL DNLM

AC
831

Nast-Kolb, Hermann, 1914–
Tilgung der Schuld und ausgleichung in den fällen der sogenannten unechten gesamtschulden. ... Tübingen, 1939.   116 p.
Inaug. Diss. - Tübingen, 1939.
Lebenslauf.
Schrifttum.

NN   0027487   ICRL

Nast-Kolb, Walter, 1900–
... Ueber laterale Halsfisteln und Halscysten branchiogenen Ursprungs ... Coburg, 1934.
Inaug.-diss. - Heidelberg.
Lebenslauf.
"Literaturverzeichnis": p. 21-22.

NN   0027488   CtY

359.05
N189

NAST. v.1-3. Nov.1943–
U.S. Naval Air Station.
1 v. illus. 24cm.
Tillamook, Oro.

No more published?

1. Air bases, Military.   Por soc oto.
I. U.S. Naval Air Station, Tillamook, Oro.

NN   0027489   OrU

Nasta, A.
...Reforma agrară şi problemele agricole ale viitorului. (Conferinţă ţinută în ianuarie 1926, sub auspiciile Minist. agric. şi dom. la casa centrală a împroprietăririi) Editat de Ministerul agriculturii şi domeniilor. Direcţiunea statistici şi publicaţiilor. [Bucureşti: I. E. Torouţiu,] 1926.   17 p.   8°.

1. Agriculture—Economics—Rumania.   2. Rumania. Agriculturei şi domeniilor, Ministerul.
N.Y.P.L.   August 14, 1928

NN   0027490   NN DNAL

NASTA, Alexander, 1886–
Der Maisbau in Rumänien. Weida i.Th.1909. 110 p.

Leipzig, Phil. Diss.

NN   0027491   MH PU ICRL CtY

W 6
P 3

NASTA, Marius
Cum respirăm. Ed. 2. Bucureşti, Editura de Stat pentru Literatură Ştiinţifică, 1954.
39 p. illus. (Colecţia Societăţii pentru Răspândirea Ştiinţei şi Culturii, 60)
1. Respiration

NN   0027492   DNLM

Nasta, Philip A.
Practical scene design and stagecraft for the dance. [New York] 1951. 37 l. diagrs. 29cm.
"Submitted in partial fulfillment for the course number 280.278, Administrative problems of the dance in education, School of education [N.Y.U.]"

1. Ballet—Scenery. 2. Stage scenery. 3. Scenery—Design.

NN   0027493   NN

W 4
M61
1953

NASTA CASTAN, Oscar
Informe médico sanitario de la villa de Coatzintla, Veracruz. Pelagra en los niños. México, 1953.
67 p.
Tesis - Univ. de México.
1. Public health - Mexico - Veracruz (State)

NN   0027494   DNLM

Nastasi, Johann.
Die lehre der nebensätze im Cligés von Chrestien de Troyes ... Linz, 1894.

NN   0027495   NjP

Nastasi, Johann.
Monographie sur Cligés de Chrestien de Troyes. Von Prof. Joh. Nastasi. Linz, In Selbstverlage der Linzer Handels-Akademie, 1893.
42 p. O. (Elfter Jahresbericht der öffentlichen Handels-Akademie in Linz a.d. Donau. Erstattet von Dor. A. Effenberger)
Contains also: Schulnachrichten von dem Director.

NN   0027496   NcD

NASTASI, Johann.
Monographie sur Cligés de Chrestien de Troves. [Progr.] Linz, 1893.

pp.28.

NN   0027497   MH NjP NcD

Nastassievitch, Douchan, 1897–
... Contribution à l'étude du syndrome de Raynaud chez le nourrisson ... Bordeaux, 1922. 25.5 cm.
Thèse - Univ. de Bordeaux.

NN   0027498   CtY

DR386
.P8

Nastasijević, Dragomir, ed.

Putnik.
Beograd. [Editor: Dragomir Nastasijević. Texts: Branko Popović et al. Translation: Milivoje V. Isailovic. Beograd, 1952]

Nastasijević, Momčilo, 1894–1938.
Из тамног вилајета. Београд, С. Б. Цвијановић, 1927.
121 p. 21 cm. (Модерна библиотека, 31)

I. Title.   *Title transliterated: Iz tamnog vilajeta.*

PG1418.N319   38-15908 rev°

NN   0027500   DLC

Настава географије у средњој школи; избор чланака. Превод с руског. [У ред. Радована Теодосића]. Београд, Знање, 1949.
255 p. 22 cm. (Педагошка библиотека, 34)
Includes bibliographical references.

1. Geography—Study and teaching (Secondary) 2. Geography—Study and teaching—Russia. I. Teodosić, Radovan, ed.
Title romanized: Nastava geografije u srednjoj školi.

G73.N317   74-275197

NN   0027501   DLC

Настава и васпитање; часопис за педагошка питања.
Београд, Педагошко друштво НР Србије.
v. illus., ports., music. 24 cm. bimonthly.

1. Education—Period. 2. Education—Yugoslavia—Period.
I. Pedagoško drustvo Narodne Republike Srbije.
Title transliterated: Nastava i vaspitanje.

L51.N35   58-25717

NN   0027502   DLC

Наставление для лиц, занимающихся гидрографическими работами. Перевод съ англійскаго. Санктпетербургъ, Въ тип. Морскаго министерства, 1863.
43 p. 24 cm.

1. Hydrography—Handbooks, manuals, etc.
Title transliterated: Nastavlenie dlîâ liîs, zanimaîushchikhsîâ gidrograficheskimi rabotami.

GB665.N28   65-58822

NN   0027503   DLC

Наставление для производства тригонометрическихъ работъ. С.-Петербургъ, Воен. тип. [въ зданіи Глав. Штаба] 1889–
v. illus. 29 cm.
Cover title.

1. Triangulation—Handbooks, manuals, etc.
Title romanized: Nastavlenie dlîâ proizvodstva trigonometricheskikh rabot.

TA583.N38   72-211516

NN   0027504   DLC

HQ760
.B524
Rare Bk
Coll

[Bet͡skoĭ, Ivan Ivanovich] 1704–1795.
Краткое наставление, выбранное изъ лучшихъ авторовъ, съ нѣкоторыми физическими примѣчаніями о воспитаніи дѣтей отъ рожденія ихъ до юношества. Въ Санктпетербургѣ, При Шляхетномъ сухопутномъ кадетскомъ корпусѣ. 1766.

VOLUME 405

Наставленіе къ добыванію нашатыря и другихъ амміачныхъ солей, употребляемыхъ въ общежитіи и промышленности. Санктпетербургъ ¡Въ Тип. Штаб. Отдѣл. Корпус. внутр. стражи¡ 1856.
52 p. 18 cm.
Bound with Наставленіе къ разведенію и уборкѣ хмѣля. Санктпетербургъ, 1856; Наставленіе къ устройству повозочныхъ и тележныхъ колесъ и осей. Санктпетербургъ, 1856; Наставленіе къ разведенію марены. Санктпетербургъ, 1856; Наставленіе къ воспитанію шелковичныхъ червей домашнимъ образомъ. Санктпетербургъ, 1856; Наставленіе къ разведенію и содержанію канареекъ. Санктпетербургъ, 1856; Наставленіе къ разведенію и содержанію камелій. Санктпетербургъ, 1856; Наставленіе къ разведенію ананасовъ. Санктпетербургъ, 1856; and Совѣты любителямъ цвѣтоводства. Санктпетербургъ, 1856.
Title romanized: Nastavlenie k dobyvaniiu nashatyrfa.

QD181.N15N3   72-212989

NN 0027506 DLC

Наставленіе къ разведенію ананасовъ. Санктпетербургъ ¡Въ Тип. Штаба Отдѣл. корпус. внутр. стражи¡ 1856.
45 p. illus. 18 cm.
Bound with Наставленіе къ добыванію нашатыря. Санктпетербургъ, 1856.
"Прибавленіе къ журналу Труды И. В. Э. общества."

1. Pineapple.   I. Vol'noe ékonomicheskoe obshchestvo, Leningrad. Trudy.
Title romanized: Nastavlenie k razvedenifu ananasov.

QD181.N15N3   72-212991

NN 0027507 DLC

Наставленіе къ разведенію и содержанію камелій. Санктпетербургъ ¡Въ Тип. Штаба Отдѣл. корпус. внутр. стражи¡ 1856.
91 p. 18 cm.
Bound with Наставленіе къ добыванію нашатыря. Санктпетербургъ, 1856.
"Прибавленіе къ журналу Труды И. В. Э. общества."

1. Camellia.   I. Vol'noe ékonomicheskoe obshchestvo, Leningrad. Trudy.
Title romanized: Nastavlenie k razvedenifu i soderzhanifu kamelii.

QD181.N15N3   72-212992

NN 0027508 DLC

Наставленіе къ разведенію и содержанію канареекъ. Санктпетербургъ ¡Въ Тип. Штаба Отдѣл. корпус. внутр. стражи¡ 1856.
59 p. 18 cm.
Bound with Наставленіе къ добыванію нашатыря. Санктпетербургъ, 1856.
"Прибавленіе къ журналу Труды И. В. Э. общества."

1. Canaries.   I. Vol'noe ékonomicheskoe obshchestvo, Leningrad. Trudy.
Title romanized: Nastavlenie k razvedenifu i soderzhanifu kanareek.

QD181.N15N3   72-212993

NN 0027509 DLC

Наставленіе къ разведенію марены, красильной гречки, шафрана и красильной цервы. Санктпетербургъ ¡Въ Тип. Штаб. Отдѣл. корпус. внутр. стражи¡ 1856.
62 p. 18 cm.
Bound with Наставленіе къ добыванію нашатыря. Санктпетербургъ, 1856.
"Прибавленіе къ журналу Труды И. В. Э. общества."

1. Dye plants.   I. Vol'noe ékonomicheskoe obshchestvo, Leningrad. Trudy.
Title romanized: Nastavlenie k razvedenifu mareny.

QD181.N15N3   72-212995

NN 0027510 DLC

Наставленіе къ разведенію и уборкѣ хмѣля, преимущественно въ средней полосѣ Россіи. Санктпетербургъ ¡Въ Тип. Штаб. Отдѣл. корпус. внутр. стражи¡ 1856.
40 p. 18 cm.
Bound with Наставленіе къ добыванію нашатыря. Санктпетербургъ, 1856.
"Прибавленіе къ журналу Труды И. В. Э. общества."

1. Hops—Russia.   I. Vol'noe ékonomicheskoe obshchestvo, Leningrad. Trudy.
Title romanized: Nastavlenie k razvedenifu i uborkfe khmelfa.

QD181.N15N3   72-212994

NN 0027511 DLC

Наставленіе къ устройству повозочныхъ и тележныхъ колесъ и осей. Санктпетербургъ ¡Въ Тип. Штаб. Отдѣл. корпус. внутр. стражи¡ 1856.
62 p. illus. 18 cm.
Bound with Наставленіе къ добыванію нашатыря. Санктпетербургъ, 1856.
"Прибавленіе къ журналу Труды И. В. Э. общества."

1. Wheels. 2. Axles.   I. Vol'noe ékonomicheskoe obshchestvo, Leningrad. Trudy.
Title romanized: Nastavlenie k ustroistvu povozochnykh i tel'ezhnykh koles i osei.

QD181.N15N3   72-212987

NN 0027512 DLC

Наставленіе къ воспитанію шелковичныхъ червей домашнимъ образомъ и къ разведенію шелковичныхъ или тутовыхъ деревьевъ. Санктпетербургъ ¡Въ Тип. Штаб. Отдѣл. корпус. внутр. стражи¡ 1856.
83 p. 18 cm.
Bound with Наставленіе къ добыванію нашатыря. Санктпетербургъ, 1856.
"Прибавленіе къ журналу Труды И. В. Э. общества."

1. Silkworm breeding. 2. Mulberry.   I. Vol'noe ékonomicheskoe obshchestvo, Leningrad. Trudy.
Title romanized: Nastavlenie k vospitanifu shelkovichnykh chervei.

QD181.N15N3   72-212990

NN 0027513 DLC

Наставленіе моему крестнику, поступившему въ военную службу въ рядовые. Москва, Въ Унив. тип., 1840.
27 p. 18 cm.

1. Soldiers. 2. Conduct of life. *Early works to 1900.*
Title transliterated: Nastavlenie moemu krestniku.

U19.N35   57-51425 ‡

NN 0027514 DLC

UG635 .R9A542   Nastavlenie po ékspluatat͡sii ... aérodromov voenno-vozdushnykh sil.
Russia *(1923-   U. S. S. R.) Ministerstvo oborony.*
Наставленіе по эксплуатаціи, содержанію и ремонту аэродромовъ военно-воздушныхъ силъ Совѣтской Арміи. Москва, Воен. изд-во, 1953.

Наставленіе правильно состязаться съ раскольниками, сочиненное въ Рязанской семинаріи по предписанію покойнаго преосвященнаго Симона, Епископа Рязанскаго и Шацкаго. Санктпетербургъ, Въ Сѷнодальной тип., 1826.
ix, 26, 362, 20 p. 20 cm.

1. Raskalniks.   I. Simon, Abp. of Rfazan', d. 1804. II. Rfazanskafa dukhovnafa seminarifa.
Title romanized: Nastavlenie pravil'no sostfazat'sfa s raskol'nikami.

BX601.N37   72-209469

NN 0027516 DLC

Nastavlenie RKKA.
Russia *(1923-   U. S. S. R.) Narodnyi komissariat oborony.*
... Наставленіе РККА; боевое примѣненіе артиллерійской авіаціи. 4. изд. Москва, Военное издательство Народнаго комиссаріата обороны Союза ССР, 1942.

Наставленіе знатному молодому господину; или, Воображеніе о свѣтскомъ человѣкѣ. Переведено съ французскаго на россійскій языкъ Иваномъ Муравьевымъ. Въ Санктпетербургѣ, Печатано при Артиллерійскомъ и инженерномъ шляхетномъ кадетскомъ корпусѣ, иждивеніемъ тип. содержателя Х. Ф. Клеена, 1778.
48 p. 20 cm.
L. C. copy imperfect: t. p. mutilated.
1. Conduct of life. *Early works to 1800.*   1. Murav'ev-Apostol, Ivan Matveevich, 1765-1851, tr.
Title transliterated: Nastavlenie znatnomu molodomu gospodinu.

BJ1568.R8N3   56-52376

NN 0027518 DLC

Nastavni plan i program predvojničke obuke za niže stručne škole (škole učenika u privredi i industrijske škole) ¡Zagreb¡ 1952.
22 p. 17 cm.

1. Military education—Yugoslavia.

U629.N3   59-31796 ‡

NN 0027519 DLC

Nastavni planovi i programi sa pravilnicima i obrascima za zavode i škole za nedovoljno razvijenu, gluvonemu i slepu decu. Beograd, Dřž. štamparija Kraljevine Jugoslavije, 1932.
165 p. forms. 25 cm.
At head of title: Министарство просвете Краљевине Југославије.

1. Blind—Education—Yugoslavia. 2. Mentally handicapped children—Education—Yugoslavia.   1. Yugoslavia. Ministarstvo prosvete.
Title romanized: Nastavni planovi i programi sa pravilnicima i obrascima za zavode i škole za nedovoljno razvijenu, gluvonemu i slepu decu.

HV2065.5.N35   78-536153

NN 0027520 DLC

Nastavni planovi i programi za industrijske škole i škole učenika u privredi; predmeti opšteg i opšteg stručnog obrazovanja. Derventa, Stamparija Gradskog narodnog odbora ¡19-?¡
102 p. 20 cm.

1. Vocational education—Bosnia and Herzegovina—Curricula.

LC1047.B63N3   68-129379

NN 0027521 DLC

Наставни програми за Виша педагошка школа. Скопје, 1953.
117 p. 20 cm.
At head of title: Совет за просвета, наука и култура на НРМ.

1. Skopje, Yugoslavia. Viša pedagoška škola.   I. Skopje, Yugoslavia. Viša pedagoška škola.
Title romanized: Nastavni programi za Viša pedagoška škola.

LB2122.56.N37   73-207221

NN 0027522 DLC

Nastavni vjesnik; stručni i pedagoški časopis.
Zagreb.
Apply for vol. desired   v. 24 cm. bimonthly.
Began publication in 1892. Cf. Union list of serials.
Issued by the Društvo hrvatskih srednješkolskih profesora.

1. Education—Period.   I. Društvo hrvatskih srednješkolskih profesora.

L51.N37   61-56660

NN 0027523 DLC MH KU IU

Nastelski, Karl.
Der aufrechnungsvertrag und die begruendung und ausschliessung des rechts zur aufrechnung durch vertrag. (Auszug)
[n.d., n.p.]

NN 0027524 ICRL

Naster, Paul.
... L'Asie Mineure et l'Assyrie aux VIIIe et VIIe siècles av. J.-C. d'après les annales des rois assyriens, par Paul Naster ... Louvain, Bureaux du Muséon, 1938.
xviii, 119, ¡1¡ p. incl. map. 27cm. (Bibliothèque du Muséon. 8)
At head of title: Université de Louvain. Institut orientaliste. Universiteit te Leuven. Institut voor orientalisme.
The author's thesis, Louvain.
"Bibliographie et liste des abréviations": p. ¡xi¡-xviii.

1. Asia Minor—Hist. 2. Assyria—Hist. 3. Assyria—Hist.—Sources.   I. Louvain. Université catholique. Institut orientaliste. II. Title.

Library of Congress   DS155.N38   39-16134
——— Copy 2.   ¡2¡   939.3

NN 0027525 DLC CU OCU ICU NN

VOLUME 405

4PJ 201 Naster, Paul
Chrestomathie accadienne. Louvain, Bureaux du Muséon, 1941.
104 p.

(Université de Louvain. Institut orientaliste. Bibliothèque du Muséon, v. 12)

InU CU ICU NNUT MH RPB NNC MiU
NN 0027526 DLC-P4 OCH NIC OU NjP NN NcD GEU-T

---

331 N189m Nasti, Agostino.
Movimento operaio e socialismo. Milano, Treves [1934]
viii, 85p. 25cm. (Quaderni dell'Istituto nazionale fascista di cultura, ser. 3 [no.] 10)
Bibliographical footnotes.

1. Labor and laboring classes. 2. Socialism. I. Title. II. Series: Istituto nazionale di cultura fascista. Quaderni, ser. 3, no.10.

NN 0027527 TxU CaBVaU CtY NN

Nastic', Đord̵e, 1884-1919.
... Finale ... Budapest, Ausgabe des verfassers, 1908.
91 p. 24ᶜᵐ.
At head of title: Georg Nastitsch.
Translated from the Serbian original by the author.
"Ich hoffe, dass diese meine auslegungen den vorbereitungen und den eventuellen versuchen der revolutionären arbeit im slavischen süden ein ende machen werden."—Einleitung, p. 12.

1. Servia—Hist. 2. Yugoslavs. I. Title.
28-20607

Library of Congress   DR360.N3

NN 0027528 DLC

DR 360 N3 1908 Nastić, Đorđe, 1884-1919.
Finale... 2. izd. U Zagrebu, Štampa C. Albrechta (Maravić i Decak), 1908.
62 p. fold. facsim. in pocket 23 cm.

At head of title: Gjorgje Nastić.

1. Serbia – History. 2. Yugoslavs. I. Title.

NN 0027529 OU CSt

Nastić, Đorđe, 1884-1919.
... Језуите у Босни. Београд, Нова штампарија Давидовић, 1906.
79, [1] p. 19½ᶜᵐ.

1. Jesuits in Bosnia and Herzegovina. I. Title.
Title romanized: Jezuite u Bosni.   41-36657
Library of Congress   BX3729.B6N3

NN 0027530 OU

Nastić, Đord̵e, 1884-1919.
Wo ist die Wahrheit? Neue Daten und Dokumente zur südslavischen revolutionären Agitation. Sarajevo, D.A. Kajon, 1908.
57 p., 1 facsim. 8°.

NN 0027531 NN

891.869 N268 1954 Nástin dějin české literatury od počátku národního obrození až do současnosti; pomocná kniha literární historie pro školy všeobecně vzdělavací, školy pedagogické a školy odborné. [Zpracovali] František Buriánek et al. Vyd.2. Praha, Státní pedagog.nakl., 1954.
208 p.

1. Czech literature--Hist.& crit. I.Buriánek, František,1917-

NN 0027532 MiU

Nástin hospodářského vývoje lidově demokratických zemí a některých kapitalistických států. [Vyd. 1.] Praha, Státní pedagogické nakl., 1955-
v. 30 cm. (Učební texty vysokých škol)
At head of title, v. 1- : Karlova universita v Praze. Katedra politické ekonomie.
Vol. 1 by K. Demuthová and others; v. 2 by E. Němeček and V. Veselý.

1. Economic conditions—1945-   I. Demuthová, K.
II. Němeček, Ed.
HC10.N3   56-43286 ‡

NN 0027533 DLC NNC

Nastitch (Nicolas) [1881-]. *De la radioscopie stéréoscopique. 82 pp. 8°. Nancy, 1908. No. 18.

NN 0027534 DNLM

Nástin filosofie J.A. Komenského
see under Kapras, Jan.

Nastitsch, Georg.
see. Nastić', Đorđe, 1884-1919.

Nastiukov, Georgii Andreevich, ed.
Denisov, F
Народные танцы. [Хореографическая ред. Г. Настюкова. Москва, Профиздат, 1954.

GV1751 .T35 Nastiukov, Georgii Andreevich, comp.
Танцы в клубе. [Запись танцев и составление сборника З. П. Резниковой и Г. А. Настюкова] Москва, Гос. издво культурно-просветительной лит-ры, 1954.

Настоящий ревизоръ; комедия въ трехъ дняхъ или дѣйствіяхъ, служащая продолженіемъ комедіи "Ревизоръ," сочиненной г. Гоголемъ. Санктпетербургъ, Въ Тип. X. Гинце, 1836.
viii, 125 p. 28 cm.

Title romanized: Nastoiashchii revizor.

PG3320.A1N3   78-213799

NN 0027539 DLC

Nastold, Karl, 1885-
Der württembergische hopfenbau; seine geschichtliche entwicklung, sein heutiger stand und die bedingungen seiner künftigen rentabilität, von dr. Karl Nastold ... Stuttgart, F. Enke, 1911.
viii, 130 p., 1 l. 25½ᶜᵐ. (Added t.-p.: Tübinger staatswissenschaftliche abhandlungen ... 15. hft.)
Published also as the author's inaugural dissertation, Tübingen, 1911.
"Quellenangabe": 1 leaf at end.

1. Hops. 2. Agriculture—Württemberg.
13-354

Library of Congress   HD9019.H7N3

NN 0027540 DLC ICRL NN

Настольная книга охотника-спортсмена. Москва, Физкультура и спорт, 1953-56.
2 v. illus., plates. 24cm.
Each vol. has also special t. p.
Bibliography: v. 1, p. 305-[307]

1. Hunting—Russia.
Title transliterated: Nastol'naià kniga okhotnika-sportsmena.
SK213.N33   55-40911 rev

NN 0027541 DLC FMU

(Nastol'naià kniga torgovykh deiàtelei)
Настольная книга торговых деятелей; справочник по вопросам торговой практики. [Под ред. и с предисл. В. П. Шеханова]. Москва, Центр. упр. печати ВСНХ СССР, 1926.
xvi, 451, vii p. 27 cm.

1. Russia—Commerce—Handbooks, manuals, etc.   I. Shekhanov, V. P., ed.
HF3627.N38   73-216847

NN 0027542 DLC

Настольный энциклопедическій словарь Товарищества "Бр. А. и И. Гранатъ и К°." 5. изд., съ дополненіями до 1901 года. Москва, Типо-лит. А. В. Васильева и К°, 1901.
9 v. illus., col. maps, ports. 24 cm.

1. Encyclopedias and dictionaries, Russian.   I. Granat, Russkii bibliograficheskii institut, publishers, Moscow.
Title transliterated: Nastol'nyi ènfsiklopedicheskii slovar'.
AE55.N3 1901   65-72991

NN 0027543 DLC

Настольный энциклопедический словарь-справочник. 3., перер. и значительно доп. изд. Москва, Прометей, 1929.
686 p. 23 cm.
Errata slip inserted.

1. Encyclopedias and dictionaries, Russian.
Title transliterated: Nastol'nyi ènfsiklopedicheskii slovar'-spravochnik.
AG55.N3 1929   51-53435

NN 0027544 DLC

Настольный календарь.
Москва, Гос. социально-экон. изд-во [etc.]
v. illus., ports. 30 cm. annual.
Began publication with 1938 issue. Cf. issue for 1941, p. 1.

1. Almanacs, Russian.   Title transliterated: Nastol'nyi kalendar'.
AY914.N2S   51-23548

NN 0027545 DLC

Настольный календарь-справочник по Дальнему Востоку. 1919 г. Владивосток.
v. 28 cm.
Issued by Otdel po narodnomu obrazovaniiù of Primorskoe oblastnoe zemstvo.

1.   I. Maritime Province, Siberia.
Primorskiy Kray. Oblastnoe zemstvo. Otdel po narodnomu obrazovaniiù.
Title transliterated: Nastol'nyi kalendar'-spravochnik.
DK771.M3N3   51-57005

NN 0027546 DLC

Настольный календарь учителя на 1941-   год. Москва, Государственное учебно-педагогическое издательство Наркомпроса РСФСР, 1941-
v. illus. (incl. ports.) plates, diagrs. 26 x 21ᶜᵐ.
Editors: 1941-   O. P. Leonova, E. I. Perovskii, N. A. Sundukov.
Includes section "В помощь самообразованию учителя" (bibliography)

1. Almanacs, Russian.   Title transliterated: Nastol'nyi kalendar' uchitelià.
Library of Congress   AY944.N3   43-37078

NN 0027547 DLC

Настольный церковный календарь для православных.
Регенсбург.
v. illus. 29 cm.

1. Orthodox Eastern Church. Liturgy and ritual—Calendar.
Title transliterated: Nastol'nyi fserkovnyi kalendar' dlià pravoslavnykh.
BX350.N3   61-21025

NN 0027548 DLC

VOLUME 405

Nastopkaitė, Halina
see
  Korsakienė, Halina (Nastopkaitė)

Nastorg (Jean-François-Xavier). I. Des complications en pathologie. II. [etc.] 29 pp. 4°.
Paris, 1843, No. 81. v. 407.

NN   0027550   DNLM PPC

Nastorg, Lionel, *joint author.*

Hesse, Raymond Gaston, 1884–
  ... Leur manière ...   Plaidoiries à la façon de ... Raymond Poincaré.—Maria Vérone.—Henri Robert ... [e. a.]
Paris, B. Grasset, °1925.

Nastorg, Lionel.
  ... Le rouge aux lèvres, roman.   2. éd.   Paris, P. Ollendorff, °1911.

  2 p. l., 348 p.   18½ᵐ.   fr. 3.50

                        11–28781

  Library of Congress   PQ2627.A7R7 1911

NN   0027552   DLC

Nastrac,   vicomte de Chalvet-
  see   Chalvet-Nastrac,   vicomte
de.

Nastri, Michele.
  ...Disegno, calligrafia, stenografia; loro sviluppo ed utilità.
Roma: Istituto fonografico, 1894.   21 p.   12°.

                   BRIDGE SHORTHAND COLL
415340A. 1. Shorthand—Systems.
N. Y. P. L.   June 6, 1929

NN   0027554   NN

Nastri, Nadège
  ... Un collaborateur s.v.p., comédie en un
acte, en prose. Paris, Maison d'éditions de
l'Impulsionnismo, 1908.
  30p., 1ℓ. 19½cm.
  "Représentée pour la première fois au Théâtre
mondain, à Paris, le 23 novembre 1907."

NN   0027555   CtY

Nastro spirituale. Cantici scelti.
Traduzione per Joseph Vital. 2d ed.
Yonkers, N. Y., [n.-p.] 1914.
64 p.

  1. Hymns, Italian.

NN   0027556   CtHC

Nast's illustrated almanac. 1871–
  New York, McLoughlin bros., °1870; Harper & brothers,
°1871–
     v. illus., plates. 20½–23ᶜᵐ.

  I. Nast, Thomas, 1840–1902, illus.

                      12–19026
  Library of Congress   AP101.N3

     MiU MiU-C RPB MH MB PPL CtY OFH
NN   0027557   DLC WU KU CU TxU NIC PHi OCl OCU OO

W 4
B87
1916
  NASTU, A   M
    Echinococcoza pancreasului.
  Bucureşti, 1916.
    70 p. (Bucharest. [Universitatea]
  Facultatea de Medicină. Teză, 1473)

NN   0027558   DNLM

QH324
.O8
  Nastuk, William L., ed.

  Oster, Gerald, *ed.*
    Physical techniques in biological research, edited by Gerald Oster [and] Arthur W. Pollister.   New York, Academic
Press, 1955–

057.87
NAS
  Nástup mladej slovenskej autonomistickej
    generácie.   roč. 1–
    apr. 1933–
    Bratislava.
    v. 32cm.

NN   0027560   IU OClBHS

Наступление; литературный сборник карельских и ленинградских писателей к xv-летию советской Карелии. Петрозаводск, Кирья, 1935.
  254 p. illus., ports.   23 cm.
  Contents.—Федин, К. Гость: четыре главы из книги II романа "Похищение Европы."—Виртанен, Я. На границе: стихи.—Норин, С. Застава номер три; звено из повести "Граница."—Грибачев, Н. Город; стихи.—Фиш, Г. Три рассказа.—Никонова, Ю. Весенний лов; стихи.—Паррас, Э. Новая земля; отрывок из романа "Юмовзарасцы."—Люфанов, Е. Три главы о счастьи.—Кутасов, И. Два стихотворения.—Линевский. Партизаны северного Беломорья.
  1. Russian literature—Karelia.   2. Russian literature—Leningrad.   *Title romanized:* Nastuplenie.

  PG3504.K345N3   72–226066

NN   0027561   DLC

Nasturel, Ioan Vasiliu-
  see   Vasiliu-Nasturel, Ioan, 1845–

Nasturtius (Philo). Eilfertiges Gutachten ... Zwelferischen Bundesgenossen, über die hochbedenckliche Attentata, tieff-ersinnte, unbesonnene und ärgerliche Defensions-Schrift eines Raphaël Schmuz von Poystorff, uhralten Neuburgischen Leib-Medici, so er aufgerichtet zu unsterblichem Lob und ewigwehrenden Siegs-Preiss des Augspurgischen Dispensatorii, wie dann auch zu schändlichem Nachtheil, Hohn und Schimpf des ... Herrn Joannis Zwelfers, weitberühmten Practici in Wien, erb- und meisterlichen Correctoris des weltbekanten Augustani. Nebenst zu End angehengter Erinnerung an den in Arte pharmaceutica ganz seichtgelehrten Lucam Schröküum Lucis filium. 5 p. l., 59 pp. 18°. [*Grein*]. 1673.

NN   0027563   DNLM

Nasturtiums bright and gay
  see under   [Gray, Bessie] 1854–1925.

QD305
.A2N26
  Nastvogel, Oscar.
    Ueber die einwirkung der hydrazine auf
  dibrombrenzstrangensaure.
  Wuerzburg, 1887.
    24p.
    Inaug. diss. Wuerzburg.

NN   0027565   DLC

                   1884–
Nastvogel, Philipp, gepr. Rechtsprakt.: Die rechtliche Natur des Pfandscheins.   Würzburg 1911: Staudenraus.   102 S. 8°
Erlangen, Jur. Diss. v. 11. Juli 1911, Ref. Oertmann
[Geb. 13. März 84 Würzburg; Wohnort: Würzburg; Staatsangeh.: Bayern; Vorbildung: Altes Gymn. Würzburg Reife 03; Studium: Würzburg 6, Erlangen 2 S.; Rig. 22. Juni 11.]   [U 11. 549

NN   0027566   ICRL NN NIC

Настыли в доменных печах; сборник статей. Под ред. Н. И. Красавцева. Москва, Гос. научно-техн. изд-во литры по черной и цветной металлургии, 1953.
  337, [3] p. illus.   23 cm.
  Bibliography: p. [336]–[338]

  1. Blast-furnaces—Addresses, essays, lectures.   I. Krasavt︠s︡ev, Nikolaĭ Ivanovich, ed.
                     Title romanized: Nastyli v domennykh pechakh.
  TN713.N26   54–16943

NN   0027567   DLC

Nasu, Hiroshi
  see
  Nasu, Shiroshi, 1888–

Nasu, Kō
  see
  Nasu, Shiroshi, 1888–

Nasu, Shiroshi, 1888–
  Aspects of Japanese agriculture; a preliminary survey, by Shiroshi Nasu ... New York, International secretariat, Institute of Pacific relations, 1941.
  ix numb. l., 1 l., 168 numb. l. incl. tables. map. 27½ x 21½ᵐ. (I. P. R. International research series)
  Reproduced from type-written copy.
  "A revised and enlarged edition of ... Land utilization in Japan, published by the Japanese council of the Institute in 1929."—Pref.

  1. Agriculture—Japan.   2. Land tenure—Japan.   3. Agriculture—Economic aspects.

  Library of Congress   HD915.N3 1941   42–13621
                                 [4]   630.952

     OCl MH CtY NN ICU
NN   0027570   DLC CaBVaU WaS OrCS Or MeB NcD GU CU OU

Nasu, Shiroshi, 1888–
  [Jinkō shokuryō mondai]
  人口食糧問題 那須皓著 [東京] 日本評論社
  [昭和2 i. e. 1927]
  2, 6, 319 p.   19 cm.

  1. Population—Addresses, essays, lectures.   2. Food supply—Addresses, essays, lectures.   I. Title.
  HB871.N28   73–815249

NN   0027571   DLC

Nasu, Shiroshi, 1888–
  (Keizai-seisakugaku no honshitsu narabini seisan seisaku genri)
  經濟政策學の本質竝に生產政策原理 那須皓著
  [東京] 岩波書店 [大正14 i. e. 1925]
  3, 8, 273 p.   23 cm.   (His 經濟政策學原理 第1卷)
  Includes bibliographical references.

  1. Economic policy.   2. Production (Economic theory)   I. Title.
  HD85.J3N46   74–815197

NN   0027572   DLC

Nasu, Shiroshi, 1888–
  協同組合と農業問題 那須皓・東畑精一 共著
  東京改造社 昭和7 [1932]
  474 p.   19 cm.   (經濟學全集 第17卷)
  Bibliographical footnotes.

  1. Cooperative societies—Japan.   2. Agriculture—Economic aspects—Japan.   I. Tōhata, Seiichi, 1899–   joint author.   II. Title.
  (Series: Keizaigaku zenshū, dai 17-kan)   *Title romanized:* Kyōdō kumiai to nōgyō mondai.
  HD3547.A4N3   J 64–1927

NN   0027573   DLC CSt-H

Nasu, Shiroshi.
  Land utilization in Japan, by Dr. S. Nasu ... Prepared for the third session of the Institute of Pacific relations.   Tokyo [The Institute of Pacific relations, 1929]
  2 p. l., II, 4 p., 1 l., 262, 6 p. plates, maps (3 fold.) plan, fold. tab., diagrs. 22ᶜᵐ.
  Preface signed: Research committee of Japanese council, Institute of Pacific relations.

  1. Agriculture—Japan—Statistics. [1. Japan—Agriculture—Statistics] 2. Land tenure—Japan. [2. Japan—Land] 3. [Land utilization] I. Institute of Pacific relations.

  Library, U. S. Dept. of   Agriculture 282N18   Agr 30–310

NN   0027574   DNAL CaBVaU OrPR CU OU WaU

VOLUME 405

Nasu, Shiroshi, 1888–
滿蒙開發と我農業移民に就て　那須皓著 [新
滿蒙の幣制及金融に就て [中野正光著　東京]
陸軍經理學校 [1932]
16 p. 22 cm.
Cover title.
1. Currency question—Manchuria. 2. Agricultural colonies—Manchuria. I. Nakano, Masamitsu. Shin Man-Mō no heisei oyobi kin'yō ni tsuite. 1932. II. Title.
Title romanized: Man-Mō kaihatsu to waga nōgyō imin ni tsuite.

HG1230.M3N33   75-815052

NN   0027575   DLC

Nasu, Shiroshi, 1888–
Nihon nōgyō no tembō
see under Nōgyō Keizaigakkai.

Nasu, Shiroshi.

Gini, Corrado, 1884–
Population. ⟨Lectures on the Harris foundation 1929⟩ by
Corrado Gini ... Shiroshi Nasu ... Robert R. Kuczynski ...
Oliver E. Baker ... Chicago, Ill., The University of Chicago
press [*1930]

Nasu, Shiroshi
... The problem of population and food
supply in Japan ... Honolulu, 1927.
cover-title, 26p. tables. 23½cm.
At head of title: Institute of Pacific relations. Preliminary paper prepared for the second
general session July 15-28, 1927.
1. Japan - Statistics, Vital. 2. Food supply -
Japan. I. Institute of Pacific relations. II.
Title.

NN   0027578   NRU CSt-H CtY NNU-W

Nasu, Shiroshi, 1888–
農業政策　那須皓著　東京　日本評論社　昭和
6 [1931]
2, 2, 426 p. tables. 23 cm. (現代經濟學全集　第15卷)
Includes bibliographies.

1. Agriculture and state. 2. Agriculture and state—Japan.
I. Title.   (Series: Gendai keizaigaku zenshū, dai 15-kan)
Title romanized: Nōgyō seisaku.

HD2092.N3   J 60-2774 rev
Hoover Institution
for Library of Congress   [r63b¾]†

NN   0027579   CSt-H

Nasu, Shiroshi, 1888–
(Nōsei ronkō)
農政論考　那須皓著 [東京］岩波書店 [昭
和 3 i. e. 1928]
2, 8, 465 p. 23 cm.
Includes bibliographical references.

1. Agriculture and state—Addresses, essays, lectures. I. Title.

HD1411.N33   73-819705

NN   0027580   DLC

Nasu, Shiroshi, 1888–
(Nōson mondai to shakai risō)
農村問題と社會理想　那須皓著 [東京］岩波
書店 [大正13 i. e. 1924]
2, 5, 412 p. 20 cm.
Errata slip inserted.
Includes bibliographical references.

1. Agriculture and state—Addresses, essays, lectures. 2. Sociology,
Rural—Addresses, essays, lectures. I. Title.

HD1411.N34   73-817550

NN   0027581   DLC

Nasu, Shiroshi, 1888–
(Nōson mondai to shakai risō)
農村問題と社會理想　那須皓著　増訂版 [東
京］岩波書店 [昭和2 i. e. 1927]
2, 5, 486 p. 20 cm.
Includes bibliographical references.
附錄　農村問題の本質を論じて福田博士に答ふ: p. [413]-486.

1. Agriculture and state—Addresses, essays, lectures. 2. Sociology, Rural—Addresses, essays, lectures. I. Fukuda, Tokuzō. II.
Title.
HD1411.N34 1927   74-817256

NN   0027582   DLC

DS701
.I 522
1931z
Orien
Japan

Nasu, Shiroshi, 1888–   ed.

(Shanhai ni okeru Taiheiyō Kaigi)
上海に於ける太平洋會議　那須皓編 [東京］太平
洋問題調査會 [岩波書店發賣　昭和7 i.e. 1932]

330.91
N269

Nasu, Shiroshi, 1838–
A study of correlation between factors of
production and the yields of arable land ... by
Shiroshi Nasu ...   Tokyo, Japan, The Japan council
of the Institute of Pacific relations [1931]
15 p.   22ᵐ.
"Prepared for the fourth bi-annual conference
of the Institute of Pacific relations to be
held at Hangchow from Oct.21st - Nov.4th,1931."
1.Agriculture - Economic aspects - Japan -
Statistics.

NN   0027584   CSt NN Or

[Nasu, Toshisuke]
The fundamentals of Japanese archery. [Kyoto, Priv. print.,
1937]
2 p. l., xiii, 84 p. illus., plates, ports. 24ᵐ.
English title on label mounted on portfolio; t.-p. and preface in Japanese.
Photoprinted, on double leaves in Japanese style, from manuscript
copy.
By Toshisuke Nasu; translated, with a foreword, by W. R. B. Acker.
Colophon in Japanese attached to end cover.

1. Archery.   I. Acker, William Reynolds Beal, tr.   II. Title.   III. Title:
Japanese archery.

Library of Congress   GV1189.N85   39-5834
——— Copy 2.   [2]   799.32

NN   0027585   DLC NcD MH InU OkU

GV 1189   NASU, TOSHISUKE
.N269   A syllabus on Japanese archery by Toshisuke
Nasu and Betty Hornish. Interpreter, Katsu
Yoshida.   Kyoto, Kyoto American School, 1949.
1 v. (unpaged) illus.

1. Archery. I. Hornish, Betty. II. Title.
III. Japanese archery.

NN   0027586   InU NNC

Nasuh Matrakçı, fl. 16th cent.
Un "Fetih-nâme-i Karaboğdan" (1538) de Nasuh
Matrakçı, par A. Decei. İstanbul, Osman
Yalçın Matbaası, 1953.
[113]-124 p. facsims.

"Extrait des Mélanges Fuad Köprülü."

NN   0027587   NNC

Nasuhi, Cevdet
Bir rapor, üç konferans. İstanbul, Ahmet
İhsan Matbaası, 1931

119 p. fold. map
Cover title

1. Cooperative societies - Turkey
2. Agriculture - Cooperative - Turkey
3. Turkey - Econ. condit.

NN   0027588   MH CLU

HD
1491
T8N18

Nasuhi, Cevdet
Kooperatif; yetirenler ve bitirenler davası.
İstanbul, Cumh[u]riyet Matbaası, 1929.
299 p.

1. Agriculture, Cooperative - Turkey. 2.
Turkey - Agriculture. I. Title.

NN   0027589   CLU

Nasuhoğlu, Rauf
Fizik. İstanbul, Maarif Basımevi [1952-55.
2 v. in 1. illus.

Contents.--v. 1. Ortaokul ikinci sınıf için.
--v. 2. Ortaokul üçüncü sınıf için.

1. Physics.

NN   0027590   NNC

---

al-Nasūlī, Anīs Zakarīyā.
الدولة الاموية في الشام، تاليف انيس زكريا النصولي.
الطبعة 1. بغداد، مطبعة دار السلام، 1927.
13, 360 p. geneal. tables. 21 cm.
Bibliography: p. 6-12 (1st group)

1. Omayyads.   I. Title.
Title romanized: al-Dawlah al-Umawīyah.

DS97.2.N3   N E 68-1757

NN   0027591   DLC

Nasus, Joannes, 16th cent.
see Nase, Johann 1534-1590.

PL5079   Nasution, A   Diapari
N3   English-Indonesian idioms.   Medan, Pustaka "Madju" [pref.
1950]
121 p.

1. Indonesian language - Idioms, corrections, errors. 2. English
language - Idioms, corrections, errors. I. Title.

NN   0027593   CU CtY NN

428.24
N269 N

Nasution, A   Diapari.
A new English course for Indonesian
students. Kursus baru bahasa inggeris.
Medan, Pustaka Andalas, c1950.
163p. illus. 23cm.

1.English language. Textbooks for
foreigners. Indonesian I.T1. II.T1.:
Kursus baru bahasa inggeris

NN   0027594   NB

420.7
D542n

Nasution, A   Diapari,
A new English course for Indonesian
students. In collaboration with Nathalie
Toms Means and Muhammad Saleh Arif. Rev.
Medan [Indonesia] Andalas, 1953–
v. illus.

1. English language – For foreigners –
Indonesian   I. Title

NN   0027595   MiD

Locked Press
Wason   Nasution, A   Diapari.
PE1130   Simplified English grammar for
I5N26   Indonesian students. Paramasastera
1949   sederhana bahasa Inggeris. Medan,
Pustaka Andalas, 1949.
87 p. 18cm.

1. English language--Text-books for
foreigners--Indonesian. I. Title.

NN   0027596   NIC

VOLUME 405

Nasution, A   Diapari.
Simplified English grammar for Indonesian students.
Medan, Andalas, 1951.
2 v. 19 cm.
CONTENTS.—pt. 1. Pramasastra sederhana bahasa Inggeris. tjetakan 4.—pt. 2. Pramasastra landjut bahasa Inggeris. tjetakan 2.

1. English language—Text-books for foreigners—Indonesian.
I. Title.
PE1130.I 65N3   55–44999 ‡

NN   0027597   DLC

Nasution, Abdul Haris, 1918–
Fundamentals of guerilla warfare, and the Indonesian defence system, past and future. ₍Djakarta₎, Information Sirvice ₍sic₎ of the Indonesian Armed Forces ₍foreword 1953₎,
338 p. illus. ports. 22 cm.

1. Indonesia—Hist.—Revolution, 1945–1949. 2. Guerrilla warfare.
I. Title.
DS644.N313   S A 64–7241

NN   0027598   DLC CtY MiU TxU NNC NIC CU IU

Wason   Nasution, Abdul Haris, 1918–
U660   Fundamentals of guerilla warfare and the
I5N26   Indonesian defence system past and future.
1953   ₍Djakarta₎ Indonesian Army Information Service
            ₍1953?₎
               324 p. illus., map. 21cm.

            Translation of Pokok2 gerilja dan pertahanan
            Republik Indonesia.

NN   0027599   NIC

Nasution, Abdul Haris, 1918–
Pokok² gerilja dan pertahanan Republik Indonesia di-masa jang lalu dan jang akan datang. ₍Tjetakan 2₎ Djakarta, Pembimbing ₍1954₎
311 p. illus., ports. 22 cm.

1. India — Hist. — Revolution, 1945–1949. 2. Guerrilla warfare.
I. Title.
DS644.N3 1954   S A 63–3148

NN   0027600   DLC NIC

Nasution, Abdul Haris, 1918–
Tjatatan² sekitar politik militer Indonesia. ₍Tjetakan 1₎ Djakarta, Pembimbing ₍1955₎
388 p. illus., ports. 24 cm.

1. Indonesia—Military policy. I. Title.
UA853.I 5N3   S A 63–3664

NN   0027601   DLC DS NIC CU

Fyb18   Nasution, Amal Hamzah, 1927–
N188   Pembebasan pertama; kumpulan 1942–1948.
P4   oleh Amal Hamzah. Djakarta, Balai Pustaka,
            1949.
               170 p. 22 cm.

NN   0027602   CtY

Wason   Nasution, Amir Hamzah.
BF38   Aku, masjarakat dan masa.   Tebing
N26A3   Tinggi, Pustaka Raya ₍1951₎
               71 p. 18 cm.

1. Psychology.   I. Title.

NN   0027603   NIC

Fyb18   Nasution, Amir Hamzah
N189   Anak-anak Bintang Pari. Dihiasi oleh
A5   Nasjah. Djakarta, Balai Pustaka, 1951.
               69 p. illus. 19 cm.

NN   0027604   CtY

Asia   Nasution, Amir Hamzah
BF77   Ichtisar hidup djiwa. Untuk kursus2 dan
.N38   perpustakaan. Medan, Sempurna, 1952.
               142 p. illus.

1. Psychology – Textbooks. I. Title.

NN   0027605   HU NIC

Wason   Nasution, Amir Hamzah.
BF38   Ilmu djiwa dalam masjarakat, teori-
N26I2   praktek. Untuk kursus2 dan perpustakaan.
            Medan, Sempurna, 1952.
               97 p. diagrs. 17 cm.   (Seri populer)

1. Psychology.   I. Title.

NN   0027606   NIC

Wason   Nasution, Amir Hamzah.
JQ763   Sedjarah dan tata Negara Indonesia.
1952   Untuk kursus - kursus dan perpustakaan.
N26   Medan, Sempurna, 1952.
               47 p. map. 17cm.

NN   0027607   NIC

Nasution, Amir Hamzah.
Sedjarah kebangsaan, untuk kursus pengetahuan umum. Tjetakan 1. Djakarta, Pustaka Aida, 1951.
126 p. illus., ports., maps. 22 cm.

1. Nationalism—Indonesia. I. Title.
DS638.N3   S A 63–3902

NN   0027608   DLC CU NIC InU

Wason   Nasution, Amir Hamzah.
Pamphlet   Sedjarah nasional dan gerakan politik
DS   praktis; pedoman. Medan, Pustaka Ahmad
Indonesia   Latif ₍1949?₎
211   47 p. maps. 19 cm.

1. Indonesia--Hist. 2. Indonesia--Pol. & govt.--1798-1942. 3. Indonesia--Pol. & govt.--1942-1949. I. Title.

NN   0027609   NIC

PL5099   Nasution, Amir Hamzah
.5   Tata negara praktis (demokrasi) pedoman
N37   pemimpin. Tjetakan 2. Medan, Penerbit
1950   Pustaka Andalas, 1950.
               48 p.

1. Indonesia - Pol. & govt.

NN   0027610   CU

Wason   Nasution, Amir Hamzah
DS644   Tata negara praktis pedoman pemimpin
N26t   untuk (kursus-kursus dan dan perpustakaan)
            Tjetakan Ketiga. Medan, Pustaka Andalas,
            1951.
               66 p. 18cm.

1. Indonesia--Pol. & govt.

NN   0027611   NIC

LOCK PR   Nasution, Amir Taat.
WASON   Kamus kata-kata politik. Tjet. 4. Medan,
JA   Pustaka Andalas, 1949.
64   96 p. 18cm.
N26
1949

NN   0027612   NIC

Nasution, Amir Taat.
Kamus-politik, oleh Amir Taat Nasution dan Usman Jakub. ₍Tjet. 7. Medan, Pustaka Madju, 1950?₎
124 p. 18 cm.

1. Social sciences—Dictionaries—Indonesian. I. Jakub, Usman, joint author. II. Title.
H49.N3 1950   S A 66–436

NN   0027613   DLC NIC

Nasution, Amir Taat.
Kamus-politik, oleh Amir Taat Nasution dan Usman Jakub. ₍Tjet. 8. Medan, Pustaka Madju, 1951₎
138 p. 18 cm.

1. Social sciences—Dictionaries—Indonesian. I. Jakub, Usman, joint author. II. Title.
H49.N3 1951   S A 66–437

NN   0027614   DLC

Nasution, Amir Taat.
Kamus politik, oleh Amirtaat Nasution. Tjet. 11. Djakarta, Energie, 1953.
165 p. 18 cm.

1. Social sciences—Dictionaries—Indonesian. I. Title.
H49.N3 1953   S A 66–438

NN   0027615   DLC

Wason   Nasution, Amir Taat.
Pamphlet   Pendidikan di rumah tangga. ₍Medan,
L   Senitulis, 1951₎
Indonesia   64 p. 18 cm.
32

1. Domestic education. I. Title.

NN   0027616   NIC

Asia   Nasution, Amir Taat.
GN480.8   Polygami. Medan, Timur ₍n.d.₎
.A55   72 p.

1. Polygamy. 2. Indonesia – Soc. life & customs. I. Title

NN   0027617   HU

Nasution, Amirtaat
    see
Nasution, Amir Taat.

Law   Nasution, B., ed.

Indonesia. Laws, statutes, etc.
    Perundang-undangan nasional; kumpulan undang-undang, undang-undang darurat peraturan-peraturan pemerintah dan pendjelasan, tahun 1951. Disusun dan dikerdjakan oleh H. Soerjanatamihardja dan B. Nasution. Djakarta, G. C. T. van Dorp, 1953.

Nasution, Basir.
The English language. Kursus lengkap untuk mempeladjari bahasa Inggeris dengan tidak memakai guru. Tjetakan 2. Medan, Toko Buku W. Hutabarat, 1950.
134 p. 26 cm.

1. English language—Text-books for foreigners—Indonesian.
PE1130.I 65N28 1950   56–36044 ‡

NN   0027620   DLC

VOLUME 405

Wason
DS634+
N26
Nasution, Basir
  Sedjarah Indonesia   Medan,
"Marsada" ₁1951₎
  v. 28cm.

  Contents.--
v. 2. 1800-1951.

  1. Indon   esia--History.

NN 0027621 NIC

Wason
DS634
N26
1951
Nasution, Basir.
  Sedjarah Indonesia. Tjetakan 2. ₁Medan₎
"A.T.B." 1951₎
  2 v. maps. 17-18 cm.

  Contents--djilid 1. Zaman purbakala sampai
1800. --djilid 2. 1800-1951.

  1. Indonesia--Hist.

NN 0027622 NIC

Wason
Pamphlet
DS
Indone-
sia
140
Nasution, Basir.
  Sedjarah tata negara Indonesia dan umum.
Tjetakan 4.   Djakarta, Perpustakaan Kesatria
₁1954₎
  109 p. 16cm.

  "Persiapan udjian penghabisan S.M.P."

  1. Indonesia--Hist.--Examinations, questions,
etc. 2. World history--Examinations, questions,
etc. I. Title.

NN 0027623 NIC

Nasution, Jahja.
  Merdeka dengan Irian. ₁Penjusun Jahja Nasution dan
M. A. Hanafiah Lubis₎ Medan, Tagore ₁1950?₎
  56 p. 19 cm.

  1. New Guinea--Pol. & govt.   I. Lubis, M. A. Hanafiah, joint
author. II. Title.
  DS646.7.N3   55-38208 ‡

NN 0027624 DLC

Nasution, M   Yunan.
  Konstituante-Parlemen dan pemilihan umum. Djakarta,
Antara ₁1953₎
  112 p. 19 cm.

  1. Election law--Indonesia.   I. Title.

                                    55-38262 ‡

NN 0027625 DLC

Nasution, M   Yunan.
  Riwajat ringkas penghidupan dan perdjuangan Ir. Sukarno. ₁Tjetakan 5. Medan, Pustaka Timur Medan, 1949₎
  64 p. 21 cm.

  1. Sukarno, Pres. Indonesia, 1901–   I. Title.
  DS644.1.S8N3 1949   55-39857 ‡

NN 0027626 DLC CU

Wason
Film
N3200
Nasution, M   Yunan.
  Riwajat ringkas penghidupan dan
perdjuangan Sukarno. Tjet. 8. Djakarta,
Pustaka Aida ₁tutur sepatah 1951₎
  64 p. port. 20cm.

  Microfilm (negative) Ithaca, N. Y.,
Cornell University, Photo Science, 1972.
1 reel. 35mm.
  1. Sukarno, Pres. Indonesia, 1901-1970.
2. Indonesia--History. I. Title.

NN 0027627 NIC CtY

Wason
DS644
N261
Nasution, Mahmud.
  Pengertian² sekitar demokrasi. Pen-
gurasian² sederhana tentang pengertian²dasar
sekitar tjara pemerintahan demokrasi.
Medan, Saiful, 1952.
  64 p. 19cm.

  On cover: Mahmoed Nast.

  1. Indonesia--Pol. & govt. 2. Representative government and representation. I. Title.

NN 0027628 NIC

Nasution, Mahmud Ahmad.
  Rahasia perusahaan dan peribadi. ₁Tjet. 1₎ Medan,
Pustaka Pergaulan ₁1955₎
  216 p. 22 cm.

  "Seri 110-P. U."
  Bibliography : p. 213.

  1. Success.   I. Title.
  HF5386.N34   S A 68-6413
                                  PL 480: Indo-6324

NN 0027629 DLC CtY CU

Nasution, Muchtar.
  Ilmu dagang dan perniagaan. Medan, Madju ₁1950₎
  64 p. 21 cm.

  1. Indonesia—Comm.—Handbooks, manuals, etc.   I. Title.
  HF3807.N3   55-59553 ‡

NN 0027630 DLC CU

Nasution, Muchtar.
  Pedoman bergaul, tuntunan bagi pemuda-pemudi diluar
dan didalam rumah-tangga, disekolah-sekolah menengah dan
lain2. Tjetakan 1. Medan, Andalas, 1952.
  66 p. 18 cm.

  1. Success.   I. Title.
  BJ1611.N3   55-56848 ‡

NN 0027631 DLC

Nasution, Muchtar.
  Tjontoh surat menjurat sehari-hari. Medan, Madju
₁1952₎
  71 p. 18 cm.

  1. Letter-writing, Indonesian.   I. Title.
  PL5079.N3   55-56624 ‡
  Library of Congress   ₁3₎

NN 0027632 DLC

NASUTION, MUCHTAR.
  Tjontoh surat menjurat sehari-hari. Tjetakan 3.
Medan, Pustaka "Madju" [1953?] 72 p. 18cm.

  1. Malay literature--Letters.

NN 0027633 NN

Nasvetevich, Vladimir Aleksandrovich, ed.
  Voenno-statisticheskoe opisanie raiona
Tambovskoĭ mĕstnoĭ brigady
          see under   Tambovskaĭa mestnaĭa brigada.

Nasvytis Algirdas, 1910–
  Die Gesetzmässigkeiten kombinatorischer Technik. Berlin, Springer, 1953.
  102 p. illus. 21 cm. (Wissenschaftliche Normung, 8)

  1. Electronic calculating-machines. 2. Punched card systems.
3. Information theory.   I. Title.
  QA76.N3   54-37037 ‡

  NBuU OrCS
NN 0027635   DLC MtU OU IEN IU NcRS RPB TxU NN GAT

891.91
N189v
Nasvytytė, Aldona Irena
  Vėjo dainos. ₁Chicago₎ Terra ₁195–₎
  50 p.

NN 0027636 MiD OCl NN

Nasz, Adolf.
  Opole. Wrocław, Nakł. Polskiego Towarzystwa Archeologicznego; Skł gł.: Wrocławska Składnica Księgarska,
1948.
  62 p. illus. ₁4₎ l. of illus. 30 cm. (Biblioteka archeologiczna, 1)
  Includes bibliographical references.

  1. Oppeln—Antiquities. 2. Poles in Oppeln.
  DD901.O6N37   74–215685

NN 0027637 DLC MH-P MoU

NASZ, ADOLF.
  Żarna wczesnodziejowe. Warszawa, Nakł.
Polskiego tow. archeologicznego, 1950. 86 p.
illus., 6 plates. 31cm. (Studia wczesnodziejowe. Seria archeologiczna, t. 1)

  Title in French on verso of cover.
  Summary in French.

  Bibliography, p.[70]-72.

  1. Crushing and grinding machinery. 2. Stone implements--Poland.
3. Poland--Archaeology.   I. Series. II. Title.

NN 0027639 NN CtY MB DDO ICU

NASZ przeglad, Warsaw. kwiec. 1937-sierp. 29, 1939
  (incomplete)
  Warszawa.   v.   47cm.

  Film reproduction. Positive.
  Daily.
  Includes supplements.

  t. Poland-Warsaw.

NN 0027640 NN

Nasz przyjaciel; ulotka religijna dla ludnosci polskiej w Iranie.
  Rok 1-3, no.8 (list.1942-maj 8,1944)

  ₁Teheran₎ 1942–44.   v. illus. 22–25cm.

  Irregular, Nov.–Dec. 1942; biweekly (slightly irregular), 1943– maj 8,1944.
  Numbering also continuous. no.1-41.
  Published by the Catholic clergy in Iran.
  Includes occasional suppl.
  Ceased publication with rok 3 ,nr.8 (maj 8,1944) ?

  1. Periodicals—Persia, Polish.   2. Catholic church, Roman—Poland.
  N.Y.P.L.   July 11, 1945

NN 0027641 NN

Nasz przyjaciel i towarzysz broni; ₁garść
wspomnień o Adolfie Bocheńskim.₎ Roma ₁Nakł.
Przyjaciół₎ 1945
  59 p. port.
  1.Bocheński, Adolf Maria,1909-1944

NN 0027642 MH

Nasz świat; ilustrowane polskie pismo tygodniowe dla wszystkich. Our world.
  Detroit.
            v. in   illus., ports. 30 cm.

  AP55.N3   59-26827

NN 0027643 DLC

Nasz świat; our world weekly. Detroit.

  1. Detroit - Periodicals and newspapers -
Polish 2. Detroit imprints - 1941-

NN 0027644 MiD

VOLUME 405

Nasza konstytucja. Cykl odczytów urządzonych staraniem Dyrekcji Szkoły Nauk Politycznych w Krakowie od 12-25 maja 1921 r., przy udziale: Wład. Abrahama ₍et al.₎ Kraków, Nakł. autorów, 1922.

228 p. 23 cm.

1. Poland—Constitutional law. ɪ. Abraham, Władysław, 1860-1941.

JN6754.N3   48-36714*

NN   0027645   DLC OU

Nasza Księgarnia, *Warsaw.*
Katalog.
Warszawa, Państwowe Wydawn. Literatury Dziecięcej.
v. illus., ports. 21 cm. annual.
Title varies: 19.   Katalog wydawnictw własnych.

Z2520.N3   59-46101

NN   0027646   DLC

Nasza myśl; miesięcznik oficerski. r. 1-
₍Warszawa, Prasa Wojskowa₎
v. in   illus., ports., maps. 30 cm.
Vols. 2-   called also no. 9-

1. Poland—Hist.—Period. 2. History—Period.

DK401.N29   60-30645

NN   0027647   DLC NcD

Nasza ordynacja wyborcza do rad narodowych. Warszawa, Tygodnik "Rada Narodowa," 1954.

21 p. 21 cm.

1. Elections—Poland.

JN6768.N3   55-29086 ‡

NN   0027648   DLC

Nasza przeszłość; studia z dziejów kościoła i kultury katolickiej w Polsce. t. 1-
Kraków, 1946-
v. 23 cm.
Published by Instytut Teologiczny Księży Misjonarzy w Krakowie.

1. Catholic Church in Poland. ɪ. Kraków. Instytut Teologiczny Księży Misjonarzy.

BX1564.N3   50-24644

NN   0027649   DLC TxU NSyU NN NIC

Nasza trybuna; pismo Żydów polskich. **Our tribune.**
New York.
v. in   illus., ports. 29 cm.
Frequency varies.
Published 1940-51.
Vols.   called also no.
Polish and English.
Editor: 194   J. Apenszlak.

1. Jews—Period. ɪ. Apenszlak, Jakób, 1894- editor. ɪɪ. Title: Our tribune.

DS133.N35   64-52189

NN   0027650   DLC

NASZA trybuna (Our tribune); pismo żydów polskich. Rok 1-12, no. 13 (whole no. 126); listop. 10, 1940-paźdz./listop. 1951. New York, Association of friends of Our tribune ₍etc.₎
12 v.   illus.,ports.   30-45cm.

Film reproduction on 2 reels. Positive.
Semi-monthly (irregular), Nov. 1940-May, 1942; monthly (irregular), June, 1942-Nov. 1951.

Continued in next column

Continued from preceding column

Vol. 5, no. 9 filmed following v. 8.
Published 1941-Jan. 1945 under the auspices of the American federation for Polish Jews.
Editors: Nov. 1940-Mar. 1950, J. Apenszlak (Nov. 1940-Sept. 1946, with A. Tartakower).
Includes Our tribune (English supplement) published July, 1943-Nov. 1951. Supplements for July, 1943-Mar. 1944 were issued by the Representation of Polish Jewry (American division). Some of these

English supplements were issued as sections of the periodical and filmed as they occurred. Others, issued separately, have all been filmed following v. 8 of the periodical. (Library file lacks v. 2, no. 4, Apr. 22, 1944, of the supplement.)

1. Periodicals--U.S., Polish. 2. Poland--Per. and soc. publ. 3. Jews in Poland--Per. and soc. publ. I. American federation for Polish Jews. II. Representation of Polish Jewry. Our tribune. III. Title: Our tribune. IV. Apenszlak, Jacob, 1894-1950,ed. V. Tartakower, Arjeh, 1894- , ed. ɪ. Subs. for *PBH

NN   0027653   NN

... **Nasza walka e szkołę polską, 1901-1917**
see under   Komitet obchodu 25-lecia walki o szkołę polską. Komisja historyczna.

Naszályi, Aemilius, 1910-
... Doctrina Francisci de Vitoria de statu. Romae, Scuola salesiana del libro, 1937.

2 p. l., ₍vii₎-xxiii, 231 p. 26ᶜᵐ.
Bibliography: p. ₍vii₎-xiii.

1. Francisco de Vitoria, 1486?-1546.

           A 40-3380

Notre Dame univ. Library   JX2159.N
for Library of Congress   ₍2₎

NN   0027655   InNd DLC

Naszályi, Aemilius, 1910-
El estado según Francisco de Vitoria. Traducción y prólogo del R. P. Ignacio G. Menéndez-Reigada. Madrid, Ediciones Cultura Hispánica, 1948.

273 p. 24 cm.
Translation of Doctrina Francisci de Vitoria de statu.
Bibliography: p. 267-271.

1. Francisco de Vitoria, 1486?-1546. 2. State, The.

JC145.F65N315   50-26432

NN   0027656   DLC NcD MiU CU-S IU DAU WU MH NjP

Nászay, Károly
... A magánalkalmazottak szolgálati és nyugdíjviszonyai. A magánalkalmazottakról szóló összes törvényes rendelkezések és nyugdíjvalorizációs törvény gyakorlati magyarázata. Irta: Dr. rákosi Nászay Károly ... Budapest, Közérdekü könyvek kiadóvállalata ₍1926₎

144 p., 1 l. 20½cm. (Közérdekü könyvek ...)
Includes legisla-   tion.

NN   0027657   MH-L

DK436.5 Nasze błędy w 1831 r. ₍n.p., 191-?₎
N269   24 p. 15½ᶜᵐ

On verso of t.-p.:"Za pozwoleniem wojennej cenzury niemieckiej".

1.Poland- History- Revolution, 1830-1832.

NN   0027658   CSt-H

Nasze gry i ćwiczenia. Praca zbiorowa pod redakcją Janiny Tworkowskiej. [Hamburg] Wydawnictwo Antoniego Markiewicza [1946]
76

NN   0027659   NNC-T IU

NASZE koło pracuje. nr. 5-17, 19-22, 25-27, 29-32, 34-35, 37-62; grudz. 1948-1949, lut.-maj, wrzes.-list. 1950, stycz.-kwiec., maj-czerw., sierp. 1951-1953
Warszawa.   v.   illus.   22cm.

Monthly.
Published by the Związek młodzieży polskiej.
Issues also numbered within   the year.

Includes occasional suppl.
Ceased publication?

1. Youth--Per. and soc. publ.--Poland. I. Związek młodzieży polskiej.

NN   0027661   NN

                   016.58
                   N188
... **Nasze piśmiennictwo botaniczne w roku 1904.** Lwów, L Związkowa drukarnia we Lwowie, 1906.
cover-title, p. [185]-202. 24ᶜᵐ.
At head of title: Odbitka z czasopisma Polskiego towarzystwa przyrodników im. Kopernika "Kosmos" r. xxxi.

NN   0027662   ICJ

F870   Nasze sprawy. v. 1, no. 1-
P7N3
         Los Angeles.
         v. in   illus. 29cm.

         In Polish.

         1. Poles in California. 2. Periodicals - California.

NN   0027663   CU-B

Naszkowski, Marian.
Ludowe Wojsko Polskie. Warszawa, Instytut Polsko-Radziecki, 1952.
24 p. 21 cm.
Errata slip inserted.

1. Poland. Wojsko Polskie. ɪ. Title.

UA829.P7N3   59-31358

NN   0027664   DLC

... **Naszym celem komunizm**
see under   ₍Bortnowska, S

Nat de Mons, *13th cent.*
Die werke des trobadors N'at de Mons zum ersten male hrsg. ɪ. teil ... von Wilhelm Bernhardt ... Leipzig, Druck von Breitkopf & Härtel, 1887.
46, ₍2₎ p. 21ᶜᵐ.
Inaug.-diss.—Bonn.
Lebenslauf.
"Sonderabdruck aus der einleitung zu der ausgabe der werke des trobadors N'At de Mons, Altfranzösische bibliothek, hrsg. v. W. Foerster, xɪ. band."

ɪ. Bernhardt, Wilhelm, 1861- ed.   CA 19-76 Unrev'd

Library of Congress   PC3330.N3 1887 a

NN   0027666   DLC NjP NN OCl PBm PU

Nat de Mons, *13th cent.*
Die werke des trobadors N'At de Mons; zum ersten mal hrsg. von Wilhelm Bernhardt. Heilbronn, Gebr. Henninger, 1887.
xlix, 169, ₍1₎ p. 19ᶜᵐ. (*Added t.-p.:* Altfranzösische bibliothek, hrsg. von dr. W. Foerster, 11. bd.)
Issued in part as the editor's inaugural dissertation (Bonn, 1886) Leipzig, 1887 (46, ₍2₎ p.)

ɪ. Bernhardt, Wilhelm, 1861- ed.

                 4-973 Revised

Library of Congress   PC3330.A7 1887

NN   0027667   DLC PU NN IaU CaBVaU MeB OU MH OCl OClW

Nat Gard, pseud.
see   Bechtel, John Adams, 1869-

VOLUME 405

Nat, Jan.
De studie van de Oostersche talen in Nederland in de 18e en de 19e eeuw ... door Jan Nat ... Purmerend, J. Muusses, 1929.

6 p. l., 188 p. front. (port.) 20½ᶜᵐ.

Proefschrift—Amsterdam.
Bibliographical foot-notes.
"Stellingen": [3] p. laid in.

1. Oriental philology—Hist. 2. Schultens, Albert. 1686-1750. 3. Semitic languages. 4. Netherlands—Bio-bibl.

34-25312

Library of Congress   PJ68.N4N3 1929   490.7

NN   0027669   DLC MiU CLU MH IU ICU

DT83
.N3
(Or)
Nat, Jan, 1895 or 6-1942.
Geschiedenis van het Oude Oosten tot de 6de eeuw voor Christus. Amsterdam, Wereldbibliotheek, 1935.
246 p. illus., maps.
"Dit werk maakt een onderdeel uit van onze serie Encyclopaedie in monografieën."
"Bibliografie": p. [211]-221.

1. Egypt—History, Ancient. 2. Egypt—Civilization.

NN   0027670   ICU

Nat, Jan, 1895 or 6-1942.
Hebreeuwsche grammatica. 3. herziene druk bewerkt door J. J. Koopmans. Leiden, E. J. Brill, 1945.

xii, 186 p. 24 cm.

Bibliographical references included in "Voorbericht voor den tweeden druk" (p. [ix])

1. Hebrew language—Grammar. I. Koopmans, J. J., ed.
PJ4564.N3 1945   A F 48-3100*
Chicago. Univ. Libr.
for Library of Congress   [1]†

NN   0027671   ICU NIC NN NNC DLC

Nat, Jan, 1895 or 6-1942.
Hebreeuwsche grammatica. 5. druk bewerkt door J.J Koopmans.   Leiden, E.J. Brill, 1951.
xii, 197 p.   24 cm.
Bibliographical references included in "Voorbericht voor den tweeden druk" (p. [ix])

NN   0027672   NcD

Nat, Jan, 1895 or 6-1942.
Oefeningen bij de Hebreeuwsche grammatica; stukken uit het Oude Testament en woordenlijsten. 2., geheel herziene druk door J. J. Koopmans. Leiden, E. J. Brill, 1945.

vi, 115 p. 25 cm.

1. Hebrew language—Grammar. I. Koopmans, J. J., ed.
PJ4567.N3 1945   A F 47-6998*
Chicago. Univ. Library
for Library of Congress   [2]†

NN   0027673   ICU NN DLC

Div.S.
492.45
N2710
Nat, Jan, 1895 or 6-1942.
Oefoningen bij de Hebreeuwsche grammatica; stukken uit het Oude Testament en woordenlijster ... 3. druk door J. J. Koopmans ... Leiden, E. J. Brill, 1948.
viii, 115 p. 24½cm.

NN   0027674   NcD

Nat, W. H. van der.
Bosboom-Toussaint, *Mevrouw* Anna Louisa Geertruida.
Don Abbondio II, Historische novellen, Een arme die rijk maakt ... Met illustratiën naar teekeningen van W. H. van der Nat. Rotterdam, D. Bolle [1899]

Nat, W. H. van der.
Bosboom-Toussaint, *Mevrouw* Anna Louisa Geertruida.
Eene kroon voor Karel den Stouten, De hertog van Alba in Nederland, De hertog van Alba in Spanje, Het rustuur van kardinaal Ximenès en Alkmaar's beleg ... Met illustratiën naar teekeningen van W. H. van der Nat. Rotterdam, D. Bolle [1899]

NAT Blake; or, The doomed highwayman. By the author of "Tom Water; or, The haunted highwayman"... Philadelphia, T.B.Peterson & brothers [n.d.]

NN   0027677   PU

Nat Blake, Author of
Bill Horton
see under title

Nat Blake, Author of.
... The life and adventures of Dick Clinton, the masked highwayman...
see under title

NAT FLEISCHER'S ring record book and boxing encyclopedia. 1941-
[New York, Ring book shop, etc.]   v.
illus., ports.   24cm.

Vols. for 1947-55 called 3d-11th suppl.
Editor: 1941- , N. S. Fleischer.

Title varies: 1941-44, Nat Fleischer's all-time ring record book; 1945-52, Nat Fleischer's ring record book. (Other slight variations.)

I. Boxing. I. Fleischer, Nathaniel S., ed. II. Fleischer, Nathaniel S., ed. All-time ring record book. III. Fleischer, Nathaniel S., ed. Ring record book and boxing   encyclopedia

NN   0027681   NN

En Nat i Slukefter. Vaudeville i een Act. Kjøbenhavn, H.P. Møller. [18- ?]
16 p. nar. 12°.

NN   0027682   NN

NAT "KING" COLE song album of recorded hits. Chord symbols included. New York, Remick, [c1954] 32 p. port 31cm.

For voice and piano.
CONTENTS.— It's only a paper moon (H. Arlen)—Body and soul (J. Green)—What is this thing called love (C. Porter)—Sweet Georgia Brown (Bernie, Pinkard, Casey)—Three little words (H. Ruby)—I'll string along with you (H. Warren)—Return to paradise (D. Tiomkin)—

I know that you know (V. Youmans)—The love nest (L. Hirsch)—Blue gardenia (Russell, Lee)—My sleepy head (L. Coleman)—Too marvelous for words (R. Whiting).

1. Songs, U.S.—Collections. I. Cole, Nat King.

NN   0027684   NN

Nat. R. K. commissie voor jeugdwerkloozenzorg
see
Nationale Roomsch-katholieke commissie voor jeugdwerkloozenzorg.

The Nat Ridley series
see under Ridley, Nat, jr.

Nat the navigator
see under   [Bowditch, Henry Ingersoll]
1808-1892.

The Nat Turner Negro insurrection in Virginia. 1831.
18 p. D.
no title page.

NN   0027688   NcD

NAT Waters' jack-knife, and how it turned up; by W.H.L.

Illustr. (Appended to the The COMICAL adventures of David Dufficks, [18-?], pp. 65-76.)

NN   0027689   MH

Nata, of Shinovi
see
Nathan Nata, of Shinovo.

Nata, André Éloi, 1888-
... Contribution à l'étude des hygromas prérotuliens ... Bordeaux, 1921.
25.5 cm.
Thèse - Univ. de Bordeaux.

NN   0027691   CtY

Nata Permana, Rd. Hasan
see   Permana, Hasan Nata, Raden.

Nata Rajan, M   S
Famine in retrospect. Bombay, Padma Publications [1944]
63 p. 19 cm. (Current topics series, no. 14)

1. India—Famines. I. Title. (Series)
HC439.N35   57-51664

NN   0027693   DLC

342(54)
N271
Nata Rajan, M   S
The Indian Constituent Assembly. New Delhi [Feb. 1947]
49 p. 24cm.

1. India (Dominion) Constituent Assembly.

NN   0027694   NNUN NN

Nata Rajan, M   S
Some aspects of the Indian war economy. Baroda, Padmaja Publications [1946?]
vii, 153 p. 22 cm.

1. India—Econ. condit—1918-1945. I. Title.
HC435.N34   57-21222

NN   0027695   DLC CaBVaU NjP NIC PU

Nata Rajan, M   S
A study of the capital market of Madras Presidency, with special reference to its evolution and indigenous institutions. [Calcutta] 1936.
76, ii p. 27 cm.

1. Banks and banking—Madras (Presidency)
HG3289.M3N3   332.1   48-33924*

NN   0027696   DLC

Wason
PL5454
N27W7
Nata Sukarja, M   E
Wira pakoentjen, karangan M.E. Nata Soekarja. Batavia, Bale Poestaka, 1931.
136 p. illus. 22 cm.

NN   0027697   NIC

VOLUME 405

Nataasmara, M. Kamit
    see   Kamit Nataasmara, M

NATABAL nu Tinamit. Composicion en dialecto Kiché.
    6pp. Ts. (Poem)
    In: Mava Soc. Quart., vol.1 (1932), p.71.

NN   0027699   ICN

Natacha, *pseud.*
    see Ituño, Angela de.

...Natación. México, Compañia general editora, 1945.   87 p.
    illus.   19cm.   (Biblioteca deportiva. 6)

1. Swimming. I. Ser.
N. Y. P. L.   September 30, 1949

NN   0027701   NN

Natadze, G   M
    Основы гигиены. ₍2., заново перер. изд.₎ Допущено в
    качестве учеб пособия для лечебных и педиатрических
    факультетов мед. ин-тов. Москва, Медгиз, 1951.
    350 p. illus., maps. 27 cm.
    Errata slip inserted.
    Bibliography: p. ₍355₎

1. Hygiene, Public.   I. Title.
              Title transliterated: Osnovy gigieny.

RA425.N34 1951   52–36685

NN   0027702   DLC

Nb   Nataf, André
1   Sur des questions d'agrégation en
1954   économétrie. Paris, 1954.
      58 p. illus.

      Thèse – Paris.

      1. Economics, Mathematical.

NN   0027703   CtY MH

Nataf, Berthe, joint author.

Jacquot, Raymond.
    ... Le manioc et son utilisation alimentaire, par Raymond
Jacquot et Berthe Nataf ... Introduction de Émile F. Ter-
roine. Paris, Hermann & cᵗᵉ, 1936.

WH   Nataf, Berthe
43   Sur la régulation de certaines activités
      enzymatiques tissulaires par des hormones
      sexuelles. [Paris? 1953?]
      113 p. illus.

      Thèse – Paris.

NN   0027705   CtY

Nataf (Edouard) [1895–]. *Arthropathie
tabétique et accidents du travail. 20 pp. 8°.
Paris, 1924. No. 153.

NN   0027706   DNLM CtY

Nataf, Félix.
    ...Le crédit et la banque au Maroc. Préface par François
Piétri... Paris: P. Geuthner, 1929.   vi, 8–217 p. incl. tables.
4°.

    Bibliography, p. ₍215–₎217.

501299A.   1. Banks and banking—   Morocco. 2. Credit—Morocco.
N. Y. P. L.   November 10, 1930

NN   0027707   NN MH CtY

T113   Nataf, François, 1912-
P21   ... Contribution à l'étude du surménage intel-
1939   lectuel; son existence dans le domaine pro-
      fessionnel ... Paris,1939.
      Thèse – Univ. de Paris.

NN   0027708   CtY

T113   Nataf, Gaston, 1868-
A215   ... Contribution à l'étude do traitement
1921   chirurgical de l'éléphantiasis des membres par
      la méthode de Walther ...
      Alger,1921.   24½cm.
      Thèse – Univ. d'Alger.

NN   0027709   CtY

T113   Nataf, Jacques, 1900-
P21   ... Le traitement de l'eczéma et du prurit par
1928   le sulfate de magnésie ... Paris,1928.
      Thèse – Univ. de Paris.

NN   0027710   CtY

W   Nataf, Raoul Aaron, 1912-
4   Le traitement de l'hémogénie par la
P23   radiothérapie splénique ... Paris,
1942   Foulon, 1942.
      56 p. (Paris. ₍Université₎ Faculté
      de médecine. Thèse. 1942. no. 44)

NN   0027711   DNLM MnU CtY

Nataf, Roger, joint author.

Cuénod, Auguste Jean, 1868–
    ... Biomicroscopie de la conjonctive. Avec 6 figures et 34
planches en couleurs hors texte. Paris, Masson et cᵗᵉ, 1934.

R10   Nataf, Roger
+Pa951   Contribution à l'étude des transitions
      interdites. Paris[1951]
      Thèse – Paris.

NN   0027713   CtY

Nataf, Roger, joint author.

Cuénod, Auguste Jean, 1868–
    ... Le trachome, avec 39 figures originales en noir et en cou-
leurs. Préface de Charles Nicolle. Paris, Masson et cᵗᵉ, 1930.

OPTOMETRY
RE321   Nataf, Roger.
N19   Le trachome; historique, clinique,
1952   recherches expérimentales et étiologie,
      thérapeutique, prophylaxie. Préf. de A.
      Cuénod. Paris, Masson, 1952.
      426 p. illus., col. plates.

      Bibliography: p. ₍367₎–416.

      1. Conjunctivitis, Granular.

NN   0027715   NNC-M MiU PU-UH-DeS   PPC ICJ DNLM

Nataf, Roger, joint author.

Cuénod, Auguste Jean, 1868–
    Trahom, yazanlar: A. Cuénod ve R. Nataf, çeviren: dr.
Murad Rami Aydın ... İstanbul, Devlet basimevi, 1938.

T113   Nataf, Roger, 1901-
P21   ... La rupture spontanée du globe oculaire
1927   dans le glaucome ...
      Paris,1927.   23cm.
      Thèse – Univ. de Paris.
      "Bibliographie": pp.₍81₎–83.

NN   0027717   CtY

T113   Nataf, Siméon Armand, 1912-
P21   ... Essai de thérapeutique de la tétanie para-
1939   thyréoprive de l'adulte par résection du sympa-
      thique cervical ... Paris,1939.
      Thèse – Univ. de Paris.

NN   0027718   CtY

PL5089   Natahamidjaja, R. B. Prasena.
.S75T5
Orien   Sugeng.
Indo   Tjinta dan kebenaran, menurut dasar tjeritera Prasena,
    karangan R. B. Natahamidjaja. Djakarta, Balai Pustaka,
    1950.

Natal, A., pseud.

    see

Natalucci, Aurelio.

Natal, Antonio

    see

Natale, Antonio, 1648–1701.

Natal, Arthur Hamilton Baynes, *Bp. of*
    see Baynes, Arthur Hamilton, *Bp.*, 1854–1942.

NATAL, GIORGIO.
    ...L'artèfice; tragedia in quattro atti... Milano [Tip.
E.Zerboni, 1933]   85 p.   18½cm.   (Collezione teatrale
moderna. [n.] 30.)

1. Drama, Italian. I. Title. II. Ser.

NN   0027723   NN

NATAL, GIORGIO.
    ...Un nome e dieci secoli... Milano: [Tip. E.Bellasio,
1935]   76 p.   18½cm.   (Collezione teatrale moderna.
[n.] 36.)

1. Drama, Italian. I. Title. II. Ser.

NN   0027724   NN

Natal, Giorgio.
    ...Sogno equoreo; tragedia marina in 3 azioni.   Rocca S. Ca-
sciano: Stab. tip. L. Cappelli, 1931.   129 p.   24cm.

    Copies numbered; this copy no. 171.

622924A.   1. Drama, Italian.   I. Title.
N. Y. P. L.   August 10, 1936

NN   0027725   NN

NATAL, Jerónimo.

    See NADAL, Gerónimo.

Natal, John William, bp. of, 1814-1883
    see   Colenso, John William, bp. of
Natal, 1814-1883.

4F   Natal e Silva, Collemar
Braz.   Historia de Goyaz. Rio de Janeiro,
213   Estabelecimento Graphico Mundo Medico,
      1935-
      v. 1-

NN   0027728   DLC-P4 ICU CSt

VOLUME 405

Natal e Silva, Collemar.
... Ruy Barbosa em seu tempo e em seu meio, traços de sua vida e de sua obra. Rio de Janeiro, Typ. do Patronato, 1928.
2 p. l., [7]–169 p., 1 l. 18ᶜᵐ.
"Conferencia realizada ... no dia 10 de agosto de 1928, no Instituto da Ordem dos advogados brasileiros ..."

1. Barbosa, Ruy, 1849–1923.

30–15003

Library of Congress   F2537.B26

NN 0027729   DLC

Natal.
Official publications of the "Colony of Natal" (before May 31, 1910) and of the "Province of Natal" (May 31, 1910–   ) are entered under the above heading.

J711
.R2
Natal.
Blue book for the colony of Natal ... Pietermaritzburg, Natal [18
25 v. [1884 has a supplement ...
"Departmental reports, 1884. Pietermaritz-burg, 1885]

NN 0028002   DLC

J711
.R3
Natal.
...Departmental reports.

NN 0028003   DLC

Natal.
Departmental reports. 1884.

see

Natal.
Blue book for the colony of Natal... 1884.

DT
868
E53
Natal.
Emigration to Natal, and conditions of govern-ment land grants, with full description of the Colony and its industries. Published under the authority of the Colonial Govern-ment. London, Jarrold [1866?]
64,12,14 p. col.map.

1. Natal.

NN 0028005   CLU

Natal.
Estimates of the additional expenditure to be defrayed from revenue. Begroting van die addisionele uitgawes wat bestry moet word uit inkomste.
[Pietermaritzburg]
v. 30 cm. annual.
Report year ends Mar. 30.
Afrikaans and English.

1. Natal—Appropriations and expenditures. I. Natal. Begro-ting van die addisionele uitgawes wat bestry moet word uit inkomste.
HJ80E.A33   354'.68'4007224   73–645770
                                                MARC-S

NN 0028006   DLC

Natal.
The game sanctuaries of Natal ...
see under Ledward, C. N.

Natal.

Pitchford, Herbert Watkins-
... Horse-sickness investigation. Introductory. By H. Watkins-Pitchford, F. R. C. V. S. Pietermaritzburg, "Times" printing and publishing company, ltd., 1903.

Natal.
List of clerks on the permanent civil establish-ment.
Pietermaritzburg, 1893–

JQ2221
1893b+

NN 0028009   DLC

25·7
5094
Natal.
...List of officers holding appointments in the civil service of the colony of Natal.
[Pietermaritzburg, 1877–

NN 0028010   DLC

Natal.
The Natal civil service list
Pietermaritzburg,
v. 22ᶜᵐ.

1. Civil service—Natal.   I. Natal. Colonial secretary's office.
II. Title.
Library of Congress   JQ2221   7–16346

NN 0028011   DLC CtY NcD

J8
'87
Natal.
Natal government gazette.

NN 0028012   DLC

J
8
B7
Microfilm
Natal.
Official gazette.   Pietermaritzburg.

NN 0028013   MBU

Natal.
Reports of resident magistrates and administrators of native law on natives ...
Pietermaritzburg,
18
v. 33ᶜᵐ.

1. Natal—Native races.
                                     CA 6—1032 Unrev'd
Library of Congress   HC517.N3A3

NN 0028014   DLC

Natal.
Rules for the gaols in the colony of Natal. Made by the governor in council under and by virtue of the pro-visions of Law 39 of 1887. Pietermaritzburg, Printed by P. Davis & sons, 1903.
2 p. l., 34 p. 24½ᶜᵐ.

4–34846†

NN 0028015   DLC

Natal.

Great Britain.
South African telegraphs ... Copy "of the Agreement made the 27th day of July 1901 between His Majesty's gov-ernment, the governments of Cape colony and Natal, the Brit-ish South Africa company, and the Eastern, and the Eastern and South African telegraph companies for the transmission of telegraph traffic to and from South Africa; together with a copy of the Treasury minute thereon, dated the 29th day of July 1901" ... London, Printed for H. M. Stationery off. by Wyman and sons, limited, 1901.

Natal. Addington Hospital, Durban.
  See
Natal. Government Hospital, Addington.

Natal. *Agent-general in London.*
... Report.
Pietermaritzburg,
v. 33½ᶜᵐ.
          have title: Report of the agent-general.

1. Natal—Pol. & govt.
J711.R25   9–3258

NN 0028018   DLC

Natal. Agriculture Dept.
  see **Natal.** Dept. of Agriculture.

Natal.   Arms and ammunition dept.
Natal. *Laws, statutes, etc.*
... The Natal mines act (no. 43), 1899. And the regu-lations framed thereunder, with regulations for the stor-age of explosives. Pietermaritzburg, Printed by W. Wat-son, government printer, 1900.

Natal. *Attorney-general's office.*
Criminal statistics, and attorney-general's report.
[Pietermaritzburg, 18
v. 33ᶜᵐ.

1. Crime and criminals—Natal. 2. Criminal statistics—Natal.
                                              9–3661†
Library of Congress   HV7384.N3A3

NN 0028021   DLC

Natal. *Audit Dept.*
  see **Natal.** *Audit Office.*

HJ9080E
.A3
Natal. Audit office.
Annual general report of the provincial auditor on the accounts of local authorities,
38th–
1953/54–
[Pietermaritzburg] 1956–
v.

1. Natal – Finance. 2. Finance – Natal.
3. USAfr. – Finance – Natal. I. Serials –
USAfr. – Annuals, etc.

NN 0028023   DS

VOLUME 405

Natal. *Audit* Office.
Auditor-general's report on the public accounts.

Pietermaritzburg, 18

v. in   32¼ᶜᵐ.
Report year irregular.
Title varies.

1. Finance—Natal.

10–32992

Library of Congress   HJ80.E3

NN   0028024   DLC

Natal. *Audit Office.*
Finance accounts (including trust, housing loan and village water supply accounts) Teachers' Pension and Provident Funds accounts and appropriation accounts ... with the Provincial Auditor's reports thereon.

Pietermaritzburg ₍etc.₎

v. in   34 cm.
Report year irregular.
Title varies: 18 slightly)—18   Auditor's report. Public accounts (varies counts.—189   -19   Auditor-General's report on public accounts. Treasurer's finance accounts, Contingencies

Fund account, Public Debt Commissioners' accounts, Suppression of native rebellion account ... and other miscellaneous accounts ... with the Auditor-General's reports thereon (varies slightly)

1. Finance—Natal.

HJ80.E3   13–17301 rex*

NN   0028026   DLC NN DS

Natal. *Audit office.*
... Financial instructions regulating the mode of keeping and rendering the accounts of receipts and expenditure. Approved by His Excellency the administrator in Council on the 16th day of June, 1898. Pietermaritzburg, Natal, P. Davis & sons, government printers, 1898.

1 p. l., vii, 58, ₍1₎ p., 1 l. 24ᶜᵐ.

4–34844†

NN   0028027   DLC

Natal. *Audit Office.*
Instructions regulating the mode of keeping and rendering the accounts of receipt and expenditure in the Colony of Natal. Pietermaritzburg, P. Davis, Govt. Printers, 1886.

16 p. 32 cm.

1. Finance—Natal—Accounting.

HJ9929.N2A3 1886   7–24504 rev*

NN   0028028   DLC

Natal. *Audit Office.*
Report upon the system of keeping the public accounts in the Colony of Natal. 1895. Pietermaritzburg, W. Watson, Printer to the Natal Government, 1895.

43 p. 33 cm.
Signed: John Bromley, Exchequer and Audit Dept.

1. Finance—Natal—Accounting.   ɪ. Bromley, John.
HJ9929.N2A3 1895   7–24503 rev*

NN   0028029   DLC

Natal. *Auditor*
see **Natal.** *Audit Office.*

Natal. *Bacteriological dept.*
Report.

Pietermaritzburg,

v. 24–33ᶜᵐ.

1. Bacteriology.

8–9987

Library of Congress   SF719.N3A2

NN   0028031   DLC

Natal. Boilers dept., Inspector of.

see

Natal. Inspector of boilers dept.

Natal. *Census board.*
Census of 1891. Report with tables and appendices. Natal, P. Davis & sons, gov't printers, 1891.

21, ₍3₎ p. map, 22 tab. (partly fold.) fold. form. 33ᶜᵐ.
Signed: W. Broome, G. Nicholls, H. Wylde-Browne, J. G. Dartnell.

1. Natal—Census, 1891.   ɪ. Broome, William.

6–16188

Library of Congress   HA2012 1891

NN   0028033   DLC NIC

Natal. *Census office.*
Census of the colony of Natal April 1904. Presented to His Excellency the governor of Natal, June, 1905. Pietermaritzburg, P. Davis & sons, government printers, 1905.

5 p. l., 926 p. fold. maps, fold. diagrs., fold. forms. 33⅓ᶜᵐ.
Census commissioner: Thos. K. Murray.

1. Natal—Census, 1904.   ɪ. Murray, Sir Thomas Keir, 1854–

7–18375

Library of Congress   HA2012 1904

NN   0028034   DLC ICJ

Natal. Central Experiment Farm.
Further report on manure experiments
see under   **Natal. Dept. of Agriculture.**

Natal. Central Experiment Farm.
Report on experiments in potato growing...
see under   **Natal. Dept. of Agriculture.**

Natal. Civil service board.
Minutes...relative to the reduction of establishments, etc., and the classification of the civil service of Natal.
Pietermaritzburg, 1906.
2 v.   f° *tables 33 cm.*

JQ 2245 .A5.

NN   0028037   DLC

Natal. Civil service board.
Report of Civil service committee.
[Pietermaritzburg? 1906]

JQ2245
D4
1906

NN   0028038   DLC

Natal. Civil Service board.
Report of the committee appointed to enquire into civil service administration. 1907... Maritzburg: P. Davis & Sons, 1907. 41 p. tables. f°.

Investigation made by the Civil Service Board with three additional members.

1. Civil service, Natal. 2. Natal.   Civil Service Board.
N. Y. P. L.   October 28, 1921.

NN   0028039   NN DLC

Natal. *Civil service commission.*
Reports on the civil service of Natal, by the civil service commissioner. 1903. Pietermaritzburg, P. Davis & sons, printers, 1903.

4 p. l., 85 p. 7 fold. tab. 31¼ᶜᵐ.
Henry Higgs, commissioner.
Contents.—Memorandum and instructions for the guidance of the civil service commissioner.— Copy of Minute, principal under secretary to heads of departments.—First report. Estimates.—Second report. Excise department.—Third report. Methods of dealing with official papers in the Natal civil service.—Fourth report. Savings bank department.—Fifth report. Volunteer department.—Sixth report. Post office.—Seventh report. Treasury.— Eighth report. Magistrates.— Ninth-Tenth and final report. General.
ɪ. Higgs, Henry, 1864–

8–5863

NN   0028040   DLC

Natal. Civil service committee
see
Natal. Civil service board.

Natal. *Coal testing committee.*
... Report of the Coal testing committee 1904–1905. Maritzburg, P. Davis & sons, printers and publishers, 1905.

1 p. l., 89, ₍1₎ p. plates, plans (partly fold.) 33ᶜᵐ.

1. Coal testing.

G S 6–518

Library, U. S. Geol.   survey

NN   0028042   DI–GS ICJ

Natal. Coffee cultivation, Commission on.
see
Natal. Commission on coffee cultivation.

Natal. Collector of customs.
Report of the collector of customs
see under   **Natal. Customs and excise dept.**

VOLUME 405

Natal. *Colonial defence commission.*
... Report of the Colonial defence commission, with minutes of evidence. Pietermaritzburg, "Times" printing and publishing company, ltd., 1903.

2 p. l., 265 p., 1 l. 33ᶜᵐ.

At head of title : Confidential.
Ernest L. Acutt, chairman.

1. Natal—Defenses.   ɪ. Acutt, Ernest Leslie.

Library of Congress   UA857.N2 1903   6–6283

NN   0028045   DLC

Natal. Colonial Secretary's Office.
    ... Natal. Annual report for 1887–1891–2
    see under   Gt. Brit. Colonial Office.

Natal.   Colonial secretary's office.

Natal.
   The Natal civil service list
   Pietermaritzburg,

Natal. Colonial secretary's office.

Natal. *Committee on test of colonial woods for railway sleepers.*
Report of Committee on test of colonial woods for railway sleepers. To the Honourable the colonial secretary. ₍Pietermaritzburg, 1892₎

Natal. Colonial secretary's office.
Natal. *Committee to enquire into the working of the public departments.*
Report of the Committee appointed to enquire into the working of the various public departments of the colony, with a view to placing them upon the most efficient footing, and simplifying the conduct of business. ₍n. p., 1875₎

Natal. *Colonial secretary's office.*
Statistical year book.

Pietermaritzburg, 18

v. 25–33ᶜᵐ.

1. Natal—Stat.   ɪ. Title.

       7—4545

Library of Congress   HA2013

NN   0028050   DLC ICU KMK CtY CU ICJ

Natal. *Commission of Enquiry to Report upon the System of Education in Natal*
    see
Natal. *Education Commission.*

Natal. *Commission on coffee cultivation.*
   ... Commission ₍appointed₎ to inquire into and report upon matters relating to coffee cultivation in the colony. ₍Report₎ Maritzburg, Vause, Slatter & co., government printers, 1881.

cover-title, 6 p. 33ᶜᵐ.

S. Crowder, chairman.

1. Coffee—Natal.   ɪ. Crowder, Samuel.

       7–34746

Library of Congress   SB269.N3

NN   0028052   DLC

Natal. *Commission on education.*
   ... Report of the Commission on education, appointed by ... Sir Charles Bullen Hugh Mitchell, ᴋ. ᴄ. ᴍ. ɢ., governor ... 1891. Pietermaritzburg, Natal, P. Davis & sons, government printers ₍1891₎

4 p. l., ₍218₎ p. 32½ᶜᵐ.

Commission : Killingworth Richard Todd, George Thomas Nicholls, George Gardner, Charles Barter, and Kenneth Howard Hathorn.

1. Education—Natal.   ɪ. Todd, Killingworth Richard, 1843–

       5–26569 Revised

Library of Congress   L667.A6

NN   0028053   DLC DHEW

Natal. *Commission on European immigration.*
Report to His Excellency Sir Henry Ernest Bulwer ... ₍Pietermaritzburg? 1885₎

10 p. 34ᶜᵐ.

Caption title.
George C. K. Richardson, chairman.
Commission appointed to investigate the management of the Land and immigration board, with all matters connected with European immigration; the extent to which lands can be utilized for agricultural settlement by irrigation; measures for encouraging erection of sugar mills, and means for encouraging fencing of lands.

1. Natal—Emig. & immig.   ɪ. Richardson, George C. K.

       8–34313

Library of Congress   JV8927.A29 1885

NN   0028054   DLC

Natal. Commission on immigration and crown lands.
Natal. *Land and immigration board.*
European immigration to Natal. The experiences of practical farmers, elicited by a circular letter and questions addressed by the Land and immigration board, in November, 1890, to farmers in Natal; also their advice to intending immigrants. Pub. by resolution of the Commission on immigration and crown lands, appointed by His Honour Francis Seymour Haden ... deputy governor ... on 28th August, 1891. Pietermaritzburg, P. Davis & sons, government printers ₍1891?₎

Natal. *Commission on importation of stock.*
   ... Report of the Commission appointed by His Excellency Sir Charles Bullen Bullen Hugh Mitchell ... to enquire into and report upon the best means to be adopted by the government with the view of improving the breed of cattle and horses in Natal. 1889–90. Pietermaritzburg, W. Watson, government printer, 1890.

1 p. l., vi, ₍429₎ p. 33 cm.
Paged : A2, B26, C39, D322, E40.
Sir Thomas K. Murray, chairman.
1. Cattle breeding. 2. Cattle—Natal. 3. Horse breeding—Natal. ɪ. Murray, Sir Thomas Keir, 1854–1936.

       6–23940

SF55.N2A4 1890

NN   0028056   DLC

Natal. *Commission on leprosy.*
Report of the Commission on leprosy. ₍Pietermaritzburg? 1886₎

21 p. 33½ᶜᵐ.
G. A. Lucas, chairman.

1. Leprosy—Natal.   ɪ. Lucas, G. A.

       7–34766

Library of Congress   RC154.8.N3 1886

NN   0028057   DLC

Natal. *Commission on magisterial divisions.*
   ... Report of the Commission appointed by His Excellency Sir Charles Bullen Hugh Mitchell ... to enquire into and report upon the sufficiency or otherwise of the magisterial divisions of the colony, &c. 1890–91. Pietermaritzburg, P. Davis & sons, government printers ₍1892?₎

2 p. l., vi, 45 p. fold. map. 32½ᶜᵐ.

At head of title : Colony of Natal.
Henrique C. Shepstone, chairman.

1. Administrative division—Natal.   ɪ. Shepstone, Henrique Charles, 1840–

       8–34312

Library of Congress   JQ2270.A5 1890/91

NN   0028058   DLC

Natal. *Commission on native mission reserve.*
Report of native mission reserve. ₍Pietermaritzburg? 1886?₎

11 p. 33ᶜᵐ.

Caption title.
Commissioners : W. D. Wheelwright, chairman, G. C. Cato, John Kirkman, H. E. Stainbank.

1. Land grants—Natal. 2. Church lands—Natal.   ɪ. Wheelwright, William Douglas.

       7–32982

Library of Congress   HD983.N3A4 1886

NN   0028059   DLC

Natal. *Commission on pollution of streams.*
   ... Commission appointed to enquire into and report upon the pollution of streams in the coast districts. ₍Report₎ Pietermaritzburg, Vause, Slatter & co., government printers, 1881.

cover-title, 5 p. 33ᶜᵐ.

A. H. Hime, chairman.

1. Water-supply—Natal. 2. Water, Pollution of.   ɪ. Hime, Sir Albert Henry, 1842–

       7–41315

Library of Congress   TD425.N3

NN   0028060   DLC

Natal. Commission on scab and stock diseases.
Third and final report. Commission on scab and stock diseases, 1894–5.
Pietermaritzburg, 1895.

SF719
.N3A4

NN   0028061   DLC

Natal. *Commission to Enquire into and Report upon the System of Education in Natal*
    see
Natal. *Education Commission.*

Natal. *Commission to inquire into the past and present state of the Kafirs.*
Proceedings and report of the Commission appointed to inquire into the past and present state of the Kafirs in the district of Natal, and to report upon their future government, and to suggest such arrangements as will tend to secure the peace and welfare of the district, for the information of His Honour Lieutenant-Governor Pine. ₍Pietermaritzburg, 1852–3 ₍1879₎

1 p. l., iv, 64 p. 32ᶜᵐ.
Signed : Walter Macfarlane, president.
On cover : Report on native affairs in Natal, 1852-3. Reprinted in 1879.
1. Natal—Native races.   ɪ. Macfarlane, Walter, of Natal.

       7–15721

Library of Congress   HC517.N3A5 1853a

NN   0028063   DLC NN

Natal. Commission to Inquire into the Past and Present State of the Kafirs.
Proceedings and report of the Commission appointed to inquire into the past and present state of the Kafirs in the district of Natal, and to report upon their future government, and to suggest such arrangements as will tend to secure the peace and welfare of the district, for the information of His Honour Lieutenant-Governor Pine. 1852–3. ₍Pietermaritzburg, 1853?₎
64, iv p. 29½ cm.

Photostatic reproduction, on 69 leaves, of the original in the British Colonial office library.

*ZS – 140

———— Film copy.

Film reproduction of the original in the British Colonial office library. 35mm. Reduction 12. Position II. Negative.

Natal. Kafirs, Commission to inquire into the past and present

*ZS – 140

———— Proceedings of the commission...   Natal: J. Archbell and son, 1852–53.   6 parts in 1 v.

Film reproduction of the original in the British Colonial office library. 35mm. Reduction 12. Position II. Negative.

1. African tribes—Kafirs.
N. Y. P. L.   November 22, 1940

NN   0028066   NN

VOLUME 405

Natal. Commission to Inquire into the Past and Present State of the Kafirs

Proceedings of the Commission appointed to inquire into the past and present state of the Kafirs in the District of Natal, and to report upon their future government, and to suggest such arrangements as will tend to secure the peace and welfare of the district, for the information of His Honor the Lieutenant-Governor. Pietermaritzburg, J.Archbell, 1852-53

6 v. in 1
Part 6 lacks t.p.

NN 0028067   MH CtY IEN

Natal. Commissioners for the Colonial and Indian Exhibition.

Catalogue. Natal contributions to Colonial and Indian exhibition at South Kensington, 1886.
    see under   London. Colonial and Indian Exhibition, 1886.

Natal. Commissioners for the Colonial and Indian Exhibition.

Natal; official handbook ...
    see under   London. Colonial and Indian Exhibition, 1886.

Natal.   Commissioners of land agricultural loan fund.
     see

South Africa. Commissioners of land and agricultural loan fund, Natal.

Natal. Committee appointed to enquire into civil service administration, 1907.
    see

Natal. Civil service board.

Natal. Committee on primary school system.

     see

Natal. Council of education. Committee on primary school system.

Natal. *Committee on test of colonial woods for railway sleepers.*

Report of Committee on test of colonial woods for railway sleepers. To the Honourable the colonial secretary. [Pietermaritzburg, 1892]

7 p. 23ᶜᵐ.

Committee: John W. Shores, chairman, P. C. Sutherland, G. Nicholls.

1. Railroads—Ties. 2. Wood—Preservation.   I. Shores, John W. II. Natal. Colonial secretary's office.

Library of Congress   TF254.N3   8—19062

NN 0028073   DLC

Natal. *Committee on the supply of intoxicating liquors to natives.*

... Report of the Committee on the supply of intoxicating liquors to natives, appointed by His Excellency Sir Charles Bullen Hugh Mitchell ... Pietermaritzburg, P. Davis & sons, government printers, 1892.

cover-title, 47 p. 33ᶜᵐ.

Henry Bale, chairman.

1. Liquor traffic—Natal.   I. Bale, Sir Henry, 1854–

                    6—15168

Library of Congress   HV5199.N2A5 1892

NN 0028074   DLC

Natal. *Committee to enquire into the working of the public departments.*

Report of the Committee appointed to enquire into the working of the various public departments of the colony, with a view to placing them upon the most efficient footing, and simplifying the conduct of business. [n. p., 1875]

31 p. 32ᶜᵐ.

Caption title.
F. Napier Broome, colonial secretary, chairman.

I. Broome, Sir Frederick Napier, 1842–1896. II. Natal. Colonial secretary's office.

                    6–15169

NN 0028075   DLC

Natal. Conservator of forests.

Report of the conservator of forests
    see under   Natal. Dept. of Agriculture.

Natal. Controller of Excise
    see   Natal. Excise Office.

Natal. *Coolie commission.*

... Report of Coolie commission, appointed to inquire into the condition of the Indian immigrants in the colony of Natal; the mode in which they are employed; and also to inquire into the complaints made by returned immigrants to the protector of emigrants at Calcutta. August, 1872. Pietermaritzburg, P. Davis and sons, government printers, 1872.

iv, 66 p. 33ᶜᵐ.

Signed: M. H. Gallwey, B. P. Lloyd.

I. Gallwey, Sir Michael Henry, 1826–

                    5–41541

NN 0028078   DLC

Natal. Council
    see   Natal. Provincial Council.

Natal. Council of education.

Income and expenditure of the Council of education for 1880–86
(n.p., 1885–86.

2 v. 31½cm.

NN 0028080   DHEW

Natal. *Council of education. Committee on primary school system.*

Interim report of the committee appointed on 26th January, 1887, "to enquire into the primary school system, with special reference to 'payment by results.'" [Pietermaritzburg, 1887]

14 p. 32½ᶜᵐ.

Henry Bale, convener.

1. Education—Natal.   I. Bale, Sir Henry, 1854–

Library of Congress   LB1564.N3A3   6–39109

NN 0028081   DLC

Natal. *Crown lands commission.*

... Report [of commission appointed to enquire into the operations of the rules and regulations, proclaimed on the 16th of October, 1880, for the alienation and settlement of the crown lands of the colony, etc.] [Pietermaritzburg] 1886]

18 p. 32ᶜᵐ.

A. H. Hime, chairman.

1. Natal—Public lands.   I. Hime, Sir Albert Henry, 1842–

                    7–32984

Library of Congress   HD989.N3A4 1886

NN 0028082   DLC

Natal. *Customs and excise dept.*

Report of the collector of customs.

Pietermaritzburg,

   [v. in 5] tables (partly fold.) 33ᶜᵐ. annual.

1900–1902. Report of the collector of customs on the shipping and trade of the colony.
1903–19   Report of the collector of customs, and Report of the collector of excise.
1902 includes "Comparison between Customs union and Transvaal customs tariffs" (p. 14–25)

1. Natal—Custom house. 2. Natal—Comm. 3. Tariff—Natal. 4. Internal revenue—Natal.
The Report of the collector   for of excise is continued in "Report of the commissioner of excise   e" (South Africa. Commissioner 8–4542 of customs and excise).
Library of Congress   HJ80.E7   8–4542

NN 0028083   DLC

Natal. *Department of Agriculture.*

Bulletin ... . Natal, Department of Agriculture. ... . Pietermaritzburg, 1902–1909.

No. 3–5, 15–16. illus., plates. 25ᶜᵐ.
Publication discontinued.

                (SB35 .A4)

NN 0028084   ICJ DLC

Natal. Department of Agriculture.

Sawer, E   R.

Cedara memoirs on South African agriculture, by E. R. Sawer ... Pietermaritzburg, Printed at the City printing works, 1909.

Natal. Dept. of Agriculture.
...Further report on manure experiments, by the Director of agriculture. [1903]

NN 0028086   DNAL

S17
.N3

Natal. Dept. of agriculture.

... The **Natal** agricultural journal

[Pietermaritzburg, etc.] The "Times" printing and publishing company, limited,

VOLUME 405

S335   Natal. Dept. of agriculture.
.A6   ... Notes on agriculture in Natal.   Maritzburg,
        P. Davis & Sons, printers [1905]
        1 p.l., 79 p.   illus.   24 cm.

NN 0028088   DLC DNAL

Natal. *Dept. of agriculture.*
    ... Report of the conservator of forests, Natal ...
Pietermaritzburg, 19

    v. tables, fold. plans. 25ᶜᵐ.

    Continued in Report of the chief conservator of forests (South Africa.
Dept. of forests)

    1. Forests and forestry—Natal.

    Library of Congress   SD103.N3A2   8—27245

NN 0028089   DLC CU

Natal. *Dept. of agriculture.*
    Report of the government entomologist.

Pietermaritzburg, 19

    v. illus., plates. 24½ᶜᵐ. annual.

    1. Insects, Injurious and beneficial.
                                                8—1614
    Library of Congress   SB919.N3A3

NN 0028090   DLC ICJ

Natal. Dept. of Agriculture.
    Report on experiments in potato growing at the Natal cen-
tral experiment farm, during seasons 1902-3 and 1903-4. Pietermaritzburg: Times Prtg. and Pub. Co., Ltd., 1905.   2 p.l., 40 p.
8°. (Bull. 9.)

1. Potato.—Experiments. Natal.
N. Y. P. L.   July 28, 1913.

NN 0028091   NN

Natal. *Dept. of agriculture.*
    Reports of Messrs. Lloyd and Vanderplank on out-
break of rinderpest. Report of commissioner of agriculture, Natal, to the Honourable the colonial treasurer ...
[Pietermaritzburg, 1896]

    6 p. 33½ᶜᵐ.

    1. Rinderpest. .. Lloyd, C. B. II. Vanderplank, F. B.
                                                8—16997
    Library of Congress   SF966.N27

NN 0028092   DLC

Natal. Dept. of agriculture.
    ... Supplementary report by Col. F.V. Corbett
on irrigation in Natal, dated 11th November, 1901
        see under   Corbett, Frank Vincent.

Natal. Dept. of native affairs

        see

Natal. Native affairs dept.

Natal. *Dept. of public health.*
    Report of the health officer
Pietermaritzburg, 1903-

    · v. in   tables, diagrs. (partly fold.) 33½ᶜᵐ.

    1. Natal—Sanit. aff.
                                                8—4886
    Library of Congress   RA352.N2

NN 0028095   DLC

Natal. *Director of Provincial Medical and Health Services.*
    Report. Verslag.
[Pietermaritzburg]
        v. 32 cm. annual.
    Report year ends Mar. 31.

    1. Hygiene, Public—Natal.

    RA352.N27   614.061684   50—56945 ‡

NN 0028096   DLC

Natal. *Education Commission.*
    Report, 1937. Pietermaritzburg, Natal Press [1938]
    x, 116 p. 34 cm.

    1. Education—Natal.

    L667.B35   58—53112

NN 0028097   DLC NN CtY

Natal. *Education, Commission on* [1891]
        see
Natal. *Commission on education.*

Natal. Education Committee, Provincial
        see Natal. Provincial Education Commit-
tee.

Natal. *Education dept.*
    Annual report.
Pietermaritzburg, P. Davis & sons, government printers
[etc., 18

    v. in   32½ᶜᵐ.

    Report year irregular: ends Dec. 31, 18   –   ; June 30, 18   –
1885–   pub. also in the Blue book for the colony of Natal, 1885–
Title varies: 18   –1894, Report of the inspector of native education.
1894–   Annual report of the inspector of native schools.

    1. Education—Natal.
                                            CA 5—2228 Unrev'd
    Library of Congress   L667.A2

NN 0028100   DLC DHEW

Natal. Education dept.
    ... Education department directory 1904, 1906.
Pietermaritzburg, 1904- 6
        3v. 8°

                            (L667 .A37)

NN 0028101   DLC

Natal. Education Dept.
    Natal education. [Mobeni, Durban, 1949]

    100 p. illus.
    Editorial Committee: C.M.Boysen, Chairman, E.A.Halm
[and others]: general editor: N.E.Nuttall.
    Title and text also in Afrikaans.

NN 0028102   MH

Natal. *Education Dept.*
    Natalse onderwys. Natal education. [Pietermaritzburg
1949]
    100 p. illus., ports., col. maps. 25 cm.
    English and Afrikaans.

    1. Education—Natal.

    LA1571.A5 1949   379.684   53—22371

NN 0028103   DLC PU NN

L81   Natal. Education dept.
.N3   Native teachers' journal.

        [Pietermaritzburg] Natal, Education department, 19

Natal. *Education dept.*
    ... Report of the superintendent of education ... Pieter-
maritzburg [1886]-19
    v. in   33ᵐ.
    Report year irregular.

    Published also in the Blue book for the colony of Natal, 18

    1. Education—Natal.   6—42767 Revised
    Library of Congress   L667.A3

NN 0028105   DLC NcD NN DHEW MBU

Natal. Education dept.
    Report on Indian schools 1886-1887

    Revenue and expenditure.   [n.p., 1887-88)
    2 v.   34 cm.

NN 0028106   DHEW

Natal. *Education dept.*
    ... Reports on government and state-aided secondary
schools ...

Pietermaritzburg,
    v. 33ᵐ.

    1. Education—Natal. 2. Education, Secondary.
                                                7—42607
    Library of Congress   L667.A35

NN 0028107   DLC

Natal. *Education Dept.*
    Tabelle van onderwysstatistiek
    see its
    Tables of educational statistics.

VOLUME 405

Natal. *Education Dept.*
Tables of educational statistics. Tabelle van onderwysstatistiek.
Pietermaritzburg, Printed by The Natal Witness (pty.) ltd.
     v.   33 cm.   triennial.
"Supplementary to the published reports of the Director of Education."

     1. Education—Natal—Stat.

L667.A25   58-38731

NN   0028109   DLC NN

Natal. *European immigration dept.*
Report.
Pietermaritzburg,
     v.   33 cm.

     1. Natal—Emig. & immig.

Library of Congress   JV8920.A4   5-41537

NN   0028110   DLC

Natal. *Excise office.*
Report.
Pietermaritzburg,   –1903.
     v.   33½ cm.
      –1902 have title: Report of the controller of excise.
     Continued in the Report of the collector of customs (Customs and excise dept.) 1903-

     1. Internal revenue—Natal. 2. Liquor traffic—Natal—Taxation.

Library of Congress   HJ80.E68   9—321

NN   0028111   DLC

Natal. Fisheries Advisory Board.
Natal food fishes. How to select and how to cook them...
Durban: Robinson & Co., Ltd., 1915.   12 p.   8°.

1. Fish, Natal. 2. Cookery.—Fish.
N. Y. P. L.   March 27, 1920.

NN   0028112   NN

Natal. Fisheries Department.
Report on Natal coast fisheries considered in relation to the methods of the fishing interests in the United Kingdom, by the principal fisheries officer.   Pietermaritzburg: P. Davis & Sons, 1913.   11 p.   f°.

1. Fisheries, Natal.
N. Y. P. L.   December 21, 1914.

NN   0028113   NN

Natal. Fisheries dept.
Report... Coast fisheries...
Pietermaritzburg, 1915- 16.
     2v. f°

     DLC SH315 .N3A3

NN   0028114   DLC

Natal. *Forest commission.*
... [Report of] Commission appointed to enquire into and report upon the extent and condition of forest lands in the colony. Pietermaritzburg, Printed by W. Watson, government printer, 1889.
     33 p. fold. tab. 32 cm.
     Signed by P. C. Sutherland, W. F. Blackburrow, and others.

Continued in next column

Continued from preceding column

     1. Forests and forestry—Natal.   1. Sutherland, Peter Cormack.

Library of Congress   SD103.N3A3   1889   6-23044

NN   0028115   DLC

Natal. Game advisory committee.
Harris, R   H   T   P.
... Report on the bionomics of the tsetse fly (*Glossina pallidipes* Aust.) and a preliminary report on a new method of control, presented to the Provincial administration of **Natal** by R. H. T. P. Harris ... Pietermaritzburg, The **Natal** witness, 1930.

Natal. Geological Survey.
Bibliography of Natal and Zululand geology. [Part I–II.]
     2 pts.   (*In* Report of the Geological Survey of Natal and Zululand. Pietermaritzburg, 1902–1904. 30 cm.   No. 1, p. [29]–36; no. 2, p. [29]–35.)
     Compiled by William Anderson, gov't geologist.

NN   0028117   ICJ

Natal. *Geological survey.*
... Report of the Geological survey of Natal and Zululand. 1st–3d and final. By William Anderson, government geologist ... Pietermaritzburg, P. Davis & sons, printers; [etc., etc.] 1901–07.
     3 v. plates, fold. maps, profiles (part fold.) 30½ cm.
     At head of title: Natal. Surveyor-general's department.
     2d–3d report have imprint: London, West, Newman and co.
     1st–2d report issued by direction of ... minister of lands and works; 3d report, issued by direction of the ... premier and colonial secretary.
     Contains a Bibliography of Natal and Zululand geology, pt. 1–3.
     1. Geology—Natal. 2. Geology—Zululand. 3. Geology—Natal—Bibl. 4. Geology—Zululand—Bibl.   1. Anderson, William.

         (QE323 .N3)   G S 14-596

Library, U. S. Geol.   survey   (786) qA

NN MtBuM NjP OU DLC
NN   0028118   DI-GS IU ICJ NNC MH-A KMK TxU GEU CU

Natal. *Glencoe colliery enquiry commission.*
... Report of the Glencoe colliery enquiry commission. [Pietermaritzburg, P. Davis & sons, 1908]
     cover-title, [1133]–1151 p. 2 fold. plans. 32¾ cm.
     At head of title: Colony of Natal.
     "Supplement to the Natal government gazette no. 20."

     1. Mine explosions.

            G S 16-126

Library, U. S. Geological   Survey 425(780) qN19

NN   0028119   DI-GS

Natal. Government asylum, *Pietermaritzburg.*
Report.
Pietermaritzburg, 18   –19
     v. fold. tables. 32–33 cm.
     At head of title: Colony of Natal.
     Report year ends Dec. 31.
     Reports for 1897–19   have title: ... Report of the medical superintendent ...

            8-6152†

Library of Congress   RC588.N3P5

NN   0028120   DLC

Natal. Government chemist.
...Report of the government chemist for the year

Pietermaritzburg,   f°.
     DLC: TP195.N2

1. Chemistry (Analytical), Natal.
N. Y. P. L.   January 11, 1922.

NN   0028121   NN DLC

Natal. Government Entomologist.
Report of the Government Entomologist
     see under   Natal. Dept. of Agriculture.

WX
28
HU5
D9A2

Natal. Government Hospital, Addington.
[Collection of publications]

     The Library has a collection of miscellaneous publications of this organization kept as received. These publications are not listed or bound separately.

NN   0028123   DNLM

Natal. Government hospital, Addington.
Report of medical superintendent.

NN   0028124   IU

Natal. Government hospital, Durban.
     see
Natal. Government hospital, Addington.

Natal. Government Laboratory.
Report of the government chemist
     see under   Natal. Government chemist.

Natal. Government museum, Pietermaritzburg
     see   Natal Museum, Pietermaritzburg.

Natal. Government observatory, Durban.
     see
Durban, Natal. Observatory.

Natal. *Government savings bank.*
Report of the controller, Natal government savings bank ...

Pietermaritzburg,
     v.   33 cm.

            8—9564

Library of Congress   HG3400.P5

NN   0028129   DLC

Natal. *Governor,* 1889-   (Sir C.B.H.Mitchell)
... **Natal. Despatch** from Governor Sir C. B. H. Mitchell ... (with enclosures) on the subject of the liquor traffic among the natives of Natal ... London, Printed for H. M. Stationery Off. by Eyre and Spottiswoode, 1890.

     18 p. 33 cm.   ([Great Britain. Colonial Office] Her Majesty's colonial possessions. no. 83)

     Numbered also as Papers by command <C.–5897.–13>   In Sessional papers of the House of Commons, 1890, v. 48.

NN   0028130   ICJ IEN

VOLUME 405

Natal. *Governor, 1901–1907* (Sir Henry E. McCallum)
... Correspondence respecting an act for a referendum in Natal on the draft South Africa union act. Presented to Parliament by command of His Majesty. March, 1910 ... London, Printed for H. M. Stationery off., by Darling & son, ltd., 1910.

10 p. 33ᶜᵐ. (Gt. Brit. Parliament. Papers by command₁ Cd. 5099)

At head of title: Natal.

"Act to provide for an electoral ballot on the proposed entry of Natal into a South African union": p. 4–5.

1. Natal—Pol. & govt. 2. Africa, South—Politics. i. Gt. Brit. Colonial office.

10–15268

Library of Congress   JF493.N3A5 1910

NN   0028131   DLC ICJ

Natal. *Governor, 1901–1907* (Sir Henry E. McCallum)

Gt. Brit. *Colonial office.*
Natal. Correspondence ₁and further correspondence₁ relating to native disturbances in Natal ... London, Printed for H. M. Stationery off., by Darling & son, ltd., 1906–08.

Natal. Governor, 1901–1907 (Sir Henry E. McCallum)
Natal. Correspondence relating to native disturbances in Natal ...
see under   Gt. Brit. Colonial office.

Natal. *Governor, 1907–1909* (Sir Matthew Nathan)

Gt. Brit. *Colonial office.*
Natal. Correspondence ₁and further correspondence₁ relating to native disturbances in Natal ... London, Printed for H. M. Stationery off., by Darling & son, ltd., 1906–08.

Natal. Governor, 1907–1909 (Sir Matthew Nathan)
Natal. Despatch from the governor of Natal forwarding a bill to make special provision for the trial of natives accused of certain crimes
see under   Great Britain. Colonial office.

Natal. *Harbour dept.*
... Chairman's minute and departmental reports ...

Durban, Natal, 18

v. in   illus., plates, fold. plans, fold. diagrs., charts. 33ᶜᵐ.

The report of the port captain, and that of the chief engineer, pub. in this series   are continued as separate publications.

1. Port Natal.

Library of Congress   TC319.N3A2   6–13292

NN   0028136   DLC

Natal. *Harbour dept.*
... Regulations of the port and harbour of Port Natal. Maritzburg, Printed by P. Davis & sons, 1903.

71 p. 21½ᶜᵐ.

1. Port Natal—Harbor regulations.

5–697†

Library of Congress   VK365.P8N2

NN   0028137   DLC

Natal. *Harbour dept.*
Report of the engineer ...
Pietermaritzburg, 18 –19

v. in   fold. plans, fold. tables. 33ᶜᵐ.

Title varies slightly.

Continuation of the reports pub. in the "Chairman's minute and departmental reports."

1. Port Natal.

Library of Congress   TC319.N3A3   6–13293

NN   0028138   DLC

Natal. *Harbour dept.*
Report of the port captain.
Pietermaritzburg, 18 –19

v. in   33ᶜᵐ.

18 has title: Annual report of the port captain.

Continuation of the reports pub. in the "Chairman's minute and departmental reports."

1. Port Natal.

Library of Congress   TC319.N3A4   6–13294

NN   0028139   DLC

Natal. *Harbour dept.*
Report of the secretary.
Pietermaritzburg,

v.   33ᶜᵐ.

1902 has title: Report of the Natal Harbour department.

9–4652†

Library of Congress   TC319.N3A45

NN   0028140   DLC

Natal. *Immigration dept.*
... Indian immigration. Laws and regulations, &c., affecting Indian immigrants and employers. Pietermaritzburg, Printed by P. Davis & sons, 1875.

65 p. 32¼ᶜᵐ.

4–34845†

NN   0028141   DLC

Natal. Immigration dept., European.

see

Natal. European immigration dept.

Natal. *Immigration restriction dept.*
Report of the immigration restriction officer.
Pietermaritzburg,

v.   33ᶜᵐ.

5–41538

NN   0028143   DLC

Natal. Indian Congress
see   Natal Indian Congress.

Natal. *Indian immigrant school board.*
Annual report.
Pietermaritzburg, W. Watson, printer to the Natal government ₁18

v. 33ᶜᵐ.

Title varies: 18   Report on Indian schools ... Revenue and expenditure.

18   –   Annual report of the Indian immigrant school board on the condition of Indian schools ...

1884–   pub. also in the Blue book for the colony of Natal, 1884–

1. Education—Natal.   i. Title.

CA 5—2229 Unrev'd

Library of Congress   L667.A4

NN   0028145   DLC DHEW

Natal. *Indian immigrants commission.*
Report of the Indian immigrants commission, 1885–7. Pietermaritzburg, Printed by P. Davis & sons, government contractors, 1887.

2 p. l., viii, ₁3₁–645 p. incl. maps. 33ᶜᵐ.

CONTENTS.—Report.—Evidence.—Short notes and observations.—Appendices.

1. Natal—Emig. & immig.

10–14058†

Library of Congress   IV8928.I 5 1887

NN   0028146   DLC

Natal. Indian Immigrants Commission.
Report of the Indian Immigrants Commission, 1885–87. Pietermaritzburg, P. Davis, 1887. 645p. illus.

Microfilm ed., positive and negative copies. Negative does not circulate.

NN   0028147   ICRL

Natal. *Indian immigration dept.*
Report of the protector of immigrants.
Pietermaritzburg ₁18

v.   33ᶜᵐ.

Cover-title.

Report for the calendar year, 1884–1890, 1896–1900. Report years ends June 30, 1891–1895.

January–June, 1891, has title: Supplementary report ...

5–41539

·NN   0028148   DLC MnU MH

Natal. *Indian immigration trust board.*
Annual report.
₁1st–   ₁ 1882–
₁Durban, 1883–

v.   33ᶜᵐ.

Report year ends June 30, 1891–19

9th covers period Jan. 1, 1890–June 30, 1891.

5–41540

NN   0028149   DLC

Natal. Indian immigration trust board.
₁Rules made by the Indian immigration trust board under the authority of section 116, of law 25, 1891. Durban, 1910.
1 l. 30½ cm.

NN   0028150   DL

Natal. *Industries and tariff revision commission.*
... Report of the Industries & tariff revision commission with appendices and evidence. January, 1906. Pietermaritzburg, P. Davis & sons, printers ₁1906₁

598, ₁4₁ p. 33ᶜᵐ.

Frederick R. Moor, chairman.

1. Tariff—Natal. 2. Natal—Indus.   i. Moor, Frederick Robert, 1853–

7–6275

Library of Congress   HC517.N3A5 1906

NN   0028151   DLC ICU ICJ

VOLUME 405

Natal. *Insolvency commission.*
Insolvency commission. To His Excellency Sir Henry Ernest Bulwer ... governor ... of Natal ... ₍Report₎ ₍Pietermaritzburg, 1886₎
8 p. 32ᶜᵐ.
Caption title.
Appointed to inquire into the insolvent and assignment laws of the colony, and to report changes needed therein ; John C. Walton, chairman.

1. Bankruptcy—Natal.   ɪ. Walton, John C.
                                       8–16813

Library of Congress   HG3769.N3 1886

NN   0028152   DLC

Natal. *Inspector of boilers dept.*
Report.
Pietermaritzburg,
    v. 33ᶜᵐ.
             have title: Report of the inspector of boilers.

1. Steam-boiler inspection—Natal.
                                   9–372

Library of Congress   TJ307.N3 3

NN   0028153   DLC

Natal. Inspector of native education.
Report
      see under   Natal. Education dept.
Annual report.

Natal. Institute of Engineers
      see   Natal Institute of Engineers.

Natal. *Land and immigration board.*
European immigration. Report of committee of the Land and immigration board. ₍Pietermaritzburg?₎ 1891₎
7 p. 31ᶜᵐ.
Caption title.
Signed: F. S. Haden, for the committee.

1. Natal—Emig. & immig.   ɪ. Haden, Francis Seymour, 1850–
                                 8–37294

Library of Congress   JV8927.A29 1891a

NN   0028156   DLC

Natal. *Land and immigration board.*
European immigration to Natal. The experiences of practical farmers, elicited by a circular letter and questions addressed by the Land and immigration board, in November, 1890, to farmers in Natal; also their advice to intending immigrants. Pub. by resolution of the Commission on immigration and crown lands, appointed by His Honour Francis Seymour Haden ... deputy governor ... on 28th August, 1891. Pietermaritzburg, P. Davis & sons, government printers ₍1891?₎
3 p. l., 3–30 p. 32½ᶜᵐ.
1. Natal—Emig. & immig.   ɪ. Natal. Commission on immigration and crown lands.
                                 8–37295

Library of Congress   JV8927.A29 1891

NN   0028157   DLC

Natal. *Land and immigration board.*
Report for the year

Pietermaritzburg, 18
    v. 32½ᶜᵐ.

1. Natal—Emig. & immig.
                                 8–36098

Library of Congress   JV8920.A25

NN   0028158   DLC

Natal. *Lands commission.*
... Evidence given before the Lands commission, (1900–01–02,) with appendix. Pietermaritzburg, P. Davis & sons, government printers, 1904.
1 p. l., 478 p. 33ᶜᵐ.

1. Land grants—Natal. 2. Absenteeism.   ɪ. Title.
                                 21–13362

Library of Congress   HD985.A4 1902a

NN   0028159   DLC CtY

Natal. *Lands commission.*
... Report of the Lands commission February, 1902. Report and appendix, with digest ... Pietermaritzburg, The Times printing and publishing company, ltd. ₍1902?₎
1 p. l., xii, 72 p. incl. tables. 33ᶜᵐ.
"Published under government notice, no. 136 of 1902."
Henry Fell, chairman.

1. Land grants—Natal. 2. Absenteeism.   ɪ. Fell, Henry.
                                 7–27310

Library of Congress   HD985.A4 1902

NN   0028160   DLC

Natal. *Laws, statutes, etc.*
... Act no. 28, 1901. "For the inspection & regulation of boilers," together with the rules published thereunder. (Government notice no. 664, 1901) Pietermaritzburg, "Times" printing and publishing co., ltd., 1901.
cover-title, 6 p. 24ᶜᵐ.

1. Steam-boiler inspection—Natal.
                                 5–702†

Library of Congress   TG642.N27

NN   0028161   DLC

622.007   Natal—Laws, statutes, etc.
N19ac   Act "to amend the Natal mines act, 1899".   n.p. 1905.
        1p.

NN   0028162   IU

622.007   Natal—Laws, statutes, etc.
N19a   Act to consolidate and amend the laws relating to mining.   n.p. 1899.
        47p.

NN   0028163   IU

Natal. Laws, statutes, etc.
Army act, 1881. 44 & 45 Vict., c. 58. Applicable under section 177 to the colonial forces in Natal when serving with Her Majesty's regular forces. Pietermaritzburg, Vause, Slatter, Govt. printers, 1881.
108p. 32cm.

NN   0028164   IEN

Natal. *Laws, statutes, etc.*
Criminal law. Pietermaritzburg, P. Davis, printers, 1901.
56 p. 25 cm.

1. Criminal procedure—Natal. 2. Criminal law—Natal.
                                 52–49395

NN   0028165   DLC

Natal. Laws, statutes, etc.
Matthews, Maynard Reginald Nelson.
Digest of the Native high court reports, Natal, by Maynard Matthews ... 1899–1909. Pietermaritzburg, Natal, P. Davis & sons ₍ca. 1910₎

        Natal. Laws, statutes, etc.
349.684   English-Zulu translation of law no. 19,
N271E   1891, to legalise the code of native law laid before the Legislative Council according to the provisions of law no. 44, 1887. Pietermaritzburg, J. Hershensohnn, 1893.
      68 (i.e. 115) p. 21 cm.
      Opposite pages ₍2₎–48 numbered in duplicate.
        1. Natal. Native races. 2. Law, Primitive. Natal. 3. Customary law. Natal.

NN   0028167   NcD

Pam   Natal. Laws, statutes, etc.
Coll   Natal code of native law. ₍Johannesburg₎
14909   Witwatersrand University Press ₍1932?₎
      cover-title, 45 p. 22cm.

        1. Natal. Native races. 2. Law, Primitive.

NN   0028168   NcD

        Natal. Laws, statutes, etc.
Nkd29   ... Natal code of native law. Pretoria,
B52   The government printer, 1932.
A2   32, viiip. 24½cm.
1332   At head of title: Union of South Africa. Interleaved.

NN   0028169   CtY

349.684   Natal. Laws, Statutes, etc.
N181n   Natal code of native law. Johannesburg, Witwatersrand University Press ₍194-₎
      26 p.

      Cover title.
      Reprinted from African Studies, v.2, no.1, March 1943.

        1. Customary law.- Natal. I. African studies. II. Title.

NN   0028170   WaU PU NSyU

        Natal. Laws, statutes, etc.
      Natal code of native law. ₍Johannesburg₎ Witwatersrand Univ. press ₍1945?₎
      cover-title, 45 p.

NN   0028171   NNC

VOLUME 405

Natal. Laws, statutes, etc.
Natal code of native law. ₜJohannesburg₎
Witwatersrand University ₜ1945?₎
45 p.

"Proclamation no.168, 1932."

NN 0028172   MBU CLSU CU-S PPiP MH-L IEN

Natal. *Laws, statutes, etc.*
... The Natal mines act (no. 43), 1899. And the regulations framed thereunder, with regulations for the storage of explosives. Pietermaritzburg, Printed by W. Watson, government printer, 1900.
xxiii, 129 p. 24ᶜᵐ.
Regulations for the storage of explosives (p. ₜ123₎-129), issued by the controller of arms.

1. Mining law—Natal. 2. Explosives.

4—9880

Library of Congress   TN249.N2A2

NN 0028173   DLC

Natal. *Laws, statutes, etc.*
""⁵²⁰ ... . The Natal mines act (no. 43), 1899, and the regulations framed thereunder, with regulations for the storage of explosives. Pietermaritzburg, printed by P. Davis & Sons, 1904.
xxiii, 135 p. 25ᶜᵐ.
At head of title: Colony of Natal.
"Regulations for the storage of explosives," p. [130]-135; issued by the Controller of Arms.

NN 0028174   ICJ

Natal. *Laws, statutes, etc.*
Natal ordinances, laws, and proclamations, comp. and ed. under the authority and with the sanction of His Excellency the Lieutenant governor and the ... Legislative council. By Charles Fitzwilliam Cadiz ... assisted by Robert Lyon ... By authority. Pietermaritzburg, Vause, Slatter & co., gov't printers, 1879-80.
2 v. 24ᶜᵐ.
CONTENTS.—v. 1. 1843-1870.—v. 2. 1870-1879.

1. Cadiz, Charles Fitzwilliam, 1832– ed. II. Lyon, Robert, joint ed.

6-11875

NN 0028175   DLC

Natal. Laws, statutes, etc.
Natal Ordinances, Laws, and Proclamations, 1845 89. Pietermaritzburg, 1891-90.

4 vol.
Vol.1,2, by Cadiz; 3,4 (entitled, Ordinances and Laws of Natal), by Broome.

NN 0028176   MH

Natal. Laws, statutes,etc.

Stafford, W   G.
Native law as practised in Natal, by W. G. Stafford ... Johannesburg, Witwatersrand university press ₜ1935₎

Natal.   Laws, statutes, etc.
... Ordinances of the Province of Natal, 1932. Published by authority ... Ordonnansies van die Provinsie Natal, 1932.Op gesag uitgegee. Pietermaritzburg, Natal press (pty.) ltd. [1932?]
87 p.   24 cm.
At head of title: Province of Natal.
English and Dutch.

NN 0028178   NcD-L

Law   Natal. Laws, statutes, etc.

Stafford, W   G
Principles of native law and the Natal code, by W. G. Stafford and Emanuel Franklin. ₜRev. ed.₎ Pietermaritzburg, Shuter & Shooter, 1950.

Natal. *Laws, statutes, etc.*
Short abstract of ordinances and laws. Maritzburg, P. Davis & sons, 1902.
viii, 279 p. 24ᶜᵐ.
Published for the general information and guidance of the police force.

4-35855†

NN 0028180   DLC

Natal. *Laws, statutes, etc.*
Statutes of Natal, comp. and ed. by R. L. Hitchins ... assisted and rev. on behalf of the colonial government by G. W. Sweeney ... being a compilation of the statutes of the colony of Natal from the years 1845 to 1899, inclusive, with foot-notes, and with appendix containing the acts of 1900. Pietermaritzburg, P. Davis & sons, 1900-02.
3 v. 25ᶜᵐ.
—— Statutes of Natal, being a supplement to volumes 1, 2, and 3 of the compilation of statutes of the colony of Natal from the years 1845 to 1900, inclusive, commonly

known as "Hitchins' statutes," containing all the statutes of the colony (acts of supply excepted) from 1901 to 1906, inclusive, which are at present in force, together with a chronological table, contents tables, and footnotes giving references to English and colonial decisions. Comp. and ed. by R. L. Hitchins ... rev. on behalf of the colonial government by G. W. Sweeney ... London, Pub. for "The Natal law journal" by A. & F. Hitchins, 1907.
xv, ₜ1₎, 754 p. 25½ᶜᵐ.
I. Hitchins, Robert Lewis, ed. II. Sweeney, George William, joint ed.

15-2955-6

NN 0028182   DLC

Natal. *Laws, statutes, etc.*
Volunteer act, 1895, and regulations under the same, for the volunteer force, Natal. Maritzburg, W. Watson, government printer ₜ1895₎
1 p. l., 131 p. 23½ᶜᵐ.
Corrected to May 2, 1901, by insertion of orders, notices and ms. notes.

1. Military law—Natal. 2. Natal. Volunteer force.
4-9681

Library of Congress   UB727.A2

NN 0028183   DLC

NATAL. Legislative Council.
Debates of the Legislative Council of the colony of Natal.
v. 1–
Pietermaritzburg: Vause, Slatter & Co., 1880-93. 24½x19cm.

Publisher varies.
Ceased publication with 1893.

NN 0028184   NN NcD

NATAL. Legislative Council.
Sessional papers. Council

Pietermaritzburg,   31-22½cm.

Ceased publication with 1893.

NN 0028185   NN

Natal. *Legislative council. Select committee on marriages of natives.*
... To His Excellency Anthony Musgrave ... ₜReport of Select committee appointed to consider the subject of marriages contracted by natives under Christian rites. Pietermaritzburg, Printed by P. Davis and sons, government printers, 1872₎
13 p. 32¾ᶜᵐ.
Caption title.
Charles Barter, chairman.
1. Natal—Native races. 2. Marriage law—Natal. I. Barter, Charles, jr. II. Title.

CA 9—5334 Unrev'd

Library of Congress   HQ1019.N3A4 1872

NN 0028186   DLC

Natal. *Local Health Commission.*
Report of the engineer.
ₜPietermaritzburg₎
v. illus. 33 cm. annual.
Report year ends June 30.

1. Hygiene, Public—Natal.

RA312.N3A3   53-26916 ‡

NN 0028187   DLC

Natal. *Local Health Commission.*
Report with abridged departmental reports together with accounts and balance sheets for the financial year.
ₜPietermaritzburg₎
v. 33 cm. annual.
Report year ends Mar. 31.

RA352.N28   54-35440 ‡

NN 0028188   DLC DNLM

W 2   **NATAL. Local Health Commission**
HU5.1   Secretary's financial report and
N2L8s   abstract of accounts for the year.

Pietermaritzburg, 194
v.
Report year ends Mar. 31.
1. Public health - Africa, South

NN 0028189   DNLM

Natal. *Magistrates' courts.*
Rules for regulating the practice and the forms of proceedings in native cases in Magistrates' courts. Pietermaritzburg, Natal, P. Davis & sons, 1903.
31 p. 25ᶜᵐ.

1. Court rules—Natal. 2. Court rules—Zululand.

14-22375

NN 0028190   DLC

Natal. *Magistrates' courts.*
Rules for the Courts of magistrates in the colony of Natal; framed under the Magistrates' courts act, 1896, and amending acts. Pietermaritzburg, Natal, P. Davis & sons, printers, 1910.
1 p. l., viii, 75 p. 24½ᶜᵐ.

1. Court rules—Natal.

14 22373

NN 0028191   DLC

Natal. *Medical and Health Services, Director of Provincial.*
see **Natal.** *Director of Provincial Medical and Health Services.*

VOLUME 405

Natal. *Medical council.*
Annual report.
Pietermaritzburg,
v. 33½ᶜᵐ.

1. Medical laws and legislation—Natal.

9–1719†

Library of Congress   RA352.N23

NN   0028193   DLC

Natal. *Medical council.*
... Regulations regarding midwives, trained nurses, and attendants or nurses of the insane. Published under government notice no. 322, 1901. Pietermaritzburg, "Times" printing and publishing company, 1901.
cover-title, 16 p. 24ᶜᵐ.

1. Nurses and nursing.

5–3338†

Library of Congress   RC439.5.N27

NN   0028194   DLC

Natal. *Militia dept.*
Report.
Pietermaritzburg,
v.   fold. plan, tables, fold. chart. 33ᶜᵐ.

1. Natal—Militia.

8–9995

Library of Congress   UA857.N15

NN   0028195   DLC NN

Natal. Mines dept.

Hatch, Frederick Henry, 1864–
... Report on the mines and mineral resources of **Natal** (other than coal) by F. H. Hatch ... London, Printed by **R.** Clay and sons, limited, 1910.

Natal. *Mines dept.*
Report on the mining industry of Natal. Pietermaritzburg, Government printer, 18 –1910.
v. in   illus., fold. plates, fold. plans, tables (part fold.) 33ᶜᵐ.
Title varies: 18   Annual report of the commissioner of mines ...
18   Departmental report ₍etc.₎
18 –1909. Report on the mining industry of Natal ... by ... commissioner of mines...
Reports for 1910 are included in the Annual reports of the Mines dept., Union of South Africa.
One report covers the years 1907 and 1908.
1. Mines and mineral resources—Natal.

6–13291

Library of Congress   TN119.N3A2

NN   0028197   DLC MH NNC

Natal. *Mines dept.*
... Report upon the coal-fields of Klip River, Weenen, Umvoti, and Victoria counties, together with tabulated statement of results obtained from a series of trials of colonial coal upon the Natal government railways, by Frederic W. North, ꜰ. ɢ. s., colonial mining engineer ... London, Printed by Harrison and sons, 1881.
1 p. l., 66 p. plates (partly fold.) 2 fold. maps, fold. tab. 33ᶜᵐ.

1. Coal mines and mining—Natal.   ɪ. North, Frederic W.

6–31671

Library of Congress   TN810.N3A3   1881

NN   0028198   DLC

Natal. *Mines dept.*
... Rules for the information & guidance of drill foremen. Pietermaritzburg, Printed by P. Davis & sons, government printers ₍1904?₎
cover-title, 1 p. l., ɪɪɪ, 15 p.   forms (part fold.) 24½ᶜᵐ.
At head of title: Colony of Natal. Mines department.
J. T. Audas, deputy commissioner of mines, superintending drills.

1. Rock-drills. 2. Boring.   ɪ. Audas, John Thomas.   ɪɪ. Title.

11—13417

Library of Congress   TN281.N3   1904

NN   0028199   DLC

J
711
N32
1906/07   **Natal. Native Affairs Commission, 1906-07.**
Report. Pietermaritzburg, 1907.
54p.

H.C. Campbell, Chairman.

I.Campbell, H   C   1. Race
relations - Natal.

NN   0028200   MBU

HC517
N3A5
f   **Natal. Native Affairs Commission, 1906-1907.**
Report of the Native Affairs Commission, 1906-1907. Pietermaritzburg, P. Davis., Govt. Print. Off., 1907.
41 p.   33cm.
At head of title: Colony of Natal.

1. Negroes in Natal - Econ. condit.   I. Title.

NN   0028201   CSt-H

Natal. *Native affairs commission, 1906–1907.*
... Report of the Native affairs commission, 1906–07. Presented to both houses of Parliament by command of His Majesty. January, 1908. London, Printed for H. M. Stationery off., by Darling & son, ltd., 1908.
41 p. 33ᶜᵐ. (₍Gt. Brit. Parliament. Papers by command₎ Cd. 3889)
At head of title: Natal.
Henry Cooke Campbell, chairman.

1. Natal—Native races.   ɪ. Campbell, Henry Cooke.

9–1500

Library of Congress   HC517.N3A5   1908

NN   0028202   DLC DNW ICJ

Natal. *Native affairs dept.*
Annual reports.
Pietermaritzburg,
v.   tables (part fold.) 33½ᶜᵐ.

1. Natal—Native races.

CA 7—1974 Unrev'd

Library of Congress   HC517.N3A2

NN   0028203   DLC MH

Natal. *Native affairs dept.*
... Blue book on native affairs ... Pietermaritzburg, 18 –19
v.   tables (part fold.) 34½ᶜᵐ.
Compiled from reports by magistrates and from records in the office of the secretary for native affairs.
Continued in Blue book on native affairs (South Africa. **Native affairs** dept.)

1. Natal—Native races. 2. Natal—Econ. condit.   ɪ. Title.

CA 7—1973 Unrev'd

Library of Congress   HC517.N3A4

NN   0028204   DLC MH

Natal. *Native affairs dept.*
Report of the expedition sent by the government of Natal to install Cetywayo as king of the Zulus, in succession to his deceased father, Panda, August, 1873. Pietermaritzburg, Printed by P. Davis & sons, government contractors, 1874.
34 p. 32½ᶜᵐ.
By T. Shepstone, secretary for native affairs.

1. Cettiwayo, king of Zululand. d. 1884. 2. Zululand—Hist.   ɪ. Shepstone, Sir Theophilus, 1817–1893.   ɪɪ. Title.

8—28340

Library of Congress   DT878.Z9A2

NN   0028205   DLC

Natal. *Native commission.*
... Evidence taken by the sub-commission for **Umvoti** County. Printed for circulation among the members. Pietermaritzburg, Vause, Slatter & co., government printers, 1882.
2 p. l., 60, 25 p. 32ᶜᵐ.

1. Natal—Native races.

7–15720

Library of Congress   HC517.N3A5   1882a

NN   0028206   DLC

Natal. *Native commission.*
Report of the Natal native commission, 1881–2. Pietermaritzburg, Vause, Slatter & co., government printers, 1882.
iv, 52 p. 32ᶜᵐ.
Sir Henry Connor, president.

1. Natal—Native races.   ɪ. Connor, Sir Henry.

7–15719

Library of Congress   HC517.N3A5   1882

NN   0028207   DLC CtY

Natal. Native high court.

Lugg, Harry Camp.
Digest of Native high court reports, 1899–1915. By H. C. Lugg ... Pietermaritzburg, P. Davis & sons, ltd. ₍1916?₎

Natal. Native high court.

Matthews, Maynard Reginald Nelson.
Digest of the Native high court reports, Natal, by Maynard Matthews ... 1899–1909. Pietermaritzburg, Natal, P. Davis & sons ₍ca. 1910₎

Natal. *Native high court.*
Reports of the decisions of the full court of the **Native** high court ... ₍v. 1–   1899– Pietermaritzburg, P. Davis & sons, printers ₍1900?–
v. 24½ᶜᵐ.
Vol. 1 printed by Munroe brothers; v. 8-11, by the Times printing and publishing co., ltd.
Reporters: 1899–1901, F. A. Farrer and R. A. Marwick; 1902, R. A. Marwick; 1903–1906, T. A. Jackson; 1907, T. A. Jackson and L. O. Oxland; 1908, W. H. Acutt and L. O. Oxland; 1909, W. H. Acutt and H. C. Lugg; 1910–   H. C. Lugg.
1. Law reports, digests, etc.—Natal.   ɪ. Farrer, Frederick Arthur, reporter.   ɪɪ. Marwick, R. A., reporter.   ɪɪɪ. Jackson, Thomas Arthur, reporter.   ɪᴠ. Oxland, Lionel St. John Oxley, reporter.   ᴠ. Acutt, Walter Hugh, reporter.   ᴠɪ. Lugg, Harry Camp, reporter.

13–24366

NN   0028210   DLC MH IU CU-AL

Natal. Natives' land committee
    see   **South Africa. Native affairs dept. Natives' land committee.**

VOLUME 405

Natal.   Parliament.

The parliament consisting of the Legislative Council and the Legislative Assembly was abolished in 1910 and a legislative body of one chamber established to take its place.

For publications after 1910.
See
Natal. Provincial Council.

J711
H6
Documents
Dept.

Natal.   Parliament
Acts.

Pietermaritzburg.

v.

NN   0028213   CU

Natal. *Pharmacy board.*
Matters under the control of the Natal Pharmacy board ... ₍Pietermaritzburg, 1896?₎
8 p.   33ᶜᵐ.

1. Pharmacy—Natal.

CA 10-3949 Unrev'd

Library of Congress   RS15.N2A4

NN   0028214   DLC

Natal. *Pharmacy board.*
Report.
Pietermaritzburg,
v.   33½ᶜᵐ.

1. Pharmacy—Natal.

9-1720†

Library of Congress   RS15.N2A3

NN   0028215   DLC

Natal. *Police dept.*
Natal police force.   Revised rules and regulations.
Maritzburg, P. Davis & sons, printers, 1902.
1 p. l., 141, xxix p.   24ᶜᵐ.

4-11802

NN   0028216   DLC

Natal.   Police Department.
Natal police force.   Revised rules and regulations.
1906. Pietermaritzburg: P. Davis & Sons, 1906.   1 p.l., xxx p., 1 l., 139 p.   8°.

1. Police—Jurisprudence, Natal.
N.Y.P.L.   December 16, 1919.

NN   0028217   NN

Natal. *Police dept.*
Report of chief commissioner of police.
Pietermaritzburg,
v. in   tables (part fold.) 33ᶜᵐ.

1. Police—Natal. 2. Crime and criminals—Natal.

8-4544

Library of Congress   HV7848.N3A3

NN   0028218   DLC

Natal. *Post-war Works and Reconstruction Commission.*
Interim report.
₍n. p.₎
v. in   34 cm.
Title from text.

1. Natal—Public works.

HD4350.N3A3   56-27995 ‡

NN   0028219   DLC

Natal. *Postal and telegraph dept.*
... Report of the postmaster-general.
Pietermaritzburg, 18   19
v.   tables (part fold.) 32½ᶜᵐ. annual.
1891/92-1894/95   have title: Report of the postmaster-general and general manager of telegraphs.
Continued in Report of the postmaster-general (South Africa. Dept. of posts and telegraphs)

1. Postal service—Natal. 2. Telegraph—Natal.

Library of Congress   HE7345.A3   8-4543

NN   0028220   DLC

Natal.   Protector of immigrants.
see
Natal. Indian immigration dept.

Natal.   Provincial Council.
For publications prior to 1911 see   **Natal.** Parliament.

Natal. **Provincial Council.**
Debates and proceedings. Debatte en verrigtinge.
₍Durban₎
v. in   34 cm.
Afrikaans and English.
Vols. for   issued in parts.

1. Natal—Politics and government.   I. Natal.   Provincial Council. Debatte en verrigtinge.
J711.H24a   328.68'4'02   73-647491
MARC-S

NN   0028223   DLC

₍**Natal.** *Provincial Council*₎
Estimates of the additional expenditure to be defrayed from revenue and capital. Begroting van die addisionele uitgawes wat bestry moet word uit inkomste en kapitaal.
₍Pietermaritzburg₎
v. 33 cm. annual.
Report year ends Mar. 31.
Order of title varies.
Vols. for 1961- 62-1966/67 issued by the Treasury.
1. Natal—Appropriations and expenditures.   I. Natal. Treasury. Estimates of the additional expenditure to be defrayed from revenue and capital. II. Natal. Treasury. Begroting van die addisionele uitgawes wat bestry moet word uit inkomste en kapitaal. III. Natal. Provincial. Begroting   van die addisionele uitgawes wat bestry moet word uit in-   komste en kapitaal.
HJ80E.A25   354.68'4'007224   72-8752

NN   0028224   DLC

Natal. *Provincial council.*
... Minutes ...
Pietermaritzburg, 1911–
v.   tables (part fold.) 32ᶜᵐ.
At head of title: Union of South Africa. Province of Natal. Includes also Ordinances (1911-   ) Estimates of expenditure (1912-   ) and Printed papers (1913-

1. Natal—Pol. & govt. 2. Finance—Natal.

29-18956

Library of Congress   J711.H65

NN   0028225   DLC NN CtY

Natal. *Provincial Audit Office*
see   **Natal.** *Audit Office.*

Natal. Provincial Education Committee.
Report. ₍Pietermaritzburg, The Natal Witness₎ 1946.

NN   0028227   MH

Natal. *Provinsiale Raad*
see
Natal. *Provincial Council.*

Natal. *Public works dept.*
Report of the chief engineer.
Pietermaritzburg,
v. in   plates (part fold.) fold. plans, tables (part fold.) fold diagrs. 33½ᶜᵐ.
Report year irregular

1. Natal—Public works.

Library of Congress   TA119.N3   8-4074

NN   0028229   DLC

Natal. *Railway dept.*
... Minutes on the subject of light railways. Maritzburg, P. Davis & son, printers ₍1901?₎
1 p. l., 12 p.   33ᶜᵐ.
At head of title: Natal government railways.

1. Railroads—Natal. 2. Railroads, Local and light.

Library of Congress   HE3419.N5   1901   6—879

NN   0028230   DLC

Natal. *Railway dept.*
... Observations by general manager of railways on the report of Mr. J. H. Smith, special railway commissioner upon the administration, organization, and working of the Natal government railways. Durban, 1903.
1 p. l., 14 numb. l. 3 tab. (part fold.) 33ᶜᵐ.
At head of title: Natal government railways.
David Hunter, general manager of railways.

1. Railroads—Natal.   I. Hunter, Sir David, 1841–

Library of Congress   HE3419.N5   1903   6—878

NN   0028231   DLC

Natal. Railway Department.
...Official tariff book for goods, mineral, vehicle and live stock traffic.   Pietermaritzburg: P. Davis & Sons ₍1910₎. 168 p. f°.

At head of title: no. 24. Natal government railways.
On recto of t-p.: Supplement to no. 4. The Natal Government Gazette...24th May, 1910...

1. Freight—Rates, Natal.
N.Y.P.L.   December 14, 1921.

NN   0028232   NN

Natal. Railway department.
Official tariff book, for passenger, luggage and parcels traffic. Pietermaritzburg: P. Davis & Sons ₍1910₎. viii, 105 p.   f°.

Supplement 5 to the Natal government gazette, 30th May, 1910.

1. Railways.—Rates, Natal : 1910.
N.Y.P.L.   October 21, 1911.

NN   0028233   NN

VOLUME 405

Natal. *Railway dept.*

report of the engineer-in-chief (Natal government railways extensions) ... Pietermaritzburg, P. Davis & sons, government printers [etc.] 18

v. in   33ᶜᵐ.

Report year irregular.
1894/95, covers period July 1, 1894, to Dec. 31, 1895.
Title varies slightly.

1. Railroads—Natal.

Library of Congress   TK119.N3A3   5–13713

NN   0028234   DLC

Natal. *Railway dept.*
Report of the general manager of railways.

Pietermaritzburg, 18

v. in   fold. maps, tables (part fold.) 33ᶜᵐ.
Continued in Report of the general manager of railways and harbours (South Africa. Dept. of railways and harbours)

1. Railroads—Natal.

Library of Congress   HE3419.N3A2   5–31561

NN   0028235   DLC ICJ

Natal. *Railway dept.*
[Report of the general manager of railways upon certain leading features in the organization of the railway system of the colony 1879–1884. Durban? 1884?]

11 p. 32½ᶜᵐ.

Signed: Dav. Hunter, general manager.

1. Railroads—Natal.   I. Hunter, David, 1841–

                                                8–37292

Library of Congress   HE3419.N5 1884

NN   0028236   DLC

Natal. *Railway dept.*
... Reports upon the doubling of the main line and the alternative main line. September, 1902. Pietermaritzburg, "Times" printing and publishing company, ltd., 1902.

1 p. l., 31 p. 33½ᶜᵐ.

At head of title: Natal government railways. Engineering department. Reports by the engineer-in-chief and the superintending engineer.

1. Railroads—Natal.

                                                6–874

Library of Congress   HE3419.N5 1902

NN   0028237   DLC

Natal. Regional and town planning commission.

See

Natal. Town and regional planning commission.

Natal. *Roads committee.*
... Report of Roads committee appointed by the administrator to enquire into and report upon a certain scheme prepared by the engineer-superintendent of roads for the construction and maintenance of the public roads of the province, etc. ... [Durban, 1919]

cover-title, 14 p. 24½ᶜᵐ.

At head of title: Province of Natal.
Geo. H. Hulett, chairman.

1. Roads—Natal.   I. Hulett, George Herbert, 1864–   II. Title.

                                                31–18478

Library of Congress   TE119.N3A5 1919   624.709684

NN   0028239   DLC

Natal. *Roads dept.*
Report.
Pietermaritzburg, 1918–

v. maps (part fold.) tables, diagrs. 34ᶜᵐ.

Report year ends March 31.
Mimeographed.

1. Roads—Natal.

Library of Congress   TE119.N3A2   33–32608
                                [2]   625.709684

NN   0028240   DLC

TE
119   **Natal. Roads Dept.**
.N3   **Report of the Chief Engineer.**
A3   [Pietermaritzburg]

          Report year ends Mar. 31.

NN   0028241   MiU

Natal. *Roads Dept.*
Report of the Provincial Roads Engineer.

Pietermaritzburg, Natal Witness.

v. 33 cm. annual.

Report year ends Mar. 31.

1. Roads—Natal.

HE367.N3A32   54–43216 ‡

NN   0028242   DLC

TE145
.L58
          Natal. Roads Dept.

          Lewis, P   C
          Report on a tour of the United States of America and England during April–October, 1951 covering the study of materials, research, planning, design, and construction developments in highway engineering. [Pietermaritzburg? 1952?]

Natal. Royal agricultural society

see

Royal agricultural society of Natal.

Natal. *Special railway commissioner.*
Natal government railways. Report of J. H. Smith, special railway commissioner, upon the administration, organisation and working of the Natal government railways. London, Waterlow and sons, limited, printers, 1903.

1 p. l., 63 p. 2 fold. map. 33½ᶜᵐ.

1. Railroads—Natal.   I. Smith, J. H., railroad expert.

                                                8–3204

Library of Congress   HE3419.N5 1903 a

NN   0028245   DLC ICJ

Natal. Superintendent of education.
Report of the superintendent of education
see under   Natal. Education dept.

Natal. Supreme court.

Broome, William, 1852–1930.
Digest of the Natal law reports [1858–1893] By William Broome ... Pietermaritzburg, Munro bros., printers, 1896.

Natal. Supreme court.

Broome, William, 1852–1930.
Digest of the Natal law reports, 1894–1901. ⟨Being vols. xv.–xxII. of the new series.⟩ By William Broome ... Pietermaritzburg, Munro bros., printers, 1903.

Law   **Natal. Supreme court.**

Natal law reports. Supreme court. New series. v. 1–31; 1879/80–1910. Pietermaritzburg [etc.] 1885–1911.

Natal. Supreme Court.
Natal. Return to an address, dated 7 July 1868...
see under   Great Britain. Parliament.
House of Commons. [supplement]

Natal. Supreme Court.
Finnemore, Robert Isaac, 1842–   *ed.*
Notes and digest of the principal decisions of the Supreme court of the colony of Natal ... 1860[–1867] Published by permission, and edited by R. I. Finnemore ... Pietermaritzburg, Natal, Natal law society, 1880–82.

Natal. *Supreme court.*
Reports of cases in the Supreme court of Natal. From its commencement, 15th April, 1858. By Thomas Phipson ... Pietermaritzburg, Printed by May & Davis, 1858

48 p. 23ᶜᵐ.

1. Law reports, digests, etc.—Natal.   I. Phipson, Thomas, reporter.

                                                10–10686

NN   0028252   DLC ICU   IU OClW CtY

Natal. Supreme court.
Rules of the Supreme and Circuit courts of the colony of Natal; "The Supreme court act, 1896", and amending acts; the criminal law procedure ordinance, no. 18, 1845, and amending acts; together with a copious index. Edited and compiled for the Natal Law society by J.J. Hillier ... Durban and Maritzburg, P. Davis & sons, 1906.

3 p.l., xxii p., 1 l., 208 p. incl. forms. 22.5 cm.

Errata sheets inserted.

NN   0028253   CtY

Natal. *Supreme court*
see also
South Africa. *Supreme court. Natal provincial division.*

VOLUME 405

Natal. *Surveyor-general's dept.*
Report of the surveyor-general.
Pietermaritzburg,
v. 33½ᶜᵐ.

1. Natal—Public lands.

Library of Congress   HD985.A2   9—320

NN   0028255   DLC

Natal. Surveyor-general's department. Geological survey.
see
Natal. Geological survey.

Natal. Surveyors' institute
see
Surveyors' institute of Natal.

Natal. Tariff revision commission.
see
Natal. Industries and tariff revision commission.

Natal. *Technical education commission.*
... Report of the Technical education commission, **May,**
1905. Report, with appendices A, B, and C, and, **Minutes**
of evidence, with appendices I–V. Maritzburg, P. Davis &
sons, government printers, 1905.
215 p. 32½ᶜᵐ.
Sir David Hunter, chairman.

1. Technical education—Natal.   I. Hunter, Sir David, 1841–
7—27423
Library of Congress   T166.N3A3 1905

NN   0028259   DLC DL ICJ

Natal. *Tesourie*
see
Natal. *Treasury.*

Natal. *Town and Regional Planning Commission.*
Natal town and regional planning reports. v. ₁1₎–
₁Pietermaritzburg, 1953–
v. in   illus. maps (part fold., part col.) 27 cm.
Vol. 1 issued without series title and numbering.
Vol. 1: 2d ed.

1. Natal—Economic policy. 2. Natural resources—Natal.
I. Title.
HC517.N3A44   65–36524

NN   0028261   DLC CSt NN IU MiU

Natal. *Town and Regional Planning Commission.*
Report.
₁Pietermaritzburg?₁
v. maps. 25 cm. annual.
Report year ends Mar. 31.

1. Cities and towns — Planning — Natal. 2. Regional planning—
Natal.
NA9277.N3A3   57–34251

NN   0028262   DLC

Natal. *Town and Regional Planning Commission.*
Tugela Basin; a regional survey of the catchment area of
the Tugela River and its tributaries. Interim report, produced for the Natal Provincial Administration and the
Natural Resources Development Council ₁by E. Thorrington-
Smith, Provincial town and regional planner. Pietermaritzburg, 1953₁
xi, 148 p. illus. (part col.) maps (part col.) 27 cm. (₁Its Natal
town and regional planning reports, 1₁)
Includes bibliographies.
1. Tugela Valley—Econ. condit. 2. Natural resources—Tugela Valley.   I. Thorrington-Smith, E.   II. South Africa. Natural Resources
Development Council. III. Title.   (Series)
HC517.N3A44   vol. 1   65–35385

IEN MH NN CU CaBVaU
NN   0028263   DLC OrU NcU FU NcD CSt CtY MBU NIC DI

Natal. *Trade commission.*
Report of the Trade commission. 1885–6. Pietermaritzburg, P. Davis & sons, printers, 1886.
xiv p., 1 l., 313, x p. 33ᶜᵐ.
F. S. Haden, chairman.

1. Natal—Comm.   I. Haden, Francis Seymour, 1850–
6–14131
Library of Congress   HF265.N3A4

NN   0028264   DLC

Natal. *Treasury₁*
Estimates of the expenditure to be defrayed from revenue
to be collected (excluding capital expenditure). Begroting
van die uitgawes wat bestry moet word uit inkomste wat
ingevorder moet word (kapitaaluitgawe uitgesluit).
₁Pietermaritzburg₁
v. 33 cm. annual.
Report year ends Mar. 31.
Order of titles varies.
1. Natal—Appropriations and expenditures.   I. Natal. Treasury.
Begroting van die uitgawes wat bestry moet word uit inkomste wat
ingevorder moet word (kapitaaluitgawe uitgesluit).
HJ80E.A28   354.68'4'00722   70–208169

NN   0028265   DLC

Natal. *Treasury.*
... Financial statement.
Pietermaritzburg,
v. 33½ᶜᵐ.

1. Finance—Natal.
8–1494
Library of Congress   HJ80.E4

NN   0028266   DLC

Natal. Treasury. Government Savings Bank.
See
Natal. Government Savings Bank.

Natal. *Treaties, etc.*
Agreement for the mutual extradition of fugitive criminals from Natal and from the South African Republic.
₁Pietermaritzburg? 189–₁
10 p. 32½ᶜᵐ.
Caption title.

1. Extradition.   I. South African Republic. Treaties, etc.
10–17390†
Library of Congress   JX4371.N3A4

NN   0028268   DLC

Natal. *Treaties, etc.*
Convention between the government of Natal and the
government of the Orange Free State, entered into on the
12th and 24th June, 1890, for the construction, equipment,
working, and maintenance of a line of railway within the
Orange Free State, from Van Reenen's pass to the town
of Harrismith. ₁n. p., 1890?₁
40 p. incl. fold. tab. 33ᶜᵐ.

1. Railroads—Orange Free State. 2. Railroads—Natal.   I. Orange
Free State. Treaties, etc.
7–33389
Library of Congress   HE3419.O6A3

NN   0028269   DLC

Natal. Treaties, etc.

South African Republic. *Treaties, etc.*
... Tractaat voor de wederkeerige uitlevering van voort-
vluchtige misdadigers uit Natal en van uit de Zuid-Afrikaansche Republiek. Gesloten 18 en 20 November 1897. In
werking getreden 22 November 1898. Opzegbaar na 22 November 1898. ₁Pretoria₁ Staatsdrukkerij van de Z. A. Republiek, 1898.

Natal. Treaties, etc.

South African republic. *Treaties, etc.*
Zululand-grenslijn-conventie, Z. A. republiek. Pretoria,
Staatsdrukkerij der Zuid-Afrikaansche republiek, 1898.

Natal. University, *Pietermaritzburg*
see
Pietermaritzburg. University of Natal.

Natal. *Veterinary dept.*
Report of the principal veterinary surgeon.
Pietermaritzburg, 18
v. fold. charts. 24½–33½ᶜᵐ. annual.
18   title reads: Report of the veterinary surgeon.

1. Veterinary medicine—Natal.
8–1621
Library of Congress   SF719.N3A3

NN   0028273   DLC

Natal. *Volksraad.*
Voortrekker wetgewing; notule van die Na-
talse Volksraad, 1839–1845, met inleiding en
aantekeninge van Gustav S. Preller. Pretoria,
J. L. Van Schaik, 1924.
xviii, 296 p.

"In opdrag van die Suid Afr. Akademie vir
Taal, Lettere en Kuns."

NN   0028274   NNC-L MH WU

VOLUME 405

Natal. *Zululand lands delimitation commission, 1902–1904.*
... Reports by the joint imperial & colonial commissioners. (With annexures and maps.) Pietermaritzburg, P. Davis & sons, government printers, 1905.
2 p. l., vii, 300 p. maps (partly fold.) 33ᶜᵐ.
Commissioners, appointed by the governor of Natal: Sir John G. Dartnell, later replaced by R. H. Beachcroft and Charles J. Renault Saunders.

1. Zululand—Pol. & govt. 2. Natal—Public lands. 3. Natal—Native races. I. Dartnell, Sir John George, 1838– II. Saunders, Charles James Renault, 1857–   III. Beachcroft, Robert Henry.

Library of Congress   HD989.N3A4   7-21684

NN   0028275   DLC

---

799   Natal, Brazil. *Ordinances.*
... Lei n.3 de 3 de setembro de 1924.
Monte-pio municipal.   Natal, Typ. Commercial.

NN   0028276   DPU

---

799   Natal, Brazil. *Ordinances.*
Relatorio ... em sessão de 1 de janeiro de 1924 ...   Natal, Typ. c'A Imprensa, 1923.

NN   0028277   DPU

---

799   Natal, Brazil. *Ordinances.*
... Resolucão n. 218.   Natal, Typ. d'A Imprensa, 1923.

NN   0028278   DPU

---

799   Natal, Brazil. *Ordinances.*
... Resolucão orcamentaria ...   15 set. 1922, 15 set. 1923.

NN   0028279   DPU

Natal, Brazil. *Preifeitura municipal.*
Natal e o seu progresso
see under title

... The **Natal** agricultural journal
 ₍Pietermaritzburg, etc.₎ The "Times" printing and publishing company, limited,
v. in   illus., plates, ports., diagrs. 25ᶜᵐ.
Biweekly (irregular)   –1903; monthly, 1904–
At head of title,   : Natal Dept. of agriculture and mines;
                             : Natal. Dept. of agriculture.
Title varies: –1903, The Agricultural journal and mining record.
1904–07, The Natal agricultural journal and mining journal.
1908– The Natal agricultural journal.
"Published for and edited in the Department of agriculture."
Published Mar. 18, 1898–Jan. 1911. Superseded by the Agricultural journal of the Union of   South Africa. *cf.* Union list of serials.
1. Agriculture—Period.   2. Agriculture—Natal.   I. Natal. Dept. of agriculture.
                          ₍2₎
Library of Congress   S17.N3   46-32501

NN   0028281   DLC IU TU

Natal. *An illustrated official railway guide and handbook of general information*
see under   Harrison, Charles William Francis, 1874–

Natal and Zululand annual.   Durban, Natal, pub. by W. S. Banting.

"With which is incorporated the "Zululand Times annual".
Superseded by The Garden colony; Natal, Zululand, and Pondoland.

NN   0028283   MiD

W 1   **NATAL** Anti-Tuberculosis Association
NA2157   Annual report.
             1st-   1934-
             ₍Durban₎
             v.

NN   0028284   DNLM

W 1   **NATAL** Anti-Tuberculosis Association,
NA216   News flash.
             Durban, Natal ₍1944?₎-
             v.

NN   0028285   DNLM

Natal bank, limited, appellant.
In the Privy council. No. 78 of 1909. On appeal from the Supreme court of the Transvaal. Between the Natal bank, limited (plaintiffs) appellants, and Hendrik Theodor Rood and others (defendants) respondents. Appellants' case. Respondents' case. Record of proceedings. Supplemental record. Travers Smith, Braithwaite & co., for appellants. Watkin Williams, Steel & Hart ... for respondents.   [London, Metchim & son, 1909]
cover-title, [110] p. incl. plan, tables. fold. tab. 28 cm.
Concerns the insolvent estate of the respondents father.

Contains autograph of W.R. Bisschop.

NN   0028287   CtY

Natal botanic gardens, Durban.
soe
Durban, Natal. Botanic gardens.

Natal Carbineers
see **South Africa.** *Army. Royal Natal Carbineers.*

The **Natal** civil service list
see under   Natal.

Natal customs union tariff. 1903. Alphabetically arranged. Pietermaritzburg, Printed by P. Davis & sons, 1903.
71 p. 25ᶜᵐ.
Interleaved.

1. Tariff—Natal—Law.   I. South African customs union.
HJ6360.A5 1903   CA 8-2634 Unrev'd

NN   0028291   DLC

Il natal d'Apollo; componimento drammatico per festeggiare la nascita di S.A.R. il principe ereditario delle Sicilie.   Napoli, Stamperia reale, 1775.
78 p. front. 21 cm. [Binder's title: Raccolta di opere diverse II]

NN   0028292   CtY

Natal Day celebrations of the Dominion of Canada and the United States of America at Nelson on Wednesday, July 1st, and Saturday, July 4th, 1891: program of sports. [Nelson, B.C., 1891]
broadside (32 x 19 cm.)

Xerox reproduction of the original.
D. Labau, chairman of Committee of arrangements.

NN   0028293   CaBViPA CaBVa

973.7   The Natal day of Gen. R.E. Lee appropriately
S727   observed throughout the South, Jan. 9, 1901.
V.28
         Southern historical society papers, v.28, p. 228-43.

NN   0028294   ViLxW

The **Natal** directory
Pietermaritzburg, P. Davis & sons, limited
v. 22ᶜᵐ.

1. Natal—Direct.
                                          15-9566
Library of Congress   DT867.N3

NN   0028295   DLC CU

Natal e o seu progresso.   [Natal ? 1940?]
cover-title, [92] p., 4 l. illus. (incl. ports.) diagrs. 22 x 31 cm.
On cover: "Administração. Rafael Fernandes Gurjão, interventor federal. Gentil Ferreira de Souza, prefeito da capital. Natal - Rio Grande do Norte".
1. Natal, Brazil. I. Natal, Brazil Preifeitura municipal. II. Rio Grande do Norte, Brazil (State) Interventoria federal.

NN   0028296   CU

Natal government gazette
see under   Natal.

Natal Government Museum, Pietermaritzburg
see
Natal Museum, Pietermaritzburg.

Natal government railways magazine
see   The South African railway and harbours magazine.

VOLUME 405

D
S Natal Indian Blind Society.
N271r Reports & financial statements.

Includes reports of the Natal Indian Blind Society Workshops and the Arthur Blaxall School for the Blind. The Society has a multi-purpose project which includes the deaf, the hard of hearing and the cerebral palsied.

NN 0028300 DGC

Natal Indian Congress.
DT872 Constitution ₍amended by fifth provincial
N271 conference 1951₎ Durban, 1951₎
f 13 p. 34cm.
Cover title.
Processed.

1. East Indians in Natal. I. Natal Indian Congress. 5th Conference, Durban, 1951.

NN 0028301 CSt-H

4DS Natal Indian Congress.
India Memorandum on civic amenities, sub-
539 mitted to the Hon. Justice F.N. Broome
[and others] members of the Natal
Indian Judicial Commission. Durban,
1944.
7 ℓ.

NN 0028302 DLC-P4

4JG Natal Indian Congress.
204 Memorandum on civic status submitted
to the Hon. Justice F.N. Broome [and
others] members of the Natal Indian
Judicial Commission. Durban, 1944.
17 ℓ.

NN 0028303 DLC-P4

4LB Natal Indian Congress.
890 Memorandum on education, submitted
to the Hon. Justice F. N. Broome [and
others] members of the Natal Indian
Judicial Commission. Durban, 1944.
30 ℓ.

NN 0028304 DLC-P4

4HD Natal Indian Congress.
2836 Memorandum on housing, submitted to
the Natal Indian Judicial Commission.
[19]
1 v. (various pagings)

NN 0028305 DLC-P4

Natal Indian congress.

Gt. Brit. *Colonial office.*
Union of South Africa. Further correspondence re
specting a bill to regulate immigration into the Union o
South Africa; with special reference to Asiatics. (T
continuation of ⟨Cd. 5579⟩ March, 1911) ... London
Pub. by H. M. Stationery off., printed by Darling an
son, ltd., 1912.

Natal Indian congress. *Provincial conference*, 1944.
... Agenda book of Provincial conference, held on the 19th
and 20th February, 1944. At the Avalon theatre ... Durban.
Opened by His Worship the Mayor, Councillor R. Ellis Brown,
J. P. President: Adv. J. W. Godfrey. Chairman of committee:
A. I. Kajee ... Durban, 1944.
1 v. 34ᶜᵐ.
Cover-title.
At head of title: Natal Indian congress. (Founded by Mahatma
Gandhi in 1894)
Various pagings.
Reproduced from type-written copy.
1. East Indians in Natal.

45-14579
Library of Congress DT866.N3 1944 c
₍2₎ 325.2540968

NN 0028307 DLC

Natal Indian congress. *Provincial conference*, 1944.
... Resolutions passed at the Provincial conference held at the
Avalon theatre, Durban, on the 19th and 20th February, 1944.
₍Durban?₎ 1944₎
5 numb. l. 33ᶜᵐ.
Caption title.
At head of title: Natal Indian congress. (Founded by Mahatma
Gandhi in 1894)
Reproduced from type-written copy.

45-7554
Library of Congress DT872.N3 1944 b
₍2₎ 325.25409684

NN 0028308 DLC

323.1(68:54)
N2 Natal Indian Organisation
Memorandum to members of United Nations
on the treatment of Indians in South
Africa. ₍Durban, 1947₎
13 p.

1. Indians - Union of South Africa

NN 0028309 NNUN

Natal Indian Teachers' Society.
Silver jubilee, 1925-1950. ₍Durban, 1950?₎
64 p. illus. 28 cm.

1. Natal Indian Teachers' Society.

L61.N1427 371.1'006'2684 74-177376
MARC

NN 0028310 DLC

Ub10 Natal Institute of Engineers.
N19 Proceedings of the ... general meeting.

Durban.
22cm.

NN 0028311 CtY

The Natal law magazine, conducted under the auspices of
the Incorporated law society of Natal. Containing reports of leading decisions in the Durban circuit court,
digest of Supreme court decisions, notes on current
events in legal matters, articles on legal subjects, reviews of law books, &c., &c., with index an dtable of
cases ... v. 1–
1908–
Durban, G. A. Riches, 1908–
v. 23½ᶜᵐ.
Editors: 1908– R. L. Hitchins, A. E. Carlisle.
Formed by the union of the Natal law quarterly and the Natal law
journal.
I. Hitchins, Robert Lewis, ed. II. Carlisle, Arthur E., ed.
III. Incorporated law society of Natal.
9–26923

NN 0028312 DLC IU

The Natal law quarterly ... v. 1–2, 4–6; Mar. 1902–1907.
Durban, Natal, Printed for the proprietors (the "Durban
moot") by Robinson & co., ltd. ₍etc.₎ 1902–07.
5 v. ports. (part col.) 24½ᶜᵐ.
Vol. 3 was not published.
W. T. Lee, editor.
In 1908, the Natal law quarterly and the Natal law journal were
united to form the Natal law magazine.
L. C. set consists of v. 1–2 only (Mar. 1902–1904); v. 4–6 wanting.

1. Law—Period. 2. Law—Natal. 3. Law reports, digests, etc.—
Natal. I. Lee, William T., ed.
7–23406 Revised

NN 0028313 DLC

Natal law reports for the year₍s₎ ₍1873–1879₎ ... Pieter-
maritzburg, Natal, Natal law society, 1881.
6 v. in 1. 24ᶜᵐ.
Cover-titles.
Editors: 1873, R. I. Finnemore.—1874–1879, A. C. Dulcken.
The old series of Natal law reports terminated with cases decided in
December, 1872; the new series commenced with November term, 1879.
These cases are some of the most important decided during the inter-
mediate period. *cf.* Pref.

1. Law reports, digests, etc.—Natal. I. Finnemore, Robert Isaac,
1842– ed. II. Dulcken, Albert Curtis, ed. III. Natal law society.
10–10689

NN 0028314 DLC CtY

Natal law reports. Reports of cases decided in
the Natal provincial division of the Supreme
court of South Africa ... v. 1–50, 1879/80–
1929; 1930–32. Pietermaritzburg, 1884–1933.
53 v. in 40. 24 cm.
Vol. 1–30 called News series.
Title varies: v.1–30, Natal law reports.
Supreme court; v. 31, Natal law reports.
Cases decided in the Natal Supreme court, 1910,
Jan.–May. Cases decided in the Natal provin-
cial division of the Supreme court of South
Africa, 1910, June–December.
Publisher varies.

Continued as the South African law reports.
Natal provincial division.

NN 0028316 MH-L OC1W

Natal law reports. Supreme court. New series. v. 1–31;
1879/80–1910. Pietermaritzburg ₍etc.₎ 1885–1911.
31 v. 25ᶜᵐ.
Vol. 31 has title: Natal law reports. Cases decided in the Natal Supreme court, 1910, January–May. Cases decided in the Natal provincial
division of the Supreme court of South Africa, 1910, June–December.
Reporters: v. 1–2, R. I. Finnemore (with A. C. Dulcken, v. 2)—v. 3, 7–10,
A. C. Dulcken (with W. T. H. Frost, v. 9–10)—v. 4–6, A. W. Mason.—
v. 11–17, W. Broome.—v. 18, W. E. Pitcher.—v. 19–26, W. S. Bigby
(with D. R. Pattison, v. 26)—v. 27, D. B. Pattison, Herbert Murray.—
v. 28–31, Herbert Murray.
Vols. 1–3, "reprinted" 1902.
Published for the Incorporated law society of Natal.

Continued by the South African law reports ... Natal provincial
division.

1. Law reports, digests, etc.—Natal. I. Natal. Supreme court.
II. South Africa. Supreme court. Natal provincial division. III. Finnemore, Robert Isaac, 1842–1906, reporter. IV. Dulcken, Albert Curtis, reporter. V. Mason, Sir Arthur Wier, 1860–1924, reporter. VI. Frost, William Thomas Hyde, reporter. VII. Broome, William, 1852–1930, reporter.
VIII. Pitcher, W. E., reporter. IX. Bigby, William Scott, reporter. X. Pattison, David Ballingall, reporter. XI. Murray, Herbert, reporter. XII.
Incorporated law society of Natal.

5–31353 rev

NN 0028318 DLC MH-L OC1W

Natal law society
see
Incorporated law society of Natal.

VOLUME 405

Natal mercury.
"Natal mercury" souvenir special. May 19th,
1900 ... [Durban,1900]
BBk21   broadside.port. 39x26cm.[Wright, H.
2b   Miscellaneous numbers of periodicals[etc.]]
Reporting the relief of Mafeking, with
portrait of Col. Baden-Powell.

NN   0028320   CtY

MZ74   Natal Missionary Conference.
N191   Report.

Durban.
v. 19-22 cm. annual.

Title varies: 1899-1912, Proceedings.
Imprint varies.

1. Natal – Missions. 2. Africa, South –
Missions. 3. Missions – Conferences, congresses, etc. 4. Missions – Statistics.   Afr

NN   0028321   CtY-D

Natal Museum, *Pietermaritzburg.*
Annals. v. 1–
June 1906–
Dorking [Eng., etc.] Adlard.
v. illus. (part fold., part col.) 26 cm. annual (irregular)
INDEXES:
Vols. 1–18, 1906–56. 1 v.

1. Science—Societies, etc. 2. Natural history—Africa, South.

Q85.N3   10–14295 rev 2*

NN   0028322   DLC UU DNLM ICJ GU CoU CU-S MsSM NcD MiU

Natal Museum, Pietermaritzburg.

Hatch, Frederick Henry, 1864–
... Catalogue of a collection of rocks and minerals from
Natal and Zululand, arranged stratigraphically. By F. H.
Hatch ... Pietermaritzburg, City printing works, 1909.

Natal museum, Pietermaritzburg.
[Descriptive pamphlet]. n.d.

[15] p. 8°.

NN   0028324   MH-Z

Natal museum, Pietermaritzburg.
Natal museum, Pietermaritzburg...[ed. by the Museum director, Dr. E.[Warren...]
[Pietermaritzburg, Pietermaritzburg publicity association, 1932?]
cover-title, [..] p. illus.,   25 cm.

NN   0028325   DSI

Natal Museum, *Pietermaritzburg.*
Report. 1st–
1904–
[Pietermaritzburg]
v. illus. 30–34 cm. annual.
Report year for 1904– ends Dec. 31; for   Mar. 31.
Reports for 1904– issued by the museum under an earlier
name: Natal Government Museum.
Vol. 2 published in London.

AM101.N3   069.09684   7–19883 rev 2*

NN   0028326   DLC ICJ PPAN IU CtY GU LU

Natal observatory, Durban.

see

Durban, Natal. Observatory.

Natal Political Association
Report of the Proceedings of the Natal
Political Association, and of a public meeting
held in the court hall, Pietermaritzburg, in
February, 1852, to petition the Home Government
on the subject of representative legislative
institutions for the Colony of Natal. Pietermaritzburg, Printed at the "Natal Witness"
office, 1852.
39p. 23cm.

NN   0028328   WU

Natal province handbook. Durban, 1911

NN   0028329   NjP

Natal regional survey.
Cape Town, Published for the University of Natal by Oxford
University Press, 19
v. illus., maps (part fold.) diagrs. 23 cm.
Prepared by the staffs of various departments of the University of
Natal.
—— Additional report. no.1–
[Pietermaritzburg] University of Natal Press [1951,]–
v. illus., maps, ports., diagrs. 23 cm.
No. 1 issued as Report no. 3 of the Durban Economic Research
Committee.
Prepared by the staffs of various departments of the University
of Natal.
                   HN800.N3N33
1. Natal—Soc. condit.   I. Pietermaritzburg. University of
Natal.   (Series: Dur-   ban Economic Research Committee.
Report no. 3)
HN800.N3N32   309.1684   52–42129 rev

NN   0028330   DLC IEdS WaPS UU NN

Natal regional survey. Report.
Cape Town, published for the University of Natal by Oxford University Press, 19
v. illus. 23 cm.

1. Natal—Soc. condit.—Collections.   I. Pietermaritzburg. University of Natal.
HN800.N3N34   58–37758

NN   0028331   DLC NcRS CU MB KU MiU

Natal Society, Pietermaritzburg.
The annals of Natal, 1495 to 1845 ...
see under   Bird, John, b.1815, comp.

Natal Society, Pietermaritzburg
Catalogue of books in the Library. Pietermaritzburg,
1893

NN   0028333   MH

Natal Society for the Advancement of Science and Art.
Proceedings.
[n. p.]
[v. 24 cm.

1. Science—Societies.
Q91.N3   51–35901 ‡

NN   0028334   DLC

Natal Technical College, Durban.
Natal Technical College, Durban, was founded in September 1907
as the Technical Institute. The name was changed in 1915 to
Durban Technical College. In October 1922 it became known as
Natal Technical College. The College assumed its new name of
Natal College for Advanced Technical Education in 1963.
Works by this body published before the change of name in 1963
are found under

Natal Technical College, Durban.

Natal technical college, *Durban.*
... Calendar ...
[Durban, 19
v. plates. 21ᶜᵐ.
At head of title: Natal technical college, Durban.

                       CA 35–431 Unrev'd

Library of Congress   T173.D8512   607.6847

NN   0028336   DLC

Natal technical college, *Durban.*
Handbook of general information.
[Durban] 19
v. illus., plates, diagrs. 22½ᶜᵐ.

                       43–28793

Library of Congress   T173.D85123

NN   0028337   DLC

Natal Technical College, *Durban*
see also
Pietermaritzburg. University of Natal. *Howard College,
Durban.*

The Natal tourists' guide and hotel and accommodation
register.
Durban [etc.] Central News Agency [etc.]
v. illus. 23 cm. annual.

1. Natal—Descr. & trav.—Guide-books.
DT876.N3   916.84   51–35148 ‡

NN   0028339   DLC

Natal town and regional planning reports
see under   Natal. Town and Regional
Planning Commission.

Natal University College, *Pietermaritzburg*
see
Pietermaritzburg. University of Natal.

Natal volunteer record; annals and rolls of
service in the Anglo-Boer war, 1899-1900
see under   [Milligan, A.], comp.

VOLUME 405

The Natal who's who; an illustrated biographical
920.0684   sketch book of Natalians. Durban, Natal.
N271   Who's Who Pub. Co. [1906]
            223 p. ports. 25 cm.

1. Natal. Biog.

NN   0028343   NcD

Natal Witness.
    ..."His Royal Highness." A full, special and exclusive record
of the life and activities of Edward, prince of Wales; issued by
"The Natal Witness" to commemorate the visit of the prince to
South Africa in 1925...   Maritzburg, Natal: Printed by the
Natal Witness, ltd., 1925.   ix, 278 p.   illus. (incl. ports.)
31cm.

    Advertising matter interspersed.

83815B. 1. Edward VIII, king of Great   Britain, 1894–   . 2. Africa,
South—Descr. and trav., 1900–   I. Title.
N. Y. P. L.   December 4, 1940

NN   0028344   NN

Natale, Alfio Rosario.
    Arte e imitazione della scrittura insulare in codici bobbiesi;
studi paleografici.   Milano, Edizioni del Capricorno [1950]   90 p.
illus.   25cm.   (Il Libro e la vita)

    Bibliographical footnotes.

    1. Manuscripts—Collections—Italy   —Bobbio. 2. Manuscripts, Irish
3. Handwriting, Irish. 4. Handwrit-   ing. Italian.

NN   0028345   NN

Z   Natale, Alfio Rosario.
115F   Il codice di Eugippius (Paris, B.N.,
N27   n.a. Lat. 1575) e l'influenza italiana
         nello scriptorium di Tours durante la
         prima metà del secolo VIII; note paleo-
         grafiche. Milano, Edizioni E S A, 1950.
         34 p. illus. 25cm. (Quaterniones, 1)

NN   0028346   NIC

Natale, Alfio Rosario.

Argegni, Corrado.
    ... Condottieri, capitani, tribuni ... Milano, E. B. B. I., Isti-
tuto editoriale italiano B. C. Tosi, s. a. [1936–37]

Z
6620.
I8   Natale, Alfio Rosario.
N3   Influenze merovingiche e studi calligrafici
         nello scriptorium di Bobbio (secoli VII–IX).
         Estratto dai Fontes Ambrosiani, XXVI; miscella-
         nea G. Galbiati, v.II, 1951.   Milano, Bibli-
         oteca Ambrosiana, n.d.
         44p plates(facsims) 30cm

         1.Manuscripts. Italy. Bobbio. i.Title.
         2.Bobbio, Ita-   San Colombano (Benedic-
         tine abbey)   Scriptorium.

NN   0028348   MnCS

Z114   Natale, Alfio Rosario.
.N27   Studi paleografici; arte e imitazione della
(C1)   scrittura insulare in codici bobbiesi. Milano,
         Edizioni del Capricorno [1950]
         90 p. 13 facsims. (Il libro e la vita)

         1. Paleography, Latin. 2. Bobbio, Italy
(Benedictine monastery)

NN   0028349   ICU CtY NIC

Natale, Alfonso R
    ... Liquidación de la moratoria hipotecaria; Ley n° 12.544.
[Rosario, Talleres gráficos Emilio Fenner, soc. resp. ltda.] 1938.
104 p., 1 l. incl. tables. 19cm.

    1. Mortgages—Argentine republic. 2. Moratorium—Argentine repub-
lic.   i. Title.

                                               43–27224

NN   0028350   DLC

Lilly
BX 2160   NATALE, ANTONIO, 1648–1701.
.A2 N2   Corona de las virtudes de Maria santis-
1774   sima, ... sacada del P. Antonio Natal en la
Mendel   Segunda Parte de Coelesti conversatione, a
           solicitud del Br. D. Juan de Dios, Fernandez
           de Cosgaya ... Reimpressa en Mexico, Impr.
           del J. de Jauregui, 1774.
           [8] p. 9.5 cm.

           Medina, J. T., Impr. en Mex., 5711.
           Unbound.

NN   0028351   InU

Lilly
BX 2160   NATALE, ANTONIO, 1648–1701.
.A2 N2   Corona de las virtudes de Maria
1786   santisima, ... sacada del Padre Antonio Natal
Mendel   en la Segunda Parte de Coelesti Conversa-
           tione, a solicitud del Br. D. Juan de Dios,
           Fernandez de Cosgaya ... Reimpresa en
           México, Impr. de la Calle de San Bernardo,
           1786.
           [8] p. 10 cm.

           Medina, J. T. Impr. en Mex., 7634.
           Unbound.

NN   0028352   InU

Natale, Antonio,   1648–1701.
    De coelesti conversatione in terris a re-
ligioso viro instituenda, seu Piarum operationum
praxis quotidiana in diariis oeconomia rite dis-
posita. Editio prima in Germania.   Ingolstadii
Joannes Franc.Xav. Crätz. 1750.
    782p 17cm

    Bound in brown leather.

NN   0028353   MnCS

Me35   Natale, Antonio, 1648–1701.
B5331   Glorie del sacerdozio rivelate a S. Brigida
R3   insieme co' suoi obblighi, e pregiudizj,
y693   ricavate dal libro autentico delle Rivelazioni
         della santa, e ponderate dal P. Antonio Natale
         ... Napoli, per Novello de Bonis stamp.
         arcivescovile, 1735.
         160p. 16cm.

NN   0028354   CtY

Natale,   Antonio, 1648–1701.
    Paradise on Earth ...
Benziger, 1878.
    146 p.

NN   0028355   WaSpG

Natale, Antonio, 1648–1701.
    ... Tesoro de las copiosas indulgencias, assi personales, como
por las animas de purgatorio, concedidas por los summos pon-
tifices a la Compañia de Jesus. Recogidas, y reducidas a compendio, por el p. Antonio Natal ... Y traducidas por otro
sacerdote de la mesma compañia ... Mexico, J. B. de Hogal,
1725.
    1 p. l., 56 p. 15cm.

    1. Indulgences.
                                               45–49715

    Library of Congress   BX2279.N35l

NN   0028356   DLC InU

913.377 Natale, Bonaventura.
N19s   Saggio storico delle antichità di Capoa; sive,
         Spicilegium Campanum ... Caserta, Tipografia
         della Intendenza, 1829.
         85p.

         1. Capua--Antiq.

NN   0028357   IU

NATALE, CARLO, ca. 1590–1683.
    Libro della descritione in rame de i stati, et feu-
di imperiali di don Federico Landi del Sac. Rom.
Imp. di val di Taro et val di Ceno principe IIII. mar.
di Bardi, conte di Compiano, barone dell' Pieve,
cavagliero del ordine del Tosone...racolte, dessignate
& intagliate p. Carlo Natale, pittor Cremonese.
[Cremona? 1617?]   [2] l., 70 plates (incl. ports.) map.
17x23cm.

    Engraved throughout.
    With added [?] plates: 1 signed G.P. Blanc, 6 by Leon Pallavicino.

                        Bequest of John L. Cadwalader
1. Landi, Federico, principe di Val di Taro e di Val di Ceno. 2. Taro
river and valley—Views.

NN   0028358   NN

Natale, Ernesto.
    ... La curva logística representativa del desarrollo numérico
de la población humana ... Buenos Aires [Talleres gráficos
Porter hnos.] 1937.
    20 p. diagr. 25½cm.

    At head of title: Universidad de Buenos Aires. Facultad de ciencias
económicas.
    "De la Revista de ciencias económicas, agosto de 1937."

    1. Population.   i. Buenos Aires. Universidad nacional. Facultad
de ciencias económicas. ii. Title.
                                               43–35148

    Library of Congress   HB871.N3

NN   0028359   DLC

N19   Natale, Francesco Antonio
             Saggio di un comento sopra lo statuto consue-
         tudinario dotale della città di Capua. Napoli,
         nella Stamperia Simoniana, 1802.
         cxixp. 27cm.

NN   0028360   CtY-L

Natale, Gaetano.
    Giolitti e gli Italiani. Pref. di Benedetto Croce. [1. ed.
Milano, Garzanti [1949]
    752 p. facsims. 22 cm. (Memorie e documenti)

    1. Giolitti, Giovanni, 1842–1928.

    DG575.G5N3   50–33019

NN   0028361   DLC ICU NN OCIW MH MB NIC

VOLUME 405

Natale, Gennaro
Con preghiera di pubblicazione, per esteso, o in riassunto. Ricorso al Consiglio di stato prodotto da Edoardo Scarfoglio contro il provvedimento del Prefetto di Roma, che soppresse il giornale Il Mattino in questa città. ₍Roma, 1898₎
7 p. 26cm.
Caption title.
Signed at end: Avv. G. Natale.

NN 0028362   MH-L

NATALE,Gennaro.
Del dolo e della frode,penale,civile e commerciale e dei relativi rimedi giuridici. Salerno,1877.

NN 0028363   MH-L PU-L

Natale, Gennaro
... La responsabilità dei genitori. Napoli, Detken & Rocholl, 1900.
24 p. 26½cm.
At head of title: Avvocato G. Natale.
Bibliographical footnotes.

NN 0028364   MH-L

Natale, Geronimo, 1507-1580
see Nadal, Geronimo, 1507-1580.

Natale, Giuseppe.
... I reati di diffamazione e i diritti della stampa, con prefazione del professor Enrico Pessina. Napoli, Detken & Rocholl, 1908.
1 p. l., ₍v₎-xv, 221 p. 19½ᶜᵐ.
At head of title: Avvocato G. Natale.
"Bibliografia": p. ₍xi₎-xv.

1. Libel and slander—Italy. 2. Press law—Italy. I. Title.
33-19102

NN 0028366   DLC

Natale, Jerome, 1507-1580
see Nadal, Geronimo, 1507-1580.

Natale, José A.
..."La base." Del método de la estructura de la palabra; consideraciones de orden didáctico-prácticas. Buenos Aires: A. Estrada y cia., 1915. 56 p. diagrs. 8°.

40217A. 1. Spanish language—   Phonetics.
N.Y.P.L.   February 28, 1929

NN 0028368   NN

Natale, José A.
"La base fonética;" tratado de fonética analógica aplicado a la enseñanza...por José A. Natale... Buenos Aires: A. Estrada y cia. ₍193-?₎ 285 p. illus. 22cm.

2096553B. 1. Spanish language—   Phonetics.
N.Y.P.L.   April 5, 1943

NN 0028369   NN MH MoSU

Natale, José A.
"La base," libro primario infantil, por José A. Natale ... Buenos Aires, A. Estrada y cía ₍191-?₎
7 p. l., 19-109 p. col. illus. 24½ᶜᵐ.
Cover illustrated in colors.

1. Primers, Spanish. I. Title.
20-6011
Library of Congress   PC4115.N3

NN 0028370   DLC DPU

Natale, Luigi di.
... Il cancro dello stomaco. Bologna, Cappelli, 1939.
275 p. illus. (part col.) 26 cm.

1. Stomach—Cancer.
Med 47-3155
U. S. Army Medical Library   [WI 458qN27ic 1939]
for Library of Congress   ₍1₎

NN 0028371   DNLM

Natale, Luigi di.
...Impressioni di teatro; prefazione di V. E. Bravetta. Bologna: L. Cappelli ₍1936₎ 93 p. 19½cm.

1. Drama, Italian—Hist. and crit.
N.Y.P.L.   July 28, 1938

NN 0028372   NN WaSpG

Natale, Luigi di.
Milizia in camice bianco. ₍1. ed.₎ Roma, Jandi Sapi ₍1951₎
173 p. 18 cm.
CONTENTS.—Faville del tricolore.—La carne dolente.—L'anima trionfante.

1. Medicine—Addresses, essays, lectures. 2. Physicians. I. Title.
A 52-6219
Illinois. Univ. Library   ₍1₎
for Library of Congress

NN 0028373   IU

Natale, Maria.
Un secentista : studio biografico-critico su Francesco Angeloni. — Fermo. Tip. sociale. 1911. 113 pp. 24½ cm.

M774 — T.r. — Angeloni, Francesco, 1559?-1652.

NN 0028374   MB

NATALE,Michele.
La lirica religiosa nella letteratura italiana. Napoli,stab.tip.M.d'Auria,1909.
1.8°.

NN 0028375   MH

NATALE,Michele.
La Vergine nella lirica italiana. Caltanissetta,Tip dell'Omnibus,1902.

NN 0028376   MH

Natale, Pasquale.
Prospetti di semeiotica medica
see under
Lucherini, Tommaso, 1891-

Natale, Remo di
see
Natale E , Remo di.

Natale, Stephanus
see Noël, Étienne.

Natale, Tommaso, *marchese di Monterosato*, 1733-1819.
La filosofia leibniziana, esposta in versi toscani dal marchese Tommaso de' Natali, dei marchesi di Monte Rosato ... Tomo I, libro I, Dei principii ... Firenze, Stamperia del Matini ₍i. e. Palermo, F. Valenza₎ 1756.
119, lxi, ₍4₎, 5 p. 21ᶜᵐ.
No more published.
"Principia philosophiæ avctore G. G. Leibnitio. Quibus additæ sunt nonnullæ meæ perbreves animadversiones": lxi p.
1. Leibniz, Gottfried Wilhelm, freiherr von, 1646-1716 — Poetry. I. Leibniz, Gottfried Wilhelm, freiherr von, 1646-1716. Monadologie.
PQ4720.N255F5   47-33300

NN 0028380   DLC CU

Natale, Vaccaro, 1881-
... Estomac biloculaire par ulcère. Résultats éloignés de 24 interventions ... Paris, 1927.
24 cm.
Thèse - Univ. de Paris.
"Bibliographie": p. 64.

NN 0028381   CtY

937.8   Natale, Vincenzo.
N191s   Sulla storia antica della Sicilia discorsi. Vol.1. Napoli, 1843. 639p.
No more published.

NN 0028382   IU

Natale Basile, Ignazio di.
Dante Alighieri; dramma storico in 4 atti per Ignazio di Natale Basile. Modica, Tip. Archimede, 1891.
vii, [8]-50 p. 21½ᶜᵐ.
3-11905

NN 0028383   DLC PU NIC MiU

Natale E , Remo di.
Revolución agraria en Bolivia. Cochabamba, Impr. Universitaria, 1953.
156 p. 19 cm. (Biblioteca social cristiana, no. 1)

1. Bolivia—Soc. condit. 2. Land tenure—Bolivia. I. Title.
HN276.N3   55-31152

NN 0028384   DLC FU NN CU MH NNC

VOLUME 405

...Natale; dramma in tre atti. Torino: Soc. editrice internazionale ₁1921?₎. 55 p. 12°.

Author's initials: F. M. R., at head of title.

1. Jesus Christ in drama. 2. Drama   (Italian). 3. R., F. M.
N. Y. P. L.   January 29, 1923.

NN 0028385   NN

NATALE - capodanno - epifania. Usi e leggende. A.P.Milano,1885.

pp.46.   25233.18

NN 0028386   MH

Il NATALE di Roma celebrato il xxi aprile
1847; Banchetto publico sul Monte Esquilino
alle terme di Tito; discorsi,etc. n.p.,₁18--₎.

NN 0028387   MH OC1

Nataletti (François) ₁1876- ₎. * Étude critique sur les traitements actuels de la luxation
congénitale de la hanche. 82 pp. 8°. Lyon,
1907. No. 96.

NN 0028388   DNLM

Natalena, *sister*
(of the Sisters of St. Joseph, Brentwood, N. Y.)
see
Farrelly, Natalena, *sister*.

Nataletti, Giorgio, 1907- , and G. Petrassi.
Canti popolari della campagna romana, raccolti e armonizzati
da Giorgio Nataletti e Goffredo Petrassi... Milano: G. Ricordi
& C., 1930. Publ. pl. no. 121335. 117 p. illus. 4°.

Italian words precede and accompany music for 1 voice with piano acc.
Two songs for 2 voices.
Illustrations by Am. Stefanori.

563680A. 1. Folk songs, Italian—   CARNEGIE CORPORATION OF NEW YORK.
jt. au. II./Stefanori, Am.,   Rome. I. Petrassi, Goffredo, 1904-
N. Y. P. L.   illustrator.
                                                  February 10, 1932

NN 0028390   NN CtY

Nataletti, Giorgio, 1907-

Società nazionale "Dante Alighieri". *Comitato di Tunisi.*
Museo strumentale.
... Catalogo descrittivo degli strumenti musicali raccolti nel
Museo strumentale, a cura di Giorgio Nataletti. Roma ₁Tip.
"La Speranza", anno xiv ₁1936₎

Nataletti, Giorgio, 1907- *ed.*
Il folklore musicale in Italia dal 1918 ad oggi; saggio
bibliografico. Conferenza internazionale della musica popolare, Basilea, settembre 1948. Roma, E. N. A. L., 1948.

39 p. 22 cm.

At head of title: E. N. A. L., Comitato italiano delle arti e delle
tradizioni popolari.

1. Folk-songs, Italian—Hist. & crit.—Bibl. 2. Folk-songs, Italian—
Bibl. 3. Folk-songs, Italian—Discography. I. Title.

ML128.F75N4   52-20224

NN 0028392   DLC

ML410
.V4S45

Nataletti, Giorgio, 1907-   joint ed.

Sindacato nazionale fascista musicisti.
Verdi, studi e memorie, a cura del Sindacato nazionale fascista musicisti, nel xl. anniversario della morte. Roma, Istituto grafico tiberino, 1941.

Natalevich, E   E
Маршрутно-контрольные устройства и их содержание.
2., перер., изд. Москва, Гос. трансп. жел.-дор. изд-во, 1952.
131 p. diagrs. 22 cm.

1. Railroads—Signaling. 2. Railroads—Traffic. I. Title.
Title transliterated: Marshrutno-kontrol'nye ustroĭstva.

TF615.N3 1952   54-18936

NN 0028394   DLC

Natalevich, E   E
Механическая централизация на железных дорогах
СССР. Москва, Гос. трансп. жел.-дор. изд-во, 1950.
290 p. illus. 23 cm.

At head of title: Е. Е. Налалевич, В. А. Шастин, А. В. Борисов.

1. Railroads—Russia—Equipment and supplies.
Title transliterated: Mekhanicheskaîa t͡sentraliza-
t͡siîa na zheleznykh dorogakh SSSR.

TF345.N3   50-39441

NN 0028395   DLC

Natalevich, E   E
Станционная блокировка (маршрутно-контрольные
устройства) для малых станций. Москва, Гос. трансп.
жел.-дор. изд-во, 1949.
80 p. diagrs. 22 cm.

1. Railroads—Signaling—Block system.
Title transliterated: Stant͡sionnaîa blokirovka.

TF630.N35   50-18963

NN 0028396   DLC

PQ4831
A7764
S3

Natali, Attilio
Segreti di un cuore; amore - verità ·
luce. Pescara, Tip. "Aternum" ₁1952₎.
318p. front. (port.), illus. 22cm.

Poems.

NN 0028397   RPB

Natali, Augusto.
Orientamenti pedagogici; natura e sovrannatura nell'educazione. Pref. del prof. Luigi Cunsolo. 2. ed. ₁Alba?₎ Edizioni paoline ₁1954₎

221 p. 18 cm. (Psychologica; collanina universale di psicologia e
pedagogia, 2)

1. Education—Philosophy.

LB775.N29 1954   56-33986

NN 0028398   DLC

Natali, Carlo.

See

Natale, Carlo, ca.1590-1633.

NATALI,Ettore.
L'arciconfraternita della dottrina cristiana
Cenni storici per Ettore Natali... Roma,F.
Cuggiani,1891.

94,[1] p. 22.5 cm.

NN 0028400   MH-AH

DS
135
I8N27
1887

Natali, Ettore.
Il Ghetto di Roma. Vol. 1.   Roma,
Stab. tip. della Tribuna, 1887.
268 p. 21cm.

No more published?

1. Jews in Rome. I. Title.

NN 0028401   NIC OU CtY NN MH PU CSt MiU

ML3809
N32
Music
Library

Natali, Filippo
Il diapason differenziale; instrumento acustico tascabile che
risolve le differenze dei suoni della scala musicale esatta ragguagliati
con quelli della scala temperata. Dimostrazione. Roma, Tip.
di G. Ciotola, 1886.
88 p. illus.

1. Musical intervals and scales. 2. Musical temperament.
3. Tuning.

NN 0028402   CU

Natali, Filippo
Lo stato libero di Cospaia nell'alta Valle
del Tevere (1440-1826). Umbertide, Stab.tip.
tiberino,1892.
176p. 22cm.

NN 0028403   CtY IU

HG 219
.N27
(Rare)

₁Natali, Francesco₎
Nuova tariffa per ridurre la moneta
con la notizia delle fiere per ogni
piazza, della partenza e arrivo delle
lettere, del peso, e valore di varie
monete di oro, e del peso, e misura che
corre nelle principali piazze di Europa
esattamente raffuagliato al peso, e
misura che si stila nela piazza di
Livorno. In questa quarta edizione
diligentemente corretta et accresciuta
a comodo de' signori negozianti.
Firenze, Nella stamperia dello Stecchi,
e Pagani, 1778.
120 p.
1. Money—Tables, etc. 2. Commerce.
I. Title.

NN 0028404   ICU

Natali, Georges.
Par monts et nuées, poèmes. ₁Avignon₎ Aubanel père
₁1950₎
252 p. 20 cm.

I. Title.

PQ2627.A73P3   A 51-3192
Illinois. Univ. Library
for Library of Congress   ₁3₎†

NN 0028405   IU DLC

Natali, Giovanni, ed.
... Bologna dal 14 luglio al 1° settembre 1848
see under   Bologna. Archivio di Stato.

VOLUME 405

B
161
.613

NATALI, GIOVANNI.
    Catone Uticense e lo stoicismo romano.
Pisa,F.F.Nistri,1910.
    74p. 25cm.

NN   0028407   ICN

Natali, Giovanni
    La crisi europea del 1848 e la prima guerra dell'indipendenza italiana. Bologna, Pàtron, 1948

    164 p. (His Lezioni di storia del Risorgimento tenute [alla Facoltà di lettere dell'Università di Bologna] nell'anno accademico 1947-48)

NN   0028408   MH

Natali, Giovanni
    L'Italia dal 1861 al 1870; il governo della Destra. Bologna, Patron, 1950

    149 p. (His Lezioni di storia del Risorgimento tenute [alla Facoltà di lettere dell'Università di Bologna] nell-anno accademico 1949-50)

NN   0028409   MH

Natali, Giovanni.
    L'Italia durante il regime napoleonico. Lezioni tenute alla Facoltà di lettere dell'Università di Bologna durante l'anno accademico 1954-55. Bologna, R. Pàtron [1955]
    159 p. 25 cm. (Lezioni di storia del Risorgimento)

    1. Italy—Hist.—1789-1815. I. Title.

DG547.N3   58-26761 ‡

NN   0028410   DLC IaU NN ICU IU MH TxU CU NcU

945.08
N191*l*

Natali, Giovanni.
    Lezioni di storia del risorgimento tenute nell'anno accademico 1946-47. Bologna, R. Pàtron, 1947.
    156p. 25cm.

    CONTENTS.--I. L'Italia negli anni 1814-15 e la campagna indipendentista di Gioacchino Murat.--II. La guerra del 1866 e il suo momento internazionale.
    On spine: Storia del resorgimento.

NN   0028411   TxU

Natali, Giovanni.
    Lezioni di storia del risorgimento tenute nell'anno accademico 1947-48. La crisi europea del 1848 e la prima guerra dell'indipendenza italiana. Bologna, R. Pàtron, 1948. 164 p. 25cm.

    1. Italy—Hist., 1815-1870. 2. Italy   —Hist.—Revolution of 1848-1849.

NN   0028412   NN

Natali, Giovanni.
    ... Lezioni di storia del risorgimento, anno accademico 1948-49 ... Bologna, R. Pàtron, 1949.
    159 p.

NN   0028413   NN

Natali, Giovanni.
    Lezioni di storia del Risorgimento tenute nell'anno accademico 1949-50: l'Italia dal 1861 al 1870; il governo della destra. Bologna, R. Pàtron, 1950.
    149 p. 25 cm.

    1. Italy—Hist.—1849-1870.

DG552.N38   52-38491 ‡

NN   0028414   DLC

Natali, Giovanni.
    Lezioni di storia del risorgimento; tenute nell'anno accademico 1950-51. Bologna, Pàtron, 1951.
    159 p. 24½ cm.

    1.Italy – Hist. – 19th cent.

NN   0028415   NjP

Natali, Giovanni
    L'opera politica del conte di Cavour. Bologna, Patron, 1952-[53]

    2 v. (His Lezioni di storia del Risorgimento tenute [alla Facoltà di lettere dell'Università di Bologna] nell'anno accademico 1951-[53])

NN   0028416   MH NN IaU TxU

Natali, Giovanni.
    L'opera politica di Vincenzo Gioberti; lezioni tenute alla Facoltà di lettere dell'Università di Bologna durante l'anno accademico 1953-54. Bologna, R. Pàtron [1954]
    162 p. 25 cm. (Lezioni di storia del Risorgimento)
    L. C. copy imperfect.

    1. Gioberti, Vincenzo, 1801-1852.

JC236.G55N3   58-30568 ‡

NN   0028417   DLC NN NIC CU DS

Natali, Giovanni.
    Il patriota bolognese Giuseppe Camillo Mattioli, 1817-1893; notizie biografiche e bibliografiche, documenti inediti. [Bologna, Stab. tip. Felsineo, 1931]
    39 p.
    "Estratto dall'annuario 1929-1930, VIII, del R. Istituto tecnico 'Pier Crescenzi' di Bologna".

NN   0028418   MH

4DG-319

Natali, Giovanni.
    La rivoluzione del 1831 nella Cronaca di Francesco Rangone. Roma, Vittoriano, 1935.
    264 p. (Regio Istituto per la storia del risorgimento italiano. Biblioteca scientifica. 2. ser.: Fonti, v.5)

NN   0028419   DLC-P4

881
S35Yn

Natali, Giovanni.
    Socrate nel giudizio dei padri apologisti; contributo alla storia delle relazioni fra paganesimo e Cristianesimo nascente. Ascoli Piceno, 1912
    56p.

NN   0028420   IU

Z8502
.8
B5

Natali, Giulio, 1875-
    Bibliografia leopardiana. Firenze, L. S. Olschki, 1931-

NATALI, Giulio, 1875-
    I canti della pasqua. Macerata,Stab.tip. Mancini,1898.

    20 cm. pp.43,(2).

NN   0028422   MH

D945.07
B655

Natali, Giulio, 1875-
    Carlo Botta; discorso tenuto in San Giorgio Canavese, il 22 settembre 1935 ... da Giulio Natali. [Urbino, Regio istituto d'arte per il libro, 1925]
    2 p. l., 3-45 p. 24ᶜᵐ.

    Half-title.
    "Estratto dal volume I delle Celebrazioni piemontesi."

    1. Botta, Carlo, 1766-1837.

NN   0028423   NNC

901
N19c

Natali, Giulio, 1875-
    Che cosa è la storia? Bologna, Stabilimento poligrafico Emiliano, 1908.
    cover-title, 10p.

    "Estratto dalla Rivista di filosofia e scienze affini ... 1908, anno X, vol.I, n.5-6."

NN   0028424   IU

851.7
L58cZn

Natali, Giulio, 1875-
    Corso e ricorso della lirica leopardiana; guida alla lettura dei "Canti" del Leopardi. Roma, A. Signorelli, 1948.
    110p.

    1. Leopardi, Giacomo, conte, 1798-1837. Canté. I. Title.

NN   0028425   IEN CU CtY ICU NN OC1 OrU

Natali, Giulio, 1875-
    ... Cultura e poesia in Italia nell' età napoleonica. Studii e saggi. Torino, S T E N, 1930.
    2 p. l., [7]-820 p., 2 l. 19½ᶜᵐ.
    "Alcuni altri lavori di Giulio Natali": 2d leaf at end.

    1. Italian poetry—History and criticism. I. Title.   A 34-541

    Title from Yale Univ.   Repr. from L. C. Union Cat.

NN   0028426   CtY IaU NcD ICU PSC OCU NN MH IU

Natali, Giulio, 1875-
    ... Dal Guinizelli al d'Annunzio, revisioni e rivalutazioni. Roma, Tosi, 1942.
    2 p. l., 7-889 p., 1 l. 20½ᶜᵐ. (Biblioteca di studi classici (n. 3))
    Bibliography at end of most of the chapters.

    1. Italian poetry—Hist. & crit. I. Title.   46-41201

    Library of Congress   PQ4092.N3

    [2]   851.09

NN   0028427   DLC IaU NcD PU CtY IU NjP MH CLU

VOLUME 405

PQ 4804 N27
Natali, Giulio, 1875–
Gabriele D'Annunzio e gli scrittori italiani. Catania, Università di Catania, Biblioteca della Facoltà di Lettere e Filosofia, 1954.
48 p. 25cm. (Catania. Università. Facoltà di lettere e filosofia. Biblioteca, 10)

1. Annunzio, Gabriele d', 1863–1938.

MH CU CoU
NN 0028428 NIC MiU RPB WU InU PU MWelC IaU OU CtY

Natali, Giulio, 1875–
…Gian Vincenzo Gravina, letterato; discorso letto in Arcadia l'8 giugno 1918 in ricordo del 2° centenario dalla morte di G. V. G. Roma: Tipografia poliglotta vaticana, 1919. 27 p. 4°.

1. Gravina, Giovanni Vincenzo, 1664–1718.
N.Y.P.L.   October 18, 1922.

NN 0028429 NN MH

Natali, Giulio, 1875–
… I giorni e le opere di Giosuè Carducci … Roma, A. Signorelli, 1935.
202 p., 1 l., ₍2₎ p. 19¹ᵐ.
"Nota bibliografica": p. ₍198₎–202.

1. Carducci, Giosuè, 1835–1907.
A C 35–2198
Title from Illinois Univ.   Printed by L. C.

NN 0028430 IU CU NcD

Natali, Giulio, 1875–
Giosuè Carducci. ₍n.p.₎ Cappelli ₍1950₎
194 p.

"La prima edizione (1935) di questo libro, I giorni e le opere di G. Carducci." Bibliography: p.₍185₎–190.

NN 0028431 CU NcD ICU IEN RPB MH

PQ4686 N3
Natali, Giulio, 1875–
Giosuè Carducci. ₍2. ed. Rocca San Casciano₎ Cappelli ₍1953₎
194 p. 20cm. (Saggi e monografie di letteratura italiana)

Includes bibliography.

1. Carducci, Giosuè, 1835–1907.

NN 0028432 CoU OrU NcU WU InU IaU

855C33 DN19
Natali, Giulio, 1875–
Giovanni Alfredo Cesareo.
(In Bollettino storico catanese. Catania. 25cm. Anni XI e XII (1946 e 1947) p.₍91₎–119)

1. Cesareo, Giovanni Alfredo, 1860–1937. I. Bollettino storico catanese. Anni XI e XII (1946 e 1947)

NN 0028433 IU

CT 1138 C86N19
Natali, Giulio, 1875–
Giovanni Mario Crescimbeni. Roma, Tip. poliglotta Vaticana, 1929.
27 p.
"Da l'Arcadia, 1928."
Bibliography: p. 20–27.

1. Crescimbeni, Giovanni Mario, 1663–1728.

NN 0028434 CLU ICN

PQ4683 C7Z82
Natali, Giulio, 1875–
Giuseppe Aurelio Costanzo; discorso tenuto a Siracusa il 4 ottobre 1939 … ₍estratto dall'opera in tre volumi delle Celebrazioni siciliane. Urbino, R. Istituto d'arte del libro, 1939?₎
50 p.

Bibliography: p.49–50.

1. Costanzo, Giuseppe Aurelio, 1843–1913.

NN 0028435 CU

Natali, Giulio, 1875–
Giuseppe Parini, uomo e poeta. ₍Bologna₎ Cappelli ₍1952₎
185 p. 20 cm.
Includes bibliographies. Bibliographical footnotes.

1. Parini, Giuseppe, 1729–1799.
A 53–3708
Harvard Univ. Library for Library of Congress ₍1₎

CtY NN CU NcU RPB
NN 0028436 MH OrU MB NcD NjP PU PBL IaU OClJC

---

854 P233N3
Natali, Giulio, 1875–
Giuseppe Parini, uomo e poeta. ₍Bologna₎ Cappelli ₍1953₎
185 p. 20ᶜⁿ. (Saggi e monografie di letteratura italiana)
Bibliography: p. ₍179₎–185.

1. Parini, Giuseppe, 1729–1799.

NN 0028437 CSt WaU

Natali, Giulio, 1875–
… Idee, costumi, uomini del settecento; studii e saggi letterarii. Torino, Società tipografico-editrice nazionale, 1916.
2 p. l., ₍7₎–356 p., 1 l. 22ᶜᵐ. L. 6
CONTENTS.—Alcune idee sul settecento.—Il pensiero storico italiano nel settecento dopo G. B. Vico.—Giuseppe Parini e il pensiero religioso nel secolo XVIII.—La guerra e la pace nel pensiero italiano del sec. XVIII.—La coscienza nazionale italiana avanti la rivoluzione francese.—Il cicisbeismo a Genova.—Per la storia del costume letterario nel settecento.—Il bastone pedagogo (noterella pariniana)—Carlo Goldoni a Pavia.—Il

pensiero sociale di C. Goldoni.—I due capolavori del Voltaire e i loro traduttori italiani.—Un'antologia barettiana.—Il ritorno di Carlo Gozzi.—Sul Bettinelli.—Il Momo pisano ₍Batacchi₎—Un enciclopedista classicista ₍Milizia₎—Il Varrone del secolo XVIII ₍Lanzi₎—Il Lanzi dantista.—Giuseppe Piermarini.—Il maestro di Alessandro Manzoni ₍Soave₎—Nel centenario di Vittorio Alfieri.—L. Mascheroni poeta della scienza.—La rivoluzione francese e le lettere italiane.—Francesco Lomonaco e il nazionalismo nell'età napoleonica.

1. Italian literature—18th cent.—Hist. & crit.
Library of Congress   PQ4083.N3
                          17–554

NN 0028439 DLC IaU CU MiU

PQ4083 N3 1926
Natali, Giulio, 1875–
Idee, costumi, uomini del settecento; studii e saggi letterarii. 2.ed. arricchita di nuovi saggi. Torino, Società tipografico-editrice nazionale, 1926.
470 p. 19cm.

Page 470 incorrectly numbered 170.

I. Italian literature – 18th cent. – Hist. & crit.

NN 0028440 CU NjP NNC PU IU MH OCU NcD CtY

Natali, Giulio, 1875–
Mascheroni, Lorenzo, 1750–1800.
… L'invito a Lesbia Cidonia, e altre poesie; introduzione e commento di Giulio Natali. 2. ed., riv., con tre tavole. Torino, Unione tipografico-editrice torinese ₍1920₎

854P21 DN19
Natali, Giulio, 1875–
La mente e l'anima di Giuseppe Parini; studii. Modena, G. T. Vincenzi e nipoti, 1900.
xi, 194p.

Bibliography: p.ix–xi.

NN 0028442 IU CU IaU NcD CtY CaBVaU

709.452 N191p
Natali, Giulio, 1875–
… Pavia e la sua Certosa; guida artistica con introduzione storica di Giacinto Romano. Pavia, Mattei, Speroni & c., 1911.
164p. front., illus., fold.plan.

Bibliographies interspersed.

1. Art--Pavia. 2. Pavia--Descr. I. Romano, Giacinto, 1854-1920.

NN 0028443 IU MB PU MH

709.452 N191p 1925
Natali, Giulio, 1875–
… Pavia e la sua Certosa; guida artistica, con introduzione storica di Giacinto Romano … 2.ed. Pavia, Tipo-libreria editrice vescovile Artigianelli, 1925.
159p. illus., port., fold.plan.

Bibliographies interspersed.

1. Art--Pavia. 2. Pavia--Descr. I. Romano, Giacinto, 1854-1920.

NN 0028444 IU

Natali, Giulio, 1875–
I pittori marchigiani anteriori a Raffaello. Roma: Stabilimento tipografico della "Tribuna," 1902. 11 p. 8°.
Repr.: Rivista moderna politica e letteraria. 15 luglio, 1902.

1. Painting (Italian).—History.
N.Y.P.L.   April 12, 1913.

NN 0028445 NN

Natali, Giulio, 1875– ed.
Foscolo, Ugo, 1778–1827.
… Poesie, con introduzione e commento di Giulio Natali. Bologna, L. Cappelli ₍1939₎

851.79 I27ZN
Natali, Giulio, 1875–
Un poeta maceratese; memoria su la vita e le opere di F. Ilàri; con appendice di lettere inedite d'illustri italiani Contributo alla storia della scola romagnola e marchigiana. Macerata, 1898.
xi, 99 p. 20 cm.
Includes bibliographical references.

1. Ilàri, Francesco, 1810–1878.

NN 0028447 NcD CU

Natali, Giulio, 1875– ed.
La rete di Vulcano…
see under Batacchi, Domenico, 1748–1802.

VOLUME 405

Natali, Giulio, 1875–   ed.

Spalletti, Giuseppe, *fl.* 1764.
    ... Saggio sopra la bellezza, a cura di Giulio Natali.   Firenze,
L. S. Olschki, 1933.

Natali, Giulio, 1875–
    Scrittori italiani antitedeschi.   Campobasso: G. Colitti e
figlio, 1917.   28 p.   8°.   (Collana Colitti di conferenze e
discorsi.   no. 35.)
        Author's name at head of title.
    "Conferenza tenuta all' Università popolare di Genova il 21 marzo 1916 e
all' Università popolare di Roma il 1° febbrajo 1917."

1. Germany in poetry (Italian).   2. Poetry (Italian).—History and
criticism. 3. Antipathies and preju-   dices (International). 4. Title.
5. Series.
N. Y. P. L.   October 17, 1918.

NN   0028450   NN MH NjP

Natali, Giulio, 1875–
    Lo scultore dei Mille [Battista Tassara] dalla
Provincia Maceratese.   Macerata, Tip.
Edit. Maceratese, 1901.
        32 p.
        At head of title: Piccola biblioteca Marchigiana,
3.

NN   0028451   MH

Natali, Giulio, 1875–
    ... Il settecento, a cura di Giulio Natali ...   Milano [etc.] F.
Vallardi, 1929.
    2 v.   25½ᵐ.   (*Added t.-p.:* Storia letteraria d'Italia ... 3ᵃ. ed. com-
pletamente rifatta.   [8])
        Paged continuously.
        "Note" at end of each chapter.

    1. Italian literature—18th century—History and criticism.
                                                     A 34–2888
    Title from Oberlin Col-   lege
    Library of Congress   [PQ4037.S8 no. 8 1929]

          PBm ViU OU NcU MH MiU
NN   0028452   OO OrU ICU NcD CU MWelC ViU CU PHC PU

Natali, Giulio, 1875–
    ... Il settecento, a cura di Giulio Natali ...   Ristampa ste-
reotipa corretta ...   Milano [etc.] F. Vallardi, 1936.
    2 v.   24½ᵐ.   (*Added t.-p.:* Storia letteraria d'Italia ... 3. ed. com-
pletamente rifatta.   [8])
        Paged continuously.
        Series title also at head of t.-p.
        Bibliographical "Note" at end of each chapter.

    1. Italian literature—18th cent.—Hist. & crit.
                                                     37–16090
    Library of Congress   PQ4037.S82 t. 8
                                 [2]   (850.9) 850.903

NN   0028453   DLC

850.9   Natali, Giulio, 1875–
St7   Il settecento. 2.ed.   Milano, F. Vallardi,
1939   1944–[47]
v.2   2v.(x, 1254p.) 25x17cm. (Storia letteraria
           d'Italia. 3.ed. completamente rifatta. [2])

           Bibliographical "Note" at end of each chapter.

           1. Italian literature--18th cent.--Hist. & crit.

NN   0028454   IU ViU MB

Natali, Giulio, 1875–
    Il Settecento. 3. ed.   Milano, F. Vallardi [1950–
        v.   25 cm.   (Storia letteraria d'Italia, 3./4. ed. [8])

    1. Italian literature—18th cent.—Hist. & crit.   (Series)

    PQ4037.S826   t. 8   850.903   54–16858 rev

NN   0028455   DLC WaSpG CtY

PQ4083   Natali, Giulio, 1875–
N32   Il Settecento.   4. ed. riv. e aggiornata.   Milano, F.
1955   Vallardi [1955]
             2 v.(x, 1260 p.)   (Storia letteraria d'Italia.   [3./4. ed.
           completamente rifatta])

           Includes bibliographies.

           1. Italian literature - 18th cent. - Hist. & crit.

NN   0028456   CU ICU MH PSt CU CSt CaBVaU MtU

Natali, Giulio, 1875–
    ... Storia dell'arte ad uso delle Scuole medie
e delle persone côlte ...   Torino [etc.] 1903.
22.5 cm.

NN   0028457   CtY

Natali, Giulio, 1875–
    ... Storia dell' arte ad uso delle scuole e delle persone
côlte.   4. ed. ... ampliata e riveduta ...   Torino, Società
tipografico-editrice nazionale, 1913–
        v.   illus. 22½ᵐ.   (*On cover:* Biblioteca d'arte.   1   )

    1. Art—Hist.   I. Vitelli, Eugenio, joint author.
                                                     14–7704
    Library of Congress   N5300.N3

NN   0028458   DLC NcD CU

Natali, Giulio, 1875–
    ... Su l'estetica di Dante.   [Rome?] Tipo-
grafia poligliotta Vaticana, 1938.
    1 p.l., p.[29]–36.   24½ᵐ.

    "Dagli Atti dell'Accademia degli Arcadi,
1936–1937, vol. XV–XVI."

    1. Dante Alighieri, 1265–1321.

NN   0028459   NNC

Natali, Giulio, 1875–
    ... Torquato Tasso.   Roma, Tariffi [1943]
    4 p. l., [11]–246 p., 4 l.   front. (port.)   19ᵐ.
    "Nota bibliografica": p. [241]–246.

    1. Tasso, Torquato, 1544–1595.
                                                     45–20430
    Library of Congress   PQ4646.N3
                                 [2]   928.5

          NcU PBm
NN   0028460   DLC CaBVaU OrU NIC OU CtY IU NjP RPB

NATALI, GIULIO, 1875–
    Torquato Tasso e Roma.   [Roma] Instituto di
Studi Romani, 1946,
    32p.   26cm.   (Quaderni di studi romani; Roma
nell' opera del genio.   13)

    1. Tasso, Torquato, 1544–1595.

NN   0028461   TxU WaSpG IEN CtY MH ICU NN

Natali, Giulio, 1875–
    ... Torquato Tasso, filosofo del bello, dell'arte e dell'amore.
Roma: Unione cooperativa editrice, 1895.   36 p.   12°.
    "Dal numero unico 'Torquato Tasso' pubblicato dal Circolo romano di studi il 25
aprile 1895."

271675A.   1. Tasso, Torquato, 1544–   1595.
N. Y. P. L.   October 13, 1927

NN   0028462   NN

808.8   Natali, Giulio, 1875–
N272T   Le tre muse; antologia per lo studio
           delle varie forme letterarie. A d uso delle
           scuole medie di secondo grado.   Roma, Ausonia,
           1922.
             ii, 808 p.   20 cm.
             Includes bibliographical references.

             1. Literature.   Collections.   I. Title.

NN   0028463   NcD

Natali, Giulio, comp.
    Le tre muse; antologia per lo studio delle
varie forme letterarie ad uso delle scuole
medie di secondo grado.   Roma, Ausonia, 1924.
    808 p.

NN   0028464   MiD

Natali, Giulio, 1875–
    Ugo Foscolo.   [1.ed.]   Firenze, "La Nuova
Italia" [1953]
    viii, 199p.   20cm.   (Collana critica, 60)

    Bibliography: p.[187]–191.

    1. Foscolo, Niccolò Ugo, 1778–1827.

          NN NBuU InU WaU NjP
NN   0028465   MiU ICU RPB MdBJ IEN PSt IaU CtY CU

Natali, Giulio, 1875–
    Viaggio col Leopardi nell' Italia
letteraria.   Milano, Montuoro editore
[1943]

    262 p.   20cm.

    "Con questo titolo..., nel settembre
del '42, feci dodici lezioni nel Centro
nazionale di studii leopardiani a
Recanati."– Avvertenza.

    1. Leopardi, Giacomo, conte, 1798–
1837.   2. It   alian literature. History and criti   cism.   I. Title.

NN   0028466   MnU IaU CoU OrU CU CtY OCU ICN NjP

VOLUME 405

PQ4724　NATALI,GIULIO,1875–
.N2　　La vita e l'opera di Giuseppe Parini.
Firenze, F. Le Monnier, 1931.
8+148 p. port.

Author's autograph on verso of title-page.

1. Parini,Giuseppe,1729-1799.

NN　0028467　InU NcD CtU

Natali, Giulio, 1875–
... La vita e le opere di Pietro Metastasio.　Livorno,
R. Giusti ₍1923₎.

4 p. l., 69 p.　16ᵐ.　(*On cover:* Biblioteca degli studenti ... v. 530-531)
"Un po' di bibliografia metastasiana": p. ₍65₎-69.

1. Metastasio, Pietro Antonio Domenico Buonaventura, 1698-1782.
26-21093

Library of Congress　　　ML429.M48

NN　0028468　DLC CU

Natali, Giulio, 1875–

La vita e le opere di Ugo Foscolo. Livorno,
R. Giusti, 1928.

103 p.　16 cm.　(Biblioteca degli studenti.)

Bibliography: p. ₍99₎-103.

1. Foscolo, Ugo, 1778-1827.　I. Title.

NN　0028469　CaBVaU MH CtY

Natali, Giulio, 1875–
Vittorio Alfieri.　Roma, A. Signorelli, 1949.
172 p. port.　20 cm.　(I Luminari della lingua nostra)
Bibliography : p. ₍164₎-168.

1. Alfieri, Vittorio, 1749-1808.

PQ4681.N3　　　　　　53-24931

NN　0028470　DLC MH NN CoU RPB CU IEN

Natali, J　　1889–
... Les sarcomes de la clavicule ...　Montpellier, 1920.
25.5 cm.
Thèse - Univ. de Montpellier.

NN　0028471　CtY

Natali, J　　B.
... Lilla; scènes de la vie corse. 3. éd.　Paris, E. Fi-
guière & cⁱᵉ, 1912.
2 p. l., 223, ₍1₎ p.　19ᵐ.

ɪ. Title.
13-7956

Library of Congress　　PQ2627.A75L5 1912

NN　0028472　DLC

Natali, J. B.
...Nos Géorgiques, par M. J.-B. Natali.　(Tableau géographique et littéraire de la vie agricole en Corse.)　Grenoble: J. Allier,
1921.　86 p.　4°.　(Soc. des sciences historiques et naturelles de la Corse.)

Cover-title.
On cover: Bulletin.　no. 429-432.

1. Country life, Corsica.　2. Fiction　　　　(French).　3. Société des
sciences historiques et naturelles de　　　　la Corse.
N. Y. P. L.　　　　　　　　　　　　　　　　August 15, 1922.

NN　0028473　NN

Natali, Jean Charles, 1905–
... L'ostéomyélite traumatique fermée ...
Bordeaux, 1930.
Thèse - Univ. de Bordeaux.
"Bibliographie": p. ₍61₎-63.

NN　0028474　CtY

Natali, Maria Linda Sommaruga
　　see　Sommaruga Natali, Maria Linda,
1915–

Natali, Martino, 1730-1791.
Critica di un Romano alle Riflessioni del
Portoghese sopra il Memoriale presentato dalli
padri gesuiti alla Santità di papa Clemente XIII
　　see under　Fabricy, Gabriel, 1725-1800,
supposed author.

Natali, Martino, *1730-1791.*
Lettera I. ad un lettore di teologia in Roma sopra
la morte di Gesù Cristo e sua discesa all' inferno.
Paris, Potro, 1776.
160 p.

NN　0028477　PU

262.8　₍Natali, Martino₎ 1730(ca)-1791.
N191v　　La venerabile antichità sull'autorità de'vescovi
₍n.p.₎ 1791.
69p.

Bibliographical foot-notes.

1. Authority (Religion)　2. Bishops.　I. Title.

NN　0028478　IU

Natali, Mauro
**Mater gratiae; preghiere e canti del Parr-
chiano.** ₍Fermo, Stab. Tip. Sociale, 1953₎

152 p.

NN　0028479　DCU

4K　　Natali, Nunzio.
Ital.-　　La legge Aquilia ossia il Damnum iniuria
1198　　datum, studi sul lib. IX, tit. II del Digesto.
Roma, Tip. dell'Unione cooperativa editrice, 1896.
271 p.

NN　0028480　DLC-P4

Natali, Pietro
　　see
Natalibus, Petrus de, *bp. of Equilio,* fl. 1370-1400.

WAA　　NATALI, Salvatore
qN272t　　　Topografia e statistica medica di
1889　　　Senigallia.　Milano, Civelli, 1889.
114 p.　illus.

NN　0028482　DNLM

Natali, Tommaso de'
　　see　Natale, Tommaso, *marchese di Monterosato,* 1733-
1819.

Natali, Vladimir Frankovich, 1890–
Классные практические работы по зоологии в средней
школе; методическое пособие для учителя.　Москва, Изд-
во Академии педагог. наук РСФСР, 1959́
ч.ʏ illus.　20 cm.

At head of title: Академия педагогических наук РСФСР. Институт методов обучения.

Contents.—
ч. 2. 7. класс.

1. Zoology—Study and teaching.　ɪ. Title.
Title transliterated: Klassnye prakticheskie
raboty po zoologii v srednel shkole.

QL51.N3　　　　　　55-29979 ‡

NN　0028484　DLC

Natali, Vladimir Frankovich, 1890–
Зоология беспозвоночных.　Допущено в качестве учеб.
пособия для педагог. ин-тов.　Москва, Гос. учебно-педагог. изд-во, 1951.
536 p.　illus., col. plates.　27 cm.

1. Invertebrates.　ɪ. Title.
Title transliterated: Zoologiía bespozvonochnykh.

QL362.N3　　　　　　55-40797

NN　0028485　DLC

274.5722 Natali-Sifola, Vincenzio Maria.
N19d　　Dissertazione istorica sull'antica esistenza
di un tempio d'Apollo in Casapulla e su i principj, e lo stato del medesimo villaggio ...　Napoli, V. Manfredi, 1802.
223p.

NN　0028486　IU

945.721 Natali-Sifola, Vincenzio Maria.
Z76sYn　　Lettera dell'abbate Vincenzio Maria Natali-
Sifola de'marchesi di questo cognome all'abbate
Mattia Zona sopra il di lui Saggio istorico intor-
no alla città di Calvi, e Sparanisi.　Napoli,
1793.
liii p.
In manuscript on fly-leaf: Dono dell'autore.
Gold-tooled leather binding.

1. Sparanise, Italy.　2. Zona, Mattia.　Saggio
istorico intorno alla città di Calvi, e Sparanisi

NN　0028487　IU

Natalia, Carmen, *pseud.*
　　see
Martínez Bonilla, Carmen Natalia.

VOLUME 405

Natalia, Aslauga's knight, and other tales. / Edited by a lady...
Boston: Jordan and Wiley, 1845.   96 p.   12°.

Contents: Natalia. La Motte-Fouqué, F. H. K.: Aslauga's knight. Blanche Rose.

1. Fiction, French. 2. La Motte-
Freiherr de, 1777-1843. Aslauga's
4. Title: Blanche Rose.
N.Y.P.L.

Fouqué, Friedrich Heinrich Karl,
knight. 3. Title: Aslauga's knight.

April 27, 1925

NN 0028489   NN MH

NATALIA, Aslauga's knight, and other tales.
Edited by a lady. Boston, Jordan and Wiley,
1845.
pp.96.
(Fireside library of popular reading.)

NN 0028490   MH

WB   Natalian, pseud.
58112   A South African boy; schoolboy life in Natal.
            London, M. Russell, 1897.
            168 p. 20 cm.

NN 0028491   CtY

Rare   Natalibus, Petrus de, Bp. of Equilio, fl.
BX   1370-1400.
4654   Catalogus sanctorum et gestorum eorum.
N27++   Vicenza, Henricus de Sancto Ursio, Zenus,
1493   12 Dec. (pridie Id. Dec.) 1493.
            [332] l. 34cm.

            Leaf [1a] (Title): Omnipotenti Deo:
            Immacvlatae semper virgini Mariae: vniver-
            saeqve caelesti cvriae splendori: et ani-
            mabvs nostris vtilitati. (red): Catalogvs
            sanctorum et gestorum eorvm ex diversis vo-

            lvminibvs collectvs editvs a reverendissimo
            in Christo patre domino Petro de Natalibvs
            de Venetiis Dei gratia episcopo Eqvilino.
            Below title: Antonii Verli Vicentini ad
            lectorem endecasyllabon. (Verses of the edi-
            tor to the reader)
            Leaf [326b] (Colophon): Catalogi sancto-
            rum per reueredissimum dominum petrum de

            natalibus uenetū episcopum equilinū editi
            opus finit: Vicentiae per henricū de
            sancto ursio librariū solerti cura Ipres-
            sum: Augustino Barbadico īclyto uenetiarū
            Duce. Anno salutis. M.CCCCLXXXXIII. ꝑdie
            id' decēbris ...
            Printer's device, with letters R. V.
            (Rigo Vicentino), follows the colophon.

            Leaves [327a]-[331a]: legends of 24 ad-
            ditional saints, apparently compiled by the
            editor.
            Leaves [331b] and [332] blank. Leaf
            [332] wanting in this copy.
            Signatures: a6, b-u8, x6, y-z8, &8, ꝑ8,
            ꝛ6, A-B8, C-O6.8, P8, Q-R8, S6.
            Printed capitals.

            Saints' lives are arranged by calendar.
            Hain. Repertorium (with Copinger's Sup-
            plement) *11676; Proctor, 7173; Brit. Mus.
            Cat. (XV cent.) VII, p. 1047 (IB. 31854);
            Goff. Third census, N-6.
            Imperfect copy: signatures C3 and C4
            wanting. Duplicates of signatures G3 and
            G4 bound in their place.

            Ex libris Cosmi Gordon e Coll. Regal.

            1. Saints. I. Verlo, Antonio, fl. 1481,
            ed. II. Title.

NN 0028497   NIC InU CU OrU CtY MH N DCU

Natalibus, Petrus de, *Bp. of Equilio, fl.* 1370-1400.
    Catalogus sanctorum z gestorum eorū ex diuersis volumi-
    nibus collectus. [Venetiis, per B. de Zanis; impensis L. de
    Giunta, 1506]

    274 (i. e. 275) l. Illus. 30 cm.

    Several woodcuts signed by the monogrammist "b" appeared first
    in the Bible of 1490 translated into Italian by Niccolò Malermi.
    Provenance: Museo Cavaleri (stamp)

    1. Saints.   I. Title.

    BX4654.N3 1506 Rosenwald Coll.   65-59127

NN 0028498   DLC

Natalibus, Petrus de, bp. of Equilio, fl. 1370-1400.
    Catalogus sanctorum & gestorum eorū ex diuersis volumini-
    bus collectus: editus a reuerēdissimo in xp[ist]o patre domino Petro
    de natalibus... [Venetiis, Bartholomeum de Zanis im-
    pensis Luceantonii de Giunta impressum, 1506]   4 p.l., 274
    [i. e. 275], f., 1 l.   illus.   33cm. (f°.)

    Sander 4940. Essling 1510. Dyson Perrins 179.   Proctor 12437.
    With colophon dated: v. idus iulii.

    Last leaf (blank) wanting.
    Edited by Antonius Verlus.
    Illustrations: numerous small woodcuts which had previously appeared in Jacobus
    de Varagine's Legendario of Venice, 1494 or in the Malermi Bible of Venice, 1491.
    Four of the former appear as a group surrounded by an ornamental border from a
    Venice, 1491 edition of Dante, on prelim. l. 4°. The same border surrounds the text
    on the opposite page. Ornamental initials of various sizes. Publisher's device on t. p.
    Rubricated.

    Slightly wormed.
    With stamp: Bibliotheca Regia Monacensis.
    With bookplates of Harry Walter Cholmley, Dyson Perrins and Hermann Marx.
    Binding, by J. Wright, of mottled calf, gilt.

    1. Saints—Lives. 2. Wood en-   gravings, Italian. 3. Bindings, 19th
    cent., British—Wright. I. Verlo,   Antonio, ed. II. Title.

NN 0028501   NN ICN MH

        Natalibus, Petrus de, Bp. of Equilio, fl. 1370-1400.
Typ   Catalogus sanctorum & gestor[um] eor[um]
515   ex diuersis voluminibus collectus: editus a
08.599 reuerendissimo in xpo patre dño Petro de
        Natalibus de venetijs dei gratis epo Equilino.
        Venūdatur Lugduni a Stephano Gueynard prefate
        ciuitatis bibliopola et ciue.In vico Mercuriali:
        vulgariter en la rue merciere:prope sanctum
        Antonium.[1508]
        4p.l.,cccxl numb l. illus. 26.5cm.
        Title within historiated border including
        publisher's de-   vice.

        Colophon: ... Lugduni impressum per Claudium
        dauost al's de troys. Impēsis honesti viri
        Stephani gueynard eiusdē ciuitatis ciuis &
        bibliopola. Anno domini millesimo quingētesimo
        octauo. xv. kalendas iunij.
        Edited by Antonio Verlo.

NN 0028503   MH

    Natalibus, Petrus De, Bp. of Equilio, fl. 1370-1400.
    Catalogus Sanctorum. Lyons, 1509.

NN 0028504   DCos

SPECIAL COLLECTIONS
B936.08
N19
    Natalibus, Petrus de, Bp., fl. 1370-1400.
    Catalogus sanctorum z gestorum eorum ex diuer-
    sis voluminibus collectus: editus a ... Petro
    de Natalibus de Venetijs ... epo Equilino.
    [Argentine impressum per Martinū Flach, 1513]
    [4], ccliii l. 1 illus. 32cm.

    Imprint from colophon. Title within decora-
    tive border, with printer's device.
    Saints' lives arranged by calendar.
    Preface by Antonio Verlo, editor of 1493 ed.
    Some leaves   wormed.

NN 0028505   NNC IU CtY

Natalibus, Petrus de, *Bp. of Equilia, fl.* 1370-1400.
    Catalogus sāctorum et gestorū eorū ex diuersis volumi-
    nibus collectus. Lugduñ., Venundantur ab S. Gueynard,
    al's Pineti [1514]

    cccxlij l. Illus. 26 cm.

    Illustrations attributed to Guillaume Le Roy. Cf. Baudrier.
    Bibl. lyonnaise, v. 11, p. 232-234.
    Inscription on t. p.: Ex libris Michaellij Pulgseruer bibliopolae
    1687.

    1. Saints.   I. Le Roy, Guillaume, d. 1528? illus.   II. Title.

    BX4654.N3 1514 Rosenwald Coll.   75-206948

NN 0028506   DLC DGU MiU CtY

    Natalibus, Petrus de, bp. of Equilio, fl. 1370-
    1400.
        Catalogus sanctorum et gestorum eoru ex
    diuersis voluminibus collectus: editus a reuer-
    dissimo in Christo patre domino Petro de Natali-
    bus ... [Colophon: Impressum Lugduni per
    Jacobum saccon. Anno dni millesimo quingentesimo
    decimoquarto. Die vero nona mensis decembris]
        [8] p., ccxlj numb. l. [i. e. 482 p.] illus.
    31 cm.
        t.-p. in red.
        Irregularities in paging.

NN 0028507   MiU

    Natalibus, Petrus de, Bp. of Equilia.
        Catalogus sanctorum gestorum eorumque ex
    diuersis voluminibus collectus; editus et
    multis novis additionibus decoratus a J.
    Gravio. Venetiis, 1516.
        4to.

NN 0028508   NN

BX   Natalibus, Petrus de, bp. of Equilio, fl.1370-1400.
4654   Catalogus sanctoruz et gestorum eorum ex
N3   diuersis voluminib⁹ collectus ... Lugduñ.,
1519   Venundantur ab Stephano Gueynard al's Pineti
Cage   Colophon: ... Impressum p Johannē de Cābray al's
        Moylin, impēsis Stephani Gueynard al's Pineti,1519.

        [4] cccxiii [1] l. A⁴, a-z⁸, A-P⁸, Q¹⁰. 4to,
        illus.
        Edited by Antonio Verlo.

NN 0028509   DFo

    Natalibus, Petrus de Bp., fl. 1370-1400.
        Catalogus sanctorum et gestorum eorum ex
    diversis voluminibus collectus. [Colophon:
    Impressum Lugduni per Jacobum Saccon, 1519]
    [4], 244 l. woodcuts. 31 cm.
        Engraved title page.
        Book plate: "EX libris Liechtensteinianis."

NN 0028510   PLatS NNUT CtY

        Natalibus, Petrus de, Bp. of Equilio.
*fIC   Catalogus sanctorum & gestorū eorum ex
N1914   diuersis voluminibus collectus: editus a
493cm   reuerendissimo in christo patre dño Petro de
        natalibus de venetijs dei gratia episcopo
        Equilino.
        [Lyons,1519]
        4p.l.,ccxlv numb l. illus. 33cm.
        Colophon: ... Impressum Lugduni per Jacobum
        saccon. Anno domini. millesimo quingentesimo
        decimonono. die vero vltimo mensis januarii.
        Title within   ornamental border

        including device of the Florentine lily
        (printer's ornament?).
        Edited by Antonio Verlo.
        In this copy, the illus. on recto of leaf
        xxviii shows the beheading of a bishop (6
        figures).
Typ   Another copy. 34cm.
515   In this copy, the illus. on recto of leaf
19.598F xxviii shows be-   heading by means of a
        guillotine (4   figures).
        A few cuts hand-   colored.

NN 0028512   MH

VOLUME 405

Natalibus, Petrus de, Bp. of Equilio, fl. 1370-1400.
Catalogus sanctorum ex diversis ac doctis voluminibus congestus a ... Petro de Natalibus de Venetiis, Dei gratia episcopo Equilino, ac iam denuo accurate revisus. ₍n.p.₎ 1521.
₍3₎, 236 ℓ. 30 cm.
Prefatory epistle by Antonius Verius Vicentinus.
Saints' lives arranged by calendar.

NN   0028513   PLatS

BQ
1417
.O4L3
1523
folio

Natalibus, Petrus de, Bp. of Equilio, fl. 1370-1400.
Catalogus sanctorum, ex diversis ac doctis voluminibus cōgestus a Petro de Natalibus, Episcopo Equilino, ac iam denuo accurate revisus ₍ab Antonio Verlo. Lugduni, Apud Nicolaum Petit & Hectorem Penet₎ 1523.
ccxxxvi leaves. 31 cm.
Bound with Gregory of Nazianzus, Saint. De theologia libri quinque. 1523.

1. Saints.   I. Verlo, Antonio, fl. 1493, ed.

NN   0028514   DCU

Natalibus, Petrus de, *bp. of Equilio, fl.* 1370-1400.
Catalogvs Sanctorum: vitas: Passiones: ꝛ miracula commodissime annectens: Ex varijs voluminibus selectus: quem edidit Reuerendissimus in christo pater dominus Petrus de Natalibus Venetus: Dei gratia episcopus Equilifi. simulꝗ ꝛ cura non vulgari: ꝛ emaculate quantum fieri potuit prelis nostris indidimus. ꝗ Prostant apud Nicolaum Petit, & Hectorem Penet. Lvgdvni, M.D.XXXIII.
4 p. l., ccxliii numb. l. illus. 25ᶜᵐ.
Colophon: Lugduni excu. typis et impensis Nicolai Parui: ꝛ Hectoris Penet. Anno 1534.

Signatures: ₵⁴, a-z⁸, A-N⁸, O⁴ (last leaf blank) Many errors in foliation.
Title within architectural border; black letter, initials, wood-cuts; publishers' device on last verso.
Saints' lives arranged by calendar.
Preface of Antonius Verius Vicentinus, editor of the 1st edition, 1493.
"De sanctis nuperrime canonizatis": fol. cclxxvij, verso, to fol. ccxciij, recto.

1. Saints.   i. Verlo. Antonio, fl. 1481, ed.

28-16972

Library of Congress   BX4654.N3

NN   0028516   DLC

Case
f*D
9877
.61

NATALIBUS, PETRUS DE, bp. of Equilio, fl.1370-1400.
Catalogvs sanctorvm, vitas, passiones, & miracula commodissime annectens, ex uarijs uoluminibus selectus... Lvgdvni, Apud AE. & I.Huguetan, fratres,1542.
₍3₎, clxxx(i.e.clxxix)numb.leaves. illus. 32cm.

Title in red and black within woodcut border.
Printers' device on t.-p.

9877
.61

Last leaf incorrectly numbered clxxx.
Preface of Antonius Uerlus Vincentinus, editor of the 1st edition, 1493.
Bookplate of Nicolas Yemeniz.
Bound by Simier.
"De sanctis nuperrime canonizatis": leaves clxxvj-clxxxvij.

NN   0028518   ICN MB NcU NRU

NE910
.F8N19
.1545
(SAP)

Natalibus, Petrus de, bp.of Equilio, fl.1370-1400.
Catalogus sanctorum. Sanctorum catalogus vitas: passiones:ꝛ miracula cōmodissime annectens: Ex varijs voluminibus select°... simulꝗ ꝛ cura non vulgari: et emaculate quantum fieri potuit prelis nostris indidimus. Veneūt lugd.apd.Jacobū Giūcti, 1545.
4 p.ℓ.,ccxliii numb.ℓ.,1 ℓ. illus. 24½ cm.

Colophon: Impressus est Lugduni anno salutis 1543 die vero vij Jullij.
Title within border; black letter, wood-cuts; publisher's device on last leaf.
Saints' lives arranged by calendar.
Preface of Antonius Verlus, editor of the 1st ed., 1493.

NN   0028520   NjP MnU

PG 1474
.N3 P6
1905

Natalibus, Petrus de, bp. of Equilio, fl. 1370-1400.
Il poemetto di Pietro de' Natali, sulla pace di Venezia tra Alessandro III e Federico Barbarossa, a cura di O. Zenatti ... Roma, Forzani, 1905.
1 p.l., [5]-98 p. VI plates (part fold.) 25cm.

"Estratto dal Bull. dell' Istituto stor. italiano, n. 26"

I. Zenatti,   Oddone, 1866-1901, ed.

NN   0028521   MdBJ NcU

Natalicio González, Juan
see
González, Juan Natalicio, *Pres. Paraguay*, 1897-

989.207
G643Bn

Natalicio González en el destierro. [Asunción] Biblioteca Colorada, 1950.
79 p. 14 cm. (Biblioteca colorada, 2.)

1. González, Juan Natalicio, Pres. Paraguay, 1897-

NN   0028523   ICarbS

Natalicivm Johannes Geffcken zum 70. geburtstag 2. mai 1931, gewidmet von freunden, kollegen und schülern; beiträge zur klassischen altertumskunde von Rudolf Helm ₍u. a.₎ ... Heidelberg, C. Winter, 1931.
4 p. L., 187, ₍1₎ p. 23½ᶜᵐ.

CONTENTS.—Helm, R. Heidnisches und christliches bei spätlateinischen dichtern.—Hohl, E. Zu Hesiods Theogonie.—Körner, O. Zwei beiträge zum verständnis Homers.—Lange, G. Xenophons verhältnis zur rhetorik.—Lücken, G. von. Goethe und der Laokoon.—Overbeck, J. Einige bemerkungen zu ₍Xenophons₎ Κυνηγετικός.—Schmitt, A. Δικαιοσύνη θεοῖς.—Schwenn, F. Studien zu Hesiodos.—Weisgerber, L. Galatische sprachreste.—Wiggers, R. Die grosse natur. Ein beitrag zur Platonforschung.

I. Geffcken, Johannes, 1861-   2 Classical philology—Collections.

Library of Congress   PA26.G4   32-8879

(2)   880.4

NN   0028524   NcU DDO MiU OCU PU CU-S NNC
                  DLC WaU NNC NBuU OrU OU NcD CSt MoU

... Natalidad, mortalidad infantil y mortalidad puerperal en las Américas ...
    see under   [Moll, Aristides Alcibiades] 1882-

Natalidad y mortalidad de la Habana en 1878, con deducción de los 2,913 que fallecieron en los hospitales militares, precedentes del interior de la isla. 1 l. 8°. [Habana, 1879, vel subseq.]
[P., v. 866.]

NN   0028526   DNLM

Natalie, pseud.
   Peterpuck
      see   Hancock, Mrs. Natalie Morris.

Natalie, queen consort of Milan Obrenovic, king of Serbia, 1859-1941
      see   Natalija, Queen, consort of Milan I, King of Serbia, 1859-1941.

Natalie, Shahan, 1884-
The gospel of revenge, by Shahan Natalie; tr. from the Armenian by Missak Turpanjian ... ₍Book 1₎-
₍New York, The Lexhein company₎ ʻ1919-
pt. illus. (port.) 22ᶜᵐ.
In verse.
On cover: Depicting our seventh ally's plight during Armageddon ("Armenia: Garden: Eden")

1. Armenian question.   i. Turpanjian, Missak, tr.   ii. Title.

Library of Congress   PK8700.N3   19-10065

NN   0028529   DLC

Natalie de Bellozane; ou, Le Testament ...
      see under   ₍Heuzé ₎ Mme. d'

Natalie, par Mᵐᵉ de *** ... 1833
      see under   ₍Montpezat, Mme. Charles de₎

Natalie Mining and Milling Company.
The Natalie Mining and Milling Company. Mines near Gladstone, San Juan County, Colorado. [Report by George C. Franklin] Boston, 1901.
40 p. illus. 29 cm.
1. Natalie Mining and Milling Company.
2. Occidental Mining Company. I. Franklin, George F. II. Title.

NN   0028532   CoU

Natalie mining and milling company.
Prospectus. Bost.,1901.

NN   0028533   Nh

Natalie und Dorothee, oder, Glanz und häuslichkeit
      see under   ₍Genlis, Stéphanie Félicité Ducrest de Saint-Aubin, comtesse de, afterwards marquise de Sillery₎ 1746-1830.

Natalie Zahle; til Minde, 1827, 1852, 1927.   København: C. A. Reitzels Forlag, 1927.   285 p. incl. pl.   front., illus. (incl. ports.)   4°.

1. Zahle, Natalie, 1827-1913.   2. Education, Secondary—Denmark—Copenhagen.
N. Y. P. L.   December 28, 1927

NN   0028535   NN MdBJ

Natalija, Queen, consort of Milan I, King of Serbia, 1859-1941.
Mémoires de Nathalie, reine de Serbie.   Publiés avec l'autorisation de Sa Majesté.   Paris: E. Dentu, 1891.   xi, 329 p.   19cm.

257661B.   1. Serbia—Hist., 1872-   1903.
N. Y. P. L.   January 20, 1944

NN   0028536   NN

VOLUME 405

Natalija, Queen, consort of Milan I, King of Serbia, 1859–1941.
Memorien der Königin Natalie von Serbien. Berlin, G. C. Nagel, 1891.
172 p. port. 19 cm.
Translation of Mémoires de Nathalie, reine de Serbie. "Autorisierte Uebersetzung."

1. Serbia—History—1804–1918.   I. Title.

DR340.3.N37A3515   72–226142

NN 0028537   DLC MH WU

Natalini (Giovanni). Diagnosi differenziale e cura degli essudati pleuritici. 35 pp. 12°.
Orvieto, E. Tosini, 1900.

NN 0028538   DNLM

[Natalini, N.]
Giacinto Carini. [Perugia, V. Bartelli, 1877]
(8) p.   1. 8°.
Signed at end: N. Natalini.
"La maggior parte di queste notizie sono state raccolte da una biografia di Giacinto Carini, compilata dall'on. Duca Colonna di Cesarò". note at foot of title-page.

NN 0028539   MH

BQ
25   Natalini, Vincenzo.
.L35   S. Pietro Parenzo; la leggenda scritta dal
v.2   maestro Giovanni Canonico di Orvieto. Studi
n.2   e testo a cura del dott. Vincenzo Natalini.
        Romae, Facultas Theologica Pontificii Athenaei
        Seminarii Romani, 1936.
            xix, 211 p. 2 plates (facsims.) 25 cm.
        (Lateranum. Nova series, an. II, n.2)
            Text of Passio B. Petri Parentii martiris
        auctore magistro Ionne Canonico Ecclesiae
        Urbevetanae, p. 152–205.
            1. Peter Parenzo, Saint, d. 1199.

NN 0028540   DCU NcD NIC MH-AH

Natalini de Oliveira, Clovis
        see
Oliveira, Clovis Natalini de

Natalis Alexander, *1639-1724*
        see Alexandre, Noel, 1639–1724.

Natalis de Wailly
        SEE
Wailly, Natalis de, 1805–1886.

Natalis, *Saint*
  see Naile, *Saint, d. ca. 564.*

PT 2440 NATALIS, ALEXANDER.
.N14 B9   Das Brustbild der heiligen Walpurga; oder,
1811   Das blutende Menschenherz. Erfurt, J.K. Müller,
        1811.
            238 p.

I. Title.   II. Title: Das blutende Menschenherz.

NN 0028545   InU

Natalis, Ernest.
    ...De l'empirisme au raisonnement logique; métodologie du
calcul. Liège, H. Dessain, 1948. viii, 301 p. illus. 19cm.

"Bibliographie," p. [297]–301.

476505B. 1. Mathematics—Study   and teaching.
N. Y. P. L.   May 16, 1949

NN 0028546   NN

B372.7
N19   Natalis, Ernest.
            De l'empirisme au raisonnement logique; méthodologie du calcul. 3. éd. Liège, H. Dessain,
        1953.
            295p.   (Méthodologie de l'enseignement primaire, t.2)

            Bibliography: p.[291]–295.

NN 0028547   NNC-T

B372.5
N19   Natalis, Ernest.
            Les disciplines d'expression matérielle;
        dessin et écriture. Liège, H. Dessain, 1952.
            245p.   (Méthodologie de l'enseignement primaire, t.4)

            Bibliography: p.[243]–245.

NN 0028548   NNC-T

B372.61
N19   Natalis, Ernest.
            Du langage spontané à la langue cultivée;
        méthodologie de la langue maternelle. 3. éd.
        Liège, H. Dessain, 1953.
            257p.   (Méthodologie de l'enseignement primaire, t.1)

            Bibliography: p.[251]–257.

NN 0028549   NNC-T

Natalis, Ernest.
    Les ressorts internes de l'éducation; essai de pédagogie
familiale. Liège, H. Dessain, 1954.
    228 p. illus. 19 cm.

1. Children—Management.   I. Title.

HQ769.N25   55–25422 †

NN 0028550   DLC

Natalis, Friedrich.
    Die Berechnung von Gleich- und Wechselstromsystemen,
von Dr.-Ing. Fr. Natalis... Berlin: J. Springer, 1924. 214 p.
diagrs. 2. ed., rev. & enl. 8°.

1. Electricity—Currents.
N. Y. P. L.   October 8, 1925

NN 0028551   NN IU NIC

Natalis, Friedrich
    Die selbsttaetige regulierung der elektrischen
generatoren.
    Inaug. Diss.   Braunschweig, 1908.

NN 0028552   ICRL DBS

Natalis, Friedrich.
    Die selbsttätige regulierung der elektrischen generatoren, von Dr. ing. Friedr. Natalis ... mit 75 abbildungen
im text und auf 4 tafeln. Braunschweig, F. Vieweg und
sohn, 1908.
    viii, 112 p. illus., 4 pl. (1 double) diagrs. 22½cm. (Added t.-p.: Elektrotechnik in einzeldarstellungen ... hrsg. von Dr. G. Benischke. 11. hft)

1. Electric machinery—Regulation.

Library of Congress   TK2851.N3   8–19088
                         (Copyright 1908 Res. no. 1829)

NN 0028553   DLC NIC MiU OCl ICJ MB PU-BZ

W 4   NATALIS, Helmut W   , 1921–
M96   Die Bedeutung der Venenerweiterungen
1951   im Epiduralraum für das Wurzel-
        Kompressions-Syndrom. [München]
        1951.
            25 l.
            Inaug.-Diss. - Munich.
            Typewritten copy.
            1. Sciatica

NN 0028554   DNLM

Natalis, Hervaeus.
        see
Hervaeus Natalis, d. 1323.

Natalis, Hieronymus
  see Nadal, Gerónimo, 1507–1580.

Natalis, Petrus
        see
Natalibus, Petrus de, bp. of Equilio, fl. 1370–1400.

Natalis Comitis Universae historiae sui temporis
        see under   Conti, Natale, 1520?–1580?

Natalis, oder die Schreckensscene ...
        see under   [Benkowitz, Karl Friedrich]
        1764–1807.

Natalité; organe...de propagande de l'Alliance nationale contre
la dépopulation.
    no.

Paris, 193   27cm.
    nos.   illus.
Irregular.

1. Birth rate—France. 2. France   —Population. I. Alliance nationale
contre la dépopulation.
N. Y. P. L.   October 8, 1942

NN 0028560   NN

VOLUME 405

CAV536

Natalitivm canticvm e Divinis utriusque Testamenti Scripturis in Verbi Incarnati, et B.^{mæ} Eivs Genetricis honorem concinnatvm novenis diebus expectationis optatissimi Virginis purissimæ partùs in Ecclesia cathedrali cæsenatensi ad fovendos in clero populoque christiano ergà salutis nostræ ineffabile misterium piæ reverentiæ ac devotionis sensus musicis numeris modulandum ac eminentissimi card.^{lis} episcopi jvssu editum. Cæsenæ, apud Petrum-Paulum Receputum, episcopalem

typographum, 1691.
8p. 26½cm.

[Archivio Cavagna Sangiuliani (Sezione seconda) v.536]

NN   0028562   IU

WS   NATALIZIO, Delia
113   Compendio de puericultura. 2. ed.
N272c   Buenos Aires [1939]
1939   216 p.   illus.
           1. Infants - Care & hygiene

NN   0028563   DNLM

WS   NATALIZIO, Delia
113   Compendio de puericultura. 3. ed.
N272c   Buenos Aires, Barro, 1941.
1941   251 p.   illus.
           1. Infants - Care & hygiene

NN   0028564   DNLM

WC   Natalizio, Delia
118   Higiene de la alimentación. 3. ed.
N272h   Buenos Aires, 1940.
1940   xvi, 301 p.   illus.

       Contains author's signature.

       1. Food   2. Nutrition   3. Autographs -
Natalizio, Delia

NN   0028565   DNLM

Il Natalizio di Dante Alighieri dopo seicento anni festeggiato dall'Istituto di scienze, lettere ed arti e Dalla Città di Venezia.   Maggio, 1865.

NN   0028566   RPB PU NIC

Natalucci, Aurelio.
   ... Les ailes de la paix ...   [Nice, Imprimerie E. Magnan] °1935.
8 p. l., [5], 187 p., 1 l. 19^{cm}.
Author's pseud., A. Natal, at head of title.
"Copyright ... by A. Natalucci."

1. Peace. 2. War. 3. Aeronautics, Military. 4. Capitalism.   I. Title.
Library of Congress   JX1953.N85   38-36706
Copyright A—Foreign   29789
                                    [3]   330.9

NN   0028567   DLC

R   Natalucci, Giuseppe
520   Medici insigni italiani antichi moderni
A1N27   e contemporanei nati nelle Marche.   Prefazione del Prof. Guglielmo Bilancioni ...
Falerone, F. Menicucci,1934.
viii, 222, [12] p. 25cm.

1. Physicians, Italian.   2. Medicine—
Italy—Marches.   I. Title.

NN   0028568   NIC

Natalucci (Giuseppe).   Quattordici casi di recidive di morbillo raccolti nel comune di Mercatello, e ne' suoi dintorni. 16 pp.   8°.   Civitanova-Marche, D. Natalucci, 1883

NN   0028569   DNLM

Natalucci (Giuseppe).   Un raro caso di glandole mammarie succenturiate. 12 pp. 8°. Civitanova-Marche, D. Natalucci, 1886.

NN   0028570   DNLM

Natalucci, Giuseppe
   ——. Sull' epidemia di tifo a Monsampietrangeli. 11 pp. 8°. Recanati, L. Simboli, 1903.

NN   0028571   DNLM

Natalucci, Mario.
   Ancona attraverso i secoli; ricostruzione delle vicende storiche della città.   Ancona, Tip. Trifogli, 1948–
       v.   illus.   23 cm.
   Bibliographical footnotes.
   CONTENTS.—1. quaderno. Dalle origini alla colonizzazione dorica.—2. quaderno. Il periodo romano, Repubblica ed Impero.

1. Ancona—Hist.   I. Title.

DG975.A5N3   51-29923

NN   0028572   DLC MH MB NN

NATALUCCI, Mario.
   La cattedrale di Ancona nella storia e nell'arte.   [Ancona, Dorica, 1940]

67 p.   illus.

NN   0028573   DDO

HE839   Natalucci, Mario.
.A62N2   La vita marinara e commerciale di Ancona nel Medio Evo e gli statuti del mare; a cura della Camera di Commercio Industria e Agricoltura di Ancona.   Ancona, "Voce Adriatica" [1953]

62p.   21cm.
Contains bibliography.

1.Ancona. 2.Maritime law-Italy-History. 3.Merchant marine-Italy

NN   0028574   CtN1CG

DG   [Natalucci, Tiberio]
975   Documenti inediti di storia umbra, pubblicati pel fausto avvenimento di nozze tra
U5N27   l'eccellentissimo dot. Ludovico Ciccaglia Romano e la egregia signora Angiola Mancini di Foligno.   Foligno, Tipografia de Feliciano Campitelli, 1861.
11 p. 22cm.

1. Umbria—Hist.—Sources.   I. Title.

NN   0028575   NIC

4K   Natalucci, Tiberio
It   Su la simulazione ne i negozj
1470   giuridici.   Milano, Tip. elzeviriana, 1908.
145 p.

NN   0028576   DLC-P4

Natan Ben Jechiel
   see   Nathan Ben Jehiel, 1035 (ca.)-1106.

Nātān ben Nātān
   see   Nathan ben Nathan, 1891–

Natan Ketilsson
   see   Ketilsson, Natan.

Natan mi-Frankfort ve-Hamburg
   see
Nathan ben Isaac Jacob Bonn.

Natan Spira ben Simson
   see
Spira, Nathan Nata, d. 1577.

943.08   Natan, Alex.
N272   Neues Deutschland.   Oxford, Blackwell, 1955.
vii, 151 p. 19cm.

"Reader for students of advanced German."
Includes German-English vocabulary.

1. Germany—History—Allied occupation, 1945–
2. German lan-   guage—Text.   I. Title.

NN   0028582   CoU MiU DS C

Natan, Zhak.
   Болгарское возрождение.   Сокр. перевод с болгарского Н. Н. Соколова и С. Г. Займовского; с предисл. Н. С. Державина.   Москва, Гос. изд-во иностранной лит-ры, 1949.
317 p.   20 cm.
Bibliography: p. 307–[315]

1. Bulgaria—Pol. & govt.   2. Bulgaria—Hist.   I. Title.
        Title transliterated: Bolgarskoe vozrozhdenie.

DR89.N317   51-40483

NN   0028583   DLC

Natan, Zhak.
   Българското възраждане.   2. разширено изд.   София, Българското историческо дружество [1947]
479 p.   20 cm.
"Библиография": p. [464]–476.

1. Bulgaria—Pol. & govt.   2. Bulgaria—Hist.   I. Title.
        Title transliterated: Bŭlgarskoto vŭzrazhdane.

DR89.N3 1947   48-17931*

NN   0028584   DLC

VOLUME 405

Natan, Zhak.
    Българското възраждане. 4. изд. ₍София₎ Български писател ₍1949₎
    543 p. 19 cm.
    Bibliography: p. ₍527₎–540.

    1. Bulgaria—Pol. & govt. 2. Bulgaria—Hist. ⌐ɪ. Title.
    Title transliterated: Bŭlgarskoto vŭzrazhdane.

DR89.N3 1949   52–25047

NN   0028585   DLC

4DR
Bulg
57
    Natan, Zhak.
    Bulharské obrození. [Ze zkráceného ruského vyd. bulharského originálu zpracovaného N. N. Sokolovem a S. C. Zaimovským, přel. Alena Maxová a Prokop Maxa. 1. autorisované vyd. V Praze] Svoboda [1950]
    318 p.

NN   0028586   DLC-P4 CaBVaU

Natan, Zhak.
    Идеологията на Христо Ботев. София, Наука и изкуство, 1955.
    107 p. 20 cm.

    1. Botev, Khristo, 1848–1876. ɪ. Title.
    Title transliterated: Ideologiĭata na Khristo Botev.

DR83.2.B6N3   57–17758 ‡

NN   0028587   DLC

Natan, Zhak.
    Икономическите възгледи на Димитър Благоев. София, Българска академия на науките, 1955.
    272 p. 21 cm.
    At head of title: Българска академия на науките. Икономически институт.
    Summary in French.
    Bibliography: p. ₍269₎–270.

    1. Blagoev, Dimitŭr, 1856?–1924. ɪ. Title.
    Title transliterated: Ikonomicheskite vŭzgledi na Dimitŭr Blagoev.

HB108.B6N3   57–45475

NN   0028588   DLC

HB75
.N36
1949
    Natan, Zhak.
    История на икономическите учения. Съставил Жак Натан при сътрудничеството на К. И. Григоров, въз основа на "Теориите върху принадената стойност" на Маркс и на труда Д. Розенберг "История политической экономии", 2. изд. ₍София₎ Народна култура ₍1949₎–

    v. ₍ ₎ 21 cm.

    1. Economics—Hist.   *Title transliterated:* Istoriĭa na ikonomicheskite uchenĭa.

HB75.N36 1949   51–32084

NN   0028589   DLC

Natan, Zhak.
    Марксистко-ленинското учение за обществено-икономическите формации; научно-популярно изложение. 3. прер. и разширено изд. ₍София₎ Български писател ₍1949₎
    759 p. 19 cm.

    1. Communism. ɪ. Title.
    Title transliterated: Marksistko-leninskoto uchenie za obshtestveno-ikonomicheskite formatsiĭ.

HX361.N3 1949   59–20015

NN   0028590   DLC

Natan, Zhak.
    Програмата на Отечествения фронт—програма на социализма. София, Изд. на Националния съвет на Отечествения фронт, 1948
    17 p. 17 cm

    1. Otechestven front.   *Title transliterated:* Programata na Otechestveniĭa front.

JN9609.A8O87   50–18016

NN   0028591   DLC

Natan, Zhak.
    Развитието на икономическата мисъл след Рикардо. Съставили: Жак Натан и К. И. Григоров. ₍София₎ Народна култура ₍1948₎
    530 p. 18 cm.

    1. Economics—Hist.   ɪ. Grigorov, K. I., joint author.
    Title transliterated: Razvitieto na ikonomicheskata misŭl sled Rikardo.

HB75.N38   51–15250

NN   0028592   DLC

Natan, Zhak
    Die Volksrepublik Bulgarien auf dem Wege zum Sozialismus ₍von₎ Jacques Nathan ₍et al.₎ Berlin, Verlag Die Wirtschaft, 1955.

DR83
.2
.S8A38
    Natan, Zhak.
    "Записките" на Захарий Стоянов и "Под игото" от Иван Вазов—идеен и социологичен разбор. ₍София₎ Български писател ₍1949₎
    94 p. 17 cm.

    1. Stoĭanov, Zakhari, 1850–1889. Zapiski po bŭlgarskite vŭstaniĭ.
    2. Vazov, Ivan Minchov, 1850–1921. Pod igoto.
    Title transliterated: "Zapiskite" na Zakhariĭ Stoĭanov

DR83.2.S8A38   54–32201

NN   0028594   DLC

PN5355
.B8D9
    Natan, Renata, ed.
    25 години "Работническо дело," орган на Централния Комитет на Българската комунистическа партия. 1927–1952. ₍Редактори: Рената Натан (отт. редактор) и др. София₎ Българска комунистическа партия ₍1952₎

Natanael och Elsa Beskow; studier och minnesbilder. Stockholm, Norstedt ₍1954₎
    253 p. illus., ports. 22 cm.
    Pref. signed: Djursholms kapellförening genom Gösta Eberstein.

    Contents.—Skärstads prästgård, av N. Beskow.—När jag var liten, av E. Beskow.—Glimtar från Elsa Beskows barndom och ungdom, av A. Gibettier.—Sagan om en bilderbok av E. Beskow.—Barndomshemmet Ekeliden, av S. Beskow.—Från Ekeliden till Ekebyajön, av. G. Beskow.—Natanael Beskows sociala livsverk och personlighet, av G. Hammar.—Uppror och trofasthet, av K.-G. Hildebrand.—En kristen humanist, av G. Landberg.—Natanael Beskows andliga sånger och psalmer, av E. Liedgren.—Några grunddrag av Natanael Beskows teologiska åskådning, av L. Eeg-Olofsson.—Natanael Beskow som

    konstnär, av A. Cassel.—Ved Elsa Beskows död, av P. Hein.—I barnets tjeneste, av S. Hagemann.—Steget in i sagans värld, av S. H. Wrangel.—Hur Elsa Beskow uppfattade naturen, av E. von Krusenstjerna.—Sagor om verkligheten, en studie i Elsa Beskows sagodiktning, av S. Hammar.—Bibliografi över Elsa Beskows konstnärliga och litterära produktion, av E. von Krusenstjerna (p. 208–215)—Bibliografi över Natanael Beskows tryckta skrifter, av L. Eeg-Olofsson (p. 216–247)

    1. Beskow, Natanael, 1865–1953. 2. Beskow, Elsa (Maartman) 1874–1953.

BX8080.B46N3   A 55–10499
Minnesota Univ. Libr.
for Library of Congress   ₍a66b₎†

NN   0028597   MnU NN DLC

BV3522
.N3
    Natanaele, Bongelemba.
    Wanga Yoane of the village of Yuli. Written by Wanga. Translated by Herbert Smith. Illustrated by Rose Wright. Indianapolis, The United Christian Missionary Society ₍1948₎
    127p. illus. 20cm.

NN   0028598   NNU-W

Natanaeli, Innocente, pseud.
    See
Casarotti, Ilario, 1772–1834.

Natanaelli, J.
    Lettere scritte a un suo nipote. Milano, 1825.
    12mo.

NN   0028600   NN

Natanānanda
    see
Natanānandanātha.

PK3931
.P8
    Naṭanānandanātha. Cidvallī.
    Puṇyānanda.
    ... The Kāma kalā vilās of Punya Nanda, with commentary. Edited with notes by Mahāmahopādhyāya Paṇḍit Mukunda Rāma Shāstrī ... Published under the authority of the government of His Highness Lieut.-General Mahārāja Sir Pratāp Singh Sāhib Bahādur ... mahārāja of Jammu and Kashmir state. Bombay, Printed at the "Tatva-vivechaka" press, 1918.

BL1146
.P8K3
1953
    Naṭanānandanātha. Cidvallī.
    Puṇyānanda.
    Kāmakalāvilāsa, by Puṇyānandanātha. With the commentary of Natanānandanātha. Translated with commentary by Arthur Avalon. With Natha-Navaratnamalika, with commentary Mañjūṣa by Bhāskararāya. 2d ed., rev. and enl. Madras, Ganesh, 1953.

Natanbluf, S.
    Zur kenntnis des styryl-Cumarons. Inaug. Diss. Bern, 1911

NN   0028604   ICRL PU

Natangen, Erminia von
    see Tortilowicz von Batocki, Erminia.

Natani Yazzie
    see
Cummings, Byron, 1860–1954.

Natani, Leopold.
    Anwendungen eines gewissen Coordinatensystems. Berolini, 1857.

NN   0028607   PU

VOLUME 405

Natani, Leopold.
Die höhere analysis. In vier abhandlungen. Mit berücksichtigung der theorie der complexen grossen und anderer neuen untersuchungen. Von L. Natani. Supplement zu den lehrbüchern der differenzial- und integral-rechnung ... Berlin, Wiegandt und Hempel, 1866.

viii, [3]-567, [1] p. diagrs. 23ᶜᵐ.

"Besonders abgedruckt aus dem Mathematischen wörterbuche [von Ludwig Hoffmann.]"

1. Calculus.

QA303.H272

NN   0028608   MiU ICU MH CtY NIC

Natani, L[eopold]
Materie, Aether und lebendige Kraft; physikalische Betrachtungen, von L. Natani. Berlin, G. Bosselmann, 1860.

vi, 49 p. 23 cm.

1. Matter—Properties.   I. Title.

QC173.N32   76-7586

NN   0028609   DLC

Natani, Leopold.
Hoffmann, Ludwig.
Mathematisches wörterbuch; alphabetische zusammenstellung sämmtlicher in die mathematischen wissenschaften gehörender gegenstände in erklärenden und beweisenden synthetisch und analitisch bearb. abhandlungen, von Ludwig Hoffmann. I.–VII. bd. Berlin, G. Bosselmann [etc.] 1858–67.

Pamphlet
QA
20   Natani, Leopold.
Methode der kleinsten Quadrate. Mit den Hülfssätzen aus der Analysis und Wahrscheinlichkeitsrechnung nebst einem Anhange über die ballistische Linie. Berlin, Winckelmann & Söhne, 1875.
42 p. 23cm.

1. Probabilities.

NN   0028611   NIC CtY MH

Natani, Leopold.
Uebersicht der Theorie der elliptischen Funktionen
see under   Hermite, Charles, 1822-1901.

Natani, Leopold.
Die Variationsrechnung. Anhang zur höheren Analysis ... Berlin, 1866.
3 p.l., [3]-53 p., 1 l. 23 cm. [Bound with his Die höhere Analysis. 1866]

NN   0028613   CtY NIC

Natannsen, Hugo: Sind die durch Salze erzeugten Ruheströme Ströme einer Boutnorschen Oelkette? [Bonn: Hager 1923; Altenburg: Pierer 1923.] S. 637—642. 8°. — Auszug: (Kiel 1923.) 1 Bl. 8°
[Aus: Pflügers Archiv f. d. ges. Physiol. Bd 196.
Kiel, Med. Diss. v. 10. Juli 1924   [U 24.5651]

NN   0028614   ICRL

Natannsen, Marta Lamm
see   Lamm-Natannsen, Marta.

NATANSOHN, B.
Papierene brück', oder die hefker welt. RIBL'S lebensbeschreibung; der ssod vun magnetism, auch was es thut sich auf jener welt, etc... Judeo-German. Warsaw, 1894.

pp. 78.

NN   0028616   MH

Natanson (A[bram]). * De l'opération radicale de la hernie inguinale chez les enfants. Ses suites immédiates et éloignées; ses indications et ses contre-indications. 53 pp. 4°. Paris, 1895. No. 113.

NN   0028617   DNLM

Natanson, Aleksander, ed.
... Przepisv o opodatkowaniu spadków i darowizn na obszarze b. dzielnicy rosyjskiej. Tekst ustawy obowiązującej wraz z nowelą ulgową z dnia 14 marca 1933 r., przepisami wykonawczemi i objaśnieniami oraz wzorami podań, opracował Aleksander Natanson ... Warszawa, Nakł. Księgarni F. Hoesicka, 1933.

61, [8] p. incl. tables. 15½ᵐ. (Hoesicka teksty ustaw, nr. 77)

1. Inheritance and transfer tax—Poland.   I. Poland (1918-   ) Laws, statutes, etc.   II. Title.

37-25709

NN   0028618   DLC

Natanson (Alexander [Vladimirovitch]) [1862-]. * Ueber Glaucom in aphakischen Augen. 74 pp. 3 l. 8°. Dorpat, C. Mattiesen, 1889.

NN   0028619   DNLM CU

Natanson, Alexandre
Catalogue des tableaux modernes, aquarelles, pastels, dessins, lithographies par A. André [et al.] composant la collection Alexandre Natanson dont la vente, aux enchères publiques, aura lieu à Paris, Hôtel Drouot... 16 mai 1929. Exposition publique 15 mai 1929. [Paris, Moderne imprimerie, 1929]

1 v. illus.

NN   0028620   MH NcU

N5260
f.N27   Natanson, Alexandre.
Catalogue des tableaux modernes, aquarelles, pastels, dessins, lithographies ... sculptures ... oeuvres importantes d'Edouard Vuillard, composant la collection Alexandre Natanson dont la vente, aux enchères publiques, aura lieu à Paris, Hôtel Drouot ... le jeudi 16 mai 1929. [Paris, 1929?]
1 v. (unpaged) illus., ports.
1. Art—Private collections. 2. Vuillard, Edouard, 1868-1940.

NN   0028621   ICU CtY

Natanson, Alexandre, ed.
La Revue blanche. t. 1–30; oct. 1891–15 avr. 1903. Paris, 1891–1903.

Natanson (Anton [Erich]) [1862-]. *Beiträge zur Kenntniss der Pyrogallolwirkung. 2 p. l., 93 pp., 1 l. 8°. Dorpat, C. Mattiesen, 1888.

NN   0028623   DNLM CU

Natanson, Bernard, 1832-
Исаак-Берк Левинзонъ, его жизнь и литературная деятельность; критико-биографическій очеркъ. Варшава, Центр. тип., 1900.
76 p. illus. 20 cm.

1. Levinsohn, Isaac Baer, 1788-1860.   Title transliterated: Isaak-Ber Levinzon.

BM755.L15N28   59-46935 ‡

NN   0028624   DLC

Natanson, Bernard, 1832-
מערכת ספרי קדש (לעקסיקאן) הכולל בתוכו תלד.. אנשי שם. זמות עמים, ארצות, ערים, הרים, עמקים וימים. אדעסא. בדפום נעללריך ושולצע, תרל"א. [Одесса, 1870.]
149 p. 22 cm.
Added t. p. in Russian.

1. Bible. O. T.—Dictionaries—Hebrew.   I. Title.   Title transliterated: Ma'arekhet sifre kodesh.

BS440.N28   55-46167

NN   0028625   DLC

Natanson, Bernard, 1832-
ספר הכליב Hand Lexicon זרים-כלאזיתיים לכל עפי המדעים והדשת המקצוע. מפרש עברית על פי מחקר הלשונות ודברי ימי עולם. ווארשא. בדפום א. גינז, תר"מ. Варшава, 1880.
148 p. 20 cm.

1. Hebrew language—Foreign words and phrases—Dictionaries.   Title transliterated: Sefer ha-milim.

PJ4843.N3   52-58679

NN   0028626   DLC

Natanson, Bernard, 1832-
ספר הזכרונת; דברי ימי היי יצחק בער לעווינזאהן. תכונת ספריו. מדוץ האגורה בינו ובין הכמי דורו בנוגע להשכלת היהודים בארצות רוסיא. ווארשא. בדפום י. נאלדמאן, תרל"ה. Варшава, 1875.
x, 144 p. 21 cm.

1. Levinsohn, Isaac Baer, 1788-1860.   Title transliterated: Sefer ha-zikhronot.

BM755.L45N3 1875   55-52778 rev

NN   0028627   DLC MH

Natanson, Bernard, 1832-
ספר הזכרונה; דברי ימי היי יצחק בער לעווינזאהן, תבונת ספריו, מדוץ האגורה בינו ובין חכמי דורו בנוגע להשכלת היהודים בארצות רוסיא. מהדורא תנינא בהר ספות ותקונים. ווארשא, תרל"ח. Варшава, 1878.
x, 152 p. 20 cm

1. Levinsohn, Isaac Baer, 1788-1860.   Title transliterated: Sefer ha-zikhronot.

A 52-5591

NN   0028628   NN DLC

Natanson, Bernard, 1832-
ספר הזכרונה; דברי ימי היי ריב"ל, תכונת ספריו ומדוץ האגורות בינו ובין חכמי דורו, במה שנוגע להשכלת היהודים בארץ רוסיא. מהדורא ה'. ווארשא, תרמ"ט. Варшава, 1889.
x, 148 p. 21 cm.

1. Levinsohn, Isaac Baer, 1788-1860.   Title transliterated: Sefer ha-zikhronot.

A 52-5590

NN   0028629   NN

VOLUME 405

Natanson, Bernard, 1852-
ספר הזכרונות; דברי ימי היי ריב"ל. תבנות ספריו ומרוץ אגרות
בינו ובין חכמי דורו. מהדורא ת. ווארשא. תרנ"ד.
Варшава, 1894.
x, 158 p. 22 cm.

1. Levinsohn, Isaac Baer, 1788-1860.
Title transliterated: Sefer ha-zikhronot.

BM755.L45N3 1894   55-52772

NN   0028630   DLC

Natanson, Eduard, 1861-
Ueber die abkuehlung der kohlensaeure bei
ihrer ausdehnung.
Inaug. diss. Strassburg, 1887.

NN   0028631   ICRL

NATANSON, Eduard, 1861-
Ueber die abkühlung der kohlensäure bei ihrer ausdehnung. Leipzig, 1887.

NN   0028632   MH

Natanson (Gregor). * Ueber das Verhalten des
Blutdruckes in den Capillaren nach Massenum-
schnürungen. 1 p. l., 39 pp., 1 l. 8°. *Königsberg i. Pr., E. Erlatis* [1896]

NN   0028633   DNLM

Natanson, Grigoriĭ Īosifovich, *ed.*
Торговая практика; пособие по организации и ведению
торговых предприятий; составлено при участии: Баранова,
А. А., Беленького, Н. С., Башаринова [и др.] ... Под общей
редакцией Г. И. Натансона и В. И. Николаева. Москва,
Издательство Наркомторга СССР и РСФСР, 1928.
vii, 422 p. incl. illus., tables, forms. 22 cm.

"Литература и пособия по вопросам торговедения и торговой
политики": p. [419]-422.

1. Commercial policy. 2. Commercial law—Russia. 3. Business.
I. Nikolaev, Vladimir Ivanovich, joint ed. II. Title.

Library of Congress   HF1007.N35

41-35662

NN   0028634   DLC

Natanson, Hermann, 1900-
Die cystoskopischen befunde bei nervenkrankheiten
mit besonderer beruecksichtigung des sphinkterphaen-
omens (schramm)
Inaug. Diss. Berlin, 1927
Bibl.

NN   0028635   ICRL CtY

Natanson, I   A
Набивка тканей по способу фото-фильмпечати. Москва, Гос. научно-техн. изд-во легкой промышл., 1952.
102 p. illus. 21 cm.

1. Textile printing. I. Title.
Title transliterated: Nabivka tkanei po
sposobu foto-fil'mpechati.

TP930.N3   54-25630

NN   0028636   DLC

Natanson [Isidor] [1867-]. * Contribution
à l'étude de l'arthrodèse dans le pied-bot paraly-
tique... 55 pp. 4°. *Paris, 1899. No. 336.*

NN   0028637   DNLM

Natanson, Isidor Pavlovich.
Einfachste Maxima- und Minima-Aufgaben. [Aus dem
Russischen übertragen von Ralf Dieter Schröter und Max
Heidler] Berlin, Deutscher Verlag der Wissenschaften,
1955.
29 p. illus. 21 cm. (Kleine Ergänzungsreihe zu den Hochschulbüchern für Mathematik, 9)

1. Maxima and minima.

QA563.N315   57-17387 rev ‡

NN   0028638   DLC MH MiU OU RPB FTaSU CSt CLU

---

517   Natanson, Isidor pavlovich.
N19kHUr   Konstruktiv függvénytan. [Forditotta
Renyi Artur] Budapest, Akademiai kiado,
1952.
515p. diagrs. 25cm.

Translation of Конструктивная теория
функций (transliterated Konstruktivnaīa
teoriīa funktsiĭ) Москва, 1949.
Bibliography: p. [509]-515.

1. Functions.

NN   0028639   IU CU

Natanson, Isidor Pavlovich.
Konstruktive Funktionentheorie. Deutsche Übersetzung
von K. Bögel. Berlin, Akademie Verlag, 1955.
xiv, 514 p. 25 cm. (Mathematische Lehrbücher und Monographien. 1. Abt.: Mathematische Lehrbücher, Bd. 7)
Bibliography: p. [497]-512.

1. Functions. I. Title. (Series)

QA331.N354   A 56-1726 rev
Cincinnati. Univ. Libr.
for Library of Congress   [r62c]†

NN NRU PSC MoU MH PPF CaBVaU MiHM ViU
NN   0028640   OCU IU OrCS TU DLC OC1W OU NcU NcD CU

Natanson, Isidor Pavlovich.
Конструктивная теория функций. Москва, Гос. изд-во
технико-теорет. лит-ры, 1949.
688 p. 21 cm.
Bibliography: p. [679]-680.

1. Functions. I. Title.
Title transliterated: Konstruktivnaīa teoriīa funkfsĭ.

QA331.N35   50-17052 rev

NN   0028641   DLC NBuU

Natanson, Isidor Pavlovich.
Summierung unendlich kleiner Grössen
(Einführung in die Integralrechnung) [Aus
dem Russischen übertragen von Bernhard
Göres. Verantwortlicher Verlagsredakteur:
Ludwig Boll] Berlin, Deutscher Verlag der
Wissenschaften, 1955.
60 p. diagrs. 21 cm. (Kleine
Ergänzungsreihe zu den Hochschulbüchern für
Mathematik, 12)

Translation of   Summirovanie beskonechno malykh   velichin.

1. Calculus, Integral. I. Title.
II. Series: Hochschulbüchern für Mathematik.
Kleine Ergänzungsreihe, 12.

CU OrCS ICU MoU NjP OrPR
NN   0028643   LU RPB NcD MiU OU InU FTaSU KU NRU MH

Natanson, Isidor Pavlovich.
Суммирование бесконечно малых величин. Москва,
Гос. изд-во технико-теорет. лит-ры, 1953.
54 p. illus. 20 cm. (Популярные лекции по математике, вып. 12)

1. Calculus, Integral. I. Title.
Title transliterated: Summirovanie
beskonechno malykh velichin.

QA7.P6   vol. 12   55-15514 rev ‡

NN   0028644   DLC

Natanson, Isidor Pavlovich.
Теория функций вещественной переменной. Допущено в качестве учеб. пособия для высших учеб. заведе-
ний. Москва, Гос. изд-во технико-теорет. лит-ры, 1950.
399 p. 27 cm.

1. Functions of real variables. I. Title.
Title transliterated: Teoriīa funkfsĭ
veshchestvennoĭ peremennoĭ.

QA331.5.N3   50-36406 rev

NN   0028645   DLC CLSU OrCS

Natanson, Isidor Pavlovich.
Theorie der Funktionen einer reelen Veränderlichen.
Berlin, Akademie Verlag, 1954.
xi, 478 p. illus. 25 cm. (Mathematische Lehrbücher und Mono-
graphien. 1. Abt.: Mathematische Lehrbücher, Bd. 6)
Eine Umarbeitung der "Die Grundlagen der Theorie der Funk-
tionen einer reellen Veränderlichen."
"Literaturverzeichnis": p. 471-478.

1. Functions of real variables. (Series)

QA331.5.N315   A 55-4777 rev
Duke Univ. Library
for Library of Congress   [r62c]†

CtY ICU DLC OCU ViU IU TU
NN   0028646   NcD OrCS MoU CU ICN NN CaBVaU MtBC NcU

Natanson, Isidor Pavlovich.
Theory of functions of a real variable (Teoria functsiy
veshchestvennoy peremennoy, chapters I to IX) Translated
from the Russian by Leo F. Boron, with the editorial collaboration of, and with annotations by, Edwin Hewitt. New
York, F. Ungar Pub. Co. [1955]
277 p. 26 cm.

1. Functions of real variables.

QA331.5.N313   517.5   54-7420 rev ‡

PSC MB AU OC1W
OrCS OrPR OrU NN PU NcU MiHM NcD OOxM PU-Math IU
NN   0028647   DLC MiU AAP PHC TxU IdPI MtU IdU CaBVaU

Natanson, Isidor Pavlovich.
Theory of functions of a real variable (Teoria
functsiy veshchestvennoy peremennoy) Translated
from the Russian by Leo F. Boron. New York, F.
Ungar Pub. Co. [1955-1960]
2 v. 26cm.

Vol. 1. contents chapter I to IX of the
Russian edition; Vol. 2. contents chapter X to
XVII and Appendices.

1. Functions of real variables. I. Title.

NN   0028648   IdU OrCS OrPR

Natanson, Jacques, 1901-
... L'âge heureux; comédie en trois actes.   Paris: La Renaissance du livre, cop. 1923].   216 p.   12°.

476340A. 1. Drama, French.   2. Title.
N. Y. P. L.   June 16, 1930

NN   0028649   NN CoU IaU

VOLUME 405

Natanson, Jacques, 1901–
   L'âge heureux; comédie inédite en trois
actes, par Jacques Natanson ...
   (In Les Oeuvres libres. Paris [1923] 18½cm.
v. 23, p. [217]–292)

NN   0028650   NRU OU

Natanson, Jacques, 1901–
   ...Les amants saugrenus; comédie en trois actes.   Paris:
La Renaissance du livre[, 1924]. 117 p.   12°.

547780A. 1. Drama, French.   I. Title.
N. Y. P. L.   September 17, 1931

NN   0028651   NN CoU

Natanson, Jacques, 1901–
   Les amants saugrenus; comédie inédite
en 3 actes, par Jacques Natanson ...
   (In Les Oeuvres libres. Paris [1925] 18½cm.
v. 45, p. [245]–346)

NN   0028652   NRU OU

Natanson, Jacques, 1901–
   El automóvil del rey; comedia en tres
actos [por] Natanson y Orbok, en colaboracion
con J.J. Cadenas y E.F. Gutierrez-Riog...
Dibujos de Barbero.   Madrid, 1928.
   64 p.   illus.   (La Farsa, año 2, num.64)

   Defective copy; p. 17-32 repeated after p.
48, p. 49-62 missing.

   I.Orbok, Attila von, 1888–   jt. auth.

   II.Cadenas, José Juan, 1872–   jt. auth.
III.Gutierrez-Roig, Enrique F
jt. auth. IV.Title. Series.

NN   0028654   AzTeS

Natanson, Jacques, 1901–
   El automóvil del rey, comedia en tres actos. Dibujos de Barbero.   Madrid, La Farsa, 1928.
66p.

   In: Teatro español, v.88, no. 5.
   Teatro Lara, 25 de octubre, 1928.
   At head of title page: Natanson y Orbok en colabo-
ración con J. J. Cadenas y E. F. Gutiérrez-Roig.
   Lists of works of Cadenas and Gutiérrez-Roig fol-
low text.

NN   0028655   NcD

Natanson, Jacques, 1901–
   Le Club des Ex, roman.   Paris, Éditions du Bateau ivre
[1948]
   469 p.   19 cm.

   I. Title.
          Full name: Jacques Joseph Emmanuel Natanson.

PQ2627.A77C5   843.91   48–20525*

NN   0028656   DLC IU

PQ2627   Natanson, Jacques, 1901–
A77E5   L'enfant truqué; comédie en trois actes.
          Paris, Mornay, 1922.
          208 p.   20cm.

NN   0028657   CoU InU NjP

          Natanson, Jacques, 1901–
842.91
N272E   L'enfant truqué; comédie en trois actes.
      Paris, La Renaissance du Livre [1922]
      104 p.   19cm.

NN   0028658   NcD

PQ 2627
A77 E5   Natanson, Jacques, 1901–
1922   L'enfant truqué; comédie en trois actes.
      Ornements de A.-H. Thomas. 3. éd. Paris,
      Éditions Mornay, 1922.
      208 p.

NN   0028659   CaBVaU MnU

Natanson, Jacques, 1901–
   L'enfant truqué; comédie en trois actes.   (Bravo: Les Cahiers de "Bravo."   Paris, 1931.   8°.   no. 20, p. 1–34.)

NN   0028660   NN MH

Natanson, Jacques, 1901–
   ... L'été; comédie en trois actes ... [Paris, L'Illustration]
°1935.
      34, [2] p. 30½ᶜᵐ.   (On cover: La Petite illustration ... no. 706, 12
janvier 1935.   Théâtre [nouv. sér.] no. 361)
      Illustrations on p. [2] and [3] of cover.

      I. Title.
          [Full name: Jacques Joseph Emmanuel Natanson]
                        A 35–1435 Revised
      Newberry library
      for Library of Congress   [PQ1223.I 62 n. s., no. 361]

      OCU OC1W PSt
NN   0028661   ICN WaTC OrU MB ViU PBm PHC MiU OU OO

Natanson, Jacques, 1901–
   L'été; comédie en trois actes. [Paris, Impr.
de l'Illustration] c1935.
   34p.   illus.   (La Petite illustration, no.706.
Théâtre [nouv. sér.] no. 361)

   Microcard edition.

NN   0028662   ICRL

Natanson, Jacques, 1901–
   Fabienne; comédie inédite en trois actes, par Jacques Natanson.   Représentée pour la première fois au Théâtre des Ma-
thurins, le 30 septembre 1931.
   (In Les Oeuvres libres. Paris [1933] 18ᶜᵐ. v. 139, p. [139]–232)

      I. Title.
          [Full name: Jacques Joseph Emmanuel Natanson]
                        A C 33–2340
      Title from Northwestern   Univ.
      Library of Congress   PQ1141.O4 vol. 139]

NN   0028663   IEN OU

Natanson, Jacques, *1901*–
   ...Le greluchon délicat; comédie en trois actes.   Paris: La
Renaissance du Livre[, cop. 1925]. 341 p.   12°.

476342A. 1. Drama, French.   2. Title.
N. Y. P. L.   June 16, 1930

NN   0028664

Natanson, Jacques, 1901–
   ... Le greluchon délicat; comédie en trois
actes. Paris, La Renaissance du livre [1926]
   341p.   20cm.

NN   0028665   MoU

Natanson, Jacques, 1901–
   Le greluchon délicat; comédie inédite
en trois actes, par Jacques Natanson ...
   (In Les Oeuvres libres. Paris [1926] 18½cm.
v. 61, p. [83]–192)

NN   0028666   NRU OU OOxM

Natanson, Jacques, 1901–
   Le greluchon délicat; comédie

   36 p.   illus.   (France illustration, le monde illustré.
Supplément théâtral et littéraire, no.151, 1954)

NN   0028667   MH OU

NATANSON, JACQUES, 1901–
   L'infidèle éperdu; comédie inédite en trois actes,
par Jacques Natanson.
   (In Les Oeuvres libres.   Paris [1926] 18½cm.
v.66, p.[185]–304)

NN   0028668   IU CoU OOxM OU

PQ2627   Natanson, Jacques, 1901–
A77 I 5   L'infidèle éperdu; comédie en trois
1930   actes.   Paris, La Renaissance du Livre
      [c1926, colophon 1930]
      145 p.   20cm.

NN   0028669   CoU

Natanson, Jacques, 1901–
   The intrigue, by Jacques Natanson; tr. by Mona Anrade.
London, H. Hamilton [1947]   135 p.   19cm.

471234B. I. Anrade, Mona, tr.   II. Title.
N. Y. P. L.   March 31, 1949

NN   0028670   NN ICU

Natanson, Jacques, 1901–
   ... Je t'attendais; comédie en trois actes et quatre tableaux ...
[Paris, Impr. de l'Illustration] °1929.
      34, [2] p. 30½ᶜᵐ.   (On cover: La Petite illustration ... no. 460, 28 dé-
cembre 1929.   Théâtre [nouv. sér.] no. 247)
      Portrait of author on t.-p. and illustrations on inside of covers.

      I. Title.
          [Full name: Jacques Joseph Emmanuel Natanson]
                        A 30–1040
      Title from Newberry   Libr.
      Library of Congress   [PQ1223.I 62 n. s., no. 247]

      OU MH CtY OrU WaTC
NN   0028671   ICN MB NcD PSt ViU PBm PU MiU OC1 ODW

Natanson, Jacques, 1901–
   ... Manigances, roman; frontispice et bandeaux de Vial ...
Paris, Les Éditions de la nouvelle France [1946]
      3 p. l., [11]–197, [8] p. incl. illus. front. 19ᶜᵐ.   (Collection Chamois.
[No. 8])

      I. Title.
      PQ2627.A77M3   46–23474

NN   0028672   DLC NN

VOLUME 405

Natanson, Jacques, 1901–
Michel; comédie inédite en trois actes, par Jacques Natanson. Représentée pour la première fois au théâtre Michel le 12 mars 1932.

(In Les Oeuvres libres. Paris [1934] 18ᵐᵐ. v. 156, p. [161]–258)

I. Title.   A C 34–3484
Title from Northwestern   Univ.
Library of Congress   [PQ1141.O4 vol. 156]

NN   0028673   IEN OU

Natanson, Joseph.
Early Christian ivories. London, A. Tiranti, 1953.

vi, 34 p. 51 plates. 19 cm. [Chapters in art series, v. 2]
Bibliography: p. 2⁸

1. Ivories. 2. Christian art and symbolism. I. Title.

NK5870.N28   736.62   53–11097

OClW MWiCA OrU NRU FMU CoU NcU CBGTU ViU OU TU
PP MiD DDO MH NN MdU CSt OrCS WaT PPiU WaS CLU
NN   0028674   DLC GU TxU CU FU OClMA OCU MdBWA NcD MB

Natanson, Joseph.
Gothic ivories of the 13th and 14th centuries. London A. Tiranti, 1951.

40 p. illus. 19 cm.

1. Ivories. I. Title.

NK5870.N3   736.62   51–13487 ‡

CtW CSt WaT NcU CSf OrCS
MdBWA CoU CLU PSt CaBVa NjR PPiU OrP MWiCA UU CU
NN   0028675   DLC TNJ GU FMU MB OClMA NIC MiD InU IU

Natanson, Józef, illus.

Zbyszewski, Karol.
The fight for Narvik; impressions of the Polish campaign in Norway. Text by Karol Zbyszewski, drawings by Józef Natanson. London, L. Drummond [1940]

Natanson, L. A., 1873–   tr.

Barrie, Sir James Matthew, bart., 1860–
L'admirable Crichton; fantaisie en quatre actes, par J. M. Barrie. Adaptation française de Alfred Athis [pseud.] Représentée pour la première fois, le 1ᵉʳ juin 1920, au Théâtre Antoine ... [Paris, Impr. de l'Illustration] ©1920.

Natanson, L. A., 1873–
Badauderies parisiennes...
see under title

[Natanson, L   A   ] 1873–
... Le boute-en-train; comédie en trois actes. Paris, Librairie théâtrale, 1908.

2 p. l., 193 p. 19½ᵐ.
Author's pseud., Alfred Athis, at head of title.

I. Title.
                                         8–36389 Additions
Library of Congress   PQ2627.A8B7 1908

NN   0028679   DLC IEN NIC

Natanson, L   A   1873–
...Le boute-en-train; comédie en trois actes. Paris, Librairie théâtrale, 1908. [4], 193p.

Author's pseud., Alfred Athis, at head of title.
Microcard edition.

NN   0028680   ICRL OrU

Natanson, L. A., 1873–   joint author.

Bernard, Tristan, 1866–
Le costaud des Épinettes; comédie en trois actes, par Tristan Bernard et Alfred Athis [pseud.] ... [Paris, L'Illustration théâtrale] ©1910.

Natanson, L. A., 1873–   joint author.

Bernard, Tristan, 1866–
Les deux canards; pièce en trois actes, par Tristan Bernard et Alfred Athis [pseud.] ... [Paris, Impr. de l'Illustration] ©1914.

[Natanson, L   A   ] 1873–
Hfr   Grasse matinée, par Alfred Athys. [pseud.]
na175   Paris. Éditions de la Revue blanche, 1901.
93 [1]p. illus. 19cm. [Binder's title: Natanson]
"Représentée pour la première fois à Paris sur le Théâtre Antoine le mardi 12 juin 1900."

NN   0028683   CtY NRU

[NATANSON, L   A   ] 1873–
Grasse matinée, par Alfred Athys [pseud.]   Paris: Bibliothèque Charpentier, 1903./ 93 p. 18cm.

"Représentée pour la première fois à Paris sur le Théâtre Antoine le mardi 12 juin 1900."

1. Drama, French. I. Title.

NN   0028684   NN

[Natanson, L. A.,] 1873–
Grasse matinée, par Alfred Athys [pseud.].   Paris: Charpentier, 1912. 93 p. 12°.

Illustrated t.-p.

1. Drama (French). 2. Title.
N. Y. P. L.   August 7, 1923.

NN   0028685   NN

[Natanson, L. A.,] 1873–
...Les manigances; comédie en un acte, représentée pour la première fois au Théâtre Antoine, le 3 février, 1905.   Paris: Charpentier et Fasquelle, 1905. 91 p. 12°.

Author's pseud., Alfred Athis, at head of title.

1. Drama (French). 2. Title.
N. Y. P. L.   August 10, 1923.

NN   0028686   NN

[Natanson, L. A.,] 1873–
Vieille renommée; comédie en un acte.   Paris: Librairie théâtrale, 1909. 70 p. 12°.

Author's pseud., Alfred Athis, at head of title.

1. Drama (French). 2. Title.
N. Y. P. L.   November 29, 1915.

NN   0028687   NN CtY

[NATANSON, L.   A., 1873–].
Vieille renommée; comédie en un acte par Alfred Athis, [pseud.].   Paris, Delamain et Boutelleau, 1926.

pp. 57.   43705.84.100

NN   0028688   MH CtY

Natanson, Ladislas
see   Natanson, Władysław.

Natanson (Louis). La circulation des forces dans les êtres animés; essai de psychologie scientifique. 74 pp. 8°. Paris, Bureau des Deux Revues, 1886.

NN   0028690   DNLM RPB

Natanson, Maurice Alexander, 1924–
A critique of Jean-Paul Sartre's ontology. Lincoln, The University, 1951.

136 p. 23 cm. (University of Nebraska studies, new ser., no. 6)
Bibliography: p. 127–136.

1. Sartre, Jean Paul, 1905–   2. Existentialism. (Series: Nebraska. University. University of Nebraska studies, new ser., no 6)

AS36.N2 n. s., no. 6   111   51–62373 rev

NN   0028691   DLC NcD MU IdU IdPI DAU MB OrPR

Natanson, Michał, 1861–
Untersuchungen ueber die wirksamkeit der thomasschlacke auf mittelboden.
Inaug. diss. Halle, 1887.

NN   0028692   ICRL

QD411   Natanson, Stanislaw.
.N27   Ueber die drei isomerentolylsulfurethane deren metallverbindungen und aether sowie deren donstitution.
Berlin, 1881.
36p.
Inaug. diss. Freiburg.

NN   0028693   DLC

ND553   Natanson, Thadée, 1868–
.B65N3   Le Bonnard que je propose, 1867–1947; tentatives. Avec 266 clichés dans et hors texte, dont 10 en couleurs. De nouvelles biographie et bibliographie. Genève, P. Cailler, 1951.

363 p. illus., plates (part col.) ports. 24 cm. (Peintres et sculpteurs d'hier et d'aujourd'hui, 18)
"Livres illustrés par Bonnard": p. 239–240.
"Catalogue d'expositions": p. 240–241.
"Bibliographie": p. 241–[244]

1. Bonnard, Pierre, 1867–1947.

                                                  A 52–573
Harvard Univ. Library
for Library of Congress   [2]

NNC IaU CtY GU
NN   0028694   MH DLC CaBVaU KU NcU CSt TxU NN CoU

Natanson, Thadee, joint author. FOR OTHER EDITIONS SEE MAIN ENTRY

Mirbeau, Octave, 1850–1917.
Le foyer; pièce en quatre actes, par Octave Mirbeau et Thadée Natanson, représentée pour la première fois, le 7 décembre 1908, à la Comédie-française ... [Paris, L'Illustration, ©1908]

VOLUME 405

Natanson, Thadée, 1868–
Un Henri de Toulouse-Lautrec. Genève, P. Cailler, 1951.
305 p. illus., 11 plates (10 col.) 20 cm. (Les Grands artistes raconté par eux-mêmes et par leurs amis, 11)

1. Toulouse-Lautrec Monfa, Henri Marie Raymond de, 1864–1901. (Series: Collection Les Grands artistes ous par eux-mêmes et par leurs amis)
Harvard Univ. Library   A 52–10189
for Library of Congress   ₍t₎

NN 0028696   MH NNC CtY PP OC1 PPPM NcU CLU CSt LU

Natanson, Thadée, joint author.

Fraser, Geoffrey.
Léon Blum, man and statesman, by Geoffrey Fraser and Thadée Natanson; the only authorised biography, with 16 illustrations in doubletone. Philadelphia, New York ₍etc.₎ J. B. Lippincott company ₍ᶜ1938₎

Natanson, Thadée, *1868–*
... Leon Blum y su tiempo; traducción de José Ramón Beltrán. Santiago de Chile, Ediciones Ercilla, 1939.
417, ₍8₎ p. incl. port. 18ᶜᵐ. (Half-title: Colección Contemporáneos)

1. Blum, Léon, 1872–   2. France—Pol. & govt.—1914–
I. Beltrán, José Ramón, tr.
                                    44–49278
Library of Congress   DC373.B5N3
                        ₍2₎   923.244

NN 0028698   DLC CSt-H

Natanson, Thadée, 1868–
Peints à leur tour. Paris, A. Michel ₍1948₎
888 p. plates. 21 cm.

1. Painters, French.   I. Title.
ND552.N3   759.4   48–23920*

ViU NFQC
NN 0028699   DLC MU MB PSt NhD CtY MiU MWiCA MH

Natanson, Thadée, 1868–

Pissarro, Camille, 1830–1903.
Pissarro. Texte de Thadée Natanson. Lausanne, J. Marguerat ₍1950₎

Natanson, V.A., joint comp.
fÚnyĬ pianist
see under Roĭzman, Leonid Isaakovich, comp.

Natanson, V   A
Из музыкального прошлого Московского университета. Москва, Гос. музыкальное изд-во, 1955.
119 p. 14 cm.

1. Music—Russia—Moscow.   2. Moscow. Universitet.   I. Title.
Title transliterated: Iz muzykaľnogo proshlogo Moskovskogo universiteta.
ML300.8.M7N3   57–24166 ‡

NN 0028702   DLC

Natanson, V   A   ed.
Русская фортепианная музыка, с конца XVIII до 60-х г.г. XIX века. Допущено в качестве учеб. пособия для консерваторий и музыкальных училищ. ₍Составление, ред., вступ. очерк и комментарии В. А. Натансона и А. А. Николаева₎ Москва, Гос. музыкальное изд-во, 1954–
v. 27 cm.
Includes biographies of the composers.

1. Piano music.   2. Composers, Russian.   I. Nikolaev, A. A., joint ed.   II. Title.
Title transliterated: Russkaᴵa fortepiannaᴵa muzyka.

M21.N24R8   M 55–633

NN 0028703   DLC ICU

Natanson, Wiktor.
Kodeks karny dla wszystkich. Nowy Kodeks karny z 1932 roku wraz z nowem prawem o wykroczeniach, omówił i przykładami objaśnił Wiktor Natanson ... Warszawa, Skład główny: Księgarnia prawnicza, 1932.
52 p. 19½ᶜᵐ.
Pages 50, 52, advertising matter.

1. Criminal law—Poland.   I. Title.
                        41–33410

NN 0028704   DLC

Natanson, Wiktor.
Nadzwyczajna danina państwowa. Co-kto-ile-jak? Na podstawie ustawy z dnia 16 grudnia 1921 r. Warszawa, Nakładem księgarni i składu NUT Perzyński, Niklewicz i s-ka, 1922.

72 p. 17 cm.
"Bibljoteczka podręczna obywatela polskiego, 1."

NN 0028705   MH CU

Natanson, Wiktor.
15 lat Dziennika ustaw, 1918–1932, w zakresie prawa prywatnego i sądowego z uwzględnieniem prawa administracyjnego, podatkowego i karnego. Podręczny źródłopis orjentacyjny do Dziennika ustaw, w układzie systematycznym, ze skorowidzem alfabetycznym, przytaczający ważniejsze dla praktyki teksty i uwydatniający wszystkie przepisy zmienione, opracował Wiktor Natanson. Warszawa, "Bibljoteka prawnicza", 1933.
104 p. 15½ᶜᵐ.
Pages 103–104, publishers' announcement.
1. Law—Poland—Indexes.   I. Poland (1918–   ) Laws, statutes, etc. (Indexes)   II. Dziennik ustaw Rzeczypospolitej polskiej.
                        40–38268

NN 0028706   DLC

Natanson, Wiktor, joint ed.

Glass, Jakub, *ed.*
... Prawo o notarjacie; rozporządzenie prezydenta Rzeczypospolitej z 27 październ. 1933 (Dz. ust. nr. 84, poz. 609), opracowali Jakub Glass ... i Wiktor Natanson ... Warszawa, Nakł. Księgarni F. Hoesicka, 1934.

Natanson, Wiktor.
Zarys prawa o notariacie. Warszawa, Wydawn. Prawnicze, 1953.
171 p. 24 cm. (Przewodnik notariatu, t. 1)

1. Notaries—Poland.   I. Title.
                        55–22677 ‡

NN 0028708   DLC CtY-L

Natanson, Wiliam
see
Nathanson, William, 1883–

Natanson, Władysław.
On the statistical theory of radiation.   Cracovie: Imprimerie de l'Université. 1911.   1 p.l., p. 134–148.   8°.
Repr.: Académie des sciences de Cracovie. Bulletin. Mars, 1911.

1. Radiation.—Theory.
N. Y. P. L.   February 10. 1912.

NN 0028710   NN

Natanson, Władysław.
On the theory of double refraction induced by an electric or a magnetic field.   Cracovie: Imprimerie de l'Université, 1910.   1 p.l., p. 256–277.   8°.
Repr.: Académie des sciences de Cracovie. Bulletin. Juin 1910.

1. Light—Double refraction.
N. Y. P. L.   March 23, 1911.

NN 0028711   NN

Natanson, Władysław.
Sur la conductibilité calorifique d'un gaz en mouvement.   Cracovie, 1902.
p. 137–146.   8°.
Cutting [cover with printed title] from: Bull. Acad. d. sc. de Cracovie. Cl. math., 1892.

NN 0028712   DNLM

Natanson, Władysław.
Ueber die kinetische theorie unvollkommener Gase. Inaug. diss. Dorpat, 1887.

NN 0028713   ICRL

Natanson, Władysław.
Ueber die kinetische theorie der Joule'schen erscheinung... Dorpat, Mattiesen, 1888.
28p.

NN 0028714   MiU

Natanson, Wojciech
Karol Adwentowicz. [Warszawa] Państwowy Instytut Wydawniczy [1955]
49 p. illus.

1. Adwentowicz, Karol, 1872–

NN 0028715   MH CtY

Natanson, Wojciech
Haf16   Szkice teatralne. Kraków, Wydawn.
N191   Literackie [1955]
          214 p. 20 cm.

1. Theater – Addresses, essays, lectures.
2. Theater – Poland – Addresses, essays, lectures. I. Title.

NN 0028716   CtY MiDW OC1

Natanson-Leski, Jan.
... Atlas historyczny szkolny. Dzieje Polski nowożytnej ... Warszawa, Dom książki polskiej, spółka akc., 1931.
cover-title, 1 p. l., 3 fold. l. (col. maps) 33 x 19ᶜᵐ.

1. Poland—Historical geography—Maps.
                        Map 47–501

NN 0028717   DLC

VOLUME 405

Natanson-Leski, Jan.
... Atlas szkolny do dziejów średniowiecza. Warszawa, Dom książki polskiej, spółka akc., 1928.
2 p. l., 6 fold. numb. l. incl. 27 col. maps 22½ᵐ.

1. Geography, Medieval—Maps.

Map 47-500

NN   0028718   DLC

Natanson-Leski, Jan
Bw75.15   ... Dzieje granicy wschodniej
1   Rzeczypospolitej. Część I: Granica moskiewska
w epoce jagiellońskiej ...
Lwów-Warszawa,Książnica polska T-wa nauczy-
cieli szkół polskich,1922.   24½cm.
(Rozprawy historyczno Towarzystwa naukowego
warszawskiego. Tom I, zeszyt 3)
"Z zapomogi Ministerstwa wyznań religijnych
i oświecenia publicznego."
"Przegląd źródeł": pp.[x]-xii.

Apparently all published under this title.
A continuation of the work appeared in 1930
under title: Epoka Stefana Batorego w dziejach
granicy wschodniej Rzeczypospolitej (Rozprawy
historyczno Towarzystwa naukowego warszawskiogo
Tom IX, zeszyt 2)

NN   0028720   CtY NN MiU

Natanson-Leski, Jan
Epoka Stefana Batorego w dziejach granicy wschodniej rzeczypospolitej. Warszawa, Nakł. Tow. Naukowego Warszawskiego, 1930.
xvi, 166 p. fold. col. map. 25 cm. (Rozprawy historyczne Towarzystwa Naukowego Warszawskiego, t. 9, zesz. 2)
Includes bibliographical references.

1. Poland—History—Stephen Bathory, 1575-1586.   I. Title.   II. Series: Towarzystwo Naukowe Warszawskie. Rozprawy historyczne, t. 9, zesz. 2.

DK429.5.N37   74-200607

NN   0028721   DLC NIC KU CtY MH-L NNC InU

Natanson-Leski, Jan.
Div. of   Szkolny atlas historyczny ... Lwów-Warszawa, Książnica-
Maps   atlas, 1926-32.

Natanson-Leski, Jan.
Zarys granic i podziałów Polski najstarszej. Wrocław, Nakł. Wrocławskiego tow. naukowego, 1953.
392 p.   fold. col. map (issued in pocket)   26cm.

Bibliographical footnotes.

1. Poland—Historical geography. 2. Poland—Hist., 1386. I. Wrocławskie Towarzystwo naukowe.

NN   0028723   NN

Natanson-Rapport, Max.
... Contribution à l'étude de l'infection puerpérale et en particulier de son traitement... Paris, Michalon, 1908.
68p.

Binder's title: Univ. of Paris.
Obstetrical and gynecological theses, 1907-1908.

NN   0028724   MiU DNLM

Natansonówna, Sabina.
...Kobieciątka, powieść współczesna w jednym tomie.
Warszawa: J. Fiszer, 1912.   225 p.   12°.

15140A. 1. Fiction (Polish).   2. Title.
N. Y. P. L   March 28, 1922.

NN   0028725   NN

Natansson, Hans, 1816-1887.
Ljóðmæli, eftir Hans Natansson.   Reykjavík: Kostnaðar-
maður: H. P. Hansson; Félagsprentsmiðjan, 1891.   viii, 152 p. 15cm.

722522A.   1. Poetry, Icelandic.
N. Y. P. L.   November 5, 1934

NN   0028726   NN MH NdU NIC

NATANSSON,Hans,1816-1887.
Rímur af Sigurði snarfara og ættmönnum hans.
Akureyri,B.Jónsson,1883.

NN   0028727   MH NIC

Natanzohn, Joseph Saul
see
Nathansohn, Joseph Saul, 1808-1875.

Natanzon, Bernard L
see
Natanson, Bernard, 1832-

Natanzon, V   IA
Крутильные колебания коленчатых валов с муфтами, обладающими нелинейной характеристикой. Москва, Гос. изд-во обор. промышл., 1943.
78, [2] p. diagrs. 22 cm. (Центральный научно-исследователь-ский институт авиационного моторостроения. Труды, № 40)
Bibliography : p. [79]
1. Cranks and crankshafts. 2. Vibration. (Series: Moscow. TSentral'nyĭ institut aviatsionnogo motorostroeniĭa. Trudy, no. 40)
Title transliterated: Krutil'nye koleba-niĭa kolenchatykh valov.

TL701.A1M72 · no. 40   51-48502 rev

NN   0028730   DLC

Natapov, Boris Solomonovich.
Термическая обработка металлов. Утверждено в качестве учебника для техникумов черной металлургии. Москва, Гос. научно-техн. изд-во лит-ры по черной и цветной металлургии, 1955.
392 p.   illus.   23 cm.
At head of title: Б. С. Натапов, Н. А. Благовещенский.
Errata slip inserted.
Bibliography : p. 391-392.
1. Metals—Heat treatment.   I. Blagoveshchenskiĭ, Nikolaĭ Arkad'evich.   II. Title.
Title transliterated: Termicheskaĭa obrabotka metallov.

TN672.N3   56-21878

NN   0028731   DLC

Nataprawira, P
Disekitar pengadjaran agama disekolah pemerintah [oleh] P. Nataprawira. Bandung, Penerbit Alma'arif [1953]
16 p.   20 cm.

1. Religion in public schools—Indonesia.   I. Title.

LC411.I44N3   78-255992

NN   0028732   DLC

Nataprawira, P
Kasusastran Sunda; pikeun di sakola guru, S. M., S. M. A. djeung sapapadana.   [Djakarta] Djambatan [*1952]
41 p.   20 cm.

1. Sundanese language—Grammar.

PL5452.N3   56-19102 ‡

NN   0028733   DLC

Nataprawira, P
Lénjĕpaneun. Djakarta, Bale Poestaka, 1950.
47 p.   illus.   15 cm.
Poems.

I. Title.

PZ90.S8N3   56-19105 ‡

NN   0028734   DLC MiU NIC

PL   **Nataprawira,P**
5454   "Palakiah", batjaeun ti wiwitan nepi ka per-
.N27   tengahan taun.   Bandung, Melodie [1953]
P15   v.

1.Sundanese language-Chrestomathies and readers. I.Title.

NN   0028735   MiU

PL   **Nataprawira, P**
5452   Paramasastra Sunda. Disusun ku:
N27   P. Nataprawira. [Tjet. 2] Bandung,
P2   Toko Buku "Atomic" [1953-
1953   v. 20cm.

1. Sundanese language--Grammar.

NN   0028736   NIC

PL   **Nataprawira,P**
5452   Pedaran basa Sunda. Djakarta, Widjaya [1952]-
.N26   53 [v.1, 1953]
v. illus.

1.Sundanese language-Chrestomathies and readers. I.Title.

NN   0028737   MiU NIC

PL   **Nataprawira,P**
5454   Rasiah basa Sunda,anggoeun di S.M.P.-S.G.B.
.N27   djspp. Bandung, Melodie [1954]
R22   v.

1.Sundanese language--Chrestomathies and readers. I.Title.

NN   0028738   MiU

VOLUME 405

PL
5452   Nataprawira, P
.N28   Tata basa Sunda, pikeun di S.R. ₍Tjitakan ka 2₎
        Bandung, Melodie ₍1953₎
        43 p.

        1.Sundanese language--Grammar. I.Title.

NN   0028739   MiU NIC

Nātaputta, *Jain leader*
        see
    Mahāvīra.

Naṭarācaṉ, Navāliyūr C
        see
    Nadarasa, S   1910-

Nataradzhan, L.
        see
    Natarajan, L

JQ271 Nataraja Ayyar, A   S
.N27   Mimamsa jurisprudence; the sources of Hindu
        law. Allahabad, Ganganatha Jha Research
        Institute, 1952.
        84 p.   (Ganganatha Jha Research Institute
        series, no. 2)

        1. Mimamsa.   2. Hindu law.   I. Title.
        II. Title: The sources of Hindu law.   Series:
        Ganganatha Jha Research Institute, Allahabad./
        Ganganatha Jha Research Institute series, no. 2.

NN   0028743   ICU

        Nataraja Guru, 1895-1973.
        ₍...₎ Le facteur personnel dans le processus édu-
        catif ... par₍Padmanabhan Natarajan ... Paris,
        Les Presses modernes, 1932.
        176 p. diagrs. 25 cm.

        Thesis, Paris.

        1.Personality. 2.Educational psychology.

NN   0028744   NNC

NATARAJA Guru, 1895-1973.
        The word of the Guru; an outline of the life and teachings of the
        Guru Narayana.   Bangalore, Gurukula pub. house [1952]   xix, 442 p.
        illus., ports.   22cm.

        "Works of the Guru Nārāyana" (p. 389-392); "Bibliography of
        works consulted" (p. 393-396).

        1. Nārāyana, guru, 1854-1928. 2. Vedanta philosophy.

NN   0028745   NN WU MiU

280.182 Natarajan, Balasubrahmanya, 1910-
N19A   Administrative machinery for the economic
        reconstruction of rural areas.   [Madras?
        1950?]
        12 p.

        1. Reconstruction (1939-   ) Madras
        Presidency. 2. Rehabilitation, Rural.
        Madras Presidency.

NN   0028746   DNAL

284.3 Natarajan, Balasubrahmanya, 1910-
N19A   Agricultural price fixation in Madras State.
        [Madras? 1951?]
        19 p.

        1. Farm produce. Prices. 2. Prices. Fixing.
        Madras Presidency.

NN   0028747   DNAL

280.2 Natarajan, Balasubrahmanya, 1910-
N19   Co-operatives and rural welfare.   [Madras?
        1949?]
        21 p.

        1. Cooperation. Madras Presidency.
        2. Sociology, Rural. India. Madras Presidency.

NN   0028748   DNAL

284.4 Natarajan, Balasubrahmanya, 1910-
N19C   Cost of living index.   [Madras? 1949]
        6 p.

        1. Cost and standard of living. Madras
        Presidency. 2. Index numbers (Economics)

NN   0028749   DNAL

284.4 Natarajan, Balasubrahmanya, 1910-
N19   Cost of living index numbers, their meaning
        and their uses.   [Madras? 1949?]
        10 p.

        1. Cost and standard of living. Madras
        Presidency. 2. Index numbers (Economics)

NN   0028750   DNAL

281.182 Natarajan, Balasubrahmanya, 1910-
N19C   Crop sampling surveys in Madras State.
        [n.p.] 1952.
        10 p.

        1. Field crops. India. Statistics.
        2. Sampling (Statistics)

NN   0028751   DNAL

280.182 Natarajan, Balasubrahmanya, 1910-
N19D   Demographic survey of India.   [n.p.]
        1951.
        13 p.

NN   0028752   DNAL

280.182 Natarajan, Balasubrahmanya, 1910-
N19Em   Economic statistics in Madras State.
        [n.p.] 1952.
        4 p.

        1. Madras Presidency. Economic conditions.

NN   0028753   DNAL

280.244 Natarajan, Balasubrahmanya, 1910-
N19   Economics of milk production and distribu-
        tion in the city of Madras.   [Madras? 1950]
        15 p.

        1. Milk. Production. 2. Madras Presidency.
        Milk supply.

NN   0028754   DNAL

Natarajan, Balasubrahmanya, 1910-
        An essay on national income and expenditure in India,
        by B. Natarajan. With a foreword by P. S. Kumaraswamy
        Raja. ₍Madras₎ Economic Adviser to the Government of
        Madras, 1949.
        xiv, 102 p. illus. 23 cm.

        1. Income—India.   I. Title: National income and expenditure in
        India.

        HC440.I 5N23   339.354   50-26049 rev

NN   0028755   DLC PU CSt-H CtY IU DNLM NcD

Natarajan, Balasubrahmanya, 1910-
        Food and agriculture in Madras State, ₍by₎ B. Natarajan.
        With a foreword by J. L. P. Roche-Victoria. Madras, Di-
        rector of Information and Publicity, Govt. of Madras, 1951.
        xxi, 257 p. illus., fold. maps. 23 cm.

        1. Agriculture — Economic aspects — India — Madras (State) 2.
        Food supply—Madras (State)   I. Title.

        HD2075.M2N3 1951   S A 63-59 rev

NN   0028756   DLC CSt-H CU PU ICU NBuU

Natarajan, Balasubrahmanya, 1910-
        Food and agriculture in Madras State, ₍by₎ B. Natarajan.
        With a foreword by J. L. P. Roche-Victoria. 2d ed.
        ₍Madras?₎ Director of Information and Publicity, Govt. of
        Madras, 1953.
        xxi, 281 p. illus., fold. maps. 23 cm.

        1. Agriculture—Economic aspects—India—Madras (State)
        2. Food supply—Madras (State)   I. Title.

        HD2075.M2N3 1953   338.1095482   60-19322 rev

NN   0028757   DLC WaU NN NIC

389 Natarajan, Balasubrahmanya, 1910-
N19F   Food decontrol in Madras State.   [Madras?]
        1953.-
        7 p.

        1. Rationing. Food. 2. Food control (Econom-
        ic measures)

NN   0028758   DNAL

269.594 Natarajan, Balasubrahmanya, 1910-
N19   Hand book of Andhra statistics.   ₍Kurnool₎
        1955.
        197 p.

        1. Andhra. Statistics.

NN   0028759   DNAL

VOLUME 405

304
N192H Natarajan, Balasubrahmanya, 1910-
1952?   Handloom industry in Madras.   [Madras?
         1952?]
         13 p.

         1. Handlooms.

NN 0028760   DNAL

284.3
N191   Natarajan, Balasubrahmanya, 1910-
       Indices of agricultural prosperity in Madras
       State.   [Madras? 1951?]
       18 p.

       1. Farm produce. Prices. 2. Prices.
       Fixing. Madras Presidency.

NN 0028761   DNAL

282.182
N19L   Natarajan, Balasubrahmanya, 1910-
       Land reforms legislation in Madras State
       since 1945.   [Madras?] 1952.
       13 p.

       1. Land reform. Madras Presidency. Law.

NN 0028762   DNAL

282.182
N19M   Natarajan, Balasubrahmanya, 1910-
       Man-land ratio in Madras State, a half-
       century changes, 1901-1951.   [n.p.] 1952.
       14 p.

       1. Land tenure. Madras Presidency.

NN 0028763   DNAL

281.182
N19N   Natarajan, Balasubrahmanya, 1910-
       A note on the census of livestock, poultry,
       agricultural machinery and implements in
       Madras State in 1951.   [n.p.] 1952.
       20 p.

       1. Madras Presidency. Agriculture,
       Statistics.

NN 0028764   DNAL

284.3
N19P   Natarajan, Balasubrahmanya, 1910-
       Prices and prosperity in agriculture.
       [Madras? 1948]
       13 p.

       1. Farm produce. Prices. 2. Agriculture.
       Economic aspects. India. Madras Presidency.

NN 0028765   DNAL

284.6
N19   Natarajan, Balasubrahmanya, 1910-
       A scheme of crop insurance for the
       Province of Madras.   [Madras] Economic
       Adviser to the Government of Madras,
       1949.
       26 p.

       1. Crop insurance. India. Madras.

NN 0028766   DNAL

280.182
N198t Natarajan, Balasubrahmanya, 1910-
       State and social services including rural
       welfare and welfare of the tribal people.
       [Madras? 1950?]
       16 p.

       1. Madras Presidency. Social conditions.
       2. Sociology, Rural. India. Madras Presidency.

NN 0028767   DNAL

281.182
N19   Natarajan, Balasubrahmanya, 1910-
       A statistical assessment of the Grow more
       food campaign in the Madras Province.
       [Bombay? 1949?]
       12 p.

       1. Grow more food campaign (India)

NN 0028768   DNAL

       Natarajan, Balasubrahmanya, 1910-
       Wealth & welfare in the province of Madras.
       Prepared for the Reception committee to the
       tenth session of the All India agricultural
       economic conference. [Madras] Pub. by the
       Economic adviser to the govt. of Madras,
       1949.
       viii, 192 p. ports., maps, charts, tables.

       1. Madras (Province) - Economic conditions.

NN 0028769   NNC DNAL

280.182
N19W   Natarajan, Balasubrahmanya, 1910-
       Women and rural welfare.   [Madras? 194-?]
       10 p.

       1. Women in agriculture. 2. Sociology,
       Rural. India. Madras Presidency.

NN 0028770   DNAL

       Natarajan, Kamkshi, 1868-   ed.
DS481
.G3G85 Gupta, Nagendranath, 1861 or 2-1940.
       ... Gandhi and Gandhism, by Nagendranath Gupta, with a
       foreword by K. Natarajan ... and an appendix, giving the
       life-sketch and an estimate of the author by the late Ramananda
       Chatterjee. Bombay, Hind kitabs [1945]

DS   Natarajan, Kamakshi, 1868-
479   Lady Tata; a book of remembrance / by K.
.T37   Natarajan. — Bombay : Commercial Printing
N37x   Press, 1932.
1932   xvi, 159p. : front.(port.), ill. ; 22cm.

       1. Tata, Lady Mehrbai Dorab. 1879-1931.

NN 0028772   KU MiU

       Natarajan, Kamakshi, 1868-
       Miss Mayo's Mother India; a rejoinder, by K. Natarajan...
       with an introduction by the Hon. Mr. G. A. Natesan...also criti-
       cisms of Tagore, Gandhi, Besant, Lajpat Rai, etc., and protests of
       British and American missionaries.   Madras: G. A. Natesan &
       Co.[, 1928.] viii, 126 p.   2. ed.   16°.

       405644A. I. Mayo, Katherine: Mother India. 2. India—Social condi-
       tions. 3. Woman—India.
       N. Y. P. L.   March 15, 1929

NN 0028773   NN ICU

       Natarajan, Kamakshi, 1868-
       Miss Mayo's Mother India; a rejoinder, by K. Natarajan ...
       with an introduction by the Hon. Mr. G. A. Natesan ... also
       criticisms of Tagore, Gandhi, Besant, Lajpat Rai, etc., and
       protests of British and American missionaries.   3d ed. Ma-
       dras, G. A. Natesan & co. [1928]
       viii, 128 p.   16cm.

       1. Mayo, Katherine, 1868?-1940. Mother India. 2. India—Soc. condit.
       3. Women in India.
                                                 28-20828 Revised
       Library of Congress   DS421.M435 1928

NN 0028774   DLC CaBVaU NjPT CtY CU-I

DS   Natarajan, Kamakshi, 1868-
421   Mother India; a rejoinder, by K. Natarajan.
M435   With an introd. by G. A. Natesan. Also
       criticisms of Tagore, Gandhi, Besant, Lajpat
       Rai, etc., and protests of British and American
       missionaries. 4th ed. Madras, G. A. Natesan
       [1928]
       135p. 16cm.
       1. Mayo, Katherine, 1868?-1940. Mother
       India 2. India - Soc. condit. 3. Women in
       India I. Title

NN 0028775   WU MiU

       Natarajan, Kamakshi, 1868-
       Our trip to America. By K. Natarajan. Bombay [Printed
       by J. R. Dubash, the Commercial printing press] Bandra, The
       Indian social reformer, limited [1933]
       3 p. l., 150, [1 p., 1 l. 19½cm.
       "These articles are reprinted practically as they appeared in the
       Indian social reformer."—Verso of 3d prelim. leaf.

       1. U. S.—Descr. & trav. I. Title.
                                                 43-22292
       Library of Congress   E169.N29
                                       [2]   917.3

NN 0028776   DLC OrU NN CU IU ICJ MB KyLoU

       NATARAJAN, Kamakshi, 1868-
       A rejoinder to "Mother India". Bombay, The
       Tatva-Vivechaka Press, 1927.

       16.5 cm. pp.82.
       Paper cover serves as title-page.
       Reprinted from the "Reformer".

NN 0028777   MH NjNbS

VOLUME 405

Natarajan, Kamakshi, 1868–
Unification or federation? Summary of a paper read by Mr.
K. Natarajan in Vasanta Vyakhyan Mala Series in Poona on May
22, 1921... Bombay: Tatatva-Vivechaka Press, 1921. 14 p.
16°.

Repr.: Indian social reformer.

1. India.—Government, 1914–   2. Title.
N. Y. P. L.
                                                        July 5, 1922.

NN   0028778   NN

Natarajan, L
American shadow over India. With a foreword by J. C.
Kumarappa. Bombay, People's Pub. House, 1952.
335 p. 19 cm.
Includes bibliography.

1. U. S.—For. rel.—India. 2. India—For. rel.—U. S.   I. Title.
E183.8.I 4N3   54–40216 ‡

           IaU PHC NNJ CU IU IU KMK
NN   0028779   DLC MiU NcD ICU MH PU CtY CSt-H NN NIC

Natarajan, L
From Hiroshima to Bandung; a survey of American
policies in Asia. New Delhi, People's Pub. House, 1955.
175 p. 21 cm.

1. U. S.—For. rel.—Asia. 2. Asia—Politics.   I. Title.
DS35.N3   327.73095   58–36259 ‡

NN   0028780   DLC MCM WU PU-SRS CtY CU DS NN

Natarajan, L
Peasant uprisings in India, 1850–1900. Bombay, People's
Pub. House, 1953.
80 p. 19 cm.

1. Peasantry—India. 2. Revolutions—India.   I. Title.
DS479.N25   *954.08   54–19862 ‡

           ICU NN
NN   0028781   DLC CaBVaU MiU IaU NNC NcD TxU CtY CU

Natarajan, M   S
see Nata Rajan, M   S

Natarajan, Padmanabhan
see Nataraja Guru, 1895–1973.

Naṭarājaṇ, Pālacuppiramaṇiya
see
Natarajan, Balasubrahmanya, 1910–

Natarajan, Swaminath, 1907–
A handbook of Indian history ₍by₎ S. Natarajan. ₍Hy-
derabad (Dn) 1949₎
vi, 690 p. 18 cm.

1. India—History.   I. Title.
DS436.A1N34   954   72–252375
                                                  MARC

NN   0028785   DLC CaOTP CtY IEN MH

Natarajan, Swaminath, 1907–
Indian parties and politics. ₍Madras, New York₎ Indian
Branch, Oxford Univ. Press ₍1947₎
31 p. 19 cm. (Oxford pamphlets on Indian affairs, no. 41)

1. Political parties—India. 2. India—Pol. & govt.—1919–
I. Title. II. Series.
JQ298.A1N3   329.954   47–28555*

NN   0028786   DLC ViU

DS401
.I 46
         Natarajan, Swaminath, 1907–   ed.

The Indian social reformer.

Bombay,

Natarajan, Swaminath, 1907–
Lalubhai Samaldas, by S. Natarajan. ₍Bombay, W. P.
Kabadi for Yeshanand Publications, 193–?₎
61 p. ports. 17 cm.

1. Lalubhai Samaldas, 1863–1936.
CT1508.L3N37   70–252144

NN   0028788   DLC MoU

Natarajan, Swaminath, 1907–
... Social problems, by S. Natarajan. ₍London, New York,
Bombay, etc.₎ H. Milford, Oxford university press ₍1942₎
31, ₍1₎ p. 18¼ᶜᵐ. (Oxford pamphlets on Indian affairs, no. 7)
"First published, September 1942."
"Printed in India."

1. India—Soc. condit.
                                                  43–8412
Library of Congress   HN686.N3
                         ₍8₎   309.154

NN   0028789   DLC TxU PU

Natarajan, Swaminath, 1907–
... Social problems, by S. Natarajan. ₍London, New York,
Bombay, etc.₎ H. Milford, Oxford university press ₍1944₎
31, ₍1₎ p. 19ᶜᵐ. (Oxford pamphlets on Indian affairs, no. 7)
"First published, September 1942 ... Third edition, November 1944."
Printed in India.

1. India—Soc. condit.
                                                  45–9419
Library of Congress   HN686.N3 1944
                         ₍3₎   309.154

NN   0028790   DLC

Natarajan, Swaminath, 1907–
West of Suez. Foreword by Sir S. Radhakrishnan.
Bombay, Indian Social Reformer [1938]
306 p.

1. Europe—Descr. & trav. I. Title.

NN   0028791   CaOTP MiU IU

Nataranjan, Jagadish, 1902–
History of Indian journalism. Part II of the
report of the Press Commission
see India (Republic) Press Commission.
Report. [Delhi, ...] 1954–[55]

PN5374
.A55
         Nataranjan, Jagadish, 1902–

India (*Republic*) *Press Commission.*
Report. ₍Delhi, Manager of Publications₎ 1954–₍55₎

Nataren, Fernando Jiménez
see Jiménez, Nataren, Fernando.

Nataren Castellanos, Ernesto.
... Reforma al artículo 4ᵃ constitucional; tesis que para obte-
ner el título de licenciado en derecho presenta el pasante Ernesto Nataren Castellanos. México, D. F., 1937.
4 p. l., ₍7₎–36 p. 23ᶜᵐ.
At head of title: Universidad nacional autónoma de México. Facultad de derecho y ciencias sociales.

1. Professions—Mexico. 2. Mexico. Constitution.   I. Title.
                                                  38–19145

NN   0028795   DLC

Nataridou, Kakia.
...Ζωγραφικη. Ἀθηνα, 1946. 95 p. illus. 22cm.

I. Painting.
                                                  April 30, 1948

NN   0028796   NN

Natarius, Abraham David, 1891–1934.
Philosophy and practical idealism; the collected notebooks
of A. David Natarius, compiled and edited by Dr. Ray Hutterer. New York, Harbinger house ₍°1941₎
425 p. 24ᶜᵐ.

I. Hutterer, Ray, ed. II. Title.
                                                  41–12343
Library of Congress   BD21.N3
                         ₍2₎   108.1

NN   0028797   DLC UU

NATAS, DR., pseud.
Populäre Betrachtung über den Menschen Jesus Christus
und seine Lehre, von Dr. Natas. Riga: R. Ruetz & Ko.,
A.–G., 1930. 120 p. 21cm.

644408A. 1. Jesus Christ—Teachings.

NN   0028798   NN

VOLUME 405

Natau, Otto.
... Mundart und siedelung im nordöstlichen Ostpreussen von Otto Natau. Königsberg (Pr.) und Berlin, Ost-Europaverlag, 1937.
vii, 308 p. incl. maps (1 fold.) tables. 22ᵐ. (Schriften der Albertus-universität, hrsg. vom Königsberger universitätsbund. Geisteswissenschaftliche reihe, bd. 4)
Folded maps counted as one page.
"Die niederdeutsche mundart der im aüssersten nordosten des Deutschen reiches gelegenen kreise Pillkallen, Stallupönen und Tilsit-Ragnit."—Einleitung.
Issued also as inaugural dissertation, Königsberg.
"Literaturverzeichnis": p. 288–293.
1. Low German language—Dialects—Prussia (East)

Library of Congress   PF5881.N3 1937
                                                    ₂₎   439.4711   41–19113

NN   0028799   DLC CU CtY ICU

Wason PL5089 N27 Natawiria, mas.
Penggeli hati, oleh Mas Natawiria dan Mas Soeratman alias Sastradiardja. ₍Batavia₎ Balai Poestaka ₍c1919₎
59 p. illus. 23 cm.

I. Suratman Sastradiardja, mas.

NN   0028800   NIC

Wason Q161 N27 Natawiria, Mas
Tjampakawarna. Weltevreden, Bale Poestaka, 1923.
37 p. illus. 21 cm.

NN   0028801   NIC

Wason PL5454 N27T16 Natawiria, mas.
Tjarios Ki santri gagal. Weltevreden, Commissie voor de Volkslectuur, 1921.
31 p. 22cm.

NN   0028802   NIC

Wason PN6519 SŪN27 1910 Natawisastra, mas.
Boekoe batjaän 100 paribasa djeung babasan. ₍Batavia, Landsdrukkerij, 1910–1915₎
5 v. in 1. 21cm.

Added t.p.: Soendaneesche spreekwijzen, enz.

1. Proverbs, Sundanese. I. Title

NN   0028803   NIC

Wason JQ770 N27 Natawisastra, mas.
Boekoe kahardjaan nagara. Dikarang djeung diatoer koe Masa Natawisastra, djeung koe Mas Padmadinata. Dibantoe koe goeroe2 bantoe Mas Sastrawinata ₍et al.₎ Batawi, Ruygrok, 1914.
74 p. 23cm. (Serie uitgaven door bemiddeling der Commissie voor de Volkslectuur, no. 162)

1. Public institutions—Indonesia.
2. Indonesia—   Pol. & govt.—Miscellanea
I. Padmadinata,   mas, joint author.

NN   0028804   NIC

Wason PN6519 S8 N27 1916 Natawisastra, mas.
100 ₍i.e. Saratoes₎ paribasa djeung babasan, boekoe batjaan. Tjitaken 2. Weltevreden, Albrecht, 1916.
v. 22cm.

Added t.p. in Dutch: Soendaneesche spreekwijzen enz.
At head of title: Serie uitgaven door bemiddeling der Commissie voor Inlandsche Volkslectuur no. 9.

NN   0028805   NIC

Wason PL5454 N28W2 1922 Natawisastra, mas.
Wawatjan Bispoeradja. Disalin tina basa Malajoe. Tjitakan 3. Weltevreden, Commissie voor de Volkslectuur, 1922.
75 p. 21cm.

NN   0028806   NIC

Wason PL5454 N28W3 Natawisastra, mas.
Wawatjan Sultan Abdoellah djeung Hasan; pitjonto'eun. Bandoeng, Sie Dhian Ho, 1911.
45 p. 15 cm.

NN   0028807   NIC

Natches, Gilbert.
Northern Paiute verbs.
(In University of California. Publications. American archaeology and ethnology. Vol. 20, pp. 243–259. Berkeley. 1923.)
Relates especially to the Piutes of Nevada.

M8806 — Piute Indians.

NN   0028808   MB ICN NN

Natchez, Tivadar
    see   Nachez, Tivardar, 1859–1930.

Natchez, Miss.
An act for the more healthy police of the city of Natchez; and to provide against infectious and pestilential diseases
        see under   Mississippi. Laws, statutes, etc.

Natchez, Miss.
Extract from the proceedings of the president and select-men of the city of Natchez at their meeting on the 4th of April, 1815 ..... J. McCurdy Pr. Broadside.

NN   0028811   DLC

Natchez, Miss. Cathedral of Our Lady of Sorrows.
Sketch of the Catholic church in the city of Natchez, Miss., on the occasion of the consecration of its cathedral, September 19, 1886. [Natchez, Natchez Democrat print, 1886?]
51 p. 22 cm.

NN   0028812   NcU

Natchez, Miss. Citizens.
At a meeting of the citizens of Natchez, on Saturday the 11th of July, 1812 . . . occasioned by the arrival of the news of a declaration of war against England, . . . [Natchez: Printed by John Shaw ? 1812.]
19 x 31.5 cm. Broadside.

Signed in handwriting by John Shaw as chairman.

NN   0028813   DLC

E457 .52 .N23 Rare Bk Coll Natchez, Miss. Citizens.
Resolutions adopted at a meeting of the officers of the army and navy and citizens of Natchez, on the death of the President of the United States ... Natchez, Miss. ₍Natchez courier print₎ 1865.

Natchez, Mississippi. Citizens.
To the honorable the representatives and legislative council of the Mississippi Territory, in general assembly convened: The memorial of the inhabitants, freeholders and house holders, of the city of Natchez, respectfully sheweth, . . . [Natchez, 18??]
28.5 x 39.5 cm. Broadside.

A petition for reforms in the city government of Natchez. Contains no clue to its date.

NN   0028815   Ms-Ar

Natchez, Miss. City Planning Commission.
The plan for the future development of Natchez, adopted November 2, 1951, approved by the Board of Aldermen of the city of Natchez, Mississippi, November 6, 1951. ₍Natchez, 1952?₎
66 p. illus., col. maps. 28 x 31 cm.

1. Cities and towns—Planning—Natchez, Miss.

NA9127.N183A5   711.09762   53–28367

NN   0028816   DLC NIC MsU IU NNC

Natchez, Miss. First Presbyterian Church.
Commemorative exercises on the fortieth anniversary of the installation of the Rev. Joseph B. Stratton...
    see under title

285.09762 N192m Natchez, Miss. First Presbyterian Church.
Manual. Natchez, 1905.
42p. illus. 19cm.

NN   0028818   TxU

WX 2 AM7 N2H8b NATCHEZ, Miss. Hospital
Biennial report.
Natchez ₍18—?₎-
v. illus.

NN   0028819   DNLM

Natchez, Miss. Ladies Charitable Mission Society
    see   Ladies Charitable Mission Society, Natchez, Miss. [supplement]

WZ 270 fN2728m 1804F NATCHEZ, Miss. Mayor and citizens
The Mayor, aldermen, assistants, medical faculty, and other citizens of Natchez humbly solicit the attention of the legislature of this territory to the following memorial. ₍Natchez, 1804₎
broadside. 30 x 35 cm. fold. to 30 x 18 cm.
Photocopy (negative) made in 1960, of the original in the Mississippi State Dept. of Archives and History, Jackson.

McMurtrie. Bibl. of Mississippi imprints, no. 30.
Dated Dec. 22, 1804.
Begins: For the promptitude and zeal with which your honorable body has already manifested to effect the establishment of a hospital in our city, we ...

return you ... thanks.
Presents for the guidance of the legislature data concerning the prevalence of disease in Natchez, particularly among transient river boatmen, and estimates of the cost of building and maintaining the hospital₎

Continued in next column

VOLUME 405

Continued from preceding column

Originally accompanied by (1) a copy of
the resolutions adopted by the medical
practitioners of Natchez on Nov. 21 and
issued by them in a printed "Circular,"
and (2) "subscription papers" (forms with
signatures of charitable donors and
amounts pledged)

The Natchez Hospital was established
according to an act of the General Assembly
of the territory, passed Jan. 18, 1805.
1. Natchez, Miss. Natchez Hospital
I. Mississippi (Territory) General
Assembly Title

NN 0028825 DNLM

WZ   NATCHEZ, Miss. Medical practitioners
270   Circular [soliciting subscriptions for
fN273c   the establishment of a hospital in Natchez
1804F   for the states and territories bordering on
          the Mississippi and Ohio. Natchez, 1804]
          [4] p. 29 cm.
          Photocopy (negative) made in 1960, of
          the original in the Mississippi State Dept.
          of Archives and History, Jackson.
          McMurtrie. Bibl. of Mississippi im-
          prints, 1945, no. 29.

Pages [2-3] are blank.
Dated Natchez, November 20, 1084
[sic]
Begins: Sir, under a firm persuasion
that you cannot but feel interested . . . we
trouble you with the following subscription
paper.
Signed by David Lattimore and six

other "medical practitioners of the city of
Natchez."
Includes a copy of the resolutions
adopted at a meeting on Nov. 21, signed
by the same medical practitioners.
Blank form for signatures of sub-
scribers with printed caption beginning
"We, the subscribers . . .": p. [4]

A meeting of interested citizens was
called for Dec. 22 to frame a memorial to
the territorial legislature. The memorial
was issued as a broadside in 1804.
1. Natchez, Miss. Natchez Hospital
I. Lattimore, David, fl. 1804 Title

NN 0028829 DNLM

Natchez, Miss. Natchez Garden Club
     see   Natchez Garden Club, Natchez, Miss.

Natchez, Miss. Natchez Institute
     see   Natchez Institute.

352.0762 Natchez, Miss.--Ordinances, etc.
N19or   Code of ordinances ... with con-
1893-1904 tracts, franchises, etc. ... to which
           is appended a list of the mayors and
           members of the Legislative department
           ... from April 9, 1803 (the date of
           the incorporation) to and including
           1904. Rev., comp. and pub. by author-
           ity of the mayor and aldermen by G. B.
           Shields ... Natchez, 1905.
           360p.

NN 0028832 IU MsU

Natchez, Miss. Ordinances, etc.
     An ordinance, to define and regulate the har-
bor of the city of Natchez. Natchez, Daily
courier, city print, 1837.
     14 p. 14 cm. Orig. lavender (faded) paper
covers.

     1. Natchez, Miss.--Harbor--Regulations.

NN 0028833 CSmH

Natchez, Miss. Ordinances, etc.
     Ordinances of the city of Natchez, with the
acts of the Legislature of the state of Mississippi, in regard to said city. Containing all
ordinances in force up to the 9th June, 1829.
Revised and published by authority of the president and selectmen. Natchez, Printed by William C. Grissam & co., 1829.
     299 p. 18 cm. Uncut.
     Ms. underscorings and markings in pen and
pencil throughout text.

NN 0028834 CSmH MH-L MsLE

Natchez, Miss. Natchez Orphan Asylum
     see   Natchez Orphan Asylum.

Natchez, *Miss. Planning Commission*
     see **Natchez**, *Miss. City Planning Commission.*

Natchez, Miss. Presbyterian Church
     see   Natchez, Miss. First Presbyterian
Church.

Natchez, Miss. St. Mary's cathedral
     see
Natchez, Miss. Cathedral of Our Lady of sorrows.

Natchez, Miss. Stanton college for young ladies
     see
Stanton college for young ladies, Natchez, Miss.

Natchez, Miss. State charity hospital.
     see
Mississippi. State charity hospital, Natchez.

Natchez, Miss. Trinity Church.
     The charter of Trinity Church, in the city of Natchez,
granted January 30, 1827. Also the bye-laws of the corporation of said church adopted July 6, 1827. Natchez, Printed
at the Ariel Office, 1827.
     8 p. 19 cm.

BX5980.N27T68   51-50085

NN 0028841 DLC

Natchez, *Miss.* (Diocese)
     see
Natchez-Jackson (Diocese)

Law   Natchez (District, Mississippi Ter.)

Natchez (*District, Province of Louisiana*)
     The Natchez court records. Abstracts of early records,
1767-1805. [Greenwood? Miss., 1954, °1953]

Natchez (*District, Province of Louisiana*)
     The Natchez court records. Abstracts of early records,
1767-1805. [Greenwood? Miss., 1954, °1953]
     v, 635 p. facsim. 29 cm. (The May Wilson McBee collection,
v. 2)
     "Natchez court records, 1781-1798": p. [1]-349. "Written evidences
of land claims, 1767-1805": p. 351-591.
     Bibliography: p. 603-604.
     1. Court records—Natchez (District, Province of Louisiana) 2.
Court records—Natchez (District, Province of West Florida) 3.
Court records—Natchez (District, Mississippi Ter.) i. Natchez
(District, Province of West Florida) ii. Natchez (District, Mississippi Ter.) iii. Title.   (Series)

976.3   54-3738

NN 0028844 DLC WaS MnU-L KyHi TxU NN

Law   Natchez (District, Province of West Florida)

Natchez (*District, Province of Louisiana*)
     The Natchez court records. Abstracts of early records,
1767-1805. [Greenwood? Miss., 1954, °1953]

MIC   Natchez.
          Jul. 20, 1825-cDec. 21, 1832//
          Natchez, Miss.
          v. illus. weekly.
          Title varies: Jul. 20, 1825-Feb. ?, 1830,
          Ariel.
          Microfilm by Bell and Howell, Micro Photo
          Division, Wooster, Ohio.

          1. Newspapers - Mississippi. Title: Ariel.

NN 0028846 MsU

Natchez, Natchez, Miss.
     see also
Ariel. Natchez, Miss.
Natchez weekly courier.

Les Natchez
     see [Chateaubriand, François Auguste
René] vicomte de, 1768-1848.

Natchez Academy.
     Constitution and bye-laws of the Natchez
Academy. Natchez: Printed by William C.
Grissam. 1829.
     13.5 x 21.5 cm. 7 p. Printed green paper
wrappers.

NN 0028849 NcD

VOLUME 405

La
385.9762 Natchez and Jackson Railroad Company.
N19c   Charter of the Natchez and Jackson
Railroad Co. Passed by the Mississippi Leg
islature, 1870. Approved July 21st, 1870.
Natchez, Democrat Book and Job Print, 1870.
cover-title [4]p. 21cm.

    1. Railroads--Mississippi. Mississippi.
Legislature.

NN   0028850   LU

MIC   Natchez Courier.
    1830-Sept. ?, 1952, new ser. Sept. 28, 1852-
1871?//
Natchez, Miss.
    v. illus.   daily [etc.]
    Title varies slightly. New series title var-
ies: 1852   Daily Courier; 1853-187 ?, Natchez Daily Courier.
    Other editions published in connection with
this paper: c1836 - Sept. 27, 1848, Courier and
journal; Sept. 27, 1854, Courier and Journal;
c1837- Jul. 2, 1844?, Daily Courier; c1837-

    Triweekly Courier; Jun. 18, 1845-1870?, Natchez
Weekly Courier; Aug. 21, - Dec. 29, 1863, Nat-
chez Union Courier.
    A courier and a Journal merged to form Courier
and Journal, c1836.
    Merged with Natchez Democrat to form the Nat-
chez Democrat and Courier prior to Aug. 12, 1873
    1. Newspapers - Mississippi. I. Title:
Courier and Journal. II. Title: Daily Courier
III. Title: Tri-weekly Courier. IV. Title:
Natchez weekly   Courier. V. Title: Nat-
chez Union Couri-   er. VI. Natchez Daily
Courier.

NN   0028852   MsSM MsU

    Natchez   Courier.
      An appeal to thinking men
       see under *title*

Western
Americana
Broadsides   Natchez   courier.
Ze52   ... The present political relations of the
836nb   United States and the republic of Texas ...
[Natchez, 1836]
    broadside. 41 x 27 cm.

    At head of title: "From the Natchez daily
courier, of the 27th Sept. 1836."
    Streeter no. 1224.

    1. U.S. - For.rel. - Texas.

NN   0028854   CtY

    Natchez courier and Adams, Jefferson and
Franklin Advertiser
      see   Natchez weekly courier.

    The Natchez court records, 1767-1805
      see under   McBee, May Wilson,
comp.

    Natchez daily courier
      see   Natchez courier.

    Natchez daily free trader. v.1-   1858-
Natchez, Miss.
    v. illus., daily.
    1. Newspapers.

NN   0028858   MsSM

MIC   Natchez Daily free trader.
    Feb. 2, 1858-cMay 18, 1861//
Natchez.
    v. illus.
    Microfilm by Bell and Howell, Micro Photo Divi-
sion, Wooster, Ohio [etc.]

    1. Newspapers - Mississippi

NN   0028859   MsSM

Natchez fencibles.
    Constitution of the Natchez fencibles, as adopted on the 21st
day of April, 1824, and revised on the 22d of January, 1827.
Natchez; Printed at the office of the Ariel. 1827.   10 p.   15cm.

Includes a list of the members of the company, headed by John A. Quitman, Capt.

NN   0028860   NN NcD Ms-Ar

    Natchez Garden Club, Natchez, Miss.

    Come to Natchez;"where the old South
still lives." Natchez pilgrimage, March 4
through April 2, 1950. [Natchez, 1950]
    cover-title, 37 p. illus. fold. map.
0cm.

NN   0028861   NcD

    The Natchez gazette.
    Natchez, A.Marschalk.
    34-42cm.

    Established July 27, 1802.
    Weekly, July 27, 1802-Jan.1804, Aug.31, 1804-
June 1808; semi-weekly, Feb.-Aug.24, 1804, July-
Nov.19, 1808.
    Title varies: July 27, 1802-June   1803,
Mississippi[1] herald; July-   1803, Mississip-
pi[1] herald, and Natchez repository;   1803-
Aug.24, 1804, Mississippi[1] herald, and Natchez

city gazette; Aug.31, 1804-Dec.1807, Mississippi
herald & Natchez gazette; Jan.-Sept.   1808,
Natchez gazette.
    The last regular issue was that of Nov.16,
1808; a supplement was published on Nov.19,
1808.

NN   0028863   CtY

    Natchez gazette. May 18, 1825- Feb. 7, 1827
      see   Mississippi gazette.

    Natchez, Jackson and Columbus Railroad Co.
    Annual reports of the officers and Board of
directors.   Natchez, 18
    broadside.

NN   0028865   NN

    Natchez Institute.
    ...Annual report of the Board of Visitors of the Natchez
Institute; also, the report of the Board of Examiners.

184

Natchez, 184   8°.

1. Education, U. S.: Miss.: Natchez.
N.Y.P.L.   March 31, 1924.

NN   0028866   NN CSmH PHi MsSM

26.6   Natchez Institute.
    Course of instruction and government of the
Natchez Institute, Adopted 1858.   Natchez:
Printed at the Daily Courier Office, 1858.
[3] 4-22 p.   22.5 cm.

NN   0028867   DLC

    Natchez Institute.
    Natchez Institute. [n.p.] 1855.
    [4], 6 p.
    Cover title.

NN   0028868   MsSM

    Natchez Institute.
    Revised rules for the government of the
Natchez Institute, adopted January 1, 1853.
From the Weekly Mirror Book and Job Office, 1853.
16 p.

    1. Natchez Institute. I. Title.

NN   0028869   MsSM

NATCHEZ INSTITUTE.
    Rules for the government of the Natchez institute.
             Natchez, 1846.   12 pp.   8°

NN   0028870   ICJ

800
.A13   Natchez-Jackson (Diocese) Bishop, 1881-1888
v.2   (Janssens)
    Pastoral of the Right Rev. Bishop of Natchez,
February the 22d, 1882.   [Natchez] Natchez
Democrat Print [1882]
    6 p.   23 cm.
    In Pastoral letters (binder's title) v.2, no.12.
    Full name: Francis August Anthony Joseph
Janssens.

NN   0028871   DCU

BV
800   Natchez-Jackson (Diocese) Synod, 1st, 1858.
.A2   Synodus dioecesana natchetensis prima,
no.7   habita ab illmo et rmo Gulielmo Henrico Elder,
episcopo natchetensi, hebdomada 2. post Pascha.
Anno 1858. Neo-Aureliae, ex typis Propagatoris
Catholici, 1858.

    xiv p.   21cm.

NN   0028872   DCU

BV
800   Natchez-Jackson (Diocese) Synod, 1st, 1858.
.A   Synodus dioecesana natchetensis prima,
reel 10   habita a Gulielmo Henrico Elder [ep.] New
bk. 186   Aureliae, ex typis Propagatoris catholici,
1858.

    Film reproduction. Positive.
    Collation of the original: xiv p.

NN   0028873   DCU

VOLUME 405

BV 800 .A reel 8 bk.134
Natchez-Jackson (Diocese) Synod, 1862.
Acta synodi dioecesanae natchetensis anno 1862 celebratae. [n.p., n.d.]
Film reproduction. Positive.
Collation of the original: xii p.
Caption title.

NN 0028874 DCU

BV 800 .A2 no.8
Natchez-Jackson (Diocese) Synod, 2nd, 1869.
Synodus dioecesana natchitochensis secunda, habita ab illmo et rmo Augusto Maria Martin, episcopo natchitochensi, hebdomada prima quadragesimae, anno 1869. Neo-Aureliae, ex typis Propagatoris Catholici, 1869.
48 p. 19cm.

NN 0028875 DCU

Film

BV 800 .A reel 9 bk.173
Natchez-Jackson (Diocese) Synod, 2nd, 1869.
Synodus dioecesana natchitochensis secunda, habita a Augusto Maria Martin [ep.] hebdomada prima Quadragesimae, anno MDCCCLXIX. Neo Aureliae, ex typis Propagatoris Catholici, 1869.
Film reproduction. Positive.
Collation of the original: 48 p.

NN 0028876 DCU

BV 800 .N27 1874
Natchez-Jackson (Diocese) Synod, 4th, 1874.
Synodus dioecesana natchetensis quarta habita, diebus 19a, 20a et 21a mensis Januarii A.D. 1874, a Revmo Gulielmo Henrico Elder, Episcopo natchetensi, in monasterio ciu nomen "St. Theresa's Retreat", patrum Congregationis S.S. Redemptoris, apud Chatawa, Mississippi. [n.p., n.d.]
76 p. 18 cm.
With this, as issued, are the fifth, sixth, and seventh synods.
I. Natchez (Diocese) Synod, 5th, 1886. II. Natchez (Diocese) Synod, 6th, 1892. III. Natchez (Diocese) Synod, 7th, 1897.

NN 0028877 DCU

BV 800 .A reel 8 book 135
Natchez-Jackson (Diocese) Synod, 4th, 1874.
Synodus dioecesana natchetensis 4. habita diebus 19a, 20a, et 21a mensis Januarii A.D. 1874, a Gulielmo Henrico Elder [ep.] in monasterio cui nomen "St. Theresa's ret reat," patrum Congregationis Ss. Redemptoris, apud Chatawa, Mississippi. [n.p., n.d.]
Film reproduction. Positive.
Collation of the original: 26 p.

NN 0028878 DCU

BV 800 .A2 no.6
Natchez-Jackson (Diocese) Synod, 5th, 1886.
Synodus dioecesana natchetensis quinta habita, diebus 16a, 17a, mensis septembris, A.D. 1886. a revmo Francisco Janssens, episcopo natchetensi. Natchez, Miss. [n.d.]
37 p. 15cm.

NN 0028879 DCU

BV 800 .A reel 14 bk.234
Natchez-Jackson (Diocese) Synod, 5th, 1886.
Synodus dioecesana natchetensis quinta habita, diebus 16, 17, mensis Sept., A.D. 1886 a Francisco Janssens ... [n.p., n.d.]
Film reproduction from typewritten copy. Positive.
Collation of the original: 25-57 p.

NN 0028880 DCU

BV 800 .A reel 14 bk. 235
Natchez-Jackson (Diocese) Synod, 6th, 1892.
Synodus dioecesana natchetensis sexta habita, mense Aprilis A.D. 1892 a Thoma Heslin [ep.] [n.p., n.d.]
Film reproduction from typewritten copy. Positive.
Collation of the original: 59-67 p.

NN 0028881 DCU

BV 800 .A reel 14 bk. 236
Natchez-Jackson (Diocese) Synod, 7th, 1897.
Synodus dioecesana natchetensis septima, habita fine Aprilis principioque mensis Maii, 1897. A Thoma Heslin [ep.] [n.p., n.d.]
Film reproduction from typewritten copy. Positive.
Collation of the original: 69-76 p.

NN 0028882 DCU

BV 800 .N27 1922
Natchez-Jackson (Diocese) Synod, 8th, 1922.
Constitutiones dioeceseos natchetensis quae in synodo dioecesana octava, die 14 julii, 1922, habita in ecclesia parochiali Bay St. Louis, ab Illmo. et Revmo. D. Ioanne Edwardo Gunn, Episcopo natchetensi, 1922 latae et promulgatae fuerunt. [n.p., n.d.]
135 p. 22 cm.

NN 0028883 DCU

BV 800 .A reel 17 book 284
Natchez-Jackson (Diocese) Synod, 8th, 1922.
Constitutiones dioeceseos natchetensis quae in synodo dioecesana octava die 14 Julii, 1922, habita in ecclesia parochiali Bay St. Louis a Ioanne Edwardo Gunn [ep.] 1922. Latae et promulgatae fuerunt. [New Orleans, S. W. Taylor, n.d.]
Film reproduction. Positive.
Collation of the original: 135 p.

NN 0028884 DCU

BV 800 .N27 1935
Natchez-Jackson (Diocese) Synod, 9th, 1935.
Acta synodi dioecesanae natchetensis nonae, habitae diebus 9a, 10a et 11a julii, 1935, Bay St. Louis, Miss., ab Illmo et Revmo D. Richardo Oliviero Gerow, Episcopo natchetensi, MCMXXXV. [n.p., n.d.]
[12] p. illus. 24 cm.

NN 0028885 DCU

BV 800 .A reel 20 book 333
Natchez-Jackson (Diocese) Synod, 9th, 1935.
Acta synodi dioecesanae natchetensis nonae habitae diebus 9a, 10a et 11a Julii, 1935, Bay St. Louis, Miss., a Richardo Oliviero Gerow [ep.] [n.p.] 1935.
Film reproduction. Positive.
Collation of the original: 12 p.

NN 0028886 DCU

BV 800 .A reel 17 book 285
Natchez-Jackson (Diocese) Synod, 9th, 1935.
Acta synodi dioecesanae natchetensis nonae habitae diebus 9a, 10a et 11a Julii, 1935, Bay St. Louis, Miss. A Richardo Oliviero Gerow [ep.] 1935.
Film reproduction. Positive.
Collation of the original: [16] p.

NN 0028887 DCU

Natchez, January 7th, 1828. Sir, at a meeting of persons opposed to the election of General Jackson,... [Natchez, 1828] Broadside.

NN 0028888 Ms-Ar

Natchez(Miss.) Volunteer Rifle Corps.
To the Natchez Rifle Corps. Attention... J. McCurdy p'r. April 4, 1815

NN 0028889 DLC

Natchez-on-the-Bluffs, *Miss.*
see
Natchez, *Miss.*

Natchez Orphan Asylum.
The eighteenth annual report of the Natchez Orphan Asylum; together with a report of the Treasurer of the asylum, and a list of the names of the subscribers, who have paid their subscriptions, since the last annual meeting: to which is added an address delivered at the annual meeting on the 2d March last by the Rt. Rev. Bishop Otey, of Tennessee. Natchez: Printed at the Office of the Daily Courier, 1836.
16 p. 15 cm.

NN 0028891 DLC MWA

Natchez Orphan Asylum.
The twentieth annual report of the Natchez Orphan Asylum ... to which is added an address, delivered at the annual meeting of the first of March last, by Mr. Winchester. Natchez: Printed by Samuel H.B. Black, Natchez Daily Courier, 1838.
17 p. 20.5 cm.

NN 0028892 MWA PPPrHi

Les Natchez, ou La tribu du serpent ...
see under [Pixérécourt, René Charles Guilbert de] 1773-1844.

Natchez Seminary
see
Jackson College for Negro Teachers.

MIC
Natchez Union Courier.
18 ?- ?//
Natchez, Miss.
v. illus. semi-weekly.
Possibly a little variation of the Natchez Daily Courier.
Microfilm by Bell and Howell, Micro Photo Division, Wooster, Ohio.
1. Newspapers - Mississippi.

NN 0028895 MsSM

Beinecke Library
Folio AN25 N22 N195
Natchez weekly courier. v.1- 1830-
Natchez, Miss.[S.H.B.Black, city printer]
61-69cm. weekly.
Supersedes Southern galaxy.
Title varies: 1830-1832, Natchez; 1833- ? 1834, Natchez courier and Adams, Jefferson and Franklin advertiser; 1834- ? 1839? Weekly courier and journal.
Ceased publication in 1871?

NN 0028896 CtY MsU

VOLUME 405

Natchez weekly courier.
1829–d Dec. 20, 1833//
Natchez, Miss.
v. illus. weekly.
Title varies: 1829–Jan. ?, 1833, Adams, Jefferson and Franklin Advertiser (no issues on file)
Microfilm by Bell and Howell, Micro Photo Division, Wooster, Ohio.

1. Newspapers - Mississippi. I. Title: Adams Jefferson and   Franklin Advertiser.

NN 0028897   MsSM

Natchitoches, La. Natchitoches trade school
see Natchitoches trade school, Natchitoches
La.

Natchitoches, La. Northwestern State College of Louisiana
see Louisiana. Northwestern State College of Louisiana, *Natchitoches*.

NATCHITOCHES, La. Ordinances.
Digest of Ordinances. Natchitoches,1907.

8vo. (4)+47+(3) p.

NN 0028900   MH-L

Natchitoches, La. Ordinances, etc.
Ordinances passed and adopted by the Mayor and City Council April 21, 1879. Natchitoches, Vindicator Book and Job Office Print., 1879.
35(1)p. 23cm.

Cover-title.
Imperfect; p.1-4 wanting.

NN 0028901   TxU

Natchitoches, La. State Normal School
see Louisiana. Northwestern State
College of Louisiana, Natchitoches.

Film
180

Natchitoches enterprise. Oct. 4, 1888–   Natchitoches, La., C.F. Powell, 1888–

Microfilm of copies in the office of the publisher, in Northwestern state college library, and in Louisiana state university library. Negative.
Collation of the original as determined from the film: v. illus., ports. Weekly.
Masthead title: The Enterprise.
Official   journal of Natchitoches parish.

For list of editors consult Historical records survey, Louisiana. Louisiana newspapers, 1794-1940.

1. Newspapers--La.--Natchitoches.
2. Newspapers--Natchitoches, La.
I. Title: Enterprise.

NN 0028904   LU

Natchitoches Parish, *La. Development Board.*
Natchitoches Parish resources and facilities; survey published in cooperation with State of Louisiana, Dept. of Public Works, Planning Division. [Baton Rouge, 1954?]
119 p. illus., maps (1 fold. part col.) 28 cm.

1. Natchitoches Parish, La.—Econ. condit.

HC107.L82N33   338.9763   57-63533

NN 0028905   DLC

Natchitoches Parish, *La. Planning Board*
see
Natchitoches Parish, *La. Development Board.*

Film
162

Natchitoches populist. v.1-5,no.27, Aug.24, 1894-Mar.10,1899. Natchitoches, Natchitoches pub. co., 1894-99.

Microfilm of copies in the Louisiana state university library. Negative.
Collation of the original as determined from the film: 5v. illus., ports. Weekly.
Title varies: Aug.24,1894-Mar.11,1898.
Louisiana populist (Masthead title: Aug.24,1894-Mar.1895. [Weekly Populist]

Mar.18,1898-Mar.10,1899. Natchitoches populist.
For list of editors consult Historical records survey, Louisiana. Louisiana newspapers, 1794-1940.
Occasional issues missing.

1. Newspapers   La.--Natchitoches.
2. Newspapers--   Natchitoches, La.
I. Louisiana populist. II. Weekly populist.

NN 0028908   LU

Film
417

The Natchitoches times, 1860–
Natchitoches, La. Louis Dupleix, 1860–

Microfilm of copies in Northwestern State College. Negative.
Collation of the original as determined from the film: v. illus. ports. weekly, semi-weekly.
Title varies: 1865– Semi-weekly times or the Semi-weekly Natchitoches times.

1865-1899. Text in French and English.
For list of editors consult: Historical Records Survey, Louisiana. Louisiana newspapers, 1794-1940.

1. Newspapers--La.--Natchitoches. 2. Newspapers--Natchitoches, La. I. Semi-weekly times. II. Semi-   weekly Natchitoches times.

NN 0028910   LU

The Natchitoches Times.
Golden jubilee edition, 1903-1953.
Natchitoches, La., 1953.
[48]p. illus. 44cm.

Issued as v.51, no.1, March 13, 1953.

1. Natchitoches, La. - Hist.

NN 0028911   TxU

La
370
L93b
no.406

Natchitoches trade school, Natchitoches, La.
...Learn to earn; free day and evening courses in auto mechanics, building trades, electricity, machine shop practice...   [n.p., 1939?]
cover-title, 12p. 16cm.   ([Louisiana. State dept. of education] Bulletin, no.406)

1. Technical education--La.   I. Title.

NN 0028912   LU

Natchitoches union. Natchitoches, La.
43 cm.
Daily, except Sunday.

NN 0028913   CtY

Natchodský, Josef, *pseud.*
see
Krapka, Josef, 1862-1909.

Natco.
The Pittsburgh Terra Cotta Lumber Co. was founded in 1889. In 1899 the name was changed to National Fire Proofing Co. and in 1962 this name was shortened to Natco. In 1967 the name was changed to Fuqua Industries.
Works by this body are found under the name used at the time of publication.

Nate, Joseph Cookman, 1868–
The history of the Sigma chi fraternity, 1855-1925, by Joseph Cookman Nate ...   [Chicago] The Fraternity, 1925–
v. front. (port.) illus. (incl. ports., plans, facsims.) pl. 24½ᶜᵐ.

1. Sigma chi.

Library of Congress   LJ75.S45N3   25-21038

NN 0028916   DLC IU NcD PU NcRS ViU OrSaW WaWW

LJ75
.S435

Nate, Joseph Cookman, 1868–   ed.

The Sigma chi directory. v. 1–
1902/08–
[Chicago] The Fraternity, 1909–

35

Nate, Mary J. E.
Down by the waves; or, sketches from the lookout.
Boston, 1866.

NN 0028918   DLC

[Nate, Raymond J   ]
New light on old subjects: a book of information and advice. By a physician in regular practice. [Chicago, Crownshield publishing co., ᶜ1892]
iv, [5]-106 p. 19½ᶜᵐ.

1. Hygiene, Sexual.   CA 11-1885 Unrev'd

Library of Congress   RC881.N27

NN 0028919   DLC

Naţeca Căstiri
see
Natesa Sastri, S   M   1859-1906.

Natekar, *Swami*
see Hamsa, *Bhagwan*, 1878–

VOLUME 405

Natella, Arthur A
Diviértase leyendo, by Arthur A. Natella ... and Chester H.
Stratton ... Illustrations by Gaetano Montone. New York,
College entrance book company [1943]

8 p. l., 149 p. front., illus. 20cm.

"Designed primarily for use in the second year of Spanish."—Pref.

1. Spanish language—Chrestomathies and readers. 2. Spanish language—Composition and exercises. I. Stratton, Chester H., joint
author. II. Title.

Library of Congress   PC4117.N3   44-21067

[3]   . 468.6

NN 0028922 DLC

NATELLA, Matteo.
Come si preparano le rivoluzioni, fisiologia
politica. Roma, A. Manzoni, 1887.

pp. 96.

NN 0028923 MH

Natelson, Samuel.
Condensation of unsaturated hydrocarbons with phenols—
mechanism for the condensation of the ethylenic bond with
phenols ... by Samuel Natelson. New York city, 1931.

13 p. 26cm.

Thesis (PH. D.)—New York university, 1931.
Bibliography: p. 13.

1. Hydrocarbons. 2. Phenols. 3. Ethylene. 4. Condensation-prod-
ucts (Chemistry)

32-1071

Library of Congress   QD258.N3 1931
New York Univ. Libr.   [3]   547.3

NN 0028924 NNU DLC MiU OU CU

Natelson, Samuel, *ed.*
Correlation of clinical and chemical observations in the
immature infant; a working manual for physicians and
chemists, compiled and edited by Samuel Natelson, Wood-
ruff L. Crawford [and] Franklin A. Munsey, with cooperation of Rockford Health Dept. and Illinois Dept. of Public
Health, Division of Preventive Medicine. [Richmond Hill?
N. Y.] 1952.

126 p. illus. 24 cm.

1. Infants (Premature)   I. Title. II. Title: Immature infant.

RJ250.N35   618.6   53-15956 †

NN 0028925 DLC Wa ICJ

Natenberg, Maurice.
The case history of Sigmund Freud; a psycho-biography.
[1st ed.] Chicago, Regent House, 1955.

245 p. 22 cm.

1. Freud, Sigmund, 1856-1939.

BF173.F85N27   [921.36] 926.1   55-11344 †

NN TxU PP Wa InU OrLgE OkU-M WaU
NN 0028926 DLC OKentU MoU MiU PPC PPT NcD CU DNLM

Natenberg, Maurice.
Freudian psycho-antics; fact and fraud in psychoanalysis.
Chicago, Regent House, 1953.

101 p. 21 cm.

1. Freud, Sigmund, 1856-1939. 2. Psychoanalysis. I. Title.

BF173.F85N3   131.3462   53-7510 †

CU OrU-M Wa WaE
OU TxU ICJ NN MB PPT PSt NNC CtY-M CLU MiU TU
NN 0028927 DLC CaBVa CaBVaU DNLM OCU UU-M ViU NcD

Nater, Hans.
Heut' besuchen wir Osterhasens! [Gar-
dernheim i. O., "Die Wende" [1947]
unno.

(Das gute Wende-Buch)

NN 0028928 NN

Nater, Hans.
... ; Ole mi tierra! Fahrten und leben in Spanien, Marokko
und Portugal. Berlin, Reuss und Pollack, 1929.

335 p. 19½cm.

1. Spain—Descr. & trav. 2. Morocco—Descr. & trav. 3. Portugal—
Descr. & trav. I. Title.

29-16452

Library of Congress   DP42.N3

NN 0028929 DLC

Nater, Henry.
Forschungen auf dem gebiete der landwirtschaft. Festschrift
zur feier des siebenzigsten geburtstages von prof. dr. Adolf
Kraemer. Mit dem porträt Kraemers in photogravüre, einer
karte, 8 tafeln und 25 abbildungen im text. Frauenfeld,
J. Huber. 1902.

Nater, Lewis.
La enciclopedia para los numismatistas; las monedas men-
cionadas en este libro son todas de los Estados Unidos. Publicado por Lewis Nater. Vega Baja, P. R. [1943]

40 p. 19cm.

1. Coins, American.

44-46269

Library of Congress   CJ1826.N3
[2]   737.4

NN 0028931 DLC

T113   **Nater, Valéry**
L37   \... Contribution à l'étude de l'hypochlorémie
1942   post-opératoire ... Yverdon, 1942.
Thèse - Univ. de Lausanne.

NN 0028932 CtY

Natera Ricci, L   A
Informes producidos ante el juzgado de primera
instancia en lo criminal del estado Bolívar...
see under Arvelo Larriva, Alfredo,
defendant.

Natera y Luna, Antonio.
Memoria sobre el libre uso de la caza, ó
sea sobre el abuso de su acotamiento, comunmente
permitido y autorizado en las fincas ó terrenos
abiertos de dominio particular dedicads. A la
Academia general de Ciencias, Bellas Letras y
Nobles Arte de Córdoba por su individuo el Lic.
D. Antonio Natera y Luna.   Córdoba, Imprenta
á Cargo de Manté, 1842.

NN 0028934 NNH

Naterer, François Xavier
Description & analyse des eaux minérales
des bains de Loeche en Valais, traduit de
l'Allemand par Mr. Scholl. Sion, S. Naterer, 1770.
4p. l., 3-151, [1]p. fold. plate. 18cm.

1. Physical medicine - Hydrotherapy - Early
works to 1800. 2. Physical medicine - Hydrotherapy
Loeche, Switzerland.

NN 0028935 CtY-M MH

Natermann, [Ernst]: Die wasserwirtschaftlichen Anlagen des Ober-
harzer Bergbaues und ihre wasserwirtschaftlichen Grundlagen.
(Mit 18 Zeichn. u. 8 Tab.) [Maschinenschrift.] 79 S. m. Taf. u.
Plänen. 4°. — Auszug: München: Pflaum (1922). 4 Bl. 4°
[Aus: Die Wasserkraft. Jg. 17.
Berlin TeH., Diss. v. 1922   [U 22.10679

NN 0028936 ICRL

Natermann, J.
[1059] Étude de l'échappement à ancre. Résumé de deux séances faites
à la Société des Horlogers de Genève. .... 35 p. il. 2 pl. O.
Genève 1880.

Reprinted from the *Journal suisse d'horlogerie*, 1880.

NN 0028937 ICJ

Naters, Aert van der Goes van, jonkheer
see Goes, Aert van der, jonkheer, 1863-

Naters, Andreas vander Goes van
see Goes van Naters, Andreas vander,
fl. 1701.

Naters, Marinus van der Goes van
see Goes van Naters, Marinus van der, 1900-

Nates, Arturo Díaz
see
Díaz Nates, Arturo.

Nates (Claude-Pierre) [1879-   ]. *A propos
d'observations de saturnins.* 64 pp. 8°. Bordeaux, 1906. No: 91.

NN 0028942 DNLM

Nates, Juan de, 1545 (ca.)-1613.
Juan de Nates; selección y estudio de Manuel Pereda de
la Requera. Santander, Librería Moderna, 1953.

cclxi, 108 p. illus. 18 cm. (Antología de escritores y artistas
montañeses, 30)

I. Pereda de la Reguera, Manuel, ed.

NA1313.N3P4   56-31369 †

NN 0028943 DLC CtY

VOLUME 405

Nato's gold ring, and other stories.
Philadelphia, [1870]

[Golden grain library]

36

NN 0028944   DLC

Natesa Aiyar, Kodanda Ramaiya.
The Indo-Ceylon crisis, by K. Natesa Aiyar ... Hatton, Ceylon, Ganesh press, 1941.

3 p. l., 162, xxix, [3] p. maps. 32ᵐ.

Reproduced from type-written copy.
Contains reports of the Indo-Ceylon relations exploratory conference, held in New Delhi, November, 1940.

1. East Indians in Ceylon. 2. Ceylon—Relations (general) with India. 3. India—Relations (general) with Ceylon. I. Indo-Ceylon relations exploratory conference, Delhi, 1940. II. Title.

Harvard univ. Library   JV8515.C4N3
for Library of Congress   A 43–1591
                                   [3]†   325.25409548

NN 0028945   MH DLC

PL4754   Natesa Mudaliar, K
N3T25   Tamil grammar for middle school I year and middle school II year [= middle school III year and middle school IV year]. Bangalore, Dept. of Public Instruction in Mysore, 1954.
2 v.

Cover title; t. p. and text in Tamil.

1. Tamil language - Grammar. I. Mysore (State) Dept. of Public Instruction.

NN 0028946   CU

Natesa Sāstrī, S   M   1859-1906, tr.
The Dravidian nights entertainments ...
see under Madana kamaraja.

Natesa, Sāstrī, S   M   1859-1906.
Folklore in Southern India ... By Pandit S. M. Natêśa Sāstrī. Bombay, Education Society's Press, Byculla, 1884–
pts.   18ᶜᵐ.
Parts I and III bound together; Part III dated 1888.
Opinions of the press: 4 p. bound between pts. I & III.

1. Folk-lore—India. I. Title.

NN 0028948   ViU CU NIC OCl MiU NN ICN MH

Natesa Sastri, S   M   1859-1906.
84447 Hindu feasts, fasts and ceremonies. By Pandit S. M. Natesa Sastri, ... With an introduction by Henry K. Beauchamp, ... Madras, printed at the M. E. Publishing House, 1903.
vi, [2], 154 p. front. (port.) 18½ᵐᵐ.

NN 0028949   ICJ OCl ICU

GR   Natesa Sastri, S   M   1859-1906.
305   Indian folk-tales. With an introd. by A.
.N3   G. Cardew. Madras, Guardian Press, 1908.
533 p.   port.   19cm.

1. Tales Indic I. Title

NN 0028950   WU ICU InU OCl

Natesa Sāstrī, S   M   1859-1906.
Mediaeval tales of Southern India in Tamil. iv, [2], 192p. Madras, Madras school book and literature society, 1897.

Text and added title in Tamil.
An enlarged edition of the work was published in 1886.

NN 0028951   OCl

Naṭeṣa Sāstrī, S   M   1859-1906.
Le porteur de sachet; traduction de J. H. Rosny [i. e., J. H. H. and S. J. F. Boëx]. Illustrations de Gambard et Marold. Paris: E. Dentu, 1892. 5 p.l., ii, 139 p., 1 l., 1 pl. 24°. (Petite collection Guillaume.)

1. Hindi literature.—Fiction.   2. Boëx, J. H. H., translator.
3. Boëx, S. J. F., translator.   4. Gambard, illus. 5. Marold,
illus. 6. Title.   illus. 6. Title.
N. Y. P. L.   January 4. 1912.

NN 0028952   NN WU MH MB OCl IEN

Natesa Sastri, S   M   1859-1906.
Kingscote, Mrs. Georgiana (Wolff) d. 1908, comp.
Tales of the sun; or, Folklore of Southern India. Collected by Mrs. Howard Kingscote and Pandit Naṭêśa Śāstrī. London and Calcutta, W. H. Allen & co., 1890.

Natesa Sastri, S   M   1859-1906.
Burgess, James, 1832–1916.
... Tamil and Sanskrit inscriptions, with some notes on village antiquities, collected chiefly in the south of the Madras presidency. By Jas. Burgess ... With translations by S. M. Naṭêśa Śāstrī, paṇḍit. Published by order of government. Madras, Printed by E. Keys at the Gov't press, 1886.

Natesan, B
In the service of the nation; a golden jubilee retrospect. Madras, G. A. Natesan [foreword 1948]

73 p. Illus., ports., facsims. 22 cm.

Cover title: 50 years.

1. Natesan (G. A.) and Company, Madras. I. Title.

Z453.N38   655.454   53–18387

NN 0028955   DLC MoU

Natesan, B., comp.

Souvenir of the sashtiabdha-poorthi of the Hon. Mr. G. A. Natesan. Thursday, 24th August 1933. Madras [Printed by G. A. Natesan & co., 1933]

B132   Natesan (G. A.) and Company, Madras.
.V3A8
1930   Aspects of the Vedanta. 5th ed. Madras, G. A. Natesan [1930]

BL1250   Natesan (G. A.) and company, Madras, pub.
.A1C5

Chaitanya to Vivekananda, lives of the saints of Bengal. 1st ed. Madras, G. A. Natesan & co. [1928]

Natesan (G.A.) and Company, Madras.
Eminent orientalists, Indian, European ...
see under title

Natesan (G. A.) and company, Madras, pub.
BL1550
.F3

Famous Parsis, biographical & critical sketches of patriots, philanthropists, politicians, reformers, scholars and captains of industry. 1st ed. Madras, G. A. Natesan & co. [1930]

Natesan (G.A.) and Company, Madras.
In the service of the nation; a golden jubilee retrospect
see under   Natesan, B

BR1155   Natesan (G. A.) and company, Madras, pub.
.I5

Indian Christians, biographical and critical sketches of poets, educationists, publicists, reformers, ministers of the church in India. 1st ed. Madras, G. A. Natesan & co. [1928]

Natesan (G. A.) and Company, Madras.
Indian reforms; the government of India bill, 1919
see under title

Natesan, (G.A.) and company, Madras.
Indian statesmen; dewans and prime ministers
see under title

Natesan (G.A.)   and company, Madras.
India's sacred shrines & cities
see under title

BL1265   Natesan (G. A.) and company, Madras, pub.
.A2L4

Leaders of the Brahmo samaj, being a record of the lives and achievements of the pioneers of the Brahmo movement. With seven portraits. 1st ed. Madras, G. A. Natesan & co. [1926]

HN682   Natesan (G. A.) and company, Madras, pub.
.M3
1908

The Madras congress & conferences. A collection of the presidential & inaugural speeches delivered at the Indian national congress, Indian industrial conference, Indian social conference, All-India temperance conference, the Theistic conference, the Ladies' conference, held in December, 1908, with an appendix containing the resolutions passed therein ... Madras, G. A. Natesan & co. [1908]

Natesan (G. A.) and Company, Madras.
B132
.V3M5

The Mission of our master; essays and discourses by the eastern & western disciples of Ramakrishna-Vivekananda. 1st ed. Madras, G. A. Natesan [1921]

VOLUME 405

Natesan (G. A.) and company, Madras.

DS475
.2
.R18A3

Rammohun Roy, *raja,* 1772?–1833.
Raja Ram Mohun Roy, his life, writings & speeches ...
Madras, G. A. Natesan & co. [1925]

BL1170
.R3

Ramanand to Ram Tirath; lives of the saints of northern India including the Sikh gurus. 1st ed. Madras, G. A. Natesan & co. [1926]

Natesan, G. A., & co., Madras, pub.

Indian round table conference, *London,* Nov. 12, 1930–Jan. 19, 1931.
The Round table conference. India's demand for dominion status. Speeches by the King, the Premier, the British party leaders and the representatives of the princes and people of India. Madras, G. A. Natesan & co. [1931]

DS479
.1
.S55A3

Natesan (G. A.) and company, Madras, pub.

Sinha, Satyendra Prasanna Sinha, *baron,* 1864–1928.
Speeches and writings of Lord Sinha; with a portrait and a sketch. 1st ed. Madras, G. A. Natesan & co. [1919]

Natesan, Ganapati Agraharam, 1873–
All about Delhi ...
see under title

Natesan, Ganapati Agraharam, 1873– *ed.*
All about the war; the Indian review war book. Edited by G. A. Natesan ... with an introduction by H. E. the Rt. Hon'ble Lord Pentland ... 1st ed. Madras, G. A. Natesan & co. [1915]
4 p. l., viii, xxiv, 440 (i. e. 556), 8 p. illus., plates, ports., maps. 25½ᵐ.
With many extra numbered pages.
"This is in the main a collection of the series of articles that have appeared in the Indian review since the outbreak of the war."—Note by the editor.

1. European war, 1914–1918.   I. The Indian review.

16–7048 Revised

Library of Congress   D509.N15

NN   0028974   DLC CtY WU KyLoU ICJ NcU

Natesan, Ganapati Agraharam, 1873–
The Indian demands; a symposium
see under title

Natesan, Ganapati Agraharam, 1873–
The Indian review; a monthly journal.

Madras, G. A. Natesan & co., 19

Natesan, Ganapati Agraharam, 1873–
India's goal; constructive criticism by leading Indians ...
see under title

DS479
.W3

Natesan, Ganapati Agraharam, 1873–
Wedderburn, *Sir* William, *bart.,* 1838–1918.
Speeches and writings of Sir William Wedderburn. 1st ed. Madras, G. A. Natesan & co. [1918]

[Natesan, Ganapati Agraharam 1873–
Three great Acharyas; Sankara, Ramanuja, Madhwa; critical sketches of their life and times: an exposition of their philosophical systems...   Madras: G. A. Natesan & Co.[, 1928?] 344 p. 1. ed.   12°.
Contents: Sri Sankaracharya: life and times by Mr. C. N. Krishnaswami Aiyar; philosophy by Pandit Sitanath Tattvabushan; by Mr. S. Venkataramanan. Sri Ramanujacharya: life and times by Dr. S. Krishnaswami Aiyangar; philosophy by Prof. T. Rajagopalacharyar; Ramanuja and Vaishnavism by Prof. M. Rangacharya. Sri Madhwacharya: life and times by Mr. C. N. Krishnaswami Aiyar; philosophy by Mr. S. Subba Rau.

1. Philosophy, Indian. 2. Sankara   Acharya, ca. 789–820. 3. Ramanujacharya, d. 1137. 4. Sayana.
N. Y. P. L.   5. Title.   April 9, 1929

NN   0028979   NN

Natesan, Ganapati Agraharam, 1873–
What India wants, by G. A. Natesan. With Forewords by Sir Narayan G. Chandavarkar [and others] Madras [Pref. 1917]
xvi, 133, x p. 17 cm.

1. India—Politics and government—1765–1947.   I. Title.

DS446.3.N34   74–204268

NN   0028980   DLC CaBVaU MH NN CtY KMK ICU MiU ODW

Natesan, K
An up-to-date text book on co-operation. B. Com. degree, pass & hons., Madras & Andhra Universities. Madras [1953?]
406 p. 19 cm.
Includes bibliography.

1. Cooperation—India.   I. Title.

HD3538.N3   334   58–36545 ‡

NN   0028981   DLC NN CtY

4HE
510

Natesan, L   A
Economic and statistical studies of current transport problems in the United States and Canada; being a report submitted after a visit to the United States under the Point Four Programme and to Canada on deputation by Government of India. Calcutta, Eastern Railway Press, 1955.
118 p.

NN   0028982   DLC-P4 MiU

Natesan, L. A., *joint ed.*

Bhattacharyya, Nirmal Chandra, *ed.*
Some Bengal villages; an economic survey, edited by N. C. Bhattacharyya ... and L. A. Natesan ... with a foreword by Sir Daniel Hamilton, kt. [Calcutta] The University of Calcutta, 1932.

Natesan, L   A
State management & control of railways in India, a study of railway finance rates and policy during 1920–37. With a foreword by Sir Ralph L. Wedgwood, bart. [Calcutta] Univ. of Calcutta, 1946.
xxiii, 496 p. fold. map, diagrs. 25 cm.
Errata slip and addendum slip inserted.
Bibliography: p. [483]–485.

1. Railroads—India.   I. Title.

HE3296.N35   385.13   47–26626*

NN   0028984   DLC NcD NSyU CU ICU MH MH-BA

Natesan, L   A
State management & control of railways in India. 1946.

Microcopy of the original.

NN   0028985   WaU

Naṭēsan, M   S
see
Nateson, M   S

Nateson, M   S
Jesus the Christ; His mission on earth, a Hindu view of the Galileean teacher... Trichinopoly, Vivekananda publishing house [1918]
46 p. 18ᶜᵐ.

NN   0028987   NjPT

Nateson, M   S
Pre-Mussalman India, a history of the motherland prior to the sultanate of Delhi. Srirangam, Sri Vani Vilas Press, 1917.
xxi, 138 p. ports. 19 cm.

1. India—Hist.—Early to 324 B. c. 2. India—Hist.—324 B. c.–1000 A. D.   I. Title.

DS451.N3   56–53131

NN   0028988   DLC

Natge, Hans, 1851–1906.
Francis Bacons formenlehre ... von Hans Natge ... Leipzig, B. G. Teubners buchdruckerei, 1890.
82 p. 20½ᵐ.
Inaug.-diss.—Basel.

1. Bacon, Francis, viscount St. Albans, 1561–1626.

                                          42–41323
Library of Congress   B1198.N3

NN   0028989   DLC ICRL NjP ICU MH OrU

---

arW
35019

Natge, Hans.
Über Francis Bacons Formenlehre. Leipzig, B. G. Teubner, 1891.
82 p. 24cm.

1. Bacon, Francis, viscount St. Albans, 1561–1626.

NN   0028990   NIC MoU

Nath, Amar.
The development of local self-government in the Punjab, 1849–1900. [Lahore, 1929]
60, xxvi p. 28 cm. (Punjab. Government Record Office. Publications. Monograph no. 8)
Cover title.

1. Local government—Punjab.   I. Title.   (Series)

JS7025.P83N3   57–50970

NN   0028991   DLC NcD

VOLUME 405

Nath, B. Viswa
see
Viswanath, Bhagavatula, 1889–

Law   **Nath, Badri,** ed.

The Jammu and Kashmir law reports. Containing cases determined by the High Court of Judicature, Jammu and Kashmir, and by the Board of Judicial Advisers. v. 1– Apr./May 1942–
Jammu, Printed by the Superintendent, the Ranbir Govt. Press, and published at the Govt. Book Depot.

Nath, Baij
    see   Baijnāth, Lālā, rai bahadur.

Nath, Bhola, 1902–
Rays of light, by His Holiness Swami Bhola Nathji maharaj (Ghulam-Rué-Zamin) founder of the Divine love society... ₍Lucknow, K. D. Seth, 1933₎
3 p.ℓ., 105 ₍1₎ p. front. (port.) 16cm.

NN   0028995   PHC MH

Nath, Bishan.
The law of insurance (applicable to British India) containing an exhaustive, critical and uptodate commentary on the law of contract of insurance and on the Insurance act, (iv of 1938 as amended up to 20th July, 1941) and rules as amended up to 14th March, 1942, by Bishan Nath ... 2d ed. Lahore, The University book agency, 1942.
6 p. L., xxxiii, 11, 5, 244 p. 22ᵐ.
"First edition ... 1939."—Pref. to the second edition.
Amendments (1 l.) inserted.
1. Insurance law—India. I. India. Laws, statutes, etc.

Library of Congress   HG8701.N3 1942   44–17429
                           ₍2₎   368.954

NN   0028996   DLC

Nath, Chuon
see
Chuon-Nath.

RA312   Nath, D   P
N4N3   Survey report on health services, Nepal, June 3, 1954.
Public   [n. p., 1954]
Health   37 ℓ.
Library
           Caption title.
           A carbon copy without the appendices included in the original report.

           1. Hygiene, Public - Nepal. 2. Nepal. Directorate General of Health Services.

NN   0028998   CU

Nath, Dina, joint author.

Husain, Mohammad Afzal, 1889–
... The citrus psylla (*Diaphorina citri*, Kuw.) ⟨*Psyllidae: Homoptera*⟩ by Mohammad Afzal Husain ... and Dina Nath ... Calcutta, Government of India central publication branch, 1927.

Nath, Dwarka, 1902–
A history of Indians in British Guiana; with a foreword by Sir Gordon Lethem. Published with the authority of His Excellency, the Governor of British Guiana. London, New York, Nelson ₍1950₎
xv, 251 p. illus., ports., fold. map. 23 cm.
"Addenda": 2 p. inserted.
Bibliographical footnotes.

1. East Indians in British Guiana.

F2391.E2N3 1950   325.2540988   51–405

            CU IU
NN   0029000   DLC CaBVaU MoU WU IaU MH CtY TxU ICU

Nath (Friedrich Wilhelm Reinhold) [1830–].
* De pseudarthroei ex fractura et resectione ossium. 37 pp., 1 l., 1 pl. 8°. *Berolini, typ. fratrum Schlesinger.* [1853].

NN   0029001   DNLM

Nath, Friedrich Wilhelm Reinhold, 1830–

——. Die neue Stellung der preussischen Hebeammen zum Staat und zur Geburtshülfe. Auf Grund der neueren Gesetzgebung und mit besonderer Berücksichtigung des neuen preussischen Hebeammen-Lehrbuches für Aerzte, besonders Medicinal-Beamte, zum Gebrauch bei den gesetzlichen Hebeammen - Nachprüfungen sowie für Hebeammen zum Selbstunterricht in gedrängter Kürze bearbeitet. viii, 96 pp. 8°. *Stuttgart.* 1879.

NN   0029002.   DNLM

HB   NATH, Friedrich Wilhelm Reinhold, 1830–
qN274z   Zur Medicinal-Statistik; die Geburts-
1876   und Sterblichkeitsverhältnisse des Kreises Oberbarnim pro 1876. Anhang: Practische Anleitung zur Gewinnung einer amtlich sicheren und leicht ausführbaren Kreis-Sterblichkeits- resp. Erkrankungs-Statistik, nach der im Kreise Oberbarnim bestehenden Organisation. Berlin, Reimer, 1878.
          iv, 92 p. illus.

NN   0029003   DNLM

Nath [Friedrich Wilhelm Reinhold] [1830–]. Zwangs-Abimpfung und Impfungs-Modus. 11 pp. 8°. [*Berlin, B. Boll,* 1876.] *Repr. from: Vrtljschr. f. gerichtl. u. öff. Med., Berl., 1876. n. F., xxv.*

NN   0029004   DNLM

4BL   Nath, G.   S
695   R. S. S.; its cult, an analysis.
          1st ed. Delhi, Kull-Samaj Publications [19]
                   25 p.

NN   0029005   DLC-P4

Nath, Gorak
see
Gōrakhanātha.

Nath, Herbert, 1903–
Die rechte des in unkenntnis seiner aufrechnungsbefugnis leistenden schuldners. ...
Marburg-Lahn, 1934.   36 p.
Inaug. Diss. - Marburg, 1934.
Lebenslauf.
Literaturverzeichnis.

NN   0029007   ICRL

Nath, Jagan
    see
Agrawal, Jagan Nath.

Nath, Jatindra Batabyal
    see   Batabyal, Jatindra Nath.

Nath, Kameshwar.
Hindī-racanā. Lēkhaka Kāmēśvaranātha 'Viśārada.' Tṛtīya saṃskaraṇa. Āgarā, Gayāprasāda ēṇḍa Sansa, 1935.
7, 252 p. 18 cm.

1. Hindi language—Rhetoric. I. Title.

                                        A 60–2400
Pennsylvania. Univ.   Library
for Library of Congress   ₍8₎

NN   0029010   PU

Nath, Kashi, rai bahadur.
The ideals of Hinduism, by Rai Bahadur Pandit Kashi Nath ... Bombay, D. B. Taraporevala sons & co; ₍1932₎
4 p. l., 86 p. 7 col. pl. 25ᵐ.
Some of the plates accompanied by guard sheets with explanatory letterpress or quotations.

1. Hinduism. 2. India—Religion. I. Title.

                                        44–14047
Library of Congress   BL1201.N3
                             ₍2₎   294.5

NN   0029011   DLC CtY MnU NN

Nath, Kedar.
India's political needs. Gaya, Pundit Brindaban Dikshit, 1917.
129 p. 21 cm.

1. India—Politics and government—1765-1947. 2. Hinduism and state. I. Title.
JQ231.N35   72–221801
                                          MARC

NN   0029012   DLC

Nath, Kidar, ed.
The cantonment laws in India, being an exhaustive and critical commentary on Act II of 1924 as amended by Act XXIV of 1936. By Kidar Nath ... assisted by Wishan Das Puri ... Lahore, The University book agency ₍1937₎
3 p. l., ii, ₍2₎ p., 1 l., iii, 692 p. 23ᵐ.

1. Military posts—India. I. Puri, Wishan Das. II. India. Laws, statutes, etc. III. Title.
                          ₍Name in transliteration: Kedāra-natha₎
                                          41–32899
                                          Provisional

NN   0029013   DLC

Nath, Lala Baij, rai bahadur
see
Baijnāth, Lālā, rai bahadur.

Nath, Lucy.
Im dom zu Naumburg, von Lucy Nath; mit abbildungen nach aufnahmen von Rolf-Dietrich Nath und Helmuth Nath. Leipzig, J. J. Weber ₍1936₎
64 p. incl. illus. (plan) plates. 17½ᵐ. (*Half-title:* Weberschiffchenbücherei. ₍bd. 22₎)

1. Naumburg an der Saale. Cathedral. I. Title.
Library of Congress   NA5586.N3N3   37–4865
Copyright A—Foreign   33384
                             ₍3₎   726.6094318

NN   0029015   DLC

Nath, Manindra Basu
    see   Basu, Manindra Nath.

VOLUME 405

Nath, Mathura bhatta
    see   Mathura Nath, bhatta.

---

arX 3434 no.1
  Nath, Max, *1859-*
    Die Psychologie Hermann Lotzes in
  ihrem Verhältnis zu Herbart.
  Brandenburg a. d. Kavel, G. Matthes
  ₍1886₎
    37 p. 26cm.

    "Beilage zum Jahresbericht der Ritter-
Akademie zu Brandenburg, 1886-7."

NN   0029018   NIC MH

AC831 B71 1887 Stack
  Nath, Max, *1859-*
    Die Psychologie Hermann Lotzes in ihrem
  Verhältnis zu Herbart. Brandenburg a. d.
  Havel, 1887.
    37 p.
    Programmschrift - Ritter-Akademie, Brandenburg.

    1.Lotze, Hermann, 1817-1881. 2.Herbart, Johann
Friedrich, 1776-1841.

NN   0029019   CSt

Nath, Max, 1859–
  Die psychologie Hermann Lotzes in ihrem **verhältnis**
zu Herbart ... Halle, 1892.
  1 p. l., 37, ₍1₎ p. 24ᵐᵐ.
  Inaug.-diss.—Halle-Wittenberg.
  Vita.

    1. Lotze, Hermann i. e. Rudolf Hermann, 1817-1881. 2. Herbart, Johann
Friedrich, 1776-1841.
                  E 14-2143

  Library, U. S. Bur. of   Education LB675.L8N2

NN   0029020   DHEW ICRL NjP OO

Nath, Max, 1859–
ᵀ⁷¹⁸⁸ Schülerverbindungen und Schülervereine. Erfahrungen, Studien
und Gedanken von Professor Dr. Max Nath. Leipzig und Berlin, B. G. Teubner, 1906.
  vi, 136 p. 24ᵐᵐ.

NN   0029021   ICJ

Nath, Minendra Basu
    see   Basu, Minendra Nath.

Nath, Pran
    see   Prānanātha Vidyālankāra.

Nath, Prem.
  Our fault. Foreword by Sir S. Radhakrishanan. Lahore,
Hero Publications, 1944.
  108 p. 19 cm.

    1. India—Soc. condit. 1. Title.

  DS421.5.N33   58-54596

NN   0029024   DLC MiU CU

Nath, R
    General-Berichte über das öffentliche Gesund-
heitswesen
      see under   Königsberg (Regierungsbezirk)

W 4 M96 1953
  NATH, Rajeshwar, 1927-
    Der derzeitige Stand der Herzchirurgie
  in der englischen und amerikanischen
  Literatur. ₍München₎ 1953.
    56, 15 *l*.
    Inaug.-Diss. - Munich.
    1. Heart - Surgery

NN   0029026   DNLM

Nath, Rajmohan, 1900–
  The back-ground of Assamese culture ₍by₎ R. M. Nath.
₍1st ed. Shillong, A. K. Nath, 1948₎
  1 v. (various pagings). illus., 2 fold. maps. 26 cm.
  Includes bibliographical references.

    1. Assam — Civilization. 2. Assam — History. 3. Ethnology —
India—Assam.   I. Title.
  DS485.A87N3   73-179744
                             MARC

NN   0029027   DLC WU OCl MH NIC CSt-H PU CtY NcD NN

Nath, Ratan
    see
    Dar, Ratan Nath, 1846-1902.

Nath, Satrughna.
  ଆମ ଯୁଗ କଥା. ₍ଲେଖକ₎ ସତ୍ରୁଘ୍ନ ନାଥ. ପ୍ରଥମ ସଂସ୍କରଣ. କଟକ, କଟକ
ଷ୍ଟୁଡେଣ୍ଟସ୍ ଷ୍ଟୋର, 19-
    v. illus. 18 cm
  In Oriya.

    1. Civics, East Indian.   I. Title.
                    Title transliterated: Ama yuga kathā.
  JQ283.N3   S A 64-8424

NN   0029029   DLC

QL1 E2 no.22
  Nath, Vishwa
    The millipede sperm, by Vishwa Nath and
  Ganpati Parshad Sharma. Hoshiarpur, 1952.
  99-118, [1] p. 4 plates on 2 l.
  25 cm. (East Punjab. University. Research
  bulletin. Zoology, no. 22)
    Cover title.
    Bibliography: p. 117.

    1. Millepeds. I. Sharma, Ganpati Parshad,
jt. auth. II. Title. (Series)

NN   0029030   DI

QL1 E2 no.16
  Nath, Vishwa
    Sperm formation in certain coleoptera with
  particular reference to chromosome numbers,
  acrosome and mitochondrial nebenkern, by
  Vishwa Nath [and others]. Hoshiarpur,1951.
  39-49, [1] p. plates. 25 cm. (East
  Punjab. University. Research bulletin.
  Zoology, no. 16)
    Cover title.
    Bibliography: p. 47.

    1. Beetles.   I. Title. (Series)

NN   0029031   DI PPAN

QL1 E2 no.31
  Nath, Vishwa
    Spermateleosis in the dragon-fly Sympetrum
  hypomelas (Selys), by Vishwa Nath and Rajindar
  Rishi. Hoshiarpur, 1953.
  [1], 67-71, [1] p. 2 plates on 1 l.
  25 cm. (East Punjab. University. Research
  bulletin, no. 31)
    Bibliography: p. [72].

    1. Dragon-flies. I. Rishi, Rajindar, jt.auth.
II. Title. (Series)

NN   0029032   DI

Nath, Vishwambhar, 1923–
  Production and marketing of milk for Washington, D. C.
₍College Park, Md.₎ 1949.
  163 l. tables. 28 cm.
  Thesis—University of Maryland.
  Typewritten (carbon copy)
  Bibliography: leaves 158-163.

    1. Dairying—Maryland. 2. Dairying—Virginia. 3. Milk supply—
Washington, D. C. 4. Dairy products—Marketing.

  SF232.A1N3   A 51-5972

  Maryland. Univ. Libr.
  for Library of Congress   ₍2₎†

NN   0029033   MdU DLC

Nath Barooah, Upendra
    see   Barooah, Upendra Nath.

Nath Chandik, Bissessur
    see   Chandik, Bissessur.

Nath Chatterji, Heramba
    see   Chatterji, Heramba Nath.

Nath Chowdhuri, Jogindra
    see   Chowdhuri, Jogindra Nath.

Nath Datta, Janaki
    see
Datta, Janaki Nath.

Nath Ganguli, Jadu
    see   Ganguli, Jadu Nath.

Nath Ghose, Nagendra
    see
Ghose, Nagendra Nath, 1854-

Nath Gupta, Phanindra
    see   Gupta, Phanindra Nath.

Nath Gupta, Som
    see   Gupta, Som Nath.

Nath Jha, Shambhu
    see   Jha, Shambhu Nath.

Nath Kaul, Manohar
    see
    Kaul, Manohar Nath.

Nath Koul, Mohan
    see   Koul, Mohan Nath.

VOLUME 405

Nath Mitra, Trailaksya

see

Mitra, Trailokyanath, 1844-1895.

Nath Mitra, Upendra

see

Mitra, Upendra Nath.

Nath Mitter, Dwarka
      see   Mitter, Dwarkanath, 1876-

Nath Mozumder, Harendra
see
Mozumder, Harendra Nath.

Nath Neogi, Dwijendra
      see   Dwijendra Nath, Neogi.

Nath Ṣaksena, Vishnu
      see   Vishnu-Natha Ṣakasena.

Nath Sarasvati, Pran

see

Saraswati, Prannath, Pandit, d. 1892.

Nath Sivapuri, Harihar, joint ed.

Oudh. *Court of the judicial commissioner.*
    The Oudh select cases (civil and criminal) containing Oudh rulings & select cases of the Court of the judicial commissioner of Oudh, (1859-1896) with copious head-notes, a comprehensive general index, a table of cases reported, and an appendix containing cases from 1859 to 1884. Ed. by Munshi Jwala Prasad ... and Pandit Harihar Nath Sivapuri. Lucknow, T. N. Sopori, 1915.

Nātha, Gorakṣa
    see
    Gōrakhanātha.

Nātha, Rājamohana
    see
    Nath, Rajmohan, 1900-

Nātha Śāstri Varakale, Vaidya
      see   Varakale, Vaidya Nātha Śāstri.

Nathabanja, *Luang.*
    Extra-territoriality in Siam. ₍Bangkok₎ Printed at the "Bangkok Daily Mail," 1924.
    viii, 344, A-N p. 25 cm.
    Errata leaf inserted.
    Bibliography: p. 326-342.

    1. Exterritoriality. 2. Consular jurisdiction. 3. Aliens—Thailand. 4. Thailand—For. rel.

    JX1579.5.Z6E96   57-57020

    ViU-L MiU CtY CoU MiEM NNMR
NN   0029057   DLC CaBVaU WU OU CtY-L CSt-H NIC IU MH

Nathalal Bhanji Dave
    see
    Dave, Nathalal Bhanji, 1912-

Nāthālāla Bhāṇajī Dave
    see
    Dave, Nathalal Bhanji, 1912-

[Nathalie de Jésus, Sister]
    Adresse à l'Assemblée nationale, de la part des Carmélites de France de la réforme de Saints-Thérèse. [Paris, imprimerie nationale, 1790?]

    4 p.
    Signed by soeur Nathalie de Jésus, and others.
                   Fr 1328.07.15
    Another issue.
    4 p.

    Another issue.
    4 p.

NN   0029060   MH

Nathalie, comtesse.
    ...La villa Galietta. Nouvelle. Paris ₍etc., etc.₎ 1856. 144 p. 14cm. (Société des gens de lettres de France. Quatre nouvelles couronnées. ₍part 1.₎)

NN   0029061   NN

Nathan Azzathi
    see
    Ghazzati, Nathan Benjamin, 1644-1680.

Nathan Babylonius

see

Nathan, the Babylonian, 2d cent.

Nathan ben Ashur, pseud.
    Signs of the times
        see under   Hoag, Joseph, 1762-1846.

Nathan ben Isaac Jacob Bonn. Shikhhat leket.

BS1225
.R88   **Reuben ben Hoschke,** *d.* 1673.   (Yalkut Re'uveni)
1901 ילקוט ראובני. על התורה. מאמרים ומדרשים. ישנים גם
Hebr חדשים. חברו ראובן בן האשקי כ"ץ. ואלה מוסיף על
       תראשונים ספר שכחת לקם. ווארשא. האחים לעווין-עפשטיין.
                         תרס"ב .Warszawa, 1901

Nathan ben Jacob Bonn
    see
    Nathan ben Isaac Jacob Bonn.

'J4935 **Nathan ben Jehiel,** 1035 (ca.)-1106. Lexikon
B4   Additamenta zu Natan ben Jechiel's "Aruch"
Iebraic Berlin, Isaiah, 1725-1799.
Sect. הפלאה שבערכין. ביאור העריך. ברעסליא.
      Breslau, 1830-59. [Hafla'ah sheba-'Arakhin.]

PJ4935 **Nathan ben Jehiel,** 1035 (ca.)-1106. (Agur)
.N35S3 **Samuel ben Jacob ibn Jam,** *fl. 12th cent.*
1887 אגור... כולל הקדמה וקצת הוספות על ספר העריך. מאת שמואל
Hebr ב"ר יעקב נ'מג. יצא פעם ראשונה לאור עולם על פי שלשה
    נתבי יד ... שנים בפארמא ואחד באמסרדם. עם מראה
    מקומות והערות והגהות ... ממני שלמה באבער. ברעסליא.
    בדפוס ש. שאטטלענדער. תרמ"ח ₍1887/88.₎

Nathan ben Jehiel, 1035 (ca.)-1106.   *3031.118
    Aruch completum sive lexicon vocabula et res, quae in libris Targumicis, Talmudicis et Midraschicis continentur, explicans
    Amst., 1690.

NN   0029069   NjNbS

Nathan ben Jehiel, 1035 (ca.)-1106.   *3031.118
    Aruch completum sive lexicon vocabula et res, quae in libris Targumicis, Talmudicis et Midraschicis continentur, explicans.
    Lemberg, 1865

NN   0029070   NjNbS

Nathan ben Jehiel, 1035 (ca.)-1106.   *3031.118
    Aruch completum sive lexicon vocabula et res, quae in libris Targumicis, Talmudicis et Midraschicis continentur, explicans. Corrigit, explet, critice illustrat et edit Alexander Kohut. Berlin. Calvary & Co. 1878-92. 8 v. in 5. 27 cm., in 4s.

    K3728 — T.r. — Targums. Dict. — ₍T₎aud. Dict. — Midrash. Dict. — Kohut, Alexander, ed. 1842-1894. — Hebrew language. Works in Hebrew.

NN   0029071   MB DCU-H NNUT

PJ4935 **Nathan ben Jehiel,** 1035 (ca.)-1106
-N3   Aruch completum sive lexicon vocabula et res, quae in libris Targumicis, Talmudicis et Midraschicis continentur, explicans auctore Nathane filio Jechielis ... cum appendice ad discendum utili per Benjaminum Mussafiam, medicum, philosophum, philologum et physicum ad contextum Aruchinum adjuncta. Praelaudetum opus ex disciplinis contextus Aruchini Venetiis (anno 1531) editi et typis mandatorum optimi ita ex hujus cum editione princip. (ante 1480-, nec non cum

    septem Aruchinis veteribus manuscriptis bono cum animo facta comparetione cirrigit, explet, critice illustrat et edit Alexander Kohut. New York, Pardes Publishing House Inc., 1955. 8 v. 28 cm.

NN   0029073   RPB

Nathan ben Jehiel, 1035 (ca.)-1106.
    Aruch completum ...
        see also his   'Arukh ha-shalem.

Nathan ben Jehiel, 1035 (ca.)-1106.
    העריך. ומוסף העריך מהחים בנימין מוספיא. והוספנו ספר
    המע"ך הבינו מנחם די לונזאנו וספר הפלאה שבערכין מאת
    ישעיה בערלין. ועתה נתוסף העתקת כל מלה מלשונות זרות אל
    לשון אשכנוי. לובלין. מ. מ. שניידמעסטער. תרפ"ב.
    W Lublinie, 1924.
    2 v. in 1. 23 cm.

    1. Hebrew language, Talmudic—Dictionaries—Hebrew. ɪ. Title. *Title transliterated:* ha-'Arukh.

    PJ4935.N3 1924   58-50495

NN   0029075   DLC

VOLUME 405

PJ4935
.A7
1511
Hebr

Nathan ben Jehiel, 1035 (ca.)-1106.
(ha-ʿArukh ha-katsar)
העררך הקצר (Constantinople, 1511;

Nathan ben Jehiel, 1035 (ca.)-1106.
(ʿArukh ha-kitsur)
ערוך הקצר sic; ועתה יצא לאור ע"י מאיר קאהן ביסטריטיש.
Prag, W. Pascheles, 1863.

PJ4935
.N3
1878
Hebr

Nathan ben Jehiel, 1035 (ca.)-1106.
ערוך השלם. זעללי מוסף העררך להרב בנימין מוספיא ... עם
הוספות, הגהות, העררת ותקונים ... אונתיו והקרתיו ודרשתיו
אנכי הנך יהודה קאהוט. (Vienne, 1878-92;

8 v. in 5. 27 cm.

Added t. p.: Aruch completum; sive, Lexicon, vocabula et res,
quae in libris, Targumicis, Talmudicis et Midraschicis continentur,
explicans; cum appendice ad discendum utili per Benjaminum Mussaflam ... Bono cum animo facta comparatione corrigit, explet, critice illustrat et edit Alexander Kohut.

--------- מפתח. ונגוה אליו מחברת הין העררך. עם תשע עשר
רשימות מיעילות ... על כל הננוע בלימוד העררך. הכינותיו
אונתיו ודרשתיו אני הנדה יהודה קאהוט. ווינע, תרנ"ב.
(Vienne, 1892;

149, vii, lxxxi, 78 p. 27 cm.

Added t. p.: Index ad citata Biblica, Targumica, Talmudica atque
Midraschica, quae in Aruch occurrunt; necnon ad collocationem rerum, quae graviores in Talmud continentur. Cum collectione vocabulorum italicorum, in Aruch adnexoque supplemento operis "Aruch completum" concinnavit Alexander Kohut.
Bound with v. 8.

1. Hebrew language.   Talmudic — Dictionaries — Hebrew.
I. Kohut, Alexander.   1842-1894, ed. II. Title.
Title
transliterated: ʿArukh ha-shalem.

PJ4935.N3 1878   60-57021
Library of Congress

NN   0029079   DLC MH IU CU DCU-H

PJ4935
.N3
1926
Hebr

Nathan ben Jehiel, 1035 (ca.)-1106.
ערוך השלם. זעללי מוסף העררך להרב בנימין מוספיא ... עם
הוספות, הגהות, העררת ותקונים ... אונתיו והקרתיו ודרשתיו
אנכי הנך יהודה קאהוט. מהדורה ב. ינה, מנורה, תרפ"ו.
(Vindobona; 1926.

8 v. port. 25 cm.

Added t. p.: Aruch completum; sive, Lexicon, vocabula et res,
quae in libris Targumicis, Talmudicis et Midraschicis continentur.
Cum appendice ad discendum utili per Benjaminum Mussaflam ...
Bono cum animo facta comparatione corrigit explet critice illustrat
et edit Alexander Kohut.

--------- תוספת העררך השלם להרב הנך יהודה קהום. הברן
נערכן והביאו לדפום, שמואל קריום. בעזרת דוב ב. גייער האורים;
וינא. היצאת קרן לזכרון אלכסנדר קהום. תרצ"ז.
(Vienna, 1937;

x, 438 p. 26 cm.

(ספרים ויצאים לאור בהוצאת קרן לזכרון אלכסנדר קהום. ברך ח;
Added t. p.: Additamenta ad librum Aruch completum Alexandri
Kohut. Congessit scripsit edidit Samuel Krauss, adiuvantibus Bern-
hardo Geiger (et al.;

PJ4935.N3 1926 Add.

1. Hebrew language. Talmudic — Dictionaries — Hebrew.   I. Kohut, Alexander, 1842-1894. II. Krauss, Samuel, 1866-1948, ed.   III.
Title.   *Title transliterated:* ʿArukh ha-shalem.

PJ4935.N3 1926   60-56990

NN   0029081   DLC NcD ICU RPB

Nathan ben Jehiel, 1035 (ca.)-1106.
ʿArukh ha-shalem
see also his   Aruch completum ...

Nathan ben Jehiel, 1035 (ca.)-1106.
Rabbinisch aramäisch-deutsches Wörterbuch
see under   Landau, Moses Israel, 1788-
1852.

Nathan ben Jehiel, 1035 (ca.)-1106.
ספר ערוך, עם ספר שולחן העררך מאתי דוד נאלאמב. וארשא.
Варшава, 1914-
תרע"ה.

v.¹ 23 cm.

1. Hebrew language, Talmudic—Dictionaries—Hebrew.
I. Golomb, David, 1861-1935. II. Title. *Title transliterated:* Sefer ʿArukh.

PJ4935.N3 1914   58-50494

NN   0029084   DLC

Nathan ben Jehiel, 1035 (ca.)-1106.
ספר הערוך, מסודר ע"י שמואל בן אלחנן יעקב מן הארקווירמ.
ויניציאה. נדפם במצות אליוסי בראנאדין. (Venice, 1553;

166 p. 29 cm.

1. Hebrew language, Talmudic—Dictionaries—Hebrew.   I. Title.
Title transliterated: Sefer ha-ʿarukh.

PJ5035.N3   56-49368

NN   0029085   DLC

Nathan ben Jehiel ben Abraham
see   Nathan ben Jehiel, 1035 (ca.)-1106.

Nathan ben Joseph, *13th cent., supposed author.*
פירוש תלמיד הרמב"ן למסכת תענית. יוצא לאור פעם ראשונה
על פי כתב יד עם מראה מקומות והערות על ידי יעקב יהודה
הלוי הופמאן. ניו-יארק, תשי"א. (New York, 1951;

x, 60 p. 24 cm.

Bibliographical footnotes.

1. Talmud. Taʿanit—Commentaries.   I. Hoffman, Jacob, 1881-
ed.   *Title transliterated:* Perush.

BM506.T23N3 1951   57-56644

NN   0029087   DLC

Nathan ben Judah, *13th cent.*
ספר מחכים. יוצא לאור ראשונה על פי כת"י חינא והאמ
בורג עם הערות ומבוא מאת יעקב פרימאנן. קראקא,
בדפוס של י. פישער, תרס"ט. (Krakau, 1909;

xiii (i. e. xxiii), 50 p. 26 cm.

Cover title: Machkim ... mit Anmerkungen und Einleitung von J.
Freimann.

1. Jews. Liturgy and ritual.   I. Freimann, Jakob, 1866-1937, ed.
II. Title.   *Title transliterated:* Sefer mahkim.

BM660.N3   52-48026

NN   0029088   DLC

Nathan ben Kalonymus, Isaac.
see
Isaac Nathan ben Kalonymus, fl. 1450.

(Nathan ben Naphtali Herz, *of Nemirov;*
עלים לתרופה. דיבורי יראת שמים והתעוררות. וכעת התעוררנו
להדפים מחדש בהוספות ותיקונים. וארשא. הוצאת "ברסלב."
Warszawa (1930;
ת"ר.

370, (45; p. 23 cm.

1. Hasidism.   : Title.
Title transliterated: ʿAlim li-terufah.

New York. Public Libr.   A 54-491

NN   0029090   NN

Nathan ben Naphtali Herz, *of Nemirov.*
(Likute hilkhot Yoreh deʿah)
ליקומי הלכות יורה דיעה ... בדרושים ובמוסר השכל. אשר
אסף הרב נתן, וסובב הולך ע"פ תורת חסד של מוהר"נ.
Zolkiew, 1848. בדפום ש. ד. מאירהאפפער.

267 l. 26 cm.

1. Caro, Joseph, 1488-1575. Shulhan ʿarukh. Yoreh deʿah—Commentaries. 2. Hasidism.   I. Nahman ben Simhah, of Bratzlav,
1770?-1810? II. Title.

BM520.88.A57N37   A 48-5596

NN   0029091   DLC

Nathan ben Naphtali Herz, *of Nemirov,* ed.
Likute Maharan
see under   Nahman ben Simhah, of
Bratzlav, 1770?-1810?

Nathan ben Naphtali Herz, *of Nemirov.*
ימי מהרנ"ת, בו יוספר מענין התקרבות מורנו הר"ר נתן אל
רבינו נחמן והעמים אשר עברו עליו מיום התקרבותו אליו עד יום
הסתלקותו. לעמבערג. בדפום י. מ. ניק. (Lemberg, 1876;

48 l. 15 cm.

1. Nahman ben Simhah, of Bratzlav, 1770?-1810?   I. Title.
Title transliterated: Yeme Maharnat

BM755.N25N3   55-52788

NN   0029093   DLC

Nathan ben Naphtali Herz, *of Nemirov.*
ימי מהרנ"ת. בו יוספר מענין התקרבות הר"ר נתן אל המר
נחמן (וקונטרוס אמונת עתיך. מלוקט מספר לקומי מוהר"ן מאדמו"ר
נחמן מברסלב ומספרי לקומי הלכות שחברם ר' נתן; לעמבערג.
תרם"ג.
Lemberg, Druck der Ester Salat, Witwe des U. W. Salat,
1903.

64 l. 14 cm.

1. Nahman ben Simhah, of Bratzlav, 1770?-1810?   I. Nahman
ben Simhah, of Bratzlav, 1770?-1810? II. Title. III. Title: Emunat
ʿitekha.   *Title transliterated:* Yeme Maharnat.

[BM755.N   ]   A 55-6346

NN   0029094   NN

Nathan ben Nathan, 1891-
... Die erbpacht; geschichte, wesen und reform.
Berlin, Welt-verlag, 1921.
119 p. 18½ cm.

At head of title: Dr. Nathan ben-Nathan.
Bibliography: p. 8-10.

1. Rent.   2. Land tenure.   I. title.

NN   0029095   NNC

Nathan ben Saddi, pseud.
Das andere Buch der Chronicka von den Kriegen
der Frantzosen
see under   Richter, Christoph Gottlieb,
1717?-1774.

Nathan ben Saddi, pseud.
Die Bücher der Chronick derer Könige von Engelland, be-
schrieben in jüdischer Schreibart durch Nathan ben Saddi (pseud;
... Nach dem Original verdollmetschet.   Franckfurth und
Leipzig, 1744-45.   126, 46 p.   pl.   18cm.

"Die Bücher der Chronick derer Könige von Engelland, drittes Buch. Im welchem
beschrieben die Geschichten unserer Zeiten, bis auf die Wallfarth des Feldhauptmann
Bell-Isle, nach dem Flecken Elbingeroda, und seine Reise über das Meer.   (n. p.)
1745," 46 p. at end.

The English original with title "Chronicle of the Kings of England" was first
published at London, in 1740; it was reprinted in Robert Dodsley's Trifles (London,
1745) and thought to be his work. It is however, usually ascribed to Lord Chesterfield. cf. Dict. nat. biogr. (under Dodsley).
Translated by C. G. Richter.—cf. British museum catalogue.

J. S. BILLINGS MEM. COLL.

886607A. 1. Great Britain—Kings and rulers. 2. Belle-Isle, Charles Louis Auguste
Fouquet, duc de, 1684-1761.   I. Chesterfield, Philip Dormer
Stanhope, 4th earl of, 1694-1773,   supposed au. II: Dodsley, Robert,
1703-1764, supposed au. III. Richter,   Christoph Gottlieb, 1717?-1774,
supposed tr.
N. Y. P. L.   April 22, 1940.

NN   0029098   NN ICU OCU NIC

Rare
AC
4
R33
no.2

Nathan ben Saddi, pseud.
The chronicle of the kings of England.
Written in the manner of the ancient Jewish
historians.   London printed, and Dublin
re-printed by S. Powell for C. Wynne, 1740.
48 p. 20cm.

The Chronicle was first published in 1740;
it was reprinted in Robert Dodsley's Trifles
(London, 1745) and thought to be his work.
It is, however, usually ascribed to Lord
Chesterfield.--Cf. Dict. of natl. biogr.
No. 2 in   vol. lettered: Reflec-
tions on mar   riage.

NN   0029099   NIC

VOLUME 405

DA
28.1
.N27

Nathan ben Saddi, pseud.
The chronicle of the kings of England. Written in the manner of the ancient Jewish historians. By Nathan ben Saddi, a priest of the Jews. London, Printed for T. Cooper, 1740-41.
2 v. 21½cm.

Vol.2 has title: The second book of the chronicle ... from the reign of Queen Elizabeth unto the present time....
Sometimes attributed to Chesterfield, but Straus in his Robert Dodsley (1910) affirms it to be by Dodsley, in whose collected "Trifles" it was reprinted in 1745.

1. Gt.Brit.--Kings and rulers. I. Dodsley, Robert, 1703--1764, supposed author. II. Chesterfield, Philip Dormer Stanhope, 4th earl of, 1694-1773, supposed author.

       MnU IU PP ICU InU CLU-C NNB MB NN
NN   0029100   MiU CtY CSmH NB MH DFo ICN OCH TxU

Nathan ben Saddi, pseud.
The chronicle of the kings of England, from the Norman conquest unto the present time. Written in the manner of the ancient Jewish historians. By Nathan ben Saddi, a priest of the Jews. London: T. Cooper, 1742. 77(1) p., 11. 8° in fours.

The Chronicle was first published in 1740; it was reprinted in Robert Dodsley's Trifles (London, 1745) and thought to be his work. It is, however, usually ascribed to Lord Chesterfield.--cf. Dict. nat. biog.
In: *C p. v. 672.

Br.--History, 1066-1742. 2.   Dodsley, Robert, 1703-64, supposed
author. 3. Chesterfield, Philip Dor-   mer Stanhope, 1694-1773, supposed
author. 4. Title.
N. Y. P. L.   December 16, 1915.

NN   0029101   NN RPB PHC IEN

Nathan ben Saddi, pseud.
The chronicle of the kings of England, written in the manner of the ancient Jewish historians. By Nathan Ben Saddi, a priest of the Jews. London, printed; Newport, Re-printed and sold by the Widow Franklin, 1744.
iv, 5-56 p. 16ᵐᵐ.

Covers the period 1066-1603.
The Chronicle was first published in 1740; it was reprinted in Robert Dodsley's Trifles (London, 1745) and thought to be his work. It is, however, usually ascribed to Lord Chesterfield. cf. Dict. nat. biog.

1. Gt. Brit.—Kings and rulers. I. Dodsley, Robert, 1703-1764, supposed author. II. Chesterfield, Philip Dormer Stanhope, 4th earl of, 1694-1773, supposed author.

3-8961 Additions

Library of Congress   DA28.1.N18

NN   0029102   DLC

Nathan ben Saddi, pseud.
Chronicle of the Kings of England. Boston, 1750
8°

NN   0029103   MBAt

---

*EC7
C4263
A740cd

Nathan ben Saddi, pseud.
The chronicle of the kings of England, from the reign of William the Conqueror (first king of England) down to his present Majesty George the Second: containing a true history of their lives, and the character which they severally sustain'd; whether in church or state, in the field, or in private life. By Nathan ben Saddi [pseud.].
London: Printed. Boston; New-England: [Re-]printed and sold by Z. Fowle and S. Draper, at the [Pri]nting-office opposite the Lion & Bell, in Marlborough-[street,] 1759.
79p. 18.5cm.
Evans 8340.
Attributed variously to Robert Dodsley and to Lord Chesterfield.
Imperfect: p.25-26,63-70 wanting; t.-p. slightly mutilated.

NN   0029105   MH MWA MBAt

942
N274c
1767

Nathan ben Saddi, pseud.
The chronicle of the Kings of England. From the reign of William the Conqueror, inclusive, to the reign of his present majesty, George the Third. Written in the manner of the ancient Jewish historians. Rev. ed. London, P. and G. Bagnell, 1767. 63p

NN   0029106   KMK

Ik
D668
740f

Nathan ben Saddi, pseud.
The chronicle of the kings of England, from the reign of William the Conqueror (first king of England) down to His present Majesty George the Third. By Nathan Ben-Saddi [pseud.]. London: Printed, Norwich, Conn., re-printed and sold by Green & Spooner, 1773.
87p. 18½cm.
The Chronicle was first published in 1740, covering the period 1066-1603; it was reprinted in Robert Dodsley's Trifles (London, 1745) and thought to be his work. It is also ascribed to

Lord Chesterfield. cf. Dict.nat.biog. "The second book ..." first pub. 1741 continued the chronicle from Queen Elizabeth to George II.

NN   0029108   CtY MHi

Nathan ben Saddi, pseud.
The chronicle of the kings of England, from the reign of William the Conqueror, first king of England, down to his present majesty George III containing a true history of their lives, and the character which they severally sustained, whether in church or state, in the field, or in private life. Philadelphia, Printed and sold by Robert Bell and Benjamin Towne, 1774.
119 p.

NN   0029109   PPL PMA PHi

Nathan ben Saddi, pseud.
The chronicle of the kings of England from the reign of William the conqueror (first king of England) down to his present majesty George the third ... Lancaster, Printed for Stewart Herbert, junior, 1775.

NN   0029110   PPL

Nathan ben Saddi, pseud.
The chronicle of the kings of England, from the Norman conquest unto the present time. Written in the manner of the ancient Jewish historians. By Nathan Ben Saddi [pseud.] ... Birmingham, Printed by T. Chapman, 1777.
103 p. 17 cm.

NN   0029111   CtY

Rare Book
Room
Ik
D668
740K

[Nathan ben Saddi] pseud.
The chronicle of the kings of England, from the reign of William the Conqueror, (first king of England) down to His Present Majesty George the Third: containing a true history of their lives ... By the late Dr. Franklin. The third American edition. Litchfield[Conn.]: Re-printed by Thomas Collier, 1791.
iv, [5]-99p. 16cm.
Signatures: A-H⁵I².
The author's   pseud., Nathan Ben-Saddi,   appears on p.[iii]

NN   0029112   CtY MB

Nathan ben Saddi, pseud.
The chronicle of the kings of England, from the Norman conquest unto the present time. By R. Dodsley. A new edition enlarged. London, Printed for Vernor and Hood; and E. Newbury [sic. ca. 1795]. Pp. ii, 156. 12.2x7.4cm.

NN   0029113   CaOTP

[Nathan ben Saddi] pseud.
The chronicle of the kings of England, from the Norman conquest to the present time. By R. Dodsley. A new ed. enl. London, Printed for Vernor and Hood [etc.] 1799.
iv, 140 p. ports. 18ᵐᵐ.

The Chronicle was first published in 1740; it was reprinted in Robert Dodsley's Trifles (London, 1745) and thought to be his work; it is, however, usually ascribed to Lord Chesterfield. cf. Dict. nat. biog.

1. Gt. Brit.—Kings and rulers. I. Dodsley, Robert, 1703-1764, supposed author. II. Chesterfield, Philip Dormer Stanhope, 4th earl of, 1694-1773, supposed author. III. Title.

6—28354

Library of Congress   DA28.1.N24

NN   0029114   DLC

[Nathan ben Saddi, pseud.]
The chronicle of the kings of England, from William the Norman to the death of George III. Written after the manner of the Jewish historians, with notes explanatory and illustrative. London, J. Fairburn, 1821.
286 p. plates. 22.2cm.
Extra-illustrated with 163 plates (2 col.) chiefly portraits.
First published in 1740; it was reprinted in Robert Dodsley's Trifles (London, 1745) and thought to be his work. Usually ascribed to

Lord Chesterfield.--cf. Library of Congress.

1. Gt. Brit. - Kings and rulers. I. Dodsley, Robert, 1703-1764, supposed author. II. Chesterfield, Philip Dormer Stanhope, 4th earl of, 1694-1773, supposed author. III. Title.

       TxU
NN   0029116   TxHU NN NNC MiD-B MdBP LNHT IU MH OCH

Nathan ben Saddi, pseud.
Chronicles of Nathan ben Saddi. Constantinople, 1778.

NN   0029117   PPL PPULC

Nathan ben Saddi, pseud.
The chronicles of the kings of England, from William the Conqueror, to the year, MDCCXCV, in imitation of the Holy writings. By Nathan ben Saddi, a Jew. Worcester, Mass., Printed for I. Thomas, 1795.
iv, [5]-196 p. 17ᵐᵐ.

The Chronicle was first published in 1740; it was reprinted in Robert Dodsley's Trifles (London, 1745) and thought to be his work; it is, however, usually ascribed to Lord Chesterfield. cf. Dict. nat. biog.

1. Gt. Brit.—Kings and rulers. I. Dodsley, Robert, 1703-1764, supposed author. II. Chesterfield, Philip Dormer Stanhope, 4th earl of, 1694-1773, supposed author.

6—28349

Library of Congress   DA28.1.N2

       MeB MWH
NN   0029118   DLC NIC CSt CtY WU MWA MH OClWHi PMA

Nathan ben Saddi, pseud.
The chronicles of the kings of England, from William the Conqueror, to the year MDCCXCV. In imitation of the holy writings. By Nathan ben Saddi, a Jew (pseud.). New York: Printed by J. Buel for C. Davis, 1797. iv, (1)6-119 p. 18°.

First published at London, in 1740; reprinted in Dodsley's "Trifles" (London, 1745), and wrongly attributed to him. Ascribed also to Lord Chesterfield. cf. Dict. nat. biog.
p. 17-20 wanting.

1. Great Britain.—History, 1066-   1797. 2. Dodsley, Robert, 1703-
64, supposed author. 3. Chester-   field, Philip Dormer Stanhope,
4th earl of, 1694-1773, supposed   author.
N. Y. P. L.   January 17, 1916.

NN   0029119   NN OCH

Z
232
.U6
I6
B39
1832

Nathan ben Saddi, pseud.
The chronicles of the kings of England, from the reign of William the Conqueror ... to His Present Majesty George the Third ... By the late Dr.B.Franklin. New-Harmony, Ind. Published by James O. Wattles. Printed by Richard Beck & James Bennett, 1832.
84 p. 14 cm.
First published in 1740; reprinted in Robert Dodsley's "Trifles" in 1745, and hence ascribed to him, also often attributed to Lord Chesterfield. The author's pseudonym appears at the beginning of the preface.
With this is bound, as issued: Franklin, Benjamin. The way to wealth. New Harmony, 1832.
1.Gt.Brit.--Kings and rulers. I.Dodsley, Robert, 1703-1764, supposed author. II.Chesterfield, Philip Dormer Stanhope, 4th earl of, 1694-1773, supposed author. III.Title.

NN   0029120   MiU CtY

942
N19cFf

Nathan ben Saddi, pseud.
Chronique des rois d'Angleterre, ecrite en anglois selon le stile des anciens historiens juifs, par Nathan ben Saddi ... et traduite en françois dans le meme stile. Londres, T. Cooper, 1743.
156p.
Title vignette.
The Chronicle was first published in 1740; it was reprinted in Robert Dodsley's Trifles (London, 1745) and thought to be his work; it is, however, usually ascribed to Lord Chesterfield. cf. Dict. nat. biog.
Translated by   Fougeret de Monbron.

NN   0029121   IU CtY CLU-C

VOLUME 405

DA
28
.1
N27
1742

Nathan ben Saddi, pseud.
The first and second books of The chronicle of the kings of England. ₍Written in the manner of the ancient Jewish historians. By Nathan ben Saddi, a priest of the Jews. London, T. Cooper, 1742₎
2 pts. (73 p.) illus. 22cm.

Half-title.
Each pt. has special t.p.
The Chronicle was first published in

1740; it was reprinted in Dodsley's Trifles (London, 1745) and thought to be his work; it is, however, usually attributed to Lord Chesterfield. Cf. Dict. nat. biog.
Contents:--1st book. From the reign of William the Conqueror to James I.--2d book. From the reign of Queen Elizabeth unto the present time.

NN 0029123 NIC

x820.8
D64
v.1

Nathan ben Saddi, pseud.
The first book of the lamentations of Nathan ben Saddi ₍pseud.₎ a Jew of the tribe of Issachar, seer of the kingdom of Atlantis. London, Published by Jacob the son of Jacob, 1745.
19p. 19cm. (In The Diverting jumble. London, 1747. v.1, no.4)

NN 0029124 IU CtY NIC

Nathan Ben Saddi, pseud.   FOR OTHER EDITIONS
                            SEE MAIN ENTRY

A fragment of the chronicles of Nathan Ben Saddi ₍pseud.₎ printed in Philadelphia by James Chattin, 1758. Facsimile. Philadelphia, The Philobiblon club, 1904.

Nathan ben Saddi, pseud.
A fragment of the chronicles of Zimri ...
see under Zimri, the Refiner, pseud.

*EC75
A100
775p2

[Nathan ben Saddi, pseud.]
Pranceriana. A select collection of fugitive pieces, published since the appointment of the present provost of the University of Dublin ... Dublin:MDCCLXXV. (Price, sewed 2s. 8d. h.)
12°. x,253p. front.,illus.,plate. 17.5cm.
Dedication signed: Nathan ben Saddi.
Collection of satires on John Hely-Hutchinson, known as Harlequin Prancer.

NN 0029127 MH MB NN NjP IU CoCA

Y
1847
.708

Nathan ben Saddi, pseud.
Pranceriana poetica; or, Prancer's garland. Being a collection of fugitive poems, written since the publication of Pranceriana and the appendix. The 2d ed., to which is added a supplement, containing many original pieces, never before published. Dublin,1779.

NN 0029128 ICN

Lmg7
D85
775nb

Nathan ben Saddi, pseud.
Pranceriana. A select collection of fugitive pieces, published since the appointment of the present provost of the University of Dublin [the Right Hon. John Hely Hutchinson, known by the nickname of Harlequin Prancer] ... 2d ed. Dublin,1784.
2v.in 1 17½cm.
Dedication signed: Nathan ben Saddi.
"These letters ... appear chiefly to have emanated from the pen of Dr.Duigenan ..." - Dict. nat. biog.

NN 0029129 CtY

Nathan ben Salomon, pseud.
An astronomical diary or almanack ...
see under title

Nathan ben Samson Spiro
see
Spira, Nathan Nata, *d.* 1577.

Nathan Benjamin, *of Gaza*
see
Ghazzati, Nathan Benjamin, 1644-1680.

Nathan, *of Hamburg*
see
Nathan ben Isaac Jacob Bonn.

Nathan Meyuhas
SEE
Meyuhas, Nathan

NATHAN, pseud.
Nathan to Lord North... London: Printed for G. Wilkie, and R. Faulder, 1780. 2 p. l., 59 p. 22 cm.

Reviewing and censuring Lord North's political conduct. Signed: Nathan.
Author identified in contemporary hand as "By H. C."

587088A. 1. North, Frederick North, baron, 1732-1792. 2. Great Britain--Politics, 1760-1783. 3. United States-- Hist.--Revolution--Contem- porary opinion.
AC901.M5, v. 208, no. 6

NN 0029135   ICN MB RPJCB
NN MiU-C InU ViU MH DLC RPB CtY MiD-B

El Nathan, pseud.
See
Whittle, Daniel W., 1840-1901.

Nathan, the Babylonian, 2d cent.

Drusius, Joannes, 1550-1616.
Apophthegmata Ebræorvm ac Arabvm, ex Ávoth r. Nathan, Aristea, Libro selectarum margaritarum, & aliis auctoribus collecta, latineque reddita, cum brevibus scholiis, per I. Drvsivm ... Ed. altera melior & auctior. Franekerae, excudebat Ægidius Radæus, ordinum Frisiæ typographus, 1612.

I.J1287
.A2
1887

Nathan, the Babylonian, 2d cent.
Aboth de-rabbi Nathan.
מסכת אבות דרבי נתן בשתי נוסחאות. א) המסראַ[?]והמפור־
סמת בחיקן הגהה ע"פ הדפומאות וכתבי יד שונים. ב) נוסחא
אחרת עתיקה בכתב יד והוכרה בקצת ספרים ולא נדכסה
עדין. עם הערות ... ועם מבוא ... ונלוו לזה ארבע הוספות
... ושלשה ממתחות ... מאת שניאור זלמן שעכטער. וינא,
תרמ"ז. ₍Vindobonae, 1887₎

Nathan, Abraham, 1890–
Das Minimallohnproblem; eine kritische Studie... von Abraham Nathan... Freiburg im Breisgau: R. Rebholz, 1920.
xii, 119 p. 8°.

Dissertation, Zurich.
Bibliography, p. xii.
Vita, last page.

1. Wages (Minimum).
N. Y. P. L.   December 7, 1921.

NN 0029139 NN ICU

Nathan, Ad.   No. 23 in *8050a.743
Nocturno. [For pianoforte. Arranged and fingered by John Orth.]
= Boston. Schmidt. [1880.] 3 pp. [Scandinavia. A collection of Norwegian, Swedish and Danish compositions. No. 2.] 35 cm.

L7413 — Nocturnes. — Orth, John, ed.

NN 0029140 MB

Nathan, Adele (Gutman)
The building of the first transcontinental railroad; illustrated by Edw. A. Wilson. New York, Random House ₍1950₎
x, 180 p. illus. 22 cm. (Landmark books ₍9₎)

1. Railroads--U. S.--Hist.--Juvenile literature. I. Title.

PZ7.N174Bu   50—10703

OrP OrU WaS WaSp
NN 0029141   DLC MnU MiU MB CLSU AAP IaU Or OrCS

Nathan, Adele (Gutman)
Famous railroad stations of the world, by Adele Gutman Nathan with W. C. Baker. Illustrated by Graham Bernbach. New York, Random House ₍1953₎
100 p. illus. 26 cm. (Gateway books)

1. Railroads--Stations. I. Title.
Full name: Adele Newburger (Gutman) Nathan.

TF300.N3   *385.1   385.3   53-6276 ‡

NN 0029142   DLC RP FU PP MB OCl PPT

Nathan, Adele (Gutman)
The farmer sows his wheat, by Adele Gutman Nathan. New York, Minton, Balch & company ₍'1932₎
₍39₎ p. illus. 21 x 27¼".
Illustrated t.-p. and lining-papers.

1. Agricultural machinery. 2. Wheat. I. Title.
₍Full name: Mrs. Adele Newburger (Gutman) Nathan₎
32—25861

Library of Congress   SB191.W5N3
₍a42r39q2₎   [631.3]   633.11

MB NN OrMonO
NN 0029143   DLC CaBVa PBa PPGi PPT OEac OClh OCl

Nathan, Adele (Gutman)
The iron horse ₍by₎ Adele Gutman Nathan and Margaret S. Ernst. New York, A. A. Knopf, 1931.
5 p. l., 37 p. illus. 21 x 28".
"First edition."

1. Locomotives--Juvenile literature. I. Ernst, Margaret (Samuels) 1894– II. Title.
₍Full name: Adele Newburger (Gutman) Nathan₎
31—28059

Library of Congress   TJ605.5.N3
₍a45v1₎   621.132973

ViU MB WaSp
NN 0029144   DLC PWcS PPFr MiU OLak OO Or OrLgE NN

Nathan, *Mrs.* Adele (Gutman)
The iron horse ₍by₎ Adele Gutman Nathan and Margaret S. Ernst. New enl. ed. New York, A. A. Knopf, 1937.
5 p. l., 44 p. illus. 21 x 28".
Illustrated lining-papers.

1. Locomotives--Juvenile literature. I. Ernst, Mrs. Margaret S. II. Title.
₍Full name: Mrs. Adele Newburger (Gutman) Nathan₎
37-27127

Library of Congress   TJ605.5.N3 1937
———— Copy 2.
Copyright A 102736   ₍5₎   621.132973

NN 0029145   DLC PP PPT PPGi OCl NN

VOLUME 405

Nathan, Mrs. Adele (Gutman) joint author.

Loeb, Elinor G.
Let's play garden, originated by Nadine L. Rand, assembled and written by Elinor G. Loeb and Adele Gutman Nathan; illustrations by Fanchette. ₍New York₎ Grosset & Dunlap, inc., ᶜ1936₎

Nathan, Adele (Gutman).
A place to live, by Adele Nathan. Wartime housing - the problem - the program. A half-hour radio broadcast ... over the NBC network as presented by National committee on the housing emergency, inc. ... New York ₍1942₎
1 p. l., 17 numb. l. 28ᶜᵐ.

Reproduced from type-written copy.
1. Housing - U. S.
I. National committee on the housing emergency, inc.

NN   0029147   NNC

Nathan, Adele (Gutman)
Seven brave companions; illustrated by Fritz Kredel. ₍1st ed.₎ New York, Aladdin Books, 1953.
164 p. illus. 20 cm.

1. Marquette, Jacques, 1637-1675—Fiction. ɪ. Title.
Full name: Adele Newburger (Gutman) Nathan.

PZ7.N174Se   53-12190 ‡

NN   0029148   DLC Or OC1 OOxM

Nathan, Adele (Gutman).
We hold these truths; a pageant, by Adele Nathan and Blevins Davis. ₍Weirton, 1943₎ 68 f. 28cm.
Caption-title.
Program inserted.

276243B. 1. World war, 1939–   —Drama. 2. Pageants—U. S.
I. Davis, Blevins, jt. au. II. Title.
N. Y. P. L.   August 28, 1944

NN   0029149   NN

Nathan, Adele (Gutman)
Wheat won't wait; illustrated by Millard McGee. ₍1st ed.₎ New York, Aladdin Books, 1952.
192 p. illus. 21 cm. (The American heritage series)

1. McCormick, Cyrus Hall, 1809-1884—Fiction. ɪ. Title.

PZ7.N174Wh   52-11820 ‡

NN   0029150   DLC Or AAP

Nathan, Adele (Gutman)
When Lincoln went to Gettysburg; illustrated by Emil Weiss. ₍1st ed.₎ New York, Aladdin Books, 1955.
221 p. illus. 20 cm.
WaS

1. Lincoln, Abraham, Pres. U. S.—Fiction. ɪ. Title.

PZ7.N174Wj   55-6509 ‡

NN   0029151   DLC Or OrP PPGi PP ViU WaS

Nathan, Adolf
Die auf die mangelhaftigkeit der kaufsache bezueglichen sondervorschriften der ...
Inaug. Diss.   Leipzig, 1908.
Bibl.

NN   0029152   ICRL MH

Nathan (Adolf). *Ueber die Bedeutung des Natron salicylicum als Antipyreticum. 31 pp. 4°. Kiel, C. F. Mohr, 1875.
In: Schrift. d. Univ. zu Kiel, xxii, 1875, vii, Med. xvii.

NN   0029153   DNLM

Nathan, Alan Hart, 1913–
The synthesis of some thioalkyl and hydroxyalkyl pyrimidines and purines, and the formation of a new type of thiazolidino-pyrimidine ... by Alan Hart Nathan. New York, N. Y., 1940.
37 p., 1 l. 23ᶜᵐ.
Thesis (PH. D.)—Columbia university, 1940.
Vita.
Bibliography: p. 35–36.
1. Pyrimidines. 2. Purin. ɪ. Title: Thioalkyl and hydroxyalkyl pyrimidines and purines. ɪɪ. Title: Thiazolidino-pyrimidine.

                          A 41-4736
Columbia univ. Libraries
for Library of Congress   QD401.N3
                ₍3₎   547.8

NN   0029154   NNC CU DLC

Wing
Z
30555
.612

NATHAN (ALBERT) & CO., firm, Hamburg and New York.
Albert Nathan & Co's printing inks, varnishes and bronze powders. American Type Founders Company, general selling agent in America. ₍New York? ca.1900₎ 94(i.e.107)+ℓ. 15x24cm.

Some interpolated leaves are numbered with added fractions (e.g.: 10 1/2)

NATHAN (ALBERT) & CO., firm, Hamburg and New York.   Albert Nathan & Co's printing

Consists chiefly of specimens illustrating various colors of inks.
Imperfect: about 10 leaves torn out at end.

NN   0029156   ICN UPB NjP

Nathan, Alfred.
"They never come back," a musical farce-comedy
      see under   Princeton University. Triangle Club.

Nathan, Alfred, 1866–1933.
Fine books, library sets, autograph manuscripts, English xvɪɪ century literature, first editions, colored plate books, choice bindings by famous binders, the library of the late Alfred Nathan. Public sale, November 27 ... ₍New York₎ American art association, Anderson galleries, inc., 1934.
3 p. l., 80, ₍2₎ p. incl. front., illus. (facsims.) 24ᶜᵐ.
"Sale number 4133."
277 titles. Priced in manuscript.
1. Bibliography—Rare books.   ɪ. American art association, Anderson galleries, inc., New York.
                              42-44051
Library of Congress   Z999.A552 no. 4133
      — Copy 2.   Z997.N27

NN   0029158   DLC IU ICN MB

Nathan, Alfred, 1909–
Album melodía, selección de música bailable americana con tonos marcados. Música de : Peter Pan. Letra de : O. C. Mir. Buenos Aires, D. I. M. A.; distribuidor exclusivo, A. V. Vivona ₍19
v. 28 cm.
Reproduced from ᴍs. copy.
For piano solo, principally with words.

1. Folk dance music—Argentine. 2. Piano music. ɪ. Mir, O. C.

M30.N   45-30509 rev 2*/M

NN   0029159   DLC

Nathan, Anne
see
Cohen, *Mrs.* Anne (Nathan) 1906–

Nathan, August
Die uebertragung des eigentums an beweglichen sachen...
Inaug. diss. Tuebingen, 1909.
Bibl.

NN   0029161   ICRL MH

Nathan, August.
Die übertragung des eigentums an beweglichen sachen mittels constitutum possessorium zum zwecke der sicherung von forderungen, von dr. August Nathan. Stuttgart, J.B. Metzler, 1909.
vii, 75 p. 23 cm.

NN   0029162   CtY-L

6176
.832

Nathan, Bernhard
Über das Verhältnis der Leibnizschen Ethik zu Metaphysik und Theologie. Jena, Vopelius, 1916.
53 p. 22 cm.
Inaug.- Diss. - Jena.
Bibliography: p.₍51₎-53.

1.Leibniz, Gottfried Wilhelm, Freiherr von, 1646-1716. I.Title.

NN   0029163   NjP CaBVaU MH CtY ICRL O

Nathan, Bruno.
Der Vorstand der Kommanditgesellschaft auf Aktien. Köslin: J. Rosenberg & Co., 1911.   viii, 26 p.   8°
Dissertation, Erlangen. Bibliography, p. vii-viii.

1. Companies (Joint-stock).—Juris-   prudence, Germany.
N. Y. P. L.   November 30, 1912.

NN   0029164   NN MH MH-L NIC ICRL

Nathan, C. J. M.

Nathan, Manfred, 1875–   *ed.*
The company law of South Africa, containing the Union companies act (Act no. 46, 1926) as amended by acts nos. 11 of 1932, 64 of 1934, 49 of 1935, 36 of 1937, 23 of 1939, 29 of 1939 and 33 of 1939. And including the amended rules, forms, and precedents, together with full commentary, by Manfred Nathan ... assisted by C. J. M. Nathan ... 3d ed. Johannesburg, Hortors limited, 1939.

Nathan, C. J. M., ed.

Nathan, Manfred, 1875–
Concise guide to South African company law and practice, by Manfred Nathan ... Johannesburg, Hortors limited, 1940.

Nathan, C.J.M.

Nathan, Manfred, 1875–
Rules and practice of the Supreme court of South Africa, Transvaal provincial division, Witwatersrand local division, and Appellate division, by Manfred Nathan ... and Harold Dugard Bowker ... assisted by C. J. M. Nathan ... 2d ed. (rev. and enl.) Johannesburg, Hortors limited, 1935.

Nathan, C. J. M.

Nathan, Manfred, 1875–
South African insolvency law; a commentary on the Insolvency act no. 24, 1936 (to consolidate and amend the law relating to insolvent persons and to their estates) With full text, notes, references to decided cases, forms, precedents and regulations, by Manfred Nathan ... assisted by C. J. M. Nathan ... 4th ed. Johannesburg, Hortors limited, 1936.

VOLUME 405

917.2
N274d
Nathan, Charles, comp.
Description of ports of Honduras, Costa
Rica, Colombia, Venezuela, the Guianas, and West
Indies. New Orleans, the nearest port for travel
and trade between the United States and South
America. Compiled by Charles Nathan, New
Orleans. ₍Louisville?₎ n.d.
58p. fold.maps. 17cm.

1. Central America — Descr. & tr. 2. South
America — Descr. & tr. 3. West Indies — Descr.

NN 0029169 LNHT

Nathan, Charles, *comp*
Description of ports of Honduras, Costa Rica, Colombia,
Venezuela, the Guianas, and West Indies. New Orleans the near-
est port for travel and trade between the United States and South
America. Compiled by Charles Nathan. New Orleans₍, 1882?₎.
58 p. maps. 16°.

1. Commerce—U. S.--La.—New   Orleans, 1882? 2. Commerce—South
America, 1882?   January 12, 1928
N. Y. P. L.

NN 0029170 NN LU

Nathan, Charles Frederick, 1879–
A schoolmaster glances back. Illus. by the author. Liverpool, A. W. Duncan, 1946.
242 p. illus., plates. 22 cm.

ɪ. Title.

LA2377.N3A3   923.742   48–846*

NN 0029171 DLC CtY

Nathan, Clarence Seixas, 1836–1924.
In memoriam Clarence Seixas Nathan
see under title

Nathan, Coral Duke, 1891–
The development, function and characteristics
of the gracioso in the drama of Pedro Calderon de
la Barca... 1916.
48 numb. l.

NN 0029173 OU

355.115 Nathan, Cynthia Rice.
N19c   Case work with ill and disabled servicemen.
Service to amputees; Social service to plastic
surgery cases; Service-men and tropical diseases
(parts I and II); Servicemen face discharge with
hope and fear ... ₍New York, N.Y., Family Welfare Association of America, 1945₎
31p.

Cover title.
"Reprinted from the Family, February, March,
May, June, July, 1945."

NN 0029174 IU PU-PSW LU DCU WaT

Nathan, Cyril H.

HV861   National society of children's nurseries (*Gt. Brit.*)
.G6N3   A four years plan for children's nurseries, by the chairman,
National society of children's nurseries. ₍London₎ The Na-
tional society of children's nurseries ₍1943₎

Nathan, Daniel, *pseud.*
see Dannay, Frederic, 1905–

Nathan, David Solomon, 1900–
Analytic geometry, by David S. Nathan ... and Olaf Helmer
... New York, Prentice-Hall, inc., 1947.
x p., 1 l., 402 p. diagrs. 23½ᶜᵐ. ₍Prentice-Hall mathematics series.
A. A. Bennett, editor₎
"Answers to odd-numbered problems": p. 375–398.

1. Geometry, Analytic.   ɪ. Helmer-Hirschberg, Olaf, joint author.
QA551.N3   516   47–4143

NN 0029177 DLC NcD OU IaU NBuC ICU NN MB MtU WaS

Nathan, David Solomon, 1900–
Groups of transformations in a composite
function space... ₍Cincinnati, 1933₎
166 l.

NN 0029178 OCU

Nathan, E., arr.
Champaigne polka
see under title

CT   Nathan, Edgar J 1860–
6950   Memorial of Michael H. Cardozo. [New
C3N3   York] Association of the Bar of the
City of New York, 1907.
6 p. 24 cm.

1. Cardozo, Michael H., 1851–1906.

NN 0029180 OCH

Nathan, Edgar J   1860–
Ownership; an address delivered before the one hun-
dred and sixth meeting of the Insurance society of New
York on Tuesday, March 16th, 1915, by Mr. Edgar J.
Nathan ... ₍New York, C. H. Jones & co., printer₎ °1915.
17, ₍1₎ p., 1 l. 23ᶜᵐ.
"Loss adjustment lectures": 1 p. at end.

1. Insurance law—U. S.   ɪ. Title.
15–13497
Library of Congress   HG9734.U6N3

NN 0029181 DLC OU

Nathan, Edmund, Arzt: Die Augenerkrankungen beim
Botulismus. Aus d. Univ.-Augenkl. Breslau. Breslau 1919:
Breslauer Genoss.-Buchdr. 42 S. 8°
Breslau, Med. Diss. v. 15. Nov. 1919, Ref. Uhthoff
₍Geb. 4. März 92 Zduny, Kr. Krotoschin; Wohnort: Zduny; Staatsangeh.:
Preußen; Vorbildung: G. Krotoschin Reife 10; Studium: Freiburg 2, Berlin 3,
München 1, Berlin 1, Breslau 7 S.; Coll. 22. Jan. 17; Approb. 18. Jan. 17.₎
₍U 19. 1198₎

NN 0029182 ICRL DNLM

₍Nathan, Elias Salomon₎ 1800–1862.
Gedanken aus dem tagebuch eines Juden über die drei grossen propheten der europäischen geschichte ... Hamburg, F. H.
Nestler und Melle ₍1837₎
xviii, ₍19₎–269, ₍1₎ p. 18½ᶜᵐ.
CONTENTS.—Vorwort.— Moses.— Das mosaische system.—Das judenthum.—Die Juden.—Christus.—Jehovah im Coran.—Islamitisches rechts-
princip.—Paradoxieen.—Theologische paradoxieen.—Rückblick, gruß an
den recensenten vom herausgeber.

1. Jews—Religion. 2. Moses. 3. Jesus Christ—Jewish interpretations.
4. Muḥammad, the prophet. ɪ. Title.
23–4492 Revised
Library of Congress   BM565.N3

NN 0029183 DLC

Nathan, Elias Salomon, 1800–1862.

Salvador, Joseph, 1796–1873.
Geschichte der mosaischen institutionen und des jü-
dischen volks von J. Salvador. Nach der 2. ausg. aus dem
französischen übersetzt für gelehrte und gebildete aller
stände von dr. Essenna, bevorwortet von dr. Gabriel
Riesser ... Hamburg, Hoffmann und Campe, 1836.

Nathan, Ernesto, 1845–1921.
Giuseppe Mazzini; conferenza al teatro Carlo
Felice di Genova il 26 marzo 1917.   Genova,
Libreria ed. moderna, 1918.
43 p.

NN 0029185 MH

HS612   Nathan, Ernesto.
N132   ... La massoneria, la guerra e i loro fini;
discorso tenuto al Teatro Costanzi di Roma il
21 aprile 1918. Milano-Roma-Napoli, Società
editrice Dante Alighieri di Albrighi, Segati &
c., 1918.
32 p.   17ᵐ.

1. Freemasons.   2. Freemasons. Italy.

NN 0029186 CSt-H

Nathan, Ernesto, 1845–1921, ed.
Memorie, edizione diplomatica ... 1907
see under Garibaldi, Giuseppe, 1807–1882.

Nathan, Ernesto.
La morale nella conquista della richezza.
Ed. 2. Roma, Soc. tip. ed. Nazionale,
1907.

NN 0029188 PU

Nathan, Ernesto, 1845–1921.
L'opera massonica nel triennio 1896-99; relazione del Gran Maestro Ernesto Nathan, 20 Settembre 1899. Roma, Stab. tip. Civelli, 1899.

NN 0029189 MH

Nathan, Ernesto, 1845–1921.
Pel centenario di Giuseppe Mazzini, discorso...
tenuto il 22 giugno 1905 nell' aula magna del
Collegio romano.   Roma [etc.] Casa editrice
nazionale, 1905.
30 p.   22.5 cm.

NN 0029190 CtY

Nathan, Ernesto.

Italy. *R. Commissario generale italiano per l'Esposizione
internazionale Panama-Pacifico di San Francisco.*
Relazione del R. Commissario generale italiano per
l'Esposizione internazionale Panama-Pacifico di San
Francisco a s. e. il ministro di agricoltura, industria e
commercio, senatore Giannetto Cavasola. Roma, Tipografia nazionale di G. Bertero e c., 1916.

HC305   NATHAN, ERNESTO, 1845–1921.
.N3   Vent' anni di vita italiana attraverso all' "Annuario." Note e commenti di Ernesto Nathan. Roma-Tori-
no, Roux e Viarengo, 1906.
410 p. incl. tables. 23cm. (On cover: Biblioteca di
scienze sociali e politiche. 52)

1. Italy--Econ. condit. 2. Italy--Social condit.

NN 0029192 ICU CtY NjP IU MiU

Nathan, Ernst.
Experimentelle Untersuchungen über das Wesen
der Wassermannschen Reaktion ... Jena, 1918.
Habilitationsschrift - Frankfurt a.M.
"Abdruck aus der Zeitschrift für Immunitäts-
forschung und experimentelle Therapie. I. Teil.
Originale. Bd. XXVII".
Bibliographical footnotes.

NN 0029193 CtY

VOLUME 405

Nathan, Ernst, Appr. Arzt: Über die Verkalkung der kleinen Gehirngefässe. Giessen 1913: Kindt. 47 S. 8°
Gießen, Med. Diss. v. 25. Juli 1913, Ref. Bostroem
[Geb. 23. Mai 89 Darmstadt; Wohnort: Darmstadt; Staatsangeh.: Hessen; Vorbildung: Neues G. Darmstadt Reife 07; Studium: Gießen 6, München 1, Berlin 1, Gießen 2 S.; Coll. 29. April 13; Approb. 9. Mai 13.] [U 13. 1890

NN 0029194   ICRL MH DNLM DLC

Nathan, Ernst, Dr. jur.
Ueber den ausschluss der rechtswidrigkeit im strafrecht unter besonderer berücksichtigung des ärztlichen wirkungskreises. Von dr. iur. Ernst Nathan. Breslau, Schletter, 1923.
5 p. l., 57 p. 23½ᶜᵐ. (Added t.-p.: Strafrechtliche abhandlungen ... hft. 206)
Type-written.
Also issued as inaugural dissertation, Jena, 1921.
"Literatur": 4th-5th prelim. leaves.

1. Crime and criminals. [1. Criminology] 2. Medical jurisprudence. I. Title. II. Title: Rechtswidrigkeit.

29—27881

NN 0029195   DLC MH

Nathan, Fernand, firm, Paris.
Petit atlas universel Nathan. Paris [1955]
[80] p. 36 col. maps. 16 cm.

1. Atlases, French. I. Title.

G1019.N24 1955   Map 57—363

NN 0029196   DLC DS

Nathan, Fernand, 1858–
Exposition universelle et internationale de San Francisco, 1915. *Classe XII*
see under   Comité français des
expositionS.

[Nathan, Fernand] 1858–
30 [i. e., Trente] histoires en image sans paroles à raconter par les petits. Premier livre d'initiation et d'élocution. [Par Jean Perrot, pseud. & Fernand Fau] Paris, Librairie classique Fernand Nathan [1902]
32 p. (chiefly illus.)

Typed unnumbered pages with conversational exercises inserted.

NN 0029198   NNC

Nathan, Frances.
Verses. [New York] Printed for private distribution, 1928.
52 p. 22 cm.

PS3527.A7V4   811.5   52—46951

NN 0029199   DLC

Nathan, Franz: Der Notstand im Strafrecht. [Maschinenschrift.] 6, 133 S. 4°. — Auszug: Greifswald 1922: Adler. 15 S. 8°
Greifswald, R.- u. staatswiss. Diss. v. 8. Mai 1922 [U 22. 6666

NN 0029200   ICRL

Nathan, *Sir* **Frederic Lewis,** 1861–1933.
The Association of special libraries and information bureaux (ASLIB) and its work, by Colonel Sir Frederick Nathan. An address delivered at the conference of the International institute of bibliography, at Zurich, August, 1930. London, The Association of special libraries and information bureaux [1930]
[11] p. 24ᶜᵐ.

1. Association of special libraries and information bureaux.

Library of Congress   Z673.A551N   38—17891
     [2]   026.006242

NN 0029201   DLC

Nathan, Sir Frederic Lewis, 1861–1933.
Gt. Brit. *Explosives in mines research committee.*
... Electrical exploders for shot-firing in coal mines. (A report of a sub-committee of the Explosives in mines research committee) London, H. M. Stationery off., 1925.

Nathan, Sir Frederic Lewis, 1861–1933.
Gt. Brit. *Explosives in mines research committee.*
... Memorandum on explosives for use in fiery and dusty mines, and the methods of testing them. By the Explosives in mines research committee. London, Printed & pub. by H. M. Stationery off., 1923.

Nathan, Mrs. Frederick

see

Nathan, Mrs. Maud (Nathan) 1862–

Nathan [Fritz] art dealers, St. Gall.
Gemälde und handzeichnungen ersten ranges von 1780 bis zur gegenwart. Ankauf – verkauf uebernahme ganzer sammlungen und wertvoller einzelobjekte, beratung für kauf und verkauf. Dr. Fritz Nathan, St. Galler ... [St. Gallen, Buchdruckerei H. Tschudy & co., 1938.]
[24] p. incl. plates (1 col.) 21 cm.

NN 0029205   DSI

759.94
N274g   Nathan [Fritz] art dealers, St. Gall.
Gemälde und Handzeichnungen ersten Ranges von 1780 bis zur Gegenwart... [Verzeichnis] St. Gallen [1938]
[2] p. 22 illus. (1 col.) 21cm.

1. Paintings, European. Catalogs. 2. Drawings, European. Catalogs. I. Title.

NN 0029206   IEN DSI

Nathan, George Jean, 1882–1958.
The American credo; a contribution toward the interpretation of the national mind, by George Jean Nathan and H. L. Mencken. New York, A. A. Knopf, 1920.
2 p. l., 7–191 p. 19½ᶜᵐ

1. National characteristics, American. I. Mencken, Henry Louis, 1880– joint author. II. Title.

Library of Congress   E168.N27   20—3354

     OCl OU OClh ViU NIC ICJ OCU WU Or OrCS OrU OrStbM
NN 0029207   DLC ICU MoU NcD ViU TxU CoU MB MiU NjP

Nathan, George Jean, 1882–1958.
The American credo; a contribution toward the interpretation of the national mind. Rev. and enl. ed. By George Jean Nathan and H. L. Mencken. New York, A. A. Knopf, 1921.
3 p. l., 3–266 p. 19½ cm.

1. National characteristics, American. I. Mencken, Henry Louis, 1880– joint author. II. Title.

E168.N272   26—9256

     InU IdPI MtU
NN 0029208   DLC CaBVaU PP MH PU TxU LU OrU OrPS

Nathan, George Jean, 1882–1958.
The American credo. [Addition. New York?, 1921?]
193–196 p. 19½cm.
Caption title.
Contains paragraphs 499–526.
Johnson, 359.

1. National characteristics, American. I. Mencken, Henry Louis, 1880–1956, jt. author. II. Title.

NN 0029209   ViU

Nathan, George Jean, 1882–1958, ed.
The **American** mercury; a monthly review. v. 1– Jan. 1924.
New York, A. A. Knopf, 1924–

AP2
.A4577   Nathan, George Jean, 1882–1958, ed.
The **American** spectator. v. 1–4 (no. 1–48); Nov. 1932– Apr./May 1937. [New York]

Nathan, George Jean, 1882–1958, ed.
The **American** spectator year book ... New York, Frederick A. Stokes company, 1934–

Nathan, George Jean, 1882–1958.
... Another book on the theatre. New York, B. W. Huebsch, 1915.
xii, [3], 358 p. 19½ cm.

1. Theater—Anecdotes, facetiae, satire, etc. I. Title.

PN2095.N3   15—26855

     KMK PSt GU OrU CaOTP MeB NIC
NN 0029213   DLC WU TU PU LU CU NNC NN OCl MB WaU

NATHAN, GEORGE JEAN, 1882–1958.
An appendix to The American credo, by George Jean Nathan and H.L. Mencken. New York, 1921.
193–196 p. 19cm.

Microfiche (neg.) 1 sheet. 11 x 15cm. (NYPL FSN 11, 873)
Running-title: The American credo.

1. Aphorisms, American. I. Mencken, Henry Louis, 1880–1956.
II. Nathan, George Jean, 1882– 1958. The American credo.

NN 0029214   NN

Nathan, George Jean, 1882–1958
Art of the night [by] George Jean Nathan. New York, London, A. A. Knopf, 1928.
4 p. l., 296 p., 1 l. 19½ᶜᵐ.
CONTENTS.— Advice to a young critic.—Comedy—polite and otherwise.—The Sabbatical theatre.—Actors and actresses.—Coprophilia.—The audience emotion.—The Kaiser's hordes.—Notes on the movies.—Literature and drama.—Writers of plays.—The question of passions.—Theatricalized theatre.—The trivial play.—Chronicle of vices and crimes.—Magnus maximus

1. Theater—U. S. 2. Drama—Hist. & crit. I. Title.

Library of Congress   PN2266.N23   28—6119

     NBuU PSt GU WaU
     MH PP PU OO OCl OClh NN CU OrCS OrU WaS WaSp WaT WaTC
NN 0029215   DLC CaBVaU InU NIC KU CSt NcD MiU NjP

Nathan, George Jean, 1882–1958.
The autobiography of an attitude [by] George Jean Nathan. New York, A. A. Knopf, 1925.
5 p. l., 3–292 p., 1 l. 21ᶜᵐ.

I. Title.

Library of Congress   PS3527.A72A9 1925   25—20050

     OU MH CaOTP Or WaS WaWW TU OrCS
     NcD MH ViU PPGi OLak OOxM OO OCl MB NN ScU IEN MeB
NN 0029216   DLC MtU CaBVaU NIC KEmT NcGU UU CoU

VOLUME 405

Nathan, George Jean, 1882– *1958.*
The autobiography of an attitude ₍by₎ George Jean Nathan.
New York, London, A. A. Knopf, 1928.
5 p. l., 3–292 p., 1 l. 20ᶜᵐ.
"Fourth printing, March, 1928."

ɪ. Title.
30–2606
Library of Congress   PS3527.A72A9 1928

NN   0029217   DLC NIC Or

₍Nathan, George Jean₎ 1882– *1958*
The Avon flows, by Derek Wallas ₍pseud.₎ . . .   ₍New York,
193–₎   37, 49, 31 f.   28½cm.
Typewritten.
"The Shakespearean line remains in every particular unchanged and intact . . ."

148843B. I. Drama, American.   I. Shakespeare, William. Plays.
Romeo and Juliet. II. Title.
N. Y. P. L.   April 30, 1942

NN   0029218   NN

Nathan, George Jean, 1882– *1958.*
The Avon flows, by George Jean Nathan. New York, Random house ₍ᶜ1937₎
190 p. 21ᶜᵐ.
"Orchestration" of Romeo and Juliet, Othello, and *Taming of the
shrew,* presenting the lives of Romeo and Juliet without a tragic *ending.*
"The Shakespearean line in this orchestration ... remains in every particular unchanged and intact."—Note, p. ₍6₎
"First edition."

ɪ. Shakespeare, William. Romeo and Juliet. ɪɪ. Title.
37–1748
Library of Congress   PS3527.A72A95 1937
—— Copy 2.
Copyright D pub. 47507   ₍5₎   [822.33] 812.5

WaS CaOTP CoU
NBuU FMU NIC NN MiU PP PU OC1 OC1W OLak OU MB WaSp
NN   0029219   DLC CaBVa OrU Or OrCS OrPS IdU InU TxU

Nathan, George Jean, 1882– *1958*
The bachelor life ₍by₎ George Jean Nathan; illustrated by
Irma Selz. New York, Reynal & Hitchcock ₍ᶜ1941₎
viii p., 2 l., 262 p., 1 l. incl. front., plates. 21½ᶜᵐ.

1. Bachelors.   ɪ. Title.
41–8558
Library of Congress   PS3527.A72B3 1941
—— Copy 2.
Copyright   ₍10₎   817.5

OC1 PPGi PU KEmT NIC WU ViU IdPI IdU WaE WaS Or
NN   0029220   DLC WaU CoU TU NcD NcC NcRS OO OU OOxI

Nathan, George Jean, 1882– *1958.*
Beware of parents, a bachelor's book for children, by George
Jean Nathan, illustrated by Whitney Darrow, jr. New York,
Toronto, Farrar & Rinehart, inc. ₍1943₎
xi, 130 p. front. (port.) illus. 21½ᶜᵐ.

1. Parent and child—Anecdotes, facetiae, satire, etc.   ɪ. Darrow,
Whitney, 1909–   illus. ɪɪ. Title.
43–3347
Library of Congress   PS3527.A72B4
₍15₎   817.5

NcC PP OC1 OEac OO WaSp
NN   0029221   DLC OrSaW Or CaBVa NcD OU NIC WU IdPI

Nathan, George Jean, 1882– *1958.*
A book without a title, by George Jean Nathan. New
York, Philip Goodman company, 1918.
5 p. l., 7–81 p. 19ᶜᵐ.

ɪ. Title.
18–14082
Library of Congress   PS3527.A72B5 1918

NN   0029222   DLC CU PU CoU Or OrU ICarbS MH NN WaWW

PS   Nathan, George Jean, 1881–1958.
3527   A book without a title. New York,
A856   Knopf, 1919.
B7   81 p. 19cm.
1919

NN   0029223   NIC NcD

Nathan, George Jean, 1882– *1958.*
Bottoms up, an application of the slapstick to satire,
by George Jean Nathan. New York, Philip Goodman
company, 1917.
3 p. l., 5–73 p. 19ᶜᵐ.

ɪ. Title.
17–21350
Library of Congress   PS3527.A72B6 1917

OOxM MiU NN MB KMK IdU OrU
NN   0029224   DLC GU ScU FMU NIC NcD NjP MH PU OO

Nathan, George Jean, 1882– *1958*
Comedians all ₍by₎ George Jean Nathan. New York, A. A.
Knopf, 1919.
6 p. l., 11–267 p. 19½ᶜᵐ.

1. Drama—Hist. & crit.   ɪ. Title.
19–27590
Library of Congress   PN2266.N25

OU OC1 OC1W OO LU WU NBuU IdU OrU
NN   0029225   DLC WaU NIC NcD NjP PSt PU MB NN ViU

Nathan, George Jean, 1882–, *1958.*
The critic and the drama, by George Jean Nathan.
New York, A. A. Knopf, 1922.
6 p. l., 3–152 p. 21ᶜᵐ.
Contents.—Aesthetic jurisprudence.—Drama as an art.—The place of
the theatre.—The place of acting.—Dramatic criticism.—Dramatic criticism
in America.

1. Drama—Hist. & crit. 2. Theater.   ɪ. Title.
22–2060
Library of Congress   PN1655.N3

WaWW WaS OrCS WaTC
NcD MB NN ICU KEmT NIC WaU FMU FTaSU DAU ViU MtU Or
NN   0029226   DLC IdU LU MiU MH PP PU OC1W OC1 OO OU

PR6019   Nathan, George Jean, 1882– *1958.*
O8E9   ₍A criticism of James Joyce's play, Exiles₎
N27   (In The American mercury. New York, 1925. 26ᶜᵐ.
              Vol.4, no.16, Apr.1925. p.501–502)
              Detached copy.

1. Joyce, James, 1882–1941. Exiles.

NN   0029227   CSt

812.52   Nathan, George Jean, 1882–1958, editor.
N274c   The critics' prize plays, introduced by
              Cleveland, World Publ. Co., 1945.

              377p. 22cm.

              I. Title. 1. AMERICAN DRAMA – COLLECTIONS

NN   0029228   OWorP

Nathan, George Jean, 1882– *1958.*
Encyclopædia of the theatre ₍by₎ George Jean **Nathan.**
New York, A. A. Knopf, 1940.
3 p. l., ₍v₎–ix, 449, ₍1₎ p. 22½ᶜᵐ.
"First edition."

1. Theater—U. S. 2. American drama—20th cent.—Hist. & crit.
ɪ. Title.
40–27010
Library of Congress   PN2266.N27
—— Copy 2.
Copyright A 136403   ₍20₎   792.0973

OU OCU OC1W OC1 MH KU PSt IdU MtU Or OrU WaS WaSpG
NN   0029229   DLC ViU NcD NjP TU PPT PSC PV PWcS NIC

Nathan, George Jean, 1882– *1958.*
... The entertainment of a nation; or, Three sheets in the
wind. New York, A. A. Knopf, 1942.
vi, 290 p., 1 l. 20ᶜᵐ.
"First edition."

1. Theater—U. S.   ɪ. Title.
42–1453
Library of Congress   PN2266.N28
₍20₎   792.0973

MtU Or OrCS OrP OrPS OrSaW WaE WaT WaSpG WaS
PP PPD ViU OU OC1 OC1W OOxM ICU InU PSt MB CoU MtBC
NN   0029230   DLC IdB IdPI WaU CaOTP NcC ODW PJB TU

Nathan, George Jean, 1882– *1958*
The eternal mystery; a play in one act.
₍New York, n. d.₎
231–250p. 25cm.

NN   0029231   TNJ

Nathan, George Jean, 1882– *1958.*
The eternal mystery; a play in one act, by **George**
Jean Nathan ... ₍New York, 1913₎
3 p. l., 2–18 numb. l. 28ᶜᵐ.
Type-written.

ɪ. Title.
23–11499
Library of Congress   PS3527.A72E8 1913

NN   0029232   DLC

Nathan, George Jean, 1882– *1958.*
The eternal mystery; play in one act.
(In Goldberg, Isaac. The theatre of George Jean Nathan. Chap-
ters and documents towards a history of the American drama.
Pp. 229–250. New York. 1926.)

NN   0029233   MB OC1

Nathan, George Jean, 1882–*1958* joint author.

Mencken, Henry Louis, 1880–
Europe after 8:15, by H. L. Mencken, George Jean Nathan,
Willard Huntington Wright; with decorations by Thomas H.
Benton. New York, John Lane company; ₍etc., etc.₎ 1914.

HLM
P2   Nathan, George Jean, 1882– *1958.*
          ₍The American credo. **Selections**₎
          A four page compendium to the American credo.
          ₍New York, 1921₎
          Gift of Elizabeth M. Snyder.
          Negatives, touched up, for production of this
          compendium printed at Christmas 1921 "containing
          articles that could not be printed in the book
          itself" (HLM: The Mencken bibliography, p. 25).
          I. Mencken, Henry Louis, 1880–1956, The
          American credo. S   elections. s/cII.gift:
          Snyder, Elizabeth   (Morrison)

NN   0029235   KU

PN   Nathan, George Jean, 1882–1958.
3527   Friends of mine. New York, Knopf, 1932.
A856   xx,12 p. 20cm.
F9
            Publisher's dummy copy, rejected in favor
          of The intimate notebooks.

NN   0029236   NIC

---

817   Nathan, George Jean, 1882–1958.
N19   From the Smart set. ₍n. p., 192–?₎
M2   1 v. (various pagings) 25cm.
v   Binder's title.
            A collection of articles by George Jean
          Nathan and H. L. Mencken extracted from
          Smart set magazine.

            I. Mencken, Henry Louis, 1880–1956. II.
          The Smart set.

NN   0029237   ViW

VOLUME 405

Nathan, George Jean, 1882–*1958* joint author.

Mencken, Henry Louis, 1880–
Heliogabalus, a buffoonery in three acts, by H. L. Mencken and George Jean Nathan. New York, A. A. Knopf, 1920.

Nathan, George Jean, 1882–*1958*.
The house of Satan ₍by₎ George Jean Nathan. New York, London, A. A. Knopf, 1926.

vii, 295, ₍1₎ p. 20ᶜᵐ.

CONTENTS.—The house of Satan.—intelligence and drama.—L'homme poudré.—Housebroken drama.—"The plain-song cuckoo gray."—The amusements of homo sapiens.—Geniuses.—The prince's tailor.—The play and the playwright.—What's wrong with the theatre.—The American taste.—Bagatelles in C minor.

1. Theater. 2. Drama—Hist. & crit. I. Title.

Library of Congress   PN1655.N33   26–14736

WaSpG WaSp WaTC
MiU PU NN MB MiU ScU PSt DAU InU OrPS OKentU NIC OrU
NN   0029239   DLC IdU MH NcD ViU NjP PP PPL OU OCl

Nathan, George Jean, 1882–*1858*.
The intimate notebooks of George Jean Nathan. New York, A. A. Knopf, 1932.

4 p. l., 3–326 p., 1 l. 19½ᶜᵐ.

"First edition."

CONTENTS.—Literary personalities.—Critical observations.—Theatrical opinions.—Random conclusions.

1. Authors, American. 2. Criticism. 3. Drama—Hist. & crit. 4. Theater. I. Title.

Library of Congress   PS3527.A72 I 6 1932   32–27067

———— Copy 2.

Copyright A 54879   ₍7₎   814.5

InU PP ViU OClW OCl NcD MB MsU MoU NIC MiU
NN   0029240   DLC IdPI IdU OrU CoU OU NN NcRS KU FU

817
N19   Nathan, George Jean, 1882–1958.
M3   Judging the shows. ₍New York, 192–?₎
v   1v. (various pagings) 29cm.
over-   Binder's title.
size   A collection of reviews and articles by
      George Jean Nathan extracted from various issues
      of Judge magazine.

      I. Judge.

NN   0029241   ViW

Nathan, George Jean, 1882–*1858*.
Land of the pilgrims' pride ₍by₎ George Jean Nathan. New York, London, A. A. Knopf, 1927.

4 p. l., 294 p., 1 l. 19½ᶜᵐ.

CONTENTS.—The new morality.—The American emotion.—The motherland.—The muse in our midst.—Aspects of the contemporary scene.—No. 18.—A few notes on American criticism.—The gastronomic capital.—Show-case samples.—Delusions.

I. Title.

Library of Congress   PS3527.A72L3 1927   27–18999

CaOTP NBuU WaU NIC KEmT CaBVaU
NcRS NcD MiU ICU NjP MH PP PU OU OCl OClh OCU MB NN
NN   0029242   DLC InU UU WaTC MtU OrPR IdPI OrU MsSM

Nathan, George Jean, 1882–*1858*.
Materia critica ₍by₎ George Jean Nathan. New York, A. A. Knopf, 1924.

4 p. l., 3–242 p. 21½ᶜᵐ.

CONTENTS.—Critic and criticism.—Art and artist.—Certain dramatists.—Certain familiar types of entertainment.—Certain actors and actresses.—Notes on the theatre in general.

1. Drama—Hist. & crit. 2. Theater. I. Title.

Library of Congress   PN1655.N34   24–21608

CaOTP WaU WaWW OrU
PP NcD TU MH NjP PPT PU OU OCl OOxM ODW NN MB MiU
NN   0029243   DLC WaS CaBVaU IdU IdU-SB MtU ViU NIC

Nathan, George Jean, 1882–*1858*.
Mr. George Jean Nathan presents. New York, A. A. Knopf, 1917.

310 p. diagrs. 19½ᶜᵐ.

"An after-piece of more or less critical confidences and memoirs touching lightly upon the various somethings which go to constitute what is called the American theatre."

1. Theater—U. S. 2. American drama—Hist. & crit. I. Title.

Library of Congress   PN2266.N3   17–24680

PV PU OOxM OU OO OCU NN MiU NcD NIC WaU PSt KMK MeB
NN   0029244   DLC WaSpG WaS OrU Or MB MtU NjP ViU

Nathan, George Jean, 1882–*1958*.
Monks are monks; a diagnostic scherzo, by George Jean Nathan. New York, A. A. Knopf, 1929.

5 p. l., 3–300 p., 1 l. 19½ᶜᵐ.

I. Title.

Library of Congress   PS3527.A72M6 1929   29–18126

IdPI CaBVaU
OCl MH ViU UU ScU CoU NIC InU ICarbS GU HU WaTC OrU
NN   0029245   DLC KEmT FU OkU NcD NjP MB PP OU OCl'

Nathan, George Jean, 1882–*1958*.
Monks are monks, a diagnostic scherzo, by George Jean Nathan. New York, A. A. Knopf, 1929.

6 p. l., 3–300 p., 1 l. 24ᶜᵐ.

"One hundred ten copies ... Number 90. ₍Signed₎ George Jean Nathan."

I. Title.

Library of Congress   PS3527.A72M6 1929 a   44–51630

NN   0029246   DLC CSt InU NIC PU

Nathan, George Jean, 1882–*1958*.
The morning after the first night ₍by₎ George Jean Nathan. New York, London, A. A. Knopf, 1938.

3 p. l., iii–ix, 281, ₍1₎ p., 1 l. 19½ᶜᵐ.

"First edition."

1. Theater—U. S. 2. American drama—Hist. & crit. I. Title.

Library of Congress   PN2266.N32   38–2532

———— Copy 2.

Copyright A 113480   ₍10–5₎   792.0973

WaSp CaBVaU
OU ODW PPL PSC PU MtU WaS Or OrCS CaBVa MtBC OrU
NN   0029247   DLC CU–I NIC MoSW NcRS TU NN OCU OCl

Nathan, George Jean, 1882–*1958*.
The new American credo; a contribution toward the interpretation of the national mind, by George Jean Nathan. Completely rev. and enl. ed. New York ₍etc.₎, A. A. Knopf, 1927.

xii p., 1 l., 223 p., 1 l. 19½ᶜᵐ.

1. National characteristics, American. I. Title.

Library of Congress   E168.N273   27–8157

WaSpG
OU OO ViU NN MB WU IEN ICarbS MtU TxU OrU WaWW OrCS
NN   0029248   DLC NcD NcRS MiU InU ICU MH OCU OClh

Nathan, George Jean, 1882–*1958*.
The new American credo: a contribution toward the interpretation of the national mind... completely rev. and enl. ed. N.Y. ₍etc.₎, Blue ribbon books, ₍1920–27₎
223p.

NN   0029249   OOxM LU PU

PS2649
.P5Z757 Nathan, George Jean, 1882–1958.
1906
     O. Henry in his own Bagdad. ₍New York,
     Dodd, Mead & Company, c1910₎
     477–479 p. 25cm.
     Detached from The Bookman, v. 31, no. 5
     (July, 1910)
     Clarkson, p. 66.

     1. Porter, William Sydney, 1862–1910.
     I. The Bookman. II. Title.

NN   0029250   ViU NcU

Nathan, George Jean, 1882–*1958*.
Passing judgments, by George Jean Nathan. New York, A. A. Knopf, 1935.

5 p. l., 3–271, ₍1₎ p. 19½ᶜᵐ.

Critical essays on the contemporary American theater and drama.
"First edition."

1. Theater—U. S. 2. Drama—20th cent.—Hist. & crit. 3. Criticism. I. Title.

Library of Congress   PN2266.N33   35–1614

———— Copy 2.

Copyright A 80243   ₍5–5₎   792.0973

WaWW WaS   CaBVa OrU IdPI
NIC NcRS PP PSC OU OCU OCl OCX MB Or WaT IdU WaSp
NN   0029251   DLC NNC MoU CoU ScU FTaSU ScCleU PSt

Nathan, George Jean, *1882–1958*.
Passing judgments. New York: Alfred A. Knopf, 1935₍, cop. 1933–35₎. 271 p. 12°.

CONTENTS.—As one critic to another. The American theatre today. The good old days. The theatre abroad. Critical presumptions—Theatrical. Critical presumptions—General. The sex appeal fiction. O'Neill. Summer theatres. A trio of reflections. Several writers for the theatre—and Miss Stein. Producers and productions. Motion picture censorship. The movies take over the stage. The Chaplin buncombe. General remarks.

1. Dramatic criticism. 2. Theatre, American. 3. Title. 4. O'Neill, Eugene Gladstone—Criticism (anal.). 5. Play production (anal.). 6. Moving pictures—Censorship (anal.). 7. Chaplin, Charles (anal.).
N. Y. P. L.   January 28, 1935

NN   0029252   NN

Nathan, George Jean, 1882–1958.
₍Mencken, Henry Louis₎ 1880–
Pistols for two, by Owen Hatteras ₍pseud.₎ New York, A. A. Knopf, 1917.

Nathan, George Jean, 1882–*1958*.
The popular theatre, by George Jean Nathan. New York, A. A. Knopf, 1918.

236 p. 19½ᶜᵐ.

1. Theater. I. Title.

Library of Congress   PN2266.N35   18–18494

OCX MiU MB NN TxU IdU WaTC WaS OrStbM CaBVaU OrCS
NN   0029254   DLC WU MsU InU ViU NjP PSC OCl OClW

PN
2266   Nathan, George Jean, 1882–*1958*.
N35   The popular theatre. New York, A. A.
1923   Knopf ₍1923,c1918₎
HRC   236p. (Borzoi pocket books)

     Second edition.
     Ex libris Frederic W. Hile.

NN   0029255   TxU PSt NjP CLU

808.2
N195po   Nathan, George Jean, 1882–*1958*.
     The popular theatre. ₍2d ed.₎ New York,
     A. A. Knopf ₍1924,c1918₎
     236p. 18cm. (Borzoi pocket books)

NN   0029256   OrU

PN2266
.N35   Nathan, George Jean, 1882–*1958*.
1924
     The popular theatre. ₍Popular ed.₎
     New York, A. A. Knopf ₍1924₎
     236 p. 18cm. (Borzoi pocket books)

NN   0029257   ViU

Nathan, George Jean, 1882–*1958*.
Since Ibsen; a statistical historical outline of the popular theatre since 1900, by George Jean Nathan. New York, A. A. Knopf, 1933.

4 p. l., 3–162, ₍2₎ p. 19½ cm.

1. Drama—20th cent.—Hist. & crit. 2. Theater. I. Title.

PN1861.N3   808.2   33–10742

WaSp WaU MtBC Or CaBVa WaSpG OrU
NN   0029258   DLC OU MB NN PPA PPD PPT NIC ICN CoU

VOLUME 405

Nathan, George Jean, 1882–1958, ed.
The Smart set; a magazine of cleverness. v. 1–86; Mar. 1900–
July 1930. New York, Ess Ess publishing company ₍etc.₎,
1900–30₎

Nathan, George Jean, 1882–*1958*.
Testament of a critic ₍by₎ George Jean Nathan. New York,
London, A. A. Knopf, 1931.
4 p. l., 3–257 p., 1 l. 19¼ᶜᵐ.

1. Criticism. 2. Drama—Hist. & crit. 3. Theater—U. S. I. Title.

Library of Congress   PN2266.N37   31–1498

——— Copy 2.
Copyright A 32714   ₍5-2₎   792.09

OrU WaSpG
OC1h OCU OC1 MiU MB MH KU MoU NlC ViU WaWW WaS CaBVa
NN 0029260   DLC CaOTP DAU InU WaU FU NcD NN PP PU

Nathan, George Jean, 1882–1958.
The theatre book of the year; a record and an interpretation by George Jean Nathan. 1942/43–1950/51. New York,
A. A. Knopf.
9 v. 22 cm.

1. Theater—United States—Yearbooks. I. Title.

PN2266.N373   43–51298

NN 0029261   DLC

Nathan, George Jean, 1882–*1958*.
The theatre in the fifties. ₍1st ed.₎ New York, Knopf,
1953.
298 p. 22 cm.

1. Theater—New York (City) 2. Drama—20th cent.—Hist. & crit.
3. Musical revue, comedy, etc. I. Title.

PN2277.N5N3   792   53–6856 ‡

WaS WaSpG WaT
OOxM MiU Or OU CaBVa OrMonO OrPR OrP OrU WaE
NN PPD ICU OO NNC PIm PRosC PSt PWcS OC1U TxU
PSt NlC GU NcD NcRS PP PPL PBL OC1W OC1 MB TU
NN 0029262   DLC IU ViU MtU CaBVaU MtBC OrCS

Nathan, George Jean, 1882–*1958*.
The theatre of the moment, a journalistic commentary ₍by₎
George Jean Nathan. New York, London, A. A. Knopf, 1936.
viii p., 2 l., 3–309, ₍1₎ p., 1 l. 19¼ᶜᵐ.
"First edition."

1. Theater—U. S. 2. Drama—20th cent.—Hist. & crit. I. Title.

Library of Congress   PN2266.N375   36–27440

——— Copy 2.
Copyright A 99798   ₍5–3₎   792.0973

OrU OrCS WaWW
PU OC1 OC1W OU OO TU NN FTaSU NlC GU IdU WaSp WaS Or
NN 0029263   DLC InU PSt WaU KU MoU MB NcRS NcD PPL

Nathan, George Jean, 1882–*1958*.
The theatre, the drama, the girls ₍by₎ George Jean Nathan. New York, A. A. Knopf, 1921.
361 p. 19¼ᶜᵐ.

1. Drama—Hist. & crit. 2. Theater—U. S. I. Title.

Library of Congress   PN2266.N38   21–877

MB NN OrU GU CoU MtBC Or IdU
NN 0029264   DLC CU-I LU PSt NcD ViU PU OU OC1 OC1W

Nathan, George Jean, 1882–*1958*
*AB9   ... The undersigned announce that they are
M5223   relinquishing the editorship of the Smart
923u   set with the issue for December, 1923 ...
₍New York,1923₎
broadside. 24x15cm.
Dated at head: New York, October 10, 1923.
Signed in facsim. autograph: George Jean
Nathan. ₍and₎ H. L. Mencken.
Announcing also their establishment of a new
magazine, the American Mercury.
Autographed   at head: H. L. Mencken.

NN 0029265   MH

PS3527 Nathan, George Jean, 1882–1958.
.A72   The world in falseface. London, John Lane
W7   the Bodley Head ₍1923?₎
1923   326p. 22cm.

Contents.- Art and criticism.- Theatre and
drama.- Men and women.- The world we live
in.

1. Theater - U.S.   2. Drama - Hist. &
crit. 3. Dramatic criticism.   I. Title.

NN 0029266   PSt MtU NlC

Nathan, George Jean, 1882–*1958*,
The world in falseface ₍by₎ George Jean Nathan. New
York, A. A. Knopf, 1923.
xxix, 326 p. 21ᶜᵐ.
Contents.—Art and criticism.—Theatre and drama.—Men and women.—
The world we live in

1. Theater—U. S. 2. Drama—Hist. & crit. I. Title.

Library of Congress   PS3527.A72W7 1923   23–1117

WaTC
OOxM OU OC1 NN OC1U TU ScU WaU MeB NcD WaSpG WaS
NN 0029267   DLC OrCS ICN NcRS MB NjP PSC PU–F MiU

Nathan, George Jean, 1882–*1958*,
The world in falseface, by George Jean Nathan.   New
York: A. A. Knopf₍, cop. 1923₎. xxix, 326 p. 12°. (The
Borzoi pocket books.)

Contents: Art and criticism. Theatre and drama. Men and women. The world
we live in.

526475A. 1. Drama—Hist. and crit.   2. Criticism. I. Title.
N. Y. P. L.   June 12, 1931

NN 0029268   NN MH

Nathan, George Jean, 1882–*1958*.
The world of George Jean Nathan; selected and edited,
with an introd., by Charles Angoff. ₍1st ed.₎ New York,
Knopf, 1952.
489 p. 22 cm.

I. Title.

PS3527.A72A6 1952   810.81   51—11986 ‡

OrP OrU WaS WaS OrCS OC1W
FMU NNC CoU KEmT OC1 CaBVa Or IdPI IdU MtU OrMonO TU
NN 0029269   DLC WaU CSt MB TxU MsU OCH ViU MiU NlC

Nathan, George Nathan,   comp.
*F129   The Newman collection of photographs of van-
B8N3   ished and vanishing Buffalo: consisting of (a)
photographs of all known early general views of
Buffalo (1811-1853) ... (b) photographs made from
original negatives still existing ... (c) a few
photographs of local interest, having historical
importance. ₍Buffalo₎ 1931.

4 vols. 156plates. 29x21cm.

Each plate accompanied by descriptive guard-
sheet.

NN 0029270   NBuG

Nathan, Gilbert.
Six plays by Gilbert Nathan. London, Minerva publishing
co. ltd. ₍1941₎
4 p. l., 7–233, ₍1₎ p. 22ᶜᵐ.
"First published March 1941."

Contents.—The education of Isidore.—Their finest hour.—The pen
of gold.—A dream and Hitler.—The taming of youth.—The old world
and the new.

I. Title.

Library of Congress   PR6027.A77S5 1941   41–18584

₍4₎   822.91

NN 0029271   DLC CtY

QE269
.G36   Nathan, Hans.
Nr. 1   Geologische Ergebnisse der Erdölbohrungen im Bayer-
ischen Innviertel. München, 1949.
68 p. map, diagrs. 25 cm. (Geologica Bavarica, Nr. 1)
"Schriftenverzeichnis": p. 65–67.

1. Geology — Bavaria — Inn River and Valley. 2. Petroleum —
Bavaria—Inn River and Valley.   (Series)

G S 50–277

U. S. Geol. Survey. Libr.
for Library of Congress   ₍2₎

NN 0029272   DI-GS CoU TxU DLC

Nathan, Hans.
... Geologische untersuchungen im Ries: das gebiet des
blattes Ederheim, von Hans Nathan. Mit einer geologischen
karte 1:25000, 3 tafeln und 2 abbildungen. München, Hrsg.
vom Bayerischen oberbergamt, 1935.
42 p. illus. 3 pl. fold. col. map (in pocket) 24ᶜᵐ. (₍Bavaria₎ Oberbergamt. Geologische landesuntersuchung. Abhandlungen hft. 19)
"Angeführte schriften": p. 41–42.

1. Geology—Bavaria—Ries. 2. Ries, Bavaria. I. Title.

G S 35–156

Library, U. S. Geological   Survey (530.2) Ab hft. 19
₍QE269.B   hft. 19₎

NN 0029273   DI-GS

Nathan, Hans.
Mitteilungen aus der geologischen aufnahme, von Hans
Nathan.
(*In* Bavaria. Oberbergamt. Geologische landesuntersuchung. Ab-
handlungen. München, 1938. 24ᶜᵐ. hft. 29, p. ₍47₎–50 incl. tables)

1. Geology—Bavaria.

G S 38–264

U. S. Geol. survey. Library   (530.2) Ab no. 29
for Library of Congress   ₍QE269.A19B hft. 29₎

NN 0029274   DI-GS

Nathan, Hans.
Quarz mit anhydriteinschlüssen im unterfränkischen Keu-
per, von Hans Nathan; mit 2 tafeln.
(*In* Bavaria. Oberbergamt. Geologische landesuntersuchung. Ab-
handlungen. München, 1935. 24ᶜᵐ. hft. 18, p. ₍41₎–51. 2 pl. (1 fold.))
"Angeführte schriften": p. 51.

1. Quartz. 2. Petrology—Bavaria.

G S 35–138

Library, U. S. Geological   Survey (530.2) Ab hft. 18
Library of Congress   ₍QE269.B hft. 18₎

NN 0029275   DI-GS

Nathan, Hans.
Eine zwischen eiszeitliche mollusken-fauna aus Südbayern,
von Hans Nathan ...
(*In* Bavaria. Bayerisches oberbergamt. Geologische landesuntersuchung. Abhandlungen. München, 1931. 24ᶜᵐ. hft. 3, p. 31–41.
pl. 6–7)
"Angeführte schriften": p. 41.

1. Mollusks, Fossil. 2. Paleontology—Bavaria.

G S 33–126

Library, U. S. Geological   Survey (530.2) Ab hft. 3

NN 0029276   DI-GS

VOLUME 405

of Breslau.

Nathan, Hans. Die arglistige Erschleichung eines Urteils. [Maschinenschrift] viii, 135 S. 4°. — Auszug: Görlitz 1922: Wagenknecht & Endler. 2 Bl. 8°

Breslau. r.- u. staatswiss. Diss. v. 23. Dez. 1922   [U 22. 1169]

NN   0029277   ICRL

1888-

Nathan, Hans. Ueber Mundveränderungen bei Leucaemie. Aus d. Privatkl. f. inn. Krankh. Albu, Berlin. [In Maschinenschrift.] 35 S. 4°(2°). — Auszug: [Berlin] (1920): Blankenfeldt. 4 Bl. 8°.

Berlin, Med. Diss. v. 27. Nov. 1920, Ref. Albu, Williger

[Geb. 21. Okt. 88 Berlin; Wohnort: Lübeck; Staatsangeh.: Preußen; Vorbildung: Marienstifts-G. Stettin bis Prima 07, Erg. Kant-G. Spandau 20; Studium: Berlin 1, München 3, Freiburg 3, Berlin 1 S.; Coll. 27. Nov. 20; Zahnärztl. Approb. 15. März 11.]   [U 20. 1391]

NN   0029278   ICRL

Nathan, Hans, 1910–
The career of a revival hymn. [n. p., 1943?]
89-100 p. music. 23 cm.

"Reprinted from the Southern folklore quarterly, vol. 7, no. 2, June 1943."
Cover title.
Bibliographical footnotes.

1. Old church yard (Tune)   I. Title.

ML3186.N17   783.7   52–49426

NN   0029279   DLC RPB MB PPC

Nathan, Hans, 1910–

Ref
NA863an   Charles Mathews, comedian, and the American negro ... [Jacksonville, Fla., 1946]
191-197p. 23 cm.

Reprinted from The Southern folklore quarterly, v. X, no. 3, September, 1946.

1. Negro minstrelsy. 2. Mathews, Charles 1776-1835.

NN   0029280   RPB

Nathan, Hans, 1910–
The first Negro minstrel band [The Virginia minstrels] and its origins. [n.p., 1952?] 132-144 p. illus. 24cm.

Caption-title.
Repr.: Southern folklore quarterly, v. 16, no. 2, June 1952.
1. Negro minstrels. 2. United States, 19th cent. I. Title: Virginia minstrels.

NN   0029281   NN

Nathan, Hans, 1910–   ed.
... Folk songs of the new Palestine ... edited and annotated by Dr. Hans Nathan; English translations by Harry H. Fein ... [New York] Hechalutz organization and Masada, youth Zionist organization of America [¹1938–39]
6 v. 30½ᶜᵐ.
At head of title: First series.
With piano accompaniment. Words in Hebrew (transliterated) English and Hebrew words on p. [2] of each cover.
Notes on the songs on p. [3] of each cover.
L. C. set imperfect: no. 5 wanting.
CONTENTS.—no. 1. Dances of Palestine: Kuma echa (Rise, O, brethen [!]) arranged by E. W. Sternberg. Banu (We've come) arranged by Aaron Copland.—no. 2. Shepherd songs: Hinne achal'la bachalili (Lo I play upon my flute) arranged by Paul Dessau. Ale giva (Atop a

hill in Galilee) arranged by Paul Dessau.—no. 3. The builders: Bring the bricks (Havu l'venim) arranged by Kurt Weill. Day after day (Gam hayom) arranged by Darius Milhaud.—no. 4. Songs in summer time: Avatinch (A watermelon) arranged by Ernst Toch. Salenu al ktefenu (Our baskets on our shoulders) arranged by Stefan Wolpe. Hashkediya porachat (The almond tree is blooming) arranged by Menashe Rabinovitz. Tel Aviv, arranged by Stefan Wolpe.—no. 5. Guardians of the night: Baa m'nucha (There comes peace unto the weary) arranged by Kurt Weill. Holem tsuadi (My step resounds in the dead of night) arranged by Darius Milhaud and Stefan Wolpe.—no. 6. Children's songs: Mi yivneh (Who will build) arranged by Lazare Saminsky. Tapuach zahav (An orange) arranged by Ernst Toch. Dunam po (A dunam here) arranged by Frederick Jacobi.
1. Folk-songs, Jewish.   I. Fein, Harry H., tr.   II. Hechalutz organization of America.   III. Masada, youth Zionist organiza-
tion of America.   44–27505
[2]
Library of Congress   M1851.N3F6   784.4956[9]

NN   0029283   DLC NN OCH FTaSU

Nathan, Hans, 1910–
Das rezitativ der frühopern Richard Wagners (ein beitrag zur stilistik des opernrezitativs in der ersten hälfte des 19. jahrhunderts) ... von Hans Nathan ... [Berlin, Buchdruckerei H. M. Dobrin & sohn] 1934.
79, [1] p., 1 l. illus. (music) 22½ᶜᵐ.
Inaug.-diss.—Berlin.
Lebenslauf.
"Literatur": p. 79.
CONTENTS.—Die feen.—Die hochzeit.— Das liebesverbot.— Rienzi.— Der fliegende Holländer.

1. Wagner, Richard, 1813–1883.   I. Title.

    35–24539

Library of Congress   ML410.W132N3   782.2

NN   0029284   DLC CtY NIC PU NN

ML3561
.C5N38   Nathan, Hans, 1910–
Two inflation songs of the Civil war, by Hans Nathan. [New York, The Musical quarterly, 1943]
[1], 242-253 p. illus. (music) plate (facsim.) 24 1/2cm.
Relates to Greenbacks by Emmett and to We're coming, Father Abram, by E. Bowers and G. W. Griffin.
Reprint from the Musical quarterly, vol. XXIX, no. 2, April, 1943.

1. Political ballads and songs, American.
2. U. S.—Hist.—Civil war—Songs and music. I. Emmett, Daniel Decatur, 1815–1904. Greenbacks
II. Bowers, E. We're coming, Father Abram.
III. Griffin, G. W. We're coming, Father Abram.
IV. Title. V. Title: Greenbacks. Song.
VI. Title: We're coming, Father Abram. Song.

NN   0029286   RPB PPCS MB

Nathan, Hans, 1910–
Walt Whitman and the Marine band, by Hans Nathan. [n. p., 1943]
cover-title, 47-56 p. 27ᶜᵐ.
Separate from More books; the bulletin of the Boston public library, February, 1943.
Bibliographical references in "Notes" (p. 55)

1. Whitman, Walt, 1819–1892. 2. U. S. Marine band.
    43–8425
Library of Congress   ML1311.M17N2
[2]   788

NN   0029287   DLC PPCS NNC

Nathan, Harry Louis Nathan, *baron.*
Free trade to-day. [London] Gollancz, 1929.
396 p. 19 cm.

1. Tariff—Gt. Brit. 2. Free trade and protection—Free trade.
I. Title.
HF2046.N3   29–27658 rev*

NN   0029288   DLC CU MB NN OC1

Nathan, Harry Louis Nathan, *baron, ed.*
Liberal points of view, with a foreword by the Rt. Hon. D. Lloyd George ... Edited by H. L. Nathan ... and H. Heathcote Williams ... London, E. Benn limited, 1927.
328 p. 22 cm.
CONTENTS.—Introductory note, by Leonard Stein.—What liberalism stands for, by Gilbert Murray.—The production and distribution of wealth, by T. E. Gregory.—Liberal foreign policy, by J. A. Spender.—Unemployment, by W. T. Layton.—Liberalism and the land, by W. McG. Eagar.—Liberalism and political trade unionism, by J. S. Hodgson.—Liberalism and the problem of inheritance, by H. D. Henderson.—Liberalism and industry, by J. M. Keynes.—The free trade movement in Europe, by W. T. Layton.—Liberalism and the Empire, by Ramsay Muir.—The international outlook, by H. W. Harris.—

After the Economic conference at Geneva: a postscript, by W. T. Layton.

1. Liberal party (Gt. Brit.) 2. Gt. Brit.—Pol. & govt.—1910-1936. 3. Gt. Brit.—Econ. condit.—1918-1945. I. Heathcote-Williams, Harold, 1896–   joint ed. II. Title.

JN1129.L45N3   28–13682 rev

NN   0029290   DLC CtY OrU MiU NN MB ScU

Nathan, Harry Louis Nathan, *baron, ed.*
Liberalism and some problems of to-day, edited by H. L. Nathan ... and H. Heathcote Williams ... London, V. Gollancz ltd., 1929.
536 p. 19 cm.
"Companion volume to Liberal points of view, published in ... 1927."—Prefatory note.

CONTENTS.—Prefatory note.—Introduction, by H. L. Nathan.—The Liberal state, by J. S. Hodgson.—Autocracy and democracy in Europe, by Moritz Bonn.—Patriotism and peace, by Sir Herbert Samuel.—The fundamental obstacle to socialism, by Philip Kerr.—The opportunity of liberalism, by J. S. Hodgson.—Imperial policy, by Philip Kerr.—

Safeguarding examined, by Sir John Simon.—The conditions of disarmament, by H. W. Harris.—The problem of disarmament, by Leonard Stein.—The future of the League, by H. W. Harris.—Liberal industrial policy, by E. H. Gilpin.—The Liberal Utopia, by W. T. Layton.—Rates and the householder, by Mrs. S. D. Simon.—Employment and national development, by H. D. Henderson.—Home rule for London, by H. L. Nathan.

1. Liberal party (Gt. Brit.) 2. Gt. Brit.—Pol. & govt.—1910-1936. 3. Gt. Brit.—Econ. condit.—1918-1945. I. Heathcote-Williams, Harold, 1896–   joint ed. II. Title.

JN1129.L45N32   29–28364 rev

NN   0029292   DLC WaS NN MiU DN

Nathan, Helene
Preussens verfassung und verwaltung.
Inaug. Diss. Bern, 1912
Bibl.

NN   0029293   ICRL

Nathan, Helene.
... Preussens verfassung und verwaltung im urteile rheinischer achtundvierziger, von dr. phil. Helene Nathan. Bonn, A. Marcus & E. Weber, 1912.
x, 135 p. 23ᶜᵐ. (Studien zur rheinischen geschichte ... 3. hft.)
Published in part as the author's inaugural dissertation, Bern, 1912.
"Literatur-verzeichnis": p. [vii]-x.

1. Prussia—Pol. & govt.—1815-1870. 2. Prussia—Constitutional history. 3. Rhine Province—Pol. & govt.

    22–21874
Library of Congress   DD491.R41S7 3. hft.

NN   0029294   DLC CaBVaU NcD FU CU CSt OC1 NN PU

NATHAN, Helene.
Sozialismus - demokratie - tagesfragen.
Leipzig, 1919.

At head of title: Deutsche zentralstelle für folketümliches büchereiwesen zu Leipzig.

NN   0029295   MH

Nathan, Helmuth, joint ed.

R727
.3
.S8   Standard, Samuel, *ed.*
Should the patient know the truth? A response of physicians, nurses, clergymen, and lawyers, edited by Samuel Standard and Helmuth Nathan. New York, Springer Pub. Co., 1955.

NN   0029296   [blank]

Nathan, Helmuth, 1901–
Über den zuckergehalt pathologischer körperflüssigkeiten ... Hamburg [1926?]

NN   0029297   MiU

NATHAN, Henry M.
Man's cosmic horizon, by H.M.Nathan; written for those in the second standard of evolution. London: Rider & Co. [1934] 157 p. 19cm.

1. Spiritualism. I. Title.

NN   0029298   NN

Nathan (Hermann). *Ein Fall von Sinusthrombose und Meningitis im Anschluss an eitrige Mittelohrentzündung. 21 pp. 8°. Würzburg, F. Röhrl, 1898.

NN   0029299   DNLM

VOLUME 405

[NATHAN, I.]
The year 1927 from an economical & financial point of
view. Public finance... External commerce... [New York,
1928?] 9, 4, 8, 5 p. 33cm.

Cover-title.
Reproduced from typewritten copy.

1. Economic history—Rumania. I. Title.

NN 0029300   NN

HE   Nathan (I.P.)yCía.
2838   Apuntes de oportunidad hechos sobre el
N386   proyecto relativo al arreglo de la deuda con-
LAC-Z solidada y flotante, a la posibilidad de una
          colonización productiva. Compra de los
          Ferro-carriles del Sur y Champerico a la
          instalación del Puerto de Santo Tomás y con-
          strucción del Ferro-carril del Norte, con
          algunos reflexiones sobre el proyecto Sarg,
          Horn y Peña. Guatemala, Tip. "El Progreso",
          1886.
          17p. 23cm.

NN 0029301   TxU

HE   Nathan (I.P.) y Cía.
2838   Ferro-carril del norte. [Guatemala?
N385   1885?]
LAC-Z 16p. 24cm.

1. Railroads - Guatemala. I. Title.
Sp.: Taracena Flores Collection.

NN 0029302   TxU

Nathan, Isaac, 1792–1864.
Kenney, James, 1780–1849.
The Alcaid, or, The secrets of office, a comic opera, in
three acts, by James Kenney ... Printed from the acting
copy, with remarks, biographical and critical, by D.—G.
... As performed at the Theatres Royal ... London,
G. H. Davidson [n. d.]

Nathan, I[saac] 1792–1864.
An essay on the history and theory of music; and on
the qualities, capabilities and management of the human
voice. By I. Nathan ... London, Printed for G. and
W. B. Whittaker, 1823.
3 p. l., [vi]–xiv, [2], 230 p. illus. 31½ x 24½ᶜᵐ.

1. Music, Influence of. 2. Singing and voice culture.

Library of Congress   ML60.N25   6–8962†

NN 0029304   DLC CtY MdBP PP NIC OCH OO PPL

W.C.L.Nathan, Isaac, 1792–1864.
M780.88
E58VB   The fair Haidee; a translation of a Romaic
no.26 song by Lord Byron. The music by I. Nathan.
          London, Falkner's Opera music warehouse [181–]
          5 p. 35 cm.
          For voice and piano.
          "From the poems subjoined to Childe Harold's
          Pilgrimage"
          Autographed copy.
          [No. 26] in a vol. with binder's title:
          Vocal music. English imprints.

1. Songs (Medium voice) with piano. 2.
Byron, George Gordon Noël Byron, baron. Mus-
ical settings. I. Byron, George Gordon Noël
Byron, 6th baron, 1788–1824. II. Title.

NN 0029306   NcD NN

Nathan, Isaac, 1792–1864.
Byron, George Gordon Noël Byron, *6th baron*, 1788–1824.
Fugitive pieces and reminiscences of Lord Byron: containing an entire new edition of the Hebrew melodies, with the addition of several never before published; the whole illustrated
with critical, historical, theatrical, political, and theological remarks, notes, anecdotes, interesting conversations, and observations, made by that illustrious poet: together with His Lordship's autograph; also some original poetry, letters and recollections of Lady Caroline Lamb. By I. Nathan ... London,
Whittaker, Treacher, and co., 1829.

Nathan, Isaac, 1792–1864.
Kenney, James, 1780–1849.
The illustrious stranger; or, Married and buried: an
operatic farce, in two acts, by James Kenney ... Printed
from the acting copy, with remarks, biographical and
critical, by D.—G. ... As performed at the Theatres
Royal ... London, Davidson [n. d.]

Nathan, [Isaac], 1792–1864.
The king's fool; or, The old man's curse
see under Millingen, J[ohn] G[ideon],
1782–1862.

W.C.L.Nathan, Isaac, 1792–1864
M780.88
E58VB   The kiss, dear maid, thy lip has left. The
no.27 poetry by Lord Byron. The music composed with
          an accompaniment for the piano forte by I. Na-
          than. London [ca. 1816]
          7 p. 35 cm.
          For voice and piano.
          Autographed copy.
          [No. 27] in a vol. with binder's title:
          Vocal music. English imprints.

1. Songs (High voice) with piano. 2. Byron,
George Gordon Noël Byron, baron Musical settings.
I. Byron, George Gordon Noël Byron, 6th baron,
1788–1824. II. Title.

NN 0029311   NcD

. Nathan, Isaac, 1792–1864.
Long live our monarch, a new national air, for voice and chorus,
with full orchestra accompaniments, poetry by H. W. Montagu...
Composed...by I. Nathan... London: Published for Mr.
Nathan and may be had of A. Lee [etc., 183–] Publ. pl. no. 107.
5 p. 36cm.

Full score: solo voice, S.A.T.B., orchestra and piano.
Arrangement for voice and piano, p. 5.
Composed in honor of King William IV.

1. Songs, with orchestra.   2. Songs. English. 3. National
music—Gt. Br.—England. I. Montagu,   H. W. Long live our monarch.
N. Y. P. L.   September 9, 1937

NN 0029312   NN

Nathan, Isaac, 1792–1864.
Memoirs of Madame Malibran de Beriot. By I. Nathan
... 2d ed. London, J. Thomas [etc.] 1836.
2 p. l., 72 p. 17ᶜᵐ.

1. Malibran, Mme. Maria Felicità (Garcia) afterwards De Bériot, 1808–
1836.
                                                                            1–5469
Library of Congress   ML420.M2N2

NN 0029313   DLC MB

Nathan, Isaac, 1792–1864.
Memoirs of Madame Malibran de Beriot. By I. Nathan
... 3d ed. London, J. Thomas [etc.] 1836.
[2] p. l., 72 p. front. (port.) 18ᶜᵐ.

1. Malibran, Mme. Maria Felicità (Garcia) afterwards De Bériot, 1808–
1836.
                                                                          10–18292
Library of Congress   ML420.M2N21

NN 0029314   DLC

Nathan, Isaac, 1792–1864.
[Miscellaneous songs by I. Nathan, words by
Lord Byron and others. 35 nos.]
In   34cm. [Bound with his Selection of Hebrew
B996   melodies ... [London]I.Nathan[1815]]
+G815 Autograph of I. Nathan on most numbers.

1.Songs, English. I.Byron, George Gordon
Noël Byron, 6th baron, 1788–1824.

NN 0029315   CtY

Nathan, Isaac] 1792–1864.
Music of the Hindus. (In: Saurīndramohana
Thākura. Hindu music from various authors ...
Calcutta, 1875. 8°. pt. 1, p. 229–232)
Repr.: "Musurgia Vocalis".

NN 0029316   NN

Nathan, Isaac, 1792–1864.
Musurgia vocalis, an essay on the history and theory of music,
and on the qualities, capabilities, and management of the human voice. 2d ed., enl. and considerably improved. By I.
Nathan ... London, Fentum, 1836.
2 p. l., vii, [1], xi, 353 p. 31 x 24½ᶜᵐ.

1. Music—Hist. & crit. 2. Voice.
                                                                            9–31526
Library of Congress   ML160.N27 1836

NN 0029317   DLC CtY WaU NNUT OCl PPL NN OCH

W.C.L.Nathan, Isaac, 1792–1864.
M780.88
E58VB   My life, I love you. Written by Lord By-
no.25 ron. The music composed by I. Nathan. London,
          H. Falkner's Opera music warenouse [181–]
          7 p. 35 cm.
          For voice and piano.
          "From the poems subjoined to Lord Byron's
          Childe Harold's pilgrimage"
          Autographed copy.
          [No. 25] in a vol. with binder's title:
          Vocal music. English   imprints.

NN 0029318   NcD

W.C.L. Nathan, Isaac, 1792–1864.
M780.88
E58C   My life, I love you; written by Lord
no.54 Byron. London, Published & sold by Mr Nathan,
          no. 7, Poland St., Oxford St. [ca. 1819]
          7 p. 33 cm.
          For voice and piano.
          [No. 54] in a vol. with binder's title:
          Music.
          1. Songs (High voice) with piano. 2. Byron,
George Gordon Noël Byron, 6th baron. Musical
settings. 3. Byron, George Gordon Noël Byron,
6th baron. Childe Harold's pilgrimage. I.
Byron, George   Gordon Noël Byron, 6th
baron, 1788–1824.   II. Title.

NN 0029319   NcD

W.C.L.Nathan, Isaac, 1792–1864.
M780.88
E58VB   Night wanes. The words from the celebra-
no.23 ted poem of Sara, written by Lord Byron. The
          music composed & arr. for the piano forte by
          I. Nathan. [London] Falkner's Opera music
          warehouse [181–]
          6 p. 35 cm.
          For voice and piano.
          Autographed copy.
          [No. 23] in a vol. with binder's title:
          Vocal music. English imprints.

1. Songs (Medium voice) with piano. 2.
Byron, George Gordon Noël Byron, baron. Mus-
ical settings. I. Byron, George Gordon Noël
Byron, 6th baron, 1788–1824. II. Title.

NN 0029321   NcD

VOLUME 405

Nathan, Isaac, 1792-1864, ed.
    Sammlung hebräischer Original-Melodien mit
unterlegten Gesängen von Lord G.G. Byron und
deren Übersetzung .. [von A.] Kretzschmer.
[no. 1] Berlin, Magazin f. Kunst, Geographie
u. Musik [182-?]
    1 v.   f.
    Joint editor: John Braham.

NN 0029322   OCH

Nathan, Isaac, 1792-1864.   (English)

    A selection of ancient & modern Hebrew melodies, the poetry
written expressly for the work, by Lord Byron, the music newly
arranged, harmonised & revised by I. Nathan...   London, C.
Lonsdale (late Birchall & co.) [ca. 1840]   Publ. pl. no. 2567.
218 p.   35cm.

For 1 to 4 voices with piano accompaniment. English words.
First edition (1815) compiled and arranged by John Braham and Isaac Nathan.

204242A. 1. Songs, English. 2. Vocal duos, Secular — Women — Keyboard acc.
3. Vocal trios, Secular—Mixed—Keyboard acc. 4. Vocal quartets, Secular—Mixed
—Keyboard acc. 5. Vocal quintets,   Secular—Mixed—Keyboard acc.
I. Nathan, Isaac, 1792-1864.   II. Byron, George Gordon
Byron, 6th baron, 1788-1824. Hebrew   melodies. III. Title: Hebrew
melodies.   *Card revised*
N.Y.L.   *June 21, 1944*

NN 0029324   NN

In   Nathan, Isaac, 1792-1864.
B996   [A selection of Hebrew melodies, ancient and
+G815   modern, with appropriate symphonies & accompani-
cop.1   ments. By I: Braham & I: Nathan, the poetry
           written expressly for the work by the Right
           Honble Lord Byron ... [London]Published & sold
           by I: Nathan[1815]]
              2v.in l. 34m.
              Paged continuously.
              "Braham suggested that he should aid in their
           arrangement, and sing them in public ... But

              ... [his] engagements did not allow him to
           share actively in the undertaking and in later
           editions his name was withdrawn", D.N.B.,v.14,
           p.122.
              T.-p. of 1st.no. and back cover containing
           advertisement wanting.
              Vocal score with accompaniment.

In   -- -- Another copy(?) of 1st.no. 34cm.
B996   Has t.-p. and advertising page.
+G815   Autographs of J.Braham and I.Nathan on t.-p.
cop.2

In   -- --- Variant of 1st.no. 36cm.
B996   Stanzas on p.40 numbered as I,II,II; adv. as
+G815b   in the above.
           Autographs of   J.Braham and I.Nathan on
           t.-p.

In   -- --- Variant of 1st.no. 36cm.
B996   Stanzas on p.40 numbered I,II,II; advertise-
+G815bb   ment has added line "And of H.Falconer, Opera
           Music Warehouse, 3, Old Bond Street."
              Autographs of J.Braham and I.Nathan on t.-p.

NN 0029328   CtY ICN InU MH NN PPL PPULC

FILM   [Nathan, Isaac, 1792-1864]
M784.3   [Songs. Selections]
B732s   A selection of Hebrew melodies, ancient and
           modern, with appropriate symphonies & accompani-
           ments by I. Braham & I. Nathan, the poetry
           written expressly for the work by Lord Byron.
           [London] I. Nathan [1815]
              Microfilm copy (positive) made in 1961 by The
           New York Public Library.
              Collation of original as determined from the
           film: 2v.(133p.)

              Vol.2 without special t.-p.
              "From the favourite airs — sung in the reli-
           gious ceremonies of the Jews."
              For voice and piano; v.1 with harmonization of
           3 of the airs for four voices; v.2 with harmoni-
           zation of 4 for 2-3 voices.
              Words printed also as text.

NN 0029330   IU

M   Nathan, Isaac, 1792-1864.
1768   A selection of Hebrew melodies, ancient
F31++   & modern, with appropriate symphonies and
          accompaniments by I. Braham and I. Nathan.
          The poetry written expressly for the work
          the right honorable Lord Byron. 2d number.
          [London, 1816?]
             65-133 p. 36cm.

             For 1-3 voices with piano acc.
             Bound with Feldborg, A.A. Danish and

          Norwegian melodies.   London [1815]

             1. Folk music, Jewish. I. Byron, George
          Gordon Noël Byron, 6th baron, 1788-1824.
          Hebrew melodies. II. Braham, John, 1777-1856
          III. Title: He   brew melodies.

NN 0029332   NIC

Nathan, Isaac, 1792-1864.
    A selection of Hebrew melodies, ancient and
modern. Newly arranged, harmonized, corrected and
revised, with appropriate symphonies & accompaniments, by I. Nathan. The poetry written expressly
for the work by Lord Byron.   [London] J. Fentum
[ca.1825]   Pl.no.102-103.   2 v. in 1 (124 p.)
30cm.

    Electrostatic reproduction.
    Nos. 1-2.
    For 1-4 voices and piano.
    First ed. (1815) compiled and arranged by John
Braham and Isaac Nathan.
    1. Songs, English. I. Byron, George Gordon Noël
Byron, baron, 1788-1824. Hebrew melodies. II. Nathan,
Isaac, 1792-1864.   III. Title: Hebrew
melodies.

NN 0029334   NN

Nathan, Isaac, 1792-1864.
    A selection of Hebrew melodies ancient and
modern, newly arranged, harmonized, corrected
and revised with appropriate symphonies &
accompaniments by I.Nathan, the poetry written
expressly for the work by Lord Byron ... [Lon-
don]Published for the proprietor [by J.Fentum,
J.and C.Adlard,printers,1829(?)]
    4v. 34½cm.
    Paged continuously.
    Explanatory notes illustrative of Byron's

character differ from those in edition printed
by T.Davison.
    The melodies are mainly a selection from the
favorite airs sung in the religious ceremonies
of the Jews.
    Vocal score with accompaniment.
    First edition, published in 1815 stated music

was newly arranged, etc. by I.Nathan and J.
Braham. In later editions Braham's name was
withdrawn.

NN 0029337   CtY

In   Nathan, Isaac, 1792-1864.
B996   A selection of Hebrew melodies, ancient and
+G815d   modern, newly arranged, harmonized, corrected
           and revised with appropriate symphonies &
           accompaniments by I.Nathan, the poetry expresaly
           for the work by Lord Byron ... 1st.no. [London]
           Published for the proprietor [by J.Fentum,
           Printed by R.Davison,1829(?)]
              4p.l.,66p. 38cm.
              P.39-40 and 37-38 misplaced,39-40 preceding
           37-38 in this copy.

              Explanatory notes illustrative of Byron's
           character differ from those in edition printed
           by J. and C.Adlard.
              Vocal score with accompaniment.

NN 0029339   CtY MH OCl

Nathan, Isaac, 1792-1864.
    A selection of Hebrew melodies
for libretti see Byron, George Gordon
Noël Byron, 6th baron, 1788-1824.
Hebrew melodies.

Nathan, Isaac, *1792-1864.*
    The Southern Euphrosyne and Australian
Miscellany, containing Oriental moral tales,
original anecdote, poetry, and music, an
historical sketch, with examples of the native
Aboriginal melodies, put into modern rhythm,
and harmonized as solos, quartettes, etc.,
together with several other original vocal
pieces, arranged to a piano-forte accompaniment
by the editor and sole proprietor, I. Nathan,
author of "The Hebrew Melodies," "The Musurgia
Vocalis", The   successful music in

"Sweethearts and Wives", "The Illustrious
Stranger", "The King's Fool", etc. London
and Sydney,Whittaker[1848?]
    viii,168p.

    Microfilm (negative). London, British
Museum Photographic Service[1968?]
    1 reel.

NN 0029342   MJ

W.C.L.   Nathan, Isaac, 1792-1864.
M780.88   Thou art not false, but thou art fickle.
E58VB   The poetry by Lord Byron. The music composed
no.22   with an accompt. for the piano forte by I.
          Nathan. London [ca. 1816]
             6 p. 35 cm.
             For voice and piano.
             Autographed copy.
             [No. 22] in a vol. with binder's title:
          Vocal music. English imprints.

             1. Songs (Medium voice) with piano. 2.
          Byron, George Gordon Noël Byron, baron. Musi-
          cal settings. I. Byron, George Gordon Noël
          Byron, 6th baron, 1788-1824. II. Title.

NN 0029344   NcD

Nathan, Isaac, 1792-1864.
    [Why are you wandering here, I pray?]

    Why wandering here? New York, B. W. Hitchcock,
[1869.
    [3] p. 27 cm.   (Hitchcock's half dime series of music for the
million, no. 51)
    First line of text: Why are you wandering here, I pray?
    For voice and piano.

    1. Songs (Medium voice) with piano. I. Title: Why are you
wandering here, I pray?

    M1621.N   M 54–142

NN 0029345   DLC

Nathan, Isaac ben Kalonymos
    see Isaac Nathan ben Kalonymus,
fl. 1450.

Nathan, Isaac Mardochai,

        see

Isaac Nathan ben Kalonymus, fl. 1450.

Nathan, Jack.
    A workbook for first- and second- year pupils
in an industrial arts high school course in
printing... [Cincinnati, 1944]
    v.p.

NN 0029348   OCU

Nathan, Jacques.
    Citations, références et allusions de Proust dans A la re-
cherche du temps perdu. Paris, Nizet, 1953.
    114 p. 20 cm.

    1. Proust, Marcel, 1871-1922. A la recherche du tempa perdu.
                                                 A 54–438

    Illinois. Univ. Library
    for Library of Congress   [3]

    DLC PSt OCl MoSU CSt
NN 0029349   IU LU ViU NN ICU PHC OCU NcU PU CtY

VOLUME 405

Nathan, Jacques.
  Encyclopédie de la littérature française. Paris, F. Nathan
[1952]
    303 p. illus., plates (part col.) ports. (part col.) maps, facsims.
35 cm.

  1. French literature—Hist. & crit.   I. Title.

PQ116.N3   840.9   53—2176

NN 0029350   NN IU CU TU C LU ScU MsSM OCU RPB NcU PPD
               DLC OO TxU MB OClW OU OCl NcD PIm ViU

Nathan, Jacques.
  Histoire de la littérature contemporaine. Paris, F. Nathan
[1954]
    322 p. 19 cm. (L'Activité contemporaine)
    Bibliography : p. 315-318.

  1. French literature—20th cent.—Hist. & crit.

                                            A 55—6766
Rochester. Univ. Libr.   PQ305
for Library of Congress   [2]

NN 0029351   OO OU MiU PHC ScU ViU GU KMK CLU WaU MiDW WaWW LN
               CLSU CU NNC CtY MH NIC VtMiM InU RPB NN IU TxU OCU
               NRU CaBVaU OrStbM OrU OrPS IdPI PU NcD

840.9   Nathan, Jacques.
N195l   La littérature et les écrivains: la litté-
1953   rature française.   Paris, F. Nathan [1953]
          159p. 22cm. (Collection. Petite his-
        toire de l'art et des artistes)

          1. French litera-   ture. Hist. & crit.

NN 0029352   KU OCl IaU CU ViU MH CLSU IEN IU

Nathan, Jacques, ed.
  Lorenzaccio; drame

  see under

  Musset, Alfred de, 1810-1857.

Nathan, Jacques.
  La morale de Proust. Paris, Nizet [1953]
    330 p. 19 cm.
    Bibliography : p. [315]-319.

  1. Proust, Marcel, 1871-1922.   I. Title.

                                            A 54—279
Michigan. Univ. Libr.
for Library of Congress   [54c2]

NN 0029354   IEdS CaBVaU OrU
               ICU NcD CtY CU IaU NcU IdPI PPT TU CU-I ViU MU NBC
               MiU MH TxU CSt MoSU DLC OU OCU PSt NN

Nathan, Jacques.
  Poeti e prosatori di Francia.   Novara,
Istituto geografico de Agostini [1955]
    303 p.   illus. (part col.) ports. (part col.)
maps, facsims. 34 cm.
    Translation of Encyclopédie de la littérature
française.
    1. French literature - History and criticism.

NN 0029355   OU

Nathan, Jacques, ed.
                  classicist,

Plautus, Titus Maccius.
  La marmite (Aulularia) de Plaute, présentée par Jacques
Nathan ... [Paris] Hachette [*1938]

Nathan, Jacques, classicist, ed.
Tacitus, Cornelius.
  Tibère de Tacite, présenté par Jacques Nathan ... [Paris]
Hachette [*1937]

Nathan, Jacques, of Sophia
  see Natan, Zhak.

Nathan, James

  see

Gotendorf, James, 1811-1888.

[Nathan, Jean Paul]
  ... Un éclaireur au maquis; illustrations de Cécile Reims,
couverture De Georgy ... Paris, Éditions du Chant nouveau
[1946]
    63, [1] p. 19ᵐᵐ. (Collection E. I. F.)
    Author's pseud., Jean-Paul, at head of title.
    "Ce roman a paru en feuilleton dans les numéros 11, 12, 13, 14, 15,
16-17 de l'E. I. F. sous la signature d'Olivier Nollet."
    1. World war, 1939-1945—Fiction.   I. Title.
    PQ2627.A82E3   47—21490

NN 0029360   DLC

Nathan, Joe.
  For his mother's sake. Words by Frank Adams. Music by Joe
Nathan.   New York, American advance music co., c1904.

    First line: It was roll-call, and was just before the battle.
    As sung by Miss Mary Conwell.
    Portrait of Mary Conwell on t.-p.

    1. Mother. 2. Conwell, Mary—   Port. I. Adams, Frank. II. Song
index (2).   May 31, 1949
N.Y.P.L.

NN 0029361   NN

Nathan, Joe.
  Lily Dale. Words by John J. Nestor. Music by Joe Nathan.
New York, American advance music co., c1904.

    First line: By a cottage where the pretty blushing roses scent the air.
    As sung by Miss Charlotte Dandridge.
    Portrait of Charlotte Dandridge on t.-p.

    1. Separation. 2. Lily. 3. Dand-   ridge, Charlotte—Port. I. Nestor,
John J. II. Song index (2).   May 26, 1949
N.Y.P.L.

NN 0029362   NN

BS   Nathan, Joel.
1227   Vocabularium zum Pentateuch תורה nebst
N3x   Biegungs-Tabellen der hebräischen Substantiva
1860   und Verba, bearb. von Joel Nathan. Vermehrt
        und verbessert von Dr. Meisel. 5. Aufl.
        Berlin, W. Adolf, 1860.
          155 p. 19 cm.

          1. Bible. O.T. Pentateuch - Study. 2. He-
        brew language - Dictionaries - German.

NN 0029363   PPT

Nathan, Joel.
  Vocabularium zum Pentateuch תורה nebst
Biegungs-Tabellen der hebräischen Substantiva
und Verba. Bearbeitet von Joel Nathan ... Durchgesehen von Dr. Meisel ... 7. vermehrte und
verbesserte Auflage.   Berlin, 1869.
    19 cm.

NN 0029364   CtY

NATHAN, Joel.
  Vokabularium zum Pentateuch...Durch-
gesehen von Dr. Meisel. 12. Auflage.
Frankfurt a. M., J. Kauffmann, 1898.
    174p 19cm.
    1.Hebrew Text Book. 2.Hebrew Grammar.

NN 0029365   NNJ

Nathan, Johann.
  Die musik im öffentlichen Gottesdienst. Vortrag gehalten im gemeindehause zu Hamburg-Eilbeck
... 1910... Hamburg, Vogel, n.d.
    24p.

NN 0029366   PPLT

Nathan, John.
  Works by this author printed in America before 1801 are available
in this library in the Readex Microprint edition of Early American
Imprints published by the American Antiquarian Society.
  This collection is arranged according to the numbers in Charles
Evans' American Bibliography.

NN 0029367   DLC

Nathan, Joseph.
  Die Influenza in ihren Beziehungen zum
Gehörorgan.   Bingen, 1897.
    29 p. 8°.
    Inaug.-diss. - Wuerzburg.
    Bibl.

NN 0029368   ICRL DNLM

Nathan, Joseph Arnold.
  Equity through the cases. 2d ed., by O. R. Marshall.
London, Stevens, 1951.
    lx, 528 p. 22 cm.
  ——————Supplement. London, Stevens, 1953.
    [46] p. 22 cm.

    1. Trusts and trustees—Gt. Brit.—Cases.   I. Title.

                347.8   51—4645 rev

NN 0029369   DLC CU CaBVaU

Nathan, Joseph Arnold.
  Equity through the cases. 3d ed. by O. R. Marshall. London, Stevens, 1955.
    584 p. 23 cm.

    1. Trusts and trustees—Gt. Brit.—Cases.   I. Title.

                347.8   58—25025 ‡

NN 0029370   DLC CaBVaU ICU CU OU

Nathan, Joseph Arnold.
  Equity through the cases and judicial exposition, by Joseph
Arnold Nathan ... London, Stevens & sons, limited, 1939.
    lv, 458 p. 22½ᵐ.

    1. Equity—Gt. Brit.—Cases. 2. Trusts and trustees—Gt. Brit.
I. Title.

                                            40—351

NN 0029371   DLC CtY WaU-L CaBVaU MH-L ViU-L MH

Nathan, Julius. Die imaginaeren begriffe.
    16 pp. (Zeits. f. philos. v. 83, 1883, p. 70.)—Grundbegriffe
der moral. 14 pp. (Zeits. f. philos. v. 86, 1885, p. 1.)

NN 0029372   MdBP

VOLUME 405

Nathan, Julius.
Kants logische ansichten und leistungen. ... Jena, A. Neuenhahn, 1878.
133, (1) p. 22½ᶜᵐ.

Inaug.-diss.—Jena.
"Quellen-verzeichnis": p. (184) Bibliographical footnotes.

1. Kant, Immanuel, 1724-1804.

NN   0029373   MiU CU NjP ICRL

Nathan, Julius, ed.
of Hamburg,
Hamburgische gerichts-zeitung. Herausgegeben von mehreren hamburgischen juristen. Begründet und redigirt von dr. Julius Nathan. 1.–7. jahrg., 8. jahrg., no. 1–17; 13. apr. 1861–25. apr. 1868. Hamburg, O. Meissner, 1861–68.

Nathan, Julius Ernest.
The census of British Malaya ... 1921
    see under   Malay States, Federated.
Census Office.

Nathan, Julius Ernest.
... Johol, Inas, Ulu Muar, Jempul, Gunong, Pasir and Terachi. Their history and constitution. By J.E.Nathan and R.O.Winstedt ... Calcutta,Published for the Committee for Malay studies, Federated Malay States, and printed at the Baptist mission press,1920.
2p.ℓ.,90p.incl.tables. 26½cm. (Papers on Malay subjects ⟨second series⟩ [no.3])

NN   0029376   CtY ICU OC1 CU NIC ICF MH

Nathan, Julius Ernest.
Johol, Inas, Ulu Muar, Jempul, Gunong, Pasir and Terachi; their history and constitution, by J. E. Nathan and R. O. Winstedt. Kuala Lumpur, Reprinted at the Federated Malay States Govt. Press, 1941.
89 p. 25 cm. (Papers on Malay subjects, 2d ser.)

1. Malay Peninsula—Hist.   I. Winstedt, Sir Richard Olof, 1878– joint author. II. Title.   (Series)

DS596.N3   959.5   50–41904

NN   0029377   DLC

Nathan, Keleph ben, pseud.
    see   Dutoit-Membrini, Jean Philippe, 1721-1793.

Nathan, Kurt, 1909–
Der deutsche Schiffahrtskampf von 1913; das Hapag/Lloyd-Problem vor dem Weltkrieg. Ein Beitrag zur Frage der deutschen Grosschiffahrtsorganisation...von Kurt Nathan... Kiel, 1935.
vii, 94 p. 22½cm.

Inaugural-Dissertation — Kiel, 1935.
Lebenslauf.
"Literaturverzeichnis," p. vi.

871114A. 1. Shipping—Germany,   1913. 2. North German Lloyd
Steamship Company, Bremen. 3. Ham-   burg-American Line.
N. Y. P. L.   March 18, 1937

NN   0029379   NN CtY ICRL

NATHAN, L.
Improvements in the production of beer; an address before the Master Brewers Association of America, in New York, on May 11, 1933, by Dr. L. Nathan. [New York, 1933] 15 p. illus. 22½cm.

752804A. 1. Brewing.

NN   0029380   NN NNC

Nathan, Lawrence.
Car driving in two weeks and hints for all motorists. Kingswood, Surrey, A. G. Elliot (1952)
139 p. illus. 19 cm. (Right way books)

1. Automobile drivers.   I. Title.

TL152.N25   629.28   52–64204 ‡

NN   0029381   DLC

Nathan, Leonard, 1915–
A wind like a bugle. New York, Macmillan, 1954.
282 p. 22 cm.

1. Underground railroad—Fiction.   I. Title.

PZ4.N275Wi   54–9963 ‡

NN   0029382   DLC TxU WaE OrSaW OU NN NcD

Nathan, Leopold.
Die juristische Konstruktion des Verlöbnisses nach dem Bürgerlichen Gesetzbuch. Berlin, 1902.
10+89+(3) p.
Inaug.-diss. - Rostock.

NN   0029383   MH-L

Nathan, Mrs. Lola Marie Thérèse (Granville Baker)
    see   Granville Baker, Lola Marie Thérèse, 1906–

NATHAN,Lynd.
Venzgyllyn,the revelation of a soul;[an heroic comedy]. Prologue and part I. Oxford,B.Blackwell,1930.

1.8°. pp. (6),51.
"250 copies."

NN   0029385   MH

Nathan, Manfred, 1875–
The common law of South Africa. A treatise based on Voet's Commentaries on the Pandects, with references to the leading Roman-Dutch authorities, South African decisions, and statutory enactments in South Africa. By Manfred Nathan ... Grahamstown, Cape Colony, African book company limited; (etc., etc.) 1904-07.
4 v. 25½ᵐ.

1. Law—Africa, South. 2. Roman-Dutch law—Africa, South. I. Voet, Joannes, 1647-1713. Commentarius ad Pandectas. II. Title.

4–31567

NN   0029386   DLC IU NNC-L PU-L PPB OO CtY

293gf   **Nathan, Manfred,** 1875–
S7   The common law of South Africa. A treatise
N275   based on Voet's Commentaries on the Pandects,
1913   with references to the leading Roman-Dutch
Law   authorities, South African decisions, and
Library   statutory enactments in South Africa. 2d ed.
        (Johannesburg) South Africa, Central News
        Agency, 1913.
        v.

NN   0029387   CU PU-L MH

Law   **Nathan, Manfred,** 1875–   comp.

Transvaal (*Colony*) *Laws, statutes, etc.*
The company and commercial laws of the Transvaal, with explanatory notes and index, compiled by Manfred Nathan. Johannesburg, Transvaal Leader, 1905.

Law   **Nathan, Manfred,** 1875–   FOR OTHER EDITIONS SEE MAIN ENTRY

South Africa. *Laws, statutes, etc.*
The company law of South Africa, containing the Union companies act (Act no. 46, 1926) as amended by acts nos. 11 of 1932, 64 of 1934, 49 of 1935, 36 of 1937, 23 of 1939, 29 of 1939 and 33 of 1939. And including the amended rules, forms, and precedents, together with full commentary, by Manfred Nathan, assisted by C. J. M. Nathan. 3d ed. Johannesburg, Hortors, 1939.

Nathan, Manfred, 1875–
Concise guide to South African company law and practice, by Manfred Nathan ... Johannesburg, Hortors limited, 1940.
3 p. l., 177 p. 25ᶜᵐ.
Revised by the author's son. cf. Pref.

1. Corporation law—Africa, South. 2. Stock companies—Africa, South. I. Nathan, C. J. M., ed.

41–1416

NN   0029390   DLC

Nathan, Manfred, 1875–
Contracts, deeds and forms; precedents and forms for contracts, and company, conveyancing, notarial, and general legal practice, with tables of fees and stamp duties, compiled and edited by Manfred Nathan ... New ed. Johannesburg, Hortors, limited, 1941.
2 p. l., (iii)–vi, 534 p. 25ᶜᵐ.
Correction slips inserted.

1. Forms (Law)—Africa, South. 2. Legal documents—Africa, South.

43–9452

NN   0029391   DLC

Nathan, Manfred, 1875–
The diamond laws of South Africa; being the statute laws relating to mining and trade in precious stones, collated and ed. with explanations, by Manfred Nathan ... Johannesburg, The Central news agency, limited, 1920.
154 p. 25ᶜᵐ.

1. Mining law—Africa, South. 2. Diamond mines and mining—Africa, South. I. Title.

Library of Congress   TN248.N3   22–6147

NN   0029392   DLC

Nathan, Manfred, 1875–
Dominion status. By Manfred Nathan ...
(*In* Grotius society. Problems of the war ... London, 1916-19 22ᶜᵐ. v. 8, 1923, p. 117-132)

1. Gt. Brit.—Colonies. 2. Imperial federation. I. Title.

A 23—1053

Carnegie endow. Int. peace.   Library   JX1302.G7   vol. 8
———— Copy 2.
for Library of Congress   (a41c1)

NN   0029393   NNCE MiU WaU-L

Nathan, Manfred, 1875–
Empire government; an outline of the system prevailing in the British commonwealth of nations, by Manfred Nathan ... London, G. Allen & Unwin ltd. (1928)
3 p. l., (9)–10 p., 2 l., (13)–256 p. 22ᶜᵐ.

1. Gt. Brit.—Pol. & govt.—1910–   2. Gt. Brit.—Colonies—Administration. 3. Imperial federation. I. Title. II. Title: British commonwealth of nations.

Library of Congress   JN231.N27   28–21131

     PPT OC1W OC1 OO NN
NN   0029394   DLC NcD CaBVaU CaBVa OrSaW Or TxU PSC

VOLUME 405

Nathan, Manfred, 1875–
Empire government; an outline of the system prevailing in the British commonwealth of nations, by Manfred Nathan ... Cambridge, Harvard university press, 1929.

3 p. l., ₉9₎–10 p., 2 l., ₍13₎–256 p. 22ᶜᵐ.
Printed in Great Britain.

1. Gt. Brit.—Pol. & govt.—1910–1936. 2. Gt. Brit.—Colonies—Administration. 3. Imperial federation. I. Title. II. Title: British commonwealth of nations.

Library of Congress   JN231.N27 1929   31—20976
                           ₍a37c1₎   354.4201

NN   0029395   DLC WaWW Or MtU UU ICN MH CtY NjN

JN231
N27   Nathan, Manfred, 1875–
1930   Empire government; an outline of the system
           prevailing in the British Commonwealth of
           Nations. Cambridge, Harvard University Press,
           1930.
             256 p. 22cm.

1. Gt. Brit. - Politics and government -
1910-1936. 2. Gt. Brit. - Colonies - Administration. 3. Imperial federation. I. Title.
II. Title: British Commonwealth of Nations.

    ViU OrSaW
NN   0029396   GU WaTC IdU OOxM OClW ODW OU OCU PV

Nathan, Manfred, 1875–
Die epos van Trichardt en van Rensburg, deur Manfred Nathan ... Pretoria, J. L. van Schaik, bepk., 1938.

68 p. 2 pl. on 1 l. 19 x 16ᶜᵐ. (Monument-reeks. ₍No. 7/8₎)

1. Trigardt, Louis, 1783–1838. 2. Rensburg, Johannes Hendrik Janse van, d. 1836. I. Title.

Library of Congress   DT844.2.T67N3   42–8024

NN   0029397   DLC CLU

Nathan, Manfred, 1875–
The finance and revenue laws of the Union of South Africa, by Manfred Nathan ... Durban, Butterworth & co. (Africa) ltd., 1936.

xxiv p., 1 l., 469, 56 p. 25ᶜᵐ.
————— Supplement, bringing the work up to December 31st, 1937. Durban, Butterworth & co. (Africa), ltd., 1938.

39 p. 24½ᶜᵐ.

1. Finance—Africa, South—Law. 2. Revenue—Africa, South. I. Title.

                              37–18982 Revised

NN   0029398   DLC

Nathan, Manfred, 1875–
Gold and base metals laws, being Transvaal
act no. 35, 1908 (Gold law), with amending
statutes the Orange Free State metals mining
act, 1936, the Base minerals amendment act,
1942 and the Natural oil act, 1942, by Manfred
Nathan. 6th ed. Johannesburg, Hortors, 1944.
  xviii, 335 p.

Earlier eds. have title: Transvaal gold
and base metals law.
  1. Gold mines and   mining - Transvaal. 2.
Mining law - Trans-   vaal.

NN   0029399   NNC

Nathan, Manfred, 1875–
Hire-purchase; being the Hire-purchase act, no. 36 of 1942, with full commentary and a statement of the general law, including the Civil imprisonment restriction act, and references to other statutes, by Manfred Nathan ... Johannesburg, Hortors limited ₍1942₎

viii, 103 p. 24½ᶜᵐ.

1. Sales, Conditional—Africa, South. I. South Africa. Laws, statutes, etc. II. Title: Hire-purchase act, no. 36 of 1942. III. Title: Civil imprisonment restriction act.

                              43–18987

NN   0029400   DLC

Nathan, Manfred, 1875–
The Huguenots in South Africa, by Manfred Nathan ... ₍Johannesburg₎ South Africa, Central news agency limited, 1939.

xii, 159 p. front., plates, map. 20½ᶜᵐ.
"Printed in Great Britain."
"First published in 1939."
"List of abbreviations and authorities": p. xi–xii.
"List of Huguenot emigrants and settlers": p. 135–149.

1. Huguenots in South Africa. 2. Africa, South—Hist.

Library of Congress   DT843.N3 1939   39–21851
Copyright A ad int. 23334   ₍2₎   968

    CU-S
NN   0029401   DLC ICU MiEM IEN NNC CSt NcU CU CtY-D

Nathan, Manfred, 1875–
The influence of war on contracts and other liabilities. By Manfred Nathan ... Johannesburg, W. E. Hortor & co., limited, 1916.

x, 120 p. 22ᶜᵐ.
On cover: War contracts, alien enemies, enemy trade.
CONTENTS.—Alien enemies.—Trade with the enemy.—The legal effects of war on contracts.—Neutral trade.—Property of enemies and neutrals.—Legal proceedings.—Termination of war.—Appendix: I. The trading with the enemy proclamations; II. War statutes of the Union: 1. The Public welfare and moratorium act, 1914; 2. The Removal of disabilities act, 1915; 3. The Indemnity and special tribunals act, 1915; 4. The Persons on active service relief act, 1915.
  1. War (International law) 2. Commercial law. 3. Contracts. 4. Neutrality. 5. European war,   1914–1918—Law and legislation. I. Title. II. Title: War   contracts.

Library of Congress   JX5270.N3   17–21493
                           ₍a45b1₎

NN   0029402   DLC PU-L PPB NN ICJ CtY

Nathan, Manfred, 1875–
The law and practice relating to interdicts (including mandamus and spoliation orders) by Manfred Nathan ... ₍Johannesburg₎ South Africa, Hortors limited, 1939.

xxxvi, 399 p. 22ᶜᵐ.

1. Interdict (Civil law) 2. Mandamus—Africa, South. I. Title: Spoliation orders.

                              40–10608

NN   0029403   DLC

Nathan, Manfred, 1875–
The law of damages in South Africa, by Manfred Nathan ... with H. J. Schlosberg ... Johannesburg, Central news agency limited, 1930.

xxiv, 268 p. 25ᶜᵐ.

1. Damages—Africa, South. I. Schlosberg, Herzl Joshua, joint author. II. Title.

                              31–10404

NN   0029404   DLC MH-L CtY

NATHAN, Manfred, 1875–
  Law of Deeds Registration in South Africa,
with the Union Deeds Registries Act (no.13,
1913),to consolidate and amend the laws in
force in the Union relating to the Registration
of Deeds and Regulations under the Act, with
explanatory notes and references to decisions.
Johannesburg,1919. By M. Nathan and Francis J. Holmes.
  (9)+255 p.
  "South African Conveyancing."

NN   0029405   MH

Nathan, Manfred, 1875–
The law of defamation (libel and slander) in South Africa, by Manfred Nathan ... Johannesburg, Hortor's limited. 1933.

₍ xvi, 398 p. 24½ᶜᵐ.

1. Libel and slander—Africa, South. I. Title.

                              34–15475

NN   0029406   DLC CtY

Nathan, Manfred, ed.

The Legal hand-book of practical laws and procedure, with tariffs of fees of office and stamps in British South Africa. Together with a law list ...

Grahamstown, Cape Colony, African book company, limited, 19

Nathan, Manfred, 1875–   *ed.*
The liquor law of South Africa; the Liquor act (no. 30, 1928) with commentary and references to decided cases, by Manfred Nathan ... assisted by H. J. Schlosberg ... Johannesburg, R. L. Esson & co., ltd., 1928.

xxi, 302 p. 22ᶜᵐ.

1. Liquor laws—Africa, South. ₍1. Intoxicating liquors—Africa, South₎ I. Schlosberg, Herzl Joshua, joint ed. II. South Africa. Laws, statutes, etc. III. Title.

                              30–10411

N   0029408   DLC MH-L NN CtY

968
N274n   Nathan, Manfred, 1875–
            Not heaven itself; an autobiography.
          Durban, Knox Pub. Co. [1944]
            343p. ports. 19cm.

1. Nathan, Manfred. 1875–   I. Title.

NN   0029409   IEN TxU CtY NNC

Nathan, Manfred, 1875–
Paul Kruger, his life and times, by Manfred Nathan ... Durban, The Knox publishing company ₍1941₎

6 p. l., 510 p. pl., ports. 22ᶜᵐ.
"First edition, September, 1941. Second edition, December 1941."
"List of abbreviations" (bibliography) : p. ₍491₎–492.

1. Kruger, Stephanus Johannes Paulus, pres. South African republic, 1825–1904. 2. Transvaal—Hist.

                              42–46793
Library of Congress   DT929.8.K8N3
                           ₍2₎   923.1682

NN   0029410   DLC TxU NcD CtY OrSaW

968.2
K94Yn.2   Nathan, Manfred, 1875–
             Paul Kruger, his life and times. [2d ed.]
           Durban, Knox Pub. Co. [1941]
             510p. plates. 22cm.

1. Kruger, Stephanus Johannes Paulus, Pres.
South African Republic, 1825–1904. 2. Transvaal. Hist.

NN   0029411   IEN

DT   Nathan, Manfred, 1875–
929   Paul Kruger, his life and times. ₍5th ed.₎
.8   Durban, Knox Pub. Co. ₍1946₎
K94   510 p. illus. 23cm.
N27
1946

1. Kruger, Stephanus Johannes Paulus,
Pres. South African Republic, 1825–1904.
2. Transvaal--   Hist.

NN   0029412   NIC FU MB MH NBuU FTaSU

          Nathan, Manfred, 1875–
614.0968   The public health, housing and slums acts of the Union of
N274P   South Africa, with regulations and commentary, by Manfred
           Nathan ... and Sir E. N. Thornton ... 2d ed. Johannesburg,
           Central News Agency Limited, 1935.
             432 p.   22 cm.

NN   0029413   NcD

Nathan, Manfred, 1875–
The public health, housing and slums acts of the Union of South Africa, with regulations and commentary, by Manfred Nathan ... and Sir E. N. Thornton ... 3d ed. ₍Johannesburg₎ South Africa, Central news agency limited, 1941.

3 p. l., 482 p. 22½ᶜᵐ.

1. Africa, South — Sanit. affairs. 2. Housing—Africa, South. I. Thornton, Sir Edward Newbury, 1878–   joint author. II. South Africa. Laws, statutes, etc. III. Title.

                              43–3374
Library of Congress   RA552.S6N3 1941
                           ₍3₎   614.0968

NN   0029414   DLC

VOLUME 405

Nathan, Manfred, 1875–
... The renascence of international law, by Manfred Nathan ... London, Sweet and Maxwell, limited, 1925.
ix, 218 p. 22 cm. (The Grotius society. Publications, no. 3)

1. International law. I. Title.
25—2310
Library of Congress   JX1311.N3

NN   0029415   CaBVaU WaU–L
DLC MiU NBuU TxU NjP OU OCU PU–L PPB

Law

Nathan, Manfred, 1875–
South Africa. *Supreme Court.*
Rules and practice of the Supreme Court of South Africa, Transvaal Provincial Division, Witwatersrand Local Division, and Appellate Division, by Manfred Nathan and Harold Dugard Bowker assisted by C. J. M. Nathan. 2d ed., rev. and enl. Johannesburg, Hortors, 1935.

NN   0029417   DLC TxU IEN MH CtY NNC CSt

Nathan, Manfred, 1875–
Sarie Marais, a romance of the Anglo-Boer war, by Manfred Nathan ... London, Gordon and Gotch ltd.; [etc., etc.] 1938.
viii, 358 p. 20¼ᶜᵐ.

1. South African war, 1899–1902—Fiction. I. Title.
39—3286
Library of Congress   PZ3.N189Sar

NN   0029417   DLC TxU IEN MH CtY NNC CSt

Nathan, Manfred, 1875–
South Africa from within, by Manfred Nathan ... with map. London, J. Murray [1926]
324 p. fold. map. 22½.
"First edition. 1926."

1. Africa, South—Hist. 2. Africa, South—Pol. & govt. 3. Africa, South—Descr. & trav. I. Title.
27—2508
Library of Congress   DT779.N3 1926

NN   0029418   DLC MU GU MiU OEac OCl OO NN WaU PU–Mu

Nathan, Manfred, 1875–
The South African commonwealth, by Manfred Nathan ... Johannesburg and Cape Town, The Specialty press of South Africa ltd., 1919.
xi, [1] p., 1 l., 483 p. 22ᶜᵐ.
CONTENTS.—The constitution of the Union.—Problems of state and government.—Politics.—Social conditions.—Appendix.

1. Africa, South—Pol. & govt.—1909– 2. Africa, South—Constitutional law. 3. Africa, South—Soc. condit. I. Title.
20—15567
Library of Congress   JQ1915.1919.N3

NN   0029419   CtY
DLC IEN NcD MiU NjP NN NjN WaU CaBVaU

Nathan, Manfred, 1875–
South African insolvency law; a commentary on the Union insolvency act (no. 32, 1916) to consolidate and amend the laws in force relating to the administration of insolvent and assigned estates, with explanatory notes and references to decided cases, by Manfred Nathan ... Johannesburg, W. E. Hortor & co., ltd., 1916.
xxx, 507 p. 22ᶜᵐ.

1. Bankruptcy—Africa, South. [2. Insolvency—Africa, South] I. South Africa. Laws, statutes, etc.
19—3439
NN   0029420   DLC CtY

NATHAN, Manfred, 1875–
South African Insolvency Law; a commentary on the Insolvency Acts no.32,1916,(to consolidate and amend the laws in force relating to the administration of insolvent and assigned estates) and no.29,1926,(to amend the Insolvency Act,1916,in certain respects and to enact certain provisions for the relief of debtors with a view to preventing insolvency),with full text,notes,references to decided cases, forms and precedents. 2d ed. Johannesburg, 1926.
11+569 p.

NN   0029421   MH–L

Nathan, Manfred, 1875–
South African insolvency law; a commentary on the Insolvency act no. 24, 1936 (to consolidate and amend the law relating to insolvent persons and to their estates) With full text, notes, references to decided cases, forms, precedents and regulations, by Manfred Nathan ... assisted by C. J. M. Nathan ... 4th ed. Johannesburg, Hortors limited, 1936.
xii, 597 p. 24½ᶜᵐ.

1. Bankruptcy—Africa, South. I. Nathan, C. J. M. II. South Africa. Laws, statutes, etc. III. Title.
37—10624
Library of Congress   [3]   [347.7] 332.750968

NN   0029422   DLC

Nathan, Manfred, 1875–
The South African law of partnership. By Manfred Nathan ... Johannesburg, The Transvaal leader, 1913.
xv, [1], 136 p. 22ᶜᵐ.

1. Partnership. I. Title.
16—23113
NN   0029423   DLC

Nathan, Manfred, 1875–
The South African law of partnership and private companies, by Manfred Nathan ... 2d ed. Johannesburg, Hortors limited, 1938.
xvi, 282 p. 21½ᶜᵐ.

1. Partnership—Africa, South. 2. Private companies—Africa, South. I. Title.
39—20717
NN   0029424   DLC MH–L

Nathan, Manfred, 1875–
South African literature; a general survey, by Manfred Nathan ... Cape Town and Johannesburg, Juta & co., ltd., 1925.
4 p. l., [v]–ix, [2], [11]–256 p. 19ᶜᵐ.

1. South African literature—Hist. & crit. 2. Dutch language—Dialects—Africa, South.
28—2140
Library of Congress   PR9806.N3
[2]

NN   0029425   DLC IEN ICU CU TxU NcD OCl NN PPT CtY

Nathan, Manfred, 1875–
The Transvaal companies act, being act no. 31 of 1909 to consolidate and amend the law relating to the incorporation, registration and winding-up of companies and other associations, with commentary and explanatory notes, by Manfred Nathan ... Johannesburg, The Transvaal Leader, 1909.
xxxii, [1], 364 p. 22 cm.

NN   0029426   CtY

Nathan, Manfred, 1875–
Transvaal company law, by Manfred Nathan ... New ed. With chapters on the company law of the Orange Free State and South-West Africa. By the author, assisted by G. Hartog ... Capetown and Johannesburg, Juta & co., ltd., 1925.
viii, 221 p. 25ᶜᵐ.

1. Corporation law—Transvaal. 2. Corporation law—Orange Free State. 3. Corporation law—Africa, Southwest. I. Hartog, Gustave, joint author. II. Title.
27—1013
NN   0029427   DLC CtY

Nathan, Manfred, 1875–
Transvaal gold and base metals law; being Act no. 35 of 1908, to consolidate and amend the law relating to prospecting and mining for precious metals and base metals, and to provide for matters incidental thereto, amending acts (of 1910, 1913, 1917 and 1918), and regulations under the acts, with notes and references to decided cases, by Manfred Nathan ... 3d ed. Johannesburg, Hortors limited, 1919.
218 p. 25ᶜᵐ.

1. Gold mines and mining—Transvaal. 2. Mining law—Transvaal. I. Transvaal. Laws, statutes, etc. II. Title.
22—15295
NN   0029428   DLC

Nathan, Manfred, 1875–
The voortrekkers of South Africa, from the earliest times to the foundation of the republics, by Manfred Nathan ... [Johannesburg] South Africa, Central news agency, ltd.; London, Gordon and Gotch, ltd., 1937.
xv, 427, [1] p. front., plates, maps. 22ᶜᵐ.
"Works most frequently cited": p. 397.

1. Africa, South—Hist. 2. Boers. I. Title.
38—3250
Library of Congress   DT773.N35 1937
Copyright A ad int. 23513   [3]   968

NN   0029429   NB MnU ICU
DLC NcD CSt NcU CU NRU TxU CtY MBAt NN

Law

Nathan, Manfred, 1875–
Transvaal (*Colony*) *Laws, statutes, etc.*
The Workmen's compensation acts, with rules, explanatory notes and references to decided cases, by Manfred Nathan. 2d ed. Johannesburg, Central News Agency, 1912.

Nathan, Manfred, 1875–
Workmen's compensation in South Africa; the Workmen's compensation act of the Union (no. 59 of 1934) with regulations, forms and schedules, and commentary, by Manfred Nathan ... Durban, Butterworth & co. (Africa), ltd., 1935.
xvi, 171, 14, [1] p. 25½ᶜᵐ.

1. Employers' liability—Africa, South. 2. Forms (Law)—Africa, South. I. South Africa. Laws, statutes, etc. II. Title.
36—11979
Library of Congress   [3]   331.8250968

NN   0029431   DLC NN CtY

Nathan, Manfred, 1875–
[Cleaver, Mrs. M M] ed.
A young South African; a memoir of Ferrar Reginald Mostyn Cleaver, advocate and veldcornet, ed. by his mother. Johannesburg, W. E. Hortor & co., ltd., 1913.

Nathan, Marcel.
Les arriérés scolaires; conférences médico-pédagogiques, par le Dʳ Marcel Nathan ... et Henri Durot ... avec la collaboration de M. Gobron ... et de M. Friedel ... Paris, F. Nathan, 1913.
vi, 360, [1] p. illus., plates, diagrs. 22½ᶜᵐ.

1. Backward children. 2. Defective children. I. Durot, Henri, joint author. II. Gobron, Louis, 1863– joint author. III. Friedel, joint author. IV. Title.
E 13–1168
Library, U. S. Bur. of   Education   LC4601.N2

NN   0029433   DHEW WaU DNLM CtY

VOLUME 405

WH
N274c
1908
NATHAN, Marcel
La cellule de Kupffer, cellule
endothéliale des capillaires veineux du
foie; ses réactions expérimentales et
pathologiques. Paris, Alcan, 1908.
96 p. illus.
Issued also as thesis, Paris.

NN 0029434 DNLM

Nathan, Marcel
L'esprit et ses maladies ... Paris,
Rieder [1930]
80p. 1x pl. on 30ℓ. (incl. facsims.) 20cm.
(Half-title: Bibliothèque générale illustrée. 15)
"Index bibliographique": p. [71]-72.

1. Insanity. 2. Psychology, Pathological.
I. Title.

NN 0029435 NRU

Nathan, Marcel, joint author.

Dupré, Ernest Pierre, 1862-1921.
Le langage musical, étude médico-psychologique par
les D⁰⁰ Ernest Dupré ... Marcel Nathan ... Préface de
Charles Malherbe ... Paris, F. Alcan, 1911.

Nathan, Marcel.
... Les malades dits imaginaires, par M. Nathan ... Paris,
G. Doin & cⁱᵉ, 1931.
ix, 133, [1] p. 18ᶜᵐ. (Collection des actualités de médecine pratique)
"Bibliographie": p. [131]-133.

1. Neuroses. 2. Pathology. I. Title.

		31-34606
Library of Congress	RC343.N38	
Copyright A—Foreign	13887	
	[2]	132

NN 0029437 DLC

Nathan, Marcel.
Manuel élémentaire de psychiatrie. Paris,
Masson, 1930.
[iv]319p. 20cm.

1. Psychiatry. 2. Mental disorders. 3. Psy-
chotherapy.

NN 0029438 NcD-MC PPC MH

Nathan, Marcel.
... Les psychoses évitables. Paris, E. Flammarion [ᶜ1929]
245 p., 2 l. 19 cm. (Bibliothèque des connaissances médicales,
dirigée par le docteur Apert)
"Index bibliographique": p. [243]-245.

1. Psychoses. 2. Paranoia.

RC512.N3	30—6722

NN 0029439 DLC

Nathan, Marcel.
... Troubles juvéniles de l'affectivité et du caractère. Paris,
E. Flammarion, 1930.
248, [2] p. illus. 18½ᶜᵐ. (Bibliothèque des connaissances médicales,
dirigée par le docteur Apert)

1. Adolescence. 2. Psychology, Pathological. 3. Insanity. I. Title.

		30-23777
Library of Congress	RJ550.N3	
Copyright A—Foreign	8074	
	[2]	136,762

NN 0029440 DLC

Nathan, Martin, 1886-
Ueber Deflorationspyelitis. Berlin, Ebering,
1914.
25 p. 8°.
Berlin, Med. Diss. v. 27. Febr. 1914, Ref.
Kraus.

NN 0029441 CtY DNLM

Nathan, Martin Gustav, 1886-
Das mitwirkende Verschulden der Vertreter
und Gehilfen des Beschädigten. (§ 254 Abs. 2
Satz 2 BGB.) ... von Martin Gustav Nathan ...
Wiesbaden, L. Schellenberg, 1909.
viii, 41, [1] p. 22½cm.
Inaug.-Diss. - Heidelberg.
"Lebenslauf": p. [42]
"Literatur-Verzeichnis": p. vi-viii.

NN 0029442 MH-L ICRL

Nathan, Marvin, 1879-
The attitude of the Jewish student in the colleges and uni-
versities towards his religion; a social study of religious
changes ... [by] Marvin Nathan. Philadelphia, 1932.
5 p. l., 5-264 p. diagrs. 23ᶜᵐ.
Thesis (PH. D.)—University of Pennsylvania, 1932.
Published also without thesis note.
Bibliography: p. 227-229.

1. Jews—Religion. 2. Students—U. S. 3. Jews in the U. S. 4. Religious thought. 5. Psychology, Religious. 6. Attitude (Psychology) I.
Title. II. Title: The Jewish student in the colleges and universities towards his religion, The attitude of.

		33-7401
Library of Congress	BM565.N35 1932	
Univ. of Pennsylvania	Libr.	
—— Copy 2.	[3]	296

NN 0029443 PU PBm PPD PSC NcU NcD NIC OrCS MB DLC

Nathan, Marvin, 1879-
The attitude of the Jewish student in the colleges and universities towards his religion; a social study of religious
changes [by] Marvin Nathan, PH. D. New York, Bloch publishing company, 1932.
6 p. l., 5-264 p. diagrs. 21ᶜᵐ.
Issued also as thesis (PH. D.) Pennsylvania university.
Bibliography: p. 227-229.
1. Jews—Religion. 2. Students—U. S. 3. Jews in the U. S. 4.
Students—Religious life. 5. Psychology, Religious. 6. Attitude (Psychology) I. Title. II. Title: The Jewish student in the colleges and
universities towards his religion, The attitude of.

		33—6806
Library of Congress	BM565.N35 1932 a	
—— Copy 2.		
Copyright A 60519	[a38f1]	296

PPT PPDrop
NN 0029444 DLC OrU MH-AH PU OOxM OCH OU OCl MiU

FILM
11761
BM
Nathan, Marvin, 1879-
The attitude of the Jewish student in the colleges and uni-
versities towards his religion; a social study of religious
changes [by] Marvin Nathan, PH. D. New York, Bloch pub-
lishing company, 1932.
6 p. l., 5-264 p. diagrs. On film (Negative)
Issued also as thesis (PH. D.) Pennsylvania university.
Bibliography: p. 227-229.
Microfilm. Original in Library of Congress.

NN 0029445 CU

Nathan, Marvin Freeman, 1922-
Thermal conductivity of gases under high pressure.
Urbana, 1948.
9 p. 23 cm.
Abstract of thesis—University of Illinois.
Vita.
Bibliography: p. 8.

1. Heat—Conductivity. 2. Gases. 3. Viscosity. I. Title.

QC323.N3	A 53-3167
Illinois. Univ. Library	
for Library of Congress	[3]†

NN 0029446 IU DLC

Nathan, Sir Matthew
see also Natal. Governor, 1907- (Sir
Matthew Nathan)

Nathan, Maude, tr.

Récy, Georges de.
The decoration of leather, from the French of Georges
de Récy by Maude Nathan; with illustrations and examples of leather decoration from various sources. London, A. Constable & co., ltd., 1905.

Nathan, Mrs. Maud (Nathan) 1862-
The justice and expediency of woman suffrage...
[1913]

NN 0029449 MiU

Nathan, *Mrs.* Maud (Nathan) 1862-
Once upon a time and today, by Maud Nathan ... With 28
illustrations. New York, London, G. P. Putnam's sons, 1933.
xvi p., 1 l., 19-327 p. front., plates, ports. 22ᶜᵐ.

I. Title.

		33-10701
Library of Congress	CT275.N34A3	
—— Copy 2.		
Copyright A 61383	[5]	920.7

NN 0029450 DLC WaS MoU NNJ OU OCH NN MB OClTem

Nathan, Mrs. Maud (Nathan), 1862-
One year's progress of equal suffrage...
1914.

NN 0029451 MiU

Nathan, *Mrs.* Maud (Nathan) 1862-
The story of an epoch-making movement, by Maud Nathan
... with brief forewords by Hon. Newton D. Baker ... Mary
Anderson ... Edward A. Filene ... Garden City, N. Y., Doubleday, Page & company, 1926.
xx p., 2 l., 245 p. front. 21½ᶜᵐ.

1. Consumers' league of New York. 2. Consumers' leagues. 3. Woman—Employment. 4. Labor and laboring classes—1914- I. Title.

		26—12652
Library of Congress	HD6957.U7N65	

MiU ODW OCl OCU OO NN ViU ICJ MB WaChenE WaS OrCS
NN 0029452 DLC GU OKentU NBuU CU ICU OOxM ICRL Or

Nathan, Maud (Nathan) 1862-
The wage earner and the ballot. Warren,
Ohio, [1908?]
2 l. 16°. (National American Woman
Suffrage Association. Political equality series,
v. 3 no. 1)
In: SNS p. v. 6.

NN 0029453 NN

Nathan, Maud (Nathan) 1862-
Woman's view of Christianity's millstone.
4 p. (N. Am. Rev. v. 162 p. 252)

NN 0029454 MdBP

812
N195f
Nathan, May Rose.
Foothills of fame ... Farcical sketch for 1 male
and 6 females ... New York city, E. S. Werner &
co., c1922.
12p.

NN 0029455 IU RPB

Nathan, May Rose, joint author.

Quaife, Elise West.
"Poor me", a comedy in two scenes, by Elise West Quaife
and May Rose Nathan ... New York, S. French: London,
S. French, ltd., c1921.

VOLUME 405

Nathan, Mirza
　　see　Mīrzā Nathan, fl. 1642.

Nathan, Mogens.
　　Undersøgelser over refektion med saerligt henblik paa stivelsens forhold. With an English summary ... København, 1935.
　　Afhandling - København.
　　"Literaturfortegnelse": p. [158]-160.

NN　0029458　　CtY

296.09763
N48Yn　Nathan, Moses Nathan, 1807-1883.
　　Consecration sermon, delivered at the opening of the new Synagogue Nefutzoth Yehudah at New Orleans, on Tuesday, the third day of Sivan, 5610, May 14, 1850.　Philadelphia, C. Sherman, printer, 5610 [1850]
　　18p. 23cm.

809330　　1. New Orleans. Congregation Nefutzoth Yehudah. 2. Sermons, Jewish - U.S. Sp.: Littlefield Fund.

NN　0029459　　TxU PPDrop

Nathan, Moses Nathan, 1807-1883.
　　A defense of ancient rabbinical interpretation of the prohibitory law of Deut. xxiii-3, being an answer by M. N. Nathan ... to a polemic essay on that subject by the Rev. J. M. De Solla ... Kingston, Jam., A. Decordova & nephew, 5621 [1861]
　　1 p.l., v. 40 p. 18 cm.

　　1. Marriage (Jewish law) 2. Bible. O. T. Deuteronomy xxiii, 3—Criticism, interpretation, etc. 3. De Solla, Jacob Mendes. A polemic essay on the prohibitory law of intermarriage with mamzerim. I. Title.

HQ1057.D52　　　[296] 173.1　　24-31228 rev

NN　0029460　　DLC NN PPDrop

NATHAN, Moses Nathan, 1807-1883.
　A defense of ancient rabbinical interpretation of the prohibitory law of Deut. XXIII-3: being an answer by M.N. Nathan to A polemic essay on that subject, by the Rev. J. M. De Solla. Kingston, Jamaica, A. Decordova & Nephew, 5621 [1861] v, 40 p. 19cm.

　Microfiche (neg.) 1 sheet. 11 x 15cm. (NYPL FSN 13,002) Schiff Collection
　1. Marriage. Jewish. 2. De Solla, J. Mendes.
　3. Marriage--Jurisp.

NN　0029461　　NN

Nathan, Moses Nathan, 1807-1883, ed.

DS101
.F5
　The First fruits of the west, and Jewish monthly magazine; a periodical specially devoted to Jewish interests. v. 1- Feb. 1844-
　Kingston, Jamaica.

Nathan, Moses Nathan, 1807-1883.
　Second annual examination of Sunday School of Mikveh Israel Synagogue, March, 29, 1840,...
　Phila., 5600.
　Æ p.

NN　0029463　　PHi

Náthán, Nándor
　I. [i.e.Első] Agrippa alakja a kereszteny es zsido történet tükreben kulonos tekintettel a talmudi irodalomra. Budapest, 1934
　46 p.
　Bölcsészdoktori értekezés
　1. Agrippa I, king of Judaea, ca.10 BC -44 AD.
X ref.: Herod Agrippa I, king of Judaea, ca.10 BC-44 A.D. (to 1)

NN　0029464　　MH

442.2
N19L　Nathan, Nathan.
　　Das lateinische suffix-alis im französischen... von Nathan Nathan.　Darmstadt, G. Otto's Hof-Buchdruckerei, 1886.
　　[2] 1., 49p. 20cm.　(Jahresverzeichnis der an den deutschen universitäten und hochschulen erschienenen schriften, v. 2, 1886-87, Strassburg 33)

　　Inaug.-diss.--Strassburg.

　　1. French language--Etymology.　2. French language--Words--History.　I. Title.

NN　0029465　　LU NjP IU MH PHC CtY

Nathan, Nathan ben
　　see　Nathan ben Nathan.

296.02
T137Z　Nathan, Nathan Max, 1879-
　　Ein anonymes Wörterbuch zur Mišna und Jad hahazaka.　Berlin, Druck von H. Itzkowski, 1905.
　　46p. 23cm.
　　Inaug.-Diss.--Strassburg.
　　Contains (p.23-45) an annotated edition of the portion of the dictionary covering א and ב. Lebenslauf.
　　Bibliographical foot-notes.

　　1. Mishnah--Dictionaries.　2. Moses ben Maimon, 1135-1204. Mishneh Torah.

NN
0029467　　IU CtY PU PPDrop MH OCH DCU-H ICU OU

NATHAN, Nathan Max, 1879-
　Das Israelitische Vorschussinstitut in Hamburg, 1816-1916. Festschrift... Hamburg, Ackermann etc., 1916. 64p fold. tables 23cm
　1.Israelitischer Vorschussinstitut... 2.History-Germany-Hamburg. 3.Festschrift-Institutions.

NN　0029468　　NNJ OCH

BM45
.S8
1925
Steinthal, Heymann, 1823-1899.
　Über Juden und judentum. Vorträge und aufsätze von prof. dr. H. Steinthal. Herausgegeben von Gustav Karpeles. 3. aufl., hrsg. von N. M. Nathan. Berlin, M. Poppelauer, 1925.

Nathan, Sir Nathaniel, 1843-1916.
　Economic heresies; being an unorthodox attempt to appreciate the economic problems presented by "things as they are." By Sir Nathaniel Nathan ... London, A. Constable & co., ltd., 1909.
　viii p., 1 l., 423 p. 23cm.
　"This book ... attempts the presentation, in a form as untechnical as possible, of the actual facts of modern economic phenomena as they are really seen and known to exist ... with the purpose of suggesting thoughts which may help in the solution of these actual and practical questions in so far as they concern the welfare of the people of my own country."--Pref.
　1. Economics. 2. Economic conditions. 3. Gt. Brit.--Econ. condit. 4. Gt. Brit.--Economic policy. 5. Socialism.
　　　　　　　　　　　　　　　9-14519
　　Library of Congress　　HB171.7.N3

PPL OCU OOxM OO ICJ NN
NN　0029470　　DLC OrCS CaBVaU CtY NcD MB MH ScU NjP

Nathan, Sir Nathaniel, 1843-1916, ed.
　The Judicature acts, 1873 and 1875 (36 & 37 Vict. c. 66 and 38 & 39 Vict. c. 77) with the rules and orders regulating the practice of the Supreme court of judicature, forms and precedents, schedules of costs and of fees, together with an appendix containing the previous enactments expressly incorporated into the new practice, and a copious index. Edited, with introductory chapter and annotations, by Nathaniel Nathan ... London, Law times office, 1875.
　xxxi, 354 p. 22cm.
　1. Civil procedure—Gt. Brit. 2. Court rules—Gt. Brit. 3. Forms (Law)—Gt. Brit. 4. Costs (Law)—Gt. Brit. I. Gt. Brit. Supreme court of judicature. II. Gt. Brit. Laws, statutes, etc. III. Title.
　　　　　　　　　　　　33-34731

NN　0029471　　DLC

LD3907
.G7
1947
.N3
Nathan, Norman, 1915-
　Prince William B.; the philosophical conceptions of William Blake...
　New York, 1944.
　2p.ℓ.,204 typewritten leaves. 29cm.
　Thesis (Ph.D.) - New York university, Graduate school, 1947.
　Bibliography: p.197-202.

NN　0029472　　NNU-W

Nathan, Norman, 1915-
　Prince William B.; the philosophical conceptions of William Blake. New York, New York University, 1949.
　10 p. 23 cm.
　Abridgment of thesis—New York University.
　1. Blake, William, 1757-1827.
　PR4148.P5N3　　821.79　　51-35043

NN　0029473　　DLC OrU

Nathan, Oscar, 1885-
　Modus und Auflage im römisch-gemeinen und heutigen Obligationenrecht ... von Oscar Nathan ... Hamburg, Berngruber & Henning, 1909.
　x, 127, [1] p. 22cm.
　Inaug.-Diss. - Heidelberg.
　"Lebenslauf": p. [128]
　"Literaturübersicht": p. [vii]-x.

NN　0029474　　MH-L

Nathan, Otto, 1893-
　Consumer spending, inflation and the wage earner in the United States, by Otto Nathan ... and Milton Fried ...
　(In International labour review. February, 1942. v. 45, p. [125]-141)
　1. World war, 1939- —Economic aspects—U. S. I. Fried, Milton, joint author. II. Title.
　　　　　　　　　　　　L 42-113
　U. S. Dept. of labor. Libr.
　for Library of Congress　[HD4811.I 65　vol. 45]
　　　　　　　　　　[2]　　　　　(331.05)

NN　0029475　　DL

Nathan, Otto, 1893-
　The nazi economic system; Germany's mobilization for war [by] Otto Nathan, with the collaboration of Milton Fried. Durham, N. C., Duke university press, 1944.
　ix, 378 p. diagrs. 23½ᶜᵐ. (Half-title: Duke university publications)
　Bibliographical foot-notes.
　1. Germany—Economic policy—1933- I. Fried, Milton, joint author. II. Title.
　Library of Congress　HC286.3.N24　　44-4754
　　　　　　　　　　[25]　　　　　330.943

　　　　WaS CaBVaU OrCS NNUN
　OO OU TU ViU KEmT MiU NIC FMU DAU OrU WaWW OrPR Or
NN　0029476　　DLC NcD NcRS NcGU PBm PSt PPD OCl OCU

Nathan, Otto, 1893-
　The nazi economic system; Germany's mobilization for war [by] Otto Nathan, with the collaboration of Milton Fried. Durham, N. C., Duke university press, 1944.
　ix, 378 p. diagrs. 23½ cm. (Half-title: Duke university publications)
　Bibliographical foot-notes.
HC286.3
.N24　—— —— Photocopy. Ann Arbor, Mich., University Microfilms, 1972.

NN　0029477　　OrPS

Nathan, Otto, 1893-
　Nazi war finance and banking [by] Otto Nathan ... [New York] Financial research program, National bureau of economic research [1944]
　iii, [1], 97, [1] p. diagrs. 22½ᶜᵐ. ([National bureau of economic research. Financial research program] Our economy in war)
　Occasional paper 20: April 1944.
　1. Finance—Germany. 2. World war, 1939- —Finance—Germany. 3. Banks and banking—Germany. I. Title.
　　　　　　　　　　　　44-6413
　Library of Congress　H11.N2432　no. 20
　　　　　　　　　　[8]　　　　(330.973) 336.43

　　WaWW
　WU MoU CoU MU TxU PPT PU OCl OClW OCU OO MtU WaTC
NN　0029478　　DLC WaS WaSpG OrU CaBViP NIC MiU CLU

VOLUME 405

Nathan (P. W[illiam]). A case of cerebral di-
plegia (so-called spastic spinal paraplegia) with
pseudo-hypertrophy. 7 pp. 12°. *New York,*
1904.
Repr. from: N. York M. J. 1904, lxxix.

NN 0029479   DNLM

[Nathan, Paul]
The cause of the unprofitable condition of the **printing
business,** and a remedy. [New York, Wood & Nathan
company, 1912?]
26 p. 21ᶜᵐ.
Signed: Paul Nathan.
Advertising the "Standard high-speed job press."

1. Printing, Practical.   I. Title.
12–28449
Library of Congress   Z244.5.N24

NN 0029480   DLC

Nathan, Paul.
How to make money in the printing business. **A book**
for master printers who realize that there is a practical
side to the art, and who desire to know the surest methods of making profits. By Paul Nathan ... with contributions from many of the leading printers of the United
States. New York, The Lotus press, 1900.
4 p. l., 375 p. illus. 23½ᶜᵐ.

1. Printing, Practical.   I. Title: Printing business.
1–29773 Revised
Library of Congress   Z244.5.N27

NN 0029481   DLC CU NcD ICJ MB ViU

Nathan, Paul.
How to make money in the printing business. A book for
master printers who realize that there is a practical side of the
art, and who desire to know the surest methods of making profits.
By Paul Nathan, with contributions from many of the leading
printers of the United States. New York: Oswald Pub. Co.,
1909. 4 p.l., 278 p. 2. ed. 8°.

1. Printing. 2. Title: Printing business.
N. Y. P. L.   August 30, 1917.

NN 0029482   NN WaS PP OCl ICN

Nathan, Paul, of the Zentral Verein Zeitung.
... Gedenknummer der central verein zeitung,
VI Jahrgang, Nr. 15.   Berlin, April 14, 1927.

NN 0029483   PPDrop

Nathan, Paul, Ph. D.
   see   Nathan, Paul, 1857–1927.

F9999   Nathan, Paul, writer on Mexico
Mexico under Cárdenas. 1952.
448 l.

Thesis--Univ. of Chicago.

1. Cárdenas, Lázaro, Pres. of Mexico, 1895–
2. Mexico--Pol. & govt.--1920–   I. Title.

NN 0029485   ICU

Nathan, Paul, writer on Mexico
Mexico under Cárdenas.   Chicago, 1952.
xii,448 p.

Film reproduction. Positive.
Thesis--University of Chicago.
Bibliography, p. 440-448.
1. Cárdenas, Lázaro, pres. Mexico, 1895–
2. Mexico--Hist., 1920–

NN 0029486   NN

Nathan, Paul, 1857–1927.
England und wir; betrachtungen über die internationale
politik, von Paul Nathan.   Berlin, W. Borngräber [1912]
32 p. 23½ᶜᵐ.

1. Germany—For. rel.—Gt. Brit.   2. Gt. Brit.—For. rel.—Germany.
I. Title.
24–20424
Library of Congress   DD228.7.G7N3

NN 0029487   DLC NN

Nathan, Paul.
Die enttäuschungen unserer gegner; august—september—oktober; ein vierteljahrsabrechnung von dr. Paul
Nathan. Stuttgart und Berlin, Deutsche verlags-anstalt,
1914.
35 p. 23ᶜᵐ. (Added t.-p.: Der deutsche krieg; politische flugschriften,
hrsg. von E. Jäckh. 11. hft.)

1. European war, 1914–   —Germany.
A 20–844
Title from Carnegie   Endow. Int. Peace. Printed by L. C.

NN 0029488   NNCE CU MiU OU NN NcD

Nathan, Paul, 1857–1927, ed.

Bamberger, Ludwig, 1823–1899.
Erinnerungen, von Ludwig Bamberger. Herausgegeben von
Paul Nathan. Berlin, G. Reimer, 1899.

Nathan, Paul, 1857–1927, ed.
Der Fall Justschinski
see under title

BM
717   Nathan, Paul, 1857–1927.
N3.2   Der jüdische Blutmord und der
Freiherr von Wackerbarth-Linderode. Ein
antisemitisch-parlamentarisches
Kulturbild. Berlin, F. Fontane, 1892.
37 p. 24 cm.
Offprint from the author's Der
Prozess von Tisza-Eszlar.

1. Jews in Tisza-Eszlar. 2. Blood
accusation. I. Title

NN 0029491   OCH OU

Nathan, Paul, 1857–1927
... Die Ostjuden in Deutschland und die antisemitische Reaktion, von Dr. Paul Nathan.   Berlin: Philo-Verlag, 1922. 11 p.
12°. (Zeit- und Streitfragen. Heft 5.)

1. Jews, Germany. 2. Jews.—   **SCHIFF COLLECTION.**
3. Series.   Antisemitic movement, Germany.
N. Y. P. L.   May 22, 1923.

NN 0029492   NN

Nathan, Paul.
... Palästina und palästinensischer Zionismus von **Paul**
Nathan. Berlin, Druck von H. S. Hermann [1914]
62 p. 22ᶜᵐ.
"Als manuskript gedruckt."

1. Jews—Restoration.   I. Title.
22–24612
Library of Congress   DS149.N3

NN 0029493   DLC UU OU PPD OCH NN

Nathan, Paul, 1857–1927.
... Das Problem der Ostjuden; Vergangenheit — Zukunft.
Berlin: Philo Verlag und Buchhandlung, G.m.b.H., 1926. 38 p.
12°.

1. Jews in Europe, Eastern. 2. Agri-   cultural colonies—Jews—Russia.
N. Y. P. L.   July 5, 1928

NN 0029494   NN OU OCH

Nathan, Paul, 1857–1927.
Der prozess von Tisza-Eszlar. Ein antisemitisches culturbild von Paul Nathan, DR. PHIL. Berlin, F. Fontane & co.,
1892.
xxxix, [1], 416 p. illus. (plan) 23½ᶜᵐ.
CONTENTS.—Vorwort.—Einleitung.—Das ereigniss von Tisza-Eszlar
und die antisemiten.—Die ausgestaltung der legende.—Der kampf zur
vernichtung der angeklagten.—Der prozess wegen mordes.—Der prozess
über den leichenschmuggel.—Beilagen: Obductionsprotokolle und medicinische gutachten. Situations-plan von Tisza-Eszlar.

1. Schwarz, Salomon, d. 1905. 2. Ritual murder. 3. Jews in Tisza-
Eszlar. I. Title. II. Title: Tisza-Eszlar, Der prozess von.
26–1576
Library of Congress   BM717.N3

NN 0029495   DLC NcU CtY OCH

NATHAN, PAUL, 1857–1927.
Der Prozess von Tisza-Eszlár; ein anti-semitisches
Culturbild. Berlin, F. Fontane, 1892. xl, 416 p.
23cm.

Film reproduction. Positive.

1. Blood accusation--   Tiszaeszlar. 2. Jews--Blood
accusation--Tiszaeszlar.

NN 0029496   NN

Nathan, Paul, 1857–1927.
Die russische Revolution und die russischen
Juden. Berlin, Haasenstein & Vogler, 1906.
31 p. 8°.

NN 0029497   NN

Nathan, Paul, 1857–1927.
Xanten-Cleve. Betrachtungen zum Prozess
Buschhof von dr. Paul Nathan... Berlin,
H. S. Hermann, 1892.

cover-title, 16 p. 23cm.

"Separat-Abdruck aus der 'Nation', Wochenschrift für Politik, Volkswirtschaft und
Litteratur."

NN 0029498   MH-L

Nathan, Paul, 1857–1927.
Die Wohnungsfrage und die Bestrebungen der Berliner Bauge-
nossenschaft. Berlin, L. Simion, 1890. 84 p. illus. 24cm.

1. Housing—Germany—Berlin.

NN 0029499   NN MB

QP999   Nathan, Paul, 1924–
Indications of metabolic changes during an
osmotic (urea) diuresis. 1953.
52 l.

Thesis--Univ. of Chicago.

1. Diuretics and diuresis. 2. Urea.
3. Metabolism.

NN 0029500   ICU

PG3463   Nathan, Paul S., joint tr.
.A19
1945   Gor'kiĭ, Maksim, 1868–1936.
... Seven plays of Maxim Gorky. New Haven, Yale university press; London, H. Milford, Oxford university press,
1945.

VOLUME 405

Nathan, Paul S., joint tr.

PQ3245
.B3

Bakshy, Alexander, 1885–   comp. and tr.
   Soviet scene; six plays of Russian life, translated by Alexander Bakshy, in collaboration with Paul S. Nathan; with an introduction by Alexander Bakshy. New Haven, Yale university press, 1946.

Nathan, Peter: Die in der Chirurgischen Klinik zu Kiel operierten Blasentumoren von 1901–1919. [Maschinenschrift.] 53 S. 4°. — Auszug: o. O. u. J. 1 Bl. 4°
Kiel, Med. Diss. v. 25. Juli 1922   [U 22. 6448

NN   0029503   ICRL

ND588
.W35N3

Nathan, Peter, 1925 –
   Friedrich Wasmann, sein Leben und sein Werk; ein Beitrag zur Geschichte der Malerei des neunzehnten Jahrhunderts. München, F. Bruckmann [1954]
   163 p. 196 illus., 8 col. plates. 27 cm.
   Bibliography: p. [119]–120.

   1. Wasmann, Friedrich, 1805–1886.

                      A 55–2070

Harvard Univ. Library
for Library of Congress   [1]

NN   0029504   MH DLC CSt NcD CtY KyU ICU NN

Nathan, Peter Wilfred.
   The psychology of fascism, by Peter Nathan. London, Faber and Faber ltd [1943]
   158 p. 21ᶜᵐ.
   "First published in Mcmxliii."
   Bibliography: p. 150–158.

   1. Fascism. 2. National socialism. 3. Social psychology.   I. Title.
                       43–4722

Library of Congress   DG571.N27 1943
                    [3]   301.156

NN   0029505   DLC TxU PPT CaBViP OrU NcD CtY

Nathan, Peter Wilfred.
   Retreat from reason; an essay on the intellectual life of our time. London, Heinemann [1955]
   262 p. 21 cm.

   1. Intellectual life. 2. Philosophy, Modern.   I. Title.

CB425.N3   55–4420 ‡

    CU NcD NN
NN   0029506   DLC CaBVa IdPI PU OO PP MH PPLas PPT

Nathan, Pierre, 1896–
   L'Adenomyone et de l'Adenoymose de la Femme. Paris, Legrand, 1929.

NN   0029507   PPF

Nathan, Pierre, 1896–
   ... Contribution à l'etude de l'adenomyome et de l'adenomyose de la femme ... Paris, 1929.
   Thèse - Univ. de Paris.
   "Bibliographie": p. 159–162.

NN   0029508   CtY

Nathan, Reuben
   The inverter circuit for small alternating current loads... [Cincinnati, 1933]
   79 l.

NN   0029509   OCU

Nathan, Richard: Der Einfluss des Krieges auf die Erfüllung schwebender Lieferungsverträge.
— Auszug: o. O. (1921). 7 S. 8°
Göttingen, R.- u. staatswiss. Diss. v. 31. Mai 1922   [U 22. 2222

NN   0029510   ICRL

Nathan, Robert.
   The plague in India, 1896, 1897. Compiled by R. Nathan. Simla, Printed at the Govt. Central Print. Office, 1898–
   v. 26 cm.
   At head of title: Govt. of India. Home Dept.

   1. Plague—India.   I. Title.

RC179.I 4N3   S A 64–4158

NN   0029511   DLC MB DLC-P4 DNLM NNC MiU

NATHAN, ROBERT
   They know what they do.
   Reproduced from the New York Times. Magazine [1944]
   Broadside.

NN   0029512   PPCS

Nathan, Robert, 1894–
   The adventures of Tapiola. New York, Knopf, 1950.
   121, 187 p. illus. 21 cm.
   Contents.—Journey of Tapiola.—Tapiola's brave regiment.

   I. Title.   II. Title: Journey of Tapiola.   III. Title: Tapiola's brave regiment.
                    Full name: Robert Gruntal Nathan.
                    A 52–7597 ‡

Missouri. Univ. Libr.
for Library of Congress   [2]

NN   0029513   MoU ICU CoU FTaSU LU MB PP CU

Nathan, Robert, 1894 –
   Atoms; a one act play. (Harvard monthly. Cambridge, Mass., 1913. 8°. v. 57, p. 31–38.)

   1. Drama (American). 2. Title.
N. Y. P. L.   May 27, 1914.

NN   0029514   NN

Nathan, Robert, 1894–
   Autumn, by Robert Nathan ... New York, R. M. McBride & company, 1921.
   4 p. l., 189 p. 19½ᶜᵐ.

   I. Title.
                  [Full name: Robert Gruntal Nathan]
                  21–17910 Revised
Library of Congress   PZ3.N195Au

    OC1 OC1W MB NN ViU IdU WaS CaBVa Or
NN   0029515   DLC WaE MtU WaT NcU CoU PP PPL OO OEac

813
N19a

Nathan, Robert, 1894–
   Autumn, by Robert Nathan ... New York, R. M. McBride & company, 1921.
   4 p. l., 198p. 20cm.

NN   0029516   IU WaWW MtBC OrU

Nathan, Robert, 1894–   N
   Autumn. New York: Robert M. McBride & Co., 1923.
   198 p. 12°.

   I. Title.
N. Y. P. L.   March 27, 1925

NN   0029517   NN OrPR GU PU MiU

Nathan, Robert, 1894–
   Autumn, by Robert Nathan. New York, R. M. McBride & company [1935]
   4 p. l., 198 p. 18½ᶜᵐ.
   "Copyright, 1921 ... reissued August, 1935."

   I. Title.
                  [Full name: Robert Gruntal Nathan]
                  35–27377
Library of Congress   PZ3.N195Au 9

NN   0029518   DLC OC1

Nathan, Robert, 1894–
   The Barly fields, a collection of five novels by Robert Nathan; with an introduction by Stephen Vincent Benét. New York, A. A. Knopf, 1938.
   3 p. l., v–xiv, [1] p., 2 l., 3–523, [1] p., 1 l. 21½ cm.
   Contents.—The fiddler in Barly.—The woodcutter's house.—The bishop's wife.—The orchid.—There is another heaven.

   I. Benét, Stephen Vincent, 1898–1943. II. Title.
              Full name: Robert Gruntal Nathan.
PZ3.N195Bar   38–27469

    OrU OrCS WaWW CaBVa
    MiU MB OC1JC NN KAS OC1W LU ViU WaT IdU MtBC WaS WaSp
NN   0029519   DLC FTaSU KMK MoU OC1 OCH OO PPD PSC

Nathan, Robert, 1894–
   The Barly fields, a collection of five novels by Robert Nathan; with an introduction by Stephen Vincent Benét. New York, Literary Guild of America [c1938]
   3 p. l., v–xiv, [1] p., 2 l., 3–523, [1] p., 1 l. 21½ cm.
   Contents.—The fiddler in Barly.—The woodcutter's house.—The bishop's wife.—The orchid.—There is another heaven.

NN   0029520   MtU CaBVa IdPI WaE WaTC KEmT

Za
N195
C938Bo

Nathan, Robert, 1894–
   The Barly fields, a collection of five novels ... with an introduction by Stephen Vincent Benét. London, Constable & company ltd. [1939]
   3p. l., v–xiv, [1]p., 2l., 3–523, [1]p. 21½cm.
   "First published [in Great Britain] 1939"
   Contents. - The fiddler in Barly - The woodcutter's house - The bishop's wife - The orchid - There is another heaven.

NN   0029521   CtY

Nathan, Robert, 1894–
   The Barly fields, ... New York, Knopf, 1942.

NN   0029522   PPT

Nathan, Robert, 1894–
   The Barly fields; a collection of five novels. With an introd. by S.V.Benét. NY, Knopf, 1946
   xiv, 523 p.
   Contents.- The fiddler in Barly. -The woodcutter's house. - The bishop's wife.-The orchid. -There is another heaven

NN   0029523   MH ViU

Za
N195
Ep935E

Nathan, Robert, 1894–   The enchanted voyage. Dutch tr. Verwey.
   ... De betoverde reis (The enchanted voyage) uit het Amerikaans vertaald door Mea Mees-Verwey. Santpoort,C.A.Mees,1937
   164p. 19½cm. (Kristallen-serie, 6)
   In case with his One more spring. Dutch tr. Eeden. ... En het werd weer lente ... 1935.
   x. His title: De betoverde reis.
   I.Verwey, Mea, 1892–   tr.

NN   0029524   CtY

VOLUME 405

Nathan, Robert, 1894-   Portrait of
Za   Jennie. German tr. Steiner.
N195   ... Ein Bildnis von Jenny, Roman.
En949S   Salzburg, Verlag "Das Silberboot"[1949]
           200,[1]p. 19½cm.
           Translated by Johannes Steiner and
           Geraldine Erben.

           x. His title: Ein Bildnis von Jenny.
           I. Steiner, Johannes, 1907-   tr.

NN   0029525   CtY DLC-P4

Nathan, Robert, 1894-
     The bishop's wife, by Robert Nathan. Indianapolis, The
     Bobbs-Merrill company [*1928]
     208 p. 20ᵐ.

           I. Title.
                          [Full name: Robert Gruntal Nathan]
     Library of Congress   PZ3.N195Bi   28-21889 Revised

WaWW OrCS
PU MiU OC1W OLak OC1 NBuU NN WaTC WaE WaT WaS WaSp
NN   0029526   DLC CoU OU TNJ KMK MB NcU ViU PP PPT

Nathan, Robert, 1894-
Za   The bishop's wife ... [London] V.
N195   Gollancz ltd, 1928
928Bd   208p. 19cm.

NN   0029527   CtY

813   Nathan, Robert, 1894-
N19bi   The bishop's wife.   New York, Grosset & Dun-
1928   lap [1928]
         192p. 19cm.

NN   0029528   IU WaSpG NcD MB CaOTP ICarbS

*
AC8   Nathan, Robert, 1894-
.A6
no.800   The Bishop's wife, and two other novels; with
1938   an introduction by Stephen Vincent Benét. New
         York, Editions for the Armed Services, ᶜ1938.

         351 p. 10 x 14cm. (Armed Services ed. 800)

NN   0029529   ViU

Nathan, Robert, 1894-
     But gently day [by] Robert Nathan. New York, A. A.
     Knopf, 1943.
     5 p. l., 3-161 p., 1 l. 20½ᵐ.
     "First edition."

           I. Title.
                          [Full name: Robert Gruntal Nathan]
     Library of Congress   PZ3.N195Bu   43-12145

WaS WaSp WaT OrU WaSpG MtBC KU
ViU PP PPL PSC ODW OC1W OO OC1 OCU CaBVa OrP Wa WaE
NN   0029530   DLC OU OrPS TNJ IaU GU CoU INS MiU MB

PS3527
.A74B8 Nathan, Robert, 1894-
1945
         But gently day. New York, A. A. Knopf,
         1945.
         161 p. 20cm.

           I. Title.
                 Full name: Robert Gruntal Nathan.

NN   0029531   ViU PHC

Nathan, Robert, 1894-
     A cedar box, by Robert Nathan; with a foreword by Louis
     Untermeyer. Indianapolis, The Bobbs-Merrill company
     [*1929]
     8 p. l., 15-48 p. 21ᵐ.
     "Of this limited edition ... fifteen hundred copies were printed for
     sale, of which this is no. 250."
     Poems.

           I. Title.
     Library of Congress   PS3527.A74C4 1929   29-8531

           NcU IU NcD PU OC1 OC1h TxU NN WaSp MtU WaS
NN   0029532   DLC AAP CoU ViU KMK InU MB MiU GU NjP

Nathan, Robert, 1894-
     The concert, by Robert Nathan.   New York, House of books,
     ltd., 1940.
     [36] p. 19½ᵐ. [The crown octavos. no. 6]
     "This first edition is limited to two hundred and fifty numbered copies
     signed by the author. This is no. 0. [Signed] Robert Nathan."

     1. Music—Anecdotes, facetiae, satire, etc.   I. Title.
                          [Full name: Robert Gruntal Nathan]
     Library of Congress   ML64.N27C5   40-8958
     ——— Copy 2.   PS3527.A74C8   1940
     Copyright   [2] [R.B.R.]   [813.5] 780.881

NN   0029533   DLC TxU MoSW NjP PP PSC NN MH

Nathan, Robert, 1894-
     The coward. [A play in one act.]   (Harvard monthly.   Cam-
     bridge, Mass., 1914.   8°.   v. 58, p. 20-28.)

1. Drama (American). 2. Title.
N. Y. P. L.   May 27, 1914.

NN   0029534   NN

Nathan, Robert, 1894-
     The darkening meadows; poems, including 'Dunkirk' [by]
     Robert Nathan. New York, A. A. Knopf, 1945.
     4 p. l., 3-85 p., 1 l. 22 cm.
     "First edition."

     1. World war, 1939-1945—Poetry.   I. Title. II. Title: Dunkirk.
                          Full name: Robert Gruntal Nathan.
     PS3527.A74D3   811.5   45-5159

TxU WaSpG
OO OU ViU NN NIC IU PSt CaBViP Or OrP WaS WaT WaSp
NN   0029535   DLC MiU NBuU NcGU PP PPD PU OC1 OEac

Nathan, Robert, 1894-
     Dunkirk, a ballad by Robert Nathan. New York, A. A.
     Knopf, 1942.
     7 p. 24½ᵐ.
     "First edition."

     1. World war, 1939-   —Poetry.   I. Title.
                          [Full name: Robert Gruntal Nathan]
     Library of Congress   PS3527.A74D8   42-17985
                          [T]   811.5

OC1 PSC NN
NN   0029536   DLC WaS WaT IEN MoSW MeB NBuU NcU InU

Nathan, Robert, 1894-   Dunkirk.
M1609
.D   Damrosch, Walter Johannes, 1862-
           [Dunkirk. Piano-vocal score. English]

           Dunkirk, a ballad; poem by Robert Nathan, music by Walter
         Damrosch, for medium voice and chorus in unison with string
         orchestra, piano, (and kettle drums ad lib.) Vocal score. New
         York, G. Schirmer, inc. [1943]

Nathan, Robert, 1894-   One more spring.
Za   Italian tr. Canino.
N195   È di nuovo primavera ... [Milano,etc.]
9949C   Bompiani[1949]
           154,[1]p.,2ℓ. 18cm. (Pegaso letterario,
           26)
           Translated by Elena Canino.

           I. Canino, Elena   tr.
           x. His title: È di nuovo primavera.

NN   0029538   CtY

Nathan, Robert, 1894-   One more spring.
Za   Dutch tr. Eeden.
N195   ... En het werd weer lente, uit het
Ep935E   amerikaansch vertaald door Hans van Eeden.
           Santpoort,N.V.Uitgeverij vh. C.A.Mees,1935
           175,[1]p. 20cm.

           x. His title: En het werd weer lente.
           I. Eeden, Hans van,   tr.

NN   0029539   CtY

Nathan, Robert, 1894-
     The enchanted voyage [by] Robert Nathan. New York,
     London, A. A. Knopf, 1936.
     viii, 187, [2] p. 19¼ᵐ.
     "First edition."

           I. Title.
                          [Full name: Robert Gruntal Nathan]
     Library of Congress   PZ3.N195En   36-18874

CaBVa WaSp WaSpG IdU PLasC
MB PP PPGi OO OC1W OC1 OLak WaWW WaE WaS OrCS Or OrU
NN   0029540   DLC CtU TNJ NcD MB TxU CoU WU ViU NN

*
PS3527
.A74E5 Nathan, Robert, 1894-
1936a
           The enchanted voyage. New York, Editions
         for the Armed Services, ᶜ1936.
           127 p. 10 x 14cm. (Armed services edition,
         737)

           I. Title.
           Full name: Robert Gruntal Nathan.

NN   0029541   ViU

PZ   Nathan, Robert, 1894-
3   The enchanted voyage.   London, Constable
.N195   [1937]
En   187 p. 20cm.

                          Full name: Robert
                          Gruntal Nathan

NN   0029542   WU IU CtY

Nathan, Robert, 1894-
     The enchanted voyage, ... New York, London,
     Knopf, 1941.

NN   0029543   PPT

Nathan, Robert, 1894-
     The enchanted voyage, by Robert Nathan.   New York,
     Editions for the armed services [1945] ᶜ1936.   127(1) p.   10 x
     15cm.   (Armed services editions. 737.)
     Original illustrated covers, with series note and advertisements, bound in.
     On original cover: Overseas edition for the armed forces.

     54R0816. I. Title. II. Armed   services editions.

NN   0029544   NN

VOLUME 405

Za
N195
Eq939F

Nathan, Robert, 1894–   One more
spring. Danish tr. Fasting.
... Enda en vår. [Oslo] J. W. Cap-
pelens forlag [1939]
232p. 19cm. (Ugle bøkene)
Translated by Kåre Fasting.

    I. Fasting, Kåre   tr.
x. His title: Enda en vår.

NN   0029545   CtY

Nathan, Robert, 1894–
The fiddler in Barly, by Robert Nathan. New York, R. M
McBride & company, 1926.
4 p. l., 194 p. 19¼ cm.

    I. Title.
Library of Congress   PZ3.N195Fi   26—19075

PPL MiU OClh OLak OCl NN MB WaTC IdU WaS WaSpG
NN   0029546   DLC OU IaU GU KMK NBuU FMU InU ViU PU

Za
N195
926Fd

Nathan, Robert, 1894–
The fiddler in Barly ... With 6 drawings
by Clare Leighton. London, W. Heinemann ltd.,
1927
vii, 137, [1] p., 1 l. 6 pl. 19½ cm.

NN   0029547   CtY NN

Za
N195
En953S

Nathan, Robert, 1894–   The river journey.
German tr. Schweinitz.
... Flussfahrt mit Herrn Mortimer, Roman.
[Braunschweig] G. Westermann Verlag [1953]
176p. 19½ cm.
Translated by Maria von Schweinitz.

    x. His title: Flussfahrt mit Herrn
Mortimer. I. Schweinitz, Maria (Brandrup)
von, 1889–   tr.

NN   0029548   CtY

---

*fAC9
B4356
LR246
v.81(3)

Nathan, Robert, 1894–
For Stephen Vincent Benét, by Robert Nathan.
(In Red book magazine. Dayton, O., 1943.
29.5cm., in case 32cm. vol.81, no.3, p.60.
1 illus. (port.))
A poem.

NN   0029549   MH

Za
N195
928F

[Nathan, Robert] 1894–
Frances Gruntal on her eightieth birthday.
[New York? 1928]
[3] p. port. 22 cm.

Poem.
Signed: "R. N."

    1. Gruntal, Frances, 1848–   - Poetry.
2. Nathan, Maud (Nathan) 1862–   - Autograph.

NN   0029550   CtY

Za
N195
En948V

Nathan, Robert, 1894–   The bishop's wife.
German tr. Schweinitz.
... Die Frau des Bischofs. Stuttgart [etc.]
Rowohlt [1948]
115, [1] p. 19 cm.
Translated by Maria von Schweinitz.

NN   0029551   CtY DLC-P4

PS3527
.A74O63

Nathan, Robert, 1894–
Frühling wird es wieder. [Deutsche Übertragung, Maria
von Schweinitz] Stuttgart, Rowohlt [1948]
123 p. 20 cm.
Translation of One more spring.

    I. Title.   Full name: Robert Gruntal Nathan.

PS3527.A74O63   813.5   52–37547 ‡

NN   0029552   DLC TxU

Nathan, Robert, 1894–
The green leaf, the collected poems of Robert Nathan.
[1st collected ed.] New York, Knopf, 1950.
xvii, 185 p. 22 cm.

    I. Title.   Full name: Robert Gruntal Nathan.

PS3527.A74A17 1950   811.5   50–7023

IdB WaSp WaE
MB TU ViU NcGU IU OC1 PP PPL WaT MiEM CaBViP Or WaS
NN   0029553   DLC AAP CoU KMK MiU CtY OOxM PSt NNC

Za
N195
950Md

Nathan, Robert, 1894–
His wife's young face ... London,
Staples press limited[1951]
159p. 20cm.
"First published in Great Britain
1951"
American edition (New York, Knopf)
has title: The married look.

NN   0029554   CtY InU

Nathan, Robert, 1894–
The innocent Eve. [1st ed.] New York, Knopf, 1951.
184 p. 21 cm.

    I. Title.   Full name: Robert Gruntal Nathan.

PZ3.N195 In   51–10299

MiU KMK OU NN MB OrP WaT WaTC OrU IdB KU
NN   0029555   DLC TxU CaBVa OrCS WaS WaE ICU TNJ GU

NATHAN, ROBERT, 1894–
"Jezebel's husband;" or, Jonah in Zebulon; a play.
[New York, Hart stenographic bureau, 1952?]
40, 44, 32 l. 30cm.

Typescript.
Produced at the Pocono playhouse, Mountainholm, Pa., Aug. 5, 1952.
1. Drama, American. I. Title. II. Title: Jonah in Zebulon.

NN   0029556   NN CtY

Nathan, Robert, 1894–
Jezebel's husband & The sleeping beauty. [1st ed.] New
York, Knopf, 1953.
209 p. 20 cm.
Two plays.

    I. Title. II. Title: The sleeping beauty.
         Full name: Robert Gruntal Nathan.

PS3527.A74J4   812.5   52—12191 ‡

WaE WaT OrCS NcWil
NN NcC TxU OOxM PSt FMU WU NSyU Or OrP OrAshS OrPS
NN   0029557   DLC MiU NIC NcD AzU OC1W PU PPT PP MB

Nathan, Robert, 1894–
Jonah, by Robert Nathan. New York, R. M. McBride &
company, 1925.
4 p. l., 3–212 p. 20 cm.
London edition (W. Heinemann, ltd.) has title: Son of Amittai.

    1. Jonah, the prophet—Fiction. I. Title.
         Full name: Robert Gruntal Nathan.
Library of Congress   PZ3.N195Jo   25–4208 Revised

NcU PU ICU OEac OClh OCl OClTem MB NN MeB WaE MtU IdU
NN   0029558   DLC TNJ NBuU CoU WU OU TxU NIC MsU PPGi

Nathan, Robert, 1894–
Jonah; or, The withering vine, by Robert Nathan; with a
new foreword by the author; wood engravings by Boris Artzy-
basheff. New York, A. A. Knopf, 1934.
x, 212 p., 1 l. plates. 19¼ cm.
"New edition, June, 1934."

    1. Jonah, the prophet—Fiction. I. Title.
         Full name: Robert Gruntal Nathan.
Library of Congress   PZ3.N195Jo 9   34–33472

ViU OCH OLak MB
NN   0029559   DLC WaTC WaS OrCS WaSp GU CaBVaU MiU

Nathan, Robert, 1894–
Journal for Josephine [by] Robert Nathan. New York,
A. A. Knopf, 1943.
v, [1], 142, [1], 1 l. 20¼ cm.
"First edition."

    I. Title.   [Full name: Robert Gruntal Nathan]
Library of Congress   PS3527.A74J6   43–2244
         [10]   813.5

CaBViP IdB OrP OrU WaS CaBVaU WaSpG
MB KMK NcD OU TxU ICU PPL OCl OCU OOxM PPGi CaBVa KU
NN   0029560   DLC KEmT TNJ KyLx MiEM IU OC1W TxFTC

Za
N195
938Jd

Nathan, Robert, 1894–
Journey of Tapiola ... [London]
Constable & company ltd[1938]
3p.l.,102,[1]. 17cm.
Illus. t.-p.
"First published in 1938"

NN   0029561   CtY

Nathan, Robert, 1894–
Journey of Tapiola, by Robert Nathan; with decorations
by Georg Salter. New York, A. A. Knopf, 1938.
4 p. l., [7]–121, [1] p. illus. 21¼ cm.
Maps on lining-papers.
"First edition."

    1. Dogs—Legends and stories. I. Title.
         [Full name: Robert Gruntal Nathan]
Library of Congress   PZ3.N195Jou   38–27957

WaT IdU WaS Or OrMonO WaSp IdPI
GU PPGi PP NIC CU NN ViU OU OEac OCl OC1W WaWW WaE
NN   0029562   DLC KEmT CaBVa OrCS IEN CoU NBuU TNJ

Nathan, Robert, 1894–
Journey of Tapiola, by Robert Nathan; with decorations by
George Salter. New York, A. A. Knopf, 1944.
4 p. l. [7]–121, [1] p. illus. 21¼ cm.
Maps on lining-papers.
"First edition."

NN   0029563   ViU

Nathan, Robert, 1894–
Long after summer. [1st ed.] New York, A. A. Knopf,
1948.
146 p. 20 cm.

    I. Title.   Full name: Robert Gruntal Nathan.
PZ3.N195Lo   48–8246*

WaT WaSpG NcGU
PSt NN ViU MB OO TxU LU OU OOxM Or OrP WaS WaE WaSp
NN   0029564   DLC NBuU KEmT ICU OCU Mi OC1W PHC PPT

Za
N195
948Ld

Nathan, Robert, 1894–
Long after summer ... London, Sampson
Low[1949]
4p.l.,102p. 19cm.
"First published in Great Britain 1949"

NN   0029565   CtY

VOLUME 405

Nathan, Robert, 1894–
A luz de manhã. Tradução de Hamilcar de Garcia. Pôrto Alegre, Livraria do Glôbo ₍1944₎
163 p. 19 cm. (Coleção Tucano, 5)
Translation of But gently day.

I. Title.
Full name: Robert Gruntal Nathan.
PS3527.A74B85   50–51473

NN 0029566   DLC CtY

Za
N195
En959W

Nathan, Robert, 1894–   The fiddler in Barly. German tr. Wagner.
... Das Mädchen aus Barly. Wien, Berlin, Stuttgart, P.Neff Verlag, 1955
236,[1]p. 20½cm.
Translated by Elfriede Wagner.

x. His title: Das Mädchen von Barly.
I. Wagner, Elfrie-   de   tr.

NN 0029567   CtY

Za
N195
En954S

Nathan, Robert, 1894–   Jezebel's husband. German tr. Schweinitz.
... Der Mann der Dame Jesabel, Komödie; deutsche Ubertragung: M. v. Schweinitz. München, Wien [etc.] Theaterverlag Kurt Desch [1954]
2 p. ℓ., 118 p. 20½ cm.
Reproduced from typewritten copy.

I.Schweinitz, Maria(Brandrup) von, 1889– tr.
x.his title: Der M⸗ der Dame Jesabel.

NN 0029568   CtY

Nathan, Robert, 1894–
The married look. ₍1st ed.₎ New York, Knopf, 1950.
195 p. 21 cm.

I. Title.
Full name: Robert Gruntal Nathan.
PZ3.N195Mar   50–13123

WaS WaT
ViU AAP TxU NcGU OC1 MiU NcU ICU OrCS OrP WaE WaSp
NN 0029570   DLC KU CSt TNJ MU CoU IU GU OU NN MB

Nathan, Robert, 1894–
Mr. Whittle and the morning star ₍by₎ Robert Nathan ... New York, A. A. Knopf, 1947.
5 p. ℓ., 3–175 p., 1 l. 19¼ᵐ.
"A condensed version of this story appeared in Cosmopolitan."— Dust jacket.
"First edition."

I. Title.
Full name: Robert Gruntal Nathan
PZ3.N195Mi   47–775

PP ICU MB MsU OrCS KEmT WaTC WaSpG
WaE KU WaSp WaS KyLx CtY NcGU TxU ViU PPGi PU PSt
NN 0029571   DLC CtU KMK CoU NcD TNJ OrP CaBVa OrU

Za
N195
Eh948C

Nathan, Robert, 1894–   Mr.Whittle and the morning star. French tr. Chevet.
... M. Whittle et l'étoile du matin (Mr. Whittle and the morning star); tr. par Vic Chevet. [Paris]Hachette[1948]
190p.,1ℓ. 19cm. (Les meilleurs romans étrangers)

x. His title: M. Whittle et l'étoile du matin. I. Chevet, Vic   tr.

NN 0029572   CtY

Nathan, Robert, 1894–
Morning in Iowa ₍by₎ Robert Nathan. New York, A. A. Knopf, 1944.
3 p. l., 3–50 p., 1 l. 20ᵐ.
Narrative poem.
"First edition."

I. Title.
Full name: Robert Gruntal Nathan
Library of Congress   PS3527.A74M6   44–3669
                                                        811.5

PP PPT PSt OU OC1 OLak OrP Or Wa WaS WaSp OrCS KU
NN 0029573   DLC MiU NcD KMK GU NcC FMU LU TxU MB

Za
N195
Ek947B

Nathan, Robert, 1894–   The bishop's wife. Spanish tr. Bazán.
... La mujer del obispo. Buenos Aires, Ediciones Siglo Veinte[1947]
159,[1]p. 20½cm. (Colección: La rosa de los vientos)
Translated by Armando Bazán.

I. Bazán, Armando, 1902–   tr.
x. His title: La mujer del obispo.

NN 0029574   CtY

PS3527
.A73N2

NATHAN,ROBERT,1894–
Nathan 3: The sea-gull cry, The innocent Eve, The river journey, three complete books by Robert Nathan. London, Staples ₍1952₎
247 p.

xI. Tc: The innocent Eve. xII. Tc: The river journey. xIII. Tc: The sea-gull cry. IV. Tc.

NN 0029575   InU CtY

Nathan, Robert, 1894–
One more spring. New York, Grosset & Dunlap ₍c1933₎
212 p.

NN 0029576   CaBVa Wa

Nathan, Robert, 1894–
One more spring ₍by₎ Robert Nathan. New York, A. A. Knopf, 1933.
3 p. l., 3–212 p., 1 l. 19¼ᵐ.
"First edition."

I. Title.
Full name: Robert Gruntal Nathan
Library of Congress   PZ3.N195Oh   33–3086

MB WaTC WaE WaT MtU IdU MtBC WaS Or CaBVa WaWW
CtY OrU KMK NcU NjP ViU MiU OC1 OCU ODW NN PSC PU
NN 0029577   DLC KU OrStbM IdB WaSpG KEmT PSt OkU

PZ
3
N195
On
HRC

Nathan, Robert, 1894–
One more spring ₍by₎ Robert Nathan. New York, Grosset & Dunlap [1934, c1933]
212p. 20cm.

"Twelfth printing May, 1934."

NN 0029578   TxU OrCS IdU OrPR

Nathan, Robert, 1894–
One more spring... N.Y., Knopf, 1934.
212p.

NN 0029579   OO

Nathan, Robert, 1894–
... One more spring. Stamford, Conn., The Overbrook press, 1935.
4 p. l., 153 p., 1 l. col. illus. 22 cm.
"Of this edition ... 750 copies have been printed ... typography, cover paper & illustrations by W. A. Dwiggins."

I. Title.
Full name: Robert Gruntal Nathan
PS3527.A74O6 1935   813.5   36–19344

NBuU NIC TxU
NN 0029580   DLC FU CSt NjN NjP ICN MH NN WU MoSW

Nathan, Robert, 1894–
One more spring ... [New York] The American mercury, inc. [1940?]
125 p. 20 cm. (On cover: Bestseller library)

NN 0029581   RPB

Nathan, Robert, 1894–   One more spring... New York. Knopf, 1942.
212 p.

NN 0029582   PU

Nathan, Robert, 1894–
One more spring, by Robert Nathan. New York, Editions for the armed services ₍1945₎ c1933. 127(1) p. 10 x 14cm. (Armed services editions. R-3.)
In original illustrated covers with series note and advertisements.
On cover: Overseas edition for the armed forces.
Imperfect: many lower edges cropped.

NN 0029583   NN

PS3527
.A74 O 6
1948

Nathan, Robert, 1894–
One more spring. New York, A. A. Knopf, 1948.
212 p. 20cm.

I. Title.
Full name: Robert Gruntal Nathan
NN 0029584   MB

Nathan, Robert, 1894–
The orchid, by Robert Nathan. Indianapolis, The Bobbs-Merrill company ₍c1931₎
198, ₍1₎ p. 19½ᵐ.
"First edition."

I. Title.
Library of Congress   PZ3.N195Or   31–9687

NBuU CoU ViU PPGi PU ICU MiU WaE WaS WaSp WaSpG OrCS
NN 0029585   DLC NcU NNC TNJ OKentU OO OC1 OEac MB

PS
3527
.A74
O6
1932

Nathan, Robert, 1894–
The orchid. ₍Decorations by Barbara Heath₎ London, E. Mathews & Marrot, 1932.
viii, 181p. 20cm.

NN 0029586   IU MiU CtY CaBVaU

Za
N195
Ek947B

Nathan, Robert, 1894–   The orchid. Spanish tr. Bazán.
... La orquidea. Buenos Aires, Ediciones Siglo Veinte [1950]
3p.ℓ.,9–171p.,2ℓ. 20½cm. (Colección: La rosa de los vientos)
Translated by Armando Bazán.
In case with his The bishop's wife, Spanish tr. Bazán. ... La mujer ... [1947]

I. Bazán, Armando, 1902–   tr.
x. His title: La orquidea.

NN 0029587   CtY

VOLUME 405

Nathan, Robert, 1894–
Peter Kindred, by Robert Nathan.   New York, Duffield and company, 1919.
4 p. l., 3–352 p.   19½ᶜᵐ. $2.00

ɪ. Title.
Library of Congress   PZ3.N195Pe   20–1889

    MiU OO NN
NN 0029588   DLC IdU ViU MoSW NBuU IU UU ICU TxU

PS3527
.A74P4   **Nathan, Robert,** 1894–
1920   Peter Kindred.   New York, Duffield, 1920.
            362 p.   20cm.

NN 0029589   ViU MB

Za   **Nathan, Robert,** 1894–   Portrait of
N195   Jennie. French tr. Delamain.
Eh947D ... Le portrait de Jennie; tr. de l'anglais par Germaine Delamain. Paris, Stock, 1947
        2p.ℓ.,[7]–165p.,1ℓ. 19cm.

        x. His title: Le portrait de Jennie.
        I. Delamain,   Germaine   tr.

NN 0029590   CtY

Nathan, Robert, 1894–
Portrait of Jennie, by Robert Nathan. New York, A. A. Knopf, 1940.
4 p. l., 3–212 p., 1 l. 20½ᶜᵐ.
"First edition."

ɪ. Title.
                          ₍Full name: Robert Gruntal Nathan₎
Library of Congress   PZ3.N195Po   40–27011

IdU–SB WaS OrMonO CaBVa WaSp OrPS OrAshS Or
NcU NcD ViU PPD PSC PPCCH OC1W OCU OOxM OO WaT IdU
NN 0029591   DLC PPT KEmT InU OU MB MU ICU CtY KMK

Nathan, Robert, 1894–
Portrait of Jennie, by Robert Nathan.   New York, Editions for the armed services ₍1945, c1939₎. 127(1) p. 10 x 14cm.
(Armed services editions. 655.)

In original illustrated covers with series note and advertisements.
On cover: Overseas edition for the armed forces.
Imperfect: lower edges of p. 127–₍128₎ cropped.

NN 0029592   NN ViU WaS WaT OC1W WaSp OC1 OC1ND

PS   **Nathan, Robert,** 1894–
3527   Portrait of Jennie, by Robert Nathan.
A74   Cleveland, World [1946]
P6   4p.ℓ.,3–212p.,1ℓ.
1946

NN 0029593   UU TxU ICU DLC–P4 CaBVaU

Za   **Nathan, Robert,** 1894–
N195   Portrait of Jennie ... London,
940Pdc Sampson Low, Marston & co.,1td.[1949]
        2 p. ℓ., 172 p. 19 cm.

NN 0029594   CtY

Nathan, Robert, 1894–
Portrait of Jennie.   New York, Knopf, 1953 [c1939]
212 p.

NN 0029595   PP

Nathan, Robert, 1894–
The puppet master, by Robert Nathan ... New York, R. M. McBride & company, 1923.
4 p. l., 221 p.   20ᶜᵐ.

ɪ. Title.
                          ₍Full name: Robert Gruntal Nathan₎
Library of Congress   PZ3.N195Pu   23–14805 rev.

    WaS OrCS CaBVa
    GU ICU PPL PPGi PU OEac OC1 OC1W MtU WaWW NcU MB KU
NN 0029596   DLC PPT OU ViU MeB UU IaU MiU KMK CoU

Nathan, Robert, 1894–
The puppet master, by Robert Nathan. With decorations by A. Wyndham Payne. London: J. Lane ₍1924₎. x, 187 p. illus. 12°.

151938A. 1. Fiction (American).   2. Payne, A. Wyndham, illustrator.
3. Title.
N. Y. P. L.   October 2, 1924

NN 0029597   NN IU MiU CtY

813
N195p   NATHAN, ROBERT, 1894–
1923r   The puppet master, by Robert Nathan .₍.
        New York, R.M. McBride & company, 1925 [c1923]
        4p ℓ.,221p. 20cm.

        "Third printing."

NN 0029598   TxU IdU OU

Nathan, Robert, 1894–
Read at a luncheon given by Fannie Hurst, Anne O'Hare McCormack & H. L. Mencken to Blanche W. Knopf on December 18, 1940. ₍Norwood, Mass., The Plimpton press, 1941₎

Nathan, Robert, 1894–
O retrato de Jennie, tradução de Erico Verissimo. ₍Porto Alegre₎ Edições Meridiano ₍1942₎
179 p. 18 cm. (Coleção Tucano, 1)

    ɪ. Verissimo, Erico, 1905–   tr. ɪɪ. Title.   (Series)
                          Full name: Robert Gruntal Nathan.
                PS3527.A74P66   48–43254*

NN 0029600   DLC

Za   **Nathan, Robert,** 1894–   Portrait of
N195   Jennie. Spanish tr. Bazán.
Ek947B ... Retrato de Jennie. Buenos Aires,
        Ediciones Siglo Veinte[1947]
        2p.ℓ.,7–156p.,1ℓ. 20½cm. (Colección:
        La rosa de los vientos)
        Spanish translation by Armando Bazán.
        In case with his The bishop's wife. Spanish
        tr. Bazán. ... La mujer ... [1947]
        x. His title: Retrato de Jennie.
        I. Bazán, Armando, 1902–   tr.

NN 0029601   CtY MB

Nathan, Robert, 1894–
Ritratto di Jennie. [Traduzione di Giovanni Fletzer] [Milano] Bompiani, 1948.
120 p.

NN 0029602   DLC–P4 OC1

Nathan, Robert, 1894–
The river journey. ₍1st ed.₎ New York, A. A. Knopf, 1949.
196 p. 21 cm.
"Serialized in the Woman's home companion ₍April and May 1949₎"

    ɪ. Title.
                          Full name: Robert Gruntal Nathan.
                PZ3.N195Ri   49–10410*

    WaSp WaT
    PPL OO PU WU GU CaBVa IdB Or OrCS OrP OrU WaS WaE
NN 0029603   DLC NN MB INS NcU OU FU KMK CoU ViU PP

Nathan, Robert, 1894–
... Road of ages. New York, A. A. Knopf, 1935.
4 p. l., 3–231, ₍3₎ p. 19½ᶜᵐ.
Illustrated lining-papers.
"First edition."

ɪ. Title.
                          ₍Full name: Robert Gruntal Nathan₎
Library of Congress   PZ3.N195Ro   35–1939

    MtBC OrCS OrU Or CaBViP WaSp CaBVaU IdPI PPT
    OC1h NN MoU WaTC MtU IdU WaS CaBVa WaE WaT
    ViU CtY KyLx MB PP PPDrop PHC MiU OC1 OC1W
NN 0029604   DLC WaSpG CoU IEN NBuU NcD KyU

Nathan, Robert, 1894–
The sea-gull cry, by Robert Nathan. New York, A. A. Knopf, 1942.
4 p. l., 3–214 p., 1 l. 20½ᶜᵐ.
"First edition."

ɪ. Title.
                                           42–13731
Library of Congress   PZ3.N195Se

    Or CaBVa OrU WaE WaSpG OrPS WaWW
    PBm PSt OCU OO OC1 OU ViU MB NcD KyLx WaS OrP IdB
NN 0029605   DLC KMK PPT InU CoU GU NBuU PHC PPD

Nathan, Robert, 1894–
Selected poems of Robert Nathan. New York & London, A. A. Knopf, 1935.
3 p. l., v–ix, 37, ₍1₎ p. 23ᶜᵐ.
"First edition."

                          ₍Full name: Robert Gruntal Nathan₎
Library of Congress   PS3527.A74A6 1935   35–29608
——— Copy 2.
Copyright A 88191   ₍3₎   811.5

    NN PP TxU OC1 OC1CC OC1h
NN 0029606   DLC CaBVaU Wa Or CoU MiU NcD MeB NcRS

Nathan, Robert, 1894–
Selected poems of Robert Nathan. London, Constable ₍1936₎
89,₍1₎ℓ. front.(port.)

First published in Great Britain in 1936.

NN 0029607   ScU CtY

Nathan, Robert, 1894–
Sir Henry. ₍1st ed.₎ New York, Knopf, 1955 ₍ᶜ1954₎
187 p. 21 cm.

    ɪ. Title.
                          Full name: Robert Gruntal Nathan.
                PZ7.N195Si   54—12039 ‡

    IdB OrCS OrP OrMonO OrU WaS WaSp WaT WaE
    OC1 IU PPT PP PPL PLF OO CaBVaU OCU NcU OOxM FU CaBVa
NN 0029608   DLC PWcS UU FMU GU OC1W PU TxU NcD NN

Nathan, Robert, 1894–
Son of Amittai, by Robert Nathan. London, W. Heinemann, ltd., 1925.
3 p. l., 166, ₍1₎ p. 19ᶜᵐ.
American edition (New York, R. M. McBride & company) has title: Jonah.

1. Jonah, the prophet—Fiction.   ɪ. Title.

Library of Congress   PZ3.N195So   26–3381

NN 0029609   DLC NN CtY OC1 PU

VOLUME 405

Nathan, Robert, 1894–
Tapiola's brave regiment, by Robert Nathan, illustrated by Kurt Wiese. New York, A. A. Knopf, 1941.
4 p. l., [7]–137, [1] p. illus. 21½cm.
Map on lining-papers.
"First edition."

1. Dogs—Legends and stories. I. Wiese, Kurt, 1887– illus. II. Title.
[Full name: Robert Gruntal Nathan]
Library of Congress PZ3.N195Tap 41—16062

OrP IdB WaT WaS Or Wa OrU
CoU MiU NcD NIC ViU PP PBm PPPD OOxM OCl OLak CaBVa
NN 0029610 DLC TNJ INS MeB OU CLU OKentU ICN KMK

Nathan, Robert, 1894–
There is another heaven, by Robert Nathan. Indianapolis, The Bobbs-Merrill company [°1929]
190, [2] p. 19½cm.

I. Title.
Library of Congress PZ3.N195Th 29-20011

MtU WaS OrCS
NBuU PPGi OU OCU OCl ViU NcRS WaTC WaSp WaE WaSpG
NN 0029611 DLC PPT TNJ OKentU KMK CoU GU OkU InU

Nathan, Robert, 1894–
They went on together, by Robert Nathan. New York, A. A. Knopf, 1941.
4 p. l., 3–191, [2] p. 20½cm.
"First edition."

I. Title.
[Full name: Robert Gruntal Nathan]
Library of Congress PZ3.N195Thy 41-2317

WaE Wa WaSp WaS WaSpG OrCS
OCl NcD MB ViU PBm PPL WaWW WaT Or MtU OrU IdU CaBVa
NN 0029612 DLC KEmT PPT CtY GU ICU OU TNJ OO OCU

Za
N195
Eq941P
Nathan, Robert, 1894– Winter in April. Swedish tr. Olson.
... Tidig vår; till svenska av E. W. Olson. Stockholm, Skoglunds bokförlag [1941]
2p. l., 7-228, [1]p. 23½cm.

x. His title: Tidig vår.
I. Olson, E W tr.

NN 0029613 CtY

Za
N195
Eq944T
Nathan, Robert, 1894– They went on together. Swedish tr. Törnell.
... Tillsammans - vidare, översättning fran engelskan av Aida Törnell. Stockholm, Steinsviks bokförlag [1944]
172p. 20½cm.

x. His title: Tillsammans - vidare.
I. Törnell, Aida tr.

NN 0029614 CtY

Nathan, Robert, 1894–
The train in the meadow. [1st ed.] New York, Knopf, 1953.
178 p. 21 cm.

I. Title.
Full name: Robert Gruntal Nathan.
PZ3.N195Tr 53–6846 ‡

OrP WaE KEmT
OCU OOxM PU PPL PP PBL OCl OO TxU NN OU CoU OrCS
NN 0029615 DLC CLU PWcS GU MB INS MiU KMK OWorP

Special Coll.
Nathan, Robert, 1894–
Two Robert Nathan pieces: A talk with Robert Nathan; Advice to my son. [Evansville, Ind., Herbert W. Simpson, Inc., 1950]
[12] p. 18 cm. (Typophile monograph no. 28)

A talk with Robert Nathan, by Harvey Breit, "from the New York Times Book Review ... 1950." Advice to my son, a poem, "reprinted from The Green leaf, by Robert Nathan."

NN 0029616 MeB ViU MH CU

Za
N195
En948L
Nathan, Robert, 1894– The enchanted voyage. German tr. Lorenz.
... Verzauberte Reise, ein kleiner Roman. Salzburg, Verlag "Das Silberboot," 1948
293, [1]p. 19½cm.
Translated by J. N. Lorenz.

x. His title: Verzauberte Reise.
I. Lorenz, J N tr.

NN 0029617 CtY DLC-P4

Za
N195
Ek947B
Nathan, Robert, 1894– The fiddler in Barly. Spanish tr. Bazán.
... El violinista de Barly. Buenos Aires, Ediciones Siglo Veinte [1949]
157p., 1l. 20cm. (Colección: La rosa de los vientos)
Translated by Armando Bazán.
In case with his The bishop's wife. Spanish tr. Bazán. ... La mujer ... [1947]

I. Bazán, Armando, 1902– tr.
x. His title: El violinista de Barly.

NN 0029618 CtY MB

PS3527
.A82R66
D8E3
NATHAN, ROBERT, 1894–
...De weg van eeuwen (Road of ages) uit het Amerikaansch vertaald door Hans van Eeden. Santpoort, C.A. Mees, 1936.
214 p. 19½cm.

NN 0029619 ICU CtY

Za
N195
En952S
Nathan, Robert, 1894– The married look. German tr. Schweinitz.
... Wer warst du Clementine, Roman. [Braunschweig] G. Westermann Verlag [1952]
178p. 19½cm.
Translated by Maria von Schweinitz.

x. His title: Wer warst du Clementine?
I. Schweinitz, Maria (Brandrup) von, 1889– tr.

NN 0029620 CtY PPG

Nathan, Robert, 1894–
... Winter in April. New York, A. A. Knopf, 1938.
4 p. l., [3]–228 p., 2 l. 20½ cm.
"First edition."

I. Title.
PZ3.N195Wi 38—27028

OrMonO OrCS OrU CaBVa WaSpG IdPI CaBVaU
PPL PPT KU NcD CtY InU CoU KMK MB WaTC IdU Or WaS
NN 0029621 DLC NN ViU OEac OLak OCU OCl PU PBm

Nathan, Robert, 1894–
A winter tide; sonnets & poems, by Robert Nathan. New York, A. A. Knopf, 1940.
viii p., 2 l., 3–54 p., 1 l. 21½cm.
"First edition."

I. Title.
[Full name: Robert Gruntal Nathan]
40—27658
Library of Congress PS3527.A74W5 1940
811.5

NcD NjP MiU ViU OrCS KMK Or CaBVaU IdPI
NN 0029622 DLC TNJ PPGi IdU WaS OClCC OCl OO NcC

Nathan, Robert, 1894–
A winter tide; sonnets & poems, by Robert Nathan. New York, A. A. Knopf, 1941
viii p., 2 l., 3–54 p., 1 l. 21½cm.
First edition, reprinted.

NN 0029623 ViU LU

Nathan, Robert, 1894–
The woodcutter's house, by Robert Nathan. Indianapolis, The Bobbs-Merrill company [°1927]
205, [1] p. 20cm.

I. Title.
[Full name: Robert Gruntal Nathan]
Library of Congress PZ3.N195Wo 27—20814

OClh OCl MB NN ViU NNC WaTC WaSp WaSpG TxU
NN 0029624 DLC KMK ICN MsSM MiU NcU IU PPL PU OEac

Za
N195
927Wd
Nathan, Robert, 1894–
The woodcutter's house ... London, E. Mathews & Marrot, 1932
vii p., 1l., 181, [1]p. 19½cm.
Decorations by Barbara Heath.

NN 0029625 CtY NN IU CaBVaU

Nathan, Robert, 1894–
Youth grows old, by Robert Nathan. New York, R. M. McBride & company, 1922.
5 p. l., 54 p. 21½cm.
Poems.

I. Title.
[Full name: Robert Gruntal Nathan]
Library of Congress PS3527.A74Y6 1922 22—7771

PCS NcD MB OClW OU MtU
NN 0029626 DLC GU MH FU NjP FMU IU ViU PU PPCCH

RC164
f.I4L33
Nathan, *Sir* Robert, *d.* 1921.
Report on the measures taken against malaria in the Lahore (Mian Mir) cantonment, by the Hon'ble Mr. R. Nathan ... Lieutenant-Colonel H. B. Thornhill ... and Major L. Rogers ... 1909. Calcutta, Superintendent government printing, 1910.
[3], 55, iv p. incl. tables. 2 fold. maps, 3 fold. diagr. 33½cm.
Maps and diagrs. in pocket.
"Authorities consulted": p. [i]–ii.

1. Malarial fever—Lahore, India. 2. Malarial fever—Prevention.

NN 0029627 ICU DLC-P4 MoU

Nathan, Robert Gruntal
SEE
Nathan, Robert, 1894–

HD9515
N34
Social Sciences
Nathan (Robert R.) Associates, Washingron, D.C.
Economic factors relating to wage negotiations in the steel industry for 1947, by Robert R. Nathan, Oscar Gass and G. Griffith Johnson. [Statistical material assembled by Jeanette M. Gillerman and Harold Seligman. Pittsburgh, Pa., United Steelworkers of America] 1947.
104 p. diagrs., tables.

"Prepared for the United Steelworkers of America by Robert R. Nathan Associates, Inc.".

1. Steel industry and trade - U.S. 2. Wages - U.S. I. Nathan, Robert Roy, 1908– II. United Steelworkers of America. III. Title.

NN 0029629 CU

VOLUME 405

Nathan (Robert R.) Associates, *Washington, D. C.*
Economic position of the steel industry, 1949. Washington, 1949.
53 p.   diagrs., tables.   28 cm.
"A survey of facts for wage negotiations prepared for the United Steelworkers of America."
Errata slip inserted.

1. Steel industry and trade—U. S. 2. Wages—U. S.   i. United Steel Workers of America. ii. Title.

HD9515.N26   338.47672   49–5526*

PPFRB
NN   0029630   DLC NcD IU CU NN OrU OU PU-W PPT PSC

Nathan (Robert R.) Associates, *Washington, D. C.*
An economic programme for Korean reconstruction, prepared for the United Nations Korean Reconstruction Agency. ⟨New York⟩ 1954.
xxvii, 459 p. tables. 28 cm.

1. Korea—Economic policy. i. United Nations. Korean Reconstruction Agency. ii. Title.

HC467.N3   338.9519   54–4582

OCU OU PBm PSt PSC PPT NcD CU NN OrU WaS
NN   0029631   DLC IdU FTaSU UU NNC CLSU ViU MB OCIW

HD
-990
P55N3   **Nathan (Robert R.) Associates, Washington, D. C.**
Evaluation of minimum wage policy in Puerto Rico. Prepared for the Joint Committee on Labor of the legislature of the Commonwealth of Puerto Rico by Robert R. Nathan Associates, inc.. Washington, 1955.
214 l.

1. Wages—Minimum wage—Puerto Rico. I. Puerto Rico. Legislature. Joint Committee on Labor. II.   Title.

NN   0029632   NmU

Nathan (Robert R.) Associates, *Washington, D. C.*
A national economic policy for 1949. Washington, 1949.
52 p. illus. 28 cm.
"Prepared for the Congress of Industrial Organizations."

1. U. S.—Economic policy. 2. U. S.—Econ. condit.—1945–
i. Title.

HC106.5.N23   330.973   49–5639*

NN DNAL NBuG OrP
NN   0029633   DLC NNUN PPFRB PSC PPT PU-W OrCS TxU

HD4975
.N24   **Nathan (Robert R.) associates, Washington, D. C.**

Nathan, Robert Roy, 1908–
A national wage policy for 1947 ⟨by⟩ Robert R. Nathan and Oscar Gass. Washington, D. C. ⟨Robert R. Nathan associates, inc.⟩ 1946.

330.9519   **Nathan (Robert R.) Associates, Washington, D.C.**
N19p   Preliminary report on economic reconstruction of Korea. ⟨Washington⟩ 1952.
193p. tables. 28cm.

At head of title: UNKRA/AG/13.
"Presented in partial fulfillment of the contract between the United Nations Korean Reconstruction Agency and Robert R. Nathan Associates, inc."

NN   0029635   IU MiD

Nathan (Robert R.) associates, inc., Washington, D. C.
Project reports prepared

see under

Tippetts-Abbett-McCarthy-Stratton.

Nathan (Robert R.) associates, inc., Washington, D.C.
...A prospectus for surveying the legitimate theatre in the United States. Prepared for Actors' equity association by Robert R. Nathan associates, inc. ⟨Washington⟩ 1948.   1 v.
28cm.

556839B. 1. Stage—Economics—   U. S. i. Actors' equity association.
N. Y. P. L.   December 1, 1950

NN   0029637   NN MH-BA

Nathan, Robert Roy, 1908–
... Camino de la abundancia; introducción de Víctor L. Urquidi; versión española de Rodolfo Selke. México, D. F., Fondo de cultura económica ⟨1944⟩

3 p. l., 9–295 p. 19¹⁄₂ᶜᵐ. (Half-title: Sección de obras de economía ⟨del Fondo de cultura económica⟩ dirigida por Daniel Cosío Villegas. ii. Manuales introductorios)

At head of title: Robert R. Nathan.
"Primera edición en inglés, 1944; primera edición en español, 1944."

1. U. S.—Economic policy. 2. Reconstruction (1939–   )—U. S. i. Selke, Rudolf, tr. ii. Title.   Translation of Mobilizing for abundance.

                                                            A 45–2964
Yale univ.   Library
for Library of Congress   ⟨3⟩

NN   0029638   CtY DPU

Nathan, Robert Roy, 1908–
Estimates of unemployment in the United States, 1929–1935, by Robert R. Nathan ...

(In International labour review, Geneva. January, 1936, v. 33, p. ⟨49–73⟩)

1. Unemployed—U. S. ⟨1. Unemployment—U. S.⟩   i. Title.

Library, U. S. Dept. of   Labor   L 36–71
Library of Congress   [HD4811.I 65 vol. 33]

NN   0029639   DL

HD5711
.N27   Nathan, Robert Roy, 1908–
Law   Estimates of unemployment in the United States, 1929–1935, by Robert R. Nathan. Geneva, International Labour Office, 1936.
27 p. 1 fold. chart.
Reprinted from the International labour review, vol. 33, no. 1, Jan. 1936.

1. Unemployed—U.S. I. Title.

NN   0029640   ICU

Nathan, Robert Roy, 1908–
... Expansion in the national income continued in 1935... ⟨Washington? 1936?⟩
6 numb. l.

At head of t.p. U.S. Dept. of commerce...
Bureau of foreign and domestic commerce...

Reprint from Survey of current business.

NN   0029641   OCl

HC106
.3
.A425   Nathan, Robert Roy, 1908–   FOR OTHER EDITIONS SEE MAIN ENTRY

U. S. *Bureau of foreign and domestic commerce.*
... Income in the United States, 1929–37, by Robert R. Nathan, chief, National income section, Division of economic research. November 1938. ⟨Washington, 1938⟩

Nathan, Robert Roy, 1908–
... Mobilizing for abundance. New York, London, Whittlesey house, McGraw-Hill book company, inc. ⟨1944⟩
xv p., 1 l., 228 p. illus., diagrs. 21ᶜᵐ.
At head of title: Robert R. Nathan.

1. U. S.—Economic policy. 2. Reconstruction (1939–   )—U. S. i. Title.
                                                            44–2680
Library of Congress   HC106.4.N32
                                ⟨25⟩   330.973

Wa WaE WaS WaSp WaWW NNUN
ViU NcD Or CaBVaU IdB IdU MtBC OrCS OrP OrSaW
NcC TU PP PHC PSt PU OCl OCU OO OU MiHM DNAL
NN   0029643   DLC OrU FTaSU KyU KyLx ScU NcRS

HC106
.3
.A424   Nathan, Robert Roy, 1908–

U.S. *Bureau of foreign and domestic commerce.*
... National income, 1929–36, by Robert R. Nathan, chief, National income section, Division of economic research. Washington, U. S. Govt. print. off., 1937.

Nathan, Robert Roy, 1908–
A national wage policy for 1947 ⟨by⟩ Robert R. Nathan and Oscar Gass. Washington, D. C. ⟨Robert R. Nathan associates, inc.⟩ 1946.
2 p. l., 71 p. incl. tables, diagrs. 28 x 21¾ᶜᵐ.
"Prepared by Robert R. Nathan associates, inc., at the request of the Congress of industrial organizations."—p. ⟨2⟩ of cover.

1. Wages—U. S. 2. Profit. i. Gass, Oscar, 1914–   joint author. ii. Nathan (Robert R.) associates, Washington, D. C. iii. Congress of industrial organizations. iv. Title.

HD4975.N24   331.2973   47–896

N DNAL ICJ MB NN NNC PHC PPFRB OrCS
NN   0029645   DLC OrU OrPR MtU NcD NIC OClCC PU-W

Nathan, Robert Roy, 1908–
Palestine: problem and promise; an economic study by Robert R. Nathan, Oscar Gass ⟨and⟩ Daniel Creamer. ⟨Washington⟩ Public affairs press, American council on public affairs ⟨1946⟩
x, 675 p. 24ᶜᵐ.
Maps on lining-papers.
"Prepared under the auspices of the American Palestine institute."
Bibliographical references included in "Notes and acknowledgments" (p. 687–661)

1. Palestine—Econ. condit. i. Gass, Oscar. ii. Creamer, Daniel Barnett, 1909–   iii. American council on public affairs. iv. Title.
                                                            46–3167
Library of Congress   HC497.P2N3
                                ⟨25⟩   330.9569

Or OrCS OrP OrPR Wa WaSp WaWW WaS PPT
OCU OOxM OCl ViU MB CaBVa MtBC NNZI IdB MtU
CaBVaU NcD NcGU TU ICU PSC PP PU TxU OEac
NN   0029646   DLC CU CoU NNC MiU CaBViP

Nathan, Robert Roy, 1908– joint author

Dewhurst, James Frederic, 1895–
... Social and economic character of unemployment in Philadelphia, April, 1930 ⟨by⟩ J. Frederic Dewhurst and Robert R. Nathan, Industrial research department, Wharton school of finance and commerce, University of Pennsylvania ... March, 1932. Washington, U. S. Govt. print. off., 1932.

HC
497
P2N2.9   Nathan, Robert Roy, 1908–
The world's newest success story. [New York, 1951?]
[1] p. (fold.) 26 cm.
Cover title.
Reprinted from the New York Post.

1. Israel—Economic conditions.
I. Title

NN   0029649   OCH

Nathan, Roger.
Politique économique de la France, par Roger Nathan et Paul Delouvrier. Paris, Les Cours de droit ⟨1949⟩
4 v. (434 p.) 24 cm.
At head of title: Université de Paris. Institut d'études politiques, 1948–1949.

1. France—Economic policy. i. Delouvrier, Paul, joint author.
                                                            A 52–5421
New York Univ. Wash.   Sq. Library HC278.N3
for Library of Congress   ⟨1⟩

NN   0029650   NNU-W MH

Nathan, Roger.
...Politique économique de la France, par Roger Nathan...et Paul Delouvrier... Paris, Les Cours de droit [1950] 4 v. in 1. (434 p.) 24cm.
(Cours de l'Institut d'études politiques publiés aux "Cours de droit" en 1948–1949)

At head of title: Université de Paris. Institut d'études politiques, 1948–1949.

576850B. 1. Economic history—France. I. Delouvrier, Paul, jt. au.

NN   0029651   NN

VOLUME 405

Nathan, Roger,
    Politique économique de la France
      For later editions see under   Delouvrier,
Paul.

Nathan, Roger.
  ... Le rôle international des grands marchés financiers.
Paris, Librairie du Recueil Sirey, s. a., 1938.

  3 p. l., ₉₎–182 p. 24ᵐ. (Publications de l'Institut universitaire de
hautes études internationales, Genève (Suisse) ... no. 19)

  1. Finance. 2. Foreign exchange. ɪ. Title.

                                            39–13645
Library of Congress   HG174.N3
      ₍2₎   332.15

NN 0029653   DLC NIC ICU CU OCU

Nathan, Roger, *betannif*
  ... Contribution à l'étude "in situ" de l'anato-
mie de ceratopteris thalictroides ... Gap, 1937.
  Thèse – Univ. de Marseille.
  "Bibliographie": p. [104]–106.

NN 0029654   CtY

Nathan, Rudolf, 1877–
  ... Über complicierte schädelfrakturen ... Bonn, J. v.
d. Walde, 1902.
  44 p. 22½ᵐ.
  Inaug.-diss.—Bonn.
  Vita.
  "Litteratur": p. 43.

  1. Skull—Fracture.

Library of Congress   RD529.N27
                                  6–46625†

NN 0029655   DLC DNLM MH

FILM   Nathan, S   R
13538   [Seamen welfare in Singapore. Singapore, 1954]
HD   137 ℓ. illus., tables, maps. On film (positive)

Microfilm. Original in Cornell Univ. Library.
"Acknowledgement" signed: S.R. Nathan.
Title-page lacking; title supplied from microfilm.
Research paper – Dept. of Social Studies, Univ. of Malaya.
Includes bibliography.

  1. Seamen – Singapore. 2. Merchant seamen – Singapore.

NN 0029656   CU

Nathan, Salomon.
  Ein Blick in die Ewigkeit. Festpredigt zur
Seelenfeier ... am Passah-Feste ... Rostock,
Selbstverl., 1879.
  14 p.

NN 0029657   OCH

W   Nathan, Sam
4   Le Trachome en Irak, sa prophylaxie;
L38   contribution à l'étude de l'épidémiologie
1947 du trachome. Lausanne, Risold, 1947.
      28 p. illus.

    Thèse - Lausanne.
    Bibliography: p. 27–28.

NN 0029658   DNLM

Nathan, Samson Philip
  ...Die Tonzeichen in der Bibel, von Dr. S. P. Nathan. Hamburg, S. Nissensohn, 1893. 42 p. 26cm.

  At head of title: Talmud Tora. Realschule. Bericht über das Schuljahr 1892—
1893.
  "1893. Progr. No. 738."

  1. Hebrew language—Accents   and accentuation. ɪ. Talmud Tora,
Hamburg.
N.Y.P.L.   February 13, 1948

NN 0029659   NN OCH PPDrop DCU–H

Nathan, Sarina, ed.
  Boncompagno *da Signa, 13th cent.*
  ... Amicitia di Maestro Boncompagno da Signa, ed. a
cura di Sarina Nathan. Roma, La Società, 1909.

Nathan, Theodore R   1911–
  The first hotel promotion work book, by Theodore R. Nathan ... and Jack Steiner ... New
York, Alden-Kent ₍c1940₎
  1 v. illus.

  Various pagings.
  1. Hotels, taverns, etc. - Management.
2. Advertising - Hotels, taverns, etc.
I. Steiner, Jack jt. au. II. Title: Hotel
promotion work book.

NN 0029661   NNC OC1

Nathan, Theodore R   1911–
  Hotel promotion, by Theodore R. Nathan ... New York
and London, Harper & brothers, 1941.
  xii p., 1 l., 268 p. incl. forms. front., plates. 24ᵐ.
  "First edition."

  1. Hotels, taverns, etc.—Management. 2. Advertising—Hotels, taverns, etc. ɪ. Title.
                                  41–22824
Library of Congress   TX911.N3
      ₍10₎   647.94

NN 0029662   DLC TU OC1 OU

Nathan, Theodore R., 1911–

  ... Hotel promotion work book ... 1st–
New York, Alden-Kent, inc. ₍ˆ1940–

Nathan, Walter. Influence of stomach upon
mind. 6 pp. (*Westm. Rev.* v. 146, 1896, p. 185.)

NN 0029664   MdBP

                      1869–
Nathan, Walter, Aus d. Klinik f. Psychisch- u. Nerven-
kranke d. Univ. Bonn. Die psychischen Störungen bei
der Huntingtonschen Chorea. Bonn: Eisele 1912. 64 S. 8°
Bonn, Med. Diss. v. 7. Mai 1913, Ref. Westphal
  [Geb. 11. Mai 89 Koblenz; Wohnort: Koblenz; Staatsangeh.: Preußen;
Vorbildung: Gymn. Koblenz Reife O. 07; Studium: Bonn 2, Kiel 1;
Freiburg i. B. 2, München 1, Berlin 1, Bonn 3 S.; Coll. 9. Mai 12;
Approb. 20. Mai 13.]   [U 12. 4858

NN 0029665   ICRL DNLM MH

Nathan, Walter Ludwig, 1905–
  Sir John Cheke und der englische humanismus ... Bonn a.
Rh., Rhenania-verlag, g. m. b. h., 1928.
  106 p., 1 l. 22ᵐ.
  Inaug.-diss.—Bonn.
  Lebenslauf.
  "Verzeichnis der benutzten werke": p. 100–104.

  1. Cheke, Sir John, 1514–1557. 2. Learning and scholarship—Gt.
Brit. 3. Humanism. 4. Classical literature—Appreciation.
                                  30–2608
Library of Congress   PA85.C55N3

NN 0029666   DLC DBS CtY PU MH IU MiU

Nathan, Mrs. Wilfrid

see

Granville Baker, Lola Marie Therese, 1906–

              There are no cards for numbers

             NN 0029668 to NN 0030000

Nathan (Wilhelm). *Ist bei Myomen während
der Gravidität die supravaginale Uterusamputa-
tion indicirt? 25 pp. 8°. *Würzburg, F. Röhri,
1896*.

NN 0030001   DNLM

Nathan (Wilhelm) [1864–   ]. *Ueber das
Verhalten der Muskelfasern in Bezug auf Vasco-
dilatation und Hypertrophie nach Nerven-
durchschneidung. 27 pp. 8°. *Bonn, C. Georgi,
1889*.

NN 0030002   DNLM CU

Nathan, Winfred Bertram.
  ... Health conditions in North Harlem, 1923–1927, by Winfred B. Nathan ... an abstract, by Mary V. Dempsey. New
York, National tuberculosis association ₍ˆ1932₎
  68 p. incl. maps. 23ᵐ. (₍National tuberculosis association₎ Social
research series. no. 2)
  The death rates were revised on the basis of the 1930 census population figures. *cf.* Foreword.
  "This study is ... largely a study of negro health."—Introd.

  1. Harlem, New York (City)—Sanit. affairs. 2. Negroes—New York
(City) 3. Negroes—Mortality. 4. Negroes—Statistics, Vital. 5. New
York (City)—Statistics, Vital. 6. Health surveys. ɪ. Dempsey,
Mary V., ed. ɪɪ. Title.

Library of Congress   RA448.H3N3   32–21038
Copyright A 53647   ₍3₎   614.097471

NN 0030003   DLC PPC InU PBm

Nathan-Chapotot, Roger.
  Les Nations Unies et les réfugiés; le maintien de la paix
et le conflit de qualifications entre l'Ouest et l'Est. Préf.
de Hans Wehberg. Paris, A. Pedone, 1949.
  xii, 292 p. 26 cm.
  "Bibliographie": p. ₍277₎–280.

  1. Refugees, Political. 2. World War, 1939–1945—Refugees. 3. International Refugee Organization. ɪ. Title.
  HV640.N28   940.53159   50–15798

NN 0030004   DLC NNUN OU PU NcU MnU NN

Nathan-Chapotot, Roger.
  ...La qualification internationale des réfugiés et personnes
déplacées dans le cadre des Nations unies... Par Roger Nathan-
Chapotot... Paris, A. Pedone, 1949. 292 p. 23cm.
  Thèse — Genève.
  "Bibliographie", p. 277–280.

  537438B. 1. Refugees. 2. World war, 1939–1945—Refugees. 3. International refugee organization.
N. Y. P. L.   November 3, 1950

NN 0030005   NN CSt-H MH-L PU CU-AL

Nathan-David, David Christian
  see David, Christian Georg Nathan, 1793–1874.

Nathan and Lina Straus Health Center, *Jerusalem*
  see Jerusalem. Nathan and Lina Straus Health Center.

VOLUME 405

NATHAN & OLSEN.
Nathan & Olsen, ₍1912₎-1922. ₍Reykjavík,
Prentsmiðjan Acta,1921.

sm.4°.
A daybook published by the firm Nathan &
Olsen which they gave to their customers New
Year's day 1922.

NN   0030008   MH

───────────────────────────

Nathan & Rosselli, London.
Monthly investment list ...
see under title

───────────────────────────

Nathan & Rosselli, *London.*
Time and Adams court; an attempt at reconstruction, issued
by Nathan & Rosselli to clients only. London, 1937.
3 p. L, 86 p. illus., pl. 26ᶜᵐ.
"This book has resulted simply from a desire to mark ... the fact of
our having occupied offices in Adams court for fifty years—from 31st
March, 1887."—Pref.

1. London. Adams court.   I. Title.

Library of Congress   DA687.A7N3   38-9718
                              ₍3₎   942.12

NN   0030010   DLC IEdS CaOTP NN NNC

───────────────────────────

Nathan bros., & Lilley.
The "legislative cyclopedia" of parliamentary laws
and usages. Specially designed for the use of public
assemblies, clubs and associations. Covering every point
of order. ₍New York, Nathan bros., & Lilley, 1885₎
₍3₎ p. 13½ᶜᵐ.

1. Parliamentary practice.   I. Title.
                              CA 25-1170 Unrev'd
Library of Congress   JF515.N3

NN   0030011   DLC

───────────────────────────

Nathan Burkan memorial competition.
Z551P
.C78   Copyright law symposium; the ₍first-   annual₎ Nathan
        Burkan memorial competition. New York city, American
        society of composers, authors & publishers ₍°1939-

───────────────────────────

CT   Nathan Covington Brooks, A. M., president
211   of the Baltimore Female College. ₍n. p.,
B61   ca. 1870₎
v.3   161-176 p. port. 23cm.
no.11   Caption title.
            At head of title: Nathan Covington
            Brooks, of Maryland.
            Detached from a vol. with running title:
            Sketches of eminent Americans (i.e., Bio-
            graphical sketches of eminent Americans₍?₎)
            1. Brooks,   Nathan Covington, 1809-
            1898.

NN   0030013   NIC DLC

───────────────────────────

Nathan der weise
    see under   Lessing, Gotthold Ephraim,
    1729-1781.

───────────────────────────

TX871   Nathan-Dohrmann Company, San Francisco.
N3   "Hints to the hostess." San Francisco [189-]
Agric.   62 p. illus.
Library

1. Table setting and decoration. I. Title.

NN   0030015   CU

───────────────────────────

WX   NATHAN Littauer Hospital Association,
2   Gloversville, N. Y.
AN6   Annual report.
G5N2N
        Gloversville [1893?]-
            v. in   illus.

        Report year ends Apr. 30.
        Principally the annual reports of the
        Nathan Littauer Hospital.
        1. Gloversville, N. Y. Nathan Littauer
        Hospital

NN   0030016   DNLM

───────────────────────────

Nathan M. Thomas ... An account of his life,
    written by himself
        see under   Thomas, Nathan M., 1803-1887

───────────────────────────

621.139 Nathan manufacturing company, New York.
N19c   ... Catalogue of injectors, injector
          attachments, lubricators, oilers,
          engine and boiler fittings.   New York,
          1907.
            175p. illus., tables, fold.diagrs.

          At head of title: Railway edition.

NN   0030017   IU

───────────────────────────

Nathan Perkins Seymour, 1813-1891 ... ₍New Haven,
Press of Tuttle, Morehouse & Taylor₎ 189-.
₍40₎ p. 19ᵐ.

1. Seymour, Nathan Perkins, 1813-1891.
                                          15-12748
Library of Congress   LD5962.8.S3

NN   0030018   DLC OFH OO

───────────────────────────

Nathan Smith medical club.
Billroth, Theodor, 1829-1894.
    Historical studies on the nature and treatment of gunshot
wounds from the fifteenth century to the present time ₍by₎ Dr.
Theodor Billroth ... Berlin—1859; translated by Dr. C. P.
Rhoads ... and published for the Nathan Smith medical club.
New Haven, Conn., 1933.

───────────────────────────

Nathan Soederblom in memoriam
    see under   Karlström, Nils, 1902-

───────────────────────────

BR45   Nathan Söderblom-sällskapet.
.R44   **Religion och bibel.**
        Lund, C. W. K. Gleerup.

───────────────────────────

Nathan Stein-Schrift
    see under   Schiff, H., comp.

───────────────────────────

Nathan Straus.   New York: J. T. White & Co., 1927.
front. (port.)   8°.
    Printed on one side of leaf only.
    One of fifty copies printed.
    "From the National cyclopedia of American biography."

342325A. 1. Straus, Nathan,   1848-
N. Y. P. L.   January 20, 1928

NN   0030023   NN

───────────────────────────

Nathan the wise; screenplay based on Lessing's
    drama, outline ...
        see under   Lengyel, Menyhért, 1880-
[Supplement]

───────────────────────────

Nathan Trotter and Company
    see
    Trotter (Nathan) and Company.

───────────────────────────

Nathan und Jotham ...
    see under   [Harsdörfer, Georg Philipp]
    1607-1658.

───────────────────────────

Nathanael ben Fayyumi, *12th cent.*
    The bustan al-ukul, by Nathanael ibn al-Fayyumi, ed.
and tr. from an unique manuscript in the library of Columbia university by David Levine ... New York ₍The
Columbia university press₎ 1908.
    xvi, 142, 88 p., 1 l. 24½ᵐ.
    Thesis (PH. D.)—Columbia university.
    Vita.
    Arabic text in Hebrew characters.
    Pub. also as Columbia university Oriental studies, vol. VI.

    I. Levine, David, 1876-   ed. and tr
                                          A 11-1230
Title from Columbia Univ.   Printed by L. C.

NN   0030027   NNC ICU NIC PPDrop PU

───────────────────────────

Nathanael ben Fayyumi, *12th cent.*
    ... The Bustan al-ukul, by Nathanael ibn al-Fayyumi;
ed. and tr. from an unique manuscript in the library of
Columbia university by David Levine, PH. D. New York,
The Columbia university press, 1908.
    xvi, 142, 88 p. 25 cm. (Columbia university oriental studies,
    vol. VI)
    Text (Arabic in Hebrew characters) : 88 p. at end.

    1. Jewish theology.   I. Levine, David, orientalist, ed. and tr.
BM550.N323L4   8-4311 rev
————— Copy 2.   PJ25.O6 vol. 6

NN   0030028   DLC MH NBuC CU NcD MiU NcD OC1 NN

───────────────────────────

Nathanael ben Fayyumi, 12th cent.
    ₍Bustan al-ukul. Hebrew & Judeo-Arabic₎
ספר בסתאן אלעקול. בן השכלים. לרבינו נתנאל בירב פיומי.
המקור הערבי עם תרגום עברי; תורגם וחונה בצרוף מבוא והארות
ע"י יוסף בן דוד קאפח. ירל פעם ראשונה בתרגום עברי.
ירושלים, האגודה להצלת גנזי תימן ₍4 or 1953 .e i 714₎.
    16, 158 p. 25 cm.

    1. Jewish theology.   I. Title: Bustan al-ukul. II. Title: Gan
    ha-sekhalim.
                        Title romanized : Sefer Bustan al-ukul.

BM550.N38   72-225690

NN   0030029   DLC NjR NjP

───────────────────────────

Nathanael ben Isaiah
    see   Nethaneel ben Isaiah, 14th cent.

VOLUME 405

NATHANAEL, converted Jew.
The confession of faith, which Nathanael a
Jew borne, made in the Parish church of Alhall-
owes, whereupon he was according to his desire,
received into the number of the faithfull and
so baptized the first of April, 1577. (In
FOXE, John.-A sermon preached at the christening
of a certaine Jew. 1578.)

NN   0030031   MH

Nathanaël, *monachus*

see

Chumnus, Nicephorus, *ca. 1250-ca. 1327.*

Nathanaël, *monk*
see
Chumnus, Nicephorus, *ca. 1250-ca. 1327.*

Nathanaël, Nicephorus

see

Chumnus, Nicephorus, *ca. 1250-ca. 1327.*

Nathanael; Zeitschrift für die Arbeit der evangelischen Kirche
an Israel. 1.–   Jahrg.; 1885–
Berlin, H. Reuther; New York, B. Westermann.
      22 cm.
Supersedes Friedensbote. Cf. Union list of serials.
Subtitle varies.
Editor: 18   H. L. Strack.

1. Missions—Jews—Period.   I. Strack, Hermann Leberecht, 1848-
1922, ed.
BV2619.N33   56-51020 ‡

NN   0030035   DLC MH-AH OCH NN

Nathanael Emmons, D.D. [n.p.] 1843
      see under Ide, Jacob, 1785-1880.
[Supplement]

Nathanael Greene memorial day, June 6, 1901.
      [1901?]
            Caption-title. 4 p. 22 cm.

NN   0030037   RPB

Nathanblut (Julian) [1877-   ]. *Beitrag zur
Klinik und pathologischen Anatomie der Pan-
creas-Carcinome. 47 pp. 8°. Leipzig, B.
Georgi, 1906.

NN   0030038   DNLM CtY ICRL

Wordsworth
AP   Nathaniel, Sir, pseud.
4   Notes on note-worthies of divers orders,
N55   either sex, and every age, by Sir Nathaniel
n.s.   [pseud.] VI. William Wordsworth.
v.109   (In Colburn's New monthly magazine.
          London. 24cm. new ser., v. 109 (1857)
          p. [379]-392)

      Healey 919.
      1. Wordsworth, William, 1770-1850. I.
Colburn's New   monthly magazine, new
ser., v. 109,   no. 436, April 1, 1857.
II. Title.

NN   0030039   NIC

Nathaniel Bacon, the patriot of 1876
      see under (Eggleston, Edward) 1837-1902.

Case
3A
1131   NATHANIEL Coffin...   [Peoria, Ill., Printed by
         N.C. Nason, 1864]
         8p. 14cm.
            Caption title.
            In case, 16cm.
            Bookplate of Frank C. Deering.

NN   0030041   ICN

Nathaniel Greene Guiberson, jr.   [Stanford,
      Calif., 1947]
         5 l. incl. mounted port. 28cm.

      1. Guiberson, Nathaniel Greene, 1917-1943. 2.
Stanford University. Nathaniel Greene Guiberson
jr. Scholarship.

NN   0030042   CSt

Nathaniel Hawthorne.   Philadelphia, J.B.
      Lippincott company, 1890
            see under [Lathrop, George Parsons]
1851-1898.

PS 1864 Nathaniel Hawthorne on England and the English.
N5   [Boston, 1865]
            245-250 p. 23 cm.

            A review of Our old home.
            "From The Reader."
            Detached from Living age, Nov. 7, 1865.

            1. Hawthorne, Nathaniel, 1804-1864. [Our
old home.

NN   0030044   OU

Nathaniel Macon in national legislation.
      (In Historical papers of the Trinity college historical society.
Durham, N. C., 1900. 21cm. ser. iv, p. 72-88)

      1. Macon, Nathaniel, 1757-1837. 2. U. S.—Politics and government—
1783-1865.
                                          A 40-2310
Duke univ. Library
for Library of Congress   [F251.D83 ser. 4]
      [2]   (975.60062)

NN   0030045   NcD AAP

Nathaniel Parker Willis ... sketch ... taken from
an early number of the N.Y.M.A. quarterly...
In The Ramble ... March 27, 1907 (v. 16;
16) Cornwall-on-Hudson, 1907. 25 cm.

NN   0030046   RPB

929.2   The Nathaniel Ropes estate. n.p., 1904.
R785   14p. 23cm. unbound. (Historical
Sutro   Collections of the Essex Institute,
            vol. 40, no. 1).

NN   0030047   C

... Nathaniel S. Cushing, May 13, 1889
      see under [Ackerman, Arthur Wilmot]
1857-

... Nathaniel S. Cushing, May 13, 1889
      see under [Ackerman, Arthur Wilmot]
1857-

      Nathaniel Usher Hill; born at Brazil, Indiana,
June 21st, 1851, died at Indianapolis, Ind., May
8th, 1908. n.p., n.pub., n.d.

      "The following address was delivered at...Indiana
university, May 11, 1908, in memory of Mr. Hill."

NN   0030050   InU

Nathaniel Wright Lord. A Memorial.   Columbus, Ohio, State University, 1912.
70p.

NN   0030051   OO PU-S

Nathanjahu, Bension
      see
Netanyahu, Benzion.

Nathans, Abraham David.
      Overzicht van de toepassing van complexe functies op natuur-
kundige vraagstukken... door Abraham David Nathans...
Zwolle: W. E. J. Tjeenk Willink[, 1923]. 67 p. 8°.

      Dissertation, Utrecht, 1923.

1. Physics, Mathematical. 2. Func-
N. Y. P. L.   August 31, 1923

NN   0030053   NN ICRL RPB CtY IU MH ICU

QC464 Nathans, Marcel Willem, 1922-
E3N5   The absorption spectra of Eu(SO$_4$)3.8H$_2$O in
the surface and the interior of a crystal.
[Berkeley, Calif., 1949.
         69 l. illus., diagrs., tables.

            Thesis (Ph.D.) - Univ. of California, June
1949.
            "Literature": p. 68-69.

            1. Europium sulphate.

NN   0030054   CU

Nathans, N.
      Die Internationale Transportarbeiter-Föderation; ihr Wesen,
Ziel und Streben, von N. Nathans...   Amsterdam: Ausgabe
der I. T. F., 1922. 31 p. 22cm.

1. Trade unions, Transport-
transport-workers' federation.
N. Y. P. L.   July 29, 1940
                        workers'. I. International

NN   0030055   NN DL

Nathans, Robert, 1927-
      Systematics of photoneutron reactions.
[Philadelphia] 1954.
         iv, 113 numb. l. diagrs. (1 fold. table)
30 cm.
            Thesis (Ph. D.)—University of Pennsylvania,
1954.
            Typewritten.
            Bibliography: l. 106-113.

NN   0030056   PU PU-Math

VOLUME 405

.N3
Hebraic
Sect.)

Nathans, Solomon P
פאפולערע ערקלערונג פון איינשטיין'ס רעלאטיוויטעט טעאריע.
מיט א ביילאגע איבער כעמיע און אסטראנאמיע.
New Rochelle, N. Y. [1931]
175 p. illus. 20 cm.

1. Einstein, Albert, 1879-1955. 2. Relativity (Physics)
      Title transliterated: Populere erklerung
QC6.N3   31–35462 rev⁴

NN   0030057   DLC

Nathansen, Henri, 1868– 1944.
Af Hugo Davids Liv...   København: V. Pio, 1917.   4 v.
8°.
   Contents: v. 1, De unge Aar. v. 2. Byen. v. 3. Flugten fra Festen. v. 4
Det fjærne Land.

1. Fiction (Danish). 2. Jews in   Denmark. 3. Title.
N.Y.P.L.   September 19, 1919.

NN   0030058   NN ViU

Hnp
N195
A4

Nathansen, Henri, 1868–1944
Af Hugo Davids liv; roman. Ny gennemset udg.
København, Nyt Nordisk Forlag – Arnold Busck,
1933.
644p. 22cm.

NN   0030059   CtY

Nathansen, Henri, 1868–
Af Hugo Davids liv.   Copenhagen,
Gyldendalske boghandel, c1938.
2 v.

NN   0030060   WaT N

839.83
N195a
1948

Nathansen, Henri, 1868–1944.
Af Hugo Davids liv; roman. [3. udg.]
København, Gyldendalske boghandel, Nordisk
forlag, 1948.
2v. 22cm.

   Contents.– 1. De unge aar. Byen.– 2.
Flugten fra festen. Det fjerne land.

NN   0030061   IU KyU KU CU WU MH WaU

Nathansen, Henri, 1868–
Die Affäre; Ein bürokratisches Lustspiel in 4 Akten.   Berlin: Oesterheld & Co., 1913.   111(1) p.   16°.

1. Drama (German). 2. Title.
N.Y.P.L.   April 29, 1914.

NN   0030062   NN

Nathansen, Henri, 1868–
... Affæren; komedie i fire akter.   København og Kristiania, Gyldendal, Nordisk forlag, 1913.
3 p. l., 164 p. 20ᵐᵐ.

  ɪ. Title.

                         13–25075

NN   0030063   DLC CaBVaU OrU

Nathansen, Henri, 1868–
Affæren; komedie i fire akten. København og Kristiania, Gyldendal, Nordisk
forlag, 1913.
164p.

Microcard edition.

NN   0030064   ICRL OrU

Nathansen, Henri, 1868–1944.
Danas Have. Idyl i tre Akter.   København,
Gyldendal, 1908.
3 p. l., 144 p.   12°.

NN   0030065   NN

Nathansen, Henri, 1868–
... Dr. Wahl; skuespil i tre akter, med et forspil og et
efterspil. København og Kristiania, Gyldendal, Nordisk
forlag, 1915.
166 p. 19½ᶜᵐ.

  ɪ. Title.

Library of Congress   PT8175.N3D6 1915   16–17171

NN   0030066   DLC NN

Nathansen, Henri, 1868–
... Dr. Wahl, schauspiel in drei akten, mit einem vorspiel und einem nachspiel, von Henri Nathansen; autorisierte uebersetzung aus dem dänischen von dr. John Josephsohn ... Berlin, Oesterheld & co., ᶜ1915.
93, [1] p., 1 l. illus. (plans) 18½ᶜᵐ.
At head of title: Unverleihbares und unverkäufliches manuskript.

  ɪ. Josephsohn, John, tr. ɪɪ. Title.

Library of Congress   PT8175.N3D63   17–15122

NN   0030067   DLC

NATHANSEN, HENRI, 1868–1944.
Dr. Wahl; Schauspiel in drei Akten mit einem
Vorspiel und einem Nachspiel. Autorisierte Uebersetzung aus dem Dänischen von John Josephsohn.
Berlin, Oesterheld, 1915. 93 p. 20cm.

Film reproduction. Negative.

1. Drama, Danish––Translations into German. 2. Drama, German––
Translations from Danish. ɪ. Title.

NN   0030068   NN

Nathansen, Henri, 1868–
Dr. [Doktor] Wahl; Schauspiel in drei Akten,
mit einem Vorspiel und einem Nachspiel.
Autorisierte Uebersetzung aus dem Dänischen
von J. Josephsohn. Berlin, Oesterheld, c1915.
93p. illus.

Microcard edition.
At head of title: Unverleihbares und unverkäufliches Manuskript.

NN   0030069   ICRL CaBVaU OrU

Nathansen, Henri, 1868–
Drömmen; Skuespil i tre Akter.   [København:] Gyldendal,
1911. 163 p.   12°.

1. Drama (Danish). 2. Title.
N.Y.P.L.   June 20, 1911.

NN   0030070   NN

Nathansen, Henri, 1868– 1944.
Den forbudne Frugt.   København: Det Nordiske Forlag,
1901.   239 p.   12°.

  Contents: Paa Tro og Love. Thi kendes for Ret-. Duft.

1. Fiction (Danish). 2. Title.   3. Title: Paa Tro og Love. 4. Title:
Thi kendes for Ret-. 5. Title: Duft.
N.Y.P.L.   October 16, 1924.

NN   0030071   NN

Nathansen, Henri, 1868–
... Georg Brandes; et portræt. Kjøbenhavn, Nyt nordisk
forlag, 1929.
351 p. port., 2 facsim. (1 fold.) 22ᵐ.

1. Brandes, Georg Morris Cohen, 1842–1927.
Library of Congress   PT8125.B8Z8   30–4618

NN   0030072   DLC CtY NcD WaS

Nathansen, Henri, 1868–1944.
Georg Brandes; et portræt. [2. udg.] København, Gyldendal, 1950 [ᶜ1929]
186 p. ports., facsims. 21 cm.

1. Brandes, Georg Morris Cohen, 1842–1927.

PT8125.B8Z8 1950   50–37046

NN   0030073   DLC ICU IU NIC NN NcU

Nathansen, Henri, 1868–1944.
Den gode Borger. Skuespil i tre Akter.
København, Gyldendal, 1907.
3 p. l., 222 p.   12°.

NN   0030074   NN

Nathansen, Henri, 1868–
... Der gute bürger, schauspiel in 3 akten, von Henri
Nathansen. Autorisierte uebersetzung aus dem dänischen von dr. J. Josephsohn. Berlin, Oesterheld & co.,
ᶜ1914.
99, [1] p. 19ᵐ.
Added t.-p.
At head of title: Unverkäufliches und unverleihbares manuskript.

  ɪ. Josephsohn, John, tr. ɪɪ. Title.

Library of Congress   PT8175.N3G63 1914   17–15123

NN   0030075   DLC

Nathansen, Henri, 1868–
Der gute Bürger; Schauspiel in 3 Akten.
Autorisierte Uebersetzung aus dem Dänischen
von J. Josephsohn. Berlin, Oesterheld,
c1914.
99p.

Microcard edition.
Cover title.
At head of title: Unverkäufliches und
unverleihbares Manuskript.

NN   0030076   ICRL OrU CaBVaU

Nathansen, Henri, 1868–
Hinter Mauern; Schauspiel in vier Akten.   Berlin: Oesterheld & Co., 1912.   3 p.l., 9–134 p., 1 l.   12°.

1. Drama (Danish). 2. Title.
N.Y.P.L.   February 6, 1913.

NN   0030077   NN OCH NBuG NBuC

VOLUME 405

Nathansen, Henri, 1868–
Hinter Mauern; Schauspiel in 4 Akten. ⌈Autorisierte Über-setzung aus dem Dänischen von Dr. John Josephsohn.⌉ **Berlin:** Oesterheld & Co., 1913. 134 p. 12°.

Date on cover 1912.

1. Drama (Danish). 2. Jews in   drama. 3. Josephson, John, trans-lator. 4. Title.
N. Y. P. L.   May 29, 1913.

NN 0030078   NN MH PU OCH

Nathansen, Henri, 1868–
Hinter Mauern; Schauspiel in 4 Akten.
Berlin, Oesterheld, 1913.
134p.

Microcard edition.

NN 0030079   ICRL OrU

⌈Indenfor murene. Yid.⌉
PT8175
N3 I 515
Hebraic
Sect.
Nathansen, Henri, 1868–1944.
הינטער מויערן, פיעסע אין 4 אקטן. יידיש דורך זלמן זילבער-
צווייג. ווארשע, "צענטראל." Warszawa, 1922.
iv, 102 p. 22 cm.

I. Title.   *Title transliterated:* Hinter moyern.

PT8175.N3 I 515   54–53255 ‡

NN 0030080   DLC

Nathansen, Henri, 1868–
... Indenfor murene; skuespil i fire akter. København og Kristiania, Gyldendal, Nordisk forlag, 1912.
3 p. l., 177 p. 19⅟₂ᶜᵐ.

I. Title.

Library of Congress   PT8175.N3 I 5 1912
                                          17–15092

NN 0030081   DLC

Nathansen, Henri, 1868–
Indenfor murene; skuespil i fire akter.
København og Kristiania, Gyldendal, Nordisk
forlag, 1912.
177p.

Microcard edition.

NN 0030082   ICRL OrU CaBVaU

PT8175
N3 I 5
1950
Nathansen, Henri, 1868–1944.
Indenfor murene; skuespil i fire akter.
4. udg. København, Gyldendal, 1950.
150 p.

NN 0030083   CU MnU

Nathansen, Henri, 1868–
Johannes Poulsen og Poul Reumert, af Henri Nathansen.
København: V. Pio, 1918. 80 p. front. 12°. (Teater-
v.⌉ 1.)

.. Poulsen, Johannes, 1881–   2. Reumert, Poul, 1883–
3. Series.
N. Y. P. L.   July 12, 1920.

NN 0030084   NN

Nathansen, Henri, 1868–1944.
... Johannes Poulsen. København, Gyldendal, 1946.
89 p. front. (port.) plates. 20 cm.

1. Poulsen, Johannes, 1881–1938.

PN2748.P6N3   47–26411

NN 0030085   DLC WaU CU MnU

Nathansen, Henri, 1868–
... Jude oder Europäer, porträt von Georg Brandes; mit 8 bildnissen. Frankfurt am Main, Rütten & Loening, 1931.
2 p. l., 7–263 p. ports. 21ᶜᵐ.
"Berechtigte übertragung aus dem dänischen von Erwin Magnus."

1. Brandes, Georg Morris Cohen, 1842–1927.   I. Magnus, Erwin,
1881–   tr. II. Title.   *Translation of* Georg Brandes, et portræt.

Library of Congress   PT8125.B8Z83   31–15230
Copyright A—Foreign   11530
                                          ⌈2⌉   928.8961

CtY IaU
NN 0030086   DLC PPDrop NcD NNC LU CLSU OCH OU MB

Nathansen, Henri, 1868–
... Karl Mantzius.   København: H. Koppels Forlag, 1926.
156 p. incl. ports. 12°.

1. Mantzius, Karl, 1860–1921.
N. Y. P. L.   June 15, 1927.

NN 0030087   NN MdBJ

Nathansen, Henri, 1868–1944.
Memento, digte i udvalg ved Tom Kristensen. ⌈Køben-havn⌉ Gyldendal, 1951.
121 p. 22 cm.

I. Title.

PT8175.N3A17 1951   52–26414 ‡

NN 0030088   DLC ViU CU WaU MnU

Nathansen, Henri, 1868–1944.
Mendel Philipsen & søn; roman. ⌈Kjøbenhavn. Nyt nordisk forlag, 1932.
457 p. 22 cm.

I. Title.

PT8175.N3M4 1932   74–207817

NN 0030089   DLC WaS KyU CU WaU MH NN

Hnp
N195
M4
1947
Nathansen, Henri, 1868–1944
Mendel Philipsen & søn; roman. ⌈7. opl.⌉
Kjøbenhavn, Gyldendal, 1947.
286p. port. 21cm.

NN 0030090   CtY MnU

Nathansen, Henri, 1868–1944.
Mor har Ret-. Komedie i tre Akter.
København, Gyldendal, 1904.
3 p. l., 108 p. 12°.

NN 0030091   NN

Nathansen, Henri, 1868–
∴ Portrætstudier. Kjøbenhavn: A. Busck, 1930. 231 p.
8°.

Contents: Henrik Ibsen. Vilhelm Andersen. Henrik Pontoppidan. Harald
Kidde. Knud Hjortø. Henrik Cavling. Olaf Poulsen. Peter Fjelstrup.

535543A. 1. Ibsen, Henrik, 1828–1906.   2. Andersen, Vilhelm, 1864–
3. Pontoppidan, Henrik, 1857–   4. Kidde, Harald, 1878–1918.
5. Hjortø, Knud, 1869– . 6. Cav-   ling, Henrik, 1859– 7. Poulsen,
Olaf Rye, 1849–1923. 8. Fjelstrup,   Peter.
N. Y. P. L.   July 27, 1931.

NN 0030092   NN MnU KU WaU CU

Nathansen, Henri, 1868–1944.
Protest mod jødepogromerne; tale holdt ved protestmødet i København den 27.11.1918 i anledning af pogromerne i Polen. Udg. af den Zionistiske organisations Københavnske bureau. København, 1919.
15 p. 25 cm.

1. Jews in Poland—Persecutions.   I. Title.

DS135.P6N28   74–208595

NN 0030093   DLC NN OCH

NATHANSEN, HENRI, 1868–
...Sommernat. Kobenhavn: Det Nordiske Forlag, 1899
192 p. 19cm.

604697A. 1. Fiction, Danish. I. Title.

NN 0030094   NN

Nathansen, Henri, 1868–1944
...William Bloch. Kjøbenhavn: A. Busck, 1928. 101 p.
port. 12°.

428291A. 1. Bloch, William,   1845–1926.
N. Y. P. L.   September 3, 1929.

NN 0030095   NN CU

AC
831
Nathansen, Max
Die mündliche verhandlung vor dem vorsitzenden des arbeitsgerichts. ... Wursburg, 1933.
Inaug. Diss. – Wursburg, 1933.
Bibliography.

NN 0030096   ICRL

Nathansky, Alfred.
Bauernfeld und Schubert. Von Dr. Alfred Nathansky.
Wien, K. Fromme, 1906.
1 p. l., 28 p. 24ᶜᵐ.
"Auszug aus dem sechsundfünfzigsten Jahresbericht des K. K. Staats-gymnasiums in Triest."

1. Bauernfeld, Eduard von, 1802–1890. 2. Schubert, Franz Peter, 1797–
1828.

Library of Congress   ML410.S3N2
                                          7–40773

NN 0030097   DLC NjP

Nathansky, Alfred.
Der graf von Gleichen...
see under   Bauernfeld, Eduard von, 1802–
1890.

VOLUME 405

Nathansky, Gerhard, joint author.

Laszky, Wolfgang.
  Kommentar zum Gewerblichen untersagungsgesetz, 1937, von dr. Wolfgang Laszky ... ₁und₎ dr. Gerhard Nathansky ... Wien, Manz, 1937.

Nathansky, Gerhard, ed.

Austria. *Laws, statutes, etc.*
  Kommentar zur Gewerbeordnung und zu ihren Nebengesetzen ₁von₎ Emil Heller. 2. nach dem neuesten Stande der Gesetzgebung gänzlich umgearbeitete Aufl. hrsg. von Wolfgang Laszky ₁und₎ Gerhard Nathansky unter Mitwirkung von Robert Heller. Wien, Manz, 1935–

Nathansohn, Alexander, 1878–   581 R200
  ··· Allgemeine Botanik, von Dr. A. Nathansohn, ... Mit 4 farbigen und 5 schwarzen Tafeln, und 394 Abbildungen im Text. .... Leipzig, Quelle & Meyer, 1912.
  viii, 471 p. 394 illus., 9 pl. (partly col.) 24½ᶜᵐ.

NN 0030101   ICJ MiU CU InU OU MH MiEM

Nathansohn, Alexander, 1878–
  Physiologische Untersuchungen über amitotische Kerntheilung ... Leipzig, 1900.
  Inaug.-diss. - Leipzig.
  "Sonderabdruck aus den Jahrbüchern für wissenschaftliche Botanik, Band XXXV, Heft 1."
  Lebenslauf.

NN 0030102   CtY

Nathansohn, Alexander, 1878–

Du Trochet, Henri, *marquis*, 1776–1847.
  Physiologische untersuchungen über die beweglichkeit der pflanzen und der tiere von Henri Dutrochet (1824) Übersetzt und herausgegeben von Alexander Nathansohn. Mit 29 textfiguren. Leipzig, W. Engelmann, 1906.

Nathansohn, Alexander, 1878–
  ... Propositions pour l'exploration océanographique de la Méditerranée occidentale. Par Alexander Nathansohn ... Monaco, 1910.
  cover-title, 15 p. 25ᶜᵐ. (Bulletin de l'Institut océanographique, no. 163)

  1. Hydrography. 2. Mediterranean sea.

U. S. Bur. of fish. Library   F 23—157
for Library of Congress   ₍a41b1₎

NN 0030104   DI MiU

Nathansohn, Alexander, 1878–
  ... Quelques remarques sur le programme hydrobiologique de Monaco. Par Alexander Nathansohn. Monaco, 1910.
  cover-title, 9 p. 25ᶜᵐ. (Bulletin de l'Institut océanographique, no. 188)

  1. International commission for the scientific exploration of the Mediterranean Sea. 2. Ocean. ₍2. Oceanography₎

Library, U. S. Bur. of   Fisheri~   F 23—174

NN 0030105   DI MiU

Nathansohn, Alexander, 1878–
  Der stoffwechsel der pflanzen, von dr. A. Nathansohn ... Leipzig, Quelle & Meyer, 1910.
  viii, 472 p. 24½ᶜᵐ.

  1. Metabolism in plants.

                                    Agr 11–572
Library, U. S. Dept. of   Agriculture 463N19

ICJ WaU
NN 0030106   DNAL GU CU PPAN PU–B NIC MiU OU CtY

Nathansohn, Alexander, 1878–
  ... Sur l'influence verticale des eaux sur la production du plankton marin. Par A. Nathansohn ... Monaco, 1906.
  cover-title, 12 p. 25ᶜᵐ. (Bulletin du Musée océanographique de Monaco, no. 62)

  1. Plankton. 2. Ocean currents.

                                  F 23—71
U. S. Bur. of fish. Library
for Library of Congress   ₍a41b1₎

NN 0030107   DI MiU

Nathansohn, Alexander, 1878–
  ... Sur les relations qui existent entre les changements du plankton végétal et les phénomènes hydrographiques, d'après les recherches faites à bord de l'Eider, au large de Monaco, en 1907–1908. Par Alexander Nathansohn ... Monaco, 1909.
  cover-title, 93 p. 10 pl. 25ᶜᵐ. (Bulletin de l'Institut océanographique, no. 140)

  1. Hydrography. 2. Plankton. 3. Marine biology—Mediterranean Sea. I. Eider (Yacht)

                                  F 23—130
Library, U. S. Bur. of   Fisheries

NN 0030108   DI MiU

Nathansohn, Alexander, 1878–
  ... Tier- und pflanzenleben des meeres, von dr. Alexander Nathansohn ... Leipzig, Quelle & Meyer, 1906.
  2 p.l., 128, [2] p. illus. 19 cm.
  (Wissenschaft und bildung ... 87)
    1. Marine biology. 2. Ocean.

NN 0030109   CU

Nathansohn, Alexander, 1878–
  Über die bedeutung vertikaler wasserbewegungen für die produktion des planktons im meere. Von Alexander Nathansohn. Mit einer karte. Leipzig, B. G. Teubner, 1906.
  4 p. l., p. ₁359₎–441. fold. map. 29ᶜᵐ. (Abhandlungen der Mathematisch-physischen klasse der Königl. sächsischen gesellschaft der wissenschaften. XXIX. bd., no. v)
  Bibliographical foot-notes.

  1. Plankton. 2. Ocean currents.

                           A C 33–4203
Title from Wisconsin   Univ.
Library of Congress   ₍AS182.S21 bd. 29, no. 5₎

NN 0030110   WU PPAmP NN

Nathansohn, Alexander, 1878–
  Ueber Regulationserscheinungen im Stoffaustausch ... Leipzig, 1902.
  Habilitationsschrift - Leipzig.
  "Sonderabdruck a. d. Jahrbüchern für wiss. Botanik, 38. Bd."

NN 0030111   CtY ICRL

                     BM 503
                     .8
                     .N3

Nathansohn, Aryeh Leibush, *d.* 1873.
  בית אל. בפלפול וסברא. לעמבערג. ז. נאמאנזאהן. תרל"ה.
  Lemberg, 1875.
  2 v. in 1. 35 cm.
  ———— Microfilm copy (positive)
  Negative film in the New York Public Library.
  (Film copy not in LC)

  1. Pilpul. I. Title.   *Title transliterated:* Bet El.
New York. Public Libr.   A 55–2536
for Library of Congress

NN 0030112   NN DLC

Nathansohn, Bernhard
  see Natanson, Bernard, 1832–

                                1887–
Nathansohn, Bruno, Referendar: Haftung des Schuldners für nach dem Verzuge eingetretene Unmöglichkeit der Leistung. Breslau 1911: Bermann. 64 S. 8°
  Breslau, Jur.-Diss. v. 26. Juli 1911, Ref. O. Fischer, Schott
  ₍Geb. 8. Mai 87 Benthen a. O.; Wohnort: Beuthen; Staatsangeh.: Preußen; Vorbildung: Städt. Gymn. Liegnitz Reife O. 06; Studium: Berlin 3, München 1, Berlin 1, Breslau 2 S.; Rig. 20. Juli 09.₎   ₍U 11. 634₎

NN 0030114   ICRL

Nathansohn, David Bernhard
  see Natanson, Bernard, 1832–

4LC–37   Nathansohn, Hans
  Die Fragen der pädagogischen Fürsorge an Eltern und Kinder, gesammelt unter besonderer Berücksichtigung der Heilpädagogik (Psychopathenfürsorge) Leitlinien zur Erschliessung geistiger und psychischer Schwierigkeiten und Leiden von Kindern und Jugendlichen. Für Jugendfürsorger, Jugendberater, Jugendhelfer, Lehrer, Erzieher und jugendfürsorgerisch tätige Aerzte. Berlin, 1930.
  99 p. (Das Kleine Lehrbuch, Bd. 5)

NN 0030116   DLC–P4

Nathansohn, Ḥayyim.
  ספר דברי חן; כולל שאלות ותשובות על סדר חלקות הרמב"ם
  ₍מאת₎ חיים נאמעגזאהן. הובא לבית הדפוס ע"י י. לעוו. חלק 1.
  פיעטרקוב. בדפוס ש. בעלכאמאזסקי. 1903.
  150 p. 34 cm.
  No more published.

  1. Responsa—1800–   2. Moses ben Maimon, 1135–1204. Mishneh
Torah—Commentaries.   I. Title: Divre ḥen.
                               Title romanized: Sefer Divre ḥen.

BM522.74.A78   HE 67–2170

NN 0030117   DLC

BM740
.N3
(Hebraic)   Nathansohn, Ḥayyim.
 Sect.   שפתי חן, על פרשיות התורה בדרך דרוש. ווילנא,
    בדפוס י. ל. מ"ץ, תר"ס. Вильна, 1900.
  216 p. 23 cm.

  1. Sermons, Hebrew. 2. Bible. O. T. Pentateuch—Sermons.
  I. Title.   *Title transliterated:* Sifte Ḥen.
BM740.N3   A 51–1326
New York. ·Public Libr.
for Library of Congress

NN 0030118   NN DLC

VOLUME 405

Nathansohn, Hugo, 1881–
Der Existenzbegriff Hume's ... Berlin, 1904.
74 p., 1 l. 23.5 cm.
Inaug.-diss. – Erlangen.
Lebenslauf.

NN 0030119 CtY MH

Nathansohn, Joseph-Girscha , 1883–
Ueber die methoden und resultate der operativen
behandlung des kryptorchismus.
Inaug. Diss. Berlin, 1908.
Bibl.

NN 0030120 ICRL DNLM NNC

BS1225
.N23
Hebraic
Sect.

Nathansohn, Joseph Saul, 1808–1875.
דברי שאול, חידושי תורה. מהדורא ב. לעמבערג, בדפוס
א. ז. סאלאט, תרל"ז–ח. Lemberg, 1877.
3 v. in 1. 25 cm.
CONTENTS.—

1. Bible. O. T. Pentateuch—Commentaries. I. Title.
Title transliterated: Divre Sha'ul
BS1225.N23 A 51-125
New York. Public Libr.
for Library of Congress

NN 0030121 NN DLC

BM522
.74
.A8
1879
Hebr

Nathansohn, Joseph Saul, 1808–1875.
דברי שאול ויוסף דעת; והוא שאול ומשיב מהדורא חמישאה,
שאלות ותשובות. לעמבערג. בדפוס של א. ז. וו. סאלאט.
Lemberg, 1879.
97 l. 37 cm.
——— Microfilm copy (positive)
Negative film in the New York Public Library.
(Film copy not in LC.)
1. Responsa. I. Title. II. Title: Yosef da'at.
Title transliterated: Divre Sha'ul
BM522.74.A8 1879 A 57-3300
New York. Public Libr.

NN 0030122 MH DLC NN

BS1225
.N23
1953
Hebraic
Sect.

Nathansohn, Joseph Saul, 1808–1875.
דברי שאול על התורה וחמש מגילות. יצא לאור עם תולדות
המחבר ע"י נפתלי ערנבערג. נידיורק, תשי"ב. New York, 1953.
208 l. 26 cm.

1. Bible. O. T. Pentateuch—Commentaries. I. Ehrenberg,
Naftali, 1920– ed. II. Title *Title transliterated:* Divre Sha'ul.

BS1225.N23 1953 54-51507

NN 0030123 DLC

Nathansohn, Joseph Saul, 1808–1875.
Imre binah
see under Armer, Akiba, of Klasno.

Nathansohn, Joseph Saul, 1808–1875, joint author.
Magen giborim
see under Ettinger, Mordecai Ze'ev,
1804–1863.

Nathansohn, Joseph Saul, 1808–1875, joint author.
Me'irat 'enayim
see under Ettinger, Mordecai Ze'ev,
1804–1863.

Nathansohn, Joseph Saul, 1808–1875
Seder ha'doroth
see under Heilprin, Jehiel,
ca. 1660–ca. 1746.

Nathansohn, Joseph Saul, 1808–1875, joint author.
Sefer Magen giborim
see under Ettinger, Mordecai Ze'ev,
1804–1863.

Nathansohn, Joseph Saul, 1808–1875.
Sha'ar ha-melekh
see under Belmonte, Isaac Nuñez,
18th cent.

BM522
.74
.A82
Hebr

Nathansohn, Joseph Saul, 1808–1875.
שאלות ותשובות שאול ומשיב. מהדורא רביעאה. לעמבערג.
בדפוס י. מ. ניק, תרל"ו. Lemberg, 1876–77.
3 v. in 1. 36 cm.
Vols. 2–3, בדפוס א. ז. וו. סאלאט
——— Microfilm copy (positive)
Negative film in the New York Public Library.
(Film copy not in LC.)
1. Responsa. I. Title *Title transliterated:* ... Shoel u-meshiv
BM522.74.A82 A 59-507
New York. Public Libr

NN 0030130 MH DLC NN

BM522
.74
.A83
Hebr

Nathansohn, Joseph Saul, 1808–1875.
שאלות ותשובות שאול ומשיב. מהדורא שתיתאה. חלק ראשון.
לעמבערג. בדפוס א. ז. וו. סאלאם. תר"ן. Lemberg, 1890.
83 l. 36 cm.
No more published.
——— Microfilm copy (positive)
Negative film in the New York Public Library.
Film copy not in L.C.)
1. Responsa. I. Title. *Title transliterated:* ... Shoel u-meshiv
BM522.74.A83 A 59-507

NN 0030131 MH DLC NN

BM522
.74
Hebr

Nathansohn, Joseph Saul, 1808–187b.
יד יוסף ויד שאול. לעמבערג. בדפוס מ. מ. באהאבא.
Lemberg, 1851.
2 v. in 1. 38 cm.
CONTENTS.— חלק א. על הלכות נדרים, הנקרא בשם יד נדרים.—חלק ב.
מולכות שבוקות על הלכות חרם.
Vol. 2 has title: יד שאול
1. Caro, Joseph, 1488–1575. Shulḥan 'arukh—Commentaries.
I. Title. II. Title: Yadot nedarim.
Title transliterated: Yad Yosef ve-Yad Sha'ul.
BM550.C35N3 A 48–2248 rev
New York. Public Libr.
for Library of Congress

NN 0030132 NN DLC MH

Nathansohn, Joseph Saul, 1808–1875.
Zeh Sefer Sifre
see under Sifre.

Nathansohn, Julius, ed.
Ex libris, buchkunst und angewandte graphik. jahrg. 1–16,
oct. 1891–1906; jahrg. 17– (neue folge, jahrg. 1–)
apr. 1907–
Görlitz, C. A. Starke, 1891–1909; Berlin, Druck von O. von
Holten, 1909–

Bb
933n

Nathansohn, Leon
Die Sammlung Leon Nathansohn – Dresden, mit
Beiträgen aus anderem Besitz. Goethe und sein
Kreis. Goethes äussere Erscheinung, Büsten,
Gemälde, Stiche, Medaillen, Goethes Schriften,
Goethe-Stätten, Alt-Weimar. Die Künstler des
Goethe-Kreises, Gemälde, Aquarelle, Handzeich-
nungen, von Carus, C.D.Friedrich, Graff, Hackert
Kniep, Schütz, Tischbein u.v.a. ... Berlin, P.
Graupe[1933]
119p. 28 pl. on 15l. incl.front.,ports.,
facsims. 25cm.
"Auktion 106 am 19.und 20.April 1933"
"Schätzungs- preise",folder ([5]p.)
tipped in.

NN 0030135 CtY

WG
24178

Nathansohn, Moriz
Ueber Derivate und Reactionen des Tetra-
methyldiamidobenzophenons. Uster-Zürich,
1889.
54 p.
Inaug.-Diss. – Basel

NN 0030136 CtY

Nathansohn, Nehemias.
שפת אמת. חיי ר"ם מלונגיאן, הערות והנהגות על ... ספריו.
תולדות הקבלה והחסירות בדרך קצרה. מהלך התשכלה חזרה.
דברי בקרת על עוינים ... שבם בני האדם נכשלים. לחעיר רוח
תכונים. ולהחיות הרות הלאומי. ווארשא, דרוק פאן ר. גינז,
תרמ"ז. Warsaw, 1887.
132 p. 21 cm.
Added t. p.: Sprache der Wahrheit enthält: das Leben des berühmten Litteraten M. Plungian, Anmerkungen über viele in seinen
Werken behandelten Gegenstände, kurze geschichtliche Darstellung
der Geheimlehre und des aus ihr entsprungenen Ḥasidismus, falsche

Richtung der jüd. Aufklärung, Kritik vieler verfänglichen Dinge die
in das Leben eingreifen, um Reform und Gemeingeist bei den Bessern
anzuregen.

1. Judaism—Addresses, essays, lectures. 2. Plungian, Mordecai,
1814–1883. I. Title. *Title transliterated:* Sefat emet.

BM45.N33 61–55206

NN 0030138 DLC

QD412
.P1N15

Nathansohn, Simon.
Ueber oxyphosphazo-verbindungen und ester der
n-oxychlorphosphine der aromatischen reihe.
Rostock, 1898.
42p.
Inaug. diss. Rostock.

NN 0030139 DLC

[Nathanson, A. George] 1908–
American-international buyers' guide; a reciprocal trade
directory. 1941. [New York? 1941?]
[29] p. 33 cm.
On cover: Argentina-Estados Unidos.
A prospectus.

1. America—Comm.—Direct. I. Title.
Library of Congress HF54.U5N3 44–23063
Brief cataloging
[2] 658.8058

NN 0030140 DLC

Nathanson (Arnold Ferdinand) [1865–].
* Beruht die nach Phosphorvergiftung eintre-
tende Fettleber auf einer Fettinfiltration oder
Fettmetamorphose? 31 pp. 8°. Berlin, G.
Schade, [1889].

NN 0030141 DNLM PPC ICRL

Nathanson, Bernhard
see Natanson, Bernard, 1832–

VOLUME 405

Nathanson, Felix, 1870–
WG   Zur Kenntnis der Derivate des Diketohyd-
22649   rinden. Berlin, 1893.
    35 p.

    Inaug.-Diss. – Berlin.

NN   0030143   CtY DNLM

Nathanson (Ferdinandus) [1827–]. *De
dyscrasia quadam affectionem cordis, strumam,
exophthalmum efficiente. 30 pp., 1 l. 8°.
Berolini, B. Schlesinger, [1850]*

NN   0030144   DNLM

Nathanson, Ḥayyim
    see Nathansohn, Ḥayyim.

Nathanson, Ira Theodore, 1904–   joint author.

Taylor, Grantley Walder, 1897–
    Lymph node metastases; incidence and surgical treatment in
neoplastic disease [by] Grantley Walder Taylor ... and Ira
Theodore Nathanson ... with a foreword by Shields Warren ...
London, New York [etc.] Oxford university press [1942]

Nathanson, jerome.
    America confronts the peace. America looks ahead; an address,
by Jerome Nathanson ... November 19th, 1944. Given at the regular Sunday morning meeting of the New York society for ethical
culture.   New York [1944]   8 f.   28cm.

1. World war, 1939–1945—U. S.   —Addresses, sermons, etc. I. Society
N. Y. P. L.   for ethical culture, New York.
                   July 8, 1946

NN   0030147   NN

Nathanson, Jerome.
    America confronts the peace. Must we have anti-Semitism?
An address by Jerome Nathanson ... November 12th, 1944, Station WQXR, given at the regular Sunday morning meeting of the
New York Society for ethical culture ...   [New York, 1944]
10 f.   28cm.

1. Jews in the U. S.—Anti-   Semitism.
N. Y. P. L.   April 25, 1947

NN   0030148   NN

Nathanson, Jerome.
    America confronts the peace. We go to the polls. Address
by Jerome Nathanson ... October 29th, 1944, station WQXR.
Given at the regular Sunday morning meeting of the New York
society for ethical culture.   New York [1944]   10 f.   28cm.

1. United States—Politics,   1933–   2. Industry and state—
U. S.
N. Y. P. L.   April 9, 1946

NN   0030149   NN

NATHANSON, JEROME.
    The crisis today [by] Jerome Nathanson. New York:
Soc. for ethical culture, 1938. 12 p. 19cm. (Democracy in action. no. 1.)

    1. Democracy—U. S. I. Ser.

NN   0030150   NN

Nathanson, Jerome.
    Ethical religion and social action; address by Jerome Nathan-
son ... June 24th, 1945, station WQXR.   New York, The N. Y.
soc. for ethical culture [1945]   8 f.   28cm.

1. Ethics, Social. I. Society for   ethical culture, New York.
N. Y. P. L.   May 10, 1949

NN   0030151   NN

Nathanson, Jerome.
    Forerunners of freedom; the re-creation of the American
spirit [by] Jerome Nathanson; introduction by Horace M.
Kallen. Washington, D. C., American council on public affairs
[1941]
    3 p. l., 177 p. 23½ᵐ.
    CONTENTS.—Ralph Waldo Emerson, prophet of democracy.—Walt
Whitman ; the poet as seer.—William James ; the possibilities of effort.—
John Dewey ; democracy as reconstruction.—Can freedom survive?—
Bibliographical notes (p. 173–177)
    1. Liberty.   2. Democracy.   I. American council on public affairs.
II. Title.

                                  41–20795
    Library of Congress   JC423.N35
                          [15]   323.44

    PP PSt OU
NN   0030152   DLC ODW OrU OrP WaS MtBC NIC ViU TU

Nathanson, Jerome.
    Hope in the face of despair; address by Jerome Nathanson ...
April 9th, 1944, station WQXR, given at the regular Sunday
morning meeting of the New York society for ethical culture.
New York [1944]   8 f.   28cm.

1. Ethical culture movement.   I. Society for ethical culture, New
York.
N. Y. P. L.   April 10, 1946

NN   0030153   NN

Nathanson, Jerome.
    John Dewey; the reconstruction of the democratic life.
New York, Scribner, 1951.
    ix, 127 p. 21 cm. (Twentieth century library)
    Bibliography : p. 123–124.

    1. Dewey, John, 1859–

    B945.D44N3   191.9   51–6859

    WaT WaWW
    CaBVa IdB IdPI IdU MtBC MtU OrCS OrP OrU Wa WaS
NN   0030154   DLC MH ViU TU MB NN MiU KEmT KyWAT Or

Nathanson, Jerome.
    Philosophies of defeat: mysticism, neo-Thomism and existen-
tialism, by Jerome Nathanson.   New York, New York soc. for
ethical culture [1947]   6 l.   23cm.

    "Reprinted from the Standard, vol. xxxiv, no. 2, November, 1947."

1. Mysticism.   2. Philosophy,   Scholastic.   3. Existentialism.
I. Society for ethical culture, New   York.
N. Y. P. L.   December 27, 1949

NN   0030155   NN

NATHANSON, JEROME.
    The reconstruction of religion. New York, Society
for ethical culture [1946?] 19 p. 20cm.

    Cover title.

    1. Religion—Future. 2. Ethical culture movement.

NN   0030156   NN

Nathanson, Jerome.
    Religious creeds and religious freedom, by Jerome Nathan-
son. New York city, The New York society for ethical culture
[1944]
    16 p. 19ᵐ.

    1. Liberalism (Religion) 2. Ethical culture movement.   I. New
York society for ethical culture. II. Title.

                                  44–12041
    Library of Congress   BR1616.N3
                      [3]   211

NN   0030157   DLC NN

HM   Nathanson, Jerome.
271   Science for Democracy. New York, King's
.C57   Crown Press, 1946.
1946   x, 170 p. (Conference on the scientific
        spirit and democratic faith, 1946)

        1. Liberty. 2. Authoritarianism. 3. Democracy.
    4. Science. 5. Religion. I. Title. (Series)

NN   0030158   DAU

Nathanson, Jerome.
    The struggle for the peace ... by Jerome Nathanson ... given at
the regular Sunday morning meeting of the New York society
for ethical culture ...   New York [1945]   4 v.   28cm.

    CONTENTS.—[no. 1] Economic and political problems of world order.—[no.] 2. Pro-
posals for world order.—[no.] 3. Dumbarton Oaks—its aims and shortcomings.—
[no.] 4. What should America demand?

1. World war, 1939–1945—Post-   war problems.
Y. P. L.   July 8, 1946

NN   0030159   NN

Nathanson, Jerome.
    The test of civilization, by Jerome Nathanson.   New York:
Society for ethical culture [1941?]   11 p.   20½cm.

1. World war, 1939–   —Ad-   dresses, sermons, etc. I. Society for
ethical culture, New York.
N. Y. P. L.   March 18, 1943

NN   0030160   NN

Nathanson, Jerome.
    The testing of democratic faith; can we re-educate the German
people? Address by Jerome Nathanson ... March 26th, 1944,
station WQXR, given at the regular Sunday morning meeting of
the New York society for ethical culture.   New York [1944]
9 f.   28cm.

1. World war, 1939–   —Educa-   tional aspects—Germany 2. Edu-
cation—Germany, 20th cent.   I. Society for ethical culture,
New York.
N. Y. P. L.   April 23, 1945

NN   0030161   NN

Nathanson, Jerome.
    The testing of democratic faith, the rational man: fact or myth?
Address by Jerome Nathanson ... April 2nd, 1944, given at the
regular Sunday morning meeting of the New York society for
ethical culture ...   [New York, 1944]   9 f.   28cm.

1. Education—Addresses, essays,   lectures.
N. Y. P. L.   March 27, 1945

NN   0030162   NN

Nathanson, Jerome.
    War, panic, and patriotism [by] Jerome
Nathanson. New York, Society for ethical
culture [1941]
    14 p. 21 cm.
    1. World war, 1939–   – U.S. 2. Patriot-
ism. I. Title. II. New York society for
ethical culture.

NN   0030163   NNC MH

VOLUME 405

Nathanson, Jonas Bernard, 1889–
A determination of e/m and v by the measurement of a helix of Wehnelt cathode rays.
7p.

(In Illinois. University. Laboratory of physics. Some contributions. 1912–1914)

NN　0030164　OCl

Nathanson, Jonas Bernard, 1889–
The reflecting power of the alkali metals ... by Jonas Bernard Nathanson ... ₍Chicago, 1916₎
1 p. l., p. 137–168, 1 l. diagrs. 24ᵐ.
Thesis (PH. D.)—University of Illinois.
Vita.
Reprinted from the Astrophysical journal, vol. XLIV, no. 3, October 1916.

1. Reflection (Optics) 2. Alkaline metals.　I. Title.

17–27005

Library of Congress　　QC425.N3
Univ. of Illinois Libr.

NN　0030165　IU　DLC

Nathanson, Jonas Bernard, 1889–
The reflecting power of the alkali metals.
32p.

(In Illinois. University. Laboratory of physics. Some contributions, 1914–1919, pt. 2)

NN　0030166　OCl

Nathanson, Joseph Saul
see
Nathansohn, Joseph Saul, 1808–1875.

Nathanson (José-G.) [1866–　　J. *Étude critique de la trépanation dans la paralysie générale*. 68 pp. 8°. *Paris*, 1897.

NN　0030168　DNLM

Nathanson, Julius, 1879–
... Ein Fall von halbseitigen chondrodystrophischem Zwergwuchs ...　[Leipzig] 1913.
Inaug.-diss. - Marburg.
Lebenslauf.
"Literatur": p. 19–20.

NN　0030169　CtY DNLM

Nathanson, Leon.
Die Sammlung Leon Nathansohn - Dresden
see under　Graupe, Paul, bookseller, Berlin.

Nathanson, Ludwig, 1906–
... Untersuchungen, ob neben den Varicen der unteren Extremität gerade Venen verlaufen, und Gedanken zur Genese der Varicen ...
[Berlin, 1932]
Inaug.-diss. - Berlin.
Lebenslauf.
"Literatur": p. 17.

NN　0030171　CtY

Nathanson (Max). * Ueber centralen Zerfall eines Uternsmyoms. [Erlangen.] 23 pp. 8°
Berlin, H. Schmidt, 1890

NN　0030172　DNLM

Nathanson, Mendel Levin, 1780–1868.
Dännemark's national- und staats- haushalt. Eine historisch-statistische darstellung... (Uebersetzt aus dem dänischen.) Schleswig, K. Taubstummeninstitut, 1837.
178p.

NN　0030173　MiU

Kress Nathanson, Mendel Levin, 1780–1868.
Room　Danmarks handel, skivsfart, penge-og finantsvaesen fra 1730 til 1830. Historisk fremstillet og oplyst ...　Kjöbenhavn, E.A. Reitzel [etc.] 1832.
v.　17.5 cm.

Part 3 has subtitle: Som tillige indeholder svar til hr. professor David.
1. Denmark - Economic history.　2. Banks and banking - Denmark.　I. David, Christian Georg Nathan, 1793–1874

NN　0030174　MH-BA MnU

AY37　Nathanson, Mendel Levin, 1780–1868, ed.
.D45
Rare Bk. Dansk folkekalender.　1848–
Coll.　Kjøbenhavn, H. J. Bing.

Nathanson, Mendel Levin
Fornødent gjenmaele paa Hr.T.Thaarups Anhang til rihs tilligemed bemaerkninger om vor handel og vort pengevaesen. Kjøbenhavn, Trykt Seidelin, 1816
153 p.

NN　0030176　MH KU

Nathanson, Mendel Levin, 1780–1868.
Historisk Fremstilling af Jødernes Forhold og Stilling i Danmark, navnlig Kjøbenhavn. Ved M. L. Nathanson...　Kjøbenhavn: F. H. Eibe, 1860.　viii, 272 p.　12°.

1. Jews in Denmark.
N. Y. P. L.

SCHIFF COLLECTION.
November 11, 1915.

NN　0030177　NN OCH MH OU

4HJ　Nathanson, Mendel Levin
498　Historisk-statistisk fremstilling af Danmarks national-og stats-huusholdning fra Frederik den Fjerdes tid indtil nutiden.　2. omarbeidede udg.　Kjøbenhavn, C. A. Reitzel, 1814.
1062 p.

NN　0030178　DLC-P4

Nathanson, Mendel Levin
Historisk statistisk fremstilling af Danmarks national og stats huusholdning fra Frederik den Fjerdes tid indtil nutiden. Kjøbenhavn, Reitzel, 1836

NN　0030179　MH

Nathanson, Mendel Levin, 1780–1868.
Historisk-statistisk Fremstilling af Danmarks National- og Stats-Huusholdning fra Frederik den Fjerdes Tid indtil Nutiden, ved M. L. Nathanson.　Anden omarbeidede Udgave.　Kjøbenhavn: C. A. Reitzel, 1844.　xx, 1062, vii p. incl. tables.　21cm.

674039A.　1. Economic history—　　Denmark.
N. Y. P. L.　　　　　　　　　　August 17, 1934

NN　0030180　NN ICU

4CT　Nathanson, Mendel Levin
373　Hofraad David Amsel Meyers levnet. Kjøbenhavn, Trykt hos A, Seidelin, 1816.
120 p.

NN　0030181　DLC-P4

DL199　NATHANSON, MENDEL LEVIN, 1780–1868.
.8　Leben des hofraths David Amsel Meyer, von grossirer
.M6N3　M.L.Nathanson. Aus dem dänischen übersetzt. Kopenhagen, Gedruckt bey A. Seidelin, 1816
xliv, 140, [1]p.　18½cm.
Translated by C.L. Sander.

1. Meyer, David Amsel, 1753–1813.

NN　0030182　ICU

NATHANSON, MENDEL LEVIN, 1780–1868.
Om klagerne over næringsløshed, en historisk-statistisk undersøgelse. Udg. af Selskabet for trykkefrihedens rette, brug.　Kjøbenhavn, Trykt i B. Lunos bogtrykkeri, 1838.　224 p. 17cm.

1. Employment stabilization—Denmark.

NN　0030183　NN MH

Nathanson, Mendel Levin, 1780–1868.
Om klagerne over næringsløshed i Kjøbenhavn, med tilknyttede bemærkninger angaaende E's skrift 1840–1860, af M. L. Nathanson...　Kjöbenhavn, Gyldendal, 1864.　108 p.　21cm.

1. Economic history—Denmark—　　　Copenhagen.　2. Krebs, Frederik
Christian, 1814–1881. Fra 1840　　　til 1860.
N. Y. P. L.　　　　　　　　　　　July 13, 1949

NN　0030184　NN

Nathanson, M₍endel₎ L₍evin₎.　　　Econ 6161.3.
Udførligere oplysninger om handels- og finants-væsenet í Christian den 7ᵈᵉ og Frederik den 6ᵗᵉ regjeringstid, som en fortsættelse af skriftet: Danmarks handel, skibsfart og pengevæsen. Kjøbenhavn, E. A. Reitzel, 1832.
pp. (4), 154+.

Denmark–Commerce

NN　0030185　MH MnU

Nathanson, Michael Leonard, 1795–1862, supposed author
Historisk Fremstilling af Jødernes Forhold og Stilling i Danmark ...
see under　Nathanson, Mendel Levin, 1780–1868.

Nathanson, Moshe, arr.

Jews.　Liturgy and ritual.　Hagadah.

Haggadah of Passover, translated by Maurice Samuel, with an introduction by Louis Finkelstein; music arrangements by Moshe Nathanson; illustrated by Rafaello Busoni.　New York, Hebrew publishing company [1942]

VOLUME 405

Nathanson, Moshe.

J2187
J54R4

Jews. *Liturgy and ritual. Grace after meals.*
רבותי נברך. ברכת המזון. תוי הנגינה וערוכים מאת משה
נתנזון. מחורגם מאת פלמיאל בירנבוים. יוצא לאור ביומת כנסית
החזנים באמריקה. ניריורק. היברו פוב. קו. ₍New York, 1954₎

Nathanson, Moshe, *ed.*
Zamru lo; congregational melodies, prayers, zemirot, hymns, compiled and edited by Moshe Nathanson. ₍New York₎ The Cantors Assembly of America ₍1955–
    v. 28 cm.
    Words in Hebrew (transliterated)
    CONTENTS.—v. 1. Friday evening service.

    1. Synagogue music.   I. Title.

M2186.N18Z3   M 56–308

NN   0030189   DLC OCH

Nathanson, Nathaniel L., *joint ed.*

Auerbach, Carl A   *ed.*
    The Federal regulation of transportation: materials illustrating problems of public utility control, by Carl A. Auerbach and Nathaniel L. Nathanson. St. Paul, West Pub. Co. 1953.

Nathanson, Nathaniel L.

HB236
.U5A547
1947a

    U.S. *Office of Temporary Controls.*
    Problems in price control: legal phases. ₍Washington, U.S. Govt. Print. Off., 1947₎

792.0945
N275s

Nathanson, Richard.
    Schauspieler und Theater im heutigen Italien; Erlebnisse und Beobachtungen aus sechzehn Jahren. Berlin, H. Steinitz, 1893.
    211p. 18cm.

    1. Theater - Italy. 2. Actors, Italian. I. Title.

NN   0030191   CLSU CLU MH

Nathanson, William, 1883–
    ... ה. ליװיק, דער דיכטער פֿון אָנקם און אױֿפקם.
    שיקאגאָ, פֿארלאג ל. מ. שטײן ₍Chicago, Ill., 1936₎
    177, ₍1₎ 22½ cm.
    Author's name מאטאנסאן at head of title.
    Title (transliterated): H. Leivick, der dichter fun onkum un oifkum.

    1. Leivick, Halper, 1888–   36–17570

    Library of Congress

NN   0030192   DLC CaBVaU UU

Nathanson, William, 1883–
    אינטעליגענט, קונסט און קינסטלער. לימעראטור אין ליכט פֿון
    פֿילאָסאָפֿיע. װילנע, ב. קלעצקין. ₍Wilno₎ 1931.
    545 p. 21 cm.

    1. Criticism.   I. Title.
    Title transliterated: Inteligent, kunst un kinstler.

PN83.N3   56–51773

NN   0030193   DLC

CB35
.N36

Nathanson, William, 1883–
    kultur un Civilizatzie. Chicago, Naie Gezelchaft, 1923.
    461 p. 23 cm.

    Added title-page: Culture and civilization; first of the series "Neo-socialism".

NN   0030194   NjR

CB19
.N3
1923
Hebraic
Sect.

Nathanson, William, 1883–
    מארקסיזם אין ליכט פֿון קולטור. עסענץ פֿון בוך "קולטור און
    ציװיליזאציע." שיקאגא. פֿארלאג "נײע געזעלשאפֿט."
    ₍Chicago, 1923₎
    96 p. 23 cm.
    "פֿון דער סעריע 'נעאָ־סאָציאליזם.'"

    1. Civilization—Philosophy. 2. Philosophy, Modern.
    Title transliterated: Marksizm in likht fun kultur.

CB19.N3 1923   54–55632

NN   0030195   DLC

Nathanson, William, 1883–
    שפינאזא און בערגסאָן, א פֿאראלעל. שיקאגא. פֿארלאג "נײע
    געזעלשאפֿט." ₍Chicago, 1923₎
    46 p. 22 cm.

    1. Spinoza, Benedictus de, 1632–1677. 2. Bergson, Henri Louis, 1859–1941.

B3998.N3 1923a   59–56491 ‡

NN   0030196   DLC

PJ5120
.5
.N3
Hebraic
Sect.

Nathanson, William, 1883–
    מענטש און קאָסמאָס. פֿילאָסאָפֿיש־לימעראַרישע עסײען. שי־
    קאגאָ, ל. מ. שטײן ₍Chicago, 1953₎
    381 p. 22 cm.

    1. Yiddish literature — Addresses, essays, lectures. 2. Philosophy—Addresses, essays, lectures. I. Title.
    Title transliterated: Mentsh un kosmos.

PJ5120.5.N3   54–45152 ‡

NN   0030197   DLC

B3998
.N3
(Hebraic)
Sect.

Nathanson, William, 1883–
    שפינאזא און בערגסאָן, א פֿאראלעל. װארשע, פֿארלאג "קולטור
    ליגע." ₍Warsaw, 1923₎
    46 p. 22 cm.

    Title transliterated: Shpinoza un Bergson.

B3998.N3   55–47366 ‡

NN   0030198   DLC

Nathanson, William, 1883–
    סאָװעטישער דעספאָטיזם, װי לאנג? ₍ניו־סאָציאלזם װערזום
    סאָװעטישן קאָמוניזם₎ ניו יאָרק, פֿארלאג "אידישער קעמפֿער."
    ₍New York₎ 1936.
    47 p. 23 cm.

    1. Communism—Russia.
    Title transliterated: Sovetisher despotizm, vi lang?

DK267.N298   52–56185

NN   0030199   DLC

Nathanson, William, 1883–
    Spinoza and Bergson (a parallel) Translated from the Yiddish by David Wollins. ₍1925₎
    117–122 p. 27 cm.

    From the Guardian; a literary monthly published in Philadelphia, vol. I, no. IV, February 1925.

NN   0030200   NNC

Nathanson, William, 1883–
    צו דער רעװיזיע פֿון נאציאנאל־ראדיקאלן געדאנק. שיקאגא.
    ל. מ. שטײן, ₍Chicago, 1935₎
    71 p. 23 cm.
    Added t. p.: To the revision of the national-radical concept.

    1. Religion.   I. Title.   *Title transliterated:* Tsu der revizye fun natsyonal-radikaln gedank.

BL50.N3   58–51660

NN   0030201   DLC

Nathanson, Yale Samuel, 1895–
    An analysis of sounds and frequency words basic to a new method of corrective speech (a presentation of orthenic material developed from the postulates of Twitmyer) ... ₍by₎ Yale S. Nathanson. Philadelphia, 1930.
    44 p. diagrs. 23 cm.
    Thesis (PH. D.)—University of Pennsylvania, 1930.

    1. Speech. 2. English language—Phonetics. 3. Twitmyer, Edwin Burket, 1873–

		30–31390
Library of Congress	BF455.N3 1930	
Univ. of Pennsylvania	Libr.	
—— Copy 2.		421.5

PBm NcU NIC DLC
NN   0030202   PU MiU OCU OCl OU IU MB MH NcD PHC

RC423
.T8

Nathanson, Yale Samuel, 1895–

Twitmyer, Edwin Burket, 1873–
    Correction of defective speech; a complete manual of psycho-physiological technique for the treatment and correction of the defects of speech ₍by₎ Edwin Burket Twitmyer ... and Yale Samuel Nathanson ... Philadelphia, P. Blakiston's son & co., inc. ₍*1932₎

612.78
N195m

NATHANSON, Yale Samuel, 1895–
    Manual of corrective speech exercises ₍by₎ Yale S. Nathanson ... and Juliet E. Nathanson ... ₍Philadelphia, J. Nathanson, c1947₎ cover-title, 36 p.

    "A condensation of 'An analysis of sounds and frequency words basic to a new method of corrective speech', Yale S. Nathanson ...; 'Correction of defective speech', Edwin B. Twitmyer and Yale S. Nathanson ...; 'The gift of speech', Yale S. Nathanson ...; and 'Stuttering', Eugene F. Hahn ...; 'Theory and therapy', Yale S. Nathanson."

NN   0030204   WaU IEN TxU NNQC UU OrU OrCS

Nathanya, *Israel*
    see
    Netanya, *Israel.*

Nathen, Stephan.
    Justitia vulnerata christiane, juridice et politice curata ... Coloniae Agrippinae, sumptibus J. Kalcoven, 1646.
    988 p. 4°.

NN   0030206   NjP

VOLUME 405

Nather, Ernst,
... Étude sur l'étendue de l'influence classique dans la poésie de Mathurin Regnier. Abhandlung..
Breslau, 1889.
29 p. 26 cm.
Programm – Städtisches evangelisches Gymnasium zu St. Maria-Magdalena, Breslau.
Programm Nr. 167.
1. Regnier, Mathurin, 1573-1613.

NN 0030207   CtY MH IU

Nather, Ernst Johann Alexander
De Vetusta Graecorum arte plastica. Pars I. Dissertatio inauguralis philologica ... Vratislaviae, C. H. Storch, 1869.
59 p. 8°.

NN 0030208   NjP

---

ar X
2838
no.22
Nather, Wilhelm.
Ueber das Wesen des Ostracismus in Athen. Olmütz, F. Slawik, 1872.
18 p. 21cm.

Accompanies "Programm"—Gymnasium, Olmütz, 1872.
No.22 in a vol. lettered: Programmes: Greek antiquities.

1. Expulsion—   Greece—Athens.
2. Athens—Pol.   & govt.

NN 0030209   NIC

Natherus, Johannes, fl. 1552, respondent.
Praesidente Jacobo Millichio ...
    see under Milich, Jakob, 1501-1559, praeses.

Nathesan, G A 1879-
    see also Natesan, G.A., & co., Madras, pub.

Nathhorst, Theophil Erdman, 1734-1804, respondent
Linné, Carl von, 1707-1778, praeses.
... Flora monspeliensis ... Upsaliæ, excud. L. M. Höier
[1756]

נתיב. במה לדעות והערכות, לספרות ולבקורת ... כרך
א׳ חוב׳ א׳-ג׳ טבת תרצ״ד-שבט תרצ״ד, תל-אביב, תרצ״ד-
[Tel-Aviv, 1934-35] .ה״צרת
1 v. 24ᵐ.
Edited by Eliezer L. Joffe.
No more published.

1. [Periodicals, Hebrew] I. Joffe, Eliezer Lipa, 1882-194A ed.
    Title transliterated: Nathiv.
                                    A 47-1314
New York. Public library
for Library of Congress
                            [2]

NN 0030213   NN

Nathji, Swami Bhola, maharaj
    see Nath, Bhola.

Nathmal Tatia
    see
Tatia, Nathmal.

Natho, Albert Hans
    see
Natho, Hans, 1877-

1877-
Natho, Hans, appr. Arzt: Aus d. chir. Klinik zu Greifswald. Zur Behandlung der appendicitis aktinomycotica. Greifswald 1910: Abel. 31 S. 8°
Greifswald, Med. Diss. v. 15. Nov. 1910, Ref. Ritter, Payr
[Geb. 6. Sept. 77 Berlin; Wohnort; Stralsund; Staatsangeh.: Preußen; Vorbildung: Falk-Realgymn. Berlin Reife O. 97, Erg. Gymn. Spandau M. 98; Studium: Greifswald 5, Berlin 2, Greifswald 4 S.; Coll. 20. März 07; Approb. 16. Sept. 06.]
                                    [U 11. 1649]

NN 0030217   ICRL MiU DNLM NN

817.69
A515.1
N275ce
1915
NATHO, T
A century in India of the American Marathi Mission, from 1813 to 1913. ... .
[Ahmedagar? 1915?]
[121]p. front., plates. 22cm.

Text in Marathi.

NN 0030218   MH-AH

4K
2734
Natho Davidson, Arturo, 1902-
Libertad provisional del procesado. Santiago de Chile, 1929.
147 p.

NN 0030219   DLC-P4

Nathoji, T.
    see Natho, T.

Nathorff, Erich, 1889-
Bandwürmer, von Dr. E. Nathorff ...
(In Neue deutsche Klinik. Berlin, 1928. 26ᵐ. Bd. 2, p. 1-35. illus.)
"Literatur": p. 34-35.

NN 0030221   ICJ

Nathorff, Erich.   8800   v.3
Echinokokkenkrankheit, von Dr. E. Nathorff ...
(In Neue deutsche Klinik. Berlin, 1929. 26ᵐ. Bd. 3, p. 1-29. illus.)
"Literatur": p. 29.

NN 0030222   ICJ

Nathorff, Erich.   8800   v.13
Oxyuriasis; Madenwürmer beim Menschen, Oxyuris vermicularis als Krankheitsursache, von Dr. E. Nathorff ...
(In Neue deutsche Klinik. Berlin, 1935. 26ᵐ. Bd. 13 (Erg. Bd. 3) p. [48]-63. illus.)
"Schrifttum": p. 63.

NN 0030223   ICJ

Nathorff, Erich, 1889-
... Versuche am überlebenden Uterus des anaphylaktischen Meerschweinchens. Berlin, Ebering, 1914.
31 p., 4 plates. 8°.
Berlin, Med. Diss, v. 7. Febr. 1914, Ref. Heffter.

NN 0030224   CtY DNLM

Nathorst, Alfred Gabriel, 1850-1921.
(Am) gingko? crenata Brauns ep. från sandsten vid Seinstedt nara Braunschweig. Stockholm, 1878.

Öfversigt af Kongl. vet. akad. för. hand. 1878. no. 3.

NN 0030225   OC1W

Nathorst, Alfred Gabriel, 1850-
... Annexe explicative a la carte géologique générale de la Suède publiée par l'Institut royal géologique de Suède à l'échelle de 1 : 1,000,000. Feuille méridionale par A.-G. Nathorst. [Tr. par J.-H. Kramer. Stockholm, Impr. centrale, 1884]
1 p. l., iv, 37 p. 24ᶜᵐ. and map. 54 x 71½ᶜᵐ. (Sveriges geologiska undersökning. (Institut royal géologique de Suède) Ser. Ba. Cartes générales avec descriptions. n: o 4)
Scale of map 1: 1000000.
1. Geology—Sweden.   i. Kramer, Jules Henri, 1827-   tr.

Library, U. S. Geol.   survey   G S 7-1331

NN 0030226   DI-GS CU

V
919.8
N276a
Nathorst, Alfred Gabriel, 1850-1921.
Antarctic. Ett minnesblad, af A.G.Nathorst. [Stockholm, 1903]

cover-title, p.[460]-471. illus. 23ᵐ.

Rare Book
Room
"Ur Ymer, tidskrift utgifven af Svenska sällskapet för antropologi och geografi, arg. 1903, h.4."

1. Antarctic (Ship) 2. Arctic regions. 3. Antarctic regions.

NN 0030227   CSt

Nathorst, Alfred Gabriel, 1850-1921.   581.998 P100
Den arktiska florans forna utbredning i länderna öster och söder om Östersjön. Berättelse öfver en med understöd af Vegastipendiet sommaren 1891 företagen forskningsresa. Af A. G. Nathorst. ... . Stockholm, Tryckt hos A. L. Normans boktryckeri-aktiebolag, 1891.
[2], 117-147 p. illus. (incl. 1 map). 224ᵐ.
"Aftryck ur tidskriften 'Ymer' 1891."

NN 0030228   ICJ

Nathorst, Alfred Gabriel, 1850-1921.
Beiträge der polarforschung zur pflanzengeographie der vorzeit. n.p. [1884?]

NN 0030229   NjP

Nathorst, Alfred Gabriel, 1850-1921.   L561 F2
Beiträge zur fossilen Flora Schwedens. Über einige rhätische Pflanzen von Pålsjö in Schonen, von Dr. A. G. Nathorst, ... Deutsche vom Verfasser revidirte Ausgabe. Mit 16 lithographischen Tafeln. Stuttgart, E. Schweizerbart'sche Verlagshandlung (E. Koch), 1878.
[6], 34 p. xvi pl. (part fold.) 30ᶜᵐ.
Published originally in Swedish, in K. Svenska vetenskapsakademiens Handlingar, vol. 14.
"Literatur-Verzeichnis," p. 33-34.

NN 0030230   ICJ MH MiU

VOLUME 405

Nathorst, Alfred Gabriel, 1850–
    Beiträge zur geologie der Bären-insel, Spitzbergens und des König-Karl-landes, von A. G. Nathorst ... Uppsala, Almquist & Wiksells boktryckeri-a.-b., 1910.
    2 p. l., p. ₍261₎-415, ₍1₎ illus., 2 maps (1 fold.) 25½ᶜᵐ.
    "Reprinted from Bull. of the Geol. instit. of Upsala, vol. x."
    Bibliographical foot-notes.

    1. Geology—Spitzbergen.

                                  G S 10–650
    Library, U. S. Geol.   survey 203(980) N19b

NN 0030231   DI-GS

Nathorst, A₍lfred₎ G₍abriel₎.
    Beitraege zur Kenntniss einiger mesozoischen Cycadophyten. Stockholm: P. A. Norstedt & Söner, 1902. 28 p., 3 pl. f°. (Kongliga Svenska Vetenskaps-Akademien. Handlingar. Ny följd. Bd. 36, no. 4.)

    1. Plants (Fossil). 2. Palæon-   tology (Botanical).
    N. Y. P. L.   January 6, 1912.

NN 0030232   NN

13545 **Nathorst, Alfred Gabriel,** 1850–1921.
Y   Beiträge zur mesozoischen Flora
v.57   Japan's. ₍Wien, K.K. Hof- und Staats-druckerei, 1890₎
        43-60 p. 6 plates. 29cm. (Akademie der Wissenschaften, Vienna. Mathematisch-naturwissenschaftliche Klasse. Denkschriften, Bd. 57)

      1. Paleobotany—Mesozoic. 2. Paleobotany—Japan.

NN 0030233   NIC

Nathorst, Alfred Gabriel, 1850–1921.
    Bemerkungen über Clathropteris meniscioides Brongniart und Rhizomopteris cruciata Nathorst. Uppsala, Almqvist & Wiksells boktr., 1906.
    14 p. 3 double plates. 31 cm. (Kungl. Svenska vetenskapsakademiens handlingar, bd. 41, no.2)
    Bound with his Nouvelles observations sur des traces d'animaux et autres phénomènes ... Stockholm, 1886; and 9 others of his writings.
    Bibliography: p. 12.
    1. Clathropteris meniscioides. 2. Rhizomopteris cruciata. i.t. ii.s: Svenska vetenskapsakade-   miens handlingar, bd. 41, no.2.

NN 0030234   NNBG MiU

Nathorst, Alfred Gabriel, 1850–1921.
    Berättelse ... om ... vetenskaplig resa till Schweiz och Tyskland. n.p., 1881.

NN 0030235   NjP

Nathorst, Alfred Gabriel, 1850–
    ... Beskrifning till kartbladen "Landsort" och "Käll-skären" (no. 65 & 66) af A. G. Nathorst. Stockholm, P. A. Norstedt & söner, kongl. boktryckare, 1878.
    11 p. 23½ᶜᵐ. and map. 45 x 59½ᶜᵐ. (On cover: Sveriges geologiska undersökning. Ser. Aa. Kartblad i skalan 1: 50000 med beskrifningar. n:o 65 & 66 ...)

    1. Geology—Sweden.

                                    G S 7–1242
    Library, U. S. Geol.   survey

NN 0030236   DI-GS DLC

Nathorst, Alfred Gabriel, 1850–
    ... Beskrifning till kartbladet "Sandhamn" och "Tärnskär" (no. 58 & 59) af A. G. Nathorst. Stockholm, P. A. Norstedt & söner, kongl. boktryckare, 1877.
    27 p. diagrs. 23½ᶜᵐ. and map. 45 x 59½ᶜᵐ. (Sveriges geologiska undersökning. ₍Ser. Aa. Kartblad i skalan 1: 50000 med beskrifningar. no. 58 & 59₎)
    Map is dated 1876.

    1. Geology—Sweden.

                                    G S 7–1236
    Library, U. S. Geol.   survey

NN 0030236–1   DI-GS DLC

Nathorst, Alfred Gabriel, 1850–
    ... Beskrifning till kartbladet "Gottenvik" (no. 64) af A. G. Nathorst. Stockholm, P. A. Norstedt & söner, kongl. boktryckare, 1878.
    40 p. diagrs. 23½ᶜᵐ. and map. 45 x 59½ᶜᵐ. (On cover: Sveriges geologiska undersökning. Ser. Aa. Kartblad i skalan 1: 50000 med beskrifningar. n:o 64 ...)
    Map is dated 1877.

    1. Geology—Sweden.

                                    G S 7–1241
    Library, U. S. Geol.   survey

NN 0030237   DI-GS DLC

Nathorst, Alfred Gabriel, 1850–
    ... Beskrifning till kartbladet "Gustafsberg" af A. G. Nathorst ... Stockholm, Kongl. boktryckeriet, P. A. Norstedt & söner, 1881.
    34 p. diagr. 23½ᶜᵐ. and map. 45 x 59½ᶜᵐ. (Sveriges geologiska undersökning. Ser. Aa. Kartblad i skalan 1: 50000 med beskrifningar. n:o 73)
    Map is dated 1880.

    1. Geology—Sweden.

                                    G S 7–1249
    Library, U. S. Geol.   survey

NN 0030238   DI-GS

Nathorst, Alfred Gabriel, 1850–
    ... Beskrifning till kartbladet Kristianstad af A. G. Nathorst. Stockholm, Kongl. boktryckeriet, P. A. Norstedt & söner, 1882.
    37 p. diagr. 23½ᶜᵐ. and map. 45 x 59ᶜᵐ. (Sveriges geologiska undersökning. Ser. Aa. Kartblad i skalan 1: 50000 med beskrifningar. n:o 85)
    Map is dated 1881.

    1. Geology—Sweden.

                                    G S 7–1259
    Library, U. S. Geol.   survey

NN 0030239   DI-GS

Nathorst, Alfred Gabriel, 1850–
    ... Beskrifning till kartbladet "Stafsjö" (no. 57) af A. G. Nathorst. Stockholm, P. A. Norstedt & söner, kongl. boktryckare, 1877.
    61 p. pl., diagrs. 23½ᶜᵐ. and map. 45 x 59½ᶜᵐ. (Sveriges geologiska undersökning. ₍Ser. Aa. Kartblad i skalan 1: 50000 med beskrifningar. no. 57₎)
    Map is dated 1875.

    1. Geology—Sweden.

                                    G S 7–1235
    Library, U. S. Geol.   survey

NN 0030240   DI-GS DLC

Nathorst, Alfred Gabriel, 1850–
    ... Beskrifning ti" kartbladet Trolleholm af A. G. Nathorst ... Stockholm, Kongl. boktryckeriet, P. A. Norstedt & söner, 1885.
    1 p. l., ii, 109 p. illus., 2 pl. (3 maps) diagrs. 23½ᶜᵐ. and map. 45 x 60ᶜᵐ. (Sveriges geologiska undersökning. Ser. Aa. Kartblad i skalan 1: 50000 med beskrifningar. n:o 87)
    Map is dated 1882.

    1. Geology—Sweden.

                                    G S 7–1261
    Library, U. S. Geol.   survey

NN 0030241   DI-GS

Nathorst, Alfred Gabriel, 1850–
    ... Ein besonders instruktives exemplar unter den medusenabdrücken aus dem kambrischen sandstein bei Lugnås, von A. G. Nathorst ... Stockholm, Kungl. boktryckeriet, P. A. Norstedt & söner, 1910.
    7 p. pl. 25ᶜᵐ. (Sveriges geologiska undersökning. Ser. C. Afhandlingar och uppsatser. n:o 228. Årsbok 3 (1909) : n:o 11)

    1. Paleontology — Sweden. 2. Paleontology — Cambrian. 3. Medusæ, Fossil.

                                    G S 10–637
    Library, U. S. Geol.   survey (583) D 1909 no. 11

NN 0030242   DI-GS OU

NATHORST, Alfred Gabriel.
    Bidrag til Japans fossile flora. [Stockholm], [1882].

NN 0030243   MH DI-GS

QE   **Nathorst, Alfred Gabriel**
946   Bidrag till Japans fossila flora. ₍Stockholm, 1883.₎
J3N19   ₍121₎-225 p. illus., pl. 24cm. (Nordenskiöld, Nils Adolf E. von, Vega-expeditionens venetskapliga Iakttagelser, bd.2)

      1. Paleobotany - Japan. 2. Paleontology - Japan. I. Title. (Series)

NN 0030244   CLU ICJ

Nathorst, Alfred Gabriel, 1850–1921.
    Bidrag till nordostra Gronlands geologi. 1902?

NN 0030245   DI-GS

Nathorst, A₍lfred₎ G₍abriel₎.
    Bidrag till Sveriges fossila flora. Stockholm: P. A. Norstedt & Söner, 1876. 82 p., 16 pl. f°. (Kongliga Svenska Vetenskaps-Akademien. Handlingar. Ny följd. Bd. 14, no. 3.)

    1. Palæontology (Botanical)   Sweden.
    N. Y. P. L.   December 21, 1911.

NN 0030246   NN ViU NjP

Nathorst, A₍lfred₎ G₍abriel₎.
    Bidrag till Sveriges fossila flora. ₍Part₎ Stockholm: P. A. Norstedt & Söner, 1878. v. f°. (Kongliga Svenska Vetenskaps-Akademien. Handlingar. Ny följd. Bd. 16, no. 7.)

    1. Palæontology, Sweden.
    N. Y. P. L.   January 30, 1912.

NN 0030247   NN ViU NjP

Nathorst, Alfred Gabriel, 1850–1921.
    Carl von Linné as a geologist. By A. G. Nathorst.
    (In Smithsonian institution. Annual report. 1908. Washington, 1909. 23½ᶜᵐ. p. 711–743)
    "Translation ... from Carl von Linné, såsom geolog. af A. G. Nathorst ... Upsala, 1907."

    1. Linné, Carl von, 1707–1778.

                                    15–21182
    Library of Congress   Q11.S66 1908

NN 0030248   DLC WaS MH-A PPL OU OCl OClMN OU

VOLUME 405

Nathorst, Alfred Gabriel, 1850-1921.
Carl von Linné såsom geolog. Uppsala,
Almqvist & Wiksell, 1907.
80p. 2 plates. 25cm.

NN 0030249 OkU

Nathorst, Alfred Gabriel, 1850-1921.

K. Svenska vetenskapsakademien, *Stockholm, ed.*
Carl von Linnés betydelse såsom naturforskare och
läkare. Skildringar utgifna af Kungl. vetenskapsakademien i anledning af tvåhundraårsdagen af Linnés fö-
delse. Uppsala, Almqvist & Wiksells boktryckeri-a.-b.,
1907.

Nathorst, Alfred Gabriel, 1850-1921.
... Contributions à la flore fossile du Japon, par A. G.
Nathorst. Avec 16 planches lithographiées ... Stockholm,
P. A. Norstedt & söner, 1883.
92 p. illus. xvi pl. 30ᶜᵐ. (Kongl. svenska vetenskaps-akademiens
handlingar. ₍Ny följd₎ bd. 20, n:o 2)

1. Paleobotany—Japan.

U. S. Geol. survey. Library
for Library of Congress   Q64.S85 bd. 20, no. 2

G S 17-453 Revised

NN 0030250 DI-GS NBuG NN DLC

Nathorst, Alfred Gabriel, 1850-1921.
... Contributions to the Carboniferous flora of north-eastern
Greenland, by A. G. Nathorst. 1911.
(*In* Meddelelser om Grønland. København, 1917. 28ᶜᵐ. bd. xliii,
p. ₍337₎-346. illus. (incl. map) pl. xv-xvi)
Danmark-ekspeditionen til Grønlands nordøstkyst, 1906-1908. bd. iii,
nr. xii.
Bibliographical foot-notes.

1. Paleobotany—Carboniferous. 2. Paleobotany—Greenland.

John Crerar library   A C 39-2466
for Library of Congress   [Q115.D89 vol. 43]
                                            (508)

NN 0030251 ICJ MB TxU DLC NN ViU CtY

Nathorst, Alfred Gabriel.
Emanuel Swedenborg as a geologis...
(In Swedenborg, Emanuel. Opera quaedam . . . de rebus natu-
ralibus. Vol. I, pp. xix-li. Holmiae. 1907.)

G6895 — Swedenborg. Emanuel. 1688-1772.

NN 0030252 MB

Nathorst, Alfred Gabriel, 1850-
Emanuel Swedenborg as a geologist, by A. G. Nathorst.
With six plates. Stockholm, Aftonbladets tryckeri, 1908.
3 p. l., ₍3₎-47 p. incl. vi pl. 27ᶜᵐ. (On cover: Emanuel Swedenborg as
a scientist. Miscellaneous contributions ed. by A. H. Stroh. v. 1, sect. 1)

1. Swedenborg, Emanuel, 1688-1772.

13-25853

NN 0030253 DLC WaU CU PBa

Nathorst, Alfred Gabriel
Emanuel Swedenborg såsom geolog. 1906.

NN 0030254 DI-GS

V
799.2998
N276e

Nathorst, Alfred Gabriel, 1850-
...Ett och annat om isbjörnen, af A.G.Nathorst.
Stockholm, Svenska tryckeriaktiebolaget, 1897.

cover-title, 14 p. illus. 22½ᵐ.

Rare Book
Room

"Särtryck ur Jägaren, illustrerad nordisk half-
arsskrift, utgifven under redaktion af jägmästare
Hugo Samzelius, Stockholm. 3:e årg., 1897:1."
Author's presentation copy to Dr.Gunnar
Andersson.

1.Bears. I.Title.

NN 0030255 CSt

Nathorst, Alfred Gabriel, 1850-1921.
Förberedande meddelande om floran i ...
norrländska kalktuffer. n.p., 1885?

NN 0030256 NjP

Nathorst, Alfred Gabriel, 1850-1921.
Förutskickadt meddelande om tertiärfloran ...
på Japan. n.p. [1881]

NN 0030257 NjP

Nathorst, Alfred Gabriel.
Jordens historia, efter M. Neumayrs "Erdge-
schichte" och andra kullor utarbetad med sar-
skild hansyn till nordens urvarld, ... Godtkop-
supplaga. Forra delen. Stockholm, G.& G.
Beijers.
2 v.

NN 0030258 PBa

Nathorst, Alfred Gabriel, 1850-1921.
... Fossil plants from Franz Josef Land, by A. G. Nathorst. ₍London, New York, Longmans, Green, and co.; etc.
etc., 1900.
26 p. illus., ii pl. 30 x 23ᶜᵐ. (The Norwegian North polar expedition,
1893-1896. Scientific results, ed. by Fridtjof Nansen. vol. i ₍no. iii₎)
Each plate preceded by leaf with descriptive letterpress.

1. Paleobotany—Franz Josef Land.   A 21-892
Title from Univ. of Chicag   Q115.N8 vol. 1 Printed by L. C.

NN 0030259 ICU MiU NNBG ICJ MB

Nathorst, Alfred Gabriel, 1850-1921.
... Kritiska anmärkningar om den grönländska
vegetationens historia ... Stockholm, 1890.
Pamphlet.
"Bihang till K. Svenska vet.-akad. handlingar,
band 16, afd. III, n:o 6."

NN 0030260 CtY

Nathorst, Alfred Gabriel. Kungaspeg-
lens "hafgärdingar" och förlianingen af
den kgl. grönländska handelns fartyg
"Hvidbjörnen." *Extr. fr.* Ymer. XV.
årg. Stockholm. 1895. 8°. pp. 253-256.

NN 0030261 NIC

Nathorst, Alfred Gabriel,

Antevs, Ernst.
... Die liassische flora des Hörsandsteins, von Ernst
Antevs; mit 6 tafeln und 4 textfiguren; mitgeteilt am 8.
januar 1919 durch A. G. Nathorst und C. Lindman.
Stockholm. Almquist & Wiksells boktryckeri-a.-b., 1919.

Nathorst, Alfred Gabriel

Halle, Thore Gustaf.
... Lower Devonian plants from Röragen in Norway, by
T. G. Halle; with 4 plates and 2 text-figures. Communi-
cated April 26th, 1916, by A. G. Nathorst and G. Holm.
Stockholm, Almquist & Wiksells boktryckeri-a.-b., 1916.

Nathorst, Alfred Gabriel, 1850-
... Die mikrosporophylle von Williamsonia, von A. G.
Nathorst. Mit 1 tafel und 11 textfiguren. Uppsala &
Stockholm, Almqvist & Wiksells boktryckeri-A.-B.; ₍etc.,
etc.₎ 1912.
cover-title, 10 p. illus. pl. 21ᶜᵐ.
At head of title: Arkiv för botanik utgifvet af K. Svenska vetenskaps-
akademien i Stockholm. bd. 12. n:o 6.
"Literatur-liste": p. 9.

G S 12-587

Library, U. S. Geol.   survey

NN 0030264 DI-GS

Nathorst, Alfred Gabriel, 1850-
... Några ord om slipsandstenen i Dalarne. Af A. G.
Nathorst. Stockholm, Kongl. boktryckeriet, P. A. Nor-
stedt & söner, 1885)
26 p. diagrs. 22½ᵐ. (Sveriges geologiska undersökning. Ser. C.
Afhandlingar och uppsatser. n:o 71)
Aftryck ur Geol. fören. förhandl. n:o 93. bd. vii. häft. 9.

1. Sandstone. 2. Petrology—Sweden—Dalarne.

G S 7-1406

Library, U. S. Geol.   survey

NN 0030265 DI-GS

Nathorst, Alfred Gabriel, 1850-
... Några ord om Visingsöserien. Af A. G. Nathorst ...
Stockholm, Kongl. boktryckeriet, P. A. Norstedt & söner,
1886.
21 p. diagrs. 22½ᵐ. (Sveriges geologiska undersökning. Ser. C. Afhandlingar och uppsatser. n:o 79)
Aftryck ur Geol. fören. förhandl. n:o 99. bd. viii. häft. 1.

1. Geology—Sweden—Visingsö.

G S 7-1413

Library, U. S. Geol.   survey

NN 0030266 DI-GS

Nathorst, Alfred Gabriel
Nachträgliche bemerkungen über die
mesozoische flora Spitzbergens. Stockholm, 1897.
(reprint from Öfversigt af. K. vetens-
kaps akademien. Förhandlingar 1897, no.8)
Followed by typed translation.

NN 0030267 MiHM

Nathorst, Alfred Gabriel, 1850-1921.
... Nouvelles observations sur des traces d'animaux et autres
phénomènes d'origine purement mécanique décrits comme
"algues fossiles." Par A.-G. Nathorst. Avec 5 planches en
phototypie et plusieurs figures intercalées dans le texte ...
Stockholm, P. A. Norstedt & söner, 1886.
58 p., 1 l. illus., 5 pl. 31ᶜᵐ. (Kongl. svenska vetenskaps-akademiens
handlingar. ₍Ny följd₎ bd. 21, n:o 14)
Plates accompanied by leaves with descriptive letterpress.
"Traduit et revu sur le manuscrit suédois par J. H. Kramer."—p. ₍2₎
1. Paleontology. 2. *Saporta, Gaston, marquis de, 1823-1895. À propos des algues fossiles. i. Kramer, Jules Henri, 1827-1910, tr.

Chicago. Univ. Library   A 43-151
for Library of Congress   Q64.S85 bd. 21, no. 14
                                            ₍2₎†

NN 0030268 ICU NNBG OU ICJ NN DLC

Nathorst, Alfred Gabriel, 1850-1921.
Nya anmärkningar om Williamsonia.
n.p. [1888]

NN 0030269 NjP

VOLUME 405

Nathorst, Alfred Gabriel, 1850–1921.
... Nya bidrag till kännedomen om Spetsbergens kärlväxter, och dess växtgeografiska förhållanden. Af A. G. Nathorst. Med 2 kartor ... Stockholm, P. A. Norstedt & söner, 1883.
88 p. 2 fold. maps. 31ᶜᵐ. (Kongl. svenska vetenskaps-akademiens handlingar. ¡Ny följd¡ bd. 20, n:o 6)
Bibliographical foot-notes.

1. Botany—Spitzbergen.

A 43–135

Chicago. Univ. Library
for Library of Congress   Q64.S85   bd. 20, no. 6

NN   0030270   ICU NN DLC

Nathorst, Alfred Gabriel, 1850–
... Nya fyndorter för arktiska växtlemningar i Skåne. Af A. G. Nathorst ... Stockholm, P. A. Norstedt & söner, kongl. boktryckare, 1877.
29 p. 22½ᶜᵐ. (Sveriges geologiska undersökning. ¡Ser. C. Afhandlingar och uppsatser. n:o 20¡)
Aftryck ur Geologiska föreningens i Stockholm förhandlingar, 1877, n:o 38, band III, n:o 10.

1. Paleobotany—Sweden—Scania.

G S 7–1359

Library, U. S. Geol.   survey

NN   0030271   DI-GS

Nathorst, Alfred Gabriel, 1850–
... Die oberdevonische flora des Ellesmere-Landes (mit 7 tafeln und 4 figuren im texte) At the expence ¡!¡ of the Fridtjof Nansen fund for the advancement of science; pub. by Videnskabs-selskabet i Kristiania (the Society of arts and sciences of Kristiania) Kristiania, Printed by A. W. Brögger, 1904.
22 p. illus. 7 pl. (6 double) 27ᶜᵐ. (Report of the Second Norwegian Arctic expedition in the "Fram," 1898–1902. no. 1)
1. Paleobotany—Ellesmere Land. Paleobotany—Devonian. I. Videnskabs-selskabet, Christiania. II. Fridtjof Nansens fond til irdenskabens fremma.

G S 19–432

Library, U. S. Geological   Survey 502(980) qN8

NN   0030272   DI-GS NNBG CU

Nathorst, A¡lfred¡ G¡abriel¡.
Om aftryck af medusor i Sveriges kambriska lager. Stockholm: P. A. Norstedt & Söner, 1881. 3 p.l., (1)4–34 p., 6 l., 6 pl. f°. (Kongliga Svenska Vetenskaps-Akademien. Handlingar. Ny följd. Bd. 19, no. 1.)
With bibliographical foot-notes.

1. Medusæ (Fossil). 2. Palæon-
N. Y. P. L.   tology (Zoological), Sweden.
             December 12, 1911.

NN   0030273   NN

Nathorst, Alfred Gabriel, 1850–
... Om de äldre sandstens- och skifferbildningarne vid Vettern. Af A. G. Nathorst ... Stockholm, Kongl. boktryckeriet, P. A. Norstedt & söner, 1880.
18 p. col. map. 22½ᶜᵐ. (Sveriges geologiska undersökning. Ser. C. Afhandlingar och uppsatser. n:o 14)
Aftryck ur Geol. föreningens i Stockholm förhandl. 1879. n:o 56. bd. IV, n:o 14.

1. Geology—Sweden—Wetter, Lake.

G S 7–1375

Library, U. S. Geol.   survey

NN   0030274   DI-GS

Nathorst, Alfred Gabriel, 1850–
... Om de svenska urbergens sekulära förvittring. Af A. G. Nathorst. Stockholm, Kongl. boktryckeriet, P. A. Norstedt & söner, 1880.
17 p. 22½ᶜᵐ. (Sveriges geologiska undersökning. Ser. C. Afhandlingar och uppsatser. n:o 38)
Aftryck ur Geol. föreningens i Stockholm förhandl. 1879. n:o 55. bd. IV, n:o 13.

1. Geology—Sweden.

G S 7–1374

Library, U. S. Geol.   survey

NN   0030275   DI-GS

Nathorst, Alfred Gabriel, 1850–
... Om de växtförande lagren i Skånes kolförande bildningar och deras plats i lagerföljden. Af A. G. Nathorst. Stockholm, Kongl. boktryckeriet, P. A. Norstedt & söner, 1880.
1 p. l., 9 p. 22½ᶜᵐ. (Sveriges geologiska undersökning. Ser. C. Afhandlingar och uppsatser. n:o 44)
Aftryck ur Geol. föreningens i Stockholm förhandl. 1880. n:o 62. bd. v. n:o 6.

1. Paleobotany—Sweden—Scania. 2. Paleobotany—Carboniferous.

G S 7–1380

Library, U. S. Geol.   survey

NN   0030276   DI-GS NjP

Nathorst, Alfred Gabriel, 1850–
... Om en cycadékotte från den rätiska formationens lager vid Tinkarp i Skåne. Af A. G. Nathorst. ¡Stockholm, P. A. Norstedt & söner, 1876¡
cover-title, 7 p. pl. 22½ᶜᵐ. (Sveriges geologiska undersökning. ¡Ser. C. Afhandlingar och uppsatser. n:o 19¡)
Extract from Öfversigt af Kongl. Vetenskaps-akademiens förhandlingar, 1875. n:o 10.

1. Cycadaceæ. 2. Paleobotany—Sweden—Scania.

G S 7–1358

Library, U. S. Geol.   survey

NN   0030277   DI-GS

Nathorst, Alfred Gabriel, 1850–
... Om floran i Skånes kolförande bildningar af A. G. Nathorst ... Stockholm, P. A. Norstedt & söner, kongl. boktryckare, 1878–86.
2 v. in 1. 34 pl. (partly fold.) diagrs. 30ᶜᵐ. (Sveriges geologiska undersökning. Ser. C. Afhandlingar och uppsatser. n:is 27, 29, 33, 85)
Pt. II. is "aftryck ur K. Sv. vet-akad. handl., bd. 16, n:o 7."
CONTENTS.—I. Floran vid Bjuf.—II. Floran vid Höganäs och Helsingborg.

1. Paleobotany—Sweden—Scania. 2. Paleobotany—Carboniferous.

G S 7–1365

Library, U. S. Geol.   survey

NN   0030278   DI-GS NjP ViU

Nathorst, Alfred Gabriel, 1850–
... Om några förmodade växtfossilier. Af Alfred Nathorst ... ¡Stockholm, 1873¡
p. 25–52. pl. XV–XIX. 22ᶜᵐ.
Caption title.
Öfversigt af Kongl. vetenskaps-akademiens Förhandlingar 1873. no. 9.

1. Paleobotany—Cambrian.

CA 10–3058 Unrev'd

Library of Congress   QE916.N3

NN   0030279   DI-GS NjP

Nathorst, Alfred Gabriel, 1850–1921.
... Om några ginkoväxter från kolgrufvorna vid stabbarp i Skåne, af A. G. Nathorst. Med två taflor. Lund, H. Ohlssons boktryckeri, 1906.
15, ¡1¡ p. illus., 11 pl. 29½ᶜᵐ. (Lunds universitets årsskrift. n. f., afd. 2, bd. 2, n:r 8)
K. Fysiografiska sällskapets handlingar. n. f., bd. 17, n:r 8. Bibliographical foot-notes.

1. Ginkgo. 2. Paleobotany—Sweden—Skåne. I. Title.

A 31–637

Title from John Crerar   Libr. 058
Library of Congress   [AS284.L8 n. f., afd. 2, bd. 2, nr. 8]
        r°.

NN   0030280   ICJ MoU NNBG NN PU

Nathorst, A¡lfred¡ G¡abriel¡.
Om spår af några evertebrerade djur m.m. och deras paleontologiska betydelse. Stockholm: P. A. Norstedt & Söner, 1881. 104 p., 11 l., 11 pl. illus. f°. (Kongliga Svenska Vetenskaps-Akademien. Handlingar. Ny följd. Bd. 18, no. 7.)
Bibliography, p. 54–59.

1. Palæontology (Zoological).
N. Y. P. L.   December 20, 1911.

NN   0030281   NN ViU MH

Nathorst, Alfred Gabriel, 1850–
... Om *Spirangium* och dess förekomst i Skånes kolförande bildningar. Af A. G. Nathorst ... Stockholm, Kongl. boktryckeriet, P. A. Norstedt & söner, 1879.
1 p. l., 13 p. 2 pl. 22½ᶜᵐ. (Sveriges geologiska undersökning. Ser. C. Afhandlingar och uppsatser. n:o 36)
Aftryck ur Öfvers. af Kongl. vet.-akad:s förhandl., 1879.

1. Spirangium.

G S 7–1372

Library, U. S. Geol.   survey

NN   0030282   DI-GS

QE923
-N3
Physical
Sciences
Library

Nathorst, Alfred Gabriel, 1850–1921
On the Upper Jurassic flora of Hope Bay, Graham Land ... Mexico, Imprenta y fototipia de la Secretaria de fomento, 1907.
1 p.l., ¡1269¡–1270p. 27cm.

NN   0030283   RPB

Nathorst, Alfred Gabriel, 1850–
On the value of the fossil floras of the Arctic regions as evidence of geological climates. By Prof. A. G. Nathorst ... Tr. from the French original by E. A. Newell Arber ...
(*In* Smithsonian institution. Annual report. 1911. Washington, 1912. 23½ᶜᵐ. p. 335–344)
Appeared originally in "Compt. rend. Eleventh intern. geol. congr., Stockholm, 1912. Reprinted ... from the Geological magazine, London, Decade v, vol. 8, no. 563, pp. 217–225, May, 1911."

1. Paleobotany—Arctic regions. I. Arber, Edward Alexander Newell, 1870– tr.

13–3784

Library of Congress   Q11.S66 1911

NN   0030284   DLC PHC MiU OU OCU OC1 MH-A ICJ WaS

Nathorst, A¡lfred¡ G¡abriel¡.
Palæobotanische Mitteilungen 1 & 2. Uppsala: Almquist & Wiksell, 1907. 20 p., 3 pl. f°. (Kongliga Svenska Vetenskaps-Akademien. Handlingar. Ny följd. Bd. 42, no. 5.)

1. Palæontology (Botanical).
N. Y. P. L.   February 20, 1912.

NN   0030285   NN DNLM MiU

Q64
.S85
ser.4
v.43
no.8
1908

Nathorst, Alfred Gabriel, 1850–1921.
Palæobotanische Mitteilungen, 7. Mitgeteilt am 2. Dezember 1908. Uppsala, Almqvist & Wiksell, 1908.
20 p. illus. 3 plates. 32cm. (Svanska vetenskapsakademien. Handlingar ¡ser. 4¡ Bd. 43, no. 8)

1. Paleobotany. I. Ser.

NN   0030286   ViU

Nathorst, Alfred Gabriel, 1850–1921.
... Paläobotanische mitteilungen 8, von A. G. Nathorst. Mit 8 tafeln und 5 textfiguren ... Uppsala & Stockholm, Almqvist & Wiksells boktryckeri-a.-b, 1909.
37, ¡1¡ p. illus., 8 plates. 30cm. (Kongl. svenska vetenskaps-akademiens handlingar. bd.45, n:o 4¡
"Mitgeteilt am 10. November 1909."
"Literatur-liste": p.32–33.
"Tryckt den 28 december 1909."

1. Paleobotany. I. Title. II. Ser.

NN   0030287   ViU RPB

VOLUME 405

Q
64
S85
bd.46,
no.4;
etc.
+
Nathorst, Alfred Gabriel, 1850-
 Paläobotanische Mitteilungen. Uppsala,
Almqvist & Wiksells,1911-
 v. illus.,plates. 32cm. (Svenska
Vetenskapsakademien, Stockholm. /
Handlingar. [Ny följd] bd. 46, no. 4;
bd. 46, no. 8)

 1. Paleobotany. I. Title. (Series)

NN 0030288 MU ViU

Nathorst, Alfred Gabriel, 1850-1921.
 Paleontologiska forskningar vid Wajgattet ...
till Kap York. Stockholm, 1885.

NN 0030289 NjP

919.8
N275
Nathorst, Alfred Gabriel, 1850-1921.
 Polarforskningen. Stockholm, P. A. Norstedt [1902]
 30 p. col. map. 21 cm. (Föreningen heimdals
folkskrifter, 74)

 1. Arctic regions. 1. Title. (Series)

NN 0030290 N

NATHORST, Alfred Gabriel.
 Polarforskningens bidrag till forntidens växtgeografi. Maps.
 (In Nordenskiöld. Studier och forskningar. Pp. 229-301. Stockholm, 1883.)

NN 0030291 MB

Nathorst, Alfred Gabriel, 1850-1921.
 Eine Probe aus dem Torflager bei Lauenburg an
der Elbe. Berlin, 1894.
 [533]-534 p. 29 cm.
 Caption title.
 From Naturwissenschaftliche Wochenschrift,
Bd.9, Nr.44.
 Bound with his Nouvelles observations sur des
traces d'animaux et autres phénomènes ... Stock-
holm, 1886; and 9 others of his writings.
 Bibliographical footnotes.
 1. Paleobotany - Germany - Lauenburg. i.t.

NN 0030292 NNBG

Nathorst, Alfred Gabriel
 ...Redogörelse för den tillsammans med
G. De Geer ar 1882 företagna geologiska
expeditionen till Spetsbergen. Meddeladt
den 14 November 1883. Stockholm, P.A.
Norstedt & söner, 1884.
 78p. 1 fold. map. (Bihang till K.
Svenska vet.-akad. Handlingar,bd.9,n6.2)
 Two copies bound together.
 Followed by typed translation.

NN 0030293 MiHM

Nathorst, Alfred Gabriel, 1850-1921.

Nordenskiöld, Nils Adolf Erik, *friherre*, 1832-1901.
 ... Studier och forskningar föranledda af mina resor i höga
Norden. Ett populärt vetenskapligt bihang till "Vegas färd
kring Asien och Europa." Stockholm, F. & G. Beijer [1883-
84]

Nathorst, Alfred Gabriel, 1850-1921.
 Den Svenska expeditionen till nordostra
Grenland. 1900.

NN 0030294 DI-GS

Nathorst, Alfred Gabriel, 1850-1921
 Sveriges geologi. 1892-4.

NN 0030295 DI-GS

Nathorst, Alfred Gabriel, 1850-1921.
 Sveriges geologi allmänfattligt framställd, med en in-
ledande historik om den geologiska forskningen i Sverige,
jemte en kort öfversigt af det geologiska systemen, af A. G.
Nathorst ... Stockholm, F. & G. Beijers bokförlagsaktie-
bolag [1894]
 2 p. l., 336 p. illus., diagrs. 27 cm.
 "Litteraturförteckning": p. 315-324.

 1. Geology—Sweden.

 G S 9—171
U. S. Geol. Survey. Libr. 208
for Library of Congress [a66c½]

NN 0030296 DI-GS PBa MH NjP

Nathorst, Alfred Gabriel, 1850-1921.
 Swedish explorations in Spitzbergen 1758-1908. A. G.
Nathorst: Historical sketch. J. M. Hulth: Bibliography.
G. De Geer: List of maps ... Stockholm, Centraltryckeriet,
1909.
 89 p. illus. (incl. maps) 23½cm.
 Reprinted from Ymer 1909, h. 1.

 1. Spitzbergen — Bibl. I. Hulth, Johan Markus.
Gerard Jakob, friherre, 1858- II. De Geer,
Gerard Jakob, friherre, 1858- III. Title.
 9—12172
Library of Congress Z6005.P7N2

NN 0030297 DLC CtY PPAN PU MiU NjP ICJ PPF

Nathorst, Alfred Gabriel, 1850-
 ... Tertiäre pflanzenreste aus Ellesmere-land, mit 2
tafeln und 2 figuren im texte, at the expense of the Fridtjof Nansen fund for the advancement of science, pub. by
Videnskabs-selskabet i Kristiania (the Society of arts
and sciences of Kristiania) Kristiania, Printed by A. W.
Brøgger, 1915.
 16 p. illus., 2 pl. 27½cm. (Report of the Second Norwegian Arctic
expedition in the "Fram" 1898-1902. no. 35)

 1. Paleobotany—Tertiary. 2. Paleobotany—Ellesmere land.
 G S 15-884
Library, U. S. Geological Survey 502(980) qN8

NN 0030298 DI-GS CU MiU

V
552.28
N275t
Nathorst, Alfred Gabriel, 1850-1921.
 ...Till frågan om det gedigna jernets förekomst i basalten på Grönlands vestkust. Af A.G.
Nathorst. [Stockholm, 1878]
 p.[203]-207. 21½cm.
 Caption title.
 At head of title: Aftryck ur Geol.föreningens
i Stockholm Förhandl. 1878. N:o 49.Bd.IV,n:o 7.
 Author's presentation copy to Bernhard Lund-
gren.
 1. Basalt. 2. Iron. 3.Petrology - Greenland - Disko island.

NN 0030299 CSt

Nathorst, Alfred Gabriel, 1850-
 Till frågan om jordens forna klimat.
Stockholm, 1893.
 16 p. 1.8°.

NN 0030300 MH-Z

Nathorst, Alfred Gabriel, 1850-
 Två somrar i Norra Ishafvet; Kung Karls Land,
Spetsbergens kringsegling, spanande efter Andrée i nord-
östra Grönland, af A. G. Nathorst ... Stockholm, Beijer
[1900]
 2 v. front., illus., plates, ports., maps (2 fold.) 24cm.

 1. Spitzbergen—Disc. & explor. 2. Greenland—Disc. & explor. 3. Andrée, Salomon August, b. 1854.
 16-8679
Library of Congress G780.N3

NN 0030301 DLC MnU MH MB

QE702
.N3
Nathorst, Alfred Gabriel, 1850-1921.
 Über abweichend gebildete Blätter der Rotbuche
(Fagus silvatica L.) Uppsala, Almqvist & Wiksells boktr., 1907.
 14 p. 3 plates. 31 cm. (Kungl. Svenska
vetenskapsakademiens handlingar, bd.42, no.7)
 Bound with his Nouvelles observations sur les
traces d'animaux et autres phénomènes ... Stockholm, 1886; and 9 other of his writings.
 Bibliographical footnotes.
 1. Fagus silvatica. i.t. ii.s: Svenska
vetenskapsakade- miens handlingar, bd.42,
no.7.

NN 0030302 NNBG ViU MH-A

QE702
.N3
Nathorst, Alfred Gabriel, 1850-1921.
 Über Dictyophyllum und Camptopteris spiralis.
Uppsala, Almqvist & Wiksells boktr., 1906.
 24 p. 7 double plates. 31 cm. (Kungl.
Svenska vetenskapsakademiens handlingar, bd.41,
no.5)
 Bound with his Nouvelles observations sur les
traces d'animaux et autres phénomènes ... Stockholm, 1886; and 9 other of his writings.
 Bibliography: p. 20-21.
 1. Dictyophyllum. 2. Camptopteris spirales.
i.t. ii.s: Sven- ska vetenskapsakademiens
handlingar, bd. 41, no.5.

NN 0030303 NNBG

Nathorst, Alfred Gabriel, 1850-1921.
 Ueber die benennung fossiler dikotylenblätter.
[Cassel, 1886]

NN 0030304 NjP

QE976
.N35
Nathorst, Alfred Gabriel, 1850-1921.
 Über die Gattung Nilssonia Brongn. mit beson-
derer Berücksichtigung schwedischer Arten.
Uppsala, Almqvist & Wiksells boktr., 1909.
 40 p. 8 double plates. 31 cm. (Kungl. Svenska
vetenskapsakademiens handlingar, bd.43, no.12)
QE702
.N3
 Bibliography: p.33-35.
 Copy 1: Gray Herbarium purchase December 1970.
 Another copy bound with his Nouvelles obser-
vations sur les traces d'animaux et autres
phénomènes ... Stockholm, 1886; and 9 of his
other writings.

NN 0030305 NNBG MiU RPB ViU

Nathorst, Alfred Gabriel, 1850-1921.
 ... Ueber die reste eines brotfruchtbaums, *Artocarpus dick-
soni*, n. sp., aus den cenomanen kreideablagerungen Grönlands.
Von A. G. Nathorst. Mit einer tafel ... Stockholm, P. A.
Norstedt & söner, 1890.
 10 p. fold. pl. 31cm. (Kongl. svenska vetenskaps-akademiens hand-
lingar. [Ny följd] bd. 24, n:o 1)
 Bibliographical foot-notes.

 1. Breadfruit. 2. Paleobotany—Greenland.
 A 43-176
Chicago. Univ. Library
for Library of Congress Q64.S85 bd. 24, no. 1

NN 0030306 ICU ViU NNBG NN DLC MH-A

VOLUME 405

QE702
.N3
Nathorst, Alfred Gabriel, 1850-1921.
Ueber pflanzenähnliche "Fossilien" durch
rinnendes Wasser hervorgebracht. Berlin, 1894.
[313]-314 p. 29 cm.

Caption title.
From Naturwissenschaftliche Wochenschrift,
Bd.9, Nr. 26.
Bound with his Nouvelles observations sur
des traces d'animaux et autres phénomènes ...
Stockholm, 1886; and 9 others of his writings.
Bibliographical footnotes.
1. Paleobotany. i.t.

NN 0030307   NNBG

Nathorst, A[lfred] G[abriel].
Ueber Thaumatopteris Schenki Nath.   Uppsala: Almquist
& Wiksell, 1907.   9 p., 2 pl.   f°.   (Kongliga Svenska Veten-
skaps-Akademien. Handlingar. Ny följd. Bd. 42, no. 3.)

Bibliography, p. 8.

1. Dictyophyllum.
N. Y. P. L.   February 20, 1912.

NN 0030308   NN NNBG ViU

QE702
.N3
Nathorst, Alfred Gabriel, 1850-1921.
Über Trias- und Jurapflanzen von der Insel
Kotelny. С.-Петербургъ, 1907.
13 p. 2 plates. 31 cm. (Научные результаты
Русской полярной экспедиціи въ 1900-1903 гг.,
подъ начальством барона Э. В. Толля. Отдѣлъ
С: Геологія и палеонтологія. вып. 2)
Записки Императорской Академіи наукъ, серія
VIII, по Физико-математическому отдѣленію.
Томъ XXI, No 2.
Bound with his Nouvelles observations sur les
traces d'animaux et autres phénomènes ...

Stockholm, 1886; and 9 others of his writings.
Bibliographical footnotes.

1. Paleobotany - Triassic. 2. Paleobotany -
Jurassic. 3. Paleobotany - Kotelny Island.
i.t. ii.s: Nauchnye rezultaty Russkoĭ poliarnoĭ
ekspeditsii v 1900-1903 gg. Otdel S: Geologiia
paleontologiia, vyp. 2. iii.s: Zapiski Impera-
torskoĭ Akademii   nauk, seriia VIII, po
fiziko-matemati-   cheskomy otdeleniiu.
t.21, no.2.

NN 0030310   NNBG MH-G

QE
282
A3
ser.Ba
no.4
Nathorst, Alfred Gabriel, 1850-1921.
Upplysningar till geologisk öfversigtskarta
öfver Sverige; utgifven af Sveriges Geologiska
Undersökning: södra bladet. [Stockholm, 1884]
iv, 35 p. tables. 24cm. and map. 74 x
55cm. (Sveriges Geologiska Undersökning.
Ser. Ba. Öfversigtskartor med beskrifningar,
no. 4)

1. Geology--Sweden.

NN 0030311   NIC

Nathorst, Alfred Gabriel
Eine vorläufige mitteilung von Prof. J.
F. Pompeckj über die altersfrage der Jura
ablagerungen Spitzbergens. [Stockholm,
P.A. Norstedt & söner, 1910.]
(Excerpt from Aftryck ur Geol. Fören
Förhandl. Nov.1910)
Followed by typed translation.

NN 0030312   MiHM

Nathorst, Alfred Gabriel, 1850-1921.
...Zur Devonflora des westlichen Norwegens von A. G.
Nathorst. Mit einer Einleitung: Das Vorkommen der Pflanzen-
reste, von Carl Fred. Kolderup... [Bergen: A/S J. Grieg, 1915.]
34 p. illus. (incl. plan.)   plates. 8°.   (Bergens Museum,
Bergen, Norway. Bergens Museums aarbok. 1914–15, nr. 9.)

Bibliography, p. 30–31.

1. Palaeontology (Botanical), Norway.   2. Kolderup, Carl Fredrik, 1869–
   3. Series.
N. Y. P. L.   May 8, 1923.

NN 0030313   NN NNBG

Nathorst, Alfred Gabriel, 1850-1921.
Zur fossilen flora der polarländer, von A. G. Nathorst ...
Stockholm, P. A. Norstedt & söner, 1894–1914.
4 v. in 1. illus., plates (part double) 29-31½m.
Contains bibliographies.
1. th., 1–3. lfg. are K. Svenska vetenskaps-akademiens. Handlingar bd.
26, n:o 4; bd. 30, n:o 1; bd. 36, n:o 3.
CONTENTS.--bd. 1. lfg. 1. Zur paläozoischen flora der arktischen zone.
1894. lfg. 2. Zur mesozoischen Spitzbergens. 1897. lfg. 3. Zur oberdevonischen flora der Bären-insel. 1902. lfg. 4. Nachträge zur paläozoischen flora Spitzbergens. 1914.

1. Paleobotany—Arctic regions. 2. Paleobotany—Paleozoic.

                                             G S 14–778 Revised
Library, U. S. Geological   Survey 690(980) qN2z

NN 0030314   DI-GS ICJ NNBG

Nathorst, Alfred Gabriel.
Zur fossilen flora der polarländer. Stockholm,
1902.

NN 0030315   IU

Nathorst, Alfred Gabriel, 1850-1921.
... Zur fossilen flora Japan's, von A. G. Nathorst. Mit
14 tafeln und 1 kartenskizze im text. Berlin. Druck und
verlag von G. Reimer, 1888.
56 p. xiv pl., map. 30cm. (Palæontologische abhandlungen, hrsg. von
W. Dames und E. Kayser, bd. 4, hft. 3)
Descriptive letterpress on versos facing the plates.

1. Paleobotany—Japan.

NN 0030316   MiU

Nathorst, Alfred Gabriel, 1850-1921.
Zur mesozoischen Flora Spitzbergens
gegründet auf die Sammlungen der schwedischen
Expeditionen.
77 p. illus., 6 plates. 31 cm.
(Kongl. svenska vetenskaps-akad. Handlingar,
Ny följd. v. 30, no. 1. Stockholm, 1897)
1. Paleobotany - Mesozoia.. 2. Paleobotany -
Spitzbergen.

NN 0030317   CtY NN MiHM MH

Nathorst, A[lfred] G[abriel].
Zur oberdevonischen Flora der Bären-insel.   Stockholm:
P. A. Norstedt & Söner, 1902.   60 p., 14 pl.   illus.   f°.
(Kongliga Svenska Vetenskaps-Akademien. Handlingar. Ny
följd. Bd. 36, no. 3.)

Bibliography, p. 52–53.

1. Plants (Fossil), Arctic regions.   2. Palæontology (Botanical), Arctic regions.
N. Y. P. L.   January 6, 1912.

NN 0030318   NN MiU NNBG IU

Nathorst, A[lfred] G[abriel] 1850-1921.
Zur palaeozoischen Flora der arktischen Zone, enthaltend die
auf Spitzbergen, auf der Bären-insel und Novaja Zemlja von den
schwedischen Expeditionen entdeckten paläozoischen Pflanzen.
Stockholm: P. A. Norstedt & Söner, 1894.   80 p., 16 l., 16 pl.
illus.   f°.   (Kongliga Svenska Vetenskaps-Akademien. Handlingar. Ny följd. Bd. 26, no. 4.)

With bibliographical foot-notes.

1. Palæontology (Botanical), Arctic   regions.
N. Y. P. L.   January 4, 1912.

NN 0030319   NN

Nathorst, Anita.
S:t Elmseld; dikter, av Anita Nathorst.   Stockholm: H.
Geber[, 1926].   80 p. 8°.

1. Poetry, Swedish. 2. Title.
N. Y. P. L.   June 15, 1927

NN 0030320   NN

Nathorst, Birgit
Kodin koristelua, ohjeita amatoimisuutoon.
[Hämeenlinna, A.A., Karisto, 1935.]
46p.

Cover title.
Finnish.

NN 0030321   OCl

Nathorst, C. E.
Commencement address...at the Constabulary
Academy, Camp Henry T. Aleen...[Benguet, P.I.,
1928]
9p.

YA 28674

NN 0030322   DLC

Egleston
D669.11
Un291
no.6
Nathorst, Helmer
Stress corrosion cracking of stainless
steels. New York, 1950.
18 p. illus., tables, diagrs. 29cm.
(Welding research council bulletin series,
no. 6)

Contents.--pt.1. Practical experiences.--
pt.2. An investigation of the suitability
of the U-bend specimen.

NN 0030323   NNC

Nathorst, Herbert.
The prognosis of exudative pleurisy in children. Stockholm, 1948.
174 p. diagrs. 25 cm. (Acta tuberculosea Scandinavica. Supplementum 17)
At head of title: From the Pediatric Clinic at Karolinska institutet
at Norrtull's Hospital, Stockholm. Head: Professor Arvid Wallgren.
From the State Institute of Human Genetics and Race Biology, Uppsala. Head: Professor Gunnar Dahlberg.
Imprint on cover: Copenhagen, Munksgaard.
Bibliography: p. 171–173.

1. Pleurisy. 2. Children—Diseases.   i. Title.   (Series)

                                             A 51–7612
Rochester. Univ. Libr.   RC306.A45 Suppl. 17
for Library of Congress   [1]

NN 0030324   NRU DNLM ViU

33.13
N19
Nathhorst, Hjalmar.
Belgiens åkerbruk. Efter Poggendorff's "Die
landwirtschaft in Belgien", annuaire des agricoles
...af Hjalmar Nathhorst.   Örebro, N. M. Lindh,
1859.
98 p. map. 21½cm.

NN 0030325   DNAL

Nathorst, Hjalmar
Landt bruket i Skåne. 1896.
unb.

NN 0030326   DNAL

VOLUME 405

33.11
N19N   Nathhorst, Hjalmar.
Några ord om vilkoren för svenska jordbrukets
utveckling, af Hjalmar Nathhorst. Stockholm,
Tidskrift för svenska landtbruket, 1858.
96 p.   22½cm.

NN   0030327   DNAL

Nathorst, Hjalmar.
De Nyaste erfarenheterna
om kaligodslingens vavide.
1896

NN   0030328   DNAL

Nathorst, Hjalmar.
Om sullguano.   1896.

NN   0030329   DNAL

Nathorst, Hjalmar.
Om Thomasfosfatets varde.
1896.

NN   0030330   DNAL

Nathorst, Hjalmar.
Swingarden and Riddersuit.   1836.

NN   0030331   DNAL

Nathhorst (Joh. Theophilus). Descriptio arte-
riarum corporis humani in tabulas redacta, cu-
jus partem primam . . . publice ventilaudam exhibit. 23 pp. 4°. *Upsaliæ, J. Edman,* [1780].

NN   0030332   DNLM

Nathhorst, Mary T.
Ellen von Platens hem, Stockholm.
8 p.   illus.
"Separattryck ur Svenska hem i ord och
bilder, 1918."

NN   0030333   DDO

Wason   Nathorst, Ruth.
DS725   Kinas kvinna i forntid och nutid, av Ruth
N27   Nathorst.   Stockholm, Sveriges Kristliga
Studentrörelses Förlag, [1924]
334 p. illus. 19cm. (Sveriges Kristliga
Studentrörelses Missionsskriftserie. N:r 19)

"Litteraturförteckning": p. [330]-331.

1. Women in China.   I. Title.

NN   0030334   NIC

4DS   Nathorst, Ruth.
China-25   Sun Yat Sen, det nya Kinas frihetskämpe.
Med förord av professor K. B. Westman.
Stockholm, Sveriges Kristliga Studentrörelses
Förlag [1933]
328 p.

NN   0030335   DLC-P4

Nathorst-Böös, Ernst Jonas, 1861-
Ernst Trygger [av Ernst Nathorst-Böös] och Nils Edén
[av Erik Thyselius] Stockholm, Svenska bokförlaget [1916]
81 p.   ports. (on cover)   18 cm.   (Männen för dagen, 9 [i. e. 13])

1. Trygger, Ernst, 1857-1943. 2. Edén, Nils, 1871-1945.   I. Thy-
selius, Erik, 1854-1924.   (Series: Männen för dagen, 13)

DL865.T7N3   24-20900 rev*

NN   0030336   DLC

792.94   Nathorst-Böös, Ernst Jonas, 1861-
B7240   Om Amerikas filmindustri.   Stockholm,
A.Bonnier [1935]
87p.   illus.,ports.   23cm.   (Svenska
Filmsamfundets skriftserie, v.1)

1.Moving-pictures - U.S. I.Title.
II.Series: Svenska Filmsamfundet. Skriftserie. 1C StL

NN   0030337   CLSU

Nathow,Helmuth,1897-
Die prozessuale urkundeneditionspflicht
im deutschen,österreichischen und französischen recht auf der grundlage der
actio ad exhibendum rechtsvergleichend
dargestellt ... Hamburg, H.Schimkus [1933]
3 p. l.,28 p.,1 l.   30½cm.
Lithographed.
Inaug.-diss. - Hamburg,1933.
Lebenslauf.
"Literaturverzeichnis" on verso of 2d
preliminary leaf and recto of 3d preliminary leaf.

NN   0030338   MiU-L

BP193   Nathr al-la' ālī.   Latin & Arabic.   1806.
.1
.A2W34   Waenen, Cornelis van, 1732-1806, comp.
Sententiæ Ali ebn Abi Talebi, arabice et latine. E codi-
cibus manuscriptis descripsit, latine vertit, et annotationibus
illustravit, Cornelius van Waenen. Oxonii, e typographeo
Clarendoniano, 1806.

Nathrath, Joh., 1872-
Ueber traumatische hydro-nephrose.
Inaug. diss. Bonn, 1897.

NN   0030340   ICRL CtY

Nathrath, Paul.
Bonn; Wesen und Werden.   Wittlich, G. Fischer [1955?]
13 p. illus. 24 cm.   (Sammlung Rheinisches Land)

1. Bonn—Hist. 2. Bonn—Descr.—Views.

DD901.B6N3   56-46165 ‡

NN   0030341   DLC

Nathrath, Paul.
Die Landschaft, Erlebnis und Fotografie; mit 75 Abbildungen. Harzburg, Heering-Verlag, 1942.
[81 p.   plates.   26 cm.

1. Photography—Landscapes.   2. Photography, Artistic.

TR660.N3   778.71   A 48-4877*
Columbia Univ.   Libraries
for Library of Congress   [1]†

NN   0030342   NNC DLC NR

---

778   Nathrath, Paul.
N275   A little guide to good photographs of
children. [Tr. by Fred Willy Frerk.
Vaduz, Heering Publications, 1954]
47 p. illus. 11 x 15 cm. (Photo in-
formation, no. 1)
Label mounted above imprint: Phila.,
Rayelle.
"Title of the original German edition:
Gute Kinderfotos."
Cover title: Good photographs of children.
1. Photog-   raphy of children.
I. Title. II.   Good photographs of
children.

NN   0030343   N NN

Nathrath, Paul.
... Die welt im licht, ein buch über fotografie, bilder und
gedanken, mit 86 abbildungen. Bonn, Verlag der buchge-
meinde [1942]
88 p. 86 pl. on 40 l. 23½ᶜᵐ.
"Die literatur": p. 84-85.

1. Photography, Artistic.   I. Title.
45-29894
Library of Congress   TR650.N28
[2]   770

NN   0030344   DLC NNC NR

Hkn   Nathrath, Paul, 1904-
ke80   Der gehaltliche Unterschied in der Lyrik
Gottfried Kellers und C.F. Meyers ... Bottrop,
1931.
Pamphlet
Inaug.-Diss.- Bonn.
Lebenslauf.
"Literaturverzeichnis": p.66-67.

1.Meyer, Conrad Ferdinand, 1825-1898.

NN   0030345   CtY ICRL PU MH

Nathrath, Wather, 1909-
... Paraesthesien und Sensibilitätsstörungen
bei multipler Sklerose und Myelose ...
Bottrop i.W., 1938.
Inaug.-diss. - Münster.
Lebenslauf.

NN   0030346   CtY

Nathschlaeger, Richard.
... U. S. A. — Letters of Credit, von Richard Nathschläger.
Vorzugsaktien und Genuszscheine, von Bernhard Reischer.
Wien: Hölder-Pichler-Tempsky, A. G., 1925.   38 p. incl. forms.
8°.   (Hochschule für Welthandel, Vienna. — Banktechnisches
Institut für Wissenschaft und Praxis. Veroeffentlichungen. Nr.
4.)

Bibliography, p. 38.

1. Credit—Letters of U. S.   2. Reischer, Bernhard.
N. Y. P. L.   March 11, 1926

NN   0030347   NN

Nathu Ram Premi
see
Premi, Nathuram.

Nathmhus, Simon von, 1865-
Unterschiede zwischen der morgen- und abendlaendi-
chen pferdegruppe am skelett und am lebend?u pferd.
Inaug. Diss   Halle, 1891.

NN   0030349   ICRL

VOLUME 405

Nathubhal, Tribhovandas Mungaldas.
The foundations of morality. Some suggestions
towards a universal moral code ... London
[n. d.]
66 p. incl. front. (port.) 18.5 cm.

NN   0030350   CtY

4K   Nathubhal, Tribhovandas Mangaldas
Ind   Hindu caste, law & custom.
262   Bombay, Printed at the "Times of
          India" Press, 1903.   ♣
              1 v. (various pagings)

NN   0030351   DLC-P4

392.5   Nathubhal, Tribhovandas Mangaldas.
N19m   Marriage ceremonies among the Kapola Banias.
         sn.p., n.d.;
         22p. illus. 20cm.

         Caption title.

             1. Marriage customs and rites--India.
         I. Title.

NN   0030352   IU

Nathuram Premi
see
Premi, Nathuram.

Nathuram Vinayak Godse
see
Godse, Nathuram vinayak, 1920-

PT   Nathusius, Annemarie von, 1874-1926.
2627   Der Befreier; Roman. Berlin, Schwert-
A69   Verlag [c1923]
B4   252p. 19cm.

NN   0030355   WU

PT   Nathusius, Annemarie von, 1874-
2627   Eros; Roman. Berlin, Bong [c1919]
A69   324p. 19cm.
E7

NN   0030356   WU PPG NN WLacU

Nathusius, *Frau* Annemarie von, 1874-
Ich bin das schwert! roman von Annemarie von Nath-
sius. 1.-4. tausend. Dresden, C. Reissner, 1914.
4 p. l., 341 p. 20ᶜᵐ.   M. 4

    1. Title.

Library of Congress   PT2627.A69 I 4 1914   14-10572

NN   0030357   DLC WU InU OClW

Nathusius, Annemarie von, 1874-1926.
...Im Auto durch Persien...   Dresden: C. Reissner, 1926
186 p. plates. 8°. (Schoepferische Kulturen.)

Plates printed on both sides.

316027A. 1. Persia—Descr. and trav.,   1910-
N. Y. P. L.   August 1, 192

NN   0030358   NN OCl

PT   Nathusius, Annemarie von, 1874-1926
2627   Im sinkenden Licht; Roman aus den acht-
A69   ziger Jahren. Berlin, Ullstein [c1922]
I4   249p. 20cm.

NN   0030359   WU

Nathusius, *Frau* Annemarie von, 1874-
Die reise nach Baden; erzählung von Annemarie von
Nathusius. Dresden, C. Reissner, 1912.
2 p. l., 244 p. 21ᶜᵐ.   M. 3

    1. Title.

                                                       12-14628

NN   0030360   DLC WU OCl

Nathusius, Annemarie von, 1874-1926.
Rheinsberg; ein märkischer Roman, von Annemarie von
Nathusius...   Stuttgart [etc.] Deutsche Verlags-Anstalt, 1922.
306 p. 19cm.

NN   0030361   NN PPG

Nathusius, *Frau* Annemarie von, 1874-
Der stolze lumpenkram. Roman von Annemarie von
Nathusius. Berlin, O. Janke, 1910.
292 p. 19½ᶜᵐ.

                                                       10-1086

NN   0030362   DLC PPG OCl

PT   Nathusius, Annemarie von, 1874-1926
2627   Das törichte Herz der Julie von Voss; eine
A69   Hofgeschichte aus der Zopfzeit. Stuttgart,
T6   Deutsche Verlags-Anstalt, 1918.
         316p. illus. 19cm.

NN   0030363   WU

PT   Nathusius, Annemarie von, 1874-1926
N276t   Das törichte herz der Julie von Voss; eine
         hofgeschichte aus der zopfzeit ... Leipzig,
         F.Rothbarth [1937]
         319,[1]p. 19cm. (Half-title: Roman-sammlung
         aus vergangenheit und gegenwart. Bd. 16)

NN   0030364   NRU PPG

Nathusius, *Frau* Annemarie von, 1874-1926.
Die trennung, roman von Annemarie von Nathusius. Berlin und Leipzig, K. F. Koehler, 1927.
267, [1] p., 2 l. 19ᶜᵐ.

    1. Title.
[Full name: Frau Anna Marie Luise (von Nathusius) von Nathusius]
Library of Congress   PT2627.A69T7 1927   27-24875

NN   0030365   DLC

Nathusius, Carolus Henricus AEmilius
see   Nathusius, Karl Heinrich Emil,
1836-

Nathusius, Christian Wilhelm, respondent.
... De ficta necessitate scabinorum in causa
criminali quae delegatur commissariis principis ...
see under   Carpzov, Friedrich Benedict,
1702-1744, praeses.

Business

Nathusius, Dietrich von
Deutsche Besteck-Industrie. Hrsg. im Jahre
des 100. Geburtstages des Begründers und Fir-
menträgers Karl August Wellner von der Firma
Sächsische Metallwarenfabrik August Wellner
Söhne Aktiengesellschaft, Aue i. Sa. [1. bd.
Aue i. Erzgeb., 1924]
40 p. illus., port.

NN   0030368   NNC NN

PZ34   Nathusius, Elsbeth Luise Friederike von, 1846-
.N38A   1903
1903   Alte Märchen den Kindern neu erzählt von E.
         von Nathusius. Bildschmuck von Hans von
         Volkmann und Otto Fikentscher. Neue, reich
         verm. Ausg. Halle a. S., Gebauer-Schwetschke
         [1903]
         148 p. illus. (part col.) 22cm.

         1. Fairy tales.

NN   0030369   ViU

Nathusius, Elsbeth Luise Friederike von, 1846-
Alte märchen den kindern neu erzählt; bild-
schmuck von Hans von Volkmann und Otto Fikentscher.
Neue, reich verm. ausg. [8],148,[1]p. col.front.
il.,col.plates. Halle a. S., Gebauer-Schwetschke
[1906]

NN   0030370   OCl

Nathusius, Elsbeth Luise Friederike von, 1846-
Johann Gottlob Nathusius, ein pionier deutscher industrie, von Elsbeth von Nathusius ... Stuttgart und
Berlin, Deutsche verlags-anstalt, 1915.
306 p. front., plates, ports. 21½ᶜᵐ.   M. 5

    1. Nathusius, Johann Gottlob, 1760-1835. 2. Germany—Indus.—Hist.

Library of Congress   CT1098.N3N3   16-1951

NN   0030371   DLC CSt NN IaU NNC ICN CU GU

Nathusius (Fridericus Guilelmus) [1815-   ].
* De erysipelate typhoso. 53 pp., 1 l. 8°. Berolini, F. G. Nietack, [1856].

NN   0030372   DNLM

---

ar X   Nathusius, Heinrich.
3224   Jacob Immanuel Pyra. Halberstadt,
no.2   C. Doelle [1874]
         18 p. 27cm.

         Separate from "Programm" (Schulnach-
         richten)--Realschule, Halberstadt.
         No.2 in a vol. lettered: Programmes:
         German literature. III, 2.

             1. Pyra, Immanuel Jakob., 1715-1744.

NN   0030373   NIC

VOLUME 405

Nathusius, Heinrich von.
Andeutungen in beziehung auf fütterungsversuche.
Landw. vers. stat. bd. 1, p. 96-98.   Dresden, 1859.

1. Metabolism.

Agr 4-2698

Library, U. S. Dept. of   Agriculture

NN   0030374   DNAL

Nathusius, Heinrich von, of Obornik, Germany.   *9330.436.24
Die bäuerlichen Verhältnisse in der Provinz Posen.
(In Verein fuer Socialpolitik. Schriften. 24. Pp. 1-51. Leip-
zig, 1883.)

E2497 — Posen, Province. Agric.

NN   0030375   MB

Nathusius, Heinrich von, of Obornik, Germany.   *9330.436.35
Der Wucher auf dem platten Lande in der Provinz Posen.
(In Verein fuer Socialpolitik. Schriften. 35. Pp. 303-324. Leip-
zig, 1878.)

E2513 — Posen, Province. Soc. sci. — Usury.

NN   0030376   MB

Nathusius, Heinrich von, of Obornik, Germany.   *9330.436.44
Die Zustände und die Reform des ländlichen Gemeindewesens in der
Provinz Posen.
(In Verein fuer Socialpolitik. Schriften. 44. Pp. 7-24. Leip-
zig, 1890.)

E2492 — Posen, Province. Pol. hist. — Local government.

NN   0030377   MB

NATHUSIUS,Heinrich von,1900-
Pferdemessungen und die vorzüge ihrer
variationsstatistischen auswertung. Inaug.-Diss
Halle (Saale),O.Thiele,[1926].

pp.30.
"Lebenslauf",p.[28].
"Literaturverzeichnis",pp.[29]-30.

NN   0030378   MH MiU

q636.4   Nathusius, Hermann Engelhard von,1809-1879
N19v   Abbildungen von schweineschædeln zu
sup   den Vorstudien für geschichte und zucht
         der hausthiere.   Berlin, 1864.
         23p. plates.

NN   0030379   IU NjP MdBP

Nathusius, Hermann Engelhard von, 1809-1879.   z262.72.2
Bemerkungen über die Schädel der Eskimohunde.
(In Koldewey, Carl. Die zweite deutsche Nordpolarfahrt. Band
2, pp. 175-177. Leipzig. 1874.)

K7969 — Skull. — Dogs. Eskimo.

NN   0030380   MB

Nathusius, Hermann Engelhard von *and* **Salviati, Carl von.**
Jahres-bericht über den zustand der landes-kultur in
Preussen für das jahr 1871.   tables.
Landw. jahrb.   bd. 1, p. 293-417.   Berlin, 1872.

1. Agriculture. Germany. Prussia.

Agr 4-1450

Library, U. S. Dept. of   Agricultr

NN   0030381   DNAL

Nathusius, Hermann Engelhard von *and* **Thiel, H.**
Jahresbericht über den zustand der landes-kultur in
Preussen für das jahr 1872.   tables.
Landw. jahrb.   bd. 2, p. 657-887.   Berlin, 1873.

1. Agriculture. Germany. Prussia.

Agr 4-1458

Library, U. S. Dept. of   Agriculture

NN   0030382   DNAL

Nathusius, Hermann Engelhard von, 1809-1879.
Landwirthschaftliches thier-album in photo-
graphien
     see under title   [Supplement]

Nathusius, Hermann Engelhard von, 1809-1879.
Die racen des schweines.   Eine zoologische kritik und
andeutungen über systematische behandlung der haus-
thier-racen.   Von Hermann von Nathusius ... Berlin,
G. Bosselmann, 1860.
2 p. l., 91, (1) p. 22½ᶜᵐ.

1. Swine.

8-26804†

Library of Congress   QL737.U5N2

NN   0030384   DLC NIC CtY MdBP

Adelmann
QL   Nathusius, Hermann Engelhard von, 1809-
737   1879.
U5N27   Ueber Constanz in der Thierzucht.
          Berlin, G. Bosselmann, 1860.
             xii, 104 p. 21cm.

             Bound with his Die Racen des Schweines,
          1860.
             First published in Zeitschrift für
          deutsche Landwirthe.

             1. Breeding.   2. Stock and stock-
          breeding. 3. D   mestic animals.

NN   0030385   NIC ICJ OU IU

Nathusius, Hermann Engelhard von.
Ueber die sogenannten leporiden.
Landw. jahrb. bd. 5, p. 503-511.   Berlin, 1876.

1. Belgian hare.

Agr 4-1451

Library, U. S. Dept. of   Agriculture

NN   0030386   DNAL MH

Nathusius, Heinrich Engelhard von.
Ueber die zucht schwerer arbeitspferde und die mittel
zu ihrer beförderung in Preussen.   2 pl.
Landw. jahrb.   bd. 14, p. 1-107.   Berlin, 1885.

1. Horse. Belgium. 2. Horse, Draught. 3. Horse. Prussia.

Agr 4-1449

Library, U. S. Dept. of   Agriculture

NN   0030387   DNAL

Nathusius, Hermann Engelhard von.
Ueber schädelform des rindes.   illus.
Landw. jahrb.   bd. 4, p. 441-459.   Berlin, 1875.

1. Osteology of the skull.   2. Skull conformation of cattle.

Library, U. S. Dept. of   Agriculture   Agr 4-1452
2 (e)

NN   0030388   DNAL

Nathusius, Hermann Engelhard von, 1809-1879.   636.2 L700
Ueber Shorthorn-Rindvieh.   Mit einem Anhang über Inzucht.
Von Hermann v. Nathusius, ... Berlin, G. Bosselmann, 1857.
[2], 83 p.   tables (1 fold.)   22ᶜᵐ.

NN   0030389   ICJ OU

Nathusius, Hermann Engelhard von, 1809-1879.
Vorstudien für Geschichte und Zucht der
Hausthiere, zunaechst am Schweineschaedel.
Berlin, 1864.

   xiv, 186 p. atlas of 6 plates and 24 p.
text. 4o.

NN   0030390   MH-Z MdBP IU

40
N19   Nathusius, Hermann Engelhard von, 1809-1879.
         Vorträge über Viehzucht und Rassenkenntniss.
         Berlin, Wiegandt & Hempel, 1872-

             1. Domestic animals. Breeding.

NN   0030391   DNAL NN CtY IaAS

Nathusius, Hermann Engelhard von, 1809-1879, ed.
   Wandtafeln für den naturwissenschaftlichen
Unterricht mit specieller Berücksichtigung der
Landwirthschaft ...   Berlin, Wiegandt, Parey,
1874-82.

NN   0030392   PU-B

QK84   Nathusius, Johanne.
.N38   Die Blumenwelt nach ihrer deutschen Namen,
         Sinn und Deutung in Bilder geordnet.   Leipzig,
         1868.
            205p. plates.

             1. Plant lore - Germany. 2. Flower
         language. 3. Plant names, Popular - Germany.
         I. Title.

NN   0030393   NcU

VOLUME 405

Nathusius, Johanne.   25228.34.21
Die blumenwelt nach ihrer deutschen namen sinn und deutung
2ª aufl. Leipzig, Arnoldische buchhandlung, 1869.
pp. (2), vi, (2), 205. + Plates.

Folklore (2)–Plants|Botany–Nomenclature

NN   0030394   MH

NATHUSIUS, Karl Heinrich Emil, 1836–
De more humandi et concremandi mortuos apud
Graecos usitato. Diss.-inaug. Halis Saxonum,
[1864]

pp. 33+.
"Vita", after p. 33.

NN   0030395   MH DNLM ICRL PU

SB
63
.R7
N28
Nathusius, Lilly von.
Theodor Roemer; Lebensabriss und bibliogra-
phischer Überblick. Halle, Universitäts- und
Landesbibliothek Sachsen-Anhalt, 1955.
131 p. port. 21 cm. (Schriften zum
Bibliotheks- und Büchereiwesen in Sachsen-
Anhalt)

1. Roemer, Theodor, 1883-1951. 2. Roemer, Theodor,
1883-1951--Bibl.

NN   0030396   MiU NNC MH

Nathusius, Maria Karoline Elisabeth Luise
(Scheele) von, 1817-1857.
Gesammelte Schriften. Halle a. S.,
Mühlmann, 1890-99.
9 v. in 8.

NN   0030397   OC1W

Nathusius, Maria Karoline Elisabeth Luise (Scheele) von, 1817–
1857.
Above her station : the story of a young woman's life. By Mrs.
Herman Philip, from the original of Maria Nathusius. New
York : Follett, Foster and co., 1863. 231 p. 17½cm.

122770B. 1. Fiction, German.   I. Philip, D. M., tr. II. Title.
N.Y.P.L.   June 26, 1941

NN   0030398   NN PPL MH

PT
2440
.N2
A68
1858
Nathusius, Maria Karoline Elisabeth Luise
Scheele von, 1817-1857
Die alte Jungfer. Eine Erzählung von
der Verfasserin des "Tagebuchs eines armen
Fräuleins." 2. Aufl. Halle, Richard Mühlmann,
1858.
228p. 19cm.

NN   0030399   TNJ PPG

Nathusius, Maria Karoline Elisabeth Luise
(Scheele) von, 1817-1857.
Ausgewählte Erzählungen ... Berlin,
Meidlinger,
1 Bd.

NN   0030400   PPG

Nathusius, Maria Karoline Elisabeth Luise
(Scheele) von, 1817-1857.
Ausgewaehlte schriften. Lpz., Fock,
1889-90.
10 v. in 3.

NN   0030401   PU

PT
2440
N2
B4
Nathusius, Maria Karoline Elisabeth Luise
(Scheele) von, 1817-1857
Die beiden Pfarrhäuser. Ringet danach,
dass ihr stille seid. Das Rektorat; drei
Erzählungen von Marie Nathusius. Bearb.
von Dr. Werner Werther. Stuttgart, Union
Deutsche Verlagsgesellschaft [1890]
72p. illus. 17cm. (Universal-Bibliothek
für Jugend und Volk, Bd. 250)

NN   0030402   WU

PZ
33
N3
B6
Nathusius, Maria Karoline Elisabeth Luise
(Scheele) von, 1817-1857
Die Botenfrau. Die Sonntagsschule. Lorenz,
der Freigemeindler. Drei Erzählungen.
Stuttgart, Union Deutsche Verlagsgesellschaft
[1900?]
79p. illus. 17cm. (Universal-Bibliothek
für die Jugend, 242)

I. Title II. Title: Die Sonntagsschule
III. Title: Lorenz, der Freigemeindler

NN   0030403   WU

Nathusius, Maria Karoline Elisabeth Luise (Scheele) von,
1817-1857.
Dorf- und stadtgeschichten, von Maria Nathusius. Nach der
verfasserin heimgang zuerst gesammelt. Halle, R. Mühlmann,
1858.
vi, 556 p. 18½ᵐ. (Added t.-p.: Gesammelte schriften ... 1. bd.)
With this is bound the author's Die geschichte von Christfried und
Julchen. Halle, 1858.

I. Title.

Library of Congress   PT2440.N2D6   1858   42-29760

NN   0030404   DLC

[Nathusius, Maria Karoline Elisabeth Luise (Scheele) von] 1817-
1857.
Elisabeth. Eine Geschichte, die nicht mit der Heirath schliesst.
Von der Verfasserin des "Tagebuchs eines armen Fräuleins." ...
2, Aufl. Halle, J. Fricke, 1858. 2 v. in 1. 18cm.

NN   0030405   NN PPG

Nathusius, Maria, 1817–
Elisabeth. Eine geschichte, die nicht mit der
Heirath schliesst... Halle, 1860.

NN   0030406   PPL

NATHUSIUS Frau Maria [(Scheele) von].
Elisabeth; eine geschichte, die nicht mit der
heirath schliesst. 7e aufl. Halle, J. Fricke,
1863.

2 vol.

NN   0030407   MH OU

NATHUSIUS, Frau Maria [(Scheele) von].
Elisabeth; eine geschichte die nicht mit der
heirath schliesst. 8e aufl. Halle, J.
Fricke, 1866.

2 vol.
Added title-page reads: Gesammelte schriften,
8-9.

NN   0030408   MH

Nathusius, Marie (Scheele) von.
Elisabeth; eine Geschichte, die nicht mit der
Heirath schliesst. 9. Aufl. Halle, J. Fricke,
1870.

2 v. in 1.
Vol. 2 has added t.-p.: Gesammelte Schriften
von Marie Nathusius. 9. Bd.

NN   0030409   MH

Nathusius, Maria Karoline Elisabeth Luise (Scheele) von,
1817-1857.
Elisabeth. Eine geschichte, die nicht mit der heirat schliesst
von Marie Nathusius ... Halle a. S., J. Fricke [1877]
2 v. in 1. 19ᵐ. (Added t.-p.: Gesammelte schriften ... 8.-[9.] bd.)

I. Title.

Library of Congress   PT2440.N2E5   1877   2-1782 Revised

NN   0030410   DLC

F
83941
.6135
NATHUSIUS, Frau MARIA KAROLINE ELISABETH LUISE
(SCHEELE) VON, 1817-1857.
Elisabeth. Eine Geschichte, die nicht mit
der Heirath schliesst. Milwaukee, Wis., G.
Brumder, 188-?
566p. 19cm.

NN   0030411   ICN MH

PT2440
.N2
E53
Nathusius, Maria Karoline Elisabeth Luise
(Scheele) von, 1817-1857.
Elizabeth: A story which does not end in
marriage. Trans. from the German of Nathusius
by S.A. Smith. Edinburgh, R. Grant, 1860.
2v. 18cm.

NN   0030412   NcU DLC

Nathusius, Maria Karoline Elisabeth Luise (Scheele) von, 1817-
1857.
Elizabeth. Translated from the German of Marie Nathusius.
By Mrs. M. A. Shryock. Philadelphia : Porter & Coates, 1891.
vii, 9–493 p. 19½cm.

122771B. 1. Fiction, German.   I. Shryock, Mrs. M. A., tr.
N.Y.P.L.   II. Title.
                             June 26, 1941

NN   0030413   NN OC1W MB

NATHUSIUS, Frau Maria (Scheele) von.
Erzählungen einer grossmutter für junge
mädchen. 4. (miniatur) aufl. Halle a.S., R.
Mühlmann, (M. Grosse), 1890.

24°.

NN   0030414   MH

[Nathusius, Maria Karoline Elisabeth Luise (Scheele) von]
1817-1857.
Erzählungen von der Verfasserin von "Martha die Stiefmut-
ter," und "Vater, Sohn und Enkel." Erstes Heft... Zweite Auflage... Halle: R. Mühlmann, 1854. 104 p. 18½cm.

No more published?
"Aus dem 'Volksblatt für Stadt und Land' besonders abgedruckt."
Bound with her: Tagebuch eines armen Fräuleins. Dritte Auflage. Halle, 1854.
CONTENTS.—Christfrieds erste Reise.—Tante Sofie.—Julchens Haushalt.—Das Rec-
torat.

905341A. 1. Fiction, German.   I. Title.
N.Y.P.L.   June 3, 1938

NN   0030415   NN PU

VOLUME 405

PT 2440 NATHUSIUS,MARIA KAROLINE ELISABETH LUISE
.N2 F2 (Scheele) von,1817-1857
        Familien-Skizzen. Herr und Kammerdiener;
        zwei Jugend-Novellen. Halle, J. Fricke, 1861.
        399 p. (Her Schriften)

        I. Title: Familien-Skizzen.   II. Title: Herr und
        Kammerdiener.

NN 0030416   InU

Nathusius, Maria Karoline Elisabeth Louise
      (Scheele) von, 1817-1857.
      Familien-skizzen, Herr und Kammerdiener;
      zwei jugend-novellen; 3d. ed. Halle, 1868.

NN 0030417   ODW

Nathusius, Maria Karoline Elisabeth
      Luise (Scheele) von, 1817-1857.
      Fra uvenskab til venskab, af Marie
      Nathusius. Fra tysk ved Olga [pseud.]
      Kjøbenhavn, C.B. Kjaer, 1897.

      252 p.   18cm.
      With this are bound: Sapira, I.N.
      Fra jøde til kristen. 1897; Vollmar, A.
      Funden. 1897; Hansen, J.M. Vejblomster.
      [1897?]
      I. Andersen, Olga, tr. II. Title.

NN 0030418   MnU

Nathusius, Maria Karoline Elisabeth Luise (Scheele) von,
      1817-1857.
      Die geschichte von Christfried und Julchen. Aus den klei-
      nen erzählungen von Maria Nathusius zuerst zusammengestellt.
      Halle, R. Mühlmann, 1858.
      4 p. l., [3]-287 p. 18¼ᶜᵐ. [With her Dorf- und stadtgeschichten. Halle,
      1858]
      Added t.-p.: Gesammelte schriften ... 2. bd.
      Imperfect: p. 285-287 wanting.

      I. Title. II. Title: Christfried und Julchen.
                                                        42-29761
      Library of Congress   PT2440.N2D6 1858

NN 0030419   DLC

NATHUSIUS,Frau Maria (Scheele) von,1817-1857.
      Die geschichten von Christfried und Julchen.
      Aus den kleinen erzählungen von Marie Nathu-
      sius zusammengestellt. 4e aufl. Halle a.S.,
      R.Mühlmann,1885.

      Added title-page: Gesammelte schriften,2.

NN 0030420   MH

Nathusius, Maria [Karoline Elisabeth Luise (Scheele) von]
      Die geschichten von Christfried und Julchen. Aus
      den kleinen erzählungen von Marie Nathusius zusam-
      mengestellt. Wohlfeile original-ausgabe. 5. aufl. Halle
      a. S., R. Mühlmann, 1890.
      4 p. l., 280 pp. 19ᶜᵐ. [In her Gesammelte schriften. 2. bd.]
                                                        2-1781-M 2

NN 0030421   DLC WU

Nathusius, Frau Maria Karoline Elizabeth Luise
      (Scheele) von, 1817-1857.
      Joachim von Kamern, ein lebenslauf & Langen-
      stein und Boblingen; zweite aufl. Halle,
      Mühlmann, 1856-1857.
      2 v.

NN 0030422   PP

PZ3   Nathusius, Maria Karoline Elisabeth Luise von.
.N199   Joachim v. Kamern; Diary of a poor young
Jo   lady. By Maria Nathusius. From the German by
        Miss Thompson. Leipzig, Bernhard Tauchnitz
        [etc., etc.] 1869.
        3 p. l., 333, [1] p. 15ᶜᵐ. [Half-title:
        Collection of German authors. [Tauchnitz
        edition] v. 12)
        I. Thompson, Miss, tr. II. Title. III.
        Title: Diary of a poor young lady.

NN 0030423   MB OC1 MiU PPL NIC

Nathusius, *Frau* Maria Karoline Elisabeth Luise
      (Scheele) von, 1817-1857.
      Katie von Walden; or, Langenstein and Bobbingen.
      By Maria Nathusius... Tr. from the German by Mary A.
      Robinson. Philadelphia, New York, The American Sun-
      day-school union, ¹1892.
      1 p. l., 5-381 p. 19¼ᵐ.

      i. Robinson, Mary A., tr.
                                                    7-25795†
      Library of Congress   PZ3.N199K

NN 0030424   DLC

PT2440 Nathusius, Maria Karoline Elisabeth Luise
.N2L3   (Scheele) von, 1817-1857.
1857   Langenstein und Boblingen; eine Erzählung.
        2. Aufl. Halle, R. Mühlmann, 1857.
        356 p. 18 cm.
        Published also under title: Katie von Walden.

NN 0030425   ViU

Nathusius, Maria von, 1817-
      Langenstein & Boblingen, eine Erzaehlung. Halle,
      Muehlmann, 1881.
      303 p.

NN 0030426   PPG

PT2440 Nathusius, Maria Karoline Elizabeth Luise
.N2L3   (Scheele) von, 1817-1857.
1888
        Langenstein und Boblingen. Eine Erzählung.
        10. Aufl. Halle a. S., R. Mühlmann, 1888.
        303 p. 18cm.

        Published also under title: Katie von Walden.

NN 0030427   ViU OC1

Nathusius, Maria Karoline Elisabeth Luise
      (Scheele) 1817-1857.
      Lebensbild der heimgegangenen Marie
      Nathusius, geb. Scheele. Für ihre Freunde
      nah und fern. Samt mittheilungen aus ihren
      noch übrigen Schriften. Halle, Fricke, 1867.
      3 v.   D.
      Gesammelte Schriften von Marie Nathusius.

NN 0030428   NcD PPG

Nathusius, Maria Karoline Elisabeth Luise
      (Scheele) von, 1817-1857.
      Lebensbild der heimgegangenen Marie Nathusius,
      geb. Scheele. Für ihre Freunde nah und fern,
      samt Mittheilungen aus ihren noch übrigen
      Schriften. [Hrsg. von Ph. v. Nathusius] 2. ver-
      kürzte Aufl. Halle,J.Fricke,1875-76. 3v.
      fronts. 18cm. (Gesammelte Schriften. 13.-15.
      Bde. Nachträge, Bd. 4-6)
      Contents.-1. Bd. Mädchenzeit.-2. Bd. Frauen-
      leben in Althaldensleben.-3. Bd. Frauenleben in
      Neinstedt.
      1. Nathusius, Maria Karoline Elisabeth Luise
      (Scheele) von, 1817-1857. I. Nathusius, Philipp
      Engelhard, 1815-   1872, ed.

NN 0030429   MWelC MH

[Nathusius, *Frau* Maria Karoline Elisabeth Luise (Scheele)
    von] 1817-1857.
      Louisa von Plettenhaus, or, The journal of a poor young
      lady. Translated from the German ... Edinburgh, T. Con-
      stable and co.; [etc., etc.] 1854.
      1 p. l., 240 p. front. 18ᵐ.

      i. Title.
                                                    42-27372
      Library of Congress   PZ3.N199Lo 2

NN 0030430   DLC

[Nathusius, *Frau* Maria Karoline Elisabeth Luise (Scheele)
    von] 1817-1857.
      Louisa von Plettenhaus, the journal of a poor young lady.
      Tr. from the German ... New York, Boston, C. S. Francis
      & co., 1857.
      233 p. 17¼ᵐ.

      i. Title.
                                                    7-23114
      Library of Congress   PZ3.N199L

NN 0030431   DLC ViU MB NN

[Nathusius, Maria Karoline Elisabeth Luise
    (Scheele) von] 1817-1857.
      Lowly ways; or, The diary of a poor young
      lady. From the German, by F. E. B. Philadel-
      phia, Claxton, Remsen & Haffelfinger, 1871.
      16°.
      I. B., F.E. II. Title.

NN 0030432   MB DLC-P4

[Nathusius, Maria Karoline Elisabeth Luise
    (Scheele) von] 1817-1857.
      Lowly ways; or, The diary of a poor young
      lady. From the German. By F. E. B. ...
      Philadelphia, E. Claxton & co., 1882.
      vii, 9-235 p. 16.5 cm.
      I. B., F.E. II. Title.

NN 0030433   NN

Nathusius, Frau Maria Karoline Elisabeth Luise
      (Scheele) von, 1817-1857.
      Martha, die Stiefmutter; [&] Marie; zwei
      Dorfgeschichten

NN 0030434   OC1

833.7   Nathusius, Maria Karoline Elisabeth Luise
N276r   (Schele) von, 1817-1857.
        Rückerinnerungen aus einem mädchenleben.
        4. Aufl. Halle a.S., R. Mühlmann, 1868.
        175p. 18cm. (Her Gesammelte Schriften,
        5. Bd., 3. Heft. 2. Aufl.)

NN 0030435   IEN

Nathusius, Maria Karoline Elisabeth Luise
      (Scheele) von, 1817-1857.
      Tagebuch einer Reise nach der Provence,
      Italien und der Schweiz. Aus dem Nachlasse.
      Halle,Fricke,1860.   370p. 18cm. (Gesammelte
      Schriften 10)

        1. Italy. Description and travel. 2. Switzer-
      land. Description and travel.

NN 0030436   MWelC

VOLUME 405

4PT Nathusius, Maria Karoline Elisabeth
Ger. Luise (Scheele) von, 1817-1857.
8718 Tagebuch eines armen Fräuleins.
  New York, Holt [ ]
    163 p.

NN 0030437 DLC-P4 OO PU

PT Nathusius, Maria Karoline Elisabeth Luise
2440   (Scheele) von, 1817-1857.
N2   Tagebuch eines armen Fräuleins. Abge-
T5 druckt zur Unterhaltung und Belehrung für junge
1853 Mädchen... 2. Aufl. Halle, R. Mühlmann, 1853.
  160p.

NN 0030438 UU

[Nathusius, Maria Karoline Elisabeth Luise (Scheele) von]
  1817-1857.
  Tagebuch eines armen Fräuleins. Abgedruckt zur Unterhaltung und Belehrung für junge Mädchen... Dritte Auflage.
Halle: R. Mühlmann, 1854. 168 p. 18½cm.

  "Zuerst im 'Volksblatt für Stadt und Land.'"
  With this is bound her: Erzählungen. Erstes Heft...Zweite Auflage... Halle,
1854.

905341A. 1. Fiction, German. I. Title.
N. Y. P. L.   May 31, 1938

NN 0030439 NN

834N19 [Nathusius, Frau Maria Karoline Elisabeth
Otl855 Luise (Scheele) von, 1817-1857.
   Abgedruckt
  zur unterhaltung und belehrung für junge mädchen.
  (Zuerst im "Volksblatt für stadt und land.") 4.
  aufl. Halle, R. Mühlmann, 1855.
  168p.

NN 0030440 IU PPG

Nathusius, Frau Maria Karoline Elisabeth Luise
  (Scheele) von, 1817-1857.
  Tagebuch eines armen fräuleins. Abgedruckt
  zur unterhaltung und belehrung fuer junge maedchen.
  8. aufl. Leipzig, Fiedler [186-?]
  225p.

NN 0030441 OO

Nathusius, *Frau* Maria Karoline Elisabeth Luise
  (Scheele) von, 1817-1857.
  Tagebuch eines armen fräuleins. Abgedruckt zur un-
terhaltung und belehrung für junge mädchen. Von Marie
Nathusius. 8. aufl. Halle, R. Mühlmann, 1864.
  210 p. 16ᶜᵐ.

  I. Title.

              18-1212

Library of Congress   PT2440.N2T5 1864

NN 0030442 DLC

NATHUSIUS, Frau Maria [(Scheele) von].
  Tagebuch eines armen fräuleins. Von Marie
Nathusius. Boston, De Bries, Ibarra und comp.,
[1866].

  pp.(2), 163.
  (Collection De Vries, German series, 17.)

NN 0030443 MH

Nathusius, Maria Karoline Elisabeth Luise von. 4879a.115
  Tagebuch eines armen Fräuleins.
  Boston. De Vries, Ibarra & Co. [187-?] (1), 163 pp. 12°.

NN 0030444 MB

Nathusius, Maria, 1817-
  Tagebuch eines armen Fraeuleins... Vierzehnte
  auflage. Halle, 1886.

NN 0030445 PPL

NATHUSIUS, Frau Maria [(Scheele) von], 1817-1857.
  Tagebuch eines armen fräuleins; abgedruckt
  zur unterhaltung und belehrung für junge
  mädchen. Leipzig, P. Reclam, jun., [189-].
   136p.
  Cover: Universal-bibliothek, 2360.

NN 0030446 MH CU

Nathusius, Maria [Karoline Elisabeth Luise
  (Scheele) von] 1817-1857.
   Tagebuch eines armen Fräuleins. Wohlfeile
original-Ausg. 16. Aufl. Halle a. S.,
R. Mühlmann, 1890.
   2 p.l., 155 p. 19 cm. (In her
   Gesammelte Schriften. Bd. 5, Hft. 1)

NN 0030447 OU

PT Nathusius, Maria Karoline Elisabeth Luise
2440   (Scheele) von, 1817-1857
N2   Tagebuch eines armen Fräuleins. Leipzig,
T3 G. Fock, 1890.
  147p. 19cm.

NN 0030448 WU NcU NN

Nathusius, Maria [Karoline Elisabeth Luise (Scheele) von]
  Tagebuch eines armen fräuleins. Wohlfeile original-
ausg. 17. aufl. Halle a. S., R. Mühlmann, 1899.
  2 p. l., 155 p. 12°. (*In her* Gesammelte schriften. bd. 5, hft. 1)

         1-20006—M 4

NN 0030449 DLC

Nathusius, Frau Maria Karoline Elisabeth Luise
  (Scheele) von, 1817-1857.
  Vater, Sohn und Enkel, eine Dorfgeschichte.

NN 0030450 OCl

PT Nathusis, Maria Karoline Elisabeth Luise
2440   (Scheele) von, 1817-1857
N2   Vier Geschichten aus Dorf und Stadt. Berlin,
V5 Meidinger [1907]
  88,88p. illus. 21cm.

NN 0030451 WU

[Nathusius, Maria Karoline Elisabeth Luise (Scheele) von] 1817-
  1857.
  Der Vormund. Eine Erzählung von der Verfasserin des "Tagebuchs eines armen Fräuleins." Halle: R. Mühlmann, 1858.
184 p. 18cm.

16986B. 1. Fiction, German. I. Title.
N. Y. P. L.

NN 0030452 NN PPG OCl

Nathusius, Marie
  see Nathusius, Maria Karoline Elisabeth
  Luise (Scheele) von, 1817-1857.

Nathusius, Marie Sophie
  Ino. Amsterdam, Arbeiderspers, 1955

NN 0030454 MH

4PT Nathusius, Marie Sophie
Dut. De ketting. Amsterdam, Arbeider-
472 spers, 1955.
    67 p.

  (De Boekvink litteratuur in
  miniatuur)

NN 0030455 DLC-P4 MH NNC

4PT Nathusius, Marie Sophie
Dut. De partner. Amsterdam, De Arbeiders-
672 pers, 1954.
    56 p.

  (De Boekvink; litteratuur in miniatuur)

NN 0030456 DLC-P4 MH NNC

Nathusius, Martin, 1883-
  Das Vertragswerk von Locarno und der
  Völkerbund ... Würzburg, 1926.
  Inaug.-diss. - Würzburg.
  "Literaturverzeichnis": p. [7]

NN 0030457 CtY CSt-H MH

Nathusius, Martin, 1883–
  Die wirtschaftliche Struktur des Gaugebietes Magdeburg-An-
halt, von Gauwirtschaftsberater Dr. Nathusius... [Magdeburg,
1936] 24 p. front., plates. 21cm. (Magdeburger Kul-
tur- und Wirtschaftsleben. Nr. 8.)

  1. Economic history—Germany— Magdeburg. I. Ser.
N. Y. P. L.   March 14, 1939

NN 0030458 NN

BR307 NATHUSIUS, MARTIN VON, 1843-1906.
.N27 Die christlich-socialen ideen der reformationszeit
  und ihre herkunft. Von d. Martin von Nathusius ...
  Gütersloh, C. Bertelsmann, 1897.
   [4], 167 p. 22cm. (Added t.-p.: Beiträge zur för-
  derung christlicher theologie... 1. jahrg. 1897. 2. hft

   1. Reformation. 2. Sociology, Christian.

NN 0030459 ICU CtY MiU NNUT

Nathusius, Martin von, 1843-   *3520.60.2
  Ernst Wilhelm Hengstenberg. Portrait.
  (In Werckshagen. Der Protestantismus am Ende des XIX. Jahr-
hunderts. Band 2, pp. 617-618. Berlin. [1902].)

F64 — Hengstenberg, Ernst Wilhelm.

NN 0030460 MB

VOLUME 405

Nathusius, Martin von, 1843-1906.
... Die Inspiration der Hl. Schrift und
die historische Kritik... Stuttgart,
C. Belser, 1895.
41 p. 22 . (Zeitfragen des christlichen Volkslebens. 20:6)

NN 0030461 NjPT

Nathusius, Martin von, 1843-
Katechismuspredigten nach der ordnung des
kirchenjahres. Leipzig, Hinrichs, 1883.
2 v.

NN 0030462 PPLT

Nathusius, Martin von, 1843-
Die mitarbeit der kircha an der lösung der
sozialen frage. I. Die soziale frage. Leipzig,
Hinrich, 1893.
310p.

NN 0030463 OO

HN31 Nathusius, Martin von, 1843-1906.
.N27 Die mitarbeit der kirche an der lösung der sozialen frage.
Von Martin von Nathusius ... Leipzig, J. C. Hinrich, 1895.
2 v. in 1. 22½ᶜᵐ.
Each vol. has special t.-p. dated 1803-94.
Contents.—I. Die soziale frage.—II. Die aufgabe der kirche.

1. Sociology, Christian.

NN 0030464 ICU

Nathusius, Martin von, 1843-1906.
Die mitarbeit der kirche an der lösung der sozialen frage,
auf grund einer kurzgefassten volkswirtschaftslehre und eines
systems der christlichen gesellschaftslehre (sozialethik) dargestellt von Martin von Nathusius ... 2. völlig neu bearb. aufl.
Leipzig, J. C. Hinrichs, 1897.
xi, 563, ₁1₁ p. 23ᶜᵐ.
Bibliographical foot-notes.
1. Sociology, Christian. 2. Social problems. 3. Church work.
I. Title.
₁Full name: Martin Friedrich Engelhard von Nathusius₁

33-19693

Library of Congress HN31 N3 1897 261

NN 0030465 DLC CU MiU

Nathusius, Martin von, 1843- 261.6 P701
⁴²³¹⁷ Die Mitarbeit der Kirche an der Lösung der sozialen Frage. Auf
Grund einer kurzgefassten Volkswirtschaftslehre und eines Systems der christlichen Gesellschaftslehre (Sozialethik) dargestellt
von Martin von Nathusius ... . Dritte Ausgabe. Leipzig,
J. C. Hinrichs'sche Buchhandlung, 1904.
viii, 563₁, [1] p. 22½ᶜᵐ.

NN 0030466 ICRL PPLT

B3191 Nathusius, Martin von, 1843-1906.
N37 Naturwissenschaft und Philosophie. Zur
Beleuchtung der neuesten materialistischen
Kundgebungen du Bois-Reymonds u A. Hiel-
bronn, Henninger, 1883.
70 p. (Zeitfragen des christlichen
Volkslebens, Bd.8, Hft.7)

1. Naturalism. 2. Materialism. 3. Du Bois-
Reymond, Emil Heinrich, 1818-1896. 4. Sci-
ence-Philosophy.

NN 0030467 CU

Nathusius, Martin von, 1843-1906.
Timotheus... Leipzig, Hinrichs'sche buchhandlung,
1881.
123p.

AC931 [Haverford-Bauer pamphlets, v. 16, no. 7]
.H3
v.16

NN 0030468 DLC

NATHUSIUS, Martin VON, 1843-
Ueber die bedeutung christlicher erkenntnis.
Barmen,[1903].

(Salz und licht, 5.)

NN 0030469 MH

Nathusius, Martin von, 1843-1906.
Das wesen der wissenschaft und ihre anwendung
auf die religion. Empirische grundlegung für
die theologische methodologie. Von Martin von
Nathusius ... Leipzig, J.C.Hinrichs, 1885.
viii,446 p. 21½ᶜᵐ.
Half-title lacking.

1.Religion and science—1860—1899.

NN 0030470 MiU NNUT IU

Nathusius, Martin von, 1843-
Wissenschaft und kirche in streit um die theo-
logischen fakultaten. Heilbronn, Henninger.
1886.
47 p.

NN 0030471 PPLT

BT1370 Nathusius, Martin von, 1843-1906.
.N27 ... Zur charakteristik der Cirkumcellionen des 4. u. 5.
jahrhunderts in Afrika. Von d. M. von Nathusius. Greifswald, Druck von J. Abel, 1900.
38 p. 23ᶜᵐ.
Wissenschaftliche beilage zu dem Vorlesungsverzeichniss der Universität Greifswald.

1. Donatists.

NN 0030472 ICU NjPT

Nathusius, Philipp Engelhard, 1815-1872.
Hundert drei Lieder...
see under Béranger, Pierre Jean de,
1780-1857.

[NATHUSIUS,Philipp Engelhard] 1815-1872.

Ilius Pamphilius und die Ambrosia.₁ Neue
ausgabe. Berlin,1857.

2 pt.
(In Arnim,Mme.E.(B.) von Sämmtliche schriften,1857,vii,viii.)
By P.E.von Nathusius and Bettina (Brentano)
von Arnim.

NN 0030475 MH

Nathusius, Philipp Engelhard, 1815-1872, ed.
DD205 Kügelgen, Wilhelm Georg Alexander von, 1802-1867.
K8A2 Jugenderinnerungen eines alten Mannes. 8. Abdruck.
1876 Berlin, W. Hertz [1876]

Nathusius, Philipp Engelhard, 1815-1872, ed.
Lebensbild der heimgegangenen Marie Nathusius,
geb. Scheele
see under Nathusius, Maria Karoline
Elisabeth Luise (Scheele) von, 1817-1857.

Nathusius, Simon von, 1865-1913. 636 Q309
⁴⁴⁶⁸⁷ Atlas der Rassen und Formen unserer Haustiere. Von Dr.
Simon von Nathusius ... . Nach Originalzeichnungen von Tier-
maler Th. von Nathusius. ... . Stuttgart, E. Ulmer, 1904-.
Vol. 1-. Text. 25ᶜᵐ. and atlas. 21 x 264ᶜᵐ.

NN 0030478 ICJ

Nathusius, Simon von, 1865-
Einiges über den einfluss der oxalsäure in futterstof-
fen. Nach versuchen an schafen ... Breslau, R. Galle's
buchdr., 1897.
1 p. l., 54 p., 1 l. 22½ᶜᵐ.
Habilitationsschrift—Breslau.

1. Feeding and feeding stuffs. 2. Oxalic acid.
12-12995

Library of Congress SF97.N27

NN 0030479 DLC DNLM

Nathusius, Simon von, 1865-1913.
Der haustiergarten und die dazu gehörigen sammlungen im Landwirtschaftlichen institut der Universität
Halle. Kurzer leitfaden für besucher und interessenten
... von professor dr. Simon von Nathusius ... Hannover,
M. & H. Schaper, 1912.
77, ₁1₁ p. incl. illus., tables. 19¼ᶜᵐ.

1. Halle. Universität. Landwirtschaftliches institut. Haustiergarten.
Agr 17-1204

Library, U. S. Dept. of Agriculture 411N19

NN 0030480 DNAL IU

Nathusius, Simon von, 1865-
Die hengste der Königlich preussischen landgestüte,
1896-1897. Ein beitrag zur kunde der pferdeschläge in
Deutschland auf grund vorgenommener messungen und
wägungen an 2448 landbeschälern. Im auftrage der
Deutschen landwirtschafts-gesellschaft bearb. von dr. Simon von Nathusius ... Berlin, Druck von Gebr. Unger,
1899.
3 p. l., 111, ₁1₁ p. incl. tables. 24ᶜᵐ. (Added t.-p.: Arbeiten der Deutschen landwirtschafts-gesellschaft ... hft. 43)

1. Horse. Breeding. 2. Horse. Weight and measurement.
Agr 11-949

Library, U. S. Dept of Agriculture 18D48 no. 43

NN 0030481 DNAL NN

Nathusius, Simon von, 1865-
Messungen an 1460 zuchtpferden und 590 soldatenpfer-
den. Dritter beitrag zur kunde der pferdeschläge; im
auftrage des Deutschen landwirtschafts-gesellschaft,
bearb. von dr. Simon von Nathusius ... Berlin, P. Parey,
1912.
vi, 247, ₁1₁ p. 26ᶜᵐ. (Added t.-p.: Arbeiten der Deutschen landwirtschafts-gesellschaft ... hft. 205)

1. Horse. Weight and measurement.
Agr 13-216

Library, U. S. Dept. of Agriculture 18D48 no. 205

NN 0030482 DNAL ICJ

VOLUME 405

Nathusius, Simon von, 1865–
Messungen an stuten, hengsten und gebrauchspferden. Ein beitrag zur kunde der pferdeschläge. Im auftrage der Deutschen landwirtschafts-gesellschaft, bearb. von Dr. Simon von Nathusius ... Berlin, Deutsche landwirtschafts-gesellschaft, 1905.
vi, 234 p. 24ᶜᵐ. (*Added t.-p.:* Arbeiten der Deutschen landwirtschafts-gesellschaft ... hft. 112 ...)

1. Horse. Weight and measurement.   Agr 6–20

Library, U. S. Dept. of   Agriculture 18D48, hft. 112

NN   0030483   DNAL ICJ NN

Nathusius, Simon von, 1865–1913.
Die pferderassen.   Stuttgart, E. Ulmer, 1904.
26 p.   24 plates.   22 x 28 cm.
(Atlas der rassen und formen unserer haustiere, ser. 1)
In portfolio.
Plate 24 wanting.

NN   0030484   PU PU–V

Nathusius, Simon von, 1865–1913, ed.
Schwarznecker, G.
Schwarzneckers pferdezucht. Rassen, züchtung und haltung des pferdes. 5. aufl. durchgesehen und ergänzt von dr. Simon von Nathusius ... Berlin, P. Parey, 1910.

Nathusius, Simon von, 1865–
Die pferdezucht unter besonderer berücksichtigung des betriebswirtschaftlichen standpunktes. Leitfaden für züchter, besitzer und freunde des pferdes. Von Dr. Simon von Nathusius ... Mit 12 abbildungen. Stuttgart, E. Ulmer, 1902.
vii, 228 p. illus., tables. 21½ᶜᵐ.   3–19856

NN   0030486   DLC ICJ

Nathusius, Simon von, 1865–
... Die rinderrassen ... Stuttgart, E. Ulmer ₍1904₎
25 p. 24ᵐᵐ. *and atlas of* 28 pl. 20½ x 27ᵐᵐ. (*His* Atlas der rassen und formen unserer haustiere ... II. serie)

1. Cattle. Breeds.   Agr 4–1803

Library, U. S. Dept. of   Agriculture 43N19.

NN   0030487   DNAL

Nathusius, S₍imon₎ von.
Die Tierzucht. (Deutschland unter Kaiser Wilhelm II. Berlin, 1914. 4°.   Bd. 3, p. 1466–1471.)

1. Animal industry. Germany.   MANDEL COLLECTION.
N. Y. P. L.   June 3, 1914.

NN   0030488   NN

636.12 Nathusius, Simon von, 1865–1913.
N19u   Unterschiede zwischen der morgen- und abendländischen pferdegruppe am skelett und am lebenden pferd. Beitrag zur rassenkunde unserer haustiere. Langensalza, 1891.
80p. diagrs.

Inaug.- diss.--Halle-Wittenberg.

NN   0030489   IU DNAL MdBP

Nathusius, Wilhelm, *ed.*
Milchgesetz nebst ausführungsbestimmungen, unter beifügung der wichtigsten hiermit in zusammenhang stehenden gesetze und verordnungen; erläutert unter mitwirkung von dr. jur. E. Bose ... und dr. phil. dr.-ing. e. h. A. Juckenack ... von W. Nathusius ... ₍und₎ H. Nelson ... Berlin, C. Heymann, 1932.
viii, 489 p. 19ᶜᵐ.

1. Milk trade—Germany. I. Nelson, Hans, joint ed. II. Bose, Ewald.
III. Juckenack, Adolf, 1870– IV. Germany. Laws, statutes, etc.
v. Title.
                                           36–5201

NN   0030490   DLC OC1W

Nathusius, Wilhelm
Milchgesetz nebst ausführungsbestimmungen unter beifügung der wichtigsten hiermit in zusammenhang stehenden gesetze und verordnungen. Erläutert unter mitwirkung von ... E. Bose ... und ... A. Juckenack ... von W. Nathusius ... H. Nelson ... mit nachtrag von 1934. Unveränderter nachdruck. ₍Berlin₎ C. Heymann, 1954.
viii, 489, 86 p. tables. 18½cm.

"Abkürzungen" (bibliographical): p. ₍vii₎-viii.

NN   0030492   MH-L DNAL

Nathusius, Wilhelm von, 1821?–1899.
Erfahrungen über die kreuzungsprodukte des Zebu mit dem europäischen hausrind und deren fruchtbarkeit.
Landw. jahrb. bd. 1, p. 61–67.   Berlin, 1872.

1. Hybrids. 2. Zebu. Hybrids with cattle.   Agr 4–1454

Library, U. S. Dept. of   Agriculture

NN   0030493   DNAL

Nathusius, Wilhelm von.
Heinrich von Nathusius († am 11. September 1890.) ein lebensbild. port.
Landw. jahrb. bd. 20, p. 237–260.   Berlin, 1891.

1. Nathusius, Heinrich Engelhard von.   Agr 4–1455

Library, U. S. Dept. c.   Agriculture

NN   0030494   DNAL

Nathusius, Wilhelm von.
Hermann von Nathusius; rückerinnerungen aus seinem leben.
Landw. jahrb. bd. 9, p. 1–25.   Berlin, 1880.

1. Nathusius, Hermann Engelhard von.   Agr 4–1456

Library, U. S. Dept. of   Agriculture

NN   0030495   DNAL

Nathusius, Wilhelm von.
Ueber die nothwendigkeit, bei der pferdezucht die verschiedenheit der gebrauchszwecke zu berücksichtigen. illus.
Landw. jahrb. bd. 2, p. 189–207.   Berlin, 1873.

1. Horse. Breeding.   Agr 4–1445

Library, U. S. Dept. of   Agriculture

NN   0030496   DNAL

Nathusius, Wilhelm von.
Über haar-formen und -farben von equiden als kriterien der vererbung, namentlich bei bastarden. 12 pl.
Landw. jahrb. bd. 26, p. 317–429.   Berlin, 1897.

1. Horse. Breeds.   Agr 4–1457

Library, U. S. Dept. of   Agriculture

NN   0030497   DNAL

Nathusius, Wilhelm von.
Ueber strukturverhältnisse von wollhaaren mit anknüpfung an die Kohlschmidt'sche erörterung der Breslauer probeschur und die letztere selbst. 2 pl.
Landw. jahrb. bd. 22, p. 469–502.   Berlin, 1893.

1. Wool judging.   Agr 4–1458

Library, U. S. Dept. of   Agriculture

NN   0030498   DNAL

Nathusius, Wilhelm von, 1821?–1899.
Untersuchungen über Harting'sche Körperchen. Leipzig, 1890.
p. 602–648. 1 pl. 8°.
Cutting from: Ztschr. f. wissensch. Zool., Leipz., 1890, xlix.

NN   0030499   DNLM

578.9   Nathusius, Wilhelm von, 1821?–1899
N19u   Untersuchungen über nicht celluläre organismen, namentlich crustaceen-panzer, mollusken-schalen und eihullen, von W. von Nathusius-Königsborn. Mit 16 lithographirten tafeln. Berlin, Verlag von Wiegandt, Hempel & Parey, 1877.
vi, 144p. 16 pl. 31cm.

1. Histology. I. Title.

NN   0030500   LU MdBP CU PPAN MH

Nathusius, Wilhelm von.
Die vorgänge der vererbung bei hausthieren. 4 pl.
Landw. jahrb. bd. 20, p. 1–86.   Berlin, 1891.

1. Heredity. 2. Zootechny.   Agr 4–1459

Library, U. S. Dept. of   Agriculture

NN   0030501   DNAL ICU

Nathusius, Wilhelm von.
Wird die perlsucht beim rindvieh durch ansteckung oder vererbung erzeugt?
Landw. jahrb. bd. 14, p. 457–463.   Berlin, 1885.

1. Tuberculosis. Transmission.   Agr 4–1460

Library, U. S. Dept. of   Agriculture

NN   0030502   DNAL

VOLUME 405

Nathusius, W₁ilhelm₁ von, 18₂1?-₁899
Das wollhaar des schafs in histologischer und technischer beziehung mit vergleichender berücksichtigung anderer haare und der haut. Von W. v. Nathusius-Königsborn. Berlin, Wiegandt und Hempel. 1866.
xvi p., 1 l., 200 p. xxiv pl. 27ᶜᵐ.

1. Hair. 2. Wool. Agr 7-1151

Library, U. S. Dept. of Agriculture 45N19

NN 0030503 DNAL CU MB ICJ OU

Nathusius-Koenigsborn, Wilhelm von
see Nathusius, Wilhelm von, 1821?-1899.

Nathusius-Ludom, Philipp von, 1842-1900.
CₙL15 Conservative Partei und Ministerium ...
1 Berlin, 1872.
Pamphlet

NN 0030505 CtY

Nathusius-Ludom, Philipp, 1842-1900. 396.1 N104
Zur „Frauenfrage", [von] Ph. v. Nathusius. Halle, R. Mühlmann, 1871.
107760 [4], 159 p. 21½ᶜᵐ.

NN 0030506 ICJ

NATHUSIUS-NEINSTEDT, Heinrich von, 1851-1906.
Beiträge zur geschichte des hauses Neufville seit der einwanderung der familie nach Deutschland bis auf die neuzeit, 1558-1897; zusammengestellt und bearbeitet von Heinrich von Nathusius-Neinstedt und Alfred von Neufville. Frankfurt a.M., [typ.anstalt A.Osterrieth], 1897

4°. pp.vi,73 + 17 plates and 5 geneal.tables
"Als manuscript gedruckt,200 exemplaren,no. 195."

NN 0030507 MH

Nathusius-Neinstedt, Heinrich von, 1851-1906.
Codex diplomaticus moenofrancofurtanus. Urkundenbuch der reichsstadt Frankfurt. Herausgegeben von Johann Friedrich Boehmer. Neubearbeitung auf veranlassung und aus den mitteln der administration des dr. Johann Friedrich Boehmer'schen nachlasses ... Bearb. von Friedrich Lau. Frankfurt am Main, J. Baer & co., 1901-05.

NATHUSIUS-NEINSTEDT, Heinrich von, 1851-
Die deutschmeister vor 1232. Inaug.-diss. Marburg, 1888.

NN 0030509 MH CU ICRL

Nathusius-Neinstedt, Heinrich von, 1851-1906.
Ebrard, Friedrich Clemens, 1850-
Die stadtbibliothek in Frankfurt am Main. Im auftrage der städtischen behörden aus anlass der vollendung des erweiterungsbaues hrsg. von dr. Friedrich Clemens Ebrard, stadtbibliothekar. Mit 19 tafeln und 22 textabbildungen. Frankfurt am Main, Druck von Gebrüder Knauer, 1896.

Nati, Augusto.
Del concordato, con speciale riguardo al concordato stragiudiziale. Roma, Foro italiano, 1936.
303 p. 24 cm.
Bibliography: p. 375-382.

1. Composition (Law)—Italy. I. Title: Concordato.
51-45499

NN 0030511 DLC CU-L

Nati, Pietro, d. 1613.
Breve discorso intorno alla natura del popone, e sopra il cattivo uso del ber fresco con la neve. Fiorenza, G. Marescotti, 1576.
17 p. 24°.

NN 0030512 DNLM

Nati, Pietro, d. 1613.
Breve discorso intorno alla natura del popone, e sopra il cattivo uso del ber fresco con la neve. In: RAC. d' opusc. scient. e filol. 16°. Venezia, 1730, iv. 373-398.

NN 0030513 DNLM

WZ NATI, Pietro, d. 1613
240 Modo facile et ispedito da conservarsi
N277m sano ne tempi pericolosi della pestilenza.
1576 Con altri trattati ... Fiorenza, Giorgio Marescotti, 1576.
[29], 17, 35 p. 16 cm.
Signatures: a, A-D⁸, E⁴ (A₈ and D₄ blank)
The two other treatises are Nati's Discorso intorno alla natura del popone, & sopra il cattivo uso del ber' frescho con

la neve; and D. A. Altomare's Trattato delle vinacce, a translation by Nati of De vinaceorum facultate ac usu.
I. Altomare, Donato Antonio, 16th cent. [De vinaceorum facultate ac usu. Ital. 1576] II. Nati, Pietro, d. 1613.

Discorso intorno alla natura del popone, & sopra il cattivo uso del ber' frescho con la neve Title

NN 0030516 DNLM DFo

Nati, Pietro, b. 1625.
Delle vinacce e sue virtù e del modo d'usarle
see under Altomare, Donato Antonio, 16th cent.

Nati, Pietro, b. 1625.
Petri Nati ... Florentina phytologica observatio de malo limonia citrata-avrantia Florentiæ vvlgo la bizzarria. Florentiæ, typis H. de Naue, 1674.
4 p. l., 18 p. incl. pl. 27ᶜᵐ.

1. [Bizzaria]
Agr 28-625

Library, U. S. Dept. of Agriculture 93N212

NN 0030518 DNAL

Nati, Pietro, b. 1625.
... Memoria sull'agrume bizzarria, ristampa integrale del testo latino con traduz. e note del dott. Attilio Ragionieri ... Catania, F. Battiato, 1929.
64 p., 2 l. double front., double pl. 19ᶜᵐ. (On cover: Biblioteca d'agricoltura e industrie affini. vol. LXX)
Verso, Latin text; rectos, Italian translation.

1. [Bizzaria] I. Ragionieri, Attilio, tr.
Agr 29-1498

Library, U. S. Dept. of Agriculture 93N212M

NN 0030519 DNAL

Nati, Publio.
... Del fallimento; formulario commentato in armonia col progetto per il nuovo Codice di commercio. II. ed. Roma, P. Cremonese [1930]
167 p. 22ᶜᵐ.

1. Bankruptcy—Italy. 2. Forms (Law)—Italy. I. Title.
35-21503

Library of Congress [347.7] 332.750945

NN 0030520 DLC

Nati, Vincio.
...Una volta...così'... Milano [etc.] Gastaldi [1949] 62 p. 19cm. (Teatro)

1. Drama, Italian. I. Title.
N.Y.P.L. August 23, 1950

NN 0030521 NN RPB

Nati da Bibbiena, M. Pietro
see Nati, Pietro, d. 1613.

Cdᵢₑₛ Natick, Mass.
1851 Order of exercises at the celebration of the
Oct.8 two hundreth anniversary of the settlement of the town of Natick,/... eighth day of October, A.D, 1851 ... Boston, Damrell & Moore, printers, [1851]
broadside, 38 x 21cm.

NN 0030523 MHi

Ov30 Natick, Mass.
N23a Reports of town officers with a statement of the receipts and expenditures ... Natick,
23cm.

NN 0030524 CtY

Natick, Mass.
South Middlesex Peculiar; or, Natick View and Review
see under title

Natick, *Mass.*
Vital records of Natick, Massachusetts, to the year 1850. Comp. by Thomas W. Baldwin ... Boston, Mass. [Stanhope press, F. H. Gilson company] 1910.
249 p. 23½ᶜᵐ.
Published under provisions of chapter 470, Acts of 1902, commonwealth of Massachusetts.
Alphabetical indexes to the manuscript records of the town, supplemented by information from church registers, cemetery inscriptions and other sources.

1. Registers of births, etc—Natick, Mass. I. Baldwin, Thomas Williams, 1849- comp.
10-8745

Library of Congress F74.N2N4

OCl WaS WaSp MH MtHi
NN 0030526 DLC ViU NcD MB PHi MiU OClWHi I NN

VOLUME 405

NATICK, Mass. Board of assessors.
    Assessed valuation of the real estate of the inhabitants of the town of
Natick. Also a list of the real estate owned by non-residents. 1892.
    Natick, 1892.   v. 8°.

NN 0030527   MB

W 2   NATICK, Mass. Board of Health
AM4.2   Annual report.
N2B6a
               Natick [18--?]-
                   v.
               Report year irregular.
               1. Public health - Massachusetts

NN 0030528   DNLM

Natick, Mass. Evangelical church.
    The articles of faith and covenant of the
Evangelical church, Natick: with a list of the
members. Boston, 1835.
    12 p.   18.5 cm.

NN 0030529   CtY

Natick, (Mass.) First Baptist church.
    100th anniversary ... 1849-1949 ...
[n.p., n.d.]
    100 p.   port.   24 cm.

NN 0030530   NRAB

Natick, Mass. First Congregational Church
    Articles of faith...and list of members.
1454. Milford, 1854
    23,[1]p. 3°

NN 0030531   MWA

Natick, Mass. First Congregational church.
    ...The confession of faith, covenant, forms
of admission, ecclesiastical principles and
rules, with an historical sketch, and list of
members, 1877. Bost., T. Todd, ptr., 1877.
    131 p. front.

        **Cover title: Manual of the First Congrega-
tional church...**

NN 0030532   MiD-B CtY CtY-D NN OO

Natick, Mass. First Congregational church.
    Report of the First Congregational church and
society in Natick, for the year *1856*
Natick, Mass., From the Observer office, 1857-
    1 v. 16 1/2 cm.

NN 0030533   CSmH

Natick, Mass. Leonard Morse hospital.
    Annual report.
Natick, Mass.,
    v. pl. 22½ cm.
    Full title of report for 1903: Annual report of the Board of trustees of
the Leonard Morse hospital.

                            CA 10-5678 Unrev'd

    Library of Congress   RA982.N34L5

NN 0030534   DLC DNLM

F74   Natick, Mass.   St. Paul's church.
N2N2   Year book.

           No imprint, 18_-
               _ vols.   illus.   20cm.
               1. Natick, Mass.   St. Paul's church.

NN 0030536   NBuG

Natick, Mass.   School committee.
    Annual report. 1861/68; 68/69 92/93 98/99 1900/01
06/07 08/09 10/11 12/13 17/26; 30-31.
Boston, Natick, Mass., 1868-1932.
    28 v. plates, plans 21½-23½ cm.
    Report year irregular.

NN 0030537   DHEW NcD

Natick, Mass. Takewambait base ball club
    see   Takewambait base ball club,
Natick, Mass.

Natick, R.I. Baptist Young People's Union
    see   Baptist Young People's Union.

Natick (South) Mass.
    see   South Natick, Mass.

The Natick directory ... for 18
[no.
Boston, W. A. Greenough & co., c18
    v. 23½ cm.

    1. Natick, Mass.—Direct.   I. Greenough, W. A., & co., Boston, pub.

    Library of Congress   8-34295

NN 0030541   DLC

---

*F74
.N2N3   Natick Federal Savings and Loan Association,
            Natick, Mass.
            The story of Natick. [Natick, Mass., Sub-
        urban Press, 1948]
            32 p. illus., maps (1 fold.) ports. 27cm.

            1. Natick, Mass.

NN 0030542   MB MiD

The Natick, Mass. (Middlesex County) directory ...
Boston, Mass., W. E. Shaw,
    v. fold. map. 24½ cm.
    Compilers: W. E. Shaw.

    1. Natick, Mass.—Direct.
                                            8-34133
    Library of Congress   F74.N2A18   Copyright

NN 0030543   DLC

868.915   Natiello, Alberto.
N277r   Romancero de la España heróica. Prólogo
           de Julio Marsagot. Xilografía de la portada
           de Jorge Gnecco. [Buenos Aires] Edita
           Tiempo Nuestro [1938]
               60p.   24cm.

               I. Marsagot, Julio. II. Title.

NN 0030544   IEN MH CLU

Natiello, Miguel V.
    ... Motivos del terruño, versos. Buenos Aires, Editorial
Tor [1928]
    78 p., 1 l. 19 cm.

    I. Title.   35-25743

    Library of Congress   PQ7797.N36M6   861.6

NN 0030545   DLC

PQ 7797   NATIELLO, NICOLAS
.N35 E8   Estilo y tabaco. Buenos Aires, A.I.A.P.E.,
           1941.
               197 p.

               Stories.

NN 0030546   InU

Natier, E., joint author.

Franc de Ferrière, Philippe Jean Jacques, 1898-
    Étude statistique du pH et de la potasse assimilable dans
quelques sols africains, par J. Franc de Ferrière et E. Natier.
diagr.
    Ann. agron. n. s. année 2, p. 683-689.   Paris, 1932.

Natier, E., joint author.

Franc de Ferrière, Philippe Jean Jacques, 1898-
    Zones climatiques et zones de pH des sols; leurs rapports
avec la potasse assimilable des sols, par J. Franc de Ferrière
et E. Natier. map, diagrs.
    Ann. agron. n. s. année 3, p. 184-209.   Paris, 1933.
    "Bibliographie": p. 209.

Natier, Léon-Alphonse, 1879-
    *Les complications nerveuses des fractures du
coude. Lille, 1904.
    88 p. 8°.

NN 0030549   DNLM

Natier, Marcel, 1860-
    Coryza et gymnastique respiratoire, par
Marcel Natier. Paris, 1912.
    16 p. illus. (Étude de respiration
(thérapeutique physique) 13)
    For English translation, see Transactions
of the American Laryngological Association, v. 34,
1912, p. 256-264.

NN 0030550   PPC

WV   NATIER, Marcel, 1860-
N277f   Fièvre des foins; pathogénie &
1888   traitement. Paris, Doin, 1888.
               159 p.

NN 0030551   DNLM

VOLUME 405

Natier, Marcel, 1860–
Statistique
see under Paris. Policlinique. Service de rhinologie, d'otologie et de laryngologie.

Natier, Marcel, 1860–
——. La surdité, son diagnostic et son prognostic établie au moyen de l'enquête par les diapasons. 14 pp. 8°. Paris, 1903.

NN 0030553 DNLM

Natier, Marcel, 1860–
——. Surdité et fièvre typhoïde. Destruction totale du tympan droit par otorrhée chronique. Traitement par les exercices acoustiques au moyen des diapasons. Rééduction physiologique de l'oreille. 7 pp. 8°. Paris, 1905.

NN 0030554 DNLM

RC423 Natier, Marcel, 1860–
N33 Voix de fausset; origine et traitement respiratoires. Altérations dentaires. Paris, Publications de La Parole, 1902.
25 p. illus.
Cover title.
"Extrait de La Parole, n°6, juin 1902."

1. Speech, Disorders of.

NN 0030555 CU MH

Natier, Pierre, 1903–
..., Contribution à l'étude du lipiodolage trachéo-broncho-pulmonaire per-radioscopique... Paris, 1932.
Thèse – Univ. de Paris.
"Bibliographie": p. [59]–65.

NN 0030556 CtY

. Natíli, Virgilio.
Le schegge. Varese, "Giornale di Poesia" [1923]
59 p. 16 cm. (Quaderni di poesia, no. 2)
"Ornamenti di Gino Maggioni";

NN 0030557 CtU

Nātil Khānlarī, Parvīz
see
Khanlarī, Parvīz Nātil.

WBJ NATILI, Peter
N277a Ärztlicher Ratgeber der Electro-
1892 Physiopathie. 4. bereicherte Aufl.
München, Staegmeyr [1892]
218 p. illus.

NN 0030559 DNLM

Natilica, conte indien, ou, critique de Catilina. 1749
see under Desforges, 1710–1768.

Natilie [!] or the maid of the mill
see [The Miller's daughter] Natilie [!]

WZ NATIN, Isaac
100 A collection of miscellaneous bio-
qN277 bibliographical material on this person, together with abstracts, résumés, etc. of his works, may be found on the shelves under the above call number.

NN 0030562 DNLM

W Natin, Isaac
1045 Antecedentes, títulos, trabajos.
N277a [Buenos Aires] 1945.
1945 23 p.

NN 0030563 DNLM

W Natin, Isaac
4 El dispensario antituberculoso. Buenos
B92 Aires, "La Semana médica", 1931.
1931 109 p. illus. (Buenos Aires. Universidad Nacional. Facultad de Ciencias Médicas. Tesis. no. 4501)

Bibliography: p. [97]–109.

Series

NN 0030564 DNLM

Natinguerra, Amerigo Bartoli
see Bartoli, Amerigo, 1890–

Natio; pismo poświęcone sprawom narodowościowym w Polsce. 1, no. 1–8; stycz.-lip. 1927. W Warszawie.
1 v. 28 cm. monthly.
Edited by P. Łysiak.
Polish, German, French, and English.

1. Minorities—Poland—Period. I. Łysiak, Paweł, ed.

DK412.N33 60–56890

NN 0030566 DLC NN

Natio Dalekarlo-Vestmannica Upsalina
see Uppsala. Universitet. Natio Dale-karlo-Vestmannica.

Natio Wiburgensis
see Helsinki. Yliopisto. Viipurilainen Osakunta.

Nation, *Mrs.* Carry Amelia (Moore) 1846–1911.
The use and need of the life of Carry A. Nation. Written and published by herself. Topeka, F. M. Steves & sons, 1904.
4 p. l., [3]–184 p. front., plates, ports. 22½ᶜᵐ.

I. Title.
4–16788 Revised
Library of Congress HV5232.N3A2 1904

NN 0030569 DLC TxU

Nation, *Mrs.* Carry Amelia (Moore) 1846–1911.
The use and need of the life of Carry A. Nation, written by herself. Rev. ed. Twenty-five thousand ... Topeka, F. M. Steves & sons, 1905.
201 p. front. (port.) illus. (incl. ports.) 22½ᶜᵐ.

I. Title.
5–18112 Revised
Library of Congress HV5232.N3A2 1905

OC1WHi OO ICJ Vi CU
NN 0030570 DLC TU CaBVaU LU IEG IU NcGU ICU MiU

Nation, *Mrs.* Carry Amelia (Moore) 1846–1911.
The use and need of the life of Carry A. Nation, written by herself. Rev. ed. Ten thousand copies ... Topeka, F. M. Steves & sons, 1908.
6 p. l., [17]–396 p. front. (port.) illus. 20ᶜᵐ.

I. Title.
8–22604 Revised
Library of Congress HV5232.N3A2 1908

MoU CU OFH OC1 OC1WHi MH WaTC WaSp
NN 0030571 DLC KEmT TNJ ICarbS ViU TxU KMK

HV Nation, Carry Amelia (Moore) 1846–1911.
5232 The use and need of the life of Carry
N3 A. Nation, written by herself. Rev. ed.
A2 Alpena Pass, Ark. [1909, c1908]
1908a 414 p. illus. 19 cm.

NN 0030572 CaBVaU

Nation, Carry Amelia (Moore) 1846–1911.
The use and need of the life of Carry A. Nation. Written by herself. Revised ed. [Topeka, F.M. Steves & sons, 1909]
414 p. ports., illus. 18 cm.

CaBVaU KU
NN 0030573 MH WaSpG DI KAS OC1WHi MiU IU IEG

TN27 Nation, Harold Turton, 1876– comp.
.B7
British Columbia. *Dept. of mines.*
Annual report.
Victoria, 18 –19

Nation, Harold Turton, 1876–
The Dewdney trail. (In British Columbia Historical Association. 4th report and proceedings. 1929. p. 30–33)

NN 0030575 CaBViPA

BP Nation, W C
565 The unseen world; being the remarkable
L4 experiences in the family of W.C. Nation,
HRC and subsequent investigations of the phenomena of spiritualism and its teachings. By the editor of The message of life. 3rd. ed., enl. Levin, N.Z. [pref. 1920]
143 p. illus. 18 cm. [With Leadbeater, Charles Webster, Life after death and how Theosophy unveils it. Sydney, 192–]

Author's signed presentation copy to Sir

Arthur Conan Doyle, Levin, N.Z., Oct. 1, 1920.
Ms. note.

1. Spiritualism. I. Title. A.F.: Nation, W C .

NN 0030577 TxU

VOLUME 405

₍Nation, William₎
The history of Freemasonry in Northern China, 1913–1937... ₍
Published with the approval of the principals of the various
Masonic bodies in China. ₍Shanghai₎ Privately printed, 1938.
xii, 435 p. illus. 21cm.

"Preface" signed: W. Nation.

1. Freemasons—China.
N. Y. P. L.

NN   0030578   NN

Nation, William, jr.
The dramatic pieces, and poetry, of William
Nation, jun. Including, The school for diffidence.
Miscellanies, a collection of songs, &c. &c. ...
Plymouth, printed for the author, 1789.
20 cm.

NN   0030579   CtY DFo

Nation, William, jr.
Old love renewed. (In his Dramatic pieces
and poetry) Plymouth, 1789.
(In Three centuries of drama: English,
1751–1800)

Microprint.

NN   0030580   MoU

Nation, William, jr.
School for diffidence. (In his Dramatic
pieces and poetry) Plymouth, 1789.
(In Three centuries of drama: English,
1751–1800)

Microprint.

NN   0030581   MoU

Nation, William, Sr.
A dissertation on the nature of heresy. 1731
see under title

Nation, William Hamilton Codrington, 1843-1914.
Bad old times; some leaves from my grandfather's diary.
By W. H. C. Nation. London: Drane's, 1913. 47 p. 12°.

1. Great Britain.—Social life, 18th   century. 2. Title.
N. Y. P. L.   October 22, 1914.

NN   0030583   NN

Nation, William Hamilton Codrington, 1843-1914, comp.

Good things from the dramatists; selected by
W. H. C. Nation exclusively from upwards of 60
pieces produced and reproduced at theatres under his management. 2d and revised ed. With
many additions. London, Gay & Hancock, ltd.,
etc. 1910.

sq. 24°. pp. (2) 108.

NN   0030584   MH

Nation, William Hamilton Codrington, 1843–1914.
Sketches from life and jottings from books. By W. H. C.
Nation ... London, T. C. Newby, 1864.
2 p. l., 288 p. 20ᶜᵐ.

I. Title.   40–20521

Library of Congress   PR5102.N4595

NN   0030585   DLC

Die Nation.
₍Berlin₎ Verlag der Nation.
v. 24 cm.

Monthly, accompanied by an annual supplement.
Began publication in 1951. Cf. Jahresverzeichnis des deutschen
Schrifttums, 1951.
At head of title: National-Demokratische Partei Deutschlands.
"Zeitschrift der Hochschule für Nationale Politik," (called
–Dec. 1952, Schule für Nationale Politik)

1. Germany—Pol. & govt.—1945–   I. National-Demokratische
Partei Deutschlands. II. Berlin. Hochschule für Nationale Politik.

DD257.4.N32   54–32865

NN   0030586   DLC

Die NATION; Zeitschrift für Theorie und Praxis
nationaler Politik. Jahrg. 1–10; März, 1951–1960.
Berlin. 10 v. illus. 24cm.

Film reproduction. Negative.
Vol. 1, 3–5, 1951, 1953–55, in EAA.
Lacking: June, 1951, Jan.–May, 1952.
Monthly.

Published by the Hochschule für nationale Politik der National-
demokratischen Partei Deutschlands, Mar. 1951–Mar. 1953; by the
Parteivorstand der National-demokratische Partei Deutschlands,
Apr. 1953–1960.
Subtitle varies.
Includes supplements.
United with Voran (not in the library) to form Der Nationale
Demokrat.
I. Germany--Politics--Per.   and soc. publ. I. National-
demokratische Partei Deutsch-   lands. II. National-demokrat-
ische Partei Deutschlands.   Hochschule für nationale Politik.

NN   0030588   NN

La Nation.
₍Bruxelles₎
no. in   v. illus., ports., maps (part fold.) 23 cm. irregular.
Issued by the Direction de l'éducation des forces armées of Belgium (called   –1950 Service d'éducation à l'Armée
(varies) 1950, Direction de l'éducation à l'Armee)

1. Belgium.   I. Belgium. Direction de l'éducation des forces
armées.

DH418.N3   55–29143

NN   0030589   DLC

The Nation; Netaji number, January 23, 1950. ₍Calcutta₎
1950.
150 p. illus. 28 cm.
On cover: "Netaji special."

1. Bose, Subhas Chandra, 1897–1945—Addresses, essays, lectures.
I. The Nation (Calcutta)

DS481.B6N35   954.03⁵/5⁰0924   74–196508
                                    MARC
Library of Congress   75 ₍4₎

NN   0030590   DLC

The Nation, Dublin.
The new spirit of The Nation
see under title

The Nation, Dublin.   FOR OTHER EDITIONS
                       SEE MAIN ENTRY

The Spirit of the nation. Ballads and songs by the writers
of "The Nation," with original and ancient music, arranged
for the voice and piano-forte. Dublin, J. Duffy, 1845.

The Nation, Dublin.
The voice of the Nation. A manual of nationality. By
the writers of the Nation newspaper. 5th ed. Dublin,
J. Duffy, 1844.

The Nation (Ireland) v.1,no.1; Oct.16,1924.
ˣSCpbG   Dublin, 1924.
.H924   1 no. 45cm.
.N47N

NN   0030594   MB

The Nation.
₍Karachi₎
v. illus. 27 cm. monthly.
"Incorporating the Middle East."

1. Pakistan—Econ. condit.—Period.

HC440.5.N3   S A 62–904 ‡

NN   0030595   DLC

The Nation, London
see
The Nation and Athenæum.

The Nation, edited by C. C. Burr. v. 1, no. 1; Sept. 1855.
New York, Burr & Long.
80 p. 27 cm.

I. Burr, Charles Chauncey, 1817–1883, ed.

AP2.N18   52–53928

NN   0030597   DLC NN

The Nation. v. 1–
July 6, 1865–
New York, Nation Associates, inc. ₍etc.₎
v. illus. 29–32 cm. weekly.

INDEXES:
Vols. 1–30, July 1865–Sept. 1880 (Issued as Q. P. indexes, no. 1)
   (AI3.G8   no. 1) 1 v.
Vols. 31–40, Oct. 1880–Oct. 1885 (Issued as Q. P. indexes, no. 18)
   (AI3.G8   no. 18) 1 v.
Vols. 1–105, 1865–1917. 2 v.

(Series: Griswold, William McCrillis, 1853–1899. Q. P. Indexes)

AP2.N2   051   4–12681 rev*

KyLoU AzTeS
CaBVaU NNJ CaBVa OrPS WaS OrSaW MU PSC PPD MH-BA
WvU CtNIC FTaSU CU-Riv KT TMG CtH CMC IdU Or OrP
NNH DCU-H PCaD CSmH NN CaOTU OAkU MWH OkTU PPT
OU ODW DL MiU NIC GEU-H InRE NcD NcRS TU MH ViU
NN   0030598   DLC TxU KEmT NR NjP MB ICJ OC1W OCU

VOLUME 405

FILM
X175
The Nation. v.1–
July 6,1865–
New York, Nation Associates,inc.⟨etc.⟩

Indexes:
Vols.1-30, July 1865-Sept.1880.
Vols.31-40, Oct.1880-Oct.1885.
Microfilm. Ann Arbor,Mich., University Micro-
films. 35 cm. (Current periodical series
publication no.90)

NN 0030600   MiU ICU OU

The Nation (New York)
Address of the carriers of The Nation
see under title

The Nation⟨ New York⟩

Near East relief. *Russian commission.*
An American report on the Russian famine. Findings
of the Russian commission of the Near East relief. Published by the Nation. New York ⟨1921⟩

The Nation (New York)
An analytical index to the political contents of
"The Nation"
see under [Griswold, William McCrillis]
1853-1899.

Pamphlet
T
129+
The Nation (New York)
Atoms for peace. Special 90th anniversary issue. ⟨New York, 1955⟩
⟨513⟩-572 p. illus. 28cm. (The Nation,
v. 180, no. 25, June 18, 1955)

Cover title.

1. Atomic energy. I. Title.

NN 0030604   NIC

The Nation⟨ New York⟩

Johnson, James Weldon, 1871–
L'autonomie d'Haïti, par James Weldon Johnson. Qurtre ⟨!⟩
articles reproduits de la revue "The Nation", comprenant le
compte-rendu d'une enquête effectuée pour le compte de l'Association nationale pour l'avancement des gens de couleur, et traduits en français par les soins de l'Union patriotique haïtienne.
New York, Association nationale pour l'avancement des gens
de couleur; Port-au-Prince, Comité central de l'Union patriotique, 1921.

The Nation⟨New York⟩
The best of the Nation; a selection of the best articles of lasting
value to appear in the Nation during the recent past. New
York, The Nation associates ⟨c1952⟩ 96 p.   20cm.

I. The Nation associates, inc.   New York.

NN 0030606   NN OrU

Pamphlet
QC
85+
The Nation⟨ New York⟩
The challenge of the atomic bomb, the
Nation's special supplement containing the
addresses delivered at the Annual Nation
Associates Forum, held at the Hotel Aster,
December 1-3. ⟨New York⟩ 1945.
⟨700⟩-720 p. 30cm.

1. Atomic bomb.

NN 0030607   NIC

The Nation (New York)
... A complete bibliography of the published
writings of the late William Graham Sumner.
[New York, New York evening post company,
1910]
[3] p.   21.5 cm.
Caption title.
From the Nation, July 21, 1910 and Sept. 1,
1910.

NN 0030608   CU

The Nation⟨ New York⟩
The conquest of Haiti...   ⟨New York,
The Nation, inc., ᶜ1920⟩
60 p. 18½cm.

Articles and documents reprinted from
The Nation.

1. Haiti - Hist. 2. U. S. - For. rel -
Haiti. 3. Haiti - For. rel. - U. S.
I. Title.

NN 0030609   DS DPU

The Nation⟨ New York⟩
The controversy between Col. George Bliss and "The Nation," newspaper. Transcribed from the Nation.   ⟨New York,⟩
1876. * 68 f. 4°.

Manuscript.
Relates principally to the extradition of Charles L. Laurence.

4036A. 1. Laurence, Charles L.   2. Criminals.—Extradition, U. S.
and Gt. Br.   3. Bliss, George,   1830-97.
N. Y. P. L.   June 22, 1921.

NN 0030610   NN

The Nation⟨ *New York*⟩
Critical and social essays reprinted from the New York
Nation. New York, Leypoldt & Holt, 1867.
iv, 230 p. 18ᵐ.
Twenty-five articles, from July, 1865 to May, 1867.

1. American essays. I. Title.

30-15363

Library of Congress   PS687.N3

MB OrU WaS
NN 0030611   DLC KMK NN NIC CU PPL MH NjP MnU OCl

The Nation (New York)
Decrees and constitution of Soviet Russia
see under Russia (1917-   R. S. F. S. R.)
Laws, statutes, etc.

The Nation (New York)
Elliott Coues as represented in the Nation

see under

McAtee, Waldo Lee, 1883–

The Nation⟨ *New York*⟩
Fifty years of American idealism: the New York Nation,
1865–1915; selections and comments by Gustav Pollak. Boston and New York, Houghton Mifflin company, 1915.
ix, 468 p., 1 l. 23ᵐ. $2.50
"Part I of this volume embodies, with various additions, the substance of my article on 'The Nation and its contributors' in the semi-
centennial number of the Nation (July 8, 1915)"—Prefatory note.
CONTENTS.—I. The Nation: its editors and contributors.—II. The Nation's views from year to year.—III. Representative essays.
I. Pollak, Gustav, 1849-1919, ed. II. Title.

Library of Congress   PN4900.N3P6   16—695

NIC WHi MH ICRL ODW OU MiU NN ICJ MB NjP
NN 0030614   DLC CaBVaU OrPR WaTC MtU WaS OrU MtBC

The Nation⟨ *New York*⟩

Vámbéry, Rusztem, 1872–
The Hungarian problem, by Rustem Vambery; introduction
by Oscar Jászi ... ⟨New York⟩ The Nation ⟨1942⟩

The Nation (New York)
Is monogamy feasible?
see under title

The Nation⟨ New York⟩
Mr. Parkman and his Canadian critics
see under title

The Nation,⟨New York⟩
... The morals and manners of the kitchen, and Baby suffrage. From "The Nation". New York, K. Tompkins, 1875.

ML60
.H16
1949
The Nation (New York)

Haggin, Bernard H   1900–
Music in the Nation. New York, W. Sloane Associates
⟨1949⟩

The Nation⟨ New York⟩

The Nation year book. 1942–
New York, N. Y., The Nation, inc. ⟨1942–

GV1507
.C7B34
The Nation⟨ New York⟩

Barrett, Jack.
The Nation's crossword puzzle book, a collection of 55 cross-
word puzzles, composed and edited by Jack Barrett. New
York, Crown publishers ⟨1944⟩

The Nation⟨ New York⟩
"Ol' rags an' bottles," by our special correspondent. ⟨New
York: National Civil Liberties Bureau, 1919.⟩ 4 l. 8°.

Caption-title.
Repr.: The Nation. Jan. 25, 1919.

1. Industrial Workers of the World.   2. National Civil Liberties Bureau.
N. Y. P. L.   November 7, 1919.

NN 0030622   NN

VOLUME 405

The Nation(*New York*)
Pages from the Nation; selections from the contributions of the editorial staff for the decade 1918–28; illustrated with cartoons and other drawings. New York, The Tenth anniversary committee of Nation readers, 1928.

1 p. l., 184 p. front., illus., ports. 16½ᵐ.

"Tenth anniversary committee of Nation readers organized in 1928 in honor of Oswald Garrison Villard's ten years' service as editor of the Nation. Chairman: William Allen White": p. ₍163₎–166.

1. Villard, Oswald Garrison, 1872–   I. Tenth anniversary committee of Nation readers. II. White, William Allen, 1868– III. Title.

Library of Congress   PS659.N3

28–10656

NN   0030623   DLC CU ICRL WHi ICN TNJ   CrPS NjP OrU

The Nation(*New York*)
Palestine, a pattern of betrayal; the role of the United States, Great Britain, and the United Nations since November 29 [1947] New York, The Nation associates, 1948.

[19] p. illus. 28 p.
Consists of articles which appeared in The Nation between the adjournment of the special session of the United Nations General Assembly on Nov. 29, 1947 and the convening of the new special session on April 16, 1948.

NN   0030624   MH

The Nation(*New York*)

Villard, Oswald Garrison, 1872–
The press today, by Oswald Garrison Villard ... [New York, The Nation, ᶜ1930]

The Nation(*New York*)
Russian reprints from the Nation of November 16th, 23rd and 30th... [New York, The Nation, 1918.

NN   0030626   MiU

The Nation(*New York*)

Johnson, James Weldon, 1871–
Self-determining Haiti, by James Weldon Johnson. Four articles reprinted from the Nation embodying a report of an investigation made for the National association for the advancement of colored people, together with official documents ... [New York, The Nation, ᶜ1920]

The Nation (New York).
The Southern Negro

see under title.

The **NATION**(*New York*)
Special western supplement.
N.Y. Nation associates.

1946   issued for the Conference of the Nation associates.

Library has:
1946

NN   0030629   WaS

The Nation(*New York*)
[Two issues of the Nation, February 26, 1936, and March 4, 1936, showing the change in design and format]
2 pts. in 1 v. 29½ᵐ.

The issue for March 4 designed by Joseph Blumental of the Spiral press - cf. The shape of things in The Nation, March 4, 1936, p. [261]

NN   0030630   NNC

The Nation(*New York*)
Unpunished homicide at the South; its social and commercial influence. An instructive and unbiassed discussion of the question. Comp. from the Nation of N. Y. New York, L. Kempner, 1883.

[41] p. 25ᵐ.

Compiled by Louis Kempner.

1. Homicide — Southern states. 2. Crime and criminals — Southern states. 3. Southern states — Soc. condit. I. Kempner, Louis, comp. II. Title.

Library of Congress   HV6524.N3

10–23612

NN   0030631   DLC

Nation (*New York*)   No. 50 in *Map 86.2
War map supplement of The Nation, ... New York, August 6, 1914.
= [New York. 1914.] Size, 19 × 15⅞ inches. Scale, none.

L5124 — European War, 1914– . Maps.

NN   0030632   MB

The Nation, *New York.*
William Dwight Whitney ... [New York, 1894]
8 p. 23ᵐ.

Caption title.
"Reprinted from the Nation, of New York, June 14, 1894."

1. Whitney, William Dwight, 1827–1894.

11–24033

Library of Congress   PK109.W6N3

NN   0030633   DLC

The Nation (New York) (Indexes)
An analytical index to the political contents of "The Nation," ...
see under   [Griswold, William McCrillis] 1853–1899.

The Nation, New York. (Indexes)
The Nation, volumes 1–105, New York, 1865–1917, indexes of titles and contributors; compiled by Daniel C. Haskell
see in   The Nation.

The Nation (New York) Tenth anniversary committee of Nation readers
see   Tenth anniversary committee of Nation readers.

FILM
X730   The Nation. 19 –
Rangoon, Burma.

Microfilm.   Washington, D.C., Library of Congress Photoduplication Service.

NN   0030637   MiU CtY

NATION [Sydney] no. 141–date; Apr. 4, 1964–date
Sydney.   no.   illus.   29cm.

Semimonthly.

1. Periodicals--Australia.

NN   0030638   NN

Nation (Victoria, B.C.) v.1, no.1–20; Mar. 5 –
July 16, 1898. Victoria.
1 v.   35 cm.   weekly.

Edited and published by D.M. Carley (cf. Victoria daily colonist, Mar. 6, 1898, p.5)
Absorbed by Nelson economist on Aug. 17 or 24, 1898.
No more published?
Also on microfilm reel 38A.

NN   0030639   CaBViPA

The Nation, a liberal weekly devoted to politics, economics, science, foreign affairs, literature, drama and the arts
see   The Nation. v. 1–
July 6, 1865–

The Nation. [A magazine published monthly]
see   The Nation, edited by C. C. Burr ...
1855. New York, Burr & Long.

The Nation, a weekly journal devoted to politics, literature, science & art
see   The Nation. v. 1–
July 6, 1865–

La **Nation**; hebdomadaire politique et littéraire.
Année 1

Québec, 1936–   62cm.
v. illus.

"Pour un état libre français en Amérique."
Editor : 1936–   Paul Bouchard (with Pierre Chaloult, Feb.– Apr., 1936).

1. Quebec (Province)—Politics—   Per. and soc. publ. 2. Canadians, French—Per. and soc. publ. I. Bou-   chard, Paul, journalist, ed. II. Cha- loult, Pierre, ed.   loult, Pierre, ed.
N.Y.P.L.

June 14, 1937

NN   0030643   NN

The **Nation** (*Hebrew periodical*)
see
ha-Le'om.

The **Nation** (incorporating "the Advent witness"). no. 1–2 (May – Aug. 1949). Pretoria, Kingdom press [1949] 2 nos. illus. 44cm.

"An independent South African quarterly journal, expressing a national and Gentile viewpoint in the English language."
Edited by Larratt Battersby.
No more published.

1. Fascism—Per. and soc. publ.—   Union of South Africa. 2. Jews— Anti-Semitic writings.
N.Y.P.L.

April 3, 1951

NN   0030644   NN

VOLUME 405

La **Nation**; organe de la Fédération républicaine de France, Parti
républicain national.

Paris, 19   27 – 29cm.
v.
Weekly.
Various mistakes in numbering.
Vols. –11, no. 9 (– March 2, 1935) lack "Parti républicain national"
in subtitle.

I. France—Politics—Per. and soc.
II. Fédération républicaine de France.   publ. I. Ducrocq, 1874-   , ed.
N. Y. P. L.   May 26, 1942

Founded by Georges Ducrocq.
Vols. 10, 15 (1934, 1939) include separately paged suppl.: Congrès national de la
Fédération républicaine de France, 1934, 1938. (Incompl.)
Includes various other suppl.

NN   0030646   NN

DD257
.A1N3
Die Nation; Politik, Wirtschaft und Kultur. 1.-
Jahrg. (Nr. 1-   ); März 1947-
[München]
      v. in]   illus. 22 cm. monthly.
"Published under political party publication license ... [of the]
K. P. D."

1. Germany—Pol. & govt.—1945-   .—Period.   I. Kommunistische Partei Deutschlands.

DD257.A1N3   51–36192

NN   0030647   DLC

Die Nation; unabhängige Zeitung für Demokratie und Volk.

Bern.
      v. illus. 50 cm. weekly.
Began publication in 1983. Cf. Das Schweizer Buch, 1988.
Title varies slightly.

AP32.N285   053   51–33847 ‡

NN   0030648   DLC ICRL

Die **Nation**. Wochenschrift für politik, volkswirtschaft
und literatur. Hrsg. von dr. Th. Barth.

Berlin, H. S. Hermann [etc., 18   –1907]
      v. 31½ᶜᵐ.
No more published.

I. Barth, Theodor, 1849–1909, ed.

                        CA 11–3011 Unrev'd
Library of Congress   AP30.N2

NN   0030649   DLC IU ICRL CU MiU MH MB ICJ

053
NA
Die **Nation**; Wochenschrift für politik, volkswirtschaft und literature. v.1-24, no.26;
1884-märz. 1907. Berlin.
24v. 31cm.

FILM
053
NA
     ---- v.1-   1884-
Microfilm. New Haven, Conn., Yale University
Photographic Services, Yale University Library;
Boston, Readex Microprint Corp. for Boston
Public Library, 1971.   reels. 35mm.

NN   0030651   IU

Die Nation. Wochenschrift ... Berlin.
Die Nation. Eine Sammlung ausgewählter
Artikel. Berlin, H.S. Hermann, 1894.
214 p. 20 cm.
Collection of articles from Die
Nation; Wochenschrift für Politik,
Volkswirtschaft und Literatur.

NN   0030652   OCH

DC150
Z5
v.15
no.10
La nation à la reine. [Paris, De
l'imprimerie de P.de Lormel, 1789?]
7 p. 20cm.
Caption title: La nation à la reine, ou
Réponse directe à l'imprimé intitulé:
Marie-Antoinette d'Autriche, reine de
France, à la nation.

1.Marie Antoinette, Consort of Louis
XVI, 1755-1793. Marie-Antoinette d'Autriche,
reine de France, à la nation.

NN   0030653   CSt NIC NN

The **Nation** and Athenæum. v. 1–48; Mar. 2, 1907–Feb. 21,
1931. London [The Nation limited, etc., 1907–31]
48 v. 34ᶜᵐ. weekly.
Supersedes the Speaker, the liberal review.
Title varies: Mar. 1907–Feb. 12, 1921, The Nation.
Feb. 19, 1921–Feb. 21, 1931, The Nation and the Athenæum (later The
Nation and Athenæum)
Published by the Speaker publishing company, Mar. 2, 1907–Feb. 15,
1908; the Nation publishing company, limited, Feb. 22, 1908–May 22,
1920; British periodicals limited, May 29, 1920–July 28, 1923; the Nation
limited, Aug. 4, 1923–Feb. 21, 1931.
Includes separately paged literary and other supplements.
Absorbed the Athenæum in Feb. 1921.
Merged into the New statesman in Feb. 1931, which continued under
title: The New statesman and Nation.

Library of Congress   AP4.N15   8–16047 Revised
                  [r32m1]   052

OC1W OU MB ICJ OO
NN   0030654   DLC MoSW NjNbS CtH FU MH   NIC MtU

Nation and Athenaeum.
The **idea** of public right; being the first four prize essays in
each of the three divisions of the Nation essay competition,
with an introduction by the Rt. Hon. H. H. Asquith, M. P.
London, G. Allen & Unwin ltd.; New York, The Macmillan
company [1918]

Nation and Athenaeum.
A **Library** of peace & war. With an introduction by Francis
W. Hirst ... London, Printed by the North of England
newspaper co., ltd., Darlington, for the Speaker publishing
co., ltd. [1907?]

The Nation and Athenaeum.
Some reflections of a soldier ... London, The **Nation**
publishing company ltd. [1916?]

GV343
.N3
The Nation and Athenaeum.
The wasted years. [Boston,
Massachusetts Civic League, 1918]
[4] p. 24cm.
Article originally published in the
London Nation on Sept. 23, 1916.

1. Physical education and training.
I. Title.

NN   0030658   MB NcD

The Nation and the Athenaeum
see The Nation and Athenaeum.

La **Nation** arabe; revue ... politique, littéraire, economique et
sociale, servant les intérêts des pays arabes et ceux de l'Orient.

Genève, Naville & cie. [19
      v. 23½ᶜᵐ. monthly (irregular)

1. Arabia.   43–21769
Library of Congress   DS201.N3
                  [2]   953.005

NN   0030660   DLC

Nation armée. Apr. 10, 1848. Paris.
1 no.

Specimen no.

NN   0030661   ICRL

Nation armée. Apr. 10, 1848. Paris.
1 no.

Microfilm ed., positive copy.

NN   0030662   ICRL

La **nation armée**; leçons professées à l'École des hautes études
sociales, par mm. le Gᵃˡ Bazaine-Hayter, C. Bouglé [etc.] ...
Paris, F. Alcan, 1909.
2 p. l., ii, 278 p. 22ᶜᵐ. (On cover: Bibliothèque générale des sciences
sociales XXXIII)
Avant-propos signed: A. C. [i. e. Alfred Croiset]
CONTENTS.—Avant propos.—I. ptie. L'école et le patriotisme. L'idée
de patrie, par A. Croiset. Le patriotisme à l'école primaire, par F. Rauh.
Le lycée et l'éducation militaire, par G. Lanson. Les universités et l'armée, par C. Bouglé.—2. ptie. L'armée et la nation. Démocratie et armée,
par E. Boutroux. La préparation au devoir militaire, par le capitaine
Bourguet. La préparation à la guerre avant et après le service militaire,

par le capitaine Potez. L'éducation morale dans l'armée par E. Bourgeois. L'éducation physique, par G. Demeny.—3. ptie. Questions diverses. L'Armée—école et la démocratie française, par le général
Bazaine-Hayter. L'éducation sociale et les "hautes écoles du peuple"
dans les pays scandinaves, par L. Pineau.

1. Military education—France. 2. France—Army. 3. Patriotism. I.
Paris. École des hautes études sociales. II. Bazaine-Hayter, Georges
Albert, 1843– III. *Croiset, Alfred, 1845–1923.
                               E 11—865
U. S. Off. of educ. Library   LC191.N2
   for Library of Congress   U565.N3

NN   0030664   DHEW NcD DLC ICJ NjP

La "Nation armée" nouvelle
see under Viri, pseud.

La nation Arménienne
see under [Asgian, Jean-Baptiste, bp. 1840-
1913]

Nation associates, inc., New York
Addresses at the dinner in honor of Dr. Thomas
Mann on the occasion of his seventieth birth-
day, Waldorf-Astoria hotel, New York, June 25,
1945. Auspices The Nation association. New
York city [1945]
23 p. 13 x 20.5 cm.
Portrait on cover.

NN   0030667   MH CU

VOLUME 405

Nation Associates, inc., *New York.*
The Arab Higher Committee, its origins, personnel and
purposes; the documentary record submitted to the United
Nations, May, 1947. New York City [1947]

9 p. plates, facsims. 28 cm.

Cover title.

1. Arab Higher Committee. 2. Amīn al-Ḥusainī, Grand Mufti,
1895-   I. United Nations.

DS125.3.A6N3   956.9   48–703*

NN   0030668   DLC NNUN OrU OCH NN TxU MH CSt-H NNZI

D840
.K5
Nation Associates, inc., New York.

Kirchwey, Freda, *ed.*
The atomic era—can it bring peace and abundance? New
York, McBride [1950]

The Nation associates, inc., New York.
The best of the Nation

see under

The Nation (New York).

Nation Associates, Inc., N.Y.
The British record on partition as
revealed by British military intelligence
and other official sources. Memorandum
submitted to the special session of the
General Assembly of the United Nations,
Apr. 1948. N.Y. [1948]
48 p.

1. Palestine

NN   0030671   NNUN NIC MiU CSt-H NNC MH

946
N277
Nation Associates, inc., New York.
The case for action against Franco and
the recognition of the Spanish Republic by
the United Nations; memorandum submitted
to the Security Council, New York, March,
1946. [New York, The Nation Associates,
1946]
cover-title, 31 p. 21 cm.

1. Spain - Politics and government -
1939 - I. United Nations. Security Council.

NN   0030672   NNUN

4DS
728
Nation Associates, Inc., New York.
Could the Arabs stage an armed
revolt against the United Nations?
Memorandum submitted to the General
Assembly of the United Nations. New
York, 1947.
77 p.

NN   0030673   DLC-P4 MH Or OrU OCH

Nation associates, inc., New York.
Oil and the State department policy on Palestine; the documentary evidence of how ARAMCO attempts to destroy the partition resolution of the United nations. Memorandum submitted
to the President of the United States, June 1948, by the Nation
associates... New York [1948] 12 p. 28cm.

1. Petroleum—Political and   economic aspects—Near East.
2. Arabian American oil company.   3. Palestine—Hist., 1917–
N.Y. P. L.   April 30, 1951

NN   0030674   NN MH NNJ OCH

DS149
.P33
Nation Associates, inc., New York.

The Palestine problem and proposals for its solution; memo-
randum submitted [by Freda Kirchwey, president, the
Nation Associates, Henry A. Atkinson, sec'y, the Church
Peace Union, Raymond Swing, and others] to the General
Assembly of the United Nations, April, 1947. [New York,
Nation Associates, 1947]

JQ
1825
P3N3.8
Nation Associates, inc., New York.
Police state: Nazi model. Palestine
under British rule. A study of the
police state created by the mandatory
power. Memorandum submitted to General
Assembly of the United Nations. New
York, 1947.
14 p. 27 cm.

1. Military law--Palestine.
I. United Nations. General Assembly.
II. Title

NN   0030676   OCH

Nation associates, inc., New York.
The record of collaboration of King Farouk of Egypt with the
Nazis and their ally, the Mufti; the official Nazi records of the
King's alliance and of the Mufti's plans for bombing Jerusalem
and Tel Aviv. Memorandum submitted to the United nations,
June 1948. New York, The Nation associates [1948] [58]p.
28cm.

1. World war, 1939–1945—   Diplomatic history. 2. Germany—
For. rel.—Egypt. 3. Egypt—For. rel.   —Germany. 4. Amīn al-Ḥusainī,
grand mufti, 1895- . 5. World   war, 1939–1945—Palestine. I. Ger-
many. Auswärtiges Amt.   N.Y.P.L.   May 4, 1951

NN   0030677   NN NNJ MiU MH NNUN

Nation Associates, inc., New York.

Security and the Middle East, the problem and its solution;
proposals submitted to the President of the United States.
[New York, Nation Associates, 1954]

... The nation at work ... London [etc.] G. G. Harrap & co.
ltd. [1934]

v. front., illus. 19 cm. (A history of England at work, ed. by
J. D. G. Davies, M. A. & F. R. Worts, M. A. [book III])

1. Gt. Brit.—Econ. condit. 2. Gt. Brit.—Indus.—Hist.   I. Davies,
John David Griffith, 1899-

Library of Congress   HC253.N3   35–103

                                           [5]   330.942

NN   0030679   DLC

La Nation Belge. 1830–1905
see under   Liége. Exposition universelle
et internationale, 1905.

Nation building; famous characters, historic
events
see under   Home educational society,
Philadelphia.

Nation building in Australia; the life and work of Sir
Littleton Ernest Groom ...
see under   [Groom, Jessie (Bell), lady]
comp.

DA18
N277

Hoover
Library
Nation building in the British Commonwealth
and empire; a programme of study and discussion.
[London? 194-]

24 p. double map. 21 cm.

Contains bibliographies.

1. British Commonwealth. 2. Gt. Brit. -
Colonies.

NN   0030682   CSt-H MH

La nation catalane
see under   Union des nationalités.

---

*FC9
D8262
Z898n
La nation & l'armée. En l'honneur de
Cavaignac à la guerre et de Sarrien à la
justice (30 juin 1898) ...
Paris, Librairie A. Pierrot, éditeur, 37, rue
Etienne-Marcel, 37. 1898.

16p. 17.5cm.
Desachy 530.
Original printed beige wrappers preserved;
advts. on p.[4] of wrappers; bound in half red
cloth and marbled boards.

NN   0030684   MH

---

*FC9
D8262
Z900n
La nation et l'armée, par un colonel.
Armand Colin et cie, éditeurs, Paris, 5, rue
de Mézières, 1900. Tous droits réservés.

vi, 192p. 19cm.
Desachy 150.
First published as "Lettres libres" in
Le Temps.
Original printed yellow wrappers preserved;
advts. on p.[4] of wrappers; bound in half brown
cloth and marbled boards with A. de Boisandré's
Napoléon antisémite, 1900.

NN   0030685   MH MiU

Nation et progrès.
L'évolution, l'homme, la race, six conférences prononcées
en 1952, par René Binet [et al.] Paris, Comptoir national du
livre [1953]

83 p. diagrs. 27 cm.

1. Ethnology—Addresses, essays, lectures. 2. Man—Origin.
I. Title.

GN325.N38   55–21629

NN   0030686   DLC

Nation Europa.
Coburg.
v. illus., ports., maps. 22 cm. monthly.
Began publication with Jan. 1951 issue. Cf. Deutsche Bibliogra-
phie. Zeitschriften, 1945–52.
Editor: A. Ehrhardt.

——— Beilage. Suchtlicht. Jahrg. [1]-
Jan. 1954-
Coburg.
v. illus., ports. 22 cm.
Vols. 1-   bound with v. 4-   of the main work.
                                 D1050.N3 4.-5. Jahrg.
1. Europe—Hist.—1945-   Period.   I. Ehrhardt, Arthur,
1896-   ed.

D1050.N3   58–47531

NN   0030687   DLC MiU

The nation in a dilemma; or, Which shall we alter?
see under   [Capps, Edward] supposed
author.

VOLUME 405

A **nation** in bondage and stupendous issues. **New York,** Latin-American news association ₍1916?₎

14 p. illus. 22½ᶜᵐ.

1. Mexico—Hist.—Revolution, 1910-   ɪ. Latin-American news association.

Library of Congress   F1234.N27   CA 25—271 Unrev'd

NN   0030689   DLC TxU LNHT NN OU

A nation in bondage, and stupendous issues.   New York, [1916]   14 p. illus. 23cm.

Microfiche (neg.)   1 sheet.   11 x 15cm.   (NYPL FSN 12,006)

1. Investments, Foreign--Mexico.   2. Catholic church, Roman--Mexico.   3. Mexico--For. rel. --U.S.   4. United States--For. rel--Mexico, 1910-

NN   0030690   NN

The nation mourns.   New York, Published by Chas. Magnus, 12 Frankfort St. ₍1865₎

Broadside.   21 x 12.5cm.

Five-stanza poem.
Portrait of Lincoln.

1.Lincoln,Abraham-Poetry.2.Poetry.3.Broadsides.

NN   0030691   MiU-C NN

The Nation mourns a martyred Father!   [Assination of Lincoln, Apr., 1865] [Philadelphia] Loag, print. [1865]
1 p.   F°.

NN   0030692   NN

A nation on wheels
see under   McCall's magazine.

308
Z
Box 863

Une nation opprimée.   Genève, Georg, 1895.
32 p.

Bibliographical footnotes.

1. Ukraine - History - Addresses, essays, lectures.   2. Ukraine - Nationality - Addresses, essays, lectures.

NN   0030694   NNC WU InU

Nation pamphlet.
no.

Durban ₍Union of South Africa₎ The Knox pub. co., 1944
nos.   illus.   18 – 21cm.

NN   0030695   NN

The **nation** preserved; or, The plot discovered.   Containing an impartial account of the secret policy of some of the South-Sea directors; with copies of their letters to each other, and the substance of their debates in several of their private conferences: taken before a notary-publick.   Also a letter from one of their agents in France. Addressed to Sir J —— B —— ...   London: Printed for the author, and sold at Mrs. James's; and by the booksellers of London and Westminster, 1720.   1 p.l., 38 p.   8°.

BANCROFT COLLECTION.
Lenox. / 1. South Sea Company.   *Revised*
N. Y. P. L.   *May 25, 1932*

NN   0030696   NN InU MH-BA MiU-C MB CtY PU NNC IU

The nation preserved; or, The plot discover'd, containing an impartial account of the secret policy of some of the South sea directors; with copies of their letters to each other; and the substance of their debates in several of their private conferences taken before a notary-publick, also a letter from one of their agents in France; addressed to Sir J—— B—— ...   Dublin, Reprinted by C. Carter, 1721.
32 p.   16 cm.
First edition 1720.

NN   0030697   MH-BA

La Nation Roumaine.   Paris.
Vol. 2, no. 24; v.5, no.103 (Jul.15, 1949-Dec.15, 1952).   (Incomplete. (Lack: v.2,nos.26-27;v.3,nos.38-40

NN   0030698   NN

---

*EB7
A100
710n2

The nation run mad.
[London,1710?]

broadside.   30.5x18cm.
Satire, in verse, on the Sacheverell trial.

NN   0030699   MH

La Nation serbe en France depuis sa fondation
see under   Brunhes, Jean, 1869-1930.
[Supplement]

La **Nation** sud-africaine, valeurs et idéaux d'une société pluriraciale.   Ouvrage collectif sous la direction de G. H. Galpin.   Monaco, Éditions du Rocher ₍1954₎
219 p.   20 cm.   (Profil des nations)

1. Africa, South—Race question.   ɪ. Galpin, G. H., ed.

DT763.N3   57-27850 ‡

NN   0030701   DLC CSt MB MH NIC NN

La **Nation** tchèque.
Paris, 19

v. 23½ᶜᵐ.   semimonthly.
Editor: Édouard Beneš.

1. Czechs.   2. Slovaks.   ɪ. Beneš, Edvard, ed.

Library of Congress   DB191.N3   CA 20-84 Unrev'd

MdBE CU OCU OU MiU OrU MB NjP
NN   0030702   DLC CaBVaU CSt-H CoCA NcU CaBVaU NN

A **nation,** to become rich and prosperous, must, through its legislation, protect its producing and laboring classes: capital, the product of those classes, will protect itself Reasons for taxing all high wines and alcohol, sold after date, instead of all made after date ...   Respectfully submitted to the members of the Senate and House of representatives of the United States.   Chicago, Beach & Barnard, printers, 1864.

6 l.   32ᶜᵐ.

1. Liquor traffic—U. S.—Taxation.

                                          CA 9-4665 Unrev'd

Library of Congress   HD9350.8.U5N2

NN   0030703   DLC

Nation und nationalität.   Beiträge von F. Hertz—Wien, S. R. Steinmetz—Amsterdam, M. H. Boehm—Berlin, G. Roffenstein — Wien, E. v. Karman — Budapest.   Karlsruhe, G. Braun, 1927.
x p., 1 l., 217 p.   23 cm.   (*Added t.-p.:* Jahrbuch für soziologie, hrsg. von prof. Gottfried Salomon.   1. ergänzungsb.)
Contains bibliographies.
CONTENTS.—Vorwort des herausgebers.—Wesen und werden der nation, von Friedrich Hertz.—Die nationalität und ihr wille, von S. R. Steinmetz.—Die nationalitätenfrage, von M. H. Boehm.—Zur soziologie des nationalismus, von Gaston Roffenstein.—Psychologie des internationalismus, von Elemér v. Kármán.
1. Nationalism and nationality.   2. International cooperation.   ɪ. Hertz, Friedrich Otto, 1878-

JC311.N28   L 27-402

U. S. Dept. of Labor.   Library
for Library of Congress   ₍a50c₎†

NN   0030704   DL ICJ CU DLC NcD

Nation und staat; deutsche zeitschrift für das europäische minoritätenproblem ... 1.-   jahrg.; sept. 1927-
Wien, W. Braumüller ₍1927₎
v.   ports.   24½ᶜᵐ.   monthly.
Editors: Sept. 1927-Mar. 1933, Jacob Bleyer, Rudolf Brandsch, Paul Schiemann, Johannes Schmidt-Wodder.—Apr. 1933—"Herausgegeben für den Verband der deutschen volksgruppen in Europa von Ferdinand von Uexküll."
Includes section "Literaturberichte".
1. Europe—Politics—1914-   2. Minorities.   3. Nationalism and nationality.   4. Europe—Politics—Period.   ɪ. Bleyer, Jakab, 1874-1933, ed.   ɪɪ. Brandsch, Rudolf, 1880-   ed.   ɪɪɪ. Schiemann, Paul, 1878-   ed.   ɪv. Schmidt-Wodder, Johannes, ed.   v. Uexküll-Güldenband, Ferdinand, baron von, ed.   vɪ. Verband der deutschen volksgruppen in Europa.

Library of Congress   D410.N3   36-12882

                           ₍3₎   053

OCl
NN   0030705   DLC TxHR NBuU NcD NN NBuG IEN DS ICJ

The **nation** vindicated, from the aspersions cast on it ...
see under   [Tindal, Matthew] 1653?-1733.

Die **nation** vor Gott; zur botschaft der Kirche im dritten reich
see under   Künneth, Walter, 1901-   ed.

Nation-wide
see   Nationwide.

The **Nation** year book.   1942-
New York, N. Y., The Nation, inc. ₍1942-
v.   illus.   19½ᶜᵐ.

ɪ. The Nation, New York.

                                                        43-1951

Library of Congress   AY21.N3

                           ₍5₎   051

NN   0030709   DLC NcRS KyU NNC

Nationaal arbeids- secretariaat in Nederland. Correspondentieblad...
see   Correspondentieblad van het **Nationaal** arbeid-secretariaat.

VOLUME 405

Nationaal arbeids-secretariaat in Nederland
Verslag van het Nationl arbeids-secretarist
in Nederland (N.A.D.); 1925/28
1 v.   21 cm

NN   0030711   DL

Een nationaal belang
    see under   Onderwijzersvereeniging,
Leeuwarden.

Nationaal bureau van vrouwenarbeid.   396.5 P903
    Beroepsklapper, excerpt uit de "Uitkomsten der beroepstelling,
in het koninkrijk der Nederlanden op den een-en-dertigsten December 1889," aangevende het aantal gehuwde en ongehuwde
vrouwen (benevens het algemeen totaal) werkzaam als hoofd
of ondergeschikte in eenig beroep of bedrijf, met inleidend woord
en eenige supplementen, door Marie Jungius. [Amsterdam,
H. J. Poutsma, 1899.]
    59, [1] p. 1 fold. map. 21½ᶜᵐ.
——— Uit de "Uitkomst ... December 1899," ... met
inleidend woord en naschrift. .... [Amsterdam, pref. 1903.]
    76 p. 20ᶜᵐ.
    Preface signed: Marie Jungius.
    "No. 2 van de reeks 'Goedkoope uitgaven' van het Nationaal bureau van vrou-
wenarbeid."

NN   0030713   ICJ

H62
.T5
    Nationaal Bureau voor Onderwijs op Economische
        Grondslag.
    Tijdschrift voor het economisch onderwijs.

    Groningen, J. B. Wolters.

Nationaal Centrum Vorming Bedrijfsjeugd.
    Karakter; handleiding voor het vormingswerk onder wer-
kende meisjes. Rotterdam, 1953.
    108 p. illus. 16 x 25 cm.
    Bibliography: p. 106.

    1. Young women—Charities, protection, etc.

    HV1441.N4N3   60-18321

NN   0030715   DLC

Nationaal comité ter herdenking van Betje Wolff
    en Aagje Deken.
    Boeket voor Betje en Aagje

    see under

Wolff, Elizabeth (Bekker) 1738-1804.

JX
4150
N21
    Nationaal Comité van Actie tegen het Verdrag
        met België.
    Het gewijzigde verdrag met België; is aan-
vaarding thans mogelijk? ['s-Gravenhage,
Martinus Nijhoff, 1926]
    xi, 44 p.

NN   0030717   NNC-L CU

Nationaal Comité van Actie tot Wijziging van het
    Verdrag met België.
    Kantteekeningen op het verdrag met België
    see under Fokker, E

JX
4150
N21
    Nationaal Comité van Actie tot Wijziging van
        het Verdrag met België.
    Het Verdrag met België in strijd met 'slands
belang. ['s-Gravenhage, Martinus Nijhoff,
192-?]
    38 p. fold. map.

    Bound with: Nationaal Comité van Actie tegen
het Verdrag met België. Het gewijzigde verdrag
met België; is aanvaarding thans mogelijk?
[1926]

NN   0030719   NNC-L

Nationaal Comité Viering Bevrijdingsdag
    5 Mei 1955.
    10 jaar vrede; nationaal gedenkboek
        see under   Veer, Paul van't.

                                            Neth 4290.90F
Nationaal Comité voor Arbeid aan Werklooze Intel-
lectueelen, 's-Gravenhage.
    Winterboek 1934-1935. Haarlem, Drukkerij De
Spaarnestad [1934]

    104 p. illus. (part col.)

NN   0030721   MH

Nationaal Comité voor Brouwgerst.
    Jaarboekje.
    [Rotterdam?]
        v. 21 cm.

    1. Barley.   2. Brewing—Societies.

    TP570.A1N3   53-32793 ‡

NN   0030722   DLC DNAL

663.3   Nationaal Comité voor Brouwgerst
N21m
    Mededeelingen. no.1-
    Wageningen, Holland, 1936-
        v. illus., diagrs. (part fold.) 25cm.
                        (Nationaal Instituut voor Brouwgerst)
    Vols. no.1-18 issued by the institute, under
its earlier name: Nationaal Comité voor
Brouwgerst.

NN   0030723   IU

Nationaal Comité voor Brouwgerst.
    25 [i. e. Vijf en twintig] jaar brouwgerstverbouw in
Nederland, door J. A. Emmens [et al. Rotterdam, 1953]
    36 p. illus. 21 cm. (Its Mededeelingen, 1953-19)

    1. Barley.   I. Emmens, J. A.

    SB191.B2N3   59-54674 rev ‡

NN   0030724   DLC RU

Nationaal comité voor de Willibrord herdenking.
    Willibrord-herdenking, 739-1939. Catalogue
van de St. Willibrordtentoonstelling. [Utrecht?
1939?]
    54, 27 p. plates.

NN   0030725   MH

Fine Arts
N
5964   Nationaal Comité voor de Willibrord-Herden-
.N4   king.
U92   Willibrord-Herdenking, 739-1939: catalogus
N28   van de tentoonstelling van vroeg-middeleeuws-
che Kunst. [Utrecht, 1939]
    73 p. illus.

    1.Art, Medieval--Exhibitions.

NN   0030726   MiU MH

Nationaal comité voor de Willibrord herdenking,
    Catalogus van de tentoonstelling van vroeg-
middeleeuwsche kunst
        see its   Willibrord-herdenking, 739-1939.

Nationaal Comité voor Geografie (*Belgium*)
    see
Comité national de géographie (*Belgium*)

E39.811
N277g   Nationaal Comité voor Hulp aan Nederland.
    Gedichten uit de bezette Nederlanden.
    Voorwoord van B. Ph. van Harrinxma thoe
    Slooten. Inleiding van J. B. Braaksma.
    Brussel, A. Manteau, 1945.
    55p. facsim. 26cm.

    1. Dutch poetry, 20th cent. I. Title.

NN   0030728   IEN

Nationaal Comité voor vervroegde Winkelsluiting, The Hague.
    De wettelijke winkelsluiting in Nederland; verslag uit-
gebracht door het "Nationaal Comite voor vervroegde Winkelsluiting," 21 november 1908-1 januari 1918. 's-Gravenhage,
1918. 74 p. incl. tables. 8°.

    1. Stores, Netherlands, 1908-18.
    N. Y. P. L.   November 6, 1922.

NN   0030729   NN

NATIONAAL COMITÉ VOOR VERVROEGDE WINKEL-
    SLUITING, The Hague.
    De wettelijke winkelsluiting in Nederland; verslag,
21 november 1908-1 januari 1918. 's-Gravenhage,
1918. 74 p. tables. 24cm.

    Film reproduction. Negative.
    Bibliography, p. 73-74.

    1. Retail trade--Jurisp.--   Netherlands.

NN   0030730   NN

Nationaal-congres der kleine burgerij
    see   Congrès national de la petite bour-
geoisie.

Nationaal congres tegen de prostitutie,   L176.06903 O900
                                            Amsterdam, 1889.
    Handelingen van het Nationaal congres tegen de prostitutie te
Amsterdam, in het gebouw "Frascati", Dinsdag 30 April 1889 en
drie volgende dagen, belegd door de Nederlandsche vereeniging
tegen de prostitutie, met medewerking van den Nederlandschen
vrouwenbond tot verhooging van het zedelijk bewustzijn. 'sGravenhage, W. A. Beschoor, 1889.
    [4], 201, [7] p. 27ᶜᵐ.

NN   0030732   ICJ CU

VOLUME 405

W 3
NA257
1947
NATIONAAL Congres voor de Geestelijke
Volksgezondheid, Amsterdam, 1947
₍Handelingen₎ Zwolle, Tijl ₍1947₎
133 p.
1. Mental hygiene - Congresses

NN 0030733 DNLM

Nationaal Congres voor Vakonderwijs, The Hague, 1919.
... Rapporten en handelingen. Bundel 1–3. ₍'s Gravenhage,
1919.₎ 3 parts in 1 v. tables. 8°.

1. Education (Professional).—Con-   gresses, 1919.
N. Y. P. L.   April 19, 1922.

NN 0030734 NN

Nationaal en internationaal Kongres van den
stedelijken en landelijken middenstand
see   Congrès national et international
des classes moyennes urbaines et rurales.

D731
.N27
Nationaal Front.

Nederlandsch dagblad. 1.–   jaarg.; 8 Juli **1940–**
s' Gravenhage, Uitgeverij "De Veste."

AP15
.W42
Nationaal Front.

De Weg; weekblad van Nationaal Front. 1.–2. jaarg., nr. 15;
27 Apr. 1940–9 Aug. 1941. 's Gravenhage.

Nationaal Indische Partij.
Ons standpunt
see under Douwes Dekker, Ernst François
Eugène, 1879–1952.

Nationaal Instituut. Departement voor
Volkvoorlichting.
Waarom? waartoe? hoe? Amsterdam. Het
Nationaal Instituut ₍1944₎

NN 0030739 NN MiU

Nationaal Instituut Steun Wettig Gezag.
Handboek veer het Nationaal instituut Steun Wettig
Gezag. Vuga-boekerij. ₍Arnhem, G. W. van der Wiel. 1955–

1 v. (loose-leaf) 22 cm.
Includes legislation.

1. Police—Netherlands. I. Netherlands (Kingdom, 1815–   )
Laws, statutes, etc.
57–40731

NN 0030740 DLC

Nationaal Instituut voor Brouwgerst, Mout en
Bier, T. N. O.
see Nationaal Comité voor Brouwgerst.
in earlier name

Nationaal Instituut voor de Lanbouwstudie in Belgisch-
Congo
see
Institut national pour l'étude agronomique du Congo.

Nationaal instituut voor de steenkolennijverheid
see Berlin. Institut national de l'industrie
charbonnière, Liege.

Nationaal Instituut voor Landbouwkrediet
see Belgium. *Institut national de crédit agricole.*

Nationaal Jongeren Verbond.
Roseboek van de muiterij [aan boord van
Hr. Ms. "De Zeven Provinciën", Feb., 1933]
Samengesteld uit de bladen der N. v. de
Arbeiderspers door den persdienst van het
Nationaal Jongeren Verbond. Den Haag, N.v.
Haagsche drukkerij en uitgeversmaatschappij,
1934.
83 p. illus. 24 cm.
1. Sociaal Democratische Arbeiders Partij.
2. Mutiny – Netherlands.

NN 0030744 CSt-H WaU

Nationaal Komiteit voor Hulp en Voeding
see
Comité national de secours et d'alimentation,
Brussels.

Nationaal Luchtvaartlaboratorium, Amsterdam
see Netherlands (Kingdom, 1815–
Nationaal Lucht- en Ruimtevaartlaboratorium.

Nationaal Lucht- en Ruimtevaartlaboratorium
see
Netherlands (*Kingdom, 1815–*   ) *Nationaal Lucht- en*
Ruimtevaartlaboratorium.

Nationaal Luchtvaartgeneeskundig Centrum, *Soesterberg*
see
Soesterberg, Netherlands. Nationaal Luchtvaartgeneeskundig Centrum.

Nationaal Maria Congres, *Brussels, 1954.*
National Maria Congres, Brussel 2-3-4-5 September
1954. ₍Brussel, 1955₎
161 p. illus., ports. 22 cm.

1. Mary, Virgin—Congresses.

BT595.N3 1954   58–21613

NN 0030749 DLC

Nationaal Nieuw-Guinee Comité, Stichting
see
Stichting "Het Nationaal Nieuw-Guinee Comité."

Wason
L597
A2N27
1935
Nationaal Onderwijs Congres, Soerakarta,
1935.
Verslag Nationaal Onderwijs Congres di
Soerakarta, pada tanggal 8 t/m 10 Juni 1935.
Jang menghimpoen commissie verslaggever.
₍Soerakarta, 1935₎
104 p. 25cm.

Signed: Soetedjo.

NN 0030751 NIC

W1
NA218B
Nationaal Protestants Centrum voor de Geestelijke
Gezondheidszorg in Nederland.
Publicatie. [Den Haag]
v.
1. Psychology, Pastoral - period.

NN 0030752 DNLM

Nationaal Schaakgebouw, The Hague.
Bibliotheek der vereeniging Het Nationaal
Schaakgebouw, catalogus. [The Hague, 1948]
18 p.
Reproduced from typewritten copy.

NN 0030753 OCl

Nationaal-socialistisch jaarboek
see Nationaal-socialistische almanak.

Nationaal socialistisch studentenfront.
Almanak.

Leiden ₍19

v. illus., plates, ports. 23ᵐ.

1. World war, 1939–1945—Netherlands.
46–42550
Library of Congress   D810.E5N45

NN 0030755 DLC

Nationaal-socialistische almanak. 1942–

Utrecht ₍1941–

v. illus. (incl. ports.) diagrs. 16½ᵐ.
"Uitgegeven in opdracht van den organisatieleider door den Materiaaldienst der N. S. B."
Title varies: 1942, Nationaal-socialistisch jaarboek.
1943– Nationaal-socialistische almanak.

1. Netherlands—Hist.—German occupation, 1940–1945. I. Nationaal-
socialistische beweging der Nederlanden.
44–26208 Revised
Library of Congress   DJ287.N3
₍r46d2₎   949.2

NN 0030756 DLC NN CU MiU MH

Nationaal-socialistische beweging der Nederlanden.
Almanak ... van het Nationaal socialistisch
studentenfront
see under Nationaal socialistisch studentenfront.

Nationaal-socialistische beweging der Nederlanden.
Antwoord van het Nederlandsch nationaal-
socialisme (fascisme) op een tiental nederlandsche
vragen. [Utrecht]
30 p. (Its Brochure IV)

NN 0030758 DLC

VOLUME 405

Nationaal-sozialistische beweging der Nederlanden.
Bouw mee! Uitgave van De Afdeeling propaganda der N.S.B. [194?]
16 p. *20cm.*
Corn. title.

NN　0030759　DLC MH

Nationaal-Socialistische Beweging der Nederlanden.

JN5985
N3A44
ed.2　Dit moet gij weten over de Nationaal-Socialistische Beweging der Nederlanden. Een practische uiteenzetting voor hen die toetreden tot de Beweging. In opdracht van den Organisatieleider der N.S.B. uitgegeven door den
Hoover
Library　Materiaaldienst. Tekst van Jan de Haas.
[Amsterdam, 1943]
63 p. illus., ports., diagr. 21cm.
"Tweede, geheel herziene druk van het boekje 'Wat was en is, wat deed en doet de N.S.B.'"
1. Nationaal-Socialistische Beweging der Nederlanden. I. Haas, Jan de. II. Title.

NN　0030760　CSt-H

Nationaal socialistische beweging der Nederlanden.
Erfelijkheidsleer. [Utrecht, 193- ?]

15 p. diagrs. 23 cm.
Cover-title.

NN　0030761　MH DLC

Nationaal sozialistische beweging der Nederlanden.
De geheime geldbronnen der N.S.B.; opzienbarende onthullingen. Een "Insider" aan het woord. Zal de regerring ingrijpen? [Utrecht? 193- ?]

Cover-title.
Signed at end; De leider van het strijd- en verkiezingsfonds, en lid der financielle commissie der N.S.B.

NN　0030762　MH

Wason
DS643
N27　Nationaal-Socialistische Beweging der Nederlanden.
Gezagsondermijning in Indië; het wanbeleid van drie Gouverneurs-Generaal. [Met een voorwoord van Mussert] Utrecht, N.E.N.A.S.U.
[1935]
61 p. 21cm.

1. Indonesia--Hist.--1798-1942. 2. Indonesia--Pol. & govt.--1798-1942. I. Title.

NN　0030763　NIC

Nationaal-socialistische beweging in Nederland.
De hagespraak; geïllustreerd gedenkboek ter herinnering aan de eerste Nationale hagespraak der N. S. B., gehouden te Lunteren op 1 Juni 1936. Kortenhoef, Hobera, 1936. 30 p. illus. 25cm.

"'Bergopwaarts,' rede van Ir. A. A. Mussert," p. 15-30.

1. Fascism--Netherlands.
N.Y.P.L.
I. Mussert, Anton Adriaan, 1894-1946.
August 15, 1950

NN　0030764　NN CtY DLC-P4

Vk13
1　Nationaal-socialistische beweging der Nederlanden.
Hou zee! liederen voor de N.S.B. ... 5e druk ...
Utrecht[194-?]
Pamphlet
With the melodies unaccompanied.

NN　0030765　CtY

Nationaal-Socialistische Beweging der Nederlanden.
Instructie voor het werk in de groep. [Utrecht, voorwoord 1941]
108 p. forms. 21 cm.

1. Fascism--Netherlands.

JN5985.A3A3　　　49-36784 rev†

NN　0030766　DLC

Nationaal socialistische beweging der Nederlanden
Jeugdstorm zakboek
see under　Nationaal-socialistische
Beweging der Nederlanden. Nationale jeugdstorm.

Nationaal-Socialistische Beweging der Nederlanden.
Kaderblad. 1.- jaarg.; 1942-
see under title

4DJ
91　Nationaal-Socialistische Beweging der Nederlanden.
Het landdag gedenkboek, ter herinnering aan den 3den Algemeenen Landdag der N. S. B., gehouden te Amsterdam op 30 Maart 1935. Amsterdam, Grafische Kunstinrichting "Hobera" [1935]
60 p.

NN　0030769　DLC-P4 CSt-H

Nationaal socialistische beweging in Nederland.
Mag een Katholiek lid zijn van de N.S.B. Ja. [Utrecht] 1941.

23 p. 10 x 20 cm.

NN　0030770　MH

DJ287
.N3　Nationaal-socialistische beweging der Nederlanden.
Nationaal-socialistische almanak. 1942-

Utrecht [1941-

DJ
287
N3　Nationaal-Socialistische Beweging der Nederlanden
Nationaal-socialistische (fascistische) staatsleer. Utrecht, 1933.
28p. 23cm. (Nationaal-socialistische beweging in Nederland, no. 3)

1. National socialism 2. Fascism - Netherlands 3. Netherlands - Pol. & govt. - 1898-1945 I. Title

NN　0030772　WU

AP15
.N574　Nationaal-Socialistische Bewegung der Nederlanden.
Nieuw Nederland; maandblad voor economie, staatkunde en cultuur. 1.- jaarg.; Juni 1934-
Utrecht, Nederlandsche Nationaal-Socialistische Uitgeverij.

4DJ
68　Nationaal-Socialistische Beweging der Nederlanden.
Programma. Utrecht, Hoofdkwartier [1932]
48 p.

NN　0030774　DLC-P4

NATIONAAL-SOCIALISTISCHE BEWEGING der NEDERLANDEN
Programma met toelichting. Utrecht [1932]
48 p. 23cm.

Film reproduction. Negative.
Cover title.

1. Fascism--Netherlands.

NN　0030775　NN

JN
5985
N3
A3　Nationaal-Socialistische Beweging der Nederlanden
Programma met toelichting. Utrecht [1932]
7, 51p. 23cm.
Cover title.

1. Fascism - Netherlands I. Title

NN　0030776　WU MH

Nationaal-socialistische beweging der Nederlanden.
... Staatkundige richtlijnen der Nationaal-socialistische beweging in Nederland. 10.-20. duizend. [Utrecht, 1936]
43 p. (Its Brochure V)

NN　0030777　DLC

Nationaal-socialistische beweging der Nederlanden.
Het tuchtrecht der beweging. [Utrecht, 1943]
28 p. 23½cm.
On cover: NSB.

I. Title.

DJ287.N33　　　47-34412

NN　0030778　DLC NN

308
Z
Box 845　Nationaal-Socialistische Beweging der Nederlanden.
Die Vereinigten Staaten von Guyana, das jüdische nationalheim; plan Mussert. [n. p., 1939]
23 p. ports., maps.

Includes excerpts from speeches of A. A. Mussert, leader of the National socialist movement in the Netherlands.
Published also in Dutch.

NN　0030779　NNC

Nationaal-Socialistische Beweging der Nederlanden.
Voordrachten gehouden binnen het kader van den burgemeesterscursus der N. S. B. te 's-Gravenhage in de Opleidingsweek 21-26 Juli 1941. 's-Gravenhage, Roepers' Drukkerij, 1941.
351 p. 24 cm.

1. Municipal government—Netherlands. 2. Mayors—Netherlands.

JS5938.N3　　　58-54411

NN　0030780　DLC

Nationaal-socialistische beweging der Nederlanden
... Voorschrift voor de vorming. (Alle vroegere voorschriften zijn hiermede vervallen)...
['sGravenhage?] 1941.
16 p. 20.5 cm.
In lower left corner of t.-p.: Bo-1 16-10.
1. Nationaal-socialistische beweging der Nederlanden. Afdeeling 10, Vorming.

NN　0030781　CSt-H

VOLUME 405

Nationaal-socialistische beweging der Nederlanden
Vormingslessen voor nieuwe leden. ₁n. p.₎ Afdeeling vorming
van de Nationaal socialistische beweging in Nederland ₁1941?₎
36 p.   port.   23cm.

Cover title.

1. Fascism—Netherlands

NN   0030782   NN DLC MH

Nationaal-Socialistische Beweging der Nederlanden.
Wat was en is wat deed en doet de N. S. B.? Een uiteenzetting voor de nieuwe leden der beweging van den aard en
het karakter van onzen strijd voor volk en vaderland.
₁Utrecht₎ Uitg. in opdracht van het Hoofdkwartier der N.
S. B. ₁1941₎
56 p.   illus.   21 cm.

I. Title.

DJ287.N34   54-52644 ‡

NN   0030783   DLC CU CSt-H MH

NATIONAAL-SOCIALISTISCHE BEWEGING DER NEDER-
LANDEN.
Wat was en is wat deed en doet de N.S.B.? Een
uiteenzetting voor de nieuwe leden der beweging van
den aard en het karakter van onzen strijd voor volk en
vaderland. [Utrecht] Uitg. in opdracht van het Hoofdkwartier der N.S.B. [1941] 56 p. illus. 21cm.

Film reproduction. Negative.

1. Fascism--Netherlands.

NN   0030784   NN

Vki3   Nationaal-socialistische beweging der Neder-
1   landen. Zomer-zangfeesten der N.S.B. [Den Haag,
         194-?]
         Pamphlet
         Cover-title.
         Twenty songs, with the melodies, unaccompanied.

NN   0030785   CtY

Nationaal-Socialistische Beweging der Nederlanden.
Zoo zingt de NSB; 20 marsch- en strijdliederen. 4. druk.
₁n. p., 194-₎
38 p.   24 cm.
For piano, with superlinear words.

1. Nationaal-Socialistische Beweging der Nederlanden—Songs and
music.   I. Title.
M1752.N3Z6   M 55-591

NN   0030786   DLC CtY

---

tD802   Nationaal-socialistische Beweging der Neder-
N4N3   landen. Nationale jeugdstorm.
         Jeugdstorm zakboek./ ₁Samengesteld door en
         verantwoordelijk voor den inhoud: Hopman F.
         Barkhuis en Oppervaandrig Jan Schuurman.
         Utrecht, Nederlandsche Nationaal-Socialistische
         Uitgeverij, 1944₎
         191 p.   illus.,ports. 14cm

NN   0030787   CU MH ICRL

Nationaal-Socialistische Beweging der Nederlanden.
Weerafdeling.
De Zwarte soldaat
see under title

Nationaal Socialistische Beweging in Nederland
see   Nationaal Socialistische Beweging der
Nederlanden.

JN5985   **Nationaal Socialistische Nederlandsche Arbeiders**
.N32N5   **Partij.**
          Het **Nieuwe** volk.   -10. jaarg., nr. 39;   -4 Oct.
          1941. ₁Utrecht₎

NN   0030790

JN5985   Nationaal-socialistische Nederlandsche arbei-
N5A33   ders-partij.
          Program der duitsche revolutie voor Neder-
Hoover   land. ₁Utrecht, n.d.₎
Library   20 p.   15^{CM}.

1.Fascism - Netherlands. I.Title.

NN   0030791   CSt-H

Nationaal-Socialistische Vrouwen Organisatie. *Landelijke*
Bibliotheek.
Boekenlijst. ₁Amsterdam, 1942?₎
24 p.   24 cm.

1. Dutch literature — Bibl. — Catalogs.   2. National socialism —
Bibl.—Catalogs.   I. Title.
Z936.N3   59-47643 ‡

NN   0030792   DLC

Nationaal Veiligheidscongres, Amsterdam, 1926.
Verslag der werkzaamheden van het Nationaal Veiligheidscongres, 1926, gehouden in het gebouw "Grand Théatre," Amstel-
straat 21, Amsterdam op 26 en 27 Maart 1926. . .   ₁Amsterdam:₎
Druk de Bussy₁, 1926₎.   294 p. incl. diagrs., tables.   illus.,
pl.   8°.

1. Accidents—Prevention—Congresses.
N. Y. P. L.   September 12, 1927

NN   0030793   NN

Nationaal verband der Christen vakvereenig-
ingen.
(Report of) Congress. 1st-   1912-
Ghent, 1912-
1 v. 24 cm.

NN   0030794   DL

Nationaal Verbond der Plaatselijke en Gewestelijke Gemeenteontvangers van België
see   Nationale Bond der Gemeenteontvangers en der Ont-
vangers van de Commissiën voor Openbaren Onderstand.

Nationaal Vlaamsch studentenverbond.
. . . Aan de Vlaamsche studenten. Rechtskun-
dige raadpleging nopens de Vervlaamsching der
Gentssche hoogeschool.   Gent, Drukkerij Pol
Saelens, 1916.
22 p.

NN   0030796   OClWHi

Nationaal vlaamsch verbond.
. . . Het vlaamsche volk tegen den centraliseerenden en ver-
franschenden belgischen staat. ₁Brussel, Drukk. van het
"Vlaamsch steunkomiteit," 1917₎
1 p. l., ii, 32 p.   24^{cm}.
Bibliographical foot-notes.

1. Flemish movement.   2. Belgium—Pol. & govt.   3. Belgium—Languages.   I. Title.
Library of Congress   DH491.N3   46-28402

NN   0030797   DLC

Nationaal werk voor hulpverleening
see   Œuvre nationale de secours (*Belgium*)

Nationaal werk voor kinderwelzijn
see
Œuvre nationale de l'enfance (*Belgium*)

Nationaal woningcongres, Amsterdam, 1920.
. . .Prae-adviezen voor het woningcongres te houden op
Woensdag 19 en Donderdag 20 Mei 1920. . .te Amsterdam. . .
₁Amsterdam, 1920₎   128 p.   23cm.

Cover-title.

1. Housing for the working class   —Congresses—Netherlands—
Amsterdam, 1920.
N. Y. P. L.   October 10, 1939

NN   0030800   NN

Nationaal Woningcongres, Amsterdam, 1920.
Stenografisch verslag van het Nationaal Woningcongres,
gehouden op 19 en 20 Mei 1920, in het gebouw voor den werken-
den stand. . .   ₁Amsterdam, 1920.₎   152 p.   8°.

1. Habitations—Congresses—Nether-   lands—Amsterdam, 1920.
N. Y. P. L.   October 10, 1927

NN   0030801   NN

Nationaal zeemansfonds.
Scheepsrampen in oorlogstijd.   Amsterdam, J. F. Duwaer en
zonen ₁1947₎   xi, 158 p.   28cm.

"Uitgegeven. . .van het Nationaal zeemansfonds."
"Aanvulling" (p. 159-166) inserted.

458746B. 1. World war, 1939-1945   —Naval history and operations.
2. World war, 1939-1945—Commercial   aspects—Netherlands. 3. Shipping
—Netherlands. I. Title.
N. Y. P. L.   January 31, 1949

NN   0030802   NN

---

*
JN5935   **Nationaale Brieven.** 1. Stukje.   Amsterdam,
.N38   J. Allart, 1785.
1785   xvi, 120 p.   22cm.

1. Netherlands—Nationality.

NN   0030803   ViU

Le NATIONAL, Paris. 1830-
Paris.   v.   illus.

Film reproduction. Positive.
Daily.

I. France--Paris.

NN   0030804   NN NNC CaBVaU MiU

VOLUME 405

Le National, Paris.
Procès du National de 1834
see under title

Le National, *Paris*.
Procès et acquittement du National, poursuivi
pour avoir défendu l'égalité, les droits de l'armée,
la loi contre le privilège et le régime des
ordonnances; contenant l'article incriminé, les
débats, le réquisitoire; la plaidoirie et la réplique
de M⁰ Michel ... Paris, Pagnerre, 1838.
40 p. 21.5 cm.
Bound with: Gisquet, H. J. Procès de M. Gisquet.
1839.

NN 0030806 NNC

The **National**; a journal devoted to the interests of the
members of the National window glass workers of
America. v. 1–
August, 1915–
₍Cleveland, O., 1915–
v. 25¼ᵐᵐ. monthly.
Editor: J. M. Neenan.

1. Trade-unions — U. S.—Period. 2. Glass-workers—Period. I. National window glass workers.

L 16–47
Library, U. S. Bur. of Labor Statistics HD6500.G5N5

NN 0030807 DL WvU

The **National**: a library for the people. Ed. by W. J. Linton.
v. 1₎; Jan. 5–June 29, 1839. London, J. Watson, 1839.
2 p. l., viii, 368 p. plates. 22¼ᵐᵐ. weekly.
No more published.

I. Linton, William James, 1812–1897, ed.

Library of Congress AP4.N17
15–3185

NN 0030808 DLC CoU NcD ICJ NjP

The **NATIONAL**: a library for the people. v. 1;
Jan. 5–June 29, 1839. London, J. Watson, 1839.
2 p.l., viii, 368 p. plates 23cm.

Microfilm.
Weekly.
Edited by W. S. Linton.

1. Periodicals—Gt. Br. I. Linton, William James, 1812–1897, ed.

NN 0030809 NN

The **National**: a library for the people. Ed. by W. J. Linton
v. 1; Jan. 5–June 29, 1839. London, J. Watson, 1839.
2 p. l., viii, 368 p. plates. 22¼ᵐᵐ. weekly.
No more published.
Radical periodicals of Great Britain.
Microfiche.

NN 0030810 WaE1C

The **National**. ₍News of the National blank book and its dis-
tributors₎
v.

₍Holyoke, Mass.₎ 19 v. illus. 28cm.
Bimonthly (irregular; v. 33, no. 4 <Sept. / Oct. 1942> not published).
Title from caption; cover-title: The National.
Published by the National blank book company.

1. Office equipment—Per. and soc. publ.—U. S. I. National blank
book company, Holyoke, Mass.
N. Y. P. L. August 6, 1945

NN 0030811 NN

National Abaca and Other Fibers Corporation.
Report.
₍Manila₎
v. 33 cm. annual.

1. Fibers.

HD9155.P64N33
55–22946 ‡

NN 0030812 DLC

National abstracters directory; abstracters, attorneys, and
title examiners.
Monroe, La., American Abstracters Directory.
v. 23 cm.

1. Title companies—U. S.—Direct.

55–33406

NN 0030813 DLC

National academic cap & gown co., *Philadelphia*.
History of academic caps, gowns and hoods. The Intercollegiate bureau of academic wear. Compiled and edited by
the president of the National academic cap & gown co. ...
Philadelphia, Pa. ₍ᶜ1940₎
63 p. incl. illus., form. 23ᵐᵐ.
"Foreword" signed : E. I. C.

1. Universities and colleges—Costume. 2. Hoods. 3. Degrees, Academic. I. Cohen, E. I. II. Intercollegiate bureau of academic wear.
III. Title.

Library of Congress LB2389.N3
40–13350
———— Copy 2.
Copyright AA 329705 ₍3₎ 378.29

NN 0030814 DLC WaTC DSI PPD LU MB

National Academic Freedom Committee
see American Federation of Teachers. *National Academic Freedom Committee.*

National Academy bulletin
see New York (City) National Academy of
Design. Bulletin.

National academy for adult Jewish studies.
Adult Jewish education in the modern synagogue
see under
Noveck, Simon.

National Academy for Adult Jewish Studies
Adult Jewish education in time of war; the
proceedings of a national conference on adult
Jewish education held Nov. 10, 1942. NY, National
Academy for Adult Jewish Studies, under the
auspices of the Jewish Theological Seminary of
America [1942?]
92 p. (Adult Jewish education series, 2)

NN 0030818 MH

National academy for adult Jewish studies.
Bulletins in adult Jewish education ... no. 1

₍New York? 19 no. 28cm.
No. 1 published under the auspices of the Jewish theological seminary of
America.

1. Education—Jews—U. S. I. Jewish theological seminary
of America. N. Y. P. L. June 22, 1945

NN 0030819 NN

National academy for adult Jewish studies.

BM197
.5
.G6 **Gordis, Robert,** 1908–
Conservative Judaism; an American philosophy, by Rob-
ert Gordis, with a special guide for study and discussion by
Josiah Derby. New York, Pub. for the National academy of
adult Jewish studies of the Jewish theological seminary of
America, Behrman house, 1945.

National academy for adult Jewish studies.

Greenberg, Simon, 1901–
The ideals of the Jewish prayer book, by Simon Greenberg,
PH. D. A publication of the National academy for adult Jewish
studies under the auspices of the Jewish theological seminary of
America. New York, 1942.

National academy for adult Jewish studies.
The laymen's institute; an adventure in Jewish
living

see under

Noveck, Simon.

National Academy for Adult Jewish Studies.
The literature of modern Zionism
see under Cohen, Armond Emanuel,
1909–

National academy for adult Jewish studies.
Maimonides: the man and his ideas

see under

Bokser, Ben Zion, 1907–

National Academy for Adult Jewish Studies.
Six approaches for adult Jewish education in
Conservative synagogues. New York, 1954.
24 p. 28 cm.
Papers prepared for the adult education session
of the Rabbinical Assembly convention, May 18,
1954 ...
1. Education. Adult. I. Title.

NN 0030825 OCH

National Academy for Adult Jewish Studies.
Suggested courses for adult Jewish study.
New York, N. Y., 1954.
193 p. 28 cm.
------- Supplement 1955-56. New York, 1955.
20 l. 28 cm.

NN 0030826 OCH ScU NN MB

National academy for adult Jewish studies.

BM502
.S5
1940z **Talmud.** *English. Selections.*
The Talmud for every Jew; readings in the Talmud, with
a brief commentary by Rabbi Ralph Simon ... New York
city, The National academy for adult Jewish studies under
the auspices of the Jewish theological seminary of America
₍194–?₎

National Academy for public purchasing.
₍Proceedings₎ First session– 1948–
₍Washington, 1948–

NN 0030828 NcU

VOLUME 405

National academy notes
    see under New York (City) National academy
of design.

National Academy notes and complete catalogue
    see New York (City) National Academy of
Design. National Academy notes.

National Academy of Administration, *Mussoorie, India*
  see
  Mussoorie, India. National Academy of Administration.

National Academy of Arbitrators.
  Arbitration today
  see its
  Proceedings of the annual meeting.

National academy of arbitrators.
  Code of ethics and procedural standards
    see under American arbitration association.

National Academy of Arbitrators.
  Proceedings of the annual meeting. 1st–7th—
1948–54—
Washington, B₍u₎reau of N₍a₎tional A₍f₎fairs,
    v. 24 cm.
  Title varies: 1948–54, Selected papers from the first seven annual
meetings.
  Each vol. has also a distinctive title: 1948–54, The profession of
labor arbitration.—1955, Arbitration today.—1956, Management rights
and the arbitration process.—1957, Critical issues in labor arbitration.
  Editor: 1948–54—   J. T. McKelvey.
  1. Arbitration, Industrial—Societies, etc.   I. McKelvey, Jean
Trepp, ed. II. Title: The profession of labor arbitration. III. Title:
Arbitration today. IV. Title: Management rights and the arbitration
process. v. Title: Critical issues in labor arbitration.

HD5481.N32   55—57413
        *331.899062 331.15406273

OrU MB NBuC   NjR IdU-L ViU MiU WaU-L CaBVaU MtU
ODW TU NcU IU DI OU TxU Wa KU-L WaBeN NNC MiD CU
NN 0030834   DLC DAU OU TxU KyU MBU GU LU NBuT NbU

National Academy of Arbitrators.
  Selected papers from the first seven annual meetings
  see its
  Proceedings of the annual meeting.

NATIONAL ACADEMY OF ARBITRATORS.
  [Statements of qualifications of applicants for
membership] November 29,1948. [Philadelphia,1948].
9 leaves.
Processed; caption title.
By the Membership committee.

1. Arbitration

NN 0030836   MH-IR

National Academy of Arbitrators. Committee on
  Research and Education.
    Report to the National Academy of Arbitrators,
January 14, 1949. [1949]
    8, 5 l.
    "Appendix: Labor arbitration studies, recently
completed or in progress, January, 1949": 5 leaves
at end.
    1. Arbitration, Industrial. U.S.
    2. Arbitration, Industrial. U.S. Bibliography.

NN 0030837   NNC

National academy of art.

American federation of arts.
  Proceedings of the convention at which the American federation of arts was formed; held at Washington, D. C., May 11th,
12th and 13th, 1909. Washington, D. C., Press of B. S. Adams,
1909.

National Academy of Art (*India*)
  see
  Lalit Kala Akademi.

National academy of commercial art, *Chicago.*
  ... Basic principles of free hand drawing ...
Chicago, Ill., National academy of commercial art, ʻ1922–
    v. illus., plates. 19½ x 27½ᶜᵐ.
  Plates (20½ x 28ᶜᵐ) laid in.
  Section two has title: Artistic and commercial composition.

  1. Drawing—Instruction. 2. Advertising. I. Title.

Library of Congress   NC997.N3   23–15588

NN 0030840   DLC

National Academy of Design, New York
    see New York (City) National Academy of
Design.

National Academy of Economics and Political
  Science.
  Special publications series.
  no. 1–
  Washington, D. C. ʻ1932–
    v. 26cm. irregular.
  Ceased publication with no. 15 (1958).

NN 0030842   NNC MH

National Academy of Engineering. *National Research
Council*
  see
  National Research Council.

National Academy of Letters, *Delhi*
  see
  Sāhitya Akademi.

National Academy of Music, New York.
  Critical and biographical sketches Prepared by
the editorial staff of the National academy of
music ...
    see under title

National academy of music, New York.
A Melhor musica do mundo; bibliotheca universal didactica
para piano, preparada pela a junta editorial da Academia
nacional de musica, especialmente para os estados unidos do
Brazil. Chefes da junta: Louis C. Elson, Maurice Dumes-
nil, Rudolph Ganz ... ₍e outros₎ A presente edição foi preparada sob a orientação artistica do illustre compositor, Oscar Lorenzo Fernández ... New York, The University society inc.; Rio de Janeiro, J. Bernades ₍ᶜ1929₎

National academy of music, New York.

The University course of music study, piano series; a standardized text-work on music for conservatories, colleges, private teachers and schools; a scientific basis for the granting
of school credit for music study ... prepared by the editorial
staff of the National academy of music; editors and associate
editors: Rudolph Ganz, Edwin Hughes, Charles Dennée ...
₍and others₎ New York, The University society, incorporated ₍ᶜ1920–

National academy of music, *New York.*
  The violinist's dictionary, prepared by the Editorial department of the National academy of music; Nicholas Devore,
editor in chief. New York, The University society, incorporated ₍ᶜ1926₎
    194 p. 17½ᶜᵐ.

  1. Music—Dictionaries. 2. Violin. I. De Vore, Nicholas, 1882– ed.
II. Title.
                           26—15198
Library of Congress   ML102.V4N2

NN 0030848   DLC OC1

National Academy of Music, New York. Extension Department.   4045–475
  How to build up a class.
  New York. [1920.] 24 pp. 20.5 cm.
  Relates to teaching music privately.
  The title is on the cover.

E617 — T.r. — Music. Economic aspects.

NN 0030849   MB

National Academy of Music, New York. Extension Department.
  School credit for outside music study ...
  New York. [1920.] 31 pp. [National Academy of Music, Educa-
tional Department, New York. Bulletin E14.] 19.5 cm.

E662 — T.r. — S.r. — Music in the public schools.

NN 0030850   MB

National Academy of Music, New York. Extension Department.
  ...School credit for outside music study; a comprehensive
syllabus outlining requirements for a course in piano playing, as a
basis for school credit for music study. New York₍, cop. 1924₎.
36 p. 19½cm. (Its: Bulletin E16.)

1. Music—Instruction and study.   2. School music—U. S.
N. Y. P. L.   June 27, 1933

NN 0030851   NN DHEW

National Academy of Music, New York. Extension Department.
  ...School credit for outside music study; a plan for its organization and administration. New York₍, cop. 1923₎. 31 p.
incl. forms. 19½cm. (Its: Bulletin E 15.)

1. Music—Instruction and study.   2. School music—U. S.
N. Y. P. L.   July 5, 1933

NN 0030852   NN DHEW

National Academy of Natural, Anatomical and Pathological Science
    see New York (City) Grand Anatomical Museum.

National Academy of Peiping
  see
  Pei-p'ing yen chiu yüan.

VOLUME 405

National academy of photography.

John, Robert.
Giving photography a new meaning; prepared by Robert John, for the National academy of photography; an outline of a simple, unified process of natural color photography ... ₍New York, E. E. Vreeland, printer, '1915₎

WM
61
qN277
NATIONAL Academy of Religion and Mental Health
₍Collection of publications₎
The Library has a collection of miscellaneous publications of this organization kept as received. These publications are not listed or bound separately.
1. Medicine & religion

NN   0030856   DNLM

National Academy of Sciences, Allahabad
see
National Academy of Sciences (India)

National academy of sciences, *Washington, D. C*
Annual of the National academy of sciences for 1863/64–1866. Cambridge ₍Mass.₎ Welch, Bigelow, and company, 1865–67.
3 v. 19ᶜᵐ.
No more published.

Library of Congress   Q11.N27   15-10606 Revised

PPAN OO OC1W OU MiU MtU
NN   0030858   DLC Wa ICJ DI-GS Nh NcD MeB NcD-MC IU

National Academy of Sciences, Washington, D. C.
Applied research in the United States
see under Scott, Eugene, W., ed.

National academy of sciences, Washington, D.C.
Mayer, Alfred Goldsborough, 1868–1922.
... Biographical memoir of Alfred Marshall Mayer, 1836–1897, by Alfred G. Mayer and Robert S. Woodward. Presented to the academy at the autumn meeting, 1915. Washington, National academy of sciences, 1916.

National academy of sciences, Washington, D. C.
Hall, Edwin Herbert, 1855–
... Biographical memoir of Benjamin Osgood Peirce, 1854–1914, by Edwin H. Hall. Presented to the Academy at the annual meeting, 1918. Washington, National academy of sciences, 1919.

National academy of sciences, Washington, D.C.
Mitchell, Silas Weir, 1829–1914.
... Biographical memoir of John Shaw Billings, 1838–1913, by S. Weir Mitchell; with The scientific work of John Shaw Billings by Fielding H. Garrison. Presented to the academy at the annual meeting, 1916. Washington, National academy of sciences, 1917.

National academy of sciences, *Washington, D. C.*
... Biographical memoirs. v. 1–
Washington, 1877–19
v.   ports.   24ᶜᵐ

1. Scientists, American.
5–26629
Library of Congress   Q141.N2

KEmT CLU MeB MShM
MdBP MsU PPiU TxDaM ScC1eU KyU FU GEU CSt MBdAF
MtU NcD NBuC UU TxLT PBL MMeT IaGG FTaSU CtN1C
MiU OU NBuU OC1 OCU ICJ MH NjP PBa IU WvU ICU
NN   0030863   DLC C OrU-M CaBVa   CU NcU NIC DNLM

National Academy of Sciences, *Washington, D. C.*
The chemistry of penicillin; report on a collaborative investigation by American and British chemists under the joint sponsorship of the Office of Scientific Research and Development, Washington, D. C., and the Medical Research Council, London. Comp. under the auspices of the National Academy of Sciences, Washington, D. C., pursuant to a contract with the Office of Scientific Research and Development. Editorial Board: Hans T. Clarke, John R. Johnson ₍and₎ Sir Robert Robinson. Princeton, Princeton Univ. Press, 1949.

x, 1094 p.   illus.   28 cm.

1. Penicillin.   I. U. S. Office of Scientific Research and Development.   II. Clarke, Hans Thacher, 1887–   ed.
RS165.P38N3   615.3292411   49–7715*

PRaW IdPI PPT OCU OOxM CaBVaU OC1W-H MiU
CSt ViU TxU ICU ICJ DNLM MB MH DNAL PPF PPSKF OU
NN   0030865   DLC KMK OC1W MtBC OrCS NNBG OrU-M IdU

QB4
.M92
National academy of sciences, Washington, D. C.
Mount Wilson observatory.
... Communications to the National academy of sciences v. 1–   (no. 1–   )
₍Washington₎ 1915–

TH9031
.N3
1952
National Academy of Sciences, Washington, D. C.
National Research Council. *Building Research Advisory Board.*
Condensation control in buildings, as related to paints, papers, and insulating materials. ₍Conference₎ February 26 and 27, 1952, conducted by the Building Research Advisory Board, Division of Engineering and Industrial Research, National Research Council ₍and₎ National Academy of Sciences. Washington, 1952.

National academy of sciences, *Washington, D. C.*
... Conduct of scientific work under United States government. Message from the President of the United States, transmitting report of the National academy of sciences ... ₍Washington, Govt. print. off.,₎ 1909₎
5 p. 23ᶜᵐ. ₍U. S.₎ 60th Cong., 2d sess. House. Doc. 1337)
Prepared by a committee of the National academy, R. S. Woodward, chairman. Read, referred to Committee on appropriations and ordered printed, January 18, 1909.
1. U. S.—Scientific bureaus.   I. Woodward, Robert Simpson, 1849–   II. U. S. 60th Cong., 2d sess., 1908–1909. House.
9–35203
Library of Congress   Q183.N22

NN   0030868   DLC MiU OO

Physics
D550
N21
1948
National Academy of Sciences, Washington, D. C.
Conference on physics, Pocono Manor, Pennsylvania, 30 March–1 April, 1948. Sponsored by the National Academy of Sciences. Princeton ₍N. J.₎ 1948.
77 l.   diagrs.

1. Physics – Addresses, essays, lectures.
I. Title.

NN   0030869   NNC

National Academy of Sciences, Washington, D.C.
Conference on the mechanisms of hormone action, with special reference to the adrenal cortical hormones. Résumé by Frank L. Engel and Jane Russell of a conference held January 17–19, 1952, at Arden House, Harriman, New York, by the National Academy of Sciences. Washington, National Academy of Sciences, National Research Council, 1952.
15 p.   25 cm.   (National Research Council. Publication 224)
1. Hormones. 2. ACTH.   I. Engel, Frank Libman, 1913–   II. Title.   (Series)
QP801.H7N3 1952a   612.015   53–60890

PBL OC1W ViU PPC CU MiD LU CaBVaU
NN   0030870   DLC WaTC OrP DNLM ICJ PSt NcD PPSKF

National Academy of Sciences, Washington, D.C.
Constitution.   n. t.-p.   ₍Washington, 1892.₎   6 p.   8°.

1. Societies (Learned), U. S.
N. Y. P. L.   January 16, 1914.
NN   0030871   NN

National academy of sciences, Washington, D.C.
Constitution and by-laws of the National academy of sciences. Washington, H. Polkinhorn, printer, 1864.
12 p.   22ᶜᵐ.
Library of Congress   Q11.N285 1864   5–11279
NN   0030872   DLC

Q
N277c
NATIONAL Academy of Sciences, Washington, D. C.
Constitution and membership. Washington ₍1863?₎–
v.
NN   0030873   DNLM MiU

RARE BKS
GN6.55
.R3
v.14
no.22
National Academy of Sciences, Washington, D.C.
Constitution and membership. 1876. Washington, D.C. The Home Secretary ₍1876₎
xix p.   21 1/2 cm.
₍Rag-bag, v. 14, no. 22₎
NN   0030874   NRU

National academy of sciences, *Washington, D. C.*
... Constitution and membership. 1879. Washington, D. C., Pub. by the home secretary ₍1879₎
xx p.   23½ᵐ.
15–10609
Library of Congress   Q11.N285 1879
NN   0030875   DLC

National Academy of Sciences, Washington, D.C.
Constitution and membership. April 21, 1882. Washington, 1882.
21 l.
Xerox copy of the original.

NN   0030876   OrU-M

National academy of sciences, *Washington, D. C.*
... Constitution and membership. April 21, 1883. Washington, D. C., The Academy, 1883.
24 p.   23 cm.
5–19601
Library of Congress   Q11.N285 1883
NN   0030877   DLC DNLM

VOLUME 405

National academy of sciences, Washington, D.C.
Constitution and rules and list of officers
and members... 1915.

NN 0030878   OC1

National academy of sciences, Washington, D. C.
Constitution and rules of the National academy of
sciences. Proposed by the Council, April 16, 1872.
[Washington, D. C., 1872?]
19 p. 22 cm.
Caption title.

NN 0030879   DSI

National Academy of Sciences, Washington, D.C.
Development of international cooperation
in science

see under

Symposium on the Development of International
Cooperation in Science, Washington, D.C.,
1951.

National Academy of Sciences, *Washington, D. C.*
A facsimile of the original signature book, National
Academy of Sciences, United States of America. [Wash-
ington, 1952]
[7] p. 28 cm.

1. Autographs—Facsimiles. 2. Signatures (Writing)

Q11.N2864 1952   53-60947 ‡

NN 0030881   DLC NNBG

National Academy of Sciences, Washington, D. C.
Health, medical and drug factors in highway
safety

see under

National Research Council. Committee on Highway
Safety Research.

National academy of sciences, *Washington, D. C.*
A history of the first half-century of the National academy
of sciences, 1863–1913. Washington, 1913.
xi p., 1 l., 399 p. plates, ports. 26 cm.
Edited by Frederick W. True.

1. National academy of sciences, Washington, D. C. I. True, Frederick, William, 1858–1914. II. Title.

Library of Congress   Q11.N286

13—35434

ICN MB NN MH-A DN MBCo MtU IdU OrU DHEW CaBVaU
CLSU NcD PBa MiD MiU OCU OU OC1 ViU NjP DSI ICJ
NN 0030883   DLC FTaSU MsSM DS TU NIC MU   NBuU

National academy of sciences, *Washington, D. C.*
Index to the first ten volumes of the Proceedings
(1915-1924)
see its   Publications of the National academy
of sciences of the United States of America (1915-
1926) ...

National academy of sciences, *Washington, D. C.*
Inquiry of the National academy of sciences concerning
the operations of the Coast and geodetic survey. [Wash-
ington, R. O. Polkinhorn & son, printers, 1884?]
cover-title, 20 p. 23½ cm.

1. U. S. Coast and geodetic survey.

Library of Congress   QB296.U85 1884

15-7528

NN 0030885   DLC

GC57
.V3

National academy of sciences, Washington, D. C.

Vaughan, Thomas Wayland, 1870–
International aspects of oceanography; oceanographic data
and provisions for oceanographic research, by Thomas Wayland Vaughan and others. Washington, D. C., National academy of sciences, 1937.

National academy of sciences, Washington, D.C.

National research council.
International critical tables of numerical data, physics,
chemistry and technology, prepared under the auspices of the
International reseach council and the National academy of
sciences by the National research council of the United States
of America; editor-in-chief: Edward W. Washburn ... associate editors: Clarence J. West ... N. Ernest Dorsey ... 1st ed.
New York [etc.] Pub. for the National research council by the
McGraw-Hill book company, inc., 1926–30.

National academy of sciences, *Washington, D.C.*
... Investigation of the scientific and economic relations
of the sorghum sugar industry, being a report made in
response to a request from the Hon. George B. Loring,
U. S. commissioner of agriculture, by a committee of the
National academy of sciences, November, 1882. Washington, Govt. print. off., 1883.
152 p. 23½ cm.
At head of title: National academy of sciences.
"Bibliography of sorghum": p. 148–152.
CONTENTS.—pt. I. Report of the committee.—pt. II. Conclusion and summary.—pt. III. Appended papers.
1. Sorghum sugar.   I. U. S. Dept. of agriculture.

Library of Congress   TP405.N27

5-35940

OCU   DNLM Or IdPI NjP OkU OrU MH-G CU
NN 0030888   DLC ICJ Nh NIC MBH KMK TU OU OFH MiU

T58
.U6
1943f

National academy of sciences, Washington, D. C.

U. S. *Training within industry service.*
The job relations training program. October 1, 1943.
[Washington] Training within industry service, Bureau of
training, War manpower commission [1943]

National Academy of Sciences, Washington, D.C.
Letter from the acting president ...
see its   Survey of the territories.

F226
.5
.H95
v.2
no.6

National Academy of Sciences, Washington, D.C.

Letter of the President of The National
Academy of Sciences, communicating in
obedience to law, a report of the operations
of that society for the past year ... [Wash-
ington, 1868]
77 p. 26cm. (U.S. 40th Cong., 2d sess., 1867–
1868.) Mis. doc. No. 106)
[Hunter pamphlets, collected, v. 2, no. 6]
Caption title.
1. Science—Societies. I. Ser.

NN 0030891   ViU

National academy of sciences, Washington, D.C.
Letter of the president of the National
academy of sciences, communicating, in obedience
to law, a report on the operations of that society
for the past year ... [Washington, 1868]
44 p.incl.tables. (40th Cong., 2d sess. Senate. Mis. doc. no. 106)

Caption title.
Bound with U.S. Congress. House. Committee
on coinage, weights, and measures. Report. 1866.

NN 0030892   MH-BA

Q11
.N283

National academy of sciences, Washington, D.C.
List of officers and members of the National
academy of sciences.
[Washington, D.C.]

NN 0030893   DLC

RARE BKS
GN6.95
.K3
v.14
no.21

National Academy of Sciences,
Washington, D.C.
[List of pending nominations]
[Washington, D.C. The Home Secretary,
1876]
1 p.l., 3 p. 20 cm.
[Rag-bag, v. 14, no. 21]

NN 0030894   NRU

National academy of sciences, *Washington, D. ...*
List of publications of the National academy of sciences. [Washington, D. C., 1918?]
cover-title, 10 p. 25½ cm.
"Reprinted from the Proceedings of the National academy of sciences,
vol. 3, pp. 743–753, December, 1917."

1. National academy of sciences, Washington, D. C.—Bibl.

CA 21-6 Unrev'd

Library of Congress   Z7403.N26

NN 0030895   DLC

National Academy of Sciences, Washington, D. C.
Manual for gaugers of spirits
see under   U.S. Treasury Dept.

National Academy of Sciences, Washington, D.C
Map standardization for a loose-leaf national
atlas
see under   National Research Council.
Committee on a National Atlas of the United States.

National academy of sciences, Washington, D. C.
Memoir of Frederick Augustus Genth. 1820–1893
see under   Barker, George Frederick,
1835–

National academy of sciences, *Washington, D. C.*
Memoirs of the National academy of sciences. v. 1–
Washington, Govt. print. off., 1866–19
v. illus., plates (part col.) maps, tables, diagrs. 30 cm.
Beginning with v. 2, issued also in the Congressional series of U. S.
public documents.
Vols. 3–4 each in two parts, with separate t.-p. and paging.
Each volume comprises one or more monographs, many of which are
issued also as separates.
A list of the papers contained in v. 1–11 is given in "A history of
the first half-century of the National academy of sciences, 1863–1913,"
p. 378–382.
Vol. 8, 6th and 7th memoirs were issued also as v. 5, no. 1–2 of the
Memoirs from the Biological laboratory of Johns Hopkins university.
1. Science—Societies.

15—10607

Library of Congress   Q11.N2

OCU MiU OC1 NcD PP MH-P MWA DSI CtY-M IdPI KyLoS
CPT LNL MtU WvU MMeT PBL MShM TxLT Nh DI-GS NjP TU
NN 0030899   DLC OrU WaS MdBP GEU IaGG CtNIC DAU

National Academy of Sciences, Washington, D.C.
Minutes of the business meetings of the National Academy of
Sciences, held at Washington, April 19–21, 1910. [Washington,
1910.] 22 p. 8°.

1. Science.—Associations, etc., U. S.
N. Y. P. L.   October 11, 1915.

NN 0030900   NN N

Q11
N214
1950

National academy of sciences, Washington,
D. C.
National academy of sciences organization,
July 1, 1950. [1950]
31 p.

NN 0030901   NNC-M

VOLUME 405

378.34
N276n　National Academy of Sciences, Washington, D.C.
　　National Research Endowment, a national fund
　for the support of research in pure science.
　Washington [1925?]
　　23p.　25cm.

　　1. Endowment of Research.　2. Endowments.
　U.S. I. Title.

NN　0030902　IEN NjP DSI MiU

Q11
.N2928　National Academy of Sciences, Washington, D.C.
　　National Research Council.
　　News report.　v. 1–
　　Jan./Feb. 1951–
　[Washington] National Academy of Sciences.

UC700
.U56　National Academy of Sciences, Washington, D. C.
no. 1　Spector, Harry, 1915-1959, ed.
　　Nutrition under climatic stress; a symposium edited by
　Harry Spector and Martin S. Peterson. [Held at, National
　Academy of Sciences, Washington, December 4-5, 1952.
　Washington, Advisory Board on Quartermaster Research
　and Development, Committee on Foods, National Academy
　of Sciences-National Research Council, 1954.

506
N27o　National Academy of Sciences, Washington,
　　D. C.
　　Officers and members.
　　　　　[Washington, D.C.]
　　v.　24 cm.

NN　0030905　N DI-GS

National Academy of Sciences, Washington, D. C.
　Organization and members ...
　　see under　National Research Council.

National Academy of Sciences, Washington, D. C.
　Physical and Chemical Aspects of Basic
　Mechanisms in Radiobiology.　National Academy
　of Sciences and National Research Council,
　Washington 25, D. C., 1953.
　　145 p.

NN　0030907　OC1W

TC777
.5
N3
1916　National Academy of Sciences, Washington, D. C.
　　Preliminary report upon the possibility of
　controlling the land slides adjacent to the
　Panama Canal ... [Washington, 1916]
　　193-207 p.　26cm.
　　"Reprinted from the Proceedings of the National
　Academy of Sciences, vol. 2, p. 193, April,
　1916."

　　1. Panama Canal.

NN　0030908　MB

National Academy of Sciences, Washington, D.C.
　[Presentation of amendments providing for division of the
　membership into classes and suggested classification.]　n. t.-p.
　[Washington, 1893.]　6 p.　8°.

1. Societies (Learned), U. S.
N. Y. P. L.　　　　　　　　　　　　　　　January 16, 1914.

NN　0030909　NN

National academy of sciences, *Washington, D. C.*
　... Proceedings.　v. 1.　[Mar. 1863-Oct. 1894]　Washington, D. C., 1877-95.
　1 p. l., 406 p.　23ᶜᵐ.
　Issued in 3 parts: pt. 1, 1877; pt. 2, 1884; pt. 3, 1895.　No more published.

　1. Science—Societies.
　　　　　　　　　　　　　　　　　　15—10605

Library of Congress　　　Q11.N25

NN　0030910　DLC DNLM PPAN NIC OC1 OU NjP MB ICJ

National Academy of Sciences, *Washington, D. C.*
　Proceedings.　v. 1–　　　　Jan. 1915–
　[Chicago] University of Chicago Press.
　　v.　illus.　26 cm.　monthly.
　Vols. 1–　issued by the academy under a variant name: National
Academy of Sciences of the United States of America.
　Imprint varies: 1915-19, Baltimore, Williams & Wilkins Co.—
1920-53, Easton, Pa., Mack Print. Co. [etc.]
　INDEXES:
　Vols. 1-10, 1915-24 (Issued as v. 13, no. 1, pt. 2) *with* v. 13. (In-
cludes list of academy publications, 1863-1926, and list of publica-
tions of the National Research Council, 1916-25)
　1. Science—Societies, etc.

Q11.N26　　　　　　　　　16-10069 rev*

NmS
TxLT PSt KyLoU MoU NNC LNL MWH ScCleU PHC PPiU
NcRS NcD DNLM GEU PBL PCarlD WvU MnRM CLWM MsU
P RP OkTU TxU NIC MiU OU OC1 ODW MB NjP ICJ PSt
NN　0030911　DLC NcU-H IEN MH-P MoU PPF NBuU MnNC

National academy of sciences, *Washington, D. C.*
　Publications of the National academy of sciences of the
United States of America (1915-1926) ... Washington, D. C.,
The Academy; Easton, Pa., Mack printing company, 1926.
　1 p. l., 197 p.　26ᶜᵐ.　(On cover: Volume 13, number 1, part II, January, 1927, Proceedings of the National academy of sciences)
　CONTENTS.—pt. I. Index to the first ten volumes of the Proceedings
(1915-1924)—pt. II. List of other publications of the academy from
1863-1926.—pt. III. List of publications of the National research council
from 1916-1925.

　1. Science—Bibl.　I. National research council.
　　　　　　　　　　　　　　　　　27—9820

Library of Congress　　　Q11.N26　vol. 13, no. 1, pt. II

NIC MiU OCU OU OC1W MH MH-A DAL ICJ IdU
NN　0030912　DLC DCU OrU Wa TU DAU KMK MH OC1 NcD

National academy of sciences, *Washington, D. C.*
　... Real property taxes on academy building; statement of
President Frank B. Jewett before the Committee on the District of Columbia of the United States Senate on August 18,
1942. Washington, D. C., 1942.
　cover-title, 32 p.　23ᶜᵐ.

　1. National research council.　2. Taxation, Exemption from.
I. Jewett, Frank Baldwin, 1879–　II. Title.
　　　　　　　　　　　　　　　　45—16565

Library of Congress　　　Q11.N282
　　　　　　　　　　[2]　　　　　506.273

NN　0030913　DLC MH

National Academy of Sciences, *Washington, D. C.*
　Report.　1863–
　Washington.
　　v. in　illus., maps.　24 cm.　annual.
　Report year for 1863-1920 ends Dec. 31; for 1921–　June 30.
　Issued in the Congressional series as Senate or House documents.
　Reports for 1868-71, 1873-77, are believed never to have been printed.
　Title varies slightly.
　Vols. for 1916–　include Report of the National Research
Council.

　1. Science—Societies, etc.

Q11.N28　　　　　　　　　15-10608 rev*

MdBP PPAmP NBuU IdPI CtN1C WaSpG NcD CU-Riv CtY
TxLT PBL ViU MH-A TxU WaTC OC1 OCU NcU MiU ODW
NN　0030914　DLC DI-GS DN DPU MWA NjP Nh TU NcGU

National academy of sciences, *Washington, D. C.*
　Report of a committee of the National academy of sciences on the condition and preservation of the Declaration of independence. [Washington, D. C., 1903]
　2 l.　26½ᶜᵐ.
　Signed: Charles F. Chandler, chairman of the committee.

　1. U. S. Declaration of independence.　I. Chandler, Charles Frederick, 1836–
　　　　　　　　　　　　　　　　17—23297

Library of Congress　　　E221.N27

NN　0030915　DLC

634.9
N213r　National academy of sciences, Washington, D.C.
　　Report of the committee appointed by the Na-
　tional academy of sciences upon the inauguration
　of a forest policy for the forested lands of the
　United States to the secretary of the interior,
　May 1, 1897.　Washington, Govt. print. off.,
　1897.
　　47p.

　　1. Forests and forestry--U.S.　2. National parks
　and reserves--U.S.　3. Forest reserves--U.S.

NN　0030916　IU OrHi OrCS MBH OO MB DLC

National academy of sciences, *Washington, D. C.*
　... Report of the committee of the National academy of
sciences on Panama canal slides. [Washington, Govt.
print. off., 1924]
　xi, 135 p.　front. (fold. map) plates (part fold.) diagrs.　31½ x 24½ᶜᵐ.
(National academy of sciences, Washington, D. C. Memoirs. vol. XVIII)

　1. Panama canal.
　　　　　　　　　　　　　　　　24—27315

Library of Congress　　　Q11.N2　vol. XVIII

OC1 OO OU OCU ICJ MB WaS OrU WaTC CaBVaU
NN　0030917　DLC FTaSU OKentU NIC TxU DN NcU MiU

National academy of sciences, *Washington, D. C.*
　... Report of the eclipse expedition to Caroline Island,
May 1883.
　(In its Memoirs. Washington, 1884.　30 cm.　v. 2, 1st memoir
(p. 5-146) 20 pl.)

　1. Eclipses, Solar—1883.　2. Caroline Island.
　　　　　　　　　　　　　　　　4—1298
Library of Congress　　　Q11.N2
———— Copy 2, de-　　tached.　QB543.83N

MiU OU OC1 OC1MN OCU NcU
NN　0030918　DLC CaBVaU WaTC OrU NIC ViU CtY ICJ

National Academy of Sciences, *Washington, D. C.*
　Report of the treasurer.
　[Washington]
　　v.　25 cm.　annual.
　Report year ends June 30.
　At head of title, 19　　　: National Academy of Sciences,
including National Research Council.

　I. National Research Council.

Q11.N2812　　　　506.273　　　51-37820 ‡

NN　0030919　DLC VU

National Academy of Sciences, Washington, D.C.
　Report [on amendments to the constitution of the academy]
presented November 2, 1892.　n. t.-p.　[Washington, 1892.]
6 p.　8°.

1. Societies (Learned), U. S.
N. Y. P. L.　　　　　　　　　　　　　January 16, 1914.

NN　0030920　NN

VOLUME 405

National academy of sciences, *Washington, D.C.*
... Report on glucose, prepared by the National academy of sciences, in response to a request made by the commissioner of internal revenue. Washington, Govt. print. off., 1884.

108 p. 23ᶜᵐ.

At head of title: United States internal revenue.

2–8650

NN 0030921 DLC DNLM ICJ

NATIONAL ACADEMY OF SCIENCES, Washington, *D.C.*
Rules, n.p., [186–].

Large paper. pp. 13.

NN 0030922 MH

National academy of sciences, *Washington, D. C.*
... Scientific explorations of the Philippine Islands. Message from the President of the United States, transmitting a report by a committee appointed at the request of the President by the National academy of sciences to consider and report upon the desirability of instituting scientific explorations of the Philippine Islands. [Washington, Gov't print. off., 1905]

22 p. 23ᶜᵐ. (U. S. 58th Cong. 3d sess. Senate. Doc. 145)
Chairman of the committee: William H. Brewer.
Plans, estimates, legislation and administration by the Board of scientific surveys of the Philippine Islands, constituted by the President March 9, 1903: p. 13–22.
1. Philippine Islands—Surveys. I. Brewer, William Henry, 1828– II. U. S. Board of scientific surveys of the Philippine Islands.

Library of Congress Q183.N27 6–14698

NN 0030923 DLC OO MiU

National Academy of Sciences, Washington, D. C.
... Scientific results of the United States arctic expedition, steamer Polaris ...
see under U. S. Navy Dept.

National Academy of Sciences, Washington, D. C.
Scientific, technical, and related societies of the United States
see under title

National Academy of Sciences, Washington, D. C.
[Scrapbook of the autumn meeting, Brown university, Providence, Rhode Island, October 23, 24, 25, 1939. Providence, 1939]
68 l. illus. (incl. ports.) 28 cm.
Includes addresses and mounted letters, programs clippings.

NN 0030926 RPB

National academy of sciences, *Washington, D. C.*
The semi-centennial anniversary of the National academy of sciences, 1863–1913. Washington, 1913.

vii p., 1 l., [2], 108 p. plates. 26¼ᶜᵐ.

G S 14–76

Library, U. S. Geol. survey S(200) N353

NN 0030927 DI–GS NjP IU OCl MH–A

National academy of sciences, Washington, D. C.
Silliman, Benjamin, 1816–1885.
Sketch of the life and scientific work of Dr. John Lawrence Smith, prepared by appointment of the National academy of sciences. By B. Silliman. April, 1884. ⟨With a complete list of his published memoirs, etc.⟩ Washington, D. C., 1884.

National academy of sciences, Washington, D. C.
... Standards for electrical measure, February 20, 1895. Printed for the Academy. Washington, Judd & Detweiler, 1895.
cover–title, 9 p. illus. 24 cm.

At head of title: National academy of sciences.
Signed: O. C. Marsh, president of the National academy of sciences, A. Hall, home secretary.

1. Electric measurements. I. U. S. Laws, statutes, etc. II. Title.

NN 0030929 Vi DI–GS OrU MB MiU DBS CtMW MiU

RARE BKS
GN6.95
.R3
v.10
no.20

National Academy of Sciences, Washington, D.C.
Survey of the territories. Letter from the acting president of the National Academy of Sciences transmitting a report on the surveys of the territories. [Washington, D.C., 1878] 27p.
(U.S. 45th Cong., 3d Sess. House. Mis. doc. no. 5)
[Rag–bag; v. 10, no. 20]
Caption title.
Includes: U.S. Geographical and Geological Survey of the Rocky Mountain Region. Report on the methods of surveying the public domain.

1. United States—Surveys
2. Surveying—Public lands—United States I. United States. Geographical and Geological Survey of the Rocky Mountain Region. Report on the methods of surveying the public domain.
II. Title

NN 0030931 NRU ViU Nh RPB

Q11
.P5
vol. 90,
no. 1

National academy of sciences, Washington, D. C.
Symposium on atomic energy and its implications. Papers read at the joint meeting of the American philosophical society and the National academy of sciences, November 16 and 17, 1945. Philadelphia, The American philosophical society, 1946.

National academy of sciences, Washington, D. C.
Symposium on climatic cycles. Wash. 1933.
p. 349–388. illus. 26 cm.

NN 0030933 DAS

National Academy of Sciences, Washington, D.C.
Symposium on the laboratory propagation and detection of the agent of hepatitis

see under

National Research Council. Panel on the Sterilization of Blood and Plasma.

National Academy of Sciences, Washington, D. C.
Technical aspects of the loss of the Macon. Washington, National Academy of Sciences, 1937.

28 p. diagrs. 28 cm. (Government Relations and Science Advisory committee. Special committee on Airships, report no. 3)

NN 0030935 WaTC

National academy of sciences, Washington, D. C.
Dutton, Clarence Edward, 1841–1912.
Volcanos and radioactivity. (Read before the National academy of sciences, April 17, 1906) By Major C. E. Dutton ... Englewood, N. J., The Englewood times, 1906.

National academy of sciences, Washington, D. C.
The will of Alexander Dallas Bache, March 18, 1862
see under Bache, Alexander Dallas, 1806–1867.

National Academy of Sciences, Washington, D. C.
see also Conference on Quantum-Mechanical Methods in Valence Theory, Shelter Island, N. Y., 1951.

National academy of sciences, Washington, D.C. Advisory committee on civil defense
... Operation green light; the evacuation of Portland, Oregon, September 27, 1955. [By] Willard Bascom. [n.p., 1955]

cover–title, 12 numb. l. illus., map. 28cm.

Reproduced from typewritten copy.

NN 0030939 MH–L

National Academy of Sciences, Washington, D. C.
Advisory Committee on Metals and Minerals
see National Research Council. Advisory Committee on Metals and Minerals.

National Academy of Sciences, *Washington, D. C. Committee on Battery Additives.*
Report. Washington, 1953.
35 p. 27 cm.
——— Appendices. Washington, 1953.
1 v. illus. 27 cm.

QC605.N312

1. Storage batteries—Additives.

QC605.N3 54–61376 rev ‡

NN 0030941 DLC DNAL MB

KQ5.2
N277ev

National Academy of Sciences, Committee on Disaster Studies. *Washington, D.C.*
Evacuation of Panama City before Hurricane Florence, by Lewis M. Killian, Sociology Research Laboratory, the Florida State University. Washington, 1954.
12, 2 p. 28 cm.

1. Hurricane Florence. 2. Hurricanes. Florida. Sept. 1953. 3. Psychology, Applied. I. Killian, Lewis M. II. Florida. State University, Tallahassee. Sociology Research Laboratory.

NN 0030942 DAS

KQ5.2
N277hur

National Academy of Sciences, Washington, D.C. Committee on Disaster Studies.
Hurricane Barbara; a study of the evacuation of Ocean City, Maryland, August 1953, by Jeannette F. Rayner. Washington, 1953.
17 p. 28 cm.

"A pilot study conducted...at the request of the Federal Civil Defense Administration."
1. Hurricane Barbara. 2. Psychology, Applied. 3. Hurricanes. Maryland. August 1953. I. Rayner, Jeannette F.

NN 0030943 DAS

National academy of sciences, Washington, D.C. Committee on government relations
see National academy of sciences, Washington, D.C. Government relations and science advisory committee.

VOLUME 405

National Academy of Sciences, *Washington, D. C. Com-*
mittee on Oceanography
    see
National Research Council. *Committee on Oceanography.*

National Academy of Sciences, Washington, D.C.
    Committee to Consider the Classification of Wool.
¹⁰⁴⁸⁴⁰ Report of a Committee of the National Academy of Sciences
concerning the classification of Donskoi wool. January 30, 1886.
Washington, Gov't Print. Off., 1886.
  24 p. incl. tables. 23^{cm}.   *[In Pamphlets on textile industries, 2.]*
  On verso of t.-p.: Treasury Department, document no. 80, Secretary — Customs.

  NN   0030946   ICJ

Q712
.A1N3   National Academy of Sciences, Division *Washington, D.C.*
    of Medical Sciences.
    Directory of the Division of Medical
  Sciences; membership of the Division and
  its committees. Washington.
    v. 28cm.

  NN   0030947   NNU

National Academy of Sciences, *Washington, D. C. Govern-*
ment Relations and Science Advisory Committee.
  Report on the role of science in national planning. Prepared in response to the request of Frederic A. Delano, chairman the National Planning Board, Federal Emergency Administration of Public Works, addressed to the President
of the National Academy of Sciences on April 24, 1934.
[Washington] 1934.
  42 l. 28 cm.

  1. Science and state—U. S.   I. Title : Science in national planning.

  Q127.U6N3   509.73   51–51308

  NN   0030948   DLC DNAL MH NN IU CU

National Academy of Sciences, Washington, D.C.
  Government Relations and Science Advisory
  Committee. Special Committee on Airships
    see   National Academy of Sciences,
  Washington, D.C. Special Committee on Airships.

National Academy of Sciences, Washington, D.C.
  Highway Research Board

    see   National Research Council.
  Highway Research Board.

National Academy of Sciences, *Washington, D. C. Library*
  see   Washington, D. C. Library of the National Academy of Sciences and the National Research Council.

National academy of sciences, *Washington, D. C.*
  National research council.
    see
National research council.

National academy of sciences,
  Washington, D.C. Science
  advisory board

    see

Science advisory board.

National Academy of Sciences, *Washington, D. C. Scien-*
tific Advisory Group.
  Reorganization of science and technology in Japan, report.
Tokyo, 1947.
  xii, 44 p. 28 cm.

  1. Science—Hist.—Japan.

  Q127.J3N28   509.52   48–3940*

  NN   0030954   DLC DI–GS DNAL CU

National Academy of Sciences, *Washington, D. C. Space*
Science Board
  see
National Research Council. *Space Science Board.*

National Academy of Sciences, *Washington, D. C. Special*
  Advisory Committee (Appointed 1947)
  see
National Academy of Sciences, *Washington, D. C. Scien-*
tific Advisory Group.

National academy of sciences, *Washington, D. C. Special*
committee on airships.
  ... Report ... no. 1/2–5. [Stanford University] Printed by
Stanford university press [1936–37]
  4 v. plates, fold. tab., diagrs. (part fold.) 26½^{cm}.

  At head of title: Special committee on airships.
  Nos. 1 and 2 are combined in one issue.
  "These reports were prepared by a committee appointed by the Science
advisory board at the request of the secretary of the navy. Later, on dis-
continuance of the board in December 1935, the committee was continued
by the Government relations and science advisory committee of the National academy of sciences."

  CONTENTS.—no. 1. General review of conditions affecting airship design and construction with recommendations as to future policy. January 16, 1936.—no. 2. Review and analysis of airship design and construction past and present. January 30, 1937.—no. 3. Technical aspects
of the loss of the Macon. January 30, 1937.—no. 4. The metal-clad type
of airship construction, with recommendations. August 11, 1936.—no. 5.
The Illespess type of airship construction, with recommendations. August 11, 1936.

  1. Air-ships.   I. Science advisory board.

                                          38—6635
  Library of Congress   TL650.N35
                      [a42d1]   629.13321

  NN   0030958   DLC WaS ICJ

National Academy of Sciences, Washington, D.C. War
  Metallurgy Committee
    see   National Research Council. War
  Metallurgy Committee.

Q
73   National Academy of Sciences (*India*)
N25   Annual number.
    Allahabad.
      v. ports. 25 cm.

    Title varies :   Business matters.
    Vols. for   issued by the academy under an earlier
  name: Academy of Sciences, United Provinces of Agra and Oudh.

    I. National Academy of Sciences (India)   Business matters.

    Q73.N25   49–31520 rev

  NN   0030960   DLC IU NNC LU ICRL CtY GU TxU

National Academy of Sciences (*India*)
  Proceedings.

  Allahabad.
    v. in   25 cm. annual.
    Began publication with 1931/32 issue. Cf. Union list of serials.
    Issued in parts.
    Papers by various authors.

    1. Science—Societies.

    Q73.N252   506.254   51–25296

        NSyU GU WU ICRL FTaSU NNCC
        OU NN KU PPF GAT TxU OU IU NIC CLU RPB PPAN CU
  NN   0030961   DLC ICRL NNC   ViBlbV PPAmP

Q73
A61A3   National Academy of Sciences (*India*)
    Silver jubilee souvenir: 1930–1955. [Allahabad? foreword
  1955]
    153 p. ports.

    Brief papers. Includes also "Presidents of the Academy"
  (p. 30–51) and "Honorary fellows of the Academy" (p. 52–112)

    1. National Academy of Sciences, Allahabad, India. 2. Science
  Biog. 3. Science - India - Biog.

  NN   0030962   CU MnU RPB IU

National Academy of Sciences of the United
  States of America
    see
  National Academy of Sciences, Washington,
  D. C.

National Academy of the Arts of Design, New York
    see   New York (City) National Academy of
  Design.

NATIONAL ACADEMY OF THEOLOGY.
  Proceedings. 1st meeting. [N.Y.] 1889.

  NN   0030965   MH–AH

National Academy of Visual Instruction.
  Visual education directory. 1924, 1926–1927,
  1930–1931, 1933.

  NN   0030966   OCl

National Academy of Visual Instruction
  see also
  National Education Association of the United States.
  Dept. of Audiovisual Instruction.

National acceptance journal
    see   American business and national
  acceptance journal.

National accident society, *New York.*
  Agent's manual of the National accident society of the
city of New York ... Adopted August 1, 1887. Arranged
... by A. N. Lockwood ... N. Y., G. W. Burnham & co.,
printers, °1887.
  44 p. 14½^{cm}.

  I. Lockwood, Adolphus N., comp.   7–12101†

  Library of Congress   HG9321.N2

  NN   0030969   DLC

657
N218   The National accountant, v.1–3, no.1. Oct.
  1936–Aug.1937. Los Angeles, 1936–37.
    3v. in 1. illus. 23cm.

    Set incomplete. June–July, 1937 missing.

    1. Accounting—Period.

  NN   0030970   LU OCl

VOLUME 405

National accountants institute.

Hutchison, John R *comp.*
Three hundred questions with answers on commercial law;
forty quiz questions with answers; the notary public examination. Compiled by John R. Hutchison ... in collaboration
with the National accountants institute and the National association of certified public accountants. Washington, D. C.,
The A. C. Mellichampe inc. press, °1934.

nF5601
.N3
National accounting conference.
Proceedings...
New York ₍1940?₋ ₎
5 v.   28-29 cm.

NN   0030972   DLC

National acme co., Cleveland.
Acme automatic multiple spindle screw machine:
reference book for operators... ₍The Firm₎
°1917.
94 p. illus. diagrs.

NN   0030973   MiD

National acme company, Cleveland.
Annual report... 7th-20th
₍Cleveland₎

NN   0030974   OCl OClWHi

NATIONAL-ACME   COMPANY, Cleveland,
Ohio.
General catalogue of "Acme automatic" and
"Acme semi-automatic" screw machines. Cleve-
land, 1908.

NN   0030975   MH

National Acme company.
Handbook for operators of Acme-Gridley multiple spindle
bar machines; design, construction, tools, operation of models
R and RA 4, 6 and 8 spindle machines. 1st ed. ... Cleveland, O., The National Acme company, °1939.
123, ₍1₎ p. incl. illus., tables, diagrs. 23½ᵐ.

1. Spindles (Machine-tools)   I. Title: Acme-Gridley multiple spindle
bar machines, Handbook for operators of.

                                        40-35329
Library of Congress   TJ1215.N3
———— Copy 2.
Copyright   ₍2₎   621.82

NN   0030976   DLC

National Acme Company.
Handbook for operators of Acme-Gridley
multiple spindle bar machines; design, construction,
tools, operation of models R, and RA 4, 6 and 8
spindle machines. 3d ed.   Cleveland, Ohio,
Author, c1942.
127 p.   illus. tab. diagrs.

NN   0030977   WaS

National Acme company, Cleveland.
Handbook for operators of Acme-Gridley
multiple spindle bar machines; design...construc-
tion...tools, operation of Models R and RA 4,
6, and 8 spindle machines. ₍The Author₎ °1944.
127 ₍1₎ p.. illus.

NN   0030978   MiD

National acme co., Cleveland.
Handbook for operators of acme, model "C", 5
spindle, automatic screw machines; covering
chiefly the design, construction, tool equipment
and operation of the machine. The Author ₍1930₎
unp. diagrs.

NN   0030979   MiD

National acme co. Cleveland.
Handbook for operators of Gridley multiple
spindle automatic screw machines, covering
chiefly the design, construction, tool equipment
and operation of model G 4 spindle machines.
The Author, °1924.
130 p. illus. charts, tables, diagrs.

NN   0030980   MiD

National acme co. Cleveland.
Handbook for operators of Gridley multiple
spindle automatic screw machines, covering
chiefly the design construction, tool equipment
and operation of model "G" & "F" 4 spindle
machines. ₍The Author₎ 1930.
132 p. tables, diagrs.

NN   0030981   MiD

National Acme company.
A handbook for operators of Gridley multiple spindle automatic screw machines, covering chiefly the design, construction,
tool equipment and operation of model "G" & "F" 4 spindle
machines. 1943. A reprint of the 1930 edition. Cleveland, O.,
The National Acme company ₍1943₎
132 p. incl. illus., tables, diagrs. 21½ᵐ.

1. Screw-cutting machines.   I. Title: Gridley multiple spindle automatic screw machines.
                                                44-12470
Library of Congress   TJ1222.N28 1943
                      ₍3₎   621.882

NN   0030982   DLC

National Acme company.

Multiple spindle automatic bar and chucking
machines. Self-opening threading dies, collapsible
taps and hollow milling heads. Industrial centrifuges for separating and clarifying. The chronolog
for controlling idle time limit, control station
and motor-starter switches, solenoids and solenoid-
counters. Cleveland, Ohio, The National Acme
company ₍1946?₎
1 v. illus., diagrs. 29½cm.
Loose-leaf.
1. Spindles (Machine-tools) 2. Milling-machines. 3.
Centrifuges. 4. Solen   oids. 5. Taps.

NN   0030983   ViU

National action conference for civil rights, Washington, D. C.,
1941.
National action conference for civil rights, Washington, D. C.,
April 19-20. . .   Washington. Nat. federation for constitutional
liberties ₍1941₎   2 parts.   28cm.

Part 2 has title: Proposals for action ...

J. Liberty—U. S.
N. Y. P. L.   September 14, 1945

NN   0030984   NN

National Action Conference on Minority Veterans
Problems, New York, 1946.
Proceedings.   New York, Stenotype
Reporting Co., 1946.
165 l.
Conference called by American Council on
Race Relations.
Typewritten.
1. Veterans. U.S. 2. Minorities. U.S.
I. American Council on Race Relations.

NN   0030985   ICU

F902"6   National Action Movement.
ᴿNA
ᴹIS
₍Miscellaneous ephemeral materials not
fully catalogued₎

NB. - Such materials are shelved in

NN   0030986   WHi

National ad-views; a review of national newspaper
advertising ideas ...   New York, Vincent
Edwards & co.
Semi-monthly,   -1932; monthly, 1933-

NN   0030987   OCl

National adequate wiring bureau.
Copper in the home...   N.Y., c1938.
30p.

NN   0030988   OU

There are no cards for numbers
NN 0030989 to NN 0032000

NATIONAL ADJUSTMENT COMMISSION.
Awards of commission from date of creation
Aug.1917 to Dec. 27, 1918.

Typewritten.

NN   0032001   MH

National adjustment commission.
... Chairman's report. 1918-
see its   Report ... 1918-1919/20.

National Adjustment Commission.
...In the matter of the demands of the deep sea longshoremen of the port of New York, as to wages, etc.   ₍New York,
1919.₎   2 v. in 1.   4°.

Caption-title.
At head of title: Before the National Adjustment Commission.
Paging continuous.
Mimeographed.

1. New York City.—Dock laborers.   2. New York City.—Wages.
N. Y. P. L.   October 8, 1921.

NN   0032003   NN

National Adjustment Commission.
...In the matter of the demands of the longshoremen of the
North Atlantic coast ports as to wages, etc.   ₍New York, 1918.₎
585 f.   4°.

Caption-title.
At head of title: Before the National Adjustment Commission.
Mimeographed.

1. Dock laborers, U. S. 2. Wages.—   Dock labor, U. S.
N. Y. P. L.   October 8, 1921.

NN   0032004   NN CU MH

National adjustment commission.
... Longshore labor; an investigation into hours, earn-
ings, labor cost and output in the longshore industry at
the port of New York ... By B. M. Squires ₍executive
secretary₎ ₍New York, 1920₎
1 p. l., 3, iv numb. l., 1 l., 4-316 numb. l. (i. e. 333 l.) incl. diagrs. 27¼ᵐ.
At head of title: National adjustment commission.
Autographed from type-written copy.
Appendices: i. Weekly summaries of incoming and outgoing deepwater
vessels and cargoes at the principal ports of the United States in 1919.—
ii. Deepwater and coastwise longshore wage rates in the United States, 1914-
1920.—iii. Retail prices and cost of living in port cities of the United States,

Continued in next column

VOLUME 405

Continued from preceding column

1914-1920.—IV. Pre-war plans to regularize employment in the dock industry in European ports.—V. Methods of handling dock labor in Great Britain during the war.—VI. Demobilization and re-settlement of dock labor in the United Kingdom.—VII. Recommendations of a Court of inquiry, Great Britain, with respect to dock labor, 1920.—VIII. National dock agreement in Great Britain, 1920.

1. Longshoremen—New York (City) 2. Labor and laboring classes—New York (City) 3. Longshoremen—Gt. Brit.   I. Squires, Benjamin Mark, 1886–   II. Title.

                       CA 22-445 Unrev'd

Library of Congress   HD5503.N35 1920

NN 0032006   DLC NN

NATIONAL ADJUSTMENT COMMISSION.
Proceedings at New Orleans, Louisiana, Oct.
31, 1918, in the matter of coastwise longshoremen.

    Typewritten. ff. 49.
"Reported by Gassie & Beary."
2 tables and ms. sheet inserted at end.

NN 0032007   MH

National adjustment commission.
    Report ... 1918–1919/20. Washington ₍etc.₎ 1919–₍20₎
    2 v. map. 23–27¼ᶜᵐ.
Title varies: 1918, National adjustment commission. Chairman's report for the period ending December 31, 1918. Washington, Govt. print. off., 1919. 23ᶜᵐ. (Chairman: Robert P. Bass. Seal of United States shipping board on t.-p.)
1919/20 (mimeographed) Report of the executive secretary of the National adjustment commission for the period January 1, 1919 to June 30, 1920. ₍New York?₎ 1920₎ 27¼ᶜᵐ. (Executive secretary: B. M. Squires)
    1. Arbitration, Industrial—U. S. 2. Longshoremen—U. S. 3. Shipping—U. S. 4. Labor and laboring classes—U. S.—1914–   I. Bass, Robert Perkins, 1873–   II. Squires, Benjamin Mark, 1886–1937.

                              19—26411

Library of Congress   HD5503.N3
                ₍a38r33g1₎   331.155

NN 0032008   DLC CU OU DFT OC1 ICJ NN MH

National administrative council, Independent
labour party (Gt. Brit.)
    see   Independent labour party. National
administrative council. (Gt. Brit.)

W 1   NATIONAL Adoption Society, London
NA221   Annual report and balance sheet.
      1943-
      London.
        v.

NN 0032010   DNLM

National Adult School Union, London.
    Achievement and challenge; a scheme of study for
the year 1938 for adult schools ...   London,
National adult school union [1938?]
    xiv, 310 p.   19 cm.
    1. Religious education. 2. Education of adults.
I. Title.

NN 0032011   CU

HV   National Adult School Union, London
245   Adult school social service handbook.
N26   Compiled by the Social Study and Service
      Committee of the National Adult School Union.
      London, 1914.
        96p. 22cm.

      1. Social service 2. Public welfare -
Gt. Brit. I. Title

NN 0032012   WU

National Adult School Union, *London.*
    The adult school study handbook
    see its
    A course of study for adult schools.

National adult school union, *London.*
    The adult school year book and directory.
    1

    ₍London, 1   no.   17cm.
    1   dated April.
    Cover-title: 1   , Directory of adult schools...

    1. Education—Direct.—Gt. Br.   I. Title. II. Title: Directory of
adult schools.
N. Y. P. L.   March 29, 1946

NN 0032014   NN

National adult school union, *London.*
    Adult schools; their aims and methods and how to establish
them. London, Nat. adult school union ₍1927?₎ 16 p. 18cm.

    1. Education, Adult—Gt. Br.   2. Sunday schools—Gt. Br.
N. Y. P. L.   November 15, 1945

NN 0032015   NN

379.19   National adult school union, London
N27a   Adult schools; their aims and
      methods and how to establish them.
      London, The Union ₍1944₎
      cover-title, 16p. D.
Educ.

NN 0032016   IaU

National adult school union, London.
    Annual report of the national council.

NN 0032017   MiU

National Adult School Union, London.
    Books of the Old Testament in colloquial
speech
      see under   Bible. O. T. English.
192- - 3-. Robinson and others.

National adult school union, *London.*
    Builders and makers; a scheme of study for the year 1944 for
adult schools...   London, National adult school union ₍1943₎
v, 146 p.   illus.   18cm.

    "Thirty-fourth of a series of annual handbooks."

    1. Reading—Courses. 2. Sunday   school—Lessons.
N. Y. P. L.   November 15, 1945

NN 0032019   NN

LC5325   National Adult School Union, London.
N3A3   A century of change, 1851-1951; a
      course of study for the year 1951 for adult
      schools. London, National Adult School
      Union ₍1951₎
      280 p.

      "Notes": p.278-280.
      Includes bibliographies.

      1. Education of adults - Manuals, text-
books, etc.   I. Title.

NN 0032020   CU NNU-W

National adult school union, *London.*
    The claims of life, a scheme of study for the
year 1930 for adult schools. London, National
adult school union [1929?]

NN 0032021   MH

National Adult School Union, *London.*
    A course of study for adult schools.

    London.
          v. 19 cm.
    Title varies: 19   A scheme of study for adult schools.
    Cover title, 19   : The adult school study handbook; 19
    Study handbook.
    Each volume has also a distinctive title.

LT310.N3   268.434   48–18761 rev*

NN 0032022   DLC

National Adult School Union, *London.*   3599.568
    Everyman faces life. A scheme of study for the year 1924   for
adult schools.
— London. [1924.] 1 v. 18.5 cm., in 16s.

    The sub-title on the cover is: Being the adult school lesson handbook.

N1565 — T.r. — Education. Adult. Pe .icals. — Adult school lesson handbook.
— Annuals and year-books.

NN 0032023   MB MiU OC1

National Adult School Union, *London.*
    The Fellowship hymn-book
    see under title

National Adult School Union, *London.*
    The Frank Metcalfe memorial lecture...
1930

    London,₍ 1930   8°
      no.

    Contents:
    1930. NEWMAN, Sir G. Some notes on adult education in England. 1930.

NN 0032025   NN

National Adult School Union, *London.*
    International affairs; a study handbook, ₍by₎ Norman Angell
₍pseud., and others₎.   London: National Adult School Union₍,
1924₎.   122 p.   12°.

    Contents: LANE, R. N. A. The ideas which are the foundations. FAIRGRIEVE, J.
History and geography. BURNS, C. D. International affairs to-day. MARTIN, G. C. The
new spirit.

422791A. 1. International relations,   2. Lane, Ralph Norman Angell,
1874–   3. Fairgrieve, James.   4. Burns, Cecil Delisle, 1879–
5. Martin, George Currie, 1865–
N. Y. P. L.   August 15, 1929

NN 0032026   NN OC1

National Adult School Union, *London.*
    ₍Minor publications.₎

NN 0032027   ICJ

National adult school union, *London.*
    New beginnings; a scheme of study for the year 1941 for adult
schools...   London, National adult school union ₍1940₎   viii,
225 p.   18cm.   (Adult school lesson handbook. 1941.)

290451B. 1. Sunday schools—Lessons.   2. Reading—Courses.
N. Y. P. L.   May 11, 1945

NN 0032028   NN

VOLUME 405

National adult school union, London.
New life, a scheme of study for the year 1921
for adult schools...London, National adult
school union (1921)
x, 196 p. 19 cm.
On cover: Adult school lesson handbook for
1921.

NN 0032029 DHEW OO

National adult school union, London.
Paths to freedom; a scheme of study for the year 1935 for
adult schools with a special contribution on "Britain and
India", by Professor John Coatman ... London, National
adult school union [1934]
x, 352 p. illus. double map. 19ᶜᵐ.
"Twenty-fifth in a series of annual lesson handbooks."—p. vi.
Includes references.

1. Religious education. 2. Education of adults. [2. Adult education]
I. Title.
E 36–475
Library, U. S. Office of   Education BV1561.N2 1935

NN 0032030 DHEW ICU

National adult school union, London.
Personality in the making; a scheme of study for the year
1936 for adult schools ... London, National adult school union
[1935]
viii, 304 p. illus. 18½ᶜᵐ.
"Adult school lesson handbook for 1936."

1. Moral education. I. Title.
A 36–593
Title from Univ. of Chi-   cago LC268.N17 1936
[3]   Printed by L. C.

NN 0032031 ICU

LC268   NATIONAL ADULT SCHOOL UNION, London.
.N17   Purpose and experience; a scheme of study for the
year 1934 for adult schools... London, National adult
school union[1933]
viii, 308 p. 19cm.
"Adult school lesson handbook for 1934."

1. Moral education.

NN 0032032 ICU

National Adult School Union, London.
A scheme of study for adult schools
see its
A course of study for adult schools.

National Adult School Union. London.
Study handbook
see its
A course of study for adult schools.

National adult school union, London.
To-day and to-morrow; a scheme of study for the year 1940
for adult schools. London, National adult school union [1939]
vi, 313 p. illus. 19cm. (The Adult school lesson handbook.
1940.)

290450B. 1. Sunday schools—   Lessons. 2. Reading—Courses.
N. Y. P. L.   April 30, 1945

NN 0032035 NN

National adult school union, London.
Towards a whole society; a scheme of study
for the year 1946 for adult schools. [1946]
vi, 216 p. illus., map, table.

Includes bibliographies.
1. Education of adults.

NN 0032036 NNC

National Adult School Union, London.
Towards adjustment, a scheme of study for the year 1948
for adult schools. London [1947]
241 p. 19 cm.

1. Religious education—Text-books for adults.   I. Title.
BV1550.N3   268.434   48–18761*

NN 0032037 DLC

National Adult School Union, London.
The Word in the world; a scheme of study for the year 1928
for adult schools... London: National Adult School Union[,
1927]. vi, 294 p. 12°.
Contains bibliographies.

1. Sunday schools—Lessons.   2. Title.
N. Y. P. L.   June 25, 1928

NN 0032038 NN

---

374   National Adult School Union, London.
N214w   A world of persons, a course of study for the
year 1949 for adult schools.   London [1948]
vi, 239p. illus. 19cm.

Includes bibliographies.

1. Education of adults. 2. Education--Gt.
Brit. I. Title.

NN 0032039 IU

National Adult School Union, London. Social
Study and Service Committee.
Adult school social service handbook
see under National Adult School Union,
London.

National Adult Work Planning Conference. Lake
Geneva, Wis., 1946.
Looking ahead in adult work, issued by Editorial committee, United Christian Adult Movement, based upon National Adult Work Planning
Conference, Lake Geneva, Wis., July 28–August 4,
1946. Chicago, International Council of Religious Education, 1947.
101 p. 23 cm.

On cover: Adult resource materials.

NN 0032041 KKcB

National Advance. Milwaukee, Wis., Jan.
1890–1909?
Title varies: 1890–June 2, 1894, Milwau-
kee Advance (scattered numbers as National
Advance) - *National advance and the Labor*
People's Party paper.   *advocate.*
Robert Schilling, ed. and manager.

NN 0032042 NbHi MH

The national advantages of government aid to
American commerce
see under [Clyde, William P   ]

National advertiser.
New York.
v. semimonthly.
Published 1878–1907?

NN 0032044 ICRL·OClWHi

National advertiser, New York.
A collection of truths for those who wish to
arouse the public in the surest and most direct
manner, together with certain facts and figures
not generally known. New York, 1887.
57 p.

NN 0032045 WaS

National advertiser, *New York.*
"Money makers." How men have succeeded by advertising ... [New York, The National advertiser, 1894]
[66] p. illus. 22ᶜᵐ.

1. Advertising.   CA 9–3961 Unrev'd
Library of Congress   HF5823.N27
(Copyright 1894: 34911)

NN 0032046 DLC

National advertisers' research, *Cleveland.*
Analysis of reports from public librarians upon reader
interest in periodicals, as observed in library reading
rooms. Cleveland, O., National advertisers' research,
°1917.
cover-title, 17 l. incl. diagrs. 23 x 28½ᶜᵐ.
"Summary of 111 reports from librarians of public libraries throughout
the United States."

1. American periodicals. 2. Bibliography—Best books—Period. I. Title.
Library of Congress   Z6945.N28   17–20041

NN 0032047 DLC

National advertising
see Advertising age and mail order
journal.

National advertising art center, inc., New York.
PN6161   Baker, George, 1882–
.B2758   Slightly soiled; a group of tales compiled and retold by
George Baker. 1st ed., December, 1944. [New York, National
advertising art center, inc., °1944.

National advertising company, New York.
America's advertisers: who they are, where they are, how
they have developed, and what they are doing at the
present time ... New York, The National advertising
co., 1893.

National advertising investments.
[New York]
v. tables. 31 cm.
Annual, 19   ; semiannual, 19
Published 19   by Magazine Advertising Bureau, inc.; 19
by Leading National Advertisers, inc.

1. Advertising — Yearbooks. 2. Advertising — U. S.—Stat.   I.
Magazine Advertising Bureau, inc. II. Leading National Advertisers,
inc.
HF5802.N3   659.1058   49–23553 rev*‡

NN 0032051 DLC MB OrU MtU CaBVaU

VOLUME 405

National advertising records ... v. 1–   Jan. 1925–
Chicago, The Advertising record company, inc.; [etc., etc.,]
1925–
    v.   35½ᵐ.
    Monthly, Jan. 1925–Mar. 1933; twice a month, Apr. 1933–
    Title varies: Jan. 1925–Jan. 1927, National advertising records; a
    monthly publication containing records of the size and cost of
    space used by all advertisers in America's leading weekly and
    monthly magazines.
    Feb. 1927–Dec. 1932, National advertising records ... a monthly pub-
    lication containing records of the size and cost of space used by
    advertisers in national advertising fields ... (varies slightly)
    Jan. 1933–   National advertising records ...
    Vols. 1–8 published in New York, etc., by Denney publishing company,
    inc.; v. 9– in Chicago, etc., by the Advertising record company, inc.
    1. Advertising—Period.
                                            35–16085
    Library of Congress   HF5801.N3
                               [2]   659.1

NN   0032052   DLC NN MiU

National Advertising Service, inc.
    College newspaper rate & reference guide...
    [19

    New York [etc.,] 19   nos.   23 x 31cm.
    Published by National advertising service, inc. (on cover of most issues: NAS).

    1. Advertising—Rates—U. S.   2. Advertising—Mediums—News-
    papers and periodicals. 3. Colleges   and universities—Student publications
    —U. S. I. National advertising   service, inc.
    N. Y. P. L.   October 26, 1950

NN   0032053   NN MiD

National advertising service, inc.
    876 college newspapers ...   New York city: National advertis-
    ing service, inc., c1937.   17 l.   28½cm.
    Caption-title.

    1. Colleges and universities—   Student publications—U. S.—Bibl.
    2. Advertising—Mediums—News-   papers and periodicals.
    N. Y. P. L.   October 27, 1938

NN   0032054   NN

National advertising service, inc.
    878 college newspapers, comprising all the known college news-
    papers publishing in the United States and possessions, and
    represented for national advertising by National advertising
    service, inc. ...   New York city: National advertising service,
    inc., c1938.   16 f.   27½cm.
    Caption-title.

    1. Colleges and universities—   Student publications—U. S.—Bibl.
    N. Y. P. L.   October 1, 1940

NN   0032055   NN

National advertising service, inc.
    Purchases and preferences in the college
    market
        see under   [Associated collegiate press]

National advisory board for fuels and structural mate-
    rials.
    Report. Proceedings of a conference of the National
    advisory board for fuels and structural materials, held
    at the Oriental hotel, Manhattan beach, New York city,
    August 10 and 11, 1906.   [New York? 1906?]
    6 p. l., 2–182 numb. l., 3 l., 10, 11 numb. l.   27ᵐ.
    Autographed from type-written copy.
    Appended: Boiler division, United States Geological survey fuel tests.
    Matters prepared for presentation at the New York conference ... by the
    engineer in charge of the Boiler division (L. P. Breckenridge) (Revised
    in accordance with action at above meeting) August 7, 1906 (10 numb. l.)—
    Brief outline of the work of the Gas producer division, and proposed lines for
    future investigations, by Prof. R. H. Fernald (11 numb. l.)
    1. Fuel—Testing.   2. Coal mines and mining.
                                        CA 22–292 Unrev'd
    Library of Congress   TP321.N3

NN   0032057   DLC DI-GS IaU

National Advisory Committee for Aeronautics
    see
    U.S. National Advisory Committee for
    Aeronautics.

HD5723   NATIONAL ADVISORY COMMITTEE FOR COMMUNITY SERVICE
.A43N27   PROJECTS.
              Conference...held Tuesday morning,May 21,1940–
           [Tuesday afternoon,Wednesday and Thursday,May 21,
           22,23,1940] ... Washington,D.C.,1940]
              2 pt. 27cm.
              Mimeographed.

              1.U.S. Work projects administration.

NN   0032059   ICU

National Advisory Committee for the Evaluation of Gamma
    Globulin in the Prophylaxis of Poliomyelitis.
        An evaluation of the efficacy of gamma globulin in the
    prophylaxis of paralytic poliomyelitis as used in the United
    States, 1953; report. [Washington, U. S. Govt. Print. Off.,
    1954]
        vi, 178 p. illus., maps. 26 cm. ([U. S.] Public Health Service.
    Publication no. 358. Public health monograph no. 20)
        Includes bibliographies.
        1. Gamma globulin. 2. Poliomyelitis. I. Title. (Series: U. S.
    Public Health Service. Publication no. 358. Series: U. S. Public
    Health Service. Public health monograph no. 20)
    RC180.5.G3N3   *616.9   616.83   54–61570

       PPT WaWW MoU PPWM
NN   0032060   DLC TU CU-M ViU DNLM OU PU-Med-TS PP

National Advisory Committee for the Evaluation of
    Gamma Globulin in the Prophylaxis of
    Poliomyelitis.
        Minutes of the 1st–   meeting, 1953–19–– .
    n. p., The Committee, 1953–
        v.   F.

NN   0032061   CaBViP

National advisory committee on agricultural
    services for Canada
        see   Canada. National advisory committee
    on agricultural services.

National Advisory Committee on Citizen
    Participation. Committee on the Role
    of the Board in Voluntary Agencies.
    First on the agenda. [n. p.] 1954.

NN   0032063   PU-PSW

National advisory committee on education.
    see.
    U.S. National advisory committee on education.

National Advisory Committee on Emergency
    Nursery Schools.
        see   U.S. National Advisory Committee
    on Emergency Nursery Schools.

HFMA83   National Advisory Committee on Farm Labor.
8N212   [Miscellaneous ephemeral materials not
MIS   fully catalogued.]

          Shelved in three different sizes.

NN   0032066   WHi

National advisory committee on illiteracy.
    ... For immediate release, June 4, 1931.
    Virginia, the hearthstone of democracy ...
    Washington, National advisory committee on
    illiteracy, 1931.

       3 numb. l.
       Mimeographed.

NN   0032067   ViU

National advisory committee on illiteracy.
    Illiteracy statistics for the state of
    Virginia, 1930. Washington, D. C., National
    advisory committee on illiteracy, 1930.

       [4] p.

NN   0032068   ViU

National advisory committee on illiteracy.
    Sub-committee on techniques.
    Gray, William Scott, 1885–
    ... Manual for teachers of adult illiterates, by William
    S. Gray. Prepared for Sub-committee on techniques ...
    Washington, D. C. [Washington, D. C., 1930]

National advisory committee on illiteracy. Subcommittee on
    techniques.
        Manual for teachers of adult literacy classes: A partial
    reproduction of Bulletin no. 1, January, 1930, by National ad-
    visory committee on illiteracy, prepared by Sub-committee on
    techniques, Washington, D. C. January 1934. Printed by per-
    mission of Sub-committee on techniques of the National ad-
    visory committee on illiteracy, Washington, D. C. and issued
    by Mississippi state Department of education in cooperation

    with Mississippi state Board of public welfare. Jackson, Miss.
    [1934]
        44 p. 23ᵐ. (On cover: Mississippi. Dept. of education. Bulletin
    no. 76)
        "Based largely on the manual prepared by the State Department of
    education of Louisiana."—Introd.
        1. Illiteracy—U. S. 2. Education of adults. [2. Adult education—
    U. S.] I. Mississippi. Emergency relief administration.
                                                E 38–434
    U. S. Off. of educ. Library
    for Library of Congress   [L166.B3 no. 76]
                                    [2]   (370.61762)

NN   0032071   DHEW

National advisory committee on illiteracy. Subcommittee on
    techniques.
        ... Manual for teachers of classes of illiterate adults (tenta-
    tive suggestions) Prepared by Sub-committee on techniques.
    Washington, D. C. [1930]
        44 p. 23ᵐ. (National advisory committee on illiteracy. Bulletin no.
    1. January, 1930)
        "Based largely on the manual prepared by the State department of
    education of Louisiana."—Introd.
        Dr. C. R. Mann, chairman.
        1. Illiteracy—U. S. 2. Education of adults. [2. Adult education—
    U. S.] I. Mann, Charles Riborg, 1869– II. Title. III. Title: Teach-
    ers of classes of illiterate adults, Manual for.
                                                E 31–831
    Library, U. S. Office of   Education LC151.N2 no. 1

NN   0032072   DHEW ViU CSt

National advisory committee on local health
    departments.
        Local health units for the nation
        see under title

National Advisory Committee on Local Health
    Units.
        Five State Regional Conference on Local
    Health Units, Salt Lake City, 1948
        see under title

National Advisory Committee on Local Health Units.
    Proceedings [of the] annual meeting.

    New York, National Health Council.
        v.   28 cm.

        1. Hygiene, Public—Congresses.   I. National Health Council.

    RA422.N15   55–38391

NN   0032075   DLC OrU-M DNLM NNC

VOLUME 405

W 6   NATIONAL Advisory Committee on Local
P3   Health Units
       Where do we stand on local health
units?   New York ₁1950?₎
     18 p. illus.
     Published jointly with the National
Health Council.
       1. Public health - U. S.   I. National
Health Council   Title

NN   0032076   DNLM

National Advisory Committee on Local Health
    Units
      see also   Missouri Valley Regional Con-
ference on Local Health Units, Omaha, 1949.

National Advisory Committee on Recreation Research
    see
National Recreation Association. National Advisory
Committee on Recreation Research.

National Advisory Committee on Recruitment,
   Training and Placement of Recreation Personnel
     see
National Recreation Association. National
Advisory Committee on Recruitment, Training
and Placement of Recreation Personnel.

National Advisory Committee on Research in the
   Geological Sciences
      see   Canada. National Advisory Committee on
Research in the Geological Sciences.

National advisory committee on research on
   egg and poultry subjects.

**Poultry products conference of scientific and technical work-
ers,** *Chicago,* 1935.
    Report of the Poultry products conference of scientific and
technical workers in connection with the fourth annual meeting of the National advisory committee on research, held under
the auspices of Institute of American poultry industries, University of Chicago, September 3–6, 1935. ₁Chicago, Institute
of American poultry industries, 1935?₎

National Advisory Committee on School Records
   and Reports.

    Financial accounting for public schools

    see under

    Foster, Emery Milton, 1891–

National Advisory Committee on the Employment of Older
   Men and Women
      see
    Gt. Brit. *Ministry of Labour and National Service. Na-
tional Advisory Committee on the Employment of Older
Men and Women.*

National advisory committee on WPA nursery schools
    see
U. S. *National advisory committee on WPA nursery schools.*

National Advisory Committee on Women's Participation, New York World's Fair, 1939–1940
    see   New York (City) World's Fair, 1939–1940.

National advisory council for physical education (*South
   Africa*)
      see
South Africa. *National advisory council for physical educa-
tion.*

National advisory council of better homes in America.
    Better homes in America; plan book for demonstration
week, October 9 to 14, 1922 ... ₁New York, Printed by the
Delineator, ₁1922₎
    cover-title, 1 p. l., 53 p. illus., diagr. 22½ᶜᵐ.

    1. Dwellings. 2. House decoration.   I. Title.

Library of Congress   NA7110.N3   CA 23–369 Unrev'd

NN   0032087   DLC DHEW OOxM

National Advisory Council on Education for Industry and
   Commerce (*Gt. Brit.*)
    see Gt. Brit. *National Advisory Council on Education
for Industry and Commerce.*

HD8072   **National advisory council on radio in education.**
.M643
    Miller, Spencer, 1891–   *ed.*
     American labor and the nation, edited by Spencer Miller,
jr. ... Chicago, Ill., The University of Chicago press ₁1933₎

National Advisory Council on Radio in Education.
    ... An annotated list of books recommended by
the American Library association for the radio
course "American labor and the nation".   New York,
author, n. d.
    9 l.
    Multigraphed.
    1. Radio lectures. 2. Arbitration, Industrial.
Bibliography.   3. Labor and laboring classes. U. S.
Bibliography.   I. American library association.

NN   0032090   WaPS

National advisory council on radio in education.
    ...Annual assembly... Scrapbook... ₁no.₎

₁Chicago? 193   v.   29cm.

    "Samples of stationery, programs, invitations, advance releases, mimeographed
speeches and speech releases, newspaper clippings. Arranged in chronological order."
    For scrapbook of fifth and final assembly, 1935, see: Institute for education by
radio. Scrapbook. Sixth annual Institute for education by radio combined with the
fifth annual assembly of the National advisory council on radio in education. May
6–7–8–1935.

    1. Radio in education—U. S.
N. Y. P. L.   July 3, 1940

NN   0032091   NN

National Advisory Council on Radio in Education,
   inc.
       ... Broadcasting abroad, ... 1932
         see under   International broadcasting
   union.

National Advisory Council on Radio in Education.
   Broadcasts on "psychology today"
      see its   ... Listener's notebook.

National Advisory Council on Radio in Education.
   Collective bargaining
      see under   Howard, Charles Pagelsen,
   1887–

₁National advisory council on radio in education₎

    Constructive economy in state and local govern-
ment; ₁a round–table discussion by₎ Thomas H.
Reed ... H. W. Dodds ... Luther Gulick ... Joseph
McGoldrick ... ₁and₎ Dorothy Straus ... ₁Chicago₎
The University of Chicago press ₁1932?₎
    1 p. l., 13 p.   23ᶜᵐ. (Government series lecture no.4)
    "Delivered September 27, 1932, over a nation-wide net-
work of the National broadcasting company."
    1. U. S.—Econ. condit.—1918–   2. Finance—U. S.
I. Reed, Thomas Harrison, 1881–   II. Dodds, Harold
Willis, 1889–   III. Gulick, Luther Halsey, 1892–
IV. McGoldrick, Josep   h Daniel, 1901–   V. Straus,
Dorothy   VI. Title.   VII. Ser.

NN   0032095   ViU

National Advisory Council on Radio in Education.
    Constructive economy in the national government
[by] Louis Brownlow [and others]   [Chicago] Univ. of
Chicago. Press [1932]
    12 p.   23 cm.   (Its Government series lecture
[ser. 2] no. 3)
    1. Finance. U. S.   I. Brownlow, Louis, 1879–

NN   0032096   ViU

National Advisory Council on Radio in Education.
    ...Consumers radio series.
Lecture no. 1–9 (April 30 – June 25, 1935)

Chicago: The Univ. of Chicago Press, 1935.   9 nos.   23cm.

    Weekly.
    Cover-title.
    At head of title: More for your money.
    Delivered over the Columbia network.

    1. Consumption (Economics)—   U. S.   2. Retail trade—U. S.
N. Y. P. L.   June 29, 1936

NN   0032097   NN OCU ICU

National Advisory Council on Radio in Education.
   Doctors, dollars and disease
      see its   Public health series lecture.

National advisory council on radio in education.
    Dramatizations broadcast as part of a series on vocational
guidance, presented under the auspices of National advisory
council on radio in education, inc., and arranged in cooperation
with the National vocational guidance association, from February 18 to April 24, 1932 over a coast-to-coast network of stations of the Columbia broadcasting system.   New York city,
National advisory council on radio education, inc. ₁1934₎
    1 p. l., 45 p.   23ᶜᵐ.
    1. Radio plays. 2. Vocational education.   I. National vocational
guidance association.   II. Title.

Library of Congress   PN6120.R2N3   38–31004
——— Copy 2.
Copyright   D pub. 59224   ₃₎   [792] 371.425

NN   0032099   DLC OrCS

National advisory council on radio in education.

    Economic aspects of the depression. [Chicago]
University of Chicago press [c1931]

    10 nos. in 1 v.   22cm.

    Contents: Reading guide. - Forerunners of the
present depression [by] Ernest L. Bogart. - Social
consequences of business depressions[by] Jane
Addams. - America and the balance sheet of Europe
[by] Harold G. Moulton. - International economic
interdependence [by] Edwin F. Gay. - Effects of
depressions on employment and wages [by] William

       M. Leiserson. - Business de-
pressions and business profits [by] William F.
Gephart. - Agriculture in relation to economic
prosperity [by] Edwin G. Nourse. - Wages in relation to economic recovery [by] Leo Wolman. -
Banking policies in relation to recovery [by]
Jacob H. Hollander. - Forward planning of public
works to stabilize employment [by] Otto T. Mallery.
    1. Economic conditions - 1918 - Add., ess., lec-
tures.   2. Social problems.   3. Panics.   I. Title:
The depression.

NN   0032101   NNCE

VOLUME 405

NATIONAL advisory council on radio in education.
Economic series presentation; lectures delivered Nov.12,1932 - June 10,1933, over a nationwide network of the National broadcasting company.
Univ.of Chicago press. 1932-33. 29 nos.
in 1 v.

nos.1-6 published as Economic series lectures.

NN 0032102   WaS Or IU OCU OO DL

National advisory council on radio in education.

Morley, Felix, 1894-   *ed.*
The economic world today, edited by Felix Morley ... Chicago, Ill., The University of Chicago press ₍ᶜ1933₎

National advisory council on radio in education.
₍Economics in a changing social order₎

₍New York?₎

NN 0032104   OC1

---

q330.973 National advisory council on radio in education.
N218e   ₍Economics of the new deal.   New York, League for industrial democracy, 1933-34₎
28 pieces in 2v.

Mimeographed radio broadcasts.

NN 0032105   IU OC1

HB34   NATIONAL ADVISORY COUNCIL ON RADIO IN EDU-
.N3   CATION.
...Economics series lecture no.[1]-
[Chicago]The University of Chicago press[c1931-
v. 22cm.

1.Radio in education--Societies. 2.Economics--Addresses,essays,lectures.

NN 0032106   ICU OC1 MB NN DL MH DNW

National advisory council on radio in education.

Reed, Thomas Harrison, 1881-   *ed.*
Government in a depression; constructive economy in state and local government, edited by Thomas H. Reed ... Chicago, Ill., The University of Chicago press ₍ᶜ1933₎

JA36   NATIONAL ADVISORY COUNCIL ON RADIO IN EDUCATION.
.N27   ... Government series lecture no.1-14; ₍ser.2₎ no.1-16; ser.3, no.1-24. ₍Chicago₎ University of Chicago press, 1932-33.
1 v.

1. Radio in education--Societies. 2. U.S.--Pol. & govt.--Addresses, essays, lectures.

NN 0032108   ICU DL MB WaS OC1 OO OCU NNU-W NN

National advisory council on radio in education.
FOR OTHER EDITIONS
SEE MAIN ENTRY
British institute of adult education.
Group listening; a report prepared for the National advisory council on radio in education, inc., by the British institute of adult education, October, 1933. Chicago, Ill., The University of Chicago press ₍1934₎

National advisory council on radio in education.
Information series.
no. 1-.
New York, National advisory council on radio in education, inc. ₍etc., 1931-
v. 19ᶜᵐ.

Some numbers issued in several revised editions -
Editor: 1931-   Levering Tyson.

1. Radio broadcasting. 2. Radio in education.
I. Levering, Tyson,   1889-   ed.

ICJ NN OC1 MH-L MiD ICRL MB
NN 0032110   NNC OrU OrCS OrLgE CU OCU MiU OO CSt-H

National Advisory Council on Radio in Education.
Labor series lecture.
no. 1-

Chicago: Univ. of Chicago Press₍, 1932   23cm.
nos.

Weekly.
Lectures "delivered...over a nation-wide network of the Columbia Broadcasting System."

NN 0032111   NN NNC OC1 MB DL

289x   National Advisory Council on Radio in
N277   Education.
1a   Law series I, lecture no.1-15. ₍Chicago₎
Law   University of Chicago Press ₍1933₎
Library   no. in   v.

Contents.- no.1. The American bar, its past leaders and its present aim, by C.E. Martin and W.J. Donovan.- no.2. Training for the bar, by Roscoe Pound.- no.3. Shall I become a lawyer? by J.G. Rogers.- no.4. The lawyers influence upon public opinion, by Samuel Seabury.- no.5. Pitfalls along the legal education road, by J.K. Clark.- no.6. Should the public distrust the lawyer? by J.H. Wigmore.- no.7. The lawyer and business, by S.H. Strawn.- no.8. What is the bar doing to improve the administration of justice? by G.A. Thompson.- no.9. Reforming the law through legislation, by H.W. Toll and E.R. Sunderland.

NN 0032113   CU OrU WaS ICU OC1 DLC

National advisory council on radio in education.

American bar association. *Council on legal education and admissions to the bar.*
The lawyer and the public, edited by the Council on legal education and admissions to the bar of the American bar association. Chicago, Ill., The University of Chicago press ₍ᶜ1933₎

National advisory council on radio in education.
Reed, Thomas Harrison, 1881-   *ed.*
Legislatures and legislative problems, edited by Thomas H. Reed ... Chicago, Ill., The University of Chicago press ₍ᶜ1933₎

National Advisory Council on Radio in Education.
...Listener's notebook.
no. 1-6

Chicago: Univ. of Chicago Press, 1931-32.   6 nos.   charts, illus.   22cm.

At head of title: no. 3-6, National Advisory Council on Radio in Education. Broadcasts on "Psychology today."
Later reissued with the Psychology series lectures in one volume. See entry under: Bingham, W. V. Psychology today.

1. Radio in education.
N. Y. P. L.   April 19, 1933

NN 0032116   NN MB MH DL

National Advisory Council on Radio in Education.
Local government legislative needs of 1933 [by] Henry W. Toll [and others]   [Chicago] Univ. of Chicago Press [1933]
12 p.   23 cm.   (Its Government series 3, lecture no. 6)
1. Local government. U.S. I. Toll, Henry W

NN 0032117   ViU

National Advisory Council on Radio in Education.
More for your money
see its   ... Consumers radio series.

National advisory council on radio in education.
... The National advisory council on radio in education. New York, Office of the council ₍1931₎
cover-title, 31 p. 19ᶜᵐ. (*Its* Information series. no. 1)
Levering Tyson, director.

1. Radio in education—Societies.   I. Tyson, Levering, 1889-
31-15061
Library of Congress   LB1044.5.N3
———— Copy 2.
Copyright A 38241   ₍3₎   371.333062

NN 0032119   DLC DHEW MB OrU OCU OEac MiU ViU

LB1044 National advisory council on radio in education.
.5   ... The National advisory council on radio in
N28   education. 2d ed., rev. August, 1931. New York
no.1   National advisory council on radio in education,
         1931.
         36 p.   21cm. (₍National advisory council on radio in education₎ Information series. no.1.
         Levering Tyson editor)

1. Radio in education - Societies. 2. Radio broadcasting.

NN 0032120   CU

National advisory council on radio in education.
... National advisory council on radio in education, inc. Rev., May, 1932. New York, 1932.
45 p. 19ᶜᵐ. (*Its* Information series. no. 1. Levering Tyson, editor)
Levering Tyson, director.
"Council publications": p. 19.

1. Radio in education—Societies.   I. Tyson, Levering, 1889-
32-21486
Library of Congress   LB1044.5.A1N3 1932
———— Copy 2.
Copyright A 53231   ₍3₎   371.333062 *

NN 0032121   DLC DHEW MiU ViU

National advisory council on radio in education.
National advisory council on radio in education, inc. ₍n. p., 1933?₎
1 p. l., 30 p. illus. 28ᶜᵐ.
"Council publications": p. ₍15₎

1. Radio in education—Societies.   I. Tyson, Levering, 1889-
E 34-594
Library, U. S. Office of   Education LB1044.5.A1N3 1933

NN 0032122   DHEW NN

National advisory council on radio in education.
... National advisory council on radio in education, inc. Rev., June, 1936. New York, 1936.
58 p. 19ᶜᵐ. (*Its* Information series. no. 1. Levering Tyson, editor)
Levering Tyson, director.
"Council publications": p.24-25.

———— Copy 2.
Copyright A 53231   ₍3₎   371.333062

NN 0032123   ViU OU OCU

National advisory council on   radio in education.
Proceedings
see its

Radio and education...

VOLUME 405

National advisory council on radio in education.
  Psychology pamphlets. Chic.University of Chicago[°1931]
  Illus.
  Contents. - Child development, bu Arnold Gesell,
and others. - Learning and forgetting, by Edward S.
Robinson. - Old prejudices and new schools in psychology, by Robert S.Woodworth. - Our social atti-
tudes, by Gardner Murphy. - Psychology: a modern
science of human management, by Walter R.Miles.

  1. Radio in ed   ucation - Societies.
  I. Tyson,   Levering, 1889-
  II. Title.

NN   0032125   OYesA

National Advisory Council on Radio in Education.   *3607.466
  Psychology series. Lecture no. 1-17. Delivered over . . . net-
work of the National Broadcasting Company. Oct. 17, 1931 -
Feb. 20, 1932.
— [Chicago.] University of Chicago Press. 1931, 32.   v. 21½
cm.

  Additional unbound parts, as received, may be found in covers on the
same call-number. They are not noted on this card until bound.

D547 — T.r. — National Broadcast. Company. Pubs. — Psychology. Period.
— Radio. In education.

NN   0032126   MB InU DL NN MH OrU

W 1   National Advisory Council on Radio in
NA231   Education
       Public health series lecture. no. 1-19;
       Oct. 1, 1934-Feb. 1935. [New York]
       19 nos.

       At head of title, no. 3-19: Doctors,
       dollars and disease.

       1. Health education - Radio broadcasts
       2. Medical economics - Radio broadcasts

NN   0032127   DNLM OCl

National advisory council on radio in education.
  Radio and education ... proceedings of the 1st
assembly of the National advisory council on radio in education, 1931-   Chicago, Ill., The University of Chicago
press [1931-
       v. 23½ cm.

Editor: 1931-   Levering Tyson.

  1. Radio in education—Societies.   I. Tyson, Levering, 1889-
ed.

LB1044.5.A1N25   371.33306273   31—28589

NN OC1 DHEW MnU NNC TxLT OC1BE
NN   0032128   DLC KEmT MB OC1 OO NcU OC1W OC1h MiU OU

National Advisory Council on Radio in Education.
  Reading guide.
  no. 1-3

Chicago: Univ. of Chicago Press, 1931-32.   3 nos.   22cm.

  "Prepared for the American Library Association by Felix Morley, the Brookings
Institution, to accompany a series of broadcasts."
  Ceased publication.
  Contents:
no. 1. Economic aspects of the depression.   1931.
no. 2. Proposed roads to economic recovery.   1932.
no. 3. New social responsibilities.   1932.

1. No subject. I. American Library   Association. II. Brookings
Institution, Washington, D. C.
N.Y.P.L.   December 20, 1935

NN   0032129   NN NNC DL ICU MB KyU

National Advisory Council on Radio in Education.
  Report of the director...
[19

[New York, 19   23cm.
  no.

1. Radio in education—U. S.
N.Y.P.L.
                                                September 6, 1934

NN   0032130   NN

National advisory council on radio in education.
FOR OTHER EDITIONS
SEE MAIN ENTRY
Koon, Cline Morgan, 1894-   comp.
  ... Some public service broadcasting; being a report on the
survey made by the National advisory council on radio in edu-
cation and the federal Office of education, compiled by Cline M.
Koon ... New York, National advisory council on radio in
education, inc., 1934.

National advisory council on radio in education.

Gruenberg, *Mrs.* Sidonie (Matsner) 1881-
  The use of the radio in parent education; report of a study
conducted by the Child study association of America in cooperation with the National council of parent education and
the National advisory council on radio in education; study
directed by Sidonie Matsner Gruenberg. Chicago, Ill., The
University of Chicago press [1939]

National Advisory Council on Radio in Education
see also **Joint Radio Survey Committee.**

National advisory council on radio in education. *Advisory
committee on engineering developments.*
  ... Present and impending applications to education of
radio and allied arts; report of the Committee on engineering developments. New York city, National advisory council on radio in education, 1931.
  5 p. l., [9]–94 p. 19 cm. ([National advisory council on radio in
education] Information series. no. 5. Levering Tyson, editor)
  A. N. Goldsmith, chairman.

  1. Radio in education. 2. Moving-pictures. 3. Moving-
pictures in education. 4. Television.   I. Goldsmith, Alfred Norton,
1887-

  Library of Congress   LB1044.5.N33   31—34921

                             [a49f1½]   371.333

NN   0032134   DLC DHEW OCU MB

National advisory council on radio in education. *Advisory
committee on engineering developments.*
  ... Present and impending applications to education of radio
and allied arts; report of the Committee on engineering developments. 2d ed., rev. New York, National advisory council on radio in education, 1932.
  5 p. l., [9]–95 p. 19ᶜᵐ. ([National advisory council on radio in edu-
cation] Information series. no. 5. Levering Tyson, editor)
  A. N. Goldsmith, chairman.

  1. Radio broadcasting. 2. Radio in education. 3. Moving-pictures,
Talking. 4. Moving-pictures in education. 5. Television.   I. Goldsmith, Alfred Norton, 1887-

  Library of Congress   LB1044.5.N33 1932   32—1864
  ——— Copy 2.
  Copyright A 45908   [5]   371.333

NN   0032135   DLC DHEW MiU ViU

National advisory council on radio in education. *Advisory
committee on engineering developments.*
  Present and impending applications to education of radio
and allied arts; report of the Committee on engineering developments. Chicago, Ill., The University of Chicago press
[1934]
  83 p. diagrs. 19ᶜᵐ.
  A. N. Goldsmith, chairman.
  "Council publications": p. 4–5.

  1. Radio broadcasting. 2. Radio in education. 3. Moving-pictures,
Talking. 4. Moving-pictures in education. 5. Television.   I. Goldsmith, Alfred Norton, 1887-

  Library of Congress   LB1044.5.N33 1934   34—40275
  ——— Copy 2.
  Copyright A 76888   [3]   371.333

NN   0032136   DLC

National advisory council on radio in education. *Advisory
committee on engineering developments.*
  ... Present and impending applications to education of radio
and allied arts; report of the Committee on engineering developments. Third revise April, 1934. New York, National
advisory council on radio in education, inc. [1934]
  83 p. diagrs. 19ᶜᵐ. ([National advisory council on radio in educa-
tion] Information series. no. 5. Levering Tyson, editor)
  A. N. Goldsmith, chairman.

  1. Radio broadcasting. 2. Radio in education. 3. Moving-pictures,
Talking. 4. Moving-pictures in education. 5. Television.   I. Goldsmith, Alfred Norton, 1887-

                                             E 35–106

  Library, U. S. Office of   Education LB1044.5.N33 1934

NN   0032137   DHEW MB CLSU OU

National advisory council on radio in education. *Advisory
committee on engineering developments.*
  ... Present and impending applications to education of radio
and allied arts; report of the Committee on engineering developments. 4th revise July, 1936. Chicago, Ill., The University of Chicago press [°1936]
  vii, 87, [1] p. diagrs. 19ᶜᵐ. ([National advisory council on radio in
education] Information series. no. 5)
  A. N. Goldsmith, chairman.

  1. Radio broadcasting. 2. Radio in education. 3. Moving-pictures,
Talking. 4. Moving-pictures in education. 5. Television.   I. Goldsmith,
Alfred Norton.

  Library of Congress   LB1044.5.N33 1936   37–199
  ——— Copy 2.
  Copyright A 99837   [5]   371.333

NN   0032138   DLC OU ViU

National advisory council on radio in education. *Advisory
committee on engineering developments.*
  ... Present and impending applications to education of radio
and allied arts; report of the Committee on engineering developments. 4th revise July, 1936. New York, National
Advisory Council on Radio in Education [°1936]
  vii, 87, [1] p. diagrs. 19ᶜᵐ. ([National advisory council on radio in
education] Information series. no. 5)
  A. N. Goldsmith, chairman.

NN   0032139   OU

National advisory council on radio in education. Committee on civic education by radio.
  National municipal league.
  Constructive economy in government ... broadcasts ... presented by the Committee on civic education by radio of the
National advisory council on radio in education and the American political science association, in coöperation with the
National municipal league. New York city, National municipal league [°1934]

National advisory council on radio in education. Committee on civic education by radio.
  National municipal league.
  The crisis in municipal finance ... broadcasts ... presented
by the Committee on civic education by radio of the National
advisory council on radio in education and the American
political science association, in coöperation with the National
municipal league. New York city, National municipal league
[°1934]

National advisory council on radio in
  education. Committee on civic education
  National municipal league. by radio.
  The 44 state legislatures of 1935 ... broadcasts ... presented
by the Committee on civic education by radio of the National
advisory council on radio in education and the American
political science association, in coöperation with the National
municipal league. New York city, National municipal league
[°1936]

National advisory council on radio in education. *Committee
on civic education by radio.*
  Four years of network broadcasting; a report by the Committee on civic education by radio of the National advisory
council on radio in education and the American political science association. Chicago, Ill., The University of Chicago
press [1937]
  v, 77, [1] p. 19ᶜᵐ.
  Account of the Committee's experience in the conduct of the "You
and your government" program over the NBC network, January 3,
1933, to June 9, 1936.
  1. Radio in education. 2. Radio broadcasting.   I. American political science association. II. Title.

  Library of Congress   LB1044.5.N35   37–24302
  ——— Copy 2.
  Copyright A 109832   [3]   371.333

NN   0032143   DLC OrU OrCS NNC OCU NN OU

National advisory council on radio in
  education. Committee on civic education
  National municipal league. by radio.
  A new deal in local government ... broadcasts ... presented
by the Committee on civic education by radio of the National
advisory council on radio in education and the American
political science association, in coöperation with the National
municipal league. New York city, National municipal league
[°1936]

VOLUME 405

National advisory council on radio in education. Committee on civic education by radio.
National municipal league.
Planning ... broadcasts ... presented by the Committee on civic education by radio of the National advisory council on radio in education and the American political science association, in coöperation with the National municipal league. New York city, National municipal league ₍ᶜ1936₎

National advisory council on radio in education. Committee on civic education by radio.
National municipal league.
Reviving local government ... broadcasts ... presented by the Committee on civic education by radio of the National advisory council on radio in education and the American political science association, in coöperation with the National municipal league. New York city, National municipal league ₍ᶜ1934₎

National advisory council on radio in education. Committee on civic education by radio.
National municipal league.
Taxation for prosperity ... broadcasts ... presented by the Committee on civic education by radio of the National advisory council on radio in education and the American political science association, in coöperation with the National municipal league. New York city, National municipal league ₍ᶜ1936₎

National advisory council on radio in education. Committee on civic education by radio.
National municipal league.
Trends of government ... broadcasts ... presented by the Committee on civic education by radio of the National advisory council on radio in education and the American political science association, in coöperation with the National municipal league. New York city, National municipal league ₍ᶜ1936₎

National Advisory Council on Radio in Education. Committee on Civic Education by Radio. 4229.419
You and your government. A listener's handbook. Prepared . . . to accompany a series of broadcasts [Government series lecture] . . . April 5–July 5, 1932, Sept. 6–Dec. 27, 1932.
— Chicago. The University of Chicago Press. 1932. 2 v. in 1. 22 cm.

D2178 — T.r. — Listener's handbo. A. — Radio. In Education. — United States. Pol. hist.

NN 0032149   MB Wa NN

National Advisory Council on Radio in Education. Committee on Engineering Departments
see   National Advisory council on Radio in education. Advisory committee on engineering developments.

National advisory council on radio in education. Committee on research.
Frost, S. E., 1899–
Education's own stations; the history of broadcast licenses issued to educational institutions ₍by₎ S. E. Frost, jr. ... Chicago, Ill., The University of Chicago press ₍1937₎

National Advisory Council on School Broadcasting.
Television in the classroom; report of a Canadian experiment
see under   Canadian broadcasting corporation.

National advisory council on school building problems.
Barrows, Alice, 1878–
Functional planning of elementary school buildings, by Alice Barrows, specialist in school building problems, Office of education ... United States Department of the interior, Harold L. Ickes, secretary. Office of education, J. W. Studebaker, commissioner. Washington, U. S. Govt. print. off.. 1937.

National Advisory Council on the Training and Supply of Teachers
see Gt. Brit. *National Advisory Council on the Training and Supply of Teachers.*

National Advisory Garden Committee.
... Report ...   Washington, D.C., 1942.
v.   28 cm.
Processed.
At head of title: Extension service, U.S. Dept. of agriculture.
1. Food for freedom program. 2. Vegetable gardening. U.S. I. U.S. Extension service.

NN 0032155   DNAL

National advisory group on 4-H postwar programs
see
U. S. *National advisory group on 4-H postwar programs.*

National Advisory Heart Council
see U. S. National Advisory Heart Council.

National Advisory Mental Health Council
see U. S. *National Advisory Mental Health Council.*

National advisory police committee on social protection
see
U. S. *National advisory police committee on social protection.*

The National advocate. v.1, no.1; Feb. 19, 1831. [Dublin]
14p. 20cm.   WB 58678

No more published?

1. Periodicals - Ireland.

NN 0032160   CtY

The National Advocate.   Independence, Ia.
v.
M.S. Hitchcock, editor and proprietor.

NN 0032161   NbHi

National advocate. v.1–
Dec.15, 1812–
[New-York]
50–58cm. daily.

Ceased publication Jan.31, 1829.
United with New York statesman to form New York morning herald.

NN 0032162   CtY OOC DLC

The national advocate. v.1-73 no.8; 178.05
1866-Oct.1938. New York, National   M277
Temperance Society.
73v.in 26cm. 10 nos.a year.

Title varies: v.1-32, 1866-1897, National temperance advocate.

1. Temperance - Period. 2. Liquor problem - Period. I. National Temperance Society and Publication House, New York.
x National temperance advocate.

NN 0032163 NcD MB CU OU   CLSU OCl ICJ OClWHi GEU OO MiU NN IEG

The NATIONAL advocate. v.1-   ; Jan.1866- New York.

Film reproduction. Master negative.

NN 0032164   NN

The National advocate. Devoted to the reclamation of the arid public domain by the construction of state and national irrigation works, and to the creation of rural homes as national safeguards. v. 1–   Jan. 1897–

San Francisco, The National advocate publishing company ₍1897–
v.   illus. 29½ᶜᵐ. monthly.
Cover portraits.
Subtitle varies.
Editors: 1897–   G. H. Maxwell.
1. Irrigation—Period. I. Maxwell, George Hebard, 1860-   ed.

Library of Congress   TC801.N3   6–3262†

NN 0032165   DLC

National advocate for the country. v.1–   Beinecke Library
Jan. 1813–   Folio
[New York, Published by Thomas Snowden,   AN33
etc.]   N5
54–56cm.   N2132

weekly, Jan. 1813–Jan. 1814; semiweekly, Jan. 1814–Jan. 1829.
Editors: Henry Wheaton;
Samuel S. Conant.
Ceased publication Jan.   1829.

NN 0032166   CtY

The NATIONAL advocates, a poem. Affection-   Y
ately inscribed to the Honourable Thomas Erskine,   185
and Vicary Gibbs, Esq....   London,J.Dabrett,1795.   .N 2
33p. 28cm.

NN 0032167   ICN CtY

National aegis, by Hector Ironside.   Rare Book
v.1, no.1-   ; Dec.2, 1801-Aug.24,   Collection
1831.   Worcester, Mass., S. Goodridge ₍etc.₎   AP2
v. illus. 49cm. weekly.   .A2 F38 Folio

Continued by National aegis and general advertiser.
Vol.1 bound with Farmer's museum, v.7,   ₍1₎ 1801-
1799.   1802 1799.

I.Ironside, Hector.

NN 0032168   NcU

NATIONAL AEGIS   Micro-card
Dec. 2, 1801-Dec. 27, 1820.   A
Worcester, Mass., R. Johnson; S. Goodridge;   6
S. Cotting; S. Nutting [etc.] 1801-1820.   .002
1 box(73 cards) 23cm.   (Early
American newspapers)   Box
Editors: "Hector Ironside"(Francis Blake),   100
Edward Bangs, etc.
For history of publication see Brigham, v. 1, p.418-19.
Microcard ed. by Readex Microprint for American Antiqua-   rian Soc., Worcester, 1966.

NN 0032169   ICN ViU

VOLUME 405

National aegis, Worcester, Mass.

₍Allen, George₎ 1792–1883.
Remarks on the attack of the "Family ægis" upon Judge
Allen. ₍Worcester, Mass., 185–₎

National Aero- and Astronautical Research Institute, *Amsterdam*
see
Netherlands (*Kingdom, 1815–*) *Nationaal Lucht- en Ruimtevaartlaboratorium.*

National Aeromedical Centre, *Soesterberg*
see
Soesterberg, Netherlands. Nationaal Luchtvaartgeneeskundig Centrum.

Gimbel
TLB
7
N27
1922

National Aeronautic Association of U.S.A.

Advance information on the second National
Aero Congress to form a National Aeronautic
Association ... Compiled by the Advance
Committee on Organization ... Detroit [1922]
30 p. illus., maps. 23cm.

1. Aeronautics - Societies, etc.

NN   0032173   CoCA OU DNW WaS

TL724
.5
.C5P8

National aeronautic association of U. S. A.

Putnam, Carleton, 1901–
Air transportation, new hope of free enterprise; an address
by Carleton Putnam, president Chicago and Southern air lines,
at the company's 10th anniversary dinner, sponsored by the
National aeronautic association, Washington, D. C., June 25,
1943. ₍Memphis, 1943₎

National Aeronautic Association of U.S.A.
Airport digest
see under   Airport digest;landing
facility development.

National aeronautic association of U.S.A.
Airports and the U.S.; an economic study
...   Washington, D.C., c1946.
1 v.   charts, tables.

Each section separately paged.
Folded table at end.
Manifold copy.

NN   0032176   MH-BA·

TL501
.N23

National aeronautic association of   U.S.A.
(incorporated)
Annual report of the president...
[Washington ? D.C., 19__]
1 pam.   8°

NN   0032177   DLC DSI

National aeronautic association of U.S.A. (inc.)
...Articles of association, by-laws, minutes of
first meeting of governors.
Washington, [1922]

TL501
.N3

NN   0032178   DLC DSI

---

q629.13
N211a

National aeronautic association of U.S.A.(incorporated)
Aviation jobs for veterans.   ₍Washington,
D.C., National aeronautic association, 1945?₎
15p.   diagrs.

Caption title.
Reprinted from National aeronautics.

1. Aeronautics--U.S.   2. Veterans--Employment--U.S.

NN   0032179   IU

TL501
.F26

National Aeronautic Association of U. S. A.

FYI, for your information; the Washington newsletter.   v. 1–
July 15, 1944–
Washington, National Aeronautic Assn.

National aeronautic association of U.S.A.
... Flight plan.   v.1, no.1-2, Mar.–Apr.
1946.   Washington, 1946.
1 v.

Merged with National aeronautics May 1946.

NN   0032181   MH-BA· WaS IU ICRL NN

National Aeronautic Association of U.S.A.
Instructions to delegates, alternates and
visitors to the annual convention of the National
aeronautic association of U.S.A. and the national
air races.   New York City,, October 8, 9, 10, 1925.

NN   0032182   DSI

National aeronautic association of U. S. A. (incorporated)
International air races; report of Contest committee, Lambert-St. Louis field, St. Louis, Mo. Sanctioned by National
aeronautic association of U. S. A., under rules and regulations
of F. A. I., October 3, 4, 5, 6, 1923.   ₍Washington? D. C., 1923₎
2 p. l., illus. (map) 8 fold. tab.   28 x 21¼ᶜᵐ.

"Compiled by B. Russell Shaw, executive vice-chairman."

1. Aeronautics.   I. Shaw, B. Russell, comp.   II. Title.

CA 29-547 Unrev'd

Library of Congress   TL740.I 6   1923 b

NN   0032183   DLC DSI

National aeronautic association of U. S. A. (incorporated)
International air races; report of Contest committee, Wilbur
Wright field, Dayton, Ohio ...   October 2, 3, 4, 1924.   ₍Washington, D. C., 1924₎
2 p. l., illus. (map) 12 fold. tab.   27¼ x 21¼ᶜᵐ.

Stamp of "Contest committee, National aeronautic association ...
Washington, D. C." on t-p.
"Sanctioned by National aeronautic association of U. S. A. under
rules and regulations of F. A. I."

1. Aeroplane racing.   I. Title.

Library of Congress   TL721.5.N3   31–4406
———— Copy 2.   629.13

NN   0032184   DLC DSI

National Aeronautic Association of U. S. A.
Joint private flying conference; ₍proceedings₎
see   Joint Private Flying Conference.
₍Proceedings₎

TL501
.N32

National aeronautic association of U. S. A.

National aeronautics.   v. 1–
Dec. 1, 1923–
₍Washington, etc.₎ National aeronautic association of
U. S. A., inc., 1923–

National Aeronautic Association of U.S.A.
National air races of 1926, "Model farms"
field, Philadelphia, Pennsylvania
see its   "Rules and entry blank; ...

Gimbel
TLC
71
N27

National Aeronautic Association of U.S.A.
(incorporated)
Official publication: 1935 National air
races, Cleveland Municipal Airport, Cleveland,
Aug. 30 to Sept. 2, 1935.   15th annual world's
premier air classic sponsored by National Air
Races of Cleveland, Inc. ...   Washington
[1935?]
52 p.   illus.   30.5cm.
1. Aeronautics - Competitions.   I. Title:
National air races.   1935.

NN   0032188   CoCA

National Aeronautic Association of U.S.A.
Official world, international and national
aircraft records, correct to April 25, 1939.
Washington ₍1939₎
Cover-title, 87 *l.*

NN   0032189   MH-BA·

TL725
.A1J6

National aeronautic association of U. S. A.

Joint airport users conference.
Proceedings. ₍1st₎   1944–
₍Washington, 1944–

National aeronautic association of U.S.A.
Proceedings ₍of the *National Aviation Clinic*₎
see under   National Aviation Clinic.

4TL
539

National Aeronautic Association of
U. S. A.
Rules and entry blank; National Air
Races 1926, Model Farms Field, Philadelphia, Pa., September 4 to 11, 1926.
1st ed. [
57 p.

NN   0032192   DLC-P4 WaS

National aeronautic association of U. S. A.
(incorporated)
Sporting aviation handbook. 1st ed. Washington, D. C.,
Contest board, National aeronautic association, °1936.

National Aeronautic Association of U.S.A.
State legislative report, 1947.   [n.p., Author,
1947]
1 v.   (Its Bulletin no. 1)

NN   0032194   Or

TL501
.W3

National Aeronautic Association of U. S. A.

Washington newsletter. v. 1–3, no. 13; Jan. 1, 1941–June
30, 1944. Washington, National Aeronautic Assn.

National aeronautic association of U. S. A.
We must get down to earth to get America into the air! A
realistic, practical program to create adequate landing facilities for both personal and commercial aircraft to serve every
community in America ... ₍Washington₎ National aeronautic
association ₍1944₎
cover-title, 1 p. l., 2-30 p. illus. 21¼ᶜᵐ.
Reproduced from type-written copy.

1. Airports--U. S.   I. Title.
                                                45–2531
Library of Congress   TL726.2.N28
                                        ₍3₎   629.136

NN   0032196   DLC

VOLUME 405

National aeronautic association of U. S. A. (incorporated)   *Academy of model aeronautics*
see
Academy of model aeronautics.

National Aeronautic Association of U.S.A. Air
Youth Division
see   Air Youth of America.

TL501
.A814
National Aeronautic Association of U. S. A.
Detroit chapter.

Aviation and yachting.

₍Detroit₎

TL501
.N325
National Aeronautic Association of U. S. A.
Greater St. Louis Chapter.

Wing tips.

₍St. Louis₎

NATIONAL AERONAUTIC ASSOCIATION of U.S.A. Southern
California chapter.
Handbook for avions. Prelim. ed. [Los Angeles
Air youth committee of Southern California chapter,
c1938] 93 l. 20cm.

1. Aeronautics--U.S., 1938. 2. Aeronautics as a profession. ₍. 1938.

NN   0032201   NN

National aeronautic association review
see
National aeronautics.

The **National** aeronautic magazine
see
National aeronautics.

The **National** aeronautic review
see
National aeronautics.

National Aeronautical Electronics Conference, *Dayton, Ohio*
see
National Aerospace Electronics Conference, *Dayton, Ohio.*

National Aeronautical Establishment
see
National Research Council, *Canada. National Aeronautical Establishment.*

TL505
N25
1928
National Aeronautical Safety Conference. 1st,
New York, 1928.
Aircraft sessions. ₍Papers presented at the₎
First National Aeronautical Safety Conference,
under joint auspices of the Daniel Guggenheim
Fund for the Promotion of Aeronautics and the
National Safety Council. ₍New York? 1928?₎
₍393₎-790 p. illus. 24ᶜᵐ.
Caption title.
At head of title: Seventeenth annual safety
congress, National Safety Council.

1. Aeronautics -   Congresses. I.National
Safety Council.   II.Daniel Guggenheim
Fund for the Pro   motion of Aeronautics,
Inc.

NN   0032207   CSt NBuG DL DAS DAL

National aeronautics. v. 1–
Dec. 1, 1923–
₍Washington, etc., National aeronautic association of
U. S. A., inc., 1923–
v. in illus. (incl. ports.) 28½-30½ᶜᵐ (v. 1-2 : 50ᶜᵐ) monthly.
Vol. 1 consists of one number only; v. 10, no. 11 (Nov. 1932) never
published.
Title varies: 1923–27, National aeronautic association review.
1928–Mar. 1930, The Aeronautic review.
Apr.–Aug. 1930, The National aeronautic review.
Sept. 1930–Mar. 1935, The National aeronautic magazine.
May–Aug. 1935, The New national aeronautic magazine.
Sept. 1935–Apr. 1937, The National aeronautic magazine.
May 1937–   National aeronautics.
Dec. 1923–   1924 published at Dayton, O.; 1928–Apr. 1929, at
Buffalo; Aug. 1929–Mar.   1930, at Baltimore.
1. Aeronautics—Period.   2. Aeronautics—U. S.   ɪ. National
aeronautic association of   U. S. A.
Library of Congress   TL501.N32   36–25980 (rev. '43)
                ₍43e2₎   629.1305

       OU FU
NN   0032208   DLC CoCA MdBE CU ICRL NN WaS OCl OCU

National aeronautics council, inc., New York.

Lyon, Thoburn Cassady, 1896–
Aerial navigation ₍by₎ Thoburn C. Lyon ... New York,
National aeronautics council, inc., 1942.

TL501
.A48
National Aeronautics Council, inc., New York.

Aeronautics.

₍Dunellen, N. J.₎ National Aeronautics Council.

TL685
.3
.G85
National aeronautics council, inc., New York.
Guthman, L   C
Aeronautics aircraft spotters' handbook, edited by L. C.
Guthman ... New York, National aeronautics council, inc.,
1943.

TL545
.A42
National Aeronautics Council, New York.
            FOR OTHER EDITIONS
            SEE MAIN ENTRY
Aeronautics, an authoritative work dealing with the theory
and practice of flying. General editor, Don Ryan Mockler;
advisory editors, Alexander Klemin, Holden C. Richardson
₍and₎ James E. Fechet. New York, National Aeronautics
Council ₍ᶜ1940–

National aeronautics council, inc., New York.

Webster, Sidney Haskins, 1908–
Aircraft and power plant accessory equipment ₍by₎ Sidney
H. Webster ... New York, National aeronautics council, inc.,
1941.

TL685
.3
.H3
National aeronautics council, inc., New York.
Hartney, Harold Evans, 1888–   ed.
... Aircraft spotters' guide ... edited by Lt. Col. Harold E.
Hartney. ₍New York, National aeronautics council, inc., 1942–

National aeronautics council, inc., New York.

Wilkinson, Paul H   1895–
Diesel aviation engines ₍by₎ Paul H. Wilkinson. New York,
National aeronautics council, inc., 1942.

TL586
.L8
1944
National aeronautics council, inc., New York.
Lyon, Thoburn Cassady, 1896–
Elementary air navigation ₍by₎ Thoburn C. Lyon ... New
York, National aeronautics council, inc., 1944.

National aeronautics council, inc., *New York.*
Elements of technical aeronautics. New York, National
aeronautics council, inc., 1942.
ix, 214 p. illus., diagrs. 22ᶜᵐ.
"The material first appeared in the magazine Aeronautics and was
largely revised for this work."—p. ix.
CONTENTS.—Theory of flight, by Alexander Klemin.—Aerodynamics of
the airfoil, by Alexander Klemin.—Forces acting on an airplane in flight,
by Alexander Klemin.—Lift increasing devices, by Alexander Klemin.—
General design data, by B. F. Ruffner.—Flutter and vibrations in aircraft, by S. B. Sherwin.—The airplane structure, by F. N. M. Brown.—
Principles of rotating wing aircraft, by V. R. Haugen.—Development and
operation of the autogiro, by O. H. Lunde.—Helicopters, by V. R. Haugen.—Aeronautical research, by S. P. Johnston.
1. Aeroplanes.   2. Aero-   dynamics.
Library of Congress   TL545.N28   43–2653
                 ₍20₎   629.13

NN   0032217   DLC WaS IEN

National aeronautics council, inc., New York.

Smith, Frederick H   1907–
Flying by instruments ₍by₎ Frederick H. Smith ... New
York, National aeronautics council, inc., 1942.

National aeronautics council, inc., *New York.*
Hand book of airplane maintenance and operation, a practical treatment of the assembly, service, maintenance and over-
haul of aircraft, engines and accessories, edited by specialists in
the field of aeronautics. New York, National aeronautics council, inc., 1944.
ix, 502 p. incl. illus., forms, diagrs. 22ᶜᵐ.
"General editor ... Ivor B. Yassin."—Foreword.

1. Aeroplanes—Maintenance and repair.   ɪ. Yassin, Ivor Benjamin,
1904–   ed.
Library of Congress   TL671.9.N3   44–6611
                 ₍7₎   629.134

NN   0032219   DLC WaS CaBVa

TL515
.R3
National aeronautics council, inc., New York.
Randers-Pehrson, Nils Henrik, 1899–
History of aviation ₍by₎ N. H. Randers-Pehrson ... New
York, National aeronautics council, inc., 1944.

National aeronautics council, inc., New York.

Harrison, Louis P.
Meteorology ₍by₎ Louis P. Harrison ... New York, National
aeronautics council, inc., 1942.

National aeronautics council, inc., New York.

Fechet, James Edmond, 1877–
Parachutes ₍by₎ Maj. Gen. James E. Fechet, Joe Crane
₍and₎ Glenn H. Smith. New York, National aeronautics
council, inc., 1942.

National aeronautics council, inc., New York.

Fechet, James Edmond, 1877–
Radio in airmanship ₍by₎ Maj. Gen. J. E. Fechet ... Lieut.
M. F. Eddy ... William P. Lear ₍and₎ Alan Bloch. New York,
National aeronautics council, inc., 1942.

VOLUME 405

National aeronautics council, inc., New York.

Moss, Sanford Alexander, 1872–
Superchargers for aviation ₍by₎ Dr. Sanford A. Moss ...
New York, National aeronautics council, inc., 1942.

TL685
.3
.H617   National aeronautics council, inc., New York.

Hoff, William Charles, 1912–   *ed.*
Warplane spotters' manual, edited by William C. Hoff ...
₍New York₎ National aeronautics council, inc., °1943.

National Aerospace Education Council.
U.S. aviation today. Washington, 1953–
v. illus., diagrs. 23 cm.
1. Aeronautics. U.S. 2. Aeroplanes. I. Title

NN   0032226   NcU

National Aerospace Education Council. Materials
of Instruction Committee.
Aircraft number 116: the story of the aircraft plant. Produced for students in aviation
education. Washington, 1954.
32 p. illus. 28cm.

"This booklet was prepared from a manuscript
submitted by Alfred J. Schutte."

NN   0032227   OrPS

National Aerospace Education Council. Materials
of Instruction Committee.
Aviation activities: produced for boys and
girls. Washington, 1954.
40 p. illus. 22 x 28cm.

"This booklet may be used to accompany
[the author's] Look to the sky."

NN   0032228   OrPS

National Aerospace Education Council. Materials
of Instruction Committee.
Helicopters. Washington [1954]
32 p. illus. 28cm. (Aviation education
booklet, 3)

NN   0032229   OrPS ViU OOxM OrP

National Aerospace Education Council. Materials
of Instruction Committee.
Jets. Washington, 1953.
31 p. illus. 22 x 28 cm. (Aviation education
booklet, 2)

NN   0032230   OrPS OrU ViU

National Aerospace Education Council. Materials
of Instruction Committee.
Look to the sky: a picture book of aviation
for boys and girls, with questions to discuss
with the children and concepts to be developed
by the teacher. Washington [1954]
32 p. illus. 22 x 28 cm. (Aviation education
booklet, 1)

First published August, 1953.

NN   0032231   OrPS OrU ViU IU

National Aerospace Electronics Conference, *Dayton, Ohio.*
Proceedings. 1952–
₍Dayton, Ohio₎
v. illus., diagrs. 24–28 cm. annual.

None published for the first 3 conferences, 1949–51.
Title varies: 1952–   Abstract of papers delivered.—19   –55,
A compendium of technical papers.
Some vols. have also distinctive titles: 1952–54, Airborne electron-
ics digest (varies slightly)—1955, Aeronautical electronics digest.
Issued by the conference under earlier names: 1952–54, National
Conference on Airborne Electronics; 1955–58, National Conference on
Aeronautical Electronics; 1959–   National Aeronautical Electron-
ics Conference.

Conferences sponsored by the Dayton Section and the Professional
Group on Aerospace and Navigational Electronics (called 1952–
Professional Group on Airborne Electronics; 19   –59, Professional
Group on Aeronautical and Navigational Electronics) of the Institute
of Radio Engineers.
1. Electronics in aeronautics—Societies, etc. 2. Astrionics—Societies, etc. I. Institute of Radio Engineers. Dayton Section. II.
Institute of Radio Engineers. Professional Group on Aerospace and
Navigational Electronics. III. National Aerospace Electronics Conference, Dayton, Ohio. Abstract of papers delivered. IV. National Aerospace Electronics Conference, Dayton, Ohio. A compendium of
technical papers. V. Title: Airborne electronics digest. VI. Title:
Aeronautical electronics digest.

TL693.N3   61–2171 rev

     ICJ WaS TxDaM
NN   0032233   DLC TxU CaBVaU OU N   NBuU NSyU MiD

National Aero-space Instrumentation Symposium
see
ISA Aerospace Instrumentation Symposium.

National affairs [Toronto]
see   Marxist review.

National Affairs Association
₍Address to the Native Affairs
Association₎ on the Native Land
Husbandry Act, February 15, 1952.
Nyasaland.
21 ℓ.

NN   0032236   MBU

M306
N19c   **National Afro-American Council.**
Constitution and by-laws of the National
Afro-American Council, held in New York City,
October 9, 10, and 11, 1906.
Louisville, Ky. Dispatch printing Co.
1907.
70 p. 19cm.

NN   0032237   DHU

National Afro-American council.
The National Afro-American council, organized 1898.
A history of the organization, its objects, synopses of
proceedings, constitution and by-laws, plan of organization, annual topics, etc. Comp. by Cyrus Field Adams,
secretary ... Washington, D. C., C. F. Adams, 1902.
29, ₍2₎ p. 23ᶜᵐ.

1. Negroes—Societies. I. Adams, Cyrus Field, comp.

                               12–2893
Library of Congress   E185.5.N27

NN   0032238   DLC

E185
.61
.M485   National Afro-American Council.

Mebane, George Allen, comp.
"The Negro problem" as seen and discussed by Southern
white men in conference, at Montgomery, Alabama, with
criticisms by the Northern Press. Prepared and compiled
for the National Afro-American Council by Geo. Allen
Mebane. New York, Alliance Pub. Co., 1900.

National agents' record.
Detroit, National Casualty Co.
v. illus. monthly.

Center has:

NN   0032240   ICRL

The national agreement of professional base ball
associations...
see under   Board of Arbitration representing
the National League of Professional Base Ball Clubs
and the American Association of Base Ball Clubs.

National Agricultural Advisory Commission
see   U.S. National Agricultural Advisory
Commission.

A225
N21   **National Agricultural Advisory Commission;**
₍directory₎
Washington.

1. U.S. National Agricultural Advisory
Commission. Directories. I. U.S. Dept. of
Agriculture. Office of the Secretary.

NN   0032243   DNAL

National Agricultural Advisory Service
see   Gt. Brit. *National Agricultural Advisory Service.*

National agricultural and industrial development
association, Dublin.
Historical record, Golden jubilee 1905–1955

see under

McCaul, J   G   ed.

National Agricultural and Rural Affairs Conference
see   National Agricultural Credit Conference.

National agricultural association [Founded 1879]

see

American agricultural association.

National agricultural association. *1st congress, Nashville,
Tenn.,* 1871.
Address to the agricultural organizations in the United
States. Prepared by a committee in obedience to a reso-
lution by the National agricultural association, together
with constitution and proceedings. Nashville, Tenn.,
Printed at Union & American book and job office, 1871.
26 p., 1 l. 22ᶜᵐ.

1. Agricultural societies.

                               15–11913
Library of Congress   S22.N26

NN   0032248   DLC TU

National Agricultural Aviation Conference. *1st, Fort
Worth, Tex.,* 1949.
Transcript. Fort Worth, 1949.
9X, 70 l. 27 cm.

1. Aeronautics—Congresses. 2. Aeronautics in agriculture.
3. Spraying.
TL722.1.N3 1949   629.13863   50–30397

NN   0032249   DLC

VOLUME 405

284.29
N215   **National Agricultural Bank of Libya.**
      Annual report of the Board of Direc-
      tors.
      ₍Tripoli₎

         1. Agricultural banks. Libya.
         2. Agricultural credit. Libya.

NN   0032250   DNAL MBU

381
N216   **National Agricultural Chemicals Association.**
      Annual report.

      Washington,

         1. Chemicals, Agricultural.

NN   0032251   DNAL

HE2321   National Agricultural Chemicals Association.
.I5D8

     Dun and Bradstreet, inc. *Marketing Services Company.*
       Cross haulage of insecticides, 1942. A survey made for
     the Agricultural Insecticide and Fungicide Association. By
     Research & Statistical Division, Dun & Bradstreet, inc. New
     York, ᵒ1943.

     National Agricultural Chemicals Association.
       Law chart; laws regulating distribution and sale of agri-
     cultural chemicals. Rev. Washington, 1955.

       sheet. 36 x 60 cm. fold. to 30 x 19 cm.

       1. Agricultural chemicals—Law and legislation—United States—
     States—Indexes.   I. Title.

     KF3959.Z95N38   1955   343′.73′08556686   74–160682
                                                  MARC

NN   0032253   DLC

     National Agricultural Chemicals Association.
Law

     Conner, John Davis, 1911–
       Manual of chemical products liability; an analysis of the
     law concerning liability arising from the manufacture and
     sale of chemical products, prepared by John D. Conner and
     George A. Burroughs. ₍Washington₎ Manufacturing Chem-
     ists' Association and National Agricultural Chemicals Asso-
     ciation, ᵒ1952.

     National Agricultural Chemicals Association.
     N.A.C. news and pesticide review
       see under title

     National Agricultural Chemicals Association.
     News and pesticide review
       see   N.A.C. news and pesticide
     review.

     National Agricultural College, Farm School,
     Pa.
       see Farm School, Pa. National Agricul-
     tural College [Supplement]

238.29
N21   **National Agricultural Communications Con-
      ference, Michigan State College, 1954.**
      Agricultural communications; operations,
      training, research, administration. A re-
      port on the National Agricultural Communica-
      tions Conference. ₍n.p.₎, 1954₎
      32 p.

        1. Agriculture. Public relations.
        2. Journalism,   Agricultural. I. Nation-
      al Project in   Agricultural Communica-
      tions. II. Title.

NN   0032258   DNAL

     National agricultural conference, *Washington, D. C.,*
     1922.
       ... Report of the National agricultural conference.
     January 23–27, 1922 ... Washington, D. C. ... Washing-
     ton, Govt. print. off., 1922.

       1 p. l., 210 p. 23ᶜᵐ. (₍U. S.₎ 67th Cong., 2d sess. House. Doc. 195)
     Ordered printed March 3, 1922.

       1. Agriculture—Congresses. 2. Agriculture—U. S.   I. Title.

     Library of Congress   HD1753 1922a   22–26269

OO OU OClW TU DFT

NN   0032259   DLC DNAL CU NcRS MtBC WaS OrU OrCS OCl

HD   National Agricultural Conference, Washing-
1753   ton, D. C., 1922.
1922b   ₍Stenographic records₎   Washington,
      1922.
      128 l.   36 cm.

       Bound with this report are *its* Program
     and list of invited delegates, *its* Committee
     assignments and *its* Report of committees
     adopted...

        1. Agricul   ture - Congresses.

NN   0032260   NIC

     National Agricultural Conference, Toronto,
     1932.
       National Agricultural Conference, called by
     the Hon. Robert Weir, Minister of Agriculture,
     Ottawa; held at the Royal York Hotel, Toronto,
     Aug. 29 to Sept. 1, 1932.

       83 p.

NN   0032261   CaBVaU

     National agricultural congress. *1st, St. Louis,* 1872.
       Proceedings of the National agricultural congress,
     held at St. Louis, Missouri, May 27 to 30, 1872. Indian-
     apolis, Sentinel company, printers, 1872.

       84 p. 23½ᶜᵐ.

       1. Agriculture—Congresses. 2. Agriculture—U. S.

                                       12–12325

NN   0032262   DLC

     National agricultural congress. 2d, Indianapolis, 1873.
       Proceedings of the National agricul-
     tural congress held at Indianapolis,
     Indiana, May 28, 29, and 30, 1873.
      66p. 22cm.

NN   0032263   OFH

     National agricultural congress. *5th, Philadelphia,* **1876.**
       Proceedings of the fifth annual session of the **National**
     agricultural congress, at Philadelphia, Pa., September
     12th, 13th and 14th, 1876 ... Chicago, Prairie farmer
     company, printers, 1877.

       74 p. 22½ᶜᵐ.

       1. Agriculture—Congresses. 2. Agriculture—U. S.

                                       18–5388

     Library of Congress   S22.N265 1876

NN   0032264   DLC CU

     National agricultural convention, *Washington, D. C.,* 1872.
       ... Proceedings of the National agricultural conven-
     tion, held at Washington, D. C., February 15, 16, and 17,
     1872. Washington, Govt. print. off., 1872.

       84 p. 22½ᶜᵐ. (₍U. S. 42d Cong., 2d sess. Senate. Mis. doc. 164)

       1. Agriculture—Congresses. 2. Agriculture—U. S.

                                   Agr 12–30 x
     U. S. Dept. of Agriculture   Libr. 1Ag85N
     Library of Congress   S22.N275

NN   0032265   DNAL MBH NcU TU ICJ

     **National agricultural cooperating committee of
     the United States.**

     **Inter-American conference on agriculture, forestry and ani-
     mal industry.** *1st, Washington, D. C.,* 1930.
       Documentary material on the Inter-American conference on
     agriculture, forestry and animal industry, Washington, D. C.,
     September 8 to 20, 1930 ... ₍pt. I–II₎ Washington, D. C.,
     1929–30.

     National agricultural cooperating committee of
     the United States.

     Inter-American conference on agriculture. *1st, Washington,
     D. C.,* 1930.
       Documentos relativos a la Conferencia inter-americana de
     agricultura, selvicultura e industria animal. pte. I₍–II₎ Wásh-
     ington, D. C., 1929–30.

     National Agricultural Credit Committee.
       Report of meeting.
     [Chicago?]
       1. Agricultural credit. U.S. 2. Agricultural
     finance. U.S.

NN   0032268   DNAL

     National Agricultural Credit Conference.
       Proceedings.
     New York, Agricultural Commission, American Bankers
     Association.

       v. diagrs. 21–23 cm. annual.

       First conference held in 1952.
       Conferences for   sponsored by the Agricultural Commit-
     tee of the American Bankers Association under the committee's earlier
     name: Agricultural Commission.

       1. Agricultural credit—U. S.—Congresses.   I. American Banker .
     Association. Agricultural Committee.

     HG2051.U5A5974   54–39389 rev

NN   0032269   DLC PPULC ScU OU IdU NcRS NBu

     National agricultural exhibition and horse fair,
                     Washington, D. C., 1867
            see
     Washington, D.C. National agricultural exhibition
                     and horse fair, 1867.

     National Agricultural Experiment Station, Tokyo
       see   Nōji Shikenjō, Tokyo.

HD
192S   National agricultural laborers' union. Execu-
.N28   tive committee.
       Evidence on the cause of the present agricul-
     tural depression obtained from practical and
     bona-fide farm labourers, issued by the authority
     of the Executive committee of the N.A.L.U. ...
     Leamington, Curtis and Beamish, 1880.

       32 p.incl.tables. 21½ cm.

       Preface signed: Joseph Arch.

       1.Agriculture   --Economic aspects--
     Gt.Brit.   I.   Title.

NN   0032272   MiU

     National Agricultural Library
       see   U.S. National Agricultural Library.

VOLUME 405

National agricultural limestone association,
Columbus, Ohio.
Dollars and sense; spreading the gospel limestone; making two dollars grow where one dollar
grew before. ₍Columbus, Ohio, The National
agricultural limestone association, n.d.₎
40p.

NN 0032274   OU

National Agricultural Limestone Association, *Washington,
D. C.*
        see
National Agricultural Limestone Institute, *Washington,
D. C.*

57.9
N219   National Agricultural Limestone Institute,
Washington, D.C.
        Membership letter.

        Washington.

        1. Limestone. Societies.

NN 0032276   DNAL

57.9
N2142   National Agricultural Limestone Institute, *Washington, D.C.*
        National Soil Conservation Committee.
        News service.
        Washington.

        1. Lime.

NN 0032277   DNAL

National agricultural organization society.
        Announcement of the National agricultural organ-
ization society, with constitution and by-laws...
Madison, Wis., [1915]

HD1485
.N3A3

NN 0032278   DLC OrCS OO

National Agricultural Organization Society.
        Announcement of the National Agricultural Organization
Society, with constitution and by-laws, created by the delegates
to the 1915 sessions of the National Conference on Marketing and
Farm Credits.   Madison, Wis. ₍1917.₎   15 p. incl. forms.   8°.
(National Agricultural Organization Soc. ₍Circular 1.₎)

1. Cooperation (Agricultural), U. S.   2. Series.
N. Y. P. L.   August 14, 1919.

NN 0032279   NN

S   National Agricultural Organization Society.
1   Circular. no. 1-8.
N28   Madison, Wis., 1916-17.
        1 v. 23 cm.

        1. Agriculture - Societies, etc.

NN 0032280   IU LNH CU OO NN OrCS WaS OCl

National agricultural society.

The **Agricultural** digest; pub. under the auspices of the
National agricultural society. v. 1-
May 1916-
New York, N. Y., The Agricultural press, inc., 1916-

NATIONAL AGRICULTURAL SOCIETY, *Victoria, Australia.*
        Report of proceedings.   1880-89.
                Melbourne : Walker, May & co. [etc.].   1881-90.

NN 0032282   MB

National agricultural society, *Washington, D. C.*
        Mode of manufacturing sugar from the corn stalk, and
of oil and stearine from lard, &c. Pub. by the National
agricultural society. Washington, J. & G. S. Gideon,
printers, 1842.

        1 p. l., 22 p. illus. 24ᶜᵐ.
        Three articles by William Webb, C. Morfit and John H. Smith, respec-
tively.

        1. Maize sugar. 2. Lard-oil. 3. Stearin.   I. Webb, William, of Wil-
mington, Del. II. Smith, John H. II. Morfit, Campbell, 1820-1897.

Library of Congress   TP149.N27   8—15631
——— Copy 2.   ₍Rural economy pamphlets, v. 5, no. 8₎
                            S405.R94 vol. 5

NN 0032283   DLC MH MiU-C

Pam
HD1485
.F25T2   National Agricultural Wheel. Tennessee.
        Constitution and by-laws of the state &
subordinate agricultural wheel, of the State
of Tennessee, together with the constitution
and by-laws of the National Agricultural
Wheel, of the United States of America.
Fulton, Ky., Toiler Print, 1887.
        19 ₍1₎ p. 22 cm.

        Cover title.

NN 0032284   T

HD5856
U52C2   National Agricultural Workers Union .
N36   American and foreign farm workers in California; statement to
Social   the President's Commission on Migratory Labor, by Ernesto Galarza.
Sciences   [Washington, D. C., 1950]
             30 p.

        1. Migrant labor - California.   I. Galarza, Ernesto, 1905-
II. U. S. President's Commission on Migratory Labor.   III. Title.

NN 0032285   CU

National agricultural workers union.
        Constitution.   ₍n. p., 1951₎   13 p.   16cm.

        Cover title.
        "America's farm union."

        1. Trade unions, Agricultural—   U. S.

NN 0032286   NN

HFBA29   National Agricultural Workers Union.
N213
MIS   [Miscellaneous ephemeral materials not
        fully catalogued.]

        Shelved in three different sizes.

NN 0032287   WHi

National agricultural workers union.
        Proceedings ... convention.   Washington, D. C.

        Supersedes National Farm Labor Union.
        Proceedings of convention.

NN 0032288   MH-IR

National agricultural workers union.
        A report on trade unions in Hawaii and recommendations sub-
mitted by Ernesto Galarza, vice-president and director of research, National agricultural workers union, September 1, 1955.
₍Washington? 1955₎   49 l.   29cm.

        Cover title.
        At head of title: Confidential.

        1. Trade unions—Hawaii.   I. Galarza, Ernesto, 1905-

NN 0032289   NN

National Agricultural Workers Union
        see also
National Farm Labor Union.
Southern Tenant Farmers' Union.

HD8039
S852U6   National Agricultural Workers Union .
N36   Research and Education Dept.
Social   The Louisiana sugar cane plantation workers, vs. the sugar
Sciences   corporations, U. S. Department of Agriculture, et. al.   Washing-
             ton, D. C., Inter-American Educational Association, 1954.
             159 p. plates, tables, facsims.

        "An account of human relations on Corporation - owned Sugar
Cane Plantations in Louisiana under the Operation of the U. S.
Sugar Program 1937-1953. "

        1. Sugar workers - Louisiana.

NN 0032291   CU

SF   National agriculturist and bee journal for
521   the farm, apiary and fireside. v. 1-
N277   18 -   New York.
             v. illus. 42 cm. monthly.

        Title varies: Bee-keepers'
journal and national agriculturist.

        1. Bees - Periodicals. I. Bee-keepers'
journal and   national agriculturist.

NN 0032292   NIC

National agriculturist and bee journal for the farm,
apiary and fireside
        see also
Bee-keepers' journal and national agriculturist.
Bee-keepers' journal and agricultural repository
for the apiary, farm and fireside.

                                                *5990.8
National Agriculturist, The, and Pennsylvania Farm Journal, devoted
to agriculture, horticulture and rural economy. Combined papers,
vol. I
Pittsburgh, Pa. Beckham & Long. 1868. v. Illus. 4°.
Contains National Agriculturist, vol. 9, and Farm Journal, vol. 14.

F5523 — Agriculture. Period. — Periodicals.

NN 0032294   MB

National air brakes ...
        see under   National brake & electric co.

National air cargo conference, *Detroit, 1944.*
        Outlook for air cargo in fresh produce; addresses delivered
at the National air cargo conference held in Detroit on March
23, 1944, under the auspices of Wayne university and the Detroit Board of commerce, to discuss the postwar prospects of
transporting fresh fruits and vegetables by aircraft, ed. by N.
Stanley Oates ... Detroit, Mich., Wayne university press,
1944.
        vii, ₍1₎, 91, ₍1₎ p. diagrs. 22 cm.   (*On cover:* Wayne university
studies in air transport, no. 2)
        1. Aeronautics, Commercial—Freight. 2. Farm produce—Trans-
portation.   I. Oates, N. Stanley, ed. II. Title.
        TL720.7.W3 no. 2   A 45—4876
                                (387.7082) 387.744
Minnesota. Univ. Libr.
for Library of Congress   ₍a51f½₎†

        ViU DLC
NN 0032295   MnU MsU NjP WaTC CaBViP TxU MH-BA

National air clinic
        see
National aviation clinic.

VOLUME 405

National Air Council.
Bulletin. v. 1, no. 1–4; Aug.–Dec. 1945. ₍New York₎
1 v. illus., ports. 35 cm. monthly.
Issued by the council under its earlier name: Air Power League.

1. Aeronautics—Societies. 2. Air power—U. S.

UG633.N32   358.405   48–14819*

NN   0032297   DLC MH-BA NN

629.13   **National air council.**
qN271   Industrial preparedness. Education in
aviation; a record of the aviation forum
held November 18, 1946, at the National
aircraft show, Cleveland, Ohio.   ₍N.Y.₎
Air power league, 1946.
37p. ports. 28cm.

1.Aeronautics. 2.Efficiency. Industrial.
I.Title.

NN   0032298   N WaS Or OrU ICJ IU MH-BA NN

TL501   **National Air Council.**
.N334
The National air review. Mar. 1949–
₍New York₎ National Air Council.

National Air Council.
Peace through air power, a report by the Air Power
League. ₍New York 1946₎
32 p. illus. (part col.) col. maps, diagrs. 28 cm.

1. Aeronautics, Military—U. S.   I. Title.

UG633.N35   358.3   47–6230 rev*

NN   0032300   DLC Or ICJ IU NNU-W MiU

National Air Council.
Report.

₍New York?₎
v. illus. 28 cm.
Reports for   issued by the council under its earlier name: ·
Air Power League.

1. Air power—Societies.

UG630.N37   48–23125*‡

NN   0032301   DLC WaS MH-BA

National air institute.
First National air institute under auspices of the Detroit aviation society. Arranged by committee representing National advisory committee for aeronautics,
Society of automotive engineers, American society of
mechanical engineers, Aeronautical chamber of commerce
of America, inc. Participated in by the foregoing and
also by members of American bankers association, American bar association, National aircraft underwriters association. Preliminary to third National airplane races
and second National aero congress ... Detroit, Mich. ...
October 11, 1922. ₍Detroit, Saturday night press, 1922?₎
46 p., 1 l. 23cm.
1. Aeronautics—Con-   gresses.   I. Detroit aviation society.
                                        CA 24–177 Unrev'd
Library of Congress   TL505.N3 1922
————— Copy 2.

NN   0032302   DLC Or

National Air Institute.
₍Papers presented at the annual meeting.₎
₍no.₎ 1–

₍Detroit, etc., 1922–
nos.   8°.

Cover-title.
₍no.₎ 1 in: VDY p. v. 27, no. 7.

NN   0032303   NN WaS

National air pilots' association.
Journal; official publication of the National air pilots' as-
sociation ...
Cleveland, O. ₍19
v. illus. 23cm. monthly.
January, July 1931. Membership number.

1. Air pilots—Societies.   I. Title.

                                        CA 33–1146 Unrev'd
Library of Congress   TL501.N33

NN   0032304   DLC OCl NN WaS

National Air Pollution Symposium.
Proceedings. 1st–   1949–
Los Angeles.
v. illus., diagrs. 28 cm. annual.
"Sponsored by Stanford Research Institute in co-operation with
California Institute of Technology, University of California, Univer-
sity of Southern California."

1. Air—Pollution—Congresses.

RA577.A1N3   614.706373   51–4370

          OrU IdPI
     NcRS ICU DNLM NNC DAS ICJ NN DAU FTaSU MH-BA CaBVa
NN   0032305   DLC Or OrP OrCS OrPR WaS CU PU-FA TxU

M10.42   **National Air Pollution Symposium, 2d, Pasadena,**
N277a   **Calif.**
Abstracts and biographies on papers and
speakers for the Second National Air Pollution
Symposium. ₍Pasadena, Calif.?₎, 1952.
1 v.(unpaged) 28cm.

Sponsored by Stanford Research Institute
with the cooperation of California Institute
of Technology, University of California at Los
Angeles ₍and₎ University of Southern Califor-

nia.
Meetings held May 5 and 6, 1952, Huntington
Hotel, Pasadena, California.
Contents.—Session I. Our knowledge of at-
mospheric pollutants: status report.—Session
II. Fundamental chemistry and physics of the
atmosphere.—Session III. Combustion as a con-

tributor to air pollution.—Session IV. Biological aspects of air pollution.

NN   0032308   DAS

National Air Pollution Symposium. 3rd,
Pasadena, 1955.
Air pollution situation in Los Angeles
see under   Hitchcock, Lauren
Blakely, 1900–

National Air Races
Official directory & log. National air races.
Cleveland, O.

Library has
8th   1939–

Sanctioned by the National Aeronautical Association, Washington, D. C.; held under rules of
the Federation Aeronautique Internationale.
On cover: 1939.   World's premier air
classic.

NN   0032310   MiD

National Air Races .
Official publication: 1935 National air races,
Cleveland Municipal Airport, Cleveland, Aug. 30 to
Sept. 2, 1935
see under   National Aeronautic Association
of U.S.A.

Press and radio manual.
Cleveland.   v.   28cm.

1. Aeronautics—Meets—U.S.

NN   0032312   NN OCl

The **National** air review. Mar. 1949–
₍New York₎ National Air Council.
v. illus., maps. 28 cm. monthly (except July–Aug.)

1. Aeronautics—Period.   I. National Air Council.

TL501.N334   629.1305   51–36539

NN   0032313   DLC TxU NN CoCA CU MH-BA .

National Air Traffic Conference.
Proceedings...
₍no.₎ 1

₍New York, 1929   8°.
v.
1929.   full title reads: Proceedings...National Air Traffic Conference of the
Aeronautical Chamber of Commerce of America, Inc...

1. Aeronautics, Commercial—U. S.   I. Aeronautical Chamber of Commerce of America, Inc.
N. Y. P. L.   July 24, 1930

NN   0032314   NN WaS ICJ

National air transport.

N. A. T. bulletin board. no. 1–
June 16, 1927–
Chicago, Ill., 1927–

National Air Transport.
N.A.T. fly paper
see under title

National air travel survey for Lockheed Aircraft
Corporation
see under   Foote, Cone and Belding.

National aircraft blue book. v.3,no.5–
Jan.1949–   Chicago, National
market reports, inc., 1949–
v.

NN   0032318   MH-BA WaS MiD OCl

A406   **National Aircraft Production Meeting, Los**
N277   **Angeles, 1937.**
Papers ₍Preprints ... to be presented at
the National Aircraft Production Meeting
of the Society of Automotive Engineers at
Los Angeles, Calif., October 7 to 9, 1937.
Los Angeles, 1937₎
1 v. (various pagings) illus. 29 cm.
Caption title.
1. Aeroplanes - Design and construction.
I. Society of Automotive Engineers.

NN   0032319   DSI

National Aircraft Standards Committee
see   Aerospace Industries Association of
America. National Aircraft Standards Committee.

VOLUME 405

NATIONAL AIRLINES, INC.
Agreement between National airlines, inc. and
NAL chapter, Flight engineers' international association.
[n. p.]   v.   23cm.

"Covering flight engineers in the employ of National airlines, inc."

1 Labor contracts. Air-line employees'--U.S   I. Flight engineers'
international association. NAL   chapter.

NN 0032321   NN

National airlines, inc.
Annual report.

Jacksonville, Fla., 19
v. illus. (incl. ports.) diagrs. 28ᵐ.

44-39342
Library of Congress   TL720.9.N3A3
[2]   387.7065

NN 0032322   DLC NN OrU

National airlines, inc.
Prospectus 113,333-⅓ shares National airlines, incorporated
common stock (par value $1.00 per share)...principal under-
writer...Lehman brothers... [New York] 1944. 24 p. map.
33cm.

1. No subject. I. Lehman   brothers, firm, bankers.
N.Y.P.L.   August 12, 1947

NN 0032323   NN

National Airlines star reporter. [Miami, Public
Relations Department, Miami International
Airport]
v. illus. 28 cm. monthly.
Organ of National Airlines employees.
Numbering varies: Sept. 1959, v. 13, no. 2;
Oct. 1959, v. 14, no. 3; Nov. 1959, v. 15, no. 4;
Dec. 1959, v. 16, no. 5; Spring issue, April 1960,
v. 17, no. 1, and vol. numbering continues from
this issue.

NN 0032324   FU

National Airport, *Washington, D. C.*
see Washington National Airport.

National Airport Conference, Chicago, 1927
see   Chicago Airport Conference, 1927.

National Airport Conference. *2d, Buffalo, 1930.*
Proceedings. [n. p.] Aeronautical Chamber of Commerce of America [*1930*]
124 p. 24 cm.

1. Airports—Congresses.

TL725.A1N3   629.136   30-21458 rev 2*

NN 0032327   DLC WaS NN ICJ

National airport conference, *Washington, D. C., 1937.*
... Proceedings of National airport conference, December 6
and 7, 1937. Washington [D. C.] 1938.
cover-title, iv, 184 p. 26ᵐ.
At head of title: U. S. Department of commerce, Bureau of air commerce.
Photoprinted.

1. Aeronautics—Congresses. 2. Airports—U. S. ɪ. U. S. Bureau
of air commerce.
38-26129
Library of Congress   TL725.N3 1937
———— Copy 2.   [5]   629.13606373

NN 0032328   DLC WaS ICJ CU

National Airport news
see Airport news.

National Airports Conference.
Proceedings.

Norman, Oklahoma.
v. 28cm.

"Sponsored by the American Association of
Airport Executives and the University of
Oklahoma with the cooperation of the Federal
Aviation Agency."
Issued   by the conference under its ear-
lier name: Conference [on] Airport Management
and Operations.

NN 0032330   IU MiU MH-BA

The national alarm; or, Seasonable admonition
to the degenerate natives of the once formidable
island of Great Britain: occasion'd by the late
rumour of a fresh invasion meditating by their
Gallic neighbours. Humbly inscrib'd to His Grace
the Duke of B--df----d, first commissioner for
executing the office of lord high ad--iral. By
J---- H------, esq; ... London: Printed and sold
by George Woodfall ... 1745.
22 p. 37½ᶜᵐ.

First edition?

Signatures: [A]-E², F¹.
In verse.
Unbound, in cloth case.

NN 0032332   CLU-C

National alcoholic beverage control association.
Annual convention. [Proceedings] 1st-
1938–   [n. p., 1938–
v. ports. 23ᵐ.

1. Liquor problem—U. S.
43-32779
Library of Congress   HV5287.N25A3
[2]   178.406273

NN 0032333   DLC

National Alcoholic Beverage Control Association
see also
Joint Committee of the State to Study Alcoholic
Beverage Laws.
National Conference of State Liquor Administra-
tors.

National alfalfa journal; published monthly. v. 2, no. 1.
Jan. 1916. f°. Sioux Falls, S. D., 1916.

NN 0032335   MBH

331.805 National alliance.
POSA
Detroit, Mich. [etc.]
v. illus. 27-31cm. monthly.
"Official organ of National Alliance of
Postal and Federal Employees" (Sept.
-Aug. 1965 National Alliance of Postal
Employees)
Title varies: Postal
alliance.
Numerous er-   rors in vol. numbering.

NN 0032336   IU NN· PP

The National alliance, *New York.*
... Tables of cost and results of the plan of life insurance adopted by the National alliance. Ed. of December,
1887 ... [New York, 1887]
62 p. diagr. 17ᶜᵐ.

7-5824†
Library of Congress   HG8963.N28A8 1887

NN 0032337   DLC

National alliance, Daughters of veterans
see   Daughters of Union Veterans
of the Civil War.

National Alliance Baseball Rules Committee.
Baseball umpires manual
see under   National Federation of State
High School Athletic Associations.

HFBP26L   National Alliance of Amalgamated Painters,
.N489   Paper Hangers and Decorators of America.
N213   District New York and Vicinity.
MIS   Constitution and by-laws. New York, 18 -
.   v. 14cm.
Library has: 1899, [1901, [1905,
1899 and 1905 issued under previous name of
the union: Amalgamated Painters and Decorators of New York.

NN 0032339   WHi MdBJ

National Alliance of Art and Industry, New York.
The Art Center and industry
see under   Art Center, New York.

National alliance of art and industry, New York.
Bulletin of progress for members of the National alliance of art and industry...New York, N.Y.,
1933.
cover-title, 12 l.   29 cm.
Mimeograph sheets in folder.
Printed on one side of leaf.

NN 0032341   DSI ICRL MBMu

National alliance of art and industry, New York.
Choosing a life career in the design arts, a
discussion of vocational guidance problems,
May 4, 1932
see under   New York region art council.

National alliance of art and industry, New York.
Exhibition of one hundred important paintings by
living American Artists, April 15 to April 27, 1929
see under   New York regional art council.

National alliance of art and industry, *New York.*
Exhibition of photographs for art and industry,
October 18 to November 5. National alliance of
art and industry, Pictorial photographers of
America cooperating. [New York, 1939?]
cover-title, [14] p. 22ᶜᵐ.

1. Photography - Exhibitions. I. Pictorial
photographers of America.

NN 0032344   NNC

VOLUME 405

National Alliance of Art and Industry, New York.
Monograph.
no. 1–

₍New York, cop. 1932   18cm.
nos.
Contents:
no. 1. SHELDON, R., Methods of purchasing designs.   cop. 1932.
no. 2. NASH, B. The manufacturer and the development of the design project.   cop. 1932.

NN   0032345   NN

National Alliance of Art and Industry, New York. — Industrial
Institute.
Talk.
no.

New York, 1931   23cm.
nos.

no.   name appears as: Industrial Institute of the Art center.

1. Design, Industrial—Per. and soc.   publ.
N.Y.P.L.   April 11, 1933

NN   0032346   NN OC1

National Alliance of Art and Industry, New York.
New York Regional Art Council
see
New York Regional Art Council.

National alliance of Bohemian Catholics of America.
"Naše dějiny," sestavil a vydává Národní svaz českých katolíků v Texas. Ndp. msgr. Josef Pelnař ... dp. Jos. C. Kunc
... senátor L. J. Sulák ... ₍a jiní₎ Granger, Tex., 1939.
718 p. incl. illus., ports. 24ᵐᵐ.

1. Bohemians in the U. S.   2. Catholics in the U. S.
                                          42–51854
Library of Congress   BX1407.B7N3

NN   0032348   DLC

National alliance of Bohemian Catholics of America.
50 let kulturní práce, na oslavu zlatého jubilea českých otců
benediktinů z opatství sv. Prokopa, Lisle, Ill., vydal Distriktní
svaz českých katolíků, květen, 1935 ... Souvenir book on the
occasion of the golden jubilee of the Bohemian Benedictine
fathers of St. Procopius abbey, Lisle, Ill. Chicago, Ill., 1935.
64 p. illus. (incl. ports.) 25ᵐᵐ.
On cover: Five decades of the Bohemian Benedictines.
Text in Bohemian or English.
Includes advertising matter.
1. Lisle, Ill. St. Procopius (Benedictine abbey) 2. Bohemians in the
U. S.   I. Title.   II. Title: Five decades of the Bohemian Benedictines.
                                          42–51598
Library of Congress   BX2525.L5S3

NN   0032349   DLC

National alliance of Czech Catholics of America
see
National alliance of Bohemian Catholics of America.

National alliance of employers and employed
₍Miscellaneous pamphlets and leaflets.
London, 1916-1918.

NN   0032351   DL

National Alliance of Employers and Employed.
Report.
19

London₍, 19   12°, 8°.
nos.

For later years see National Industrial Alliance. Report.

1. Employer and employed—Assoc.   and org.—Gt. Br.   2. Arbitration
and conciliation, Industrial—Gt. Br.
N.Y.P.L.   December 28, 1926

NN   0032352   NN

₍National Alliance of Legal Aid Societies.₎
Final report on uniform legal aid records, including classification of nature of cases, classification of source of cases, classification of disposition of cases, classification of data as to clients, by
the Special Committee on Classification and Standardization of
Records. ₍Philadelphia, 1923.₎   iii, 90 p.   8°.

1. Charities (Legal), U. S.
N.Y.P.L.   November 28, 1924

NN   0032353   NN NNU-W MH-L

National alliance of legal aid societies
Proceedings

SEE

National conference of legal aid bureau and
societies.
Proceedings.

NATIONAL ALLIANCE OF POSTAL EMPLOYEES.
Constitution and by-laws as adopted by sixth
biennial convention, Pittsburgh, Pennsylvania,
including the amendments of succeeding conventions. Prepared at national headquarters, Oct. 4,
1937. n.p., [1937].

pp. 42.
Paper cover serves as title-page.
                                    Sch. Pub. Adm.
Amendments codified by G. N. T. Gray. n.p.,
[1939?].
pp. [1].

NN   0032355   MH

National Alliance of Postal Employees.
National alliance
see under title

National Alliance of Russian Solidarists
see
Narodno-trudovoĭ soĭuz.

DB665   National alliance of Slovak Lutherans.
.S4
Šebík, Michal Múdry.
Stručné dejiny Slovákov, podl'a uvedených prameňov, sosta-
vil: dr. Michal Múdry Šebík. Pittsburgh, Pa., Národný svä̈z
slovenských evanjelikov, 1940.

National Alliance of Television & Electronic
Service Associations.
NATESA scope
see under title

National Alliance of Theatrical Stage Employees of the United States and Canada
see   International Alliance of Theatrical
Stage Employees and Moving Picture Machine
Operators of the United States and Canada.

National alliance of Unitarian and other
liberal Christian women

see

Alliance of Unitarian and other liberal
Christian women.

National Allied Bazaar, Boston
see Boston. National Allied Bazaar.

National allied relief committee.
The Allied bazaar...
see under   Allied bazaar, New York, 1916.

₍National allied relief committee₎

The crisis in Italy; American aid is
urgently needed to strengthen our southern
ally against the German and Austrian
campaign of Frightfulness ... ₍New York,
1918?₎
₍4₎ p.

NN   0032364   OC1WHi

National Allied Relief Committee.
Exhibition and sale of the war cartoons...
see under   Raemaekers, Louis, 1869-

National allied relief committee.
Exhibition of the paintings by François Charles Cachoud for the benefit of Les amis des artistes association,
under the auspices of the National allied relief committee, at the Anderson galleries (incorporated) Monday,
March 26th to Saturday, April 7th, 1917. ₍New York,
Priv. print. by G. T. Washburn & co., Irving press, ʿ1917₎
1 p. l., 25 p. front. (port.) plates. 28⁴ᵐᵐ. $1.00

1. Cachoud, François Charles, 1866-   2. Paintings—Exhibitions.
I. Amis des artistes association.   II. Anderson galleries, New York.

Library of Congress   ND553.C23N3   17–11802

NN   0032366   DLC OC1MA MiD WaS PP PPPM MB

National allied relief committe.
German horrors as practiced on the
thousands of Belgian prisoners, soldiers
and civilians, in the Kaiser's detention
camps ...
₍4₎ p.

Cover-title.

NN   0032367   00

National allied relief committee.
The relief of the children of eastern
Europe. An account of the condition and
needs of the unfortunate children of the
newly liberated war-ravaged countries of the
Baltic states, Poland, Czecho-Slovakia,
Roumania, and Jugoslavia. ₍New York City,
National allied relief committee, inc.,
1919?₎
cover-title, 8 p.

NN   0032368   OU

National allotments & gardens journal
see The Allotment & home garden.

SB1   National Allotments and Gardens Society.
.A33
The Allotment & home garden.
₍Bognor Regis, Sussex₎

282.9   National Allotments and Garden Society.
N214A   Allotment holders' companion and calendar.
[London,

NN   0032371   DNAL

282.9   National Allotments and Garden Society.
N214   Annual report.   London₍.

NN   0032372   DNAL NIC NN

VOLUME 405

HD
1519
G7
N2M
National Allotments and Gardens Society

₍Miscellaneous publications₎ London
₍193?₎
3 nos. in 1.   26 cm.

1. Working-   men's gardens - Gt. Brit.
2. Gardens - G   t. Brit.

NN   0032373   NIC

84
N2122
National Allotments and Garden Society.
**Notice of special general meeting.   Lon-
don, 1955.**
18 p.

1. Allotment gardens. Societies. 2. Cooperation. Societies. Gt. Brit.

NN   0032374   DNAL

National allotments journal
see The **Allotment** & home garden.

National Allotments Society
see National Allotments and Gardens Society.

National almanac.
19
Chicago, The Chicago daily news, inc.,
c19
v. 20ᶜᵐ.

Supersedes the Chicago American national
almanac and year book?
Cover-title: 19   , Chicago daily
news almanac.

NN   0032377   NNC NBuHi NUtHi

The **National** almanac and annual record for ... 1863–64.
Philadelphia, G. W. Childs; ₍etc., etc.₎ 1863–64.

2 v. 18½ᵐ.
1864 edited by W. V. McKean.
According to Sabin, the American almanac and repository of **useful**
knowledge was succeeded by the National almanac.
No more published.

I. McKean, William Vincent, 1820–1902, ed.

1–2509

Library of Congress   AY64.N25

ICRL Or CaBVaU
OU NjP NIC ViHaI MB ICJ DN Nh NN ViU NjR NdU KMK AAP
NN   0032378   DLC NcD NNH NNUT OFH DI OC1W OC1 OO

...National almanac and guide of the Philippine
Islands. Almanaque-guia nacional de Filipinas...
Manila, ₍19

AY1124
.N3

NN   0032379   ₍₎DLC NN

National almanac and pocket-calendar for the
year of our Lord, 1840. By J.W. Herschell.
New York
36 p.

NN   0032380   OO

... **National** almanac and year book for 1938 ... **Chicago, Ill.,**
The National survey and sales corporation, °1937.

960 p. incl. illus., diagrs. 20ᶜᵐ.

At head of title: Chicago American.
On cover: Chicago American national almanac and year book.
Edited by C. D. MacDougall and others.
Supersedes the Chicago daily news almanac and year book.
No more published.

1. Almanacs, American. I. MacDougall, Curtis Daniel, 1903– **ed.**
39–8294 Revised
Library of Congress   AY67.C4N52
₍r40c2₎   317.3

ICJ
NN   0032381   DLC NcU OCU CU IU NN ICRL Or OC1 OrU

Le National almanach.   1889, 1892–93.
Paris [1888–92]
12°.
Title from cover. Title-page reads
Almanach.

NN   0032382   NN

National Altrusan
see   International Altrusan.

National aluminate corporation, *Chicago.*
Nalco demonstration book. Copyright ... by National aluminate corporation. ₍Chicago₎ °1932.

1 v. plates, ports., diagrs. 29ᶜᵐ.
Loose-leaf; the text and plates are mounted.
Bibliography: p. 18–19.

1. Feed-water purification. 2. Sodium aluminates. I. Title.
CA 32–632 Unrev'd
Library of Congress   TJ379.N3
Copyright AA 95391   621.1943

NN   0032384   DLC

National aluminate corporation, Chicago.
Straub, Frederick Guy, 1896–
... A study of the reactions of various inorganic and organic
salts in preventing scale in steam boilers; a report of an investigation conducted by the Engineering experiment station,
University of Illinois, in coöperation with National aluminate corporation, by Frederick G. Straub ... Urbana, University of Illinois ₍1936₎

Bf7
26a
National alumni association, New York.
Dinner time questions for pleasant family
discussions in homes where learning is
cultivated and knowledge prized. The true
answers ... in ... World epochs. [New York]
National alumni association[c1937]
34p. 22½cm.

NN   0032386   CtY

National amalgamated association of iron, steel and tin
workers of the United States
see
Amalgamated association of iron, steel and tin workers.

National amalgamated society of operative
house and ship painters and decorators.
Annual reports....

NN   0032388   DL

National amalgamated society of operative **house and**
ship painters and decorators.
Rules...

NN   0032389   DL

National Amalgamated Union of Labour.
...Annual report and financial statement...
₍no.₎

Newcastle-upon-Tyne, 1
no.   tables.   8°.

1. Trades unions, Gt. Br.
N. Y. P. L.   September 13, 1922.

NN   0032390   NN DL

National amalgamated union of labour
Rules...Newcastle-on-Tyne, 1904
44 p. 16½cm

NN   0032391   DL

**National Amalgamated Union of Shop Assistants, Ware-
housemen and Clerks.**
Annual report and balance sheet.

London.
v. 24 cm.

1. Clerks—Societies. 2. Clerks—Gt. Brit.
HD6668.M4N3   49–32630*‡

NN   0032392   DLC DL WU

HD6668
.M4D5
National amalgamated union of shop assistants,
warehousemen and clerks.
Distributive trades journal. v. 1–   (no. 1–   );
Jan. 1939–
₍London, Dilke house publications, ltd., 1939–

National amalgamated union of shop assistants, warehousemen and clerks.
(Miscellaneous pamphlets)

NN   0032394   DL

The National amateur.
₍Roanoke, Va., etc.₎
v. in   ports. 26 cm. quarterly.
Official organ of the National Amateur Press Association.

1. Amateur journalism—Societies, etc. I. National Amateur Press
Association.
PN4826.N2A3   070.489   55–58236

NN   0032395   DLC NjR NN

National amateur athletic federation.

Coops, Helen Leslie, 1901–
High school standards in girls athletics in the state of
Ohio, by Helen Leslie Coops ... New York, 1933.

National Amateur Athletic Federation.
Minutes of the annual meeting of the Board of Governors.
₍no. 1

New York, 1922   8°.
no.

1. Athletics—Assoc. and org.—U. S.
N. Y. P. L.   April 8, 1929

NN   0032397   NN

National amateur athletic federation.
Proceedings 7th–   annual meeting
(n.p., 1929–
1 v. 27½ cm.
Mimeographed.

NN   0032398   DHEW OU

National Amateur Athletic Federation. Men's Division.
Report of the proceedings of the annual meeting.
₍no.₎

New York₍, 192
no.
192   cover-title.

1. Athletics—Assoc. and org.—U. S.
N. Y. P. L.   August 5, 1926

NN   0032399   NN DHEW OU

National amateur athletic federation.
Women's division.
Bulletin ... New York, ₍1934₎

NN   0032400   WaPS

VOLUME 405

National amateur athletic federation.
    Women's division.
    ...Group of student leadership. Papers
presented at the third annual meeting. May,
1926. (N.p., 1926)
    cover-title, 48 p incl. form. 23 cm.

NN   0032401   DHEW

National amateur athletic federation. *Women's division.*
    ... Membership list
New York ₁19

    v. 23 x 9½ᵐ.

                                                    42-40688
                                                    Brief cataloging
    Library of Congress   GV709.N27

NN   0032402   DLC

796.06 National amateur athletic federation.
N2112n   Women's division.
           News letter ... New York, 19

           Mimeographed.

NN   0032403   WaPS

National Amateur Athletic Federation. Women's
    Division.
    Report of conference on training ...
       see under   Conference on Training for
    Leadership in Athletic Activities for Girls and
    Women, New York, 1925-1926.

National amateur athletic federation. *Women's division.*
    Report of the ... annual meeting of the Women's division,
National amateur athletic federation. ₁1st₁–
    1924–
    ₁Chicago, etc., 1924–
       v. 23-28ᵐ.

    Title varies slightly.
    Mimeographed (except 2d–   1925–

    1. Athletics—Societies. 2. Woman—Societies and clubs.
                                                    42-40688
    Library of Congress   GV709.N25₁.

NN   0032405   DLC DHEW NN

371.74 National amateur athletic federation. Women's
N213ag   division.
           A study of girls' athletic associations in
        the secondary school: objectives, organization,
        program ... ₁New York City, author, 1934₁
           cover-title, 16 p.

           Processed.

           1. Athletic clubs 2. Physical education and
        training I. Title: Girls' athletic associations
        in the secondary school, objectives, organization,
        program, A study of.

NN   0032406   WaPS

National amateur athletic federation. *Women's division.*
    A study of women's athletic associations in colleges and uni-
versities. New York city, Women's division, National amateur
athletic federation ₁1936₁
    ₁1₁, 11 p. 21ᵐ.
    "Made under the auspices of the Women's division, National amateur
athletic federation ... ₁by₁ the committee ... Willie Dean Andrews ...
chairman."—p. 1.
    Multigraphed.

    1. Physical education ₁and training₁—U. S. 2. ₁Physical education—
Universities and colleges₁ 3. Woman—Health and hygiene. ₁3. Woman—
Physical education₁ I. Andrews, Willie Dean. II. Title. III. Title:
Women's athletic associations in colleges and universities.
                                                    E 36-187
    Library, U. S. Office of   Education GV709.N2

NN   0032407   DHEW OO

National amateur athletic federation. *Women's division.*
    Women and athletics, compiled and edited by the Women's
division, National amateur athletic federation. New York,
A. S. Barnes and company, incorporated, 1930.
    v, 95 p. 23½ᵐ.
    Bibliography: p. 94-95.

    1. Athletics. 2. Woman.
                                                    30—18946
    Library of Congress   GV709.N3
                                   ₁41o2₁   796

        OrPR WaS OrCS OrU TU
NN   0032408   DLC IU PSt OCU ODW OU MiU IdU MtBC

National Amateur Baseball Federation, Inc.
    Amateur baseball; its organization,
    promotion and administration. ₁n.p., 1950?₁
       1 v. (unpaged)

    Cover title

NN   0032409   MoU

National Amateur Gardeners' Association.
    The amateur world of horticulture...
       see under title

National amateur journalist
    see   Mail order journal.

The NATIONAL amateur mineralogist. v. 1, no. 1.
    v. 2, no. 2 - v. 3, no. 8, v. 4, no. 5-7, 9 - v. 5, no. 3 - v. 5,
    no. 12, v. 7, no. 3-6, v. 8, no. 2-6, v. 9, no. 2-3, 5;
    Nov. 1938, Mar. 1940-Dec. 1943, Oct. 1944-May, 1945.
    May, 1946-Aug. 1947, Dec. 1948, Apr. -Dec. 1949.
    Mar. -Dec. 1950, Feb. -Apr., Aug. 1951.
    Kenmore, Wash. ₁etc. ₁ O. B. Brown ₁etc. ₁
    v   illus., maps. 23cm.

        Irregular.
        Vol. 2, no. 4, Oct. 1940 lacks numbering; v. 7, no. 3, Apr. 1949
    incorrectly called Apr. 1948.
        Title varies: v. 1-2, no. 5, Nov. 1938-Nov./Dec. 1940, The Miner,
    chemist and engineer.
        Ceased publication with v. 9, no. 5, Aug. 1951?

    1. Mines and mining—Per. and soc. publ. I. Title: The Miner,
chemist and engineer.

NN   0032413   NN WaU

GV881 NATIONAL AMATEUR PLAYGROUND BALL ASSOCIATION OF
.N3   THE UNITED STATES.
           ...Official handbook... 19
         New York, American sports publishing company
         ₁19
              v. ports.,illus. 17cm. (Spalding's
         athletic library)

         1.Playground ball.

NN   0032414   ICU

**National amateur playground ball association of the
United States.**
    ... Official handbook ... New York, American sports
publishing company ₁1908₁
    35 p. front. (port.) illus. 17ᵐ. (Spalding's athletic library. Group ı.
no. 306)

    1. Playground ball.
                                                    8-15714
    Library of Congress   GV883.N3
                           (Copyright 1908 A 205522)

NN   0032415   DLC

796.35 National amateur playground ball asso-
N27o   ciation of the United States
1909   ...Official handbook. O.C. Reichow,
            associate ed.   New York, American
         sports pub. co. ₁c1909₁
              72p. front.,illus.,ports.,diagrs. D.
         (Spalding's athletic library. Group I.
         no.321)

NN   0032416   IaU

National amateur press association.
    Constitution of the National amateur press association. ₁Jer-
sey City, V. B. Haggerty, 1941₁ 14 l. 12cm.

NN   0032417   NN

National amateur press association
    ₁Miscellaneous material₁
    P 17, 709

NN   0032418   OClWHi

---

*
Z123
.N3   ₁National Amateur Press Association₁
1900
           ₁Miscellaneous publications of private
         presses in the United States. v. p., 19
              v. 27cm.

         1. Private presses.

NN   0032419   ViU

National Amateur Press *Association.*
    The National amateur
    see under title

4-Serials

National Amateur Press Association.
    Year-book.

NN   0032421   DLC-P4 NBu

The **National** American. no. 1-2 (May 15 – Sept. 1, 1942).
    Drums, Pa., 1942. 2 nos. 29cm.
        Irregular.
        Edited by Frank Emerick.
        No. 2 (Sept. 1, 1942) includes "Supplement giving the Atlantic charter and the
    Declaration."
        No more published.

        1. United States—Politics,   1933–   I. Emerick, Frank,
    1892-   ed.
    N. Y. P. L.   May 16, 1946

NN   0032422   NN

National American; official organ of the American National Labor
    Party.
    v. 1

    New York: Zenger Press Inc., 1935   41½cm.
    v. illus. (incl. ports.)

        Weekly.
        Vol. 1, no. 1-10 also called no. 44-53 "D. B." in continuation of the numbering of the
    Deutscher Beobachter of New York, which it supersedes.
        Vol. 1 complete in 10 nos.; v. 2, no. 1 omitted in numbering?
        Includes the current suppl. in German: Der Nationale Amerikaner, v. 1–

NN   0032424   NN

VOLUME 405

National American croquet association.
Croquet guide and official rules governing the game.

₁Annual₎. New York, American sports publishing co.
₁1893–

v. diagrs. 17ᶜᵐ. (*On cover:* Spalding's athletic library, v. 1,
no. 10; v. 2, no. 22; v. 4, no. 38A; v. 5, no. 52; v. 6, no. 68₎
Title varies: 1893, Croquet; the rules governing the game.

1. Croquet.

Library of Congress   GV935.N27   5–23421†

NN   0032425   DLC IU CtY

National America Denmark Association
see
America Denmark Relief.

The **National** American Indian memorial at Fort
Wadsworth, harbor of New York. ₁Philadelphia, J.
Wanamaker₎ ⁀1913.

₁12₎ p. illus. 23ᶜᵐ.

1. Wadsworth, Fort, New York. National American Indian memorial.

Library of Congress   F127.S7N25   13–9464

NN   0032427   DLC

The **National** American Indian memorial, harbor of New York...
₁Philadelphia: Wanamaker, cop. 1913.₎   48 p.   illus. (incl.
facsims., map, ports.)   f°.

Caption-title.
Repr. from various newspapers

1. Indians, N. A.   2. Monuments, His-   torical—U. S.—N. Y.—New York.
N. Y. P. L.   January 8, 1927

NN   0032428   NN

---

fF127   The National American Indian memorial ₁harbor
S7N3   of New York; being an account, as voiced by
        the press of the whole country, of the of-
        ficial opening of the ground at Fort Wads-
        worth.   New York? 1922?₎
        cover-title,48 p.   illus.,ports. 42cm.

1. Wadsworth, Fort, New York.   National
American Indian memorial.

NN   0032429   CU

National American kennel club.
The **American** kennel club ... stud book. Official. v. 1–
          1879–
St. Louis, National American kennel club; ₁etc., etc.₎
1879–

National American Kennel Club.
Stud book
see
American Kennel Club.
Stud book register.

National American legion auxiliary

see

American legion. Auxiliary.

NATIONAL AMERICAN MUSICAL CONVENTION AND CHAUT-
AUQUA.
National American musical convention and Cha-
utauqua, promoted in the interests of American
music and musicians, Thurston auditorium,Lock-
port, New.York, Sept. 30th to Oct.6th,1917,
[Lockport, N.Y., 1917.]

1.8°. Ports. and other illustr.

NN   0032433   MH

ML38.B9   National American Music Festival, 6th,
N2   Buffalo, 1921.
            Official program.   ₁Buffalo, Kenworthy
          Printing Co., 1921₎

64p.   illus.   23cm.

1. Music festivals.

NN   0032434   NBuG

National American Party
see   American Party.

National American Patriots' Union.
The singing patriot
see under   Murray, Oliver E

National American Wholesale Grocers' Association,
Washington, D.C.
Bulletin
see   Facts and figures; an authoritative
food trade magazine.

National-American Wholesale Lumber Association.
Summarized report of proceedings ... annual convention,
National-American Wholesale Lumber Association, Inc. ...
New York ₁1924–   ₎

Library has 1924 to date. 26–28ᶜᵐ.
Organized in March 1923 as a merger of the National Wholesale Lumber
Dealers Association and the American Wholesale Lumber Association.
Title varies: 1924–1926, Year book and complete report of proceedings ...
     1927–1928, Report of proceedings ...
1931–   called 39th–   annual convention.
Wanting: 1937.

NN   0032438   ICJ OU

National-American Wholesale Lumber Association.
Year book and complete report of proceedings
see its   Summarized report of proceedings...

National American Woman Suffrage Association.
Formed in 1890 by the union of the National Woman Suffrage
Association and the American Woman Suffrage Association. In 1920
the association's section, League of Women Voters, became an in-
dependent organization under the name National League of Women
Voters (later League of Women Voters of the United States)

National American woman suffrage association.
Catt, *Mrs.* Carrie (Lane) Chapman.
An address to the Congress of the United States, by
Carrie Chapman Catt, president of the National Ameri-
can woman suffrage association ... New York, N. Y.,
National woman suffrage publishing company, inc. ₁1917₎

National American Woman Suffrage Association.
Anna Howard Shaw; a memorial, prepared by a committee
appointed from the board of directors of the National American
Woman Suffrage Association.   ₁New York: National Woman
Suffrage Pub. Co. ₁1919?₎   4 p.l., (1)6–26 p. incl. port.   pl.   8°.

1. Shaw, Anna Howard, 1847–1919.   2. Woman.—Suffrage, U. S.
N. Y. P. L.   June 11, 1920.

NN   0032442   NN DLC ICJ

National American Woman Suffrage Association.   5586.172
Anna Howard Shaw: a memorial.
=   [New York. National Woman Suffrage Publishing Co., Inc.
     1935.] (3), 26 pp. Portrait. Plate. 23 cm.

D8987 — Woman suffrage. — Shaw, Anna Howard, 1847–1919.

NN   0032443   MB

NATIONAL AMERICAN WOMAN SUFFRAGE ASSOCIATION
Annual report.   505 Fifth Ave., New York
City, 1912 –

NN   0032444   Or

National American Woman Suffrage Association.
An anti-suffrage monologue. [1912]
see under   Howe, Marie (Jenney)

National American woman suffrage association.
Catt, *Mrs.* Carrie (Lane) Chapman, *comp.*
The ballot and the bullet, comp. by Carrie Chapman
Catt. Pub. for the National-American woman suffrage
association ... Philadelphia, Press of A. J. Ferris, 1897.

National American woman suffrage association.
The biological argument against woman
suffrage...1914.

NN   0032447   MiU

National American woman suffrage association.
Catalogue and price list of suffrage literature, National-
American woman suffrage association. New York city
₁1911₎

cover-title, 15 p. 16ᶜᵐ.

1. Woman—Suffrage—Bibl.

                                                    11–7860

Library of Congress   Z7963.S9N2

NN   0032448   DLC

National American Woman Suffrage Association.
₈₇₆₈₃ .Catalog and price list of woman suffrage literature and supplies.
New York City, National American Woman Suffrage Association,
[1911?].
cover-title, 21, [1] p. 24ᶜᵐ.
"What to read on suffrage, a monthly bulletin."   4 p. tipped in at end.

NN   0032449   ICJ NN

CT99
.A628N3   National American woman suffrage associa-
            tion.
            Celebration in honor of Susan B.
          Anthony's eighty-sixth birthday. Church
          of Our Father, Washington, D. C. February
          15, 1906 eight o'clock, p. m. Under the
          auspices of the National American woman
          suffrage association. [Washington? D. C.,
          1906]
            [2] p., port. 23cm.
            1. Anthony, Susan Brownell, 1820–1906.

NN   0032450   DLC

VOLUME 405

NATIONAL AMERICAN WOMAN SUFFRAGE ASSOCIATION.
The college evening of the thirty-eighth
annual convention held in Baltimore, February
8, 1906. n.p.,n.d.

NN 0032451   MH OO

National American Woman Suffrage Association.   *5586.174
Condensed minutes of the Victory Convention (1869–1920), National American Woman Suffrage Association and 1st Congress, League of Woman Voters.
= Chicago. 1920. 1 v. 23.5 cm.

D9917 — Double main card. —   National American Woman Suffrage Association. (M1) — National League of Woman Voters. (M2) — Woman suffrage. (1,2) — Societies. Proc., trans., etc. (1)

NN 0032452   MB

National American Woman Suffrage Association.   9324.373
Congressional reports in favor of an amendment to the National Constitution prohibiting the disfranchisement of United States citizens on account of sex.
= [New York, 1894?] 12 pp. 8°.

E6234 — Woman suffrage.

NN 0032453   MB

National american-woman suffrage association.
Fales, Imogene C.
... Coöperation, by Imogene C. Fales. New York, For the National-American woman suffrage association, 1897.

National American woman suffrage association.
Disfranchised men. n.d.

NN 0032455   MiU

National American woman suffrage association.
Do you know? [1916]

NN 0032456   MiU

National American woman suffrage association.
Cobbe, Frances Power, 1822-1904.
The duties of women; a course of lectures, by Frances Power Cobbe. New York, The National-American woman suffrage association. 1898.

National American woman suffrage association.
Eminent opinions on woman suffrage. New York: National American Woman Suffrage Association [1912]. 55 p. nar. 16°.
Title from cover.

1. Woman.—Suffrage, pro. 2. National American Woman Suffrage Association.
N. Y. P. L.

NN 0032458   NN OrU

National American woman suffrage association.
Eminent people declare for equal suffrage. n.d.

NN 0032459   MiU

National American Woman Suffrage Association.
Frederic C. Howe on suffrage
see under   Howe, Frederic Clemson, 1867-1940.

National American Woman Suffrage Association.
Fruits of equal suffrage
see under title

National American woman suffrage association.
Handbook ... and proceedings of the ... annual convention, 18

Washington, 18
v. 22½ᵐ.
Editor: 18   H. T. Upton.

1. Woman—Suffrage—Societies. 2. Woman—Suffrage—U. S.
I. Upton, Harriet Taylor, ed.

Library of Congress   JK1881.N28   CA 5–2230 Unrev'd

OC1WHi ODW MiU OC1 ViU
NN 0032462   DLC NcD Or MB WaS WaSp ICJ Wa Nh OO

National American Woman Suffrage Association.
Headquarters news letter.
v.
New York. 19   4°.
v. illus.
Monthly.

1. Woman.—Suffrage: Per. and soc. publ.
N. Y. P. L.   May 9, 1922.

NN 0032463   NN

National American Woman Suffrage Association.
JK1888
1896   U. S. *Congress. House. Committee on the Judiciary.*
Hearing of the National American Woman Suffrage Association. Committee on the Judiciary, House of Representatives, Washington, D. C., January 28, 1896. Washington, Govt. Print. Off., 1896.

National American Woman Suffrage Association.
The history of women suffrage
see under   Stanton, Elizabeth (Cady) 1815-1902, ed.

National American woman suffrage association.
Saunders, *Mrs.* Jessie Jane (Cassidy) 1861-   comp.
The legal status of women, comp. by Jessie J. Cassidy. New York, The National-American woman suffrage association, 1897.

National American Woman Suffrage Association.
Mayors of five states recommend municipal suffrage for women
see under title

NATIONAL AMERICAN WOMAN SUFFRAGE ASSOCIATION.
[Miscellaneous publications]

NN 0032468   Or

National American Woman Suffrage Association.   q324.3
N22p   [Pamphlets and press releases]. New York [etc.] 1913-20.
19 pieces in envelope. 35cm.

NN 0032469   IU

National American woman suffrage association.
Catt, *Mrs.* Carrie (Lane) Chapman.
Perhaps. [By Carrie Chapman Catt. Warren, O., 1910?]

National American Woman Suffrage Association.   396.3
P191   Political equality leaflets. Warren, O.,
no.3   [1904-08]
28 nos. 16cm. (In Pamphlets on woman suffrage, no.3)

1. Woman. Suffrage. Periodicals, societies, etc. I. Title.

NN 0032471   OrU

National American Woman Suffrage Association.   396.3
P191   Political equality series. v.1-4.
no.4   Warren, O., 1904-08.
4v. 16cm. (In Pamphlets on woman suffrage. no.4)

Not bound in consecutive order.
Library has: v.1, no.1-7, 9-11; v.2, no.1, 3-4,7-8,10; v.3, no.1-3, 6, 11-12; v.4, no.1-2, 7-8, 23.

NN 0032472   OrU

NATIONAL AMERICAN WOMAN SUFFRAGE ASSOCIATION.
Political science study series.
New York.   v.   19cm.

Quarterly.
Vol.3, no.4 in SNS p.v.15.

1. Woman--Suffrage--Per. and soc. publ.--U.S.

NN 0032473   NN DLC

National-american woman suffrage association.
President's annual address... before... annual convention...
JK881   [Washington, D.C. 1904]
.N35

NN 0032474   DLC

National American woman suffrage association.
Proceedings of the ... annual convention
see its   Handbook ... and proceedings ...

National American woman suffrage association.
Program of the annual convention.
Washington,
v. 23½cm.

Library of Congress   JK1881.N3   CA 5—2231 Unrev'd

NN 0032476   DLC

National American woman suffrage association.
Progress. v.   -10;   -June 1910.
[New York, etc., National American woman suffrage association] 1902 -10.

VOLUME 405

National American woman suffrage association.
International woman suffrage conference. *1st, Washington, D. C., 1902.*
Report first International woman suffrage conference held at Washington, U. S. A., February 12, 13, 14, 15, 16, 17, 18, 1902, in connection with and by invitation of the National American woman suffrage association. New York [1902]

National American women suffrage association.
Report of the annual convention
see its Handbook ... and proceedings ...

National American woman suffrage association.
The revolution in women's work makes votes for women a practical necessity. n.d.

NN 0032480   MiU

JF851
.C7   National American woman suffrage association.
Rare Bk. Curtis, George William, 1824–1892.
Coll.   Speeches of George William Curtis [and] Henry Ward Beecher. New York, The National-American woman suffrage association, 1898.

National American woman suffrage association.
Phillips, Wendell, 1811–1884.
Speeches on rights of women, by Wendell Phillips. Pub. for the National-American woman suffrage association ... Philadelphia, Press of A. J. Ferris, 1898.

National American woman suffrage association.
Suffrage and government...
see under Austin, Mary (Hunter), 1868–1934.

National American woman suffrage association.
Susan B. Anthony, 1820–1906.
[Warren, 1906?]

JK1899
.A6N3

NN 0032484   DLC

National American woman suffrage association.
McCrackan, William Denison, 1864–
... Swiss solutions of American problems, by W. D. McCrackan ... 2d ed. New York, Printed for the National American woman suffrage association by Concord co-operative printing co., 1897.

National American woman suffrage association.
Testimony from Idaho. [1914]

NN 0032486   MiU

National American woman suffrage association.
Testimony from Wyoming. [1914]

NN 0032487   MiU

La
324.3   National American Woman Suffrage Association.
N21c   The thirty-fifth annual convention...
1903   will be held at the Athenaeum, New Orleans, March 19th to 25th, 1903. [New Orleans, 1903]
              cover-title, [23]p. incl. advertising. illus. 24cm.

1. Woman   suffrage—Congresses.

NN 0032488   LU

National American woman suffrage association.
Thirty-ninth annual convention, Chicago...
February 14 to 19, 1907: [program.]
23 p.   23 cm.
Victory convention, Chicago. Feb. 12 to 18, 1920.

NN 0032489   ICHi

F884
P8P2   National American Woman Suffrage Association.
v. 3;21   Thirty-seventh annual convention ... June 28 to July 5, 1905, First Congregational Church, Park and Madison Streets, Portland, Oregon. [Portland, 1905]
[24] p. (incl. cover) illus. 24cm. [Pamphlets on Oregon, v. 3. no. 21]

In portfolio.

1. Woman - Suffrage - Portland, Or. 2. Woman - Suffrage - Congresses. (Series)

NN 0032490   CU-B

National American woman suffrage association.
A tribute to Woodrow Wilson. New York, National American woman suffrage association, 1919.
46 l. 35½ᶜᵐ.
Includes a testimonial to Woodrow Wilson from each of the state branches of the association and his Address to the United States Senate, September 30, 1918.

1. Wilson, Woodrow, pres. U. S., 1856–1924.
                                                   43–47411
Library of Congress   E767.N3

NN 0032491   DLC NN

National American woman suffrage association.
The truth about Colorado. [1913]

NN 0032492   MiU

National American woman suffrage association.
The truth versus Richard Barry ...
[191-]

NN 0032493   MiU

National American woman suffrage association.
Twenty facts about woman suffrage. n.d.

NN 0032494   MiU

National American woman suffrage association.
Twenty-five answers to antis; five minute speeches on votes for women by eminent suffragists. New York, National woman suffrage publishing company, inc., publishers for the National American woman suffrage association [1912?]
cover-title, 43 p. illus. (ports.) 25½ᶜᵐ.
"Delivered ... at a meeting ... March 11, 1912, at the Metropolitan temple in New York."—Foreword.

1. Woman—Suffrage. I. Title.
                                                   34–12355
Library of Congress   JK1901.N32   324.30973

NN 0032495   DLC CaBViP NIC

National American woman suffrage association.
Two years of equal suffrage in California-its results. [1914?]

NN 0032496   MiU

National American woman suffrage association.
United States senators and representatives on woman suffrage... n.d.

NN 0032497   MiU

National American Woman Suffrage Association.
Victory Convention (1869–1920) of the National American Woman Suffrage Association including the Susan B. Anthony centenary celebration and the Anna Howard Shaw memorial, together with the first National Congress of the League of Women Voters. Congress Hotel, Chicago, Illinois. February 12th to 18th, 1920. [Chicago, Illinois, Englewood Print Shop, 1920.]
[72] p. 27½ᶜᵐ.
Unpaged.
Advertisements interspersed.

NN 0032498   ICJ OO MB ICHi

National American woman suffrage association.
Victory, how women won it; a centennial symposium, 1840–1940, by the National American woman suffrage association. New York, The H. W. Wilson company, 1940.
8 p. l., [3]–174 p. front., pl., 6 port. 21 cm.
Each portrait accompanied by a leaf with biographical sketch.
CONTENTS.—Preliminary agitation, by Mary F. Morrisson.—First organized action, by Mary G. Peck.—Rampant women, by Mildred Adams.—"That word male," by Mary F. Morrisson.—Wyoming: the first surrender, by Carrie C. Catt.—Campaigning, state by state, by Maud W. Park.—The opposition breaks, by Gertrude F. Brown.—

Appeals to Congress, by Penelope P. B. Huse.—A decisive victory won, by Gertrude F. Brown.—The winning plan, by Maud W. Park.—The secretary has signed the proclamation, by Mary G. Peck.—Appendix: Bibliography (p. [155]–156). The National American woman suffrage association. Interesting events in the woman movement. The electoral thermometer. Partial suffrage gains. Directions for state work in supporting 19th amendment. Directions for lobbyists. Chronology of congressional action. Author's who's who.

1. Woman—Suffrage—U. S. 2. Woman—Suffrage—Hist. I. Title.
JK1896.N3   324.30973   40—35249

CaBVa OrU Or OrSaW WaWW OrPR OrCS Wa
RP MtBC NIC KyU KyU-A WaS MtU IdU WaSp WaTC OrStbM
NN 0032500   DLC OC1 OFH OO MiU ViU NcU NcD CoU KEmT

JK
1896   National American Woman Suffrage Association.
.N28   Victory, how women won it; a centennial
1940a   symposium, 1840–1940. New York, H.W.Wilson, 1940.
              174 p. illus., ports.
              Photocopy. Ann Arbor, Mich., University Microfilms, 1966. 174 p. (on double leaves)

1.Woman—Suffrage—U.S. I.Title.

NN 0032501   MiU

*BROAD-
SIDE   National American Woman Suffrage Association.
1912   Votes for women. [Includes map showing
.N37   the states with full suffrage, partial
              suffrage, no suffrage and the states where
              the question of suffrage will be voted on
              this year] New York, Allied Printing, 1912?
              broadside. map. 30 x 22½cm.

1. Women—Suffrage. I. Title.

NN 0032502   ViU

National American woman suffrage association.
Cowles, James Lewis, 1843–
What women might do with the ballot; reasonable postal laws, by James L. Cowles. New York, National American woman suffrage association [1911]

VOLUME 405

⌈National American woman suffrage association⌉
Woman suffrage, arguments and results. ⌈New York,
National American woman suffrage association, 1910?⌉
cover-title, ⌈313⌉ p. 15ᶜᵐ.
Various pagings.
Contributions by various authors.
CONTENTS.—Materials for debates.—Endorsements.—History.—General
arguments.—Equal suffrage in practice.

1. Woman—Suffrage.   I. Title.

Library of Congress   JK1901.N33   19–13099

NN   0032504   DLC OO ViU TxU InU

National American woman suffrage association.
Woman suffrage, arguments and results; a collection of
eight popular booklets covering together practically the
entire field of suffrage claims and evidence. Designed
especially for the convenience of suffrage speakers and
writers and for the use of debaters and libraries. New
York, National American woman suffrage association
⌈1911?⌉
⌈222⌉ p. 15½ᶜᵐ.
Various pagings.

CONTENTS.—Why women should vote. By Jane Addams.—Objections
answered. By Alice S. Blackwell.—Where women vote. By Frances M.
Björkman.—Do you know? By Carrie C. Catt.—A common sense view of
woman suffrage. By J. L. Williams.—Why women want to vote. By
Frances M. Björkman.—Measuring up equal suffrage. By George Creel
and Judge B. B. Lindsey.—Eminent opinions.

1. Woman—Suffrage.   I. Title.

Library of Congress   JK1901.N35   19–13098

NN   0032506   DLC GU MH

National American Woman Suffrage Association.   324.3 R261
Woman suffrage. Arguments and results. A collection of eight
popular booklets covering together practically the entire field of
suffrage claims and evidence. Designed especially for the convenience of suffrage speakers and writers and for the use of debaters and libraries. New York, National American Woman Suffrage Association, ⌈1912?⌉.
⌈2⌉, 55, ⌈1⌉ p. 15½x9ᶜᵐ.
Contents.—Addams, J. Why women should vote.—Blackwell, A. S. Objections
answered.—Björkman, F. M. Where women vote.—Catt, C. C. Do you know?
—Williams, J. L. A common sense view of woman suffrage.—Björkman, F. M. Why
women want to vote.—Creel, G., & Lindsey, B. J. Measuring up equal suffrage.—
Eminent opinions.

NN   0032507   ICJ WaU

National American Woman Suffrage Association.
Woman suffrage; History, arguments and results...
see under   Maule, Frances, 1879–   ed.

National American Woman ⌈ Suffrage Association.
Woman suffrage in practice
see under   International Alliance of Women.

National American woman suffrage association.
Woman's centennial congress, November 25, 26,
27, 1940
see under   Woman's Centennial Congress,
1940.

National American woman suffrage association.

Woman's century calendar, ed. by Carrie Chapman Catt,
pub. by National American woman suffrage association ... New York, N. Y. ⌈1899⌉

National American woman suffrage association.

The Woman's journal. v. 1–48; Jan. 8, 1870–May 26, 1917.
Boston and Chicago ⌈etc.⌉ 1870–1917.

JK1880
.W58
National American woman suffrage association.

The Woman's journal. v. 1–16, no. 6; June 2, 1917–June
1931. ⌈New York, The Woman citizen corporation, etc.,
1917–31⌉

National American woman suffrage association.

The Woman's tribune. v. 1–25, v. 26, no. 1; Aug. 1883–Mar.
6, 1909. Beatrice, Neb., The Nebraska woman suffrage association; ⌈etc., etc.⌉ 1883–1909.

⌈National American woman suffrage association.⌉
The working of equal suffrage...⌈1914.

NN   0032515   MiU

National American Woman Suffrage Association
see also
American Woman Suffrage Association.
National Woman Suffrage Association.

National American woman suffrage association. Dept.
of study in political science.
Question book. Department of study in political science of the National-American woman suffrage association. ⌈New York, The National-American woman suffrage association, 1896⌉
48 p. 17ᶜᵐ. (On cover: Political science study series. vol. II, no. 2,
Sept. 1896)

1. Economics—Outlines, syllabi, etc.   I. Title.

Library of Congress   HB171.5.N3   19–13100

NN   0032517   DLC

National American Woman Suffrage Association.   League of
Women Voters
see   League of Women Voters of the United States.

National Americana society, New York.

Ellsworth, Lincoln, 1880–   ed.
Air pioneering in the Arctic; the two polar flights of Roald
Amundsen and Lincoln Ellsworth ... New York, National
Americana society, 1929.

CS69
.N3
National Americana Society, New York.
American families of historic lineage, being a genealogical, historical and biographical account of representative
families of eminent American and foreign ancestry, recognized social standing and distinguished achievements; historic families. New York ⌈19—⌉
345 p. illus. (part col.) ports. 37 cm.

1. U. S.—Geneal.   I. Title.

CS69.N3   66–59323

NN   0032520   DLC

National Americana Society, New York.
American families of historic lineage; being a genealogical, histori-
cal and biographical account of representative families of eminent
American and foreign ancestry, recognized social standing and
distinguished achievements. Historic families... New York:
Americana Soc. ⌈191–⌉   3 v. fronts., col'd plates, ports. f°.

1. U. S.—Genealog.
N. Y. P. L.   August 3, 1921.

NN   0032521   NN

National Americana Society, New York.
American families of historic lineage. Long Island edition.
Issued under the editorial supervision of W. S. Pelletreau and J. H.
Brown.   New York: National Americana Soc. ⌈1913⌉   2 v.
pl., port. f°.

Paging continuous.
no. 16 of fifty copies printed, édition étoile d'argent.
Bound in dark brown crushed levant morocco.

1. Genealogy, U. S.: N. Y.: Long   Island. 2. Long Island.—History.
3. Brown, John Howard.
N. Y. P. L.   March 14, 1914.

NN   0032522   NN MiD-B

E171
.A53
National Americana society, New York.

Americana. v. 1–37; Jan. 1906–Dec. 1943. New York, The
American historical company, inc.; ⌈etc., etc., 1906–43⌉

National Americana Society,   New York.
Annals of American families; issued under the
editorial supervision of Cuyler Reynolds...
J. Collins Pumpelly...⌈and⌉ John W. Jordan...
New York, National Americana soc. ⌈191–?⌉ 365 p.
illus. 37cm.

Contents.—Van Rensselaer.—Stuyvesant.—Cuyler.
—Van Cortlandt.—Schermerhorn.—Read.—Spencer.—
Snow.—Dewey.—Duke.—Delano.—Lawrence.—Livingston.

—Schanck.—Van Alstyne.—Jackson.—Bissell.

1. United States—Geneal. I. Reynolds, Cuyler, 1866–
1934, ed. II. Pumpelly, Josiah Collins, 1839–1920,
ed. III. Jordan, John Woolf, 1840–1921, ed.

NN   0032525   NN

National Americana Society, New York.
Annals of American families.
3v.por.pl.col.pl.   N.Y.Nat.Americana
soc.[1921?]

Half-title: Historic families.
Edition etoile d'argent, limited to
fifty numbered and registered sets, of
which this is no.16.

NN   0032526   NJQ

National Americana society, New York.

Lawrence, Ruth, ed.
Colonial families of America, issued under the editorial
supervision of Ruth Lawrence ...
New York, National Americana society ⌈1928–

National Americana society, New York.
The Ellsworth family ... New York, National Americana
society, 1930–
v. front. (col. coat of arms) plates, ports. 35½ᶜᵐ.
Allied families: Holcomb, Loomis, Eaton, Birge, Oviatt, Dawes.
CONTENTS.—L. James William Ellsworth, his life and ancestry.

1. Ellsworth family (Josiah Ellsworth, 1629–1689) 2. Ellsworth,
James William, 1849–1925. 3. Ellsworth, Lincoln, 1880–
Library of Congress   CS71.E475 1930   30–7781

NN   0032528   DLC IU OCl OClMA OClW OClWHi OClMN

National Americana society, New York.

Lawrence, Ruth.
Genealogical histories of Crane-Starkey and allied families. Issued under the editorial supervision of Ruth Lawrence ... New York, National Americana society, 1931.

VOLUME 405

NATIONAL AMERICANA SOCIETY, New York
Morris, Hennen, Shepard, Vanderbilt and allied
families; genealogical and biographical. New York,
1954. 66 p. 37cm.

1. Morris family. 2. Hennen family. 3. Shepard family. 4. Vanderbilt family.

NN 0032530 NN

385.0973
qV22Z National Americana Society, New York
N2 Vanderbilt genealogy. Extracted from
pamphlet prepared in 1934 by National Americana Society, Inc. and New York Social Register of 1945. New York, 1945.
8L. 29cm.

Typescript.

1. Vanderbilt family (Jan Aertsen Van der
Bilt., fl.1650) I. Title.

NN 0032531 TNJ

National Americanization Committee. 3575.210
Americanization war service. What you can do for Americaniza-
tion.
= New York. 1918. 12 pp. 20½ cm.

L6847 — T.r. — Americanization. — European War, 1914- . United States.

NN 0032532 MB

National Americanization committee.
Americanization—what women's organizations can do... ᵉ191-?ᵉ

NN 0032533 MiU

National Americanization committee.
Americanizing a city; the campaign for the Detroit
night schools, conducted in August–September, 1915, by
the Detroit board of commerce and Board of education,
under the auspices of the National Americanization committee and the Committee for immigrants in America ...
issued by the National Americanization committee and
the Committee for immigrants in America. New York
city, 1915.
23 p. illus. 23cm.
1. Evening and continuation schools—Michigan—Detroit. 2. Detroit—
Foreign population. I. Committee for immigrants in America. II. Detroit board of commerce. III. Detroit. Board of education. IV. Title.

18-9653

Library of Congress LC3733.D6N3

NN 0032534 DLC NN MB DHEW OC1 OO

National Americanization Committee. 3575.211
A call to national service.
= [New York. 1916.] 16 pp. 21½ cm.
On the work of the organization.
The title is on the cover.

L6843 — T.r. — Americanization.

NN 0032535 MB

National Americanization Committee.
A call to national service. ᵢNew York, 1916.ᵢ 8p nar.
8°.
Cover-title.

1. Emigrants and immigrants, U. S.
N.Y.P.L. 2. Americanism.
October 30, 1916.

NN 0032536 NN

National Americanization Committee. 3575.207
Circular. No. 7, 9, 10, 11. Pay envelope series.
= New York. [1918.] v. Illus. Portrait. 15½ cm.
Deals with citizenship in the United States.

L6845 — Americanization.

NN 0032537 MB

National Americanization Committee.
The engineer and social changes... ᵢNew York, 1917.ᵢ
6 p. 8°.
Repr.: Engineering news-record. April 12, 1917. Editorial.

1. Labor.—History and conditions.
N.Y.P.L. June 6, 1919.

NN 0032538 NN

National Americanization Committee.
Partial record of alien enemy activites, 1915-
1917
see under Providence journal.

National Americanization committee.
Professional course for service among immigrants;
prepared for the use of colleges and universities, schools
of civics and philanthropy, to fit men and women for
service among immigrants. Adapted also for study by
clubs, institutions and conferences of workers of social
organizations. New York, N.Y., The Committee for immigrants in America ᵢ1915ᵢ
24 p. 21½cm.
On cover: Prepared for the United States Bureau of education by the
Committee for immigrants in America.
1. U. S.—Foreign population. I. U. S. Bureau of education. II. Title.

E 16-67

Library, U. S. Bur. of Education HV4010.N2

NN 0032540 DHEW

National Americanization Committee.
Sickness insurance. Prepared by a special committee of experts.
118499 New York, Reprinted for the Committee for Immigrants in America, [1913?].
60 p. 24cm.

NN 0032541 ICJ

National Americanization Committee. 3575.213
A startling statement of facts. A new era in the industrial world.
= New York. 1918. (4) pp. 21 cm.
Urges Americanization work in industrial concerns as a means to retain
immigrant workers.

L6845 — Americanization.

NN 0032542 MB

National Americanization Committee.
War Americanization for states. New York: National
Americanization Committee, 1917. 50 p. 8°.
Cover-title.

1. Emigration and immigration. U. S. 2. Title.
N.Y.P.L. April 15, 1918

NN 0032543 NN DL

National Americanization Committee. Committee on Man-Power 3575.212
Engineering. No. 4.
Americanization of foreign-born within controlled districts.
= New York. [1918.] (1) p. 33 cm.
On industrial Americanization.

L6841 — T.r. — Americanization. — Citizenship. United States.

NN 0032544 MB

National Ammonia Company.
The ammonia-chlorine treatment of water; a
digest and bibliography
see under Berliner, Julius Frederick
Thomas, 1902-

TP490
.N35 National ammonia company.
The National diamond. v. 1-7, no. 10; July 1931-Dec. 1937.
New York, Philadelphia, National ammonia division, E. I.
du Pont de Nemours & co., inc.; ᵢetc., etc.ᵢ 1931-37.

National Ammonia Company
see also
Du Pont de Nemours (E. I.) and Company.

National amnesty committee for the Smith Act
victims
See
National committee to win amnesty for Smith Act
victims.

National Amvet.
v.
Washington, D. C., 1946– v. illus. 22–43cm.
Film reproduction. Positive.
Monthly (irregular).
Published by American veterans of World war II.

1. World war, 1939-1945— Veterans—Per. and soc publ.—
U. S. I. American veterans of World war II ond Korea.

NN 0032549 NN

National Anaesthesia Research Society
see International Anesthesia Research
Society.

National Analysts, Inc.
Curb parking survey and central city shopping
survey. Done on behalf of Philadelphia Committee
for Relief of Traffic Congestion. Submitted by
National Analysts, Inc., October 1945. Philadelphia, 1945.
47 l. tables.

Parking regulations by sides of
blocks surveyed. ᵢPhiladelphia, 1945ᵢ
p.47-A-77. maps.

1. Parking.

NN 0032552 PPBMR

National Analysts, inc.
Fibers; opinions and practices among manufacturers of
cordage and twine. Washington ᵢU. S. Govt. Print. Off.ᵢ
1953.
98 p. tables. 26 cm. (U. S. Dept. of Agriculture. Marketing
research report no. 51)
"One of a series of industrial consumer preference studies conducted by the Division of Special Surveys, Bureau of Agricultural
Economics; written by National Analysts, inc."
1. Fibers. (Series)

[HD1751.A9183 no. 51] Agr 53-258

U. S. Dept. of Agr. Libr. 1Ag84Mr no. 51
for Library of Congress ᵢ3*ᵢ

NN 0032553 DNAL PP PU-W

National Analysts, inc.
Housing market analysis, a symposium
see under
American Marketing Association.

VOLUME 405

National Analysts, ınc.
  The service station and the motorist
    see under Du Pont de Nemours (E.I.)
  & Company, Wilmington, Del. Petroleum
  Chemicals Division.

₁National analytic corporation, *Detroit*₁
  Your estate problems. ₁Detroit, The National analytic
corporation, °1929₎
  ₁40₎ p. incl. illus., diagrs., forms. 27½ᶜᵐ.

  1. Estates (Law) 2. Wills. 3. Forms (Law) ɪ. Title. ɪɪ. Title:
Estate problems.
                                      cA 29–461 Unrev'd

NN   0032556   DLC

SF967   National Anaplasmosis Conference.
A6   Proceedings.
N37   1st–
          1948–
          v.p.
          v.

NN   0032557   CU-A ·IdU MBCo OrCS LU KMK

National Anatomical Museum, New York
    see
  New York (City) Grand Anatomical Museum.

The **National** ancient monuments review. v. 1–
1928–
  Manchester, The Wykeham press ₁1928–
    v. illus., plates (part fold.) fold. plans. 25ᵐ. quarterly.
    Editor: 1928–   John Swarbrick.
    Nos. 1–   include "Tour & pilgrimage supplement."

  1. Monuments—Preservation—Period. 2. Monuments—England.
ɪ. Swarbrick, John, 1879–   ed.

  Library of Congress   DA655.A1N27   38–14079
                              ₁3₎   708

NN   0032559   DLC NN

National ancient monuments year book...
₁1927

₁Manchester:₎ Wykeham Press, 1927   8°.
  v. illus., plates.
    Editor : 1927–   J. Swarbrick.

1. Monuments, Historical—Gt. Br.
N. Y. P. L.   November 21, 1928

NN   0032560   NN CU

National and American miller
  see
  American miller and processor.

DS   National and domestic customs of the Jews;
112   with a large and valuable map of Palestine;
N37   and an appendix, containing scripture
          allusions to various customs and opinions.
          Prepared by a Friend of Youth. New York,
          Leavitt; Boston, Crocker & Brewster, 1830.
          iv,144p.

      1. Jews—Social life and customs.

NN   0032562   UU MH

The **National** and English review. v. 1–   (no. 1–   );
Mar. 1883–
London.
    v. ın   illus., maps. 26 cm. monthly.
    Title varies : Mar. 1883–May 1950, The National review.
    Absorbed the English review, Aug. 1937; the English review maga-
zine, June 1950.

    AP4.N25   9–17515 rev 2*

      MH MB ICJ MNS CoU CaBVa WaS DNW
NN   0032563   DLC MMeT CtH CU NNC NcD NIC TxU NjP

National and Freemason
              see
National Freemason.

The **National** and English review.
  "Germany on the brain"; or, The obsession of "a
  crank"; gleanings from the National review, 1899–1914;
  with an introductory note, by L. J. Maxse ... London,
  "The National review" office, 1915.
    368 p. 24ᶜᵐ.
    CONTENTS.—Introductory note.—Table of dates.—The disclosure, and
exposure of German anglophobia.—The fight for the emancipation of
British foreign policy from the German yoke.—A new chapter in British
policy.—From Paris to Algeciras.—From Algeciras to the Anglo-Russian
agreement.—From the Anglo-Russian agreement to "shining armour."—
From "shining armour" to Agadir.—From Agadir to the eve of Armageddon.—Approaching Armageddon.
    1. Gt. Brit. — For. rel. — Germany. 2. Germany — For. rel. — Gt. Brit.
3. Europe—Politics—1871–   4. European war, 1914–   —Causes.
ɪ. Maxse, Leopold James,   1864–   ɪɪ. Title.

  Library of Congress   DA47.2.N3
                                            18–19229

NN   0032565   DLC CtY DNW ICJ NN

The **National** and English review.   *P.19.547.3
  Woman: the question of her higher education, her position in the
  political and industrial world and as a social reformer. A collection of articles thereon which appeared in the National Review
  from 1884 to 1897.
  — Cleveland. 1914. 33 pph. in ɪ v. 24½ cm., in 8s.
  The title-page is type-written.

  This card was printed at the Boston   Public Library, October 10, 1914.
  K3402 — Women.

NN   0032566   MB

RH   National and grand army songs, compiled by
B552   a blind soldier, for the support of his
          family. Ottawa, Kan., N. Waring, 1884.
          19p. 14cm.

          Cover title.

          1. U.S. Army—Songs.

NN   0032567   KU-RH

National and Grindlays Bank Limited.
  The National and Grindlays review
  see under title

National and Grindlays Bank Limited
  see also
  National Bank of India, ltd.

The **National** and Grindlays review. v. 1–
Oct. 1954–
₁London₎
    v. ın   25 cm. quarterly.
    Title varies: Oct. 1954–Oct. 1957, N. B. I. review.—1958, The Na-
tional overseas and Grindlays review.
    Issued Oct. 1954–Oct. 1957 by the National Bank of India, ltd.;
Jan. 1958–   by the National and Grindlays Bank Limited
(called in 1958 National Overseas and Grindlays Bank Limited)

    1. Commerce—Period. 2. Finance—Period. ɪ. National Bank of
India, ltd. ɪɪ. National and Grindlays Bank Limited.

    HF41.N2   330.5   58–22172 rev 2

NN   0032568   DLC OrU HU

₁National and Inter-American Music Week Committee₎
  The 1944   letter to local Music week
  chairmen and workers, National and inter-American
  music week. ₁15 Fourth Ave., New York, Author,
  1944₎
    v.

NN   0032569   Or

National and international bureau of information, *New York.*
  The universal telegraph cipher code. Arranged for general correspondence ... New York, The National & international bureau of information ₁°1885₎
    66 p. 17½ᶜᵐ.

    1. Cipher and telegraph codes.
                                            cA 7–4988 Unrev'd

  Library of Congress   HE7673.N27

NN   0032570   DLC

HQ 114   **National and International Council of Women from**
. N3   **1894 to 1904.**
          ₁Scrap book: a collection of newspaper
          clippings, magazine articles, programs, etc.₎
          4 vols.   illus. (port.)   30 cm.

NN   0032571   DLC

National & international employment handbook for specialized personnel.
  Chicago, World Trade Academy Press.
    v. 28 cm. annual.
    "By Juvenal L. Angel," 19

    1. Vocational guidance—Yearbooks. 2. U. S.—Occupations.
ɪ. Angel, Juvenal L.

    HF5381.A1N37   371.425   53–4549

NN   0032572   DLC OU NIC

371.425 **National and international handbook for**
qN2732   **specialized personnel.**
           New York.
           v.

           Issued by World Personnel Service, Chicago.

           1. Occupations. 2. Professions. I.
           World Personnel Service, Chicago.

NN   0032573   N NBuG NNC OCl WU UPB

National and international measures for full
  employment ...
    see under United Nations. Dept. of
  Economic Affairs.

National and Jackson Democratic association.
  Burke, Edmund, 1809–1882.
    ... Taylor Whigery exposed. Letter from the Hon. Ed-
mund Burke. ₁Washington? National and Jackson Democratic association committee, 1848₎

**National and local government officers' associ-
  ation.**

      See

National association of local government officers

National and Municipal Association.   320.6161–ɪ
*₁Call for the National and Municipal Association, charter and
articles of incorporation.₎ ₁12₎ p. sq. D. Chicago, Ill., c. 1897.

NN   0032577   ICJ

VOLUME 405

National and municipal association.
ₑCharter, etc.₎
n.p. ₑcl897₎
ₑ9₎ p.   O.

NN   0032578   00

National and Ohio state Republican and Democratic
     platform, 1896
        see under   Democratic party. Ohio. Con-
vention, 1896.

National and Pan-American Press Congress
    see Pan American Press Conference.

... National & patriotic songs, with English and original
    words ... Sydney, Brisbane, W. H. Paling & co. limited
    ₑᵉl942₎
cover-title, 32 p. 31ᶜᵐ.   (Paling's album series, no. 23)
Publisher's plate no.: W. H. P. & co. ltd. 1178.
With piano accompaniment.

1. National songs. 2. United nations (1942-   )—Songs and music.
                                               44-31063
Library of Congress   M1627.N2615

NN   0032581   DLC

The national and private advantages of the African
    trade considered: being an enquiry, how far it
    concerns the trading interest of Great Britain ...
        see under   [Postlethwayt, Malachy]
ca. 1707-1767.

National and regional economic tendencies
        see under   Maryland. University. Bureau
of Business and Economic Research.

... National, and state auto-highways and their
    concourse of industries and institutions ...
        see under   [Owen, Albert Kimsey]

National and state legislation on exemption from taxation of be-
quests and gifts to education, philanthropy and religion... Issued by representatives of the free public educational, philanthropic
and religious institutions of the city of New York, May 29, 1917.
ₑNew York. 1917.₎   1 p.l., 18 p.   8°.

1. Taxation.—Exemption, U. S.   2. Inheritance tax, U. S. 3. Gifts.
—Taxation, U. S.   May 20, 1918.
X. Y. P. L.

NN   0032585   NN Or 00

National and state live-stock associations and
     allied organizations
        see   Live-stock associations

National and state revenues and expenditures
     1913 and 1903 ...
        see under   U.S. Bureau of the census.

National and state rights, considered by "one
    of the people", reply to the "Trio"
        see under   [McDuffie, George] 1790-1851.

National and state taxation: their operation and
    results as affecting life insurance. To which are
    appended the action of the American life
    underwriters' convention, at its last session,
    and an extract from the report of the Massachu-
    setts insurance commissioners. New-York,
    1862.
        20 p.   23 cm.

NN   0032589   CtY

National and University Institute of Agriculture, *Reḥovot,
Israel*
    see
    Reḥovot, Israel. National and University Institute of
Agriculture.

National and University Library of the Socialist Republic
of Macedonia
    see
    Skopje, Yugoslavia. Narodna i univerzitetska biblioteka.

National anecdotes, interspersed with historical
    facts ...
        see under   Thiselton, William Matthew, ed.

National Anesthesia Research Society
        see   International Anesthesia Research
Society.

**National aniline & chemical company, inc.,
New York.**

    Acid colors. National U. S. A. colors. New
York, Boston, Toronto ₑetc.₎ National aniline &
chemical company, incorporated ₑ1919?₎
₂p.l., 3-31 p., front., illus.(mounted samples) pl.
23½ᶜᵐ.

    1. Coloring matter. 2. Dyes and dyeing—Wool.
I. Title. II. Title: National U. S. A. colors.

NN   0032594   ViU CtY IU OU

National aniline & chemical company, inc., *New York*
    Acid dyes for worsted piece-goods. New
York, National aniline & chemical company, inc.,
n.d.
    xv, ₑ19₎ p. front. 23cm.
    Contains colored samples.

    1. Dyes and dyeing - Wool.

NN   0032595   DP MdBJ

National Aniline & Chemical Company, Inc., New York.
    American colors vs. German colors; the dye situation today
...by Dr. Louis J. Matos...   New York: National Aniline &
Chemical Co., Inc. ₑ1918.₎   14 p., 1 l.   front. (port.), illus.
12°.

    Partly reprinted from Women's wear.

1. Dyes, U. S. 2. Matos, Louis   Joseph.
N. Y. P. L.   May 2, 1919.

NN   0032596   NN

National aniline & chemical company, inc., New
    York.
    Chrome colors on yarn, giving complete direc-
tions concerning the methods by which chrome dyes
are applied and also tabulations of fastness
properties, etc. 2d rev.ed. New York ₑetc.₎
National aniline & chemical company,inc. ₑn.d.₎
    xxii p. front.,plates. 23cm.

    Each plate, except the last, contains samples
of dyed wool.

NN   0032597   MoU

National Aniline & Chemical Company, inc.,
    New York.
    Cotton colors. Colorants pour coton.
New York ₑ19 - ₎
    67 p. illus., samples. (National U.S.A.
colors, no. 29)
    In French and English.

    1. Dyes and dyeing - Cotton. I. Title.

NN   0032598   NBPol

National aniline & chemical company, inc., *New York*
    Direct dyes for cotton. New York, National
aniline & chemical company inc., n.d.
    xxv, 29 p., 1 l. front. 23cm.
    Contains colored samples.

    1. Dyes and dyeing - Cotton.

NN   0032599   DP

National Aniline & Chemical Company, inc., *New York,*
    Defendant.
    ₑDocuments and correspondence relating
to the case of Grasselli Chemical Company vs.
National Aniline & Chemical Company, inc.₎
        see under   Grasselli Chemical Company,
complainant.

National aniline & chemical company, inc., New
    York.
    Dyes for astrakan. New York, National aniline
& chemical company, inc. ₑn.d.₎
    2l. front.,fold.plates. 23cm.

    Each plate, except the last, contains samples
of dyed astrakan.

NN   0032601   MoU

National aniline & chemical company, inc., New
    York.
    Dyes for paper. 2d rev.ed. New York ₑetc.₎
National aniline & chemical company, inc. ₑn.d.₎
    4l. front.,fold.plates. 23cm.

    Each plate, except the last, consists of
samples of dyed paper.

NN   0032602   MoU

B 5945   National aniline & chemical co., inc., *New York.*
598*   Dyes for paper.
            National aniline & chemical company incor-
porated,executive offices: 21 Burling slip,
New York[ca.1920] ...
    [4]p.,9l.of mounted specimens. 2 plates.
23cm.,in case 24.5cm.
    The 9 leaves of specimens are folded
accordion-style, with specimens mounted on one
side only.

    Original gilt-stamped green cloth; in cloth
case.
    Imperfect: 1 mounted specimen wanting.

NN   0032604   MH

VOLUME 405

NATIONAL ANILINE & CHEMICAL COMPANY, Inc., New York.
Dyes for paper. Third revised edition. Buffalo, N.Y.:
National Aniline & Chemical Co., Inc.[, 193–?] v, 21 p.
front. 23cm.

Mounted col'd samples, p.1–21.

675279A. 1. Dyes and dyeing, Paper.

NN 0032605 NN

National aniline & chemical company, inc., New
York.
Dyes for skein silk. New York [etc.] National
aniline & chemical company, inc. [n.d.]
3ℓ. front., fold.plates. 23cm.

Each plate, except the last, contains samples
of dyed silk.

NN 0032606 MoU

National Aniline & Chemical Company, inc., New York,
defendant.
The Grasselli Chemical Company, plaintiff,
vs. National Aniline & Chemical Company, inc.,
defendant. Record
see under   Grasselli Chemical Company, complainant.

National Aniline & Chemical Co., Inc. New York.
Manual of hosiery and knit goods dyeing;
including processes for the application of "National"
... dyes. 2d ed. rev. Author, 1923.
46 p.

NN 0032608 WaS

National Aniline & Chemical Company, Inc.
Memorandum in the Matter of Title V. -
Dyestuffs. Act of September 8, 1916. Prepared
expressly for the United States Tariff Commission.
[New York, 1918]
2 p.l., vii, 256 p., 14 l. tables. (part. fold.)
24 cm.
1. Tariff on dyestuffs - U.S. 2. Dyes and dyeing.
I. Title: Title V. - Dyestuffs.

NN 0032609 ViU MH

National aniline & chemical company, inc., *New York.*
"National certified food colors," certified to the Bureau
of chemistry, Department of agriculture. New York,
Boston [etc.] National aniline and chemical company, inc.
[1922]
vii p., 7 col. pl. 23cm.

Each plate consists of samples in colored celluloid.

1. Coloring matter in food. I. Title: Certified food colors.

Library of Congress   TX571.C7N3   22–12250

NN 0032610 DLC

TX571
C7N3   National Aniline & Chemical Company, inc.,
1922   New York.
"National certified food colors," certified
to the Bureau of chemistry, Department of
agriculture. New York, National Aniline &
Chemical Company, inc. [1922?]
v p. 4 col. pl. 23cm.

Each plate consists of samples in colored
celluloid.

NN 0032611 GU

QH   NATIONAL Aniline & Chemical Company,
237   inc., New York
N277n   National pharmaceuticals; certified
1938   stains, biological stains, vital stains,
staining solutions, indicators, laboratory
reagents, certified colors. January 1,
1939. New York, c1938.
47 p. illus.
1. Stains and staining - Catalogs

NN 0032612 DNLM

National Aniline & Chemical Company, inc.,
New York.
Union colors. New York [19 _]
16 p. illus., samples. (National
U.S.A. dyes, no. 107)

1. Dyes and dyeing - Wool. 2. Dyes and
dyeing - Cotton. I. Title.

NN 0032613 NBPol

National Aniline and Chemical Company, inc., *New York*
see also
Allied Chemical Corporation. *National Aniline Division.*

National animals' friend society, London.
The "A. F." pamphlet series. London, Animals'
friend society, 19--
v.

NN 0032615 OO

National animals' friend society, London.

The Animals' friend, or The progress of humanity.

London, Steuart, 18

National anniversary. A copy of the remarks
introductory to the reading of the Declaration of
Independence by Samuel R. Miller, and a copy of
the oration delivered by Bellamy Storer, were
furnished the committee of arrangement, at the
request of that body, and furnished for
publication.   Cincinnati? 1829.
12 p. 16.5 cm.
n. t. p.; caption on p. 3. Oration delivered at
the Methodist Reformed Church in Cincinnati,
Ohio, on the 4th July, 1829. By Bellamy Storer.

NN 0032617 OClWHi

NATIONAL ANNUITY LEAGUE, INC., OF COLORADO.
Constitution of the National annuity league, inc., of
Colorado. Denver, Colo. [1937] 2 l. 13½cm.

1. Pensions, Old age—Assoc. and org.—U.S.—Colorado.

NN 0032618 NN

National antarctic expedition 1901–1904.
... Album of photographs and sketches with a portfolio
of panoramic views. London, The Royal society [Printed
by Oliver and Boyd, Edinburgh] 1908.
xvi, 303, [1] p. incl. 97 pl. front., 43 pl. (11 fold., 7 col.) 31½ x 24cm.
and atlas of 24 fold. pl., 2 fold. maps. 31½ x 27½cm.
Prefatory note signed: Arch. Geikie, secretary, Royal society.
Introduction by Edward A. Wilson.
1. Antarctic regions. 2. Ice—Antarctic regions. I. Royal society of
London. II. Wilson, Edward Adrian, 1872–1912. III. Title.
Library of Congress   Q115.N32   9—7739
———— Copy 2.   G850.1901.D66
Plate [xt, and 2 maps   (A and B) wanting.

NN 0032619 DLC CtY MH-Z OrCS DAS NN CU MiU ICJ

National Antarctic expedition, 1901–1904.
The Antarctic manual
see under *title*

National Antarctic Expedition, 1901–1904.
The charts of the "Discovery" Antarctic
expedition
see under   Mulock, George F. A.

National Antarctic expedition, 1901–1904.
Earthquakes and other movements recorded in the Antarctic regions, 1902–1903.
In National Antarctic expedition 1901–
1904. Physical observations with discussions by various authors. London.
1908. p.37–96.
28653

NN 0032622 DAS

q559.99
N213g National Antarctic Expedition, 1901–1904.
Geol   Geology (Field-geology: petrography) London.
Lib'y   Printed by order of the Trustees of the British
Museum, 1907.
160p. illus. 32 x 24cm. (It's Natural history,
v.1.)
842257   Edited by L. Fletcher.
1. Geology – Antarctic regions. I. Fletcher, Sir
Lazarus, 1854–1921, ed. II. British Museum (Natural History) III. National Antarctic Expedition,
1901–1904. Natural history, v.1.

NN 0032623 TxU CSt DLC

National antarctic expedition, 1901–1904.
... Magnetic observations. Prepared under the superintendence of the Royal society. London, The Royal society, 1909.
vii, 274 p. front., XLIII pl., tables, diagrs. 31 x 23cm.

1. Magnetism, Terrestrial—Observations.

Library of Congress   QC826.A6N3   10–1783
———— Copy 2.   Q115.N35 .

NN 0032624 DLC NN MH-Z CtY OrCS DAS CU MiU ICJ

National antarctic expedition, 1901–1904.
... Meteorology ... Prepared under the superintendence of the director of the Meteorological office with the
co-operation of a committee of the Royal society. London, The Royal society [Harrison and sons, printers]
1908–13.
2 v. front., illus., plates (part col.) fold. maps, charts, diagrs. 31 x
24cm.
Pt. II: Prepared in the Meteorological office, under the superintendence
of M. W. Campbell Hepworth.
CONTENTS.—pt. I. Observations at winter quarters and on sledge journeys with discussions by various authors.—pt. II. Comprising daily syn-
chronous charts 1st October, 1901, to 31st March, 1904.
1. Meteorology—Antarctic regions. II. Gt. Brit. Meteorological office.
II. Royal society of London. III. Hepworth, Melville Willis Campbell, 1849–1919.
Library of Congress   Q115.N28   8—32354
———— Copy 2.   QC994.9.N3

NN 0032625 DLC OrCS DAS CtY MH-Z NN CU MiU ICJ

National Antarctic Expedition, 1901–1904.
The National Antarctic Expedition. "The South
Polar Times." ... [London, 1903]
broadside prospectus.

NN 0032626 RPJCB

National Antarctic Expedition, 1901–1904.
The National Antarctic Expedition. "The South
Polar Times." Prospectus ... [with] "South
Polar Times." Subscription form. [London, 1904]
caption title.

NN 0032627 RPJCB

National antarctic expedition, 1901–1904.
... Natural history ... London, Printed by order of the
Trustees of the British museum, 1907–12.
6 v. illus., plates (part col., part fold.) maps, charts. 31½ x 24 cm.
Maps with v. 1 and 2 folded in pocket.
Preface to v. 1–4 signed: E. Ray Lankester; v. 5, Sidney F. Harmer;
v. 6, L. Fletcher.
Vol. 1 edited by L. Fletcher; v. 2–6, by F. Jeffrey Bell.
Synopsis and Classified summary of the contents of vols. I–VI: v. 6,
p. [xi]–XVI.

Continued in next column

VOLUME 405

Continued from preceding column

CONTENTS.— I. Geology (field-geology : petrography) 1907.— II. Zoology (*Vertebrata: Mollusca: Crustacea*) 1907.— III. Zoology and botany (*Invertebrata:* marine *Algae, Musci*) 1907.— IV. Zoology. (*Various Invertebrata*) 1908.— V-VI. Zoology and botany. 1910–12.

1. Geology—Antarctic regions. 2. Zoology—Antarctic regions. 3. Botany—Antarctic regions. I. Fletcher, Sir Lazarus, 1854–1921, ed. II. Bell, Francis Jeffrey, 1855–1924, ed. III. British museum (Nat. hist.) IV. Title.

Q115.N26   8—3924
——— Copy 2.   QH84.2.N25

OClW MiU PPAmP CU NcD CaBVaU OrCS ICF-A
NN   0032629   DLC CtY IU NIC FMU ViU FTaSU MH ICJ

National Antarctic expedition 1901–1904.
... Physical observations with discussions by various authors. Prepared under the superintendence of the Royal society. London, The Royal society [Harrison and sons, printers] 1908.
v. 192 p. illus, 21 pl. (7 col., 1 fold.) 2 maps, diagrs. 31 x 24ᶜᵐ.
Preface signed: Arch. Geikie, Sec. R. S.
CONTENTS.—I. Tidal observations in the Antarctic regions, 1902–1903.— II. Pendulum observations.—III. Earthquakes and other earth movements recorded in the Antarctic regions, 1902–1903.—IV. Antarctic observations of aurora, 1902–1903.—V. Antarctic magnetic observations, 1902–1904.
1. Tides — Antarctic regions. 2. Gravity. 3. Earthquakes — Antarctic regions. 4. Auroras. 5. Magnetism, Terrestrial — Antarctic regions. I. Royal society of London.

Library of Congress   Q115.N3   8–23353
——— Copy 2.   G850.1901.D65

NN   0032630   DLC MH-Z CtY OrCS DAS CU AU MiU ICJ

National Anthem Competition.
Prize winning poems in ... contest ... [which] closes May 1, 1929. New York, 1929.
15 p.   23 cm.
Cover title.

NN   0032631   RPB NcD

The national anthem for India. [London, 1883?]
1 p. l., ii–iii, 23, v–x, [1] p., 1 l., [4] p. 38½ᶜᵐ.
Caption title.
"On the good results that may attend the establishment of a national anthem in India [by F. K. Harford]": p. [1]–23.

1. God save the king. I. Harford, Frederick Kill, 1832– II. National anthem for India fund.

      CA 6–2698 Unrev'd
      [5b1]
Library of Congress   ML3658.N2

NN   0032632   DLC

National anthem for India fund.

The national anthem for India. [London, 1883?]

The national anthem in Urdu. [Lahore, Anjuman-i-Punjab press, 18–?]

17, [12] p.   23cm. [Miscellaneous papers on India, Afghanistan, etc. v.4, no.10]

Caption title.

1. God save the king (Song)

NN   0032634   MnU

National anthem of Syria, arr. by Thomas F. Darcy, Jr. Traditional. New York, Bourne [1945]
parts.   14 x 17 cm.
Cover title.
For band.

1. National songs, Syrian (Instrumental settings)

M1258.N   M 59–238

NN   0032635   DLC

National anthems and patriotic airs of all nations. Arranged for the pianoforte... London: Boosey & Co.[, 189–?] Publ. pl. no. H. 129.   32 p.   f°. (The Cavendish music books. no. 109.)

1. Songs, National.
N. Y. P. L.   July 6, 1928

NN   0032636   NN

M
1627
N27++
  National anthems and patriotic airs of all nations. Arr. for the pianoforte. London, New York, Boosey [190–?]
32 p.   36cm. (The Cavendish music books, no. 109)

Without words.

1. National songs. 2. Piano music, Arranged.

NN   0032637   NIC

The National anthems of the Allies. London, etc., etc., G. Schirmer, Ltd. [1916?]
13 + p.

NN   0032638   MH

The national anthems of the Allies: Great Britain, France, Belgium, Russia, Japan. London, New York, G. Schirmer [191–]
9p.   26cm.

Words in the original, Russian and Japanese transliterated, with English translation.

1. National songs.

NN   0032639   CLSU

M1627
N278
  The National anthems of the Allies: Great Britain, France, Belgium, Russia [and] Japan. London, New York, G. Schirmer. [1914]
10 p.   music.   25cm.

1. National songs.

NN   0032640   CSt-H NjP

The National anthems of the Allies; United States, Great Britain, France, Belgium, Russia, Japan, Serbia, Italy, Rumania, Portugal, Cuba. New York, G. Schirmer, ©1917.
24 p.   31 cm.
For voice and piano.
Words in English and the language of each country. The words of the Russian and Japanese anthems are transliterated.

1. National songs.
M1627.N263   1917a   52–55980

NN   0032641   DLC CaBVa WaSp Wa IU NN MB CLSU

National anthems of the United Nations and associated powers ...
see under   Treharne, Bryceson, 1879–   ed.

National (The) Anti-Compulsory Vaccination Reporter. Mary C. Hume-Rothery, editor. Supplement, Jan. 1, 1878. 16 pp. 4°. [London.]

NN   0032643   DNLM CLM

National anti-contagious diseases acts association.
Southampton branch.
The application of the contagious diseases act to Southampton. [Report of proceedings] Southampton, Eng. [1870]
8 p.   21.5 cm.   [Pamphlets on contagious diseases acts, v.1]

NN   0032644   CtY

National anti-convict-contract association.
... Proceedings of the national convention, held at Chicago, August 26th, 1886. Together with other interesting matter relating to convict-contract labor. Ed. by Prof. L. D. Mansfield, M. A., assistant secretary. Chicago, Pub. by the Association, 1886.
ix, [1], 78 p.   25½ᵐᵐ.
At head of title: National anti-convict-contract association.

1. Convict labor—U. S. I. Mansfield, L. D.

Library of Congress   HV8908.N3 1886   10—28547

NN   0032645   DLC OrU OFH DL

The National anti-corn-law league
see   Anti-corn-law league.

National anti-food-trust leag, *Washington, D. C.*
Food bulletin, no. 1–
[Washington, D. C., National anti-food-trust leag, ©1910– pt. 23ᶜᵐ.

1. Food—Societies.
Library of Congress   TX341.N3   10–6504

NN   0032647   DLC

National anti-masonic convention, *Baltimore, 1831*
see
United States anti-masonic convention, *Baltimore, 1831.*

National anti-masonic convention, *Philadelphia, 1830.*
see
United States anti-masonic convention, *Philadelphia, 1830.*

Seligman
Per.
N214
  National Anti-Monopoly Cheap-Freight Railway League.
Document ... Monthly circular of the National Anti-Monopoly Cheap-Freight Railway League, for promoting reform in railroad management, by securing equal rights and cheap transportation, with consequent increased development of industrial energies and national resources ... Arranged for publication by Henry O'Rielly.

New York, Published by the National Anti-Monopoly Cheap-Freight   Railway League,

v.   23–24cm.

Sabin 51921.

NN   0032651   NNC NN

VOLUME 405

National anti-monopoly cheap-freight railway league.
... Practical statesmanship and commercial enterprise connected with improvement of means & reduction of cost in the
American railway system; and incidentally involving reforms
in the express and telegraph systems. Opinions of public
journals, prominent men, and popular meetings, in different
parts of the world, indicating the increasing popularity of the
important principles involved in the national anti-monopoly
cheap-freight railway bills presented in Congress by Senator
Henderson of Missouri, Senator Harlan of Iowa, and Senator

Nye of Nevada ... Arranged for publication by Henry
O'Rielly. New York, National anti-monopoly cheap-freight
railway league, 1867.
cover-title, p. ₍141₎–170. 22ᶜᵐ. (Document VIII–December 31, 1867.
Monthly circular of the National anti-monopoly cheap-freight railway
league ...)
No. 4 in a volume of pamphlets lettered: Ferrocarriles. 1867 a 1873.

1. Railroads—U. S.   I. O'Rielly, Henry, 1806–1886, ed.   II. Title.
30–29615

NN   0032653   DLC MH-BA

National anti-monopoly cheap freight railway league.
Proposed national system of cheap freight railways ...
Freight capacity ten-fold over the present double-tract.
Cost of transportation to be reduced to one-third of present
charges. Letter from the president of the National cheap
freight railway league, and others, to citizens of Texas.
₍Washington? 1867?₎
HE2123.N3
8 p. 23½ cm.
Caption title.
——— ₍Washington? 1867?₎
8 p. 23½ cm.
Another impression.
1. Railroads—U. S.
HE2123.N312
CA 7–6843 Unrev'd

NN   0032654   DLC

National anti-monopoly cheap-freight railway league.
Reform in railroad management, by securing equal
rights & cheap transportation. Statement of the views
and objects of the National anti-monopoly cheap-freight
railway league, with an abstract of the congressional railway bills introduced by Senator Harlan ... the nature of
which bills ... being fully explained in the annexed statements concerning the development of our industrial resources, by the Hon. Lorenzo Sherwood ... New York,
National anti-monopoly cheap-freight railway league,
1867.
4 p. l., 22, ₍2₎ p. 21½ᶜᵐ.
Edited by Henry O'Rielly.
The development of our industrial resources ... by Lorenzo Sherwood:
p. ₍1₎–22.

1. Interstate commerce.   I. Sherwood, Lorenzo.   II. O'Rielly, Henry,
1806–1886, ed.
5—39105
Library of Congress   HE2757.1867.N3

NN   0032656   DLC ICJ MH-BA

NATIONAL ANTI-MONOPOLY CHEAP-FREIGHT RAILWAY
LEAGUE.
Statement of the views and objects of the
National Anti-Monopoly Cheap-Freight Railway
League. New York. May,1867.

NN   0032657   MH

National anti-monopoly cheap-freight railway league.
... Supplement to statements in former publications about
the National anti-monopoly cheap-freight railway bills presented in Congress by Senator Harlan of Iowa, Senator Henderson of Missouri, Senator Fowler of Tennessee, and Senator
Nye of Nevada, further extracts from correspondence, and from
public journals in different sections of the Union, showing the
advantages and popularity of the proposed reformation and
improvement of the railway system. Including a letter of
Governor Peirpont, advising the adoption of the proposed

reform in Virginia ... Arranged for publication by Henry
O'Rielly. New York, National anti-monopoly cheap-freight
railway league, 1867.
cover-title, ₍25₎–40 p. 23ᶜᵐ. (Document IV—August, 1867. Monthly
circular of the National anti-monopoly cheap-freight railway league)

1. Railroads—U. S.   I. O'Rielly, Henry, 1806–1886, ed.
45—49803
Library of Congress   HE2757 1867.N33

NN   0032659   DLC

National anti-monopoly league.
Address to the people. The National antimonopoly
league. Our principles ... ₍New York, 188–?₎
24 p. 14¼ᶜᵐ.

1. Monopolies—U. S. 2. Trusts, Industrial.
CA 9–3404 Unrev'd
Library of Congress   HD2795.N2

NN   0032660   DLC NN WHi

National Anti-Opium Association of China.
China in the grip of Japanese drug traffickers. Memorandum
presented to the Commission of Inquiry of the League of Nations,
by the National Anti-Opium Association of China. Shanghai,
China, 1932.   16 p.   22½cm.

752807A. 1. Opium—Trade and stat.—   China.   June 12, 1935
N. Y. P. L.

NN   0032661   NN

National Anti-Opium Association of China.
The Commission of Inquiry and opium
monopoly
see under Dai, Bingham, 1899–

NATIONAL ANTI-OPIUM ASSOCIATION OF CHINA.
The National opium suppression committee and its policy;
the Opium suppression act and regulations, by Bingham Dai,
secretary... Shanghai, China: National anti-opium assoc.
of China, 1929. 18 p. 18cm.

1. Opium—Trade and stat.—China, 1929. I. Dai,
Bingham.

NN   0032663   NN

National anti-opium association of China.

Opium, a world problem; published quarterly by the National
anti-opium association of China.
Shanghai, China ₍192

National Anti-Opium Association of China.
Traffic in opium
see under International Anti-Opium
Association. Peking.

DKLA   National Anti-Polygamy League.
+N277   Petition. ₍New York, 1899₎
P   ₍1₎ ℓ.   53 x 21 cm. fold. to 21 x 13 cm.
            Blank printed petition form.
            Sub-title: Anti-polygamy petition to the
          U.S. House of Representatives.
            On reverse: Membership ₍list₎ of the
          National Anti-Polygamy League.
            "...effort to prevent the seating of the
          Polygamous Mormon, Brigham H. Roberts, of
          Utah, in the   Fifty-sixth
          Congress..."

NN   0032666   WHi

National anti-prohibition monthly

see

Law and order magazine.

National antiquarian association, Dubuque, Ia.

The Cultural antiquarian; history, art, science. v. 1–
autumn 1936–
Dubuque, Ia., The National antiquarian association, Columbia museum ₍etc.₎, 1936–

National anti-saloon convention
see Anti-saloon league of America.

Micro   National Anti-slavery Bazaar, Boston.
3   Gazette. v. 1–
          Boston, 18
            cards. 7.5x12.5cm. (Slavery Pamphlets)
          Micro-opaque. Louisville, Ky., Lost Cause
          Press, 1964.

NN   0032670   PSt ICN OU

National anti-slavery bazaar, Boston.

The Liberty bell. By friends of freedom ... Boston, Massachusetts anti-slavery fair, 1839–46; National anti-slavery
bazaar, 1847–58.

National anti-slavery bazaar, Boston, Mass.
(Notice of the opening of the 16th
national anti-slavery bazaar) broadside.
5x 8 in.
P 13, 465

NN   0032672   OClWHi

National anti-slavery bazaar, Boston..
Report of the ... National anti-slavery bazaar ...

Boston, 185
v. 15ᶜᵐ.

CA 6–2040 Unrev'd

ViW NIC
NN   0032673   DLC OClWHi MB TU MWA NcD TxU MiD ICN

Micro-   National Anti-slavery Bazaar, Boston.
fiche   Report of the ... National anti-
          slavery bazaar. Boston, 1857.
            2 sheets.   10.5 x 14.8 cm.
          (₍Slavery, source material and critical
          literature₎)
            Microfiche (negative) of typescript.
          Collation of the original: 34 p. 15
          cm.

NN   0032674   OOxM

National anti-slavery festival.
see National anti-slavery bazaar, Boston.

National anti-slavery standard. v. 1–30, June 11, 1840–Apr.
16, 1870; new ser., v. 1, May–July 1870; new ser., v. 1–3,
July 30, 1870–Dec. 1872.. New-York, American anti-slavery
society; ₍etc., etc.₎ 1840–72.
34 v. in 11. 23½–66ᶜᵐ.
Weekly, June 1840–Apr. 1870; monthly, May–July 1870; weekly, July
30, 1870–Dec. 1871; monthly, Jan.–Dec. 1872.
Title varies: June 1840–Apr. 1870, National anti-slavery standard.
(66ᶜᵐ)
May–July 1870, The Standard. A journal of reform and literature.
(23½ᶜᵐ)
July 30, 1870–Dec. 1871, The National standard ... An independent,
reform, and literary journal. (44ᶜᵐ)
Jan.–Dec. 1872, The National standard ... A temperance and literary
journal.

Editors: June 1840–May 13, 1841, N. P. Rogers.—May 20, 1841–May
1843, Lydia M. Child (with D. L. Child, June 1841–May 1843).—Aug.
1843–May 23, 1844, D. L. Child.—May 30, 1844–July 1854, S. H. Gay
and others.—Aug. 1854–May 1863, not ascertained.—June 1863–May
1865, Oliver Johnson.—Jan.–May 1866, Parker Pillsbury.—May 1866–
Dec. 1872, A. M. Powell.
Absorbed the Woman's advocate in May 1870.
Merged into the National temperance advocate.

1. Slavery in the U. S.—Period.   I. Rogers, Nathaniel Peabody,
1794–1846, ed.   II. Child, Mrs. Lydia Maria (Francis) 1802–1880, ed.
III. Child, David Lee, 1794–1874, ed.   IV. Gay, Sydney Howard, 1814–
1888, ed.   V. Johnson, Oliver, 1809–1889, ed.   VI. Pillsbury, Parker, 1809–
1898, ed.   VII. Powell, Aaron Macy, 1832–1899, ed.   VIII. American anti-
slavery society.

Library of Congress   E449.N28
30–17868

CtY CSt ViU NcRS CU-S ICRL N OCl OO MeB
NN   0032677   DLC ICRL ICN NIC AAP NNC InU MiU MB

VOLUME 405

Micro-
film
So-14
National anti-slavery standard, v. 1-
30, June 11, 1840-Apr. 16, 1870; new ser.,
v. 1, May-July 1870; new ser., v. 1-3,
July 30, 1870-Dec. 1872, N. Y., American
Anti-slavery Society, 1840-72.
Library has: June 11, 1840-
Microfilm copy.   Reels.   Negative.
35mm.
Collation of original: 34 v.
Title varies: June 1840-Apr. 1870, Nation-
al anti-slavery standard; May-July 1870, The
Standard; July 30, 1870-Dec. 1872, The Na-
tional standard.
Absorbed the Woman's advocate in May 1870.
Merged into the National temperance
advocate.

NN   0032678   CL FTaSU MoU KMK NSyU OU NcU ICU PSt

National Anti-Steel-Trap League.
Anti-Steel-Trap League news
see under title [supplement]

National anti-steel-trap league.
New hope for the Biological survey ... Washington, D. C.,
National anti-steel-trap league, inc. [1939]
31, [1] p. illus. 23ᶜᵐ.

1. U. S. Bureau of biological survey. 2. Wild life, Conservation of—
U. S. 3. Trapping.   I. Title.
44-46096
Library of Congress   SK361.N3
[2]   799

NN   0032680   DLC Or ICRL CtY LNHT NN

HV4763   National anti-steel-trap league.
.A7B7
1926   Breck, Edward, 1861-1929.
The steel-trap, a manual of information by Edward Breck ...
Washington, D. C., Anti-steel-trap league, 1926.

National antisuffrage association.
... Woman suffrage. Argument submitted by the National antisuffrage association in opposition to the adoption of the socalled Susan B. Anthony proposed amendment to the Constitution of the United States extending
the right of suffrage to women ... Washington, Govt.
print. off., 1916.
27 p. 23½ᶜᵐ. ([U. S.] 64th Cong., 1st sess. Senate. Doc. 408)
Presented by Mr. Dillingham. Ordered printed April 17, 1916.

1. Woman—Suffrage—U. S.
16-26383
Library of Congress   JK1903.A2N3

NN   0032682   DLC MiU OO OrU

National anti-sweating league, *London.*
... Annual report ... 1st-
1906/07-
Manchester, 1908-
v.   21½ᶜᵐ.
At head of title: National anti-sweating league to secure a minimum
wage.
Report year ends June 30.
List of publications on sweating included in each report.

1. Sweating system. 2. Wages—Minimum wage—Gt. Brit.
15-16112
Library of Congress   HD2339.G7N3

NN   0032683   DLC DL

National anti-sweating league, London.

Mallon, James Joseph, 1880-
... Extending the Trade boards act. By J. J. Mallon ...
[London, 1914?]

National anti-sweating league, London.

Mallon, James J.
... Minimum wage in practice, by J. J. Mallon (secretary of the National anti-sweating league ...) [London,
1914]

National anti-sweating league, *London.*
Miscellaneous pamphlets on the sweating
system and minimum wage. London, 1907-18]
7 pam. 22-28 cm.

NN   0032686   DL

National anti-sweating league, London.
"Never had a holiday" ... [191-?]

NN   0032687   MiU

National anti-sweating league, *London.*
... Report of conference on a minimum wage, held at
the Guildhall, London, on October 24th, 25th, & 26th, 1906.
London, Co-operative printing society limited, 1907.
97 p. 21½ᶜᵐ.

I. Sweating system. 2. Wages—Gt. Brit.—Congresses.
9-15100
Library of Congress   HD4918.N3

NN   0032688   DLC MiU DL ICJ NN

National Anti-Sweating League, *London.*
A short bibliography of "sweating," and a list of the principal
works upon, and references to, the legal minimum wage.   [Lon-
don, 1906.]   24 p. 8°.
Title from cover.

1. Sweating system.—Bibliography.   2. Wages (Minimum).—Bibliography.
N. Y. P. L.   October 22, 1913.

NN   0032689   NN MiU ICJ DL

[National Anti-Sweating League, London.]
Sweated workers and trade boards; impressive conference
at Sunderland House ...   [London, 1913.]   11 p.   8°.
Compiled from various newspapers.
Title from cover.

1. Sweating system, Gt. Br.
N. Y. P. L.   November 25, 1914.

NN   0032690   NN DL

331.8   National anti-sweating league, London.
N21sw   Sweating as it is.   [London, 1910?]
8p.

NN   0032691   IU

National anti-sweating league. Leicester branch.
First report of an investigation into the
home industries of Leicester by the investigation
joint-committee of the Christian social union
(Leicester branch), and of the Anti-sweating
league (Leicester branch.)   15 p.
21½ cm.

NN   0032692   DL

National anti-sweating league of Victoria.
... 14th annual report; 1910 Melbourne,
1910
1 v.

NN   0032693   OU

National Anti-Trust Conference, *Chicago,* 1900.
Official report. Chicago [G. S. Bowen, 1900]
xv, 586 p. ports. 19 cm.
"Official directory of the American Anti-Trust
League": p. [1]

1. Trusts, Industrial—Congresses. 2. Trusts, Industrial—U. S.

HD2783.A3 1900d   48-43353*

ICJ MU
NN   0032694   DLC OrU NIC WaU MiD DFT OClWHi NjP IU

W 1   NATIONAL Anti-Vaccination League, London
NA233   Annual report.
1st-   1896-
London.
v.

NN   0032695   DNLM DLC-P4

WC   NATIONAL Anti-Vaccination League, London
588   [Collection of publications]
qN277
The Library has a collection of
miscellaneous publications of this
organization kept as received. These
publications are not listed or bound
separately.
1. Vaccination

NN   0032696   DNLM

National Anti-Vaccination League, *London.*
Facts about smallpox and vaccination. A reply to the 1924
edition of the pamphlet issued by the British Medical Association
... London[, 1924?]. 52 p. 8°.
"The author of the pamphlet is Dr. John C. McVail."

1. Vaccination, Anti. 2. McVail,   John Christie, 1849-   : Facts about
smallpox and vaccination.
N. Y. P. L.   July 29, 1926

NN   0032697   NN

W 6   NATIONAL Anti-Vaccination League, London
P3   An inquiry into vaccine "lymph"; its
origins, varieties, nature and effects as
disclosed in original official publications,
together with a brief history of its
compulsory inoculation in England under
the vaccination laws and departmental
regulations. [London, 1922?]
91 p.

NN   0032698   DNLM MH

National Anti-Vaccination League, *London.*
...The present position of the vaccination question. The case
for a final settlement on lines of personal freedom. London[,
1925]. 76 p. 8°.
Cover-title.

1. Vaccination—Anti.
N. Y. P. L.   February 24, 1926

NN   0032699   NN DNLM Or

National Anti-Vaccination League, *London.*
Vaccination at work. What it is; and what it does.   London: The National Anti-Vaccination League, 1913. 32 p. illus.
3. ed. 8°.
Title from cover.

1. Vaccination, Anti.
N. Y. P. L.   January 19, 1914.

NN   0032700   NN

National anti-vaccination league, London.
Vaccination at work; what it is; and what
it does. 4th ed. (with additions) London,
1924.
40 p. illus., ports., facsims.

1. Vaccination. I. Title.

NN   0032701   NNC

VOLUME 405

National anti-vivisection society, inc.
    The dog's scrap book. ₍Chicago₎ Published
by the National anti-vivisection society, inc.,
c1933.
    48 p. illus. 10½x22½cm.

    1. Dogs. 2. Dogs - Poetry. I. Title.

NN 0032702   ViW

National anti-vivisection society ₍Gt. Brit₎
The Animals' defender and zoophilist.

    London, 18 –19

NATIONAL ANTI-VIVISECTION SOCIETY ₍Gt. Brit₎
    British vivisections recorded in 1897.
==   [London, 1898.] 7 pp. Sm. 8°.

NN 0032704   MB NN

    National Anti-vivisection Society (*Gt. Brit.*)
    Minutes of the extraordinary council meeting summoned
to consider the situation created by the reported determination of the Royal Commission on Vivisection to hold its
meetings in secret, and held at the offices of the society, 92,
Victoria Street, on Monday, the 29th October, 1906. ₍Lon-
don, 1906₎
    8 p. 28 cm.

    I. Gt. Brit. Royal Commission on Vivisection (1906)

HV4943.G55N2   59–55910

NN 0032705   DLC MB

    National Anti-vivisection Society (*Gt. Brit.*)
    The Pasteur "cure" for rabies. 1,220 reported deaths!
Rev. to January 1st, 1901, and issued as a supplement to "The
Zoophilist and animals' defender," February 1, 1901. ₍Lon-
don, 1901₎
    229–251 p. tables. 28 cm.
    Caption title.

    1. Rabies. I. The Animals' defender and zoophilist. II. Title.

RC148.N3   7–27548 rev*

NN 0032706   DLC

    National Anti-Vivisection Society ₍Gt. Brit₎
    ... Selections from the admissions, assertions
& evasions of the witnesses
        see under Gt. Brit. Royal Commission on
Vivisection (1875)

JX1416   National Anti-War Congress, Washington, D.C.,
N276   1938.
      Proceedings. Washington, Keep America Out of
War Congress, 1938.
    1 v. (various pagings) 28cm.

    1. U. S. - Neutrality. 2. U.S. - For. rel.
- 1933-1945.

NN 0032708   CSt-H NN CtY

National apartment owners association.
    The property owner: "Victim of error and discrimination."
A request for relief from gross error in the imposition and administration of rent control by the Office of price administration.
Prepared for presentation to the Banking and currency committee, House of representatives, June, 1945, by Eugene P. Conser
on behalf of National apartment owners association. Washington ₍1945₎ 36 p. illus. 28cm.

    1. Rent—U.S. 2. World war,   1939–1945—Economic aspects—U.S.
I. Conser, Eugene P.
N.Y.P.L.   August 25, 1947

NN 0032709   NN

National Appeals Information Service.
    Register of Jewish social service agencies in
Palestine
        see under Bureau of Jewish Social
Service Research.

National appeals information service.
    ₍Reports on Jewish institutions₎
₍no. 1–

    New York, 192   28 – 29cm.
    nos.   charts, tables.
    Numbering supplied.
    Reproduced from typewritten copy.
    Various numbers published by the Bureau of Jewish social research.

    No more published? The functions of the service were taken over by the Council
of Jewish federations and welfare funds in 1932.
                  CONTENTS.
    no. 1. Report on Jewish social service institutions in Jerusalem, Tel-Aviv, Jaffa and
        Haifa, Palestine; summary statement on index compiled under the direction
        of Dr. J. L. Magnes and Mr. Harry Viteles of Jerusalem.   April, 1928.
    no. 2. Leo N. Levi memorial hospital, Hot Springs, Ark.   July, 1928.
    no. 3. Hebrew sheltering and immigrant aid society (HIAS), New York, New York.
        Sept., 1928.
    no. 4. Ex-patients' tubercular home of Denver, Colo.   Oct., 1928.

    no. 5. Jewish consumptives' relief society of Denver, Colorado.   Nov., 1928.
    no. 6. Denver national home for Jewish children.   Nov., 1928.
    no. 7. National Jewish hospital at Denver, Colorado.   Dec., 1928.
    no. 8. Jewish consumptive and ex-patients relief association, Los Angeles, California.
        Feb., 1929.
    no. 9. Jewish agricultural society ... New York city.   March, 1929.
    no. 10. National farm school, Doylestown, Pa.   March, 1929.
    no. 11. Menorah movement ... New York city.   March, 1929.
    no. 12. Bureau of Jewish social research, New York.   May, 1929.
    no. 13. National council of Jewish women ... New York.   May, 1929.

    no. 14. National desertion bureau, New York. N.Y.   Jan., 1930.
    no. 15. B'nai B'rith, Wider scope committee; by Michael Freund.   May, 1931.
    no. 16. Report on the National home for Jewish children at Denver; supplemental to
        the report issued in November, 1928.   Aug., 1931.
    no. 17. Jewish publication society of America; by Michael Freund.   Oct., 1931.
    no. 18. Jewish consumptives' relief society; supplemental to the report issued in Novem-
        ber, 1928.   March, 1932.
    no. 19. Report on the Ex-patients' tubercular home at Denver; supplemental to the
        report issued in October, 1928.   March, 1932.
    no. 20. National Jewish hospital; supplemental to the report issued in November, 1928.
        April, 1932.

NN 0032714   NN

    National apple congress (British)
    Barron, Archibald Farquharson, 1835?–1903.
    British apples. Report of the Committee of the National
apple congress, held in the Royal horticultural gardens, Chiswick, October 5th to 25th, 1883. Comp. and prepared by Mr.
A. F. Barron ... London, Macmillan and co., 1884.

National apple institute.
    The annual meeting...
₍no.₎

    ₍Cincinnati, etc., 193   28cm.
    nos.
    Reproduced from typewritten copy, no.
    Caption-title, no.

    Title varies: no.   Minutes of the annual meeting...
    no.   The annual meeting...
    ——— Midsummer meeting...
    193
    Reproduced from typewritten copy, 193
    193 includes a suppl.

NN 0032717   NN

280.3939   **National Apple Institute.**
N21A   **Apple crop "guesstimate" by varieties.**

    [Washington]

    1. Apple. Varieties.

NN 0032718   DNAL

93.31   **National Apple Institute.**
N21   **Apples.**

    Washington.

    1. Apple.

NN 0032719   DNAL

---

280.   National apple institute.
3939   ... Bulletin [irregular] no.
N21B   Washington, D.C.
    [etc.] 1940-
    Ceased. Info. by phone from issuing office,
Oct. 2, 1963.
    No. –59,   -Dec. 17, 1941,
published in Columbus, O.
    No. 403 repeated in numbering.
    Beginning with no. 414, June 1959, incorporates
its Crop prospect by varieties (280.3939 N21A)

NN 0032720   DNAL

280.3939   **National Apple Institute.**
N21N   **The national apple news. v.1**

    ₍Washington₎

    **Includes information formerly issued as its
Apple crop "guesstimate" (280.3939 N21Ap)**

    1. Apple. Statistics. 2. Apple. Market-
ing. I. Title.

NN 0032721   DNAL

National apple institute.

    [Reports and addresses of] the Fifth annual
meeting of National apple institute, Shenandoah
hotel, Martinsburg, W.Va., March 17 and 18,
1939. [Martinsburg, W.Va., National apple
institute, 1939]
    16 p.   27 cm.
    1. Apple - Societies. 2. Fruit - Marketing.

NN 0032722   OrCS

284.393   National apple institute.
N21   Statement [concerning apple ceilings]
[Wasington, D.C.] 1943.
    5 l.
    1. Apple. Cost of production. 2. Apple.
Prices. Fixing. I. Benz, Reuben G.

NN 0032723   DNAL

National apple shippers association
    see International apple association.

National Appliance and Radio-TV Dealers Association.
    Annual cost-of-doing-business survey.
Chicago.
    v. 28 cm.
    Cover title: 19   NARDA's annual costs of doing business
survey.

    1. Household appliances. 2. Radio industry and trade—U. S. 3.
Television industry—U. S.   I. Title: NARDA's annual costs of
doing business survey.

HD9999.H8N3   66–97454

NN 0032725   DLC LU OrCS NIC

HD9697   National Appliance and Radio-TV Dealers
.U4N33   Association.
    Home appliance trade-in blue book.
Madison, Wis.

HD9697   National Appliance and Radio-TV Dealers Association
.U4N33
    Official NARDA trade-in guide.

    Madison, Wis., NARDA Guide Co.

HD9697   National Appliance Trade-In Guide Company,
.U4N33   Madison, Wis.
    Home appliance trade-in blue book.
Madison, Wis.

VOLUME 405

HD9999   National Appliance Trade-In Guide Company,
.L42U64   Madison, Wis.
    Home laundry trade-in blue book.

    Madison, Wis., National Appliance Trade-In Guide Co.

HD9999   National Appliance Trade-In Guide Company,
.S934U58   Madison, Wis.
    Kitchen appliance trade-in blue book.

    Madison, Wis., National Appliance Trade-In Guide Co.

HD9999   National Appliance Trade-In Guide Company,
.T373U65   Madison, Wis.
    National TV data handbook. 1951–

    Madison, Wis., National Appliance Trade-In Guide Co.

    National appraisal committee
      see
    United States community improvement appraisal. *National committee.*

National Appraisal Company, Boston, Mass.
    A solution of the valuation problem...   Boston, Mass.:
National Appraisal Co.₍₁₉₁₄.₎   87 p.   8°.

    Cover-title.
    Consists mainly of copies of letters of recommendation, and list of clients.

    1. Valuation, Industrial.
N. Y. P. L.   December 30, 1927

   NN   0032733   NN

    National appraisal forum.
    Proceedings of the general sessions and urban group meetings, National appraisal forum, held under the auspices of the Joint committee on appraisal and mortgage analysis. 1937–

    ₍Washington, D. C., 1937–

      v. 27ᶜᵐ.

    Held in Washington, D. C., 1937–
    Mimeographed.

    1. Valuation—Congresses.   I. Joint committee on appraisal and mortgage analysis.
    Library of Congress   HD1387.A1N3   38–26569

   NN   0032734   DLC LU DNAL OClFRB

    National appraisal forum.
    Proceedings of the rural group sessions, National appraisal forum, held under the auspices of the Joint committee on appraisal and mortgage analysis. 1937–
    ₍Washington, D. C., 1937–

      v. maps, tables, diagrs. 26½ᶜᵐ.

    Cover-title.
    Mimeographed.
    Held in Washington, D. C., 1937–

    1. Valuation—Congresses.   I. Joint committee on appraisal and mortgage analysis.
    Library of Congress   HD1387.A1N33   38–17703
    ————— 2d set.   ₍3₎   333.3

   NN   0032735   DLC OClFRB

336.292   National Appraisal Institute.
N21g   Guide for setting assessed values for 1949.
    Assessments. Iowa ed...   Davenport, Iowa,
    Printed by Fidlar & Chamber Co. for National
    Appraisal Institute, °1949.
      v.p. 23 cm.

      Loose-leaf.
      With this is bound: National Appraisal Institute. Iowa field assessors' instruction book.

   NN   0032736   III

336.292   National Appraisal Institute.
N21g   1949 Iowa field assessors' instruction book...
    Davenport, Iowa, Printed by Fidlar & Chambers
    Co. for National Appraisal Institute, °1949.
      v.p. 23 cm.

      Loose-leaf.
      Bound with: National Appraisal Institute.
    Guide for setting assessed values for 1949 assessments, Iowa ed.

      1. Assessment. 2. Land—Taxation—Iowa.

   NN   0032737   LU

    National apprenticeship and training
      standards ...   *Asphalt*
      see under   National Cement Masonry,
    and Composition Joint Apprenticeship Committee.

    National arbitration and peace congress
      see
    American peace congress.

National Arbitration Committee.   7574-84
    A memorial to the Senate of the United States.
— [Washington. 1897.]   (4), 96 pp.   8°.
    A statement concerning the treaty of arbitration between the United States and Great Britain, concluded January 11, 1897.

    G2636 — Great Britain. For. rel. Unit. ₋tates. — United States. For. rel. Great Britain. — Arbitration. International

   NN   0032740   MB NN MdBJ

NATIONAL ARBITRATION COMMITTEE.
    A memorial to the Senate of the United States.
[Washington, 1897]   96 p.   21cm.

    Microfiche (neg.)   2 sheets.   11 x 15cm.   (NYPL FSN 13, 244)

    1. Arbitration, International—   Treaties—U.S. and Gt. Br.,
    1901. 2. Arbitration, Interna-   tional—Treaties—Gt. Br. and
    U.S., 1901.   I. Subs. for   XBL p.v. 4, no. 5

   NN   0032741   NN

    National arbitration conference
      see
    American conference on international arbitration.

NATIONAL arbitration convention.
    Resolutions adopted in Washington on the 30th and 31st
of May, 1882.
        N.t.p.   [Wash., 1882.]   (6) pp.   4°.

   NN   0032743   MB

    The national arbitration law
      see under   [Stimson, Frederic Jesup]
    1855–1943.

National arbitration league.
    The National arbitration league ... ₍Washington?
D. C., 1884?₎

      1 p. l., 21 p. 23ᶜᵐ.

    Library of Congress   JX1908.U6N4   10–16214†

   NN   0032745   DLC NN OWibfU

    National Arboretum, *Washington, D. C.*
      see Washington, D. C. National Arboretum.

    National Archaeological Museum, *Athens*
      see
    Athens. Ethnikon Archaiologikon Mouseion.

    National archaeological news. v. 1–2, no. 3; Mar. 1937–
May 1938. ₍Lancaster, Pa., Conestoga publishing co., inc.,
1937–38₎

    2 v. in   illus. 20ᵐᵐ.   monthly.
Editor: 1937–   G. B. Fenstermaker.

    No more published.   cf. Union list of serials.
    L. C. set incomplete : v. 2, no. 2–3 wanting.

    1. U. S.—Antiq.—Period. 2. Archaeology—Period. 3. Indians of
North America—Antiq.   I. Fenstermaker, Gerald B., ed.
                           44–38530

    Library of Congress   E51.N25
                ₍2₎   913.73

   NN   0032748   DLC NBuG NN

    National archery association of the United
      States of America.
    Elmer, Robert Potter, 1877–
    American archery; a vade mecum of the art of shooting with a long bow, comp. by Dr. Robert P. Elmer. ₍Columbus? O.₎ 1917.

    National Archery Association   of the
      United States of America.
    The archer's handbook. 1st ed. Ronks, Pa.
    n.d.
      112 p.   illus.   23 cm.

    N.A.A. constitution and by-laws: ₋p. 63–73
    Official N.A.A. tournament rules: p. 74–95

      1. Archery.   I. Title.

   NN   0032750   CSf

GV1185   National Archery Association of the United States
.A68   of America.
    The **Archers'** magazine. v. 1–
    July 1952–
    ₍Philadelphia₎

    National Archery Association of the United States
of America.
    Archery. Boston, Mass.
      see under title

    National archery association of the United States
of America.
    Wilkinson's score book for archers, adapted to all rounds
      see under   Wilkinson, John.

    National architect.
      v. 1, no. 11–

    Detroit, 1945–   v. illus. 28cm.

    Monthly.
    Official publication of the National council of architectural registration boards.
    Vol. 1, no. 11 (Nov. 1945) was the first issue published independently. Jan.–Oct. 1945 (without numbering and with title: National council of architectural registration boards. Weekly bulletin) were issued as a monthly number of: Michigan society of architects. Weekly bulletin. (See entry under latter title.)

    1. Architecture—Per. and soc.   publ. I. National council of architectural registration boards.
N. Y. P. L.   January 3, 1950

   NN   0032754   NN GAT

VOLUME 405

The **National** architect.

₍Philadelphia, The National architect co., 19
     v.   illus., plates, plans. 33½ᶜᵐ. monthly.
     Editors: -Aug. 1914, Horace Trumbauer.—Sept. 1914-
     A. H. Granger.

     1. Architecture—Period.   I. Trumbauer, Horace, ed.   II. Granger,
Alfred Hoyt, 1867–   ed.

                               CA 16–474 Unrev'd

     Library of Congress   NA1.N2

NN   0032755   DLC

National Architects' Union.   *8102.30
     Artistic one-story houses.
     New York. [1893?] (59) pp. Plates. Plans. 27½ × 30½ cm.

K890 — T.r. — Country and seashore houses.

NN   0032756   MB

     National architects' union.
         Colonial houses for modern homes
            see under   Child, Edward Southwick, 1859-

National architect's union.
     Modern homes. The perspective views and building
plans for sensible low cost houses. Arranged, designed,
illustrated and published by National architects union ...
Philadelphia ₍1889₎

     ₍56₎ p. incl. illus., plans. 35½ᶜᵐ.

     1. Architecture, Domestic—Designs and plans.

     Library of Congress   NA7130.N3   11–34058

NN   0032757   DLC

National architect's union.
     Modern rural homes. The perspective views and build-
ing plans for twenty-five sensible low-cost houses. Philadelphia, National architect's union ₍1891₎

     26 p. plans. fol. (National architect's union. Sensible low-cost
houses. v. 3)
     Copyrighted by A. C. Child.

                              1–1437

NN   0032758   DLC MiU MSaE

National architect's union.
     Picturesque houses for forest and shore. Perspective
views and floor plans. Arranged, designed, illustrated,
and published by National architects' union ... Philadelphia ₍1891₎

     28 l. illus. (incl. plans) 37ᶜᵐ.

     1. Architecture, Domestic—Designs and plans.

     Library of Congress   NA7130.N35   11–34059

NN   0032759   DLC MSaE

     National architects' union.
         Sensible low-cost barns and stables
            see under   Child, Edward Southwick, 1859-

National Architects' Union.   *81002.20
     Sensible low cost houses.   Vol. [1–] 3.
     New York. [1893?]   3 v. in 1.   Plates. Plans.   27 × 30½ cm.
     Copyrighted by A. C. Child.
     Contents. — 1. 35 houses costing from $400 to $1800.   2. 35 houses
costing from $1800 to $4000.   3. 35 houses costing from $3000 to $9000.

K6338 — Houses. — Child, A. C.

NN   0032761   MB

     National architectural competition
           see   National small house competition.

     National archives
           see
     U. S. *National archives.*

     National Archives and Records Service
           see   **U. S.** *National Archives and Records Service.*

     National archives project.
     Alphabetical list of ship registers, district of Barnstable,
Massachusetts, 1814–1913. Compiled from original documents
stored in the New Bedford Custom house. Prepared by the
National archives project, Division of women's and professional
projects, Works progress administration, the National archives,
sponsor. Boston, Mass., 1938.

     2 p. l., ii–x, 163 (i. e. 164) numb. l.   37½ᶜᵐ.
     Mimeographed.
     Includes extra numbered leaf 12A.

     1. Ships—Registers.   I. Title.

                               39–26140

     Library of Congress   HE565.U7N3
     —————— Copy 2.   ₍2₎   656

NN   0032765   DLC CU ViU MB IU

     National archives project.
         Bibliography of the Navy department and the
naval shore establishment
           see under   Survey of federal archives.

     National archives project.

     Survey of federal archives.
     The eleven original customs districts established in the com-
monwealth of Massachusetts, in geographical order, from the
New Hampshire to the Rhode Island borders; together with
the names of collectors who served in them between 1789 and
1913. Compiled by the Survey of federal archives, Division of
professional and service projects, Work projects administration. The National archives, cooperating sponsor. Boston
Mass., The National archives project, 1941.

     National archives project.

     Historical records survey.
     Inventory of federal archives in the states. Prepared by the
Survey of federal archives, Division of women's and professional projects, Works progress administration. The National
archives, cooperating sponsor ... Oklahoma City, Okla. ₍etc.₎
The Historical records survey ₍etc.₎ 1937-

     NATIONAL Archives Project
         Letters ₍1796–1878₎ transcribed
     from original letters at Custom House,
     Boston, Mass.   Boston, 1940.
         9 v.

         1. U. S.   Marine Hospital, Boston

NN   0032769   DNLM

     National archives project.

     Survey of federal archives.
     Ship registers and enrollments of Boston and Charlestown.
Compiled by the Survey of federal archives, Division of pro-
fessional and service projects, Works progress administration.
The National archives, cooperating sponsor ... Boston, Mass.,
The National archives project, 1942-

     National archives project.
     Ship registers and enrollments of Machias, Maine, 1780–1930.
Prepared by the National archives project, Division of com-
munity service projects, Work projects administration. The
National archives, cooperating sponsor ... Rockland, Me., The
National archives project, 1942.

     2 v. plates, tables. 27½ᶜᵐ.
     Reproduced from type-written copy.
     "Publications prepared by the Survey of federal archives, Division of
community service programs, Work projects administration in Maine":
pt. 1, leaf at end.

     1. Ships—Registers.   2. Shipping—Machias, Me.   I. Title.

                              42–50709

     Library of Congress   HE565.U7N32
                       ₍6₎   656

NN   0032771   DLC MeB ViU CU MU OrU IaU OClWHi

     National archives project.

     Survey of federal archives.
     Ship registers and enrollments of Newport, Rhode Island,
1790–1939. Prepared by the Survey of federal archives, Division of professional and service projects, Work projects administration. State of Rhode Island, Department of state, Division of archives, sponsor. The National archives, co-operating
sponsor ... Providence, R. I., The National archives project,
1938–41.

     National archives project.

     Survey of federal archives.
     Ship registers and enrollments of Providence, Rhode Island,
1773–1939. Prepared by the Survey of federal archives, Division of community service programs, Work projects administration. State of Rhode Island, Department of state, Division of archives sponsor. The National archives, co-operating
sponsor ... Providence, R. I., The National archives project,
1941-

     National archives project.
     Ship registers and enrollments of Saco, Maine, 1791–1915.
Prepared by the National archives project, Division of com-
munity service programs, Work projects administration. The
National archives, cooperating sponsor. Rockland, Me., The
National archives project, 1942.

     2 p. l., xiii, 108 numb. l., 1 l. incl. tables. plates. 27½ᶜᵐ.
     Reproduced from type-written copy.
     "Publications prepared by the Survey of federal archives, Division
of community service programs, Work projects administration in Maine":
leaf at end.

     1. Ships—Registers.   2. Shipping—Saco, Me.   I. Title.

                              42–50710

     Library of Congress   HE565.U7N324
                       ₍6₎   656

NN   0032774   DLC OClWHi MeB MU

     National archives project.

     Survey of federal archives.
     Ship registers and enrollments, ship licenses issued to vessels
under twenty tons, ship licenses on enrollments issued out of
the port of Bristol-Warren, Rhode Island, 1773–1939. Pre-
pared by the Survey of federal archives, Work projects administration, state of
Rhode Island, Department of state, Division of archives,
sponsor. The National archives, co-operating sponsor. Providence, R. I., The National archives project, 1941.

     National archives project.

     Survey of federal archives.
     Ship registers of Dighton-Fall River, Massachusetts, 1789–
1938. Compiled by the Survey of federal archives, Division
of women's and professional projects, Work projects administration. The National archives, cooperating sponsor. Boston, Mass., The National archives project, 1939.

VOLUME 405

HE565 .U7S76
National archives project.

Survey of federal archives.
Ship registers of New Bedford, Massachusetts. Compiled by the Survey of federal archives, Division of professional and service projects, Work projects administration. The National archives, cooperating sponsor ... Boston, Mass., The National archives project, 1940.

HE565 .U7S815
National archives project.

Survey of federal archives.
Ship registers of the district of Plymouth, Massachusetts, 1789–1908. Compiled by the Survey of federal archives Division of women's and professional projects, Works progress administration. The National archives, cooperating sponsor ... Boston, Mass., The National archives project, 1939.

National archives project

see also

Survey of federal archives.

BV2000 .N27
National Armenia and India relief association.
Helping hand series. v.1–29, no.4, 1899–Sept., 1927. Barre, Mass., 1899–1927.
27v. illus. 14cm. quarterly.
v.15–16 omitted in numbering.

1. Missions--Armenia.   2. Missions--India.
3. Refugees--Armenia.   I. Title.

NN   0032780   IEG

The national armories. A letter to the Hon. George T. Davis...1853.

see under

ₗStearns, Charlesₗ

The national armories, a review of the systems of superintendency...1852.

see under

ₗStearns, Charlesₗ

National armory. An appeal to congress by the citizens of Rock Island
see under   Rock Island, Ill. Citizens.

National army and navy Spanish war veterans

see

Spanish war veterans

N5020 .W6
National art association.
Catalogue of the national loan exhibition... 1st– 1892–   . In the chapel of the Smithsonian institution, Washington, D.C. 1892.
ₗWashingtonₗ 1892

NN   0032785   DLC

National art-collections fund, *London.*
Annual report. 1st–
1903/04–
London, 1905–
v. illus., plates. 26½–27½ cm.
List of members in each volume.

1. Art--Gt. Brit.

N12.N3   17—27818

NN   0032786   DLC CaBVaU WaS PPPM OC1MA DSI CSt

National Art-Collections Fund, *London.*
Art treasures for the nation; fifty years of the National Art-Collections Fund. Introd. by the Earl of Crawford and Balcarres. London, Thames and Hudson ₗ1953ₗ
40 p. 80 plates. 26 cm.

1. Art patronage.   2. Art--Gt. Brit.--Galleries and museums.
3. Art--Collectors and collecting.   I. Title.

N12.N32   708.2   53–4108

NN   0032787   DLC WaS MdBWA CaOTP NNC NN MH

National art-collections fund, *London.*
A catalogue of an exhibition of old masters in aid of the National art-collections fund: Grafton galleries, 1911; ed. by Roger E. Fry and Maurice W. Brockwell ... ₗLondonₗ P. L. Warner, publisher to the Medici society limited, 1911.
xiv, 132, ₗ1ₗ p., 1 l. front., LXXX pl. (incl. ports.) 27½ᵐ.

1. Paintings--Exhibitions.   I. Fry, Roger E., 1866–   ed. II. Brockwell, Maurice Walter, 1869–   joint ed. III. Medici society ltd.

13–1984

Library of Congress   N5055.G7 1911

PPPM MB MnU MWiCA CSmH CaBViP
NN   0032788   DLC MdBWA CtY PPD MiDA MH TxU NjP OO

National art-collections fund, *London.*

London. Exhibition of Spanish old masters, 1913–1914.
Catalogue of the Exhibition of Spanish old masters, in support of National gallery funds, and for the benefit of the Sociedad de amigos del arte española, Oct. 1913 to Jan. 1914. 1st ed. Grafton galleries ... ₗLondon, Printed by Odhams limited, 1913ₗ

National Art Collections Fund, London
The Ernest Cook bequest to the nation; a selection from more than 150 pictures and works of art. [L, 195-]
32 p. illus.

NN   0032790   MH-FA

National Art-Collections Fund, *London.*
Exhibition in honour of Sir Robert Witt, C. B. E., D. LITT., F. S. A., of the principal acquisitions made for the nation through the National Art-Collections Fund. ₗThe National Galleryₗ 23rd Nov. 1945 to 5th Jan. 1946. ₗLondon, 1946ₗ
48 p. front. 22 cm.
Cover title.
"Exhibition ... confined to Western pictorial art."

1. Witt, Sir Robert Clermont, 1872–   2. Paintings--Exhibitions.
I. London. National Gallery.

A 49–3822*

Harvard Univ. Library
for Library of Congress   ₗ1ₗ

NN   0032791   MH CtY

National art-collections fund, *London.*

London. Exhibition of Spanish old masters, 1913–1914.
Illustrated catalogue of the Exhibition of Spanish old masters in support of the National gallery funds and for the benefit of the Sociedad de amigos del arte española, Oct. 1913 to Jan. 1914, Grafton galleries. ₗLondon, Printed by Odhams limited, 1913ₗ

National art-collections fund, *London.*

Blake, William, 1757–1827.
Illustrations to the Divine comedy of Dante by William Blake. London, Priv. print. for the National art-collections fund, 1922.

708.2 N213
National art-collections fund, *London.*
The national art-collections fund. ₗLondon, 1950ₗ
16p. illus., col. cover illus.

Cover title.

NN   0032794   MiDA

National art-collections fund, *London.*
Twenty-five years of the National art-collections fund, 1903–1928. Glasgow, Printed for the Fund by R. Maclehose & co., limited, the University press, 1928.
5 p. L., 253, ₗ1ₗ p. incl. front., plates, facsims. 29 x 22½ᵐ.
"This volume has been produced under the general editorship of Mr. D. S. MacColl, in conjunction with a publication committee."
CONTENTS.--Introduction, by Sir Robert Witt.--Chronological list of acquisitions.--Topical list of acquisitions: Paintings: old masters, by Sir Charles Holmes.--Paintings: modern, by Charles Aitken.--Egyptian and classical art, by A. H. Smith.--Sculpture from medieval to modern

times, by Eric Maclagan.--Prints and drawings, by Campbell Dodgson.--Eastern art, by Laurence Binyon.--Coins and medals, by G. F. Hill.--Minor arts of medieval and other periods, by O. M. Dalton.--Manuscripts, by Sir Frederic Kenyon.--Ceramics and glass, by Bernard Rackham.--Textiles, by A. F. Kendrick.--Silver and other metalwork, by W. W. Watts.--Furniture and woodwork, by H. C. Smith.

1. Art patronage.   2. Art--Gt. Brit.--Galleries and museums.   3. Art--Collectors and collecting.   I. MacColl, Dugald Sutherland, 1859–   ed. II. Title.

Library of Congress   N12.N34   39–3612
                             ₗ2ₗ   708.2

CLCM
NN   0032796   DLC NN MH CSmH OC1MA CaBVaU NcD CaOTP

National Art Committee.   4079-432
Catalogue of war portraits by American artists. [Exhibited] under the auspices of Yale University and by courtesy of the American Federation of Arts [at the] New Haven Public Library, 16–30 June 1921.
= [New Haven. 1921.] (64) pp. Portraits. Autograph facsimiles. 19 cm.
The catalogue was compiled by Florence N. Levy.
The title is on the cover.

M3653 — Portraits. Exhibs. —   New Haven, Conn. Public Li-
Library. Free Public Library. — Levy,   brary.
European War, 1914–1919. Portraits.   Florence Nightingale, compiler, 1870–.—

NN   0032797   MB

National Art Committee.
Catalogue of war portraits by American artists under the auspices of Yale university & by courtesy of the American federation of arts; new Haven library 16–30 June, 1921. Washington, D.C., National art committee, c1921.
unp.

NN   0032798   PU

National art committee.
Exhibition of war portraits; signing of the Peace treaty, 1919, and portraits of distinguished leaders of America and of the allied nations painted by eminent American artists for presentation to the National portrait gallery; organized by the National art committee. ₗNew York, ʼ1921ₗ
ₗ64ₗ p. incl. front., illus. (ports.) 20ᵐ.
"January 18 to February 11, 1921, Metropolitan museum of art, New York."
"Catalogue of the portraits, by Florence N. Levy."
1. European war, 1914–   2. Portraits--Exhibitions.
I. Levy, Florence Nightingale, 1870–   II. New York. Metropolitan museum of art.

Library of Congress   D507.N3   21–1092

NN   0032799   DLC NN ViU

National art committee.
Exhibition of war portraits; signing of the Peace treaty, 1919, and portraits of distinguished leaders of America and of the allied nations, painted by eminent American artists for presentation to the National portrait gallery; organized by the National art committee. ₗNew York, 1921ₗ
ₗ64ₗ p. incl. front., illus. (ports.) 20ᵐ.
On cover: National gallery of art under direction of the Smithsonian institution, Washington, D. C., May 5 to 22, 1921.
"Catalogue of the portraits ₗcompiledₗ by Florence N. Levy."
1. European war, 1914–1918 — Portraits.   2. Portraits — Exhibitions.
I. Levy, Florence Nightingale, 1870–   II. Smithsonian institution.
National collection of fine arts.

43–38927

Library of Congress   D507.N3 1921 a

NN   0032800   DLC MiU OU OC1WHi

VOLUME 406

National Art Education Association.
Art and human values
see under title

N81
.A86

National Art Education Association.

Art education. v. 1-
Jan./Feb. 1948-
₍Kutztown, Pa.₎

. **National Art Education Association.** Art education organizes
see its Yearbook.

NATIONAL ART EDUCATION ASSOCIATION.
Convention. [Program] 1st- ; 1951-
Cleveland [etc.]   no.   illus. 24cm.

Biennial.

1. Art.--Education--U.S.

NN 0032804   NN Or

375.706 National Art Education Association.
N277d   Directory. [1st-

[Washington]
v. ports. 26cm. (Art education)

1.Art - Study and teaching - Societies,
etc. - Direct.

NN 0032805   CLSU WaS

National Art Education Association.
N   Research in art education, Manuel Barkan,ed.
11   Kutztown,Pa., State Teachers College ₍1954₎
.N28   151 p.   tables.   26 cm.   (National Art
1954   Education Association,5th Yearbook,1954)
Prepared by the Research Committee of the
National Art Education Association.
Errata slip inserted.
Includes bibliographical references.

1.Art--Study and teaching.

NN 0032806   MiU PPPL

National Art Education Association.
Yearbook. 1st-
1949-
₍Kutztown, Pa.₎
v. illus. (part col.) ports. 23 cm.
Each vol. has also a distinctive title: 1949, Art education organizes.

1. Art—Yearbooks. 2. Art—U. S.

N11.N15   707   50—13830

NcU
TxLT ScU KMK TxU CU TU OC1 NN UU CoD TNJ OrCS OrU
NN 0032807   DLC CaBVa MtBC KEmT NNU MsU MiU IU InNc

National Art Education Association
see also   National Education Association of the United States. Dept. of Art
Education.

National Art Galleries, inc., New York.
Collection of American, French and Dutch
paintings...
see under   Dudensing, Richard and son, N.Y.

National art galleries, inc., New York.
Collection of important paintings
see under   Brothers, Ernest.

National Art Galleries, Inc., New York.
A collection of XVII and XVIII century English
furniture and decorations ...
see under   Cooper, W.F.

National art galleries, inc., New York.
Important Americana ... New York,
National art galleries
see under   Michaelsen, Cornelius.

NE
2415
C7   National Art Galleries, inc., New York.
N3   Important collection of Currier & Ives prints. Unre-
1932a   stricted public auction, Thursday evening, December 1st
[1932]   New York [1932]
35 p. illus. 23 cm.

Title from original paper cover.

1. Currier & Ives. 2. Lithographs – Catalogs.

NN 0032813   Vi

National Art Galleries, inc., New York.
The important collector's library of first editions
... January 12th and 13th, 1933
see under   Darrow, Carolyn B

National art galleries, inc., New York.
Period English furniture, French & Flemish
tapestries...
see under   Charles of London, firm., New
York.

ML462
.N38   National Art Galleries, inc., New York.
Rare musical instruments, collected mainly
by the celebrated opera singer Marcella Lindh,
sold by order of G. S. Jacobson, including
musical autographs, American and Italian
furniture, fine paintings, bibelots and art
objects, with additions. Public auction sale,
Saturday afternoon, March 12th, 1932, at
2 o'clock. New York, 1932.
46 p. illus. 24cm. (Its Sale no. 38)

Cover title.

Catalogue compiled by C. C. M. Michaelsen.

1. Musical instruments--Catalogs.
2. Paintings--Private collections. 3. Furni-
ture--Catalogs. I. Lindh, Marcella. II. Title.

NN 0032817   ViU

National art galleries, inc., *New York.*
Sculptures by Alceo Dossena, to be sold at public auction
... March 9th, 1933 ... in the Grand ball room of the hotel
Plaza ... New York, National art galleries, inc., 1933.
85, ₍5₎ p., 2 l. incl. front. (port.) illus. (incl. facsims.) 27½ᶜᵐ.
"Foreword" signed: Dr. Alfred M. Frankfurter.

1. Sculpture—Catalogs. 2. Dossena, Alceo, 1878-   ɪ. Frankfurter,
Alfred M.
36–15084
Library of Congress   NB623.D75N3
₍2₎   735.0945

NN 0032818   DLC PPPM MiU MWelC NNC OO

NK
2406   National Art Galleries,inc.,New York.
.N28   XVII and XVIII century American furniture
and contemporary decorations,comprising the
collection exhibited during the summer at King
Hooper mansion,Marblehead,Mass.,owned and operated by King Hooper,inc. Also choicest specimens from the collection of Hyman Kaufman,Bos-
ton,and the collection of silver of Herbert
Lawton,Boston,sold by their order; unrestricted public auction sale,Thursday,Friday and Saturday,December 3rd,4th and 5th,1931 ... New
York,1931.
318 p. illus.
"Sale number twenty-two."
1.Furniture--Catalogs. 2.Furniture,American.
3.Silversmithing--U.S. I.King Hooper,inc.
II.Kaufman,   Hyman. III.Lawton,
Herbert.   IV.Title.

NN 0032819   MiU NCorniC

NE
2415   National Art Galleries, inc., New York.
C7   200 rare Currier & Ives lithographs from the Michael-
N3   sen Gallery; unrestricted public auction sale Thursday
1932   evening, January 14th, 1932. New York, 1932.
73 p. illus. 23 cm.

Title from original paper cover.
At head of title: Sale number twenty-seven.

1. Currier & Ives. 2. Lithographs – Catalogs. I. Michaelsen
Gallery, New York

NN 0032820   Vi

National Art Gallery, *Madras*
see
Madras. National Art Gallery.

National Art Gallery, *Sydney*
see
Sydney. Art Gallery of New South Wales.

National art gallery, Washington, D. C.
see
Washington, D.C. National glalory of art.

National art gallery of Canada
see
Ottawa. National   gallery of Canada.

National Art Gallery of New South Wales, *Sydney*
see
Sydney. Art Gallery of New South Wales.

National art library, London
see   South Kensington museum, London.
National Art Library.

VOLUME 406

N8530
.A67
National Art Materials Trade Association.

Art material trade news. v. 1–
May 1949–
Chicago ₍E. H. Ellison₎

National Art Service Company, Inc.   **W.38.4N19
The history of Mount Vernon, America's patriotic shrine. Revised
edition.
= [Washington, D.C.] 1932. 27, (4) pp. Plates. 21½ cm.

D2079 — Mount Vernon, Virginia. — Washington, George. Mount Vernon.

NN   0032828   MB DI

National art society.

New York. World's fair, 1939 *–1940.*
American art today. New York World's fair. ₍New York₎
National art society ₍ᶜ1939₎

National art society.

Robertson, Elizabeth Wells.
Art appreciation workbook, by Miss Elizabeth Wells Robertson ... issued in connection with "Art for your sake," a new
National art society NBC presentation, 25 educational drama-
tizations of the lives of famous painters, directed for National
art society by Dr. Bernard Myers ... every Saturday ... October 7–March 30. New York, The National art society ₍1939₎

₍National art society₎
Art for your sake. ₍New York, ᶜ1939₎
₍14₎ p. illus. 21ᶜᵐ.

Statement of the activities of the National art society.
"Membership application": 2 leaves laid in.

1. Art—Societies.   I. Title.
                                                                40–18385
Library of Congress   N11.N2A5
——— ——— Copy 2.
Copyright AA 329524   ₍2₎   706.273

NN   0032831   DLC CaBViP

National art society.
Art for your sake; a National Broadcasting
Company public service feature...
see under title

N11
.N2A2
National art society.
Report of the president, National art society. 1st–
1940–   ₍New York, 1940–
          v. 23ᶜᵐ.

The first report covers the period from the incorporation of the Society
October 7, 1939 to May 15, 1940, inclusive.

1. Art—Societies.
                                                                S 41–14
Smithsonian Inst. Library
for Library of Congress   ₍2₎

NN   0032833   DSI DLC

National art society, Chicago.

Buckley, Edmund, 1855–   *ed.*
The fine arts; a university course in sculpture, painting,
architecture and decoration in their history, development and
principles. Editor-in-chief, Edmund Buckley ... consulting
editors, J. M. Hoppin ... Alfred V. Churchill ... Chicago,
National art society ₍ᶜ1907₎

National art society, Chicago.
Representative judgments on the principles of
art
            see under   Churchill, Alfred Vance, 1864–
1934.

National art society, Chicago.
The technique and principles of art
            see under   Sturgis, Russell, Jr.

National art student

see

American art student and commercial artist.

National Art Survey of Scotland.
Examples of Scottish architecture from the 12th
to the 17th century
            see under title

National art theatre society, *New York.*
Manual of the National art theatre society of New
York. Incorporated, March, 1904. New York, Pub. at
the offices of the Society, 1904.
          157 p. 12 pl. 20½ᶜᵐ.

The plates are to accompany the articles on the endowed theaters of
Europe.
Imperfect: plate 1, "The Théâtre français," wanting.

CONTENTS.—A foreword ₍by₎ Arthur Hornblow.—Our aims and pur-
poses, by J. I. C. Clarke.—History of the National art theatre society, by
H. P. Mawson.—What an endowed theatre might do for America, by
A. M. Palmer.—The players for a national art theatre, by H. D. French.—
The repertory of a national art theatre, by Rupert Hughes.—The drama
from a churchman's point of view, by the Rev. Minot J. Savage.—The
Comédie française and what it has done for the French people, by Jules
Claretie.—What the Comédie has done for French literature, by Prof.
Adolph Cohn.—How Germany fosters her national drama, by W. W.
Whitelock.—Denmark's endowed drama, by Julius Moritzen.—Subsidized
art in Italy, by Lionel Strachey.—Constitution of the society.—Life mem-
bers.—Members.

1. Theaters—Europe.
                                                                14–2642
Library of Congress   PN2017.U6N2

NN   0032840   DLC NjP NIC

National art training school, South Kensington

see

London. Royal college of art.

National Art Views Company.
New York. [1903]
see under title

National artistic hair work company, *Chicago.*
Catalogue of designs for artistic hair scenery and ornaments, executed by National artistic hair works of Chicago, Ill. ... ₍Chicago, 1886₎
          2 p. l., 150–175 numb. l. 24 x 31½ᶜᵐ.
Cover-title: Catalogue of artistic hair work for mementos and souvenirs.

1. Hair-work.   CA 10–2593 Unrev'd
Library of Congress   TT976.N27 1886

NN   0032843   DLC

National artistic hair work company, *Chicago.*
₍Hair ornaments. The art of working in hair. Chicago, ᶜ1886₎
          66 p. illus. 18½ᶜᵐ.
Caption title.
p. 65–66 repeated.

1. Hair-work.
Library of Congress   TT976.N26   8–34030†

NN   0032844   DLC

NATIONAL ARTISTS CORPORATION, New York.
Lectures and special attractions ₍New York₎
          illus., ports. 10 x 23 cm.
Annual.
Only current issue kept.

NN   0032845   MH-FA

---

*
PS3503
.U64B8   National Artists Corporation, New York.
no.21   Poet's theatre with Vincent Godfrey Burns.
          ₍New York, n. d.₎
          1 l.   38 cm. ₍Burns pamphlets, no. 21₎

Reproduced from typescript.

1. Burns, Vincent Godfrey, 1893–
I. Title.

NN   0032846   ViU

National arts broadcast
            see   National arts club, New York.
                    Bulletin.

CT
211
A52   **National Arts Club, New York.**
v.10   Addresses on the occasion of the
no.2   presentation to Mr. Timothy Cole of the
          National Arts Club gold medal of merit,
          February 16, 1916. [New York? 1916?]
          [18] p. 23cm.

1. Cole, Timothy, 1852–1931.
I. Title

NN   0032848   NIC OO NN

National Arts Club, New York.
American paintings from the collection of Mr.
William T. Evans
            see under   Evans, William Thomas, 1843–
1918.

National arts club, New York
A brief sketch of the Graphic group organized in 1911 for the betterment of the
graphic arts. ₍New York₎ Published for the
members ₍Wm. E. Rudge₎ 1929.
          15 p., 1 l., front., 4 plates (ports.) 30 cm

Plates printed on both sides.
Autographs of eighteen members on fly-leaf.

1. Graphic group.   I. American institute
of graphic arts.
Title from Peabody Inst., Baltimore.

NN   0032850   MdBP

VOLUME 405

NATIONAL ARTS CLUB, New York.
   Bulletin.
New York,   v.   illus.   21-23cm.

   Monthly, except July-Sept. (slightly irregular).
   Title varies: 1939-June, 1946, National arts broadcast (Oct. 1946-
June, 1947, lack title).
   Ceased publication with v. 42, no. 2, Nov. 1962?
I. Title: National arts   broadcast.

NN   0032851   NN

National Arts Club.
   Catalogue; special exhibition of the work of members...
Jan. 8 - Feb. 9, 1913.   New York [1913].   4 l.   8°.

1. Paintings.—Exhibitions, U. S.:   N. Y. City.   2. Sculpture.—Exhibitions, U. S.: N. Y. City.
N. Y. P. L.   September 9, 1913.

NN   0032852   NN

National Arts Club, New York.   4073.28
   Decoration of the National Capitol. [Circular sent by the Club.]
=   [New York, 1900.]   (3) pp.   4°.

*D6542 — United States Capital and Capitol.

NN   0032853   MB

National arts club - New York
   Exhibition catalogues. 1917.

   An exhibition of etchings by contemporary
American artists, February 28 to March 23,
1917. The American institute of graphic arts.

NN   0032854   OC1MA

National Arts Club, New York.
   Exhibition of Japanese paintings on silk by
Yokoyama
      see under   Nippo-Bijitsuin.

National Arts Club.
   Memorial exhibition of paintings and drawings by W. Shirlaw
...March 8th to April 5th, 1911.   New York [1911].   6 l.   8°.

1. Shirlaw, Walter.
N. Y. P. L.   September 20, 1911.

NN   0032856   NN

National arts club, New York.
... Memorial exhibition of paintings by John Leslie
Breck ... catalogue. [New York, 1899?]
[7] p. port. 21ᶜᵐ.
Biography, preceding catalogue, signed: Benjamin Kimball.

1. Breck, John Leslie, 1860-1899.
                                          CA 11-2784 Unrev'd
   Library of Congress   ND237.B8

NN   0032857   DLC MB

National arts club, *New York*.
   The National arts club, New York ...
[New York,
   v. fronts. plates. 21ᶜᵐ.
Officers, exhibitions, lectures, constitution, members.

                                          CA 8-2823 Unrev'd
   Library of Congress   N11.N55

NN   0032858   DLC MiDA NjP MdBJ MWA MP

NATIONAL ARTS CLUB. New York.
   New club house of National Arts Club. New
York, 1906.

NN   0032859   MH

National arts club, New York.
   ...Pictures by the late William Hamilton Gibson
with a relief portrait of him by K. K. Bush-Brown.
tenth exhibition, May 31st to June 14th, 1900.
[New York? 1900]

NC134
.G4N8

NN   0032860   DLC MB

National arts club, New York.
   Pictures by the late William Hamilton Gibson, with a relief portrait of him by H. K. Bush-Brown. Tenth exhibition, May 31st
to June 14th, 1900. [New York, 1900]   [4] l. port. 22cm.

Film reproduction. Positive.
Cover title.

1. Gibson, William Hamilton,   1850-1896 .

NN   0032861   NN

National arts club, New York.

Ruckstull, Fred Wellington, 1853-
   Social art; an address delivered to the Open table of
the National arts club, by Mr. F. W. Ruckstuhl, January
twenty-fifth, 1915. [New York, The Open table of the
National arts club, 1915]

National Arts Club.
   Special exhibition of contemporary art, January...1908.
[New York,] 1908.   2 l.   8°.
   In : MAW p. v. 4, no. 16.

1. Architecture.—Exhibitions, U. S.:   New York City.
N. Y. L.   August 25, 1913.

NN   0032863   NN CtY

National Arts Club, New York.
   Summer sketch exhibition, National Arts Club...New York
City. Sketches and studies by painter members of the club...
[New York, 1916.]   6 l.   8°.

   Catalogue of the exhibition.

1. Paintings.—Exhibitions, U. S.:   New York City.
N. Y. P. L.   November 24, 1916.

NN   0032864   NN

National arts club, New York.
   ... "The Tilden mansion--home of the
National arts club;" ...
      see under   Lamb, Charles Rollinson.

National Arts Club, New York.
   A tribute to William Winter...   [New York, 1909.]   30 p.
ports.   8°.

   Cover-title.
   "Dinner in honor of William Winter at the National Arts Club of New York
City, Wednesday, December fifteenth, nineteen hundred and nine.

1. Winter, William, 1836-1917.
N. Y. P. L.   January 29, 1924.

NN   0032866   NN ViU

National arts club, New York.

Vollbehr, Otto Heinrich Friedrich, 1869-
   The Vollbehr incunabula at the National arts club of New
York from August 23 to September 30 мсмxxvɪ, by George
Parker Winship. [New York, Pynson printers, 1926]

National arts committee for the celebration of
   Washington's 200th birthday.
   Washington pre-eminent; thirty-five key
scenes, presenting the high-lights in the lives of
Washington's parents & ancestors and of
Washington's own life, from childhood to death,
as revealed & established by newly discovered
records
      . see under   Bartlett, Mrs. Alice (Hunt)
1870-

TE270   National Asphalt Conference.
.N3   [Proceedings] 19 -
         Held under the auspices of the Asphalt
         institute and the Association of asphalt
         paving technologists.   New York, The
         Asphalt institute, 19 -
            v. illus. 23 cm.

         1. Asphalt. 2. Roads--Congresses. I.
         Asphalt Institute.   II. Association of
         Asphalt Paving   Technologists.

NN   0032869   TU DLC KyU ICJ CU OO MiD MtBC WaS DPR

National Assembly for Moral Re-Armament,
   Washington, D.C., December 30,1950-
   January 8,1951.
   Report ... on an ideology that can win
the world.   Wash.The Assembly,1951.
   40p.illus.ports.sq.Q.

NN   0032870   OrP CaBViP

National Assembly Library, Seoul, Korea
      see   Kukhoe Tosŏgwan, Seoul, Korea.

National Assembly of Civil Service Commissions
   see
Public Personnel Association.

National Assembly of France
      see   France. Assemblée nationale constitu-
ante, 1789-1791.

National Assembly of Scotland
      see   Church of Scotland. General assembly.

TF7   National assembly of student Christian associa-
N221c   tions, Miami university, Oxford, Ohio, 1942.
         Christian faith and social reconstruction, for
         use now and at the National assembly of student
         Christian associations, Miami university, Oxford,
         Ohio, December 27, 1941-January 3, 1942. [New
         York, National student assembly committee, 1941?]
         45 p. 22 cm. (Assembly paper, no. 2)

         At head of title: Program priorities for 1941-
         42.
         Includes bibli-   ographies.

NN   0032875   CtY-D

National Assembly of the Church of England
   see Church of England. *National Assembly*

VOLUME 405

National associated clans.
Ritual of the National associated clans ... ₍Chatta-
nooga, Chattanooga printing & engraving co.₎ ᶜ1922.
39 p. illus. (plan) 20½ᶜᵐ.

ɪ. Title.

CA 23–20 Unrev'd
Library of Congress   HS2330.N22A5 1922

NN   0032877   DLC

National Associated Marine Suppliers.
N. A. M. S. directory of American ship suppliers.

New York.
v. 23 cm.
Cover title,   : A directory of American ship suppliers.

1. Ship chandlers—U. S.—Direct.   ɪ. Title.   ɪɪ. Title: A directory
of American ship suppliers.

VM470.5.N3   56–27650

NN   0032878   DLC MiU

**National associated schools of scientific
business, Chicago**
National business ability tests.
₍Chicago, National associated schools of
scientific business, c1915₎
24 p. incl. forms. 20½ cm. (Bulletin
no.1. March, 1915)

NN   0032879   DHEW

National Associa**t**ed School of Scientific Business, *Chicago*.
National business ability texts (Advance proofs)
Chicago [191–]
14 p.   4°.
Inserted at end are five tests in English,
spelling, etc., p. (19)

NN   0032880   MH

National Associated Studios of Music, Inc.
Catalogue. 1928/29.
= Boston. [1928.]   v. Portraits. 21 cm.
   Additional unbound parts, as received, may be found in covers on the same
   call-number. They are not noted on this card until bound.

NN   0032881   MB OCl

National Associated Veterans of the Mexican
War
        see   National Association of Veterans
of the Mexican War.

National Association, London.
Address of the National Association, London,
to the people of Ireland. London, Cleave
₍etc., etc., 1843₎
8 p. 18cm.

Volume of pamphlets.

NN   0032883   NNC

**National Association and Council of Business
Schools.**

HF1101
.D5

Directory of business schools in the United States; a hand
book for vocational advisors and guidance officers. ₍1st₎–
ed.; 1943–
Washington, National Association and Council of Business
Schools.

**National Association and Council of Business Schools.
Secretaryship**

see under

Purvis, Elgie G

National Association and Council of Business Schools
see also
**National Association of Accredited Commercial Schools.
National Council of Business Schools.**

National Association and Council of Business Schools. *Accrediting Commission for Business Schools*
see
Accrediting Commission for Business Schools.

National association boards of pharmacy
        see   National Association of Boards of
Pharmacy.

National Association Democrati**c** Clubs
        see   National Association of Demo-
cratic Clubs.

National association for adult education.
        see   Adult education association.

**National Association for American Composers and Conduc-
tors, inc.**
Annual bulletin.

₍n. p.₎
v. 23 cm.

ML27.U5N14   781.606273   49–32153*‡

NN   0032891   DLC N NN

National association for American composers
and conductors, inc.

₍**Berthoud, Paul P**   ₎
The musical works of Dr. Henry Hadley, compiled and listed
in two parts. Part 1. Alphabetic. Part 2. Descriptive. New
York, N. Y., The National association for American composers
and conductors and the Henry Hadley foundation, 1942.

M24
.B882S8

National association for American composers
and conductors, inc.

Browning, Mortimer, 1891–
₍Suite, piano, D minor₎

... Suite in D minor for piano ... by Mortimer Browning ...
New York, N. Y., J. Fischer & bro. ₍1940₎

National association for art education.
Bulletin.
v. 1

New York, 1936–   30cm.
v. illus.
Monthly during the school year.

1. Art—Education—Per. and soc.   publ.
N. Y. P. L.   May 4, 1938

NN   0032894   NN

National Association for Bank Audit, Control
and Operation
        see   NABAC, the association for Bank
Audit, Control and Operations.

**National Association for Better Radio and Tele-
vision.**
Annual report on Children's radio and television
programs.   Los Angeles, Calif.,
1955
v.

NN   0032896   Wa

NATIONAL ASSOCIATION FOR BETTER RADIO AND TELEVISION.
Children and television--some opinions. Los Angeles
[1954]   16 p.   22cm.

1. Television and children.

NN   0032897   NN InU

791.4
N215r

National Association for Better Radio and
Television.
Radio and television guide to better programs.

Los Angeles,
v. 23cm.

At head of title,   : "NAFBRAT."

NN   0032898   IU

PN1992
.8
.R3T4

National Association for Better Radio and
Television. Evaluation Committee.
Television for the family.
₍Los Angeles, National Association for Better Radio and
Television₎

National association for Business Teacher
Education.
... Annual conference of the National
association of commercial teacher-training
institutions. Abstract of proceedings 3d–
1930– ₍n.p., 1930–
v. (Its Bulletin no. 1, 3, Feb. 1930,
July 1933)

NN   0032900   OU LU

National association for Business Teacher
Education.
... Bibliographies and directory of members.
₍n.p., The National association of commercial
teacher-training institutions, 1938.
39, ₍1₎ p. (Its Bulletin, no.15, May, 1938)

NN   0032901   OU

National Association for Business Teacher Education.
Bulletin. ₍no.₎ 1–
₍n. p., 1930₎–
no. in   illus. 23 cm.
Cover title: no.   NABTE bulletin.
No. 1–   issued by the association under earlier names: no. 1–20,
National Association of Commercial Teacher-Training Institutions;
no. 21–   National Association of Business Teacher-Training Insti-
tutions.
Includes reports of the association's annual meetings.

1. Business education—Societies, etc.

HF1101.N2   650.711   59–4188

OU OrU MtU DCU CoU FTaSU IdU OrCS OrLgE
NN   0032902   DLC MiU IU KyU PBL TNJ-P OAkU MsU MBU

VOLUME 405

National association for Business Teacher
Education.
[... Commercial teacher-training curricula
in 94 accredited teachers colleges and normal
schools in 1938
see under Sipe, John Marvin, 1905-

National Association for Business Teacher
Education.
An evaluation of the graduate courses in
business education offered in the colleges and
universities of the U.S. in 1943
see under Garrett, Robert Norval,
1904-

National association for Business Teacher
Education.
... Handbook for studying business education
see under Reynolds, Helen.

650.7 National association for Business Teacher
N21b   Education.
no.10   [...Methods requirements in commercial teacher
training. Prepared by following committee:
Frances B. Bowers, chairman...] [n.p.] 1936.
caption-title, 43p. 22½cm. (Bulletin no.10)

1. Teachers, Training of--Business education.
2. Business education. I. Title.

NN 0032906   LU PPT OU

650.7 National association for Business Teacher
N21b   Education
no.28   [...National association of business teacher-
training institutions, Ed. by Benjamin R. Haynes
...] [n.p.] 1942.
caption-title, 47p. 22½cm. (Bulletin no.28)

1. Future business leaders of America. I. Title.
II. Haynes, Benjamin Rudolph, 1897- ed.

NN 0032907   LU

650.7 National association for Business Teacher
N21b   Education.
no.11   [...Practice teaching and business experience
in commercial teacher training...] [n.p.]
1937.
caption-title, 30p. 22½cm. (Bulletin no.11)

1. Teachers, Training of--Business education.
2. Business education. I. Title.

NN 0032908   LU OU

National Association for Business Teacher
Education.
... Practices and problems in commercial
teacher-training institutions
see under Studebaker, Mark Earl, 1888-

National Association for Business Teacher
Education.
... Report of the work committee on a
rating scale for secondary business education
see under University of Chicago
Conference on Business Education, Chicago.
Work Committee.

National association for Business
Teacher Education
Research in commercial teacher training
prepared by E. G. Blackstone, chairman,
Ann Brewington, B. R. Haynes, H. A. Tonne.
[N. Y.: The association, 1934.
28 p. (Bulletin no. 5)

NN 0032911   OU

National Association for Business Teacher
Education.
Research in commercial teacher training.
1936.
see under Brewington, Ann.

National Association for Business Teacher
Education.
The selection of persons to be trained as
teachers of business subjects
see under Hunsinger, Majorie.

National Association for Business Teacher
Education.
A study of student teaching in business
subjects in state teachers colleges ...
see under Gilbreth, Harold Brite, 1908-

National Association for Business Teacher
Education.
Suggested programs for commercial teacher-
training institutes
see under Shover, William Glen.

National association for Business
Teacher Education.
... Training of teachers in service. [n.p.]
The National association of commercial teacher-
training institutions, 1937.
24 p. (Its Bulletin, no. 13, December 1937)

NN 0032916   OU

National association for Business Teacher
Education.   Committee on policies.
... Committee on policies progress report.
[n.p.] The National association of commercial
teacher-training institutions, 1940.
cover-title, 30 p. (National association of
commercial teacher-training institutions.
Bulletin no. 19, February, 1940)

NN 0032917   OU

650.7 National association for Business Teacher
N21b   Education. 12th conference, Cleveland,
no.17 Ohio.
[...Proceedings of the twelfth annual conference
of the National association of commercial teacher-
training institutions. Ed. by Ann Brewington...
Held at the Hotel Hollenden, Cleveland, Ohio, Saturday, February 25, 1939.] [n.p., 1939]
caption-title, 34, [1]p. 22½cm. (Bulletin
no. 17)

1. Business education--Societies. 2. Teachers,
Training of--Business education. I. Brewington,
Ann, ed.

NN 0032918   LU OCU

650.7 National association for Business Teacher
N21p   Education. 14th conference, Atlantic City, 1941.
1941   ...Proceedings of the fourteenth annual conference
of the national association of business teacher-
training institutions. Edited by Ann Brewington...
[n.p.] 1941.
42p. 22½cm. (Bulletin no.22)

1. Business education--Societies. 2. Teachers,
Training of. 3. Teachers--Training--Business schools.
I. Brewington, Ann, ed.

NN 0032919   LU

650.7 National association for Business Teacher
N21b   Education. 15th conference, Chicago, Ill.
no.27 [...Proceedings of the fifteenth annual conference of the National association of business
teacher-training institutions. Ed. by Ann Brew-
inton... Held at Hotel Sherman, Chicago, Illinois
December 29 and 30, 1941.] [n.p.] 1941.
caption-title, 41p. 22½cm. (Bulletin no.27)

1. Business education--Societies. 2. Teachers,
Training of--Business education. I. Brewington,
Ann, ed.

NN 0032920   LU

National Association for Community Development
Community development
see under title

HC28   National Association for Conservation Education
N24   and Publicity.
Annual convention

[n.p.]
v. 28 cm.
Cover title.

1. Natural resources – Study and teaching.
2. Natural resources – Congresses.

NN 0032922   DI

National Association for Constitutional Government.
Bulletin.
v. 1
Washington, 1920   8°.
v.

NN 0032923   NN MiU OO

National Association for Constitutional Government.   *4329.303
Constitution. Adopted May 6, 1916.
=   Washington. [1916.] (4) pp. 15 cm.
The title is on the cover.

NN 0032924   MB DLC

National association for constitutional government.
The Constitutional review; a quarterly magazine advo-
cating the maintenance of constitutional government
and recording its progress at home and abroad. v. 1-
Apr. 1917-
Washington, D. C., 1917-

JK1541   National association for constitutional
.W4   government.   FOR OTHER EDITIONS
1915 a   SEE MAIN ENTRY
Watson, David Kemper, 1849-1917.
Invalid legislation. The power of the federal judiciary to
declare legislation invalid which conflicts with the federal Con-
stitution, by David K. Watson ... Washington, D. C., The
National association for constitutional government [1915?]

JK1541   National association for constitutional
.M73   government.
Moschzisker, Robert von, 1870-1939.
Judicial review of legislation; a consideration of the war-
rants for and merits of our American system of judicially re-
viewing legislation to ascertain its constitutional validity, by
Robert von Moschzisker ... [Washington, The National asso-
ciation for constitutional government, 1923]

JK3   National association for constitutional government.
.N25   List of members of the National association for
constitutional government
Washington, D.C.
v. 16 cm.

NN 0032928   DLC

VOLUME 405

National association for constitutional
government, Washington, D.C.
Hill, David Jayne, 1850–
Our great inheritance: an address before the Daughters
of the American revolution, Sons of the revolution, and
the Sons of the American revolution, on February 22nd,
1919, by David Jayne Hill. Washington, D. C., National
association for constitutional government ₁1919₎

National association for constitutional
government.
U. S. *Constitution.*
Pocket edition of the Constitution of the United States;
with an introduction by Merrill E. Gates ... Washington,
D. C., The National association for constitutional government
₁1919₎

National association for constitutional government.
Proceedings of the ... annual meeting and dinner of
the National association for constitutional government ...
1st–   1916–
₁Washington↑ D. C., 1916–
v. 23ᶜᵐ.
List of members inserted.

1. U. S.—Pol. & govt. 2. U. S. Constitution.

17–19296

Library of Congress   JK3.N2

NN 0032931   DLC OC1WHi MB KyU

National association for economic expansion
see   Association nationale d'expansion
economique.

378.3 National Association for Foreign Student Affairs .
N214f Foreign student advisers and others officially
concerned with foreign student welfare and
counseling. Teachers of English as a foreign
language. Based on a survey of NAFSA, September,
1953.   New York ₁1953₎
84p. 28cm.

1. Students, Foreign. 2. Counseling. 3. English language--Study and teaching. I. Title.

NN 0032933   IU

LB3602 National Association for Foreign Student Affairs.
.N2A52 General directory of foreign student advisers.
The NAFSA directory.
New York.

LB2376 **National Association** for Foreign Student
.N3   Affairs.
**Handbook for counselors of students
from abroad. Experimental ed.   New
York, 1949.**
vi, 214 p. 28 cm.

"Prepared by members of the Practicum
for Foreign Student Advisers, Teachers
College, Columbia University, Summer
Session, 1948."

NN 0032935   TU NN KMK IdU PSt NNU MiDW

National Association for Foreign Student Affairs.
Immigration regulations for foreign student
advisers
see under   Cooper, Leland H

LB3602 National Association for Foreign Student Affairs.
.N2A2 Meeting; ₁special report₎
National Association for Foreign Student Affairs.
Report of the conference. 1st–
1949–
New York.

LB3602 National Association for Foreign Student Affairs.
.N2A52 The NAFSA directory.
New York.

National Association for Foreign Student
Affairs.
NAFSA newsletter
see under title

National Association for Foreign Student Affairs.
Report of the conference. 1st–
1949–
New York.
v. 23–28 cm. annual.
Vols. for   issued as its NAFSA publications. CR. (LB.
3602.N2A18)
Title varies: 1949, Meeting; ₁special report₎
Some reports have also distinctive titles: 1961, New directions in
international educational exchange.—

1965, Overcoming barriers to educational and cultural communications.
Conferences for 1950–   held as Conference on International Educational Exchanges.

Vols. for 1949–   issued by the association under its earlier name:
National Association of Foreign Student Advisers.

1. Students, Foreign—U. S.   ɪ. Conference on International Educational Exchanges. ɪɪ. National Association for Foreign Student
Affairs. Meeting; ₁special report₎ ɪɪɪ. Title: New directions in
international educational exchange. ɪᴠ. Title: Overcoming barriers to
educational and cultural communication.   (Series: National Association for Foreign Student Affairs. NAFSA publications. CR)

LB3602.N2A2   52–26394

NN FU AAP PSC MiU KKcB PLF
NN 0032941   DLC CaBVa Wa WaWW OrCS OrU OC1CC NNC

WA   National Association for Maternal and Child Welfare.
1
N272
[Collection of publications].

The Library has a collection of miscellaneous
publications of this organization kept as
received. These publications are not listed or bound
separately.
1. Child Welfare 2. Maternal Welfare

NN 0032942   DNLM

National Association for Maternal and Child Welfare.
Report of annual conference.
₁London₎
v. 22 cm.

1. Maternal and infant welfare—Gt. Brit.— Societies, etc.

HV700.G7N3   58–18132

NN 0032943   DLC DNLM KMK MiU

National Association for Mental Health, London
see   National Association for Mental
Health (Gt. Brit.)

National Association for Mental Health, New York
see   National Association for Mental
Health (U.S.)

NATIONAL ASSOCIATION FOR MENTAL HEALTH (Gt. Brit.)
Child guidance inter-clinic conference.
Author, 1951.
1 v.

NN 0032946   Or

WM   NATIONAL Association for Mental Health
1   (Gt. Brit.)
qN277 ₁Collection of publications₎

The Library has a collection of
miscellaneous publications of this
organization kept as received. These
publications are not listed or bound
separately.

NN 0032947   DNLM

National Association for Mental Health (Gt. Brit.)
The family approach to child guidance
see under
Inter-clinic Conference for staffs of Child
Guidance Clinics, 11th, London, 1955.

National association for mental health (Gt. Brit.)
Finding foster homes; an experiment
see under   Maw, Mary.

National Association for Mental Health (Gt. Brit.)
MH news letter
see under title

W 1   NATIONAL Association for Mental Health,
NA235 (Gt. Brit.)
Minutes ₁of the₎ annual general
meeting.
London ₁1948?₎–
v.

NN 0032951   DNLM

National Association for Mental Health (*Gt. Brit.*)
Notes on legislation relating to mental defectives. London ₁1946₎
11, ₁1₎ p. 22 cm.

1. Mental health laws—Gt. Brit. ₁1. Mental defectives—Laws and
legislation—Gt. Brit.₎ ɪ. Gt. Brit. Laws, statutes, etc.

Med 48–1578 rev

U. S. National Library   of Medicine [W6P3]
for Library of Congress   ₁r60c₎

NN 0032952   DNLM

National Association for Mental Health (Gt. Brit.)
136.7 Periods of stress in the primary school;
N277P report prepared by an Expert Group ... London, Published with financial support from
UNESCO by the National Association for Mental
Health ₁1955₎
ii, 38 p. 21½cm.

Includes bibliography.

NN 0032953   NcD

National Association for Mental Health (Gt. Brit.)
The practical application of research and
experiment to the mental health field

see under

Conference on the Practical Application of Research
and Experiment to the Mental Health Field,
London, 1958.

VOLUME 405

RA790
A1N22
1955
Public
Health
Library

National Association for Mental Health (*Gt. Brit.*)
 Preventive aspects of mental health work. Proceedings of a conference held at County Hall, London ... 24th to 25th March, 1955. [London? 1955?]
  110 p.

 "Conference on Preventive Aspects of Mental Health Work. Chairman: Kenneth Robinson."

 1. Mental hygiene - Gt. Brit. - Congresses. 2. Psychiatric social work - Congresses. I. Conference on Preventive Aspects of Mental Health Work, London, 1955. II. Title.

NN 0032955   CU DNLM

National Association for Mental Health (*Gt. Brit.*)
 Report. 1946/47–
 [London]
  v. illus. 22-25 cm. annual.

 Report years ends Mar. 31.

  RA790.A1N14   131.3206242   52–23103 rev ‡

NN 0032956   DLC NN DNLM

W 6
P3

NATIONAL Association for Mental Health, (*Gt. Brit.*)
 Some special educational problems of physically handicapped children; report of an enquiry conducted in 1949 by the National Association for Mental Health in conjunction with the Central Council for the Care of Cripples. [London, 1950?]
  71 p. illus.
  1. Children - Exceptional - Education
I. Central Council for the Care of Cripples London

FU-HC
NN 0032957 DNLM OrU-M NNU-W TxDaM MiU Wa CaBVaU

National Association for Mental Health (*Gt. Brit.*)
 Strain and stress in modern living

 see under

Conference on Strain and Stress in Modern Living: Special Opportunities and Responsibilities of Public Authorities, London, 1954.

National association for mental health (*Gt. Brit.*)
 Why delinquency?
 see under Conference on the scientific study of juvenile delinquency, London, 1949.

National Association for Mental Health (*Gt. Brit.*)
 see also International Congress on Mental Health, London, 1948.

National Association for Mental Health (*U.S.*)
 And you never know
 see under
Stirling, Nora, 1900–

WM
1
qN275

NATIONAL Association for Mental Health (*U.S.*)
 [Collection of publications]

 The library has a collection of miscellaneous publications of this organization kept as received. These publications are not listed nor bound separately.
  1. Mental hygiene

NN 0032962   DNLM

RC443
.D5

National Association for Mental Health (U. S.)
 Directory of outpatient psychiatric clinics and other mental health resources in the United States and territories.
 [New York]

National Association for Mental Health (*U. S.*)
 Eating patterns of children; a guide for doctors and nurses. [New York, 1951]
  16 p. illus. 22 cm.

 "Based on ... 'Child guidance leaflets' ... prepared by Nina Ridenour for the New York City Committee on Mental Hygiene of the State Charities Aid Association, in collaboration with the staff of the Bureau of Child Hygiene and the Bureau of Nursing of the New York City Department of Health."

 1. Children—Nutrition—Psychological aspects. I. Title.

  RJ206.N26   613.22   51–6056 rev ‡

NN 0032964   DLC TU DNLM OrCS

National Association for Mental Health (*U. S.*)
 Eating problems of children; a guide for parents. [New York, 1951]
  17 p. illus. 22 cm.

 "Based on ... 'Child guidance leaflets' ... prepared by Nina Ridenour for the New York City Committee on Mental Hygiene of the State Charities Aid Association, in collaboration with the staff of the Bureau of Child Hygiene and the Bureau of Nursing of the New York City Department of Health."

 1. Children—Nutrition—Psychological aspects. I. Title.

  RJ206.N27   649.3   51–6057 rev ‡

NN 0032965   DLC

Pamphlet
RC
8+

National Association for Mental Health (*U.S.*)
 Facts and figures about mental illness and other personality disorders. New York, 1952.
  9 p. 26cm.

 Cover title.

 1. Mentally ill—U. S.

NN 0032966   NIC MiU

W 6
P3

NATIONAL Association for Mental Health (*U.S.*)
 Forgotten children. New York [1955?]
  30 p. illus.
  Cover title.
  1. Children - Exceptional Title

NN 0032967   DNLM OCU

National Association for Mental Health (U.S.)
 Handbook for psychiatric aides
  see under National Mental Health Foundation.

National Association for Mental Health (U.S.)
 If your child is slow. (New York, 1952)
  (8) p. illus. 20 cm.

NN 0032969   OCU

National association for mental health (U.S.)
 Mental health publications and audiovisual aids. N.Y., N.A. for M.H., 1954.
  23 p. 23 cm.

NN 0032970   NRCR

RA790
.A1M5

National Association for Mental Health (U. S.)
 Mental hygiene. v. 1–
 Jan. 1917–
 New York.

National Association for Mental Health (*U.S.*)
 Notes for after fifty

 see under

Stern, Edith (Mendel) 1901–

W 1
NA241p

NATIONAL Association for **Mental Health** (*U.S.*)
 Proceedings of the program sessions [of the] mental health assembly and annual meeting.

  [New York? 1951?]–
   v. illus.
   1. Mental hygiene

NN 0032973   DNLM

RA790
N216
1952

National Association for Mental Health (*U.S.*)
 Recommended books for a mental health library. New York, 1952.
  [4] p. (Its Education bulletin, no. 2, rev. 1952)

 ----- ----- Supplements A-F. Rev. New York, 1952.
  6 l.

NN 0032974   NNC-M MoKU MtBC

National association for mental health. (*U.S.*)
 Report.
 1st–
 1950/51–
 New York [1951?–
   v. 23cm. annual.

NN 0032975   NNC OC1 CaBViP NcU NN CaBVaU

National Association for Mental Health (*U.S.*)
 Some special problems of children aged 2 to 5 years

 see under

State Charities Aid Association, New York. New York Committee on Mental Hygiene.

W 6
P3

NATIONAL Association for Mental Health (*U.S.*)
 A study of administration of state psychiatric services [by] Raymond G. Fuller. New York [1954]
  60 p.
  Preprinted from Mental hygiene, vol. 38, no. 2, Apr. 1954.
  "This article reports the major findings of a project undertaken by the National Association for Mental Health under a research grant from the National Institute of Mental Health of the Public Health Service."
  1. Hospitals - Psychiatric - U. S.
I. Fuller, Raymond Garfield, 1886- ed.

NN 0032978   DNLM Wa LU MiU NNC-M OU CaBVaU Or

~GOD PLUS NOTHING~

Our lives in Papua New Guinea

By D. Arvalee Palmer

The Memoirs of

R. Dale Palmer
And
D. Arvalee Palmer

"Not unto us, O Lord, not unto us,
but unto thy name give glory,
for thy mercy and for thy truth's sake."
Psalms 115:1

"Many, O Lord my God, are thy wonderful works...
if I would declare and speak of them,
they are more than can be numbered."
Psalm 40:5

Patrick Palmer Publishing

Tucson, Arizona

Published by Patrick L. Palmer
Photography and art work by R. Dale Palmer
Digital imaging and restoration by Patrick L. Palmer
Edited by Greg Melendes
Cover design by Laura Melendes
Printer preparations by Ghost River Images

Library of Congress Control Number 2014913013
ISBN 978-0-9906265-0-3

Scripture quotes from the King James Version

Printed in China

Photographic and Artwork Credits

The two palm tree trademark belongs to R. Dale Palmer.
Read as "R. D. (Palm)er" or "D. n A. (Palm)er" in later years.
Artwork and maps are original works by R. Dale Palmer.

Original WWII photographs by Blair Freiberg's father, used by permission.
The majority of photos are from the family albums, slides and snapshots.
Others by R. Dale Palmer, D. Arvalee Palmer, Peter D. Palmer and Patrick L. Palmer.

Cover background: Highlands mountains of PNG, Laura Melendes.
Front cover: Dale, Rabibi (Hapato's dad) and Danny, family album.
Back cover: Dale with literacy class, family album; Arvalee and Dale, Patrick L. Palmer.

~Acknowledgements~

First of all, Dale and I owe special thanks to our daughter, Julie Melendes, who enrolled us in the Creative Writing Class in 2002 at Waukesha County Technical College in Wisconsin.

Also, special thanks are given to Gail Grenier Sweet, the instructor of that writing class who critiqued our early writings, and gave much valuable help and many suggestions.

I wish to express my sincere thanks to Mary Condit who, along with her husband Robert, now deceased, read our stories and responded with genuine enthusiasm which spurred us on to continue writing the next chapter of our book.

Words cannot express my gratitude to our children and the inspiration they all have been to me. I am particularly thankful for my son Pat's help, who has given so willingly of his time and expertise, encouraging me in getting the book published, and especially in seeing this work through to completion; spending innumerable hours on picture selection, editing and placing them in the book.

Many thanks go to my editor, friend and fellow missionary in Papua New Guinea, Greg Melendes, who has lovingly critiqued the entire book, offering many helpful suggestions.

I'd like to express my sincere thanks and gratefulness to Laura Melendes for her expertise and help on the beautiful design of the book cover.

I would like to express my grateful thanks for my daughter Julie's help with editing and her critique of the book, in which she gave many valuable suggestions and corrections.

Finally, I am truly appreciative for the help of my grandson, Michael, (Pat's son) for keeping the computers and their programs running.

I am grateful to all the churches and many friends who helped us through the years with their prayers and gifts of support. Each one contributed to this story ever taking place by keeping us on the foreign field. And, above all, to the Lord God who truly showed us that it was indeed, "God Plus Nothing."

D. Arvalee Palmer

~Dedication~

To our five children: Pat, Peter, Paul, Julie, Dan and their families.
This includes our twelve grandchildren:
Stephanie, Anthony, Angela, Michael and Shawna;
Jeffrey and Christopher;
Natausha and Jessica;
Emily;
Trevor and Nicole.

Also our twelve great-grandchildren, by birth:
(1) Eliana, (2) Daniel, (3) Daniella, (4) Ana, (5) Olivia,
(6) Alexandria, (7) Benjamin, (8) Judah, (9) Esther,
(10) Jacob, (11) Isabel, and (12) Kayden.

I trust our story will inspire each of you to
keep looking to the Lord, always
believing that God can use your lives
to do great things for Him
as you honor and obey Him.

Our desire in writing our memoirs is that each
of you would know about our lives,
that we would be remembered, that our story
would inspire you to give your lives to God, and
above all, that the story of what God has done in the hearts of the
people of Papua New Guinea would be told.

~Contents~

Acknowledgements 5

Dedication..6

Foreword..8

Preface 10

Words, Phrases and Meanings 16

Introduction 17

~PART ONE~   Our Vision

Chapter 1   How I First Heard of New Guinea, 1942 25

Chapter 2   Entering Missionary Training, 1950.......................37

Chapter 3   Sailing for Australia, 1953 49

~PART TWO~   New Beginnings

Chapter 4   On to New Guinea, 1953 59

Chapter 5   The Turning Point 81

Chapter 6   A Choice Land Site 93

~PART THREE~   Our Dream…A Reality

Chapter 7   The Old Water Race 109

Chapter 8   Memories…Arvalee Remembers 133

Chapter 9   Family Moving to the Gimi, 1958 147

~PART FOUR~   God's Faithfulness

Chapter 10   Home in the USA, 1959 179

Chapter 11   Co-Workers Again 207

Chapter 12   Moving On; Another Surprise 231

~PART FIVE~   Starting Over

Chapter 13   Our Third Term; First Days in the Sepik, 1972 275

Chapter 14   Exciting Days in the Sepik 289

Chapter 15   An Unexpected Turn of Events, 1982 305

~PART SIX~   A Rewarding Ministry

Chapter 16   We Return to PNG, 1987, Via England and Ireland 315

Chapter 17   We Return to the USA, 1993 325

Chapter 18   A Major Decision, 2002 369

APPENDIX   (Dale's Complete Diary, 1955 and 1959) 379

Epilogue # 1 453

Epilogue # 2 455

Epilogue # 3 457

Epilogue # 4 459

CONTENTS LISTING INDIVIDUAL STORIES.................................461

GLOSSARY 467

CONTACT INFORMATION 475

~Foreword~
Snapshots of Dale and Arvalee Palmer
By Jim Covington

Today, July 1st, 2007 is Dale Palmer's birthday. I could not think of a more appropriate time to reprint what I wrote a little over ten years ago after I traveled with Dale and Arvalee to Papua New Guinea in 1997.

If you want to get to know who someone is, travel together. That journey was like rummaging with them through the old photographs of their lives, then discovering several priceless masterpieces. What hinders me from a more revealing exposé about who the Palmers really are is what they can say about me.

I listened to their stories and discovered the first snapshot to be of a pastor who was committed to going to the "regions beyond," but couldn't, so he exposed his congregation to God's greatness and the necessity of obeying the first word of the Great Commission: "Go!" Of course, this is a picture of Brother Kermit Byrd, the pastor of Bell Gardens Baptist Church in the 40s and 50s. Many of the Palmer's peers were challenged to serve the Lord and several explored the vast opportunities and began their lifetime ministry. In those days, these couples were continually "spurring one another to love and good works." Proverbs 27:17 says, "As iron sharpens iron; so a man sharpens the countenance of his friend."

Dale was so eager to serve God that he would ask every missionary he heard at the church services how he and his wife could also become missionaries. Often, the reply was, "get some training." Dale knew this would be almost impossible because he never finished high school. God challenged Dale to do something and then threw a huge obstacle in his way, which served as a lifelong reminder that God's work is accomplished "not by might, nor by power, but by my Spirit, saith the Lord of hosts," (Zechariah 4:6).

Without adequate qualification, credentials, or encouragement, what did the Palmers do? They followed the Lord's leading, choosing what some considered a "fly by night" organization that early on had a horrible reputation. Five of their first missionaries were martyred! Dale and Arvalee were not deterred by the ministry's reputation, nor, that they were sent off by their home church in 1953 without any commitment of financial support. Maybe that is what faith is. Dale repeated several times, "But God hath chosen the foolish things of the world to confound the wise; and God hath chosen the weak things of the world to confound the things which are mighty;" (1 Corinthians 1:27).

Frankly, I didn't understand how the church could let the Palmers go without offering any financial support, but this was one of those panoramic shots. Pointing near the edge of the picture, Dale brought to mind a story he must have been told by others of how their home church stepped out in faith to financially support them.

While home on furlough from Africa, Dr. Nathan Barlow, a missionary medical doctor, told the church leaders that they should take his support and give it to "that young couple" (the Palmers), if the church didn't have the money to support them. What a selfless act of Biblical love at tremendous personal sacrifice! God provided and He also stirred the home church in its faith to partner and participate in taking the gospel where Christ had not yet been preached.

Arriving in Papua New Guinea all my familiar State-side impressions of Dale and Arvalee disappeared. This was a snapshot I was not accustomed to seeing. I think I know why, too. No suit, no tie! I had never seen Dale in his "element" on his turf. When he spoke, it was with authority, the "thus saith the Lord" kind, with inflection and great affection!

There is one final snapshot. Upon our arrival in each location we were greeted by missionaries and nationals. Dale and Arvalee are dear to the missionaries. They had become like the grandparents of the mission; respected, loved, and highly esteemed because their work as pioneer missionaries in all the regions of Papua New Guinea had inspired so many others. To see this response to the Palmers was overwhelming.

The nationals added a unique dimension to this photo. Their affectionate love for Dale and Arvalee was breathtaking. At our home churches we greet one-another and shake hands. We might even give one of those hurried "arm around the shoulder" kind of hugs—not too long, not too close. In Papua New Guinea, when the brothers and sisters in Christ saw Dale and Arvalee, they would cling to them like a child who had been lost, found, and reunited with his parents. Those were no ordinary embraces. They were embraces for the ones who introduced them to Jesus Christ as the Savior of the world. They were tears of genuine love for the ones who gave their lives for these dear people.

So happy to see the Palmers!

It was evident in our travels, as Dale and Arvalee told and lived their life story, how the Refiner's fire had so carefully perfected His image in them until you could clearly see Jesus, (2 Cor. 3:18).

I add these snapshots to a photo album from my childhood. Somewhere along the way, Dale and Arvalee became two of my heroes. As a little boy, my parents made heroes of them by leading us to pray for the Palmers when they were working in the Gimi tribe. Little boys have lots of heroes. They talk about them, imitate them, even display memorabilia. Not all boys have the privilege of venturing with their hero into his realm. If Dale and Arvalee aren't already two of your heroes, come trek with them through their story and let them introduce you to our True Hero.

Jim Covington with a baby kangaroo

Jim Covington

One of the pastors at Bell Gardens Baptist Church in California

~Preface~

We were very young in the early 1940s and we were each introduced to the beautiful land of New Guinea in a different way…..but God knew our hearts and used this exposure as we grew up to give us a burden for the New Guinea people, ultimately leading to a desire to serve Him as missionaries. Our hearts were challenged as we listened to various missionary speakers; always with the vision of service in New Guinea.

The following pictures and throughout the book give a glimpse of our lives there with the people and their customs.

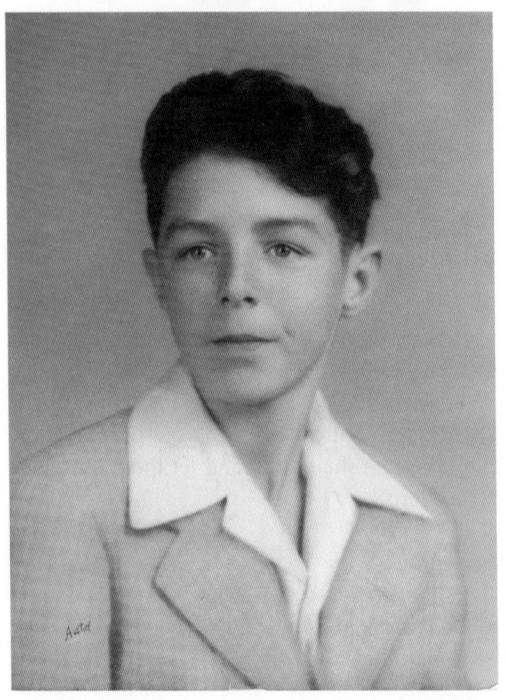

Dale heard stories of New Guinea from Luther Briggs, his dad's friend, a Marine who served in New Guinea in the Pacific Theater during World War II.

Arvalee read in the newspaper a series of articles about an Army plane crash that killed all but three of the passengers, known as the *Shangri-La Diary* by Corporal Margaret Hastings, WAC.

At home in our small cabin at Boot
Camp in Fouts Springs, California.

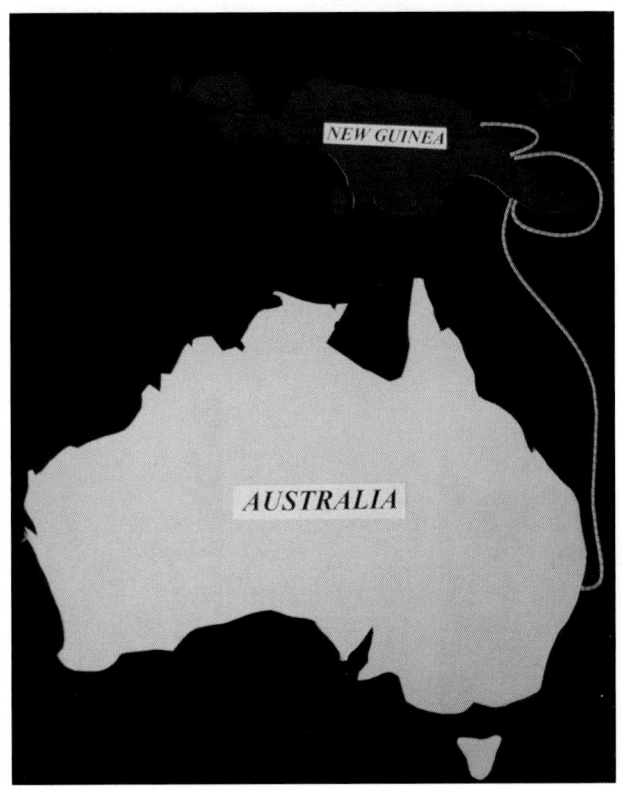

Who could have known? The large island of New Guinea lay over the ocean, in all its beauty with a people, many of whom had never seen a European or Western person.

We sailed across the Pacific Ocean on the M/S *Parrakoola*, disembarking at Sydney, Australia.

About three months later we sailed from Sydney to Port Moresby, then on to Lae and Madang on the M/V *Bulolo*.

The Early Days ~ En Route

Departing on the M/V *Bulolo* in Sydney, for New Guinea.

Ferns

Frangipani

Relaxing days were enjoyed during this voyage on the M/V *Bulolo*.

A beautiful landscape and the area surrounding the Kami mission base.

An orchid in bloom

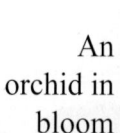

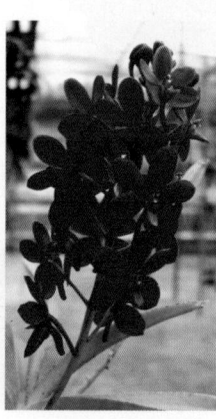

The Early Days ~ At Kami

The Driver and Palmer families, 1955.

Chuck, Jean, Marlene and Kathy with the Palmers.

Orchid flower

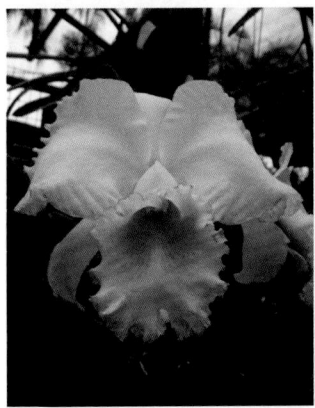

We enjoyed sweet fellowship with the Driver and McCurdy families.

An orchid blossom

Don McCurdy became our supply man, shopping for us at the stores in Goroka.

Don, Gwen, Dale and Mark with the Palmers.

The Early Days ~ At Kami

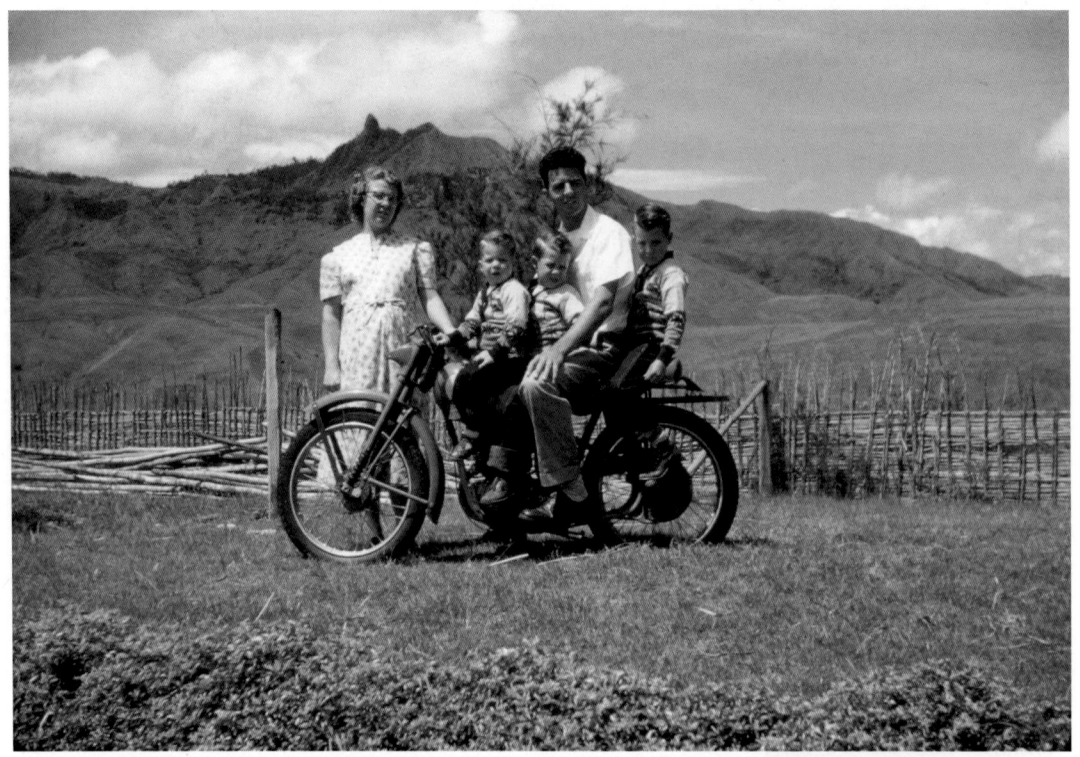

Arvalee, Paul, Peter, Dale and Pat at Kami.

Orchids

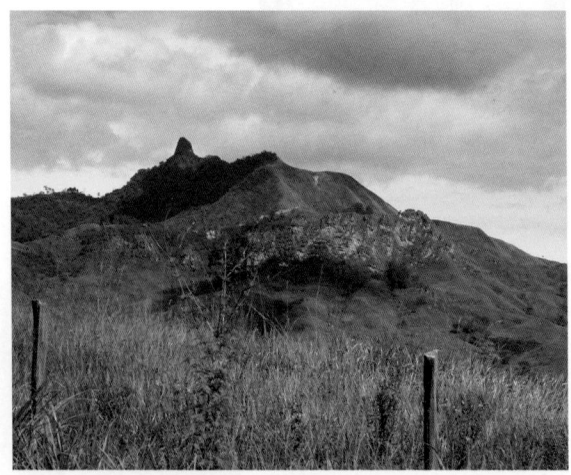

A widely known landmark in this valley,
known as "The Thumb".

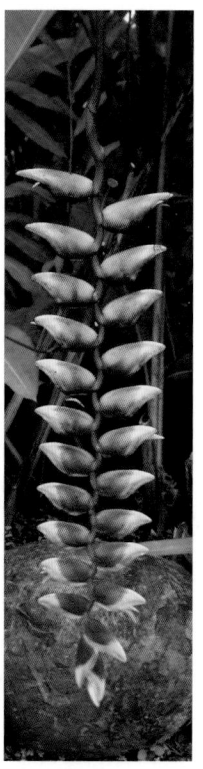

The Palmer and McCurdy kids, 1957. While spending hours together, these kids became more like siblings, playing and sharing their toys.

Ginger flower

A young Bird of Paradise

A Blue Crown Pigeon

Words, Phrases and Meanings

Throughout this book one may find many words or phrases that are unfamiliar or foreign to the reader. Because of the language and cultural differences encountered it is unavoidable and actually adds intrigue to the narrative. To help immerse you into the story, the translations or meanings have been added; a short description within the text and the longer version in the glossary.

Immediate definitions or translations are placed in parentheses following the word or phrase which is italicized. Examples: *a cuppa* (a cup of tea) or *"Yu kam kwiktaim. Hos i gat pikinini!"* (You come quickly. The horse has a baby!) The glossary begins on page 467.

Many words in Gimi use glottal stops; an example is A-o-bana. The hyphen indicates an obstruction of air flow between the spoken letters. Our English exclamation *uh-oh!* is an excellent example, and our words with double 't' like *butter* could be written *bu-ter* because the first 't' is actually not spoken. This does not apply to Pidgin words, none of them have glottals. Pidgin often uses a word repeat like *Laplap* or two words have a singular meaning like *haus sik* which means clinic or hospital.

Gimi is written phonetically, in the case of A-o-bana the 'b' is a 'b fricative' and sounds like a cross between 'v' and 'w' with the upper lip on the lower lip. Refrain from putting your lips tightly together at the 'b' and you are saying it correctly.

Dates throughout are written as MM/DD/YY

~Introduction~
Our Early Lives, (1929-1950)
Dale's Birth and Early Life
By Arvalee

A quote from a birthday greeting card sent by one of Dale's friends states: "GOD MADE YOU SPECIAL…On the day that you were born, no one could have imagined what a blessing you would become to so many! But, I bet God knew all along."

Dale was born in Ft. Worth, Texas on July 1st, 1929. But sadly, before he was two years old, his parents had divorced, leaving much of his care to his maternal grandmother, Rosalie Lynch, who died from pneumonia, when Dale was only five years old.

Shortly afterwards, Dale's mother, Roberta Mildred (Lynch) Palmer, now a single parent, gave him to his paternal grandparents, Wade R. and Virginia J. Palmer, to bring up. They moved to Los Angeles, California when Dale was eight or nine years old. His grandmother was a godly woman and prayed for him faithfully. His dad, Lester J., better known as Bud, was present in the home most of the time during Dale's formative years. All his life Dale was troubled by the fact that his mother didn't want him. In later years when he asked his Aunt Hazel why his mother had given him away, she didn't have an answer. However, his cousin did. Gene said, "Why, we all know that if Dale's godly grandmother hadn't raised him, he wouldn't have become the man he is today." This seemed to settle any question he had about his mother's rejection. Dale grew up calling his grandmother Mom, as that is what his dad called her. She was the only mother he ever really knew.

Dale's grandparents, Wade R. and Virginia J. Palmer.

After Dale went to live with his paternal grandparents, his grandmother would read Bible stories to him before he took an afternoon nap on the screened-in porch where they lived in a house located on Lake Worth. He remembered when his Aunt Hazel cleaned his finger-nails, because it hurt! Another memory was

17

playing with small china figurines of dogs and cats belonging to his grandmother Palmer. He had many good memories of his childhood.

His Vision

From the time Dale was saved at seventeen years old, he had a passion to serve the Lord. Gradually, the Lord changed his desire, not to just serve Him, but to serve Him as a missionary in the land of New Guinea.

I'll admit that Dale's desire and vision to follow the Lord was stronger than mine, but to me the world revolved around this guy. I was head over heels in love with him. His desire to follow the Lord to the ends of the earth became my desire too.

Many folks, including our beloved pastor, thought we would never succeed as missionaries. But somehow, God had given us both the faith to believe the words we read in the Bible; that He would supply all our needs as it states in Matthew 6:33, "But seek ye first the kingdom of God, and his righteousness, and all these things shall be added unto you."

Dale read the Word of God and took it literally. It meant exactly what it said. When people asked him how he would provide for his family, it was a simple matter to Dale.

Dale as a teenager.

"Why, God will take care of us," he would answer them. When he read Romans 15:20, it changed his life. "Yea, so have I strived to preach the gospel, not where Christ was named, lest I build upon another man's foundation."

His deepest desire was to serve the Lord, yet at first we both had more than one idea how we would do that. But gradually the Lord showed him, and ultimately me, that He wanted us to serve Him full time as missionaries. With that goal in mind, we took every available opportunity to get involved in our local church. We taught a Sunday school class and also helped with the Vacation Bible School. We took our turn attending the monthly service at the Gospel Rescue Mission, where Dale often preached. He joined the other men who met on a busy street corner to preach the gospel. On several occasions people approached him and hurled insults, and one lady even cursed him. He also went door-to-door witnessing with other men from church. Some of the other young men at the church met for prayer as early as 4:30 in the morning. Dale worked until 3:00 a.m. and would often fall asleep on the carpeted floor. Fearful that he would fall back asleep and miss his turn, he always asked to pray first. Along with all these activities, we held a little Bible Class in our home for the neighborhood children.

As involved as we were on the home front, Dale's interest in missions was always apparent. When missionaries were visiting, Kermit Byrd, our pastor, would often invite them to speak in the church services. After the service, Dale would go talk to them, asking them how we could join them in their work. Little did he know that someday others would be approaching him asking that very same question.

His Heart

Dale often quoted one of his favorite verses: "But God hath chosen the foolish things of the world to confound the wise; and God hath chosen the weak things of the world to confound the things which are mighty," (1 Corinthians 1:27).

I believe this verse meant a lot to Dale, because he didn't hold himself in high regard. This was partly because of his struggle in school, and with reading in particular. He loved to quote this verse to an audience when he was giving a missionary challenge to let people know that if God could use him, then He would use anyone who would give his life in service.

Because he had a lifelong struggle with his reading, his confidence was not in himself, however, but in the great God he served. Therefore, God gave him the courage to pursue his goal of reaching the tribal people with the gospel, people who had never heard of God.

Once, when he was speaking with his grandmother about his desire to serve the Lord, he asked her "How can I serve the Lord, when I can't read very well?" She answered by telling him a story. She had an uncle who faced a similar dilemma. He was a farmer and when he was plowing his field with his mule one day, God spoke to him that He wanted him to be a preacher. He said, "How can I preach when I can't read?" But he obeyed God and God gave him the ability to read, but the only book he could read was the Bible. Dale's grandmother then gave him the verse in James 1:5, "If any of you lack wisdom, let him ask of God, that giveth to all men liberally, and upbraideth not…." Then she said, "Those words 'upbraideth not' mean God will not embarrass you."

During our time of missionary training in Fouts Springs, California, from mid-1950 through 1952, Paul Fleming, the founder and Chairman of New Tribes Mission, often told the students, "Remember, if you become a missionary, it is **God Plus Nothing**. In God's eyes, you can do nothing in your own power; it will all be the work of God if you serve Him successfully on the foreign field."

His Faithfulness

Over the years, the zeal and heart Dale had for serving the Lord and the people of New Guinea never diminished. He longed for these tribal people to come to know his Lord and Savior. Many times I heard him tell an audience, "I have a disease and it's contagious. Be careful, you might catch it." Of course, he was referring to the fact that his burden for reaching lost men with the gospel was like an infectious disease, and if they were not willing to obey God's leading and follow Him, they should beware of listening to his message.

In another respect, Dale did suffer through many days of physical illness throughout his entire life. On the field he had repeated attacks of malaria, as well as pneumonia and hepatitis and other less severe ailments. Many missionaries would have given up and returned to their homelands, but Dale was committed to prove that 'God plus nothing' would be enough to reach tribes for Christ.

Arvalee's Birth and Early Life
By Arvalee

I was born in the panhandle town of Lamesa, Texas on February 22nd, 1930. My dad, John Paul Price, worked on a water drilling rig and my mother, Zelda Opal (Wilkinson) Price cooked for the crew of men who worked with Dad. They lived in rough quarters in the work field. These were the Great Depression years and times were hard. Because work was scarce, the crew and our family moved from place to place in order to survive.

My earliest memory is of a long, screened-in porch the length of the house and of calling to my mother to come push me as I was swinging. She was usually nearby at her treadle sewing machine. She would stop sewing and come to give my swing a shove, and I would be content for a few more minutes until the swing eventually became still once again. Many years later she told me that I was about two years old when we lived at the house in Tularosa, New Mexico.

When I was five years old, we moved to Normandy, Texas, southeast of Del Rio, to virgin farmland in the Rio Grande Valley. This farm was shared with my dad's parents, James Marion and Mary Leanna (Huddleston) Price, and two of my dad's brothers.

About a year after we moved to Normandy, we had a flood that destroyed all we owned. The wonderful people of this farming community took up a collection and built a small, one-room frame house for us, with a corrugated metal roof. Our new house was built on the high side of the creek, not too far from my grandparents' home. The neighbors were so kind and generous; besides building us a house, they also gave us a shower of food, clothing and many other basic necessities.

When I was about eleven years old I went to San Antonio with a group of 4-H Club girls, accompanied by one of our school teachers. A river ran through the city and this was used for swimming. The teacher told us to be careful because a short ways out there was a drop off, and the water would be very deep. My friend and I were having so much fun, laughing and cutting up that we forgot about the drop off. Before we knew it, we were in water over our heads. My friend didn't know how to swim at all, and in her fear, she constantly clung to me, pushing me under. I thought I could swim, but this experience showed me that I really could only dog paddle. It was a very frightening time for me, but we were saved from drowning when an older girl noticed us and pulled us out, me by the hair on my head! This near drowning caused me to have a lifelong fear of water.

I was twelve years old when we moved to Los Angeles, California in 1942 because my father was in pursuit of work. Living on a farm was a hard existence. So when World War II started, my dad left for California and got a job in a defense plant. After saving enough money, he found a furnished house to rent. He then sent for my mom and me, my sister and three-month-old brother, and we joined him in June 1942. In the summer of 1944 we moved once again, but this time my folks had found a small house to purchase in Bell Gardens, where we settled and I enrolled in school. Dale and I met there in 9th grade. We both graduated from Junior High School in 1945. He was so shy he would hardly speak to me, but I had a crush on this tall, gangly guy with black curly hair. I believed he liked me, too.

Arvalee as a teenager.

That summer following the ninth grade we began dating and each Sunday he would go to church with my mother and me. One Sunday the Pastor gave an invitation, and Dale went forward to be saved. I had been saved when I was eight or nine years old, but I followed him down the aisle anyway. That night we were baptized together. It was on June 23rd, 1946. I have many happy memories of those early years of my life.

It was my privilege to serve the Lord alongside this humble man of God. What an exciting life we had as we learned to trust God through many times of crisis. We raised five children on the mission field and never regretted our decision to give our lives in service to the God we loved.

It was Dale's fondest wish to write about his life in New Guinea and have the stories published. My final task to accomplish on Dale's behalf in our lifelong service for the Lord is to compile our stories and have them published. I have combined our writings, told chronologically, and I trust you will enjoy reading about our lives. With the exception of a few brief words or sentences to clarify meaning, Dale's stories are told in his own words, in his unique style.

Now, I present the true stories of Dale and Arvalee Palmer, pioneer missionaries to Papua New Guinea (*PNG*) 1953-1993. They are lovingly compiled by D. Arvalee Palmer, wife and devoted companion.

~PART ONE~

Our Vision

Chapter 1

How I First Heard of New Guinea, 1942
By Dale

The year was 1942, about a year after World War II had started. We were living in San Diego, California where my dad and grandpa had secured work in the defense plants.

The phone rang and Dad was saying, "Sure, you can come out here. Yes, I'll come to get you. I'll be out as soon as I can."

Dad looked over at me and asked, "You want to go for a ride Dale?"

"You bet. Who was that on the phone, Dad?"

"That was an old buddy of mine, who has been out in the South Pacific, fighting the Japanese. He's a Marine. He's in the Camp Pendleton Hospital with a broken ankle and asked if he could come out and visit with us for a few weeks."

As Dad was going out the back door I was following close behind. I told Mom I was going with Dad to get his friend.

Dad had *Huli* running when I jumped in. *Huli* was the name Dad called his 1929 De Soto. I loved that car, and Dad gave it to me when I got my driver's license at fourteen-and-a-half years of age. We were off and soon going downhill into Mission Valley, one of the suburbs of San Diego. *Huli* always ran better downhill. Dad said that I could turn the kerosene on now. I liked doing that, so I reached down and felt the handles just near my left foot. I looked at Dad and asked, "Are you ready now?"

Dale as a young teen with Hudi.

"Yep," he answered. I turned the kerosene on first and then turned off the gas quickly. Once the engine was hot, *Huli* could run just as well on kerosene as it did on gas. Gas was hard to get in the war days and my grandpa was real smart with things like that.

25

Grandpa and Dad had put a fuel tank in the floor of the back seat for kerosene. Grandpa always called it coal oil but I called it kerosene like Dad and everyone else. But when I was working with Grandpa, I called it coal oil. *My grandpa, whom I idolized, was a great guy and I learned so much from him. He could tell some wild stories, too.*

Before I knew it, we were turning into the gate of the camp hospital. There Dad's friend was, standing on the sidewalk with his crutches, waiting for us. He got in the front seat with Dad, and I sat in the back seat with the crutches and put my feet on the kerosene fuel tank.

When we arrived home, Dad's friend, Luther Briggs, sat on our living room couch with his leg resting on the coffee table. Mom gave him a little pillow to keep the cast from rubbing the table. I was thirteen years old when Luther Briggs came to our home. While he was with us, he talked about this place where he had been fighting the Japanese. He called it "New Guinea". The stories he told about the people of New Guinea were so fascinating to me.

When Luther was talking about the New Guinea people, his voice would soften and he would get a faraway look in his eyes. "I tell you the truth. These national men could walk in the jungles like ghosts. You think you are all alone out there in the jungles then one of these men suddenly steps out from behind a bush. All the service men fighting in New Guinea called them the '*Fuzzy Wuzzy Angels*' (see glossary). You see, their hair is fuzzy, kind of like sheep's wool. When these New Guinea men walk in the jungles they are as quiet as a ghost and when you're wounded or need someone to help you, they are as welcome as an angel."

The Army medics were doing all they could to get the wounded out of the jungles, but they could not always find their men. One outstanding ability of the New Guinea nationals was that they not only knew where the wounded were, but they were also aware of where the Japanese were located most of the time and could avoid them.

Luther Briggs and Bud, Dale's dad.

Luther explained that when the medics carried a wounded man on a stretcher they used two men to carry it with the wounded man's

26

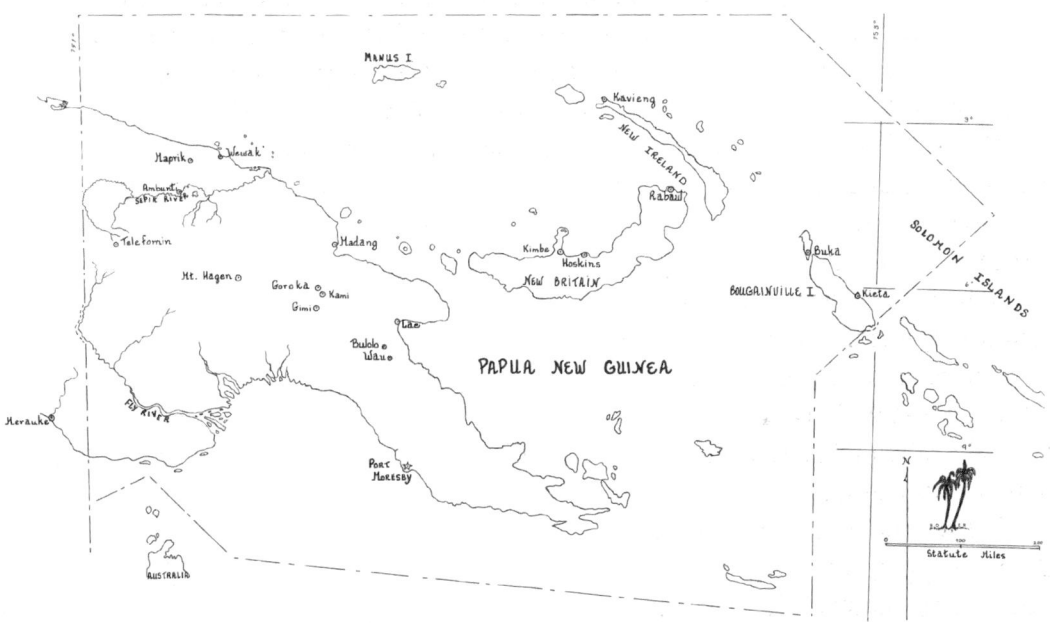

Dale's map of New Guinea © R. Dale Palmer.

arms hanging down and the stretcher low to the ground, in case they dumped their *cargo* (load). In contrast, the *Fuzzy Wuzzy Angels* used four men and carried the stretcher on their shoulders, providing a more secure base.

Luther said, "Many American and Australian soldiers would have died out in the jungles if there had only been the military medics to rescue them. Many soldiers would have perished, if it had not been for the *Fuzzy Wuzzy Angels* finding them and carrying them back to where they could get medical help."

When Luther was telling me these things there was a look of tenderness in his face as he talked about these national men. Understand that my Dad and Luther grew up in a culture at the turn of the 20th century when most Texans looked down on black people and had very little respect for them. Now, here is a tough Marine from Texas bragging how these *Fuzzy Wuzzy Angels* were doing a better job of finding the wounded men and bringing them out of the jungles than our own medics.

As I look back on my time with Luther Briggs, I see God at work in my young life. It reminds me of the Bible story about God's plans for Jeremiah before he was in his mother's womb. Before Jeremiah was even born, God had appointed him to be a prophet to the nations, (Jeremiah 1:5).

I thank God for preparing me for New Guinea before I even knew Him.

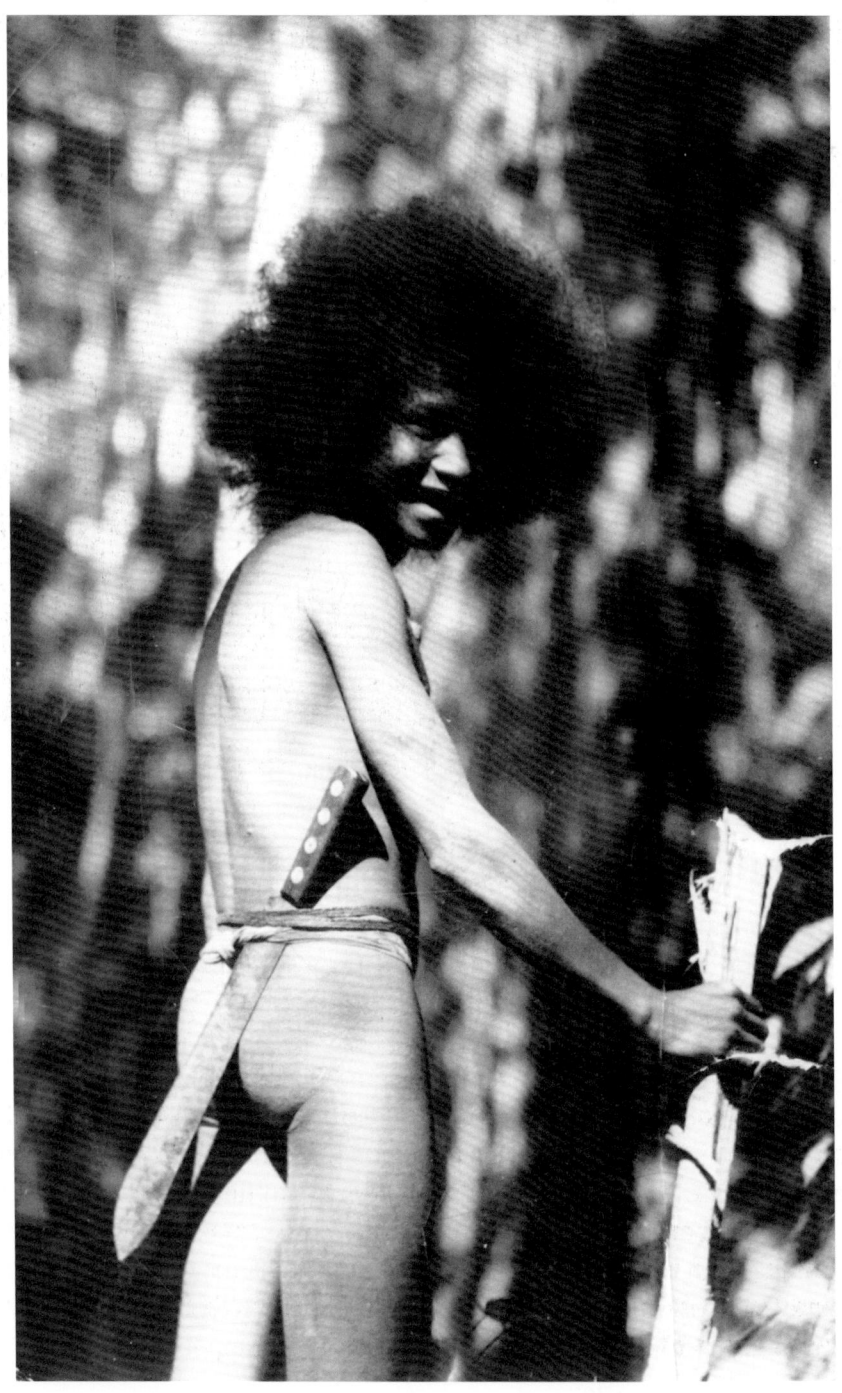

A Fuzzy Wuzzy Angel with machete.

Fuzzy Wuzzy Angels with stretchers.

Our Marriage
By Arvalee

Dale and I first met when we were both teenagers in the ninth grade. Of all the kids in the classroom, he was the most shy. However, a couple of years later when he trusted the Lord as his Savior through the shed blood of Jesus Christ on the cross, his character changed. He told me many years later that when he was saved and turned his life over to God, he finally had something to talk about.

Dale and I were married at Bell Gardens Baptist Church on April 12th, 1948, on a Monday night. That was Dale's day off from work.

Brother Byrd and Bell Gardens Baptist Church.

Times were hard, and my dad didn't even have a job when we got married. He had a friend who owned a bakery, and my folks bought our wedding cake from him. Mamma made my beautiful two piece wedding dress.

Mamma and I were window shopping one day when I saw a dress I liked so much that I told her, "I want my wedding dress to be made like that." Right then and there she took an envelope out of her purse and sketched the pattern on it. Later, she bought white crepe fabric for the dress, and wide, white lace for the sleeves. She drew and cut a pattern from newspaper, then used an old sheet to sew the dress at first, to make sure it fit me perfectly. After making any necessary adjustments and when she was satisfied, Mamma ripped it apart. Only then did she cut the white crepe material.

The fitted bodice closed with tiny, fabric-covered buttons and there were inserts of wide lace in the bell shaped sleeves. The wide French cuffs were also fastened with tiny fabric-covered buttons. Each button closed with a loop. She lovingly made all those loops and covered buttons by hand.

When we went to get the marriage license, we discovered that Dale was too young! He had to have his father's permission and signature

Our wedding, April 12th, 1948.

before we would be granted the license. Dale phoned his dad, Bud, and he came down from Bakersfield, where he worked, to sign the papers for our license!

Dale's Uncle George and Aunt Margaret gathered red roses from the neighbors' gardens on Fry Street and decorated the church. Uncle George made a heart-shaped arch from wire and built and painted a small white picket fence. The arch and picket fence were intertwined with the roses and green leaves. These were placed on the platform at the front of the church. Dale and I stood underneath the arch and the pastor stood just behind it. There were white Calla Lilies in tall vases on either side of the arch. It was very much a family affair and a beautiful wedding.

Dale and I each had one attendant. Dale asked Bill Holeman to be best man. Bill made sure no one got to our car to decorate it with *Just Married* signs or tin cans. He kept it locked in the garage until it was time for us to leave after the reception. Then he simply drove down and exchanged his car for ours and actually chauffeured us from the church.

My maid of honor was Nancy Capehart, who was my best friend all through high school. She wore a short pink dress for the wedding ceremony. Later that year in June, she wed Forest Stine, and I was her matron of honor. They had met at the church youth group activities before he went in the Navy, where he served for several years.

Dale wanted to go to San Diego for our honeymoon, so that is where we went. On the way, we stopped and got a motel in Corona del Mar for our first night together. We were blissfully happy, just two kids who knew they belonged together. The next morning, at a small café, we both ordered ham and eggs for breakfast.

We had gone together for over three years, and would have married sooner, but we were too young! I remember telling Dale I felt like a bird let out of a cage. My mother had wisely kept a strict vigil over me, lest we should do something foolish! Now, our marriage gave us the freedom we desired.

After arriving in San Diego, we checked into a motel. Then we went to see Dale's friend, Ted Pendleton, and his family. We were glad we had booked a room at the motel, because Mrs. Pendleton wanted us to stay with them. We had anticipated this and that was the reason we had found our room before we visited them. We didn't want to spend our honeymoon visiting with friends; we wanted to be alone.

The next morning, before we got up, there was a knock on our door. When Dale opened it, there was his friend, Ted. We never did figure out how he knew where we were staying! But it turned out just fine, because Ted acted as our guide and showed us around town to visit several tourist attractions. The town had changed considerably since Dale had grown up there during the war.

We had three wonderful days together, before Dale had to be back to work on Friday. We discovered we had left our marriage license in one of the motels; hence we only have a copy of it, and not the original document!

I went back to school on Monday to finish twelfth grade. I had promised my mother that I would finish school if we got married in April instead of waiting until June, as we had originally planned. We had decided to get married in April because several couples from church had set their wedding dates for June. We thought there weren't enough weekends for everyone to get married in the month of June. Besides, we had been engaged longer than most of them, so we changed our wedding date to April.

In June I graduated from twelfth grade. Our attire was a black cap and gown. Dale would have graduated too, but he had quit school in November when his boss offered him a full-time time job as the night cook at Don's Barbecue. This was a considerable promotion and at the time, this seemed the right thing to do. Though he never did finish high school, accepting this position made it possible for us to get married sooner.

Our first home was a small house trailer which Dale had bought from Gene Scott, a cook with whom he worked. It was parked on the lot where Dale's grandparents had a homemade trailer and a double garage. At the back of the garage there was a cement slab where we kept the washing machine.

Dale's grandparents lived and worked at the Naval Base in Ridgecrest, California, in the Mojave Desert east of Bakersfield. When they came down to visit in Bell Gardens, they stayed in their homemade trailer.

We continued to attend Bell Gardens Baptist Church, singing in the choir and teaching classes in the Sunday school where we had several teachers working with us. We were also involved in street preaching and witnessing. A group of us from the church went to the Union Rescue Mission each month to share our testimonies. We usually taught in the Daily Vacation Bible School (DVBS) each summer as well. Since these classes were held in the morning and Dale worked the night shift, he was free to help.

A few months after Dale and I were married, my folks moved to the desert too. Daddy opened a restaurant there in the small town of Inyokern, located near Ridgecrest. After my graduation, and our wedding, I felt lost without my folks and my siblings around. I especially missed my baby sister, Glenda Sue, who was just a year old. I called her *Susie*. So Dale and I decided I should go visit them for a few days and he put me on a Greyhound bus.

After several days with them I was ready to go home again, however, I persuaded Mamma to let me take Susie home with me. To my annoyance, when I arrived in Los Angeles the small suitcase with her clothes had been lost and she had nothing to wear. It was found after a few days, but in the meantime, my good neighbor and friend, Lorene Speers, bought some clothing at yard sales to tide her over.

A frightening thing happened the first night Susie was with us. I woke up to check on her and discovered that she was uncovered. She felt so cold that I was really scared she would get sick, so I brought her to bed with us, until she warmed up. Following that fright, I used safety pins to secure her blankets!

After a week or so with us, Susie wanted to go home. She missed her mamma, and Mamma was more than glad to have her back home again.

Just as Dale and I settled down together, we soon discovered that we were going to have an addition to our own family! Typical of first time parents, we began talking about names for the new baby. Of course, those were the days before ultrasound, so we had no idea if the baby would be a girl or a boy. Dale liked the name Patrick, if we had a boy; and we both liked the idea of Lee, for the second name, after Arvalee. We both agreed if we had a girl, she would be called Julie Dale, with the second name after her daddy.

Our Lives Continue

Even before we were married, Dale and I had talked about serving the Lord. At one time we thought it would be great to run a Christian old folk's home. I even took some bookkeeping in my senior year of high school thinking that would be profitable in the operation of this type of home. We thought that I would keep the books and Dale would do the cooking. He was already working at Don's Barbecue, so he had plenty of experience. I'm sure this line of thinking was inspired by the fact that Dale's grandparents were getting up in years, and Dale had a desire to look after them.

Gradually, the Lord laid foreign missions on our hearts and thoughts of the old folk's home diminished. Our pastor, Kermit Byrd, used to invite missionaries to speak and would give up his pulpit whenever they were available. Dale would often go up and ask them how he could join them in their work, and they usually told him that he should start by going to Bible school. Since Dale had found school quite difficult and had not finished high school, the thought of attending Bible school seemed beyond us. We were expecting our first baby and knew we would need an income, which would probably require me to work and Dale was very much against this. So, Bible school didn't seem a possibility.

God blessed us with the first addition to our family when Patrick Lee was born on March 28th, 1949. Dale was twenty and I was only nineteen years old. By this time my folks had moved back to Bell Gardens. Their move was timely for us, as Dale and I had learned that we would require an adult to accompany us to the hospital when the time came for the baby to be born. So, there we were, about midnight, calling for my mother to go to the hospital with us!

A baby didn't stop us from attending the meetings at the Union Rescue Mission, or any church services for that matter. We just took Patrick along with us! When people heard of our desire to be missionaries, many questioned us about going to the mission field with a baby, but we believed God would take care of him as well as the two of us.

Shortly after Pat was born, my folks moved back to Inyokern and opened the family-style restaurant there again. Dale and Forest Stine had looked into opening this restaurant, but God had closed the doors. Soon we would know why this new business venture was not to be.

Some time previously, Dale had met a man named Oscar Torneby at the Youth for Christ meetings and had told him that we wanted to be missionaries. One day Oscar brought us a small book called, *Adventures with God in New Guinea* by Paul Buckman. Reading this book about New Guinea was very timely for Dale. It brought back memories of the visit from his dad's friend, Luther Briggs, when he was just thirteen years old. His heart was gripped by the needs of these heathen people. He firmly believed New Guinea was where we should set our sites in looking forward to the mission field. He stated, "This is where we need to go."

After reading the book, Dale passed it on to me. It was during World War II that I actually heard of New Guinea for the first time. I was about fifteen years old when I read a story in the daily newspaper called the *Shangri-La Diary*, by Corporal Margaret Hastings. I was enthralled with the story of a United States Army plane crash in New Guinea in which twenty-one passengers were killed. Only three survived. Corporal Margaret Hastings told how she and two others, Sgt. Kenneth Decker and Lt. John McCollom, though horribly wounded and burned from the plane crash, survived forty-seven days until the Army rescued them. Medicine and food supplies were dropped by air, until finally the rescue team arrived by parachute. The eventual rescue of the three survivors was accomplished with a glider plane, which was quite a feat.

While reading *Adventures with God in New Guinea*, I too, was impressed that New Guinea was where we should go. Indeed, most of the United States had never heard of this place, a place inhabited by *Stone Age* (see glossary) people who had never seen white men before.

A few weeks later, Oscar brought over two *Brown Gold* magazines, the New Tribes Mission publication, for us to read. We had never heard of this organization, but we were very impressed by what we read. One article specifically mentioned the fact that New Tribes Mission (NTM) trained both a husband and wife for ministry.

Dale was particularly interested in this, because he felt strongly that we both needed training to become missionaries. That, however, was not the philosophy of the organizations in which some of our friends were involved. There, the husbands were being trained for the ministry while the wives worked to support them.

Not long after reading these magazines, we wrote for application forms to enter missionary training, which NTM called *boot camp*.

The following spring, Pastor Kermit Byrd asked Dale, "You and Arvalee will be able to help us again in DVBS, won't you?"

Even though we were still waiting for a reply from NTM, Dale answered by faith, "Why no, we'll be in *boot camp* by then."

Pastor Byrd said, "Oh, have you heard from them then?"

Dale replied, "No, but we will."

We believed with our whole hearts that God was leading us and we would begin training that summer. We absolutely believed this was what God wanted us to do. Shortly after Dale's conversation with our pastor, a letter came from New Tribes Mission. Dale was practically walking on air as he brought the envelope from the mail box. The letter informed us that we had been accepted as missionary candidates. This was very exciting news to us!

As we read the letter we learned that Johnny Greiner, the man who processed the applications, had been killed along with fifteen others on the DC-3 mission airplane that had crashed in Venezuela on a trip in June 1949. Our applications had been placed on his desk, awaiting his attention.

The letter also informed us that the next class for missionary training was to start on July 1st, 1950, so our preparation accelerated as we now had a date set for our departure.

Using the front axle and wheels of a Model T Ford, Dale's granddad built a small two-wheeled trailer, to assist in moving our household goods to Fouts Springs, the location of the training camp, in north central California. The trailer was painted silver and Dale painted a sign on it in red letters that read, Jesus Is the One. Meanwhile, we were busy packing all our earthly belongings, getting ready to leave for missionary training. What an exciting time it was in our lives!

When we told all our friends and our folks that we wanted to be missionaries, and that we were planning to go into missionary training, we got various reactions from them. Dale's dad, Bud, came to visit us, and although he was not a believer at that time, he encouraged us in our plans. The day we told him of our acceptance by the mission and of the date of departure, he told us he had an errand and would be back shortly.

When he returned, he put a small square box about 15 inches high, on the table saying, "I thought if you're going to be missionaries, you'll need one of these." We opened it to find a Coleman pressure lamp. Giving us this lamp seemed to express his approval of our desire to serve the Lord.

That night, like an excited kid, Dale lit the lamp, and hung it from the ceiling. It was certainly not as bright as an electric bulb, but it both fueled the fires of our dreams of the mission field and gave us a glimpse into the future. We were encouraged to press on.

Regretfully, the time came to turn off the lamp and get to bed. As the mantle slowly cooled and the light faded, we drifted off to sleep wondering about the future and all that might lie ahead of us.

The church gave us a farewell service on the last Sunday before we left for Fouts Springs. Dale and I were asked to give our testimonies, so we both went up to the platform. Dale wanted me to go first, so with trembling knees, I shared verses from Matthew chapter 6, and verse 33 in particular.

> all these things.
> 33 But *seek ye first the kingdom of God, and his righteousness; and all these things shall be added unto you.
> 34 Take therefore no ⁵thought for

God had laid these verses on my heart as different people would ask us, "How will you live and provide for your son? How will you buy food and clothing, since Dale won't be working?" I shared in my testimony that I believed God's Word and His promises that He would provide all our needs if we put Him first in our lives and served Him. I tried to communicate to the audience that we were really just trusting God to keep His Word.

It was now Dale's turn to speak. He just about brought the house down when he said, "I don't know what to say. My wife used the verse I had planned to share!" I'm still not sure what else he did say. We had not discussed with each other what we planned to communicate. We just knew that God would take care of us, and He had given us both the same verse and had individually impressed on our hearts that there was nothing to fear if we put our lives in His hands.

After the service, the church family gave us a shower of clothing, food, and quilts, as well as gifts of money. One lady, DeEsta West, had made a sheet cake and decorated it using pipe cleaners and food color. There was a round, thatched-roof hut that represented a national house. Under a pipe-stem palm tree, was a figure with a cut out photo of Dale's face on it! It was complete with green coconut icing for the grass.

When we arrived at Bakersfield to say goodbye to Dale's dad, he gave us two large, burlap bags full of potatoes and onions that he had gleaned from the surrounding fields. Little did we know how much we would appreciate this gift of food; during our first weeks at *boot camp* it met a real need.

Family before leaving for Boot Camp.

Chapter 2

Entering Missionary Training, 1950
By Arvalee

We drove into Fouts Springs over a steep, winding, mountain road. It was July 1st, 1950, Dale's twenty-first birthday. Pat was 15 months old at the time. The weather was miserably hot, 115 degrees, and the radiator was boiling on our black 1937 Packard. When we came to a spring, Dale stopped the car. We learned later that this place of respite was called *Candy Bucket*, and over time we stopped there many times for the refreshing water it provided.

As Dale took the cap off the over-heated radiator, rusty hot water sprayed into the air, and then came to settle on his starched shirt. Alas, his shirt was no longer crisp and white, but was spattered with spots from the brown water. He looked like an old, speckled bird! I was embarrassed knowing that we would arrive at camp hot and dirty. I had wanted to make a good impression! What a blow to my pride! We certainly weren't looking our best on that day.

We drove on into camp and Dale stopped the car in front of a building that said Office over the door. A man with a bald head and a full black beard came out to meet us.

When Dale introduced us, the man said, "Hi, my name is Harold Jackson. We'll drive through camp and find you an empty cabin."

This was our introduction to Harold Jackson, who was the leader of the boot camp. We had never met anyone from New Tribes Mission, so when this bearded, balding man appeared we were a bit taken aback. He told us that he had just returned from jungle camp, where the missionary trainees built and lived in temporary houses, learning how to rough it, before actually going to a foreign field. That explained the beard, because we knew beards were not allowed by New Tribes Mission!

A few days later, although Harold had shaved off the beard, Dale told me that he was thinking *what have we gotten into? He looked like what I imagined a prophet might look like.*

As Harold stepped onto the running board he put his arm through the open window around the door post and Dale drove through camp so Harold could select a cabin for us. We passed a number of small one-roomed cabins, all painted brown, the Forest Service color, because the camp was situated in the Mendocino National Forest. Remember, it

37

was very hot and dusty.

"Let's look at this cabin and see if it's ready," Harold said, as he jumped off the running board to go have a look.

Meanwhile, I was looking at the next cabin just down the way with big cracks in the walls and paint peeling off its wide wall boards. I was thinking to myself, *I hope we don't get that one.*

Then Harold was back. "Nope, that one has not been cleaned yet. Let's look at the next one." Sure enough, we got the cabin with the paint peeling and the cracks in the walls. That was another blow to my pride.

Harold talked to us for a while as we were unloading our things and moving into our new home, and then he went back to the office. He and his family were to become dear friends to us in the days ahead.

We unloaded the rest of our belongings and began the task of settling in. The wide cracks between the broad, wooden, floor boards were filled with dirt. I found a table knife and began digging the dirt out. Because of my up-bringing, it was important to me to have a really clean floor. I could remember my mother scrubbing a floor similar to this on the farm in Texas. She used wood ashes to bleach the boards. She took pride in having a spotless floor, and I was determined to follow her example.

Family at Boot Camp.

Before long, folks were coming around to greet us and make us welcome. Someone said to me, "Come winter time you'll wish those cracks were filled with dirt so the cold air won't blow in." So I decided it was best to leave the cracks filled, even if it was with dirt.

Clayton and Nina Templeton invited us over for supper that night. They had three young sons. The only seating they had was long wooden benches or simple wooden boxes. Yet we were grateful for their hospitality and friendliness.

We got settled and classes soon started. I was bewildered by it all. One teacher, Miss Ethel Coy, taught us skills in how to learn a foreign, unwritten language. It didn't make much sense to me. There was no course for Pidgin English, which was the trade language of New Guinea, so Cheryl Fleming taught us some Malaysian… another south Pacific language.

We had Bible classes also. One of these was taught by Mr. McNaughton, who served occasionally as a guest speaker. He was an excellent teacher. All guests were listed on the bulletin board along with a meal schedule and the students were encouraged to sign up to invite them in for a meal. During our time of training we invited Mr. McNaughton into our home many times for meals.

Another Bible teacher, Lance Latham, one of the founders of the AWANA clubs, came from Chicago once a year to teach Romans and Ephesians. His main focus was the grace of God. He was an excellent pianist as well, and loved to entertain the students and younger children on the keyboard.

On special occasions Paul Fleming, the founder and Chairman of New Tribes Mission, would fly in from Chico, California, in his Stinson airplane, to challenge and encourage us. His classes usually ran on for about three hours. I found these hard to sit through, for I was expecting our second baby by then.

Classes were held in the mornings, with afternoons taken up by work detail for all the men and single women, or married women without children. Sometimes, Dale would lie down on the floor after lunch and go to sleep. He was tired; we were not used to the long hours of study each night, trying to figure out the difficult, new subjects assigned to us. I thought taking a little time for a nap wouldn't hurt. Inevitably, the work detail leader, Wes Brazil, would come around looking for Dale. Dale would go off to work until 5:00 p.m. The men worked at many tasks to keep up the grounds around the camp. They also went into the surrounding mountains to cut wood for heating the cabins during the winter.

Throughout the long, hot summer, some of the folks would take time out to go to the creek for a late afternoon swim. Dale would often go down with Bud, the teenaged son of Homer and LaVera Hancock, the couple who operated the little store in camp.

Bud would come by on his bicycle and Dale would ride double with him down to the swimming hole. I went there with Pat so he could paddle in the water and cool off, but pregnant women didn't go swimming in those days. It just wasn't the proper thing to do.

Once while swimming, Dale had a terrifying experience. There was a diving board, but unknown to Dale someone had cracked the board. Dale went out for a dive, and just as he sprung to make the dive, he heard the board break; but it was too late to stop! It thrust him into the depths and he didn't know which way was up! He was almost out of breath and he suffered several seconds of terror as he struggled to make it to the surface.

Although we went into missionary training as planned, we went without any promised support. Yet God kept His promises and our needs were always met. We never missed a meal, and we learned how to wisely manage the money we had to work with. Dale and I carefully counted our pennies and managed to buy what we needed for the next meal. I remember going to the store and dividing a box of crackers with Rosemary Etherton because neither of us had enough cash to buy a full box. If we didn't buy very much, Homer took notice, and in a day or so would drop off a box of groceries on our doorstep as he drove his truck down through camp. I wonder how many folk Homer looked after in his generous, quiet way.

At another time, our cupboards were almost empty and other supplies were low. I was beginning to wonder what to prepare for supper. At his work detail that afternoon, Dale had been assigned the task of cleaning out a small house trailer of some missionaries who departed with short notice. They ran out of time, because they got word to leave suddenly for the field. Karl Getteman, the work detail leader, told Dale to use or dispose of anything he found. That evening Dale brought a box home and it seemed there was everything we needed in that box. It contained a box of rolled oats, sugar, even some laundry soap and much more food. Why was Dale chosen to clean out the house trailer? We believed it was of the Lord and that He used it to meet our needs.

Although we frequently didn't have an abundance of food, there were many times we invited folks to come share a meal with us. Dale had become acquainted with a Forest Ranger; a single man who seemed lonely, so naturally Dale wanted to invite him for a meal. I will always remember what a wonderful surprise it was when he brought us a whole canned chicken as a gift. It seemed to me this was God's blessing for sharing our meager fare with a friend.

Dale's grandparents with Pat and Peter.

It was shortly after this that Dale's dad and grandparents came to visit us in Fouts Springs. They wanted to check out the organization we had joined. Many years later, Grandma Palmer told Dale she wished they had joined the mission themselves at that time.

Dale was sick so often during our training days that he was nicknamed Job by some of the men in camp. We already knew that he was allergic to penicillin and sulfa drugs and as time went by, he developed allergies to several other medicines.

Once, when he had flu-like symptoms, Rosemary Etherton, the camp nurse, gave him some medicine but he was allergic to it and had a bad reaction, resulting in huge welts or hives all over his body. The hives were so bad that he couldn't sleep and he walked the floor for three nights. He was miserable. Even after he stopped taking the medicine, he was still dangerously sick. Fortunately, we were able to go to Chico to see the doctor. Rosemary and her husband Ken were making a trip and invited us to ride with them.

In Chico, we stayed in a small room at the mission headquarters and planned to see the doctor the next day. Dale still had hives all over his body and his face was swollen as well. As if these were not problems enough, he also needed a laxative. Leaving him in the room, I went to the other apartments in the building to see if I could borrow some. I knocked on several doors, but no one was home.

Finally, at the next try, a man answered the door and went to look in his bathroom cabinet for a laxative. While I waited anxiously, I noticed several men sprawled on the floor, looking at a map of South America. One man seemed to be staring at me. I felt very embarrassed because it was only a month before the baby was due. As I walked back down the hall, laxative in hand, I heard footsteps following me. Glancing back, I spotted the man who had been staring at me. By then I realized that he was Ken Finney, one of the leaders of the mission.

He caught up to me and said, "You're frightened. What is the matter?"

I told him all about Dale's sickness, and that we had a little boy, with another baby due any day, and that I felt I would be left alone to care for them because Dale was going to die. His words were such a comfort to me. He said, "This is of Satan. If Dale were going to die, God would prepare your heart." Then he went to our room, and prayed for Dale and me. What a tremendous encouragement that was to me in this time of trial.

The next day we saw the doctor, who gave Dale some medicine to relieve the hives. In a day or so, he was well enough for us to return to camp.

Because of the Korean War, men Dale's age and older were required to register with the draft board and Dale's classification was 1A. I cannot remember how much of a concern this was to us at the time, but I'm sure we felt we should continue with our plans to follow the Lord. Soon after we entered training, we received news that he had been reclassified as 4F, because he was in training for the ministry of the gospel. This ensured that he would not be drafted to serve in the United States Army, but he was in God's Army.

A New Baby and Tragic News

After Dale recovered, he got permission from Paul Fleming to take Pat and me to the mission's headquarters in Chico, to await the birth of our baby. While we were waiting, Dale kept busy helping to load the mission airplane, scheduled to take a group of missionaries to South America.

Finally the day came for the birth and God blessed us with another son we named Peter. He was born on November 16th, 1950. When the nurse came by with the birth certificate, asking me what name to put on it, I had to think quickly. I had been so positive we were having a girl that Dale and I hadn't decided on a name for a boy. I knew that Dale liked the name Peter and I liked David, so I answered, "Well, I guess we'll call him Peter David."

We were blessed to have Dale's grandmother come to Chico to help me with the new baby and with Pat, who was only twenty months old. There we all stayed in the apartment belonging to one of the single ladies.

On November 21st, 1950, Dale helped load the mission plane headed for South America. He helped Edna Greiner, the widow of Johnny Greiner and her five children board the plane, as well as Donna Wetherald and her baby son, Mark. Her husband Ben was a pilot who was killed on the first plane crash in Venezuela in June 1950. A short while later the plane departed, with plans to stop in Billings, Montana, for a meeting, before continuing on to the field. There were twenty-one passengers on board, including Paul Fleming, the Chairman of New Tribes Mission. This airplane, a DC-3, was named the Tribesman II, because it replaced the first one that had crashed earlier in Venezuela. It was piloted by two former United States Army pilots, Jack Dennis and Sterling Lowrey, who were also in the Missionary Training program. The Tribesman II had been refitted to transport missionaries to the foreign field, because commercial flights in the 1950s were infrequent and very costly. Therefore the mission decided to purchase and operate their own airplanes.

Peter was five days old, and Dale had an opportunity to ride back to camp with some other folks. He left us in Chico, planning to come get us later after I had regained my strength.

The phone, in our building, located in the hall across from our room, rang that night about ten o'clock. Harold and Elsie Wallin's teenage son, Rod, answered it. Soon word spread throughout the building that the mission plane had not arrived at its destination. We learned later that it had crashed because of bad weather, near Jackson Hole, Wyoming, on Mount Moran in the Grand Teton Mountain Range. What a blow that was to all of us. Grandma Palmer never could understand why God allowed a whole planeload of missionaries to die such a tragic death.

The Tribesman II, the plane that crashed.

Meanwhile, as the car carrying Dale and the others pulled into camp at Fouts Springs, folks were standing outside with their lanterns lit, singing, "He giveth more grace, when the burdens grow greater, He giveth more strength as the labors increase…" Only then did Dale and the other travelers hear about the plane crash.

We had already faced the fact that lives might be lost in following and serving the Lord. We fervently believed God was in control, and although we didn't understand why, we trusted God to bring good out of these hard times. John 12:24 dwelt in our minds: "Except a corn of wheat fall into the ground and die, it abideth alone."

Extra Duty

Since the training camp was in the Mendocino National Forest, the male students who were physically fit were often summoned by the forest rangers to join them in fighting forest fires. Everyone knew that when the huge bell in the center of the camp rung, it meant one thing: FIRE! Either there was a forest fire or there was a fire in camp in one of the cabins.

The bell rang one day, and everyone vacated the chapel building to find the reason for the alarm. It soon became apparent that one of the cabins was ablaze. As I passed by the burning cabin, I didn't recognize whose it was, so I asked Velma Kennell, who was standing nearby, "Whose cabin is it?"

Bursting into tears, she answered, "It's mine!" By that time, some of the men, including Dale, were busy extinguishing the flames. Fortunately, there was not too much damage done to their cabin.

Dale on the forest service truck.

During the summer, Dale and most of the other men were called out quite frequently by the forest ranger. Because of his experience, Dale sometimes was appointed fire team cook, which paid quite a bit more than regular firefighting. Because there were no cooking utensils, he told of having to cook steaks on shovels over hot coals. Talk about roughing it! At times, when there was food left over, he was required by the authorities to bury it in the ground. This was one of the more difficult tasks for him, knowing his family and others in camp would have relished that fresh meat or those canned hams.

After one forest fire when Dale came home his clothes and boots were worn out. His shirt was covered with small holes caused by flying sparks. These fires were extremely dangerous and we women often wondered if all the men would come home. Although fire fighting was hazardous work, it helped with our student fees and we managed to stay debt free. We were thankful for this provision, dangerous as it was.

While the men were gone fighting fires, the leaders in camp wanted to keep the women busy, so some ladies were given the assignment of picking up stones with shovels and throwing them into the bed of a big truck. Lucky for one woman, she knew how to drive a truck, so she escaped the hard work. I was delegated to look after the children, since I was expecting our second baby. I reasoned that *picking up stones was a complete waste of time. The camp was situated on a mountain of stones and the women could have picked up stones all day for weeks and there would still be stones.* Of course, I didn't express my sentiments on the subject!

Daily Life

It seemed there was never a dull moment in boot camp. All the students took turns minding the nursery while the rest of us were in classes. We were on a schedule, so no one missed too many classes. Most of the time, the men watched the pre-school children or toddlers, while the women took care of the babies. It was a big responsibility looking after all those active little children.

One morning, Gordon Strongathorm's little boy fell down the steep cliff to the creek. Without giving it a second thought, Genny Hare, the woman looking after the nursery that day, scrambled down the steep slope to rescue him. The boy's head was bruised and cut, and Genny was scratched up pretty badly on her legs and thighs. This created some excitement, but both injured parties recovered nicely.

Hanging the wash.

I was not sick too often, but one time my throat was so sore that I could hardly swallow. We thought it must have been strep throat. After this went on a few days, I asked Dale to call the Elders, to anoint and pray for me. About ten o'clock that night, several men came to our cabin, anointed me with oil, and each one prayed for me. I remember throughout the night, in my restlessness, reminding the Lord that we had obeyed His Word, according to James 5:14 and 15, and asked Him to heal me. The next morning there was absolutely no sign of my sore throat. I knew the Lord had worked a miracle and I gave Him all the praise.

On a lighter note, I must write down one thing that our family has often laughed about, although I was a bit upset at the time. Peter was about a year and a half old and Pat was about three. I had been shopping at the little camp store and only had twenty cents left. Homer had glazed doughnuts for sale and they were just five cents each. I decided to splurge, spend my last twenty cents and buy four of them.

At dinner that night, our two little boys sure were eyeing those doughnuts. We had taught our children to clean up the food on their plates before they had dessert. Just as the treats were put onto each plate, Dale pointed up to the ceiling and exclaimed, "Look!" As was intended, both boys looked up. Meanwhile, Dale reached over and snitched Peter's doughnut. When the boys realized there wasn't anything on the ceiling, they looked back at their plates. Of course, there were tears when Peter found that his doughnut was gone. I also was quite displeased with this incident, but for a different reason. I thought *"Daddy" had carried his practical joke a bit too far!* Our children learned from a very early age that their father delighted in teasing them.

When Peter was about twenty-months old, he woke up in the middle of the night screaming. Dale and I were frantic because we could find no way to comfort him. He was obviously in much pain, but was too young to tell us what was wrong. After we prayed for him, he finally quieted down, and went back to sleep. As he was growing up Peter often had earaches, and we reckon they must have started around this time.

Brothers

Once, while all the men except one were away fighting a forest fire and the women and children were left behind, there was some unusual excitement in camp.

Living next door to our cabin with her two young sons, was Lori Dennis, the widow of one of the two pilots who had been killed in the mission plane crash in Wyoming. Each evening, just before dark, Lori's young sons would take a walk up the hill to the *latrine*. As they left their cabin on this particular evening, Jackie, the older one, rushed ahead of Freddie, his younger brother.

I was washing dishes and could see them through our window. I thought to myself, *You are a little rascal, Jackie, leaving your little brother to walk by himself.* A few minutes later, Jackie ran back to their cabin, yelling, "Mommy! Freddie fell in the *latrine*!"

Families came rushing out of their cabins and headed up the hill to the latrine to see what had happened. Sure enough, Freddie was up to his armpits in muck. He had lifted the lid, and while swinging on the cross bars, had lost his grip and fallen in! No doubt, he had seen the older, stronger boys performing this trick.

There was only one man in camp, and he, too, hurried up the hill to see if he could rescue the boy. It soon became apparent that the only way was to lower a rope, have Freddie put it under his arms, and pull him up.

Mr. Street queried, "Does anyone have a rope?" There was complete silence. It seemed no one had a rope.

Reluctantly, I spoke up, "I have a clothesline rope." *I really didn't want to use it, but I couldn't leave him there, knowing my rope could be used to retrieve him, so I ran after my new clothesline to help rescue Freddie.*

Mr. Street tied a loop in the rope and told Freddie to put it under his arms. Freddie cried, "I can't!"

To which Mr. Street replied, "Just stay down there then." Freddie quickly changed his mind. He decided he could do it after all. What a mess that child was in! The stench was repulsive. His mother was planning to take him down the steep cliff trail to wash him in the creek. I protested and persuaded her that the water would be much too cold. Besides, it was almost dark and the trail down to the river would be difficult to navigate in the near-darkness.

Lori took my advice, ushered him to the washhouse instead and put him in one of the laundry tubs. In the end it would have been much simpler to have cleaned him up in the river! She was very upset with me. I'm sure she could have killed me for my suggestion!

Training Days are Over and…
Our Third Baby

The time came in the spring of 1952 when our training days were over and we returned home to Bell Gardens. We settled down in our house trailer that had doubled in size, because Dale's granddad had built a room onto the back of the garage and moved the trailer alongside. Dale got a job across the street in a small cabinet shop while we were waiting for our visas to be granted to enter the country of New Guinea. We started an afternoon Bible class for the neighborhood children. We enjoyed teaching these little kids the stories of Jesus and the Bible. One weekend we went camping in the mountains with a group from Bell Gardens Baptist Church.

Since our visas had not been granted as quickly as we expected, after Christmas we decided that our time could be better spent if we returned to Fouts Springs for extra training to hear and write a tonal language. Both the mission and Ethel Coy, the linguistics instructor, agreed to this arrangement, so we made the move back to Fouts Springs soon after the new year of 1953. The fact that I was expecting our third child helped us make this decision, as well. Economically, it was to our advantage to have the baby while living at the mission, instead of in a city hospital in the county of Los Angeles. We decided to go to Colusa because it was closer to the training camp than Chico, where Peter had been born. On one of our last trips for a prenatal checkup, our old Packard broke down and Dale knew the motor was ruined. We walked back to a farmhouse to use a telephone to arrange for someone at boot camp to come pick us up.

Those gracious farm folks invited us in, two perfect strangers, let us use their phone and then invited us to join them for dinner. Imagine our surprise when we sat down to a *banquet*! We were served roasted wild duck (an entire duck for each person), artichoke, and a scrumptious, chocolate layer cake. It was a weekday, but this seemed to be their normal dinner. Neither of us had previously eaten artichoke or roasted duck, which was served with individual little scissors that were especially made for serving duck. We simply watched our hosts and did likewise.

Before long, Les Foster came to pick us up. This dear friend and brother also loaned us his car when we went to have the baby. After our car broke down, I went into Colusa for another check up. Because the doctor thought the birth was imminent, he recommended that I stay in town. He knew of a home where I could stay for a week, but Dale went back to camp, since we had left Pat and Peter there with a babysitter. I tried to keep busy during the week, mainly through writing letters. A week later, Dale came back to check on me. When I saw the doctor, he decided to induce me. Then he said, "You can go now, and when the pains become close together, come back to the hospital."

From there, Dale and I went to a large grocery store that had a soda fountain. We ordered milkshakes and whiled away the time. Before long, I told Dale, "I think we'd better go to the hospital now." Our baby was born soon after I was checked in that day. Paul Len was born on February 28th, 1953 in Colusa, California.

When it was time to go back to camp, Dale came to get me, bringing Ethel Coy along. She was eager to hold the baby for the return trip to camp, which we allowed her to do. She delighted in cuddling and watching this marvelous newborn baby.

Our relationship with Ethel had started when we first arrived in Fouts Springs. We were not the brightest students in the linguistics course, but she was always patient with us. She often invited us to her small cabin for a meal. When I was sick with strep throat, she cooked breakfast for us; a pan of hot cream of wheat. As she left, she stated, "I didn't know how much to cook, but if it's too much, it's always good fried."

Our passport photograph, 1953.

Now we had three precious little boys, Pat, Peter, and Paul. When Paul was five weeks old we received our visas and were able to leave for New Guinea, but first we visited our family in Southern California.

Paul's passport photograph, 1953.

Since we no longer had a car, it was Dale's dad, Bud, who came to get us and drove us home to Oxnard. We stayed with Grandma and Grandpa Palmer and Dad Palmer until it was time to leave for New Guinea.

Chapter 3

Sailing for Australia, 1953
By Arvalee

After a short time with family in Oxnard, we began making contacts and inquiries about ships leaving for New Guinea. Ken Johnston, the new Chairman of the mission who had been appointed after Paul Fleming's death, phoned from headquarters in Chico, and told Dale that a freighter was leaving from Los Angeles, bound for Sydney, Australia, the end of June. He told us we had $475 in our account at headquarters. This was money we had saved from Dale's forest fire pay. We needed another $1,025 to purchase the tickets. Dale asked if the $475 was enough for a down payment.

Ken said, "Yes, that will hold a booking for you."

Dale told him, "Go ahead and book the tickets for us." This gave us three months before we had to leave. We trusted the Lord for enough money in hand to purchase the tickets by the date required.

One day, we borrowed the car from Dale's dad and went to visit Forest and Nancy Stine, our longtime friends from Bell Gardens.

Forest declared to Dale, "It sure is good to hear that you have your tickets to sail in June."

Dale said, "Oh, we haven't purchased the tickets yet. We've only made a down payment on a booking."

After that, we drove to San Diego to see my parents one last time before we sailed. They had let us know previously that they didn't want to see us leave on the ship, for it was too hard for them, not knowing when they would see us again. My dad, at that time, wasn't a believer and was against us going to the mission field. He wouldn't even talk to us about it. Mamma told us that Daddy had asked her how much our tickets would cost. When she told him, he then asked her how much money we still needed.

When she replied that we needed just over a thousand dollars, he exclaimed, "Why, they will never make it! You don't need to worry about them going anywhere." In his thinking, it was impossible, because he knew Dale wasn't working; he had no idea where that kind of money would come from. He didn't know that our wonderful, faithful God, who always keeps His promises, had promised to meet all our needs. We believed and were trusting in this God to provide for us, including the funds we needed to buy those tickets. We believed it was in God's plan for us to go to New Guinea.

En route back to Oxnard, as we drove through Los Angeles, we stopped by Redlands to visit our friends who were living in a trailer park, as an outreach ministry for New Tribes Mission. We knew several families there.

When getting ready to leave, imagine our surprise when we discovered an envelope containing a large gift of over $500 tucked under the steering wheel. These student missionaries had taken up a collection for us to help with the purchase of our tickets. This, along with the gifts from our wonderful friends at Bell Gardens Baptist Church, provided the means to purchase our tickets.

Grandma Palmer and our family.

It was years later, after serving in Papua New Guinea and returning to the United States for our first furlough, that we learned our friend Forest Stine, who was also a deacon in the church, had informed the folks there of the situation. He simply shared with them our need and that we were looking to the Lord to supply the funds to purchase our tickets to leave on the ship in June.

A few weeks before we were due to depart, we moved to Bell Gardens and stayed with Ray and Ina Orsburn, who always took us in when we visited town. It was in their back yard, under the avocado tree, that we packed our four 55-gallon drums of equipment for the field.

On June 23rd, 1953, we sailed from San Pedro, California, on the M/S *PARRAKOOLA*, a Swedish freighter. Sailing with us was Tom Palmer, (no relation to Dale) who finished the training with New Tribes at Fouts Springs about the same time as we did. Dale's folks came from Oxnard to visit us aboard the ship. Some folks from Bell Gardens also came on board to see us before we left. There were Forest and

The M/S *Parrakoola*.

50

Nancy Stine and her mother, Mrs. Capehart; Charles Congdon and daughter Barbara; Dick and Lee Kelso, and Sonny Covington. Folks from Redlands were there as well; Al Cole and his mother, and Bernie and Doreen Ketchum, and others. This was an exciting time for all of them, as well as for us.

Other friends, Charles and Virginia Taylor, with whom we'd been in missionary training, came to see us, too. When they found out that Gospel Recordings had given us a number of phonograph records with wonderful hymns, they went shopping and brought back a wind up Victrola record player for us. They also provided us with several chil-

Friends and family on board ship.

dren's records. This wonderful gift would provide us with many happy hours in the days to come. Our little sons especially enjoyed playing the children's records.

We spent that night anchored in the harbor. The next morning, Dale's folks came to see us off, but they had to stay on the wharf. Waving goodbye to us were Grandpa and Grandma Palmer; Dale's dad, Bud, and his brother, Uncle George and his sons, Brian and Allen; and Mrs. Dixon, their grandmother. Aunt Evelyn, his

dad's sister and her son, Davis Wade Bogue, were there as well. Margaret, George's wife, was in the hospital with a new baby, whom they named Lester Dale, and couldn't be there. This was the last time we saw Grandpa Palmer and Aunt Evelyn, because they both passed away before we returned for our first furlough.

After being underway just one night, we discovered the following morning that Pat and Peter were both covered in red spots. Then we remembered that some relatives had come from Texas about two weeks before we left, and their kids had the measles. Sure enough, our boys both had the measles. Fortunately, this happened

A last good-bye from the dock.

after we were well out to sea, or we may not have been allowed to sail! Unfortunately, there was no doctor on board the ship.

Our first three days and nights on board turned out to be miserable, because not only were the boys sick, but Dale and I were both seasick! We took turns minding the boys, and Paul, who had to be bottle fed. The stewardess had belatedly told us that we should keep on eating. But for us, this advice came too late, since we were already seasick. By now, it was impossible for us to eat anything. I told Dale there was only one good thing about it; now he knew exactly

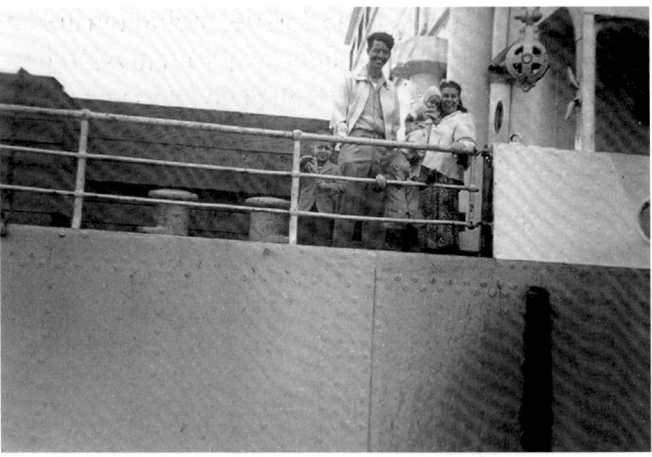

Our family on the M/S *Parrakoola*.

what morning sickness was like! Years later, on another voyage, we did keep munching on fruit and crackers, and managed to overcome seasickness, which proved that the stewardess was right.

Once we were over that misery, our days were spent relaxing and enjoying many hours of leisure on deck. We'd had such a busy schedule before leaving that we were fairly exhausted. So we relaxed and enjoyed watching the ocean for porpoises and flying fish that often landed on deck. Dale took naps in the deck chairs, while the boys played deck games and we all swam in the makeshift pool, formed of canvas and filled with ocean water. Pat and Peter enjoyed those times, and we were free to keep a close eye on them, as a sweet Australian lady offered to watch four-month-old Paul when we were swimming. She always told me, "He's as good as gold," with her *Aussie* (Australian) accent, which was still very pronounced, although she had spent years in the United States. There were several other Australians on board, too. One man took the time to explain to us the Australian money system, which was based on pounds, shillings and pence. This was quite different from the decimal system of the United States.

Tom Palmer was a great help to us also by looking after the boys; Peter especially, who was still being potty trained. This was the life of luxury, but we looked forward to arriving in Australia. It took twenty-one days to cross the Pacific Ocean, and during that entire time we only spotted land once, way in the distance.

The seas must have been extra rough one night, because Paul, who slept in the lower bunk, was tossed out onto the floor. Peter slept at one end of the bunk and Paul was tucked in the other end. Climbing down from the top bunk, I quickly went to Paul's rescue. It seemed he cried forever, being terrified and hurt as well. I had to go to the galley to find his bottle and warm it up myself, because none of the crew was on duty through the night. I don't think anyone else on the entire ship heard a thing, because the ship's powerful engines were extremely noisy. Even Dale and Pat slept uninterrupted in the cabin next door.

The next morning I told the stewardess some other sleeping arrangements had to be made for the baby, so she made a bed for him in a large drawer. He was safe the rest of the journey.

Every night, the twenty-one passengers, including our family, had dinner at the Captain's table. At one meal, there were glasses for champagne, which we declined. Inside each of the children's glasses was a silver dollar!

One thing marred our pleasant days. There was a man on board who was quite a heavy drinker, who took a fancy to me, despite the fact that he had a lovely, dark-haired wife. He seemed to look for opportunities to come alongside me, at which time he would lean toward me and say, "Oh Ginger, would you let me stroke your beautiful hair?" This was very annoying to me, but I would ignore him and walk away.

Finally, on the day we landed in Sydney, this man advanced, speaking the same words to me. I broke down crying. I had been under a lot of stress, trying to get everything packed and all of us ready to disembark. This impudence was the last straw. When Dale found me crying, he approached the man and in very firm words told him, "Leave my wife alone." Of course he did, since we were all disembarking. Thankfully, we never saw him again.

What a wonderful sight it was, to come into Sydney Harbor! There, bounding up the gang plank were two friendly faces. Although we knew neither one of them, Charles Driver (Chuck) and a missionary student, Arnold Davis, had come to meet us. We had corresponded with Chuck since he was the field leader in New Guinea. He was in Sydney, organizing a group of Australian folk who wanted to join the New Tribes work on the field. With their days of training over, they were all looking for passage to the field.

Shortly after our arrival, Chuck asked Dale, "Have you heard about the forest fire that killed fourteen New Tribes men?"

Dale replied, "No, we didn't hear any news while we were aboard ship." Chuck proceeded to tell us about the devastating disaster. Later, after we had more details, Dale realized that he knew most of those men who died. They were fellow students in training with us, men he knew from work detail, and fighting fires together.

There were Cecil Hitchcock, Sergio Colles, David Johnson, Stanley Whitehouse, Allan Boddy, Benjamin Dinnel, Harold Griffis, Paul Gifford, Robert Mieden, Howard Rowe, Raymond Sherman, Daniel Short, Stanley Vote and Darrel Noah. Our friend,

Darrel Noah had planned that he and his wife would join us as partners in New Guinea, once they had finished the training. This fire came to be known as the Rattlesnake Fire in the Mendocino National Forest.

It was painful to think of the deaths of these men and to begin work on the field without Darrell, but again we knew the Lord was in control. We would continue to trust His plan for our family.

Our Time in Australia

Chuck had made bookings for our accommodations at the Sydney Missionary Home, located in Turramurra. We hired a vehicle to take us and our luggage there. After three weeks aboard ship, it surely was a welcome sight to see that lovely old two story house, where we had a large guestroom with a fireplace and with beds for each of us. Our room was booked for a month. During that time, we ate in the home's dining room with several other guests. One guest was a single lady, Malia Santoro, also with New Tribes Mission. Meals were cooked and served by Miss Preen.

This home had been recently purchased and put into service as a missionary home. The yard suffered from many years of neglect. Dale and Tom Palmer worked many long hours, cutting out overgrown shrubs, and clearing away rubbish, so they had hearty ap-

The Sydney Missionary Home.

petites each meal. The food was dished out onto plates, and a plate served to each of us, but everyone got about the same amount of food on his plate. I noticed that Dale or Tom quickly *offered* to help Pat or Peter, if either of them said they couldn't finish their dinner.

We left the States during the summer and didn't realize that it was winter in Australia in July! We about froze, so to speak, during those first days in Sydney. Pat and Peter were dressed in short pants and sandals. Trying to keep the baby warm enough while bathing him in front of the fireplace, stoked with bits of coal, was a very trying experience for me! But we survived. In those days, we learned many lessons about the Australian climate and culture.

Since our monthly allowance, to be sent to us by the mission, had not yet reached us, we were not able to proceed to New Guinea, as planned. Therefore, after the month's reservation had expired at the missionary home, we had to look for other accommodations.

We found a small vacation cabin in Cronulla, on the bay, and moved there. This was across town from Turramurra. The cabin had a living room, a kitchen with a sink, a hotplate with an oven underneath it for baking, a table and chairs and two bedrooms, a porch and a large closet. There was also a bathroom, but it only had a bathtub and a chip heater that we stoked with bits of coal. The toilet was outside up a long flight of steps.

Staying in the cabin with us were Tom Palmer and Malia Santaro, who had moved with us from the missionary home. Malia occupied the small bedroom and Tom slept in the closet. We and our three sons crowded into the larger bedroom.

Soon, Don and Gwen McCurdy and their small son, Dale arrived from the States and joined us in the cabin! There had to be some shifting around to make enough room for everyone. The men put up a tarpaulin on the porch to keep out the dampness, and Tom moved from the closet to the porch. Malia moved from the small bedroom to the closet. McCurdys now occupied the small bedroom; Dale and I were the only ones who didn't have to move!

A frightening thing happened one day when Peter was playing on the small settee or couch. An electrical outlet was located on the wall at the door to the kitchen, just above the back of the settee. The switch was located just above the outlet which was designed to hold a light bulb, but it was empty. Peter, a curious two-and-a-half year old, put his finger in the outlet. Amazingly, it did him no harm, as immediately his hand hit the switch and turned off the current! The incident was over before we had time to be alarmed, but we immediately realized what a narrow escape he had, making us keenly aware of the watch care of our Heavenly Father. We wasted no time before covering the outlet with some tape.

Time went by and our money still had not reached us. We found out it was being sent to New Guinea. We had an immediate need for money to buy food and pay for our accommodations, so Dale went to a group of men working nearby who were building a new house and asked about work. They directed him to the boss. This kind man put Dale to work across the bay, clearing some ground to build a new house. This kind of work was just what Dale had done when he worked on the forest fires. He was paid for each day's work, and this helped us buy the food we needed and pay our rent. We believed this was God's provision to meet our immediate needs.

One day while Dale was burning some brush, the lady next door came to the fence and called to him, bringing a tall frosty glass of cold beer! He offended her greatly when he felt he had to refuse it, although he was extremely hot, thirsty and exhausted from the heat.

We had some interesting experiences while shopping for food those early days in

Australia. We were able to buy rabbits for about thirty cents each, so we had lots of rabbit stew, stretching it with plenty of vegetables to feed all ten of us. I remember asking about purchasing milk, since all I could see in the store was powdered milk. I asked the clerk, "Don't you have any *sweet milk*?" She surely didn't understand my Texas brogue or choice of words. I had to explain that I wanted to buy some fresh milk.

It was my turn to be perplexed, when she answered, "Oh, you have to put out the billy tin by your front door." This was how I learned that the milkman came around each morning in a little horse-drawn cart, and ladled out the milk into a small covered tin, left by the door for that purpose. Somehow this fact had escaped me while we were staying at the missionary home.

During this time, contacts were made, and the men were able to have several meetings in churches, where they shared about the work we would be doing in New Guinea. They learned how to travel about using the electric train system.

Dale tells about the time he and Tom were heading to a meeting, when they found they had to change trains to get there. This left each of them short of a ticket to get back home. They didn't have enough money with them to buy another, and they didn't know what they would do. After the meeting, a lady pressed some money into Dale's hand. It was enough to buy the return ticket home for both of them! The lady was Nell Dreghorn, who turned out to be one of our new Australian co-workers. She traveled with us by ship to New Guinea a short time later. This was just one of the wonderful ways in which the Lord provided for us during those days.

There was so much for us to learn about this Australian culture. When we were still at the missionary home, Dale and Tom were invited to a meeting and were told to come for *tea* as well. Since our dinner was about to be served, they ate before they left. How surprised they were, when they arrived at the meeting, to find *tea* was actually dinner! Since they were both young and had healthy appetites, they didn't have much trouble eating dinner twice that night!

~PART TWO~

New Beginnings

Chapter 4

On to New Guinea, 1953
By Arvalee

Dale and I have fond memories of those days in Australia as we waited to go to New Guinea.

Before Chuck Driver departed for New Guinea, he and Dale discussed possible allocation sites for our family. Because Harold and Mary Sellers were working alone in the Highlands, they decided that we should join them in that work. This meant we would work at the mission base at Kami, about 36 miles from the town of Goroka.

We and the McCurdys loaned Tom Palmer the money to purchase his airplane ticket and he preceded us to New Guinea, paying us back later. Then the McCurdys helped us buy our tickets on the ship, and they were able to follow about a month later after we had paid them back.

So in October 1953, Dale and I traveled on the M/V *BULOLO* with the Australian folk who were joining the work in the Watut, where Chuck was stationed.

After departing from Sydney, the ship first docked in Brisbane, Queensland, to take on more supplies and passengers. While there, the stewardess who helped with the children in the dining room told us we had to purchase a small saucepan to cook our baby's food. Paul was about seven months old and was eating mashed or strained food by then. So Dale and I went to some stores near the wharf and finally found a very cheap pan. It was all we could afford, but it served the purpose.

The next day, the ship continued on its voyage north to New Guinea. Again, Dale and Pat shared a cabin, and Peter, Paul and I were in the cabin next door. After one evening meal, as we were all going back to our rooms, Pat and Peter ran down the long passageway ahead of us. Suddenly, there was a piercing scream, and Peter ran back towards us as fast as his little legs would carry him! He had spied a huge cockroach on the floor. This was very frightening to a little boy, just a month short of three years old. Never had we seen such a huge insect! Little did we know that we would spend considerable effort trying to eliminate cockroaches during our entire time on the field!

Port Moresby, the capital of New Guinea, was the next scheduled stop. It was thrilling to finally see the land and people we had dreamed of for so many years! The porthole to my room was level with the dock, and I could see the industrious wharf workers. Wanting to be friendly, I waved to one of them. Big mistake! Later, I discovered this man squatting down, peering into the porthole, and he remained there, more or less a permanent fixture! I finally had to cover the opening to have some privacy. I was very naïve at that time, especially of the New Guinea culture. I learned a foreign woman had to be very careful in her attentions to the national men, lest they give them the wrong ideas.

After leaving Port Moresby, the ship rounded the far eastern end of the island and we docked at Samarai Island. We had enough time there to enjoy walking around the small isle on its lovely white sand beach. Next, we anchored offshore at Lae, on the northern coast of New Guinea, where the Australian folks disembarked. Chuck and Ed Erke were there to meet them and drove them to the Watut mission station.

A couple of days later, our family disembarked at Madang, located farther west on the northern coast of the island. Harold Sellers met us there, having flown in from Goroka. He had booked us a room at the hotel. At breakfast the next morning we had our first taste of papaya. We were not impressed, because we had been told it was like cantaloupe! But before too long papaya was a real treat to all of us. We also greatly enjoyed the bananas. The varieties grown in New Guinea were the sweetest bananas we had ever eaten.

Harold helped us set up a checking account at the Bank of New South Wales, where our money from the mission had been deposited. We also established an account at the Madang Burns Philp store, since we would order and buy everything by mail via the store's Country Orders Service. Each order had to be prepaid by check.

The second day in Madang we boarded a DC-3 and flew to the Eastern Highlands Province, landing on a grass airstrip in the town of Goroka. It was an old World War II airstrip. We stayed that night in the Goroka Hotel, in a small round bush house. The next morning, a young national man knocked on our door, saying, "*Mi laik kisim wok,*" or some such thing.

We didn't have a clue what he was saying, so we found Harold and told him that a young man was at our door but we didn't know what he wanted. Harold came to our room, talked with the fellow, and then relayed, "He just wants to work for you." That was our introduction to Pidgin English, the trade language of New Guinea.

Settling at Kami
By Arvalee

Harold hired a World War II jeep and a trailer from another mission group to take us and our drums out to the Kami mission base. We traveled over a narrow mountainous road for about two hours until we came to the muddy swift-flowing Dunantina River, which was traversed by a swinging footbridge. That was the end of the road. Our drums were unloaded, and Harold helped Dale get them across the bridge. Some young national men who worked for Harold were there to help us. Harold informed us, "The mission base is two miles up the trail, there in the foothills. Just follow the trail and you will find it." He went on ahead, leaving us to fend for ourselves! He was anxious to get home.

The nationals headed up the trail with our *cargo* (baggage). Dale carried Paul, and I followed along with the diaper bag. Pat and Peter ran on ahead of us on the trail, through the tall *kunai* grass. Suddenly, both boys were scooped up in the arms of young national boys, who ran off up the trail with them. They were telling us something, but we didn't understand a word in this strange garble! All we could do was follow the path and keep going. In another hour or so we came to the mission base, and there were our boys, playing happily with the Sellers children. Their three older boys ranged in age from about eleven to seven years old, their little girl was about five, and the baby boy was about a year old.

Our first house at Kami.

Our first home was a small two room, 12 X 24 foot grass-roofed bush house which was used by the Sellers as a guesthouse. We settled in, using the front room for cooking and eating. Mary, Harold's wife, was so hospitable and willing to help during those days with our makeshift setup. We were cooking on a one burner kerosene Primus stove, while she had a cast iron cook stove. Many times she invited us over for a meal, which we appreciated immensely; however, it wasn't the same as cooking for ourselves. Before long, we realized we needed more space. Dale asked Harold about moving a small building from another location and joining it to the existing house to use as a cookhouse. Harold was in agreement and soon we had a real kitchen of our own.

While we were in Australia we had purchased a small cast iron cook stove, which was being shipped to New Guinea. Unfortunately, it was a long time in arriving. In the meantime, Dale designed and built a stove, from a 55-gallon steel drum. This sure made it

Family in front of our house.

easier for me to cook our own meals. It was complete with an oven in the center which he constructed from a square flour drum. The thin metal of this square drum became very hot, with a fire alight in the bottom of the steel drum for the oven and another fire above the oven to heat the stovetop. Once, I came close to burning the house down, which was very scary indeed. We had kept the kindling wood in the corner, behind the stove. I had some food cooking, and when I came back to tend to it, I found the kindling wood smoking, just ready to burst into flames. That was the last time the kindling wood was stored behind the stove!

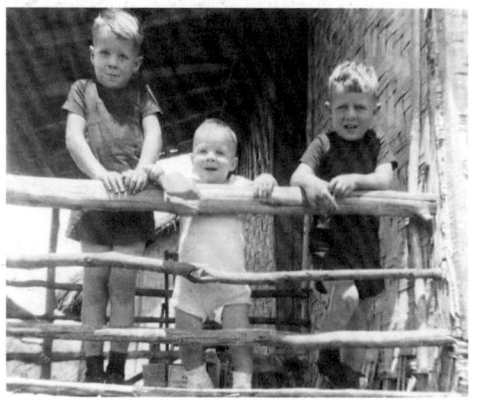

Our boys on the porch.

In the beginning, I followed Mary's leading as she washed the clothes for her family on a rub board. I found I had to wash clothes every day to

The drum stove Dale made.

keep enough clean clothes for our family. In the tropics you have to change clothes every day, or they mildew very quickly. This hard work was getting me down physically so Dale and I decided I must have some help. We began training some of the local teenage boys to work for us; not only to help wash clothes, but they prepared fresh vegetables as well, another very time-consuming task. This not only helped me to manage the work load, but it gave me an excellent opportunity to learn Pidgin English.

Although it was a blessing and tremendous help to have these willing workers, it was an unimaginably hard job trying to train them. First of all, my limited knowledge of Pidgin English made communicating instructions quite a challenge. Added to that, these boys had never worked for Europeans and didn't know what a clean shirt really meant. Besides this, we found out that several of them were quite adept at stealing! We learned many lessons in patience and dealing with people in those days.

It was a treat, though, to have an abundant supply of fresh produce, which we bought from the people who lived in nearby villages. The women would carry the garden produce to our houses in woven string bags, which we learned were called *bilums*. During

Yatyou washing clothes.

that first year, we learned to eat sweet potatoes in abundance cooked in many different ways, since that was the staple of the people. These people were true farmers who grew corn, green beans, pumpkins, cucumbers, and green onions, as well as papaya, bananas and pineapple. We seldom saw Irish potatoes, and the ones they brought were very small. The next year, however, the potato crop was abundant, and the potatoes were much larger.

We kept table salt on hand for the purpose of trading for food and firewood. We purchased it in seventy pound bags, which were quite difficult to transport. Each huge bag had to be carried on poles from Goroka by our national workers. Sometimes, someone would ask for a small box of matches instead, but the most valued trade item was salt.

While living at Kami many people would come to us from the nearby villages with terrible sores on their bodies. Dale went to Goroka and told Dr. Sims about these sores. He told Dale it was yaws, a form of venereal disease and could be cured with penicillin shots. He offered to give Dale the penicillin, needles and syringes, but we had no refrigerator in which to store the medicine. The doctor then told him he would give him powdered penicillin and small bottles of distilled water, to mix together. Dale accepted, and that was the beginning of the first medical aid clinic at our Kami Mission Station. We both learned to give penicillin shots to the people, but it wasn't always easy. Since the scant attire of both men and women continuously exposed them to the elements, the skin of their buttocks grew very tough; so tough in fact, that we would sometimes bend needles in the process of giving them a shot!

We not only gave shots for yaws, but we often had to diagnose a fever or other sickness in order to help people get well. A few years later, when the Government Officer came into that area to take a census, he told us that yaws had been eradicated in a five mile radius of the Kami Mission Station.

At first, sick people came every day, at any time of day, and it really became a burden. Soon, Dale came up with a plan to give each patient a slip of paper with their names, record, and when the next treatment or shot was due. He asked them to come only on Monday, Wednesday and Friday; those days were set aside as the days for *haus sik*; or house sick, (clinic).

With the help of Harold and Mary, and in spite of making many blunders, we were learning to speak Pidgin English. Soon Dale was adept enough at the language to share the gospel story with the people. He would do this before giving out any medicine or dressing any sores at the first aid clinic.

These were exciting days! Our dreams of working with people who had never before heard the gospel story had at last become a reality!

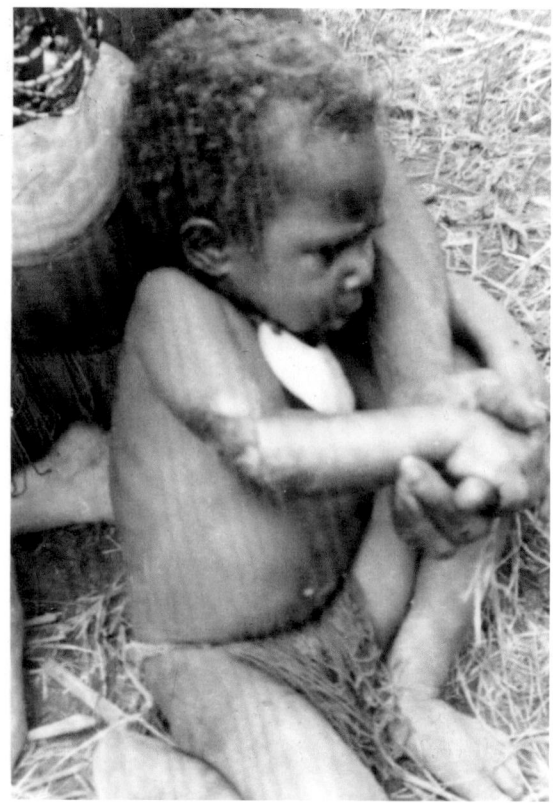

Child with a burn on her elbow.

My First Gimi Patrol, 1954
By Dale

This true story took place half a century ago when I was twenty-four years old. My wife, Arvalee, and I had come to the Territory of New Guinea because we believed God's command was for us to go to the remote places of the earth and preach the gospel. We arrived the sixth day of October, 1953, with our three little boys, Pat, Peter, and Paul, joining Harold and Mary Sellers with their five children at the Kami Mission Station in the Eastern Highlands Province.

In spite of the obstacles of language acquisition and of learning to work effectively with these primitive people, we were simply thrilled to be in New Guinea, in the land God had called us to, to serve Him.

Those were Colonial days and the country was still under the authority of the Australian Government, having been mandated to them after World War II. This Government sought to bring peace to warring tribal areas, along with roads and first aid clinics. It built airstrips and provided schools in very remote locations. The Patrol Officers or Kiaps (see glossary) were in charge and kept law and order in the interior tribal areas and took the census as well. They were stationed at the Patrol Posts (see glossary), far inland and many miles away from civilization.

Harold had been burdened to reach the Gimi tribe, the yet untouched people beyond the mountains to the south. The Gimi was classified as an uncontrolled (see glossary) area by the Government because the national people were hostile to neighboring villages, and clan wars were frequent. The Government believed it was a dangerous place and for that reason would not allow any Europeans to visit there. Harold and I both had to apply for a special permit from the Government to make this patrol into the Gimi.

Now, with permits in hand, our plans were finally in place and I was to accompany him on a trek to the Gimi tribal area. This was my first chance to walk through the area beyond Mt. Michael and make contact with the Gimi people.

Our Departure
By Dale

There was excitement in the air that morning in the cool highlands of the Territory of New Guinea. This was a very special day to me. It was my first time to go on patrol in this country and it was also my son Paul's first birthday, February 28th, 1954.

Harold came down to our bush house early that morning to tell me the national carriers had arrived. "Are you ready to go Dale?" he asked.

"Yes, I'm ready," I replied. Harold helped carry my things up to his place where the carriers were waiting. Arvalee and the boys walked up with us. The carriers took the *rucksacks* (backpacks) from Harold and me, swung the packs onto their shoulders and stood there ready to go. Their copper skin and the beads of water in their black curly hair were shining in the early morning light.

We said our good-byes and headed off into the mountains as the sun came up. We were hiking in the sun most of the day and I could see Harold's ruddy complexion was getting quite sunburned from the reflection off the tall *kunai* grass. Climbing out of the steep Kuru valley in the late afternoon, the sun was beating down on our backs and we were all exhausted. Then we came over the crest of the mountain, and we were looking into a lush, cool, dark green valley with long finger-like shadows closing in around the new Government Patrol Post at Tarabo.

When we arrived at the post a handsome, young Australian Patrol Officer, John McArthur, greeted us with a cup of hot tea.

My throat was so dry; I'll never forget how good that tea tasted. John's *kukboi* (cook) prepared a delicious meal for us, which we enjoyed in John's comfortable bush home made of woven bamboo, round poles and *kunai* grass roof. We talked far into the night and drank pot after pot of hot tea.

John couldn't have been friendlier and told us he had walked twice through the area behind Mt. Michael. He said, "The Government is now calling this area the Gimi." John showed us his hand-drawn map of the Gimi area. "I have an extra copy. Would you like it?"

"Yes, thank you," I replied.

John leaned over and whispered, "One of my national officers is leaving at five a.m. with a group of porters heading to the south Gimi. They're going to Amusa to cut bamboo and carry it back to Tarabo to finish building the patrol post. You could follow them into the area, if you'd like."

Excited? There must have been a better word for how I felt. Sleep would not come to me that night; my head was swimming with dreams.

> *Had these Gimi people ever heard of God? Mr. George Greathead, the District Commissioner of the Eastern Highlands, had told Harold that no mission group had ever been in this area. Maybe we're the first missionaries to set foot in this tribal nation! I was wide awake, thinking about the words of Acts 1:8 "...to the uttermost part of the earth." In a few hours we'd be off to the ends of the earth where these Gimi people lived.*

When I first arrived in New Guinea, Harold had told me how he met Mr. George Greathead.

He related: "I was flying by DC3 aircraft from Bulolo to the Sepik, but a large thunderstorm blocked our route; the plane had to land in the town of Goroka, on a World War II grass airstrip. I walked over to the District Office and asked if I could talk to the District Commissioner.

"'How can I help you?' Mr. Greathead asked.

"'I'm with New Tribes Mission and we are looking for tribes that have no other

Dale and Harold Sellers at the house sick.

missions working with them,' I answered.

"Mr. Greathead walked over to his office window and pointing due south he said, 'See that big mountain? It's called Mt. Michael. There is a large group of people living on the other side of the mountain. We are just starting to bring these people under the control of the Government to stop the clan fighting. No mission has been allowed to work there yet.'

"I thanked Mr. Greathead and knew when I walked out of his office that God had blocked my route so that we had to land in Goroka, and there learn about the Gimi people."

With a few hours' rest, a new map in hand, and a guide to show us the way, we were off again into the mountains with high hopes of soon seeing the Gimi people. We came down the mountain that evening to the Henagaru Government Rest House, a small round, grass roofed hut for housing the patrol officer or other travelers.

We asked at Henagaru where the Gimi people were located. A spokesman pointed south. "That mountain is Negibi. All the people beyond Negibi speak the Gimi language."

The next day, we dropped off the steep ridge to a fast flowing whitewater river. We followed the river along the base of Mt. Negibi as it twisted and turned to the south. The canopy of big trees that grew along the river shaded us from the hot tropical sun in the afternoon. We could look up and see the sun peeking down on us every now and then. Late that evening we arrived at the village of Amusa.

Dale and Harold Sellers.

I was tired and glad when Harold said, "Maybe we could rest a day here at Amusa." We were as far south as we planned to go on this patrol.

When we walked into the village we were met by the red-skinned *luluai* (chief). There was fear in his eyes and we were not sure what was going on. Later, having visited with the people and shown ourselves to be friendly, he seemed to relax. After that, he was very friendly; and his people brought us all kinds of food, including sugar cane; a good token of friendship.

It was good to spend that extra day with the Amusa people and the *luluai*. The *luluai* and I remained friends for many years thereafter.

The next day we walked in a westerly direction to Uvai, just a few hours away. Uvai lies in a small valley and upon our arrival the people were anxious to show us something. They led us away from the village houses and into a clearing to show us the remains of a small engine block. We had no idea what it was from or how it had gotten there.

> *Years later Pat Smith, an Australian fellow missionary, was with me at Uvai and I showed him the engine block. He said it was from a Tiger Moth aircraft that was used during the war as a reconnaissance plane.*

We saw men carrying stone axes and wearing woven bark string capes that hung from their shoulders down to their heels. There were all kinds of colorful feather head-dresses and yellow possum's fur on the men's heads. Men and women alike wore different kinds of shells as decorations.

When I woke up the next morning, the early morning birds were still singing. Lying there in my sleeping bag, I thanked the Lord for allowing me to see these Stone Age people with my very own eyes. This was no dream. We were in a large valley of Stone Age people whom we had come to find.

"From this map John gave us, it looks like we will have to go through the Mani area to get to the Umi village," Harold said.

"Yes. It looks like it will take us two days hiking from here to get there," I responded.

The following night we stopped at a village in the Mani. That night one of our carriers was sick and wide-eyed with fear. He was afraid of the local people, thinking they had cast a spell of sorcery on him. A local shaman came into the house, which made all of us uneasy, so Harold escorted the shaman out of the bush house. We stayed in the same house with our carriers that night to reassure them that all would be fine.

The next day, we hiked northeast toward the village of Umi. By this time all the carriers were so afraid that you could see the fear in their eyes. Harold and I talked it over and agreed that we must keep them close to us. Our carriers were not from the

Gimi and they had heard rumors about the power of the Gimi sorcerers. We were still three days' walk from home and we didn't want them to run away and leave us. As a precaution, I took the lead as we came down the narrow ridge near the Umi village, and Harold brought up the rear.

> *Three months before this patrol, a group of Umi men came to our Kami Mission Station looking for work. They worked well for six weeks, and then said, "We want our pay. A big man (a tribal fight leader) died at Umi village and we are all going home."*
>
> *We told them their pay had not arrived yet; they could come back later to get it. These rugged mountain men were very upset with us. They wanted their pay immediately. At that time we paid in trade goods: glass beads, shells, knives and cloth.*
>
> *That night, in the moonlight, we could see them hunkered down talking in the yard. We were scared they might do something foolish. It was a relief to see that they were all gone when morning came.*

As I walked down that narrow ridge, I recalled their anger over the earlier pay problem and thought to myself, *Will these Umis receive us well?* Just then, I heard loud wild yodeling coming up from the village. The sound was echoing off the mountains, "*A-o-bana-ooo -i-o- a-nau-obe.*" I could see the yodeler running up the trail towards me. His powerful arms were outstretched and his muscular body was glistening with red grease in the afternoon sun. His eyes were flashing and he didn't stop yodeling, "*A-ru-aru a-nau-ooo A-o-bana-i-o a-nau-ooo.*"

When he reached me, I stopped right in the middle of the trail. *What's next?* I thought. As this five foot tall chief danced up and down in front of me, facing his village, he gave another loud yodel. Then this young chieftain spun around and picked me up, holding me in a tight grip around my thighs. He was still yodeling and dancing as we came down the trail to the village. The two of us together were over eight feet high! I had no control over where I was going. I felt helpless, having another person's legs dancing me around. We came bobbing right into the village like old Scottish dancers.

The village was on a high flat ridge and all the grass huts were facing the small path with a sharp drop-off on the far side. From eight feet up, that path didn't look very wide. The men and women chanted loudly as we came into the village. I thought, *What is going on?* You're not thinking real clear when you're up off the ground and bobbing up and down like an old butter churn! But one thought was spinning around in my head, *Should this chief stub his toe, over that cliff we will go.*

This powerhouse of a man just kept on dancing with my 150 pound body and six foot two inch frame in his arms. My legs were going numb and the people were still chanting all around me. I thought, *Are we heading for the village cooking pot?* It seemed like an hour, but I know that it was just minutes. To my great relief, the chief finally put me down. I looked back and saw that Harold was also surrounded by people.

You should have seen my clothes after all the men finished hugging me. I had bright red *abai grease* on my white shirt and khaki shorts. By now, there was no doubt in my mind that these were friendly people. We had been given the royal welcome into the Umi clan. While they were surprised to see us walking into their village, they were glad to see us at the same time. I think it was just a bit overwhelming to them.

> *Abai is a vegetable that grows on the pandanus tree. After it is cooked, they squeeze the seeds releasing the thick red grease. The people rub the grease on their bodies to keep their skin from getting dry, as most of their body is exposed to the tropical sun. The Gimis say, "Our skin feels good when we rub the abai grease on it." They also use the red vegetable grease or sauce on their food for seasoning.*

When the Umi men who had worked for us appeared, Harold spoke to them. "Your six weeks' pay is at Kami. You can come get it when you like," he told them in the trade language. All the men shouted, *"Hanare."* We learned fast that *hanare* means, "That's good."

I sat down on a log and pulled my boots and socks off. *"Nanonebo,"* ("Oh, Mother") all the kids shouted at once. It seemed like everyone wanted to touch and rub my soft white feet. It was obvious they had never seen white feet before. I thought of the words in Isaiah 52:7, *"How beautiful upon the mountains are the feet of him that bringeth good tidings...."*

The people wanted us to try all the different kinds of food. It was lots of fun until I was given some dry cooking bananas. It was like chewing on balsawood.

I slept well most of the night in the men's lodge, although it's more like a smoke-house, (to stay warm in the high altitude coolness, open fires burned all night). I had to lie down, even before bedtime, to get underneath the smoke. The men talked way into the night, most likely about the day's happenings. Every now and then someone would say something and they would all crack up laughing. You couldn't keep from laughing with them, even though they might be laughing at you. This was the last night we spent in a Gimi village, and a day not to be forgotten.

The next night, we arrived back at Henagaru and slept in the same little bush house as we had before. The last day's hike was a long day, even though we took a shortcut around the east end of Mt. Michael. It was the hardest hiking of the patrol. The sun was scorching hot and we were all exhausted when we arrived home at our Kami station that night. Both Harold and I were jubilant about our patrol into the Gimi and wrote reports to our field leader, Chuck Driver.

> *Arvalee and I both realized that, rather than continuing to live in the Sellers' guest house, we needed our own larger home, so I had started building a new house. It was 24 feet x 24 feet, with a porch at the back and another on the front of the house. It was built entirely of bush material, except for some nails. Round poles or trees were used throughout and the floor was made of bamboo mats, woven with large flattened bamboo. The walls were made of woven pit-pit, a sort of hollow cane, and the roof was made from kunai grass thatch. The windows were covered with plastic window material.*

A month later, after the Gimi patrol, Chuck Driver and Arnold Davis, a new missionary we had first met in Sydney, flew from Bulolo to Goroka. They walked to Kami, wanting to hear more about this new tribe. Our visitors strolled down with Harold and me to see the new bush house that I was building. The new bamboo floor was tightly woven and the warm tropical sun had turned the bamboo a deep golden yellow. The four of us sat on the bamboo floor.

Harold started talking, "The people were friendly and everywhere we went they gave us sugar cane."

"Let's ask the Lord what He wants us to do about working with these tribal folks," Chuck suggested.

Each of us prayed and when we finished, Chuck said right away, "You know Harold, God gave you the burden to help these Gimi people, but I don't believe you're the one to open this new work. I believe Dale is."

Arnold said, "Yes, I agree with you. Dale's the one to open this new work."

Harold was quiet for a moment, before speaking, "Yes, I'm in agreement with you. I'm not the one to start this work, but Dale is."

It was clear to me that God wanted me to work with these Stone Age people. I shared my excitement with Arvalee and she was one hundred percent in agreement. It had been our dream for the last five years to bring the gospel to a people who had never heard the Name of Christ. Now our dream was coming true.

"Will You Help My People?"
By Dale

As the sun was setting over our Kami Mission Station in the Highlands of New Guinea, I noticed the shadowy figures of some twenty men advancing up the hill towards me. They were armed with bows and arrows, and most of them were wearing feathered headdresses.

When they were just a few feet from me, this party of warriors opened up and a stocky man stepped forward and stood gazing at me. He was speaking to me, but I had no idea what he was saying. As he glanced back over his shoulder, a young man stepped up beside him. Standing there tall and straight, he looked me right in the eyes and identified the group as Gimi men.

"Our leader wants to know, '*Yu inap salim sampela man long helpim ol manmeri bilong mi*?'" (Will you send someone to help my people?)

I told the chief that we were just now making plans to come and help his people.

The young man restated to his chief, in their language, what I had said. I could tell the chief was pleased with my answer.

Then the chief put his open hand on his chest and said something that made me think he was telling me his name. I always carried a small notebook in my shirt pocket with a pen or pencil, and I wrote it in my notebook the best I could. It sounded like, *"Esema."*

A Gimi man.

Then the young interpreter said with a big grin, *"Nem bilong mi Meniba."* (My name is Meniba.) That, too, was entered into my record book. I didn't realize it that evening when Meniba came with the chief, Esema, but I had met him before. One night, not too long before, Meniba and three other men came through Kami carrying the body of a man who had died in Goroka. I had given them some food and then they had moved off silently into the night.

Looking to the south, Meniba said, "My people live on the other side of that big mountain."

"Yes," I replied in Pidgin English. "We made a patrol into your area about four months ago."

Meniba returned, "Yes, we saw you at the village of Uvai when you passed through and spent the night. We are not from Uvai but from Negibi."

Here I am again with the Gimi people only this time I am standing before Esema, a powerful tribal chief asking me to send someone to help his people. This is the invitation for which we had been praying.

As I was marveling at this revelation, Esema gave a signal, and the party of men turned and headed south in the cool night air, leaving me gazing after them as they disappeared over the first hill. They were going home. I wondered *would their home soon become my new home… Would my dreams of working with the Gimi people soon become a reality?*

The District Commissioner of Goroka
By Dale

In 1952, about one year before we arrived in the Territory of New Guinea, there was a change of Government personnel in Goroka. Mr. George Greathead, the man that Harold Sellers had been working through, resigned to develop a pioneer passion-fruit-pulp industry near Goroka for Cottees Passiona (N.G.) Ltd. He was succeeded by Ian Downs, unquestionably one of the most outstanding District Commissioners in the Eastern Highlands.

Mr. Downs was a Coast Watcher in New Guinea during World War II. The Coast Watchers were brave men who helped to defeat the Japanese Imperial Army by spying on them and sending radio signals of their coastal movements back to the Allied forces. Downs was a man with strong ideas and a vision to make this newly liberated land productive. His dream was to build a network of roads throughout the Eastern Highlands Province of New Guinea.

Downs started off with a bang, right in the town of Goroka. There was a well-groomed golf course that was joined to the top end of the Goroka Airport. The European Country Club and bowling greens were in the center of this beautiful golf course. If you needed to go from one side of the airport to the other you were forced to walk across the top end of the grass airfield where the airplanes were landing because the Country Club people would not permit anyone to cross their lovely golf course.

Well, Ian Downs was not in office long before he *marked out* (surveyed) and built a road right through the beautiful Country Club Golf Course! Now, if you needed to go from one side of the airport to the other you could travel on the new road. Consequently, Ian Downs was not at all popular among the Europeans at the Country Club in Goroka.

Ian Downs also had a dream to make this beautiful province of the Eastern Highlands productive by introducing coffee trees as a cash crop. It was called the "coffee gospel," and it worked! Highlands's coffee beans are the main cash crop for the highlands people to this day.

These were the colonial days of the Territory of New Guinea. When you went into the office of the District Commissioner, you were required to dress in long white pants, a white shirt, tie and a white coat. That is how I dressed when going into the office to talk with Ian Downs. His patrol officers were ordered out of his office if they were not dressed properly. I never knew how I would be received when it was my turn to enter his office, and in 1954 and 1955, I was in Mr. Down's office quite often. I'm writing all this to help you understand the man I had to go through to get permission to work in the East Gimi.

Because of the clan fighting in that area, Mr. Downs was not sure how the tribal people in the eastern part of the Gimi would receive me. He said it would be better if I would do patrols in the west side of the Gimi for the time being. Many times we talked, yet Mr. Downs could not understand my passion to go into the eastern part of the Gimi. Only Government Patrols were going into this area at that time because it was actually designated as "*Uncontrolled Territory*" (see glossary) by the Government.

I knew about the clan wars. Meniba had told me the fighting between the clans was so bad in the Northeastern Gimi around Mt. Negibi that his clan had moved down south to Uvai. Downs was trying to keep me out of this fighting zone until his patrol officers could work with the people to persuade them to stop the clan fighting.

I wrote a letter to our field leader, Chuck Driver, telling him about every meeting that I had had with Mr. Downs. To my surprise, Chuck told me to go over Downs' head and write to the higher officials in Port Moresby and ask them for a permit to work in the East Gimi. I did so, and in time, I received the permit.

However, this did not set well with Mr. Ian Downs. He called me into his office and told me that from now on he would expect a full type-written report every ninety days on all my activities with the people. He said, "The Government wants to know how the tribal people are accepting you as a person." I was not really sure just how much to write, so I sent another letter off to Chuck and asked him. He wrote right back to me and said, "Tell Mr. Downs about every mud puddle you walk through. Flood him with information in every report." So that is what I did. My dear wife used reams of paper, typing my reports on her little Smith Corona portable typewriter. As required, these type-written reports were delivered personally to Mr. Downs every ninety days.

Our Vision for the Gimi
By Arvalee

Dale knew that God had spoken to him and had burdened his heart for the Gimi tribe. After the survey to the Gimi and being among these Stone Age people, Dale's burning desire was to reach them with the gospel. This desire was confirmed to be of God. When Chuck and Arnold visited, they along with Harold had agreed that Dale was God's man to reach the Gimi. We understood this would be sometime in the future.

Shortly after the Gimi patrol, the Sellers family moved back to Rising Sun, where Chuck Driver lived. New missionaries, Ken and Donna Stewart and their two little girls joined us at our Kami Mission Station.

We had been in New Guinea just over a year, living at the first highlands base called Kami. During that time we had become friends with the Wertz family; Ben, Tilila and Ruth, who were with another mission group. They had established a station a hard day's hike farther into the mountains, in the village of Gono.

While Dale was waiting for the required permit from the Government to enter the Gimi, he began making visits to the people on the western side of Mt. Michael, just beyond the village of Gono. To reach these villages in the western part of the Gimi, Dale had to travel through Gono where the Wertz family lived. They often encouraged him to bring the kids and me up to see them.

While Dale was on one of these treks, the men of the village (residents) made a successful pig hunting trip. Several of the men brought their prize, tied to a long pole, and presented it as a gift to Dale. This gave him an opportunity to learn the names of the body parts as they butchered the animal, preparing it for cooking in a *mumu,* (the traditional New Guinea way of cooking food in the ground over hot rocks). Dale quickly retrieved his notebook and pencil, asking the name of each part as they removed it. He learned the words for heart and liver and other internal parts. He had heard phrases spoken before with the word for liver. It was in this way that he first learned it was the *ru-a-au* (liver), and not the heart, that was referred to as the center of emotions for the Gimi people.

On one trip he stayed in the village of Hegaturu, camping in the Government Rest House, as was his custom. One evening a *longlong man* (a crazy man) came to the house and was yelling at the top of his lungs. All the people visiting with Dale made a hasty departure. Being deranged, the man fully drew his six-foot bow and arrow on Dale! No wonder the people fled. Thinking quickly, Dale turned to the man and commanded the demons "to come out of him in the name of the Lord Jesus Christ." Upon hearing this, the man turned and let the arrow loose. It went flying into a nearby picket fence, shattering it into a hundred pieces. The people told Dale the man had been like this ever since he had been sick with a high fever. They knew him well and he was to be feared.

Our Trip to Gono, 1954
By Arvalee

Ben Wertz usually stopped by our house and spent the night with us on his way home from shopping in Goroka. There was no road past the Dunantina River, so he parked his vehicle in a bush garage that he had built at the river and walked the two miles to our house. We would give him a meal and a bed, and the next morning he'd be refreshed and ready to go on his way home. We enjoyed his visits and we usually stayed up late sharing stories. Ben was fun loving. I remember when we'd ask him to come in and sit down, he would sort of sing, "I just got to *heben*, (heaven) and I can't sit down."

One morning, in December 1954, after an unusually late night, we woke up, looked out the window, and spied Ben walking down the trail on his way home. He was so quiet that we had not woken up. He had decided to leave for home, without disturbing us. We really felt bad that we had slept in and had not given him any breakfast to sustain him for the long hike home, but it was too late to stop him.

Since the Wertzes had invited us to come visit them many times, Dale and I talked it over and decided to take them up on their offer. In a day or so, we were ready to go, having assembled the bare necessities for the trip. Dale had contacted two men from the village of Kemasi, and they had agreed to carry our two oldest sons because the boys were too small to walk such a long distance. Pat was almost six years old and Peter had just turned four. We had decided to leave Paul with Ken and Donna Stewart, our co-workers, who later left the field. We thought he was too young to enjoy the long tiring trip; he was two months shy of his second birthday.

It was a hot, sunny day when we set out from Kami for Gono causing us to perspire profusely as we walked along. I was glad we had worn hats and long sleeved shirts to protect us from the hot tropical sun. We were thankful it did not rain that afternoon, as it often did in the highlands of New Guinea. Our two little boys walked for some distance, until their little short legs gave out. Then the two carriers bravely hoisted them upon their shoulders, carrying them throughout the long day, except for short periods of rest. Although New Guinea men are small in stature, they are lean, wiry, and strong.

The first day's walk was over the new road site, which was being built by the national people with pick and shovel. They worked under supervision of the Government, which was pushing the building of roads into the interior of the country. On that first day, we walked through mudslides that were up to my knees. I lost my shoes more than once in the mud, and Dale would go digging for them with his bare hands and then we would be on our way again. I had borrowed a pair of shoes from Donna, but they were too large for me, so it was hard to keep them on my feet.

Dozens of the national people were still working on the road. As we approached, our family caused a lot of excitement because many of these people had never seen white people before, much less a white family. They descended upon us, rubbing our arms and legs, shouting, "*Missisio, Missisio,*" (white woman, white woman). We had to stay alert or their wandering hands would find more *intimate* places to rub! It was the custom of New Guineans, we found out in time, to greet people by touching them in private places. Of course this was unacceptable to us, and though we may have offended some, we slapped their hands away.

The first day, we only got to Lufa, the Government Patrol Post. The Patrol Officer, John Thyer, had often stopped by our house on his way to Goroka. That night he provided us a most welcome meal and put us up for the night. After supper, John treated us to cups of hot Milo, a chocolate flavored drink that is favored among the Australians. We were so exhausted that it felt wonderful to lie down on the large chair cushions that he put on the floor for us to sleep on.

The next morning, although we felt refreshed, the first half hour of walking was quite painful. Our muscles were screaming in protest from the strenuous hiking we'd done the day before, yet we had to press on to our destination.

We reached Gono by midday, and walked into the Wertz's mission base, surprising them all. Ruthie, their eight-year-old daughter, saw us first at the top of the hill, and went running down to the house, calling excitedly to her parents, "Mommy, Daddy, the Palmers are here! The Palmers are here!" They were very surprised to see us, because we had no way to let them know ahead of time that we were coming for a visit.

Besides the sore muscles from walking, the toenails on my big toes had loosened and turned black and blue from wearing the shoes that were too large. Sometime during the night I got up with one of the boys and stubbed my toe. It hurt so badly that it was all I could do to keep from crying out, but I bit my tongue. I didn't want to waken everyone in the house.

We enjoyed our time with the Wertz family, simply spending time together, laughing and telling stories. We spent a lot of time playing games and working jigsaw puzzles. Ruthie was an only child, so she and our boys had a great time playing together.

Ben had a goat that he asked Dale to kill, butcher, and prepare for our Christmas dinner. Ben knew Dale's background; that he was a chef and had experience cutting and cooking meat, so he knew this would not be an imposition upon Dale. We seldom had fresh meat of any kind, so this was a great treat. Tilila always prepared delicious meals, but she made this one a festive occasion for us.

Before long, it was time to leave and go back home. We had all enjoyed our time together and would remember it well for years to come.

On the return trip, we reached Lufa before noon. It was too soon to stop for the night, so we decided to keep going toward home even though we knew there was no place to spend the night. When it began getting dark, our carriers called out to the people in a village we passed, asking them to bring us a torch, but they wouldn't help us. Our carriers were very upset that the people in this village wouldn't help us when we really needed them. Then it began to rain, but we had to keep walking. I was so tired that I could hardly put one foot in front of the other, but somehow I numbed my mind to my feelings and kept pressing on.

Our two little boys were exhausted, too. They had fallen asleep atop the carrier's shoulders, with their heads resting on the men's heads. We had nothing with which to shelter any of us from the rain; we were all cold and dripping wet. It was pitch dark and we couldn't see where we were going. Sometime after dark, the carriers began calling out to the workers at the Kami base. They would call out or holler to a close village, usually across a valley, who would then call or relay to the next village and so on until the message got to the base. So Ken got the message and brought the horse to meet us. Dale put me onto the horse and was leading it when he stepped into a ditch and wrenched his knee, which laid him up for several months.

When we finally arrived at home that night, it was 10:30. We had walked eighteen hours from the time we set out that morning! Thankfully Donna had lots of hot water and some hot, nourishing food ready for us. We were more than grateful for these provisions. We all took hot tub baths in a big galvanized wash tub, and that warmed us up. I bathed the two boys first and got them ready for bed. The water had to be warmed again after each of us finished, so Donna kept a large teakettle of water heating on the wood stove for this purpose. After we had a quick bite to eat, we were all more than ready to go home to our own beds. It was so good to be safely home.

We were ecstatic to see our little Paul again, but we were disappointed that he wasn't too excited to see us! He was calling Ken and Donna, *Daddy* and *Mamma*. We had only been gone ten days, and he had already forgotten us. Happily, that changed after a few days.

Dale's wrenched knee was sore and swollen for about three months after the trip, and I did lose the nails on my big toes, as I knew I would. But thankfully our bodies soon healed. In spite of the pain and hardships we had endured, we both felt our little adventure was well worth it. We enjoyed many more good times with Ben and Tilila, but that visit was the most memorable of all.

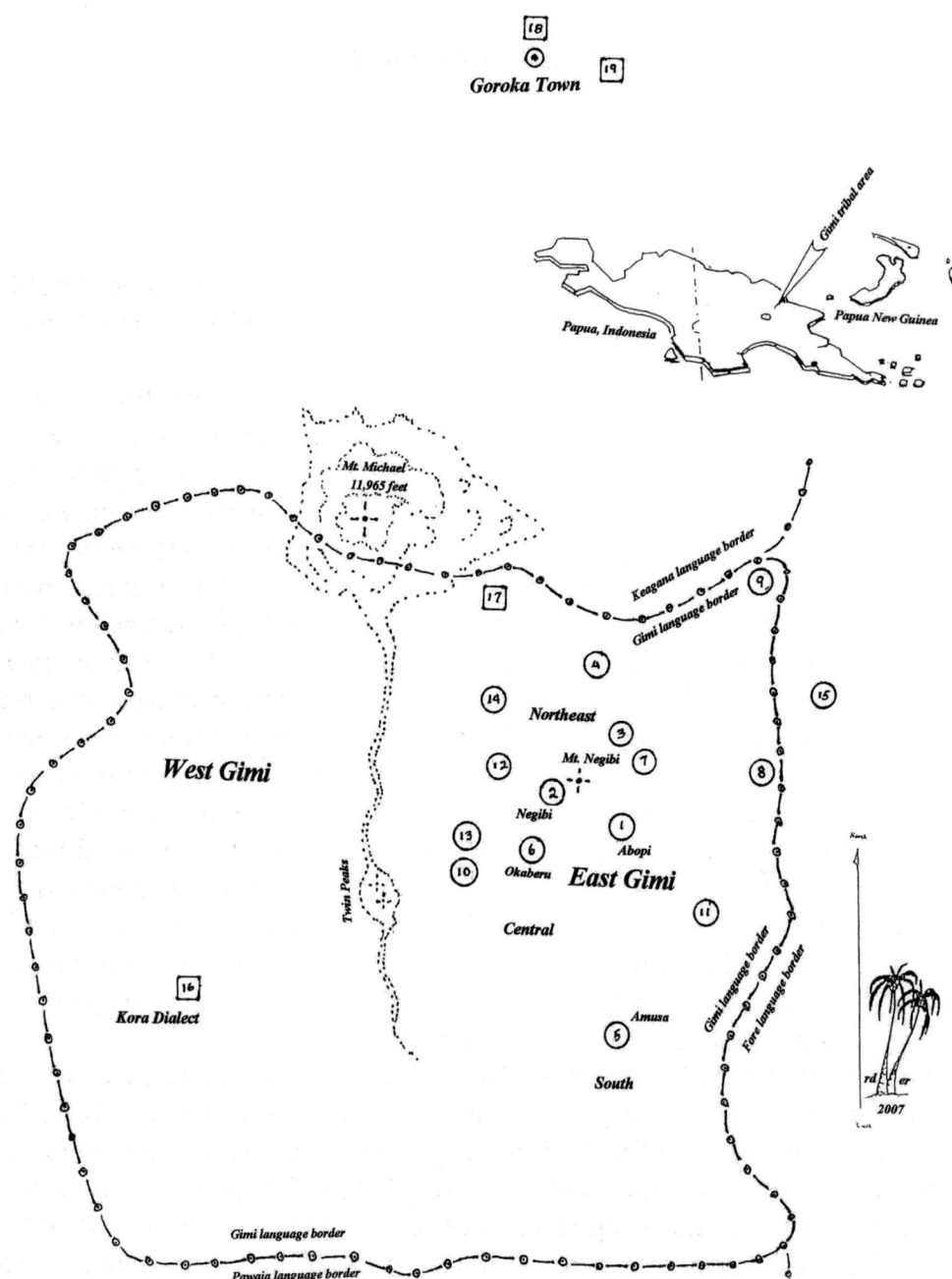

Dale's map of the Gimi tribal area © R. Dale Palmer.

Chapter 5

The Turning Point
By Dale

Mr. Downs, the District Commissioner, had wanted me to work in the West Gimi, so, after the Stewart family arrived, I did make several patrols into the area behind Mt. Michael.

Going along the west side of Mt. Michael, I arrived at the new patrol post at Lufa, around mid-afternoon. If the patrol officer should be on the station, I would visit with him over *a cuppa* (a cup of tea). Then I continued on up to Ben Wertz's place at Gono, arriving in time for dinner. Tilila, his wife, would always have a nice evening meal.

After a good night's sleep at Gono, I would swing east from Gono, hiking on to the village of Mekino. I slept the second night there. The next day, I had to cross three deep gorges to get to Hegaturu village. Then there was another deep gorge before I started climbing the ridge that divides the West Gimi from the East Gimi. Scaling this ridge required climbing up on vines and roots. The pass on the other side must be close to eight or nine thousand feet, with a breathtaking view from the top of the ridge. I was looking down on the East Gimi and turning around I could see for miles into the West Gimi.

All the time I was out on patrol in the Gono area of the West Gimi, where Mr. Downs thought I should work, I was really thinking about my promise to Esema and Meniba. I had told them that we were making plans to come and help their people in the East Gimi.

After being with us eight months, the Stewart family became discouraged and left the field. This was quite a blow to us. Following their departure, it was necessary for me to stay close to home, to look after my family. That is when I started going out to the nearby Kami villages on Sunday to preach.

If I got an early start, I could make a loop around these villages before dark. I would make the first stop at Fore Village, the village nearest us, to teach a few folks. Then I would climb up the steep cliff to Kemasi village, where quite a number of people came to hear the message. The village leader was very keen and gathered his people to hear God's Talk. Next, I would swing down under the waterfalls and have a bit of lunch, before going over to Leptapenega for a short meeting. Close by was Numago, where a few folks gathered upon my arrival. By early afternoon, I arrived at Haga village where Zona lived. Zona was the *luluai* of the village of Haga. These people were very open, and we always had good meetings at their village.

During this time, we received a letter from our fellow missionaries at *Rising Sun* saying:

> *"The work at Kami was not started right and with only one family left in the Highlands we should close the Highlands work down and move the Dale Palmer family to Rising Sun and all work together there."*

Arvalee and I were devastated, to say the least. It was like our little world was falling apart. It seemed everything was coming down around us. It was so hard losing Harold and Mary Sellers when they moved from Kami to Rising Sun. My conflict with Ian Downs, the District Commissioner, over a permit to work in the Gimi, was also very draining. Then Ken and Donna Stewart left the field. Now, our fellow missionaries wanted to close the Highlands work, just as it was getting started!

We cried out to God, "We know Lord that You are in control of all that is happening in our lives. You must be bringing us to the end of ourselves to teach us something." The old song that Paul Rader wrote in 1921 sustained us then and is still very meaningful to us today.

> *Fear not, little flock, from the cross to the throne,*
> *From death into life He went for His own;*
> *All power in earth, all power above,*
> *Is given to Him for the flock of His love.*
>
> *Only believe, only believe; All things are possible, only believe;*
> *Only believe, only believe; all things are possible, only believe.*
>
> *Fear not little flock, He goeth ahead,*
> *Your Shepherd selecteth the path you must tread;*
> *The waters of Marah He'll sweeten for thee,*
> *He drank all the bitter in Gethsemane.*
>
> *Fear not, little flock, whatever your lot,*
> *He enters all rooms, 'the doors being shut;'*
> *He never forsakes, He never is gone,*
> *So count on His presence in darkness and dawn.*
>
> *(By Paul Rader, Public Domain)*

We were broken. We did not know what to think. How could God open a work so wonderfully, and then later show twenty missionaries that He had changed His mind? How could we leave, after giving our word to Esema and Meniba that we would come and help their people? What should we do now? Arvalee and I were so upset we could hardly keep going.

After about a week, we were able to write a letter back to our fellow missionaries at Rising Sun. We shared our hearts with them, stating that we were not in agreement with their decision. We believed we had to stay in the Highlands and do all we could to keep the promise we had made to Esema, the Gimi chief. We reminded Chuck, Arnold and Harold that God had made it very clear to all four of us when they had visited us at Kami, that Arvalee and I were the ones to open the work in the Gimi tribe.

We sent our reply off, knowing it would be a month before we could receive any word back. We were praying that God would intervene on our behalf, leaving it in His Hands. Never before had we felt so alone. It was like our dearest friends had misunderstood why we were in the Highlands. All we knew for sure was that God had said in His Word that He would never, never, never leave us or forsake us. He was all we had to cling to during that very long month.

Those were the days that I was using a 125cc *BSA* (British Small Arms) street motorcycle, to transport our supplies from the town of Goroka to our Kami Mission Station. Several weeks after we sent our plea, I was in Goroka for supplies. Before leaving town, I went by the post office to see if we had received any mail. A letter was there from the Bulolo Post Office. I could not open the letter fast enough. It read:

> *"Dear Dale and Arvalee,*
>
> *The Don McCurdy family and my family will be moving up to join you and Arvalee soon.*
>
> *In the Bonds of Christ,*
>
> *Chuck"*

What a wonderful ride back home it was, with the fresh wind of hope blowing in my face! Crossing the old swinging footbridge was not hard this time, and going up the steep hill by Ludi Schmidt's place was just as easy. When I arrived at the house and showed Arvalee the letter, we cried and thanked God for this wonderful answer.

We don't know how many folks were praying for us at this time, but my dear grandmother was for sure, as was a dear lady in Australia, named Mrs. Billings, who had a prayer meeting for missionaries in the little chapel at the Church of England in downtown Sydney every Friday about noon. Christians would come in on their lunch break and pray for the missionaries on her list. We were blessed to be on that list.

In those days, decisions for the direction of the field in New Guinea required 100% agreement of the missionaries on the field. Some twenty missionaries at Rising Sun had all agreed that the Highlands work should be closed. For them to now be in agreement with Arvalee and me, we knew that God had done a wonderful work in their hearts. We thanked God that He had given us the courage to write that letter to our fellow missionaries.

It would be wonderful to have Chuck and Jean Driver and Don and Gwen McCurdy join us in the Highlands work. To Arvalee and me, this was a major turning point for New Tribes Mission in New Guinea in 1955.

The Wrong Goat
By Arvalee

After being in the country for just a year, we'd inherited a small herd of goats from Harold. We were very thankful for these goats as they provided fresh meat once in a while, instead of our steady diet of canned meat.

Dale wanted to do something special for the *luluais* (chiefs) from the five Kami villages where he'd been preaching. So he decided to kill and butcher a couple of goats and invite these men to share in a feast. We planned to cook the meat in a *mumu* (steam cooking).

Butchering a goat.

We'd been in New Guinea about three years with our three little boys, Pat, Peter and Paul. Wherever their daddy went, they wanted to go too. On the appointed day for the feast, their dad headed for the barn, a short distance away. He took his rifle and the boys walked down with him.

I looked out the front door and saw Dale walking up to the front porch, rifle in hand. He had only been gone a half hour! His slumped shoulders and the

Preparing a mumu.

downcast look on his face told me that he was upset. He looked so miserable, like he was ready to burst into tears. I rushed outside to ask him why he had come home so soon. I could only think that he must have had an accident! My mind raced, *Has Dale shot one of our sons? Oh, dear God, I hope not.* I called out, "What's the matter? What happened?"

He answered, "I shot the wrong goat. As it came around the corner, I aimed and pulled the trigger, and then I could see its eyes. It was the young goat I killed!"

Dale had planned to kill the old billy goat and an old nanny goat. In addition to these, we had about six younger nanny goats and a young billy goat that looked exactly like its father, except in its eyes, which were clear and bright. The whites of the old goat's eyes were red and terrible looking. When he told me he had mistakenly killed the young billy goat, I was so relieved that I seemed to have the right words for the moment. I simply said, "Well, you might as well shoot the old billy goat too, for he's of no use. We can find another one for breeding."

Dale went back to the barn and shot the old one, as well as the old nanny goat, as he had originally intended. Now he had three goats to butcher. Then we proceeded with our plans for cooking and preparing a feast for the chiefs.

Dale and our New Guinea helpers were busy on a nearby hillside preparing the *mumu* (steam cooking). First the rocks were heated in a wood fire. After the rocks were hot they were put into a hole in the ground and covered over with banana leaves. The food, which consisted of pumpkin, sweet potato, greens, beans and other vegetables, as well as the meat, was placed on top of these leaves and covered with more leaves. Then, earth was put over the top layer, a hole was made in the top, and water was poured into the hole through a long length of bamboo. As the water trickled down over the food, it hit the hot rocks, creating steam, cooking the food to perfection in about an hour.

While the men were butchering the goats and preparing the *mumu* on the hill, I was busy in the house washing canning jars. I planned to preserve some of the meat, because it was more than we needed for the feast. I was using a borrowed pressure cooker canner, but the weight gauge wasn't functioning properly. I propped a flat iron on the weight gauge, thinking that would help to hold it steady. However, keeping the wood burning stove at the correct temperature, stoked with just the right amount of firewood to maintain the correct heat, was a difficult task. Opening the firebox door and leaning forward to put the wood on the glowing coals exposed my face to the intense heat and presented the risky business of burned fingers as well. The day was hot enough without the task of canning all this meat. But, we had no other means of preserving it.

I had built up the fire just right and the pressure gauge seemed to be keeping a steady pressure. The last of the meat was in four quart size canning jars in the pressure cooker, so I thought I would go over and see how the *mumu* was progressing. Just as I went out the back door, the over-pressure plug blew, and steam and hot meat spewed out that tiny hole! I thought to myself, *I must have closed the door too forcefully and jarred the pressure gauge!* Meat spewed all over the ceiling! *What a mess! All that work and now all those jars of meat are lost. How in the world will we be able to clean it off the ceiling?* My worry turned to relief, however, when I realized that no one had been in the house at the time, so thankfully no one had been burned.

When we opened the cooled pressure cooker, we found only one jar of meat was lost. Much later, when money was scarce, we were very thankful to the Lord for all those jars of delicious meat on our shelves, even though it seemed to be a disastrous mistake. Then we knew why Dale had shot the wrong goat.

The next day, we tackled the huge job of cleaning the ceiling, which was constructed of woven bamboo mats. Fortunately, when building the house, Dale had placed a piece of galvanized sheet iron around the stove pipe on the ceiling for safety purposes, and that is where most of the meat had collected. Before washing the ceiling, the meat had to be scraped off the sheet iron, but Dale was so tall he was able to get the job done quite easily.

After it was all over, we remembered Romans 8:28, "And we know that all things work together for good to them that love God, to them who are the called according to His purpose."

Horses, 1955
By Arvalee

When the Sellers family left Kami, we inherited Prince, their horse. It was a stallion, a very high-spirited horse and hard to control. It was not only hard to handle, but mean. Many times, as Dale was mounting him, the beast would reach around and bite Dale on the leg. Dale had grown up riding horses, but he didn't know how to manage this one.

One day when Peter was about five years old he was standing on the other side of the fence watching Dale saddle Prince, who was tied to a fencepost. That mean, ornery horse reached across the fence and bit Peter on the shoulder. It was very painful I'm sure, because it made him cry. I was furious when I heard that the horse had bitten my little son.

A short time later, Dale went to the Government Agricultural Station in Goroka, and talked to Mr. Bell, the manager. He asked, "Mr. Bell, what can I do to control a horse that is just mean and ornery? He bites me when I start to mount him, and he bit my little son on the shoulder. What can I do?"

Mr. Bell gave Dale some advice that many might consider cruelty to animals these days. But something had to be done, short of getting rid of the horse. He told Dale, "You get a sturdy 2" x 2" board about eighteen inches long and lay it across the saddle. Then, when you put your foot in the stirrup, put your hand on the board. When the horse turns around to bite you, whack him across the top of his nose as hard as you can."

Dale did as Mr. Bell advised him and got a board ready. Sure enough, the day came when Dale was mounting the horse and it turned its head around to bite him. Dale hit him as hard as he could and a big knot swelled up across his nose.

From then on, Prince never bit anyone again. Many times, when Dale was about to mount, the horse would turn around like he used to do, but slowly turn his head back. It was as if he remembered and had decided not to bite. He had learned his lesson.

Dale still needed another horse to use for packing supplies into the Gimi. Don Mc-Curdy had an idea to buy shelled peanuts from the local people, haul them to Goroka in his Willys jeep and resell them, making a small profit to cover the cost of hauling them. This saved the people from carrying the bags of peanuts on their backs to town. He suggested to Dale, "We can use the profits from the peanuts to buy another horse."

The men had heard about an auction in Goroka where some horses would be sold. Before the event, Don and Dale went to inspect the horses and talk to the auctioneer. They saw a large mare that was a draft horse and she looked like a good horse for packing supplies. They told the auctioneer they'd like to bid on it.

When the bidding started, a local businessman started bidding against Don and Dale. Almost ignoring the businessman, the auctioneer stopped the bidding and pronounced, "Sold!" pointing to Don and Dale. It seemed they were favored by the auctioneer, perhaps because they had talked to him beforehand. Later, the businessman came to Dale offering to buy the horse for a higher price than they had paid. But Dale wasn't tempted because he needed another horse for the work. They decided to call the horse "Peanuts" because they bought her with peanut money, (money earned from hauling peanuts to market for the people).

Don was a help to us in so many ways. After the purchase of the mare, he bought a riding saddle and a pack saddle for us. He knew that these would be very helpful in opening the Gimi tribal work, and that we could not afford them because he knew our finances were short.

In time Dale tried to teach me to ride the horses. He believed it would be helpful to me to have this skill when we were ready to move into the Gimi. I had never been very athletic; therefore I had never had a desire to ride a horse. And I was, by nature, too afraid to attempt it on my own. Once, as I was riding Peanuts down the little hill that led to our house, I fell off. The horse turned to go around the curve but I didn't turn with it, so off I went! I made about three summersaults, and as I came to a stop I put my hands over my head because I thought the horse would step on me. Dale, watching from the house, saw me fall. He came out, saying, "Well, I'm glad to see you're not hurt, but you need to get back on the horse. If you don't, you may have a fear of falling and never ride again." So he helped me mount the horse again and I rode the short distance to the house. I never was a real cowgirl, but later on I did appreciate that I knew enough to stay in the saddle.

After we'd had Peanuts several months, one of the young national boys working with the horses came to the house calling, "*Yu kam kwiktaim. Hos i gat pikinini!*" (You come quickly. The horse has a baby!) We couldn't believe what he was telling us. We went with him as soon as we could to the barn, and sure enough, there was a newborn foal, still wet, with very wobbly legs. The mother was gently nuzzling it, coaxing it to suckle. We didn't even know Peanuts was expecting a baby so we called the foal "Bonus!"

Twenty-Seven Bee Stings, 1955
By Arvalee

The land where the mission station was built was parched from lack of adequate rain. As we walked down a trail, there were many places where the ground had dried out, creating great crevasses. It was quite useless to put a metal roof on the houses to catch rain water, for it seldom rained and it would never meet our needs. The necessity for water was quite desperate for our two families because we had three sons, and Don and Gwen had two little boys.

For our water needs we relied on a small spring which produced a trickle of water that accumulated in a deep pool. Using a horse with a pack saddle, we hauled water in four drums of five gallons each, an arduous journey up and down the hill. We were concerned this might not be very healthy water so we boiled every drop of it for drinking.

We urgently needed a better supply of water for our families so Dale and Don decided to dig a well on a location a good ways over the hill from our houses. Our little boys would go over day after day to watch the men and their helpers dig. Paul was about three and a half; he was a little *tag-along*, following our two older boys and Dale Mc-Curdy. The men were digging with picks and shovels, so this was taking quite a long time. After all their effort, I don't believe they ever found water.

One day the older boys came charging in, all excited about the day's adventures. I asked them, "Where's Paul?"

"Oh, he's coming," they replied offhandedly.

A few minutes later, Dale came rushing in, carrying Paul in his arms. This caused me some anxiety because I couldn't see immediately that anything was wrong with him. There were death adders in the grasslands, I knew, and I feared he might have been bitten by a snake.

Dale called, "Get the baking soda. Paul has been stung with *kunai* bees (hornets)."

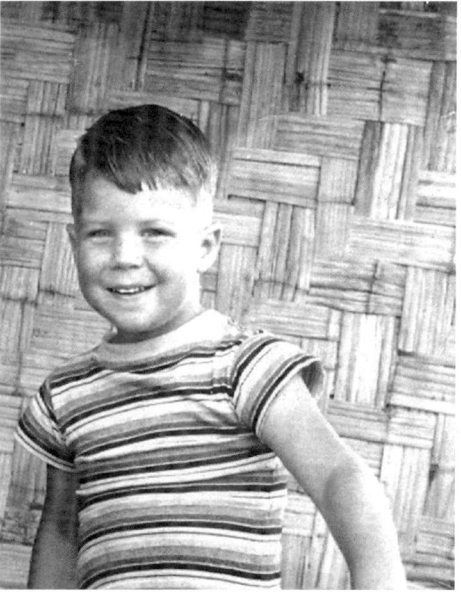

I got the soda immediately, and mixed it with a little water to make a paste. We had often used this method when one of us would get stung with a bee, so we knew that it did relieve the pain. But the sting of these bees was quite different than the sting of a honey bee. After a honey bee stings, it looses the stinger; therefore, it quits stinging. However, *kunai* bees, a small type of hornet, can sting repeatedly and must be picked off a person, one by one.

Paul on his 4th birthday.

Dale had found Paul rolling and writhing in pain on the ground. He was helpless to get up because his body, head, and face were covered with *kunai* bees. We later realized that as the older boys had run through the high *kunai* grass they had stirred up the bees, which were nesting amidst the tall grasses. In their excitement to get home, the older boys were not aware that they had stirred the bees from their nest. Little *tag-along* had been outrun by the three older boys, and the bees caught him. Dale found him just in time.

As we applied the baking soda, we counted at least twenty-seven stings. He was soon asleep and the swelling gradually subsided. We knew God surely had His hand on our little Paul that day, for we knew many people were allergic to bee stings and would never have survived such a severe attack.

Meniba and Our Dream of a Horse Road
By Dale

Before my permit to enter the East Gimi came through from Port Moresby, I wanted to find out if Meniba would work for me. I thought he would be a good man to have around. He was a young man who was familiar with five languages in the area where I would be traveling, and I needed this kind of helper at my elbow all the time. Along with the Gimi, Meniba understood and spoke some of the Yagaria, the Keagana and the Fore languages. In addition, he knew the trade language, Pidgin English. So I went off to find Meniba.

Without authorization to enter the East Gimi, I could only go as far as the Henagaru Government Rest House (GRH). When I arrived there I explained to some Henagaru men that I needed to contact Meniba in the Gimi. One of them offered to call out for Meniba to come over to Henagaru to see me, and proceeded to do so.

This *calling* is a beautiful thing to witness. The man crouches down with one knee on the ground and cups his hands over his mouth. Then he begins to call. The sound which he makes comes from deep down inside, and the blood vessels in his neck bulge as his voice carries over the mountains with a resounding echo. It sounded more like a yodel as it bounced off the cliff walls. I love watching them yodel.

To my delight, Meniba walked over the next morning. I talked to him about working for me out at Kami. Meniba stood in front of me and said, "I have three things that I want to do if I work for you. First, I want a bank book," which meant he wanted a savings account book at a bank. "I want to learn to shoot a shot gun and I want to learn to ride a horse."

"We can do all those things, and more," I told him. I could tell that he was pleased with this job offer. Then I asked, "Do you think your wife would come out to Kami and work for my wife and help her learn the Gimi language?"

"I don't know if she will come," he replied. "I will need to go talk to her." So off he went, back to his village at Mt. Negibi. The next day, about noon, I could see a group of people coming up the ridge. There were some women with them.

Meniba's wife must not have been even five feet tall, and she was very young. She was dressed in traditional Gimi fashion. She wore a pony tail skirt made from bark string around her waist, which leaves the hips bare. Her head was covered with a bark string cap, decorated with *girigiri shells*, (small sea shells), spaced all around the edges. Her beautiful dark eyes were focused on me, and she spoke to me. Meniba translated, "She wants to know if there is *iremu* (edible greens) out there."

"Yes." I told her, "We have all kinds of greens."

This young woman was much smarter than most civilized people when it comes to a well-balanced diet. You see, their staple food is sweet potatoes but one cannot eat sweet potatoes alone. They need greens, and lots of them, to balance their diet. So when she asked me if there were greens out where I lived, she was thinking of her health.

She was speaking again and wanted to know, "Can I have a space to make a garden?"

"Yes, you can," I told her.

I asked her name and Meniba replied, "It's Mu-u-nabi."

In the Gimi culture one will rarely say his or her own name for an introduction, someone else always says their name for them.

She was one spunky little gal. Mu-u-nabi and Arvalee learned a lot from each other.

Mu-u-nabi's arrival at Kami was her first experience outside the Gimi and the first time she had entered the home of a white person. We had a simple bush house, made of woven bamboo mats and a grass thatched roof, but imagine her amazement at seeing a braided rag rug on the floor and curtains on the windows! I'm sure it was all overwhelming to this little Gimi woman, perhaps no more than 16 years old. Her top was bare but she was not embarrassed in the least. She could not speak nor understand Pidgin English, and Arvalee had no knowledge of the Gimi language, but they began trying to communicate with each other.

Mu-u-nabi worked for Arvalee in the house for several years. Arvalee taught her to help in the kitchen with food preparation, and to sweep and wash the woven bamboo floors. After a few months we realized she was expecting. When the time came, she wanted to have her baby at home in the Gimi, so Meniba took her back. Afterward, we learned her baby and our little girl were born within two weeks of each other.

Arvalee with our helpers at Kami.

Mr. Downs' main objective was to construct a car road into the Lufa and Gono areas on the northwest side of Mt. Michael. This would not help us, because we needed to skirt the southeast side of Mt. Michael. For our purposes at this time, a car road was not necessary. We only needed a small trail for our pack horses to use. We needed a supply line into this remote area and that is how the horse road idea was born.

My permit to work in the East Gimi came through from Port Moresby, and the Drivers and McCurdy families arrived at approximately the same time. This freed me to start making trips into the East Gimi.

Whenever Meniba and I walked between Kami and the Gimi we were always looking for a place to make a horse road. We would talk about it at night when we made camp. We would talk about it when we were walking. Meniba knew enough language in the Keagana and Yagaria tribes to find out if they would let us cut a road through their areas.

One night, after we had eaten and were sitting around the fire talking, Meniba said to me, "You're going to get killed."

I asked him, "Why?"

"You don't look where you're going."

This was a shock to me, for I thought I was a pretty fair hiker.

"You must always be watching for trouble," he said. "Your eyes should be scanning out in front of you and above you, and to each side, and you should watch where you are putting your feet. Glance behind you often, and don't take a step off the trail, because there are pig trap holes that have sharpened bamboo spikes down in the bottom."

I thanked Meniba for telling me this. I know it helped me travel these trails more safely. *"See then that ye walk circumspectly, not as fools but as wise"* (Ephesians 5:15). I believe Meniba was teaching me to walk circumspectly, like a wise man should. Meniba became a very dear friend and God used him greatly in the birth of the Gimi church.

Dale and Meniba off to road work.

Chapter 6

A Choice Land Site
By Dale

In choosing a site to build a home for my family, and the first mission station in the Gimi, my primary thought was the availability of water. This was greatly influenced by the location of the previous site, at Kami, where we were always in need of it. On this morning, the five chiefs and I had looked at three possible land sites for building a mission station. Two of the plots of land had water several hundred feet below the land site, which made them undesirable.

When Esema led me further up the mountain to a spring, I knew this third piece of land (where we had been staying), would be the ideal spot I had hoped for. The spring was about a quarter of a mile up Mt. Negibi, quite a bit higher than the ridge we had been staying on. There were lots of trees obscuring our view, but I could tell we were higher than the landsites on the other ridges the chiefs had shown me. I could envision a water race carrying a supply of clean, spring water down the mountainside to our mission station on the ridge. Because of the fresh spring water, I felt this piece of ground would make a better mission station.

As the sun was set-ting and the highland air was getting cooler, one of the Gimi men reached into his net bag and took out a small rattan vine, some three feet long. He placed the rattan around a stick of wood with some dry moss and started pull-ing the rattan back and forth until there was smoke coming from the moss. In a short time,

Mt. Negibi in the 1960s.

we all hunkered down around the warm fire, which felt good to me, wearing shorts and a shirt, and to the men with me, who only wore loin cloths and bark string net capes on their backs. (These net bags and net capes are woven for the men by the women of the tribe. The net bags are called *bilums*.)

The *luluais* (chiefs) pulled out their bamboo pipes from their net bags and started smoking. We sat around the glowing fire, talking well into the night. Finally, I told the five *luluais* that this ridge we were on would be a very desirable location for a mission station. They talked for some time in the Gimi language, which I didn't understand. Then Esema, the main chief who had invited me into the Gimi, stood up and said, "*A-o-bana* (pink man) you can have the ridge, the water and all the trees around the ridge and up to the source of the spring. They are yours to build a mission station. If anyone cuts a tree from this land they must first get your permission."

All five men were in agreement that this was in fact the best place for us to live. Wow, how these words encouraged me and thrilled my heart! Now I could proceed with my plans to build the mission station and I would figure out a way to bring that water down the mountain. In time, all of the five clans started clearing the ridge and built a large round bush house for me. Later, I learned that this very ridge was the crossroads for many travelers.

Arvalee and the kids had been waiting for four years to move into the Gimi. I was looking forward to having my family with me, so we could live together on this pictur-esque mountain ridge that we would call home, hopefully for many years.

The Gimis called me *A-o-bana* for a long time. *A-o* means red or pink in color and *bana* is the Gimi word for man. When more Europeans came into the Gimi they started using my name, which they pronounced *Deo*.

Esema, the Leader of His People
By Dale

As I sat and rejoiced on this high, cloud-covered ridge in the heart of New Guinea, my thoughts drifted to the five men sitting with me. They were all tribal chiefs, called *luluais* by the Government. The rippling muscles on their bodies were shining from the red vegetable oil they rub on their skin, called *abai* in the local Gimi language. They say this oil keeps their skin from getting dry. It looks like ketchup, feels like olive oil, and tastes, well, maybe a bit like avocado with the stretch of your imagination. *Abai* is the fruit of one species of the *pandanus* tree family.

While watching these handsome young men, with their stout chests and powerful arms and legs, it made a lasting impression on my mind. These tribal men, who had formerly been fight leaders, were the leaders of five northern clans around Mt. Negibi.

As I look back over the years, I realize that these young men were all about my own age. They all remembered the Second World War was going on as they were going through their tribal initiation ceremony. Gimi boys start their first of five initiations into manhood when they are around ten or twelve years old. So depending on what stage of initiation they were in at the time they saw their first airplane and heard the explosions of the bombs, it gives a rough idea of how old they might have been at the time of the war. I was between thirteen and fifteen years old when the fighting was going on in New Guinea, so we were roughly the same age.

It was good to have the full support of Esema in this and our future endeavors. I am so thankful the Lord allowed me to know and work with such a noble fight leader. It was an honor to just be with men like Esema and Meniba. They were exceptional leaders, and I count it a privilege to have worked so closely with them throughout the years in the northeast Gimi area. Both of them passed away several years ago and are now being rewarded for all they did to bring the Good News to countless tribal people in the Gimi.

I believe God put it into the heart of Esema to walk into our humble mission station there at Kami and ask me if I could send someone to help his people. God had me in the right place at the right time to hear this request. I thank Him often for choosing me to do His biddings.

Our Bridge Washed Out
By Dale

A few days before the Drivers and McCurdys were to arrive at our Kami Mission Station, we had a flash flood that washed out our swinging footbridge. This bridge spanned the river that separated us from the town of Goroka to the north, so in reality we were cut off from the outside world.

Mind you, this bridge was not much to look at. The handrail was barbed wire fencing, which was all Ludi Schmidt had to work with at the time he did the construction. But it was our only way of crossing the fast-flowing Dunantina River. So, we had to look where we were stepping to stay on the one-by-six inch planks and at the same time avoid getting snagged on the barbed wire.

Ludi built this small footbridge to get supplies in from Goroka and to provide a way of transporting the coffee beans from his young coffee plantation. This river was not only swift, but was also deep and maybe fifty to sixty feet across. All things considered, we were so thankful for this little bridge that spanned the Dunantina River.

It was quite a trick to get my 185 pound *BSA* motor bike across this swinging bridge.

On the northern approach, I had to walk beside the running cycle as we climbed a ramp about fifteen to eighteen feet long. At the top of the ramp, I would stop, mount the cycle, put it out of gear, and use the right hand brake with one hand while clutching the barbed wire railing with the other. I had to steer with the brake hand and at the same time skip my other hand along the wire, hoping to avoid all the barbs. Because the bridge was sagging in the center, I had to get off the cycle in the middle of the bridge, but before I got off, I had to kick start the bike so it could pull itself up the other side. I did try riding it up once, but that was not really too smart. It was better to walk the bike up under its own power. There was also a ramp exiting the south side of the bridge. This ramp was steeper, and the brakes would not always hold the bike back. I remember losing it a few times coming down that ramp.

As much trouble as I'd had on that old cable foot bridge, it was a great loss to lose our only link to the outside world!

The Old Swinging Foot-Bridge Crossing The Durnantina River

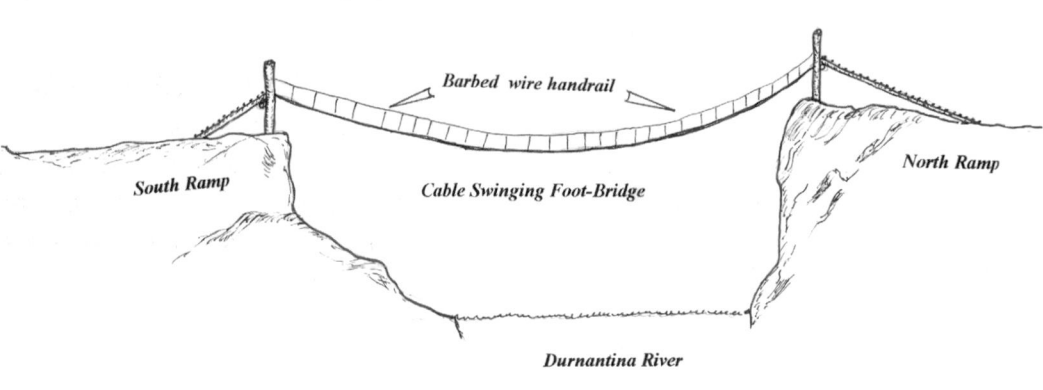

© R. Dale Palmer.

John Thyer was the Australian Patrol Officer at Lufa at this time, and he was on our doorstep the day after the bridge washed out asking me to help him build a raft to cross the river. John was a fine young man and I surely enjoyed working with him on this raft project. I discovered he was a very strong swimmer. Without the footbridge, John and I had to swim the river and then walk most of the 36 miles to the town of Goroka. In Government stores we chose six good 44-gallon drums, two sizes of cable, wooden planks and all we needed to build a raft.

Upon our return we chose one strong tree on each side of the river to anchor the larger cable to. Each end was about four feet off the ground. With the cable now stretch-

The Walkway on the Foot-Bridge

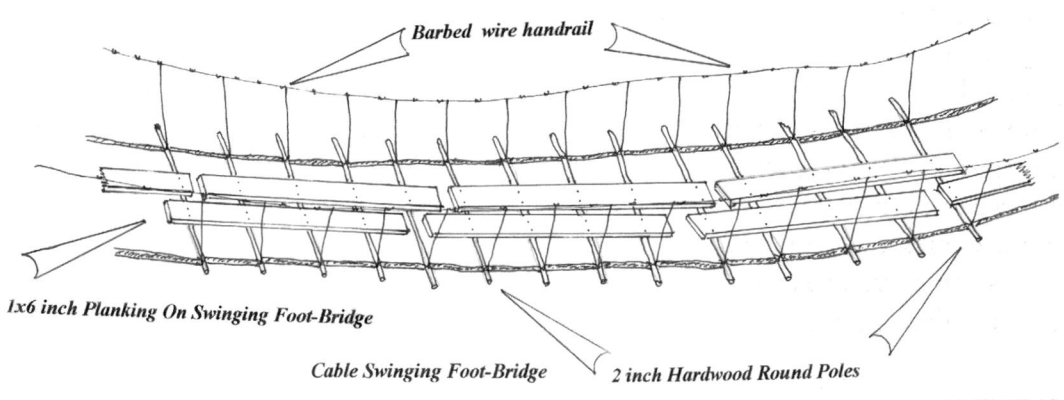

Barbed wire handrail

1x6 inch Planking On Swinging Foot-Bridge

Cable Swinging Foot-Bridge   2 inch Hardwood Round Poles

ing tightly across the river, we were ready to construct the raft. We wired the six large drums together and built a platform on top of these using the wooden planks.

We fastened one end of the smaller cable to the raft and the other to the big cable across the river. In this way we could navigate the crossing by standing on the raft and pulling ourselves across, hand over hand, using the larger cable. It took us just a few days to construct this efficient system to get us across the river.

The Raft that John Thyer and I Built to Cross the River.

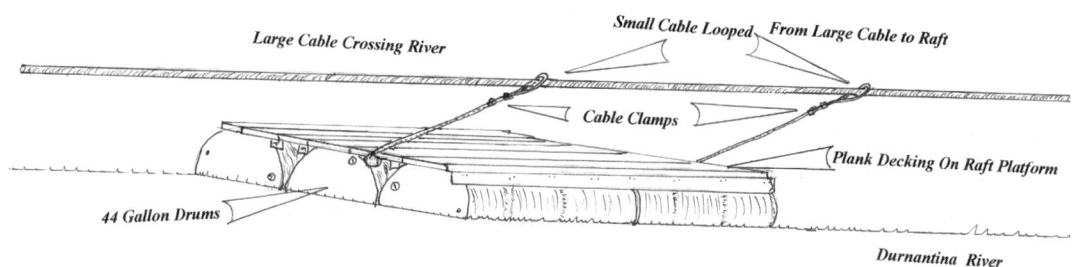

Large Cable Crossing River

Small Cable Looped   From Large Cable to Raft

Cable Clamps

Plank Decking On Raft Platform

44 Gallon Drums

Durnantina River

We could stand on the raft and pull ourselves across with the large cable.

We were grateful that by the time the Driver and McCurdy families arrived we had a sturdy means for crossing the Dunantina River. It was also a good feeling to once again have a route to the outside world.

The Gimi Horse Road
(Excerpts from Dale's Diary, 1955)
(See Appendix, page 379 for entire diary.)

Dale planned a trip to the Gimi with Meniba, so he could hire men to help with constructing a road for the horses to bring in supplies after we moved in. Without a supply line, he knew we couldn't live there as a family.

08/31/55. I had prayer this morning with Chuck and Don. Don closed in prayer. Chuck and I left Kami about 8 a.m. on the motorbike, a 125 cc *BSA*. We met Meniba and Lamafu at the spring near the old Casarina tree near Olaguti village. Chuck took the bike back to Kami, and the three of us started off hiking down the little trail, bound for Fusa. We stopped at the river and had a short swim.

We arrived at Fusa *GRH* (Government Rest House) about 3:00 p.m. Later, I walked up on a hill where I could see a road site from Fusa to Kisivero. We will have to work a new road through this area. Tonight Lamafu and I prayed together. Meniba was there, too.

09/01/55. Read the first chapter of Philippians. Left Fusa about 6:00 or 6:30. We walked hard all day, stopping very little. We got to Henagaru about 4 p.m.

09/02/55. I had a little meeting in the house last night for the local people. The nationals of Henagaru said that they knew nothing about God. Some of the young men said that they would come and work for me and I could teach them more.

Looking to the northwest from Henagaru I can see a high white rocky cliff. Below is the *Zani* (Thani) River that runs up into the east corner of Mt. Michael. The mountain looks to be about 9,000 or 10,000 feet. Our destination today is Amusa.

Everything has been going very well, but, as Mel Wyma used to say, "There is always calm before a storm." I never know what to expect from the Enemy.

As we headed toward Amusa, we were walking south, going along the broad *Zani* River, which is moving along at about four or five miles an hour, faster than I can walk. I think that I must walk about three miles an hour. The *Zani* is the big river here in the Gimi. It is well over my head in most places and from 20 to 30 feet across along here. About noon today we had a heavy rain. It just poured. We quickly cut some banana leaves and covered up our *cargo* (supplies) as well as we could, but we all got wet. Praise the

Lord, the bedding and clothes didn't. The rain made the river look like it was boiling. This morning it was a deep green color. We stood and watched as the *Zani* turned to a color like coffee with cream. We arrived here at Uvai about 3:00 p.m. and it was still raining. So I thought it best to sleep here tonight, in the Government Rest Houses.

09/03/55. Saturday. Meniba and I walked down to Amusa this morning to pick up my camping things that had been stored there in an old trunk for about four months. We got some fellows to carry them back to Uvai. We were back about 1:00 p.m. The pots, pans and dishes that had been in the trunk were all covered with mold, so Lamafu had a big dish washing job.

We had a talk today about the *cargo cult*. If a national believes in the *cargo cult*, he thinks material objects like canned meat, pots, pans, shoes, clothes and tools are sent from their ancestors and just fall from the sky. Meniba showed the local nationals the jar of goat meat that Arvalee had canned, hoping to give the people a better understanding of where things such as *tinned* (canned) meat come from. Meniba told them, "This canned meat doesn't come from God or our ancestors, but from big pigs (referring to any large animal) that the white man (pink man or European) has. They kill the big pigs and cook the meat and put it in the *tins* (cans) and bottles." No one said anything, but everyone was listening.

Praise God for the book of Philippians that I've been reading. God, through Paul, is teaching me more how to live for others. Also, my spiritual life has a lot of room for improvement. Paul said in chapter 3:10, "That I may know Him, and the power of His resurrection, and the fellowship of His sufferings, being made conformable unto His death:" I like to read it from the Williams version. There it reads a little differently. Paul is referring to our spiritual and moral resurrection, not the final physical resurrection.

The Devil is trying to discourage me because we didn't see the 10 fellows come in today, these whom we were hoping to hire to work on the road. We were counting on them to go out to Kami and work on the road with us. Praise the Lord. I believe they will be in. He won't let me down. I told Meniba we would get them, but he said that he didn't know where. I told him that I believed God would send in the ten men to work.

09/05/55. We are still at Uvai. We had a meeting this morning, and I taught on the creation and the fall of man. I feel a real open spirit with the folk. Wa-uwa's *luluai* (chief) asked me, "Where do we go when we die (where do the dead go)?" I told him what the Bible said.

Praise the Lord! Eleven fellows were lined up to work. I knew they would come.

The Word has been a real blessing as I've been reading in the book of Philippians. If we just tell God what we want, and not man, then because of our union with Christ Jesus, we have the peace of God. God is at peace and wants us to be. That must be in our minds, since He said it "surpasses all human thought." What I especially like is that He said He would keep guard over our hearts and thoughts. I've been looking for some way to guard my heart and thoughts.

09/06/55. Then Paul tells us to "practice" thinking. I like that. He says, "Practice thinking on things that are true, honorable, right, pure, and lovable, high toned, excellent, and praise worthy." This is a lot to practice thinking about. I have surely received a lot of help by reading Philippians at this time.

We got to Amuraisa this afternoon.

I've been asking God to show me how to teach these people. I am sure He is, starting now. Tonight I was outlining some thoughts on teaching about God. I feel I should teach at the same time about Jesus. Then it came like the lights coming on. Where does the Holy Spirit come into the picture? Looking into God's Word and seeing the place of the Holy Spirit, it is clear that He has just as much importance in the teaching of the gospel. I would just like to stay here and teach them.

09/07/55. We got the seven *cargo boys* (carriers) off to Fusa this morning. We now have ten men to work.

We didn't get away from the *GRH* (rest house) until 8:00 or 8:30 and we got to Muye late, about 5:00 p.m. this afternoon. We got rained on a little, but not bad. Sure was tired tonight. I will send Lamafu and the carriers on to Fusa, and Meniba and I will walk up in the hills and see if we can find a good road site across from Fusa to Muye. It's about two hours closer than following the old trail.

09/08/55. We got here to Kosotaka rest house today about 1:00 p.m. We will make this our first base camp for the road work. I've had an upset stomach for two days, so I was not very strong for walking.

I think there is a real possibility of putting the road over on the east end of Mt. Michael. Also, it looks good from Fusa to Kisevero, but from there to here, I don't see the way yet.

I trust we'll be able to get going on the road on Monday, from the Yali tree (at Olaguti) this way.

09/12/55. Went down to Kami for the weekend, and had some good fellowship with the folks. It was good to see the wife and kids again. Chuck said the *luluai* (chief) and the leader from Kemasi told him they have received Christ Jesus as their Redeemer. Praise God.

We got the road started today and I'm looking for Satan to hit any time now. How it will be, we will never know. I came back to the house about noon and Prince (the horse) and I walked over to the place where I thought the road should go. It looks really good, and I'm planning on *marking* it tomorrow, Lord willing.

I think I will just start teaching from Genesis and about God. I feel the rest will come later.

Satan came over me, in a way, saying there was no peace for me. Then the Holy Spirit reminded me of Philippians 4:4–10, *"Let your forbearing spirit be known to everybody...keep on making your wants known to God..."* Praise God for showing me this.

09/15/55. Lamafu quit work on the 13ᵗʰ and I've been doing all of my housework. It's best that he did quit, because then I didn't have to fire him. I'm asking God to send me a good worker to help in the house. (My camping house)

The road is moving along, slowly, but looking right good.

I've been teaching the workers about the fall of man. I feel my real job is to feed these sheep, or lambs. They are really lambs.

09/16/55. I had Meniba in for supper last night. When we were done, Meniba sat back in the chair and said, *"Bel bilong mi i-tait"* (my stomach is full). He said it was sure good, and then he thanked me two or three times.

We had all the workers come up and, as we washed the dishes, we played the records in Pidgin from Gospel Recordings. I feel that God is going to give us some real followers out of these fellows. I have got to pray more for them.

09/18/55. The nationals came this morning from Kosotaka and wanted to hear the talk from the Bible about God. I felt really bad because I had no one to interpret for me, so I couldn't talk to them. At times like this I don't know what to do. We have got to make the gospel available soon to these poor people living in darkness.

Wa-uwa came in from Kami with a big apple pie from the Kami bakery (Arvalee). It surely is good. The guys all came up and asked if they could play the recorder, so Wa-uwa is playing it for them. Meniba should be up in a bit with a *pas* (letter) from Arvalee.

Meniba got back all right, and a letter from Arvalee let me know that she and the boys would like to come up and stay a while. This idea had never entered my mind. I prayed and felt a real peace about it.

09/20/55. Today the carriers and I went down to Kami to get Arvalee and the kids. We all got back to Kosotaka just before sunset. We have all enjoyed this week. Arvalee said it was like camping out. Well it is camping out, but just not like at home in the States.

The nationals have been bringing plenty of food, for which we have been thanking the Lord. Also the people of Kosotaka have been coming and asking to hear God's Word. Today we got down to some good points, but they haven't shown a conviction as of yet. We must pray more for them. Each morning I have been teaching a bit from the Word, to the men that are working. I'm teaching from the Old Testament.

09/24/55. Pat, Peter and Paul have been having a great time with all the little boys and girls up here. They climb trees and play with their bows and arrows, which the nationals have made for them. They play like they are pigs, grunting like pigs at each other. There are plenty of real pigs here.

This is the end of two weeks and the road is well on its way down to the first river. We should be there by the middle of the week. We will be to the river tomorrow and have started up the other side of the river. We are going slowly, but I feel we will have a good road for the horse to carry *cargo* (supplies) on and for the motorbike. It will save a few steps.

We've asked Meniba and Mu-u-nabi to come for a fried chicken dinner tonight. They gave us one of the chickens and we bought the other. I have felt that the Lord is going to save Meniba someday soon. Meniba has shown nothing to build up my hopes, but as I've been praying, the Lord has given me this peace.

10/21/55. During the month Arvalee and children spent with me here, in Kosotaka, I didn't get much writing done, but we surely had a wonderful time together. They are back at Kami in our little home now and I'm here alone again. It's sure quiet around here without them and it is terribly lonesome now without them. The Kosotaka kids enjoyed having three little white boys to play with. They played kickball a lot and we had so many bananas that we had a banana eating contest. It was just a good time for our family to be out with the village people. We all had a lot of fun together.

We are moving our camp closer to the road work.

These days are real days of testing. The Devil is using his blinded sheep to cause all types of trouble. As we started working on the road today, one *luluai* (chief) from Olaguti (PoPo) said that I had to buy a *matmat* (burial place) for one pound. I told him I didn't think he was right, for I was just following the old trail at this place. I left the matter there.

> *Last Saturday the 15th, when I was sick in bed, Meniba came up and said a luluai was going to kill all of the workers for working the road on his ground. So the fellows had all stopped working. I got up and rode the horse to the road site.*
>
> *Before I went, Arvalee, the kids and I prayed and asked the Lord to really work in the luluai's heart. He did! Praise His Name! When I got there, the luluai said we could make the road there, and he even helped. I saw him today, and he was really nice.*
>
> *Arvalee and the kids are back at Kami in our little home now and I'm here alone again. It's quiet around here without them. We are moving our camp closer to the road work.*

The old *luluai* (chief) of this valley of Olaguti has been a real help to me in *marking* the road so far, but tonight he has just told me that he wants pay for the entire road. Everything must be placed in God's hands. I cannot bear these burdens alone. There is peace when God is holding everything. (These kinds of incidents happened about once a week during the entire two years that we were working on the road.)

Off and on for two years, Meniba and I did most of the *marking* of the road. We had 200 men digging with picks and shovels and four work leaders overseeing 50 men each.

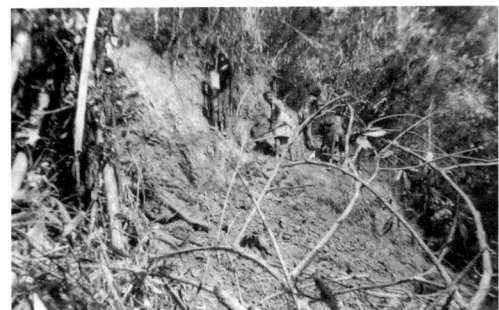

I could buy shovels without handles by the dozen, and the men would make their own handles. The shovel was part of their pay for working. I paid the 200 workers with other trade goods as well, such as steel bush knives, and red cloth for a wrap-around sarong, called a *laplap*. The four work leaders were paid with money.

Digging the road using shovels.

Two of the work leaders, Bebu and Meniba, were good friends, so Meniba wanted Bebu to work with him. Bebu was a very hard worker but had no idea how to lead and manage the 50 men working under him. So Meniba would go show Bebu how to lead the workers so they could get some road made. Wa-uwa was a young Gimi teenager and could keep his 50 men

Meniba and Biru, Dale's helper and cook.

The boss boys 'foremen' for the road work crews; Kalabus, Wa-uwa, Bebu and Meniba.

working well. One thing Wa-uwa had going for him was that he knew some of the Yagaria language, and got along well with the men working under him.

Each morning before we started work, I would teach

a Bible story to all our workers with the gospel woven into it. One day Meniba and Bebu told me that they believed that Jesus died for their sins. These were the first Gimi believers. It was about Christmas time when Meniba and Bebu shared with me how they believed the Good News about Jesus Christ. We stopped working on the road for a month during Christmas and the new year. When Bebu returned from his Christmas break in the Gimi he told me this story.

"When I arrived back in my home village of O-aberu, some of the men were working sorcery on the chest of a teenage girl. She had died and the sorcery was to find out which clan had killed her."

A man holds a bamboo about 18 inches long on the chest of the dead person and there are some arrows in the bamboo with the arrow tips pointing up. The man holding the bamboo calls out the names of the clans one at a time, and if the chest should jerk at the time of calling that clan's name, the people believe they are the ones who are responsible for the death.

Bebu went on. "I told the man to stop. I prayed and asked Jesus to raise the girl up. She woke and then sat up. Everyone was shocked. The girl is still alive and doing fine."

I asked Bebu, "How did you know to do this?"

He replied, "I don't know. I knew what the man was doing was wrong and I just told him to stop and he did. All I knew to do then was pray for this young girl on the platform in the center of the village. Everyone's eyes were watching me."

I had never told any Bible stories about Jesus healing or raising people from the dead. All I can say is that God gave this new believer childlike faith to believe that God was big enough to raise the dead and bring honor and glory to Himself among these *Stone Age* (see glossary) tribal people.

The End of the Road
By Dale

With this many men working, we were able to cut a four-foot-wide horse road through the Northeast foothills of Mt. Michael quite rapidly. Meniba and I had *marked* (surveyed) the road well into the Keyagana, and the horse road was finished about two hours past Anupuru, the village where we had built the new rest house.

I would like to tell you why I chose Anupuru to build my rest house. It is about an eight hour walk from the Kami Mission Station for one thing, but the real reason is because the people of Anupuru were so warm and friendly to me and my workers. Many men from Anupuru worked on the horse road. They were just nice folks and always brought us lots of food to buy. We sometimes say Nupuru because the initial *a* is a soft *a*. When the local people speak the name of their place, you can hardly hear the *a*, because it is so soft.

I recall this incident one day, as we were building our own rest house at Anupuru. The workers were putting the *kunai* grass on the round roof house when a man walked over to me and said, "The way they are putting the *kunai* grass on is not right. Your house will leak when it rains. I can show them how to do it right."

"Okay," I said. "Give it a go."

This stranger climbed up on the roof and started taking all the *kunai* grass off and setting it beside him. The men on the roof stopped working and watched the stranger. He took a handful of *kunai* grass and twisted it several times before folding it over and tapping it tightly against the other grass, and then he tied it tightly with vines. In this way he did a full row around the house and then asked, "Who wants to try the next row?" He watched as the men followed his instructions.

After awhile, he came down off the roof and I asked him if he was looking for a job.

"Yes, I would like a job working for you, but you may not really want me working for you."

"Why is that?" I asked.

Meniba with a log for the bridge.

He replied, "I have been in prison for killing a boy in my home village." He told me he had just been released. I talked it over with Meniba that night and we felt he had served his time in prison for his crime and that maybe we could help him. I gave him 50 men to be in charge of. We just called him *Kalabus*, the Pidgin word for jail or prison. By the way, *Kalabus* was a good overseer of his men and that *kunai* grass roof never leaked, but lasted for years.

About a 12 to 15 hour's walk into the northeast Gimi, the people had started clearing the land at Mt. Negibi on the south ridge of the mountain to build our Mission Station. Meniba and I were spending time in the Gimi and on the horse road. We finally had to stop the work on the horse road to be able to spend more time in the Gimi.

The bridge beams.

The bridge decking.

George Fatzinger, a single missionary, would continue working on the road, to see the project to completion. This was a great relief to me to know the horse road would be finished.

Indeed, these were exciting days as we had made good progress on the horse road and now that the land at Negibi was being cleared where our Gimi home would be built, I could begin to hope for the future when the family would be able to join me.

~PART THREE~

Our Dream…A Reality

Chapter 7

The Old Water Race
By Dale

During those years of waiting, I was always thinking, *How in the world are we going to get that water on Mt. Negibi down that rugged mountain ridge to our mission station?*

Someone had given me a Boy Scout book before we came to New Guinea. It stated that for water to flow, it needed to have a one inch drop every 12 feet. I thought, *well, that doesn't sound too hard. Now how do we go about getting that water from its source to our home?*

We needed a channel to carry the water down the mountain ridge. One problem was that I had very little money to work with. Because there was no jeep road, anything brought in from the town of Goroka would have to be carried on the backs of the people for three days, over a rugged trail, and this would be very expensive. So we had to improvise like old Robinson Crusoe did and use whatever we had on hand.

I wanted to see my dream of installing a water race become a reality before Arvalee and the children were scheduled to move in. I had watched the Gimi people making bush salt, using a split *pandanus* tree, with the soft pithy inside chopped out to make a channel. And there were a number of long straight *pandanus* trees between the mission station and the water source. I talked it over with Meniba and he thought we could use these trees to make a channel, so he chose 20 young men and they started cutting down the tall trees.

The *pandanus* tree has a hard bark on the outside like a palm tree. Some of these great trees were quite long; maybe 20 to 30 feet long and eight to ten inches in diameter. The men split the trees in half lengthwise, then chopped out the pithy inside of the tree with their bush knives. It was, for sure, a rough looking trough for water to flow through.

The men working with us on this project were now getting excited. To construct the water race, these *pandanus* troughs had to be raised off the ground and rested on crisscrossed poles that zigzagged down the mountain slope. The area between the spring and our station was a feeding area for village pigs, so the water race had to be raised to keep the pigs from rooting it up and making a mess of everything. The water from the spring on Mt. Negibi was channeled to flow into these rough troughs down the mountain ridge to our home. We used a line level to be sure each channel had enough slope to keep the water flowing.

This rough channel worked just great. We had a 24-hour water supply of about one inch in depth and about three inches wide. It was fresh, pure mountain water and it met all the needs of our family, and our partner's family as well. Plus, there was enough for all the people in the nearby village. That old water race was a blessing to many people.

The Water Race in the Gimi from Mt. Negibi to the mission station.

© R. Dale Palmer.

One morning I went outside to find that the trough was dry. No water was flowing at all, so I put on my boots and started up the muddy ridge to see what was wrong. *Maybe a tree had fallen over in the night and broken the water race. Or maybe pigs had somehow broken down the race.* I guess I always thought the worst had happened.

About half way up the ridge I could hear water splashing. When I got closer, I could see that falling leaves had made a dam and blocked the water and it was spilling over onto the ground. The leaves had drifted down into the open trough of water and had floated along the channel to where the logs were joined or over-lapped. There was a slight turn at this joint, and because the channel was rough and had some fibers sticking out where the two logs joined, the leaves had piled up to form a dam. The leaf dam had cut off the water supply from the mission station and the water was spilling on the ground, of no benefit to anyone.

It was a very simple repair job. All I did was reach down and remove the leaves from the channel, and what do you know, the water was off and running down to the house once again.

Some 34 years later, in August of 1991, my son Peter and his sons, Jeff and Chris and I were invited to a new church opening at the village of Negibi. That night we were having a great time of singing and fellowship in the little church. Our old time friend Hapato started talking about the water race that he and other men there had helped to build. "You know those old *pandanus* logs we used to bring the water down that ridge worked really good. Dale and his family and Dave Lawrence and his family needed that water, but we all got to use it too. That water was good."

Hapato stopped for a minute and started again. "Dale, you are like those old *pandanus* logs. God used you to bring the water of life into the Gimi. We have drunk of that water and now God wants each of us to be logs to carry His water of life to those who need it. There are still lots of people in the Gimi who have not drunk of the water of life."

Yes, Hapato was right. My life has been much like those old *pandanus* logs. Those split logs we used were rough with lots of fibers sticking out in the channel. I'm sure some would have thought that this rough looking thing will never work. But God seems to delight in using the nothings and nobodies to do extraordinary things. It was true, this water race was not much to look at, but it did the job of carrying the water to where it was needed. That is all God needs, just an empty channel that He can pour His love through.

A channel is really nothing more than the vehicle to carry the water from its source to a given area; a means of carrying or expressing ideas. God has chosen to use weak human beings to carry His life-giving message to the world in need of the water of life. All that really matters is that the vehicle or the channel be totally given to the Master so He can prepare it for use. How He does that is up to Him. Where He places that channel is also His choice.

Had you seen it, you might not have been impressed with the Gimi water race. The *pandanus* tree, when split in half and the inside chopped out, was not very fancy to look at. But that's all we had to work with. The truth of the matter is it carried a flow of water down to our homes. Impressive or not, it was functional and many enjoyed this fresh spring water.

Stepping back in time, when we first entered the missionary training program of New Tribes Mission, life seemed much simpler. We students filled the big chapel building at Fouts Springs, California and sang great old hymns. One that we learned and came to love was called, "Channels Only". That wonderful old song gripped our hearts in a way that's hard to express. I'm sure many of our fellow students felt the same as Arvalee and I did. We were challenged to be an empty channel, so that God could use us for His Glory.

You know, I have thought about that old water race a lot over the years. Hapato didn't say anything about the leaves, but he might not have known about them. I will never forget how that little dam of leaves stopped the flow of water. Big crises that come into our lives are not always the things that stop the flow. Sometimes they make the water flow better. But it's those persistent little leaves that so quietly flutter into our lives that do so much harm. They are so small you hardly notice them. I guess what we first notice is that the water is not flowing. There is dryness of soul, an emptiness that was not there before.

Those little leaves that fluttered down and clogged the water race, remind me of how selfish I have been sometimes...all the little selfish thoughts that could have been tossed out as soon as they entered my mind, *Ah, they are just little things*, we say to ourselves. Maybe it was just something a friend said, or a look. It could be that we asked a question of someone we trusted and never received an answer. There are all kinds of selfish thoughts bombarding us daily. God is more than willing to keep the leaves cleaned out if we want Him to. Our loving Father is right there at our elbow whenever we call on Him.

Why is it we don't ask God to remove those bad thoughts (the leaves in our channel)? Well, sometimes we like them and don't want to let go of them. We just let them float around in our hearts and minds, thinking they are little and will do no harm. Yet, in time they will build up and soon those little leaves will become a dam and block the flow of the water of life to ourselves and others. But the Master of our water race is an expert at maintaining His personal property. The Bible says that, "If we confess our sins, He (God) is faithful and just to forgive our sins, and to cleanse us from all unrighteousness," (1 John 1:9).

The selfish thoughts that we have are like leaves that clog the water race. God promised that He would clean out all the unrighteous thoughts, so that the water of life will flow freely through these human channels. When we come to that place in our lives when we no longer want that dryness and emptiness to continue and we cry out to God for help, He truly is faithful and more than willing to reach down and remove the dam of leaves in our lives.

There are still many people on spiritually dry mountain ridges in the world today and God has not changed His feelings towards them. He still wants them to drink of this water of life. The words in the Bible have not changed since Jesus stood up on the last day of that great feast and cried, "If any man thirst let him come unto Me and drink. He that believeth on Me, as the scripture has said, out of his belly shall flow rivers of living water," (John 7: 37, 38). If you have truly drunk of the water, then just as truly, that living water still flows from your innermost being. As it does, you know the true joy of the Lord.

If it's not flowing, check for leaves. Let's get on with the job! Let God have our lives and clean out any little leaves, so He can work freely through us to bring honor and glory to His Name as He wraps up His Great Work.

(No message has more impact than one growing out of the messenger's own experience. RDP)

The End of the Stockades, 1957
By Dale

A few months before the Chuck and Jean Driver family were to leave for furlough, Chuck asked me if he could come into the Gimi to take some 16 millimeter movie film of the Gimi people. "Yes, I would be delighted to have you visit with me in the Gimi," I assured him. It was quite lonely, during the weeks I was in the Gimi with no one to talk to in my own language and fellowship with. So it was extremely exciting for me to have Chuck come visit. He was the only other missionary to come to the Gimi since Harold Sellers and I had made the survey back in February of 1954. It wasn't that I didn't enjoy my friendship with my new brothers in Christ, Meniba and Bebu, but it was just different having Chuck with me. You will see what I mean.

The horse road was open all the way past Anuparu where my rest house was located. Chuck rode behind me on the buddy seat of my 125cc *BSA* motorcycle from Kami Mission Station to Anuparu. At one place, I had to get a run at the hill on the other side of the creek. Before we crossed the creek, I told Chuck to hang on. He did, and we went flying down to the creek. There was a fence just before coming to the creek bed and the opening in it was barely wide enough for the handlebars of the motorcycle to go through. We got through that okay and then hit the little bridge of small poles with a clatter and up the rise on the other side we went. I could see that Chuck was quite shaken by the time we got to the top of the hill, where I stopped the bike. He was in a sweat!

"How in the world did you get through that?" Chuck exclaimed.

"I missed it once, but I'm getting better at it," I told him.

Our Gimi carriers had left early from Kami and were almost to the Fusa Mountain when we caught up to them. When cutting the road up this mountain, we had to make switchbacks several times for the pack horses. Chuck got off the bike and walked with the carriers, while I mounted the bike and started up the switchbacks. A little over halfway

Dale on motor bike crossing a creek.

up, the cycle became so hot that the engine seized up, so I leaned the bike onto the cut bank of the road and had a nap. After awhile, Chuck and our carriers caught up to me. By then, the bike was cool and I rode it on up to the top, where I waited once again for Chuck. By this time he was happy to get back on the bike.

"We are not far from Anuparu where my rest house is," I encouraged Chuck.

That night when we were eating our dinner, Chuck kept saying, "I don't see how that motor-cycle stands up to all the punishment you put it through, Dale. You ride it so hard and it just keeps going even with two of us on it."

We left the bike in the house at Anuparu and started walking into the Gimi from there.

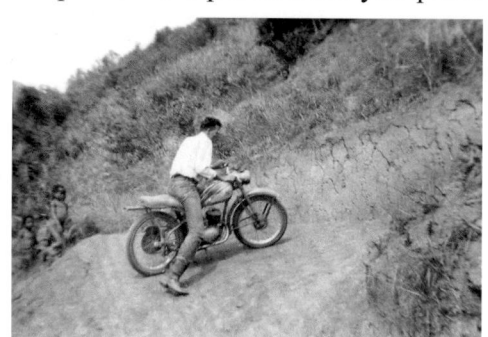

Dale on motor bike going up a hill.

Chuck loved to sing when he was hiking. One great song Chuck taught me on the trail was:

> *"And can it be that I should gain*
> *An int'rest in the Savior's blood?*
> *Died He for me, who caused His pain?*
> *For me, who Him to death pursued?*
> *Amazing love! How can it be*
> *That Thou, my God, shouldst die for me?*
> *Amazing love! How can it be*
> *That Thou, my God, shouldst die for me?"*
> *(By Charles Wesley, Public Domain)*

We would sing so loudly, I'm sure we could be heard for miles. Another song that was good to march to was:

"Lo, the conflict of the ages is upon us today,
And the armies are assembling all in battle array;
Are you number'd with the faithful, one of God's loyal few,
Who have sworn Him full allegiance?
Can He count upon you?

Have your eyes caught the vision?
Have your hearts felt the thrill?
To the call of the Master do you answer, 'I will?'
For the conflict of the ages, told by prophets and by sages,
In its fury is upon us, is upon us today."
(By Mrs. C. H. Morris, Public Domain)

It was wonderful hiking with Chuck and it seemed to make the trail shorter than before.

That night we stayed on the north slope of Mt. Negibi at the Government Rest House that was in Esema's village. The next day, as we were walking over to the south side of Mt. Negibi to see how things were going on the new mission station, we passed an old stockade on the west side of Mt. Negibi.

Chuck got so excited when he saw it. "Dale, you never told me that the Gimis have stockades!" he exclaimed.

"Well, I never thought much about it. There were several stockades in the valley when I first came here. I guess I just thought that's the way it is everywhere."

Chuck told me that not many tribes in New Guinea built stockades. "This is the only one I have seen and this would be the ideal place to shoot the movie."

"We'll ask Esema about shooting the movie here, Chuck," I responded.

It was fine with Esema, and Chuck asked if the men could put on a mock war. Did they ever like that! They painted their faces and bodies with war paint and made blunt arrows out of *pitpit*. It was really something to film. Chuck was running the old wind up 16 millimeter camera and I was reading the light meter as we were both dodging the arrows. I was disappointed that I never saw any footage of that mock war or of the old stockade. It might not have been any good. I don't know.

In those days I didn't have a camera so I never had a picture of a stockade. But I can still remember what they looked like. The fortifications were built on a high ridge. When

I think about the tools they had then it's amazing to me that these tribal people could build such grand stockades as they did. The only tool they had was an obsidian stone adze. No steel axes then. The stockade was nothing more than a rectangular enclosure with walls of 13 to 15 foot long adzed boards standing on end and tied together with strong rattan vines. There was only one door and it was like a tunnel with lots of dry banana leaves hung on the interior so they could hear anyone coming in or going out. There were little cubicles along the inside walls about eight feet up, where men sat and watched for anyone coming that was not of their clan. These lookouts were guarded day and night. The men's large lodge was near the tunnel doorway. The women, children, and pigs lived in small, individual round houses behind the lodge. During tribal wars the old stockade was a safe place for a clan to live.

Gimi Stockades

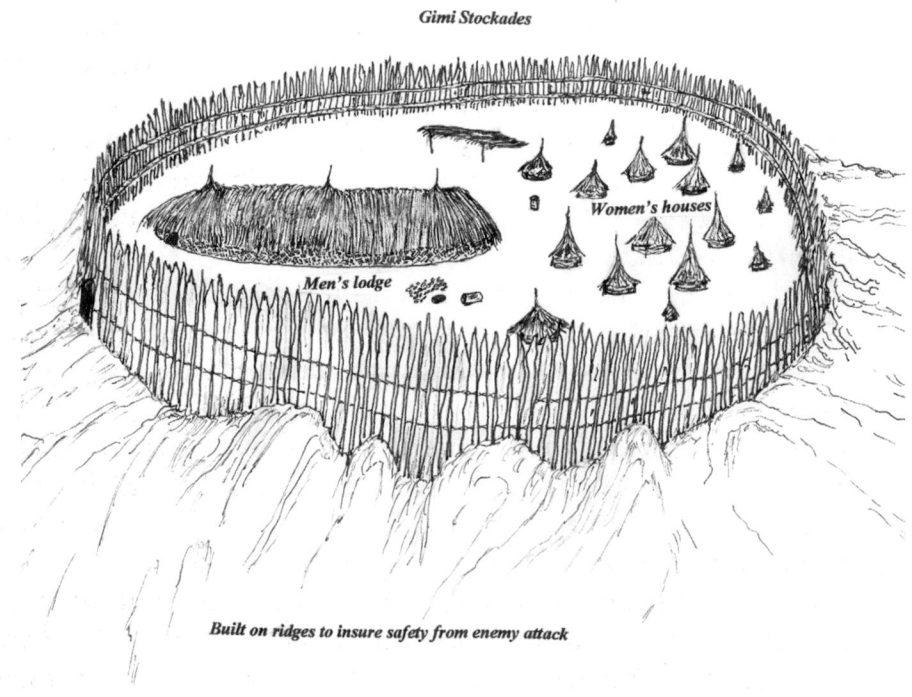

Built on ridges to insure safety from enemy attack

© R. Dale Palmer.

Chuck was really taken up with this old stockade. He was still talking about it the day he left.

It was wonderful having Chuck in the Gimi with me for a few days. I enjoyed his fellowship so much. He was an outstanding leader and I was surely going to miss him.

I arranged for a few men to carry his camera and tripod back to Kami and he walked off down the mountain never to see the Gimi again.

New Co-Workers at Kami
By Arvalee

Because we were alone, we were thrilled when we learned that Chuck and Jean Driver and Don and Gwen McCurdy and their families would join us at Kami. A few months after they joined us, Don was able to acquire a Willys jeep. This was necessary due to our dire need for transportation. Prior to their arrival, Dale had been bringing supplies from Goroka for our family on his motorcycle, although this was a very difficult task. Imagine him balancing a 35 pound steel drum of flour or a four gallon tin of kerosene across the fuel tank, with a backpack strapped onto his back and two more sacks fixed across the rear wheel of the motorcycle. That was no easy accomplishment!

With the arrival of two more families, and their need for groceries and supplies, Dale felt he would require help hauling them from Goroka. After each man took turns with Dale going to Goroka for supplies on the motorcycle, Don ordered a new Willys jeep and he became our supply man. We wrote out an order with the supplies we needed, gave him a check for the estimated amount, and he would shop for us, doing his best to purchase the items we needed.

Since the Drivers and McCurdys had arrived at Kami, Dale could continue his work in the Gimi. Before they joined us it had not been wise to leave the children and me alone on base, but now we had ample support should a problem arise. Dale made many trips into the Gimi to work with the people and study the language. He even hired Gimi helpers to work for me at Kami, and I was trying to learn Gimi phrases from them. Meniba had brought his wife Mu-u-nabi out of the Gimi and I was teaching her to help me with the housework. Meniba was Dale's main helper, and it worked out well for his wife to be at Kami as he was spending most of his time there, too.

Dale was working on a horse road to the Gimi, with the view of transporting supplies by pack saddle once our family was able to move into the Gimi. Meniba was a big help on the road work, too. They would spend five days working on the road, and then come home on the weekend.

At intervals, the road work was discontinued, just to give everyone a break. At those times Dale would go to the Gimi and he would be gone for several weeks at a time. Once, the time stretched to six weeks, and I honestly thought I had forgotten what he looked like. The days Dale spent in the Gimi were lonely days for the kids and me.

The kids and I were always thrilled when Daddy came home. When he was getting ready for a trip, I always baked fresh bread, banana bread and other goodies, so he could take some with him. His main staple was leaf tea (loose tea leaves) and sugar! That was before the days of tea bags! He drank many, many cups of hot sweet tea in those days. And he always took rice and small *tins* (cans) of mackerel with him, too; these he could share with a village family who happened to invite him in for a meal.

Julie Dale: A Special New Arrival, 1956
By Arvalee

After having three little boys, I very much wanted a baby girl. I would turn the pages in a magazine and look longingly at the pictures of infant girls. One was an advertisement for pink knitting yarn! I cut that picture out and hung it above our bed. Later, when I discovered a new baby was on the way, I kiddingly said, that picture was surely what did the trick!

From the time we were expecting our first baby, we'd had the name *Julie Dale* picked out for a girl. Alas, we had three boys in a row. Not that we were disappointed, but I still longed for a girl. However, by the time we were expecting our fourth child, we had begun toying with the possibility of a different name for a girl. Finally, just two weeks before the baby was due, Dale said, "If we have a girl and call her by a different name than *Julie Dale*, it won't be like it's our baby." So that settled it. We decided if the baby were a girl, she would be named *Julie Dale*.

It was the day after Christmas, 1955, and towards the end of the day I began having pretty severe contractions. By nightfall, we decided it was time to leave for Goroka. There was no road up to the Kami base, so we had to walk to the river, about two miles away, where Don parked his Willys Jeep. Dale let Don know in ample time that he needed to take me to the hospital, so he could get ready. It would be an overnight trip. Then, Dale told the carriers that we would be leaving for the Dunantina River. Four of them would carry me to the river in Dale's steel framed carrying chair, which had been attached to two poles.

In the darkness, we left for the river. The bridge had been washed out and Dale had to swim across the Dunantina, fighting the strong current, just to bring the raft over to our side. After carefully placing the chair and me on the raft, he worked very hard pulling on the cable, moving our conveyance across the river. About midnight we finally made it to the hospital in Goroka.

By the time the doctor came and examined me, all the contractions had stopped. I felt very relieved because I could smell liquor on the doctor's breath, and I certainly didn't want a drunken doctor delivering our baby. I spent the rest of the night in the hospital, but was released the next morning.

Dale went to see our Papuan friends, Kama and Maria, who operated the Kwato Mission, and they gave us the use of one of their rooms so I could remain in town. Dale went shopping at the new Buntings store run by Snow Blakely and found they had one single innerspring mattress for sale. Always thinking of my comfort, he bought that mattress for me so I would have a comfortable bed while I was awaiting the birth of our baby. That afternoon, he and Don went back to Kami.

I stayed there at the Kwato Mission for the next four weeks, cooking my meals on a one burner Primus stove. One day Dale brought our three little boys in on the motorcycle to see me. Pat sat behind Dale on the buddy seat and Peter and Paul sat on the gas tank in front of Dale. Peter had to hold onto Paul, who kept going to sleep.

Another missionary family, also expecting a new baby, had asked to stay at Kwato Mission at that same time. They were Cleon and Aletha Laughlin and their little boy, Douglas. They worked with Ben and Tilila Wertz, and lived farther interior past our mission base.

In January Dr. Zigas did some blood tests, and found that my blood type was RH negative A. He was worried that he would have to *change* the baby's blood, because he didn't know that Dale's blood type was the same as mine. He decided to induce me so the baby would be born during the day, as there was the possibility of a power failure and he didn't want to risk delivering the baby by lamplight.

Our little girl, Julie Dale, was born on January 26th, 1956. At one stage, the doctor told me *to hurry and push*, but I was remembering when one of the boys was born the

doctor had told me to take my time. But I did as the doctor told me, and soon the baby was born. Then I found out that the cord was around her neck so the doctor had a good reason to tell me to hurry and push.

After our daughter was born, Dale went to town to the little store run by Mrs. Snow MacFarland and bought the shoes I had admired during the weeks of waiting. I thought those pretty brown and tan shoes were beautiful and had even tried them on. Dale had told me then that if I had a girl, he would buy them for me!

After a week in the hospital, Dale and Don came to take me home. Exciting things had been happening during the month I was in town awaiting the baby's birth. The Government had built a bridge across the Dunantina River; however, at this point it was not completely fin-

Arvalee and Julie at two
weeks old.

Don's Willys Jeep on the Dunantina bridge.

ished. It still needed the decking fully secured and the Marsden matting for the tires to run on. This would be the first time a vehicle had crossed the bridge! Don was prepared for this and carried wide planks in the truck to assist in times of need.

In order for us to cross the bridge Dale had to place these wide planks, just ahead of the truck, instead of the Marsden matting. Don would drive that distance over the planks and then the process would have to be repeated, until they had crossed the entire length of the bridge. Moving these thick, heavy planks from behind the truck, to the front of the truck, putting them in place on the deck again and again and again, was very exhausting for Dale.

At the same time, the jeep road had been finished from the river up to our mission station, a distance of about two miles, but the culverts were not yet installed. When we came to one of these, Dale would again get out of the truck and place two planks across the culvert and Don would very carefully drive across them.

While I had been away in Goroka, Dale had been busy at home, too. He had built an addition onto our bedroom by enclosing half of the front porch with walls. Then he had taken one of the windows out in our bedroom and replaced it with a doorway into the new room. This new addition would be Julie's room. I had been wondering where she would sleep!

The baby also needed a crib, and Dale had made one using screen wire to enclose the sides and ends of the bed. We used mosquito netting over the top to keep mosquitoes or other insects out. It was painted blue. Another special surprise for me was the chest he built for the baby's clothes. It had two doors opening to reveal two shelves. He taught our five-year-old son, Peter, how to use a paint brush, and he painted it pink. Everything was ready and waiting when we brought the new baby home. Dale had not told me about the new room, the crib or chest, so they were a complete surprise to me. I was delighted with all his accomplishments and with his thoughtfulness.

Visitors
By Arvalee

We were excited to hear that Tom and Corinne Palmer were visiting us in April of 1956 while on their honeymoon! Dale and Tom had been close friends ever since the days at Fouts Springs when we were in training together. We didn't often have company, so we were looking forward to seeing them.

One day, Dale and I decided to go to the village of Kemasi and see how the folks were doing. This was one of the villages where Dale visited and preached the gospel, when doing the circuits of the Kami villages. Tom and Corinne were going with us. Dale knew many of the people and it had been a while since he had seen them. The mountain was so steep I almost fainted going up! It was the first time I had done any hiking since the baby had arrived, and it was almost too strenuous for me, especially with a young baby. However, I slowed down, drank some water, and was fine the rest of the way.

One day while Dale was working in his workshop, Pat and Peter were playing in the sand box nearby that Dale had built for them. They left playing and came to Dale, telling him, in tears, that they wanted to be saved and go to heaven. He wasn't surprised, because we had been teaching Bible stories, telling them about heaven for the ones who put their trust in Jesus' blood to cover their sins, and hell, the place of punishment. Soon after this, Don McCurdy drove us to a small creek up the road from our base and he and Dale baptized them both. Of course this thrilled our hearts, knowing they had understood the gospel and accepted the truth of the shed blood of Jesus to wash away their sins.

About a year later, we had a visitor named Vaughn Collins, who was with Gospel Recordings. He stayed with us a few days. Gospel Recordings made cardboard record players with a record that could be heard by using a pencil to turn the machine. They gave these small record players to the national people with recordings of the gospel message in their own language. Our son Pat was about eight years old, and he was fascinated with these record players. Julie was a toddler by then and Vaughn used to kid around, saying that he would wait until she grew up and then he would marry her!

Julie at 15 months old outside our new house.

While Vaughn was visiting us, three men on motorcycles rode in to our base one day. They were from another mission and had come to *ask Dale* why New Tribes Mission was in the area, since their mission had been there first. The other men on our station were away, so Dale was grateful for Vaughn's presence and support as he talked with these men. We believed the gospel had not been fully preached in the area, so, our presence as a mission was necessary for the people to hear the full message of Jesus dying on the cross for their sins.

An Angel to the Rescue, 1957
By Arvalee

Don McCurdy went to Goroka about once a week for supplies and mail, or to take care of any business at the bank. It became a practice of the little boys to meet Don at the gate and open it for him before he turned into the oval driveway around our houses. After Don drove through the gate, he would stop the Willys jeep and the boys would climb onto the front bumper and ride around with him, finally coming to a stop at his house. He was going less than five miles an hour and we all thought it was perfectly safe; which it usually was.

Once, however, it proved otherwise. Paul was about four years old and he climbed up on the bumper with the older boys, Pat, Peter and Dale McCurdy. We don't know what happened, but Don said that when he looked out the jeep window, he saw Paul rolling out from underneath the front tire, just before the back tire would have crushed him.

The boys with the bicycle from Grandpa Palmer.

At that same time, James Yanepa, a young national fellow working for Don, came over and told Don that, "I saw an angel pull Paul out from underneath the tire." When this incident occurred, Dale was away in the Gimi and only heard the story second-hand. That was the beginning of many miracles that God performed for Paul. Through the years there were to be many instances when it was obvious that God was at work on his behalf.

Years later, Dale wanted to hear the story from James himself. James had become the Premier (or Governor) of the Eastern Highlands Province of Papua New Guinea. When Dale went to see him in the Government office, James told Dale, "I never saw an angel before that day, and I have never seen one since then, but I saw a white form pull Paul from underneath the jeep."

Don had reminded us of Hebrews 1:14, "Are they not all ministering spirits, sent forth to minister for them who shall be heirs of salvation?" He said that, "We should have no fear for Paul, for God would not have sent the angel to rescue him from the wheel of the jeep if He did not intend to grant him salvation." These words greatly encouraged us to keep trusting God for our son.

Entertaining Angels Unawares, 1957
By Arvalee

"Be not forgetful to entertain strangers: for thereby some have entertained angels unawares," (Hebrews 13:1).

Our Saturday afternoon nap was interrupted when we heard two old Army jeeps drive up. Going to the door, we saw these strangers piling out of the two vehicles. Very friendly they were, too. There was the father, mother, teenage son, young son and their nurse. Oh, yes, there was the taxi driver too, who drove them from Goroka to our base. The father of the group drove the other jeep. The taxi driver came into the house with them. He owned the local bakery in town, and wore many other hats as well; this day he was the taxi owner and driver!

The last people you would expect to see on an isolated mission base in the heart of New Guinea, in 1957, are tourists. Our visitors were from Chicago and were traveling around the world in their yacht, which was docked in the Port Moresby harbor. Another son, who was the twin of the teenage son who came with them to visit us, was flying over the mountains in a chartered DC-3 and taking moving pictures of the area.

Since we were having a *siesta,* I had left our lunch dishes on the table. I was embarrassed to have company arrive with the clutter still on the table. Since then, I seldom, if ever, leave the table without clearing away the dirty dishes!

We learned that when these tourists had landed in the chartered DC-3 at Goroka, the driver and owner of the taxi was there to offer his services. When they wanted to do something interesting, he told them he knew where some American missionaries lived!

Trying to be hospitable, I put on the teakettle and made a pot of hot tea. I also had some banana ice cream

Our family, 1958.

in our small kerosene refrigerator. There were only two tiny trays, the size that would make six ice cubes each. But it was a treat for us and I usually made it several times a week, since we always had an abundance of bananas. Before long, Gwen McCurdy came down to our house, bringing a banana cake she had baked! It was our custom to share everything with our co-workers, and they shared with us.

As I served the guests hot cups of tea, ice cream and banana cake, they plied us with questions. "Why and what were we doing way out here in *the wilds* of New Guinea?" they asked. They posed every conceivable question one could think of and we answered them truthfully, giving them the gospel as we shared the reason that we were in this foreign land. They must have spent a couple of hours there with us in our little bush house with its thatch roof, *plaited* (woven) bamboo floor and *plaited pitpit* (woven cane) walls. On the floor, there were braided rag rugs that I had made. There were *kanda* (rattan) chairs and other homemade furniture. This was our home and we were happy to have these guests.

When they got up to leave, the man stuffed something into Dale's shirt pocket and then they drove away. When Dale reached into his pocket, he pulled out some money! There were 70 English pounds, about $150 at that time. That unexpected gift tided us over during a time when we only had about $35 a month support. Today we do not even remember our visitors' names. It was as if God had sent His angels to our house that day! God had met our needs again, and in a most unusual way. Is it any wonder we take Matthew 6:33 to mean exactly what it says? "Seek ye first the kingdom of God and His righteousness, and all these things shall be added unto you."

Hepatitis, 1956
By Dale

Watha-mo-re-e came storming into my bush house one morning, loudly demanding that I give him a steel axe. He claimed his father's burial ground was near the place where my new house was being built, and he wanted payment for disturbing his father's burial site.

This was not my first encounter with this red-skinned sorcerer. His light-brown eyes danced as he paced back and forth in front of me, shouting all the while. I let him rant and rave for some time until he ran out of things to say. Some children were peeking in the doorway and Watha-mo-re-e chased them away. Then he reached in his *bilum* (string bag) and pulled out some human bones. "These are my father's bones that were buried near your house site," he said. He must have gotten his second wind, for he was storming around me again. After he cooled down a bit, I told him that he would need to go and tell the five *luluais* (chiefs) who gave me the land, about his claims.

"No," he shouted. "It is your land now." His wild eyes were wide and flashing. "Give me a steel axe to pay for upsetting my *papa's* burial ground. That's all I want, then my talk will be finished."

"I'll talk it over with Esema and Meniba and let you know about the axe later," I said.

"No! No! Give me an axe now," he demanded.

"You are not really sorry that I upset your burial ground, you just want to get a steel axe from me," I replied.

He stormed out the door shouting something that I didn't understand.

I later talked it over with Meniba and he thought Watha-mo-re-e might have gone up at night and put the old bones at the base of the big tree that was going to be cut down the next day. Meniba told me not to give him an axe.

The value of a steel axe at this time was great as the Gimi men were still using stone axes. So to have a new steel axe would give Watha-mo-re-e a lot of prestige.

Things seemed to cool down so the people kept working on clearing the land of trees and brush where my house would be built. A number of clans worked together to build this first mission station in the East Gimi. I still remember some of the clans that helped; they were from Negibi, Avopi, O-aberu, Aibeisu and Tha-arai.

It was about two weeks after Watha-mo-re-e had come to me about the axe that I started getting sick. I would take a bite of food and the second bite would meet the first bite coming up. Everything I tried to eat would come up. After a few days, I told Meniba that I was going out to Kami until I could start feeling better. I thought I just had an upset stomach from something I ate.

"I will try to be back in about two weeks," I told him.

Meniba thought I should have some men carry me out in my steel framed chair. He said, "It's a long walk and you are weak." I had not been able to keep anything down for three days.

"I think I'll be alright. I just need someone to carry my backpack," I replied. Meniba chose Bainaba, his brother-in-law, to go with me. He was a strong young man, about 17 years old.

The first day we arrived at Muye before dark. It had been a hard day, because I still couldn't keep anything in my stomach. The next day was some of the hardest walking I had ever done. I was much weaker than the day before and I could tell I had no strength since I had taken in no food for several days. As I walked along, suddenly I found myself face down, spread eagle in the middle of the trail. Several times I would just collapse like this. Bainaba faithfully stayed beside me, but he was helpless to really assist me other than sitting down beside me, crying, wringing his hands, and saying, "*A-o-bana nau ru-a-au, nau ru-a-au.*" (Pink man, [the name the Gimis called me] my *liver is crying*, my *liver is crying* [heart is breaking], literally: I'm so sorry for you.) Each time I fell down Bainaba would help me up and support me the best he could, and we'd walk a while longer.

I had a few more down times before arriving at Kami the following day. I had sent a note to Arvalee with a runner before I left the Gimi asking her to send the horse to meet me. We were only about two hours walk away from home when the horse met us, and it was a great relief to be able to ride the remaining distance.

I was glad to be safely home at last. But after two weeks, I still saw no improvement and continued vomiting after every attempt at eating. Chuck Driver looked at me and said, "Your eyes are yellow; you must have yellow jaundice. You'd better go see the doctor in Goroka." So Don McCurdy drove me to the Goroka Hospital and Dr. Sims asked me what was going on. I told him that I thought I might have yellow jaundice. "You sure do," he said. "We call it hepatitis now. It's a good thing you don't drink alcohol or you would be dead. You have the worst case of hepatitis I have ever seen. You need quiet, a lot of rest and lots of fresh beef. We can find a home here in town for you to stay in." (The hospital was very small with only one room set aside for Europeans.) I didn't want to stay in town away from my family! "Oh, I'll be alright at home," I responded. "It will be quiet there."

So I went home, but Arvalee had a hard time keeping our four children quiet. The children didn't understand how sick I was. One day while the kids were playing outside, Peter fell and cut his face quite badly. All the kids came rushing into our house crying. They were all in tears. I was in bed, but got up to see what was going on. I don't know if it was all the blood on Peter's face or what, but I almost fainted. Arvalee had to help me get back in bed.

My two-week promise to Meniba turned into eight months before I could return to the Gimi. Many Gimis believed for years that Watha-mo-re-e had worked sorcery on me, because of my reluctance to give him that one little steel axe.

It was really something the way my needs were met during this time. At the time I saw the doctor, he told me that I needed lots of fresh meat. Bunting Store in Goroka had just bought a freezer and they were now able to order beef steaks and roasts from Australia. These items had never been available before. It was just like the Lord to pour out His blessings on everyone in Goroka town and the surrounding area when one of His kids had a need. I'm thrilled to know that God keeps His Word. He said, "...all these *things* shall be added unto you." We don't need to ask, "What shall we *eat*? Or what shall we *drink*? Or wherewithal shall we be *clothed*?" He sent the meat just when I needed it. He is always on time, (Matthew 6:33).

One night, about five months into my hepatitis, I had been feeling so much better that Arvalee cooked some beef sausages that I enjoyed eating. In a short time my head was swimming and Arvalee had to keep me sitting up in the chair in order to keep me from falling. Through that experience we realized that I still had to be careful of what I ate. Greasy foods in particular had to be avoided for a long time.

Dale's Hepatitis
By Arvalee

A note came from Dale in mid-December 1956 that he was sick and was hiking out of the Gimi on his way home. After being home for two weeks with no improvement, Chuck encouraged him to go see the doctor.

Dr. Sims told him he had hepatitis and that he needed rest and quiet to recuperate. The doctor told Dale he needed fresh lean beef, and to follow a special bland diet, particularly avoiding greasy, fried foods.

Those were stressful days for all of us. Children cannot understand the need for quiet when someone is sick. The three boys would race through the house, in the front door and out the back, just having fun. But this was not the quietness Dale needed! His nerves were frazzled by any kind of noise or excitement. Finally I had to make a rule; I told the boys, "Once inside the house, stay inside and find something quiet to do. No more running through the house."

Julie was only eleven months old, and she thought this was great fun having Daddy home and in bed most of the time. She would climb up on the bed, expecting Daddy to give her a piggyback ride while sitting astride him. I surely had my hands full, trying to take care of a sick husband and keep the children happy for eight long months while Dale recovered. During all that time, Dale could hardly write a letter, which was a great frustration to him.

When Peter had his accident, Dale got out of bed to see what all the commotion was about, but he was not up to dealing with the problem and had to go back to bed. I was so grateful when Gwen and Don McCurdy came to our rescue. Gwen came and helped me clean up Peter's face and patched him up with butterfly patches, and Don drove him to the hospital in Goroka. Peter had a bad cut on his cheek and another on his forehead that needed stitches. The hospital staff told Don that it was good he brought Peter to the hospital when he did. After 24 hours they would not have been able to stitch the wound because the risk of infection would be too great in the tropics. Don and Peter slept in town that night and came home the next day. Peter remembers that he and Don had baked beans for supper, which Peter thought was a real treat.

Not too long after Peter's accident, Julie was playing and crawled behind the living room door. I had forgotten to spring the large rat trap. It went off and the lever struck her just above the eyebrow, narrowly missing her eye! We were so thankful for God's protection and gave Him praise for His watch care over her.

After the episode with the beef sausages, Dale went back on a bland, non greasy diet. After that he slowly began to improve and regular food was gradually introduced into his diet. But it was eight months before he was able to resume his work in the Gimi.

Cargo Cult
By Dale

During the time I was sick with hepatitis some Gimis would come out to Kami and check on me from time to time. They also gave me a little report about the progress there.

One time they told of a prophet who came from the coast and told all the Gimis that a rope would hang down from heaven and if each of them would give the prophet a shilling (about 10 cents) they could climb the rope. In three days they could come back down and there would be a straight road from the Gimi to the town of Goroka. Between Goroka and the Gimi stands Mt. Michael at 11,965 feet. That would be quite a road, straight through to Goroka. On this new road there would be all kinds of *cargo* they could gather for free. Things like canned meat and fish, clothes, bush knives and steel axes would be theirs in abundance!

I sent a letter to the District Commissioner in Goroka about this prophet. And his reply was that the Government could not interfere in a religious act.

The prophet actually used verses from the Bible to base his teaching upon. "The voice of him (the prophet) that crieth in the wilderness (the Gimi). Prepare ye the way of the Lord (the rope will hang down), make straight in the desert a highway for our God. Every valley shall be exalted, and every mountain and hill shall be low: and the crooked shall be made straight and rough places plain:" (Isaiah 40:3, 4) (a straight road from the Gimi to Goroka).

That was just one form of *cargo cult*. The Coastal Prophet got his bag of shillings and went back to the coast and the Gimi people were left holding the rope, longing to see that new road to Goroka.

Making Bush Salt
By Dale

The Gimis had amazing survival skills. One example was how they made their own *thobi* (Gimi bush salt).

As I was walking through the woods with some Gimi men, we came upon some folks sitting around a fire, so we stopped and talked with them. They told us they were making *thobi* (salt). They showed me the plant or vine they had gathered from the nearby woods. It was waxy like a balsam plant but bigger around, and had no flowers. They said the plant just grows along on the ground; it must have been 10 to 15 feet long. Then the folks showed me a 20-foot-long *pandanus* tree cut in half lengthwise with the soft pithy inside chopped out. The *pandanus* tree lay at a slight angle and was propped up at one end.

The balsam vine was chopped into small pieces before it was cooked in the fire. After the ashes of the balsam have cooled they are placed at the elevated end of the *pandanus* trough. Water is poured over the ash and it runs down the trough and a large wooden dish at the lower end of the trough catches the ash and water. This mixture is left to set for a time, and then the water is poured off, leaving the homemade *thobi* (salt).

When the homemade salt is still damp they form it into a ball and wrap it in clean, new, wet bark strips about one inch wide. Then the ball of salt is placed inside the men's lodge up in the roof area to dry. It does not taste like our salt to me, but more like *Mrs. Dash* with lemon pepper; that is, if you have a real good imagination.

I just thought you might like the recipe for making bush salt, should you ever get lost in the woods.

Gimi Initiations
By Dale

Eight months later, after I was feeling better, I was able to resume my Gimi trips. Shortly thereafter I was invited by Esema to attend his son Masis' (Matches) nose piercing initiation.

It was a great honor to be a part of this initiation. I was seated on the ground beside men that I knew. There were maybe 10 to 12 men on each side of me, sitting in a half circle. An older man I could see across the way was removing the bark rope (string) that was tied around a ball of homemade salt. Then he took the ball of salt and scraped the salt into his mouth with his top front teeth. With his mouth full of salt he turned and spat it out like a spray, over a large wooden dish of cooked pork sitting on the ground.

When he was finished, another man picked up the dish of meat and carried it over and placed it in front of me on the ground. It was clear to me that I was the guest of honor.

That was one fat pig. The fat was thick on all the meat. I knew enough Gimi culture to know what I should do next, but before I did it, I quietly asked God to please bless this greasy meat to my weak stomach. Then I took a bite out of the top piece of meat and passed it to the oldest man next to me. I repeated this ritual of taking a bite and passing the meat on to the men on each side of me until each piece of pork on that wooden dish was gone.

I was thinking to myself, *Boy, I'm sure glad that's over.* Then I saw some feet in front of me and looked up to see Esema standing before me with another wooden platter of greasy pork! I was starting to say, "I'm full, I've already eaten," when he set the platter of meat down in front of me. With his big arms crossed over his large-barreled chest, he looked down at me and said, "Eat it!" I then realized that this was the *real* ceremonial meat for the nose piercing initiation for his son.

Now that is when you really need a second blessing! I did eat and God blessed it, because I didn't get sick.

Esema's son Matches was not the only boy in the initiation. These boys looked to be about 10 to 12 years of age, and the nose piercing is the first of five initiations they go through to become a man.

This is the time in the boy's life when he stops living in his mother's home and eating the food she cooks. Before he can live in the men's lodge, the boy must be clean of all food women have fed him. To ensure this, the men forced down the boy's throat a long piece of small rattan that is bent in half, thus bringing up all the food cooked by a woman. He is now clean inside.

Then the boy is wrapped in a bark cape and laid on the ground and beaten with a larger rattan stick. If the boy should cry at this time they will keep beating him until he stops. You know, real men don't cry. After this they pierce the septum of his nose with a sharp bone.

After the initiations were over some men cleaned the intestines of the pigs that had been killed. I just stood by and watched as they were stuffing all the fat into the intestines and then they cooked it over some hot rocks.

Later, I was sitting talking with some other men, when one of the men, who had been cooking the stuffed intestines, came over towards me. He handed me a green leaf with a slice of intestines full of fat on it. I felt that every eye was on me to see if I would eat it. That is when you must forget you have a sense of smell and take that bite. It really didn't taste that bad, but the smell was something I will never forget!

These people love to eat pig fat. A few years later I lived in the village of Raro and had been there for a few weeks. My host invited me to go with him to the village of A-e-aru Mane. It was not far away, but up a steep hill. When we arrived we were greeted by many wanting to shake hands. One old man called me over to him and handed me something wrapped in green leaves tied with small vines.

I sat on the ground beside him and began to untie my treasured gift. It was a large slice of pig fat with the blackened skin and hairs still attached. It had been cooked over an open fire. Remember, I had been in the village without any meat for about two weeks, eating only vegetables and fruits with the people, so that pork fat tasted so good to me. That seemed to only prove to me that I was on the mend and my liver was working well again!

Chapter 8

Memories…Arvalee Remembers
By Arvalee

Eight months had passed before Dale was feeling well again after his bout with hepatitis. Jim and Sylvie Spence came from the Watut to visit us. Jim was very ill with leukemia and knew his time was short on this earth, but his longtime dream had been to see the Gimi tribe. Dale felt the trip would be too hard for Jim, but Jim persuaded Dale that he could make it.

Dale and Jim left Kami riding the two horses, Prince and Peanuts, and traveled as far as Anuparu the first day, and part of the next until the end of the road. The horses were then taken back to Kami. Jim had to be carried the rest of the way, so Dale fixed up his steel framed chair by lashing two poles to the armrests.

This was Dale's first trip to the Gimi since his sickness. Many of the people believed that Watha-mo-re-e, the local sorcerer, had cast a spell of witchcraft on him and they thought that Dale wasn't returning to the Gimi. But God allowed him to return.

Dale's heart was in the Gimi and he always had thrilling stories to tell us when he came home to Kami. His stories of the Gimi people and their hunger and eagerness to know more of the gospel message gave me a keen desire to join him there. Even though these were years of hardship, our dream was to be together, one day, in the Gimi.

Memories So Clear Are Still Ringing in My Ear
By Dale

"Dale, I want to go to the Gimi with you."

"But Jim, it's a hard trip into the Gimi. With your advanced leukemia, the trip could finish you."

"I know my time is short, Dale, but I need to see the Gimis before I die."

Jim had lived and worked with the Hamtai tribal people since coming to New Guinea in 1950 and, before he died, he wanted to see the second tribal area New Tribes Mission had opened.

By now, the people had finished the large round house they had been building for me. It was August 1957. I had never seen the house completed, because I'd gotten sick and had to leave the Gimi for those eight months.

I was quickly able to get Jim a permit for a short visit into the Gimi. The horses were ready and we had a good line of carriers waiting for us. We left early that morning, leaving Arvalee and Jim's wife, Sylvie, at Kami. The first night on the trail we slept at Anuparu, in my small round house. The next day we rode the horses about three more hours to the end of the cut horse road. Then, Lamafu, the national man who cared for the horses, took them back to Kami. Now on foot, Jim, the carriers and I all started off down the trail. We had not gone far until I had the carriers cut two long poles from nearby trees and tie them to my steel framed chair with some vines. Jim sat in the chair and four men carried him most of the way to the Gimi. Jim told me later that it was quite tiring to hold on to the chair, but he didn't fall out.

Jim and Sylvie
Spence and Joey.

This part of the trail was not much more than a pig track and we were moving more slowly than usual. This was partly because I, too, needed to rest more often. Jim was very tired and I was still weak from my hepatitis, so we stopped at Muye at the Government Rest House (GRH). I was glad to see that little rest house. The next day we could ease our pace and travel more slowly and still arrive home at Negibi in five hours.

When we came over the crest of the hill, we were looking down on the large round house the people had built for me. It was forty feet in diameter and had a woven bamboo floor, plaited bamboo walls and a thatched roof. The house was beautiful! It more than met my dreams as I had imagined it to be.

The Gimi round house.

Jim was very weak, and while we were there he just rested on a small folding cot most of the time. The people came inside the house to see this new *A-o-bana* (pink man). They rubbed his hands, feet and legs and chattered away in Gimi to him. Jim would prop himself up on his elbow and talk to them in Pidgin English, but he knew they couldn't understand him. I could tell Jim was really enjoying seeing and getting to know the Gimi people.

Opisha and Peter (two of the four Watut believers who came with Jim) wanted to share the Good News with the Gimi people but could not speak to them either. Meniba was the only Gimi that knew any Pidgin English at that time, so Opisha and Peter would stay close to Meniba and ask him to tell the people what they were saying. They were teaching from the wordless book.

Jim and I were also talking to a lot of people through Meniba. At that time there were hundreds of tribal people that made professions of faith. Many were truly born again, but we found out later there were some that did not clearly comprehend the message. This was very understandable because we were so limited in communicating the Good News in the trade language, yet it was a thrill to see the change in so many lives. I know it was a work of God for I saw it with my own eyes.

One morning, just before Jim and I left the Gimi, we saw three people coming up the trail. As they came closer we saw that an old man was being led by two teenage girls, one on each side, helping him to walk. He came inside the house and sat beside Jim's cot. Meniba was there and interpreted what Jim was saying. Jim then explained to Abu-o-ne that he himself was old and would die soon. Abu-o-ne thought about this, and about Jim's message, and then he told Jim that he wanted to follow God's talk.

After three weeks in the Gimi, Jim was looking really worn-out and he needed to get to a doctor. I was not sure that Jim could make the trip out because he was so weak. Yet we headed out, and after we arrived at Kami we were able to take Jim to see a doctor right away.

It was about four months after Jim visited the Gimi that he went home to be with the Lord. It reminded me of how Simeon of old was ready to depart this earth after he had seen the Christ child. Jim just had to see the Gimi, even if it killed him.

About three months after Jim's Gimi visit, I was preaching at the village of O-aberu. I shared that God is a jealous God. Old Abu-o-ne, who was almost blind, stood up and said, "I am going to throw away my ancestors' bones and follow God's Talk." This was a bold step for this dear old man.

Word came to me on January 14th, 1958, that old Abu-o-ne had died. I believe that Abu-o-ne may have been the first Gimi to enter Heaven. It was about this same time that Jim died in Bulolo. I have always wondered what it must have been like when Jim and Abu-o-ne saw each other in Heaven.

I would like to close this story about my good *Aussie* mate Jim Spence by saying that I always felt so honored that our field leaders, like Chuck Driver and Jim Spence, wanted to be with me and share in this great work in the opening of the Gimi.

(For more details of this time in the Gimi you can read the book *In Search of Brown Gold* by Fred Morris. Pages 122 to 151.)

The next big event was Arvalee's first visit to the Gimi tribe. This was a very exciting thing for me, to take my beautiful, little redheaded wife in among these wild and excitable tribal women, who would see their first *A-o-batha* (pink woman). I was not sure how Arvalee would handle all this attention from these loud tribal women…but she did great. I'm sure she felt the warm friendship these dear women bestowed upon her.

My First Trip to the Gimi, 1957
By Arvalee

Dale had just come home from one of his long trips to the Gimi and the children and I were so excited to have Daddy home again! I cooked some of his favorite foods and made fresh bread and a special dessert. The kids all talked at the same time, trying to tell him what had happened while he was gone. They had missed him so much.

Those were hard days for me because I had all the responsibility for the children and running the home, as well as overseeing the hired help. These helpers performed most of the chores around the house. They swept, mopped and cleaned the house, prepared fresh vegetables, washed the dishes and sometimes assisted me with the cooking. In addition they also chopped firewood, washed clothes on a rub board, and ironed the clothes with a gasoline iron. Nevertheless, supervising all this, as well as looking after the four kids under the age of eight and home schooling our two older sons was very hard for me as a young mother.

I was using a correspondence course from Queensland, Australia, for the boys' schooling and much of it was unfamiliar to me. They even spelled some words differently! For instance, they spelled tire as *tyre* and Savior as *Saviour*. Color was spelled *colour*. Those are just a few examples.

In addition, I suffered from hay fever every day, making me extremely miserable. The medication I was taking gave me some relief, but it made me dreadfully sleepy and nervous. If the door slammed, I would jump. I badly needed the help and support of my husband.

The night Dale returned, he said to me, "You keep talking about moving to the Gimi to be with me. Before we make a final decision to move, I want you to visit the Gimi. You should see the people and be there long enough to decide for yourself if you can handle this rigorous, primitive life style."

"You know we agreed with Chuck and the other men that we were the ones to open the new mission work in the Gimi," I said.

"Yes, but at that time I had no idea how hard it was to work in that isolated place, among such primitive people. I want you to know it's a very difficult place to live. It's a rugged three day hike to get there and perhaps you'd see none of our fellow missionaries for months."

I responded, "Then maybe it's time to plan a trip so I can see what it's really like. I'm tired of being alone and looking after the children by myself. I've been looking forward to the time when the children and I could join you."

After our discussion, we talked to Don and Gwen McCurdy, our partners, about the best time for me to make a trip to the Gimi and asked if they would look after our children while we were away. We decided that we would visit after Christmas so Dale applied for a special permit from the Government so I could visit the area.

Finally, the big day came. It was the day after Christmas, 1957. That morning we ate breakfast with the McCurdy family, and left our children in their care. We planned to be gone for seventeen days. Saying goodbye to our four children was certainly difficult for me. Julie started crying when she realized that Mommy was going away. I comforted her and soon she was happily playing with the McCurdy boys.

Mounting our horses, we started off on this three day trek to reach the Gimi. Dale was riding Peanuts, the big draft horse, and I was on Prince, the smaller gelding quarter horse. I'm not much of a rider, but it was better than walking all the way. As we rode slowly along, the tropical sun grew hotter with each passing hour. Since I have fair skin, it was good that I had worn a large, wide brimmed hat and a long sleeved shirt.

We followed the new jeep road that went to Lufa, the Government Patrol Post.

To the Gimi on horses.

Before noon, we reached the narrow horse road that Dale and his hired national workers were digging out of the mountainous terrain into the Gimi. It would enable pack horses to carry supplies into the Gimi once our family moved in and were settled. The horse road in this section was terribly muddy because of the heavy rains and loose soil yet we were glad that it was the horses wading through the mud, slipping and sliding, instead of us! We crossed numerous creeks in this section. Dale had built log bridges across the creeks, but they weren't safe for the horses so we rode them down into the creek bed. Sometimes I dismounted and Dale led or rode my mount across the creek. A few times, I rode across myself and the horse would take a great leap over the creek to the other bank. I wondered if I would stay on, but I did.

That afternoon, it started to rain. I said, "I'm sure glad we wrapped up our bedding."

"Yes, it's better to use the raincoats for the bedding. I get too hot if I wear a rain-coat," Dale answered.

I put up my umbrella to keep my head and shoulders dry but my lower body got wet. Dale used a *national raincoat*, which the tribal people made by sewing together the long, narrow leaves of the *pandanus* tree. It resembled a folded newspaper, but it didn't give him much protection, so he got wetter than I did.

All day long we rode the horses along that six-foot-wide horse road through the mountains. The local tribal people had made the road with the picks and shovels that Dale had given them, part of their pay for doing the work on the road. They were excellent compensation because the people could use them in their gardens instead of their traditional digging sticks.

By this time, we were leaving the grasslands and getting into some forest. To look at the steep slopes around us, one would think it impossible to dig a road with no more than hand tools to work with.

Whenever we came near a village or garden, the people came out to greet us. The women yelled in Pidgin English, "*Missisio! Missisio!*" (A term used for a European woman).

"Why are these boisterous people so excited?" I asked.

"You're probably the first European woman they've ever seen," Dale answered.

Once, an elderly man gave us a few bananas to eat and they tasted mighty good. As we passed through this area called Frigano, I realized that these people, too, having no mission group working among them, had never heard about God.

About 4:30 p.m., after nine and a half hours in the saddle, we reached our destination for the day, a place called Anuparu. Dale already had a bush house built there with some camping equipment inside.

We had hired fourteen Gimi men to travel with us and carry our supplies for the trip. One of them, Biru, was Dale's right-hand-man, helping him prepare the food and cleaning up. These fellows were helpful especially to the *Missisio,* whom they knew was not used to roughing it. Without the help of these men, I wouldn't have been able to make such a trip, especially if I'd had to carry my own belongings. But it was also a help to them. The people were happy to have someone show an interest in them. They wanted to work for us as it gave them the chance to earn a little money or trade goods.

These carriers soon had a fire built inside the bush house. It felt cozy and warm but the house quickly filled with smoke. We had to either lie down or go outside to keep our eyes from smarting. After the smoke dissipated somewhat, we had a cup of refreshing hot tea. Then we had our meal, some steak which Gwen had pre-cooked for us, which was a real treat, and some potatoes that Biru cooked under the coals. After a time of prayer and thanking the Lord for a good trip that day, we settled down early for a much needed rest.

In the round house, there was ample room to spread our sleeping bags on the bamboo floor. Dale and I chose a spot close to the wall, away from the central fireplace. That was a hard bed, but I was so exhausted that it felt wonderful to just lie down. The carriers settled down on the floor with their feet pointed towards the fire. During the night, as the room became chilly, one of them would rouse up to place more firewood on the coals, keeping the fire from dying out. Occasionally we could hear them talking in low voices among themselves.

The next morning we were awakened by the rustling movements of the men stirring from their night's rest. The fire was rekindled and the smell of food cooking sharpened our awareness that it was time to break our fast. Biru was tending the thick slices of bread browning over the open coals on a sharpened stick, while hot, bubbling oatmeal cooked in a billy tin, a 6-inch can with a wire handle. It was a nourishing breakfast that would strengthen us for the long hike ahead. The carriers preferred a hot sweet potato baked in the coals during the night!

By the time we got the chores finished, it was 7:30 and time to be on our way.

Lamafu had the horses saddled and waiting. Dale said in Pidgin English, "*Ah, yu gut pela man, Lamafu. Yu lukautim hos gut pela tru. Tenkyu.*" (Ah, you're a good man, Lamafu. You took good care of the horses and got them ready. Thank you.)

As we mounted our horses, I exclaimed, "Oh, I didn't know I was so sore."

This section of horse road was in excellent condition, although it was often muddy in the heavily forested areas. Here the sun was hidden by the tall trees, keeping the road wet. As the road wound and twisted through the mountains, it crossed numerous little forest streams of clear, sparkling water. I observed many varieties of trees in various shades of green, unusual wild flowers, vines, and other lush undergrowth. The beauty of the jungle almost made me forget my aching limbs.

We rode the horses that morning about three hours, to the end of the cut horse road. From there Lamafu took the horses back to Kami base to feed and groom them.

For the first time since starting our trip, we had to walk and I realized the trip would be really difficult for me from here on. The narrow trail, worn into ruts by years of trudging feet, led us down a steep hill, then up the other side, often times under vines and undergrowth and over protruding tree roots, huge boulders, and occasionally a large fallen tree. Although I enjoyed the beautiful foliage, I had to watch where I placed my feet, lest I trip and fall.

It seemed every muscle in my body was aching after sitting in the saddle for almost two days. And now my leg and thigh muscles were screaming in protest against the hiking. I wasn't used to this rigorous lifestyle!

The people that we met along the way were friendly and excited to see a European woman. They grabbed my hands, and rubbed my arms and legs. Several times they tried to touch me in more inappropriate places as well, so I had to keep quite alert! At least this was no surprise to me. We'd had the same exposure to the village people when we visited the Wertzes in Gono. This way of greeting is the acceptable show of friendliness among the New Guinea people.

The trail was wet and slick, making it almost impossible to stay upright. My feet kept sliding out from under me so one of the men cut a walking stick for me, which helped me to keep my footing. It was much harder going uphill than going down for me because I was so short-winded. At times, I thought I would never make it; I wanted to give up and lie down. My thighs ached from the strain of going up and my knees trembled with the pressure of the steep descent. When I felt I couldn't make it any further, I stopped in my tracks, rested, and took deep breaths. Sometimes, I found a place to sit on a smooth rock. After catching my breath a few minutes, I was ready to proceed.

All through the day, Dale was only a few feet behind me, continually encouraging me. He would call out, "Take your time, Honey. There's no hurry." Usually, he allowed me to take the lead, to set the pace, as I had to take three steps to his one, his legs being so long!

We had hiked four hours before we came to the Government Rest House, at Muye. These small bush houses are provided by the Government for the *kiap* (patrol officer) and for other travelers like us. We stopped here to spend the night.

After a cup of hot tea, a sponge bath and a bite to eat, I felt much better. However, I certainly didn't feel up to a game of kickball, as our carriers did! I said to Dale, "How do they have enough energy to play ball?"

He said, "Oh, the carriers are only stopping because they know you are so tired. They would much rather go on."

Towards evening, sitting on the grass outside the house, we had a meeting with the men who traveled with us. It was a joyous time of sharing some thoughts from the Word of God, singing, and praising the Lord. Many of these men were new Christians and Dale took every opportunity to teach them more about walking with God.

The next day we continued on. When we came upon a mountain stream we stopped for a drink of water. Once, we decided to walk up the shallow stream on the large, flat rocks. Suddenly, my feet slipped out from under me and down I went! I hadn't realized how slick those stones were from the moss that grew on them. I was soaked, but the water was cool and refreshing and my clothes soon dried. I was surely thankful that the fall didn't hurt me. This was no place to break a bone.

Later in the day, we encountered new people who spoke another language. Although Dale and I were covered with mud, these nationals didn't seem to notice as they shook our hands and acted so glad to see us. About noon we came to a small garden with three or four houses inside the rough picket fence. A couple of men and women came out to greet us and gave us a long stick of sugarcane. Dale peeled away the tough outer layer with his pocket knife and cut off bite-sized chunks, which we chewed to extract the sweet, succulent juice. We found it truly refreshing, and the sugar gave us much energy. Dale had learned that the gift of sugarcane was a sign of hospitality and friendship.

That day we crossed three or four wide, fast flowing rivers. Those bridges! You've never seen anything like them! They were usually placed at a narrow gorge, with the river flowing far below. Some were made by placing a single log across the stream. Others were made by tying vines together with a few hand-hewn planks tied across the vines to walk on. The bridge bounced from my body weight as I crossed, giving me a giddy feeling. I had to focus carefully on where to place my feet instead of on the water below. I crept slowly across, carrying nothing, while the carriers crossed quickly with their *cargo* (loads). Each time, I was greatly relieved to reach the other side. Need I tell you that I was terribly frightened?

Crossing a stream on a log foot bridge.

For awhile we walked alongside a large river. As the water tumbled over the huge boulders it made a deafening roar. It was a magnificent sight. We were surrounded by forest, with the exception of the small trail we were walking on. A few brightly colored birds were flying overhead. It seemed to me that walking through the forest was the hardest part of the trip because of the rough trail, but it was so beautiful I soon forgot the difficulties.

At last we came to Mt. Negibi. Dale's house was located on the far side of the mountain. I began to wonder if I could make it the rest of the way and stopped quite often to rest. One of the men encouraged me, saying, *"Em i klostu longwe liklik, Missisio."* (It's not too much farther, Mrs.) First, we had to climb the mountain and then go

A swinging foot bridge made of jungle vines.

down the other side. My feet kept slipping on the steep, muddy trail. I even fell down a few times.

Finally, two of our carriers, Asumuyaba and Ani-ani-mo, each took hold of my upper arms and propelled me forward. They physically took me down the mountain. I don't think I took one step; my feet just slid down, with these men holding me up and guiding me all the way. It seemed they had decided that this "*Missisio*" had fallen down enough, and this was their way of helping me. I was indeed grateful!

Then, I saw the clearing on a ridge and Dale's huge, round, bush house for the first time. Now we hastily made our way down the trail where I eagerly inspected my future home and I soon discovered that the walls and floor were made of plaited or woven bamboo and the roof from thatched grass. It was a full forty feet in diameter, which would give ample space for our family and for meetings with the people on rainy days. One half of it was partitioned off for the bedrooms; another fourth was used for the kitchen and storage. The remaining fourth was open for the people who loved to come in and sit around the open fireplace, which consisted of a circle of large rocks. I was glad to finally see the home in the Gimi that the people had built for Dale, which was to be my home for the next eleven days... and hopefully where our family would live in the near future.

The people seemed so glad to see me. You can imagine how they looked at me, since most of them had never seen a European woman. Many of them wanted to touch my hands and arms and stroke my long, red hair.

Just after we arrived someone brought us some hot food. It was delicious, having the distinctive flavor of food cooked over hot rocks in the ground called a *mumu* (steam cooking). There were sweet potatoes, beans, corn, and several kinds of locally grown greens. During my visit, we also had as many fresh mushrooms as we cared to eat. The little boys gathered the mushrooms that grew wild in the forest and we bought them for a few spoonfuls of salt, which they valued for seasoning their food.

I was glad the long trip was over. I could hardly move the next morning, because every muscle in my body was dreadfully sore, and my upper arms were awfully bruised as well. But I was not sorry that I had come with my husband to visit these people, who had become his devoted friends.

One morning, a young girl about ten years old was carried to the house on a crude stretcher. They said she had been *poisoned* by sorcery, and the entire sole of her foot was sore and painful. Having no medicine, they had chewed up bark and leaves and made a poultice to put on it. After soaking her foot, Dale carefully cut away the dead skin. The entire sole of her foot was rotten, and it fell off, exposing raw flesh! It was a terrible thing to clean. During the next few days, we administered a series of penicillin injections which worked a miracle. After treatment, her foot was like a newborn baby's foot; tender, pink skin covered the sole. Before we left for our home at Kami it was practically healed. How rewarding it was to be able to help this young girl recover her health.

When Dale was in the Gimi alone, he had trained Biru to give injections of penicillin and bandage sores, which saved him much time. Since the Government had not yet set up medical aid posts, he usually did medical work three days a week. While I was there visiting, I sometimes helped him by cleaning and bandaging sores.

It was during my visit that the people of Negibi wanted to start working on the horse road from their end, which would eventually join the section already finished. Meniba spent a couple of days walking through the bush, laying out the route the road would follow. After a few days, the people started digging away the ground with their shovels. They hadn't gone far from the house when the hard work of cutting down huge trees began.

Throughout the day we heard trees crashing through the jungle, with a final thud indicating another had fallen. In the evening Dale and I walked down the newly dug horse road to see their progress. Those people were amazing; even though they had worked hard all day, most of them had a smile and a few words of greeting. They considered themselves very privileged that a missionary had come to live in their village, even though it meant hard work to build a road. They seemed to accept that they were only improving their living conditions in the process.

The higher altitude of the Gimi made the climate a great deal colder than Kami. We wore our sweaters most of the day and kept a fire going in the open fireplaces in the middle of each room. We really enjoyed the nice warm sunshine around noon, the warmest part of the day.

Looking in any direction from the house at Negibi, one could only see mountains and the pristine beauty of the jungle. What a fantastic place to live! In the early morning, clouds settled over the river valley and it looked like a bed of pure, fresh snow. At times the sunsets were gorgeous. I enjoyed each day there, but I felt incredibly idle with no children to care for.

Before our return to Kami, I knew in my heart that I should move to the Gimi with the children, to be with Dale. I was already aware of some of the trials of working with primitive people. Now I had experienced what a long, tiresome trip it was to reach this isolated place. Yet, I felt confident that the Lord would enable me and give me the strength I needed. Providentially, the Government had informed us that the restrictions for working in the Gimi were to be lifted in 1958.

The day finally came to leave for Kami. Since I was weak from diarrhea Dale decided I should be carried over the steep places in the steel framed camp chair. The chair was tied with bush vines onto two poles with a man on each end of the poles. Four men hoisted the poles to their shoulders. It was remarkable how these carriers, transporting me in a chair, could go so quickly up steep, narrow places, chattering happily all the while. Many times I was almost tipped out, but I managed to hang on. We traveled much more quickly when they were carrying me than when I was walking!

We spent the night again at Muye and started out early the next morning. About noon, as we went up the last hill, there was Lamafu waiting with our two horses. We were surely glad to see him and the horses!

The third day, January 11th, we spent all day in the saddle. We were about four miles from the Kami station when we noticed rain clouds so we began running the horses. We didn't run them all the way, but we beat the rain and didn't get wet.

The children were so glad to see us and, needless to say, I was ecstatic to see them. Perhaps the McCurdys were the happiest, because seventeen days with seven children was a very long time. We were extremely grateful that they were willing to look after our children, thereby making this trip feasible. How we praised the Lord for our co-workers. We know the Lord had made it possible for us to work together in real love and harmony.

Harold and Thelma Jackson's Visit
By Dale

Shortly after Chuck Driver returned to the States and Jim Spence died, The Executive Committee of New Tribes Mission sent Harold Jackson, one of its members, to New Guinea to set up the first Field Committee. Because many students in the training in the U.S. were planning to come to New Guinea, they realized the field would grow quickly and they wanted to have leadership in place.

Meetings were held in the Watut to discuss the forming of this new committee. Don McCurdy was able to represent the Highlands area and flew down to the Watut, where most missionaries were living. Just before Harold arrived, I'd had a fall on my motorbike. My right leg fell on the hot muffler, burning the back of it on the calf just above my high-topped boot. It was very painful and the burn turned into a crater ulcer that was larger than a silver dollar. Tropical ulcers are very common in the tropics and I was not able to do much for about three months. I was not able to attend these meetings because of this injury.

Harold appointed Arnold Davis, Ed Erke, Tom Palmer, Dave Lawrence, Don McCurdy and me to the first Field Committee.

Before Harold set up the new Field Committee, the field of New Guinea had been functioning on 100% field guidance. Because our field was small in number this worked fine. Everyone had to be in agreement on a decision before we would implement it. Group guidance had some good points as we all needed to draw on the Lord and work closely together with our fellow missionaries in order to function.

After these meetings, Harold went to Australia and started a training center for prospective new missionaries. The following year Harold returned to New Guinea with his wife, Thelma, and asked if I would take them to see the Gimi tribal people where I worked. By this time the Dave Lawrence family had moved from the Watut to our Kami base with plans to join us in the Gimi work.

We set a date for their visit, received their permits and set off. They rode our two horses, while Dave and I walked with the carriers.

The second day out, we came to a group of people blocking the trail. A man standing on a large stone asked me in a loud voice, "Why are you going so far inland when we are here and want a missionary?" This question made quite an impression on Harold, because he had never before heard people ask for a missionary.

After we arrived at my home in the Gimi, Thelma wanted to see inside a men's lodge. I talked to some of the big men (village leaders) and they thought that was funny that an *A-o-batha* wanted to go inside a lodge.

"If that's what she would like, that's OK with us," they said.

Thelma had white socks on when she went into the lodge and when she came out five minutes later her socks were black. I pointed to her feet and said, "What is that?" She looked down and was in shock to see that her socks were black! They were covered with fleas! Inside the men's lodge, the floor is covered with several layers of sugarcane pulp that makes a nice warm home for the family of fleas who live there. I don't think Thelma had seen fleas like this before and she certainly was not happy that they had found a new home on her socks.

The people laughed and had a lot of fun with Harold. He had a good time teasing and showing off his false teeth and they kept trying to pull their teeth out like he did. I don't remember much more about that trip, but we surely had a lot of laughs and a good time together.

This friendship with Harold and Thelma went back to 1950 when we first started our missionary training, which we recounted in Chapter 2.

I remember Harold telling us about this lady who was visiting the camp. She asked Harold how the students lived when they didn't work at a paying job.

*"Well, we live by faith out here and if that shouldn't work, we have
a place out back where we bury them," he told her.*
*Harold was full of fun and we became good friends with him and
Thelma during our missionary training.*

The next big event, after Harold and Thelma's visit to the Gimi, was moving part of our family into the Gimi. Again, Arvalee tells that part of our history.

Chapter 9

Family Moving to the Gimi, 1958
By Arvalee

For nearly five years, we had lived at Kami in our bush house that Dale had built. Once again the residents on the station were changing. The Drivers had left for furlough. Don McCurdy had built a new house for his family at the new mission station called Olaguti, up the road a few miles from Kami. This location was chosen because it was near a spring of water that flowed year round. The land was leased from the local people who owned it.

Earlier that year, the Lawrence family had joined us at Kami. They were living in the old Sellers house where the McCurdys had lived prior to their move to Olaguti.

Finally the time had come for us to move to the Gimi. When everything was packed, we abandoned our bush house at Kami, since the mission base was being moved to Olaguti. It was October, 1958. The Lawrences were also making preparations to move into the Gimi to join us a month later.

We packed all our household belongings in parcels that could be carried by one person. The only way to make the move was for the Gimi people to carry our things into the Gimi for us because at that time there was no road for a vehicle. But before making our big move, we planned to spend a week or so with the McCurdys at Olaguti.

Dale had had many attacks of malaria since we'd been in New Guinea, so after our move to Olaguti, a doctor in Goroka recommended a malaria eradication treatment for Dale. He thought this would prevent future attacks while living in the bush location, which was a great distance from the hospital. But this doctor didn't know Dale's medical history of allergies to many medicines. After a day or so on the new medicine Dale became very nauseous. Soon he was vomiting every five minutes. At five o'clock on Sunday morning, he said to me, "I think I'd better get to the hospital."

Although I knew that Dale was vomiting frequently, I didn't realize how seriously ill he was until he told me he should go to the hospital. Then I knew how desperately ill he was. He had been sick many times, but he was never one to complain so it was hard for me to judge how sick he really was. This was before I was aware of the danger of dehydration.

Getting to the hospital, however, presented a problem. Don had gone to a village for the weekend and he had the only vehicle, so I needed to send him a note to tell him of the urgency to get Dale to the hospital. I dressed quickly and walked down the path in the darkness to the workers' houses and asked one of them to take a note to Don.

When Don came with the vehicle a couple of hours later, Dale and I were ready to go. We put a mattress in the bed of the pick-up truck for him to lie on and I sat beside him. He was so sick he couldn't even hold his head up. I knew he needed my support, so I insisted on staying beside him, even though Don encouraged me to sit in the cab.

After traveling a couple of hours over the bumpy mountainous road, we arrived at the hospital in Goroka. Dale was put on an I.V. immediately because he was very severely dehydrated. The doctor told us that a man had died a few months before from dehydration. It was at this time that I was enlightened as to the insidious danger of dehydration. Dale told me later that as long as he was vomiting, a nurse was always at his bedside, looking after him. It was a great relief to have Dale safely in the care of the wonderful hospital staff that paid close attention to his needs.

Ready to move to the Gimi.

Once Dale was settled in the hospital, Don and I returned to base because I had no place to stay in Goroka. It was difficult for me to leave him, knowing how sick he was. We had no radio or other means of finding out how he was getting along. The next week we returned to check on Dale and found that he was ready to be discharged. I was greatly relieved to hear he was doing so much better. Now, Dale had to recuperate and gain his strength back. His sickness set our move to the Gimi back by six weeks and Don and Gwen graciously looked after us. During this time we became more like one family.

While we were staying with the McCurdys, another missionary's *cargo* (baggage) arrived by ship, and along with it came a large metal box that Dale's granddad had made. It was full of wonderful things from Dale's family; among them new clothes for each of us and a baby doll and buggy for Julie.

Now that Dale was feeling well again, we set the

Unpacking the large metal box.

new date for the big move for the end of November, 1958. Since Dale's first visit to the Gimi in February, 1954, we had anticipated this move. Since that time, he had worked alone in the tribe. Our dream of being together as a family was slowly becoming a reality because the Government had lifted the restrictions.

As it happened, we still would not move in as a complete family. Pat and Peter stayed behind temporarily in order to continue their schoolwork. I'd had quite a bit of difficulty teaching them their school lessons. During this time Gwen had been teaching Pat while Peter was being taught by Althea, so the obvious solution was to continue on with what we had been doing. So, Pat stayed with Don and Gwen at Olaguti and Peter stayed with Dave and Althea at Kami.

When moving day arrived a group of Gimi people came to carry our things and assist us in the move. We had learned how difficult it was for the children to be carried by the national men when we made the trip to Gono, so Dale built a little chair each for Paul and Julie to be carried in. Paul was five and a half years old and Julie was almost three. Each chair was lashed to a pole and carried on the shoulders of two men. The first day of travel, Dale and I rode the horses, Peanuts and Prince, to Anuparu. There we spent the night, camped in the small round house that Dale had built for his use while going to and from the Gimi. The things he had stored there were very useful to us.

After sleeping at Anuparu, we sent the horses back to base. From here we would walk with our helpers the rest of the way to the Gimi, stopping at Muye the second night.

When Dale first began trekking to the Gimi, he tried to get there as quickly as possible. A friendly patrol officer once told him, "You should slow down when trekking over these rugged mountain trails, or you will burn out in this tropical climate. The people will still be there, whether you get there in one day or three." Dale took his advice and usually took three days for the Gimi trip.

Julie and Paul in carrying chairs.

As we walked along the narrow, mountainous bush trail, twisting and winding down the mountain, we could usually spot below us the carriers with Paul and Julie sitting in their carrying chairs. Once, the transporters got way ahead of us and we could no longer see them. Dale, not knowing these men personally, was concerned for the welfare of our two little ones, so he began running down the mountain to catch up with them. He was relieved to find the kids were fine and the carriers were continuing their steady pace. He stopped them for a rest, allowing me to catch up. He knew I would want to know, too, that everything was all right.

After three days on the trail, it was a great relief to know we had finally reached our destination. We were at last in our new home! The people had built this wonderful, unique house for Dale. We had spent a lot of time planning the 40-foot diameter house so that the rooms would be partitioned just right.

I was pleased to see that Dale had finished making the partitions for the children's bedrooms. But we still had a lot of work to do, getting things unpacked and putting the house in order. While we were still at Kami, Dale had pre-cut the plywood for the kitchen cabinets and dressers for the bedrooms. All this material was moved in with us and Dale now had to assemble the furniture. I knew all this would take a lot of time, but I was anxious to get settled again, this time in our brand new round bush house.

The largest and most difficult item to transport was our large cast iron cook stove. Dale had removed the doors, stove top lids and legs, anything that could be taken off to reduce the weight, but it was still tremendously heavy. In fact, the men who carried it had given out along the way and left it in a vacant house, planning to return for it at a later date, which they did. The men finally delivered it to us four months later, on March 22nd.

Of course we missed our two sons and were eagerly anticipating the day Pat and Peter could join us in the Gimi. Our plan was for Peter to come in with the Lawrences when they moved in December, and Pat would come in the new year, after the school year was finished.

A Near Death Experience
By Arvalee

It was the middle of December 1958. We had been in the Gimi for just two weeks and now Paul and Julie had both come down with measles. I recognized the red rash as measles right away, because Pat and Peter had already had them on the voyage across the Pacific Ocean.

I felt dreadful, thinking that we had brought measles to the Gimi people. I mentioned this to Meniba, Dale's faithful language helper, and he said, "Oh, Missus, many of our children have already had this sickness." That was a great relief to hear, because I had feared that many Gimi children might die if they contracted measles.

I knew that I needed to keep the children quiet and warm, make some good, soft food for them, and they would be fine in a day or so. At least this is what I thought. This was true for Julie. She did just fine. In about three days, she was feeling well again and the red rash was gone.

Sadly, it was a different story with Paul. He became really ill with a high fever and a bad cough. His eyes had turned blood red, and to protect them I put a dark blanket over the window. Spasms of coughing caused frequent vomiting. This turned him off all desire for food, lest he throw up again. Paul had already been sick for a week, when, one morning, as Dale held his little arm, his thumb left a distinct impression. It was then we realized he was dehydrated. We knew this was very serious, because of Dale's recent bout with dehydration from the drug allergy. Paul needed treatment at the hospital in Goroka, but we knew the journey there would be impossible for him. If we had tried to carry him out on a stretcher he would never survive the three day trip.

We were totally dependant on the Lord and knew in our hearts that unless the Lord did a miracle, we would soon be digging a grave. We were beside ourselves with anxiety. Nothing we tried had helped him.

The Lord tells us, "Cast all your cares upon me" (1 Peter 5:7) and, "If any are sick, pray for him and anoint him" (James 5:14). That is just what we did that morning. I brought the bottle of cooking oil, and Dale took a little on his fingers to anoint Paul. George Fatzinger, a fellow missionary, was there with us. Also, two of our Gimi workers were there. Nu-u-da and A-a-mo-aba had both made a profession of faith in the Lord. We all gathered around his bed, knelt down, and each of us prayed for him.

Have you ever seen the Lord heal someone? There was no doubt in our minds that the Lord did perform a miracle that day! After we prayed, Paul did not throw up again. The cough didn't go away immediately, but the vomiting ceased! He began eating the soft foods I prepared---soup, egg custard and soft Jell-O. Because we did not have a refrigerator, I had to make Jell-O with half the boiling water and less cold water. That is why I called it *soft Jell-O*. Each day Paul improved, until he was completely well again.

Oh, how happy we were to see him gaining strength each day. With hearts overflowing with gratitude and awe, we thanked the Lord for answering our prayers. But why wouldn't He? He wants us to be obedient to His commands to cast all our cares on Him and to pray and ask, believing in faith that He will heal, according to His will.

> *In speaking with Paul about this incident years later, he told me the scariest part of his illness, was that during those first critical days, he couldn't see! He must have temporarily lost his sight, but had not mentioned it to us at the time. If it had been for an extended time, we certainly would have noticed, because we were watching him very closely day and night. Praise the Lord, He was merciful in that we were not aware that he had lost his sight and of the full danger he was in. In healing Paul, the Lord performed a greater miracle than we were aware of; raising him up from the measles and healing his eyes!*

Early Months in the Gimi
By Arvalee

Having moved to the Gimi, without Pat and Peter, we eagerly looked forward to the time our family would again be complete. Now it was a few days before Christmas and Peter arrived at last to join us, along with Dave and Althea Lawrence and family.

Peter was so excited to be with us again that he ran the last few hundred yards up the trail to the house. I can still picture him vividly as he came towards me. He was only eight years old, and that month was a long time for him to be away from Mom and Dad and his siblings.

It was to be a much longer time before ten year old Pat would join us. He was still living with the McCurdys at Olaguti, as Gwen was his school teacher. We knew he would be there until May when school finished. What a long time that would be, to be separated from his family. But a surprise was in the making! Unknown to us, arrangements had been made for him to come for a visit in January! Jerry Sherman accompanied him on the trip and they arrived on the 24th. That was a thrilling time for us all and it gave Pat a glimpse of what "home" was like in the Gimi. While he was there, he asked if we could have his birthday party early while he was home with us, so we did that, although his birthday was actually on March 28th. But alas, his vacation was soon over, and he had to return to Olaguti to finish the school year. Our family was no longer complete!

Dale himself continued having trouble physically. Consequently, he spent most of his time around the house. When he felt up to it, he taught the workers at their houses, located just down the hill from us. He was not often able to trek to the villages, lacking the stamina necessary for more distant hikes.

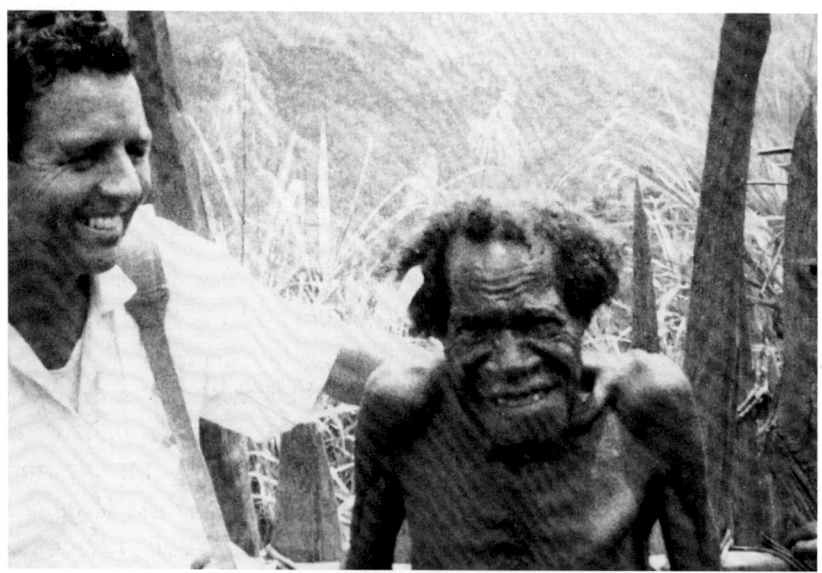

Dale and a Gimi grand-father.

152

We were far from civilization and more medical problems were ahead but it was our son Peter who needed a doctor this time.

Dale was making preparations to kill and butcher a goat. Peter was on the spot, standing there holding the tame goat, which was tied, for his dad. That goat must have sensed its days were numbered because it hooked Peter with one of its long horns and flipped him into the air. He came down on his head, but it knocked the wind out of him, too. Ruthie Stone was visiting us and we decided that Peter should see a doctor. So when she left the Gimi a few days later we sent Peter along to see the doctor in Goroka. We had Dale's carrying chair ready, so Peter could be carried in that. Peter told me recently, "It was so miserable trying to hold on to that thing that I got out and walked. Once I was in Goroka, the doctor examined me, but I don't remember if they took an x-ray or not. He just told me, 'Have bed rest and lay on your back for two weeks.'" Imagine the doctor giving Peter this advice; after all, it took two days for him to walk to town and now another two days back home again! After four days of walking, now you should rest?

After we had been in the Gimi for some time, Dale thought I should have a little break from the isolation, so he arranged for me to go out to Olaguti to check on some new items that had come for us by ship. After sorting through them, I would decide if we needed them in the Gimi. We planned that several national men would travel with me and we would stay overnight at Anuparu in Dale's rest house. We had stayed there on my visit to the Gimi and again when the children and I had moved into the tribe. Lamafu, the man who looked after our horses, would bring Prince to meet me there.

After walking most of the day, we came to Anuparu and I was faced with the decision of where all these national men would sleep that night! I hadn't even thought of that when Dale and I were planning the trip! But now here I was, a lone woman, traveling with these national men. I quickly decided they could not sleep in the house with me, so I told them they would have to go to the village just down the hill and sleep there. I gave one of them the key and padlock to the door and instructed him to lock it and pass the key back to me underneath the door. I told him that he could come back in the morning and unlock the door. "*Yu mas lokim dua na givim key bek long mi. Long moningtaim yu kam bek, na opim dua,*" I said.

They followed my instructions and then off they went to the nearby village. They probably thought this was a very strange *Missus*. I settled down in my sleeping bag, but disturbing thoughts kept coming to my mind, preventing me from going to sleep. No doubt it was the enemy making these suggestions. *What if the crazy man from the village comes and sets the house on fire? How would you get out?* After a few minutes of being plagued by these worrisome thoughts, I felt the enemy had indeed brought them to mind. After walking most of the day, I was extremely tired and realized that it was crucial that I get a good night's sleep. I thought, *All right, Lord, if that is the way you want me to depart this world, I'm ready.* And I went to sleep!

When morning came, the carriers returned from the village and I passed the key to them underneath the door. Soon I was preparing to leave for Olaguti. Lamafu had arrived with the horse, which I rode all day to the mission base.

I was so exhausted by the time I arrived at Olaguti that it took me a day or so to recuperate. Then I accomplished my task of sorting the newly arrived items and was ready to return home. When I got home, Dale informed me that one of the carriers who had accompanied me on the trip was the local *witch doctor*. I thanked him for not telling me this bit of information before I made the trip!

The Lawrence Family
By Arvalee

Dave and Althea had settled down temporarily in three small round houses, located just behind our larger round house. Earlier, Dave had contracted with the people to build these in preparation for moving his family to the Gimi area. Now that they were settled in, he was constructing a larger, family house on the hillside above our house.

They used one of these small houses for sleeping quarters, one for cooking and eating, and the third for a schoolroom. Althea resumed teaching Peter along with her own children soon after their arrival.

Althea was expecting and about the middle of the year, Dave took her out to have the baby in Goroka. They planned to be away six weeks before the birth and six weeks afterwards. They had arranged with us to keep their three children, Steve, Joy and Craig. It's a good thing our house was a large one! A new room was fabricated in part of our living room for them. Dave hiked back from Olaguti to the Gimi several times to keep in contact with his kids and check on how they were doing in their parents' absence.

I remember an amusing incident that happened because of the likes and dislikes of food in our respective families. For lunch, I occasionally served sardines to our family, who thought this was a special treat. After lunch one day, I found sardines on the floor underneath Joy's chair. It was only then that I discovered that she didn't like them. She told me years later, that when I served them after that, she simply put them in her pocket!

It was indeed a happy day when Dave and Althea returned to the Gimi with a healthy new baby boy whom they named Dana. Now, each of our families had three boys and a girl.

Later, Dale and Dave went to Olaguti to attend the yearly mission conference, leaving Althea and me alone in the tribe with our children. While they were away a frightful incident happened. One of the national couples fought periodically, which usually resulted in Aaron beating up on his wife, Sadieboro. Aaron had worked often for Dave as his language informant and we all knew of the trouble this couple had experienced.

One day, I heard loud screaming and looked outside to see Aaron chasing his wife up the trail with an upraised hatchet. At that point, I rushed outside and yelled to Althea. We went together up the trail to rescue Sadieboro. When Aaron saw us approaching, he turned suddenly and crashed the hatchet into the picket fence alongside the trail. Althea and I brought Sadieboro back to my house and began patching up the small wounds that her husband had inflicted earlier that morning. It was an hour or so later that we realized how foolishly we had acted! To interfere in a marital dispute was not culturally acceptable. We realized too late that we should never have tried to help Sadieboro, and we were indeed fortunate that Aaron had not turned the hatchet on us!

Disturbing Thoughts
By Arvalee

Our house was a huge round house, with the bedrooms taking one half the space of the house. The kitchen, dining room and living room made up the other half of the house. This area was divided in half, each taking a quarter of the space. Alongside the dining table, a couple of feet away, there was a dividing wall about the height of the table. The living area was an open space and the national people were allowed to enter our house freely into this open area. They loved to stand alongside the dividing wall while we were eating! They had never observed people who sat down to eat around a table so we were quite a fascination to them.

Usually, I didn't mind their presence, since they stood outside the dividing wall. However, there was one man who really began to grate on me. He persisted on coming inside the wall and standing at the end of our table, day after day. Most of the time, he was coughing and he had a discharge from his nose! Dale knew it upset me that the man was spreading germs every time he coughed so he politely asked him, three times, to stand on the other side of the wall. In response, he would only grunt and nod his head, but he would never move.

One day, I had all I could take. I got up and left the table. I could not eat another bite. As I went away, the Lord was speaking to me. It seemed He told me, *You do not love these people. You only think you do.*

Right then, I had to really examine my heart, and I knew beyond a doubt that I really did not love the people. I was not big enough nor did I possess in myself the capability to love these culturally different people coupled with their lack of 20th century hygiene.

It was only God's love that made me willing to go into the Gimi, and I realized that day that it was only God's love that would keep me there with these unlovely people.

A major victory was won that day. From then on I had a different outlook when the people came around. God took care of the problem in my heart, and surprisingly, before long we heard that the man, Eviraisa, had moved to the south Gimi!

Our Pet Cockatoo
By Arvalee

After Peter arrived in the Gimi, he had a pet lorikeet that he kept in a cage. One day he found his pet dead. It appeared that the bird had been caught in the door as it closed. Peter was distraught, and when Meniba saw him crying he asked him what had happened. Peter told him, and Meniba said, "Don't you cry anymore, Peter. I know where there is a nest of *cockatoos*, and I will get a baby and bring you one."

True to his word, the next day Meniba borrowed the shotgun from Dale, took two shells and in a few days he brought back a baby *cockatoo* for Peter. He told Dale he was able to shoot both parent birds with one shell, enabling him to get the baby from the nest. Shooting these birds was no problem to Meniba because the people only thought of these beautiful birds as another meal for their family and more feathers for a headdress.

We kept this new baby *cockatoo* in a cage to protect it from the cats. At first it didn't even know how to perch on the branch in the cage. The first night we had it, I was awakened several times by its raucous squawking. The next day, I complained to Meniba about my sleeplessness. He said, "It's just hungry, Missus." He then told me how to feed it; by taking bits of banana or *kaukau* (sweet potato) and poking it down its gullet! The bird would squawk, holding its beak open, at which time I would poke the food in. Indeed, this stopped the terrible noise! Dale kidded me, saying that bird thought I was its mama!

After awhile, we began taking it out of the cage and it would walk awkwardly across the kitchen floor, flapping its huge wings, exercising them in preparation for its first flight. The cats ran away when the bird began flapping its wings so after we saw that the cats were actually afraid of it we no longer feared for the bird's life. Then the bird discovered the tin of milk kept underneath the kitchen stove for the cats! It was quite amusing to watch the bird taking sips of milk alongside the cats!

As it grew, the antics of this bird were most entertaining. Our entire family enjoyed watching it but as time went on, it became a nuisance too. When it did learn to fly it would swoop down to the clothesline and chew up my clothespins, which was extremely annoying.

Sometimes the *cockatoo* would fly off into the jungle, no doubt foraging for food.

One day we saw that it had landed in a distant tree down the mountainside from our house. Peter was worried that it wouldn't come back and persuaded some young boys to climb the tree to rescue it. They did and brought it home. After that, the bird frequently flew away but always came back home. It would perch on the railing by our back door, which was fashioned as a Dutch door.

We usually kept the top part of the door open during the day. At lunchtime one day we heard the bird squawking and knew it was nearby. It was learning to talk, and as it flew overhead it called out, "*Peto, Peto, Peto,*" a perfect imitation of the way the young Gimi kids said Peter's name. Suddenly, it flew kitty-cornered right through the Dutch door and made a perfect landing, right in the middle of our table, scattering dishes all over. Placing my hands over its folded wings, I picked it up and took it to the door, tossing it none too gently into the air, and it flew away!

Almost every morning the bird made a practice of following Dale down the pathway to the national worker's houses, where Dale led the group in devotions. Instead of flying, it actually walked down the trail, awkwardly putting one foot in front of the other much like a penguin. As people approached, it would cock its head to one side saying, *"erane"* (meaning "hello" in Gimi). We often said to each other, "That bird thinks it's a person." One morning Dale heard his name, "*Masta Deo, Masta Deo.*" Looking up to the thatch roof, there he saw the bird swinging from a pole by one claw, calling his name in the Gimi pronunciation, of course!

Sometime later, as we walked down the rough road, leaving the Gimi for our first furlough, our beautiful white *cockatoo* flew overhead. It followed us to the first village, then turned and flew back towards our house. A few weeks later, we heard from the Lawrences that they had found white feathers on the path, and they believed a village dog had killed it. In its entire life it had never feared walking down the path, instead of flying! Alas, it died because it felt so secure.

Ordering and Buying Supplies
By Arvalee

A vital part of living successfully in the Gimi was being able to order and receive all our necessary supplies from town; from laundry soap to tooth paste and all food items. However, we could buy fresh produce from the local people, who grew a wide variety of garden produce, including bananas, tomatoes, cucumbers, greens, spring onions, pumpkin, sweet potato, taro, green beans, corn, snake beans (a locally grown type of green bean) and mushrooms. These were usually available in abundance all year round. Best of all, we could buy all these wonderful vegetables at very reasonable prices.

Usually we ordered supplies about once a month. I carefully calculated which items and amounts were needed, wrote out the order and sent it by hand carrier to our mission's supply man. A post-dated check accompanied each order. Items such as butter and eggs presented a problem to the supply man. Once, the rolls of coins, which we needed to pay the carriers and buy produce, had been packed in the plastic container along with the butter! Imagine my frustration upon opening that container, to find the coins mingled with the butter, which had melted! Receiving unbroken eggs was truly a miracle. I ordered four dozen at a time and they had to be carefully packed. In time, the carriers learned to identify which rucksack contained the eggs and treated them with TLC.

How long would that thirty-five pound drum of flour last, or the sugar, or powdered milk? I miscalculated on the very first order I made, when we had an extra mouth to feed, so when Christmas came there was no flour to make bread and those extra treats, or to make bread stuffing for our baked chicken. I solved the problem when I found a recipe in the cook book for rice stuffing. Missionaries often have to learn early on to make substitutions for items that are not available. I found this ability enhanced my cooking and I learned to be very creative in my use of the locally grown produce, as well.

I baked all our bread and was thankful for that previously mentioned wood cook stove. It was the largest model available and I could bake six loaves of bread at once. In addition to the loaves of bread, I regularly made banana bread, pies, cookies or sweet rolls, all of which were relished by the family.

We bought processed cheese which we sliced before serving. It was packaged in small round *tins*. Once when Ireso and his wife, O-o-nasi (or Coconuts) were having lunch with us, she exclaimed, "Soap! Imagine having soap to eat." We quickly informed her that it wasn't soap and then we tried to explain to her what cheese is. This was nearly impossible, as the Gimi people were not familiar with the process of milking animals or the concept of food produced from the milk! The foods of the missionaries are truly as foreign to the national people as their food is to us, so we all had to be educated to learn each others' customs and habits.

For many years, anything we ordered from the stores in Goroka had to be carried to the Gimi by the people in rucksacks. What a blessing it was, especially to the people, when the jeep road was finally finished and supplies could be hauled in by vehicle.

Life In The Gimi
Excerpts from Dale's Diary
(See Appendix, page 379 for entire diary.)
January, 1959

01/01/59. We have been in the Gimi for 5 weeks now. It is so good to have the family in here with me.

I feel that the work here in the Gimi is just beginning. Yet, in another way we have a good head start. I feel the greatest thing that has been done for these people to deliver them from the power of Satan is that Christians from the homeland have written over and over that they are praying for the Gimi. Without prayer we would have no start at all in here. Mom (Palmer) has written me that she prays for Meniba and his wife all the time, and I know for sure that Meniba would have lost heart by now and have fallen by the wayside if someone hadn't been praying and holding him up before the Lord all the time.

Peter's little parakeet died today. When he found it, he couldn't keep from crying. Meniba saw him crying and told him that he would go down to A-ibu to try to get him a (baby) *cockatoo*. He said, "I'll go in the morning."

01/06/59. It's been so cold in the mornings. I thought we might try to meet in the firewood house, so we could have a fire. Meniba said after the meeting that Asumuyaba's brother had died and he was going over to see him. He said he was a Christian.

01/07/59. Meniba said that they had already buried the man, (who died on the 2nd), so he didn't see him. They all feel sorcery was worked on this man, too, just like Meniba's brother. The fear of sorcery is very strong. We have got to believe the gospel of Jesus Christ is truly the Power of God and it can break the powers of the evil one in this place. It can also do in the hearts of these poor benighted people what dynamite can do to a hard stone that is blocking a roadway. The power of the gospel, I know for sure, can break these cold, hard hearts of the people and open them to the warm love of Christ. I know God has done this very thing for me some 10 years ago and He's the same today as He was 10 years ago.

01/10/59. The weather is still cold this morning, it must have rained most of the night and the wind woke me this morning. This must be the coldest time of year back here.

The Lord helped me this morning in our family devotions by Peter's example. He got up singing a song about the Lord, then he stopped singing and Arvalee saw him praying. We talked some about how God helped Joshua. Paul said Joshua 1:9 for us, The Lord commands us to be strong and brave, not to be afraid or over-taken, and He promises to be with us always.

01/17/59. Meniba is going to take some time off. There is a custom here that when a close relative dies, his relatives have to kill pigs and feed more distant relatives. This is where Meniba is right now, but he has no pigs to kill so he's trying to buy some. I told him he could have two weeks off.

Meniba came in tonight telling me that his only pig is gone now. He thinks someone stole it. He said tomorrow he is going to look for it. Satan is working on Meniba overtime these days. He thinks everyone is down on him. I feel he's on the rock bottom. Now, to see the Lord take over in his life and bring him out on top would be great. Meniba is walking through the valley of the shadow of death these days. But he has got to see that the Lord is with him. He knows that the Lord is near, He is over all, but he doesn't know and really believe it for his own life. When the Lord opens his eyes to this he will be able to say, "I will fear no evil, for you are with me Lord." This will be the day for Meniba.

01/18/59. Meniba went to look for his pig today, but didn't find it.

The kids and I went for a nice walk up the road this afternoon. There are so many things to look at and the kids have so much fun.

01/19/59. As I was looking out the window this morning, I saw Meniba and his wife going down the road. I don't know where they are going, but they must be looking for their pig yet. He is sure low these days. I don't know what to do to help him, only pray. He didn't get back for the morning devotions.

Meniba came in time to help Arvalee with the wash, then right after the wash was over, he said his pig had come back and someone had stolen it, for its ears were cut off. He wanted to track it back, said the ears were bleeding, and he could follow the drops of blood. He left about noon and it rained about 4:00 p.m. real hard. He came in about 5:30 and said he tracked the blood back to a village down below us here. He said he talked to the man down there, who said he found the pig down on the *Thani* River. Meniba said he told the man he could give him a pig for stealing his and cutting its ears. He came up here to talk to me about it.

"Alright Meniba, lets pray about it," I said. "God will show you what to do if you will only be willing to obey Him." I prayed first and Meniba prayed in Gimi and I couldn't understand him at all, because he was talking so low. I could hear someone call, Meniba, MENIBA. Come quickly, they're going down to fight.

Meniba looked at me and said, "Mu-u-nabi is calling me, I must go now."

I told him, "Walk softly before the Lord and He will help you."

"Yes, I will sir, pray for me." He went out the front door and I got up and went out the back door, going over to tell Dave. I saw about 15 men with bows and arrows running down the road over by U-i-mo's house. Meniba was now down the road a bit, making good time; Mu-u-nabi was calling out to Meniba about something, as he went running by the house but I couldn't understand her. All the men were over the hill by then and Meniba was right behind them. I went on over and told Dave about it, for he had been in school all day and didn't know much about what had happened. After I told him, I went for a short walk up the road. I told the Lord that it was up to Him to show Meniba about his motive about this pig and to give him love and wisdom in all of this.

Arvalee called me for supper, but I was feeling a bit sicker, so didn't eat much and went right to bed. I lost all my supper and was in bed for the night when Meniba came in the front door. He asked Arvalee if I was here. Arvalee said yes, but he is sick. Meniba came to the bedroom door and said, "Are you sick?" He was all smiles and said, "God helped me. When I left you some of my clan had come and was going down to burn the little hamlet. They had their bows and arrows ready to fight. The arrow tips were unwrapped and the razor bamboo edges were in each man's hand. I told them to stop, that I would talk to the fellow and we weren't going to fight. They were sure mad, but somehow God made them hear what I had to say, but some even got mad at me. As I walked up to the man's house alone, my people kept shouting, 'Let's burn the houses and kill all their pigs.' By the time I got to the man's house he was standing in front of his house. I told him not to be afraid for my people were not going to fight. The Negibis had circled the hamlet and were shouting yet, 'Burn the houses, kill the pigs.' The Father helped me to speak softly and I asked the man why he had stolen my pig. He said he found it down on the *Thani* River and he was going to take care of it. I said, 'Have I ever come to your village and stole your pigs or anything from you?'"

"No."

"Well then why did you steal my pig and cut his ears off?" Then the man told me that he had stolen my pig and he was sorry. I told him that he was full of sin and following Satan, that he was always doing something to me or my people and making it hard for us. I told him I wasn't mad, but felt sorry for him. The Negibis had quieted down a bit by now.

The man said, "I liked your pig, so I stole it and cut its ears off and ate them, but the pig got out of the fence I made and ran away. I will give you one of my little pigs for my stealing."

Meniba said, "God spoke to my *liver* (heart) and told me if I take that pig from him, that I would be stealing his pig. So I told him that I would buy the little pig from him, and then everyone would be happy." So Meniba and the man shook hands and said it was finished. But this did not make Meniba's people happy. They said that he must give the pig, no pay. The man said he was willing to just give the pig to Meniba, but Meniba said, "NO. God told me to pay for the pig." Meniba said, "*Master* (Dale), God really helped me today." I said to him that we should thank God for hearing us when we called on Him for help. So with a big smile all over his shiny black face, he said, "Yes, let's do." We both thanked God for helping him this afternoon. He just kept saying, "*Papa God*, (Father God) you helped me, it was you that made me strong." After praying he said he thought it would be good if he would make a fence to keep his pig in from now on. I told him I thought it would be good and I might be able to give him a bit of pig wire to make a strong fence. He said good night and strolled out the front door.

It has done me a world of good to see a victory over Satan like this. Believe me, Meniba is standing alone in his beliefs; his wife and his people just don't understand him. But God does and He is doing a good work in this young man's life. We see today that God is willing to help those who are willing to obey Him and not listen to what others say. This is one light in a very dark tribe, but others will see that this one is following a new Master and they will know that the one they are following is not the right one.

We had a test in language today and I missed all but two; my stress is all wrong. You would think I would know better. The *boys* (see glossary, here meaning young men) got here with the mail tonight. Pat and Jerry Sherman (later married to Ted Fitzgerald) are to leave from Olaguti in the morning.

01/22/59. No rain today. About 3:30 Biru and two *boys* went to meet Jerry and Pat.

01/24/59. Pat and Jerry got in about 10:30 this morning. James Yanepa from Yagaria (Kami) and several believers from the Watut came with Jerry.

01/26/59. Pat doesn't seem to know what to do with himself so Jerry, Pat and I played Scrabble all morning.

01/27/59. Jerry read to our family this morning. Had a birthday party for Julie and Asumuyaba (Meniba's first born) and Ani-animo (A-a-mo-aba's little boy). Julie was three years old, (and we think the others were, too).

01/28/59. A-a-mo-aba killed two chickens for supper tonight. It was nice to have Dave and Althea over for supper. I told them after eating that we might try to go on furlough some time in August or September of this year.

01/29/59. Pat has been having a good time back here. The kids go up the road and find so many things to do in the bush.

01/30/59. Meniba came in this morning, said he was a bit sick, so he came on home last night. He said they had a good meeting at Misapi and the Christians were glad to see them.

01/31/59. The three visitors went down with Dave this morning to have devotions with our workers and local people who attend the meetings.

February, 1959

02/01/59. Biru and I went down to Ore-ua-bipi. Pat went along, too.

02/04/59. Meniba started working on Dave's house today.

02/06/59. I did the teaching this morning. Meniba doing well on the house.

02/15/59. Dave said they sure had a good time at the baptism. There were about 30 baptized. Hu-a-ni-aba had the communion all ready, all on his own.

Had Pat's birthday celebration today, he is 10 years old. He asked if we could have it for him now. (His birthday is on March 28th.) We had a good time singing tonight too.

02/18/59. Pat and Biru got away at 5:00 a.m. this morning, it was real dark but they should get to the horses easily by noon.

02/21/59. Meniba came in about 3:30 and said U-i-mo was bleeding from his nose. So I went right over there. They all feel that someone came up to the fence and worked sorcery on him today some time.

When I came up to the house U-i-mo saw me and tried to climb into his house. But his mother and another man that were holding him up pulled him back and set him up. I had stopped and was standing on the outside of the fence with one foot on the sty. When they got him pulled back and sitting up again, I stepped over the sty and down into the small yard. I walked over to U-i-mo and sat in a squatting position just to his left. His Mother was crying as she helped hold him up. There were men milling in the yard and some old fellows were sitting by a fire just behind me. Some were saying, "It's sorcery and it's the A-bo-pisa clan that did it." I could hear all this chatter, but all this time I was looking at U-i-mo. I took his pulse and it seemed to be normal, maybe just a bit slow. Then he looked right at me, asking me "Will I die tonight?" I told him, "No! I believe that God wants you to be made well." I told him that Meniba and I came and wanted to pray for him and that all three of us must put our trust in God at this time. Then I told him that I would like to read from my Bible James 5:14. Pidgin English: *"Sam pela man I gat sik, em I ken singaut long strong pela boi bilong Yesusu, em I ken pre long em nau putim gris long nem bilong Yesusu"*. I told them that it was good for us to obey God; that this was not my idea, but this is the way God told us to pray for the sick. I told them I didn't have any oil and asked if they did. After a bit a man came up from behind me and gave me some bark that was rolled loosely in a ball, saturated with pig grease. I thanked him and took it from him. I rubbed a bit on his forehead and we prayed for U-i-mo.

02/22/59. Last night at the supper table it was just getting dark when the front door flew open and in walked eight men fully armed with bows and arrows over their shoulders. Esema, the *luluai* (chief) of the Negibi clan, walked on into the dining room and I asked him what he had come for. He said that he had come for nothing at all. I told him that I knew better. We shook hands and exchanged greetings and then he looked around a bit, then he and four other men walked out. He must have told three of the men to stay here, for that is just what they did. They sat down in the chairs in the living room and played with Paul and Peter for some time. I felt a cold coming on, so went in and went to bed. I could hear the fellows talking and picking on the auto harp, and then I went off to sleep. Arvalee said that she was typing and they were in there talking low until about 9:30 and then the big lamp that lights the living room and dining room ran out of kerosene and went out. She said they went outside then and went off. A bit after that, Meniba came up and Arvalee told him that I was asleep and had a cold and she didn't want to wake me up. She asked him if he wanted anything. "No, I just came up." And he went out. He came up this morning and got some soap to wash up, but didn't say anything about last night, so I didn't ask. About 3:00 this afternoon I walked down to Meniba's house and saw U-i-mo's wife sitting in the door way. I looked in and there sat U-i-mo, so I went in and sat down beside him. He said his head just had a little pain. I then walked up to the house and saw Etha-o chopping on a tree. He spoke to me and said, "Red man, hello." So this made me feel good.

02/23/59. After the meeting, I asked if there was anything we could pray for. Meniba said U-i-mo was alright now, but there might be trouble for the men going down to the village the other night. He also said that he was afraid that someone would work sorcery on him. So I prayed and then Meniba prayed.

March, 1959

03/01/59. Meniba, Biru and A-a-mo-aba all went down for the baptism. Meniba said that everyone was asking where *Master* Dale (see below and glossary) was and could they baptize without the missionaries around. Meniba asked them "Who were they getting their strong from, the missionaries or God?" He told them, "We may not always have the missionaries with us. God can help us and make us strong." I was sure glad that Meniba spoke up and said this. This is just what these Christians need, to have some of the crutches taken away from them, so they can stand on their own two feet. He said when they were talking to the people about baptism that it thundered and Meniba told A-a-mo-aba that it was like when Jesus was baptized. He said 46 people were baptized.

See 'My First Gimi Patrol' which explains Colonial days. During this period, the native people referred to and addressed all Europeans, or foreigners, as Master and Missus. This was a term of respect. In later years these terms became obsolete as the name of each person was commonly used. Section edited by Arvalee

03/12/59. Wrote to Don (McCurdy) today and told him to put 100 pounds (£100, Australian currency) down on a booking for a ship in September.

03/22/59. Carriers got in this afternoon with the stove that has been stored in a village since we moved here last November.

The cast iron cook stove was so heavy the carriers had worn out and left it in a vacant house until they felt strong enough to bring it the rest of the way into the Gimi. Rune, one of those carriers, actually had a large cyst develop on his shoulder, which had to be surgically removed. These Gimi men and sometimes women, who carried our supplies, even though we paid them, were very faithful and dedicated: playing a key role in keeping us missionaries in this remote Gimi tribe. By Arvalee.

03/24/59. One of the carriers who went down to work on the *kanda* (rattan) bridge yesterday, fell in the water, but was able to swim over to the bank and got out. Praise the Lord.

03/25/59. Arvalee left for Olaguti this morning.

03/28/59. Got word from Arvalee today, said she was sore (from walking). Work on the house is coming along good.

03/30/59. Still teaching Paul. Sent *cargo boys* (carriers) to Olaguti today.

April, 1959

04/01/59. Thought maybe Arvalee would be coming today but she wrote that she was going to town today to see the doctor.

04/02/59. The people are bringing lots of planks for shingles for Dave's house. Meniba is working hard and should be finished with this one side by the end of the week.

04/04/59. Meniba got the roof on one side yesterday, so is taking the day off today.

04/06/59. Dave has been working with Meniba on the house and it's been going much faster.

04/07/59. Arvalee got here today about 3:00 p.m.

04/15/59. Carriers got here from Olaguti this afternoon. We had no rain today. Got some good mail today; from Stines and Mom.

04/16/59. Meniba got back from Misapi and had a lot to talk about. Meniba is starting to put into practice what he believes. He is truly growing in the things of the Lord, but I feel it's the prayers of the many saints that are praying for him.

04/19/59. Had a good talk to Meniba tonight. He has been working so hard that he doesn't come by to talk like he used to. We talked about goats, cows, roads, my trip to Porosa. I sure enjoy talking to him, he just understands.

04/20/59. Praise the Lord for bringing Dave and I to Kigupa today (on the way to Olaguti for conference). I saw the Lord's hand on my life for I had not the strength to come this far. The last two hours we had to stop a lot for me. We tried to get enough fellows to carry the chair, so I could ride some, but the Lord didn't see fit for this. We got here about 4:30 and must have left about 9 or 9:30.

04/21/59. Got here to Anuparu about 2:30. The horses sure look good.

04/22/59. We left Anuparu at 9:00 this morning and got here (Olaguti) a bit after 5:00 p.m. Dean (Van Vliet) went to town and Tom (Palmer), Arnold (Davis) and Al (Cole) came. Tom and I are in the guest room together.

04/23/59. Tom and I talked for some time last night. The conference started today at 9:00 a.m.

04/26/59. Played ball with Dale and Pat this morning and then Pat and I had some good fellowship in the Word.

04/30/59. I spoke this morning on our fellowship. I sang Amazing Grace and told what a blessing it was to my heart when I was sick.

Got word from Arvalee today, said that Meniba had got mad at Aaron and knocked him down. Aaron was fighting Mu-u-nabi, Meniba's wife and Sadieboro and their mother, so this made Meniba real mad and he came and told Arvalee and Althea that he was wrong in getting mad and they all three had prayer together. I do feel that Meniba is going through these hard times to really make him a man for the great job of building a strong New Testament church in the Gimi. When he comes to the end of the rope and there is no one to help him but God then and then only will Meniba see the Lord can do anything for him.

May, 1959

05/01/59. The conference was over today. I believe in my heart that this was the best conference that we have ever had in New Guinea. There was a spirit of needing each other's fellowship that I have never sensed before. I know myself that the Lord had done a real work in my heart before I ever got here. We talked about some big things but I believe most everything came out with an answer and there was an overall unity.

We closed with the Lord's Supper. So praise the Lord for meeting with us this year. To God be the Glory, Great things He hath done. Dave is going to leave for the Gimi in the morning.

05/07/59. We left Olaguti at 8:00 a.m. Told Don and Gwen good-bye for it may be a long time before we see them again. (I think they left for furlough before we did. Arvalee) Let George (Fatzinger) ride twice. *(He must be referring to riding the horses; not clear. Arvalee)*

I cooked dinner for the three of us. We had rice and potatoes and fresh tomatoes for dinner. (*I think Pat returned to the Gimi with Dale at this time, because he had been living with Don and Gwen and they were leaving for furlough. Dale doesn't make this real clear. Arvalee.*)

05/08/59. Left Anuparu at 7:00 a.m. and got to Negibi at 5:00 p.m. Sure glad to be home. Went to bed with the chickens. Dave came in and talked for some time, and then after the kids were in bed, Arvalee and I talked for some time.

05/11/59. Had a long talk with Meniba, he was asking me if I was coming back. (After our furlough) I told him that I sure wanted to and I would write him and let him know. Hobe-aba said he was teaching Meniba to read when I was at Olaguti.

05/13/59. Right after prayer meeting today, Arvalee saw Aaron walking up the road, so I thought I would walk up the road, too. Found him down the hill cutting some pickets for a new garden. I called to him and went down part of the way. I asked him if we could talk, he said yes. I told him that I wanted to know what all the trouble with Meniba was all about. He stopped chopping and came up close to me and sat down. I told him that we, Dave and I, had come for one thing and that was to help him and many others to come to know the ways of the Lord Jesus Christ. He sat there for a long time, neither of us talking. Then he started talking. He said when he walked past my house that he had a big shame and his *liver* (heart) was heavy. I knew this was what we have wanted to see for a long time. I read to him from Ephesians 4:29-32. I told him that now that we are Christians we should want to do the things that God wants us to do. He wants us to be kind and loving like the Lord Jesus was and is, 5:25. We should do all we can to make our wives good and pure, this will make our home happy and our *livers* (hearts) will be happy when we have that love of Jesus for our wives. He said that he knew he was wrong and that it was a bad fashion to fight his wife all the time. This doesn't make the home happy.

05/14/59. Dave said that he and Meniba had a talk with Aaron this morning. They told him that they were not mad at him, but just wanted to help him. Meniba and Zasibini got a room made (in our house) for the Lawrence children. Arvalee likes it now that we have our living room inside the wall. Althea said that they got to Kami one year ago to-day. I told them that Meniba had been working for me for four years since May 1st, 1955.

05/15/59. Today was the close of the Negibi School for Peter and Steve. They had a little program and we all went to it. Dave and Althea came over to see what we wanted to get rid of, so we talked for some time. Told Dave that these things that I have made will help him so that he won't have to spend a lot of time building things and he could spend more time in the language work.

05/18/59. Today was a big day. Got the three Lawrence kids moved into their room. We killed three chickens for supper and made Dave and Althea's lunch for tomorrow, for hiking out to Olaguti. We are all out of meat. Had a nice dinner, a good salad of lettuce and tomatoes.

05/27/59. Dave came this afternoon.

05/28/59. Dave helped Meniba get the roofing *iron* on the top of the house today. It was quite a job.

05/29/59. Dave went down to teach the *boys* this morning. Teaching the kids about *Pilgrim's Progress* in the morning. Dave and Morobe did the wash this morning. Dave is willing to do anything that he sees is in need. He's a real blessing to me this way.

June, 1959

06/01/59. We are having a lot of fun teaching from the *Pilgrim's Progress* book; most of the kids understand parts of it, even Joy and Julie. They know that the big bag on Graceless' back is sin. Dave is teaching literacy this afternoon.

06/13/59. Dave worked on the house till dark. Arvalee said she gets tired of just cooking and being in the house all the time. I will have to help her more. Yesterday, I took all the kids, but Pat, who was in school and we all went for a walk up the road. Julie keeps asking me to go with her up the road. So today Pat and I played ball for a bit, then I helped them make some little car roads just before lunch.

06/16/59. Dave got off for Olaguti at 7:00. Cold and windy this morning, the kids spent the morning in the house. Carriers were back by 3:00 p.m. today.

06/18/59. Last night Paul prayed for Saubai, so this morning he came to the meeting for the first time in a long time. He sat right next to me. I reviewed yesterday's lesson. We had a good time with the kids this morning, (teaching from *Pilgrim's Progress*).

06/19/59. Yesterday, Arvalee and I prayed for the Bolivian field. Asked Arvalee if she would like to pray for the school at Tambo. She told the Lord that it was hard for her to think of leaving the kids in a school, but now she does see that if they are in a mission school they will grow in the things of the Lord, just like they do at home. The cross is not greater than His grace.

06/20/59. I walked up the road this morning. Told the Lord I was in great need and needed my heart warmed with His love for the ones I teach each morning. The Lord is so good and gave us some good fellowship this morning. I read first from 2 Corinthians 6:1.

I cut hair for all the boys this morning.

06/22/59. At night when we pray together, the children have been praying for someone around here; for the young boys like Nu-u-da and Saubai. Julie asked if she could pray for Hobe-aba. We are now on our 5th missionary book at our bedtime stories. The older kids sure like them. I have been reading it first to them and then telling it, and the little ones listen much better.

06/27/59. Pat, Pete and I went up to the end of the water race this morning. It's not as far as I thought. We were able to get a bit more water running in it. We had lots of fun.

06/28/59. Not much doing this Sunday. We all went up the road to the big tree today and had an outing. I think it was good for all of us to get out and Arvalee said it did her good. Had our lunch on the road and a little Bible story.

06/30/59. Sidi came in this morning and his little boy is sick with *pekpek blut*, (dysentery). I gave him some medicine, but he can't keep it down. Hope he will stay so we can help his little boy. There is real fear in Sidi, so we might be able to help him. Meniba told him to make a new hole (a toilet hole), so we all wouldn't get sick. That's using your head. Etha-o has started work on the house. I helped them in the morning.

July, 1959

07/01/59. It was really cold this morning. We had the meeting in Morobe's house. Sidi was there for the meeting. I started giving his little boy shots today at 10:00 then one at 3:00, (probably sulfa shots). Then I'll give him one more about 8:00 or 9:00 tonight. Sidi came up this afternoon and said that some men came up from his place and want him to bring his little boy home so they can kill some chickens and eat them before he dies. Sidi was upset, you could tell, by looking in his eyes. I told him that he had come to me and asked me to give his son some medicine and I asked him if they would stay here so I could take care of him. "We will stay and not run away," he said.

Dave walked in about 5:00 this afternoon. Althea had their baby boy June 22. The Lord sure was good.

07/02/59. Spirits were a bit higher this morning in the meeting. Sidi's son is much better.

We talked about the upcoming conference with the native leaders and tried to plan the time and agenda.

07/03/59. Sidi said that his little boy had dysentery again. I wanted to get down there to see him, but with all the cooking I couldn't get away. I may start the shots again tomorrow if he's not better.

07/04/59. I tried to give Sidi's little boy some sulfa orally. By dark I felt we would have to give him some more shots. Arvalee felt better so she went with me. Sidi cried. Oh, how they love that little fellow. After we gave the shot they cried for some time, then after they stopped I prayed; then Nu-u-da, Morobe, Arvalee and Sidi. I wish I could understand the language. I'm sure I could be a real help to Sidi at this time.

07/05/59. Gave Bede a shot this morning and afterwards Sidi and his wife started crying. They said that when I started giving him the shots, he stopped eating. I gave him another one this afternoon when I got back from Negibi. Bede looks bad tonight. Sent some milk down to see if he could drink it. The kids are sure praying for this little fellow to get well.

07/06/59. In the night I felt that if I gave Bede any more shots that the shock would kill him. Oh, he just really fights. He is so thin.

This morning we had a good meeting. Sidi said that when his little boy drinks the water it comes up, but the milk stays down. I told him he could have more milk. By noon they hadn't come up to get any more, so I sent Meniba down to see why. Said he still had some and Morobe was the only one who could get him to drink. Dave went down tonight and said he was eating some things now, so we will just have to pray it will stay down. And we won't have to give him more shots. Dave is coming along well on his house.

07/07/59. Sidi's little boy is looking better and eating *kaukau*, (sweet potato) now. Praise the Lord for answering our prayers.

07/08/59. The carriers went to get *cargo* (supplies) this morning. Arvalee thinks that she just has morning sickness.

07/13/59. Dave is coming right along on the house. He sure is praising the Lord for the way it's been going up. We talked tonight about what our schedule would be during the conference.

07/14/59. The kids have been trying these days; the little ones talk *kros* (speak in anger) at each other so much. Dave has been trying to help them in the morning devotions along this line.

07/15/59. Several are planning to sing at the conference and have been practicing their songs. We hope they can sing at the conference.

07/19/59. I find that I get upset over little things, like the kids not coming when it's time to eat. This morning, I just saw that it was nothing but the Lord that could love one so full of self and He is so merciful to me.

07/20/59. Last night I was up with the kids at 12:00 and 3:00 a.m. and never could get to sleep. I don't think I slept a bit.

Fixed lunch, read till 1:30, studied the Word till 2:00 then we had prayer meeting. Told Dave how I wanted to teach, using sticks: 1 stick is not strong, but tie them together and they are strong: Christian fellowship. We are God's house, Jesus is the center post, and we must lean on Him.

07/23/59. GIMI NATIONAL CONFERENCE STARTED TODAY

There were five of us in the prayer meeting this morning. The first meeting was teaching on the sticks, how we are like sticks, and we are not strong. We need to be in a fellowship and this will make each of us strong. We can break one stick, but when all the sticks are together they are strong. The rope is a picture of Jesus' Talk and it ties us together. Meniba had the afternoon meeting on the gospel presentation. Today Roland Boye and Fred Morris walked in from Olaguti. James and Ausoka came too.

07/24/59. In the meeting this a.m., I spoke on Jesus as the Good Shepherd, how we need to have the Lord make our hearts ready for the day in the morning.

07/26/59. We had prayer again this morning and Fred (Morris) came to the meeting too. At one time I counted about 200 but more came after that.

Meniba talked for some time on Jesus dying on the cross and going back to Heaven. Just as Meniba was giving out the *kaukau* (sweet potato) for the Lord's Supper, it started raining. After the rain stopped we had an arrow shooting contest for three small four gallon drums. Two fellows from Uhezuihutai and a fellow from Oaberu won them.

THE CONFERENCE ENDED TODAY

07/27/59. I have sure enjoyed the fellowship with Fred (Morris); he is a real swell fellow in the Lord.

07/28/59. The fellows got off this morning about 7:30. Dave took Craig with him.

07/30/59. Today has been beautiful all day. This morning I spoke to the group on God's plan for husband and wife to live together and be happy. I see more and more that we have got to help these young people in their married life, if we are going to have a strong leadership in the church of God.

07/31/59. Went down this morning to the meeting; it was cold so we met in Meniba's house. I read to them again from Ephesians 5:22 through 33. Husbands love your wives; God tells us to, and we must obey Him. Before, we didn't know what we should do, but now we have God's Word to help us.

August, 1959

08/01/59. We talked to the men this morning. I tried to show them that we have got to love our wives even when they do the wrong thing. We have a big job as husbands, for how can we love with a love like the Lord has for us? He must fill our hearts with love for our wives.

08/03/59. Teaching about husband and wife. Mu-u-nabi came to the last part of the meeting.

08/05/59. Yesterday Dave and Althea got here about 4:00 p.m. in the rain.

08/07/59. The Lawrences ate at their house this morning. Arvalee went down with me to the meeting this morning.

08/08/59. We went up to Dave's for supper tonight.

08/09/59. We had a good meeting this afternoon. The people were saying they were sorry we were going on furlough. I told them that they mustn't *[sic]* be sad, because we were going, but now they had met the Friend of all Friends. White men will come and go, but Jesus will always be with you. We have most everything packed. We had some *kumu* (greens, sort of like spinach) and beans that the natives cooked tonight.

08/10/59. Things are coming along well with the packing. Meniba made a big *mumu* (steam cooking) this afternoon. We had two chickens.

08/11/59. We had a hard time getting off this morning. It was 9:00 a.m. and then we had to stop two or three times before we got to the river. When we got down to Tabaribo's place, Julie asked if we were at Grandma's. We were four hours getting to the horses. We stopped at Aniaru for the night.

08/12/59. Got away at 8:45 this morning from Aniaru. After we stopped and had lunch, the *boys* carried Arvalee in the chair to Kosotaka. We got here, Olaguti, at 5:45 p.m. Sure good to meet all the folks.

08/13/59. Arvalee was quite sore all day today. Been talking a lot to Fred and all the others. Jake (Queener) doesn't say much.

08/17/59. Arvalee went to town today and Julie went, too. The doctor said she is four months along, anyway. Fred left for the Watut.

08/20/59. Harold came down from Lufa and he said that I told him we would be up today, but I thought I said Friday. We thought it best to go back with him. So we did.

08/21/59. Harold and Mary (Sellers) are very hungry for fellowship. We went up to see Ben and Talila (Wertz) this afternoon. They sure have a beautiful place.

08/22/59. We went down and saw Cleon and Aletha (Laughlin) for a bit.

08/23/59. Had a nice rest this Sunday. We got some more packing done.

We flew from New Guinea to Australia a few days after the entries for August were written. After being at Plumpton, N. S. W. near Sydney, for about three weeks, we flew home towards the end of September 1959. Arvalee

Our First Furlough, 1959
By Arvalee

We had been in the Gimi about two months when Pat came for a visit during his school break. It was great having him home with us, even though we knew it was only for his vacation from school and he would have to go back to Olaguti. We received a note by carrier, letting us know that a visitor was coming with him. Jerry Sherman, a young widow whose husband perished in the Rattlesnake Forest Fire in 1953, accompanied him on the hike to the Gimi to see us.

They got here on the 24th of January and Jerry informed us that evening that the field leaders had sent her to give us a special message. They all knew of Dale's limited physical abilities and frequent illnesses and felt it was time for us to go on furlough. Furthermore, everyone was in agreement with this decision. This was disturbing news to Dale, for he was not ready to leave his beloved Gimi people!

But we had been on the field for over five years. Much had been accomplished and we had fulfilled our dream of living among the Gimi people. Dale had learned to communicate with the people, although he never felt that he knew the language fluently.

The next morning, after Jerry's announcement, Dale was broken out in hives all over his body. At first we thought he had eaten something that he was allergic to, but nothing he had eaten was out of the ordinary, so I thought the hives were caused by the distressing news Jerry had brought! After a few days, Dale finally accepted the fact that in light of his physical condition and that the entire group of missionaries felt it was time for us to go on furlough, we should make plans to do so.

It was an exciting time for me, especially, thinking about seeing our families again. I guess my thoughts were mainly about seeing my parents and siblings. They had never seen our little girl, and Paul had been an infant when we'd left. Pat and Peter had grown up a lot since we'd been on the field as well. There truly had been a lot of changes in our family.

Since we were going on furlough we all needed clothes, so I began sewing on my treadle sewing machine like my mother before me! I ordered some material from the store in Goroka to make short pajamas for the boys. I had a terrible time trying to figure out how the neckline opening was done. Maybe that is the reason I remember those particular garments. As I recall, there were 36 different articles of clothing that I had sewn, mainly for the children.

Soon the time came for Dave and Althea to leave for Goroka for the birth of their baby. Dale got Meniba to construct another room for their children, in a corner of our living room. These were especially busy days for me, since I was now looking after the Lawrence children as well as our own.

But before we left the Gimi, I was having a lot of episodes of nausea each morning, and I finally realized we had another baby on the way!

As we left the Gimi departing for our furlough, we walked past the village just down the mountain from us. Julie, only three and a half years old, looked around and said, "Mommy, where is Grandma?" We had been telling her for weeks that we were going home to see her Grandma, but she had no idea of who "Grandma" was, or where she lived. The Gimi area and our national friends were the only world she knew.

Our home church sent this poem to us, written to encourage people to help buy our tickets home.

"THEY NEED TO COME HOME

I may be ragged and my patches may look funny,
But under each patch is money, money, money.
These are our gifts be they great or small,
To help Dale and Arvalee climb over a $2,000.00 wall.
With the help of the Lord and a small patch by you,
Dale can recuperate and say HOWDY to me and to you.
They have worked hard and it's now time for a rest,
So it's up to us folks to do our best.
So give and give and the Good Lord will bless
All those that help God's children that sent out this S.O.S.
Now I have a front and a back and two sleeves,
So cover me with patches and hurry up please.
For Dale and Arvalee are waiting for these."

A poem sent from friends at our home church, Bell Gardens Baptist.

After we had spent a week or so with the McCurdys at Olaguti, I really was in need of some maternity clothes. Before we left New Guinea, Gwen helped me make a skirt, providing some black gabardine material for it. This was material she had salvaged from a pair of men's dress pants, and it made a lovely skirt for which I was indeed very grateful.

Meanwhile, Don had secured passage for us on a ship. We left New Guinea by air and arrived in Sydney, Australia, staying at the missionary training center in Plumpton, New South Wales. Here at the mission headquarters, dear Mrs. Wallin, whom we knew from Chico, California, came to my rescue. She told me where I could buy a pattern and material for sewing the maternity top I needed. She said, "Arvalee, you cannot ask for a *pattern* in Australia. You will have to ask for a *pattin* or they will not understand you!" Boy, I was still learning much about the Australian language and culture. Sure enough, I pronounced it like she had told me to, and came home with my *pattern*.

During the three weeks we were at Plumpton, each of the kids came down with bronchial flu, and then I contracted it as well. Much to our dismay, a few days prior to our departure, Dale became sick, too. It's a tough enough job to travel with a large family, but being sick certainly multiplies the difficulties.

Thanks to Dale's mother and stepfather, Roberta and Jim McKeon, who sent us extra money, we were able to exchange our tickets on the ship for airline tickets. Traveling by air was more expensive than by ship, so their help with this purchase was a huge blessing to us. Our sickness made us dread an ocean voyage. The airplane we flew on, a Boeing 707, was one of the earliest flights to cross the Pacific Ocean. We were grateful that it was finally possible to fly to the States.

It was quite a thrilling experience departing from Sydney, Australia, at 7:30 on a Friday evening and watching the lights of the city, and then the sky became completely dark as we flew over the ocean. We first flew to the Fiji Islands, where the plane refueled. When we arrived in Honolulu it was 7:30 in the morning of the same day we had left Australia! We had flown all night. We arrived there 12 hours before we had left Sydney. This was a new experience, crossing the International Date Line in the air! Upon our arrival we successfully passed through the USA customs and were able to enter the country officially.

Our connecting flight to Los Angeles left that afternoon at 4:30. We had an entire day before we would board our next flight and we were all exhausted, so we asked the taxi driver to take us to a hotel. We were at the mercy of the taxi driver, who may have received a generous tip from the hotel, as he took us to one on the famous Waikiki beach, where we booked a hotel room and all six of us slept for several hours. That afternoon Dale bought hamburgers for each of us. This was a real treat, as we had not had an American hamburger for six years. These expenditures took most of our meager dollars, leaving us almost broke.

Of course the kids wanted to swim in the ocean at the famous Waikiki Beach, so I went out and waded in the surf while they played in the shallow water, because Dale still wasn't feeling well enough to take them.

Soon it was time to leave for the airport. Dale went to the desk to check out and pay the bill and asked the clerk to phone for a taxi and for a bell boy to move our suitcases downstairs. Either they were extremely busy, or they knew they wouldn't receive a very generous tip, because there was no bell boy available! Dale had to go back to the desk and ask for the keys to our room and he and the boys moved the suitcases, while I waited at the hotel entrance doors with Julie. The taxi was waiting by the curbside when they brought the remaining suitcases. Dale said, "Come on, we don't want to be late." I quickly grabbed Julie's hand and we got in the taxi. On the way to the airport, which was quite a distance, Dale began searching for our tickets in his breast pocket. Realizing he didn't have his coat on, he said, "Where is my coat with the tickets?"

I gasped, "Oh my, they are in your coat and I left it hanging on the railing at the hotel!" In my haste, I had forgotten it.

By this time, we were too close to the airport to return to the hotel for the coat. When we arrived, Dale went to the counter and explained our predicament to the agent. He replied, "Oh, there is nothing that can be done. You will have to stay another night in Honolulu and take the next plane tomorrow."

What a blow! My heart sank! *That man didn't understand that we didn't have enough money to spend another night in that fancy hotel!* Just then, another agent came over to Dale. He had overheard parts of the conversation. He asked Dale, "What is the problem?" So Dale repeated to him that we had left his coat with the tickets at the hotel.

Right away this agent said, "That's no problem. What hotel were you staying in?" Dale told him and the man phoned the hotel and told them where we had left the coat. The hotel employee looked on the railing and found the coat, intact, with our tickets and passport. (In 1959, the family members were all on one passport; however the passport and overcoat could be mailed later as we had already cleared U.S. customs in Hawaii.)

In the meantime, three of the engines on the airplane were running. The man at the counter told Dale that the kids and I should board the plane while things got sorted out. As soon as he confirmed with the hotel that indeed our tickets were in the coat, he told Dale to board the plane. By then the fourth engine was running and Dale literally ran across the tarmac to get on board before they hoisted the steps. He was in a sweat when he joined us.

> *I remember the second ticket agent was a big black man; isn't it interesting that a black man, the race of people Dale cared so much for, would be the one to see a need and help so dramatically?*

We arrived in Los Angeles on a Friday night in late September, 1959. We were without our passport, but we had already gone through customs in Honolulu so it was not an issue. The coat with tickets and passport were flown to us the next day.

Many of our friends from Bell Gardens Baptist Church were there to greet us. Though we knew their faces, we couldn't think of their names! Dale's dad was there as well as Great-grandma Palmer. How wonderful it was to see their smiling faces again. Sadly, Great-grandpa Palmer and Aunt Evelyn had passed away while we were on the field.

~PART FOUR~

God's Faithfulness

Chapter 10

Home in the USA, 1959
By Arvalee

As Dale's dad, Bud, drove us home to Oxnard, he asked Dale if he would like to drive the car. Dale answered him firmly, "No!" He surely didn't want to drive, as this was his first time to experience freeway traffic! Since Dale hadn't had too many opportunities to drive in the six years we were overseas he felt more like hiding underneath the dashboard.

Soon we began the task of settling in, trying to fit our large family into Bud's three bedroom house, which he shared with Great-grandma Palmer. Dale and I occupied the guest room, which was large enough for a crib. We knew it would be needed soon enough for the new baby. It was decided that Pat would sleep in Bud's room in the spare twin bed. Peter and Paul slept together on the hide-a-bed in the living room which meant they couldn't go to bed until the adults were ready for bed. Most of the time I put them to bed in our room, then woke them up and moved them to the living room. This seemed to work very well. Great-grandma said Julie could share her bed. That didn't work too well for great-grandmother, as the little one just kicked too much. So before long we had to find a cot for Julie to sleep on, which was placed at the end of Grandma's bed.

For some time, Dale and I both experienced terrible leg aches every day and we finally came to the conclusion that these were caused by the tile floors. We found the floors hard to get used to, having lived on springy bamboo floors for the entire term in New Guinea. In addition, I was suffering from continual morning sickness.

Right away Grandpa gave three of the kids a nickname. He called Julie *Little Aus,* because her accent sounded so different to him. Paul was nicknamed *Bunyan* and he called Pat *Big Daddy* when he noticed that Pat felt responsible to help us keep track of the other kids.

On Monday morning, we enrolled the three boys in the nearby grammar school. Looking back, that wasn't such a smart decision! We could have given them a little time to adjust to being in the United States and to learn such things as how to cross the street! As the school year went on, we learned that one of the boys didn't know the meaning of hearth. We expressed our concern to their teacher that they might be behind in their lessons, as they had grown up in a very different environment and had been taught by various methods on the field. The teacher replied, "You don't need to worry about your children. The experiences they have had, traveling and living overseas, make up for anything they might have missed in school here."

At first the boys came home for lunch each day. Before long, Great-grandma, observing how tired I was, said, "Why don't you pack a lunch for them, Arvalee? That would be so much easier for you." So I took her advice and started sending them to school with their lunches.

One day, Paul, who was in first grade, told me he didn't want to take his lunch to school anymore, but would rather come home. He wouldn't or couldn't give me a reason, so I insisted he take his lunch. Much later, Pat or Peter told us that Paul had thrown up in the lunchroom one day, and an older boy had threatened him by saying he would beat him up if he ever did that again. The poor little kid… and to think that his mother hadn't known the real reason he wanted to eat his lunch at home.

Adjustments were, at times, humorous. Some school friends came home with one of the boys one day and expressed their surprise that Julie was white, because they knew she had been born in New Guinea!

Julie came to me one day and said she wanted someone to play with. Without thinking, I said, "Why don't you go outside in the front yard? There are sure to be some children around for you to play with." So she went outside and a little later I went to check on her. She was nowhere in sight! I was terribly frightened, imagining what might have happened to her. Dale and I both started walking up and down the streets looking for her. Finally we found her, two or three streets away, pushing her doll buggy. You can be sure I kept a closer watch on her after that.

Once, on Wednesday evening, when Dale and Great-grandma went to prayer meeting, and I was home alone with the children, the doorbell rang. I went to the door, trembling with fright. There stood two young men. They were salesmen and could probably tell I was afraid, because they hurriedly stated their business and left! Before long, I began feeling more at home and lost my extreme fear of strangers.

Naturally, we tried to help Dale's folks with food costs because we didn't want to put a strain on their budget. It seemed to me that Grandma thought we had to have bacon or ham and eggs for breakfast every morning. In New Guinea, we were used to eating quite simply. I gradually tried to change the menu, so that we were eating more like we were used to, which included a lot of hot oatmeal porridge and toast for breakfast.

Another thing that was very difficult for me was Grandma's use of the newly installed garbage disposal. She would get up from the meal, and if Lassie, the dog, couldn't eat the leftover food, she would put it in the garbage disposal. Soon I quietly began putting the leftovers away, before she got up from the table. Sometimes she would say, "Why,

Arvalee that isn't enough to save."

I would reply, "Oh, I think that will be just enough for Dale's lunch tomorrow." Stating it in that way seemed to be acceptable to her.

It wasn't too long after we arrived home that a teacher noticed that Peter had trouble hearing. So we took him to the doctor who told us he needed an operation. Soon afterwards he had his tonsils and adenoids removed. He recently reminded me that after the surgery he never had those bad recurring ear aches again.

It took Dale some time before he was comfortable driving a car, as he had not driven in such a long time. I remember the time Forest and Nancy (Stine), our longtime friends, came to see us. Forest was eager to show Dale his car so they went for a drive. Forest finally convinced Dale to get behind the wheel. Dale said he just about put Forest through the windshield when he applied the brakes at a stop sign. He had never heard of power brakes before, much less used them!

Naturally, I was anxious to see my parents, so a short time after we got home I went to see them. The boys were in school and we really didn't have the money for all of us to go on a trip, so Dale and I decided I should go with Julie by train. Even though driving was hard for Dale, he borrowed the car from his dad and we drove down to see Forest and Nancy, who were living in Covina at the time, and from there Dale put us on a train for Phoenix. We really were broke; after buying the tickets, Dale had two dollars left; one he gave to me, and one he kept! The train seemed to stop at every little wide spot all night long, but it finally arrived. I couldn't let my parents know of our arrival, because I didn't have a telephone number. All I knew was the name of their restaurant and its location on the Bee Line Highway.

When we got off the train, the woman in the ticket office was going off duty. I asked her if she knew the location of Paul's Café on the Bee Line Highway. She knew of it and offered to take me out there, but she said, "You'll have to pay me for driving you out there." I agreed to do so. Even though I probably didn't have enough money to pay her, I knew my dad would.

On the drive out to the restaurant, the woman unloaded her ideas and dislike of men in general to her captive audience. When she finished talking I told her all about my life in serving the Lord in New Guinea! When we pulled up in front of the café, she said, "You don't owe me a dime."

"Thank you very much," I responded.

As he looked through the big glass windows, I could see my dad watching her car. I waved to him, and heard him call out, "Oh, you don't know me."

Then Julie and I got out of the car and walked inside and surprised both my dad and my mother. What a wonderful reunion we had after six long years away.

Danny Boy
By Arvalee

Dale's dad knew we would eventually need a car of our own so he took Dale shopping for one. They found a 1953 Plymouth four door sedan, which served us well for some time.

We were quite comfortable living in Oxnard, with Dale's dad and grandmother, although we knew it would be temporary. We had found a good doctor, named Dr. Crites, and my pregnancy was progressing. This would be our fifth child and I was hoping for another girl. In those days, we waited until the baby was born before we knew if it was a boy or girl!

We wanted to spend Christmas with my parents in Arizona, but the doctor wouldn't allow me to travel--he actually thought I might be having twins, and he thought the birth could be at any time. But the holidays came and went and still there was no baby.

Finally, two months later, we had our new little bundle of joy. He was born on February 25th, 1960, in Port Hueneme, California. He weighed in at ten pounds and one ounce; quite a bundle for a newborn. He was a beautiful baby, but he looked like he was three months old when we brought him home from the hospital! We named him Danny James; but he changed it to Dan James when he was grown.

By the time the baby was a few days old, he had a very sick mother. During the delivery, my blood pressure went up alarmingly high. Nevertheless, the doctor allowed me to go home the day after he was born. The third day, I was awakened early in the morning by severe pains in my temples, accompanied by a very frightening dream.

In my dream, it seemed I was swimming in a river in New Guinea and became entangled in vines underneath the water. I was drowning! As I gasped for air and inhaled, it seemed water went into my lungs. It was then that I awakened with excruciating pain in my temples. The pain was almost unbearable. As I cried out, Dale woke up, and a short time later he took me to the doctor, who put me on some strong medication which sedated me. I spent the next week sitting up in a recliner because the pain returned when I tried to lie down.

Before starting the medication, I had enough presence of mind to give details to Great-grandma and Dale on how to prepare the baby bottles with formula. That done, I slept most of the next week. Dale would awaken me, give me the medicine and then I was off to sleep again.

A day or so after my first dream, I had a second one, similar to the first. In this dream, my little girl, just four years old was drowning. It was so vivid, I can still visualize it. Thankfully I soon woke up, again with horrible pain in my temples.

After a week had passed and I had taken all the medicine, I seemed to be much better. However, I continued to have severe headaches from time to time for about twenty years, usually accompanied by a dream of water and drowning. After all those years I came to recognize an episode as a mere dream, and the Lord enabled me to wake up before there was any pain. The source of these dreams was easy to trace… I had almost drowned when I was twelve years old. I believe the Lord showed me that the devil was using that incident to torment me with these terrible dreams and by giving me a fear of water. After I understood this, the dreams ceased altogether!

By the time I was on my feet again, our little Danny boy was a bottle-fed baby accustomed to Great-grandma feeding him and rocking him to sleep! Long after the bottle days were over, I continued to rock him to sleep. Dale liked to tease me, saying I rocked Danny until his feet were dragging the floor.

Moving to Modesto and Traveling, 1960
By Arvalee

We felt like the house was too cramped for all of us, although we loved being with Great-grandma and Grandpa Bud after not seeing them for such a long time. At times though, things did get a bit tense for both Dale and me in this small house. I recall one incident in particular when Dale had to spank one of the boys. He took him out to the garage because Grandpa Bud could hardly tolerate us disciplining the children, especially if it involved a spanking.

The answer to our housing problems came through a phone call from Ken Johnston, the director of New Tribes Mission. He said they needed someone to join Karl Getteman on staff at the mission training center in Modesto, California. He asked, "Would you and Arvalee be able to help us out?"

We had to decide if we felt this was what the Lord wanted us to do, and it only took us a few days to make a decision. We would move to Modesto. The move took place when Dan was two months old. It didn't take us long to pack, as we had very few household items.

At the training center in Modesto, we were assigned to a two-bedroom apartment in the staff building. It had a living room, a kitchenette and a small bathroom as well. The apartments didn't have full kitchens, as the camp was set up so that everyone ate the two main meals together in the dining room. The women took turns cooking for the group of about fifty people, including the children.

I was really concerned about my ability to cook for such a large group, mainly because occasionally I was laid low by one of the severe headaches that I first experienced when the baby was born. Secondly, I was concerned because I had never cooked for fifty people. However, along with the other women on staff, I was assigned a work schedule with two student helpers. Together, we were able to cook a nice meal for the group, and the Lord proved faithful in seeing me through. I learned the secret to being able to cook for a large group, was to start early! Eventually, we were able to cook a turkey dinner with all the trimmings for Thanksgiving; quite an accomplishment!

We enjoyed getting settled as a family in the apartment. We put the baby's crib in our bedroom, and the other four children shared the other bedroom, sleeping on two bunk beds. At first, Paul was on one of the top bunks, but he fell off once during the night, hitting a chest of drawers and hurting his rib cage. After that, we changed the kids around; the two older boys slept on the top bunks, and Julie and Paul on the two lower ones.

The children each had a large drawer and there was closet space for hanging their clothes. One day when I was putting their folded clothes away, I found Pat's drawer was full of wires and batteries. He had no other place to keep these treasures, his prized possessions. I think this was the beginning of a lifelong interest in the electrical field.

Once again we enrolled the boys in the local school. Sometimes they walked home from school barefoot, wading in the irrigation ditch along the way. Pat came home one day with his instep bleeding. He had stepped on a broken bottle and cut his foot quite severely. Dale was away at the time, so Karl Getteman took him to the doctor to get it stitched up. Pat remembers picking cherries on the way home from school and he says I used to make pies from them.

Julie learned to ride a bicycle on the volleyball court at the camp. The boys taught her to ride their bicycle, but she was too small to sit astride the seat and reach the pedals. She had to put her foot through the bars. The boys took turns pushing her around until she was riding on her own.

Classes and prayer meeting for the students were held each morning in the room directly below our apartment. Meanwhile, our family was busy preparing for the day ahead. Sometimes the boys, getting ready for school, would reach into their pants' pockets and accidentally drop three or four marbles onto the tile floor. I fancied this could be heard in the room below. On most mornings, I put Dan, who was now several months old, on a blanket on the floor. He would lie on his tummy and kick his feet, clad in soft soled shoes, against the floor. I worried constantly that our children were too noisy, and would disturb the students below.

Finally, I came to terms with the situation. Since no one had complained, I realized the kids must not be as noisy as I imagined they were. I reasoned within myself, *If they are too noisy, then I guess the leaders will come tell us and find another apartment for us.* After that, I was able to relax more and quit fussing at the kids to be quiet.

Dale taught a class every morning, but then he usually had to come home and spend the rest of the day lying down. He was still far from well. We had established our family with a local doctor, who had served with a mission board in Africa and was recognized as a tropical disease specialist, but he didn't know what Dale's problem was. We heard through the mission that there was a doctor in Chicago, Dr. Adolph, who treated tropical diseases. We were encouraged to go there to see if he could help Dale.

Dale agreed to do so, but was concerned that he would not be able to drive such a long distance. The drive out to the local doctor usually left him exhausted and it was only eighteen miles there and back. Since I did not drive and the boys were too young, I told him, "We will just have to go as far as you feel like driving, and then find a place to sleep." We did that, sometimes sleeping on the side of the road. Surely God was watching over us!

That summer we were able to visit relatives en route to Chicago. We stopped in Carlsbad, New Mexico, and saw my Uncle Ewell and Aunt Dortha Wilkinson. Some of us went to the Carlsbad Caverns, but Julie had the mumps and wasn't able to go with us, so she stayed home that day.

We drove on to Lubbock, Texas, to see Dale's Aunt Hazel and Uncle Harper Pate. They had a nice home with light beige carpets on the floor. I told the kids, "If you don't drop any food on the carpets when we're eating, I'll give you fifty cents!" They remembered that a long time, and often reminded me of it.

Afterwards, we drove on to Ft. Worth, to visit Dale's mother and step-father, Roberta and Jim McKeon. Pat got the mumps while we were there and I believe Paul may have had them at the same time. Peter and the baby escaped them.

Roberta and Jim lived on a farm and raised and fattened pigs to sell, feeding them on day old bakery goods the stores could no longer sell. The boys would join Jim in the truck after he picked up the load. Standing in the truck bed, the kids opened plastic wrappers on cakes, bread, cookies and all kinds of goodies, taking a bite of each and throwing the remainder of it to the pigs! Roberta made homemade freezer ice cream just about every day. She would ask, "What kind do you want today? How would you like peach?" Those were indeed the hot, lazy days of a Texas summer.

After our visit we headed to Chicago so Dale could consult with Dr. Adolph. We stayed at the mission headquarters, which was then located at Woodworth, Wisconsin. Dale drove from there to Chicago, where they took (stool) tests at Mt. Sinai Hospital. They told him the results would be mailed to him.

God's Promise to a Frightened Young Man
By Arvalee

We then headed back to Modesto, California, planning to visit Mr. and Mrs. Cole, Al Cole's parents, in Colorado. Al was one of the missionaries in New Guinea. I don't remember how long it took us to get to Colorado, but the 1953 Plymouth broke down a few miles before we got to the Cole's ranch.

There we were on a lonely country road in Colorado and it was already dark. After a few minutes talking things over, Dale and I decided that I would remain in the car with the children, while he hiked back to the town we'd passed through, just a few miles away. There he telephoned our friends, explaining our predicament.

I felt somewhat uneasy, sitting there in the dark, so I began to sing. I told myself it was to calm the children, but perhaps it was to calm myself as well. I had heard stories about travelers being attacked and robbed when their cars broke down. Although I tried to put on a brave face for the kids, who ranged in age from five months old to about 12 years old, you can be sure all the car doors were locked.

Now, here we were, waiting for Dale to return. The kids were being very patient; the three boys shared the back seat, and the baby and Julie were in the front with me. That's the way we traveled, mile after mile, in this four door sedan. No air conditioner and no extra room for anyone. The baby was put to sleep on the bench seat between Dale and me, and little Julie slept curled up on the floor at my feet. As we traveled throughout the hot summer, we bought bags of crushed ice to munch on to soothe and keep everyone as cool as possible.

Suddenly, Pat broke the silence, saying quietly, "Mom, I saw some writing over against the mountain."

I asked him, "What did it say? What did it look like?"

Then he said, "It was all bright and lit up like lights, and it said, 'Fear not, I will never leave you or forsake you.' Then, as soon as the words appeared, they were erased. I could just read them as they appeared, then they were gone."

I told him the Lord must have shown him those words from the Bible to encourage him so that he wouldn't be afraid while we were sitting here waiting. I thought to myself, *That is just like the Lord, to give words of encouragement to a child, for he needed his faith to be strengthened, maybe in a much greater way than I needed it for I knew the Word of God, and deep down I knew the truth that God would never leave me or forsake me.*

Truly, He had kept His promises in keeping us safe the many miles we had traveled, and during the times we had slept along the roadside.

After a while, Dale returned, to wait with us. He had been able to contact the Coles and someone was coming to get us. Soon they arrived and we left the car and trailer parked just off the road. We were hoping it would be safe, as the trailer held our suitcases and other belongings. Taking some of our things to use that night, we went to the Coles' house. Arrangements were made for Dale and someone else to come the next day to tow the car and trailer back to their place.

It turned out that we spent three weeks with Mr. and Mrs. Cole. Dale had caught a cold or the flu and was sick most of that time. While he was recovering, Mrs. Cole taught him how to work on leather goods and he made a beautiful leather belt for himself with an intricate tooled design. Then he chose some leather to make a purse for me. I have kept that beautiful purse all these years.

Mrs. Cole cooked delicious meals, using the fresh vegetables from her garden. She jokingly said that "the Palmers were canning her vegetables." I'm sure there were none left for canning after feeding our large family for three weeks.

Since it was not possible to repair the car, we continued our trip back to California by train. We were met in Los Angeles by our missionary friend, Bill Key, who was on furlough from Bolivia. We then continued our trip to Modesto by car, as Dale's Dad had come to get us.

We had been home about two weeks when the results of the medical tests arrived. Dale's illness was diagnosed as amoebic dysentery, or intestinal amoeba. The prescription for treating it called for a medicine called Mystilin V. Although we had a diagnoses and a prescription for the medicine, we were not able to get it filled. We were broke and couldn't afford to buy it because it was quite expensive.

A few nights after we received the prescription, our friends, Dorwin and Alta Stennit and their family came over to visit. He asked if we had heard from the doctor. When we told him yes, but hadn't gotten the medicine, he very pointedly asked us why we hadn't. We had to tell him that we just couldn't afford it.

He then grabbed Dale by the arm and said, "Come on, we're going to get your medicine." They went to the drug store right then to buy it, and after one week that medicine had worked a miracle and Dale was well again. He was like a different person.

We figured Dorwin was one of God's special servants, maybe one of those ministering spirits as mentioned in Hebrews 1:14, sent at just the right time to meet our need.

More Travel Experiences
By Arvalee

It was great to be home again in Modesto, but hard to shop or go anywhere without a car. Harold and Marietta Piovesan passed through Modesto as they were departing for the field of New Guinea. Before they left they decided to give their car, a panel van, to us, which was a real provision. Now we could at least go to church and to the store when we needed to without depending on others.

Later, we drove this car to Oxnard, to see Great-grandma and Grandpa Bud. On the way to Oxnard we had to pass by Chowchilla, so we decided to stop and visit Ethel Coy, who had been our linguistics teacher in boot camp. She now lived on the family farm with her elderly father.

She asked me, "You're planning to have supper with us, aren't you?"

I told her, "No, I don't think so. Dale wants to get to Oxnard before dark."

She was quick thinking and replied, "I can catch that chicken, wring its neck, and have it cooking, while he is still visiting with Dad."

She proceeded to do just that. We had a nice dinner, topped off with frozen peaches from their farm for dessert. We always enjoyed sweet fellowship with Ethel and her father. *A number of years later, on our second furlough, we were able to attend Mr. Coy's funeral with Ethel. After his death, Ethel went to the field of Panama where she served as a missionary for a number of years.*

It was after dark before we got to Oxnard, but it was probably just as well. The weather was very hot and traveling was more comfortable after dark.

While we were visiting Grandpa Bud, he found a good deal and traded the Piovesan's car in on a Ford station wagon, which suited the needs of our large family much better.

We were so thankful Dale was feeling better. Now, he began taking some of the students out on meetings, but I stayed home with the children most of the time. One couple was from Santa Barbara, and they were able to get a meeting in their home church. We made some lifelong friends in this church.

We had been in the States about two years and now, in the summer of 1961, it was time to return to the field. We began planning our trip back and started packing our drums with items necessary to live comfortably in New Guinea. We purchased tickets on a ship with the P and O Lines to sail again to New Guinea via Australia.

Almost everything was packed, yet we wanted to go to Seattle to visit my sister and family, Johnnie and Len Lonning. Leaving our things in the camp apartment in Modesto, we set out to visit several friends along the way.

We stopped to see Ron and Susie Lovern and family in Roseburg, Oregon. While we were there, another family came by. It was Kirk and Carole Glenn and they had several children as well. We knew both these couples from a church in Arroyo Grande, California. (Eventually this church, later called Grace Bible Church, started supporting us.) I can't remember where we all slept that night, but we surely enjoyed our time there.

The next morning, as we were leaving for Seattle, Kirk gave Dale some money. On the way to the Seattle area, we had to stop for gasoline and a bite to eat, spending most of our money. We had enough gasoline to get to Johnnie and Len's place, so we were not concerned about it. We had arranged with the mission headquarters to send our next check to my sister's address in Gig Harbor, so we felt confident we would have enough money there to make the return trip to Modesto.

As we came to the bridge that connected the mainland to the peninsula where my sister lived, we found it was a toll bridge. This was a surprise! Dale said, "I don't have any money. We can't cross the bridge!"

The boys in the back seat, said, "We'll look underneath the seat. There may be some change there." So they did and actually found some.

Then Pat said, "Look in the ash tray, Dad. You may find some coins there, too." So Dale looked in the ash tray and found a few more.

Julie chimed in, "I have some pennies in my purse." So, with everyone's help, we found enough change to cross the toll bridge!

Years later, as we related the story to Kirk, he said the Lord told him, as we drove away that day, that he hadn't given Dale enough money. After that, he continued to support us throughout all our years on the field and beyond.

We had a good visit with Johnnie and her family. She and Len had three boys and owned a big German shepherd dog. Len owned and operated a garage and filling station with a small store attached.

We planned to visit King's Garden while we were in the Seattle area. They had printed our letters for some time, as well as printing letters for other missionaries. In addition to this ministry, they operated a Christian radio station, had a Youth ministry, and had a Thrift Shop. The group on the King's Garden staff gave us a gift coupon to use at the Thrift Shop.

Visiting King's Garden.

In the Thrift Shop, we didn't find anything we needed. Then we spied a lovely old Seth Thomas seven-day chiming clock. It had a rich, resonate "Bong, bong, bong" chime on the hour and the half hour. That clock was a real treasure and became a part of our household for many years. We packed it well and took it back to New Guinea with us.

A couple in Bremerton had been supporting us financially so Dale and I wanted to look them up. We phoned them and were invited to lunch. When we arrived we found they were an elderly couple. Mrs. Walters began showing us around the house; there were new draperies, as well as a lovely wall-to-wall carpet on the floor and stairway. Their children had installed these for their 50th wedding anniversary.

Lunch was ready; a complete chicken dinner with all the trimmings, if I remember correctly. As I was helping, setting the table, and putting lunch on, Mrs. Walters turned to me and said, "You wouldn't mind if we put newspaper underneath the table would you? I sure wouldn't want the children to drop any food on the carpet. And, would it be all right if we put the highchair for the baby here in the kitchen doorway?"

I replied, "I wouldn't mind at all. I'll put the newspaper under the table and the baby will be fine there just inside the door." This was an obvious relief to her.

After the delicious dinner, Mr. Walters took Dale and the older children down to the waterfront, where he had a little boathouse. They had a very enjoyable time and spent most of the afternoon there. Later, they came back to the house and we visited some more. Mrs. Walters insisted on making some sandwiches which we ate before we left for my sister's house.

As we were departing Mrs. Walters drew me aside and said, "I just have to tell you this. The last missionaries that visited us had five children, too. They were little monsters. They climbed on my furniture with their shoes on and swung the poker from the fireplace around their heads. I thought they would break my chandelier." Then she said, "I can see I didn't have to worry about your children. They behaved themselves perfectly."

That was the most gracious compliment I have ever received from anyone. We knew that many people didn't welcome large missionary families into their homes. Now, we knew exactly why. We were so thankful God had given us wisdom to train our children so they were acceptable to the people we visited. We certainly didn't want to be poor testimonies or set a bad example as missionaries serving the Lord. We didn't want the Lord to be dishonored by the way our family behaved.

Loading the packed drums in the trailer.

When our visit in Washington was over, we left for Modesto again. After cleaning the apartment, we loaded our things and the drums in a trailer and left for Oxnard, where we spent some time with Dale's dad and grandmother. It was hard to leave them, as Great-grandma was failing in health. But Dale's dad, Bud, had found a girlfriend, and we knew there would be a wedding one of these days soon. Her name was Joye.

We now had a sailing date and knew we had to press on. We went to the Orsburn's house in Bell Gardens. They took us in again, except this time we had five children, and the baby slept in a dresser drawer! They had a huge avocado tree in the back yard and a picnic table where we could spread our things out for packing. We got it all done in good time and left on the ship, sailing in August, 1961, from San Pedro for Australia, via Honolulu.

Return Overseas, 1961
By Arvalee

While staying with the Orsburns in Bell Gardens, Dale attended a missionary conference in Anaheim and stayed in the home of Dr. and Mrs. Brunemeier. At this time they told him that their son Byrd and family were missionaries working in the Philippines with New Tribes Mission and FEBC (Far East Broadcasting Company) setting up radio transmitters.

After Dale became acquainted with them, he thought the doctor would know how to treat our baby son, Dan, who had not been well for some time with a bad cough. So we decided to take him to Doctor Brunemeier, who diagnosed him with whooping cough. He said Dan wasn't contagious at that stage and we would be able to proceed with our plans to sail for Australia.

We learned some twenty plus years later, that Byrd was killed on July 27th, 1983, while he was working in Saipan setting up a radio transmitter. "From our earthly perspective, Byrd fell into the high voltage on the KSAI 10KW transmitter, and was instantly electrocuted. From his perspective, he stepped instantly into his heavenly home. What a wonderful surprise for him! For those of us left behind, the only word to describe our initial reaction was shock…exactly what happened we will never know this side of eternity. Somehow he tripped or slipped or in some way lost his balance before he had a chance to turn off the high voltage…and fell directly into the transmitter. Death was instantaneous." (Quote from his widow Angie Brunemeier).

This sad news made us realize in a new way, just how fleeting life on earth really is but that God is in control of when He calls us into His presence. Our responsibility is living a life that is ready for His calling at any time.

My parents drove up from San Diego to see us before we left on the ship. They knew the Orsburns from the time they had lived in Bell Gardens, and Mamma knew them from church as well. A few days later, we set sail as planned and arrived in Honolulu, where we had arranged for Vic and Lorita (Enti) Dizon to meet us.

They took us to see an Aloha parade which was a delightful experience. After the parade, they took us to eat at a Chinese restaurant, and we enjoyed the delicious food very much. Later at their house, Dan began throwing up repeatedly. He really was quite sick. At the time we thought he was possibly sick from the Chinese food, as there wasn't much on the menu that a young child could eat.

Vic was a doctor and tried to help Dan, but because we had to be aboard ship by midnight, he didn't have time to do so. Danny continued throwing up for three days. We realized that he must be suffering sunstroke from too much sun exposure at the parade. I don't remember too much more about the rest of the trip, except they were difficult days.

We were met at the Sydney wharf by Mission personnel and were taken to the Mission training center in Plumpton. We were set up in a Quonset hut apartment, similar to student's housing, but ours was double in size. The apartment had a kitchen, living area, dining area and our bedroom in the first half, and the kids' bedrooms were in the adjoining half. It was not a typical guest apartment, but a permanent dwelling. In fact, it seemed like it was planned for the Palmer family! Harold and Thelma Jackson were the directors of the training camp and it was good to see our friends again.

After we'd been at Plumpton a short time, Harold approached Dale and asked if we could stay on staff while he and Thelma took a much needed furlough.

Boy, was that a surprise to us! We really had been looking forward to getting back to the Gimi tribal people and settling into our home again. We had already spent eighteen months on staff at the training camp in Modesto. Now we were being asked to stay at Plumpton until Harold returned. Of course we diligently prayed about this, but eventually Dale and I felt this was the least we could do. We agreed to stay and help out.

Even though we were temporarily living in Australia, we badly needed a car. The Mission had a van that needed some work on it and Dale was able to get it running. It was called a Fordsom. We borrowed this van for a while, and then Dale was able to buy a small four door Vauxhall that met our needs very well while living in Plumpton.

Fordsom van.

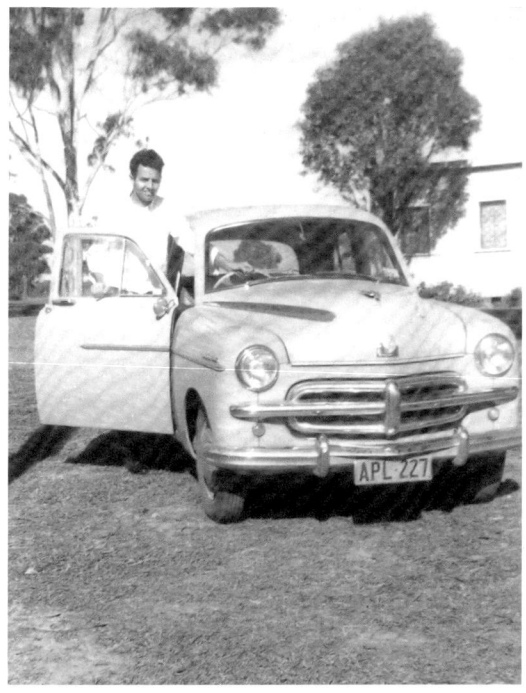

The Vauxhall.

There were many lessons for all of us to be learned in this Australian culture, which was so different from the American culture. Although we had worked with Australians on the field, we found there were many more differences in our ways of thinking and speaking.

Dale was teaching the students in missionary training classes each day, while my duties consisted only of cabin inspection. We had several amusing experiences during this time. Once, the boys' dorm invited our sons over for a meal. Imagine the boys' surprise when they sat down to a plate of green peas with a pat of butter on the top. That alone consisted of their supper. The fellow in charge of cooking that week was quite inexperienced in preparing meals!

Our children were all enrolled in school, with the exception of Dan, and because of the differences in curriculum the boys were each put back a grade! Julie started first grade. The differences in arithmetic and spelling, particularly, were hard for the boys to adjust to. I have mentioned these things previously, but I'm sure each of them could write about those experiences in more graphic detail than I ever could.

Once, when Julie was asked by her teacher what she sometimes had for breakfast, her answer was, "eggs", which Julie pronounced as "aigs" (with a drawl, just like her Texan mother!). Upon hearing that, the teacher said it was properly pronounced eg, as you'd say leg, and continued drilling her to no avail!

One day Peter came home from school with a broken nose! There had been some squabble on the school grounds and he got the bad end! I was very upset about this incident, but there was nothing I could do about it!

The kids learned that baked beans, salad, or spaghetti were quite acceptable sandwiches that could be purchased at noon from the school Tuck Shop.

I found it somewhat demanding, keeping up with all the responsibilities living at Plumpton with our large family. In New Guinea I'd always been able to employ one of the nationals to help me, which I'd come to rely on. Here, we did all the house work ourselves.

One of the new students, a married lady named Faye Albrecht, drove her car to take some of us shopping for groceries. Four other ladies usually went with us. Faye taught me much about shopping and using the foods available in Australia.

I learned to buy a pumped leg of lamb (corned) instead of corned beef. Also, you could get a cheaper cut of meat if you asked for hogget, instead of lamb. It was a cut from a mature sheep. Those shopping days were long and tiresome with us ladies arriving home at suppertime. By the time the food was put away and dinner cooked, it made dinner very late. I began teaching our boys to help by preparing the family meals for me on shopping days. This proved to be a tremendous blessing to me. In this way, we could eat dinner soon after I got home.

This was also valuable training for the boys' future. I taught them how to cook a meal, in consideration of their ages. Pat, who was almost thirteen, learned to make meatloaf, mashed potatoes and a vegetable. Peter, not quite twelve, was taught to make an Irish stew. Paul, who was just nine years old, made simple stove-top macaroni and cheese and a salad. When they were older, they were very appreciative of this training. They also helped me in other ways. The two older boys learned how to iron their shirts, while Paul ironed pillowcases. Julie, only six years old, learned to iron handkerchiefs! I'm sure you find this hard to believe, as most of these items are not even ironed today! But in those days, we ironed almost everything, because wash and wear clothing and polyester had not yet been invented.

Since we were staying in Plumpton on staff, we had unpacked our drums to find dishes, linens, clothes, and other things we needed. In December, which was the beginning of spring or summer in the southern hemisphere, the weather turned quite cold and damp because it was raining frequently. We were cold and I had to hunt for sweaters and jackets in the drums, which were kept outside our apartment, under the eaves of the roof. When we opened the drums again, imagine our surprise to find a couple of them were full of water! Some things were ruined, but I was able to wash and dry other articles. A roll of red crepe paper had permanently stained a few things a light pink color. The most difficult thing to deal with was trying to dry my supply of new spices, which were to last for the entire next term on the field. Trying to save them, I opened each tin, and spread the contents of cinnamon, nutmeg, or whatever, on cookie trays, to dry. I soon ran out of trays and had to borrow some from my neighbors! I put them out to dry in the sun, and when it would begin to rain, I would have to dash out and bring them inside the house. Surprisingly, most of these spices had not lost their potency and I was able to use them later. However, I had to store them in small jars, as the original *tins* were ruined.

We had a large studio photograph of Julie and Dan when he was six or eight months old. This picture was rolled up in one of the drums and suffered water damage also.

After we dried it out, Dale mounted it on a piece of plywood. The water marks are on it to this day, but it rests in an honored place in Julie's bedroom!

Since New Tribes Mission was not well known in Australia, Dale and I took two students, Lyle Mumford and David Scoble, both young single men, on a ministry trip to South Australia. While we were away, a young married couple, Ron and Faye Jarlott, students in the missionary training, came to stay with our children. We had several opportunities to share in different churches along the way and we were able to give our testimonies and challenge other Christians to get involved in missions, either by praying, giving, or going.

It was on this trip that we met and stayed with friends of Lyle and his family. They were an elderly couple, Mr. and Mrs. Reichenbach, who owned and operated a sheep farm. Mr. Reichenbach also grew strawberries, and gave all the proceeds from sales to missionaries. Mrs. Reichenbach had a horse named Prince that she asked Dale to ride. She said the horse needed a good run and workout. The horse was so high spirited that Dale had a hard time controlling him. He had to pull on the bit as hard as he could to stop the horse before it crashed into a fence! I think it was Dale who got the workout!

Besides the horse incident, I can remember the intense cold. In Australia, in the 1960s, there was no central heating in most homes. The bedrooms were not heated like the rest of the house, which usually had a fireplace in the living room. Before going to bed we were each given a hot brick to place at the foot of our beds so we would warm up. I had just fallen off to sleep when I heard the brick from Dale's bed hit the floor. He had stretched out in relaxation and pushed the brick onto the floor. Dale often preached while wearing his overcoat over his suit, as even the churches were not heated. At times he even wore his flannel pajama pants

Dale riding Prince.

195

underneath his suit pants. Those in the audience kept their coats on too, plus covering their laps with a blanket!

During Christmas break the students were given a holiday, or a vacation, when they visited family or friends. There were two cows at the Mission training center that had to be milked twice a day. Since the students usually did this as part of their work detail, this chore fell to Dale. There was so much milk and cream that our family couldn't use all of it. However, Dale came up with an idea to use some of it. We made homemade ice cream from pure cream that holiday. We were spoiled indeed!

Norma was a single student whose mother, Mrs. Walsh, often came to camp to visit or attend the Tuesday night fellowship meetings. We became good friends with her and as time went on, it became her custom to spend an afternoon at our house, helping me with mending! What a tremendous blessing this was to me. She taught me how to rip out the inner seam of the pants leg of the boys' jeans, mend the worn out knee, then sew up the seam again! This made the chore of mending that knee so much easier than trying to turn it around in such awkward angles to sew it on the sewing machine. One day when she arrived at our house she presented our Dan with two hand-knit sweaters which she had made from her scraps of leftover yarn. As long as we were in Plumpton, Dan never forgot who gave him those sweaters. When Nana Walsh arrived he would run to his chest of drawers and bring out the sweaters to show her.

While in Australia we met another dear lady who was a genuine prayer warrior, Mrs. Else Billing. She was acquainted with Jim and Sylvie Spence and had prayed for them and the mission work in New Guinea for years. She held a weekly prayer meeting in downtown Sydney where folks prayed for missionaries from all over the world. Over Christmas break that year, Mrs. Billing invited us to spend a few days with her in her cabin in the mountains at Kootoomba and attend the Keswick convention meetings with her and other friends. That was a delightful time for our family although we were sort of roughing it, as there were not too many conveniences in the cabin. I remember the only place to wash a few clothes was in the bathtub. Then we had a hard time drying them, as the weather wasn't too cooperative, and continued to rain. I managed to dry our clothes by hanging them in front of the fireplace.

Des Oatridge and his family, whom Dale and I had met on the previously mentioned ministry trip, were there also, staying in their caravan or travel trailer. After washing their clothes, Des could not get his undershorts dry, so I offered to dry them in front of the fireplace. I wasn't too successful and somehow managed to scorch them. I was frequently reminded of it in future visits with them!

Mrs. Billing was favorably impressed by the fact that our kids washed their hands each time after using the outhouse. Of course, since they had been raised in New Guinea and grew up using an outhouse, they had been taught to wash their hands from the time they were small.

During our time on staff at Plumpton, Pat and Barbara Smith and four children came into the missionary training. Later, they came to work with us in the Gimi tribe and we became close, lifelong friends.

A few weeks before Pat and Barbara were due to enter the missionary training, her folks, Mr. and Mrs. Alan Barham came from Brisbane, to visit the Mission and check out this organization they were joining. They stayed in our home and it was such a pleasure to get to know them. Mr. Barham delighted us each morning as he sang praises to the Lord, even though he was severely handicapped from the effects of polio in his early life. What a wonderful testimony he was to the glory of the Lord.

These are but a few remembrances of our time while living in Plumpton. We not only had many exciting experiences, but we learned to love Australia as a country and to love and appreciate the Australian people. We made many lasting friendships.

New Guinea Bound, 1963
By Arvalee

A few months before our return to New Guinea, we heard the shocking news that Althea Lawrence had given birth to triplets in the Gimi. Expecting a baby while living in such a remote location is a huge challenge in the best of circumstances, but there was still no road into the Gimi. Coming or going, everyone had to make an arduous journey over the rough mountainous trail each way. To the best of their capabilities, the Lawrences had made plans ahead of time to ensure a safe delivery at the hospital in town. They were planning to leave the Gimi for the birth of the new baby, like they had previously done. Then, six weeks before they were to depart for Goroka, the unexpected happened. Althea took a tumble going down the slippery hill to the washhouse, and the fall brought on premature labor. At the time of birth, much to their amazement, there were triplets, but one of the babies was stillborn. Jake and Martha Queener had joined the Lawrences in the Gimi, and assisted them the best they could during this traumatic time.

Ultimately, they sent a *runner* with a letter to Olaguti, requesting that Rosemary Etherton, a registered nurse, come to the Gimi to help them. When Rosemary arrived she realized these two premature babes needed more help than she was able to administer under the conditions. Plans were made to transport the babies to Olaguti in a roughly made incubator, carried on two poles by national men. Besides needing to keep the babies warm, they had to be fed more frequently than full term babies. This was difficult to do while hiking over the rough trail, as this necessitated stopping the caravan, making a fire and heating water for the formula, as well as the water bottles. The plan was to take them to the Goroka Hospital where they could receive medical care, but sadly, one of the babies died en route and the third babe died shortly after their arrival at the Olaguti base.

Our hearts bled for Dave and Althea when we heard this sad news. Losing a baby must be heart wrenching, but to lose three at the same time would be devastating indeed. We saw them briefly as they passed through Plumpton on their way for a much needed furlough. Dave had been very ill with hepatitis, and was still a very sick man. Since we were still living at Plumpton, Dale was able to assist them in getting to the airport and help them in boarding their flight for the States.

After a year and a half in Australia, it was time for us to return to New Guinea. We began making tentative plans, but we really didn't have the money to purchase our tickets.

The Jacksons had arrived back in Australia and took over their responsibilities once again. Harold and Thelma needed to pick up the car they had shipped over from the States, so Dave Scoble borrowed the Vauxhall from Dale to take them to the wharf. While driving to the wharf, Dave was involved in an accident. He was thrown into the street, but he told us later, "I wasn't even hurt, it just tore me *strides,*" (his pants). Thankfully, the Jacksons only suffered a few minor cuts. Dale reported the accident to the insurance company, and the car was totaled. When the check came from the insurance company, it was the exact amount we needed to purchase our airplane tickets to return to New Guinea! In a most unusual way, God had met our needs once again!

Back to the Gimi, 1963
By Arvalee

As we were traveling back to New Guinea, we stayed with Mr. and Mrs. Alan Barham in Brisbane. It was a pleasure visiting in their home and getting acquainted with some of their friends.

It was the end of May before we arrived back on the field. We stayed at Olaguti, the main mission station where a number of missionaries lived. We lived in a large, vacant bush house while we organized our equipment to move into the Gimi.

Our children had grown up during the time we had been away from New Guinea. Pat was now fourteen and a half years old, Peter was thirteen, Paul was ten, Julie was almost seven and Dan was three years old. Dan had never seen national people before and, much to our surprise, he was afraid of them. When he spotted them standing just outside the fence he would run crying into the house! Thankfully it didn't take long for him to adjust and make good friends.

Ken and Rosemary Etherton and their four girls lived a short distance from us on the Mission grounds. Julie was happy to have friends near her own age and wanted to be like the other girls. She started begging me to cut her hair, which she wore in a beautiful long pony tail that curled into one long ringlet and it had never been cut. Finally, I gave in and cut it short like the Etherton girls!

Everything was finally organized and the day came for our move to the Gimi.

But just as the children had grown, things had changed in the Gimi while we were away. The original round bush house had deteriorated and had been torn down while we were away. We needed to build a new house so we lived temporarily in a smaller bush house that was generally used for guests. It was too small for our large family so our three boys slept in the Lawrence's old bush house, a short distance from the house we were staying in.

Return to the Gimi.

While we were on furlough Jake and Martha Queener moved into the Gimi to join the Lawrences. Jake built a small house from *pit sawn* (see glossary) lumber on the mission grounds not too far from the Lawrence's house. Since the Lawrences had gone on furlough the Queeners had been alone, so they were happy that we had returned.

One day, Jake came down to our house to tell us that he heard on the radio that President John F. Kennedy had been assassinated! That was November 22nd, 1963. What a terrible blow! It was almost unbelievable that something this horrible could happen in our beloved homeland. I believe it was about six months after this that the Queeners went on furlough, leaving us alone in the Gimi.

A New House, 1964-1965
By Arvalee

When we were faced with the need to build a new house, I don't think either of us realized how much hard work it would entail. This time, Dale was planning to build a wooden frame house, using *pit sawn* timber, because he knew that a house made from bush material wouldn't last very long. We had spent many hours drawing up the plans for our new home. It would be situated alongside the Lawrence's old bush house, which needed to be demolished as it was beyond repair.

Dale hired a crew of eight strong, young men to help him. They would need to learn how to use the *pitsaw* (see glossary) and then cut down the trees that had to be dragged to the work site and sawn into lumber. All this was extremely difficult and physically exhausting work for Dale, even though he had Gimi men to help him.

Dale had another major interest. Besides building a new house, he was working on the Gimi language each day. He never felt he really knew the language well, even though he studied it diligently for years. He was able, however, with the help of several of his Gimi brothers, to successfully put out a one page monthly bulletin in the Gimi language with news articles and health and cleanliness information.

One article gave instructions on the use of the upcoming new currency. This was in preparation for when Australia was planning to replace pounds, shillings and pence with dollars and cents. The decimal system was a new concept the people needed to learn to use, or they faced the possibility of being shortchanged when they sold their coffee. Some of the unscrupulous buyers would try taking advantage of them, so this information was very helpful.

After the bulletins were typed to our satisfaction on our portable typewriter, the first draft was sent to a dear lady friend in Melbourne, Australia, who reproduced them on a mimeograph machine. She then sent us a sufficient number of copies to distribute to the men who were promising leaders of the fledgling Gimi church. They, in turn, shared the news with the smaller groups in their villages. Of course, giving this reading material to these men was helpful only because they had previously learned to read the Gimi language.

Dale teaching the men's literacy class.

Dale hired a young man named Ireso to help him acquire the Gimi language. Ireso was a lot of fun to work with and had a unique sense of humor, even though learning

Ireso and Dale working on
translation.

language was serious and intense work. One morning, as they were working away on the language, I took them their customary cup of tea and some cookies. Dale said to me in English, "Thank you. You are my number one wife."

I replied, "Where is the number two wife?" At this exchange of playful words between us, Ireso burst out laughing. It was customary for many national men to have several wives at once, but he knew that missionaries did not have more than one wife, so found our words hilarious. Although he didn't speak English, he understood more of what we were saying than we realized.

Ireso lived at Avopi village, which was located beside the *Thani* River, about 2,000 feet down the mountainside from our planned house site, at the top of the ridge. Thinking ahead, Dale asked Ireso to choose a large flat rock and carry it up the mountain to the house site each day. These large rocks would be used for the foundation of our house. Ireso eventually carried enough rocks, on his shoulders, to place one underneath each foundation post.

When the men on the *pitsaw* crew were adequately trained and the sawing was actually in progress, Dale started laying out the house foundation. The *pitsaw* crew brought the sawn boards down to the house site and they were stored in the nearby Lawrence house. By the time the *pitsaw* crew had enough planks sawn, Dale was ready to use them in the new building. I often walked down in the evening to inspect the progress Dale had made that day. As the months went by, work on the house steadily progressed. Those were extremely long, tiring days, and Dale was exhausted by the end of each one.

Looking back, we often wonder how we managed to cover all the expenses we incurred—the usual expenses of buying our supplies from Goroka, paying the carriers who brought them in from Olaguti in backpacks, and paying the *pitsaw* crew. But

Ireso, Dale's
friend and helper.

The pitsaw.

God was always faithful in supplying our needs, sometimes in very surprising ways.

As the building took shape, the time came when we needed to order the corrugated roofing *iron* (steel) from Goroka. What a tremendous blessing it was when we learned that Don and Gwen McCurdy had purchased this roofing *iron* (steel) for us. It was all carried into the Gimi by the people, who balanced it on their heads. What exciting days those were as we saw the house nearing completion!

A note came through the mail one day that a guest was coming to visit. He wanted to help Dale with the building. Pat and Peter hiked out of the Gimi to meet him at the end of the Government jeep road and accompany him the rest of the way to the Gimi. Our visitor was Vern Appleton, Barbara Smith's cousin. We had met him and his family when we were passing through Brisbane on our return to the field. When Vern was a young man, he had been in a motorcycle accident and had lost his left leg just below the knee. He used a prosthesis and had actually acquired a peg leg for his hike and time in the Gimi. The nationals came for miles to view this wonder. They had never seen a European man with only one leg! There was a national man at A-ibu, in the south Gimi, who had also lost his left leg in an accident. He, too, came to see Vern. These two could identify with one another, although they couldn't understand each other's language. Vern wasn't a bit embarrassed when these people came to see his leg. He would roll up his pant leg to display the stump. The people had to feel his leg, rubbing their hands over it, oohing and aahing in exclamation as they touched it. If he was working on the building, he would take the prosthesis off and hop around on one leg, whether on the floor joists or at another location of the building. For us, it was a bit scary to see him hop from one place to another, not knowing if he would be safe, or miss his landing!

By the time Vern arrived, our three boys had moved into the new house because the Lawrence's old house was leaking so badly they could hardly find a dry place for their beds! Only parts of the floor had been laid and the house was far from finished, but the roof was on and the walls were up. Vern slept in what would eventually become Julie's bedroom.

We still didn't have windows for the house, so we covered each window opening temporarily with plastic mesh. Then out of the blue, Vern said he wanted to take care of this expense for us! As it turned out, his family's business in Brisbane manufactured louvers for windows! Before leaving the Gimi, he measured each window, and later shipped us the louvers and the glass, all expenses paid, to finish the house! Words cannot describe how blessed we were for this huge act of generosity. It truly was a most thrilling day when Dale was able to install the windows. No more plastic mesh, and no longer would we have the worry of bugs and moths flying inside the house when the Petromax lamp was lit at night! This was pure luxury! Imagine having glass windows in this remote location on the mission field. Now we could see the glorious view of the distant mountains all day long.

Dale chose *thaso* wood or brown pine for the floor boards. He planed each board by hand and coated it with varnish. He went to a great amount of trouble and hard work to provide me with a beautiful floor in our new home. He was determined that it would not only be nice, but easy to care for as well. To our disappointment, in time this wood proved to be too soft and all the varnish wore off. Eventually, Dale replaced it with boards made from a much harder wood, called *emo*. It was more suitable for the daily wear a floor receives.

It was a pleasant surprise to learn that one of the single missionaries, Dave Yarral from New Zealand, was coming to build the kitchen cabinets for us! What a boost to know a skilled tradesman would craft them for us. Imagine my delight, knowing we would have a beautiful, efficient kitchen! Dave had a hearty appetite and as expected, I made as many tasty dishes as I could manage. This was not a problem, though, since I was used to cooking for our large family. And Dave was a farm boy so he didn't expect fancy food! I remember, after one meal, he questioned, "Why all the bother of making special food? Oh, just for some good old boiled mince!" (Hamburger meat)

Dale had chosen long, wide planks for the cabinet tops, each of which he hand planed as smoothly as possible. To finish these cabinet tops, we chose light apple green enamel paint, trimmed in light grey. We had purchased a double well, stainless steel sink, complete with two fitted, stainless steel drains on each end. My new kitchen was beautiful as well as functional. I was anxious to get moved, so after the cabinets were finished, Dale and I, along with Julie and Dan, moved into the house, too! Our three boys had slept there for some time, but after months of living in that small bush house, we were ready to move!

Our new house more than met our expectations. It was far more comfortable and practical than a bush house. I had never even dreamed of having such a wonderful house in the remote land of the Gimi. We were so isolated, a coffee buyer once exclaimed, "Where in the world am I! Is this at the end of the world?"

In the years we lived there, we had many visitors who came to spend time with us. Let me name a few: Ken and Lily Johnston, the Director of New Tribes Mission; Don Hay, who hiked to a village with Dale and dropped his new camera in the river because he didn't trust a national to carry it! Chippy and Edna Trigg, and at

Our Gimi house almost finished.

Dale's request, Edna treated us by making homemade doughnuts; Dale and Jerry Brown and daughter; Ken and Rosemary Etherton and girls; Dean and Laurel Van Vliet; Ted and Faye Albrecht and their three girls, along with Sue their grown daughter; Lyle Mumford; Rollie Boye; Don and Gwen McCurdy and boys; and Lou and Miriam Willand and family. Then there were the many friends of our children who came for school vacations.

A visiting fellow missionary once said, "What a terrible road we traveled over to get here!"

Dale replied, "It depends on which end of the road you live, whether you think it is terrible or not." We thought it was quite a remarkable road; constructed by the national people using only picks and shovels, climbing steep mountains and passes, and crossing numerous rivers. This road followed most of the horse trail Dale had built previously. Now, instead of a three day walk, you could cover the 40 some miles in about eight hours, not counting landslides, flat tires or some other problem. We were very thankful for it and for our rustic but comfortable home in this distant bush area. Many people would pay thousands of dollars for real estate such as this, with the wonderful view of the mountains that surrounded us, and the spectacular sunsets which were our delight. What a privilege. God had indeed blessed us richly, not only with a lovely home amidst wonderful surroundings, but with friendly "neighbors" who were open to the gospel... all praise to God.

Vacation Gimi Style, 1965
By Arvalee

It was about 1965 that we felt badly in need of a vacation, but we didn't have enough money to go to Goroka or the coast and stay in a guest house. Instead, we planned a vacation in the jungle; we would go camping. We had plenty of food in the cupboards to take with us and all of us were excited about getting away for a few days.

However, going to the jungle for a vacation took a lot of planning, because we had to take everything we would need with us. I packed bedding for each of us, consisting of blankets, quilts, and our pillows. I had to pack dishes for food preparation and eating; silverware, knives, pots and pans, a bucket to carry water in and a basin to wash the dishes. Matches and kerosene were also needed. We took along a kerosene Primus stove in case wet firewood prevented us from starting a camp fire, and a lamp. In addition, we thought we might need a pressure cooker in the event the hunters in the group were lucky enough to shoot some game! The boys were eager to try their skill with the gun and I believe one of them did kill a small wallaby. We relied mostly on *tinned* (canned) meat, though.

Dale had set things up with a man from a village across the river. We called him the *Dog Man*, because he owned several hunting dogs, which he used to hunt opossums. *Dog Man* arranged with the people of his village to build a rough house in the forest for us to stay in. He told us that it was in a very isolated location, but it had a shallow stream nearby, the main requirement for the chosen location.

Dale hired several men to accompany us and carry our belongings, as there were far too many bundles for us to carry by ourselves. To reach our *vacation house*, we had to cross the *Thani* River. The trail descending to the river was a steep, rough track, filled with ruts from heavy rains of many years. We didn't just casually stroll along, but watched closely as we took every step, lest we lose our footing and tumble down, head first. We crossed the river over a swinging footbridge, and then started the hike over an ill-defined, seldom used track through the thick forest. Total silence enveloped us as we walked along, with the exception of an occasional bird call far above us in the towering canopy of trees. Even here, we had to watch every step, for the trail was filled with ruts and tree roots that could easily trip us. The forest was so dense that without our guide we would have been totally lost. After walking about an hour we came to the spot where our house was located. We could hear a small stream rippling nearby; our supply of water for our daily needs.

The house was very rough, with broad leaves defining the roof and wide bark strips for the walls. It was all tied together with jungle vines, and though we could see daylight through the walls and the roof, it was sturdy enough for a temporary house. We thought it would keep the rain off, but when it began raining in the middle of the night, several of us found water dripping on our beds. The next day, it was a chore trying to dry the wet bedding, as the canopy of trees was very dense and there wasn't much sunlight coming through.

Inside the house, a bed for each of us was attached to the outer wall. Each bed was made from small tree trunks, about one inch in diameter, placed together lengthwise, sort of like a bench. These pole beds were about a foot and a half off the floor. When we spread our blankets over them they looked just fine—that is until we lay down. If we moved around too much while sleeping, the poles spread apart and there was an open space between our body and the floor!

We cooked our food over the open fire—food that I had prepared before we left home and carefully measured, so there was just enough for each day. I brought oatmeal, powdered milk and sugar for breakfast, along with fresh baked loaves of bread. One meal was pigs in the blanket. All we needed to do was add some water to the flour mixture to make the dough. Then we put the small canned Vienna sausages on long sticks and formed the dough around them. The kids took turns cooking these over the open fire, turning them until the biscuit dough browned just right and supper was ready in a jiffy.

Although roughing it was enjoyable, we found it took a lot of time just to prepare our meals and wash up the dishes. Once a day a few people came by to bring us some sweet potato and other fresh food to supplement our diet. They were probably checking up on us, too, to make sure these crazy European people were all right! These people were strangers to us, but friendly, and it was always a welcome sight to see them coming down the trail through the forest.

I'll never forget how I felt when we arrived back home five days later. As we came through the front door, that old Gimi house truly looked like a mansion with its varnished floors and shiny, smooth cabinet tops. It actually had windows that we could see out of! And it looked so clean! Most of all we enjoyed a nice, hot shower. The beds were soft, clean and comfortable! It really was wonderful to be home again.

Chapter 11

Co-Workers Again
By Arvalee

Soon after the camping trip, Pat and Barbara Smith arrived with their four teenagers, Ken, Lorene, Jim and Don. They moved into the former Queener house. Pat needed to do some extensive remodeling before it was suitable for a family of six.

These were exciting days for the Palmer family. Dale and I enjoyed having co-workers once again. On most mornings we had a *cuppa* tea together, either at our house or with Pat and Barbara at their house. Dale appreciated having someone to accompany him to the villages, too. On one trip, as they were hiking along, Dale was singing, "Go Tell It on The Mountain." When Pat caught up with him, Dale said, "Isn't this view breathtaking?"

Pat replied, "Yes, it certainly is breathtaking," meaning he was short of breath. He was not yet physically in shape and found hiking in these Gimi mountains, at an altitude of over 7,000 feet, to be quite strenuous.

Barbara, Lorene and I had literacy classes for the Gimi women, as none of them were able to read. We were trying to prepare the women for the future when they would have the scripture in their own language. Barbara and I also decided to teach the women to use a needle and thread. Supplying cloth, we instructed them in the art of sewing together simple skirts with an elastic casing waistband. Some of them seemed to catch on quite well, but others never mastered the art of using a needle and thread. It was much easier for them to buy inexpensive clothes from town.

The Lord had supplied for us a Maytag washing machine through our dear friends, Cline and Virginia McFerran, in California. It was run by a small gasoline motor, which made a deafening noise. This was set up outside our basement door. Many times, when I would be thoroughly absorbed in the task of washing the clothes, Pat would appear on the small hill above, shouting "Gut moning *misis*, yu stap gut?" (Pidgin English for "Good morning, Missus, are you well?") This startled me, and usually made me jump. It never failed to amuse Pat, and he would enjoy a hearty laugh!

The Smith kids and our kids all spent many happy hours together. They had fun playing games, having sing-alongs, jam sessions and playing ping-pong in our basement. Peter made a drum using a large, empty, metal tin with a goat skin stretched over the top! Ken Smith used an old tea chest on which he strung strings and called it his box-o-bass! They all had such wonderful times together.

Two single lady missionaries from the Summer Institute of Linguistics (*SIL*) were also learning the language, in order to translate Scripture. Nancy Knippel (later married Sam McBride) and Jean Smith enjoyed coming to our house for homemade soup. Dale sometimes stopped at their house for a cup of tea when he passed through their village at Tunakau, an hour or so away, as he was coming home from a trip. They teased him about using so much sugar in his tea and placed before him a large cooking spoon used to stir food on the stove. Dale was a great tease himself, so took all this teasing in a good nature.

My Aussie Mates, Pat and Barbara Smith
By Dale
(A step back in time; how I met Pat and Barbara Smith)

The old, log church in Brisbane, Queensland, was full of people that night as I stepped out of the rain onto the wobbly, log step and into the church hall. I was ushered up to the front of the building and a hush settled over everyone as they stopped talking. All you could hear was the scuffling of the chairs on the old wooden floor as folks started sitting down. Their keen eyes were giving this American stranger the once-over.

Most of the time when I'm asked to speak, I know what I'm going to preach, but not this night. I'm still not sure just how it all started, but I ended up preaching on the life of Moses. I do remember saying that Moses was about eighty years old when God came to him in the burning bush and said, "I am sending you to the King of Egypt. Go! Bring My people, the Israelites, out of Egypt!" Never before had I spoken on the life of Moses, and I never have since.

Before I brought the message that night, I had asked Ted Albrecht and Bill and Rosie Hay, who were traveling with me, to share their testimonies. They were Australian students at the New Tribes Mission Training center in New South Wales, located at Plumpton, near Sydney. Arvalee and I were on staff there, filling in temporarily for Harold and Thelma Jackson, who were taking a badly needed furlough.

After I closed the meeting in prayer, we all kept very busy talking to folks long after the meeting was over. I remember an older white-haired man in a dark overcoat handing me a roll of money. We talked to a lot of enthusiastic people that night, in that century old United Protestant Church. One did not find many independent churches in Australia like that one.

The next night was Monday and we had two meetings scheduled. Bill, Rosie and

Ted took our borrowed car and went off to the one meeting, and Alan Barham loaned me his French Peugeot and I went to the other meeting.

> *That borrowed car we drove to Brisbane belonged to a Real Estate man near the training center in New South Wales. We were praying about this trip up to Brisbane when Art Bowcher came to me and said, "Dale, you can use my new Holden car to drive to Queensland and I will use your Fordsom until you get back." What a blessing and answer to prayer that was!*

Art Bowcher.

It was dark when I got in Alan's car. I had not driven it before and did not know that in order to shift gears in the Peugeot it was the opposite of most other cars, but I got the hang of it. At the meeting I met a young single man named Bob Bagley, as well as Tony Rigsby and his wife. After the meeting, we went over to the Rigsby's home for supper. (Supper, or as the *Aussies* say it, suppa, is mainly a hot cup of tea and a piece of cake.) We talked way into the night. Bob was very eager and so were the Rigsbys. They asked many good questions about what we believed and how New Tribes Mission trained people for the mission field. It was wonderful being with excited folks like this. They kept our tea cups full, and it was after 11 p.m. before I could get away.

When I arrived back at the Barham's home, where we were all staying, a big note was tacked on the door, "Dale, call this num-

Art's Holden.

ber right away." I think it must have been well after 11:30 p.m. by then. I was not sure if I should call so late, but after some hesitancy, I dialed the number. The lady on the other end of the phone said, "We have been waiting for you to call. We want to talk to you."

I asked her, "When?"

She said, "Now. It's the only time my husband has to talk. He is at work all day."

I found my way over to their farm and we drank more tea and talked until about 3:00 a.m. I remember their first question. They said, "In the meeting you

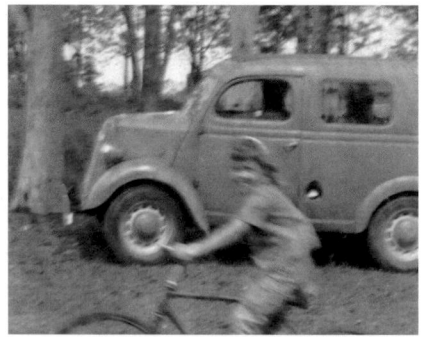

The Fordsom.

mentioned that God did not start using Moses until he was eighty years old. Did you mean that New Tribes Mission will take folks like us, who are in our forties?" I assured them we had a number of folks over forty doing a great job on the mission field. I can still remember Barbara looking at me and saying, "Does New Tribes take families with four children?"

I laughed and said, "Many of our New Tribes missionary families have five children, and some even more. I have five children myself."

Pat and Barbara Smith told me that morning that they had been turned down by an Australian mission board because they were too old at forty and they had too many children. I gave them applications to fill out and asked them to come to Plumpton for a personal interview with our New Tribes Mission staff.

Pat and Barbara did fly down to Sydney and all of us on staff enjoyed their fellowship. A few weeks later Mr. and Mrs. Alan Barham drove down to the training camp to check

The Smith family.

out this new mission that Pat and Barbara were considering. The Barhams stayed in our home and we had a wonderful time with them. Alan would wake up in the morning singing in bed. He just filled our home with joy and happiness. You see, Alan was severely handicapped; his left leg and spine were fused and unmovable, but his joy in the Lord didn't rest on his physical condition. They had a good look around our campus and met students and staff during their visit. From then on Alan Barham was behind New Tribes Mission 100%.

Alan and Lena Barham were Barbara Smith's aunt and uncle. They raised Barbara after her father and mother died, so they wanted to make sure Pat and Barbara were joining a reputable organization.

Pat told me later, that selling their farm was not really hard, as they knew they were being obedient to the Lord. Yet, when they loaded his little milk cow in the trailer to be taken away, it really broke him up. Pat and Barbara Smith went through the training in Australia in 1963 and later wrote to ask if they could join us in the Gimi tribe. We wrote back and said we would love to have them. I also wrote Bill Hay who was teaching the language course at the time, "Bill, you must help Pat and Barb to learn how to make a flapped R as it seems like it is in every other word in the Gimi language."

Most Australians do not use a flapped R in their everyday talk. When they say "butter" and "Betty" they use a T like they do in jolly old England. They pronounce it 'buTer' and 'BeTy,' *[sic]* whereas most Americans use a

The Barhams.

flapped R and say 'buRer' and 'BeRy.' *[sic]* Well, Pat mastered the flapped R but Barb just couldn't get her tongue to make that strange sound. But, you know, her love for the Gimi people was so strong that the Gimis overlooked the way she spoke their language.

Our years together in the Gimi were wonderful. At 10 o'clock and at 3 o'clock almost every day we had a *cuppa* (tea) together. This was a time to fellowship and talk about the work. During these years God knit our hearts together.

In 1972 we moved to the Sepik Region and were heading up the work there. In 1977 we were in need of a furlough. The mission leadership asked Pat and Barbara if they would come up from Queensland, and fill in for us until we returned from the States. So, they came out of retirement to fill in for us. Pat and Barb went out and visited each of our missionaries in their tribal allocations, just like we had been doing. What a blessing they were to all the Sepik teams.

When we returned from our furlough, Pat and Barb were planning to move out of the little mission house we had lived in and into the unfinished apartment downstairs, but we asked them to just stay with us until the apartment was finished. Arvalee just had a major operation and was not fully recovered yet, so we needed Pat and Barb's help for a while. It was so good to be with them again. Pat was such a blessing as he always fixed breakfast for the four of us. Barbara took charge of all the household duties which allowed Arvalee to recuperate.

After several more years in the Sepik, we were transferred in 1982, to the Highlands Region, where I served as the Field Chairman. In 1990 we moved to the island of New Britain to serve as the Government Representative for New Tribes Mission in the town of Rabaul, East New Britain. When new missionaries were looking for a tribal allocation, there was often a need to put this request before the Government officer in charge of the tribal area. Sometimes there was a problem in a tribe that had to be brought before the Government, so I was the one to go to their office to try and solve the problem.

Again Pat and Barb were asked if they could come back to Papua New Guinea to help teach literacy to a local tribe near Kimbe, West New Britain. They gladly agreed, and when they had a break they flew over to Rabaul and stayed with us for about a week. It was like old times again. We went sightseeing, took picnics to the beach and went swimming. It was just great being together with them again.

Pat and Barbara Smith, our dear Australian co-workers, left Arvalee and me with many fond and lasting memories. Arvalee and I both really miss our dear *Aussie* mates.

Today, Pat and Barbara are enjoying the fruit of their eternal investment in the lives of Papua New Guineans as they fellowship with many who are there in heaven with them.

I'm so glad they waited up for my phone call that night. I'm humbled that God gave me a little part in the lives of these two great missionaries, and I really look forward to heaven where we can spend time in fellowship with each other, not for a week, or months, or even a few years, but for all eternity.

Home Life in the Gimi and Home School
By Arvalee

Those were idyllic days in the mid-1960s for our two families. The boys roamed freely throughout the jungle, often swinging from vines hanging from the tall trees. They would often take the gun and go to the river, hoping to shoot some wild ducks. The only danger to them might be a wild mother pig, with a few piglets trailing along behind her.

This happened on one occasion when Pat had gone up the mountain to check on the water flow in the water race. Dale had found the water was not flowing that morn-ing and asked Pat to go check on it. The water race was our only supply of water, so it was an important part of our daily life that it be well maintained. He was gone for an unusually long time. When he returned, he told us that a mother pig was blocking the trail on his way back home. Rather than risk her charging him, he decided to go back up the mountain and follow another trail home.

When we had first moved into the Gimi tribal location in 1958, we relied upon Althea Lawrence, who was a trained school teacher, to teach our children, along with her own kids. Now, arriving back on the field in 1963, the Lawrence's had gone on furlough and the schooling for our children fell totally upon me. Dale and I explored various home schooling courses, but the ones from the States were so very expensive, that we finally decided to enroll each of the children in the Queensland Correspondence Course, provided by the Australian Government. Pat was enrolled later in the American Course for high school.

Pat at his school desk.

Although this was difficult for me, it was likely easier for the kids because of their prior enrollment in the Australian schools. At least they were already familiar with the different spelling of certain words, which I have mentioned before. I had a very difficult time learning to teach the Australian money system, which was in pounds, shillings and pence, based on the monetary unit of twenty shillings per pound, a shilling being equal to twelve pence. Division and multiplication in particular, were hard for me, which I had to understand in order to teach it to the kids.

Dale built a school desk for each of the kids, which we situated in their respective bedrooms. There weren't many distractions, but they all looked forward to a vehicle coming into the Gimi, usually a Government truck or a coffee buyer. *By now the horse trail had been widened and made into a road by the Government.* The drone of the laboring engine could be heard long before it reached our house as the vehicle climbed the steep mountain road. At these infrequent times, the kids knew Teacher-Mom would allow a mad dash through the house and outside to watch as the truck passed on the road below our house. Sometimes, if we knew the driver, travelers would stop and chat awhile and have a cold drink.

Paul at his desk.

Dale had made a fourteen foot tall pegboard for the boys to use for exercise. He had bored two sets of holes at twelve inch intervals from the bottom to the top of the tall board. Two round pegs about eight inches long, made from a broom handle, were placed in the bottom two holes. When climbing, a peg was removed from its hole and put in the peg hole above, next in line. Then, once they reached the top, the process was reversed. It was a challenge, but Pat and Peter, as they became stronger, were able to climb the board. They each earned a coveted pound, or about two dollars, which Dale had promised to them, if they could reach the top of the board.

However, we watched many young Gimi men who never were able to lift themselves up, even to the height of two peg holes. Dale was surprised to find that the men who had worked on the *pitsaw* and had very strong arms and shoulders, were not able to succeed in this feat. They were very frustrated that they couldn't accomplish this challenge!

During this era, all the New Tribes missionary children in New Guinea were home schooled. In time, the missionaries unanimously decided that the field needed to start a school for missionary's children. It opened with a few children and, over time, almost all of them

Peter climbing the 14 foot peg board.

went out to boarding school, which was first set up at the Olaguti base in January, 1966.

Dale Critically Ill
By Arvalee

Sometime after the Smiths joined us, Dale became sick with what we thought was malaria. I tried to nurse him back to health, but he didn't respond to the treatment. Finally, after more than a week, we decided he needed to see a doctor.

A trip to Goroka was in order, but we didn't have a vehicle. By this time, the Government jeep road had been completed all the way to our mission base. Without a vehicle, the only thing I could do was appeal to the Government for help. So I wrote a note to the medical orderly at the nearest Government Aid Post, twenty-five miles away at Okapa, explaining our situation. One of our young Gimi men hastily ran with the note and gave it to him.

When Medical Orderly Carroll, whom we knew personally, arrived in late afternoon in a Government vehicle, he marched into our house and took command. He said, "Where is the patient?" and headed down the hallway to the bedroom. It's a good thing I had packed a few items to take with us, for I'm sure he would have left without me if I wasn't ready to go! He gently ushered Dale to the waiting vehicle and I followed. I had a mattress ready to be placed in the bed of the truck for Dale to lie on.

After traveling the twenty-five miles on the rough, unpaved mountainous road, the Government vehicle deposited us at an orphanage operated by the Lutheran mission, a short distance from Okapa. Medical Orderly Carroll took us to a vacant house, where we spent the night. He told us that the Lutheran mission truck was going to Goroka the next morning and the driver was willing to take us, if we would be ready to leave at 5:00 a.m.

This house was obviously not set up as a functioning guest house, and the staff probably was not aware that anyone had arrived. There was no one present to meet us... no one to bring us a cup of hot tea, much less supper. I must have brought a few food items with us to snack on. Yet we were both so exhausted from the two-hour trip and Dale was so very ill, that we were very grateful to have a roof over our heads.

There was a bed in the house, but not much else! There wasn't even a lamp to light so that we could see our way around in the darkness. Fortunately, I had brought a torch, or flashlight, with us, but sadly the batteries were almost gone so I used it very sparingly. I was thankful for the dim light it provided, enabling us to get to bed and arise on time the next morning. Somehow we managed to get dressed and ready to meet the driver at that very early hour.

We had a very long and tiring journey ahead of us, one that would take at least three hours before we reached our mission base. The road to Olaguti was built over a very treacherous steep mountain called the Kuru. Ascending the Kuru Pass required a four-wheel drive vehicle. Once we neared the base, I asked the driver to stop at Olaguti so I could let the missionaries there know that we were on the way to Goroka to take Dale to the hospital.

At Olaguti, Dean Van Vliet came out to the truck and prayed for Dale while I went to several houses to let people know how ill Dale was, asking them for their prayers.

It was such a relief to finally have Dale safely in the hospital and in the hands of the capable medical staff. He was soon diagnosed with malaria and pneumonia. I was able to stay with some dear Australian friends, Evelyn and Alec Sinclair. I don't remember much about that time except that I was so exhausted I slept for eighteen hours before I awoke.

I don't remember how long Dale was in the hospital or when or how we got home to the Gimi again. Before leaving our home for Goroka, I had made arrangements for Julie and Dan to stay with the Smiths. Barbara was planning to prepare the main meals for all the kids while we were away. Pat, Peter and Paul would be fine staying at home and looking after themselves for breakfast.

When we arrived home again, imagine our surprise when Barbara told us that our Pat had baked fresh bread so he and the other two boys could continue having their breakfast at home. He had found the recipe for bread in my cookbook and simply followed the directions to replenish their bread supply!

A Vehicle at Last
By Arvalee
(Details provided by Pat)

Although the Government road had been finished for some time, Dale's illness once again highlighted our need for our own vehicle. Without one, we still had to rely on the national people to carry all our supplies in back packs. They had faithfully and laboriously carried our supplies for eleven years, ever since Dale had first gone into the Gimi by himself in 1954.

So in 1965, a Gimi delegation came to Dale to inform him that since there was now a road, we needed to purchase a vehicle to haul our supplies. They were obviously tired of this burden of carrying supplies for us.

Of course we knew we needed a vehicle, but there was no money in hand to buy one, and we didn't know of an acceptable way to inform our supporters of this need. What could be done, except continue to pray and look to the Lord?

Then Dale remembered a friend in Brisbane, Allen Scanzella, who once told him if there was anything he could do to help us, to let him know. Dale wrote Allen and told him of the need, asking to borrow some money to purchase a vehicle.

During this time, a friend, Hap Skinner, with *SIL*, came up with an idea. He ran a shop he called Cycle Weld, a welding and machine shop with a specialty in motorcycles, to support missionaries. Dear Hap offered to help us build a Land Rover! He knew of places all over New Guinea where there were wrecks and abandoned vehicles. He thought by finding these parts and used pieces, along with the few items lying around his shop, we could build a vehicle. In looking back, this was really a farfetched notion!

So, our son Pat, who was 16 years old at the time, moved to the *SIL* base at Ukarumpa, and rented a small house. Pat began locating and moving the parts into the shop but there were only a few parts, so soon he was done with that stage of the project.

There were many tradeoffs as the building began. Hap always had lots to do, so in return for Hap's help and expertise, Pat was given jobs like bending pipe on a hydraulic bender for welding roof trusses. There was machine shop work to do also, and Pat was able to help there, too; sometimes working on a motorcycle engine or annealing and then hardening newly cut gears in the furnace and quench tank. Pat recalls this time as one great learning experience, sort of like an apprenticeship.

Between all these tasks, Pat started to inventory all the vehicle parts on hand. The frame, front drive train, rear drive train, drive shafts, brake drums and on and on. They didn't have an engine or any body parts, so Hap and Pat travelled all over to scout out different sites. They found front and rear leaf springs and shackles, bought them and hauled them back to the shop, but they held off buying any body parts because they couldn't haul them with Hap's little Jeep.

It became obvious that they were never going to find a wiring harness; there just wasn't any wiring no matter where they looked. We think the people liked to use the copper wire for making things and simply stripped all wrecks and abandoned vehicles of the wire. They searched for ways to wire this project, but there seemed to be nothing in the country, and no one to help. I wrote to the American School, Pat's high school correspondence course in Chicago, and explained the problem to them. The staff went to the library and found the wiring schematics for the Land Rover, photocopied several pages and sent them directly to Pat at *SIL*. These pages of schematics, which included wire sizes, would turn out to be invaluable in the next few days.

One day, as Pat was working at Cycle Weld, a stranger walked in and began asking what he was doing. Pat explained that he was collecting parts to build a Land Rover. This guy poked around a bit, then went to find Hap. Soon they were back, looking, turning parts over and measuring things. Then they concluded they had a collection of mismatched parts from both long wheel base and short wheel base Land Rovers! While some parts might work together, the brake parts certainly would not. The smaller brake drums just would not be able to stop the long wheel base vehicle. This man pointed out other problems, too.

Hap had been putting out feelers for parts all over and his search actually brought this kind stranger to his shop that day. We believe this man (whose name we cannot recall) told Hap of a Land Rover in Lae that did not run and was up on blocks. He said this might be purchased "as is" for a reasonable price. Hap called the party in Lae that afternoon and probably worked out a purchase price.

There was telephone service between major cities in New Guinea, but only HF (high frequency) radio into the tribal locations. Hap went to the radio room and talked to the *SIL* translators in the Gimi, our friends, Nancy and Jean, but they were at Tunakau, and Dale was at Negibi. The ladies sent a runner to Negibi and Dale went down to Tunakau to talk this over with Hap on the radio. The vehicle would need a lot of work, but Hap thought it could be fixed up. Since the radio frequencies are shared among many groups, Hap finished the conversation with: "Everyone in New Guinea knows about this now, so if you want it, you'd better get down to Lae!"

After the radio conversation, Dale decided the vehicle in Lae would be a good deal. By now the money had arrived from our friend Allen to purchase it, so Dale got to town and flew to Lae the next day. There he could use the telephone to get more details, and then he went to look the vehicle over. He found that the front leaf springs and shackles had been removed and he made a list of other items that were needed. He sent a message to Pat to bring the parts and added, "Bring the wiring schematics." Pat packed up the springs, parts, and schematics and hitched a ride to Lae with a plumber from *SIL*.

While Dale and Pat were in Lae, the three younger kids, Paul, Julie and Dan and I went to Ukarumpa to stay in Pat's rental house at *SIL*. By this time Peter was in school at Olaguti. He had been chosen to be the first student and left home in January, 1966. He had contracted hepatitis, so he was allowed to join us at *SIL* shortly after we arrived there. One day we had gone to the little store for a few groceries and Peter was helping me carry them back to the house. He was simply exhausted by this simple task and then I realized how very ill he was. Our time at Ukarumpa turned out to be a good time for Peter to recuperate and for the rest of us to have a little break from our routine at home.

Pat and Dale were able to stay in a room at the *SIL* guest house in Lae while they worked on the Land Rover. This was quite a change for both of them, leaving the cool highlands climate for the hot humid weather in the coastal town of Lae. They worked for two days just to get the springs on the front, inflate the tires and lube the drive train parts. Then they borrowed a truck to tow it back to the guest house. During the tow, Dale tried to put it in gear and turn the motor by engaging the clutch. The rear wheels just skidded on the gravel. The answer was simple; just put the transmission into four-wheel-drive; now all four tires skidded!

One of the men at the guest house loaned them his complete set of mechanics tools and they began working on the Land Rover. The only trouble they got into with the tools was when the owner found Dale and Pat wiping the grease off them! He said not to wipe them off as the grease and oil kept them from rusting in the tropics. With the Land Rover parked under a shade tree at the guest house, they pulled off the engine's head. The engine was completely seized, and Dale tells how he poured kerosene over each piston and gently pounded each with a hammer and a block of wood until they gradually loosened. The cylinder bores were rusted badly, so more kerosene and emery cloth were used over and over in each cylinder until they were smooth. These vehicles had hand cranks so they sanded until the engine would turn easily with the crank.

In the whole town of Lae there was not a new head gasket to be found. A man told them to lightly coat the existing one with grease and torque the head bolts down twice, then run it up to temperature and re-torque the bolts. Neither Dale nor Pat can remember changing that used head gasket for a new one! When they look back, it was a miracle an engine in that condition would even run. The piston rings survived the pounding, the cylinders the sanding, and no one ever suggested doing a valve job or flattening the head. This little four-cylinder flathead engine ran for many years without any further work.

They found that white ants or termites had eaten all the electrical wiring so it all had to be replaced. Although Pat had never been around vehicles, he instinctively knew how to rewire it with the schematics and wire sizes from his school in Chicago. Together they worked on this vehicle until they were able to get it running and road worthy again!

Though the Land Rover was ready to go, there was no place to go! The Highlands Highway, from Lae to Goroka, was closed. The Kassam Pass is a section of the highway that starts in the Markham Valley at 1,000 feet and over six miles rises to 5,000 feet. Thus the Kassam Pass is a maze of switchbacks stacked on the side of the mountain and it was closed due to heavy rains and landslides. All the construction work just caused more landslides as the debris was pushed from one road surface to the one below.

So, after they got the vehicle running and were waiting for the road to be opened again, Dale and Pat drove the vehicle to the Watut base, where many of our missionaries lived. This was a good test run and everything went well except for a small leak in the water pump. They parked the Land Rover where the car road ended, near the foot bridge where the mission parked their vehicles. Then they walked the three or so miles to the Watut mission base.

Dale was in meetings in the Watut, so Pat would walk down to the river to work on the water pump. After a few days it was back together and Pat tried to start it up to give it a test run. The engine would not start; crank and crank, but it would not start. Not wanting to run down the battery, Pat started the long walk back to the base. About halfway back, Pat put his hand in his pocket and there was the rotor from the distributor cap! Removing the rotor was a common practice to keep a vehicle from being stolen. Pat went back, replaced the rotor, and the vehicle was back in service!

While in the Watut, Dale and Pat stayed with Adolph Bowen, one of the single NTM missionaries. Adolph had one of the first new transistor radios. Pat was fascinated and asked Adolph if he could look at it. A couple of hours later, Dale felt horrified when he looked in the kitchen and found the radio in pieces, spread all over the table. Pat was looking at it! Dale thought to himself, *Well, I guess I have bought a radio.* But, to his surprise, Pat put it all back together and it worked. After that, Dale knew beyond doubt that Pat had unusual abilities when it came to anything electrical, whether it was rewiring an old Land Rover or assembling a radio.

After hearing on the radio that the road, although rough, was open to traffic, Dale and Pat left for the Highlands. They drove back to Lae and bought some trade goods:

bundles of blankets, cases of canned meats, bags of rice and crackers, known as biscuits. They only bought an amount that could be locked in the cab in the event they had to leave the vehicle and walk. The supplies could serve three purposes; if they had to camp on the road they could sleep and eat, the weight would give better traction on the slippery roads, and if they didn't need them, the Gimi people would love to have some trade goods at Negibi as the nearest store was an eight hour walk away. This would also be a 'thank you' gesture to the Gimis for their many years of carrying supplies into the Gimi for us.

Having finished up in Lae, they slept a couple of hours and drove through the night up the Markham Valley so they could reach the Kassam Pass at daybreak. They reached the base of the mountain at 3 a.m., so they spent the rest of the night in a village schoolhouse. There they fed the mosquitoes well, as they didn't have nets with them. At daybreak when they reached the road construction site, the line of fully loaded big trucks seemed to be a mile long. In talking to some drivers who had been there a week or more, they said some small vehicles had been getting through. Pat stayed with the Land Rover as Dale set off to talk to drivers and workers. He found a bulldozer driver sitting on his D-9 eating lunch and had a nice chat with him. He said the road crew was not responsible for getting trucks through; their job was only to get the road opened again. This bulldozer driver told Dale, "It's a gamble if we can pull you through or not. I just towed another vehicle and the whole front of the truck was pulled off." But this driver was assigned to work at the bottom of the trouble area. It seemed to Dale like they were stuck there for a few days so he went back to the Land Rover and took a much needed nap.

About midafternoon, a shout went down the line of drivers, "They want the Land Rover up at the front of the line!" Dale quickly rolled up a couple of blankets he was resting on and they got going, very slowly moving past the line of trucks. At the front of the line they found the D-9 driver Dale had talked to earlier. He said he had been as-signed to a job at the top of the problem area, so they should follow him and he would pull them through any tough spots.

After a few hundred yards of creeping behind the D-9 they came to a "ditch" that went straight up the side of the mountain. This ditch was lined with slippery red clay about three feet wider than the D-9's blade. It was about ten feet deep and had big ruts in the bottom. To get through it, they looped the one inch diameter winch cable around the front bumper of the Land Rover; "Better to pull the bumper off than pull the truck in half," the driver reiterated. The driver played out about 100 feet of cable, locked the winch drum and started into the ditch.

As the bulldozer towed them along, they were first in one deep rut, then another. Most of the time the mud was up over the cab level on either side of the vehicle. Sev-eral times the Land Rover and the D-9 came to a stop even though its tracks were still running. The driver would stop the tracks, release the winch drum and move the D-9 a few hundred feet forward. Then he would bury the blade and ripper claws into the clay and winch the Land Rover through. There was no driving involved; they just sat there with the little Land Rover rolling over to one side then the other as it moved through the huge ditch. About two hours later they were at the top of the pass and once again began moving under their own power.

Soon something smelled hot; the red clay had packed tightly into the wheels and brake drums and was heated up by the friction. They only had a tire iron with which to remove the clay and had to be careful not to cut the brake lines. As they checked for other damage they noticed clay streaked along the roof of the cab, too. Thankfully they were safely through, and seeing no other damage they went on their way, since it was only a short drive to the *SIL* base at Ukarumpa.

What an exciting day that was when they arrived and Dale drove all of us home to the Gimi in our very own new vehicle - new to us, that is! And by the way, that front bumper had a permanent

The first Gimi vehicle.

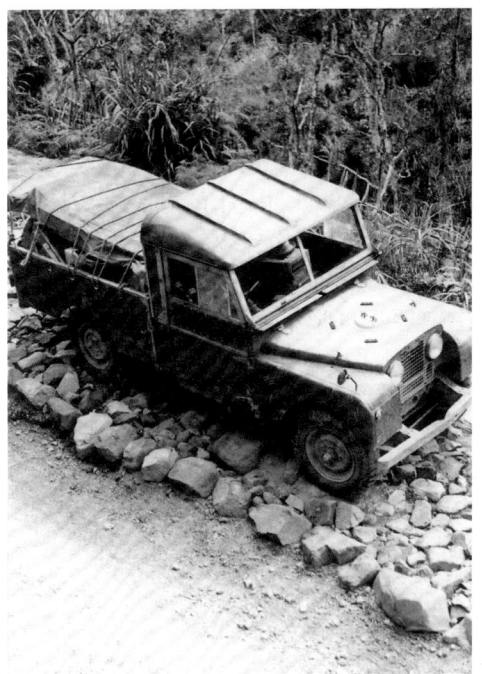

The Land Rover on rock paved road.

kink in it as a memento of that ordeal on the Kassam Pass!

After a few years of good service, except for some broken axles, we were able to replace the Land Rover with a new Toyota Land Cruiser pickup truck.

Boarding School, 1966
By Arvalee

In 1966 the entire field decided we needed a boarding school for the educational needs of our children. We decided it would be established at the Olaguti base. Lou Willand was used of the Lord to get the school started and served as its first principal. Some of the first teachers were Lou's wife, Miriam, Stella Beatham, Dave and Althea Lawrence, Dean Samuels and Dean Van Vliet, who later served as the school principal. These were a few who served in the beginning, yet there were not enough teachers to accommodate each grade. Therefore, the kids went to school as teachers became available for their grade.

The idyllic days in the Gimi came to an end when each of our children, one by one, went to school. Peter had already gone to Olaguti as the first student in January, 1966. Paul left in April, Julie in May and Pat left us on July 1ˢᵗ of that year. Dan was the last of our kids to go to school. It was decided that I would continue to teach him preschool for a year, so he stayed home until January of 1967, when he entered first grade. Stella Beatham was his first teacher.

The kids left shortly after we got the Land Rover. We were very thankful to have a vehicle, but the roads and bridges were often in poor condition. The heavy rains caused mud slides on the roads and the rough-hewn wooden bridges to rot. This made the bridges dangerous for a vehicle to cross. A trip out of the Gimi was no joy ride, usually taking at least six hours. Even without trouble, it was an exhausting task for Dale. I recall one trip taking twelve hours because of the many mud slides that made it necessary to use the wench to get the vehicle through.

These were very difficult days for me as a mother. I found it a very heart wrenching experience to send my children away. I knew home schooling them was far from satisfactory and that they would each benefit greatly from a certified school with trained teachers. It is so easy to write down the month that our kids left for boarding school, but in reality that was one of the most traumatic times I had ever experienced on the field. Even though the three boys were older, it was still very difficult for me to see them go. I worried about little things concerning their care; what kind of food they would be eating, would their clothes be washed properly, etc. After all, no one looks after your kids like you do.

However, I found it was even more difficult to let Julie go. She was just ten years old, and she was my only daughter. One day, after she had been gone a month or so, as I passed her bedroom door and glanced in, it suddenly struck me that I wouldn't be seeing her for several more months. At that moment, I was sorely distressed; I rushed to my bedroom, flung myself across the bed and sobbed my heart out for a few moments. Afterwards, I was more at peace with being apart from my precious children.

> *But let me go back to another very difficult time, eleven years earlier. Dale and I, with our three little boys were in the Watut, for the second missionary conference in February, 1955.*
>
> *During a business meeting, the topic was a school for missionary children. Having been influenced by an older woman, I voiced my opinion, saying, "I will never send my children to a boarding school. They should be at home with their parents."*
>
> *Chuck Driver, our field leader, questioned me very carefully, asking, "Arvalee, if the Lord asks you to send your kids to school, would you obey?"*
>
> *I replied, "Of course, I would obey. I always obey the Lord."*
>
> *This was a very humiliating experience for me, especially in front of all the missionaries present.*

Obviously God changed my heart over the years. Even though I found it so hard to be separated from the children for months at a time, I now knew in my heart they were in the right place, a place designed by the Lord. I believe the Lord allowed me to experience home schooling long enough to really see the need for a mission operated school where our children could receive the help they needed from qualified teachers. I knew our children were not getting the help they really needed with me teaching them at home. So by the time the school was organized, with enough qualified teachers, I was more than ready to let them go. Even though it was a hard time for me, I was finally ready, and I was thankful to the Lord for this provision.

Raro Village
By Arvalee

After Dan left for boarding school, I was able to accompany Dale on his rounds when he visited the Gimi villages. One place we visited was Raro, in the Mani area. He'd had a small house built there and had outfitted it with essentials; a few dishes, some pots and pans, some bedding and a very small wood burning stove for cooking his food. The stove was appreciated as well on the chilly mornings, as it warmed the house.

Dale had spent many days in Raro, visiting the people and writing down their names and mapping the village in order to become acquainted with their family genealogies and history. One elderly woman told Dale the history of her family, their names, how they died and how many children were in each family.

On one visit, I was honored in a special way. Through trading, Dale was able to procure an opossum tooth necklace for me. These necklaces are very difficult to obtain because they are used as a bride price. A young man seeking a bride would climb a tree and put his hand into the opossum's den, which is a hole in the tree. When the opossum bit his arm, he would pull out his arm with the animal still attached! When one talked with a young man about his bride price, the man would proudly show his arm with the scars from the opossum bites.

One day, Dale asked the old woman about the opossum tooth necklace she was wearing and told her that he would like to buy one for his wife. Right away she took the necklace off, called a man over and said a few words to him. Then she gave him the necklace and he walked away.

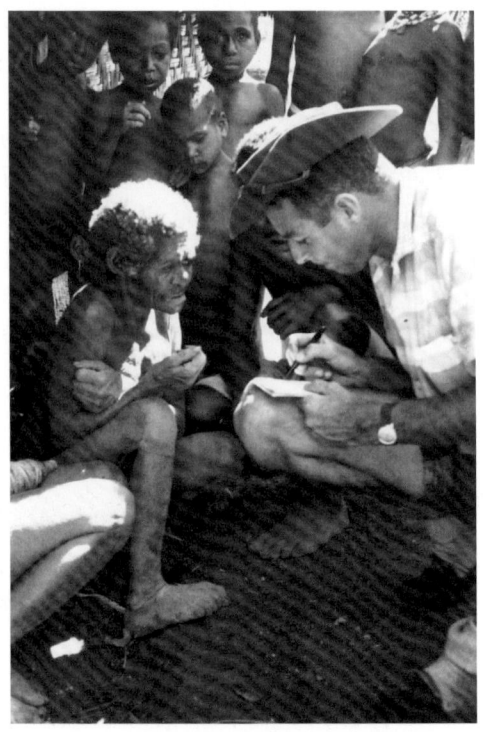

Dale taking genealogy at Raro village.

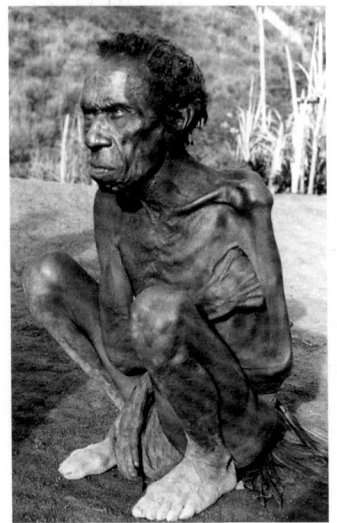

An old Gimi man with withered arm.

Dale was still learning the language and didn't understand what she had said. He thought he had offended her and that he had lost his chance of purchasing the necklace. The next time he visited, he was surprised when the woman came to him and gave him the necklace; it had been re-strung with clean, new string, made from the bark of certain trees. There are 171 opossum teeth on the necklace representing 85½ opossums, as the two front teeth are used from each opossum. Dale paid her well with trade good items; a new blanket, some *tinned* fish, skeins of yarn for making *bilums* (woven string bags) and a cooking pot. These things were valuable to her because the Gimi people lived so far from a trade store and they didn't have much money.

There was one man there who was severely handicapped

224

with a withered arm. He was literally skin and bones. Regardless, he had his place in the village, taking his turn minding the children when their mothers went to work in their gardens. Most of the older people in the village took care of the children at one time or another; they seemed to have their own schedules worked out, just not written out and posted to a roster like we would do it. The men took advantage of this time, telling ancestral stories to the children. Some were actually called a "Story Telling Man," or *Mono iri bana.*

From Raro, we could launch out to visit other people in more distant villages towards the west. On one of my trips to Raro, we hiked to the village of Tha-bi-nama-ta-ba-rai where a family kindly invited us to eat with them and spend the night. I enjoyed the visit but the conditions were difficult for me. I slept in the clothes I had worn all day, which by nighttime were quite dirty and sweaty! The next morning, we awoke, splashed our faces with water from a tin can and were back on the trail again!

The Mono Iri Bana.

The hike back to our little village house at Raro was uneventful. What I do remember vividly is that I told Dale I had to have a bath! After two days hiking and spending a night in the village I felt filthy, and I was most uncomfortable! Of course we had no bathroom at Raro, but my wonderful husband did his best to provide me with the necessities for a bath. He heated buckets of water on the little stove and spread large banana leaves over the ground in the outhouse. I had to be careful not to step towards the center, lest I fall through the hole! As I splashed warm water over my body, soaped up, rinsed off and dried, I felt as if I'd had a bath in a luxurious hotel bathroom!

Hiking back to the jeep road the next day, we were most thankful for our vehicle, which we'd left parked by the side of the road. Soon we were back in our home at Negibi. After a village trip, I had a new appreciation for our rough-hewn, but comfortable, mountain home, and for those many lonely trips that Dale had made in the early days of the Gimi work!

Big Changes, 1967-1969
By Arvalee

The next few months brought a big change for our family, one that came as a complete surprise.

Dale and I had made a supply trip to Goroka and at the same time visited our children in the boarding school at Olaguti. The *dorm mother* in the home where the boys lived told me she just no longer could cope with the demands of the dorm and that some changes had to be made.

A few months earlier, this *dorm mother* had told me that she had a hard time knowing what to make for meals. I suggested that she occasionally make pancakes, as they were easy, and my guess was that kids love them! I later learned from our boys that whenever she didn't know what to cook she made pancakes, whether it was for breakfast, lunch or dinner! I realized too late that this was the wrong suggestion to give her.

I told Dale about my discussion with her and we immediately went to Dean Van Vliet, who was now the school principal. As a result of our visit with Dean, it was decided that Dale and I would temporarily leave the Gimi work and fill in as *dorm parents*. As it turned out, this temporary position lasted for the next two school years.

When we took over the dorm, Julie and Dan, who had been in another dormitory, came to live with us. Now, we had ten kids to look after, our five, plus five others. This certainly wasn't a piece of cake and we often felt that it was one of the hardest assignments on the field. Yet the Lord had given us peace that we were in God's will in moving into this position.

After a year at the school, it was time for our furlough, but the money wasn't forthcoming to purchase our tickets. We concluded this must not be the Lord's timing, so we settled down for another school year.

Pat had completed his senior year of High School during our first year at the school, 1967 and 1968, so during the following school year, 1968 and 1969, he actually functioned as an associate missionary. He had a good reputation as a very willing and capable worker, plus he had capabilities in several useful areas. He supplemented his keen interest and talents through independent study of electricity and electronics. He was virtually self-taught in this field and his talents would soon be put to their biggest test yet!

The school base had used kerosene to fuel their lamps and refrigerators, as did all the other New Tribes missionaries in New Guinea. It was cumbersome and dangerous, so they had long realized the need for electricity.

The field leaders, in looking for an upgrade, approached Pat about installing a diesel generator and wiring the school base for electricity. This would involve about 15 build-

Pat and Hure-ere hanging
the wires.

ings altogether. He would also have to build a small shed to house the generator. He accepted this work as a challenge and it was a tremendous responsibility as well. He had a young Gimi man working with him, named Hure-ere. Peter and Paul helped out too, when they didn't have school; cutting trees for the poles, hauling them, creosoting them, digging the holes, and much more.

Besides working on this project, Pat was asked to help in the school, too. The school was short of teachers so Pat taught three classes on Science and Health to the students in first through sixth grade. These grades were divided into three groups, so he had three separate classes each day.

Pat on an electric
pole.

As we were running out of room at Olaguti, the mission had purchased land at a place called Numonohi. The new land was much nearer to the town of Goroka, in a more desirable location and had the acreage necessary for future expansion. Eventually mission headquarters would be built there, as well as the new school.

Pat with the new generator.

Besides these responsibilities, Pat often took our new Toyota pickup truck to help on the development of the new property. Peter and Paul were also able to go along on several occasions. They helped load sand and gravel, taken from the river, which was used to mix the cement for the new buildings.

Loading river sand for making cement.

Our Second Furlough, 1969
Santa Paula, California
By Arvalee

By the next summer, we had received the necessary funds to purchase the airplane tickets for our second furlough. We departed for the States on September 5th, 1969, flying via Cairns on TAA (Trans-Australia Airlines) from New Guinea to Sydney, Australia.

We spent a week in Cairns in a little motel and had a real family vacation. Dale rented a car and we drove to the Atherton Tablelands to enjoy the wonderful scenery and we visited an alligator farm as well. We also took a launch to beautiful tropical Green Island. I remember well that short trip on the launch to the island as Paul and I both suffered from seasickness!

The beach on the island was splendidly white, formed completely of coral. I was surprised to find palm trees were growing there, even in the absence of sand. We enjoyed the novel experience of snorkeling among the coral reefs, and the glass bottomed boats offered a unique view of the multicolored tropical fish. Since we'd lived in the highlands of New Guinea, we'd not had this opportunity before.

As we were enjoying the warm water, a man nearby exclaimed that he had lost his wedding ring. He and his wife were on their honeymoon, and his too large ring had slipped off his finger. We all helped him look in the coral sand, but alas, it was gone forever!

After our wonderful vacation was over in Cairns, we went to Brisbane to visit our friends there. Ron and Eric Barham, and their friend Allen Scanzella, took us to the Gold Coast which was very enjoyable. They wanted to spear fish, but found they didn't have enough spears. They simply made some more in the family's workshop. Attached to the workshop were guest facilities, where we stayed,

After our visit there, we traveled to the Australian training center at Plumpton, NSW, which was a short distance from Sydney. From there we departed to the USA.

We had secured bookings on a Greek passenger ship, the *Australis*. As the date for our departure approached, we discovered that all male passengers were required to wear a suit, with a white shirt and tie to dinner. Of course this was a huge unexpected expense for us. Now we needed to buy clothing for Dale and our four sons, besides having the expense of purchasing our tickets! We had to pay full fare for everyone except Dan, as he was only nine years old. Our fare in Australian currency was $2,162.50.

Thankfully, our needs were not a surprise to the Lord. We were acquainted with Ray Albrecht, the grown son of Ted and Faye Albrecht, who were in the missionary training. Ray worked at a department store in downtown Sydney. He offered to take us shopping to purchase suits for Dale and the boys, and was able to use his employee's discount, which gave us a really good deal. Dale and the three older boys left the store that day with a suit coat, two pairs of pants, two shirts, a tie, and shoes and socks for each of them. We had to go to a different store to find clothing for Dan. Once again we were overwhelmed by God's ways of meeting our needs at the last moment.

As for Julie and me, I had sewn nice dresses for both of us before we left New Guinea. A wonderful new fabric had been manufactured, called Crimplene in our part of the world, or polyester in the USA. I was able to purchase several yards of material, a lovely woven striped pattern in white for Julie and a nice woven design in beige for myself. From this yardage I made each of us a spring coat and dress to match.

Upon our return to the States we settled in our new location, Santa Paula, California, and started going to church where we made many new friends. One of these couples, Margaret and Jake Schrock, invited us out for pie one Sunday evening. I was wearing the new beige outfit and Margaret asked me, "Did you make your outfit?"

I thought to myself, *Oh my goodness; it's obvious that it's homemade*. But I answered her modestly, saying, "Yes, I did."

Then, she gave me the compliment of a lifetime, saying "I thought you must have made it. Otherwise, you wouldn't have been able to afford such a lovely outfit."

What a boost to my morale and self-esteem. I realized then that I had nothing to fear, for the Lord had indeed gifted me with my unusual abilities of sewing. Maybe because of that compliment I was confident in sewing other garments for Julie and myself during that furlough.

Prior to our departure from New Guinea, we had made arrangements with Dale's dad, Bud, to purchase a house for us to live in while we were home, with the understanding that we would make the payments on it, in lieu of rent. Dale would make any improvements it might need, such as painting or other repairs, and then when we returned to the field, Bud could sell the house, perhaps making a profit. We lived at 326 E. Santa Paula Street for our extended furlough of three years, until we returned to the field in September of 1972. This worked out ideally for us.

Dale had experienced a lot of stress while serving on the Field Committee that term and almost had a nervous breakdown. Working on the house was therapeutic for him and he literally spent hours scraping paint, in preparation for repainting the house.

During this time we asked the leaders of New Tribes Mission for an extended furlough to enable our two sons to finish high school and to get settled before our return. Pat enrolled at the John Brown University in Arkansas. I still remember his departure by plane. Again, I experienced the separation anxiety from my children. Once in school, he found it was next to impossible to find work because the school was in the country and he needed a car to get around. We regretted that we could not help financially, and eventually he dropped out of college due to the lack of funds.

After Pat returned home to Santa Paula, he worked at a local lemon packing plant where he loaded and unloaded many crates of lemons. Besides his work, he was often called on to repair some of the machinery to keep the plant running. After working there for several months, he decided to go to Camdenton, Missouri, and volunteer to work at the New Tribes Language Institute.

Peter enrolled as a junior in the Santa Paula High School just across the street from our house. At the same time he had to register for the military. He worked really hard and took extra classes and was able to complete both his junior and senior classes in one year, enabling him to graduate at the end of the 1970 school year. Almost immediately, his draft number was called and he enlisted in the US Army for three years, serving in Korea.

Paul graduated the next year, 1971, from Santa Paula High School as well. After graduation he had several jobs, but finally settled on working for a moving van company. We helped him set up his first apartment before our departure for New Guinea.

Julie enrolled in the eighth grade at the Junior High School, and graduated in 1970, and then went to the Santa Paula High School for the next two years.

Dan was enrolled in his grade school classes at the Barbara Webster Grammar School. He had saved his money and bought a ten speed bicycle which he rode all over town. One day, when he had parked it in front of a store in town, it was stolen! That was a hard lesson for a kid his age to learn.

Since our three oldest boys were now adults and fairly settled on their own, it was time for us to return to the field. We left for our third term in New Guinea, with only Julie and Dan to accompany us.

Chapter 12

Moving On; Another Surprise
By Arvalee

After three years in the States, September, 1972 found us traveling once again, but this time with only two of our kids, which seemed very strange.

The route of our flight took us through Tokyo, Japan, a rough flight as Dan was suffering from swimmer's ear and I had a severe headache. Besides not feeling well, neither of us, nor Julie, could eat the food served to us on the plane. The menu of pickled eggs and raw fish was not appealing to us, but Dale didn't have a problem eating.

We arrived in New Guinea, after three years away, to find the new school at Numonohi well established. The mission headquarters was located there as well. The base had grown so much; there were houses everywhere.

After getting Julie and Dan settled in a dormitory, Dale and I eagerly looked forward to returning to the Gimi, to our home and friends in the tribe, and getting settled again.

At dinner that first evening, with our dear friends, Ted and Faye Albrecht, I remarked to Faye how excited we were to get back and settled again in our own home in the Gimi. I can recall her words distinctly as she answered me, "I wouldn't count on it."

Perplexed, I asked, "What on earth do you mean?"

At that point Ted spoke up. Speaking directly to Dale, he said, "Dale, the men on the Field Committee and the Executive Committee in the States all feel that you should be the one to open the new work in the Sepik Region. They need someone to lead a team of new missionaries to work in the lowland regions."

Wow, what a surprise to both of us! We were not prepared for this in the least. No one had even hinted to us of this possibility.

Yet our hearts were set on returning to the Gimi. Dale had longed to get back and teach the people; he had a keen desire to see these babes in Christ grounded in the Word of God. We'd even had new prayer cards printed, that indicated we would be working among the Gimi people.

Dale told Ted that he would surely have to pray about this before making a decision and then he said, "I think I need to go talk to the rest of the men on the Field Committee, to get the thoughts and opinions of them all."

I recalled that while we were on furlough attending NTM's summer mission conference the previous year that Dale was asked to narrate the slides of the Sepik Region, even though he had never visited the Sepik. The Field Committee had decided to open a work in this region, and since no one else from New Guinea was attending the conference at the time, they asked Dale to describe the slides.

At the time I hardly paid attention to the slides or listened to Dale as I was quite content to keep working with the Gimi people. Besides, I thought, who would want to go to the Sepik? The Sepik was the least desirable of all the places I had heard about, full of mosquitoes, malaria, humidity, swamp and the mysterious occult practices and sorcery that everyone knew about. Knowing all I did about it, I certainly had little desire to go there.

I now write this to my shame because I knew at that time about the lost and needy people in that region. Instead, I was thinking of my own desires and creature comforts, not of the needy lost people that God wanted to reach with the gospel.

However, Dale was at least open to the possibility. He rented a mission vehicle and we traveled many miles over the rough unpaved roads to visit mission leaders. Dale felt he needed to talk to each of the men on the Field Committee, so we made the difficult trip to visit with each of them. We traveled first to the Chimbu, and then to the Watut, and Dale met personally with each of the men. Each one assured Dale that he was in agreement with the other leaders. Each one believed Dale was the man to spearhead this new venture and open the new work in the Sepik Region. After praying about it ourselves, Dale too, was convinced that this was God's will for us.

By now, I also felt this was what we should do. I know it was the Lord preparing my heart, for I was actually excited about this new venture, whereas, previously, I had no interest whatsoever in it.

Before we could move to the Sepik we needed to collect our belongings stored in our house in the Gimi. Our shipment of new equipment had not yet arrived in New Guinea, but we could manage on the few possessions we had stored. We realized we might have to buy a few other necessities as well.

Again we rented a vehicle for the trip to the Gimi. As we drove up Mt. Negibi, word spread from village to village that we were back. The people gathered around the house and many were excited to see us after our lengthy furlough.

Before long, Ireso, Dale's faithful language helper, came too. As he looked on, it was obvious to him that we were loading the vehicle to leave, not unloading things to move back into the house! After awhile, he spoke to Dale, "Eravenai?" he asked. "What are you doing?" Dale told him that the Field Committee, "the big men," had asked us to open a new work in the Sepik Region.

It seemed he was silent for a long time. We wondered what he was thinking… *That perhaps we were deserting our beloved Gimi people*. Dale was worried that Ireso might be upset and disappointed to hear we were leaving the Gimi. At last Ireso spoke, saying simply, "That is good. You brought us the Good News. You broke through the rough places (the barriers) and brought the gospel to the Gimi people. Now it's our work to take the Good News to the rest of our people. Your work in the Gimi is finished. Your job is to go reach the Sepik people with the gospel."

Instead of condemning us for leaving, he was giving his blessing and approval for us to begin a new work in the Sepik. With those words, a great weight lifted from Dale's heart, and he was finally certain this was indeed the Lord's will for us to go to the Sepik.

Ireso went on to become one of the key leaders of the Gimi church. What a joy to know he is now in God's presence.

The Story of Zato
By Dale

Now, before we leave the Gimi, here is another story, told in Dale's own words about one little Gimi boy, who grew up to be a wonderful Bible teacher. Arvalee

When Dan was about five years old we were living in the heart of the Gimi tribe. Several Gimi families lived in a nearby village. One little tribal boy named Adahuo, clad only in a loin cloth, would come over daily to our place to play with Dan. As he and Dan played toy cars together they became good friends. When Dan came in the house asking for cookies and milk, Adahuo was right behind him. He was in and around our home for several years.

Adahuo's mother, a widow, wore a mourning necklace made of large, red, seed pods that were about an inch in diameter and it hung nearly to her waist. Her head was always covered with a woven string cap. A cape fashioned from the same woven string hung down her back. The rest of her attire was the typical grass skirt that all Gimi women wore. It covered the front and back of her waist area, with the sides of her hips left bare. She always carried her garden digging stick, leaning heavily upon it, using it as a walking cane. Adahuo was her youngest child, although I knew she had at least one grown son.

Both Dan and Adahuo grew up and Adahuo would eventually go through the tribal initiation. He would no longer live with his mother nor would he be called by his boyhood name. When Gimi boys start their tribal initiations into manhood they take a man's name, so Adahuo became Zato. When Zato was older, he became a Christian, and a very good Bible teacher.

One Christmas, Zato was explaining in the church service, how Jesus was born on the ground where they kept the animals. He said, "Jesus was born on the ground just like we are. He did not have to be, because Jesus is God and He could choose where He wanted to be born. I believe Jesus chose to be born on the ground for He had us ground people in mind long ago. Jesus came down to our level so we could understand clearly all He did for us.

"We dig in the ground to make our gardens and we dig our root crops out of the ground with our hands. We heat rocks and put them in the ground and put the wooden cooking drum over the hot rocks. We line the bottom of the drum with banana leaves and put our food in the wooden drum and steam cook our food. We call it a *mumu* (steam cooking). We sit on the ground and our houses are on the ground to keep them warm. Yes, we are ground people. The Bible says in Ephesians 1:4 that Jesus chose us before He made the world. He saw us ground people and was thinking of us when He picked His place of birth."

Not only had God saved Zato for a very special purpose, He also provided him a very special wife. Remember the story about Bebu, one of the first Gimi men to put his faith in Christ? (See Part 2.6. The Gimi Horse Road, October, 1955.) Bebu returned from the Gimi after Christmas to work on the road again and told about praying for a young Gimi girl who was dead and she came back to life. Well, that young girl grew up and had a daughter. Zato married the daughter whose name is Tarabu. Zato and Tarabu have six children now, and this family is endeavoring to live for and serve the Lord in the Gimi tribal area.

Zato is still teaching the Bible and training others to be teachers of the Word of God. In the seventeen Gimi churches there are over forty men like Zato going out to teach in new villages. Yet there are many tribes in Papua New Guinea still waiting for someone to bring them the Good News of salvation.

God's Network
By Dale

We had returned from Papua New Guinea in 1993 and retired from
the field. We were living in Oregon at that time. Arvalee.

In 2001 we were traveling through the Brisbane airport returning to New Guinea to visit our dear friends. We had just stepped off the airplane from Tasmania, Australia, into the domestic terminal. Arvalee had a colorful Papua New Guinea woven net string bag, known as a *bilum*, hanging from her shoulder. A very distinguished Papua New

Guinea man walked over and spoke to us. "You must be from Papua New Guinea to have a *bilum* like this," he said. We assured him we were and talked for some time. He was flying to Port Moresby, the capital of Papua New Guinea, on the same aircraft. We rode the train together over to the International terminal, and talked more along the way.

Once on the plane, Mr. Misty Baloiloi came over and asked us if we would be in Lae at any time during our visit. We told him yes, that we were indeed planning to visit Lae.

Upon hearing that, he said, "Do give me a call when you arrive in Lae and I will show you around the Wildlife Habitat where they breed the Papua New Guinea *Birds of Paradise* at our University."

Mr. Baloiloi did all that and even more for us when we arrived in Lae. We learned he was the Vice Chancellor of the University of Technology in Lae, the chief administrative officer of the university. This all took place because Mr. Baloiloi spotted the beautiful Papua New Guinea *bilum* Arvalee was carrying. We were all total strangers in a foreign airport, but this colorful *bilum* prompted Mr. Baloiloi to feel a connection of kinship. He felt free to approach us and make our acquaintance because of the *bilum*.

Back in the 1990s Pastor Hagen's wife placed a new *bilum* on my shoulder and said, "I made this *bilum* for you, Dale, to carry your Bible and other books in." That was so meaningful to me. I felt accepted into this special *bilum* society, and I'm thrilled to carry my handmade *bilum* over my shoulder wherever I go in Papua New Guinea, or in the world.

It is hard to explain how the *bilum* links you to the Papua New Guinea people, but it does. It is nothing more than a woven, net string bag, but somehow these woven bags have become a part of the unique culture of Papua New Guinea. *Bilums* are used by men, women, and children. They are evident everywhere; in the city, the village, the bush, at the open air market and supermarket, at the airport, the community school, in the garden, the home, at church; almost anywhere you look. It is not uncommon to see women and teenage girls sitting around talking and working on their *bilums*. They are one of the most useful objects in the country, and, more than this, they reflect the flavor of society and social values at large today. They are a form of culture that nothing can suppress; they are Papua New Guinea's most animate art form.

A baby asleep in a bilum.

In 1983 Air Niugini (Pidgin spelling for New Guinea), Papua New Guinea's airline, published a calendar that was entitled Our Network, and included many beautiful pictures depicting the wide variety of *bilums* made throughout the country. There was a small map on each page of the calendar that showed all the towns that

235

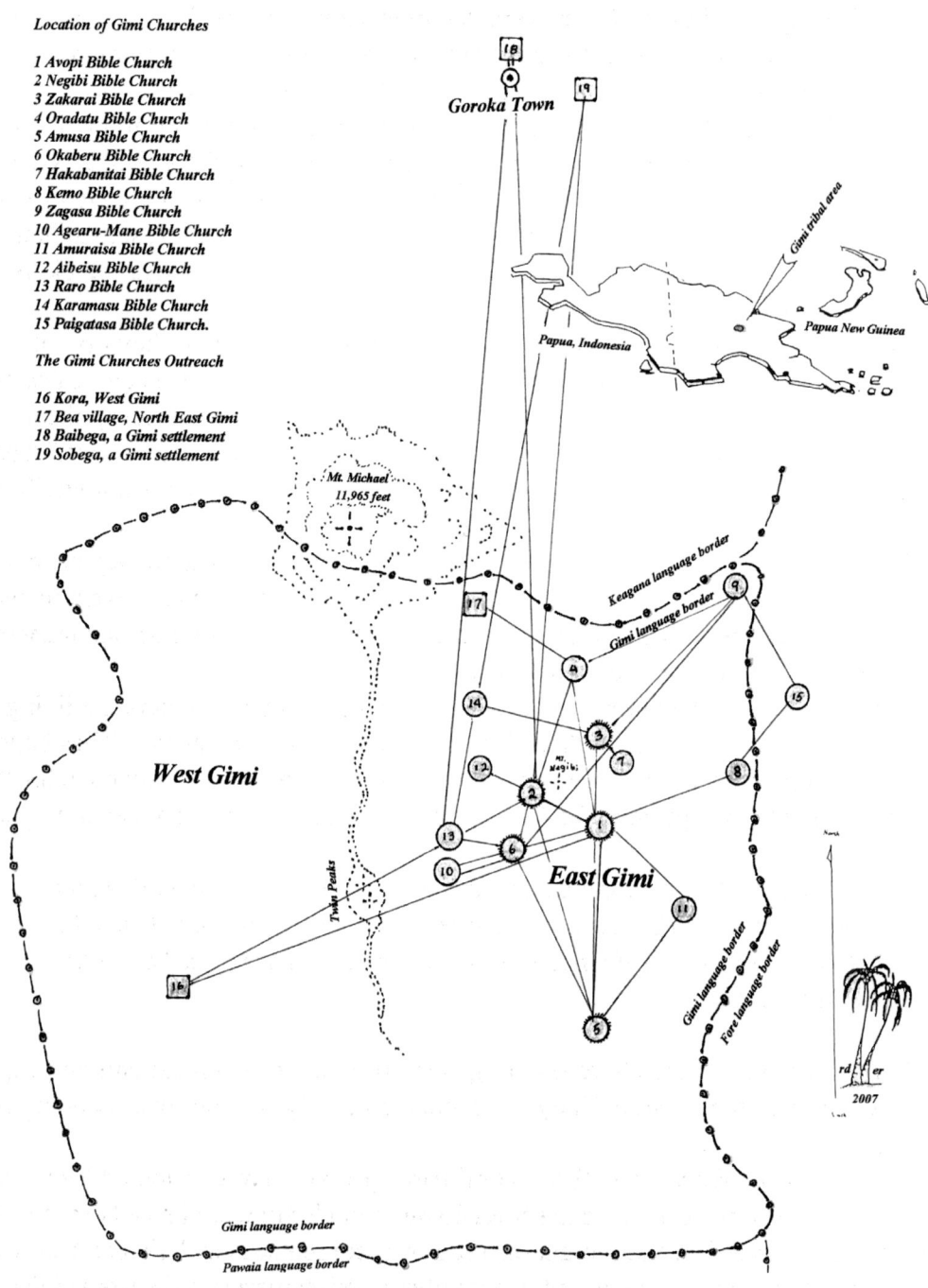

Location of Gimi Churches

1 Avopi Bible Church
2 Negibi Bible Church
3 Zakarai Bible Church
4 Oradatu Bible Church
5 Amusa Bible Church
6 Okaberu Bible Church
7 Hakabanitai Bible Church
8 Kemo Bible Church
9 Zagasa Bible Church
10 Agearu-Mane Bible Church
11 Amuraisa Bible Church
12 Aibeisu Bible Church
13 Raro Bible Church
14 Karamasu Bible Church
15 Paigatasa Bible Church.

The Gimi Churches Outreach

16 Kora, West Gimi
17 Bea village, North East Gimi
18 Baibega, a Gimi settlement
19 Sobega, a Gimi settlement

The Gimi church network © R. Dale Palmer.

236

were serviced by Air Niugini. Lines were drawn to show how the flight patterns of the aircraft reflected the unique net string patterns in the Papua New Guinea *bilums*.

I was recently drawing a new map of the locations of the Gimi churches and their outreaches. The thought came to me: *The Gimi Bible Teachers going from village to village are similar to the aircraft that fly from town to town. The Bible Teachers are really a network of men and women walking from village to village teaching God's Word.*

These seventeen Gimi churches are all indigenous, self-propagating, self-supporting and self-governing New Testament churches. What do those characteristics look like in the Gimi church?

Indigenous. Elder Avo-i Jack from Amusa was telling me that they do not need much money to live on. He said, "We have our gardens to feed us, we have a few coffee trees and we can sell the beans for money to buy a few things we need, like salt to cook with, kerosene for our lamp, a few clothes and sometimes we buy books." These Gimi believers are so natural and relaxed and at ease in their local surroundings. To me that spells indigenous.

Self-Propagating. The Gimi tribal people marry into other clans so they have relatives in different clans. When they hear some good news, they naturally want to share it with family members living in other places. These Gimi believers are spontaneous, their families close-knit and very communal.

Self-Supporting. The Gimi missionaries, Elders and Bible Teachers are living by faith. These dear people are expanding God's Kingdom in the Gimi Nation. They believe God will meet their needs as they trust Him to keep His Word as in Matthew 6:33, "… But seek ye first the kingdom of God,… and all these things shall be added unto you."

> *When national missionaries rely on foreign money for their daily support, their ministries often turn into jobs. If that money should be cut off, they will feel the need to look for other employment like in the secular world.*

Self-Governing. These churches are governed by their own local church people, not someone from the outside. They are accountable only to God, who is doing this great work.

Ten years after World War II the Gimi tribal people were considered Stone Age people by the Western world. God has been doing a wonderful work in the Gimi Nation. Today the Gimi church leaders organize their own conferences and choose their own keynote speakers. They have sent out two families as missionaries to the Kora dialect in the far away West Gimi. These families are supported with money and prayer by their local home churches. Their Bible Teachers, Elders, Deacons and Missionaries have never been to a traditional Bible school. These church leaders have been taught the same way the Apostle Paul taught Timothy, in II Timothy 2:2.

> *"...the things that thou hast heard of me*
> *...the same commit thou to faithful men,*
> *who shall be able to teach others also."*

This is how we started teaching the Gimi leaders, and they are still following the Apostle Paul's instructions.

These Gimi Churches are truly a network of God's matchless design.

One giant step in the growth of the Gimi church was when Trevor McIlwain came from the Philippines to share how to teach the Bible chronologically. One basically teaches the Bible stories the way they are arranged according to sequence in time, highlighting the attributes of God, nature of man and opposition of Satan. We began by starting in Genesis 1:1 and taught the key redemptive stories of the Bible in the order in which they happen.

Before this, I randomly selected stories from the Bible to teach the people, or I would select a topic to teach, like the Holiness of God, or the Trinity. The people didn't know if Abraham and Moses or other Old Testament characters were friends of Jesus and Paul or not. They were confused, to say the least, in regards to how it all fit together historically.

The chronological teaching fits in well with the Gimi mind set and the way they remember their ancestors. Often times it is a grandparent teaching the village children about their great-great-great grandparents in an orderly way, going back as far as they can remember, sometimes relating stories from five and six generations of ancestors. This constant review helped these tribal people develop remarkable memories.

John White, who followed us in the Gimi work, fully embraced Trevor's explanation of the chronological outline. The believers went back to their home at Amusa village in the South Gimi and started sharing this new concept with the local Amusa believers. Then John felt the Northern Gimi churches, a five hour hike away, should also hear about this wonderful new way of teaching. John shared with the church leaders from Negibi, Avopi, and O-a-beru the concept of teaching chronologically.

The Gimi grapevine traveled very fast in the northern churches. These three churches began receiving requests from churches and villages in the areas that had not heard this new teaching, asking someone to come and help them understand these new ideas. The response to the chronological teaching was like dark rain clouds had been lifted and the warm sunshine was coming out and embracing the Gimi churches. This method of teaching was clearly understood by the Gimi church leaders, and it caught on like a windblown wildfire.

In English, Trevor McIlwain calls this new chronological teaching Building on Firm Foundations. The tribal people in Papua New Guinea call it, *Planim Pos*. The meaning is: to sink house posts deeply into the ground.

We all know that building a house without a good foundation is foolish, because the building may not stand when a storm hits. The Gimi people also understand how to build a strong house that will not fall down when the storms come. It is similar to the Bible teaching in Luke 6:47 and 48, "Whosoever cometh to me, and heareth my sayings, and doeth them, I will show you to whom he is like: He is like a man which built an house, and digged deep, and laid the foundation on a rock: and when the flood arose, the stream beat vehemently upon that house, and could not shake it: for it was founded upon a rock".

This new teaching method made the Bible stories come alive and brought revival to the churches. A renewed love for the Lord Jesus Christ came to many. The understanding of the Old Testament redemptive stories was the foundation needed to build strong believers and churches. They now understood the Old Testament meaning when John the Baptist said, "Behold the Lamb of God, which taketh away the sin of the world," (John 1:29). The Bible stories of Abel offering a lamb, of Abraham finding a substitute for his son on Mt. Moriah, and the Passover Lamb, all took on new meaning for the Gimi believers.

Chronological Bible teaching and the Gimi church growth started in the early 1980s and continues to this day, 2007. It is incredibly encouraging to see how these Churches and Bible Teachers obey the great commission and crisscross their nation to humbly share what they know.

Bible teachers like Zato, from Negibi, took young Soma to train him when he was teaching the believers at O-ra-datu. During the time Zato was teaching the believers there, he was called back to Negibi for a few days. O-tu-bare, better known as O-tu, sent word that he could fill in until Zato could return. O-tu asked Zato what part of the lesson he was teaching. "I'm just ready to start the story of Moriah," he answered.

"Good. That is where I will start teaching," O-tu answered. O-tu is from O-a-beru. Siri-o, from A-bo-pi also went down and helped teach the O-ra-datu believers.

It is wonderful to see these different Bible Teachers from the three churches teaching together as a team. The churches seem to be stronger when more than one man is teaching them.

Shortly after this, Ane-avu from O-a-beru went to Raro to teach the unbelievers there in that village. Orio from A-bo-pi went with Ane-avu for some time but later had to drop out.

A few years later, Soma from Negibi, took A-mo-tha-bi and Ate-pisa with him to teach believers and unbelievers at Ai-be-isu.

This method of teaching was easy to reproduce in new disciples and leaders. Three faithful men, from O-ra-datu who were taught by Zato, O-tu and Soma, are now going to the village of Bea sharing God's Word with the hungry Bea people. Meu, Ba-tha-mo and Rex were asked by the Bea people if they would come and teach them the Bible. I know Bea is a long hard walk from O-ra-datu.

Today the Raro Bible Church has Taitus (Titus) and Benedik teaching 17 people to read and write in the Gimi settlement of Baibega, near the town of Goroka.

There is another young couple from Raro who are teaching unsaved Gimis from Sobega settlement, also near Goroka. Zato encouraged Rame-i to teach this group.

Three brothers from Tha-a-rai were helping the believers at Ha-abani-tai to come to a clear understanding of the new teaching. A couple from the village of Aramasu came to the Tha-a-rai Bible Church and asked if someone would come and teach their people. "We will look after him," they said. Thabiava, better known as Thabi, the word for sugar or sugarcane in Gimi, said he would go and teach them.

The stories go on and on, but these few may suffice to show you the handiwork of God's beautiful network of Gimi churches.

As Air Niugini has its flights marked out from town to town, their airplanes are crisscrossing the nation of Papua New Guinea to service all their passengers. The flight coordinator has a unique network of flights on his map.

The same is true about the Gimi Bible Teachers. They are crisscrossing the Gimi Nation on foot to share God's Word with those who desire to hear.

God is the Master Coordinator of this great network among the Gimi Church leaders. His bond servants have been obeying His command to go and teach for many years. God has chosen these faithful men and women to face the hardships of life so they can proclaim His message to lost tribal men, women, boys and girls who God is personally drawing to Himself.

What more can be said, "The works of the Lord are great, sought out of all them that have pleasure therein", Psalms 111:2.

Map of Gimi Villages

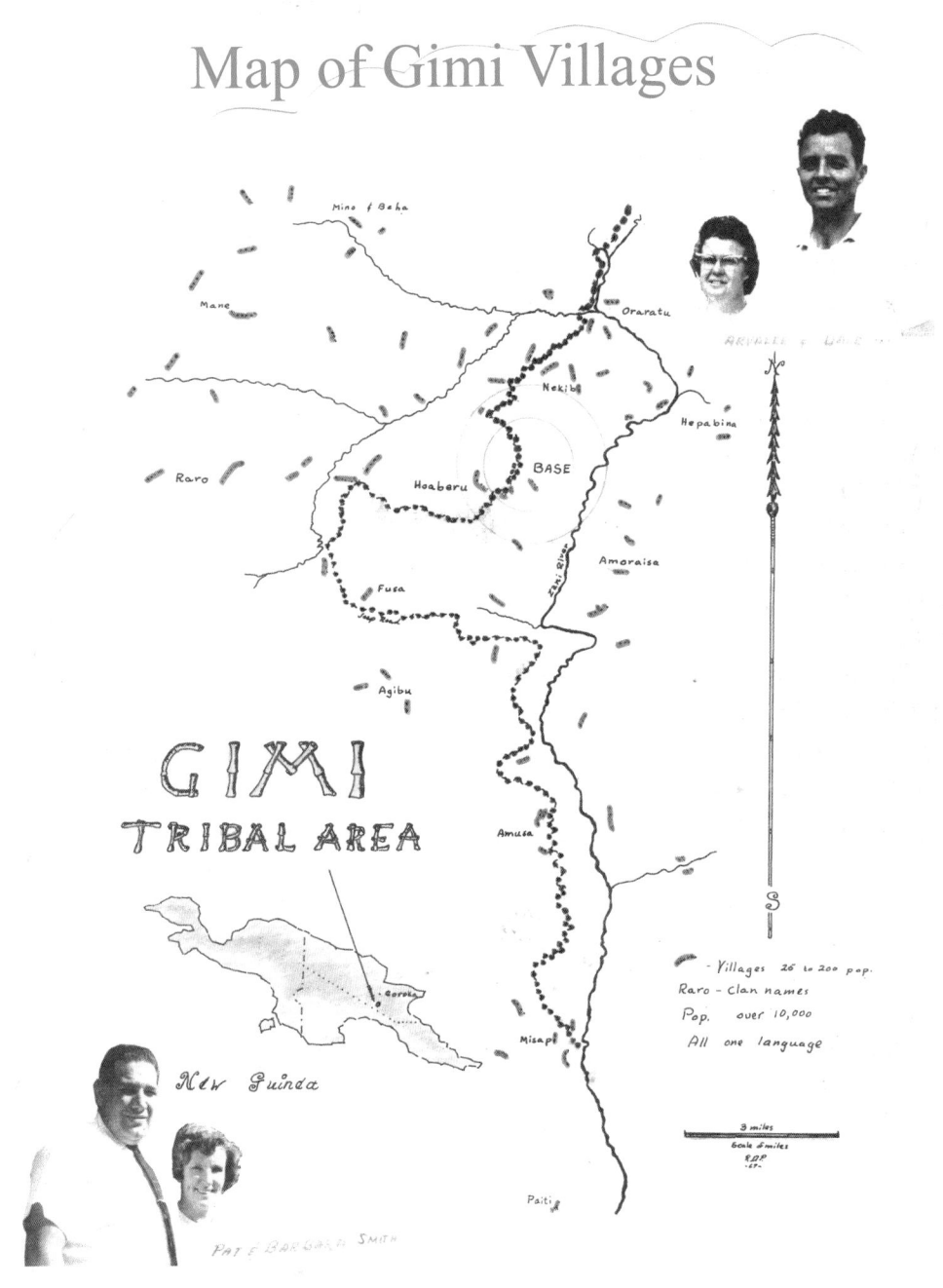

GIMI
TRIBAL AREA

- Villages 25 to 200 pop.
Raro - Clan names
Pop. over 10,000
All one language

New Guinea

PAT & BARBARA SMITH

The Gimi and Negibi

The north slope of Mt. Negibi.

Esema in 1997, an old man here, the
Gimi chief who gave Dale the land on
Mt. Negibi.

New Guinea Impatiens.

Negibi base after frame house and jeep road, about 1965.

Visiting the Negibi base site in 2001.

Early Days in the Gimi

Early morning, the Gimi valley is covered with a blanket of clouds.

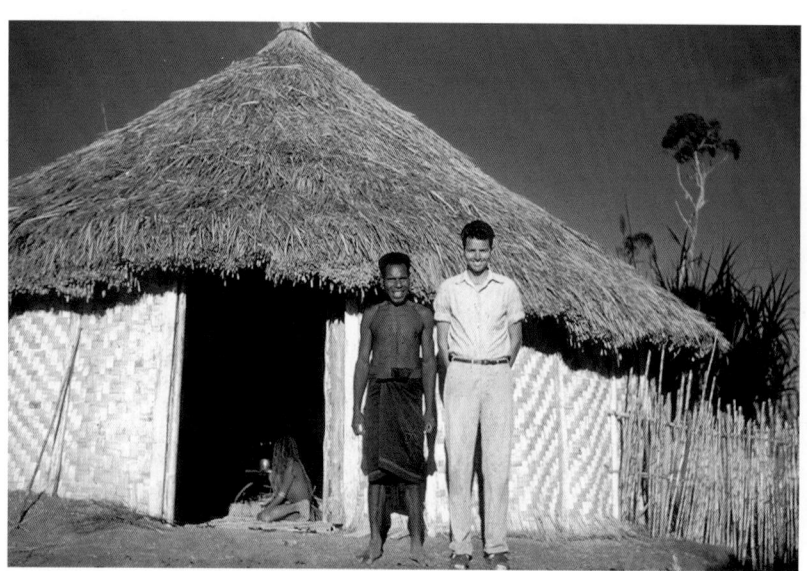

Meniba and Dale in front of the first house at Negibi.

Gimi Travel Options

Modern day mountain road to the Gimi.

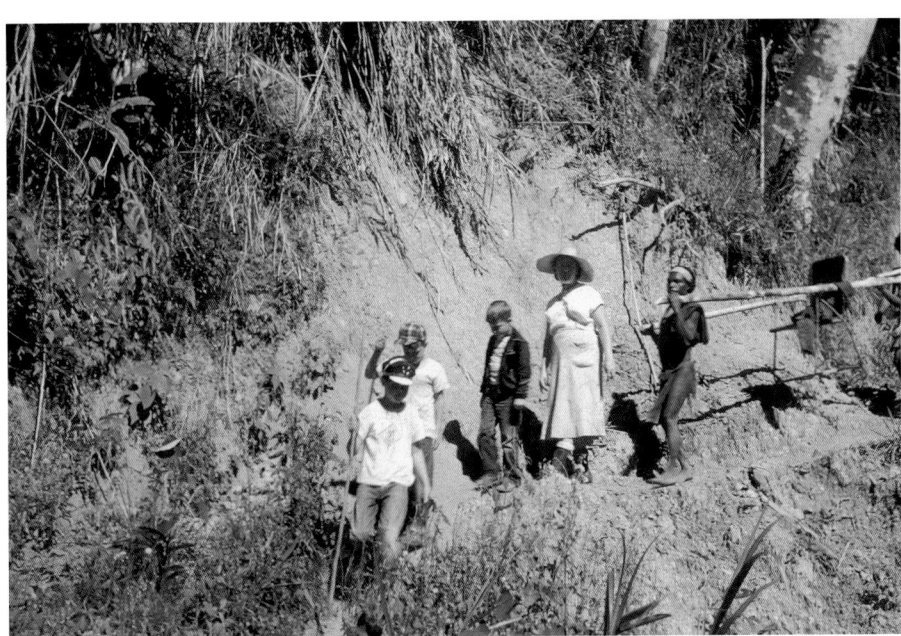

On the trail to the Gimi, a three day hike.

The Water Race

The water race, a framework of poles supported the Pandanus logs.

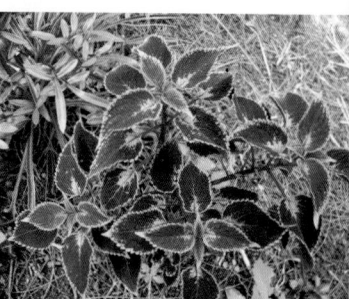

The water fills the barrel at the wash house; Althea Lawrence
is at the wringer.

Another view of the wash house and water race. The washing was done
in tubs with rub-boards but we didn't have to carry water!

Years later the Pandanus was replaced with bamboo. Then in the
1960s a 1/2 inch polyethylene pipe was used to bring a constant
flow of spring water to each house.

247

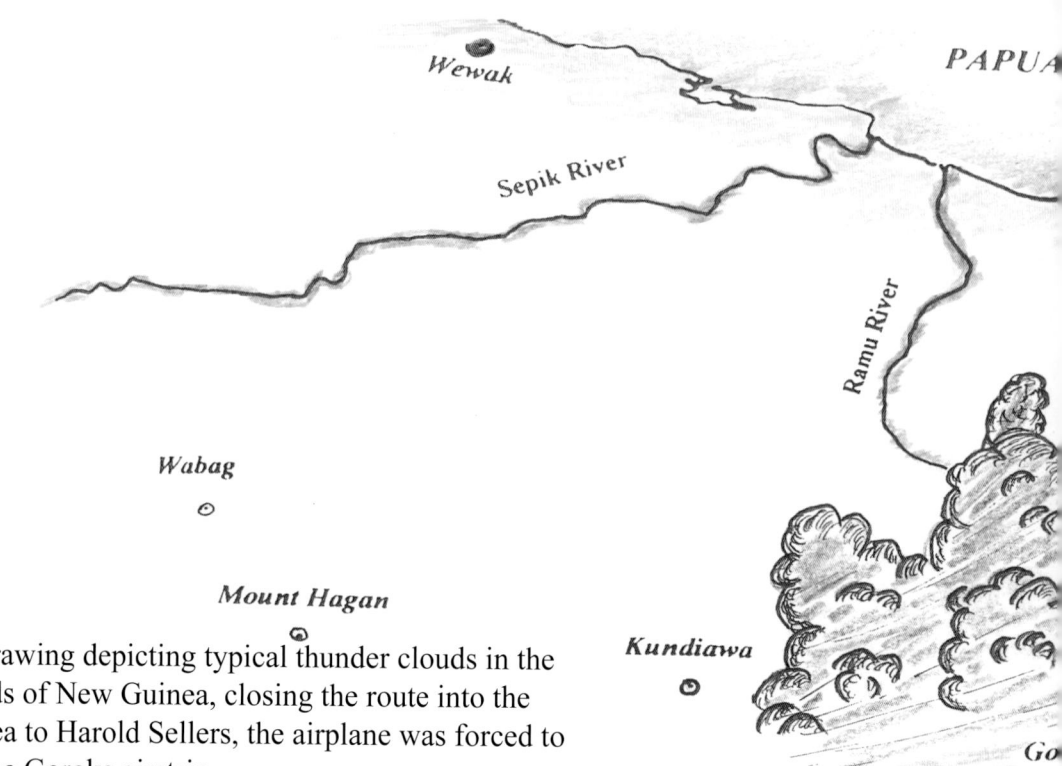

PAPUA

Wewak

Sepik River

Ramu River

Wabag

Mount Hagan

Kundiawa

Dale's drawing depicting typical thunder clouds in the Highlands of New Guinea, closing the route into the Sepik area to Harold Sellers, the airplane was forced to land at the Goroka airstrip.

North

South

Mt. Michael
11,950 Feet

Go

GIMI TRI

Gulf of Papua

248

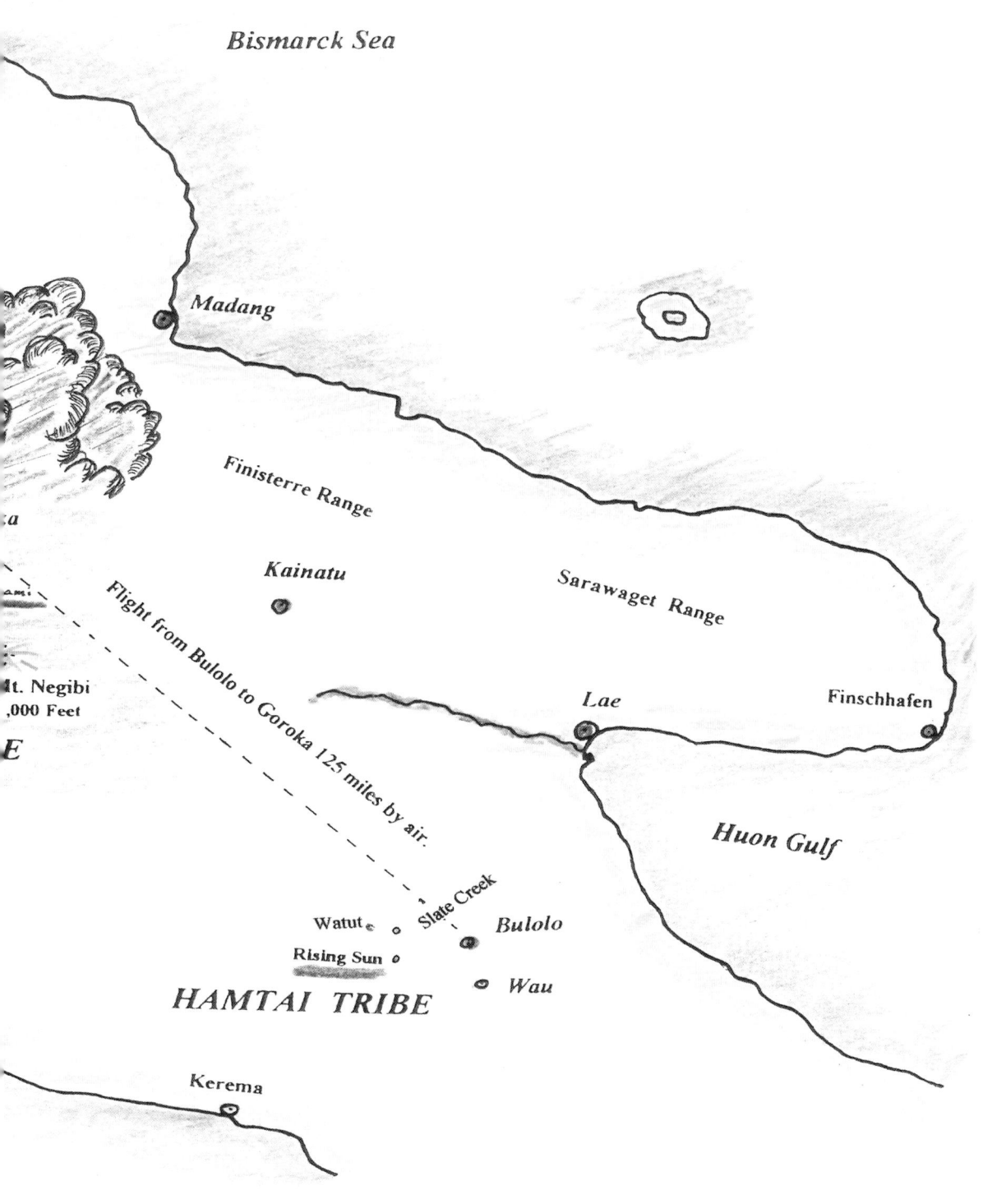

Bismarck Sea

Madang

Finisterre Range

Kainatu

Sarawaget Range

Mt. Negibi
,000 Feet

Lae

Finschhafen

Flight from Bulolo to Goroka 125 miles by air.

Huon Gulf

Slate Creek

Watut

Bulolo

Rising Sun

Wau

HAMTAI TRIBE

Kerema

Making Lumber with a Pitsaw

The pitsaw crew learned many skills like using a level and reading a ruler.

The pitsaw is set up on a hillside, a small place is leveled to stand and a pole frame is built to support the log that will become lumber.

The pitsaw crew at work, they lift the saw and plunge it down following the charcoal string line markings, over and over. Wedges hold the new planks apart so the saw will not bind.

The pitsaw crew making planks.

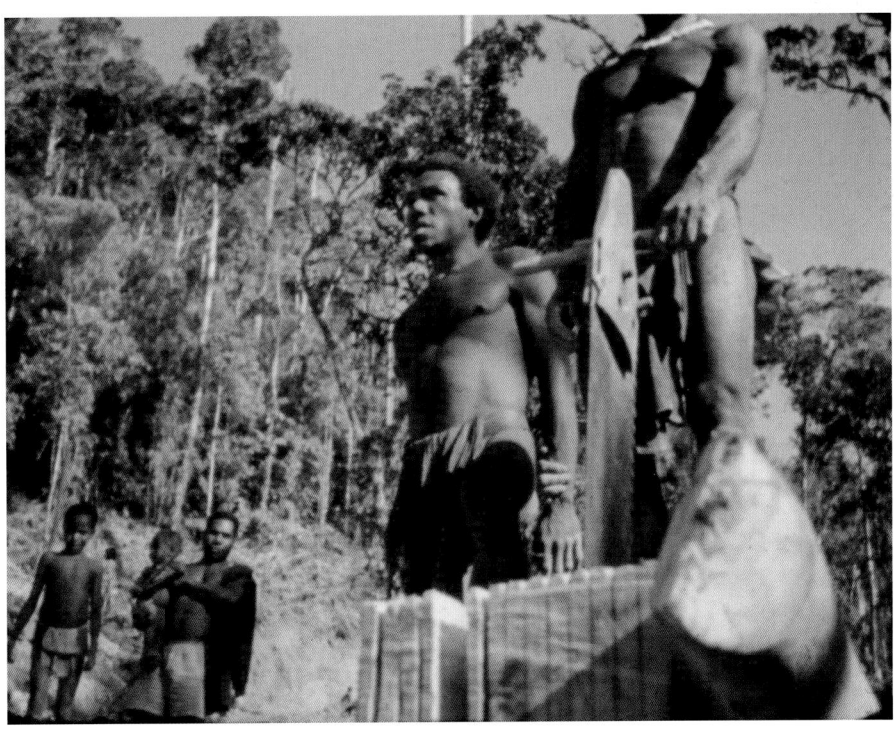

Very hard work and the men trade places often.

Making Lumber with a Power Saw

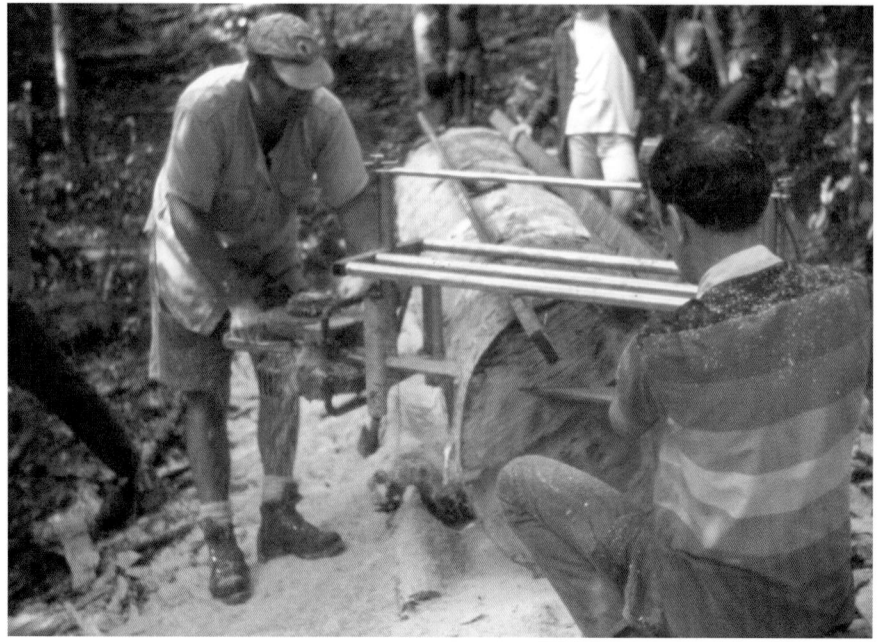

Cutting slabs with an Alaska attachment on the Homelite chainsaw.

Lyle Mumford and Ben Kulp making the first cut.

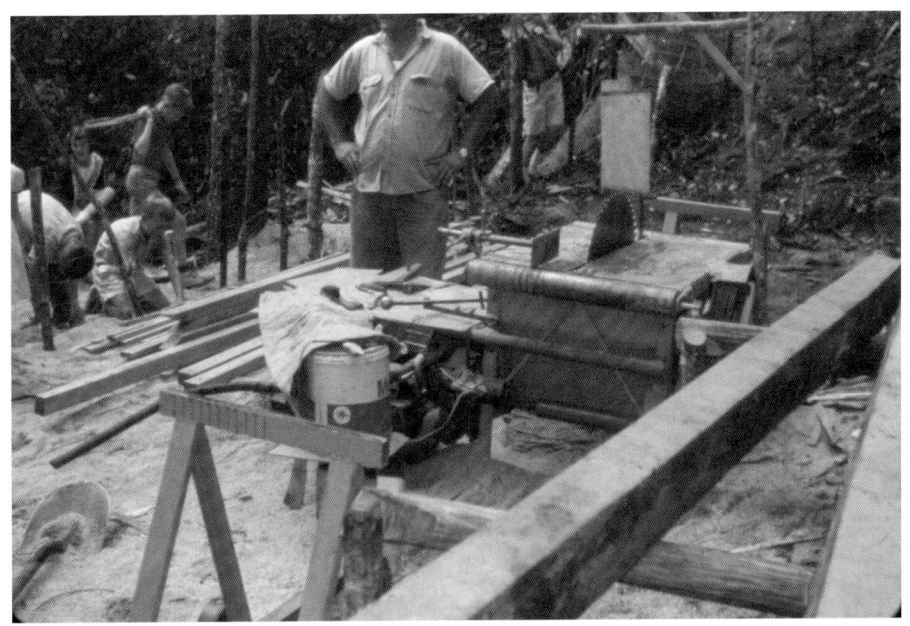

Eric Barham, Alan and Lena Barham's son and Barbara Smith's cousin built this sawmill for us. Powered by a Volkswagen engine it was portable; we took the sawmill to the tree.

The top slab being cut on the sawmill.

Our Dear New Guinea Friends

Ireso's family.

Ireso, Dale's faithful
helper and language
assistant.

Siri-o and
his family,
Ireso's son.

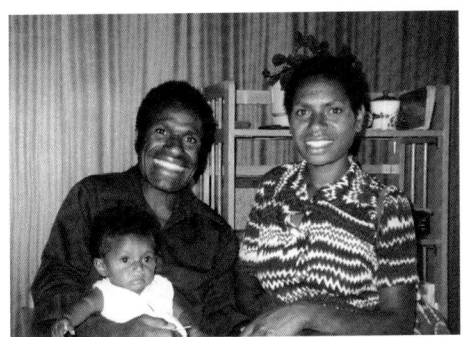

Zato and Tarabu with
their first baby, 1984.

Zato and Tarabu with family.

Somaisa, David and Lydia, Zato's
oldest children, during their high
school days.

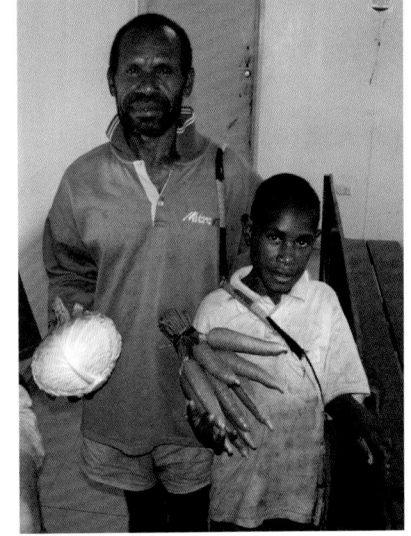

Inabera and son.

Inabera and his family bring
dinner in the Gimi. Then he
shows up at the Goroka airport!

The bilum holds
a cabbage and
bunch of carrots
just fine.

More New Guinea Friends

Balus, missionary to the Kora area and Dale with a chronological book.

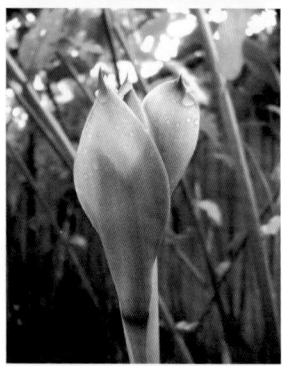

Aba-ena hiked about an hour to come see us.

Hugs for all.

Somaisa and Lydia and their children.

Saubai and Pat had played together as children.

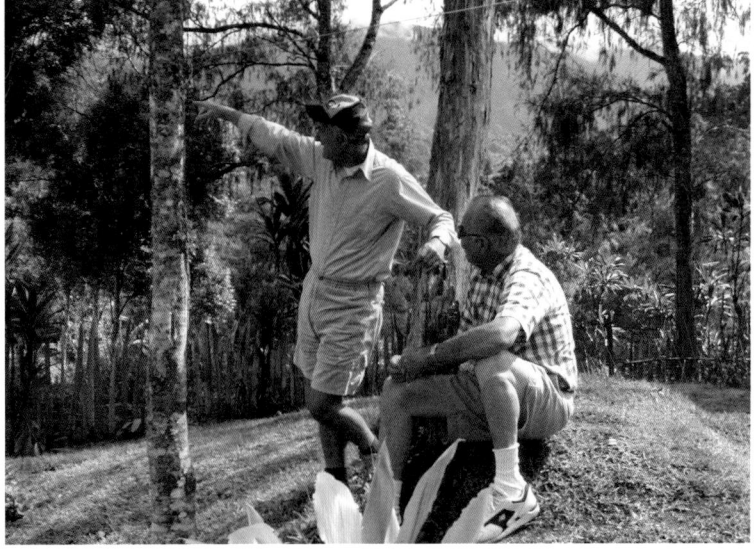

Arvalee and Ani-ani-mo, who in 1957 helped to keep me from falling by holding my arms on my first trip into the Gimi.

John describing the three day walk into the Kora area.

A Few of Our Missionary Partners

The Smith Family, left to right:
Lorene, Ken, Barbara, Jimmy,
Pat and Donnie, early 1960s.

Pat and Barbara Smith, 1997.

John and Gail Middleton, 2001.

Dale with John and Lynn White, 1997.

John and Lynn White, 2001.

Dave and Barbara Schrag, 1982.

The Prohaskas, Palmers and Kellers at
Maprik, early 1970s.

Pete and Joy Palmer, Jeff
and Chris, 1982.

Julie Dale Palmer.

Tom and Corinne Palmer.

Conference time at May River.

Making a Mumu

The wood is laid with the rocks piled on top.

The hole is ready and the rocks are heating.

The women prepare the food.

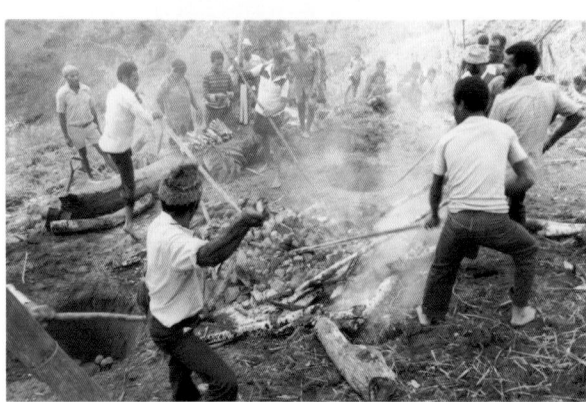

The men flip the rocks into the hole.

Almost time to put the mumu together.

Fresh banana and fern leaves are used to cover the rocks and line the hole.

Water is poured in from a bamboo.

The mumu is sealed with leaves and earth.

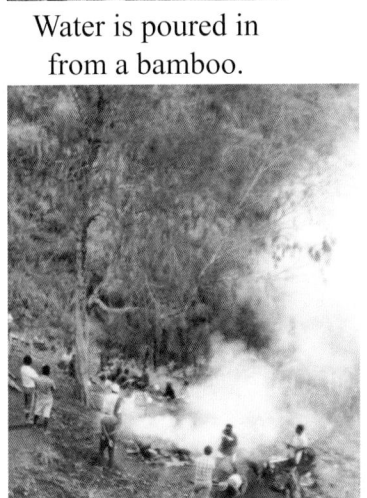

Steam rises; everyone waits as the food is cooking.

Women and men remove the food.

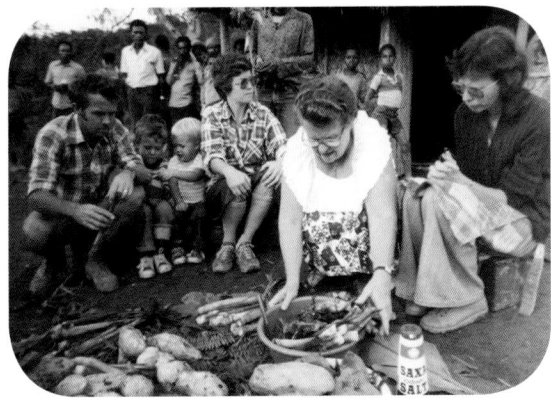

Dinner is served!

The Bilum

Bilums are given as gifts, Arvalee with Mu-u-nabi and Sadieboro.

Colorful bilums.

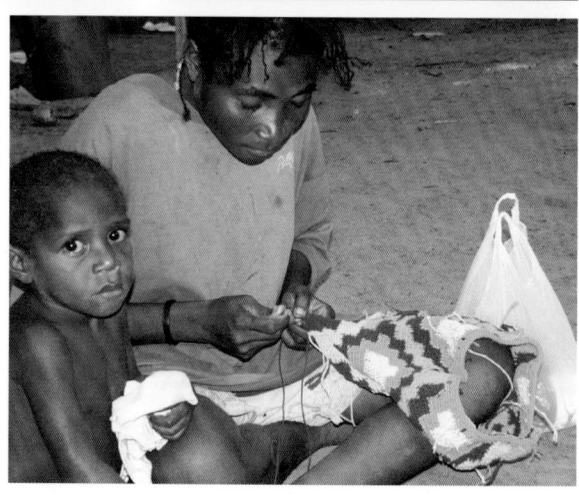

Making a bilum, adding the final touches.

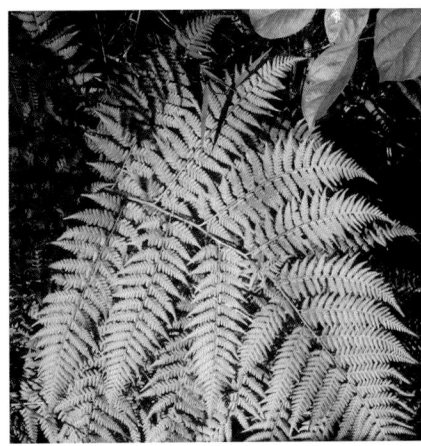

Ireso's grandson in his bilum.

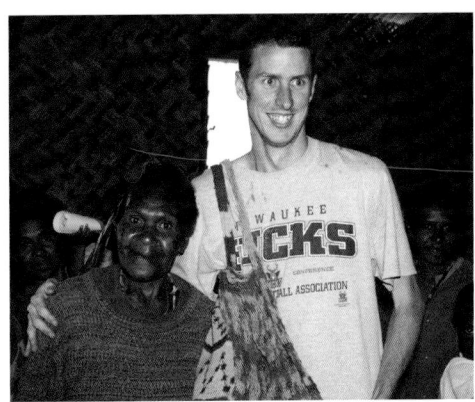

Anthony being gifted with bilums
by a kind grandmother.

Many colorful designs are woven
into a bilum.

Mr. Baloiloi and his Son, we met in
the Brisbane Airport because we were
carrying a bilum.

Unique Gimi Items

A carved wooden bowl.

Necklace close-up.

Arvalee's opossum tooth necklace.

Arrow heads.

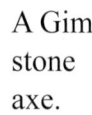

A Gimi stone axe.

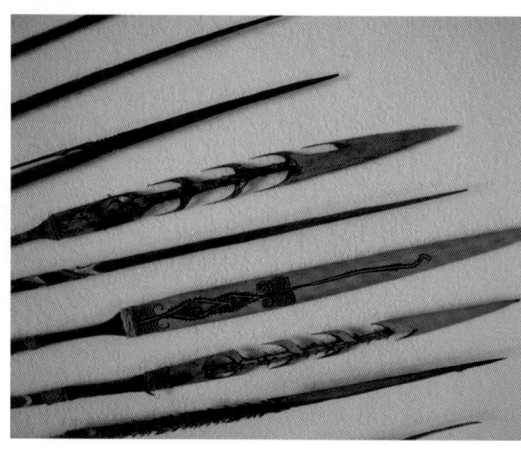

50th Anniversary of NTM in PNG

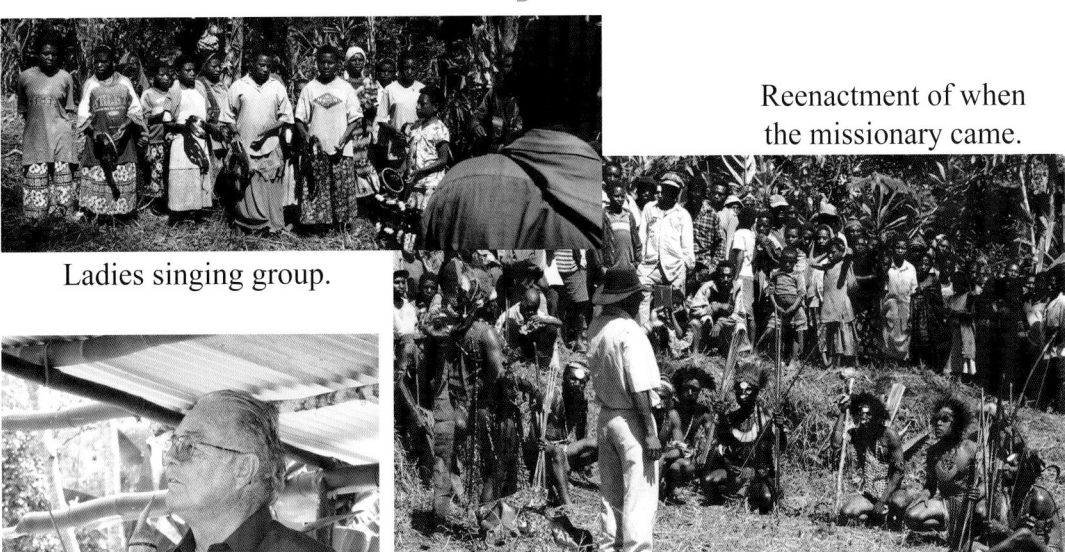

Ladies singing group.

Reenactment of when
the missionary came.

Dale sharing about the
early days.

Tom Palmer, Larry Brown and FNBC
leaders also spoke.

Attendees at the 50th anniversary.

Hiking and Bridges

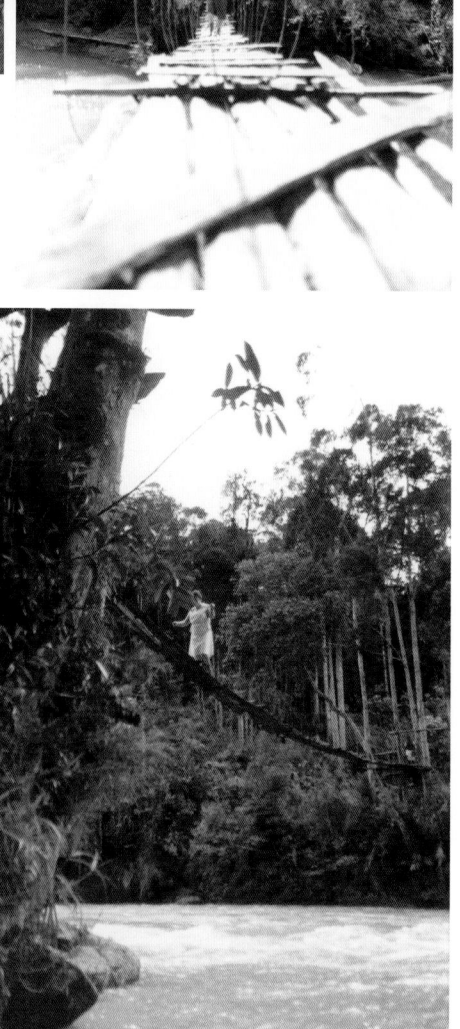

Clockwise: Hiking a trail in the South Gimi, bridge made of jungle vines and axe hewn decking, more than half way across, descending the bridge ramp.

In the Bush

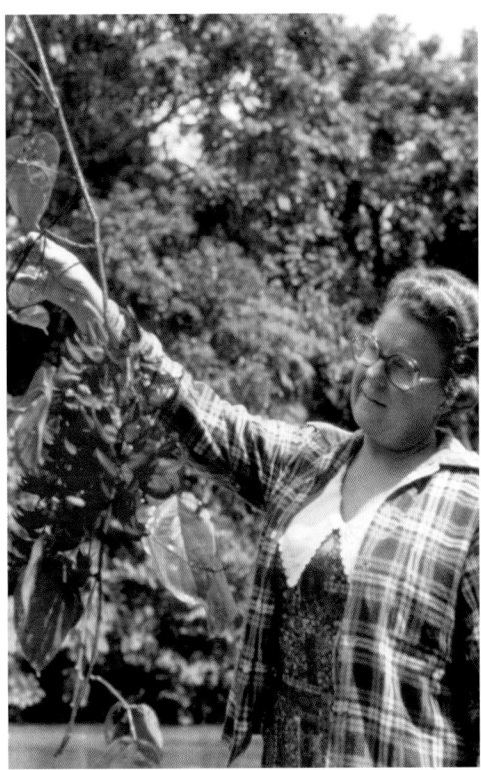

Clockwise: Dale by a clear stream. Arvalee with Jungle Flame or New Guinea Creeper. Dale, in his element, the jungle!

Maprik and Rabaul

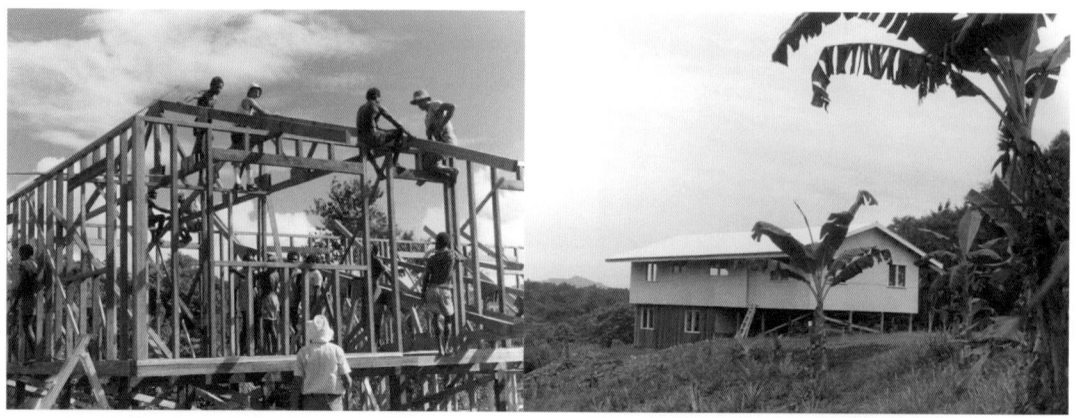

Work on our house in Maprik.

Finished Maprik house.

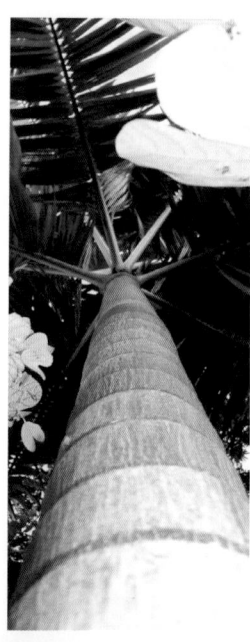

Clockwise: Dale looking toward a volcano in Rabaul.
NTM house in Rabaul. NTM house after the volcano.

Travels

The Arvalee Townland sign.
Department of Environment (DOE)
Arvalee Depot and North Ireland
Electric Service (NIES) Area Office.

Dale and Pastor Hagen with sons
Tama and Paul.

Christmas with our kids, 1981.

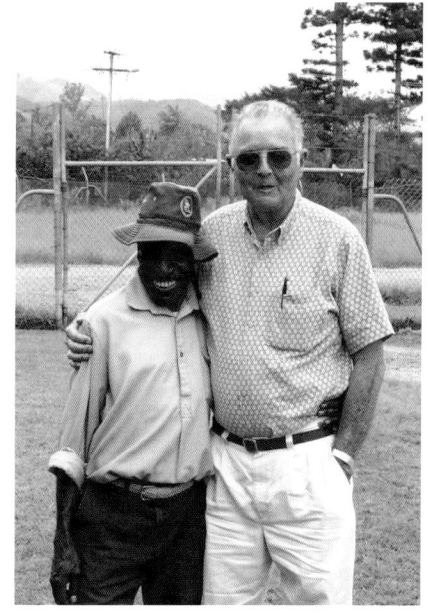

Dale with Pastor Hagen at
the NTMA hanger in Goroka,
2001.

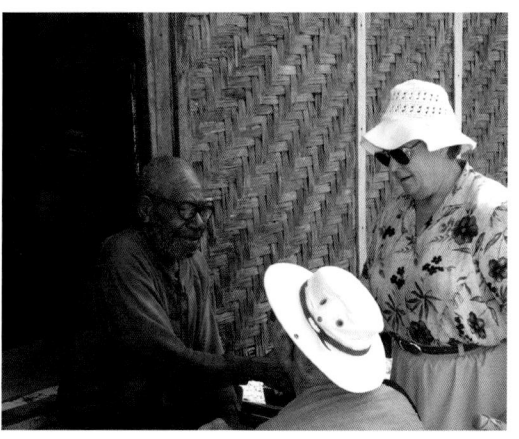

Visiting with Jonah in
the Yagaria, 2001.

The Gimi Church at Negibi

The Fellowship of National Bible Churches at Negibi, Gimi, Papua New Guinea.

Arvalee speaking to the women
in an open air meeting.

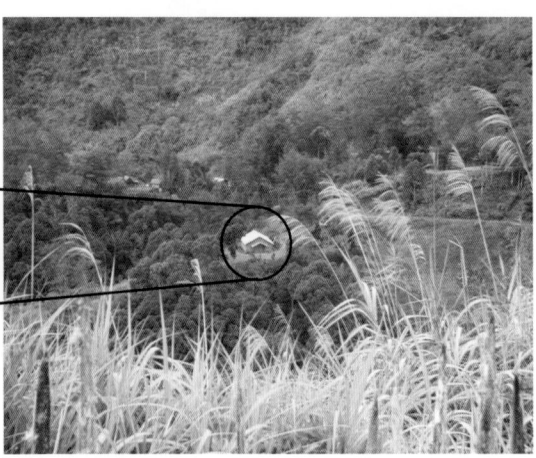

The church
building at Negibi.

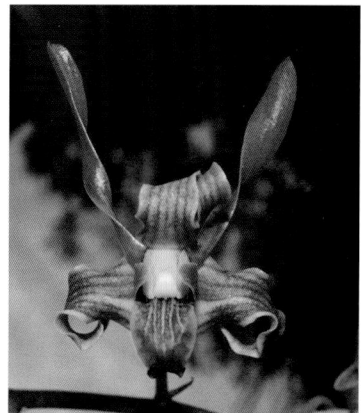

Anthony sitting on the men's side.

The women and girls all sit together.

Dale speaking in Pidgin and Zato interpreting into Gimi.

Some of the church leaders and missionaries to their own people.

The Gimi New Testament

Zato preaching in Gimi; John translates Gimi back into English so we can understand.

Gimi New Testament: "God Is Speaking".

Men and women are diligently following the scripture reading in their own language.

~PART FIVE~

Starting Over

Chapter 13

Our Third Term; First Days in the Sepik, 1972
By Arvalee

Shortly after our return from the Gimi trip, we were able to move to the Sepik Region. It was such a great relief to both of us to have Ireso's blessing to make this move.

"Bravo Hotel, Bravo Hotel, Foxtrot Gulf."

"Go ahead Foxtrot Gulf," I answered.

"Hi, Honey. How're you doing?" Dale asked.

"Fine," I responded. "I was just waiting to hear from you. Do you have any news?"

"Well, I found us a place to live, but it's sure not much to brag about. It's in a village. I couldn't find anything in Maprik town, but the people in the village are willing to rent us a little house. It's just down the road a ways from the mission property, about a mile from town."

"That sounds great; how much do they want for it?"

He replied, "It's only three kina a month, (approximately three dollars) but it's very small, about 10 ft. x 15 ft., and there is no floor. We'd be living on the ground. It used to be a trade store, but a baby died there so no one wants to live in it. It has a thatch roof, *pangal* walls (the sago palm leafstalk or stem, used for making walls, etc.) and a dirt floor. It's nothing fancy," he said.

"We've lived on the ground before, so we'll do alright. I'll book the next flight with *MAF* (Mission Aviation Fellowship) and come down right away," I promised.

He thought that was just great! After several weeks of separation, we would be together again. By this time, Julie and Dan were settled in a dormitory, so I felt good about leaving them in school at Numonohi.

It was November, 1972. Dale and Tom Palmer, along with Oliver and Alice Smith, had booked a plane with *MAF* to fly from the Highlands to Ambunti, located on the Sepik River. Ambunti was to be the supply station for our upriver and downriver allocations. Oliver and Alice had found a small frame house to rent in Ambunti. It was just out of town at the end of the airstrip, on the edge of the jungle. The house was quite isolated. Ambunti consisted of a Post Office, a Government post and one or two trade stores, where a few simple food items were available.

Dale had gone with Tom to survey the region and find us a place to live at Maprik, where the orientation base was to be located. Tom and Chuck Turner had done the initial patrol of the Sepik region a few years before. At that time, they had negotiated with the local people and the Government for the piece of undeveloped land about a mile from Maprik. This, too, was a quiet, sleepy little town, boasting a Post Office, a police station and two or three little trade stores where we could buy the most basic necessities. Maprik was located about 35 miles north of the Sepik River, and the coastal town of Wewak was 80 miles northeast. We would shop for the bulk of our supplies in Wewak, but Maprik was designated as the headquarters for the Sepik work.

After arrangements were made with *MAF* to fly to the Sepik, I told Julie and Dan good-bye. We would see them again at Christmas during the school break, when they would join us at Maprik.

I left Goroka for the Sepik in a small *MAF* Cessna 206 a week before Thanksgiving. After flying about an hour, the terrain below us changed from high, rugged, tree covered mountains to the flat lowlands of the Sepik. There below us, the mighty, sprawling river was visible as it wound snake like, back and forth through the flat terrain. As I looked out the airplane window I was amazed to see mile upon mile of jungle and swamp. I had never seen such lush terrain! Glimpses of swamp water, glistening from the sunlight overhead, could be seen through the thick canopy of green jungle. This swamp was made from water backed up from the slow flowing Sepik River during the rainy season.

As the airplane lost altitude, even before landing, I began to feel the oppressive heat. Before I realized it, the plane had touched down on the Ambunti airstrip. I could see my smiling husband waiting for me as the plane taxied toward the end of the airstrip. It was great seeing him again! He knew I didn't care where we lived. After being married almost 25 years, the only thing that mattered to me was to be there with him, to join him in the task of starting this new work.

Waiting with him were Oliver and Alice Smith, Tom Palmer, Don Meyer and Heinz Rempel. Don and Heinz and their families were two of the new missionaries planning to work in the Sepik with us.

We all walked back to the little house on the edge of the jungle. The men were all excited about the survey they would be going on the next day. That was the main topic of conversation that night. Tom, Oliver, Heinz, Don and Dale took turns telling about their plans. They would be looking for new tribal groups where the new missionaries would work.

That little two bedroom house was bursting at the seams as we all bedded down for the night. All was silent in the surrounding jungle, except for the sounds of insects and the occasional call of a night bird.

The next morning the five men set off in a 40 foot dugout canoe powered by an outboard motor. They had planned for a week long trip on the Sepik River. Don was interested in opening a work in the Iwam Tribe, located on the May River, a tributary of the Sepik, while Heinz was still surveying the area.

We two women watched as the canoe pulled out into the deep water and headed upstream on the mighty Sepik River. Alice and I waved good-bye, and headed back to the little house, walking through the sleepy little town and down the length of the airstrip. Two other missionary families with another mission group lived a short walk from the Smith's house. Also, the Australian Army was camped on the other side of the airstrip from their house. The national people always seemed friendly, but Alice had not been there long enough to make any acquaintances. In spite of the isolated location, we really felt quite safe.

While the men were away, we two ladies kept busy so the time would pass more quickly. In the mornings we did chores and sometimes walked to town to collect the mail, or buy a loaf of bread. At night, after lighting the kerosene Petromax lamp, we spent the time sitting at the table writing letters. I had tacked a pretty little card with a scripture verse on the wall beside the place where I was sitting. It was sent to me by a friend months before, and I carried this little card with me in my writing case. It gave me a homey feeling, even though I was still living out of a suitcase!

Scared Stiff
By Arvalee

One night, after supper and cleaning up our dishes, Alice and I had just settled down at the table, listening to the hum of night insects in the surrounding jungle.

The heat from the lamp only magnified the oppressive heat of the tropics, compelling us to leave the solid wooden door open, with only the screen door latched. We had even left the curtains open over the two windows, hoping to catch a breath of moving air. This heat and humidity was new to me. I had only known the coolness of the Highlands before.

As we sat there, our feelings of tranquility and peace were suddenly shattered as the entire house began to shake and the screened windows and door started rattling. As if the insects were aware of what was happening, the jungle all at once had become completely silent. Then, a noise came out of the jungle, sounding like a giant sheet of plywood being slapped down on a large body of water! Our hearts were instantly terror stricken!

Thoughts ran swiftly through my mind, *that sound couldn't have come from the river, it's too far away. The stream near the house is too small. It's only a foot or so wide and very shallow. What could it be?... It must be evil spirits,* my thoughts continued.

Even while those thoughts were going through my mind, we both sprang into action. One of us quickly closed the door and locked it, while the other pulled the thin curtains over the windows.

As I sat down again at the table, my eyes fell upon the card with the scripture verse on it. It read, "In quietness and in confidence shall be your strength" (Isaiah 30:15). That verse calmed my heart and reminded me that God didn't want us to be fearful, but wanted us to put our trust in Him and He would give us strength. I said to my companion, "I believe evil spirits are trying to scare us. Satan wants to frighten us, so we'll tell our husbands we can't work here in the Sepik. Let's pray!" So we prayed and the Lord quieted our hearts. We were both determined that Satan wouldn't have a victory, so we prayed and read our Bibles together, looking to the Lord to calm our fears.

After this experience, we changed some of our habits. We made sure our outside chores like getting water from the stream and filling the kerosene lamps were done early. We didn't want to go outside again if at all possible. At dusk, we'd close the door and pull the curtains. We no longer went outside after dark, not even to use the outhouse! We never did learn the source of this strange and frightening noise. We honestly believed it was an act of Satan to frighten us.

A night or so later, while I was busy writing some letters, Alice was taking a shower by the light of a small wick lantern that dimly lit the bathroom. Suddenly, she gave an ear piercing scream and burst through the bathroom door dripping wet, screaming that there was a national man looking in the narrow six inch wide screen opening at the top of the six foot high shower stall. I quickly grabbed a towel and she wrapped herself in it. Then we sat on the end of my bed, and began praying earnestly. This time we knew who our enemy was. Investigation in the morning showed he had placed a wooden sawhorse beneath the window opening, enabling him to peer through.

That night, I left my bedroom door open, with my head at the end of the bed, so I could see the outside door. Then I put a large butcher knife underneath my pillow. But as the fitful night wore on I knew in my heart that I could never defend myself with a knife! My trust and confidence must be in the Lord alone. Finally, the long night was over, with no further incidents.

We were indeed very fearful! We even talked about going to the other missionaries to tell them our preposterous story. Maybe we could move to one of their houses until the men returned. Or maybe we could ask the Australian Army to post a guard around our house!

But we decided neither of these plans would be what the Lord wanted us to do. The Lord wanted us to put our confidence and trust in Him and not in ourselves, or in what others could do for us. In Hebrews 13:5b we read, "For He hath said, I will never leave thee, nor forsake thee." Then in Joshua 1:5, God is speaking with Joshua and tells him, "As I was with Moses, so I will be with thee; I will not fail thee, nor forsake thee."

God wanted us to claim these promises for ourselves, which we did that night. Deuteronomy 31:6 tells us, "Be strong and of a good courage, fear not, nor be afraid of them: for the Lord thy God, He it is that doth go with thee; He will not fail thee, nor forsake thee." We were also blessed by verse 8, "And the Lord, He it is that doth go before thee; He will be with thee, He will not fail thee, neither forsake thee: fear not, neither be dismayed."

The remaining few days that Alice and I spent alone in Ambunti were peaceful ones. The Lord had taught us to depend on Him for our safety and peace of mind. When walking to town for the mail, we saw various men and we often wondered if one of them was the man who had looked in the window. We were very careful not to be too friendly with any of them.

Thankfully, while waiting for the men to return from their trip up river, we were not frightened again by scary sounds from the jungle or from any man coming to the house. We proved God's Word and "saw them again no more forever," as it says in Exodus 14:13. Nevertheless, we were two very thankful and happy ladies when the men returned from their trip. I believe that was the longest week either of us had ever experienced. You can guess what the conversation was about that night!

Further Reflections
By Arvalee

How easily I could have missed the blessing of being a part of this exciting and wonderful work the Lord has been doing in the Sepik Region. If I had allowed Satan to frighten me away during those first few days at Ambunti in November, 1972; if I had not been willing to heed God's Word and claim the promises for myself, I would have missed out on the opening of the Sepik work, and I would have missed helping missionaries reach the tribes with the gospel. And I would have missed the excitement and blessing of seeing the tribal people come to know the Lord.

Would the work in the Sepik have gone on? Yes, I believe it would have been accomplished. God would have touched the hearts of others to do His bidding, others who were willing to trust Him in the hard, fearful times. None of us are indispensable to God. If we do not obey Him, others will be raised up, and they will get the blessing that could have been ours if we had only obeyed. I am so thankful I didn't allow Satan to scare me away!

In reading and reflecting on Isaiah 30:7b in the Defender's Study Bible, Dr. Henry Morris, writes: "Their strength is to sit still." There are times when God's people have done all they could to solve a desperate situation to no avail. They are then tempted to turn to unbelievers to help them, but this is a dangerous compromise. These are the very situations in which God delights to honor true faith. Man's extremity is God's opportunity. In such circumstances, the believer is best advised to sit still and let God be his strength. Compare Exodus 14:13, "And Moses said unto the people, Fear ye not, stand still, and see the salvation of the Lord, which He will shew to you today: for the Egyptians whom ye have seen today, ye shall see them again no more forever."

I can clearly see that it would have been wrong to go to the Australian Army, or even to the other missionaries, as this would have directly disregarded God's Word. Instead, we received grace to trust Him to take care of us. We believed Isaiah 30:15 and found our strength in the quiet confidence that comes from Him.

Settling in at Maprik Village
By Arvalee

Oliver Smith had brought Don Meyer, Dale and me to Pagwi in the 40 foot motorized dugout canoe from Ambunti, where we'd been staying with him and Alice. After our two hour river trip, we climbed out of the canoe, looked down the road, and there wasn't a *PMV* (public motor vehicle) in sight. Pagwi is the small river town where the road to Maprik joins the river, so it was usually a fairly busy spot…but not today. It happened to be Thanksgiving Day, 1972. (Thanksgiving is not celebrated in *PNG*.)

While waiting for a *PMV* to appear, we ate the lunch of corned beef and beet root sandwiches that Alice had packed for us. Thankfully, we didn't wait too long before a pickup truck arrived. The driver was willing to take us to Maprik, 35 miles away over a rough dirt road, for a small fee.

As we entered the small town of Hayfield, a few miles from Maprik, we stopped at a small store and bought a few sheets of roofing metal. We set up the roofing for a temporary means of catching rainwater, which we would need in our rustic living conditions.

Dark was almost upon us as we drove into the village and Dale pointed to the house. It really did look small! But no matter, we were looking forward to getting some rest, as it had been a very long, tiring day. Dale found a couple of young village boys who took our buckets and brought us some water for cooking and washing up before going to bed. About that time, I realized my arms and legs were quite badly sunburned. I had not been prepared for the hot Sepik sun as I sat for those two hours in the canoe.

Dale and Don found the bedding as I hastily cooked rice and *tinned* corned beef, seasoned with a packet of chicken noodle soup. We had hardly given a thought to the fact that this was our Thanksgiving Day dinner!

The next morning, one of the first priorities for the two men was to build an outdoor shower and outhouse! Later that day, a young Australian woman stopped her car and asked if we would like to come to her house for a shower that evening. Would we ever! Kerry and her husband, Terry Liddicoat, lived a short distance down the road. Terry worked for the Coffee Co-Op Board.

That evening, well before dark, the three of us took our towels and clean clothes and headed down the road about a half mile away. It was an odd experience going to shower at the home of folk whom we had never met, but we became fast friends after that! While I was showering, Kerry came out with steaming cups of coffee. Neither Dale nor Don appreciated coffee in those days; but they didn't dare refuse and risk offending her, lest they miss out on their shower! Afterwards, we often kidded Don about his first cup of coffee! Later on, Kerry delighted in relating stories to us about the town folk asking her, "Do European people actually live there in that village?"

She would respond, "Yes, they actually live there."

Setting up the roofing metal was another critical job. With it, we could catch ample rainwater for cooking, washing clothes and showering.

Before he left the Highlands, Dale had made arrangements to buy a used pickup truck from Lyle Mumford, one of the missionaries. It needed some work done on it before it was sent by ship from Lae to Wewak, so it had not yet arrived in Maprik. Before it came, we had to walk the mile to town, where we bought our food in small stores and the open air market.

The long awaited day finally came when the vehicle arrived in Wewak. We were most thankful to have it at last! That little vehicle was used to haul supplies from Wewak to Maprik for all the missionaries in those early days. Before long, however, Dale was spending more time working on it than driving it. We desperately needed another vehicle.

We were fairly well settled in our village house when Don's family joined the team, setting up the first tent for their living quarters. Don and Becky had two little ones, Nicky and Noelle. We cooked our meals together, using a two burner kerosene wick stove. Shortly afterwards, Julie and Dan arrived for their Christmas school vacation. We made our temporary village home quite comfortable as we were to live there for about three months.

During those three months, Dale and Don had their work cut out for them as they began clearing the brush from the land where the mission base would be built. During our days in training, Dale had worked on forest fires in California so he knew about the difficulties of extinguishing a fire. But this was an entirely new situation. It was quite a task to get the fire started and hot enough to burn the jungle cuttings, kept wet by the heavy, daily rains. They finally resorted to setting old tires on fire to get hot enough to burn the wet jungle brush and cane.

Oliver and Alice then came from Ambunti and set up their tent on the property. They would live there while Oliver prepared to build the first little mission house on the base, which was named Kapmora. It would be our home until our own house could be built.

As we planned to move to the Sepik, there was one thing I knew we would need; a washing machine. Don Nutting, the mission supply man, had only one gasoline driven washer left at that time. It was a well-known Australian model wringer washer and we bought it before making the move. We did without refrigeration for over five months, but I was very thankful for that Simpson washing machine, especially when Dale and Don began clearing the land. Their clothes would have been impossible to wash by hand as they were full of soot, dirt, sweat and ashes.

A year or so later, the Lord supplied our need for a more reliable vehicle by providing the money to purchase a brand new van. He answered our prayers by speaking to a special friend of ours, Cline McFerran, who had been saving money to buy a 15 passenger vehicle for his bus ministry in California. Instead, he sent all that money to us and we were able to purchase a new van. What a blessing that was to all the Sepik missionaries. Cline and Virginia were the ones who gave us our first washing machine when we lived in the Gimi.

God was so good and faithful to us; blessing us all abundantly. As new missionaries arrived, there were more needs, yet God always met the needs as they came up. One special provision was a two-way radio, which meant the men no longer had to hike to Hayfield to use the radio belonging to the AOG (Assembly of God) Mission. God also supplied airplanes, land in Wewak, supplies to build houses at Maprik base and in Wewak. Other provisions like boats and motors allowed missionaries to travel upriver and downriver. Finally, a river truck was purchased that moved missionaries and supplies (cement, water tanks, and roofing iron) to their tribal allocations up and down the Sepik River. More radios, and eventually a jet barge...and so much more...stories of God's provisions too numerous to tell. God always provided in miraculous ways. He not only supplied for the mission, but met the needs of the individual missionaries for their own boats, outboard motors and houses in the tribal allocations.

What a special privilege it was to be a part of the Sepik work from the very beginning. There were lots of hard times, both physically and spiritually. God had so much to teach us, especially me, in how to work with others and how to form a team that pulled together to get the job done.

GOD WANTS HIS JOB OF REACHING THE LOST WITH THE GOSPEL COMPLETED. GOD IS FAITHFUL AND HE WILL DO IT AS WE KEEP LOOKING TO HIM. Arvalee

Life Goes on at Maprik
By Arvalee

After three months, we had moved from the village into the new house at Maprik, built by Oliver Smith. Although small, it more than met our needs. We were now able to have the new missionaries in for meals and fellowship. Some of those early arrivals probably remember the army of croaking frogs that still occupied the swales and the water filled holes. They almost deafened us every night! Once the ground was leveled and the holes filled, the frog problem was solved. Another problem was the fruit bats that kept us awake every night when they visited a tree just outside our bedroom, to feed on the fruit. Their huge flapping wings made a terrible whooshing noise as they flew from one fruit to another. Dale tried several means of frightening them away before he finally resorted to having the tree chopped down!

As new folks joined us, each family put up a tent for their first dwelling. Most of them extended the living space of the tent by enclosing a marked off area with screen wire. This area was used for living and dining. They used a communal outside shower and toilet. These were indeed rough conditions for our new folks.

I'm sure those missionaries living in tents thought Dale and I lived in a mansion…hardwood floors, our own tiny bathroom with shower, basin and toilet, a tiny compact kitchen complete with white painted cabinets, a propane gas stove and running water with a stainless steel sink. After five months we were able to purchase a small kerosene refrigerator, as well.

But I had my problems, too. The house had large window openings, which were only covered with screen. When we had a blowing rain, that end of the house always got soaked. In time I learned to pull all the furnishings out of the room, in-

Becky Meyer outside their tent at Maprik.

cluding the mattresses and everything in the closet, and pile them in the living room in the center of the house. It was far better to set the room up again than to deal with wet bedding and other items.

In time, as the Lord provided the funds, a duplex for orientating missionaries was built; each apartment had two bedrooms, a small kitchenette, a living area and a bathroom. It was nothing

Missionaries and workers at Maprik.

fancy, but with cement floors at least they were not living on the ground, as before. We were even able to purchase a washing machine shared by the orientating missionaries.

Mission house framed up.

One of the hardest adjustments for these folks, as for me, was adjusting to the tropical climate. Often, while typing letters on my portable typewriter, perspiration actually dripped from my elbows. Dale once found a new missionary stretched out on the cement floor, trying to cool off. I always felt the best part of the day was the evening, after a cool shower.

When another new family was shown the apartment where they would be living, the man exclaimed; "Where I come from, our chicken coops are better than this!"

But the families adjusted and eventually thrived at Maprik. It was a great launching

Arvalee beside the new water tank.

pad as Dale took the men to survey the tribal areas without the gospel. Upon their return, the missionaries and leadership would seek God's will as to where these families would eventually settle and work.

Palmer Family Events and First Wedding, 1973
By Arvalee

We had been in the Sepik several months, when we heard from our son Pat that he and Debbie Huckaby were planning to be married on June 16th, 1973. The wedding was to be held in Tennessee. He and Debbie had met at Camdenton, Missouri, where her parents, Jim and Sarah Huckaby, were attending NTM's Language Institute.

We regretted that we could not attend such an important occasion due to a lack of finances. Maybe it was lack of faith on our part, but at that time, it was not customary or widely accepted to return to the States for these kinds of family events. We learned Pat's second brother, Paul, was the best man. Also, that Don and Gwen McCurdy stood in for Dale and me since we could not be there. Two of their sons were in the wedding also; Bruce was the photographer and Ricky was a junior usher. Their two youngest, Grace and Lynne were the flower girls. We received a lovely album with beautiful photos of the wedding. This helped relieve our disappointment in not being able to attend.

The next year, on July 10th, 1974, we received a telegram informing us that Pat and Debbie had their first baby. The telegram stated "Stephen Dennis, mother and daughter are doing fine." It turns out they had a girl, Stephanie Denise; even with new and fast communication, the translation and language barrier was evident! What an exciting time this was for us; we were actually grandparents! Then on February 15th, 1976, Anthony David made his appearance into their family. This, too, was an exciting time for us.

Now, we had a grandson to carry on the Palmer name! Later, Angela Dawn was born on March 3rd, 1978. I remember visiting Pat and Debbie in Milwaukee on our furlough, and seeing our grandchildren for the first time. Later on, Pat and Debbie's family increased with the birth of two more children. On April 4th, 1988, Michael Patrick was born, and Shawna Danielle was born on September 13th, 1989. We were back in New Guinea by the time both of them were born.

Our daughter, Julie, graduated from high school in 1974 at the Numonohi Christian Academy, near the town of Goroka. During the next year she helped Chuck and Wanda Turner with their translation project in the Sinasina tribe. She and her school friend, Alice Huestis, helped Wanda type the entire New Testament in the Sinasina language. Working as a team, they were able to complete this monumental, yet tedious project. She also worked in the NCA school library before she returned to the USA.

When she came home to Maprik, to spend some time with us, she had a narrow escape that really frightened us. While taking a shower, she had cut her ankle with the razor. Knowing the high infection risk in the tropical climate, we immediately cleaned it with peroxide and put a bandage on it. However, a few days later she was not feeling well and had a red streak going up her leg.

She had planned to bake cookies that day and continued to do so, even though she wasn't feeling well. Then I realized she was actually running a fever and she mentioned having a lump in her groin. The next morning when she awoke, she said that she had a stiff neck. I recognized these as symptoms of lock jaw, or tetanus. I called Barbara Schrag, who was an RN, to look at her. Immediately, Barb said, "You'd better get her to the hospital right away." By that time, she was so ill that she couldn't even sit upright in the truck.

Arriving at the small Maprik hospital, the Filipino doctor took one look at her and pronounced that she had tetanus! Then he said, "Ninety-nine percent of those in the Philippines who get tetanus die!" We knew how serious tetanus was; we didn't need his added pronouncement of doom to further frighten us! He gave her a tetanus injection, started her on penicillin and told us to bring her back two or three times a day for more injections.

It took several more days of very careful ministrations before Julie was well again. God showed His marvelous power and loving kindness when He healed her. How we thanked the Lord for being so merciful. This story of Julie's near fatal experience reminds me of another very frightening incident that occurred while living at Maprik.

Dale was sharpening his knife in preparation for cleaning a catfish we had purchased at the open air market, when his knife slipped, cutting through the nail of his right thumb. He sat down on the bottom step (of our stairs), with blood dripping onto the ground.

Finally, I had enough presence of mind to put a tourniquet on his arm. Dave Schrag drove us to the hospital. This time, the doctor was French Canadian. I don't believe he spoke any English, but he could communicate with Dale in Pidgin English! After stitching up the wound, he said, "Don't let that thumb get infected."

The thumb was healing well and the stitches had been removed. We both thought it was on the mend. Then he did what turned out to be a very foolish thing. At the time, he thought nothing of accompanying Dave Schrag, to butcher beef for some Government workers. This was a real provision for us missionaries as the men usually gave Dave his choice of the meat. Since Dale had been a cook in the bar-be-cue, he knew his cuts of meat, and Dave valued his expertise. He helped Dave with the butchering, then a day or so later, he noticed that his thumb was sore again. We finally realized the wound was still open from the stitches and bacteria had entered through these tiny wounds. It gave him a great deal of pain, especially at night. He managed to sleep fitfully, and only when his arm was propped upright. In the end he almost lost his thumb.

When he returned to the hospital, the doctor was visibly annoyed "that he had let the thumb get infected", and was not too gentle with Dale. Since Dale was allergic to penicillin, there was no medicine to give him. The little national nurse at the hospital was changing the dressing one day and said, "Mr. Palmer, I think I should tell you, you will lose your thumb without antibiotics. You should either go to Lae or Port Moresby, so you can get some help."

When we got home from the hospital, we radioed and learned that an *MAF* airplane was passing through and landing at the Hayfield airstrip in 30 minutes. I hastily threw some clothes into a case, and Dave drove us to the airstrip to meet the plane. We spent one night in Wewak with Bob and Virginia Huestis and flew the next morning to Lae, where Harold Piovesan met us and took us directly to the doctor's office.

The doctor in Lae took x-rays and told Dale that osteomyelitis was already eating a niche in the bone of his thumb. The infection was serious and Dale was immediately started on antibiotics. The doctor stated, "You will lose your thumb if that medicine doesn't start working very quickly."

We were so thankful the nurse at Maprik had advised him to go to a hospital in the city. Her advice surely saved his thumb, and perhaps his entire hand.

Meanwhile, the young children in Althea Lawrence's class started praying for Uncle Dale's thumb. In the end, because the infection was not responding to the medication, the doctor changed medicines three times before finally putting Dale on Ampicillin, a form of penicillin. That medicine finally stopped the infection. One morning, however, he awoke with hives on his eyelids. He knew he couldn't tolerate any more of the Ampicillin. He phoned the doctor, who confirmed that he shouldn't take any more. But thankfully, his thumb continued to heal even without it.

To this day Dale is very grateful to have his right thumb, although the scar is quite visible. Again, God was very gracious to take care of him, as well as our daughter, Julie.

Julie left for the States in 1975, where she attended New Tribes Bible Institute in Waukesha, Wisconsin.

Chapter 14

Exciting Days in the Sepik
By Arvalee

Our time in the Sepik was a very rewarding experience. While leading the group of new missionaries, God brought us through many trials and taught us many valuable lessons.

During our time there, a number of families passed through the orientation at the Maprik base. It was first known as Tent City, because the very first missionaries had to set up tents in which to live. Those were the days before we were able to put up permanent buildings.

Everyone arriving in the Sepik had many adjustments to make, the main one being the drastic climate change. The oppressive heat seemed to actually drain all of one's energy, especially in the afternoon. Seldom was there a refreshing breeze. Thankfully, the nights seemed to be a bit cooler.

Dale kept in regular contact with the Government officials, who informed him of the tribal groups that were open to our mission working among them. After some careful planning, Dale would take the new men to survey the villages. These new folks didn't know which tribal group they would work with when they arrived in the Sepik, but these surveys exposed them to the needs of the various unreached tribal groups. One or two men would accompany Dale on a survey into a particular area, then after a trip the Lord confirmed in their hearts which area they would move into. Some of these tribal people had never seen a white man before; some were visibly trembling as the missionaries approached.

Sometimes the survey teams were transported by river, traveling by canoe, either paddling or with a motor; at other times a helicopter was hired. Dale was once deposited by the helicopter on the sandy banks of a river and the helicopter took off to bring in another missionary. As it departed, Dale looked towards the river, to see a raft with two national men drifting down the river! They only stared at him as they obviously had never seen a white man before. A short time later, these men came around the bend on the bank of the river to greet Dale. Fortunately they were friendly!

From 1972 through 1982 there were ten new Sepik tribes opened for missionary work. This all came about through the contacts that had been made during the various surveys.

The first couple to join us at Maprik was Don and Becky Meyer. Later, there were Steve and Elaine Bram, Dave and Barbara Schrag, Heinz and Helen Rempel, Jack and Betty Bounds, and Doug and Bev Croot. Following them were Bob and Virginia Huestis, along with Peter and Joy Palmer, our second son and his wife. Marlin and Pat Keller joined us as we desperately needed a mechanic to keep all the vehicles, boats and generators running. Others were Dick Hill and Jake Wieb, Rick and Collette Beckman, Dean and Eleanor Theobald, Ed and Aggie Esau, Tom and Sandy Peterson, Ron and Raema Johnston, Grahame and Carole Townley, Peter and Frieda Green, Greg and Laura Melendes, Steve and Gay Lawrence, Paul and Blair Robinson, John and Kathy Krykowski, and Jack and Jane Housley, to name a few. After we left for furlough in 1977, Bob and Noby Kennell and George and Harriet Walker joined the team.

During those first few years, we saw the Lord provide for the needs of the field in marvelous ways. It was thrilling when supplies were delivered that had been ordered from Wewak to put up a new building. Things such as water tanks, cement for septic tanks, roofing iron, screen wire, and nails were needed in abundance.

Although there were physical hardships while living in primitive conditions, there was an excitement among us. We knew there were unreached tribal people out there in the jungle, waiting for missionaries to come and live among them, learn their language, and preach the gospel. Getting these missionaries oriented was the only purpose for establishing the Maprik orientation base. Most of these new missionaries had been looking forward for several years to the day when they could spearhead a move into a tribe.

Food and Fellowship at Maprik Base

It was the custom of the ladies living on base to go to the open market on the edge of town each week, usually on Friday morning. Most of us relied on the fresh produce to feed our families, which was healthy and economical food. Such things as cucumbers, tomatoes, spring onions, corn, snake beans, taro, yams, sago, tapioca, bananas, papaya, pineapple, coconut, bush nuts, smoked fish (Tilapia), and more, could be purchased from the local people at very reasonable prices. The national women laid their wares out on mats or pieces of plastic on the ground and we could go down each "aisle" at our leisure, filling our *bilums* as we walked.

Almost every week, those of us living on base had a community potluck, setting our tables out on the grassy lawn, where we enjoyed each other's fellowship while eating. Often times I made fried rice as my contribution to the menu.

Once, Dale had been on a trip down river and when he got home he had brought a bushel or two of fresh shrimp with him. He had met the women on the river who had been fishing and they wanted him to buy the shrimp. So he decided to buy all they had! He got home about dark and immediately let me know we needed to contact several girls in the village and ask them to come help us clean shrimp! Fortunately, we found girls who were more than willing to work for the pay they would receive. Bringing their knives, they cleaned shrimp until they were done, which took more than an hour. As fast as they cleaned them, I cooked a batch in my small pressure cooker, and then quickly cooled them, so they could be frozen. These would be saved for special treats later.

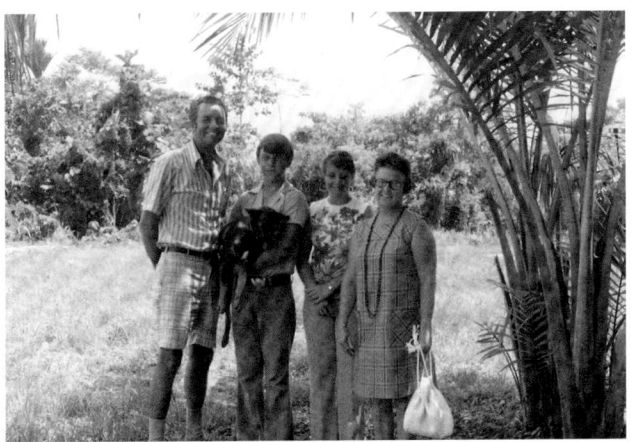

Our family at Maprik, 1972.

Dave and Barbara Schrag had been on a trip up river and we were expecting them back at Maprik that evening. I can remember when the pickup truck arrived back at Kapmora after someone met them at the river, possibly Dale, and their two little boys, Jared and Jeremy, were asleep on two spare tires in the bed of the truck, exhausted from the long hours of traveling. I had cooked a large pan of Johnny Manzetti (baked spaghetti with meat sauce) and had dinner wait-ing for them. When the Parmesan cheese was passed around, Jeremy said, "Something stinks!" I guess he had never had it before and the new smell was quite offensive to him. We all had a good laugh!

Another time, Jack Housley and Bob Kennell came back after a trip on the river. They had trouble getting a ride, so they arrived about 11 p.m. I think they had to walk a long ways. We were not expecting them, but lucky for them, all Dale and I could think of to feed them at that hour of night was steak! We had some that were frozen, so Dale put them in the skillet and they thawed as they cooked. I don't know what else we served them; but that was indeed a special treat for them that night.

I often made Bear Claws or sweet rolls which I liked to serve on Sunday mornings when some of the folks would come over to our house. Several of the men enjoyed the perked New Guinea coffee that I usually made every morning. Dale never was a con-noisseur of coffee, but I drank it regularly for years. The men knew they could count on enjoying a cup at our house. It gave us a chance for fellowship and to get to know them better.

Our Third Furlough, 1977

It was July, 1977, and time for our third furlough. We planned to travel via England and Ireland. This was the first time we had been in either of these countries.

Before we left *PNG*, we received some exciting news. Peter wrote that he was getting married to Joy Lynette Connelly in Pennsylvania in August. When setting the date for their wedding, they were thinking of our upcoming furlough.

Leaving New Guinea from Port Moresby, Dale, Dan and I traveled to Hong Kong on an airplane full of Chinese who all seemed to be smoking. (That was in the days before there were no smoking laws!) By the time we arrived in Hong Kong I had a severe case of allergies and a bad headache. We stayed overnight in a YMCA hostel.

The next day we proceeded to England. We made two fuel stops in Muslim countries. In each place the airline hostess informed all the women on board that if they wanted to disembark, to relax in the waiting room, they must make sure their arms and legs were covered. That was our first introduction to the bondage that Muslim women are required to live under.

In London we stayed at the Foreign Missions Club. Dan and another young man who was also staying there went to see Madame Tussauds' famous wax museum. Dale and I just wanted to rest as we were exhausted from the long flight.

After a day or two in London, we flew to Northern Ireland. We had been encouraged by some of the Sepik missionaries from Ireland to visit their parents, friends and churches there. With as much contact as we had with our Irish co-workers, we thought we knew their culture and could understand their accents as well. But we had a few surprises ahead of us!

In both England and Ireland, we found ourselves in situations where we couldn't understand what they were trying to tell us. Once, at a sandwich shop, when told how much we owed for our lunch, Dale could only hold out his hand and hope the cashier would take only the amount we owed for the food!

In Ireland, we were met at the Belfast airport by Megan, the daughter of Johnston Maybin, the New Tribes Mission representative. Driving back to their home, there were soldiers on a hill, with their rifles trained on the highway! Megan said, "You'd better get down Arvalee, with that green blouse on." I had sewn a bright green blouse to wear on this trip, and Dale was wearing an orange shirt with *Birds of Paradise* on it. We didn't realize that those are the colors of the opposing sides of the political parties in Ireland, the green of the Catholics and the orange of the Protestants!

New Irish friends drove us to our contacts. We met Ian Paisley, pastor of Ron and Raema Johnstone's church and an MP (Member of Parliament) with the Government. As an elected official, it was necessary he have bodyguards surrounding his office. When we attended prayer meeting at his church, The Martyr's Memorial, he asked Dale to give a brief testimony. After Dale sat down, Mr. Paisley called down to him, "How much will that two-way radio for Ronnie cost?"

Dale answered, "I don't know how much that would be in English pounds."

Mr. Paisley said, "Then tell us how much it would be in dollars."

Dale replied, "Twelve hundred dollars." Shortly thereafter we departed. We couldn't stay for the rest of the meeting because we had to leave on our trip to Port Stewart.

After prayer meeting that night, Johnston Maybin drove us to Port Stewart to visit Stanley and Irene Bishop, who operated a small guest house. We stayed a week in this lovely home and felt we were treated like royalty. Irene served a different menu for dinner every night for seven days. Stanley took us sightseeing, and we stood on a rocky cliff overlooking the ocean. He pointed north, over the sea, and told us, "There is no land between us and the north pole!" No wonder we were so cold. Dale and I felt like we would freeze…and it was the middle of July.

Upon our return to Belfast, Mr. Paisley's secretary, Billy Balmer, told us, "We lifted (took up an offering of) twelve hundred dollars Wednesday night for a two-way radio for Ron Johnstone!" Of course, this made a tremendous impression upon us.

We met William John and Florence McConnell, and Leslie and Ruth McConnell at their parents' home. They lived on a real Irish farm, with the potato fields planted within a few feet of the house.

We enjoyed the fellowship meeting at their house that night. We met many dear friends of our missionaries serving with us in the Sepik. The ladies served "suppa" (supper) afterwards, with so many delicious sweets, that I found I had to refuse the next serving.

During this time, our Dan found himself sitting on a little stool beside Mr. McConnell, who took advantage of this captive young American lad, regaling him with stories, all told in his Irish brogue. Unfortunately, all those stories were lost on Dan; he could barely understand a single word. He could only guess at what the dear old man was saying. He couldn't help himself and dissolved in laughter. But the more Dan laughed, the more it encouraged Mr. McConnell to carry on with his story telling!

We stayed overnight with the McConnell's, and the next day Ronnie Johnston, Ken Johnston's cousin, came and picked us up to take us to their house. Ronnie owned and operated an apple orchard. On the way to their home, we stopped at a fancy hotel for lunch. A wedding was in progress there and the men attendants were all dressed in beautiful grey tuxedos. This was our last night in Ireland. Unfortunately, I missed out on most of the fellowship at the Johnston's home because I was suffering from a terrible headache.

We had been very favorably impressed with that beautiful green isle and the most hospitable people we had ever been among. I told Dale, "I guess it's my Irish heritage that makes me feel right at home among all these people."

We loved driving through the countryside, with miles and miles of the greenest landscape we had ever seen. From north to south, throughout the land, the fences in the pastures were made of heaped up rocks. Occasionally, there was a tiny rock cabin in the middle of a pasture, practically in ruins. I kept thinking, *This could be where my great-great-grand-parents lived!*

The next day, Ronnie took us to catch our flight from Belfast back to London, and then we flew on to Philadelphia, where Peter and Joy met us.

Wedding Bells Again, 1977
By Arvalee

It was great to see Peter's familiar face at the airport, and of course Joy was with him! We had never met her, but could tell right away that she was the right one for Peter! They had met at the Fredonia, Wisconsin Boot Camp, where Joy's parents, John and Louise Connelly, were staff members.

Fortunately, we arrived a few days before the wedding, because Dale needed a suit for the big occasion, so Joy took us shopping for one. Before leaving New Guinea, I had sewn a long lavender dress for myself to wear.

We were happy that Pat, Debbie and family and Julie were able to attend, too, driving together from Wisconsin. Pat and family were living in Milwaukee at that time and Julie was nearby in Fredonia Boot Camp. She was one of the four bridesmaids; all clad in different colored pastel dresses.

Of course, we had not seen Pat and Debbie since they had married, and they now had two children, Stephanie and Anthony! What a joyous occasion it was; like a mini family reunion plus a beautiful wedding, which was held on August 6th, 1977. Both dads officiated at the ceremony, Joy's dad, John, and Dale. Pat and Dan were ushers.

Later that summer, at the NTM Language Institute, in Camdenton, Missouri, Dale, Dan and I underwent medical examinations by Dr. Sterling Theobald. When I mentioned the bad headaches and shaky feelings I'd had for several years, he sent me for a glucose tolerance test. This test was what determined that I had hypoglycemia or low blood sugar. Dr. Theobald instructed me to go on a special diet; consisting of high protein, low carbohydrates, no sugar, and no coffee. I also bought a book entitled: Low Blood Sugar and You. Through studying this book, I came to understand a bit of what was happening in my body. I changed the way I was eating, and after a few months, I started feeling much better. What a great difference this change in my diet made in my life.

From Missouri, we traveled west. Our destination was the missionary training center at Baker City, Oregon. Before we left the field, we had written them to ask if we might stay there during the time we were on furlough.

En route, we visited one of our supporting churches; Bible Fellowship Church, in Ventura, California. At prayer meeting, Elaine Musselman, one of our friends, told everyone about our plans to go to Baker City. She said something to the effect that it would be good if we could live close to the church instead of living in far-off Oregon.

After the meeting was over, a lady came to tell us there was a vacant town house apartment for rent in the Ventura Village Green Apartment complex, which she managed! It even had three bedrooms! This was just what we needed, because Julie was coming to stay with us for awhile. After looking it over, we changed our plans and decided to rent the apartment. Our many friends loaned us everything we needed to set up, from dishes and silverware to furniture, so we quickly got moved in and settled. Dan started his senior year at the Ventura High School a few days later, and graduated in June, 1978.

Julie was homesick, so she dropped out of boot camp to come home and spend time with us. The leaders were very understanding and agreed that she could finish the training later, which she did. It was great to have her home again. She got a job at a Ventura retirement center preparing desserts for the residents. She enjoyed that work immensely. Besides working, she was able to travel to meetings with us on the weekends.

One Sunday morning, Dale and Dan left for a meeting in Palmdale. Julie and I had decided to stay home that day. When coming out of the bathroom, Julie tried to open the door, but it wouldn't open! The lock had broken! I knew I had to get some help, because Dale would not be home until late in the evening. Not knowing what to do, I walked down the street and knocked on several doors, but no one answered. I finally came home and called the police station. The officer told me to phone the fire department. A short time later, they came in the fire engine with the sirens blaring, although I'd told them it was not an emergency.

When the firemen arrived, they came inside the house to evaluate the situation and found that the door would have to be removed from inside the bathroom because the hinges were on the inside! They decided the smallest fireman would have to climb through the narrow bathroom window, which was on the second floor. How fortunate it was that I had stayed home that day, too!

After Dan's graduation, we were planning to return to the field. With that in mind, we packed up our apartment, and returned all the items we had borrowed. A family at the church had offered to let Dan live with them, so we settled him in their home. We found out much later that this didn't work out for him at all.

The next day the three of us left for Missouri where Dale and I planned to attend Refresher Course. Julie would return to the missionary training in Fredonia. En route, we stopped in Arizona to see my parents, who were living in their mobile home at Tonto Creek, just north of Phoenix.

My dad had a wonderful garden growing. They actually lived in an area that had very fertile soil. While Dad was digging a cellar, he had struck water! So he installed a pump and had all the water he could ever use for his garden. Everything was growing profusely.

As usual, Dad prepared dinner the night before we left for Missouri. He cooked several fresh vegetables from his garden, plus he had prepared a delicious pork roast. The next morning we arose at 4:30 because Dale wanted to get an early start to cross the desert before the heat of the day.

After leaving Missouri, Dale and I visited his mother and Jim at their home in Ft. Worth. They had moved into a new house, and Dale was able to help Jim by attaching the TV antenna to the roof.

At this time, I was still suffering a lot from allergies. I'd heard of an allergy clinic in La Crosse, Wisconsin. I desperately needed help and wanted to go there and be tested. So Dale put me on an airplane and I flew to Wisconsin. In the meantime, Dale stayed a few more days with Jim and Roberta, and then drove on to Phoenix.

Since Julie was in missionary training at Fredonia, I first visited her there. A day or so later, Bill Keele drove me over to the clinic in La Crosse, with Julie to accompany us.

A 50th Wedding Celebration and Another Wedding, 1978
By Arvalee

Meanwhile, a celebration for my parents' 50th wedding anniversary was being planned in Phoenix. One of the staff members at Fredonia took me to the airport and I flew from Wisconsin to Phoenix where Dale and I met up again. I arrived in time to attend Dad and Mom Price's 50th anniversary celebration. They'd been married on September 15th, 1928. This anniversary celebration turned out to be another family reunion for us.

While we had been traveling, Paul, our third son, married Cindy Case in Las Vegas, Nevada, on August 12th, 1978. We were happy they had decided to get married, even though we had not been there. They drove over to Phoenix, along with Dan, to attend this happy occasion for Dad and Mom Price. Pat and his family drove from Wisconsin to be there as well. By this time, they had three children.

When we returned to Ventura, Lelda and Paul Lawhead gave Paul and Cindy a wedding shower in their backyard. Many of our friends from Ventura, and some even as far away as Los Angeles and Bell Gardens, attended to congratulate them.

Since we had given up our apartment before the trip to Missouri, we stayed for a while in the lovely home of Vern and Carmen Palmer, who were on vacation. At the clinic in Missouri, Dr. Theobald had told me I needed a hysterectomy. In Ventura, I went to Dr. Luttrell for a medical checkup, and he agreed that I would benefit from having the surgery.

In the first week of December, 1978, Dr. Luttrell performed the surgery, free of charge. The hospital also added me to their list for free hospital care. God had provided for us in a miraculous way! We surely gave Him all the praise, because we had no medical insurance. God had met our needs once again.

After the surgery, when the Vern Palmers returned, we were offered a place on Pelican Street to house sit. There I was able to recuperate. It was an added blessing that Dan came to stay with us until we were able to return to the field. He was working in the oil fields at the time.

After six weeks Dr. Luttrell gave permission for us to travel, so we left for Papua New Guinea on January 12th, 1979.

Our Fourth Term, 1979
By Arvalee

Leaving for New Guinea by ourselves was indeed difficult, yet we did so with mixed emotions. As hard as it was to leave all the kids, we were anxious to get back to *PNG* as we had been away a year and a half.

We flew to *PNG* via Hawaii and the Marshall Islands. Our planned route would take us through Nauru and then proceed to Port Moresby. However, once we landed at Majuro, in the Marshall Islands, we were informed there was cholera on Nauru. The plane would not be allowed to land there but would have to return to Hawaii.

We had to spend one night on the island of Majuro. After getting settled in the hotel room, we took a short tour of the island. The taxi driver gave Dale a hat which could be rolled up and put in his pocket. It was made from coconut fibers. We bought a few artifacts, among them a colorful tray decorated with small shells. The hotel was located on a beautiful lagoon, where Dale enjoyed a short swim in the pleasantly warm water. After dinner, we strolled on the glorious, white, sandy beach, enjoying the lovely view of the tall coconut palms and the crystal clear waters.

The next day we boarded the plane again and went back to Honolulu! Because of the interruption to our schedule, we were flown first class from Honolulu to Fiji, at the airline's expense. The plane then proceeded to Sydney, Australia, where we had another one night layover.

We took a taxi to the missionary training center in Plumpton, and surprised our friends, Ted and Faye Albrecht, George and Erma Davidson and Trevor and Fran McIl-waine with a quick visit. The next day we resumed our flight and traveled on to Papua New Guinea.

Arriving back at Maprik, we were happy to see Pat and Barbara Smith. They had joined us in the Gimi in 1965 and we worked together there for several years, becoming fast friends. They had retired some years previously. During our absence from Maprik, they had been asked by the mission leaders to come to the Sepik to help out with the orientation program. They stayed on with us in the little mission house for quite some time. Pat and Barbara were such a blessing to us. Pat loved to cook breakfast each morning, often serving us *bubble and squeak*, made from the leftovers from our dinner the night before.

Barbara, knowing that I'd had major surgery, was quite adept in managing the household chores, including the laundry. We appreciated their help immensely, and we truly functioned like one family.

In May, Peter and Joy arrived on the field. What a delight this was, having them there, joining the Sepik team for orientation. A special joy to us was five month old Jeffrey Dale, born on December 3rd, 1978. He was a precious baby. We have many fond memories of that time.

Then we heard from Paul and Cindy about the birth of their first baby, Natausha Dawn, who was born on November 15th, 1979. However; we didn't get to meet her until she was almost four years old.

Orientation Continues
By Arvalee

During this time, the orientation program continued at Maprik. New missionaries were arriving so fast, that we had a hard time keeping up with housing for them.

Dale went on many surveys into the bush to locate tribes that had never heard the gospel. Most of the time one of the new missionaries accompanied him. After a few months of orientation, learning the trade language of Melanesian Pidgin English, they were ready to choose a tribal allocation in which to work. Many times Dale accompanied them into the tribe to help them get settled.

Dale also traveled frequently on mission related business, and when necessary I went with him. On some occasions, he had particularly hard issues to deal with. These times were difficult for Dale, but necessary.

On March 31ˢᵗ, Jake Wieb, one of the single men, had to be flown out of Krosmeri River location by helicopter to the hospital in Wewak. Dale and Peter were there when he was admitted. The nurse started the intravenous, but when the doctor arrived, he told her to get a larger needle to administer the intravenous fluid, as Jake was severely dehydrated. The actions and quick thinking of this national nurse and the doctor literally saved Jake's life. We were so thankful for the hospital staff who gave him the care he needed for his recovery. God was merciful to spare his life. The next morning Dale went to visit Jake, and found him sitting up in bed eating a T-bone steak, smiling from ear to ear!

Building a New House at Maprik
By Arvalee

After years in the small mission house, the time had come for us to build our own house at Maprik. We'd spent many hours designing our dream house and were eagerly looking forward to it becoming a reality. In our absence, Pat Smith had started sawing the lumber for it, using a circular saw powered by a Volkswagen engine that Eric Barham had built. Dale joined Pat in sawing the lumber, but in time this proved too strenuous for Dale. Thankfully, some of the younger missionaries were able to help; Dean Theobald and Dick Hill in particular, come to mind.

On August 11ᵗʰ, 1979, the first load of cement arrived from Wewak, and the following Saturday the 18ᵗʰ, work started on the basement of our house. It was thrilling to finally have the house in progress!

During this time, an unexpected thing happened, which was a huge blessing for us. New people, John and Coral Paine, now occupied the house down the road from us. Through the company John worked for, the Coffee Co-Op Board, electric lines were being installed at their house. This was a considerable expense for the company, but a necessity. When the electric company's technician came out, he came to see Dale. He told him he would put the transformer right across the road from our base, enabling New Tribes Mission to connect to the electric line, at very little expense to the mission! What a blessing this was, and it was especially beneficial to our work. A short time later we also had telephone service.

Pat and Barbara Smith, who had returned to Australia a few months after we'd arrived back at Maprik, phoned us from Brisbane on September 7ᵗʰ. They relayed the sad news that their oldest son, Kenny, had been operated on for a malignant brain tumor. He died just four months later, on December 13ᵗʰ. He was only 33 years old, and he left a wife and children behind.

Soon after hearing that sad news, we learned that Dale's mother, Roberta McKeon, had passed away on October 15th. She'd had several heart attacks. We were glad for our recent visit with them during our furlough.

Meanwhile, work was progressing on our house. On January 15th, 1980, Dale completed the septic tank with the assistance of his faithful helpers. Twice each day, I carried cold water and snacks down to the house site, so Dale and the other workers had nourishment and enough water to drink. The hot tropical climate quickly caused dehydration, and could even lead to death without adequate fluids.

Dale and I would often walk down in the evenings and sit on a log, to view the progress made on the house each day. Our dog, Buka, a lovely coal black Labrador mix puppy, was usually with us. Dale had brought him to me from the Highlands for an anniversary present. He would run and jump and as he landed, I would catch him in my arms. He was growing so fast; one day Dale said, "You'd better stop playing with him like that because he'll soon be so big he will knock you over." So we didn't play like that anymore!

On February 4th the ground was filled in around the cement block wall that formed the basement rooms. Now, it was beginning to look like a house!

We were more than grateful for Ted and Faye Albrecht, who agreed to come to Maprik from Numonohi, to build the house for us. They arrived on February 29th. Ted was a top-notch builder and we were fortunate that he was willing to help us out. He told Dale, "You know, Dale, I wouldn't have taken on this job for anyone except you." Ted really suffered in the hot tropical sun, and he usually had a sunburned nose and lips. He started working on the house on March 3rd, 1980, just three days after they had set foot in Maprik.

Ted brought their dog Buster with them to Maprik. Being a smaller dog, Buster was very nimble and could climb the ladder and walk out on the floor joists of the new house. Our dog Buka, being a much larger breed, couldn't climb the ladder. After trying a few times and falling, he sat on the ground watching Buster and whining. He wanted to keep up with Buster so badly. It was absolutely hilarious watching the two of them. Until then, we didn't know a dog could be jealous!

One day, Ted threw a block of wood into the jungle, knowing that Buka would fetch it. The dog managed to find it, but his collar got tangled in some vines, and he started howling fiercely! I told Ted, "You threw the block of wood out there so you have to go rescue him." Of course, he did, and the dog was happy to be free again.

When we were at the market in town one day, a lady with another mission group asked me if the house being built was mine. I told her yes, and she said, "Well, don't get too excited about it. If your mission is like most, you will be transferred before you live in it for very long!" That sure wasn't too exciting for me to hear.

The Lord had provided a new Toyota long bed truck for the Sepik work. Peter, Joy and Jeffrey Dale, now working in Wewak, made the first trip in it from Wewak to Maprik with a load of lumber for our house.

The walls of the house were stood up on March 28th; just three weeks after Ted started the framework. Most of the new missionaries helped in some way with building the house, from pouring cement for the foundation and septic tank, to hauling lumber from Wewak. Peter phoned us from Wewak on April 22nd to tell us the roofing iron had arrived. Dale and Frank Low drove to Wewak and brought it back. By April 25th the roof was on the house! Can you just imagine how exciting this was for me? I loved to go down and wander through the house, although I had to be careful because the floor wasn't yet laid!

But, I didn't have to wait too long. The floor was laid by May 1st, and shortly there-after it was sanded with the electric sander which was borrowed and sent down from the mission workshop at Numonohi. The inside walls were stood up on September 1st. Of course, there was still much work to do to complete the interior. We were very grateful for the skilled help of many of our new missionaries. Dave Schrag built the kitchen cabinets, while others helped in many other ways; wiring the house for electricity, painting walls, varnishing the hardwood floors and laying tile in the kitchen and bathrooms. We were finally able to move in on April 27th, 1981. It had been a work in progress since we had arrived back on the field in January, 1979.

Our new house was just fantastic, especially so because it was on the foreign field. It had two bedrooms, two baths and another room we used for an office, besides a wonderfully designed kitchen, a large dining room and living room. It also had screens and louver glass in all the windows…no more rain blowing in…and of course, electricity. The hardwood floors were simply beautiful, made from the tongue and groove hardwood Kwila flooring Dale had ordered from Madang. This added a warm, dark, brown tone to our home.

The Missionary Cat, 1981
By Arvalee
A true story I like to tell to children's Sunday School classes.

Do you know that a "cat" can be a missionary? You didn't know that, did you? Well, I want to tell you a true story of how God used a cat, and it happened to me.

This story happened after we had been in New Guinea for many years. It shows God's love and faithfulness in looking after us, when we put our faith and trust in Him.

Many years ago, when we first knew that God wanted us to be missionaries, the Lord gave me a verse that told me I could trust Him to provide the food, clothing and shelter we would need, in bringing up our family and raising them on the foreign mission field.

During the time we had been on the mission field, I had suffered from severe headaches for a total of about 18 years. I had mentioned these headaches to different doctors, and gone to chiropractors, but none of them could help me nor did they know what caused them. Then, I told our mission doctor about the headaches, as well as the "shaky" feelings I would get whenever a meal was delayed and how I would get relief from the shaky feeling if I ate something. The doctor ordered a test which proved that I had "low blood sugar" or hypoglycemia. For the treatment, a change in diet was ordered. He told me, "You should go on a high protein, low carbohydrate, no sugar and no caffeine diet. After a while, you should start to feel better." So I began experimenting with what I could and could not eat. With the help of a small book, I began to understand the problem. Soon, I was feeling much better.

We had returned to New Guinea from furlough and after following this diet for about a year, I had proven it was beneficial for my health. One of the things I needed was eggs, which provided protein. We were in the Sepik Region, living at the small town of Maprik at the time this story happened. We bought eggs from another mission group located nearby, but one day they told us all their hens had been stolen, so there would be no more eggs.

We bought supplies in the coastal town of Wewak, which was about 80 miles away, and a supply trip wasn't planned for a while. We couldn't make a special trip just to buy eggs!

After about a week of eating other foods for breakfast, I began to feel the need for some eggs. I began to realize how much I depended on the eggs and how necessary they were for my health.

On this particular day, I was in our little office, typing letters; this was before we had computers. I paused, and in my thoughts I just cried out to the Lord; *Lord, I need some eggs for breakfast, but I don't know where they are coming from. If I don't have some eggs soon, I'll be getting those headaches again.* Then I went back to my typing.

As I sat there at my desk, I heard a knock at the back door. Since there were no steps at that door, I wondered who it could be. We were living in our new house, but there were still projects to be finished, like the steps, so none of our friends ever came to that door. Our house was built up at least four feet from the ground.

As I opened the door and looked down, there stood a little national woman and a young boy. I did not know either of them. With both hands she held a rather tall, sturdy plastic bag. And what do you think was in that bag? Why, it was eggs, a bag full of large, fresh eggs! I could hardly believe my eyes. I was almost speechless.

Dale had come to the door too. I told him about my silent plea to the Lord for some eggs. By this time we both had tears in our eyes. I asked her, "Did you bring eggs for me to buy?"

"No, I would like a baby cat," she answered. A kitten! What a surprise to hear her say that. Recently, my mother cat had delivered another bunch of kittens. They were such a bother, sometimes I didn't know what to do with them. We couldn't keep all of them. And here was a woman asking me for a kitten in exchange for her eggs. You know what? I was so thrilled to see those eggs, I gave her two kittens. But I'm getting ahead of my story.

The lady came into the house through the other door and I took the eggs. There were 18 lovely fresh eggs. But they were different than the ones I was used to. She told me, "These are duck eggs." The Lord had used my cat and the unwanted kittens to provide eggs, just when I needed them, just when I had cried out to Him and told Him that I needed some eggs.

Isn't that a wonderful story of how much God loves us and takes care of His children? Just as He promised to do in Matthew chapter 6. In verse 25, Jesus is telling us to take no thought for our lives or what we will eat, or drink or what we will wear. Then in verses 26 through 30 He tells us that the heavenly Father feeds the birds and they don't work or gather food into barns. He makes the lilies of the field grow and there are many beautiful flowers in many different colors. Yet, they do nothing to be arrayed in such glory. Jesus said, even Solomon, the great King, was not clothed in such glory as the flowers in the field. Then in verse 33, He says, "But seek ye first the kingdom of God, and His righteousness and all these things shall be added unto you." I believe this is telling us when we put God and His work first, when we serve Him, He will take care of us and meet our needs. As we trust Him and believe Him to provide for us, He will do so.

After telling this story to some girls at a summer camp recently, one of them asked me how long it took for God to answer my prayer. At first I said about a half hour. Then, as I reflected, I began to realize He must have answered EVEN BEFORE I prayed. This lady, who was used by God to meet my needs, walked from her village to my house. I don't even know which village she lived in. Perhaps it was the village near the river, which was maybe a mile away. It could have taken her an hour, maybe longer to walk down the hot, dusty road to my house.

After the lady had gone, Dale and I sat down at the table to thank the Lord for providing these eggs for me. We thanked God for meeting my need, for keeping His promises, and for His faithfulness in keeping His Word.

Happy Arrivals, 1980, and Dan and Sandra's Wedding, 1981
By Arvalee

Julie Dale arrived in Papua New Guinea on August 6th, 1980, and came to visit us in Maprik. She planned to work in the Highlands as the field secretary, so we only had a short visit with her before she left us on August 22nd, for Numonohi, where she lived with a couple of other single ladies. After some time, she finally had an opportunity to purchase a small house from missionaries who were leaving the field. She was one happy young lady to have her own place at last.

On September 23rd, 1980, Christopher John was born to Peter and Joy in Wewak. Dale and I happened to be in town when he was born and I was privileged to give him his first bath!

Our next piece of family news was that Dan and Sandra Dawn Fitzgerald were getting married. They had been high school sweethearts at the mission school at Numonohi. The ceremony was held in Seattle, Washington, on June 20th, 1981. Sandra's parents, Ted and Jerry Fitzgerald were able to attend as they were on furlough from the Island Province at Hoskins, West New Britain. Pat, Debbie and family drove out from Wisconsin. Pat was the photographer. Pat's little boy, Anthony was the ring bearer and Stephanie and Angela were the flower girls. Grandpa Bud and Granny Joye drove from Eagle Point, Oregon, up to Seattle to stand in for us, since we were still on the field. But after that long trip, Grandpa Bud got sick with pneumonia and was not well enough to attend the wedding. We were very disappointed that it wasn't possible for us to be there, either.

Dan and Sandra were blessed with the arrival of Trevor Brandon on January 4th, 1984. They were attending the New Tribes Bible Institute at Jackson, Michigan, at the time of his birth. We had come on furlough the year before, so I was able to fly to Jackson to see this precious new arrival. I loved cuddling him and rocking him to sleep. After completing Bible School, Dan and Sandra enrolled in the missions training center in Baker City, Oregon. Nicole Rochelle was born there on June 2nd, 1985. We got acquainted with her the following year when she was already a year old.

Chapter 15

An Unexpected Turn of Events, 1982
By Arvalee

True to the words of the lady at market, after living in our new house at Maprik for only fifteen months, we were transferred! Dale was asked to take Tom Palmer's place as Field Chairman, so we moved to Goroka in July, 1982. Tom and Corinne left for furlough, and Dennis Plett was the co-chairman, working in the office with Dale. Julie now worked as secretary for her dad, and continued to do so, for almost a year.

During the time Dale was Field Chairman, the country was changing the Papua New Guinea Bylaws and Articles of Association. This act required the mission to change its bylaws and articles as well. Years later, in referring to this time, Dale said, "There were stacks and stacks of papers to read, and much of it was written in legal terms, which was far beyond my limits of understanding."

But the Lord came to Dale's rescue. To assist in setting up new bylaws and articles of association for New Tribes Mission, he was able to enlist the help of Colin Lamb, who was working in the Dom Tribal area. Colin was from England and understood the legal terminology being used. The mission also hired the law firm, Coopers and Lybrand, to help with the legal work required.

Dale and Colin made many trips to Port Moresby, and with the help of this firm, they were able to set up new bylaws and articles of association for New Tribes Mission. What a tremendous help and blessing this was to Dale, to be able to accomplish this task, knowing it was all done with the help of someone who had knowledge in those matters.

As Field Chairman, Dale often traveled to other areas of the country to visit the missionaries in their isolated stations. Many times I was able to accompany him. On September 7th, 1983, we were visiting the Sepik, staying with Greg and Laura Melendes, at Wenim, on the Korosmeri River. Early that morning, we heard a motorboat approaching. We knew it was one of the missionaries from up river at Bisorio. It turned out to be Bob Kennell. He was coming to tell us some sad news. During the night, Jack and Jane Housley's home had burned to the ground. They were the care takers at the airstrip. The radio was in Housley's house, so Bob had no other way to let us know, except to come in person. Thankfully, the Housley's had gone to Wewak the day before, so they were safe, but they lost all their worldly possessions.

When Jack heard this devastating news, he said, "My treasures were all in Goroka (referring to his four sons). These worldly things can all be replaced." The field took up an offering for the Housley's and a substantial amount was given to help replace their possessions.

Later that same morning, Greg listened to the morning radio *sked* (short for schedule). We learned that Harold Williams, at Numonohi, had died on the 6th, the day before the fire. Dale and I returned to Goroka and Dale performed the funeral service for Harold. Harold was a retiree who came to *PNG* to help in the mission finance office.

Shortly after returning to Numonohi, we started packing our things, as it was time once again for furlough. Colin Lamb would serve as the next Field Chairman. We departed on October 2nd, 1983, for our fourth furlough.

Our Fourth Furlough at Lompoc, California, 1983
By Arvalee

Paul and Cindy were living in Lompoc, California, and had invited us to live there with them and Natausha, who was now four years old. They had a large house and had enclosed the garage. They made it into a nice bedroom so that we would have a room to ourselves.

We didn't have a car, so we traveled by air to see Grandpa Bud and Granny Joye in Eagle Point, Oregon, and then flew on to Phoenix, to visit my parents, the Prices.

We flew back east as well. In November we visited Pat and Debbie who were in the Kentucky Boot Camp. They met us at the airport. Pat took us to see Bill and Joyce Holeman when he took us back to catch our plane for Columbus, Ohio. Bill had been the best man in our wedding. He and his wife Joyce are missionaries with the Kentucky Mountain Mission.

We wanted to go to Columbus to visit Bible Literature International and see Jim Falkenburg again. He and some of the other men had visited us in New Guinea and had gone into the Gimi. I remember scrubbing the red Gimi mud out of their clothes when they got back to Numonohi. After visiting the Gimi, they were very interested in the translation of the Gimi New Testament. On this visit to their headquarters, we learned more about the organization. They raised money for Bible Translations, and invited us to return to Columbus at a later date.

After that visit we flew on to Jackson, Michigan, to see Dan and Sandra who were in Bible School there. After our visit with them we flew home to Lompoc.

When Trevor Brandon was born to Dan and Sandra, I flew to Jackson on January 9th to visit them for two weeks. I got back home on the 23rd.

My plane was late arriving in Los Angeles, so I missed the connecting flight to Santa Maria, where Dale was to meet me. I remember having to walk by myself along the street to the domestic terminal to catch the small plane. I was a bit nervous, but I got there safely. I found out they had already informed the airline in Santa Maria that my flight would be late. I was relieved to know that Dale wouldn't be wondering where I was.

Dale and I felt the need to visit and keep in touch with our friends and supporters, so during the time we lived with Paul and Cindy we made a trip by bus to Ventura. Though only a short distance away, it turned out to be a very long and physically taxing trip. After that short bus trip we knew we couldn't handle a longer bus trip to future destinations.

Jessica Michelle was born to Paul and Cindy on May 7th, 1984. Now, Natausha had a baby sister.

Shortly after the baby's birth, Paul loaned us their car, a Saab, and we traveled back east once again. While still on the highway in Kentucky, on the way to see Pat and Debbie, Dale had to watch carefully in order to miss the chunks of coal that had fallen from trucks. The road going up the mountain to the training camp was so rough that Dale was worried the car would drag on the high spots in the road.

Leaving Kentucky, we headed for Columbus, Ohio to revisit Bible Literature International. The Saab broke down in Columbus, and we had to put it in a garage. Since it was a foreign car a part had to be ordered for it, meaning it wouldn't be repaired for two weeks. BLI provided a motel for us to stay in for a few days. On this visit, Jim Falkenburg, the president, gave Dale a check for $6,000 to buy a computer for John White, the translator of the Gimi New Testament. Jim had met the Whites on his first visit to the Gimi.

We phoned Dan and told him the car was in the garage, so Dan and his friend Dave Bruce came from Jackson, Michigan, to get us on June 1st. We attended the Missions conference in Jackson and met many of the students at Bible School. Then on June 14th, after the Bible School course was finished, Dan and Sandra took us back to Columbus to pick up the Saab.

After leaving Columbus, we traveled together with Dan and Sandra, and went to see Gary and Vickie Gray, our friends and supporters in Frankfort, Indiana. The rough county road broke the cruise control on the Saab. This little car was evidently not meant for long or difficult road trips! Dan was invited to speak at the Gray's church. After we left there, Dale and I attended the Refresher Course at Camdenton, Missouri, an annual conference for NTM missionaries. Meanwhile, Dan and Sandra stayed at Gwen McCurdy's place in Ironton, Missouri, to look after her plants for the summer.

After the conference was over, we traveled back to California, returning the car to Paul. We then left for Papua New Guinea from LAX on September 25th, via Honolulu and Fiji, because we had to be back in the country within a year of our departure. We arrived in Port Moresby on October 1st, 1984.

Our Fifth Term, 1984
Computer Frustrations
By Arvalee

Returning to the field, Dale once again stepped into the Field Chairman's position, with Julie working as his secretary. While we were on furlough, Julie worked as Colin's secretary. Now, it was time for her to go on furlough, and she left in the spring of 1985. I would be working as Dale's secretary and Donna Plett would work for her husband, Dennis, who was functioning as the co-chairman, working with Dale. She and I were both facing the same dilemma; neither of us knew the computer! To make things worse, all the Field Committee letters and other information for the mission were stored on one computer!

While we were still in the Sepik, if anyone told me I needed to learn the computer, I always replied that I knew how to type and I had a good typewriter. I didn't think I would ever need or want to learn to use a computer. Now it was an absolute necessity so I could do the secretary's work. On December 6th, Donna Plett and I started computer lessons with Mike Ludwig as our instructor.

The Lord proved faithful to meet our needs. I think I can safely say that without the help and patience of Mike neither of us would have learned what we did! The thing I found most frustrating in those days was learning to use one program, and then having to change to a newer, more advanced program shortly thereafter. Through all the frustrations, Donna and I somehow managed to get the necessary correspondence done for the men.

After I felt fairly confident on the computer, I had volunteered to type some lessons in the Gimi language for Zato, one of our Gimi leaders. To accomplish this, I usually went to the office at night after dinner and spent an hour or so working on these lessons. One evening a most discouraging thing happened. I was so upset and distraught I was almost in tears.

I had diligently spent about three months typing the lessons into the computer, so I was nearing the end of the project. When I was finished work that night, I thought I had saved everything, but to my dismay the screen went blank. I had hit the wrong key and lost everything! At least, I thought all my hard work had been lost. There was nothing to do but to go home. When I walked in our front door, Dale could tell that I was very upset. In my frustration, I grabbed a load of clothes to fold, and furiously tore into them. I was completely devastated!

The next morning, as I was leaving our house, I looked toward the office, and there was Mike Ludwig. He gave me a thumbs up sign! Unknown to me, Dale had told Mike about my predicament and he had come down to the office early and was able to retrieve all my work! A huge feeling of relief and thankfulness surged over me. Thankfully he knew more about computers than I had ever imagined was possible.

Dan and Sandra wrote us with the good news that they were blessed with the arrival of Nicole Rochelle, who was born on June 2nd, 1985. Trevor now had a baby sister.

Joy Amidst Sorrow
Our Fifth Furlough, 1986
By Arvalee

We heard through Pat that Grandpa Bud was having a real hard time in Shady Cove, where he and Granny were living. Pat said Grandpa was even talking about suicide. When we heard this, we felt it was necessary for us to return to the States and try to take care of the situation, as best we could.

We began making plans to go back to the states for only a few months, or so we thought. Our plans were falling in place when Julie phoned to tell us that she and Dan Melendes were engaged to be married. Julie had written to tell us about Dan, whom she had first met in June of 1985, at the Waukesha Bible School where she was visiting shortly after her return from New Guinea.

Before returning to the States, we had asked Peter and Joy to look after Hudi, while we were away. Hudi was Julie's dog that we'd been taking care of. We flew the dog to the Sepik in the pod of a Cessna 185 airplane. Hudi seemed to adopt their little Blue Heeler puppy that they called Pepper.

Dale and I left Papua New Guinea on May 1st, 1986, returning to Oregon for a personal furlough. In our absence, Colin Lamb served as the Field Chairman once again.

Dale and I rented a small house in Eagle Point as we needed a place of our own. It was just ten miles from Shady Cove where Grandpa Bud and Granny Joye lived. After living in the rented house for only three months the landlord asked Dale to look after his house during the winter. In light of our caring for Grandpa Bud and his needs, we felt that was too much responsibility. Besides, the rent was getting to be too much for us to afford and since the house wasn't well insulated, we knew it would be very expensive to heat, as well.

Grandpa Bud told us we could stay in his tiny travel trailer in Shady Cove, situated on the same lot where they lived. We moved out to Shady Cove, and while there we began to understand Grandpa's problems quite a bit better.

Grandpa and Granny Joye were living in a nice mobile home, next door to Elmer and Denise Fernandes. Elmer had moved them into this home which he owned, because of problems with their previous landlord who was quite cantankerous. This was all done out of the goodness of Elmer's heart.

Julie and Dan's Wedding, 1986
By Arvalee

Shortly after Dale and I got to the States we visited Julie in Waukesha, Wisconsin. She was staying with Grandma Tony, Dan's paternal grandmother, who lived near the Bible School. We got there in time for me to attend her bridal shower. It was exciting to meet Dan and see the house they had purchased where they would be living after their marriage, and still do to this day.

Julie and Dan's wedding was on June 28th, 1986. Naturally, Grandpa wanted to attend her wedding, but Granny Joye didn't want to go. We bought Grandpa a new suit, and were prepared to buy Joye a dress for the occasion, but she wouldn't be persuaded. In the end, a family friend accompanied Grandpa on the plane to Wisconsin so he could attend the wedding.

My parents were both able to attend the wedding, and my sister Johnnie and her boyfriend attended, too. The four of them flew up from Arizona. Pat and his family were also in attendance. It was Pat who met my folks and others at the airport. In addition, Pat was the photographer for the wedding. For accommodations, we booked rooms for everyone at the Bible School, since all the students were gone for the summer.

The wedding was held at Faith Bible Church at the bottom of the hill from the Bible School. Dale officiated at the ceremony. Julie's gown was a gorgeous white lace and the three bridesmaids wore beautiful long gowns in a lovely blue. Dan's three brothers were the groomsmen and Dan Palmer was an usher.

After their honeymoon in Door County, Julie and Dan settled in their little house on Oakland Avenue. The years went by and on March 28th, 1992, Emily Jean was born. By this time we were back in Papua New Guinea.

Moving Grandpa and Granny to Eagle Point
By Arvalee

When we returned to Oregon after the wedding, we realized that Grandpa Bud and Granny Joye needed to be living in town as Shady Cove was quite a ways out in the country.

To our surprise, Granny Joye had already found a mobile home for sale in a park in Eagle Point! We were able to purchase for them the very mobile home she had found for sale. That seemed to be just what she wanted, because it was closer to her daughter, Phyllis.

As we were in the process of moving the folks, Elmer kindly offered Dale and me the mobile home to live in, the one that had just been vacated by Grandpa and Granny Joye. We needed a place to live ourselves, so we accepted his offer. We rented a truck, and as we moved the folks to Eagle Point, we exchanged their furniture for the furnishings in the place we had just bought, as it was fully furnished. We appreciated having this furniture, because we didn't even have a bed to sleep on.

The Pastor of the Brownsboro Community Church, which we attended, came to help us with the move. Pastor Fred DeVos and his wife, Priscilla and two sons were a tremendous blessing to us. Priscilla actually cleaned underneath the refrigerators on her hands and knees in both homes. Their acts of kindness spoke volumes to us. During a very hard time, we appreciated their acts of love immensely. I remember the church service we attended following this difficult time and singing, "Because He Lives, I Can Face Tomorrow." Thankfully, this move seemed to be just what Grandpa needed and they lived there happily for several more years.

~PART SIX~

A Rewarding Ministry

Chapter 16

We Return to PNG, 1987, Via England and Ireland
By Arvalee

We lived in the Fernandes' mobile home on the river in Shady Cove for several months. When the time came for us to return to the field, Elmer told us we could store all our packed belongings in his barn while we were gone. Dale made a crate and we began packing the things we needed to ship back to New Guinea.

During our time living beside the beautiful Rogue River in Elmer's mobile home, Dale and I both had numerous opportunities to share the gospel with Elmer and Denise. But neither of them had come to the point of putting their trust in the Lord.

We were planning to give our car to Pat, so at the appointed time, he flew from Arizona to Oregon. He drove us to the airport in San Francisco, pulling a trailer containing our crate. He would deliver the crate to the shipping agent a few days later near Long Beach. As we were getting into the car to drive away, the last words Elmer said to Dale were, "Dale, since talking to you, I think about God all the time."

Dale told him, "That's good Elmer. You just keep thinking about God." There was no time then to speak further on the subject because we had a long drive ahead of us and a plane to catch.

Praise the Lord for his faithfulness, for He was truly at work in the hearts of both Elmer and Denise. A few months after we left, Pastor Fred DeVos came to visit them. He had met them both when he helped us move Dale's folks back to Eagle Point. Denise told me later that when she saw him coming in the gate, she knew they were going to get saved that day! Fred was the one God used to bring them to a saving knowledge of faith in Christ.

We had sent our passports away to the Papua New Guinea Embassy in Washington D. C., to have the necessary visas stamped in them for our planned stops in England and North Ireland. But they had not been returned before it was time for us to leave for San Francisco. Before leaving Shady Cove, Dale phoned the Embassy once again, and found out that the agent we had been working through had been out of the office because of illness. After speaking with her, she arranged to send the passports to the FedEx office near the airport in San Francisco by overnight courier service. When we arrived in San Francisco, we located the FedEx office and picked up our passports. What a relief to have them in hand, just an hour or so before our departure time!

Pat dropped us off at the International terminal and then headed south to Los Angeles to deliver our crate to the Fellowship Crating agency in Bellflower. We had previously arranged for it to be shipped to us in Papua New Guinea.

Our flight was scheduled to leave from San Francisco near the end of April, 1987. We had no problem boarding the plane and did not pay extra for our luggage, though we knew it was overweight. We had packed in such haste, we didn't sort it well. It wasn't a surprise to us when we had to pay an enormous fee during our stops en route to New Guinea.

Our first stop was in England and we visited the Bible School at Matlock. We wanted to see this new facility and we also wanted to visit Jack and Isa Douglas, who were on furlough from New Guinea.

We had planned to take a bus to make this visit, but were advised that it would be a long and tedious trip. Karl Mosby, one of the students, offered to loan us his car, which Dale decided would be a good thing to do.

Unfortunately, the car broke down near Blackpool. We were so thankful that we had applied for and received a credit card before leaving the States! Otherwise, when we needed the towing service to haul the car to a garage, we would have been refused. We had never before seen the need of having one. Again, we knew the Lord had led us in this decision.

We were also thankful that Jennifer Quinn was traveling with us, whom we knew from New Guinea. Jennifer knew that John and Minnie Gibson lived nearby. She phoned John, and he and his son-in-law, Grahame Townley, came to help us. They loaned us a car and we were able to continue the trip to visit Jack and Isa. Months later, the Gibson's and Grahame and his wife Carole came to New Guinea. Sadly, while living in the Sepik, the younger couple lost their baby to an accident involving antimalarial tablets.

After our visit with Jack and Isa, Karl, the owner of the broken down car, met us at the garage, to join us for the return trip. Dale drove the car, towing the broken down one back to Matlock, while Karl was steering it. That was a hair-raising trip to say the least! It was pouring rain, and the rope which tied the two cars together, kept breaking. Dale and Karl had to get out in the rain several times and tie the cars together again. Dale found driving on the opposite side of unfamiliar roads, through strange towns and roundabouts was very stressful! It was truly a relief to finally be back at the Bible School.

A few days later, we flew from Manchester over the Irish Sea to Belfast. We wanted to visit our friends in Northern Ireland, again. This time, Dale rented a car and we drove to the places we wanted to visit.

We drove to Kilkeel and spent a night with Mrs. McConnell, whom we had met on our first visit to Ireland. Sadly, her husband had passed away. We remembered him as the man who told stories in his Irish brogue to our Dan that made him laugh, because he really couldn't understand him.

Jennifer had given us the names of several people to contact. We stayed almost a week in Londonderry in a cottage belonging to Jennifer's aunt. What a great vacation to have that lovely little house all to ourselves. We went to Omagh, Jennifer's home town, and visited her parents and her church.

We had dinner one night with her friends, the Ian McClure's. Ian and their fifteen year old son, Keith, asked Dale many questions about the kinds of wood available in New Guinea. Afterward, Keith asked Dale if he would mind sending him some Kwila, a hard wood from the Sepik, because he wanted to make himself an electric guitar. He got a scolding from his mother for asking this question! But, once we arrived at Maprik, Dale found a suitable piece of Kwila and sent it to him.

After dinner, Ian asked me, "How do you spell your name? Do you spell it, A-R-V-A-L-E-E?" I told him yes, and he said, "I work at Arvalee Townland. Would you like to see it?" This was so exciting to me, because I had never seen my name in print! He took us nearby, to a building that housed the offices where he and many others worked.

There, a roadside sign read: D.O.E. (Department of Environment) Arvalee Depot N.I.E.S. (North Ireland Electrical Service) Area Office. It was a large two story building. Inside there were rows and rows of desks. When we came to Ian's desk, he gave us a map showing all the transformers in the Arvalee Townland area. Each transformer was labeled, Arvalee A, Arvalee B, etc. up to Arvalee Z. This may seem trivial, but it was thrilling to me, just to find my name in Ireland where I knew my mother's parents came from. I knew I must still have distant relatives around that area.

Upon leaving Omagh, we came to a tourist attraction center called "The Ulster American Folk Park." We sincerely desired to stop and visit there, but we were pressed for time, since we had a meeting that evening in Portadown. We stayed with Ronnie Johnston again, whom we had met on our first visit in 1977. We left for the airport the next day from his place.

Our 6th Term, 1987
By Arvalee

We arrived back on the field on April 30th, 1987, to begin our 6th term of service in Papua New Guinea and Dale resumed his duty as Field Chairman.

While living at Numonohi Dale usually attended Pastor Hagen's church in Goroka, located in the area called Genoka. Pastor Hagen was from the Frigano tribal group, located near the Yagaria and our mission base at Olaguti. I believe he was one of Dean Van Vliet's converts and worked for Dean when he was a young man. He had a thriving church and many of those who attended were from the Yagaria and surrounding villages. He and his wife, Anna, had five children and they were all a testimony for the Lord.

While we had been away for that year on furlough, Colin and Brenda had looked after our dog Hudi for us. When we got back, Hudi was confused and didn't know where home was supposed to be! Brenda finally told her to go home and pointed to Julie's little house where we lived, and she obeyed the command and came home to us.

It was the next year that Hudi got lost when Pam McCurdy took her for a walk down by the river, and she was missing for eleven days. It was a very stressful time for Dale and me. Even missionaries get very attached to their pets and it is upsetting when things like this occur. The people had told us that she wouldn't be found, because they said, "By now someone would have killed her for a nice pot of soup." Fortunately, she was found on the twelfth day. From then on she was afraid when the people came around our house.

The RI Class, 1990 and 1991
By Arvalee

In the next year or so, an opportunity came for Dale to teach the RI (Religious Instruction) class in English at the Goroka Demonstration High School one day a week. The students were in Grades 7 through 10.

Dale knew the principal of the school, Ben Malarie, as they had met several years previously, when Dale first became the Field Chairman. Ben came to the mission base one day, needing to talk to someone who could give him spiritual counsel, and was shown to Dale's office.

He told Dale he was a volunteer with a mission organization who worked in one tribal group of the Eastern Highlands. In fact, he had even signed a two year contract with them. His family was living there with him; they had come from the Philippines, their homeland. Now, because of certain practices of this mission group leader, he was having a lot of questions about serving with them.

Dale knew about this group. Indeed, it was definitely not a group of which New Tribes Mission, or we personally, would approve. In fact, the leader had been denied the privilege of staying at our Guest Houses because of his known life style.

Dale advised Ben to break the contract and leave the group immediately, which he did. He returned to the mission station and packed up his family and belongings. We believe it was because of this godly man, that New Tribes Mission had been invited to participate in the RI class at the high school.

Some of the students were boarding at the school, but many of them lived with their parents or relatives in town. These students usually had a sponsor or patron, who paid for their school expenses; such as books and school uniforms. Because of this, they were accountable to their patron which insured they would attend classes regularly.

However, the RI class was a volunteer class; the students only attended if they were interested in learning about various religions or a specific religion. There were other RI classes as well as the one we taught.

The first day that Dale taught the class, there were seven girls in attendance. He didn't feel comfortable in a class made up entirely of girls. When he got home, he said, "You've got to come with me next week. I can't teach a room full of girls by myself." So that is how I got involved.

To Dale's surprise, the next week there were several boys there as well. The class grew each week because many of these students were familiar with New Tribes Mission, having come from tribal areas where our missionaries were working, learning language and presenting the gospel.

We taught this class in 1990 and 1991 and the numbers increased to about 70 students; the room was so crowded, some were standing at the back. To our surprise, some students were standing outside as well, listening and looking on through the louvered glass windows.

Long before the two years were over, we had invited other missionaries to join us. Rei Ramos was of particular help to us. Rei was from Puerto Rico and really struck a chord of identification with these kids. Besides assisting with some of the stories, he would bring his guitar and lead us in singing at some of the evening meetings.

John Gibson also joined us each week. We had first met John in England when the car we had borrowed broke down! John was a real help to us in these classes, even though he was not too successful in the teaching part, because the students could not understand his English accent. However, he enjoyed this ministry of being involved with these high school students and didn't want to give it up. Dale came up with the idea of asking him to read the scripture, which he faithfully did for us each week. His accent presented no problem in this instance, because the students could follow along in their Bibles as he read.

On a few occasions, we invited several of the students to come to our house at base for special times of food and fun. One Saturday morning a group of the boys from the RI class, including Paul and Tama, two of Pastor Hagen's sons, put on a skit near their father's church. Before beginning the skit, several of them sang together, accompanied by one who played the guitar. They sang "God has changed my life," and also, "There's a Way back to God:"

> *"There's a Way back to God,*
> *Jesus is coming very soon,*
> *I Know, I Know, I Know,*
> *Write My name in the Book of Life."*

The skit depicted the Great Judgment Day when all mankind will stand before our Father God. Using their own ideas, the students put together this skit. They made a large circle of ashes on the ground, and liberally sprinkled it with kerosene and set it alight! It was quite realistic. Three of them were draped in white. One represented the Judge who was reading from the Book of Life. Two were angels standing on either side who assisted him. Standing before these three, were several of the students, and Dale. Each had chosen a name which he stated when it was his turn to stand before the Judge. Paul Hagen was Mr. Moneybags. Another was Mr. Church Member, another Mr. Baptized. Dale called himself Mr. Whiteman. When the Judge couldn't find the name of the person in the book the two angels led him away to the ring of fire and threw him inside. One actually tried to escape by going the other way, but the two angels had a firm grip on him. All the while the person being led away was protesting loudly against being thrown into the fire. Once they were sitting on the ground inside the ring, they wailed, "Oh, sorry, sorry. Oh, God has left me now. Oh, sorry, sorry me."

When the skit was finished, one of the students read from Revelation 20 and Pastor Hagen explained it to the audience. The skit ended with the singers again singing, "God has changed my life."

It is with fond memories that we look back to those days of teaching the RI Class and attending Pastor Hagen's church. Interacting with those students and seeing their new found faith in God was especially rewarding. It was the highlight of that term on the field in the Highlands of Papua New Guinea.

A Frightening Encounter
By Arvalee

Once while we were living at Numonohi, Dale had an errand to do and was driving out to Olaguti in a truck. One of the missionaries on base thought he should not go alone, so offered to go with him. This was because there had been a lot of rascal (criminal) activity on the roads, and travelers had been stopped, robbed at gunpoint and sometimes worse things had happened.

Dale completed his errand and they were driving back to Numonohi. They came to a section in the road where there was a slight incline. Suddenly, several masked men jumped out of the bushes onto the road. One held a shotgun, which he pointed right at Dale's face.

There was no time to think! But instinctively, Dale accelerated and swerved the truck in the direction of the man holding the gun. Of course, the robber reacted by dropping the gun and jumping off the road to safety! Thankfully, that ended the holdup and Dale sped on his way home.

This was but another reminder of the Lord's faithful watch care over us and how we need to look to Him constantly for help and direction each day.

Angels Watching Over Us
By Arvalee

Sometime during this period, Dale's left shoulder became stiff and very painful. It was impossible for him to button his shirt or comb his hair with his left hand because he couldn't lift his arm high enough. We had heard of a doctor at the Nazarene Hospital some distance away in the town of Kudjip, who might be able to help. To see this doctor, we had to rely on one of the other missionaries to drive us there.

The doctor told Dale he had a frozen shoulder and recommended that he have surgery to break it loose. It turned out that one of our own missionaries, Elaine Good, a physical therapist, had traveled with us that day and went into the office with us to see the doctor. When the doctor recommended surgery, Elaine spoke up, suggesting to the doctor that she believed if she worked with Dale, the shoulder could possibly be improved so that he could avoid surgery. We were thankful that the doctor accepted her suggestion. She worked with Dale for several months and thankfully he didn't need to have surgery.

Some of these manipulations were very painful for Dale. Once, as Elaine was working with him, the pain was so intense, it lifted him off the bed! As it did so, he actually swung at her with his right arm, and narrowly missed hitting her right in the face! Thankfully, over time, as the exercises continued, his arm did improve and he gained full use of it again.

On one trip Paul Jarot had graciously agreed to take us to see the doctor. On the return trip, the car broke down and we were stuck on the side of the road. I was reminded later by someone that at the time of the break down, I said, "We don't need to worry. God will take care of us and send His angels to watch over us." The Lord was indeed faithful and before long, a car came along, stopped and two men got out of the car. They told us they were teachers from the Lae Vocational Tech School, and they asked if they could help us. Looking under the hood of the car, they discovered that the fuel pump had gone out. They said, "We just happen to have a fuel pump with us." So they changed it for us, and we were soon on our way home.

Were these men angels sent by God? On this earth, we will never know. But we do know that God was truly watching over us and sent those men to help in our time of need. And the amazing thing is that they had the right part for our car, which was a very unusual model in New Guinea! It was a Toyota Crown Super Saloon station wagon. We had bought it from Alfred Coleman, who had imported it from Australia a few years previously. Now, he was leaving New Guinea and he wanted to sell it. The two men were driving a different model car, yet carried a part with them for a Crown Super Saloon!

We Move to Rabaul, East New Britain, 1991
By Arvalee

Two years of teaching the RI class had come to a close. In a most unusual way it came about that we moved to Rabaul, East New Britain.

One day, we were told by one of the men on the Field Committee that there would be a vacancy in Rabaul. Our son Dan and family, who had served as Mission Representative to the *PNG* Government there, was to leave on furlough and there was no one to replace him.

Dale and I had flown over to see Dan and Sandra twice while they were living in New Britain. The first time was while they lived in the tribe of Mamusi. The second time they were living in Rabaul, in a small rented house which belonged to the Nazarene Mission. Rabaul was a beautiful, tropical island paradise with beautiful beaches; a swimmer's dream. It sported the most fantastic national farmer's market known in the whole of New Guinea. There were quite wonderful hotels and restaurants, as well. Best of all, the local people were peaceful, warm and friendly. Rabaul was a much desired location, being the island paradise that it was known to be.

When we were told of this need in Rabaul, I spoke up in an offhanded way, saying, "Oh, we could go there!" Much to my surprise, that casual remark was taken seriously. The committee men asked Dale and me to consider moving there!

Before we knew it, we were packing our things, preparing to make this move. We planned to ship a crate over on a coastal freighter, and Dale and I and Hudi would fly over with NTM aviation. It was December, 1991.

Because a Labrador mix is a large dog, the pilot had to lay Hudi on her side to slip her into the cargo pod underneath the airplane. After flying for two hours over the open sea, we stopped en route at the Mouk tribe, about halfway to our destination. We wanted to visit Mark and Gloria Zook and see the marvelous work God was doing among the people. We were ready to stretch our legs, and knew the dog would enjoy a break, too. It was amusing to see Hudi following along beside us, enjoying a run. After a short visit we were ready to leave; the dog headed straight to the airplane and stood beside the cargo pod, ready to begin the journey again. She seemed to know we had not reached our destination!

In Rabaul, Dale and I stayed at the *SIL* Guesthouse until Dan and Sandra left for furlough, a short time later. Then we moved into the small rented house where they had lived and looked after their two Rottweiler dogs, Trusty and Roxanne.

Many who read this story may wonder about missionaries owning these large dogs. Those of us who lived in towns or on mission stations found it reassuring to have a large dog about the yard to deter thieves from entering our yards or houses. A barking dog, especially a large one, would ward off unwanted visitors. I recall a few amusing times while living in Rabaul.

Once, two women came to our six foot chain link fence and gate; they were about to open it and come inside the yard, but the ever vigilant Trusty rushed to the fence, jumped and thrust all four feet against the gate. Somehow that dog knew they were not welcome visitors. They hastily went on their way!

Because of the hot, humid weather, we bathed the dogs at least once a week. We chose to do this underneath the house, on a cemented area near the water faucet. While we washed Hudi, Trusty and Roxanne would line up, awaiting their turns. The dogs actually looked forward to this ritual!

Both dogs knew Hudi had first place with Dale and me. When I petted Hudi's head, she would place her head on my knees and before long one of the other dogs would come along and nudge my arm to get my attention. They were gentle, lovable, friendly dogs, but extremely jealous of Hudi.

The mission was planning to build a new house for the mission representative in Rabaul. The headquarters for the island of New Britain was located in Hoskins, West New Britain. As mentioned before, Rabaul was in East New Britain. Two teams of missionary men came to Rabaul from Hoskins at two different times and brought several national workers with them to assist in the project.

Dale and I helped by purchasing the food for everyone, and I cooked for the missionary men. Dale also functioned as the "gopher" for the builders, making many trips to the local hardware stores for needed supplies. The house was being built on the lot next door to the house we were living in. Although it was a very demanding time for all of us, it also was rewarding. In the end, Dale and I had the privilege of moving into the finished house.

Most satisfactory, however, is the knowledge that we had a part in the lives of our fellow missionaries and long lasting friendships were made.

The Gentle Island People
By Arvalee

We had spent just 15 months in Rabaul, but we had fallen in love with the place and the people, who were so different than the people in the Highlands of New Guinea.

Once, while in town shopping, Dale was leaving the drugstore, when a crowd gathered around a van across the street. He found out that a child had run into the street and the van had run over him, pinning the child underneath the wheel. Dale went over to see if he could be of assistance, when suddenly the van was lifted off the ground by the men surrounding the vehicle. It was Dale who reached under the vehicle and lifted the little boy up and placed him, unharmed, in the arms of his mother! Everyone was so grateful and rejoicing that the child had not been injured! Instead of casting the blame on the driver, they expressed their thankfulness.

This was in such stark contrast to what we had been used to in the Highlands of Papua New Guinea. We had always been warned not to stop, but drive directly to a police station, even if hitting a pig, because the people had been known to chase and kill the driver of a vehicle involved in an accident.

Chapter 17

We Return to the USA, 1993
Eagle Point, Oregon
By Arvalee

We departed for furlough on March 4th, 1993. We had exciting plans to return to Rabaul and build our own house but God has ways of changing a man's best laid plans. We found out once again that our ways are not necessarily His ways!

Before leaving, we first flew to Maprik to see Peter and Joy. It was nice to see some of our friends from the village as well. Then we went through Port Moresby and left for the States.

Before leaving the field, we had contacted the Brownsboro Community Church in Eagle Point, Oregon, and inquired about a place to stay until we could find a place to rent. Although we had never met her, Dawn Lyon graciously offered to let us live with her in the home she shared with her daughter, Linda, and her young son, Jim. We lived with them temporarily, until we found an apartment to rent in Eagle Point on Royal Street. Dawn played a key role in our lives for a number of years. After we got settled in the apartment, Pat and his family came from Arizona to visit us. Again, Dawn helped us out by offering Pat's family a place to stay, because she and Linda were away on a trip.

While living in the apartment, Julie and Dan came to visit us too, when Emily was about two years old. At the same time, my sister Johnnie came to visit us from the Seattle area, as well. Johnnie had a pet rabbit and Emily was so fascinated with it; she wanted to pet it and followed it all over the house.

In November, 1993, we had some sad news when Dale's dad, Bud, was diagnosed with lung cancer. This changed our plans in a big way. We knew he would need our help and support during the ordeal that was before him. Dale was an only child and he had known for years that when his dad was in need, it would be his responsibility to look after him.

Together, Dale and I made the difficult decision not to return to the field as we had planned. Little did we know that his Dad's illness was just the beginning of many sorrows in our family over the next twenty-two months.

Two Volcanoes Destroy Rabaul Town, 1994
By Arvalee

As it turned out, two volcanoes erupted on the island of New Britain, on September 19ᵗʰ, 1994, the very month we had been scheduled to return to Papua New Guinea. *However, you will recall, we had changed our plans when Dale's dad was diagnosed with cancer.* Sadly, those volcanoes destroyed the town of Rabaul in East New Britain, as well as the mission's home we had a part in building, and where we had lived. Most of our things that we had in storage were lost. We were very thankful, in God's foreknowledge, that He had spared us from going through that traumatic event.

Several of the missionaries who lived at the mission base in Hoskins, West New Britain, went to Rabaul to check out the damage to the mission house. They found it utterly destroyed and took pictures to send us. The pictures showed the destruction of the house; the roof caved in, the water tank, washing machine and stove, to name a few of the objects that they photographed. One photo showed the inside stairs of the house. Other pictures showed buildings in town where we had shopped…the pharmacy, post office and others.

However, they were able to retrieve one drum of our belongings that we had stored in the attic of the house and took it back to Hoskins.

The photos impressed on us how fortunate we were, in that the Lord had not allowed us to be in residence at the time of the eruptions. We could only acknowledge that the Lord had our best interests in mind. He was in complete control of our lives.

Shady Cove, Oregon
By Arvalee

Peter and Joy were coming on furlough and asked us to find them an apartment to rent in Eagle Point, because they wanted to be near the Palmer families. We had been thinking about trying to find somewhere cheaper to live, anyway, since we were finding that it was very expensive for us to continue renting. Elmer Fernandes graciously offered to let us live in a travel trailer on his lot out in Shady Cove. We decided to let Peter and Joy move into the apartment and we would move to Shady Cove. In June, 1994, we turned the apartment over to Peter and Joy.

The first night we spent in the trailer, my sister Johnnie phoned to tell us that my mother had died earlier that night in Phoenix, Arizona. It was June 9ᵗʰ, 1994. Zelda Opal (Wilkinson) Price was 86 years old and died from a massive heart attack. She had not been well for some time. It was a great comfort to know she was safe in the arms of

Jesus, free from all pain and suffering.

Dale borrowed Paul's pickup, and we drove to Phoenix for the funeral. Pat came up from Tucson and attended the funeral with us. After the funeral we drove to Tucson to visit Pat.

Even during this distressing time, Dale was planning ahead. He had borrowed Paul's pickup so we could retrieve some of our belongings that were in storage. We drove through the night to Ventura, California as the pickup didn't have air conditioning and it was much cooler to travel at night. We went to the yard where the things were stored in a container, and Dale loaded our mattress onto the back of the pickup. As he was tying the load down, our friend Colgate Clark came over and took one look at Dale and could tell he was very ill. He said, "Dale, you are not well enough to drive back to Oregon now. Come home with me, Brother, and go to bed."

Fortunately, Dale listened to Colgate, and we went home with him and Dale went to bed. After a visit to the doctor, he was diagnosed with pneumonia. A day or so later, even though he was being treated with antibiotics, he was still running a high fever. We started treating him for malaria. We had learned from experience to always have the antimalarial tablets in our travel bag. A few days later, after completing both courses of medicine and regaining his strength, Dale was ready to travel again, and we made the trip home to Oregon. We returned to the travel trailer in Shady Cove where we spent the rest of the summer.

In late September, my sister Johnnie phoned to tell us that she would like to come for a visit. When Dawn Lyon learned of our situation, she invited all of us to stay in her home, since she was going on a trip. Dale and I would use her bedroom, and Johnnie would stay in the guest bedroom, near Linda's room.

Because of some car trouble, Johnnie was late arriving that day. As she got out of her car at Dawn's place, she was experiencing great pain in her legs. Even as she came into the house, she complained of the intense pain she was enduring.

The next morning, a Saturday, Dale had an errand, and I needed to go out to the travel trailer and finish cleaning out the refrigerator. Johnnie and I spent a delightful day together, talking about old times and laughing a lot. Because of her painful legs, she sat with them propped up in the recliner most of the time. When the mail came in the afternoon, there was a video tape from Julie. That night, back at Dawn's house, the three of us watched it together. How we enjoyed watching little two years old Emily opening a package and seeing the surprised look on her face at the contents! Johnnie had sent the package containing a toy stuffed rabbit, a replica of her live, pet rabbit, which Emily had enjoyed when Johnnie visited us earlier in Eagle Point.

After enjoying the evening together, Johnnie said she was tired and needed to go to bed. We casually said good-night and each of us headed to our rooms.

At about 5:00 a.m. there was a knock on our bedroom door, and Linda called out to us, "There is something wrong with your sister. I can hear her in the bathroom."

I jumped up quickly and went to the bathroom at the other end of the house. As I entered, I saw Johnnie was sitting on the commode with her head leaning against the wall. She was as white as the paint on the wall. I asked, "What's wrong, Johnnie?"

She answered me, "I don't know. I felt all right when I came in here." Those were the last words she ever spoke.

By then, Linda had called to Dale and he came to see what was happening. Together, Dale and Linda lifted Johnnie, and laid her down in the hall. But it was too late to help her; she had passed away. I had called 911 and the paramedics tried to resuscitate her but it was not possible. We followed the ambulance in our car to the hospital. There I had to take care of all the last minute details and fortunately, I had taken her purse with me.

Of course, there would have to be an autopsy, since she had died while visiting us at home. It was determined that the cause of death was massive blood clots in her lungs. Johnnie Pauline Lonning was 58 years old. She passed away October 2nd, 1994.

Dale immediately phoned Phoenix, Arizona, to let the rest of my family know about her death. It was decided that her memorial service would be held in Tacoma, where she lived near Seattle. A few days later, Dale and I drove to Tacoma to attend the memorial service. Another memorial service for her was held in Phoenix a short while later.

Buying a House in Eagle Point
By Arvalee

Dale and I continued to live in the travel trailer throughout the winter, but since we would be staying in the States indefinitely, we felt the Lord would have us find a house to buy.

In December, 1994, Julie, Dan and Emily came to visit us again, traveling by train. Once again, we faced the dilemma of having visitors with not enough room for everyone to sleep! This time, friends in Shady Cove, Don and Judy Savage, loaned us a motor home, which we parked close beside the travel trailer, and Julie and family slept there. Then, the senior Hubbards, Will and Jo, told us we could all move to their house in Eagle Point, where we could celebrate Christmas together, as they were going away on a little trip.

In this larger home, Julie and I were able to prepare a nice dinner for Christmas and invited Grandpa Bud and Granny Joye, and the rest of the family including Dan and Sandra, Peter and Joy, Paul and Jean, and all their children. Pat came from Tucson, and he stayed with Grandpa and Granny. There were 20 of us for dinner.

When we got back to the travel trailer, I discovered my back was giving me some real problems. We were thankful that Peter and Joy were able to drive Julie, Dan and Emily to Klamath Falls to catch the train back to Wisconsin as that was the nearest station.

In January, I went to the doctor and met Dr. Henderson who took x-rays of my back which determined my problem to be spinal stenosis. Dr. Henderson told me that I would need back surgery and explained the procedure that would be done. He gave me a shot of cortisone, which eased the pain until a date could be set for surgery. Somehow, God gave me complete confidence that Dr. Henderson would be able to help my back and I did not hesitate in making the decision to have the surgery.

In all of these trials we knew God's hand was upon our lives and that He was in control of all that came our way.

Since we had decided it would be wise to buy a house, Dale had inquired of a friend, Larry Olson, if he knew of anything for sale. He told us that his mother owned a house that had been a rental for several years. He thought she might be willing to sell it. He gave us the address, and told us to drive past it and if we thought we might be interested, he would approach his mother and ask her if she was willing to sell it.

In January we drove past the house. The outside of the house sure didn't make a favorable impression on us! But, it was in an ideal location, being only three blocks away from where Grandpa and Granny lived in the trailer park. This added to the attraction of buying it. We definitely wanted to have a look inside. Mrs. Olson, the lady who owned it, was willing to sell it so arrangements were made to have a look inside.

We had one tour through the house, and could tell from that brief inspection that the house had possibilities. We knew it would need a lot of fixing up, inside and out. It was a real blessing to us when we learned Mrs. Olson had reduced the price on it considerably, due to the fact that we were missionaries.

Finally, the day came in March when escrow closed and we signed the papers on it. We got possession of the house on April 15th, 1995. Now we were able to start work on it. We found that major work needed to be done, to even make it livable! It had three bedrooms and two baths and was located at 599 Sherman Way, Eagle Point, OR 97524.

We had to completely gut the kitchen and start over. Dale and I designed a lovely kitchen plan and were able to hire a local cabinet maker, Roger Gratzinger, who built and installed top of the line oak cabinets to our specifications. Our friend, Hank Kleker, worked alongside Roger to get our cabinets finished. While redesigning the kitchen, a new larger window was installed over the sink. A dishwasher, stove top, wall oven and a new refrigerator were purchased, too.

A furnace and air conditioner had to be installed, as well. All the inside rooms had to be painted and the living room ceiling had to be repaired. Wall-to-wall carpets were installed in the living room and bedrooms. New subflooring had to be laid in the dining room and linoleum was laid in the kitchen, dining room and the two bathrooms.

It was a blessing that two of our sons, Peter and Paul, each devoted several days of hard work assisting Dale in some of the remodeling work on the house. However, most of the work had to be done by skilled workmen who had to be hired for the job.

What a thrilling day it was when we moved into our new home on May 24th, 1995. The kitchen cabinets were not completed, so we had to sort of make shift at first, but do you think we minded? Not a bit! It was just wonderful to finally be in our own home.

On the 31st of May, Peter, Joy, Jeff and Chris came to stay with us until they caught their flight to Florida to visit Joy's family before leaving for the field. While they were with us we had quality family times when Paul and Jean and Dan and Sandra and all their kids came over for picnics.

Some of our friends from Brownsboro Community Church gave us a house warming party, organized by Marilyn Maloney. That was a wonderful memorable time to make them all welcome to our new home, while they welcomed us into the community.

After several years, we added a front and back porch and painted the outside of the house. Then we planned extensive landscaping to the front and back yards which Paul did for us. This landscaping included planting many varieties of beautiful flowers, shrubs and bulbs.

When we bought the house, Dale told me he was looking to the Lord to have the house paid for within a year. I really thought he was being unrealistic. What a miracle it was when we actually had the house completely paid for within a year! We not only made the payments on time, but often we were able to make larger payments than required.

Earlier we had invested in the purchase of building materials for the house we planned to build in Rabaul. We had also purchased two Jeeps that we planned to use there. All these things were stored in a container in Ventura, ready to be shipped. When our plans changed, we had no use for them but instead, we were able to sell everything. The field of Papua New Guinea bought all the building materials and one of the Jeeps. The other Jeep was bought by our local mail delivery lady. The money from the sale of these things was applied to the house payments.

We had quite a surprise when our dear friends, Forest and Nancy Stine, sent us a very large gift from an inheritance he received from his sister, Stella. This, too, was applied to the house.

It was indeed a thrilling day when we had the deed to the house in our possession. This house was such a wonderful improvement to the community and it was no longer an eyesore in the neighborhood.

A Sad Time
By Arvalee

During all this time, my dad, down in Phoenix, was having a lot of difficulties since my mother had passed away. We heard on November 19th, 1995, that my dad passed away. John Paul Price was 88 years old and the cause of his death was a heart attack.

My dad's spiritual condition had been a concern to us for years. But my mother wrote when he was about 72 years old that he had accepted the Lord as his Savior. A short time after that, when we were on furlough and visiting them, he and Dale were in the kitchen. Dale was writing letters and my dad was standing beside the refrigerator. He said, "You know Dale, all those years ago when I tried to stop you from going to New Guinea; I don't know what was the matter with me."

Dale got up and hugged him, saying, "Why, Paul, you weren't a believer at that time. You didn't understand why we were going. You just didn't want me to take Arvalee and the grandchildren over there."

When I was still at home, the only time my dad would go to a church service was on the rare occasion when I would be playing my steel guitar. Then he would come with me and most of the time he would accompany me, playing the chords on his guitar.

On a Sunday morning, he would sit reading the newspaper and my mother would ask him repeatedly if he was ready to take her and us children to church. Finally, he would get up and drive us there. Most of the time, we were late, which was an embarrassment to me, and I know it must have embarrassed my mother as well.

In spite of such things, all during my growing up years, my dad was a very special person in my eyes. I thought anything my dad did was all right. He was a very honest, upright, hardworking man, who never drank or abused my mother or us kids in any way.

When Dale and I were leaving for the mission field in 1953, Daddy wouldn't even converse with us about it. I remember trying to talk to him about the Lord, but that, too, was a closed subject.

On our second furlough from New Guinea, my parents came to visit us in Santa Paula, California, where we were living. We had a missionary's book, *Commandos for Christ,* by Bruce Porterfield, lying on the coffee table. My dad, an avid reader, sat up most of the night reading that book until he had finished it. After that it seemed he had mellowed considerably, and slowly his attitude changed towards us.

Knowing all this, we were confident when Dad died that he was now in a much better place.

Dale and I drove to Phoenix to attend his funeral. Pat again drove up from Tucson to be there with us. Wayne and Vern, my two brothers, and my youngest sister, Sue, and some of their families, attended Dad's funeral, too. They were the only ones left of my family.

Back Surgery
By Arvalee

Finally, near the end of that year, I started having severe pain in my back again. Dr. Henderson told me it was time to have surgery. The cortisone shots had enabled me to be practically pain free for almost a year. Surgery was done on December 22nd, 1995, because that was the next date the doctor had available. I didn't mind spending Christmas in the hospital; I just wanted to get the ordeal over with.

Before surgery, Dr. Henderson told me that when I woke up after the surgery I would feel like a semi-truck had run over me. The surgery went fine, but I had a close call afterwards when I almost didn't wake up from the anesthetic! I recall the nurse's aide calling my name and gently slapping my face to arouse me. I can distinctly remember thinking, *leave me alone and let me sleep.* Fortunately, an RN, who was just going off duty, came into the room and recognized the problem. She told Dale I was having an adverse reaction to the morphine I had been given for pain, so she gave me an injection to reverse it. Later Dr. Henderson told Dale that I should never again take morphine, as I couldn't tolerate it.

I was making good progress and was able to walk unassisted up and down the halls for several days. I came out of the hospital wearing a brace, which I had to wear for about six months. Dale had to assist me in bathing and dressing because I was quite limited in what I could do.

That surgery was life changing for me and I have been thankful ever since for the skill of Dr. Henderson, who made it possible. Ultimately, I gave praise to the Lord for leading me to this wonderful surgeon and giving me the faith to believe he would be able to help me and the courage to undergo the surgery.

More Sadness with Rejoicing
By Arvalee

On January 18th, 1996, Dad Palmer passed away. Lester James (Bud) Palmer was 87 years old. He died from lung cancer.

What a privilege it had been to live nearby, so that when Grandpa needed assistance, Dale was there. Ever since Grandpa had been diagnosed with cancer and radiation had been prescribed by his doctor, Dale had been able to help. He drove his dad two or three times a week to the appointments for his treatments.

Many times, these trips turned out to have amusing results. Once, Dale needed to stop on the lower floor of the building, but he put his dad on the elevator to go up to the doctor's waiting room. Upon arriving there, the receptionist asked him where his son was that day. Bud replied, "Oh, I rode my bicycle today."

She replied, "Oh, it's much too hot to ride a bicycle."

To which he answered, "Oh, I used my umbrella." This caused her, the other assistants and even the people in the waiting room to about double over in laughter, because they knew he was just kidding. Even though he was a very sick man, he never lost his sense of humor.

Towards the end, he was no longer able to eat the things he enjoyed. Once, he asked Dale to stop and buy him a hot dog. After one bite he couldn't eat any more. The radiation had affected his esophagus so that he could hardly swallow his food.

Dale recalls the day, about six or eight months before he died, when Bud and Joye were going over their papers that had instructions about their burial plans. They had written down that they would like the local Baptist minister to perform their burial services. Dale said to them, "But there is no longer a Baptist church here in Eagle Point, Dad. Remember, it closed a few years ago? Would you like my pastor to come talk with you?"

Bud answered, "Yes, I would like that."

Dale had tried to talk to his dad many times about the Lord, but finally Bud had told him, "Never talk to me again about this." Our kids had talked to him, too, but no one had ever been successful. We were all concerned that Grandpa did not know the Lord. He knew, as we all did, that he didn't have much longer on this earth.

Dale asked our pastor, Darrel Backus, to come visit his dad, whom he had never met. Dale was there when Darrel came and he introduced them. Getting right to the point, Darrel simply asked him, "What are you going to say to God when you stand before him, Bud?"

At that, Grandpa said, "I don't know."

Then Darrel asked him, "Would you like to know what to say?"

He answered, "Yes, I would."

Then, Darrel explained the gospel to him and led him to the Lord. Grandpa acknowledged his sin and asked the Lord to save him. What great rejoicing this wonderful news brought to our hearts. Greater joy, we know, was offered to God by the angels in heaven when another sinner was saved by grace.

About two months before his death, Granny Joye decided it was time to move to a rest home. It was in the rest home that he passed away. But he was ready, and we all rejoiced to know that his sins were forgiven and that he was in Heaven.

On February 11th, 1996, Joye (Carter) Palmer passed away. She was 92 years old. She and Bud had been married for thirty-five years. She was buried beside Grandpa in the Antioch Cemetery in Sam's Valley near White City, Oregon.

Dale and I had been under a lot of stress, with my surgery, and the deaths of our parents, so with the doctor's permission, we took a trip back east on March 12th, 1996. We first visited the headquarters of New Tribes mission in Florida. We also made a stop in Ft. Worth, Texas, to see Dale's relatives.

The best part of the trip was the time we spent with Julie and her family in their home in Waukesha, Wisconsin. I was still limited in my activities, so Dale had been doing all the housework and cooking, as well as looking after me. I know it was a relief to him to be there with Julie, who looked after us extremely well. It was just what we both needed; healing in body and soul.

Our Trip to PNG, 1997
By Arvalee

After being in the States for four years, the way was opening up for us to make a trip to Papua New Guinea. We planned a visit of six months. We left in March and returned in September.

We invited Jim Covington, one of the pastors from our home church in Bell Gardens, California, to go with us. He could only go for three weeks but we felt blessed that he would take that time to accompany us to the field and see some of the work we had been involved in throughout our missionary career, and to meet some of our national friends and our fellow missionaries, as well.

Dale and I left home in Eagle Point on March 23rd and, en route to the airport in San Francisco, visited our friends Homer and LaVera Hancock and Olive Grove in Redding, California. Then we drove to Sebastopol, California, where we stayed with Kirk and Carol Glenn. Kirk drove us to the airport in San Francisco where we boarded the plane on March 25th.

We met up with Jim at the Los Angeles airport and saw his parents and others who had come to see him off. Thus began our long flight across the Pacific Ocean to our destination in Australia.

We had a very busy but pleasurable visit in Plumpton where the New Tribes Mission headquarters was located. A special event was having dinner in the home of our beloved friends and co-workers, Ted and Faye Albrecht. Ted was the one who came to Maprik to build our house way back in 1980. Faye was an excellent cook and served us a delicious roast leg of lamb dinner, with all the trimmings. Adding to the enjoyment was the presence of other guests; one of their grandsons, Rick, and our mutual longtime friend, Arnold Davis, whom we had first met in 1953 when our ship, the *PARRAKOOLA,* first docked.

We had visitors on two different days during the time we were there. One day Norma Walsh came to see us. Another day Arnold Davis came over. It was great catching up with these old friends who served in New Guinea with us in the 1950s, although they lived in the Watut and we generally saw them only once a year at conference time. It was a special pleasure to be able to introduce them to Jim, and to show him around the mission's training camp and Bible School.

Our friend, Gail Middleton, took the three of us to the Featherdale Park where we saw many Australian animals, including kangaroos, a koala bear, a cassowary, a dingo, an echidna, penguins, a kookaburra, a wombat, an eagle, and a crocodile. All this was a great opportunity to expose Jim to the land down under. We especially enjoyed it since we were personally escorted by our dear *Aussie* friend.

Jim even ventured out on his own, and later presented us with nice pictures of the famous Sydney Opera House, and the Sydney Harbor Bridge, known locally as The Coat Hanger. We three spent a day in the Blue Mountains, again with our friends the Middletons, as our guides.

We spent an enjoyable day with Trevor and Fran McIlwain. Trevor is the author of the Firm Foundations Chronological Bible Approach to teaching the scriptures, which has been very successful in many parts of the world and has been used by many mission groups.

At the Bible College we met many of the students, some of whom we had known as children, when their parents were on the field in New Guinea. Others were new to us, but it is thrilling that some of them continue serving the Lord on the mission field. One couple, Seong and Mina Mun, are laboring in the Kora dialect of the West Gimi tribe in Papua New Guinea.

April 3rd found us in Port Moresby, the capital of Papua New Guinea, where we had a delightful night's rest in the mission's guest house. It was thrilling to see this beautiful home in operation because Dale had been instrumental in purchasing the original building on behalf of New Tribes Mission. It had been thoroughly refurbished and was a facility greatly used by the Lord in ministering to the traveling missionaries. Some were just arriving on the field for the first time, while others were on their way to their homelands for a much needed furlough or for medical treatment.

At that time it was managed by Lawrence and Shirley Verduyn, whose oldest daughter, Laura, would marry our grandson, Chris, a few years later! Chris and Laura went to school together in the Highlands. What a fantastic ministry and gift of helps these folks had, reaching out to travelers and meeting their need for rest, as well as providing wonderful meals. We surely appreciated this beautiful home and the ministry of the Verduyns.

While in Port Moresby, the three of us visited the FNBC (Fellowship of National Bible Churches) Bible Training Center, and our national friends working there, Iteve and Lidia Amole, and Samuel and Jullie Goro and their families, who were all from the Highlands. Iteve and Samuel held night classes to teach the Chronological Bible Approach to those who were newly converted to Christ and to those interested in learning more about the Bible.

The next day, the three of us departed for Goroka, in the Eastern Highlands via the Twin Aztec. It was piloted by Ole Ottosen and John Mark Estelle who served with the aviation department of New Tribes Mission. In Goroka, we were met by many of our friends, both nationals and missionaries. There was Pastor Hagen, who continued to preach the gospel in the Genoka settlement, where we had attended services back in 1990 and 1991. This dear friend faithfully served the Lord although he had meager funds for ministry and the support of his family of five children. At one time, Hagen collected pop bottles, which he sold for funds to pay tuition fees for his kids' schooling. Now he was working as a gate watchman at the hanger for the New Tribes Mission Aviation Department.

We visited the mission headquarters, at Numonohi, and visited with many friends there. We had an enjoyable time over lunch one day with Bob and Noby Kennell. Bob was now serving as the Field Chairman, with Noby right by his side assisting him in whatever capacity necessary.

One day, a vehicle was hired and Dale drove us out to Olaguti. Originally, it was the base where the school first started for our kids. This was the base where we had a dormitory for the missionary children, taking care of ten to twelve children. Now this base was serving as the National Missionary Training Center. We met most of the national students who were in attendance there, whose desire was to serve the Lord as missionaries to their own people. We had many fond memories of days gone by in Olaguti.

Along the way we passed the hill that Dale used to transverse on his motorcycle in the 1950s, while hauling supplies from Goroka for three families. He carried food and other items in backpacks, while at the same time balancing five gallon drums of fuel or drums of flour on the fuel tank. This was a very tricky and dangerous maneuver! In time, he learned to remove the load at the bottom of the hill, walk beside the running cycle and guide it up the hill. Then he returned and carried the items up one at a time. This method was not nearly as risky or physically taxing. This was in the days before there was a road!

It had been a pleasure showing Jim around and acquainting him with some of our friends. However, we were disappointed that bad weather prevented a visit to the Gimi tribal area for Jim to see the work that Dale had spearheaded in the early 1950s and where we had labored for many years.

Now it was time for the three of us to move on. On April 7th, we flew to Wewak, in a 206 Cessna with the New Tribes Aviation. It was so familiar flying over the mountainous terrain, viewing the miles of dense jungle, and finally seeing below us the broad, slow flowing Ramu River as we headed to Wewak. As we flew over the Madang Province, on an island in the distance, we could see a smoking volcano. Then before us was the Wewak airstrip, with Peter and Joy there to greet us. It was wonderful to see their smiling faces once more.

What an enjoyable time we had in the East Sepik Province. Once again we had an opportunity to show Jim around. While we were in Wewak, Peter took us all to Wom Beach. There we had spent many pleasurable hours on vacation with our kids, Julie and Dan, when they were still on the field with us. Wom Beach is the site of the World War II Memorial Park and commemorates the Japanese surrender and signing of the Peace Treaty to the American and Allied Forces in 1945. There are rows of small white crosses to mark the gravesites of many of the soldiers lost in battle. Guns are on display and plaques tell the story in some detail.

Flying on to Maprik, we attended the Sepik Field Conference, celebrating the 25th year since the Sepik work was established. Although some of the first missionaries were no longer in the work, new missionaries had come to the field to join the laborers. It was thrilling to hear the reports from some of these folks, which made it a reality of just how much the field had grown and made the gospel available to even more tribes.

At the present time, there are works in the May River Iwam, the Ama, the Owininga, the Nimo, the Abelam, the Bisorio, the Waxe, the Iteri, the Mugumute, the Siawi, the Inaru, the Nakwi, the Sorimi, the Saniyo, and the Malamuamanda tribes.

The time at conference was an opportunity for Dale and me to celebrate our 49th wedding anniversary on April 12th. Joy made the day one of remembrance for us with a cake she had baked and decorated for the occasion.

Conference was always a time the missionaries looked forward to, as most of them worked in a tribe in a bush location. Most of them had not been out to civilization in many months and looked forward to seeing their friends. A carnival and special games were planned for the children. Songs and music were greatly appreciated by all, and the more talented missionaries entertained us with special songs, and even managed to put on skits for our enjoyment.

Always, there was a gifted speaker to minister from the Word of God. Sometimes one was chosen from among our own missionaries. At other times, a man with spiritual gifts and qualifications was asked to come from overseas. These messages were challenging to us spiritually and especially satisfying for ones who were devoid of fellowship, having spent extended times in remote tribal areas.

In addition to the above activities, a Commissioning Service was held for Peter and Joy's oldest son, Jeff, and his fellow senior graduates from the Numonohi Christian Academy, located at the main mission base in the Highlands about ten miles from Goroka. These students all had parents who worked in the Sepik. This was a special time for them as they each were looking forward to the day they would go out into the world as adults.

We especially wanted Jim to see one of the tribal works in the Sepik area. From Maprik we were able to visit the Pukapuki tribal area. We traveled by air with one of the mission's aircraft to reach this tribe. After landing on the airstrip cut out of the jungle, we had a short ride by speed boat to the base of a steep hill, which we had to climb to reach the houses of the three families working there; Tim and Laurel Schroeder, Dave and Cindy Wall and Dave and Debbie Rodges.

We met some of the very primitive tribal people and saw some of their simple artifacts which they were offering for sale. The national houses were unique, being built about ten feet off the ground on seemingly spindly tree saplings.

Tim and Laurel Schroeder were holding literacy classes each day, teaching the people to read and write in their own language. These classes were attended by young and old alike, as none of them could read, since their language had never been written before.

In corresponding with Jim recently about this visit he wrote in answer to some of my questions: "Yes, Tim was my tour guide. He took me all around the village, showing everything to me."

He continued, "The Rodges were most helpful in taking care of building tasks and other things of that nature, which freed up Dave and Tim to work on their teaching. What a spirit of unity and cooperation they showed, willing to work without fanfare for the common goal! I don't remember if the Schroeders were teaching literacy classes just yet or if they were in their beginning stages. They were within just a few months of presenting the gospel when we were there. In my video, I had a picture of one of the men we talked to. At that time he was not yet saved. Of course, as Tim and Dave continued their teaching, when the news hit the NTM Daily Bulletin and the letters from Pukapuki came in, this man was listed as one of the new believers. I showed that video in Wyoming in October, and seeing his face again was a bit overwhelming because I met him as an unbeliever and now he was a brother in Christ."

After these excursions from Wewak, it was time for Jim to depart and return home. His allotted time for the trip was over, and he caught a commercial flight back to the States.

From the Sepik, Dale and I flew back to Goroka with Peter and Joy, where we attended Jeff's graduation from high school. We were included in the family dinners at the beautiful Bird of Paradise restaurant in Goroka, which the entire senior class had planned in honor of their graduation. It was a truly memorable occasion.

After this, we were able to return to the Sepik and spend quality time at Maprik. We even stayed in the original mission house on base which had been built in 1972, where we'd first lived. It was now set up as a guest house and had been enlarged considerably. While there, we visited more of the tribal people in the local church at Maprik. Peter and Joy and Gordon and Janet Woghlemut had worked in the Abelam tribe and some folks had been saved and a church had been established. Alas, some of our dear friends had never trusted the Lord as their Savior.

Dale and I made several short trips to tribal areas and became better acquainted with some of the new missionaries working in these areas. A couple of these areas were the Malamuamanda and the Inaru.

During this period of time Dale and I visited Pukapuki again. We assisted with a team of young people who were in Papua New Guinea with the Interface (ITF) program. The program was designed to expose them to tribal work, learning language and reaching the lost with the gospel. Many of the young people who have been introduced to missions through the Interface program have had their lives changed, and the Lord has directed them into full time missionary service. It was a pleasure being able to work with them and get to know them. We trust our lives made an impact on them, as they were at the crossroads of making a decision about their future.

Our time in the Sepik had been an exceptional time, but now it was over, and it was time to say goodbye. We departed for the Highlands again where we looked forward to completing our tour and visiting more of our friends. Our main desire was to visit the Gimi area, trusting the weather would permit a flight into Negibi.

Back To the Highlands
By Arvalee

We had many national friends in the Highlands tribal areas, having begun our work in 1953 at Kami, the first mission base in that part of the country. From there we worked in the Gimi for many years and finally lived in the Yagaria tribal area while looking after the school dormitory at Olaguti. Then there were the years we lived at the mission headquarters at Numonohi, near Goroka. Those were the years that Dale served as the Field Chairman. And we worked in the Government high school in Goroka as well, teaching the RI class. During all these years Dale served on the Field Committee.

After our arrival at Numonohi, an opportunity was presented for us to attend the national conference in Aziana along with John and Lynne White and Bill and Lynette Cottom. We felt honored that the national Christians would invite us to be a part of their conference. Dale and John shared the responsibilities of being the main speakers at this conference, which was conducted in the trade language, Pidgin English, as there were so many groups in attendance speaking different tribal languages.

This conference was remarkable in that it was planned and organized completely by the national church leaders. Folks came from as far away as the Sepik and the Watut tribal areas, and many tribes were represented from the Highlands. It was quite an expense and effort for most of the attendants. While the majority of them were able to fly in by air, some of them hiked many miles over rough mountainous trails. There were about 500 people in attendance.

All the food, except some local vegetables, had to be ordered from Goroka, and flown to the Aziana. Rice and lamb flaps (ribs) were some of the items ordered. The preparation, cooking and serving of the food was done by the local people. The food was cooked in huge copper pots over open fires. We were impressed that it was all so well organized.

As Dale and I were standing in line one day, waiting for the food to be served, a lady whom we knew from Numonohi turned to us with tears running down her cheeks and stated, "I just want to tell you that we are so thankful for you missionaries who came to New Guinea and brought us the gospel. If you hadn't been willing to leave your homelands, we may never have heard about God sending His Son to die for us." This touched our hearts so much to hear her tell us that face to face. It humbled us, too, to hear her words, and we told her that we were just thankful that we had obeyed the Lord when He called us to the mission field so many years ago.

During one of the conference meetings, while Dale was speaking, he related the story about a trip he had made with another missionary, Peter Banfield, to a remote village in the South Fore in the 1950s. Peter had heard that two tribal men had come out of the *uncontrolled* territory where they lived, and visited this village. Peter asked Dale to accompany him to this village, using two motorcycles, in hopes they could find these men and do a language check. Peter wanted to find out if they were related to the Hamtai tribe where he worked in the Watut. It was too bad, that after this strenuous trip, they didn't find the men they were looking for; they had already gone.

But let me tell you what happened from the time Dale and Peter left our home, until they arrived at the village. By the time the two of them came to the fork in the road, where they would turn towards the Fore village they were planning to visit, Dale was feeling very ill. He told Peter he could not proceed, but that he knew he could get some help if they went a few more miles to the Wycliff (*SIL*) headquarters at Aiyura.

There, after Peter inquired at the office, they were directed to the home of Walt and Vonnie Steinkraus, some very loving, caring, people, who took them in and nursed Dale back to health. He had a classic case of malaria, which prevented him from traveling on until he recovered.

Now, that is not the end of the story. Several years later, on March 21st, 1971, just before we began the Sepik work, we heard the very sad news that Walt, Vonnie and their two daughters, had died a horrific death when a landslide had completely covered their house and the village where they lived. Dale was very saddened at hearing this news. He realized this was the couple who had taken such good care of him at Aiyura way back in the 1950s. God was so gracious in taking their entire family to heaven at the same time. Their entire story is told to the glory of God, in the small book, *The Measure of Greatness,* by Hugh Steven.

After that conference meeting was over, a man named Kusi came to speak to Dale and related a most interesting story. He said, "My dad was one of those men you were looking for. When I was a young boy, my dad went on a trip out of our area. When he got back from his travels, he tried to explain to us all about the things he had seen. He told about men riding on a machine that had wheels, and about them wearing strange things on their feet. While my dad described these objects to his people, he took bamboo and rattan vines and other objects and tried to fashion wheels and a steering wheel and boots, in an effort to explain to the people what he had seen."

Kusi and his family had made a very strenuous hike over the mountains to attend the conference. While talking to Dale, Kusi told him that he had been working on an airstrip so that missionaries could come into his area with the gospel. However, he had not been successful in building one that would pass the strict codes of the Government.

It was a rewarding experience for both of us to be able to attend this conference. To see these precious people sitting down together, many of whom had been enemies a few years before was a miracle to behold right before our eyes. To see the excitement of the people firsthand, listening to the Bible messages and singing songs of praise to the Lord in the trade language, was thrilling to witness.

After the conference was over, we returned to the guest house at Numonohi and began making plans to visit the Gimi, Lord willing. It all depended on good weather. It wasn't possible to make a flight with heavy cloud cover or in rainy conditions because of poor visibility.

Our Gimi Visit
By Arvalee

Working through our New Tribes Mission Aviation flight coordinator, it was finally possible to book a flight with the *SIL* helicopter pilot. To make this trip, we had to first fly from Goroka to Aiyura, the *SIL* flight base, in a New Tribes fixed wing airplane. Then, Bill Cristobal, the pilot with *SIL*, flew us from there to Negibi, where John White had a helicopter pad near their house.

John and Lynne were prepared for our arrival because all these arrangements were made through the use of two-way radios. The trip to the Gimi only took minutes by air, whereas it took all day to travel the same distance by road.

We arrived at Negibi on Friday, August 21st. Many of our old time friends came to see us. Mu-u-nabi, who came out to Kami with her husband, Meniba, in 1955 to work for me, came to see us the first day. She hugged me and then we cried together, remembering olden times. Her first baby and our daughter, Julie, were born a few weeks apart in 1956.

Later, Inabera came to see us with his wife and family. Inabera came to work for us when he was a young boy. At that time I had told him that he wasn't big enough to chop wood and carry the very large pieces of firewood into the house. He stood as tall as he could and exclaimed, "Yes, I'm big enough and I'm strong, too." He worked for us many years and he proved to be a strong, willing and faithful worker in spite of his size.

On Monday, Soma and Lidia and their children, came for lunch. They brought some cooked rice and local greens, which we enjoyed immensely. Jekob, Soma's brother, was there, too. They told us that he had been saved the previous Sunday.

Zato and Tarabu and their family came to see us, also. We have known Zato ever since he was a very small boy, when he used to play with Dan, our youngest son. He was known as Ara-hu-o in those days. Now he is one of the church leaders and well respected in the tribe.

Bebu, a very old friend, came early Friday morning to see us. Bebu was one of the first Gimis to be saved when he was building the horse trail into the Gimi with Dale. He grabbed Dale and then me and hugged us both several times and kept calling our names.

Saibai came to see us that day, too, and he did the same thing as Bebu, hugging us to show he was glad to see us. He wanted to see pictures of our kids. As he looked at them he kept saying, "They were my friends, I played with them when we were all young." Then he started crying and big tears ran down his face. To our knowledge, Saibai had never been saved.

Bau, John's neighbor, and his wife and their two children, came Friday night to see us. Bau cared for our goats when he was young. Sometimes he came back to Dale, saying the goats had gotten into a garden. Then Dale had to pay a fine to replace the garden they had destroyed.

O-tu-bari came to see us Friday morning with his family, and brought the pastor from another mission group, who had been saved. We took a photo of all of them together. O-tu-bari is Nana-o-aba's son. Nana-o-aba was a leper when we lived in the Gimi. He used to come three times a week to our house for his medicine called Dapzone. It was the medicine the Government gave for outpatient leprosy treatment. O-tu-bari led the singing in Gimi the second half of the meeting on Friday. What wonderful singing! It thrilled our hearts to sit among these Gimi Christians and hear this great group singing praises to God. Too bad we didn't have a tape recorder with us. We made a note to ourselves, that we must get a recording of our Gimi people singing.

Honepa was down on the road Friday morning when we left John's house for the meeting. He hugged Dale and started crying. "My brother," he said with tears running down his face.

Also on Friday morning, Esema, who was the Gimi tribal chief when we lived at Negibi, met us on the trail as we went down the mountain on our way to the church and the *mumu* (steam cooking). He is all stooped over and very feeble, but he was glad to see us. Later in the meeting, Dale told the group how thankful he was that Esema had invited us to come to the Gimi. That was many years ago, when Esema and Meniba came to our mission station at Kami and told Dale they would like him to come help the Gimi people.

Hapato came to the meeting late, but he came forward to shake hands with Dale and then me. I didn't recognize him, so I asked the young man who carried my chair that morning who he was. Hapato was a little older than our son Pat when we were living there before. He used to be a very handsome young man and wore a red hibiscus flower in his hair almost every day. Now, he was visibly showing the advancement of years,

R. Dale And D. Arvalee Palmer

common in all of us.

Ani-ani-mo met us in the church yard before the meeting on Friday and greeted us. I recognized him, but I mistakenly called him Asu-mu-yaba, then I corrected myself. I asked him about Asu-mu-yaba and he said he would come to see us later. Ani-ani-mo and Asu-mu-yaba were the two men who walked with Dale and me when I made my first trip into the Gimi back in 1957. These two men had helped me cross the *Zani* (Thani) River, holding my hands to prevent me from slipping off the log bridge and falling into the water far below. I had fallen down several times on the hike, and they knew it was possible again! As we hiked up Negibi Mountain and down the other side, they positioned themselves on either side of me, each gripping my upper arms, to prevent me from falling down again. I literally slid down the mountain, not needing to take any steps, since they had a firm grip on my arms. Indeed, the next day, I found both arms were quite sore and bruised. These men remained my trusted helpers and friends during all the years that we lived in the Gimi. It was great to see them again.

Sadieboro met us on the trail going down the road and held my hand and walked with me down to the church. Her sister is Mu-u-nabi, my first Gimi house helper.

On Saturday, Ha-tha-na-bo led the singing at the meeting. It was wonderful hearing the group singing again, because I had not heard Gimi singing in such a long time. The Gimis have such a unique style of singing…the men lead out with the main phrase of the song in their deeper voices and are joined by the women in their high, often shrill voices, repeating the same phrase of the song.

At the meeting that morning, Dale spoke on Cain and Abel and their offerings, and how God was pleased with Abel and his offering. Then he said God was pleased with Noah and his offering, too. He spoke on Abraham and his offering of Isaac. O-tu-bari *turned the talk*, as we say in Pidgin English, into the Gimi language, or he interpreted for Dale, who was speaking in Pidgin English. Then Dale spoke on Mary of Bethany from the Gospels. He brought out the points that:

On Mary's first meeting with Jesus-- He was a good teacher.
On her second meeting-- she knew He was the Son of God.
On her third meeting-- she came to worship Him (Matthew 26:6-13 and Mark 14:3-9).

He also shared from Ephesians 5:2 that Jesus offering His life was a sweet smell to God. Dale continued speaking each day to the group of many Gimis who gathered. On Saturday, he spoke on the yoke, and again, O-tu-bari was the interpreter. He shared from 1 Corinthians 1:9, Matthew 11:25-30, and 1 Kings 19:19.

He spoke on Missions: Pray, Give and Go from Rev 5:8, 9, and then he challenged the believers from Matthew 9:35-38: Pray God will send missionaries to those who have never heard the gospel message. O-tu-bari again interpreted the message for Dale.

On Sunday, for the 3rd meeting, Dale talked on Giving and gave his testimony of how God provided through other missionaries and friends to buy our tickets for the ship in 1953. (He spoke from Philippians 4:15, Matthew 6:19-21, Haggai 1:1-11, Matthew 28:19, 20, and Matthew 24:14). We were in Australia for three months and we helped each other to get to New Guinea. There were Tom Palmer, Don McCurdy and family and us with our three sons.

When our allotted time was over in the Gimi and we were ready to leave, another *SIL* helicopter picked us up. Our flight path took us south via Amusa because John White wanted to visit the Christians there. This saved him a long strenuous hike. After dropping John off, the pilot then flew Dale and me to the Wantakia tribal area to visit Mike and Sally Cordle. We had a quick visit with these special friends while the pilot waited for us.

It was time to leave the Highlands, but we had another little journey to make before we made the final departure for the States. We had a real desire to visit Rabaul, East New Britain again. Of all the places we had lived during our years in the land of Papua New Guinea, some of our fondest memories were of the years 1991 and 1992 that we had spent in Rabaul. It was also the most beautiful and idyllic location.

We needed to see for ourselves the devastating results of the two volcanoes that had erupted on September 19th, 1994; Vulcan and Tavuvur, which were located on opposite sides of Simpson Harbor and upon which the town of Rabaul was situated.

Visiting Rabaul, 1997
By Arvalee

We departed from Goroka airport on August 29th, 1997, and arrived in Port Moresby at 10:05 a.m. Iteve Amole and Samuel Goro were waiting for us at the gate. They would be our tour guides for the day. They helped Dale load our large suitcase in the truck as well as our carry-on luggage. Then they drove us to the guest house to leave the larger luggage. We would only take a small case with us to Rabaul.

Dale surprised Norman McCready calling out, "Hello, wee man." Norm was the Irish missionary who had headed up the house building project in Rabaul, when we lived there. Now, Norm and his crew were in Port Moresby, building an addition onto the guest house.

Iteve then drove us to the Christian Book Store and we ordered a book in Pidgin English. Then we went to the Mobile Station Snack Bar at Ela Beach, where we had an enjoyable meal of hamburgers and chips and a good visit with Iteve and Samuel.

Before we returned to the States, Dale wanted to find a friend that we had first met in Rabaul. We knew he had been transferred to Port Moresby, so Iteve drove us to Ela Motors at Badili. There Dale found out that James Agi did indeed work there, but he was out to lunch. Dale left word that he would come back later.

Again, Iteve drove us back to the airport and dropped us off so we could catch our flight to Hoskins, West New Britain. We had to spend a night there at the Island's New Tribes Mission headquarters, before proceeding to Rabaul the next day.

It was a nice day for flying. We had a good flight to Hoskins and the plane was quite full. We arrived on time and Dave and Nancy Brunn were there to meet us. We went to the mission base and stayed in the # 4 apartment at the mission guest house. The base was like a new place, as there were so many new buildings that we had never seen before. We showered and went to Brunn's house for a nice baked chicken dinner.

The next morning, on August 30th, we flew to Rabaul; a one hour flight. We didn't recognize anything as we came in for landing, as the old airstrip had been destroyed by the volcanoes.

The new airstrip is called Tokua. There was nothing around the airstrip that looked familiar. In the distance we could see the barrenness and the volcanoes still standing. We caught an airport bus that took us to the former town of Rabaul. There was a sign reading Kokopo 10 km and Rabaul 40 km. Now, we realized the new airstrip, Tokua, was a good distance from Kokopo. It seemed Kokopo had not suffered from the eruption, as the wind had been blowing the ash away from it. As we traveled along, we could see the volcanoes in the distance and the results of the eruptions. Beyond Kokopo, there was utter devastation in every direction. Completely barren mountains, covered with powdery grey ash, now replaced the lush green vegetation that we had been accustomed to. And this was four years since the eruptions had taken place! We could only imagine what it was like during, or immediately following, the eruptions.

As we traveled along, we passed by the caves where the Japanese had kept their barges. These caves had been dug by the prisoners of war and also some of the national people who were used as forced labor. These five huge barges were hauled out to sea using railroad like tracks. The Japanese used the barges, under cover of darkness, to transport supplies from their submarines to the caves.

We passed a church and many villages along the road. Finally, we came to Vulcan, the first volcano. Before the eruption, Vulcan was a small mountain rising up from the ocean floor quite near the shore. Now, it covered four times the area in the ocean as well as covering a large area of land. The road had been completely covered with ash for several miles and we now drove over the top of it. There were huge crevasses, ten to fifteen feet deep, made by the mud flows and flow of ash all along the sides of the road. It is hard to describe.

Finally, we came to the paved road again. All the trees showed signs of immense heat… some were nothing but tall charred posts sticking up out of the ground. A few coconut palms had dried brown outer leaves, but surprisingly, there were some green leaves growing from the center of the tree. This was evidence of life still trying to spring forth.

Farther along, we came into the town of Rabaul. At first, there was not much evidence of the eruption. We recognized the coconut factory, Barlow's Supermarket, and a few trade stores. Some of the stores were still standing along that stretch of the road. However, once we turned onto Malaguna Road we began to see more evidence of the eruption.

When we arrived at the Hamamas Hotel it was almost noon. It was about an hour's drive from the airport. We had quite a shock when we found out the bus was not an airport courtesy bus, but they charged K20 for each person! It was fortunate that we had the cash with us. You'd think by now we'd have learned to ask a few questions!

After settling into our room, we took a walk around town and took a few pictures. The swimming pool at the club was filled almost to the top with ash and the post office had been destroyed. We only recognized the cement steps leading up to it. The giant I-beams from the roof were crumpled on the ground. The frames of the walls were all that was standing.

Dale took a picture of me standing in the doorway of the pharmacy and I could touch the top of the doorway because the ash was piled so high. The words PHARMACY above the door and at the side looked as bright as when they had first been painted. Inside was a pile of rubble covered over with ash. Everywhere before us, it looked like it could have been a war zone.

Arriving back at the hotel, I discovered my white bobby sox infiltrated with grey, talcum powder like ash. The streets, still covered with layers of ash, had been smoothed with bulldozers and most of the ash had been piled high onto the sides of the road, as if it was a pile of snow.

The Hamamas Hotel had been refurbished after the eruption, and once inside the grounds and the building, there was no visible sign that any catastrophe had occurred. We were able to spend one night in the hotel then our plane left the next day. We would have liked to stay longer, but we were fortunate to be able to purchase tickets for an overnight flight, as the number of flights into Rabaul was restricted.

Mike, the manager of the hotel, was very friendly and remembered us from when we had lived in Rabaul. Back then he was the manager of the pharmacy. He offered to drive us around town and showed us the former mission property and other places that we had been familiar with.

Norman McCready had sent pictures of the mission house and property showing all the devastation, so we knew the house had been completely destroyed, even though parts of it remained intact. The building was no longer safe and the damaged house had been demolished to prevent any squatters from occupancy. However, it was sad to see that the house where we had lived, and where so many willing hands had worked, was no longer in existence. Now all that was left was a heap of rubble.

We could see the Maytag washing machine; the legs buried in ash. The stove likewise had been destroyed. Rust from sulfuric acid had eaten away many metal parts, like the stove door and the galvanized water tank. The remains of the chain link fence were all buried in ash, leaving only a couple of feet visible.

Next door to the mission property the Nazarene Church once stood. It had been destroyed also. One of the huge I-beams was lying on the ground. Dale stepped on it and it crumbled under his weight.

That afternoon, the 31st of August, we took a local *PMV* (public motor vehicle) bus back to the airport. We had made a few inquiries and found that it was cheaper than the airport bus we had taken before. Our fellow passengers were still as friendly as we remembered the island people to be! They chatted to us in Pidgin English and showed their friendliness to us as visitors, especially when they learned that we had lived in Rabaul before the eruptions. The driver even stopped the bus so that we could take more pictures.

Our flight took us back to Hoskins where we were told that some of our belongings, rescued from the house in Rabaul, were stored. Regretfully we had learned about it too late as our flight was departing in half an hour and it was pouring rain at the time. We hurriedly peeked in one or two of the drums, and rescued a plastic button box, of all things, and left for the airport!

We left instructions directing Tim and Sharon Simmonds to have a sale and get rid of everything that had been packed, and to use the proceeds for their literacy project. Doesn't the Word of God instruct us to hold on to earthly possessions lightly?

When we arrived back in Port Moresby, that long awaited visit with James Agi and his wife was possible. They took us out to lunch at one of the hotels and we spent a great afternoon catching up on old times.

On September 9th, 1997, upon our arrival back at Numonohi, a friend of Julie's, Matella Urakowi, looked us up at the guest house. She now worked at the mission clinic at Numonohi, while her husband, Simon, who is a teacher, was still working in Port Moresby. He would be there until December and then return to Goroka to continue his schooling. She was presently staying with Pinami and his second wife, Sarah, and Pinami's son, Sam. She wanted to hear all about Julie and her family and how they were doing. Of course, she wanted us to pass on news of her and her family to Julie, as well.

It seemed our six month visit to New Guinea had passed all too quickly. What a wonderful six months it had been, traveling to the various places of interest and visiting our many friends, both missionaries and nationals. It was certainly a time we would long remember. The time had come to return to our home in Eagle Point, Oregon.

En route to the USA, we traveled through Brisbane and visited our dear friends and co-workers, Pat and Barbara Smith. It was a joy to Dale and me to be in their home again. From the day of our arrival, it was like we had never been apart. Those few days were filled with sweet fellowship. They had suffered much heartache in their family since we had last seen them, losing two of their sons to cancer; Ken, their eldest, and Jim, who was third in their family.

An Unforgettable Trip
By Arvalee

Life had settled down for us again in Eagle Point after our return from Papua New Guinea.

One Thursday morning, on November 7th, 2002, we left home at 5:25 a.m. for Baker City, Oregon. Dale was to speak in the chapel service at the New Tribes Institute on Friday morning. The weather was beautiful, with evidence of snow in the foothills and on the sides of the road as we neared the Crater Lake area. We were hoping to make the entire trip without encountering severe weather.

Unknown to us, weather was to be the least of our troubles on this particular trip! After two hours of driving, Dale pulled into the first rest stop area to wash his face and revive himself, as he was beginning to feel a bit drowsy. As he went to put his glasses into his shirt pocket, he realized something was missing! The wallet with his driver's license was not there, and he knew immediately he had forgotten it.

He said to me, "Well, I forgot my wallet with my driver's license, so we'll have to go back home."

Turning around, we knew it would be an additional four hours driving for this trip, which normally is between 8 ½ to 9 hours, but we knew it had to be done.

Arriving back in Shady Cove, Dale dropped me off at the Two Pines Restaurant to have coffee and place our breakfast order while he went home to pick up the wallet. As planned, he arrived at the restaurant just a few minutes before they brought our food.

We both felt better after a good breakfast, and continued on our way, arriving in Baker City exactly 12 hours after first leaving home. We stopped and had a quick bite to eat and continued on to the mission where we had reserved a room. We were glad to reach our destination and be able to relax. Dale was especially tired as he does all the driving. The next morning found us refreshed and Dale's chapel service was good. We enjoyed meeting several of the new students. It was always thrilling for Dale to tell about Papua New Guinea and challenge the students to serve on the field and visit and fellowship with the folks on staff.

On our return trip to Eagle Point, we had an accident that could have been fatal.

We were making good time as there wasn't much traffic on the highway that morning. I was dozing with my seat reclined, when suddenly there was a very loud noise and a terrific thump. I was awake instantly and exclaimed, "Oh my, what did you hit?"

Dale said, "I don't know. I didn't see anything in the road. It must have been a piece of metal or something." However, the car didn't show any signs of damage in the way it was handling, so we continued on without even slowing down.

When we made a rest stop, a man coming from the parking lot asked Dale, "Does that gray Mercury in the parking lot belong to you?"

Dale said, "Yes, that's my car."

The man said, "Well, there's gasoline pouring out of the fuel tank, and it's all over the parking lot." We realized immediately that the gasoline tank must have been damaged by whatever the car had hit in the road, many miles behind us.

Dale phoned AAA but they wouldn't touch the car with a gas leak. The fire department was called and they sent a fire truck with nine firemen and the fire chief himself came in a pickup truck. Finally, a tow truck was called to haul our car away. The tow truck driver asked us where we wanted to go. I guess we were in shock, as we really didn't know.

He asked us, "Where do you live?"

Dale told him, "We live in Eagle Point, Oregon, 400 or more miles from here."

He said, "Where have you been staying?"

Dale answered, "At New Tribes Mission in Baker City."

He said, "I could take you there, if you have AAA+. It covers towing for 100 miles." Since we did have AAA+ insurance, we told him that is what we should do. We could stay at the mission again.

When we got to the mission, Dale had the car towed around to the back of the property where it would be out of the way. The next day some of the students worked on the gas tank and actually patched up the leak which took care of the problem until Dale was able to have the gas tank replaced after we got home again.

It is truly a miracle that our car didn't catch fire or explode immediately. God had even provided for us in the fact that these students in training were capable of welding the gas tank to make the necessary repairs. We were so grateful for His watchful care over us and for God's protecting hand and looking after us in a wonderfully miraculous way. We were safe and could make the return trip back home to Eagle Point.

We remembered hearing about an incident several years before involving a family from Illinois who were traveling to Wisconsin. As Scott and Janet Willis were driving that day, their van hit a piece of steel in the road, causing it to ignite immediately. They lost six of their children in that blazing furnace and the parents themselves were badly burned as they stood by helpless; unable to save their children. They barely escaped with their own lives.

We began to realize what a huge miracle God had performed for us, protecting us and sparing our lives. We could both have died, or been horribly burned. Indeed, GOD IS GOOD!

Our Trip to PNG, 2001
By Arvalee

Dale and I had talked about making another trip to visit Papua New Guinea some time, but we had never set a date. We had a keen desire to visit the believers and Peter and Joy once more. It's a very expensive trip; besides the cost of the air fare, there are many things to consider, such as the cost of domestic air travel, meals and housing, just to name a few. It was a decision not to be made lightly, but we knew if a trip such as this was in the Lord's plans for us, he would provide abundantly for it.

And the Lord did just that, providing in a wonderful way to enable us to make the trip again in 2001.

In February, we received an invitation from the Papua New Guinea believers to attend the 50th anniversary celebration of NTM's arrival in the country. We mentioned to some of our supporters the possibility of returning for this celebration. The next thing we knew we received a check for $500 from the Ambassador's Sunday School Class at Bible Fellowship Church. This seemed to be confirmation from the Lord to pursue our plans to make this trip.

One day we were talking on the phone to our son Pat, and Dale asked him if he would like to visit *PNG* with us. After only a moment's hesitation he said, "Yes, I would like to do that." It had been 32 years since he had left the country with us on furlough in 1969. That was after he had graduated from high school the year before.

A week or so later, we had a phone call from Anthony, Pat's eldest son. He said, "Grandpa, can I go to *PNG* with you?"

Dale said, "Oh Anthony, I think it would be better if you went with a mission group, such as Summit or Interface."

He said, "I know about those programs, and I already want to be a missionary. I want to go with you, to see the places and people you worked with."

Dale replied, "Oh, that's great. We'd be happy for you to go with us."

It's quite a story, how Pat got his vacation time from work, not only for the six weeks he had due him, but for eight weeks. He was able to travel to Australia and Papua New Guinea for seven of those weeks.

When his company was reluctant to give him his full six weeks off, our daughter Julie told him, "I'm going to pray you will be able to get your full six weeks off."

Then one day he told us on the phone, "Tell Julie she can get off her knees."

We asked, "What do you mean?"

He said, "Well, she told me she would pray that the company would give me my six weeks vacation time. So, they told me today I can have the six weeks off." Later, it turned out they gave him eight weeks off work.

Since our itinerary included traveling to Tasmania, Australia, to visit our friends, John and Gail Middleton, we left a couple of weeks before Pat and Anthony did. Later they joined us in Wewak, a northern coastal town in *PNG*, where Peter and Joy were living.

We started our trip on June 18th departing from our home in Eagle Point, Oregon. Chris, our grandson, had been living with us for several months. It was hard to leave that day because he was scheduled to have surgery on his right knee, which he had injured while playing sports. But since the trip had been scheduled for some time, we felt we should continue with our plans, trusting the Lord would look after Chris.

We visited friends along the way to San Francisco, where we boarded the airplane. In Redding, we visited our longtime friends and prayer warriors, Olive Grove, and Homer and LaVera Hancock, enjoying great fellowship with them. After our visit there, we drove on to Chico to visit our good friends, Bill and Shirley Pittenger, and spent the night. The next morning, we departed for Sebastopol and spent the night again with Kirk Glenn and his new wife, Glenn. His first wife, Carole, had passed away since we'd made the other trip to New Guinea. Kirk would drive us to the airport again and keep our car at his place.

As we were visiting after dinner, the phone rang. Kirk said, "Dale, it's for you or Arvalee."

Dale got up to take the call; after a moment he came back and said, "It's Bill. He said they found our Australian money on the bed." I couldn't believe it! I was so positive the money was in my purse that I got up and looked. Sure enough, the money was missing. I had left it on the bed! It must have blended into the cover of the patchwork quilt top, and I didn't see it! Dale and I talked a few minutes, and decided the best thing to do was for them to mail the money to us in Australia.

The next day Kirk drove us to the airport in San Francisco. There was a layover in Los Angeles before our departure. Jim Covington and our grandson Jeff came to see us there and we all went out to eat. Then it was time to go back to the airport where we boarded the plane for Melbourne, Australia.

In Melbourne we were met by a longtime friend of the Middleton's, Keith Pitt. He took us to his home for lunch. His wife Francis was at work. We had a nice lunch and took a refreshing shower and had a much needed nap, after our 14 hour flight. We almost missed the plane later, because he took us via the scenic route! He dropped us off at the curb, found a cart for the luggage, and drove away. When we went through the doors, all we could see were lines and lines of people.

Then, we heard the announcement that our flight was boarding for Burnie, Tasmania. It looked impossible to get to the counter in time to check in and board our plane. Then the most amazing thing happened. The people in those lines began lifting up the rope barriers and making a path for us to go through! I followed as Dale pushed the cart right up to the counter, like we were someone special! The attendant quickly gave us some papers, and directed us to follow her. Our hand luggage was screened and we rushed down the corridor to the boarding station. There, the boarding agent told us we needed a boarding pass. Feeling very frustrated, we turned around, and there the lady from the ticket counter was, holding our boarding passes!

They were handed to the agent, and she motioned us to proceed and board the plane! What a relief to be seated on that small plane and heading for Burnie. We had barely made it, so we were very thankful to be on the way. It was only an hour's flight over the south channel and before we knew it, the plane landed, and there were John and Gail waiting for us.

We were thankful we had our coats with us, since it was winter in the southern hemisphere, and very cold. On Sunday, while we were in church, it actually hailed so hard that it was piled up alongside the road.

A delightful week was spent with John and Gail in their small, but cozy home. It was a joy to meet and fellowship with some of their friends. We even met the Ross Palmer family, and there was much kidding about the possibility of them being Dale's long lost cousins.

We felt like real tourists, as John and Gail took us around the island to see the attractions that many people make special trips to see. We visited The Nut, a famous mountain that has a ski lift where the especially brave can go all the way to the top of the mountain. I wasn't even tempted, as it was a very cold, windy and rainy day. Instead, we had a delicious lunch of fish and chips at the little shop near the foot of the mountain.

Then we drove around the island to view the coast and the harbor. One day we visited a well-known cheese factory and bought some of their special cheeses. I enjoyed seeing John and Gail's lovely garden. Some of the plants were unique to Tasmania and I had never seen them before.

The time passed so quickly, and before we knew it, it was time to make our departure. In Melbourne, Keith was there to meet us again. That evening we met his wife Francis and took them out to eat at a special cafeteria type restaurant, which was very enjoyable. We spent the night, and the next morning we left for the airport at 5:00 o'clock, bound for *PNG*, via Brisbane.

Arriving in Brisbane, we had to change planes for the international flight. We met a man from New Guinea who was also traveling to *PNG*. We learned that he worked in Lae. Upon our arrival at the check in desk, we found out our plane would be delayed for about four hours, due to riots at the *PNG* University in Port Moresby. When we finally boarded our flight, the *PNG* man found us, and introduced himself. Misty Baloiloi was the Vice Chancellor of the University of Technology in Lae. He told us if we were coming to Lae on our trip, to look him up and he would escort us to the Wildlife Habitat where they breed the beautiful *PNG* Birds of Paradise. We also found out he is a Christian brother and we enjoyed getting to know him. He had identified us as travelers to *PNG* in the terminal because I carried a *PNG bilum*, a string bag used throughout the country. After we arrived in Port Moresby, we didn't see him again.

We had no trouble going through customs, and Marlin Keller was there to pick us up and take us to the mission's guest house, operated by Marlin and his wife, Pat. She had a delicious meal ready for a good number of guests, besides us, and our rooms were fixed up beautifully. Marlin and Pat seemed well suited to the guest house ministry; very warm and welcoming and making everyone feel very comfortable.

We spent four days in the capital city and visited the National Training Centre (Center) where Samuel and Jullie Goro continue their ministry. Iteve and his family had returned to the Highlands, due to health problems. After church on Sunday, Samuel and Jullie very graciously invited us into their home for a meal. We felt quite honored, as they prepared the food and served us. They have two little boys now, and we found out they were adopted. Their two daughters are both in high school and they are quite grown up. Before leaving, they presented us with a *PNG bilum*, a token of friendship and appreciation.

Dale had his 72nd birthday while we were in Port Moresby, and Pat had decorated the dining room with streamers over the tables and had baked and decorated a birthday cake for him. Everyone sang happy birthday to him.

The next day we left Port Moresby and arrived in Wewak. Peter and Joy were there to meet us! It was so good to see our kids, faithfully serving the Lord there in the Sepik, where we had opened the work 29 years earlier. We marveled at the growth of the Wewak base. It was now the headquarters for the Sepik work and also the orientation base for new missionaries.

We were so happy to see the lovely new apartment that had been built just for Peter and Joy. It was so clean and new looking and they had it fixed up so nice. Most of our meals were eaten on the balcony just off the kitchen, where we enjoyed the glorious view of the bay, sunsets, the hospital and the Wewak airstrip.

We were there for about a week and Pat and Anthony arrived on the next Sunday evening. It was good to see them again and great to have a mini-family reunion at Peter and Joy's house.

The next morning, Pat was out at 9:00 o'clock to start working. Peter had asked him to wire the generator into the buildings to serve as the electrical back-up during power failures. He worked on that project for a week, with Dave Rodges assisting him, but it would require much more work to complete it.

One of the local licensed electricians came to help with the work, thus making it legal. He was speaking in English but quickly switched to Pidgin English, when he realized that Pat spoke the language. Pat had been away from New Guinea for over thirty years, but he hadn't forgotten the trade language!

After that, the four of us flew to Lae, and spent a night in the mission's guest house. We were en route to Bulolo, where we would meet up with Tom Palmer. We were looking forward to the 50th anniversary celebration.

We were able to look up Mr. Misty Baloiloi, whom we had met in the Brisbane air terminal. He sent his chauffer to the mission guesthouse where we were staying and he drove us to the Wildlife Habitat. There we were met by another assistant, who showed us around the fantastically beautiful park. Throughout the paradise like sanctuary there were raised walkways, leading from one display to another. Many gorgeous birds, beautiful trees and other tropical plants were located in the park as well. It was a unique experience to have the wild Birds of Paradise flying overhead. One especially friendly bird even tried to land on Anthony's head. Inside the sanctuary, Pat took many pictures which we are still enjoying.

When the tour was over, the chauffer took us back to Mr. Baloiloi's home, where we met his family and had a cool refreshing drink. Then he most graciously took us out for lunch.

Our mission personnel then drove us to the airport at Nadzab, twenty-five miles from Lae. There we took a small New Tribes Mission Aviation plane and flew on to Bulolo with pilot David Douglas, whom we had seen grow up in New Guinea. Larry Brown, the NTM Field Chairman, along with his young son had flown into Bulolo from Goroka and were there waiting for us.

In Bulolo we were met by Tom Palmer in his new Toyota Land Cruiser. We set off for Tom's house near Asiki, the location of the 50th anniversary celebration. This was an arduous three hour trip from Bulolo. There were several trucks loaded with people, many were walking along the road, all making their way to the celebration. Several times, Tom stopped the vehicle when he saw folks he knew. Our hearts were touched, as some were not too well and could hardly continue the trip for lack of strength. Sadly, the vehicle was too full to take on any additional passengers.

The road was in terrible condition from Bulolo to Tom's location. The ruts were so deep the four wheel drive was constantly pitching from side to side. We had to hold on and brace ourselves to stay in our seats. It was a relief to be there at last! We realized that our discomfort was only for this short trip. Tom and Corinne endured the same distresses time and again as they traveled back and forth along this road.

Dale and I slept in Tom and Corinne's small guest bedroom. Pat and Anthony shared a room, and Larry and his son had a room in a house nearby belonging to Tom's helper.

The next day was the day of the celebration, held down the road from Tom's place, a 30 minute drive away, hosted by the national folks from the Hamtai Tribe. The people had cut a rough track to the top of the hill, enabling the vehicle to drive up the steep slope. We then had to walk down the other side of the hill, to where brush had been cut from the jungle to prepare a place for the meeting and where the people could sit.

As we walked along, the smell of wood smoke was in the air, as the stones were already being heated for cooking the food in a *mumu* (steam cooking). They had killed four cows and fifty-two chickens to feed the crowd of attendees. All the food would be cooked the traditional way, in a giant *mumu* in the ground. As we arrived at the designated place for the meeting, the women were busily peeling sweet potatoes and preparing other food for the *mumu*. There must have been 1,000 or 1,500 people in attendance, or maybe more.

They had prepared a grandstand, with a metal roof, to shade us from the tropical sun. To my surprise, they even prepared iced drinks and provided folding chairs for us to sit on.

The Yagaria and Hamtai believers had planned this gathering to honor and remember the missionaries who had arrived fifty years before. They each had prepared skits, which were all too realistic, showing how they used to be, in the olden days, before the missionaries arrived.

One skit portrayed how the tribal fights began; in one instance with the stealing of a bunch of bananas from a garden. In another, a couple was working in their garden, and their pig was stolen from the place nearby where they had it tied. When these deeds were discovered, it provoked the people into a fight, involving most of the men from a village, culminating in death and a house being burned to the ground. Each of the groups depicted how the gospel had changed them. The arrival of the European missionary was portrayed by an albino tribal man, wearing a felt hat!

As Anthony was sitting among them on the ground, watching the crowd, he observed an old woman silently wiping away the tears as they were streaming down her face. Perhaps it brought back memories of a real tribal fight in which she had lost a husband or a son.

Soon it was time for the speeches from some of the national men; Malcolm and Nathan from the Hamtai, an older man from the Sina-Sina and one man from the Yagaria tribe. From among the missionaries Larry Brown, Tom Palmer and Dale all spoke. It was all very well organized and impressive.

When I think of that day, I regret that neither Dale nor I thought to introduce our son and grandson, Pat and Anthony, to the crowd of people. I thought about it when the day was ended. All the while, Pat was keeping busy taking pictures, mingling in the crowd, and Anthony was sitting in their midst.

When the speeches were over, it was time to go up the mountain again, where the food had been prepared. We missionaries were directed to a building, possibly a school and church combined, where there were tables and benches for us to sit on. They brought food for each group in large aluminum pans. Corinne had thoughtfully brought metal plates and forks for our use. There were all kinds of vegetables; sweet potatoes, pumpkin, greens, corn and beans, besides the beef and chicken. None of us left the gathering hungry!

We were thankful for very pleasant weather, as it would have been quite miserable had it rained, as the people had nowhere to take shelter. We made our way back to Tom's vehicle and he drove us back to their house, passing by a trade store owned by one of the believers.

As Tom's vehicle came near the store, we noticed there was quite a gathering of excited people. Tom told us what had happened, as he and Corinne were the only ones in our group who could understand what was being said. He said two men, with their faces covered, had come into the store with guns and held them up. They got away with some bags of money but some of the younger men chased them on foot, and they soon dropped the bags.

When we arrived at the house, Tom couldn't unlock the padlock on the front door with his key. Pat looked at it, and discovered someone had jammed a stick into the keyhole, attempting to open the lock. The lock was ruined, but fortunately Tom had a key that opened his tool cabinet, which he kept on the back porch. This enabled him to get a hacksaw, and Pat sawed through the hasp, opened the door and we went inside.

When we had left the house that morning, Corinne had carefully taken the silver-ware, the cooking pans, the two-way radio and many other things out of the main room, and locked them away in the office and/or bedroom. Now I understood why she went through this ritual upon leaving the house.

I found it hard to comprehend why the people would want to break into their house after all Tom and Corinne had done for them, giving years of their lives in sacrificial service to the Hamtai people. Not only did they bring them the gospel and translate the Scriptures into Hamtai, they also taught them to read and write in their own language.

Perhaps it was someone passing by on the road that did this, not someone from among their own people. It could have been the same ones who held up the trade store.

We were all thankful to have a clean, quiet place to sleep that night. Dale and I were quite comfortable in the little guest room, except for some visitors during the night! We were disturbed a bit as we slept, by some very familiar squeaking sounds and running of tiny feet across the woven floor mats. The next morning we told Tom and Corinne there were mice occupying the guest room!

We were up very early as Tom wanted to leave for Bulolo at 7:00 o'clock. The NTMA airplane was coming to meet us there and fly us back to Nadzab to board a commercial plane for Madang.

Peter and Joy made arrangements to meet us in the coastal town of Madang and booked us rooms in the elegant Madang Resort Hotel, where many folks came for a holiday. Joy's mother, Louise Connelly, joined us as well. We found out that even an elegant hotel has its problems. There was a water leak and it flooded Pat and Anthony's room. They couldn't even walk across the floor without getting their feet wet. Other than that, we had three delightful nights there, enjoying each other's company and exploring the town.

We also visited Lyall and Martha Mankey, who were in charge of the new work for NTM in the Madang Province. They drove us out to the new mission property where they already had a mission house built with a family living there. Later, we drove to the Jais Aben diving resort, on the bay, where our two grandsons, Jeff and Chris, had taken diving lessons. We enjoyed some delicious fish and chips for lunch while we were there.

One day we went to the open market, where there were various things for sale; artifacts, clothing and even food. Anthony bought a beautifully carved walking stick, for a very reasonable price, as a souvenir. I bought a *PNG* skirt and blouse each, for Shawna and Emily, our two youngest granddaughters.

The hotel minivan came early Saturday morning to pick us up for the airport, where we caught a commercial plane back to Wewak. On Sunday morning all the missionaries gathered for a fellowship meeting. Joy played hymns on her electronic piano while we all sang. The next morning began a new week, and Pat was back to working on the generator project.

During our time in Wewak, Peter arranged to hire a speed boat for all of us to take a picnic lunch out to Mushu Island. We were joined by the Rodges family, and we all had an enjoyable time on the beach and swimming. On the return trip, it began raining. We were all damp and felt quite chilly because of the speed of the boat.

Another day, we enjoyed going out to Wom beach, where we used to take our kids, Julie and Dan, when we were still living at Maprik. Spending our vacations in Wewak was a time we looked forward to.

This day at Wom was quite a memorable experience for me, and one I will never forget. Although I am not an accomplished or confident swimmer, I felt quite comfortable swimming out towards the coral reefs, since we had done so many times before. I thought I could rest my feet on the smooth coral should I need to.

However, before either of us realized it, Dale and I were in deep water, way past the coral reefs. In our absence of several years, the terrain of our favorite swimming spot had drastically changed! We were both too tired to swim back to the beach. It was quite frightening to me, wondering if I would be able to keep afloat treading water, until help came. Fortunately, upon hearing us calling out, Peter and Pat quickly swam to us bringing floating devices to our rescue. It was such a relief to have something to hang on to. Thankfully, they towed us to the safety of the shore.

Many of the missionaries, who work in the Sepik tribes, were out on vacation while we were there, so there was not an opportunity to visit their tribal areas.

However, we did fly to Maprik, where Dale and I had started the work in the Sepik region in 1972. Bill and Leslie Smith were occupying the house that we had built, and graciously served us a nice meal and gave us a bed for the night.

We were able to see some of our old friends in the village, who are still living much the same as they did in the 1970s...cooking around the tiny, open fires and living in small, thatched roof bush houses. Although the gospel has been preached in this tribe, there were not too many people following the Lord. We visited briefly with Patrick and Jael, and Clemence and Miriam, who were the national missionaries working in the Abelam tribe.

The next morning the mission plane met us at the Hayfield airstrip and flew us to the Inaru tribe where Chris Moore was working alone. Chris got out some frozen shrimp, and I helped him prepare dinner that night. We enjoyed our visit with him so much and admired his dedication to the Lord; staying there alone for all those months, with only the national people for company. We talked; it seemed like far into the night.

It rained heavily during the night and the next morning we looked out the window to see that the river was swollen out of its banks, and the water was just a few feet from the house! After getting dressed, I looked out the front door and saw the water had completely covered the airstrip! I wondered if we would be spending another night at Inaru, but Chris assured us the water would go down by noon. Sure enough, the water receded, and the plane landed on time. We left as scheduled and found ourselves at Wewak again with Peter and Joy.

Our time in the Sepik was over and it was time to move on. We carried many wonderful memories with us of our visit to the Sepik Region. We told Peter and Joy good-bye and left for the Highlands. We had booked rooms previously in the Numonohi guest house at the mission base.

Visiting the Gimi, 2001
By Arvalee

On Friday, July 27th, we flew from Wewak to Goroka; Dale, Pat, Anthony and I. Our pilot was Brent Dodd. We had lunch in town at the Bird of Paradise restaurant. At the guest house, our rooms were ready. Louise Connelly had invited us for dinner at her little apartment. She was alone now, having lost her husband, John, a few years before. We had lots of memories to share since her daughter, Joy, had married our son, Peter.

On Saturday, July 28th, we rented a mission van and drove to Olaguti and had lunch with Carol Gutwein. She had invited Iteve and Lidia too, who had worked in Port Moresby previously. It was great seeing them again.

After lunch, we walked up the mountain to see Jonah, one of the first Christians among the Yagaria tribal people. He was sitting in the doorway of his small house, and he called out, "*Master* Dale Palmer," reverting to the custom of bygone days when the nationals called all white men by the title of *Master*. He is quite elderly now, but when we first knew him he was a young man.

On Sunday, the 29th of July, the four of us drove to town and visited Pastor Hagen's church. There we saw many of our friends from the days when we lived at base and when we taught the RI classes.

We had lunch at the Mandarin Chinese Restaurant. On the way back to Base, we visited Sobega, the Highlands Headquarters. We saw Phil and Fiona Emery and renewed our friendship with them. Phil and I had worked in the field office together and had many shared memories of that time.

We met some of the new missionaries as well; Seong and Mina Mun, as well as Debbie Orr, who is David Orr's widow. David was the soccer coach when Jeff was in high school.

That night, back at Base, we were invited for dinner in the dorm with Jim and Barbara Hubbard. It was good to see them functioning on the field; they were from the Brownsboro Community Church we attended in Eagle Point, Oregon. They were doing a good job as dorm parents.

On Monday, July 30th, I washed all our clothes. It was a big help when Anthony hung them on the clothesline to dry. Dale met with Larry Brown all morning, discussing field issues. After their meeting was finished, the four of us went to town and had a late lunch. We drove back to Base and had dinner that night with Marvin and Chris Crockett. It was sure good to see them again and to get caught up on their family. After dinner we went back to the guest house and finished packing for the Gimi trip.

We Fly to the Gimi via Tarabo
By Arvalee

It was Tuesday, July 31st, the day we were flying to the Gimi. We got an early start at 5:15, and at 6:00 we met the Tribal Air van that transported us to Goroka. However, our flight had to be cancelled because it had rained all night and the clouds hung too low. Disappointed, we were driven back to the guest house to wait until further notice.

Finally, the weather cleared and the 206 aircraft was cleared for flight at 1:00 p.m. with John Mark Estelle piloting the plane. The *SIL* helicopter met us at Tarabo and flew to the Gimi in only seven minutes. What a blessing that was; instead of a long, six hour road trip like we used to do when we lived at Negibi!

We landed at John White's helicopter pad, which was located near their house at Negibi. It was thrilling to see John and Lynne again and to see the many old friends who had come to greet us. There was so much excitement seeing all those friendly faces after several years.

John and Lynne most graciously gave us their bedroom and they went down to their old village house nearby. Pat and Anthony slept on cots in the living room. Later that morning, we all went to the meeting, which was held in the church building down the mountain from John's house. To get there, we had to walk down a slippery trail to the jeep road. Zato held my hand or arms all the way down the trail to keep me from falling. Dale spoke to the group that morning through an interpreter. During the meeting, Pat and I took quite a few pictures of the people; snapshots that we still enjoy.

Dale and I were thrilled to learn that Saibai had been saved since we had visited in 1997. He had always been such a trouble maker when he was younger!

Anthony taught the kids a tag game and had a lot of fun with them. One of the young guys, Nu-u-da, was trying to teach Anthony to speak Pidgin English.

The people gave us taro and sweet potato from the *mumu* (steam cooking) and a bamboo of *iremu* (edible greens) and *pitpit* (an edible shoot)! Food cooked in a *mumu* is so delicious; we enjoyed it immensely. At home, later that day, Lynne made sweet rolls. John and I were supposed to look after them while they baked, but we got the oven too hot and burned the first pan.

Anthony, Dale and I all had showers, heating water on the wood heating stove and filling the shower bucket for each shower. When using a bush shower, you have to make sure you don't run out of water. After getting wet, it's best to turn off the shower head and then soap up. Then you have to turn the shower head on again to rinse off.

One day, the men had some opportunities to help John by working on a few things around the house. Dale tightened the loose legs on a chair, while Anthony worked on the front door hinges. Pat spotted things needing attention on the generator, and he used a piece of leather from my make-up box to make a tiny gasket for it!

I made egg sandwiches for lunch. While we were eating, Inabera, his wife and family brought a large dish of *mumu* (steam cooked) food, including a huge chicken. Since we were already eating, we divided all the food they brought, took some for ourselves and gave the rest back to them, which they ate and shared with the guys visiting from Amusa. The Amusa guys stayed all afternoon and Dale and I told them stories about our lives. Inabera's wife gave Pat and me *bilums*, putting them over our shoulders, as is their custom.

On Friday we all went down for the meeting about 10:00 o'clock. The women sat on the grass outside the church building, under the trees. I spoke to the women and Tarabu, Zato's wife, interpreted for me. She did a good job. The sun was filtering through the trees so I got a bit sunburned.

On Saturday I did the washing for the four of us. A woman hung them on the clothesline for me, a very kind gesture which I really appreciated. It was a very nice day so the clothes dried quickly. We were supposed to go to Zato's house for dinner that evening, but it rained hard, so the trail was too slick! Later, Zato and Tarabu brought the food they had cooked over to the house for us. They are used to the wet, slick trails.

Earlier in the afternoon, Siri-o's wife gave me a pretty green and blue *bilum*; then their little boy, Noah, gave Anthony one, putting it on his shoulder.

On Sunday, Dale and the others went to the meeting, but I stayed home as I wasn't feeling well. Dale thought he was taking a cold.

On Monday, Dale was speaking and John was interpreting for him. John knew the Gimi language very well and spoke like a national, a feat neither Dale nor I could ever master. After the meeting, Aba-ena and Hapato came back inside the church, where we were sitting to eat our lunch. These men presented Dale with a pretty orange and green *bilum* and a letter. John told Dale they were bringing him a big letter, and that it took two men to carry it! It had a stack of money inside and a letter to us. It was so touching to receive this gift of love from these dear people.

Monday evening, we went down to Bau's house to eat. Dale stayed home as he had gotten a chest cold and wasn't feeling well. Soma took a plate of food up to him. Pat was able to take a lot of pictures. Aba-ena and Soma were there with their families, too.

Tuesday I made scrambled eggs with ham for all of us for breakfast. I made toast and burned some of it, again. After so many years, I was not used to cooking the toast with the old fashioned toaster on the open burner, or cooking on a wood burning stove either!

Earlier that morning Anthony left for his hike to Numonohi with Zato and his six year old son, Jonathan. They were gone when we all got up. We heard on the evening radio *sked* (short for 'schedule') that Anthony had arrived safely at Numonohi. The work girls had told us earlier that Zato and Anthony had caught a ride by Cliff Heller's place, so they didn't have to walk all the way. Anthony told us later that Jonathan marched along beside him and Zato, never complaining about being tired. Anthony was quite impressed that a six year old boy was capable of such a long hike.

Dale, Pat and I left about 10:00 o'clock that morning to walk to our old house site, which is down the road, going south. It's a good hike from John's house. We met Aba-ena (the older man) and his wife just below John's house and he hugged Dale and me. He seemed so glad to see us. We asked them to wait at John's house until we got back. We went on and got back about 1:30. It was quite a long walk. Although we were on the road all the way, I had very sore feet.

When we got back, Lynne, bless her heart, brought me a basin and a kettle of hot water so I could soak my tired, hurting feet. Later I found a large blister on the big toe of my left foot. We had a good visit with Aba-ena and his wife and drank many cups of hot tea while sitting on the porch.

Leaving the Gimi
By Arvalee

Our visit in the Gimi was over and it was time to leave for Numonohi. It was Wednesday, August 8th. The helicopter arrived a little before 10:00 to take us to Tarabo, where Ole Ottosen met us with the fixed wing airplane. We got to Goroka and Bob Yarnell from the guest house was waiting at the hanger to pick us up. Anthony was there to meet us, too.

We all had a shower and then I started washing our clothes to get the red Gimi mud out of them! Anthony helped me. We got the clothes almost finished before Dale and I had to go to the finance office to meet with Chris Ramsey, the financial officer. We had to get our account in order and settled before we left the country.

That night we had dinner with Mike and Donna Ludwig and their son, Nolan. Donna made creamed chicken over rice which was delicious and we all enjoyed it very much. Then she offered to make copies of the video she had made of the Gimi for us, Pat and Julie. Later, Nolan brought them up to the guest house for us.

Later that night, Zato came to visit with his kids, Somaisa, Lydia and David, who are in school in Goroka. Somaisa was so glad to see us that she grabbed me around the waist and tried to lift me up! We talked and visited with them for two hours and showed them the snapshots of our kids and house.

On Thursday, August 9th, we left the Goroka airport for Port Moresby. Some of our Gimi friends were there to see us off; Zato, Sidi-o, Tapero and Noah. Then Inabera came with a big cabbage and some lovely carrots. Since he had worked in Port Moresby some years earlier, he knew how scarce and expensive fresh vegetables were in that town. They fit nicely in the large *bilum* I planned to carry onto the plane. I told Inabera that Pat Keller at the guest house would surely appreciate the veggies.

As we talked, a man nearby was listening. I gradually included him in our conversation and explained to him that we were missionaries and had come to New Guinea many years ago and had worked in the Gimi tribe. He said, "It's because of missionaries like you that *PNG* is where it is today. I want to thank you and God bless you." He was a very nice man and very well spoken. Later I asked Dale to come shake hands with him.

Departing for Port Moresby
By Arvalee

As we were going out to board our plane, I realized we hadn't seen Pastor Hagen and his family there. They had told us earlier that they would come to see us off. Now it was too late to find out if they had come. The airport security guard doesn't let everyone into the waiting room, so he may have refused them entry.

We got to Port Moresby in about 50 minutes and were picked up by Marlin Keller. He drove us to the guest house and Pat, his wife, had some lunch ready. Then Marlin took us to the Botanical Gardens to see the orchids. We spent two hours there and Pat took dozens of pictures. When it was time to go it was hard for him to leave, because he enjoyed the orchids so much.

Pat and Anthony were leaving for Australia that evening. When we all arrived back at the guest house, Pat Keller had an early supper ready for them. Then it was time for them to leave and Marlin drove the two of them to the airport to catch their plane for

Cairns, where they planned to do some sightseeing. We would see them again on Monday, in Brisbane, Queensland.

That evening, I found out that the sightseeing had caught up with me. I was exhausted and my feet were terribly sore! The hiking in the Gimi and all the rest of the walking we had done since then didn't help them at all. But it was well worth it when we remembered the wonderful times we'd had visiting with everyone and traveling to the various places. That night I got our suitcases reorganized and we both showered early. We were in bed by 7:30 as we were both extremely tired.

This trip to New Guinea would be remembered for years to come. We are so grateful the Lord made it possible and that we got to see many people and were able to visit so many places. I think the highlight of our trip was the time we spent in the Gimi and in fellowship with the Gimi Christians. It was thrilling and encouraging to see what the Lord was doing in their lives and hearts and the growth of the Gimi Church.

Visiting Australia
By Arvalee

We caught up with Pat and Anthony in Brisbane, Australia. They had flown down a few days before to do some sightseeing in Cairns. We visited with Don and Joanne Nutting and their daughters and families at their home in Bli Bli. John Brenden and Faye Fassett were there at the time as well. We had a wonderful visit with everyone.

In Brisbane, we stayed in Barbara Smith's little house, where she lived alone, since Pat had gone to be with the Lord a year or so before. Sadly, Barbara was in the hospital. Her daughter, Lorene, made us welcome, and set us up in the guest bedrooms. Lorene even arranged a gathering of some of our old time friends and fellow New Tribes missionaries. There was Mike Tidy, whose wife Beryl had gone to be with the Lord, and Bill and Beth Zaubzer, Graham Goodhew, and Tony Rigsby and his wife, as well as others. Some of these we'd worked with in New Guinea years before.

Some who'd been in the mission training program at Plumpton in the 1960s were there to see us, including Bill and Rosie Hay, who had gone into mission work with a group working with the Australian Aborigines.

Finally, Barbara was able to come home for a day or so but had to return to the hospital.

Pat rented a Toyota SUV and leaving Brisbane, we drove down the coast to Laurieton, NSW, where the new mission training camp was being built. Laurieton, later called Lakewood, is situated on the eastern coast of New South Wales. There we toured the beautiful new grounds of the training facility. All the duplex apartments for students were modern, with all the amenities any home owner would expect when renting a home for his family.

We stayed with Ted Albrecht and his daughter, Sandra Lee, in the little house that Ted had bought after selling the family home near Sydney. Sandra took us on tours of the local area, which included the oyster beds located in the nearby bay. We had a picnic lunch of fish and chips on a mountainside, where the view was most spectacular.

We left Laurieton heading for Sydney, where we would board our flight for the States. Ted traveled with us, as he still had his apartment at the Mission property in Plumpton. Along the way, we arranged to meet Trevor and Francis McIlwain and Bruce and Lee Haste, at Newcastle. We had lunch together and enjoyed a delightful visit talking about old times. We had seen the McIlwaine's in Papua New Guinea when they were there visiting, but this was the first time we'd seen Bruce and Lee since the 1960s, when they were students at the Plumpton Missionary Training School. Since then, they had been missionaries in Panama for years and had a very rewarding ministry there.

We stayed a night or so with Ted at Plumpton. It was interesting touring the old grounds where we had lived for eighteen months in the 1960s and where our kids had all been enrolled in the public school. One day we visited Ted's dear wife, Faye, who was in residence at a local nursing home since she'd had a stroke.

Soon it was time to leave and we headed for Sydney airport. Pat planned to drop us off at the terminal and then he would return the rental SUV to the agency. Anthony and I waited, while Dale and Pat left with the vehicle. It seemed they were gone an exceptionally long time and I kept looking at my watch! We sure didn't want to miss our flight.

Finally, they returned and told Anthony and me what had happened. As they unloaded our luggage at the airport, they both kept smelling gasoline, and finally they figured out why. When they had filled the gas tank earlier, they had left the gas cap on the top of the pump! So they returned to the gas station and hoped they would find it! Thankfully, it was still there, so they retrieved it, put it on the tank and returned the van to the agency!

We were four very thankful people to finally board the plane for our flight back to the USA. Pat and Anthony flew on to Tucson. Dale and I flew to San Francisco, where our friend, Kirk Glenn, was waiting for us with our car. We spent a night or two visiting with Kirk and Glenn in their home before we returned to Eagle Point, Oregon, and our own home. It was sure good to be back in our lovely little home again.

We were very tired from all our travels, but it had been well worth it to see our kids and so many of our Papua New Guinean friends. God had blessed us immeasurably by allowing us to visit again, our place of ministry in our adopted homeland.

It was so rewarding to witness first-hand the change God had made in the lives of many of the tribal people. Most thrilling was the fact that many of these Papua New

Guinean Christians were burdened to reach out to their fellow tribesmen with the gospel and were going to other areas preaching the good news. They had caught the vision and were serving the Lord, just as we had done many years before.

How thankful we were that when God chose us and gave us an opportunity to serve Him, we obeyed His call to go and preach the gospel to people who had never heard it before. Now, we were rejoicing to see the wonderful fruits of our labors!

Chapter 18

A Major Decision, 2002
By Arvalee

A few months had passed since Dale and I had returned from our trip to New Guinea in 2001. We no longer felt like Eagle Point was the place for us to spend our years of retirement. Since New Tribes Mission had a retirement center in Sanford, Florida, we thought about moving there. We corresponded with the directors of the center and were in the process of making a decision to move there.

However, before we made a final decision, we wanted to speak to each of our children and get their thoughts and opinions. First, we drove to Tucson to see Pat and then we planned to fly to Wisconsin and see Julie. Peter and Joy were home from New Guinea at that time, staying at the Waukesha Bible School, so we would be able to talk to Peter as well.

When we told Pat about our tentative plans to move to Florida, he said almost immediately, "If you move to Florida, we'll never get to see you again. Why don't you sell your house in Eagle Point and move down here? I'll look after you."

Wow! We had never even thought about moving to Arizona. But those words from Pat meant far more to us, as parents getting up in years, than I can ever express. To think that Pat cared about us so much that he was willing to look after us in our declining years, spoke volumes. This drastically changed our way of thinking. When we told Julie and Peter, separately, of our plans to move to Florida and what Pat had said, they both told us that they, too, would much rather see us move to Tucson, than to Florida!

After the trip, when we were back home in Oregon, we talked to Paul and Dan who basically agreed with the other three kids, that Tucson would be preferred over a move to Florida. I guess Florida just seemed too far away to all of them.

A move to Arizona had not been a part of our wildest dreams. It came as a complete surprise to us that we would be moving to Tucson. But as we talked about it, the idea became more attractive to both of us.

Another factor that came into play was the fact that I had two brothers and a sister living in Phoenix. I had fond dreams of being able to visit them since they would not be so far away. I also had a maternal uncle and aunt living in Carlsbad, New Mexico. Dale had a paternal uncle and aunt living in Las Cruces, New Mexico as well. For both of us, these were our only living relatives, besides our own children.

So, that is how we came to the decision to move to Arizona.

We already had a buyer for our house. Dale had talked to Tom and Sandi Chambers, dear friends of ours, sometime before and told them that one day we would be selling the house and that we would like to see them become the new owners.

We told them the time had come and that we were planning to move to Tucson. Tom and Sandi needed to sell two mobile homes before they could buy our house! In the Lord's time, buyers came for their homes and the deal went through. They signed the papers to buy our house in May the next year.

We kept in touch with Pat so he would know how things were progressing as to the sale of our house, so that he could come up at the appropriate time to help us with the move.

While making these plans we really didn't know how things would work out once we were in Tucson. But we knew the Lord would lead us and guide us as we walked in fellowship with Him.

Moving to Tucson, 2003
By Arvalee

Saturday, June 21st, at 11:40 p.m., Pat arrived at the Medford, Oregon, air terminal from Tucson. He had flown up to help us finish packing and to get us moved to Arizona. He planned to drive the moving truck, loaded with our household goods, while Dale drove our car.

Hank and Jeanne Kleker graciously offered us a place to stay during those final days of packing. We spent Monday through Wednesday nights with them. It was such a blessing to be able to stay with them, while we finished cleaning and packing.

Dale and Pat went to the Budget Rental facility and rented a moving truck on Tuesday and began loading it when they got back. Our good friends Jim Hubbard, Michael Campanelli, and a young fellow, Alan Overdorf, came to help us. After Michael left that day, we discovered that he had left us one of his photographs on the truck seat. Michael was a professional photographer. It was a beautiful photo of the cross at Fish Lake, where Grandpa Palmer had gone to fish many times. We treasured it and knew it would have a special place in our new home.

On Wednesday the 25th, we arranged to have the carpet cleaned and had the utilities and phone disconnected. We went to the post office and had the mail redirected to Tucson.

Tom and Sandi Chambers came to tell us good-bye the day before we left. They moved some of their things over at the same time. They were so grateful and thankful to be able to buy our house. For our part, we were just thankful they were the ones moving in and not strangers. We loved that house and yard because we had many special memories of buying it and fixing it up. It was a real act of faith on our part when we bought it, that God would enable us to make the payments. God had provided for it in such a wonderful way that we had it paid for before a year was over. Our son Paul had landscaped the yard for us, helping us lay it out to display many beautiful flowers. There were too many fond memories to leave it in the hands of strangers!

We departed for Tucson on Thursday the 26th, at 5:00 a.m. Pat drove the truck and we were following in our car. The truck had trouble going up the Siskiyou Mountain, a very steep incline. About halfway up the mountain Pat had to turn around. We phoned the Budget for a tow truck to tow us back to Medford. Dale thought for sure we would have to unload and get another truck, but the company changed the fuel and air filters and the truck was ready to go. We were late in departing from Medford, but it was sure better than having to get another truck and reload it.

During the time the truck was being repaired we had breakfast at the new Denny's restaurant in Ashland, then we visited Tom and Sandi as they were moving into their house, said good-bye to our neighbors once again, and visited Jim and Barbara Hubbard, who were home from Papua New Guinea.

We arrived in Merced, California, and found Mike Gleaves' place, a fellow New Tribes missionary, who had invited us to spend the night. They were on a mission trip, so we had the pleasure of using their home, but missed having fellowship with them.

The next day we made it to Ventura, California, where we stayed with Margaret (Schrock) and Jim Delameter, our longtime friends. It was good to be with them again and enjoy their fellowship. We surely appreciated their hospitality.

The next morning, we departed at 5:00 a.m. and had another long but uneventful day on the road. We arrived in Tucson at 6:30 Saturday evening, June 28th. It was the hottest day of the year at 113 degrees Fahrenheit. We stood in the street in front of Pat's house and could see the Catalina Mountains were burning. The flames were reaching skyward as that beautiful mountain burned. That was not a welcome sight.

We were very thankful for a safe trip. It was good to be there at Pat's home on 7013 N. Northlight Drive. Pat had moved out of the master bedroom into the small guest room to allow us more space. He was really cramped in the small bedroom with his desk and computer in there as well.

There was new carpet in the whole house, and new flooring had been laid in the kitchen. We found out in the next few days that Pat had worked really hard getting the house fixed up before we arrived. It really looked nice. We knew that eventually we would need to buy a larger house, perhaps a place of our own. At that stage we really didn't know what kind of place we were looking for.

The next day Dale and Pat got our things unpacked, and the following day they returned the rental truck. It was the last day of the month, June 30th, 2003. We had used the truck just six days. It cost about $1,000 to make the move plus the cost of fuel. The trip was a total of 1,440 miles.

Dale bought some plywood and enclosed part of the back porch for a space to store our furniture, because there wasn't room in the house for all our things. In the next few days, we set up our computer on a makeshift table in the office adjoining the master bedroom.

As time went on, I began thinking about how things would be if Dale and I bought our own house. It was working out just fine with me doing the cooking and housekeeping. I told Dale that it wouldn't make much sense for us to buy our own house and live by ourselves and for Pat to live by himself.

In moving to Tucson, we wanted to be a blessing and help to Pat, too. We wanted to assist him in the visitation of his two minor children, who still lived with their mother. We didn't want to only think about the benefits to ourselves, but wanted the move to be beneficial to him as well.

Around the first of October, Pat brought a newspaper home and said maybe I could look at some listings for houses that were up for sale. I found one that I thought we'd like to look at. I tried to look it up on the Internet, but I never did find the house I was looking for.

What I did find was a house on W. Medici Drive, with 1.2 acres of land and it had four bedrooms and three bath rooms. I printed the information given on it, including several nice pictures, and showed them to Dale and Pat. They decided we should go look at it. Pat knew from the address that it was only a five minute drive from his place of work.

On the 4th of October the three of us drove over to have a look. It was only a few blocks away. Pat said to me while he and I were walking around the back yard that "We should make a move on this place." I could tell that he liked the place.

It had a swimming pool and a Jacuzzi. Dale had told me, "We don't need a place with a swimming pool," so I thought this would not be the place for us.

However, after the three of us discussed it further, things began moving fast. On the 7th of October, Pat wrote a check for an earnest deposit, and the next day it was accepted by the owners. We began packing again!

Pat made a quick business trip to Tennessee with a short trip to Wisconsin thrown in. He returned on the 27th of October.

On November 5th the three of us signed the papers for the purchase of the house. Dale and I had a check from the bank from the sale of our house in Eagle Point, which we invested in the new house. The following week, after procuring the keys, we began cleaning the house. Much to our surprise, we found that two large cats were still inside the house! With difficulty, we got them corralled and locked them in the rooms that Pat would later occupy. Pat phoned the folks and asked them to please come collect their cats. We certainly didn't want cats, as Pat is allergic to them. Fortunately, we had Eco-Quest air purifiers to set up in the house to remove the cat odors.

We had the carpets cleaned the next day. Friends from Thornydale Family Church came to help us move the furniture; Pastor Denny Howard, Marc Withers, and George and Valerie Hires were a real help and blessing to us. Valerie helped me clean the kitchen and line the shelves with new shelf paper. I got two of the bathrooms cleaned, too.

Dale and I slept in the house for the first time on Thursday the 13th. Pat waited a few more days before he moved in, to give the air purifiers a chance to clean up the odors.

Julie and Emily, our daughter and granddaughter, came the next week on the 20th to help us get unpacked and settled in. They were a great help and blessing to us. Besides helping us unpack and arrange the furniture, Julie helped enormously with placing pictures on the walls and helping me with some other wall decorations, even designing and making some new arrangements.

Emily kept busy all the while, too, sweeping the entry ways and pool area, painting my two ceramic dolls I'd brought from Eagle Point, and helping in other ways. However, she was not too busy to enjoy the swimming pool, actually swimming more than once on some days.

We were not too busy to take them to several popular tourist attractions and we even fit in a quick trip to Nogales, Mexico. While there, Julie kept looking for souvenirs to take home to Waukesha. She wanted to find a donkey and cart for Dan. She finally found one and she and Pat lugged them around the busy streets as we finished up our shopping. This was no small chore as the donkey is over a foot long and about that tall. When we got back home, she surprisingly presented it to me, knowing I wanted one for our house. She had surprised me by pretending it was for Dan. She had found something smaller to take to him.

Their visit came to an end much too quickly for us all. The house seemed empty and all too quiet after they had gone home.

A Near Tragedy
By Arvalee

On March 8th, 2004, we left home in Tucson to attend the mission's conference at Bible Fellowship Church in Ventura, California. We drove to San Diego and spent the night with Harry and Marianne Hobby. The next day, on the way to Los Angeles, we spent a night with Greg and Laura Melendes. While at the conference we stayed with Jim and Margaret Delameter, our longtime friends where we always feel welcome.

When the conference was over we left for further points north, where we had a couple of meetings scheduled in Arroyo Grande, at Grace Bible Church. We were planning to drive to Oregon, too, to visit several friends and to see our sons, Paul and Dan.

We spent a night with Fred and Carol Schaeffer once again in Goleta and left the next morning, March 17th for Arroyo Grande. When we came to a park we decided to stop and stretch our legs. The Nojoqui Falls were a short walk up a trail, so we decided to take the walk. As we began the fairly steep climb, we stopped on a bench to catch our breath. While we were sitting there, a youngish man and woman passed on their way back to the parking lot. Both were dressed in singlet shirts, as it was a fairly warm day. I noticed the man had tattoos on his arms.

Soon, we were off and made it to the falls, had a look around and headed back down the trail. As soon as we got to the car, we saw that the back passenger window had been smashed! What a blow! The back seat was empty! Then we saw a large rock on the floor of the car; it had been thrown through the window, breaking it.

The thieves took everything in the back seat which included my briefcase containing our Dell laptop computer, Dale's briefcase with his Gimi Bible and his own Bible with all his notes. Also, a small case holding about $500 worth of prescription medicines was gone. The overnight bag, my make-up case and Dale's shaving case; all had been taken as well.

Fortunately, the thieves, in their haste to get away, had overlooked my purse which I had left on the floor beside the front passenger seat. I had covered it over with a pillow; it not only contained our credit card, check book and a bit of cash, but also the cell phone. Immediately, I dialed 911 and reported the crime and our location to the local Sheriff.

Yet no matter how difficult the situation, there is always something to praise the Lord for. We realized that had we returned sooner and caught the thieves in the act, we could have been injured or even killed. My purse could have been stolen, too, which would have made the crime far more serious.

After phoning 911, we got in the car and Dale drove back to the campground manager's house, near the park entrance. They were kind folk and gave us some water, but there wasn't much they could do. Within twenty minutes, the Sheriff arrived and took down all the particulars; our address, the make and model of the computer, and a list of all the items that were stolen.

Though we felt devastated, we had to press on to our destination as we had the meeting to attend that night. Arriving in Arroyo Grande, we drove directly to Lois Krantz's home, where we had made arrangements to stay. We stayed with Lois before, when her husband Lee was still alive, and had become good friends.

That night at the women's meeting, I shared with them about our mishap. A lady spoke up, saying they would pray for the thieves who broke into the car. She said, "Maybe they have never been prayed for before." Afterwards, one of the ladies gave me a check because she wanted to help out.

Lois was more than helpful to us. The next morning, she arranged for a company to come and replace the glass in the broken window; broken glass fragments were found everywhere; even in the pocket behind the seat. She took us shopping and we found some necessary items to tide us over. Then she took us to her pharmacy, where the druggist was able to supply us with a week's supply of our medications.

Then, she told us she wanted to replace the stolen computer! We suggested to her that it would be best to order one through our mission headquarters in Sanford, Florida. They would install the necessary programs for us. She agreed to this, and gave us a check to cover the cost. Talk about being a blessing to someone, her kindness blessed our hearts beyond measure.

While still in Arroyo Grande, we went to fellowship with the folks at Berean Bible Church, and Pastor Jim Wickstrom asked Dale to speak to the congregation. Much to our surprise, two couples each gave us large checks to help cover our loss. What a tremendous blessing this was to us. In the end, our losses were more than covered through the kindnesses of our dear fellow believers! God is good to His children.

The rest of our trip north was made without incident. We had an enjoyable time visiting friends and family, but it was good to be home again in Tucson, on April 6th.

Late in the evening, on May 20th, I answered the telephone and was surprised to hear it was the police in Hayward, California, near San Francisco, asking for Arvalee Palmer. They told me immediately that they had recovered my computer when they were searching the car of a man they had arrested! What an absolutely wonderful surprise! Arrangements were made and they sent it back to us via UPS.

Thankfully, when it arrived, there was no damage to the computer and all the contents were untouched…including the beginning chapters of God Plus Nothing!

Turn Down the Volume
By Dale

The years had passed, oh, so quickly and there were many changes in our lives…even to living in another locality. But the one thing that never changed was our memories of our adopted country, Papua New Guinea, and thoughts of our dear friends there. Dale always looked forward to sharing our experiences with a new audience, whether it was a church or a group of children or a home meeting. From his memoirs, here is another true story. Arvalee

The volume grew louder as the village people mourned the death of the little boy. He had gone down to the stream alone to get a drink of water and some enemies had killed him. The crying of the loved ones was getting to me, deep down inside. Then across the auditorium came the kind but stern voice of the pastor of the church, "Could you please turn the volume down a little?"

I came back to my senses. We were on furlough and were viewing a movie of one of the primitive tribes of the large island of New Guinea.

Some years later, we were back in Papua New Guinea. My teenage son, Dan and I, drove into the parking lot at the hospital to pick up one of our missionary couples. There we saw a large crowd of people and a policeman taking pictures. My first thought was to grab the camera in the glove compartment! We went over and saw a man with his head almost chopped off, and other wounds on the shoulder and legs. He had been killed during the night in a village up in the hills beyond the town. I could not begin to lift my camera to take a picture! But maybe I should have, so that you could feel the pang of sorrow for souls going into eternal darkness.

A couple of other missionaries told me that a man had died in their village and the people wailed for days and nights, mourning the loss of their loved one. There is only one way we missionaries can turn the volume down on these very real episodes, and that would be to leave the field.

Never in the history of this old world has the mission field been brought so clearly into our homes. We have been given a vision of peoples of many lands; it comes in the forms of TV, travelogues and widely known magazines. These people, working on large commercial endeavors, are willing to even give their lives to get some good pictures or write a thesis. Many organizations will spend thousands of dollars taking photos to show you glimpses of primitive people or wildlife on some of the last frontiers of the world.

People don't mind hearing or viewing these underprivileged people from their arm chairs, just as long as they have control of the viewing and the volume, so that it doesn't upset them.

Why is it that we Christians are so slow to respond to the needs of these tribes who sit in the shadow of death with no hope? Could it be that we have developed a way to turn the volume down when it comes to God speaking to our hearts about the unreached tribes remaining in the world today? When we come to places in the Bible that say, "He is not willing that any should perish," do you feel the responsibility to give your life so that these will not perish? Or is it just nice that God feels this way toward mankind?

I trust the Holy Spirit can speak to us clearly in these last days about how important our part is in fulfilling God's will. By R. Dale Palmer

(From Dale's article *Turn Down the Volume* published in *Brown Gold*, the New Tribes Mission magazine, about 1974.)

THE END

~APPENDIX~
(Dale's Complete Diary, 1955 and 1959)

The Gimi Horse Road
August, 1955

08/31/55. I had prayer this morning with Chuck and Don. Don closed in prayer. Chuck and I left Kami about 8 a.m. on the motorbike, a 125 cc *BSA*. We met Meniba and Lamafu at the spring near the old Casarina tree near Olaguti village. Chuck took the bike back to Kami, and the three of us started off hiking down the little trail, bound for Fusa. We stopped at the river and had a short swim.

We arrived at Fusa *GRH* (Government Rest House) about 3:00 p.m. It looked like it was going to rain. Had some fellowship with the Father, then I walked up on a hill where I could see a road site from Fusa to Kisivero. We will have to work a new road through this area. The people of Fusa brought no *kaukau* (sweet potatoes) to us this evening, so I shared my rice with the two men. Tonight Lamafu and I prayed together. Meniba was there, too.

September, 1955

09/01/55. I had rice for breakfast this morning. Read the first chapter of Philippians. Left Fusa about 6:00 or 6:30. We walked hard all day, stopping very little. We got to Henagaru about 4 p.m. We bought *kaukau*, *pitpit* (an edible shoot from a type of cane), sugar cane and onions today. After eating, I felt like sleeping.

09/02/55. I had a little meeting in the house last night for the local people. The nationals of Henagaru said that they knew nothing about God. Some of the young men said that they would come and work for me and I could teach them more.

Looking to the northwest from Henagaru I can see a high white rocky cliff. Below is the *Zani* (Thani) River that runs up into the east corner of Mt. Michael. The mountain looks to be about 9,000 or 10,000 feet. Our destination today is Amusa.

Everything has been going very well, but, as Mel Wyma used to say, "There is always calm before a storm." I never know what to expect from the Enemy.

As we headed toward Amusa, we were walking south, going along the broad *Zani* River, which is moving along at about four or five miles an hour, faster than I can walk. I think that I must walk about three miles an hour. The *Zani* is the big river here in the Gimi. It is well over my head in most places and from 20 to 30 feet across along here. About noon today we had a heavy rain. It just poured. We quickly cut some banana leaves and covered up our *cargo* (baggage) as well as we could, but we all got wet. Praise the Lord, the bedding and clothes didn't. The rain made the river look like it was boiling. This morning it was a deep green color. We stood and watched as the *Zani* turned to a color like coffee with cream. We arrived here at Uvai about 3:00 p.m. and it was still raining. So I thought it best to sleep here tonight, in the Government Rest Houses.

09/03/55. Saturday. Meniba and I walked down to Amusa this morning to pick up my camping things that had been stored there in an old trunk for about four months. We got some fellows to carry them back to Uvai. We were back about 1:00 p.m. The pots, pans and dishes that had been in the trunk were all covered with mold, so Lamafu had a big dish washing job. These people sure have a sense of humor and love to play on words. Lamafu had peeled some sweet potatoes and had the peelings wrapped in an old piece of cloth. He told one of the young boys sitting by the door to *rausim* (to get rid of it). The boy laughed and picked it up and ran outside, saying he was going to raus the cloth too (meaning he would keep the cloth for his own use, maybe as a loincloth).

We had a talk today about the *cargo cult*. If a national believes in the *cargo cult*, he thinks material objects like canned meat, pots, pans, shoes, clothes and tools are sent from their ancestors and just fall from the sky. Meniba showed the local nationals the bottle or jar of goat meat that Arvalee had canned, hoping to give the people a better understanding of where things such as *tinned* (canned) meat come from. Meniba told them, "This canned meat doesn't come from God or our ancestors, but from big pigs (referring to any large animal) that the white man (pink man or European) has. They kill the big pigs and cook the meat and put it in the *tins* (cans) and bottles." No one said anything, but everyone was listening.

Praise God for the book of Philippians that I've been reading. God, through Paul, is teaching me more how to live for others. Also, my spiritual life has a lot of room for improvement. Paul said in chapter 3:10, "That I may know Him, and the power of His resurrection, and the fellowship of His sufferings, being made conformable unto His death:" I like to read it from the Williams version. There it reads a little differently. Paul is referring to our spiritual and moral resurrection, not the final physical resurrection.

The Devil is trying to discourage me because we didn't see the 10 fellows come in today, whom we were hoping to hire to work on the road. We were counting on them to go out to Kami and work on the road with us. Praise the Lord; I believe they will be in. He won't let me down. I told Meniba we would get them, but he said that he didn't know where. I told him that I believed God would send in the ten men to work.

We got a lot of good food today—mushrooms, *pitpit* (edible shoots), sweet potatoes, cucumbers, onions, bananas, pumpkins, and beans. We bought five chickens, too.

09/05/55. I just didn't have time to write yesterday. We are still at Uvai. We had a meeting this morning, and I taught on the creation and the fall of man. I feel a real open spirit with the folk. Wa-uwa's *luluai* (chief) asked me, "Where do we go when we die (where do the dead go)?" I told him what the Bible said.

After a good lunch of fried mushrooms, baked *yo-o* (the other kind of *pitpit*) and stew, we set off for a walk, going west of Uvai over the hill, looking into another valley. The national people in that area said they wanted to give me a plot of ground there. The ground is about 600 yards long and not too wide, maybe about 100 yards, and runs north and south. The north end is high and runs down like terraces. About 300 yards of this could possibly be made into a landing strip. Also, I like the place for its location, since it is central. We could put the road in without too much trouble, too. It looks good. I just don't know.

We got back to Uvai about 3:00 p.m. Praise the Lord! Eleven fellows were lined up to work. I knew they would come. Two are too young. One boy is not filled out very well yet, but I am going to give him a try. There are seven real good looking *boys* (young men). One is married and looks to be a fine fellow. I gave them a real talk, telling them just what we were going to do.

The Word has been a real blessing as I've been reading in the book of Philippians. If we just tell God what we want, and not man, then because of our union with Christ Jesus, we have the peace of God. God is at peace and wants us to be. That must be in our minds, since He said it "surpasses all human thought." What I especially like is that He said He would keep guard over our hearts and thoughts. I've been looking for some way to guard my heart and thoughts.

09/06/55. Then Paul tells us to "practice" thinking. I like that. He says, "Practice thinking on things that are true, honorable, right, pure, and lovable, high toned, excellent, and praise worthy." This is a lot to practice thinking about. I have surely received a lot of help by reading Philippians at this time.

We got to Amuraisa this afternoon. Lamafu and I had a good swim in the *Zani* this evening for an hour or so. Then I crossed the swinging bridge and went up to the *GRH* (rest house). I tried to have a little quiet time this afternoon and went for a walk in the woods, but the little national boys and girls followed me and, just like kids anywhere, were talking and laughing all the time. I did have a nice walk though.

We got some sugar cane and *kaukau* (sweet potato) and one little hen from the people. I treated and bandaged one bad sore on a woman's foot.

I've been asking God to show me how to teach these people. I am sure He is, starting now. Tonight I was outlining some thoughts on teaching about God. I feel I should teach at the same time about Jesus. Then it came like the lights coming on. Where does the Holy Spirit come into the picture? Looking into God's Word and seeing the place of the Holy Spirit, it is clear that He has just as much importance in the teaching of the gospel. I've been thinking a lot about what to teach these people first. I would just like to stay here and teach them. I'm going to hit the sack now. We've got a big day tomorrow.

09/07/55. We got the seven *cargo boys* (carriers) off to Fusa this morning and there were 15 more who wanted to work, so I picked three big *blokes* (big strong fellows, from Australian slang). We now have 10 men to work. The last three were from Negibi.

We didn't get away from the *GRH* (rest house) until 8:00 or 8:30 and we got to Muye late, about 5:00 p.m. this afternoon. We got rained on a little, but not bad. Sure was tired tonight. I'm writing this in bed (my sleeping bag). I will send Lamafu and the carriers on to Fusa, and Meniba and I will walk up in the hills and see if we can find a good road site across from Fusa to Muye. It's about two hours closer than following the old trail.

We bought *kaukau* (sweet potato) and sugar cane here at Muye. I'm running low on salt, so just bought a little food, (salt was used as payment). The nationals gave us the rest. It is time for bed now.

09/08/55. We got here to Kosotaka Rest House today about 1:00 p.m. We will make this our first base camp for the road work. I've had an upset stomach for two days. I don't think it was anything I ate. I think maybe the cook is not washing the dishes well enough. It made me not care to eat, and so I was not very strong for walking.

I think there is a real possibility of putting the road over on the east end of Mt. Michael. Also, it looks good from Fusa to Kisevero, but from there to here, I don't see the way yet.

I trust we'll be able to get going on the road on Monday, from the Yali tree (at Olaguti) this way.

09/12/55. Went down to Kami for the weekend, and had some good fellowship with the folks. It was good to see the wife and kids again. Chuck said the *luluai* (chief) and the leader from Kemasi told him they have received Christ Jesus as their Redeemer. Praise God.

We got the road started today and I'm looking for Satan to hit any time now. How it will be, we will never know. I came back to the house about noon and Prince (the horse) and I walked over to the place where I thought the road should go. It looks really good, and I'm planning on *marking* (setting surveying stakes) it tomorrow, Lord willing.

I think I will just start teaching from Genesis and about God. I feel the rest will come later.

Satan came over me, in a way, saying there was no peace for me. Then the Holy Spirit reminded me of Philippians 4:4–10, "Let your forbearing spirit be known to everybody… keep on making your wants known to God…" Praise God for showing me this. We do not want to be known for what we really are, but we want people (as opposed to God) to know what we need. This is not God's way of doing it and if we are going to have the Peace of God, we have got to do it God's way. The only way that I can let everybody know what I am is to face the cross. Matt. 16:24 tells me to "deny myself daily and take up the cross and follow Jesus." This has got to become a reality to me. When I move into the cross life, Satan has no ground under him. Do I want everybody to know that I am a failure in my flesh? Oh, but praise God, I can do all things through Jesus Christ.

09/15/55. Lamafu quit work on the 13th and I've been doing all of my housework. It's best that he did quit, because then I didn't have to fire him. I'm asking God to send me a good worker to help in the house, (my camping house).

The road is moving along, slowly, but looking right good.

I've been teaching the workers about the fall of man. One *boy* (young man), Turebe, has been taking in most everything very well. He gives an answer almost all the time. I feel my real job is to feed these sheep, or lambs. They are really lambs.

09/16/55. I had Meniba in for supper last night. I have not felt like fixing a good meal, so I thought I would fix for someone else, and I did. We had scalloped potatoes and meat; a cooked tomato and bread dish with sugar, which makes it a bit sweet; cheese and bread and butter on the side; along with tea and salted peanuts afterwards. When we were done, Meniba sat back in the chair and said, "Bel bilong mi i-tait" (my stomach is full). He said it was sure good, and then he thanked me two or three times.

We had all the workers come up and, as we washed the dishes, we played the records in Pidgin from Gospel Recordings. I feel that God is going to give us some real followers out of these fellows. I have got to pray more for them.

09/18/55. The nationals came this morning from Kosotaka and wanted to hear the talk from the Bible about God. I felt really bad because I had no one to interpret for me, so I couldn't talk to them. At times like this I don't know what to do. We have got to make the gospel available soon to these poor people living in darkness.

Wa-uwa came in from Kami with a big apple pie from the Kami bakery (Arvalee). It surely is good. The guys all came up and asked if they could play the recorder, so Wa-uwa is playing it for them. Meniba should be up in a bit with a *pas* (letter) from Arvalee.

Meniba got back all right, and a letter from Arvalee let me know that she and the boys would like to come up and stay a while. This idea had never entered my mind. I prayed and felt a real peace about it.

09/20/55. Today the carriers and I went down to Kami to get Arvalee and the kids. We all got back to Kosotaka just before sunset. We have all enjoyed this week. Arvalee said it was like camping out. Well it is camping out, but just not like at home in the States.

The nationals have been bringing plenty of food, for which we have been thanking the Lord. Also the people of Kosotaka have been coming and asking to hear God's Word.

Today we got down to some good points, but they haven't shown a conviction as of yet. We must pray more for them. Each morning I have been teaching a bit from the Word, to the men that are working. I'm teaching from the Old Testament.

09/24/55. Pat, Peter and Paul have been having a great time with all the little boys and girls up here. They climb trees and play with their bows and arrows, which the nationals have made for them. They play like they are pigs, grunting like pigs at each other. There are plenty of real pigs here.

This is the end of two weeks and the road is well on its way down to the first river. We should be there by the middle of the week. We will be to the river tomorrow and have started up the other side of the river. We are going slowly, but I feel we will have a good road for the horse to carry *cargo* on (supplies on) and for the motorbike. It will save a few steps.

We've asked Meniba and Mu-u-nabi to come for a fried chicken dinner tonight. They gave us one of the chickens and we bought the other. I have felt that the Lord is going to save Meniba someday soon. Meniba has shown nothing to build up my hopes, but as I've been praying, the Lord has given me this peace.

October, 1955

10/21/55. During the month Arvalee and children spent with me here, in Kosotaka, I didn't get much writing done, but we surely had a wonderful time together. They are home now and I'm by myself again. It is terribly lonesome now without them. The Kosotaka kids enjoyed having three little white boys to play with. They played kickball a lot and we had so many bananas that we had a banana eating contest. It was just a good time for our family to be out with the village people. We all had a lot of fun together.

These days are real days of testing. The Devil is using his blinded sheep to cause all types of trouble. As we started working on the road today, one *luluai* (chief) from Olaguti (PoPo) said that I had to buy a *matmat* (burial place) for one pound. I told him I didn't think he was right, for I was just following the old trail at this place. I left the matter there.

About two weeks later, we *marked* the new road down to another crossing of the river and up the other side. The *luluai* (chief) and work leader had *marked* it for me. We had finished working it, and while the men were putting a few rocks in the river, a fellow, a new man to us all, came up and said that we couldn't make the road here. He would like compensation, because his old father was buried near here. I asked him why he hadn't told me before. I told him he should have come and told us before and we would have made the road in another place. He said that if I would give him some money now, he would forget about it. I told him that he would have to forget about it without any compensation. That was the end of the talk with that fellow and I haven't heard any more about it yet.

Then a few weeks after that, I went to *mark* (stake out) some more road and another *luluai* (chief) said I couldn't *mark* (survey) the road through this one place. We talked some about why I was building a horse road through his land, and then somehow he changed his mind and said, "You can put the road through my land." The *luluai* (chief) then told me there had been a Lutheran Mission teacher living on this ground a few years ago, but he had pulled out and was gone. I don't know what that had to do with the horse road.

Another time a leader from Kosotaka was talking to some of the workers and said he was going to let me work the road through a *matmat* (a burial ground) and then later *court me* for it (to ask for payment or compensation; or take to trial). When they heard this, the workers came and told me, so we went around the place.

> *Last Saturday the 15th, when I was sick in bed, Meniba came up and said a luluai was going to kill all of the workers for working the road on his ground. So the fellows had all stopped working. I got up and rode the horse to the road site.*
>
> *Before I went, Arvalee, the kids and I prayed and asked the Lord to really work in the luluai's heart. He did! Praise His Name! When I got there, the luluai said we could make the road there, and he even helped. I saw him today, and he was really nice.*
>
> *Arvalee and the kids are back at Kami in our little home now and I'm here alone again. It's quiet around here without them. We are moving our camp closer to the road work.*

Today we had a new problem coming up from a *turn talk* (a translator) on the Government jeep road. He said that when we get to his place he is going to get pay for the road we construct there. If not, he will *court* us (take us to trial), for he thinks he's in good standing with the new *kiap* (patrol officer). But he's not in good with my Heavenly Father. Praise God!

The old *luluai* (chief) of this valley of Olaguti has been a real help to me in *marking* (surveying) the road so far, but tonight he has just told me that he wants pay for the entire road. Everything must be placed in God's hands. I cannot bear these burdens alone. There is peace when God is holding everything. I told the *luluai* (chief named Kire) that the way the Government *marks* (surveys) the road is when the road is all finished. Then each mile is *marked* (staked) and paid for. Nothing more was said. So closed another day. (These kinds of incidents happened about once a week during the entire two years that we were working on the road.)

A funny little thing happened with Kire. He was a good leader and we have become good friends since he wanted to help me *mark* (stake) out where the horse road would go. One day I had some Juicy Fruit chewing gum. I took a stick of gum and popped it into my mouth and then caught up to Kire and asked if he wanted some gum. "Yes," was his reply, so I handed him a stick of gum still wrapped up in the tinfoil. We kept *marking* (surveying) road and later we sat down under a tree to rest in the shade and Kire was still chewing his gum. I could see silver paper in his mouth as he chewed! I hadn't thought to tell him to take the paper off the gum before chewing it. I didn't say anything to him because he was enjoying it so much.

Off and on for two years, Meniba and I did most of the *marking* (surveying) of the road. We had 200 men digging with picks and shovels and four work leaders overseeing 50 men each. I could buy shovels without handles by the dozen, and the men would make their own handles. The shovel was part of their pay for working. I paid the 200 workers with other trade goods as well, such as steel bush knives, and red cloth for a wrap-around sarong, called a *laplap*. The four work leaders were paid with money.

Two of the work leaders, Bebu and Meniba, were good friends, so Meniba wanted Bebu to work with him. Bebu was a very hard worker but had no idea how to lead and manage the 50 men working under him. So Meniba would go show Bebu how to lead the workers so they could get some road made. Wa-uwa was a young Gimi teenager and could keep his 50 men working well. One thing Wa-uwa had going for him was that he knew some of the Yagaria language, and got along well with the men working under him.

Each morning before we started work, I would teach a Bible story to all our workers with the gospel woven into it. One day Meniba and Bebu told me that they believed that Jesus died for their sins. These were the first Gimi believers. It was about Christmas time when Meniba and Bebu shared with me how they believed the Good News about Jesus Christ. We stopped working on the road for a month during Christmas and New Year's. When Bebu returned from his Christmas break in the Gimi he told me this story.

"When I arrived back in my home village of O-aberu, some of the men were working sorcery on the chest of a teenage girl. She had died and the sorcery was to find out which clan had killed her."

A man holds a bamboo about 18 inches long on the chest of the dead person and there are some arrows in the bamboo with the arrow tips pointing up. The man holding the bamboo calls out the names of the clans one at a time, and if the chest should jerk at the time of calling that clan's name, the people believe they are the ones who are responsible for the death.

Bebu went on. "I told the man to stop. I prayed and asked Jesus to raise the girl up. She woke and then sat up. Everyone was shocked. The girl is still alive and doing fine."

I asked Bebu, "How did you know to do this?"

He replied, "I don't know. I knew what the man was doing was wrong and I just told him to stop and he did. All I knew to do then was pray for this young girl on the platform in the center of the village. Everyone's eyes were watching me."

I had never told any Bible stories about Jesus healing or raising people from the dead. All I can say is that God gave this new believer childlike faith to believe that God was big enough to raise the dead and bring honor and glory to Himself among this Stone Age tribal people.

In the Gimi
January, 1959

01/01/1959. We have been in the Gimi for 5 weeks now. It is so good to have the family in here with me.

I feel that the work here in the Gimi is just beginning. Yet, in another way we have a good start. I feel the greatest thing that has been done for these people to deliver them from the power of Satan is that Christians from the homeland have written over and over that they are praying for the Gimi. Without prayer we would have no start at all in here. Mom (Palmer) has written me that she prays for Meniba and his wife all the time, and I know for sure that Meniba would have lost heart by now and have fallen by the wayside, if someone hadn't been praying and holding him up before the Lord all the time.

We all feel, Dave, Althea, Arvalee and I, that Meniba is our key man for the building of the Gimi church. I feel this new year of 1959 is going to be a great year in the Gimi. By faith, we will see the walls of tribal customs fall down at our feet and we will see Christian families step over these broken walls of fear; fear of sickness, of death, and of sorcery being made on them.

Peter's little parakeet died today. When he found it, he couldn't keep from crying. Meniba saw him crying and told him that he would go down to A-ibu to try to get him a *cockatoo*. He said, "I'll go in the morning."

01/02/59. A-a-mo-aba is sick today with an upset stomach and a big pain in his back. Meniba left for A-ibu this morning.

01/03/59. It rained almost all day today. This morning we had our meeting in Me-niba's house. Aaron turned talk (interpreted) for Dave. A-a-mo-aba is not much better today. I went over and prayed for him and sent him some *Aspro* (aspirin) to help the pain in his back.

01/04/59. This morning at about 10:00 we went to Ore-ua-bipi (to Bebu's place) for a meeting. Biru went with us to interpret for Dave and he did well. Dave spoke on the Holy Spirit dwelling in a believer when he first believes. Hu-a-ni-aba remembered the story from before and had a lot of comments. Dave said the Holy Spirit teaches us to pray for big things, like sickness, but He also wants us to pray about small things, like going to our gardens, making a fence, cooking our food etc. Rune spoke up and said, "We see the way you live and we pray and thank God for all our food and when we go to Kami we ask God to make us strong." Hu-a-ni-aba's oldest son came up in the meeting and was standing in the back just looking; his dad motioned for him to sit down, and so he did. Hu-a-ni-aba said that he and his wife always prayed, but no one would come to pray with them. Bebu has a chapel started. I told the Christians that it was their chapel and they should help with the building of it. Some of them said they would. We had some *iremu* (greens) and *ire-* (greens) with a small piece of *kaukau* (sweet potato) with the people. Then we got home about 3:30. Meniba had some *abai* cooking (the fruit of the *pandanus* tree, which makes a thick sauce for serving with other foods) in a *mumu* (steam cooking), so about 5:30 we went down to his house for dinner. Came back, and had tea and Jell-O at the Lawrence's house.

Meniba came over to our house and we had a talk about starting meetings about 11:00 a.m. in the morning, so we could teach the people that come up to see us during the day. He thought it would be good.

The walk down to Bebu's was quite tiring for me. But I think if I don't try to go too far, I will be all right. I would like to try to get down there each week and maybe I could take care of that church, so Dave could get over to the Christians farther away. The *luluai* (chief) from Ubai came up today and I paid him for the chicken he gave Peter and me before. He returned the two shovels that he had borrowed.

01/05/59. Today A-a-mo-aba is feeling some better. He came up this morning to make a fire in the stove. He also interpreted for Dave this morning. Meniba helped him a bit. Dave reviewed the crucifixion and told the story of the resurrection. Mu-u-nabi (Meniba's wife) never comes to the morning meetings. Yesterday she was working in her garden when we were having the meetings.

Dave and I got together about language study. Dave is going to get some short sentences from Aaron, and then we may try to get them on tape. He hopes to start a class by next Monday. Althea hopes to start school by then too. Meniba came up, so we had a good talk. Dave came over too, so we had some good fellowship together. Meniba said that Mu-u-nabi didn't want to come to the morning meetings and he felt that Satan was influencing her. He said that he would ask her to come to the meeting, but he had heard her say to someone, "I don't like to go to the meetings." Only God can give Mu-u-nabi that hunger for the Word of God. Oh, I need to pray more for her and Meniba.

We also talked about U-i-mo and his dad fighting. Meniba said that Aromuti and U-i-mo never did get along good. We had a good time in prayer; we all three prayed in Pidgin.

01/06/59. Dave taught this morning on the ascension. A-a-mo-aba came to work today. Mu-u-nabi still didn't come to the meeting this morning and two other women joined her in her house. I feel Satan is using Mu-u-nabi to influence the other women not to come to the meetings.

It's been so cold in the mornings. I thought we might try to meet in the fire-wood house, so we could have a fire. Meniba said after the meeting that Asu-mu-yaba's brother had died and he was going over to see him. He said he was a Christian. I also talked to U-i-mo a bit this morning about fighting his dad; that Jesus was not happy with this old way of life. I encouraged him to go tell his dad that he was sorry and make up. He laughed when he told me about it and Mu-u-nabi came up about the same time and was laughing too. They just don't see the sin they are in. Oh, that God will bring great conviction of sin upon these people.

01/07/59. The meeting was long today. Dave reviewed the life of Christ. A-a-mo-aba had a good attitude as he was interpreting the message. I had to send Biru, Hobe-aba, Morobe and Ibuna-ada to meet the horses at Yagana.

Mcniba said that they had already buried the man, (referring to the one who died on the 2nd), so he didn't see him. They all feel sorcery was worked on this man too, just like Meniba's brother. The fear of sorcery is very strong. We have got to believe the gospel of Jesus Christ that it is truly the Power of God and it can break the powers of the evil one in this place. It can also do in the hearts of these poor benighted people what dynamite can do to a hard stone that is blocking a roadway. The Power of the Gospel, I know for sure can break these cold, hard hearts of the people and make them broken and open for the warm love of Christ to flow in. I know God has done this very thing for me some 10 years ago and He's the same today as he was 10 years ago. In our prayer meeting we talked some about the fellows we are teaching in the mornings. They need to be encouraged to give out what they are taking in.

Paul fell down this afternoon and I went to help him up and Meniba came over and was talking to Paul. It made Paul mad and he started kicking and hitting at Meniba and myself. I lost my temper and whipped Paul when I was mad. I went down to Meniba and told him that this was wrong and I knew God had spoken to me about it. Meniba said he didn't understand Paul, why he should be mad at him. Meniba likes the kids so much. I could tell he was hurt. It was rainy and bad all day today.

01/08/59. This morning Mu-u-nabi, Wietho (A-a-mo-aba's wife) and Nanoi (Biru's wife) came to the meeting. We had it outside. I spoke on God being over all and how he cast Satan out of Heaven. God is going to judge everyone; Satan and his angels and all people of the earth.

Dave and I had a good talk this morning about language study, getting out with the people etc.

It rained for the most part of the afternoon. Meniba cooked some *abai* (red sauce) and *ina* (taro) in a *mumu* (food cooked in the ground over hot rocks) and brought it up for our supper. The carriers got in from Yagana about 5:30 p.m.

01/09/59. We taught this morning that God is the Great One, over all, over Satan and all the powers of darkness. God will help us to overcome the powers of Satan. God cast Satan out of Heaven and He will some day cast him and all that follow him into the pit of Hell. We are trying to get across that a Christian is on God's side and Satan is lying and doing all he can these last days to slow down the work of God.

The school room floor and windows are in as of today, so all Althea has to do is get things in order by Monday. Meniba did most of the building; it's sort of rough, but it gives Dave and me more time to do other things.

The sun came out for some time today, but the wind is cold. It's hard to keep the kids in the house.

01/10/59. The weather is still cold this morning, it must have rained most of the night and the wind woke me this morning. This must be the coldest time of year back here.

Hobe-aba told me what the song meant (Yesusu Amapi). Biru told the story of creation and went into the fall of man on his own. He is remembering the stories well. A-a-mo-aba and Wietho went down to A-ibu today. Mu-u-nabi came to the meeting this morning in good spirits. Hobe-aba closed in prayer.

The Lord helped me this morning in our family devotions by Peter's example. He got up singing a song about the Lord, then he stopped singing and Arvalee saw him praying. We talked some about how God helped Joshua. Paul said Joshua 1:9 for us, The Lord commands us to be strong and brave, not to be afraid or over taken and He promises to be with us always.

Etha-o has been coming around and is being a bit friendlier toward us the last two days. Praise God He will bring him back into fellowship with Himself. I do believe the Lord for Etha-o.

After talking to Meniba this afternoon, I know why he didn't want to go down to

Ore-ua-bipi last Sunday with us. He yet thinks that some trouble will befall him if he goes there. He thinks that Watha-mo-re-e is doing all the bad talk down there and Bebu is not willing to stand up and be strong for the Lord. I told Meniba that fear of death or sorcery is from the pit.

We got together tonight, I read I John 3:23, 24, how that God has commanded us to believe on the Name of His Son Jesus Christ and to love everyone. And if we keep this command we know for sure that the Spirit of God is living in our hearts. Oh, if only we can show in our teaching that God is over all and Jesus is King of all Kings and the Holy Spirit lives in each believer, we can stand in the Power of these three. They will be able to overcome Satan in their everyday lives.

01/11/59. Good day today, with no rain. Went down to Ore-ua-bipi today and had a good talk to the men. Watha-mo-re-e said that they were willing to come up tomorrow and get things straight with the Negibi clan. I was encouraged by going down today. They have been working well. We asked them last week to build a toilet for us, so we could come down and stay for a few days at Bebu's old house. So they have a hole dug now and started working on a woven blind for the walls. Hu-a-ni-aba was a blessing in the meeting today. I feel he's going to be a real church leader.

I was sure tired when I got home today. Dave wants to go down some time this week for a few days. Teaching today was about how God is going to judge all men for the works they have done. Dave is using the pictures that Althea painted. Teaching on the Holy Spirit in a believer and how He helps us.

Tonight we had the Lord's Supper and sang songs. It's sure good to have co-workers so we can have fellowship together. It's very cold tonight.

01/12/59. A-a-mo-aba said he would be back to work this morning, but he hasn't showed up yet, so Meniba is helping Arvalee wash the clothes today. Meniba said this morning that Esema (the big chief) told him he was coming over today to see if we would come over and teach them, for they weren't getting strong for the Lord. I feel this is an answer to prayer. The meeting this morning was about us all being Adam's children and we are all sinners. Some people think they are good, and some like the life of sin and some know they are sinners and want to turn to God and His new way of life. Meniba said that he went over to his place yesterday and told them that Satan's line killed Jesus and now they were killing the Negibi's because they were following Jesus. He said, "That's all right, if they killed Jesus they can kill us too. We won't return the evil they do to us."

We had our first language class today. It's good to work together in this language learning. Meniba made a little porch on our house this afternoon. The Lawrence's came over for dinner tonight. We had the other 2 pound ham that Don sent us; it was sure good. All of us took a short walk up the road after supper. I told the kids a bedtime story about

Koko, a little native boy who was very bad and how his big brother helped him to find the Lord Jesus Christ. Peter thanked me for telling him the story.

Arvalee was sure glad she washed clothes today, the sun was out all day and everything got dry.

01/13/59. Arvalee was sick with an upset stomach most of the night, so I had to get up with Julie. I couldn't get back to sleep after being awake, so I was *all in* (Australian term for tired or worn out) this morning. Arvalee, my darling wife, gave me breakfast in bed this morning.

Language (class) was good today. I think that I will have to re-learn some things which might be hard on the flesh. Praise God. I do feel Dave knows what he's doing and we will get the language if we can stick with these classes.

01/14/59. We reviewed creation and the fall this morning. Mu-u-nabi didn't come to the meeting, but was in the house with some folks. Nu-u-da reviewed the creation with the picture. Biru spoke some on the fall.

A-a-mo-aba hasn't showed up yet. Meniba and Biru made the clothes lines today and Hobe-aba worked in the house for Arvalee all day. Prayer meeting today was for U-he-zui-hu-tai and Imetai and when we sat down a woman from U-he-zui-hu-tai came in and Biru and I had a little meeting with her. Biru was not too good on turning talk (translating), I don't think. He said the woman said something and she only said about three words and he talked to me for 5 minutes about what she said. I can understand enough of the language to tell that he is telling her what to say back to me. I talked to him some about it, but I will have to show him that he is just lying to me and not helping anyone either.

Language class was very upset today, as the carriers came from Kami with *cargo* (supplies). No rain today.

01/15/59. A-a-mo-aba came in last night. He said that he knew he was disobeying but he just did it. I told him he just lied to me and God doesn't like liars. He has no sorry about it at all. Must think we have to put up with this for we need him so bad. Wietho sold us a leg of pig for three shillings.

I spoke to the ones this morning about sin and how God hates all sin, lying and getting *kros* (angry). U-i-mo and Aaron, I spoke to on being *kros* (angry). They must confess this and not hold it in their *livers* (hearts). I told Meniba, Biru and A-a-mo-aba that they had all lied to me at one time; Meniba about the gun, Biru about turning talk (translating) and A-a-mo-aba about not coming back to work when he said he would. Dave closed in prayer. Oh, that they will see what sin is.

Language class was better today. We met in the school house. I got the window on the back door up this afternoon. Julie was not eating well tonight. Arvalee said, I think she has lost her appetite. Julie spoke up, "Where?" she said. I told her maybe outside, to hurry up and eat and we'd go look for it. No rain today.

01/16/59. During the morning hours, some kind of a bug fell on Arvalee in her sleep. It bit her on the eye lid and when she knocked it off, it bit her on the finger. It was dark, so I couldn't find it; but it is giving her considerable pain. I put Benadryl Cream on it.

Althea is sick with sinus today, so Dave is teaching school. Meniba is putting a fence post up for a chicken fence today. A *dokta boi* (medical orderly) came today looking for Arasau to take him back to Okapa.

Dave and the kids had supper with us tonight. No rain today. I'm receiving a blessing from reading a little book, Sit, Walk, Stand on the studies of Ephesians.

Teaching this morning was on the birth of Christ; point stressed, Jesus is the Son of God.

I asked two Christians to pray this morning, so Meniba and U-i-mo prayed. I trust U-i-mo is coming back into fellowship.

01/17/59. Julie kept us up a lot last night. She says her neck is *pen* (hurting). It gives us more time in the mornings when A-a-mo-aba comes to fix breakfast. I have been so tired in the mornings that it's so hard to get up before 7:00 a.m. Reading this morning for our devotions, Col. 4:1-4. Teaching this morning on Christ; How He was with God in the beginning. When He came to earth He was yet the Son of God, but had a body like ours, but not our sin nature. He had a body like man, but He pleased God in His body to show us it could be done. And He is willing to do the same for us. I asked Nanoi this morning to pray. She prayed for a long time. Mu-u-nabi was there too. Meniba is going to take some time off. There is a custom here that when a close relative dies, the relatives have to kill pigs and feed other relatives not so close. This is where Meniba is right now, but he has no pigs to kill and he's trying to buy some. He's going to Kigupa then over to the Fore country to see if he can find some pigs. He said it was hard work when someone died in the family. I told him he could have two weeks off.

Meniba came in tonight telling me that his only pig is gone now, he thinks someone stole it. He said tomorrow he was going to look for it. Satan is working on Meniba overtime these days. He thinks everyone is down on him. I feel he's on the rock bottom. Now, to see the Lord take over in his life, and bring him out on top would be great. Meniba is walking through the valley of the shadow of death these days. But he has got to see that the Lord is with him. He knows that the Lord is near, He is over all, but he doesn't know and really believe it for his own life. When the Lord opens his eyes to this he will be able to say I will fear no evil, for you are with me Lord. This will be the day for Meniba.

01/18/59. Dave went down to Ore-ua-bipi this morning but Sidi sent some *boys* up to see if Dave would come down to Iri-bia-bipi today. So I don't know what David will do.

Meniba went to look for his pig today, but didn't find it. Dave said he had a good meeting at Ore-ua-bipi. Sidi was there, but Dave told him that his wife was sick and he had to get back.

The kids and I went for a nice walk up the road this afternoon. There are so many things to look at and the kids have so much fun. Our *koki* (cockatoo) is sure growing these days. Julie sure loves him. Althea is not feeling good yet, so Dave is going to give her some Chloromycetin. No rain today.

01/19/59. As I was looking out the window this morning, I saw Meniba and his wife going down the road. I don't know where they are going, but they must be looking for their pig yet. He is sure low these days. I don't know what to do to help him, only pray. He didn't get back for the morning devotions.

This is wash day and it's raining today. It's been raining most every night and the gardens have radishes coming up now and some lettuce. Peter planted his garden on the 13th and Paul and I on the 14th.

Se-o and some women came up today with some *kunai* grass for Biru's house. I'm buying it with salt. I paid three spoons for a big bundle, two or one for smaller ones.

Meniba came in time to help Arvalee with the wash, then right after the wash was over, he said his pig had come back and someone had stolen it, for its ears were cut off. He wanted to track it back, said the ears were bleeding, and he could follow the drops of blood. He left about noon and it rained about 4:00 p.m. real hard. He came in about 5:30 and said he tracked the blood back to a village down below us here, A-bo-pisa, is the clans name, ground name Misapi-biraisa. He said he talked to the man down there, who said he found the pig down on the *Thani* River. Meniba said he told the man he could give him a pig for stealing his and cutting its ears.

He came up here to talk to me about it. I was a bit sick in the tummy, so was lying down when he came. He told me all that had happened and that he was going back now to see if he could get a pig from this fellow. I told Meniba that I thought he was going to cause trouble if he tried to get a pig from these people. He said, "Yes, but they stole my pig and cut it's ears off and my brother Ma-o had cut a little mark in my pig's ear and now this man from A-bo-pisa has cut them off and I'm sorry for I can't remember my brother. Ma-o is dead and now my pig's ears are cut off. I think he should pay me back a pig." "Alright Meniba, lets pray about it," I said. "God will show you what to do if you will only be willing to obey Him." I prayed first and Meniba prayed in Gimi and I couldn't understand him at all, because he was talking so low. I could hear someone call, Meniba, MENIBA. Come quickly, they're going down to fight. Meniba looked at me and said, "Mu-u-nabi is calling me, I must go now." I told him to walk softly before the Lord and He will help you. "Yes, I will sir, pray for me." He went out the front door and I got up and went out the back door, going over to tell Dave.

I saw about 15 men with bows and arrows running down the road over by U-i-mo's house. Meniba was now down the road a bit, making good time; Mu-u-nabi was calling out to Meniba about something, as he went running by the house but I couldn't understand her. All the men were over the hill by then and Meniba was right behind them. I went on over and told Dave about it, for he had been in school all day and didn't know much about what had happened. After I told him, I went for a short walk up the road. I told the Lord that it was up to Him now to show Meniba about his motive, about this pig and to give him love and wisdom in all of this.

Arvalee called me for supper, but I was feeling a bit sicker, so didn't eat much and went right to bed. I lost all my supper and was in bed for the night when Meniba came in the front door. He asked Arvalee if I was here. Arvalee said yes, but he is sick. Meniba came to the bed room door and said, "Are you sick?" He was all smiles and said, "God helped me. When I left you some of my clan had come and were going down to burn the little hamlet. They had their bows and arrows ready to fight. The arrow tips were unwrapped and the razor bamboo edges were in each man's hand. I told them to stop, that I would talk to the fellow and we weren't going to fight. They were sure mad, but somehow God made them hear what I had to say, but some even got mad at me. As I walked up to the man's house alone, my people kept shouting, 'Let's burn the houses and kill all their pigs'. By the time I got to the man's house he was standing in front of his house. I told him not to be afraid for my people were not going to fight. The Negibis had circled the hamlet and were shouting yet, 'Burn the houses, kill the pigs'. *Papa* God helped me to speak softly and I asked the man why he had stolen my pig. He said he found it down on the *Thani* River and he was going to take care of it. I said, 'Have I ever come to your village and stole your pigs or anything from you? No. Well then why did you steal my pig and cut his ears off?' Then the man told me that he had stolen my pig and he was sorry. I told him that he was full of sin and following Satan, that he was always doing something to me or my people and making it hard for us. I told him I wasn't mad, but felt sorry for him. The Negibis had quieted down a bit by now. The man said, 'I liked your pig, so I stole it and cut it's ears off and ate them, but the pig got out of the fence I made and ran away. I will give you one of my little pigs for my stealing'". Meniba said, "God spoke to my *liver* (heart) and told me if I take that pig from him, that I would be stealing his pig. So I told him that I would buy the little pig from him, and then everyone would be happy." So Meniba and the man shook hands and said it was finished. But this did not make Meniba's people happy. They said that he must give the pig, no pay. The man said he was willing to just give the pig to Meniba, but Meniba said, "NO. God told me to pay for the pig." Some said it was all right, but some are yet mad at Meniba for this. Meniba said, "*Master* Dale, God really helped me today." I said to him that we should thank God for hearing us when we called on Him for help. So with a big smile all over his shiny black face, he said, "Yes, let's do." We both thanked God for helping him this afternoon. He just kept saying, "*Papa* God, you helped me, it was you that made me strong." After praying he said he thought it would be good if he would make a fence to keep his pig in from now on. I told him I thought it would be good and I might be able to give him a bit of pig wire to make a strong fence. He said good night and strolled out the front door.

It has done me a world of good to see a victory over Satan like this. Believe me, Meniba is standing alone in his beliefs; his wife and his people just don't understand him. But God does and He is doing a good work in this young man's life. We see today that God is willing to help those who are willing to obey Him and not listen to what others say. This is one light in a very dark tribe, but others will see that this one is following a new Master and they will know that the one they are following is not the right one.

01/20/59. It rained during the night, making the garden grow good. Read Luke 1:35… that the Holy thing which shall be born of you shall be called the Son of God. I want them to see this, which the angel of God said to Mary, not a man, then how God spoke out of a cloud, "This is my beloved son, hear him." Luke 9:35. Meniba interpreted in the meeting today. Meniba has all the fellows working on the chicken house using *Karuka* (Pandanus) for flooring. We prayed today for the Negibi clan. We went over to Dave's bedroom, so Althea could be in the language study. She's feeling some better.

Some men from Yumi brought some pig meat over this afternoon to sell. For four legs I gave 12 shillings, one big mirror and a small knife. The guy was happy with the pay and we were happy to get the pig. Gave the Lawrence's one leg, we kept one and gave our workers the other two.

01/21/59. Julie was sick from 2:00 on, vomiting 6 times since then. Meniba is a bit sick today, too. He said he was cold all night and didn't sleep, just sat by the fire all night. Nu-u-da came in and made passion fruit juice this morning. *Boys*, the carriers, got here with the 25 chickens today. Also, they brought the wire and 4 pieces of roofing iron. I bought some corn today and before we could get outside to divide it for sharing, Biru took some and sent a couple of little boys to his house with it. Arvalee saw it and told me. I got a bit mad and spoke *kros* (in anger) at them, and then I had to go tell Biru I was sorry for getting *kros* (angry), but that it would be much better if he would think about us too. I told him it would be good if he would come first and divide it or ask if someone had already done so, so we could all have some. I told him that they like to eat the older more mature corn much better than we do, so if it was all right with them we would like the new corn. He said he wasn't thinking, so I hope everything is all right.

We had a test in language today and I missed all but 2; my stress is all wrong. You would think I would know better. Julie is feeling much better this afternoon. The *boys* got here with the mail tonight. Pat and Jerry Sherman (later married to Ted Fitzgerald, Arvalee) are to leave from Olaguti in the morning. The *boys* who went to get the horses' *cargo* (supplies the horses brought) don't know anything about a small square tin that I gave them the week before. Said they didn't get it, but I'm sure I gave it to them. They felt I should pay them for walking to Muye last week even though they didn't get the *cargo* (supplies); they were late, so Lamafu got some kids from Amusa to carry the things, so I had to pay them for carrying. But the Negibi guys felt I should pay them too. This week they must have got there on time. I told them it was up to them.

01/22/59. Meniba didn't come to the meeting this morning. He is taking Nivaquine, and said he's cold most all the time. He did say he slept better last night. His wife came to the meeting this morning. A-a-mo-aba turned talk or interpreted. Spoke on Jesus telling His followers not to forbid the little boys and girls from coming to him, but little children don't think of bad things like we big people do and up in Heaven we will all be thinking like little boys and girls. Jesus was kind to all, big or little. Meniba came up about 10:00 a.m. and said some old man was calling for him to go over to Negibi; he was going to kill a pig and wanted Meniba there to help divide it out among the clan. I told him it wasn't the best for him to go, being sick and taking Nivaquine and walking over there. He was too sick to come outside at the back of his house, and feed on the Word of God, but not too sick to walk over to another village to eat some pig a few hours afterwards.

I bought 3 big eggs today with a small *marrow* (squash) for 9 pence. We had a full day today. I fixed George's boots with nails and then wrote a letter to Don. I was late to prayer meeting, and late to language class. It's so hard for me to say things the way Dave has them written. When I get out with the people I have so much fun talking to them, but in language class it seems I don't get anything right. I just don't know how to learn when something's written on paper. Only the Lord can help me to get and say the phrases in class.

No rain today. Biru and two *boys* went to meet Jerry and Pat about 3:30 P.M.

Dave tried to play a tape recording from his friends in the states, but the *Butoba* (tape recorder) went off and we couldn't get it to play. We worked for some time and gave up.

01/23/59. I had a real good night's rest last night and I am so thankful when I have one. Teaching this morning on the calling of the twelve. Jesus told the twelve that they must go and tell the Jews that God was going to rule over all soon and this is what Jesus wants all people everywhere to know. The Jew will be first, Matt. 10:6, and Rom. 1:16. I told them that Jesus was a Jew man.

Meniba said this morning that he was feeling much better, he came to the meeting, but he didn't work today. Mu-u-nabi didn't come to meeting this morning. Her mother has mud all over her these days and so does Horobe, Etha-o's wife.

Asked the Lord to help us fix the tape recorder and got it working now.

01/24/59. Had a good rain in the night. Each morning you can see the little plants have grown. It makes one feel good to see things growing; we have to believe that the seed has been planted in good ground. As I walk by the garden each morning to go down to teach the *boys*, I realize we have to believe by faith in the Lord in the same way, that the seed sown in them will grow and that they will grow up in Him. A farmer breaks the ground, plants, weeds and helps in any way he can, but only God can make that seed grow and bring fruit. We have got to keep believing that God is able to bring these souls to faith in Him.

Pat and Jerry got in about 10:30 this morning. James Yanepa from Yagaria (Kami) and several believers from the Watut came with Jerry. The day was full. We talked some, ate lunch, opened boxes, had prayer meeting, talked more and had a meeting with our workers and the visitors about next week and where and who should go. Tomorrow we'll be going to the villages close by. Then Monday, Biru said he would go with the visitor fellows down to Misapi and A-ibu. We talked about the Lord's Supper and that we would all teach on it tomorrow. One of them said that at Kami they just use one cup, but at the Watut they each have a cup. James spoke up, said it was all right, that it was the same and we were all thinking about Jesus and His death for us.

The Watut *boys* started talking about asking for the blood of Jesus, and James spoke up again that some men from Kami say that if we have asked the blood of Jesus, and then are baptized then we can go to Heaven and everything will be all right. James said this is not right, they don't really know the whole story of Jesus or they would not live in their sin and think it's all right. I told the fellows that we could ask for the blood of Jesus but that would not save us. We could do a lot of good things, but the only thing that will truly save us is to know (believe) that Jesus was born with a body as ours, walked and lived a pure life, before all men and is now at God's right hand. He died for you and me, and rose again. And He has given us all things. Good thoughts, talk, work, everything, now we must take it.

01/25/59. To God Be the Glory, Great things He has done. Meniba and Joseph went over to Negibi to teach this morning. Said they were going to Tu-uibe's hamlet. This may help Meniba to see the need of going over and teaching his own people.

A-a-mo-aba and Nathanial went down to Ore-ua-bipi to teach. This may show A-a-mo-aba that the Lord would use him to teach others what he knows. Biru and James have gone to U-he-zui-hu-tai to teach this morning. Dave and Aaron went down to Iri-bia-bipi. Sidi asked Dave last week to come down to his place, so Dave felt he should go this week. I woke up this morning with hives on my left arm and face. I don't know what is causing it, so haven't taken anything but *Aspro* for it. We had our meeting in Pidgin English tonight. I spoke for some time, and then asked Nathanial if he would give us the Lord's Supper. He misunderstood me and told the whole story of Jesus' life and it was a bit long. All the kids went to bed.

01/26/59. The hives are not much better this morning. Didn't get up till 10 a.m. Meniba went with the *boys* to A-ibu this morning with Biru.

Pat doesn't seem to know what to do with himself so Jerry, Pat and I played Scrabble all morning. Had a good prayer meeting this afternoon. Big rain this afternoon. Dave had the meeting with the *boys* today.

01/27/59. I slept better last night, but the hives are still there. Dave is teaching the *boys* this morning. Jerry read to our family this morning. Had a birthday party for Julie and Asu-mu-yaba, Meniba's first born and A-ni-ani-mo, A-a-mo-aba's little boy. Julie was three years old, and we think the others were too. We had 12 dark complexioned friends with black curly hair at the party and 12 *A-o-bana* (Europeans). We just had cake. Althea, Jerry, Arvalee and I played Chinese checkers.

01/28/59. Felt much better today. They are still itchy, but the hives are going down. Arvalee read to us from Ephesians 4 this morning. Nu-u-da worked on the chicken house all day today. A-a-mo-aba killed two chickens for supper tonight.

This afternoon, Dave and I were teaching and playing deck-quoits with the kids. As we were playing we saw a beautiful sunset. I'm sure Heaven will be beautiful like that all the time. A young native boy named A-enabu said that it was *bita ina* (good talk) when we were looking at it.

It was nice to have Dave and Althea over for supper. I told them after eating that we might try to go on furlough sometime in August or September of this year. The schooling will be too much for Althea if we try to stay another year and everyone on the field feel that I should go home for a rest. I do feel since Dave will be going out to Goroka with Althea when she has the new baby that it would be best if we stay here until he gets back, so that someone will be here at all times. This is a very crucial time back here and if we all pull out at one time, no telling what could happen here. Even if some new folk came right now, they should be here for 6 months to see how we deal with these tribal people. And find out a few things about them. Dave is doing real well, but Meniba needs to get to know him a bit better. I feel that this is partly up to me to help Meniba to confide in Dave, so that when I pull out, Meniba will feel free to seek help from Dave and I feel that I should tell Dave all I know about the people's customs. There are many things I want to do before we go home.

Sent Morobe and another fellow to Olaguti this afternoon. No rain today.

01/29/59. Read this morning from Matt. 10:29 – 42. We know that God loves our *koki*, (cockatoo, used as "His eye is on the sparrow") but he loves us much more and he knows how many hairs we have. Jesus wants us to follow Him each day of our lives. Didn't do much this morning. Rested some on the bed. Had a test in class today. I didn't do too well with the written part; I need to work on stress more. A-a-mo-aba helped a bit in the spoken language part. Sent Nu-u-da and Iniabuta down to Iri-bia-bipi to see if we could find someone to go get our things at Yagana tomorrow.

No rain today. Pat has been having a good time back here. The kids go up the road and find so many things to do in the bush. Dave asked A-a-mo-aba to tell the story in the morning. So Dave is going to the meeting, but A-a-mo-aba will take over, we hope.

01/30/59. Meniba came in this morning, said he was a bit sick, so he came on home last night. Said the *boys* would be in today some time. He said they had a good meeting at Misapi and the Christians were glad to see them. They told of one fellow from a village just down a ways from Misapi that had been saved, and he said he had quit smoking. The fellows got here about 1:30 p.m. They were sure rejoicing over their trip.

We had our prayer meeting with the three visiting guys today, mostly in Pidgin.

Meniba killed the Billy goat that we got from the medical officer. We have the two back legs and ribs, gave the *boys* (our workers and visitors) all the rest. Meniba shot the goat with the 22 rifle. He gave the three *boys* (visitors) quite a bit of the meat. Pat is trying to dry the goat skin.

A-a-mo-aba told the story this morning, did quite good. Dave had to help him in asking some of the fellows the questions. Sidi and O-so were here this morning.

01/31/59. The three visitors went down with Dave this morning to have devotions with our workers and local people who attend the meetings. Dave said that Joseph told the folks how people used to come to Tanameo (a village in the Watut) thinking someone would tell them about this new way of life. But he said that they would just talk to them about other things and not about the things of the Lord. He told the Christians here that they should tell each person that comes here the way of life. Dave said it was sure good. James said that it was not just the *Master's* (European's) job to tell everyone but each Christian should go tell others.

February, 1959

02/01/59. Dave and A-a-mo-aba went down to U-he-zui-hu-tai this morning; said they had a good meeting and they listened well. There wasn't as much confusion as it was at Ore-ua-bipi. Said I-saru was there and he said he would work for us.

Biru and I went down to Ore-ua-bipi. Pat went along too. They said that the fellow that was working on the toilet cut his foot and went to the *haus sik*. Then someone died and they haven't been working on the chapel for some time. Hu-a-ni-aba called the *lu-luai* (chief) from Misapi-biraisa, so he and some of his *boys* came over for the meeting. I started telling about God and how He was everywhere, how He kicked Satan out of Heaven. Satan was *kros* (mad) at God and now at Jesus. Ha-amiaba said that he wasn't afraid to die, because he would go to Heaven and see God's face and Jesus' face. Then an old man said that he had asked for the blood of Jesus to make him clean and now he is a Christian. I asked him if he was afraid to die now. No, he said. I will go to heaven now, he said. Then I showed the little picture of the Baby Jesus and told the story and then the picture of Jesus when He was a young boy and how he was helping Joseph and He always obeyed him. Then I went right into the full life of Christ and His death. I told Biru that he could give each the *kaukau* (sweet potato) and tomato juice and tell what it was for and that we should eat it and think about Jesus and His broken skin and His blood that was shed for us. Afterwards, I told the Christians they should get together each Sunday and have the Lord's Supper. I asked Biru if he would take care of the cooking of the tomatoes and having things ready each Sunday. And I told them it would be good to get the chapel finished.

02/02/59. Dave went down this morning to teach. We read Rom. 12:1 this morning. Was a real blessing to me.

02/03/59. I had the meeting this morning. Told about the angel coming to Mary and telling her that Jesus was the Son of God. Then when Jesus was baptized God said that Jesus was His Son. Then Jesus said Himself that he was the Son of God. Jesus, we must know as the true Son of God; His father is not Joseph.

02/04/59. Hobe-aba reviewed the story this morning and did well. Dave went to Ore-ua-bipi. Meniba started working on the house. I had to help him quite a bit to get started. Feel very tired today. O-so came in this afternoon. He said Jerry went to Olaguti in one day. George (Fatzinger) is having trouble *marking* road.

02/05/59. I was so tired last night that I didn't rest too well. Asked A-a-mo-aba to take the meeting this morning, he and Meniba. It's very cold this morning. My feet were cold until noon. Some *boys* from U-he-zui-hu-tai went to get the *cargo* (supplies) from Yagana.

02/06/59. Teaching this morning, Jesus tells his disciples that he is going back to Heaven. He promises them that God will send the Holy Spirit, to help them at all times. Meniba doing well on the house. It rained this afternoon, so we had a meeting with the *cargo boys* (carriers). One of the *boys* had never been here, so he got to hear the story of the birth of Christ. I hope to teach them some more soon.

02/07/59. Two of the *boys* didn't come to work this morning. Don't know just what to do with them. They told Dave that they would work until noon on Sat. All the rest have been working quite good. Rain today. Very tired these days. A-a-mo-aba has a boil on his knee. I asked him if he would like to go someplace this weekend. Said he would, so I suggested U-he-zui-hu-tai. Dave came up last night, said that Bebu is coming to all the meetings and gets others to come.

02/08/59. All of us went down to Tabaribo's place this morning. Most of the Christians were there. They said that they were not following the new way good any more. Satan was *pulling* (enticing) them and they obeyed him and were not strong for Jesus. They said that if I would come and teach them each Sunday at Tabaribo's place that they would come to hear and then they could come up strong for Jesus. A-a-mo-aba and I-saru went to U-he-zui-hu-tai today, said they had a good meeting. Teaching on the birth of Christ. My teaching was how God is over all, even Satan. How He kicked him out of Heaven. Very tired from my walk over there.

02/09/59. We read from John chapter 10 with our kids this morning. Teaching the *boys* this morning on the ascension of Jesus.

02/11/59. We read about Lazarus rising from the dead this morning. Teaching the *boys* about the Holy Spirit in each believer. I'm not doing much work, drawing a bit. At 1:00 p.m. it started raining. About 1:30 Lamafu and Ya-no-no came in soaked. Asked the Aumaraisa fellows if they would like a meeting since it was raining. Asked Lamafu if he would like to speak to them. He told them about Adam, the fall, God sending His Son, Jesus dying for us, His blood paying for all our sins. It was good, what he said. Lamafu said that he couldn't get the sores well on the horses. He wants to work for the new *master* when he comes, so we need to find a new horse boy.

02/12/59. Our reading this morning was in John 11:47-57. Verse 50 was good, the high priest said that one man should die for the people and that the whole nation would not perish. Quite a few were here this morning from A-ibu. Aaron came too; Meniba is doing quite good in leading the singing. We reviewed the same story as yesterday, about the Holy Spirit in a Believer. Told them some of the work of the Holy Spirit, showing us what sin is, teaching us to be Holy and clean. And the spirit tells us that God is over all and will someday judge the world. Four of the Aumaraisa fellows didn't come to work today at all. Dave talked to them about being late to work all the time. He has gone down to Ore-ua-bipi this afternoon to talk to them about baptism, for this Sunday.

Dave came in tonight and said that he felt that Biru was a bit light hearted when he turned talk for him. We had a good long talk, and then had prayer together.

02/13/59. Teaching more this morning about the work of the Holy Spirit in the life of a believer. Will the Holy Spirit that came into a believer when he puts his trust in Christ, go out of the believer if he should sin? Hobe-aba said, "No." I told them that the Bible tells us that we are sealed with that Holy Spirit that God promised. This is one thing I would like to get across these days. The men from Aumaraisa came up this morning and said that they were all quitting work. I could tell Dave felt bad about this, but I told him that we were able to have a few meetings with them and got a bit of work out of them, so we shouldn't feel too bad. I said, "Well, the Lord will send us some more men to work." We thought it best to start working on shingles, so I went down the hill with him and the *boys* from A-ibu. The tree was big, but he said it didn't grow straight; the wind made it twist. We made a few and he wanted to go try another tree.

02/14/59. The reading this morning was from John 12:20 – 36 about a corn of wheat falling into the ground and dying. If we don't plant, then we don't get any fruit from the seed. If we are not willing to go to the cross with the Lord Jesus now, if we love and think we are too good to identify ourselves with the death of our Lord Jesus, then we will lose our life, but if we will really identify ourselves with all that Jesus is, then we will have life after death. Then we reviewed the work of the Holy Spirit. He shows us what sin is and teaches us the new way of life. Meniba said that the Holy Spirit had helped him, that he knew he wasn't strong but it was the Holy Spirit that made him strong.

Esema came over this afternoon, and said that he had *atope* (potatoes) and he would bring them Monday. He asked if he could take one of our kittens home to get the rats in his house and bring it back Monday. Meniba came in tonight and said he hadn't known if the Negibi would come to the baptism or not, said they all had a big shame because the red skin was not talking true. He says that he will hold poison in one hand and feed us with the other hand.

02/15/59. Dave said they sure had a good time at the baptism. Bebu and Biru started doing the baptizing, and then Hu-a-ni-aba and Meniba did the rest. There were about 30 baptized. Hu-a-ni-aba had the communion all ready, all on his own. The Negibi didn't come at all. Meniba came in and said that the *luluai* (chief) from A-ibu said to him that many groups are trying to come into their place, but they don't want them and it is confusing; he ask Meniba when were we going to come down to teach them. They said that they were not strong and if we didn't come to teach them soon that their teachers would *pull* (entice) them. Meniba seemed to see the need to get out and teach them.

Had Pat's birthday today; he asked if we could have it now for him. (His birthday is on March 28th.) We had a good time singing tonight too. I gave Dave a shot for the sore on his leg.

02/16/59. Reading in Luke 1:1-10 showing how in Mark that he wrote right to the point and gave an overall picture of the work of Jesus Christ. Then in Luke we have more of a detailed picture of the life and work of Christ. Teaching the *boys* this morning. Biru reviewed the story a bit about the first picture. Then I went on to teach on the second picture, about the Christians and his sick baby. The Holy Spirit teaches us that we should pray, but the fashions of this world tell us to run away, be afraid, call for the *dream man* or kill a pig for the place *masara* (graveyard). I said that I-saru ran away, Meniba called for the *dream man* (witchdoctor), Biru killed a pig for the place *masara* (graveyard) and A-a-mo-aba did too. The Spirit of God living in us did not tell us to do this. These are the fashions of the ground, (the ways of the world, Pidgin). And we don't always hear the Holy Spirit. Meniba is leading out in the singing and I feel he's doing well. A-enabu looks bad today, so I gave Dave and him both a shot.

02/17/59. Read from the Bible this morning, Luke 1:5-27. Saw how John received the Holy Ghost before he was born, how that Zechariah had to have a sign so he got one. Teaching the *boys* this morning about meetings and how the Holy Spirit will help keep the meeting in order. He will show us when someone is speaking, if they are telling something that will build up the believers or if they are just talking 'nothing'. If the Holy Spirit speaks to our *'liver'* (heart) that someone is out of order in the meeting, we should speak up, so that it will keep order in our meeting.

Dave has been able to hire 4 new *boys* to work. Meniba has a lot of small sores on his feet and legs, so I gave him a shot along with Dave and A-enabu today.

02/18/59. Pat and Biru got away at 5:00 a.m. this morning, it was real dark but they should get to the horses by noon easy. Read this morning Luke 1:25-55. Reviewing the stories this morning Hobe-aba told the first two then Meniba did the one on meetings. I only reviewed what I taught yesterday.

Went over to see U-i-mo yesterday, he looks a bit sick, I gave his wife some sulfa tablets tonight for him to take. Don't know just what's wrong with him. They said his head and back had a big *pen* (pain) and Meniba said that he could die with this sick quickly. Got word from Don, don't know just what will happen, if they will go home in June or not.

Told the kids another story about Koko tonight and how the kind man helped him across the log that went across the big river. Jesus is our friend and he is always willing to help us if we will only put our little hand in His.

02/19/59. Reading in Luke 1 to the end of the chapter today. Dave used the picture this morning teaching on God casting Satan out of Heaven and God made everything. Biru turned talk.

Meniba said U-i-mo was not feeling too good when he saw him a bit before the meeting. So I felt I should give him shots of sulfa so gave 6 bottles at 10:00 a.m. and 2 bottles at 4:00 p.m. I will go down now and give 2 more bottles at 9:30. The *boys* are coming along on Dave's house. Biru and Dave going to Tunakau in the morning. Arvalee a bit sick tonight, she didn't eat her supper. We had *isapa*, *yo-o* and *abai* (sweet potato, a vegetable and red sauce).

02/20/59. Read this morning from Mark 1:10 showing that in Luke we have 80 verses to explain about John and Jesus birth. Mark gets right to the point.

Teaching the *boys* from the pictures; on heaven and Satan cast out and that Satan is mad at God and wants to *bagarap* (destroy) all of His work. U-i-mo said that he didn't feel much better this morning. Had Dave's literacy class tonight, the two *boys* are doing real good I feel. Meniba sure wants me to teach him to read.

02/21/59. Reading in Mark 1:10-21. We talked about what the gospel was. Jesus was preaching the gospel of the kingdom of God.

Teaching the *boys* more about Satan and how God is over him in power, how he was mad at God and saw all the good things that God had made and was going to bring man to obey him with all his power. This he did.

Meniba came in about 3:30 and said U-i-mo was bleeding from his nose. So I went right over there. They all feel that someone came up to the fence and worked sorcery on him today some time. This type of sorcery is done with real magic. He had been lying out in front of his grass house in the small yard. There is a small garden with corn, beans and tobacco between the yard and the picket fence, and then there is nothing but bush. Some foot prints were found there and just outside the fence. The sorcerer must have left them and this kind of sorcery is made with a small split bamboo that is held with the thumb and the forefinger. Then with the other hand a small stone is placed in the split bamboo and pulled back with the fingers; when the stone is in motion, the name of the person is called by the sorcerer and then this person whose name was called will die shortly. When I came up to the house U-i-mo saw me and tried to climb into his house. But his mother and another man that were holding him up pulled him back and set him up. I had stopped and was standing on the outside of the fence with one foot on the sty. When they got him pulled back and sitting up again, I stepped over the sty and down into the small yard. I walked over to U-i-mo and sat in a squatting position just to his left. He didn't look at me for some time, just stared straight ahead, maybe at Meniba who was sitting in front of him by this time. His Mother was crying as she helped hold him up. There were men milling in the yard and some old fellows sitting by a fire just behind me. Some were saying, "It's sorcery and it's the A-bo-pisa clan that did it." I could hear all this chatter, but all this time I was looking at U-i-mo. I took his pulse and it seemed to be normal, maybe just a bit slow. His eyes looked clear but he kept doing his mouth funny, but now I think it must have been the blood that had run from his nose down into his mouth and was dry and made him keep trying to get it out and off of his lips. Then he looked right at me, asking me "Will I die tonight?" I told him,

"No! I believe that God wants you to be made well." I told him that Meniba and I came and wanted to pray for him and that we must all three put out trust in God at this time. Then I told him that I would like to read from my Bible James 5:14 in Pidgin English: *"Sam pela man I gat sik, em I ken singaut long strong pela boi bilong Yesusu, em I ken pre long em nau putim gris long nem bilong Yesusu."* ("Is any sick among you? Let him call for the elders of the church; and let them pray over him, anointing him with oil in the name of the Lord:" James 5:14) I told them that it was good for us to obey God; that this was not my idea, but this is the way God told us to pray for the sick. I told them I didn't have any oil and ask if they did. After a bit a man came up from behind me and gave me some bark that was rolled loosely in a ball, saturated with pig grease. I thanked him and took it from him. I rubbed a bit on his forehead and we prayed for U-i-mo. After prayer we talked some on how Satan is under God and that we were not asking Satan to help us, but we know that God is willing to help his children whenever they call on Him and He is stronger than Satan and can break all of his power. I told U-i-mo to think on these things. He said that he couldn't think well now, he said he couldn't hear well and his mouth felt tired. Meniba said, "That's what this kind of sorcery does to a person, blood comes from their nose and they feel *longlong* (crazy)." Someone handed him some cooked bananas and he ate them. A big fellow stepped in to the yard with his bow and arrows over his shoulder and said that they were going down to the small hamlet that stole Meniba's pig last month and watch tonight and see if he came out to do some more evil. I left shortly after this, but they were still talking when I left. There were quite a few people around. Etha-o was sitting by a fire near the door way of the village, but didn't even look up when I went by.

02/22/59. Last night at the supper table it was just getting dark when the front door flew open and in walked eight men fully armed with bows and arrows over their shoulders. Esema, the *luluai* (chief) of the Negibi clan, walked on in to the dining room and I asked him what he had come for. He said that he had come for nothing at all. I told him that I knew better. We shook hands and exchanged greetings and then he looked around a bit, then he and four other men walked out. He must have told three of the men to stay here, for that is just what they did. They sat down in the chairs in the living room and played with Paul and Peter for some time. I felt a cold coming on, so went in and went to bed. I could hear the fellows talking and picking on the auto harp, and then I went off to sleep. Arvalee said that she was typing and they were in there talking low until about 9:30 and then the big lamp that lights the living room and dining room ran out of kerosene and went out. She said they went outside then and went off. A bit after that, Meniba came up and Arvalee told him that I was asleep and had a cold and she didn't want to wake me up. She asked him if he wanted anything. "No, I just came up."

And he went out. He came up this morning and got some soap to wash up, but didn't say anything about last night, so I didn't ask. About 3:00 this afternoon I walked down to Meniba's house and saw U-i-mo's wife sitting in the door way. I looked in and there sat U-i-mo, so I went in and sat down beside him. He said his head just had a little *pen* (pain). I then walked up to the house and saw Etha-o chopping on a tree. He spoke to me and said, "Red man, hello." So this made me feel good.

02/23/59. Read this morning from Mark 1 to the end of the chapter about the calling of the four fishermen. This just tells about some of the wonderful works of our Lord.

Reviewing the pictures; Hobe-aba taught on Satan being cast out of heaven, but Meniba added that Satan didn't want to be under God's hand. I-saru gave the creation story with a bit of help from Meniba and me. Hobe-aba gave the story of Adam and Eve and the fall. I talked a bit on how Adam and Eve were not ashamed when they were naked in the garden and they had good fellowship with God. Their sin was disobeying, not being naked.

Asked if there was anything we could pray for. Meniba said U-i-mo was alright now, but there might be trouble for the men going down to the village the other night. He also said that he was afraid that someone would work sorcery on him. So I prayed and then Meniba prayed. Morobe doesn't remember the stories well at all. I-saru said they had a meeting when he went down to his village.

02/24/59. I was sick today with a cold. A-a-mo-aba is teaching today.

02/25/59. Sick today, too. Dave got home at noon. A-a-mo-aba and Meniba are teaching.

02/26/59. Feeling a bit better today. Went out to help Meniba some on the chicken house roof. Dave had the meeting this morning.

02/27/59. I was feeling better today. Rained most all day today. Dave teaching. I haven't been going to the meetings.

02/28/59. Doing alright again now. I don't know what Dave is teaching in the mornings. He asked the fellows, Meniba, Biru and A-a-mo-aba if they would like to go down to Tunakau and baptize. They said they would. Dave said he wanted to stay home today. Meniba got the entire roof on but it leaks badly. Don't know what we will do.

March, 1959

03/01/59. Dave stayed home today. Meniba came in this morning and asked if Dave was going down for the baptism. I didn't know, so I told him to go and ask. He wanted Dave to go; I could tell he did. Meniba, Biru and A-a-mo-aba all went down. Meniba said that everyone was asking where the *Master* (Dale) was and could they baptize without the

Masters (Dale and Dave) around. Meniba asked them, "Who are you getting your strong from, the *Masters* or God?" He told them that we may not always have the *Masters* with us. God can help us and make us strong. I was sure glad that Meniba spoke up and said this. This is just what these Christians need, to have some of the crutches taken away from them, so they can stand on their own two feet. He said when they were talking to the people about baptism that it thundered and Meniba told A-a-mo-aba that it was like when Jesus was baptized. He said 46 people were baptized.

03/02/59. I didn't sleep too good last night. Dave said Althea has a cold. Dave is going to teach school today. I went down to teach the workers this morning, hoping to get across what belief and trust is. We started like this: A man was walking down the road with a heavy bag over his shoulder. When he came to the river he met a man, who asked if he liked the heavy bag he was carrying. He said No, I am very tired and would like to put it down or throw it away, but I don't know what to do. I will die some day and then it will all be over. Do you know where you will go when you die? No, I have always been afraid to die. Some say that we will go where the sun comes up. But I do not know for sure; it's unknown to all of us. Would you like to hear about a new way to live, a new fashion? Yes, you can tell me. If you have this new way, you can be rid of the heavy bag and you can go to the good place when you die, where there is no sick or trouble. How can I receive this new fashion? You must go to the other side of the river. There you will be told more. But there is no bridge, how can I ever get across? You can swing across on that *kanda* rope (a jungle vine). You must put all of your weight on that *kanda* (rope) as you swing across the river. So the man did it and when he was swinging and had all his weight out in the middle of the river, the bag's rope over his shoulder broke and all of his heavy load fell below into the deep river and was carried away. Then he was soon on the other side and standing on the ground. A man called to him to come and sit down by the fire and talk some with him. He was kind and spoke softly to the tired man.

03/03/59. Yesterday afternoon, Arvalee and I had some misunderstandings. Last night she spoke to me about them and felt that I was not willing to face them and wanted to just forget it all as if nothing had happened that afternoon. I could see where I was wrong, but at first I was quite bitter about it all. I felt condemned about sleeping in, in the morning and resting so much through the day, and that I have been thinking too much on sex. These made me feel down, and that I couldn't have a ministry with anyone. I told Arvalee all of this and she wanted to pray with me about it all. I'm so thankful for a loving wife that is willing to be a help mate when one is down spiritually. How thankful I am for her this morning. Truly the Lord knew that man needed a help mate. The words came to me, that there is no condemnation to those who are in Christ Jesus. All I know is that it is true and I am in Christ Jesus. This is my position in Christ. This is all I can stand on. I would go under if I didn't believe this. I rested well in the night. We are now reading to the kids in the Golden Bible book. Today was about the fall and broken fellowship with God. A-a-mo-aba reviewed the story that I told yesterday. Meniba turned it to Pidgin English. I told them that this story is a picture of how we become a 'boy belong Jesus' (saved). The *kanda* (rope) will take us all the way over to the other side if we are willing to put our trust in it. Jesus is able to make us a new man and save us if we will just put our trust in him, just the same as we put our trust in the *kanda*. The heavy bag is all of our bad fashions.

03/04/59. I broke out in hives last night. Arvalee used calamine lotion on them and I went to sleep right away. Have some new hives today, but they are not bad. Reading this morning about Cain and Abel to the kids.

Retold the story about trusting the *kanda* (rope) and teaching on the bag that is full of all our sins. The *kanda* is like trusting and the friend across the river is Jesus who died for us.

Dave feels that it would be good if Morobe and Hobe-aba would start teaching Meniba and A-a-mo-aba in the reading class. I asked him if he would be able to keep up if quite a few learned to read and if some really need more reading material right away. He thought he could. Dave also wants to go with A-a-mo-aba down to A-ibu next week and thinks it would be good if Hobe-aba could go too.

03/05/59. Arvalee played her first game of Chess last night. Had a good night's sleep. The hives that I had when I want to bed were all gone by this morning.

Reading was about Noah this morning. A-a-mo-aba reviewed the story this morning. Asked what the bag was a picture of and Biru didn't know, but A-a-mo-aba did. I was trying to show this morning how the *kanda* is like Christ and we put all of our weight on the *kanda*. You don't put half on the *kanda* and half on the ground. The same goes with putting our trust in Christ, no half way trust will do, as it must be all the way trust. Biru came in tonight and we had a good talk. Oh, that we could understand them better. When A-a-mo-aba was asked how to say that Jesus is enough, he said he was strong and we think strong. Biru was unable to even know what I was getting at. Don't think he got much tonight, but it helped me to understand more how to explain some truths. Jesus knows when we know for sure, that He is the Son of God, that He is the only one that can redeem us from our sins and give us a new fashion, make us a new man, can give us life after death. He knows the heart of man. Some people confess their sins and ask for the blood of Jesus, but then they try to quit doing the bad things and fail and fall away from the truth. I feel this is our (or my fault), for I haven't been able to make it clear what a person is to do after they are saved. The little book that Sylvie sent up helps along this line, Sit, Walk and Stand.

03/06/59. The Bible reading this morning was about Noah. Dave went down this morning to teach the workers. Hobe-aba told that the bag was full of sins. Then Biru told what the *kanda* was a picture of. I do think that the light is slowly breaking. We sent the *passes* (letters to post) with the *boys* last Sunday or Monday night and today they said that they are going tomorrow.

03/07/59. Dave, A-a-mo-aba and Hobe-aba got off for A-ibu this morning. He hopes to get down to Misapi too.

03/08/59. Went over to Negibi this morning, not too many there but feel we had a good meeting. I had a few hives when I went over and when I got home there were more. The calamine lotion was the thing for this time.

03/09/59. I was in bed all day today. Not feeling too good.

03/10/59. Swelling on face and arms today.

03/11/59. Have a few hives today but feeling some better so got up at noon and got dressed. Meniba said tonight that Morobe was mad at him because he won't give him some of the feathers from the big bird he shot Monday.

03/12/59. Almost all the hives are gone today. Wrote to Don (McCurdy) today and told him to put 100.00 pounds (£100, Australian currency) down on a booking for a ship in September.

03/13/59. Went down this morning and had prayer with the *boys*. Morobe said he was sorry for *krosim* (getting mad at) Meniba about the bird feathers. He didn't impress me as being really sorry for he had a big smile all the time he was talking. Talked to I-saru after the meeting and told him why I was letting him go. He didn't like it one little bit, said he didn't want to go home, but would stay here and work for nothing. I told him that he was *pulim* (influencing) the other *boys* to *sakim tok bilong mi* (to disobey my instructions) and I wanted him to go. I told him that I would still pray for him and hoped some day that he would be strong again like he was before.

At 5:00 p.m. there was a fight down at Misapi-biraisa and an old man that is said to be a Christian got shot twice, once in the arm and once in the stomach. Meniba said he was sorry for him.

03/14/59. Meniba went down to Misapi-biraisa today. Someone sung out (called) for him, and he was gone all day.

03/15/59. I went down this morning to ask Meniba if he wanted to go over to Negibi with me this morning. He said that he was just coming up to tell me that he was going over to teach them. He thought that I wouldn't be going and that the trip last week made me sick. I told him no. The family went too and we had a good time, had a little lunch on the way back. Meniba told me this morning that someone had stolen some of Mu-u-nabi's *pulpul* (her grass skirt) and that someone was trying to work *poison* (sorcery) on Meniba. He said you can pray for me.

03/16/59. This morning I went down and just had prayer with the fellows. Meniba said he was afraid that someone would work sorcery on him and asked us to pray for him. I told him that he shouldn't be afraid of Satan and his talk, but to know that Jesus is strong and will look after him.

Talked to Biru about Nanoi, she just sits around and looks at us all day and holds her baby. She won't even cook the *cargo boys'* (carriers') food. I told Biru that if she didn't want to work a little that she should go home, that she was *pulling* (influencing) Wietho to be like herself. I told him that Mu-u-nabi told Wietho and Nanoi that they could have some old gardens that were yet good, just needed a bit of work. They both said that they didn't want to work. Biru said he didn't know anything about this.

03/17/59. Slept good last night. When I went down this morning, Nanoi was packed up and went off in a huff. Biru didn't have much to say. Just said she didn't like it one bit when he talked to her. She got real mad at him.

Felt we had a good meeting this morning. I talked to the *cargo boys* (carriers) and told them that they were all sinners and that they could put their trust in Jesus, just like the man who went across the river on the *kanda*. When we know that we are sinners and without hope, we know that Jesus is the true Son of God and died for our sins, *oure ami*, (bad works) and His blood can wash away all our sins, can make us new men and give us hope after death. When we hold these things and really believe them, it's like holding the *kanda* (rope) and *isiosi* (swinging) across the river. The river is like the power of Satan to keep us away from God and believing in Him.

03/18/59. Peter is not feeling good this morning. He said yesterday that he felt tired and didn't eat any supper last night. He says he is cold and just tired.

I was going over to Biru's house this morning and I think Nanoi told Morobe to tell me to stay over at Meniba's to have the meeting. I need to pray much for this woman, she is out of the Lord's will. The meeting was cold and no one wanted to talk. Meniba and I prayed. Sent 4 *boys* down to the river with the *kanda* (jungle vine) that the Misapis brought up.

03/20/59. Felt the meeting was good this morning; then after I asked Meniba and Biru about Nanoi, Meniba said she started on a garden yesterday. (Her and Wietho). We went over and had a talk with them, Nanoi, Wietho and Mu-u-nabi. Nanoi said that she didn't want to go to her place, so was working a garden so she could stay here. I told her that if she was just working a garden to please me she was all wrong and she would fail. The thing that I want to see is that these women will see that it's right to work in their gardens and look after their husbands' food. I feel that I have been a bit at fault myself in not finding something for them to do before. I told Wietho that she was wrong by running away from A-a-mo-aba and that I wanted her to go back with Hobe-aba to A-ibu tomorrow. Spent most of the morning up on the hill with Dave and Meniba showing them what I thought would be best and some of my ideas.

Had a long talk with Meniba, said he thought that it would be good if he could have Saturday off and go help Mu-u-nabi in the garden then. He needs to help her more. She gets mad at him for not helping her. He gives her some money every now and then… one pound last month.

03/21/59. In the meeting this morning, I couldn't find words to express myself. So didn't talk long. Feel real burdened about Wietho today. She and A-a-mo-aba's sister are living in the house with all the *cargo boys* (carriers). Satan has an open door to her life; sin is the fruit of disobedience. She is disobeying her husband. Only God can break her stubborn will.

Meniba had the day off today. Dave and I had a good long talk today and went for a walk in the bush and had prayer together. Seems Satan is working on each of us these days in an all-out effort to stop or hinder the work of God.

03/22/59. Went over to Tabaribo's this morning. Just Meniba and I went over. Tabaribo and Etha-o reviewed the story, then I spoke on the power of Satan and that Jesus won (won the victory over) Satan on the tree. Esema said that he always prayed and was not going to follow any other talk…all of these things that came up will not change my mind; I am holding (following) this talk good.

Biru didn't go with Dave today. I don't know what to say, I guess it's up to him.

Been raining some for the last week, but not too much. More rain at night than in the day. *Cargo boys* (carriers) got in this afternoon with the stove that has been stored in a village since we moved here last November.

> *The cast iron cook stove was so heavy the carriers had worn out and left it in a vacant house until they felt strong enough to bring it the rest of the way into the Gimi. Rune, one of those carriers, actually had a large cyst develop on his shoulder, which had to be surgically removed. These Gimi men and sometimes women, who carried our supplies, even though we paid them, were very faithful and dedicated: playing a key role in keeping us missionaries in this remote Gimi tribe. By Arvalee.*

Meniba was telling me last night a bit more about Esema. He said the *luluai* (chief) from Oraratu sent word up to Esema for him not to be baptized now, but they could be baptized together. He is in jail again now. Meniba feels Esema is a good fellow, but is just a bit shy when we have a meeting.

03/23/59. In the meeting this morning I had real liberty. Speaking on the topic, that we are lost in our sins and without hope. We will try to go good and say we won't do this or that again, but we are not strong and we fall into sin time after time. I told them that there is a way and a friend that is strong and understands us. He will help you if you want Him to. You must believe that He is the true Son of God and He died for all of our sins. He will make you a new creature, a new man. You will never make yourself new. Only Jesus can do this, as we rest in Him. Told them that Jesus wants us to follow Him, but first we must sit down with Him and hear what all He has done for us. He will ever be with us, as the closest friend that we can have.

03/24/59. Had a big rain in the night. One of the *cargo boys* (carriers) that went down to work on the *kanda* (rattan) bridge yesterday, fell in the water, but was able to swim over to the bank and got out. Praise the Lord. Felt the meeting was of the Lord this morning. Reviewed some of the things I spoke on yesterday. Don't know what to say to A-a-mo-aba about Wietho yet. We had a big rain this afternoon.

03/25/59. Arvalee left for Olaguti this morning. Not feeling too good. Dave is having the meetings now.

03/26/59. Got word that Arvalee got to George's o.k. Dave teaching on the home. Not feeling too good.

03/27/59. Very tired today, haven't been sleeping well until 1:00 or 2:00 a.m. Hard to get up in the mornings. Dave said the women came to some of the meetings.

03/28/59. Got word from Arvalee today, said she was sore. Work on the house is coming along good. Not feeling good today.

03/29/59. Was in bed most all day today. Not feeling good at all. Was able to fix lunch, was glad that the Lawrences asked us over for supper tonight.

David went to Ore-ua-bipi today. Hu-a-ni-aba was gone and Bebu was not there either.

Stopped taking some vitamins that Don sent me. I don't know if that's what is making my stomach upset or not. I feel so weak. Been reading from Hebrews the first three chapters. I can see now, God's grace, even in Hebrews, almost the same as Ephesians.

03/30/59. Feeling some better today. Still teaching Paul. David is still teaching on the home. Said the women come sometimes, mostly Nanoi. Sent *cargo boys* (carriers) to Olaguti today.

03/31/59. My stomach is better today.

April, 1959

04/01/59. I started taking the vitamins again today. Dave feels that Wietho is in real rebellion to A-a-mo-aba. Nanoi comes to most of the morning meetings. She takes part in the meeting, too. Thought maybe Arvalee would be coming today but she wrote that she was going to town today to see the Dr. about her itch.

04/02/59. The people are bringing lots of planks for shingles for Dave's house. Meniba is working hard and should be finished with this one side by the end of the week. Feeling much better today.

04/03/59. Dave went down to see if he could see Hu-a-ni-aba and Bebu. Had a good talk with Hu-a-ni-aba, but Bebu was at the *haus sik* (clinic) at Tunakau. Hu-a-ni-aba said he went to Mulki and they were having a big meeting. Said it was a new talk.

04/04/59. Meniba got the roof on one side yesterday, so is taking the day off today.

04/05/59. Meniba and Biru went down to Ubai today to see or hear the big meeting there. Said that their talk was strong; and they said that they will bring all of the things they use to work *poison* (sorcery) with and burn them and all clap their hands and put one hand up and it will all be over. Meniba and Biru said they wouldn't put their hands up or take part in the meeting. They just looked. Sounds a bit like spiritualism. Would like to talk to Hu-a-ni-aba first.

> *Not sure which meeting this was, many groups were holding meetings and baptisims throughout the tribal areas of New Guinea during these days, it certainly was not one condoned by Dale or Dave or the men they had been teaching. Arvalee.*

04/06/59. Feel a bit depressed today spiritually. Dave has been working with Meniba on the house and it's been going much faster. He had to fire two *cargo boys* (carriers) for not working well. He is still teaching on the home and the family. Althea had a meeting last week with the women and wants to have another one today.

04/07/59. Arvalee got here today about 3:00 p.m. Paul is sick with a cold.

04/08/59. Paul is better today and we had school again.

04/09/59. Meniba is out of nails so will not be able to work tomorrow. He has wanted to go down to Misapi for some time to teach them, so he might go now.

Today Biru saw Nanoi hitting their mother goat that just had twins; Biru had put her in his yard to look after them. He called to her and asked her why she was hitting the goat and she yelled at him that the baby was eating the goat droppings and she yelled back some foul talk at him. This made Biru very mad and he went down, and he said, I almost hit her. He came up to tell me about it and I read to him from Ephesians chapter

5, how the husband should love his wife and take care of her the way he does his own body. Also, how that Christ loves us, his bride, when we were very bad sinners. We should love our wives just like Jesus loves us his children.

He wanted to send her home to A-ibu at first, but after I talked to him, he felt better. We had prayer together and I feel he understood what the Word of God was teaching him. A-a-mo-aba is not feeling too good this afternoon, he has a cold. I told him it would be good if he could go over and help Biru some; but he said that he was in no place to help Biru, for his wife was just as bad.

04/10/59. Biru didn't come up last night to wash dishes and A-a-mo-aba was not feeling good. Hu-a-ni-aba came up today and I had a talk with him. I found out that the Lutheran man has just come to see what the big meeting was all about and had no part in it. The natives told the Gimi fellows that they didn't know about this new talk and they would all go to hell. Men confessed that they had worked sorcery on people and if they had worked sorcery on someone and he didn't die, he would yell to the sorcerer, Thank you! In confession the man would place his two fore fingers together to make a house roof, and then they would all clap their hands and put one up in the air. The departed spirits of the ancestors will come back at some time. I don't know too much about it, but I don't think it's good. Even Hu-a-ni-aba was quite impressed with all this talk. I feel it's some type of spiritualism. (See the note above).

04/11/59. Dave went down to Uhezuhutai today. They are having a *hi-i* (the root of a special bean) feast (festival) down there. We had the *Brown Gold* prayer requests today. Arvalee and Althea spent the afternoon talking about sewing and all kinds of little things.

04/12/59. Arvalee was in bed all day today with hay fever. Went down to Tabaribo's but before I got there, Aida and his wife met me to tell me all had gone to the bean root feast and they were coming to tell me. Aaron was with me, so I read them the Word from Ephesians 2:8 and we had a good little talk. Aaron went on to Uhezuhutai and Aida and family came back home with me.

04/13/59. I didn't sleep a bit last night, so feel quite tired today. Biru washed clothes today before he went down to Uhezuhutai. It rained almost all day, so the clothes didn't get dry. Went to sleep after lunch and couldn't get up until about 4:00 p.m.

Had the literacy class again tonight. Morobe and Hobe-aba are sure coming along good. A-a-mo-aba was there to hear it all. I talked to them a bit about their motives for learning to read. A-a-mo-aba told me at first that it was so we could read the Word of God. Then he asked me is that true or not. I told him it was true; then Morobe said about the same thing. I feel we had a good time of fellowship also with the fellows. Hobe-aba saw the word 'bao.' Got word from Dave, he's having good fellowship with Mainaha.

04/14/59. Got to sleep about 1:30 this morning, woke up about 5:00 a.m. Received a blessing from reading 2 Timothy 2:22-26 in the Williams. We need to turn our backs on evil impulses, strive for uprightness, faith, love and peace in fellowship with other Christians.

04/15/59. Slept quite good last night. Find it hard to get up in the morning. Didn't feel too good in the morning, so went to bed. Felt better this afternoon. Just feel weak and tired. *Cargo boys* (carriers) got here from Olaguti this afternoon. Don sent a note about the salt and said there was 30 pounds in each bag. So when I weighed them I found one was 24 pounds and the other 28. I know that our scales were not that far off, so I asked the five *boys* that carried, about it and they said that they got salt out of the one bag at Muye to buy *isapa* (sweet potato). They said they didn't take any out of the other bag. Don told me that he would tie the knots square, for natives don't tie square knots. So I knew that both bags had been opened. I didn't know what to do, but I came in the house. No one came to get their pay for carrying so I didn't call them. We prayed about it, not knowing what we should do. We had no rain today. Got some good mail today; from Stines and Mom. Had literacy class tonight. Just went over the same thing as Monday.

04/16/59. Didn't sleep too well last night...I don't know why. Arvalee and I had a good heart to heart talk in the night before we went to sleep. She helped me to see that I need to be speaking the truth at all times and not exaggerate. I see this is nothing more than a lie. Reading in Matthew 11:25-30 Jesus prays and thanks the Father for not showing the wise and learned the way of life but shows it to the meek and humble. Jesus said, come to me, all of you that carry the heavy load of sin and I will take it away from you and give you my load that is not heavy at all. Jesus is gentle and humble to those who truly seek His help, who come to him as little children.

Dave got back from Uhezuhutai today at noon. He told us of the good time he had and the fellowship with the people. Said he started learning names. The Lord showed him that there would be no work done in the lives of these people until he started praying more for them.

Just went down to see A-a-mo-aba, he looks quite sick; it must be the flu; am giving him sulfa drugs and Nivaquine...prayed for him. Wawa came in about 5:00 p.m. so asked him if he would like to eat with us. He was quite friendly and talked a lot. Meniba got back from Misapi and had a lot to talk about. Dave came over and we talked; all four of us for some time. Meniba is starting to put into practice what he believes. He is truly growing in the things of the Lord, but I feel it's the prayers of the many saints that are praying for him.

Peter shot his little bow up the hill at a flower and the arrow went flying up the hill and hit a boy just under his eye. The boy was crying and Peter started crying and I feel he learned a good lesson.

04/17/59. I was so tired this morning, didn't get up till 9:00 a.m. Arvalee has hay fever this morning. Went down to see A-a-mo-aba, he's not feeling much better, but felt a bit more like talking. We had prayer together and as A-a-mo-aba was praying the words were coming fast to my mind and it reminded me when someone is trying to get a station clear on TV. I could just see it faintly; at times the words were clearer than at other times. It's so good to be getting close (to understanding the language). It's so hard to think of giving up and going home just when I'm about to get contact.

04/18/59. Arvalee was in bed most all day with hay fever. She sure has it bad this time. My body is aching all over today. Hope I'm not getting what A-a-mo-aba has had.

04/19/59. Arvalee and I were quite sick this morning. We were in bed most all morning. Felt much better in the afternoon. Meniba went over to Negibi to have a meeting but all were gone. So he came back. A-a-mo-aba was feeling better. Had a good talk to Meniba tonight. He has been working so hard that he doesn't come by to talk like he used to. We talked about goats, cows, roads, my trip to Porosa. I sure enjoy talking to him, he just understands.

04/20/59. Praise the Lord for bringing Dave and I to Kigupa today. I saw the Lord's hand on my life for I had not the strength to come this far. The last two hours we had to stop a lot for me. We tried to get enough fellows to carry the chair, so I could ride some, but the Lord didn't see fit for this. We got here about 4:30 and must have left about 9 or 9:30. The *boss boy* (foreman) from Yagana (Bulimakau) came by with a line from Muye and Yagana; they had been working on the road at Henagaru. He wanted to tell me about being saved and how he had moved down near the road and was building a meeting house. Said he was teaching the Muyes and then he would go back up to his place and teach them. I told him we would come by to see him in the morning. He said that most of his people were baptized now and a lot from Muye want to be. We have got to give these ones some spiritual food and trust it won't be too long before we can have literacy going back here. Will bring this up at conference time.

04/21/59. Had a good night's rest last night. Read Matthew 16, about Peter saying that Jesus is the Christ the Son of God. Jesus tells him that flesh and blood didn't tell him that, but the Father which is in Heaven showed him. Yes, we must believe this basic truth that Jesus is truly the Son of God. It will never be that we can understand how he is, but we must believe it by faith, not by what men say. God said it, I believe it.

Got here to Anuparu about 2:30. Lamafu was sick, we tried to get him to ride but he wanted to walk. Gave a short talk at Yagana to the people there. They were building a meeting house and are making a new village there. Told them that we wanted them to have the Word of God in the Keagana language, but we didn't know when we will get to them. Told them to keep praying and following God's talk. The horses sure look good.

04/22/59. We left Anuparu at 9:00 this morning and got here a bit after 5:00 p.m. Lamafu is still sick. Dean (Van Vliet) went to town and they didn't get back till about 7:00 p.m. Tom (Palmer), Arnold (Davis) and Al (Cole) came. Tom and I are in the guest room together. Last night Dave and I had a long talk. We talked about a lot of things. I did most of the talking, and then we had prayer together and went to bed. After some time, Dave asked me if I was asleep, said he felt like talking. He told me his life story and some of his ups and downs in life. It was so humbling to me for Dave to tell me so much about himself. It made me feel so small. Truly the Lord is preparing my heart, so I can know more about men and to understand them and even myself.

04/23/59. Tom and I talked for some time last night. Then Tom went to sleep, but I didn't sleep too well, so I feel a bit tired today. Reading in Deut. 32:15-23, showing me that God abhorred sin. Thinking of Ephesians 2, But God.

The conference started today at 9:00 a.m. We talked about the things we thought should be discussed. The field report was given on the Watut area. Arnold started, Al told a bit about Angea, Tom told about literacy. Started breaking out in hives about noon, don't know what's wrong.

I don't feel close to my son Pat. I just pray that we might get together and have real love and will be able to talk together. I know that I have a lot to learn, so that I can be a good father and know how to get next to my boys. Not feeling real good, doesn't help too much; (it might help) if I felt better, where I could get out and play ball or something.

04/24/59. Had hives all day today, haven't felt good all day. Don and Dean gave a report this morning on the Kami work. Al spoke to us on our fellowship with Jesus. He said that we had to be in fellowship with Jesus. We can do a lot of work in the flesh and not be in fellowship with Jesus. He said that we have to maintain this fellowship.

I gave a report about how the work started here in the Highlands up till the time when we moved into the Gimi with our families. Dave gave the report from there till now, and then our plans. George gave a report on the road work and the many believers we have there.

04/25/59. Arnold spoke to us about Joseph. Genesis 39, how that Joseph was abiding in the Lord and this helped him to turn from open sin. He showed us that Satan will do all he can to keep us from abiding in the Lord. He told how sometimes, he doesn't feel like reading and praying and it's just Satan trying to keep him from abiding in the Lord, John 15:5.

We spoke on literacy all morning and it was sure good for me. To see how others are working and how Dean and Dave want to work. Arnold asked me to give brief thoughts about what we could be thinking about over the weekend. Had no hives this morning, but by noon they were up again.

04/26/59. Hives were bad last night but went away in the night. Tom and I got to talking about Ann Crozier who lives at Sandy Creek. Said she has been a real blessing to each of their hearts. Told how the Lord answered her prayers about a type writer to help type for the missionaries. How she now prays more for her unsaved husband and not trying to force him. How the other gold miners are poking fun at Ann for becoming a Christian. We talked about what a blessing Chuck was to our lives when he was with us. (Chuck and Jean had left for furlough).

Dean and Dave went down to Forapi and Fore to have meetings this morning and Don, Arnold, Al, and Tom went over to Higibabi for a meeting. George and I were here with Gwen all morning. Played ball with Dale and Pat this morning and then Pat and I had some good fellowship in the Word. Ephesians 2:8, 9 was what we talked about. Had quite a long rest this afternoon. Not a lot of hives today. Don showed slides. Felt better today than I have since I've been here. Sleeping much better now.

04/27/59. Sleeping till about 6:30 or 7:00 a.m. Feel I need that rest. George spoke on Hebrews being the book that we could use as a pattern for our teaching. He reviewed the book as a whole, but was a bit hard to follow. Dean said that he had been thinking about how we were going to teach some of the New Testament without Old Testament stories. Tom said some give the Old Testament story just before they teach it in the New Testament.

Feeling quite good these days. Been raining a lot since getting here. Talked to La-mafu and *boys* about the Garuka and Haga people getting up no good about the men at the saw mill and giving them back all the money and telling them to get out. I didn't know these natives would be that strong.

04/28/59. Had a good night's sleep; sure feeling better. Dave spoke to us this morning about Job. When trials come to your life don't lose heart for God is going to teach you something good if you will let Him. Eliphaz was like a commander, told his soldiers to get out and fight some more. Job 5:17.

Had a good talk to Dean as we had supper, he was telling me a bit about how the mission committee works. They put something before a person, and then have fellow-ship with the person about it. If the person feels the Lord is not leading the same as the committee then it's dropped.

04/29/59. Don spoke to us on baptism and what he wrote to Chuck and the mission. We had a long talk about baptism and then went into communion. The Hughes came by today. Sellers came up this afternoon. Al went down to Kami with them. Don and Gwen not feeling too good tonight. Arnold and I had a long talk this afternoon about horses. Dean came over this evening and played the tape of Ken Finney, (a teacher from boot camp days) it was sure good to hear Ken talk again. On the tape he was answering questions from the boot campers. I'm sure it will be a bit like that when we get home. Oh, that we might show the true picture of the work here. I was talking to Arnold tonight about what we will be doing in the near future to enter new tribes. I think we might bring this up in our meeting tomorrow.

04/30/59. Not much rain yesterday, some in the night. Sleeping much better these days. I spoke this morning on our fellowship. I sang Amazing Grace and told what a blessing it was to my heart when I was sick, how it would just help me to feel better. Brought out how it was God's grace that we are what we are and what a wonderful fellowship we are in.

Got word from Arvalee today, said that Meniba had got mad at Aaron and knocked him down. He was fighting his wife, Mu-u-nabi and their mother, so this made Meniba real mad and he came and told Arvalee and Althea that he was wrong in getting mad and they all three had prayer together. I do feel that Meniba is going through these hard times to really make him a man for the great job of building a strong New Testament church in the Gimi. When he comes to the end of the rope and there is no one to help him but God then and only then will Meniba see the Lord can do anything for him.

Arvalee said that A-a-mo-aba ran away, he was sick when I left, but thought he was all right spiritually. Oh that the Lord will work in his heart in a real way.

May, 1959

05/01/59. The conference was over today. I believe in my heart that this was the best conference that we have ever had in New Guinea. There was a spirit of needing each other's fellowship that I have never sensed before. I know myself that the Lord had done a real work in my heart before I ever got here. We talked about some big things but I believe most everything came out with an answer and there was an overall unity. Tom spoke this morning, and that was a great blessing to my heart and Dean spoke this afternoon that just fit right into what Tom spoke on and Arnold said that it would be good if we could each one really pray about the needs that we have talked about and look for a real answer to prayer this next year. Dean showed us that Paul had the care of so many churches but at the same time he rolled the burden onto the Lord. Dean showed where the word care is used in the Word and how we can be taken up with the cares of this life, the work, the many problems that will be facing us this next year.

We closed with the Lord's Supper. So praise the Lord for meeting with us this year. To God be the Glory, Great things He hath done.

Dave is going to leave for the Gimi in the morning. Al and Arnold want to go to Gono on the two bikes.

05/02/59. Dave got off this morning. We tied Bonus (the colt) up this morning, she didn't like it much. Kept her tied all day, then we put her in the fence in the late afternoon. She didn't know where to go so she stayed in.

Arnold and Al went off on the bikes with Norman. The Sellers came up for supper tonight. Don showed all his slides. Dean asked me if I had a camera and I said no. He said that I need some slides when I went home to show in the churches. I asked him where that was found in the Bible. I told him that I didn't know but if the Lord wanted me to have some slides He would supply them.

05/03/59. I stayed home today and packed the drum. Dean went down to Fore and Kami for meetings. I wanted to go but wasn't feeling real good. Don, Gwen and Tom went to Higibabi. Al and Arnold got back from Gono.

05/04/59. Tom and I went up to Lufa with Harold today. He asked if they could come to our fellowship meetings and I told him whenever he was down and we were to have a fellowship meeting they were welcome to come and also to talk about the work in the churches.

When we got home, I found myself very tired and went to bed. Al gave me a good rub down in my back and felt much better. Ate a big dinner. Gwen said that I know Dale isn't sick for he doesn't eat if he is sick. Everyone has been so good to me and wants to help me all they can. There is real love in our fellowship these days. I think Harold misses this love in the fellowship.

05/05/59. This morning I felt tired. Did some lettering this morning, and had a long sleep. Then at 2:00 p.m. we met for prayer, it was good that we could pray for each field and the work as a whole. Felt real tired after prayer meeting, so rested some of the afternoon. Tom and I had a good talk; I read the 8th chapter of Romans from the Williams NT. Tom was telling me how he has been teaching Wekoto, how that before Jesus came to die for our sins and now he is with the Father and praying for us, and after he will come back to get us, His church. He said that it's best to teach like this, than to keep harping on a person's sins. I can sure see this. I told Tom how that I had been teaching on the word trust and how I wanted to make it like Pilgrims Progress in the native culture. Tom sure liked the idea and said he would like to try it. I hope that I can enlarge it and work on it quite a bit before I go home. Tom and I have sure had good fellowship together this past two weeks.

05/06/59. The fellows got away at 5:00 a.m. this morning. George is helping Dean on his water tank today. Didn't feel too good all morning just feel tired and felt like sleeping. I could push myself a bit and get more work done, but mostly rested. Gwen read to the kids this morning, some Christian stories on obeying. Gwen tells the kids to do something and if they feel like it, they do it when they get ready.

05/07/59. We left Olaguti at 8:00 a.m. Told Don and Gwen good-bye for it may be a long time before we see them again. Let George ride twice, he was *all in* (worn out) when we got to Anuparu, asked him if he wanted to go to Aniaru, and he said no. (Dale must be referring to riding the horses; not clear. Arvalee)

I cooked dinner for the three of us. We had rice and potatoes and fresh tomatoes for dinner.

I think Pat returned to the Gimi with Dale at this time, because he had been living with Don and Gwen and they were leaving for furlough. Dale doesn't make this real clear. Arvalee.

Asked the *boys*, Lamafu, Ifina and George's new *boy*, if they would like a story. They sang 3 songs in their own language, (Yagaria) that James has made up to the native tunes. They sure sang well together. Lamafu told me that one song said that our works would not save us, our money either; it was just the blood of Jesus. Another song was that we should always be happy and not sad for we are Christians. The *boys* said that the Lord had given James these songs and they liked them. I told them the story on 'trust'.

05/08/59. Left Anuparu at 7:00 a.m. Got to George's at 11:30 and met the Gimi *boys*, 12 of them. Had lunch with George and got away at 12:00 noon. I was carried most all the way and got to Negibi at 5:00 p.m. Sure glad to be home. Went to bed with the chickens. Dave came in and talked for some time, and then after the kids were in bed, Arvalee and I talked for some time. Very tired in my back.

05/09/59. I was *all in* (worn out) this morning and didn't get up till late. Meniba tells me that Biru didn't want to go down just to be with A-a-mo-aba when he was sick, but he went down to the Fore for something else. He told me a week before I left for Olaguti that they were *singing out* (calling out) for him to come down to Fore to get his *abai* (Pandanus fruit). He didn't like it when I told him he had to work. I don't feel that I can hire him back after this. He has lied to me over and over now, and I know that he can't be used of the Lord as long as he holds these lies in his heart. I will pray that he might see lying as sin. Was in bed most all day today. My back is so tired and achy. Peter is a bit sick today. Went over to Lawrences for a bit of cake and Milo tonight.

05/10/59. Feel a bit more rested this morning. Slept good last night. Dave, Meniba, Morobe and his girl friend went down to Iri-bia-bipi to have a meeting and talk about the girl. They didn't get back till after dark tonight. Had dinner tonight at Lawrences. Had our first lettuce in a salad, man it was good. Today, Pete is still not feeling good; has a fever and a cold I think.

Meniba said the girl came back and he thinks that it will take the *kiap* (patrol officer) to straighten it out. Dave said that the man that *marked* (chose) the girl has another wife and wants her to go to some other man, but the girl wants Morobe and he loves her too. The man that chose her said that Morobe is just *'pulim em'* (enticing her), but Dave and Meniba feel the man is wrong.

I was quite tired after today.

05/11/59. I'm feeling quite a bit better today and I had a good night's sleep. Arvalee has hay fever. Peter is feeling better. Julie is sick with a fever, has been in bed all day sleeping. In the afternoon, my eyes *pened* (hurt) a lot. Maybe from my long sleep.

Had a long talk with Meniba, he was asking me if I was coming back. I told him that I sure wanted to and I would write him and let him know.

Hobe-aba said he was teaching Meniba to read when I was at Olaguti. I hope that I can understand enough Gimi to be able to write to him in Gimi. I have a long ways to go.

Romans 12:2 showed me a bit more light on why we should always remember the work of love and grace of our Lord. This is why the Word of God is never growing old, but new and fresh. We shouldn't want to be conformed to the ways of the world, but we can be changed. How? By renewing our minds.

We have to get a new permit each year for our shot gun, we have to have it renewed and it's good for us as Christians to renew our minds about God's love and Grace and Mercy for us. There is nothing that will make you stronger than to think back on our Lord's wonderful sacrifices for us. When we are striving to pass a test, we review the problem well, and by reviewing we prove it to ourselves that the answer is right. As we study about the Grace of God and review over and over in our minds what has happened to us, we prove to ourselves and know for sure that we believe. We prove in our minds and hearts that God's will or desire is good for us. He desires things that are acceptable in His sight and things that are perfect.

05/12/59. I felt real good today. Julie's little neck was so sore that she couldn't get up till about 3:00 p.m. but she played the rest of the afternoon.

Dave said the girl that wants to marry Morobe is still hanging around and he talked to Morobe about it this morning. Meniba and Dave have done about all they can do to make her go away. We talked about Harold Sellers today in our meeting. I told how I had talked to Harold and he was tender and humble. We talked about some of our goals in the work here. For centers, we have been thinking of: 1. Negibi. 2. Uhezuhutai. 3. Inibiabipi. 4. Orehabipi. 5. A-ibu. 6. Misapi, and after this we're not so sure, but it might be Mani, Raro, Amuraisa, Hepafina. As time goes on we will understand better where we will work, but I do feel it's good to think of the best places and about how many centers we want to have. I was thinking that if we had about 12 centers and cover these good this would take care of about 600 or 700 people in a center. This way, we won't be running here and there seeing nothing done.

Tonight I told the children the story of trust in English. I see it needs a bit of work on it and could be used of the Lord to get a much needed truth across to each of our hearts. We need to understand more of what trust and belief really is.

05/13/59. Julie is not feeling too good this morning. Read about the hand writing on the wall this morning.

Right after prayer meeting today, Arvalee saw Aaron walking up the road, so I thought I would walk up the road too. Found him down the hill cutting some pickets for a new garden. I called to him and went down part of the way. I asked him if we could talk, he said yes. I told him that I wanted to know what all the trouble with Meniba was all about. He stopped chopping and came up close to me and sat down. I told him that we, Dave and I had come for one thing and that was to help him and many others to come to know the ways of the Lord Jesus Christ. He sat there for a long time, neither of us talking. Then he started talking. He said when he walked past my house that he had a big shame and his *liver* (heart) was heavy. I knew this was what we have wanted to see for a long time. I read to him from Ephesians 4:29-32. I told him that now that we are Christians we should want to do the things that God wants us to do. He wants us to be kind and loving like the Lord Jesus was and is, 5:25. We should do all we can to make our wives good and pure, this will make our home happy and our *livers* (hearts) will be happy when we have that love of Jesus for our wives. He said that he knew he was wrong and that it was a bad fashion to fight his wife all the time. This doesn't make the home happy.

05/14/59. We read about Daniel in the lions' den this morning. Paul is sick now; Julie has a crick in her neck each morning. Peter is feeling better, but has a bit of a cold yet.

Dave said that he and Meniba had a talk with Aaron this morning. They told him that they were not mad at him, but just wanted to help him. They told him that it would be good if he would come to the fellowship meetings from now on. Meniba said that he had not talked to us when he told Aaron that we all felt that Aaron would have to move to some other place. He told Aaron he was sorry and knew it was wrong. Dave went down to Ore-ua-bipi this afternoon, said he had a good talk to some of them. They told him that some of the unsaved ones kept them from having their meeting all the time. Meniba and Zasibini got a room made for the Lawrence children. Arvalee likes it now that we have our living room inside the wall. Althea said that they got to Kami one year ago today. I told them that Meniba had been working for me for four years since the 1st of May.

05/15/59. Arvalee got hay fever in the night and she is not feeling good this morning. Meniba is sick too. Paul is better this morning and so is Julie.

Today was the close of the Negibi School for Peter and Steve. They had a little program and we all went to it. Dave and Althea came over to see what we wanted to get rid of, so we talked for some time. Told Dave that these things that I have made will help him so that he won't have to spend a lot of time building things and he could spend more time in the language work.

05/16/59. All the kids are well again and it's sure good. We finished reading the Bible Story book this morning.

The age old problem has come up again today: How much to pay the natives for things. Some natives came up from A-ibu with some *tiri* (bamboo). Dave had said that he felt he should pay them 1d. for each stick, but the fellows said they wanted more, for they carried it a long ways. Dave said he felt sorry for them and gave them more. Then he came and talked to me again. I told him that we just can't let them put us over a barrel. We need to stick as close as we can to what we have told them. If not, they think they can get what they want out of us. When we got together for prayer this afternoon, I brought it up again, for I knew it was troubling Dave a bit. I told him that we have got to keep unity in our fellowship whatever the cost. This very thing about pay and little disagreements like this is what makes missionaries with other mission groups want to have their own station and run it the way they want to. One fellow told me that he couldn't work with anyone. Some haven't said it but they show it by what they do. We talked or I talked until 2:30 this afternoon about this. We need to have a balance in all that we do, we all have things to learn and we have got to get together and work together in all things. *(NTM is all about teamwork, unity on each mission station and unity as a field, Arvalee).* Dave said he was sure glad we could talk about these things.

05/17/59. Today is Sunday. Hobe-aba, Morobe, Aaron and David have gone to Uhezuhutai to a baptism. There are quite a few wanting to be baptized. We need real wisdom. Dave is sure feeling the burden that so many are professing Christ, but there seems to be so few really walking in the light they have.

We had a fellowship meeting tonight. It's good to sing with the kids.

Dave was telling us how the baptism went today. He saw one old man that he thought would be baptized and he asked him, and he said he would. Then Ori-o the *luluai* (chief) was helping baptize and said that he didn't think that this older fellow really understood the gospel yet and it would be good to teach him more. There was a young fellow that wanted to be baptized, but some of the men said that he never comes to their fellowship meeting and he didn't really understand well. Some fellows came up tonight and said that Biru and A-a-mo-aba were down at their houses. We had the Lord's Supper tonight.

05/18/59. Today was a big day. The wind came from the south all day today. Got the (3 Lawrence) kids moved into their room. We killed three chickens for supper and made Dave and Althea's lunch for tomorrow. We are all out of meat. Had a nice dinner, a good salad of lettuce and tomatoes.

Teaching this morning about Isaac and Rebecca, and the buying of a bride. Abraham was rich and sent 10 horses loaded with the bride's price. The servant was to get a good wife.

After the meeting this morning, talked to A-a-mo-aba for a long time. He said that he wanted to go back to his place and stay there. I don't know if he feels he was *poisoned* (a sorcery or spell) or not. He just said that this sick was in his neck and some men die from it. They cut the top of his forehead and bleed it; blood, water and air came out. Then an old man put some native medicine in it, then up his nose. Afterwards, he was able to talk some. Biru said if I didn't want him to work that he would stay here and work on his garden and get some schooling. I told him that for right now he could work his garden and maybe after he could work for us, but maybe not. He was happy. I told him that he would have to look after his food. He and Meniba had talked about it that night and felt it would be wrong to eat our food if not working for us.

About 5:30 Meniba came in and said that U-i-mo was here and wanted to know if I would doctor Nebaza, the *tultul* (assistant chief), for he has the same sick as U-i-mo had. I told him I would, for I felt it would be a good contact with Nebaza for he is unsaved. Meniba came up about 8:00 p.m. and he said he had a *pen* (pain) in his side like a nail sticking his heart. Pneumonia, his pulse was slow, about 30 beats for ½ minute. I gave him 4 cc of penicillin and some *Aspro* (Aspirin) tablets to sleep. U-i-mo, Meniba and I all prayed before we gave the shot.

05/19/59. I went down to teach the *boys* this morning. Not feeling good, just lay around most of the day.

05/20/59. I didn't sleep any last night; I must be getting the flu. I was sick in bed all day.

05/21/59. Looks like all the kids are getting sick too. Paul and Peter have a bad cough and Joy and Steve don't look good. No sleep in the night.

05/22/59. Pat and Julie getting sick now. Arvalee is not feeling good. No sleep yet, still in bed.

05/23/59. Slept from 3:00 a.m. to 7:00 a.m. Arvalee getting bad cough. Craig is not coughing yet. I'm feeling some better. I slept a bit during the day.

05/24/59. I slept most of the night. Sure feel better today. Paul and Peter better. Pat and Julie still sick. Joy is too. I slept a lot today.

05/25/59. Well the past week was like the lost week. I'm feeling so much better. Slept all night and so did the kids.

05/26/59. Had another good night's rest. I'm so thankful to the Lord for the sleep I'm getting.

05/27/59. Doing much better these days. Arvalee and I had a nice bath this afternoon, as we cooked our chicken dinner. Dave came this afternoon too.

Meniba called for a group to come up from Bebu's place. Biru came up from A-ibu with a story that Bebu had stolen part of a *pulpul* (grass skirt) from one of Zuino's wives and had sent it down to A-ibu with Biru's little brother. The man at A-ibu told the boy that this was an old fashion (a former practice; literally, 'sorcery was non-Christian') and he wouldn't work sorcery on her. He told the boy to take the *pulpul* (grass skirt) back to where he got it. So the kid gave it to Biru. Biru came right to Meniba and Meniba called for Bebu to come up and talk about it. He said he had a big shame and told Bebu that this was not a Christian fashion (practice). Meniba said that all of these rumors he thought were just lies but now he knows they are true. I knew that something was wrong with Bebu for some time, for he and Meniba were such good friends before Meniba's brother died. Then Bebu said that he thought Meniba was working sorcery on them for O-apo's brother died a short time after, over at Raro and now Bebu was trying to get back at Meniba by having sorcery worked on one of Meniba's line (clan).

05/28/59. Sleeping a lot these days. David went down to see the *boys*, as we had devotions with the kids.

Dave helped Meniba get the *iron* (Galvanized steel folded for a ridge cap, as the roof was wooden shingles) on the top of the house today. It was quite a job. I rested almost all morning, felt better this afternoon and tonight. We played the record player this afternoon some.

05/29/59. Dave went down to teach the *boys* this morning. Teaching the kids about *Pilgrim's Progress* in the morning. Dave and Morobe did the wash this morning. Dave is willing to do anything that he sees is in need. He's a real blessing to me this way.

05/30/59. Dave went down to Hu-a-ni-aba's place today. Didn't have anyone to go that could *turn talk* (translate) so he went down to Aaron's and wrote down a little story in Gimi. Then read it at the village. I told him that the Lord was forcing him to use the language. We talked some that we need to do something that will (encourage) these fellows to become leaders. It would be good, if we could get all the fellows that are Christians together somewhere and teach them for a few days. There are some problems. One is that so very few see the need of further teaching. Satan has blinded their hearts in this way and it will only be through much prayer that we will see a (truly) deep hunger for the Bread of Life. Also, many of the men don't like to go to some other place for fear of someone working sorcery on them, so to get a few fellows from other villages to meet together, would indeed be miraculous.

June, 1959

06/01/59. Meniba is feeling some better today. Hobe-aba and Morobe are both working today. We are having a lot of fun teaching the *Pilgrim's Progress* book; most of the kids understand parts of it, even Joy and Julie. They know that the big bag on Graceless' back is sin. Dave is teaching literacy this afternoon. Was talking to Dave tonight that I would like to make small maps of the clans and mark all the villages and then give the names of each Christian family and just where they live. This might help people to understand how to pray better and see the villages the way we see them. I want to see how many Christians we can find and show them the needs and get little prayer groups praying for a clan like Tunakau. We need to find out all we can about these villages, so that we can make it interesting to the prayer partners. A map of their village, showing village life, and problems in the village with men, women and young people, and little kids (would be great).

06/03/59. Got word from Olaguti today. George has hepatitis. Don't know what will happen about the road work now.

06/04/59. I had bad sinus all day and spent most of the day in bed.

06/05/59. Dave was down spiritually this morning. He came and talked to me, said he had a cold heart towards Arvalee and me and that Meniba told him this morning that he was just talking nothing, for they were all sick and no one was hearing the talk. I feel so small, but I know that it's up to me to enter into this battle with Dave and be a real help and encourage him. Only the Lord can show me how to do this.

This afternoon Arvalee called me and said that she saw Hobe-aba wrapping up something in his *laplap* (sarong). When I came in he started unwrapping his *laplap* and a piece of newspaper fell out on the floor. He said that he didn't steal it, but he just wrapped up his *laplap* and towel. I told him he was lying, and he said the Missus was lying. I told him that I saw the paper fall from his *laplap* (sarong) and I knew he was trying to steal it. He denied it over and over. Only God can show him that this is sin. We all talked to Hobe-aba for some time but he kept to his story. I told Dave that I thought it best for him not to work in the house any longer until he confesses his lie. Meniba told Hobe-aba about when he lied and had to confess to me and then his *liver* (heart) was happy.

06/07/59. Meniba went over to Negibi today. Dave went to Iri-bia-bipi and was gone most of the day.

06/08/59. Arvalee was in bed most of the day today with a sore throat. Meniba said he was so weak he could hardly walk back. He asked me if he could have a liver shot again, so I told him o.k. Dave said he had a good meeting this morning.

06/12/59. Dave is teaching Morobe and Meniba to read and write. He said that

Meniba was coming right along. Dave gave me a bit of his out-line of what he's been teaching the past three weeks.

> God: Life of Christ
>> Marriage at Cana
>> Purging the temple
>
> Personal: Holy Spirit
> Life: (pictures)
>> Forgiveness, (Teaching confession of sin.)
>> Family Life: Husband's responsibility
>> Wife's responsibility
>> Training children
>
> Purpose for sickness:
>> Trouble
>> Purify
>> Strengthen by teaching us to draw on the Lord.
>
> Church Life: Discipline
>> How purpose
>
> Gifts of Spirit: (Pictures)

Dave told me today that he wanted to help me with my English. I always use, "He don't", and "I have saw". I know that I don't use good English, but I don't know when I do it. My dear wife is telling me something all the time, but I forget what it was. As the little song goes, "I will ask Jesus to help me." I don't want to bring shame to his Name or to the Mission.

06/13/59. Sure have been feeling better this week, much stronger too. I went up to Dave's house and talked to some old men this morning and helped Dave a little. At rest time I went down in the wood house and talked to the fellows all through rest time. This is the first time I have missed my rest after lunch for months. I was a bit tired tonight.

In our prayer meeting today, we prayed for all the work at home. We always pray for our Mission leaders and all the boot camps on Saturday. We also prayed for associate missionaries (with other missions): Harold Sellers, Cleon Laughlin and Ben Wertz.

Dave worked on the house till dark. Arvalee said she gets tired of just cooking and being in the house all the time. I will have to help her more. She's having a hard time these days, so much sewing and all the kids too. Yesterday, I took all the kids, but Pat, who was in school and we all went for a walk up the road. Julie keeps asking me to go with her up the road. So today Pat and I played ball for a bit, then I helped them make some little car roads just before lunch.

Meniba told Dave this morning that there were two things troubling him. When he was with other men that were smoking that it was hard for him not to smoke and that he was so afraid that someone was going to work *poison* (sorcery) on him.

06/14/59. Dave had to go down to U-he-zui-hu-tai by himself. He was going to ask Aaron to go with him, but he got away before Dave could ask him.

Meniba and I went over to Ana-i-tapi, a village of Negibi. We two had a good talk as we walked over. We talked about making a kick ball field up the road by the water race. Meniba was telling me how the ridge we live on ran all the way to Fusa and A-ibu then on down to Misapi. This is the place to build the road, but the Government may not see this. He said he would help me with my map of the Gimi.

There were 12 at the village meeting; Tabaibo and Etha-o were there. Anaiza was sick and asked if I would give him a shot. So after the meeting I told him to come over and I would. I told the story of the prodigal son and then asked if anyone remembered it. No one did, so I told it again, and then told them that God is our Father and He loves us and will feed us and take care of us, if we will but come to Him. Ibu came home with me. We saw a DC-3 fly over again today. This is twice this week that they have flown over Mt. Negibi going to Papua.

Dave went to U-he-zui-hu-tai and then over to Tunakau at the *haus sik* (clinic) and had a meeting. He left here at 10:00 and got back at 4:00. Dave, Arvalee and I had a good talk tonight. Dave said that he wanted to fellowship with us about our children. Said he felt Pat was having a hard time liking school work and he thought Arvalee might be well to encourage him a bit more and not ask him why he did something this way or that way. He said that we have got to teach our children to obey us when we talk to them whatever the cost may be.

06/15/59. I went down this morning to fellowship with the fellows. I told the story of Jesus driving the traders out of the temple court yard. I told it once, then Meniba went over it again, then Morobe remembered about half. I told him that our bodies are God's temple and Jesus cleaned and drove out all the cows and goats, but tells us to take the pidgins out. Meniba said, "that's a good story, *Master*" (colonial).

Teaching the children the story of *Pilgrim's Progress* each morning, the older kids understand it quite good. Meniba is feeling much better, said the liver shots were helping him. Said he worked hard today. I gave the two men shots, 4 cc today, (probably penicillin).

A bit of wind today, not much rain these days. Dave spent this morning up at the house and this afternoon packing here. Arvalee has hay fever some today. Aidano told me that he went down to his place yesterday and said that Sidi got them altogether and got out the book and told them the stories from the little picture book that I made. Sure good to hear about Sidi going on in the things of the Lord. Aidano said O-so and Se-o were at the meeting too. Dave said that he has been a bit troubled about Iri-bia-bipi and the believers down there. Oh, we must pray. Village life is so hard for a Christian. Dave said that we should have the books with these pictures ready in a short time.

06/16/59. Dave got off for Olaguti at 7:00. Arvalee got hay fever bad this morning. Cold and windy this morning, the kids spent the morning in the house. Went down to Biru's house and gave the two old men shots. They both have the same name, Ana-i-da. After the shots we had a meeting there. I told them that they never come to hear our talk, but now that they have come for shots we wanted them to hear the good talk and know the way to Heaven. The two old men and the one old woman didn't act like they cared if we came or not. I told them the story that I gave yesterday, the cleansing of the temple. It was a bit too deep for them, I can see now.

Had a talk with Etha-o this afternoon, he has been much friendlier for some time now. He asked me if I wanted to buy a net cape. I told him that I would like one very much. He brought me a beautiful butterfly yesterday. I've never seen one like it in my life. I hope to mount it to take home.

Boys were back by 3:00 p.m. today. Dave said the road was about ½ hour from the Abu River. We should be able to bring the horses through soon.

06/17/59. Went down this morning and gave the two old men shots again. We sang Yesusu Amapi and I told them that Jesus left his home in Heaven to come to earth to help the people of the earth and died for them. I was speaking to the two old men. The one old fellow who is Morobe's father, (maybe an uncle?) acts like he is listening anyway.

Nu-u-da was here this morning. Then I told Meniba that I wanted to give them some of God's talk, from Hebrews 12:1 and 2. Mu-u-nabi, Aizano and Morobe were there. They all seemed to be listening. I told them that if they are to run in a race, at the Government Christmas *singsing* (festival) they must take off the things that will keep them from running fast, for they want to win and get the prize. Meniba could see this. I told them at the close that God and Jesus loves them and wants to help them to lay aside the things that hinder their testimony. Felt they understood this morning. Nu-u-da asked me if he could work again, said, *"nautene"* (I would really like to). So I'm letting him work peanuts (shell peanuts). I sure like him and I feel he will be a lot of help and we might be able to help him spiritually.

Bebu came up and brought some bamboo to sell. I asked him if we could have a little meeting. His wife and baby boy were with him, sure good to see them up here again. I told him the stories on the calendar pictures. The first one was about the birth of Jesus. Point was: The Angels said Jesus was the Son of God. Then next, how Jesus helped Joseph with the work. Story of John the Baptist, baptizing Jesus and pointing out that twice we have heard that Jesus is the Son of God. Told Bebu that he could teach his people this story and to come back and I would teach him more.

06/18/59. I thought of a way we could build a smaller house last night and I was thinking that the three boys would be going to school, maybe a mission school by the time we come back. Arvalee feels that I have no love for the children because I said the boys would probably be in school out away from us. I told her that there were three things we could do. 1. Let the children go to a mission school if we get one and we live in the bush. 2. Or, for us to have our home near the school and she be there and I would work in the bush as we did the first 5 years on the field. 3. To drop out of tribal work altogether and try to fit in somewhere in supply work or running a base or something like that. Arvalee was a bit upset and didn't feel like talking or praying with me for some time. After reading to myself Psalm 50:15 "Call upon me in the day of trouble, I the Lord will deliver you." Psalm 73: 23 and 24, "I am continually with thee: thou hast holden my right hand, You shall guide me with Your counsel." I received much strength from these words. I will be guided right if I will counsel with the Lord. After some time, Arvalee said that we could pray now. She prayed that the Lord would have His will in her life and in our family. It is going to be the cross more and more in this job of reaching lost men for Christ. I'm sure that I don't have the answers, but I know if we will counsel with the Lord about this problem, He will give the right answer. Arvalee was in a happier mood this morning and even came in to where I was fixing breakfast and wanted to be loved and made over. I want to be in the place where I can help Arvalee in her needs.

This morning as we were about to sit down to eat this little boy who is staying with Morobe kept teasing the kids like he always does. I told him to go outside three times. He said, "No, I'm staying here." When I went to put him out, he ran like mad and I ran after him and caught him down by Meniba's house. He was calling for Meniba to help him. I talked to him for some time and told him that he was going to have to mind me from now on. These kids just need a good sound whipping when they disobey. But I sure don't want to do it.

Last night Paul prayed for Saubai, so this morning he came to the meeting for the first time in a long time. He sat right next to me. I reviewed about yesterday. We had a good time with the kids this morning. Christian and Hopeful were in the dungeon today and saw how Christian was so down hearted that he thought it might be best to commit suicide and Hopeful was always looking up and told Christian that the Lord was with them. Then Christian remembered that they had forgotten to pray. After prayer, he remembered the promises of God. It was a key to open the dungeon door and the kids were sure happy they got out.

Today after lunch I went outside and saw a man from Negibi with some nails in his hair. He said Meniba gave them to him. I called Meniba and then the fellow confessed he had stolen them. I talked for some time with him and he said that he was sorry and wanted to pray and get things right. He prayed and after Meniba said that he didn't ask for the Blood of Jesus. I told Meniba that God knew his heart and if he was truly sorry and repenting in his heart and not just with his lips God would make him a new man in Christ Jesus. Ime-reaba is his name.

06/19/59. Yesterday, Arvalee and I prayed for the Bolivian field. Asked Arvalee if she would like to pray for the school at Tambo. She told the Lord that it was hard for her to (think of leaving) the kids in a school, but now she does see that if they are in a mission school they will grow in the things of the Lord just like they do at home. The cross is not greater than His Grace.

Was very tired last night and didn't feel really rested when I woke this morning. Not feeling up to par all day. But, for about two weeks now, have been feeling real good, just a bit on the weak side.

I stopped giving shots to the two old fellows this morning. In the meeting this morning, I asked if any one remembered the story I had been teaching. Not one. So I went over it again. It was very hard teaching this morning. Meniba couldn't remember to turn the talk (interpret) good. Sometimes Satan has walls around our lives. It could be, that is, I feel that I was a bit unprepared this morning. I have asked the Lord to show me another way to get my point across.

Meniba is buying lots of bamboo these days. Got some *pitpit* (cane for weaving mats) today.

06/20/59. I walked up the road this morning. Told the Lord I was in great need and needed my heart warmed with His love for the ones I teach each morning. The Lord is so good and gave us some good fellowship this morning. I read first from 2 Corinthians 6:1, "We then, as workers together with him (God) beseech you also that ye receive not the grace of God in vain." Using chapter 5:17 and chapter 4:7, and Eph. 2:10. God didn't save us to live just any way we want to, He has a plan for each of our lives. But we have got to be willing to obey His commands. Satan comes and tells us that we partly belong to Jesus, but can carry a bit of *cargo* (baggage) for him. It's these small things that keep us from walking in the light. Morobe looks so blank these days. I tried to show them how God would be so glad to help them.

Not feeling too good today. We reviewed some Bible verses and Peter gave the New Testament poem. I cut hair for all the boys this morning.

Meniba had the day off today, so after cutting the boys' hair I had to go buy bamboo and *pitpit* (cane), when I really didn't feel much like it. Bebu came and wanted me to teach him another story. I asked Peter to go see if Aaron would come and *turn talk* (interpret). Bebu understands a lot of Pidgin but he's not able to talk it. I feel that Aaron received a blessing along with Bebu. I told about two pictures, Jesus with the little children and the prodigal son. I brought out that God is very loving with us and will help us if we do wrong. We all three prayed together and I spent the rest of the afternoon in bed. We had our first rain this afternoon in a week. Our *meme* (goat) had twins today, a male and a female. This gives us 20 goats here now. Biru has 3, A-a-mo-aba. 2, Dave has 3, and Meniba 3 and me 9.

06/21/59. I didn't sleep any last night. It rained all night. Feel some better this morning. I had a talk to Meniba this morning. He told me a bit more about fighting and the fight leaders and their jobs.

Told Meniba some stories using the little pictures from the calendar. He said he was going over to Negibi and told Tabaribo yesterday that he would be there. I'm glad to see him getting out and if I can just help Bebu and Meniba these days it will be worth great riches in Heaven in the eyes of the Lord. Been cold and rainy all day today.

Eromaro and some men came up from Ore-ua-bipi and said they were hunting for a wild pig, but it got away. Asked them if they had a meeting this morning with Bebu. He just said that Bebu was at his place. I don't think these Christian fellows will meet with Bebu. I believe Bebu is really trying to do the right thing now, but he will be alone and I must pray much for him these days.

Meniba came in about dark tonight. Said Tabaribo and the other people were there. Etha-o didn't come. Tabaribo could remember everything about the stories. Ime-ere-aba told Meniba that he was going to come to all the meetings now, but before he wasn't a Christian and now he was a Jesus boy and wanted to do the things that were right now. Meniba said he talked to Anaiza and his wife, the old people and asked them if they had been thinking about what we told them, said I told them that they never come to hear what we had to say, but come to us when they got sick. Anaiza said that his mouth didn't have any talk to back us. In other words he didn't have anything to say. Meniba told him that they didn't know when they would die and if they die in their sin they will go to a bad place. "You might die in the night, you're both old now." This is the way a man becomes a soul winner when he sees people going to hell and wants to help them.

06/22/59. Didn't sleep till after 3:00 a.m. so felt quite tired this morning. Pat went down and asked Meniba if he would take the morning meeting. Got 2 more hours sleep this morning from 9 to 11:00 a.m. The people from Negibi are bringing lots of *pitpit* (cane). The goat boy, Ori-o left the mother goat and the twins. The male fell into the hot coals of the fire and was burnt bad. He couldn't live long, so I shot him. We had goat for supper.

At night when we pray together, the children have been praying for someone around here; for the young boys like Nu-u-da and Saubai. Julie asked if she could pray for Hobe-aba. We are now on our 5th missionary book at our bed time stories. First we had David Livingstone, then Hudson Taylor, Adoniram Judson, Mary Slessor and now we are telling about Allen Gardiner. The older kids sure like them. I have been reading it first to them and then telling it and the little ones listen much better.

06/23/59. Slept good last night, went down to teach the fellows this morning. Aizano remembered the story that Meniba told him yesterday, the Prodigal Son. I was trying to show them that the Father loves them and will help them if they will only come to Him. The son was sorry and asked the father to forgive him. This made the father very happy and he was willing to give him many good things. I trust this will help them to see that they must always be willing to repent and be truly sorrowful for sin. Arvalee not feeling too good today with hay fever. Had supper early today so we went for a walk. Aaron gave us a nice big *ina*, a taro, when we walked down past his house. Told me he went down to the house where the *anosa bana* (chief, literally: big man) died. I asked if he was a Christian. No, was the answer. Had a good look at the goats, brought the new baby up to the house for a bit. Julie called it her Billy goat, she loved it and played with it till the goat boy wanted to go home with it. Talked to A-ori-o this morning and told him that we would have to *pull* some of his pay for not looking after the baby goat that fell in the fire. He said that's all right. Said he had paid for some corn and *he-re-* (pitpit) that the goats had eaten. We told him to take the goats over to the other side by Mt. Negibi from now on.

06/24/59. I slept well again last night; so thankful for a good night's rest. Didn't wake up this morning until after 7:00 a.m. Find it so hard to wake up these days.

Told the story of the talents found in Matt 25:14, 30. Esema and some other believers were there. Told them that our Master is Jesus and He will be coming back soon, will He say well done to us or will He be ashamed of us? Esema said that he always tells people about God, but many times they don't want to hear him. I told him that we must be faithful and keep telling them. Some men didn't want to hear Jesus' Talk but he kept talking about the new way and about God his Father.

Esema said he was going down to where the *anosa bana* (big man) died; his name was Misapi; he was an old fight leader that was known from Misapi to Henagaru as a strong fighter. He asked if I would like to go along. Meniba thought it was a bit too far for me to walk and Arvalee was sick in bed too, so I couldn't go. Meniba was going down with them at noon.

Been upset most of the afternoon. First over Nu-u-da, then tonight over Pat and Peter. The Lord is going to have to teach me many things. Told Pat that I was wrong for getting mad.

06/25/59. This morning felt that Morobe was just not there. Said he didn't remember any stories and after Aizano repeated the story again, Morobe couldn't remember it. I told him that this story was not my talk but that Jesus told this story when he was living here on earth and it was written in God's book and we need to hear God's Word and remember, for some day we will stand before Him and if we don't remember anything we will have a big shame.

Read to the kids this morning from the Philippian Letters to Young Churches. How, when we get angry we should not do it out of wounded pride or bad temper. Went up and helped Meniba till noon laying out the rooms.

06/26/59. Spoke this morning to Morobe, Aizano, Nu-u-da, Hotshot and Meniba about how Jesus is light like the Sun. The sun was out bright this morning and I had them look at it. They said it made their eyes *pen* (pain) and then I was able to tell them how strong Jesus is and how he holds 7 stars in one hand and his talk is like a sword that goes right to our *liver* (heart). But this same Jesus who is so strong and Bright, is also loving and Rev 1:5 shows us this, for he washed us with his own blood so that we might be clean from our old sinful life. If He our King is Bright as the sun when it is strong and can hold seven *obu* (stars) in his right hand at one time; well surely He can wash our sin away.

Morobe prayed with me this morning. He also told me his other name, Thatota-a.

Arvalee was in bed most of the day with hay fever. Meniba came up tonight said he was going down to A-ibu tomorrow and would be back Sunday night. He said that Biru took his and A-a-mo-aba's goats to A-ibu yesterday. Meniba said he wanted to go see how they were doing and if they were meeting. I told him that I thought that A-a-mo-aba was afraid of *poison* (sorcery) here at Negibi. Meniba said he knew that was why he left. I can see that Satan has these Christians blinded in fear of death, so I spoke to Meniba about it again tonight. Only the Lord can open his eyes that Satan is blinding him and making him weak. Meniba will be of little help spiritually to the A-ibu Christians until he finds victory over this fear and casts his life into the Lord's hands and gives up his will.

06/27/59. About ten fellows came by this morning and said they were going to A-ibu. Now, I wonder what they are going to A-ibu for? Biru must have told them something, for them all to go down. Meniba tried to let me think it was a trip to help the believers.

Pat, Pete and I went up to the end of the water race this morning. It's not as far as I thought. We were able to get a bit more water running in it. We had lots of fun.

06/28/59. Not much doing this Sunday. Morobe came up and said that everyone was gone and he was all alone. I sure would like to get close to Morobe. We all went up the road to the big tree today and had an outing. I think it was good for all of us to get out and Arvalee said it did her good. Had our lunch on the road and a little Bible story.

Meniba got back from A-ibu just before dark, said he had a meeting with the people from the village of A-ibu. A-a-mo-aba is living up at Beha by Biru and he didn't see them. Some old man told Meniba that he knew that this talk was true and all this other talk of the ground was just a big lie. Meniba told them that we were thinking about them and he was working now and couldn't come down all the time and that his *Master* (Dale, colonial term) was not strong and *Master* Dave was working now.

06/29/59. Went for a walk up the road this morning. We had a cold north wind this morning. It was so cold that after a short walk I came back to the house where the fire was. Told the story of Jesus as the Good Shepherd. We are his little *meme's*, goats or sheep, and He is our *Meme Iri-ara* (Good Shepherd). John 10:11. Aaron was at the meeting this morning, the first time in a long time. Told him that any time he had some time to come up and talk and I would be glad to teach him some Bible stories. Said he would.

06/30/59. It's a good thing that I'm feeling better. Today was full of many jobs. I was up early this morning. I can see that I need to pray more for the believers around me here. As I see the need for more prayer, I can also hear Satan trying to condemn me for having a cold heart toward the Lord and not having a warm heart of love for the Lord and the believers. I do know the Lord would have me pray for my weaker brothers in the Gimi. But I must stand against Satan in the victory of Jesus Christ on the cross. This is the only place of safety for me. When I think of my position in Christ Jesus and what He went through to put me in this wonderful position, it makes my heart full of love and warmth for Him and this makes me want my brothers to know Him better. Oh that I might understand how to pray for the people that God has sent me to. Moses said or prayed the Lord his God to show mercy to the people he had been sent to. Exodus 32:7-14.

Sidi came in this morning and his little boy is sick with *pekpek blut* (dysentery). I gave him some medicine, but he can't keep it down. Hope he will stay so we can help his little boy. There is real fear in Sidi, so we might be able to help him. Meniba told him to make a new hole (a toilet hole), so we all wouldn't get sick. That's using your head. Etha-o has started work on the house. I helped them in the morning.

July, 1959

07/01/59. It was really cold this morning. We had the meeting in Morobe's house. I was teaching from a picture that I drew. Jesus is a good *Meme* boy (meme iri-ara bitara), a Good Shepherd. He will help us in the mornings. We need morning prayer to make us strong. We must follow Jesus and hear His voice. Satan will try to *pull*, entice, us into sin and darkness.

Sidi was there for the meeting. I started giving his little boy shots today at 10:00 then one at 3:00, (probably sulfa shots). Then I'll give him one more about 8:00 or 9:00 tonight. Sidi came up this afternoon and said that some men came up from his place and want him to bring his little boy home so they can kill some chickens and eat them before he dies. Sidi was upset, you could tell, by looking in his eyes. I told him that he had come to me and asked me to give his son some medicine and I asked him if they would stay here so I could take care of him. "You told me you would Sidi and now you have another talk. Were you lying to me yesterday?" I also told him that I felt that the Lord had told him to come up here to us, and now Satan was telling him to run away. "Three of your other children have died and now the Lord spoke to you and led you to come up here so we could save your little 6 year old boy." He looked at me and nodded a yes; then said, "You are telling the truth. We will stay and not run away."

Dave walked in about 5:00 this afternoon. Althea had their baby boy June 22. The Lord sure was good.

07/02/59. I went to bed late and couldn't get to sleep till about 2:00 a.m. I find it hard to get up in the morning when I don't sleep well. I was able to have some time with my Lord. Oh, He is so sweet to me.

Spirits were a bit higher this morning in the meeting. Sidi's son is much better. Teaching on the Good Shepherd. It's been a real blessing to my own heart.

Arvalee has hay fever almost every day now. She's in bed this morning.

We talked about the coming conference with the native leaders. When? Dave said the primers should be ready in two weeks. So could be the last of July. I told Dave that I thought it would be good to speak of fellowship and try to help them to see the need to meet for fellowship.

We also talked about Sylvie (Spence, widow of Jim) and Ruth (Parry) coming up here to work in the Gimi. It's rough but there is a need. Will have to write to Sylvie.

Arvalee a bit sick tonight, lost her supper.

07/03/59. Arvalee was in bed all day today. Sidi said that his little boy had dysentery again. I wanted to get down there to see him, but with all the cooking I couldn't get away. Tried to give Sidi the medicine and told him to give it to him. I asked him this afternoon if he gave it to him and he said some of it. I may start the shots again tomorrow if he's not better.

This afternoon about 5:00 p.m. some men from U-he-zui-hu-tai came up with half a pig. They said a man from Oraratu had killed it and they wanted to bring it up and show it to us. I told them that we should pray for this fellow that the Lord would work in his *liver* (heart). Then we need to pray that the Lord will keep us from getting mad and saying and doing things that are wrong. No one said anything. I said let's pray and looked at the *tultul* (assistant chief) who is a Christian and was the spokesman. He then told me that they wanted us to write a *pas* (note) to the *kiap* (patrol officer). I replied, "No, we won't write a *pas* (note), but we are willing to help you spiritually and would like to pray with you." He gave the command to go and they all went running off with their bows and arrows in hand. I prayed; then Dave and Meniba.

I feel tired tonight. I must not have rested in the Lord enough today.

07/04/59. Arvalee was sick most of the day. Meniba went over to Esema's place for the day. I feel the meetings have been good in the mornings.

I tried to give Sidi's little boy some sulfa orally. By dark I felt we would have to give him some more shots. Arvalee felt better so she went with me. Sidi cried. Oh, how they love that little fellow. After we gave the shot they cried for some time, then after they stopped I prayed; Nu-u-da, Morobe, Arvalee and Sidi. I wish I could understand the language. I'm sure I could be a real help to Sidi at this time.

Talked to Meniba as we were coming back from Sidi's house; he said the Lord told him to go down to Oraratu and have a meeting tomorrow. I told him it would be good to go and fellowship with those Christians. They have been asking us to come down for some time. The *tultul bana* (assistant chief) just asked me again the other day, when we were going to come and teach them. Meniba asked me if I was going to Negibi. I told him yes, he said he would be back by *belo* (noon), and could *turn talk* for me. Good.

07/05/59. Dave went to Ore-ua-bipi, had fellowship with Hu-a-ni-aba, but didn't see Bebu and his line, clan, till on the way back and met them on the road. They were out hunting wild pig. Dave said Bebu acted like he knew it was wrong. He did have a meeting there on the road.

Went over to Negibi about 10:30 this morning, Peter went with me. It rained on us all the way over. When we got there they were cutting up a pig. I had a little story about the Good Shepherd. Etha-o helped me some. We got 7 pictures when the sun came out. Peter said he was hungry and wanted to go home. Just then, a little girl came up and gave us some corn she had cooked over the open fire. He did get tired of just sitting around. Meniba came about 3:30, and then we had a good meeting. Meniba spoke first, I didn't understand too much, but I knew he was talking about living in darkness. I spoke for a short time after Meniba finished. Esema said that when everyone was sick that he told them that to walk in darkness, would only make more trouble for all of them. He was meaning that when someone died not to work sorcery in return. He also said that when he saw someone walking in darkness he would come and tell us. I think he means well.

Gave Bede a shot this morning and afterwards Sidi and his wife started crying. They said that when I started giving him the shots, he stopped eating. I gave him another one this afternoon when I got back from Negibi. Bede looks bad tonight. Sent some milk down to see if he could drink it. The kids are sure praying for this little fellow to get well.

07/06/59. In the night I felt that if I gave him any more shots that the shock would kill him. Oh, he just really fights. He is so thin.

This morning we had a good meeting. Sidi said that when his little boy drinks the water it comes up, but the milk stays down. I told him he could have more milk. By noon they hadn't come up to get any more, so I sent Meniba down to see why. Said he still had some and Morobe was the only one who could get him to drink. Dave went down tonight and said he was eating some things now, so we will just have to pray it will stay down. And we won't have to give him more shots. Dave is coming along good on his house.

Arvalee has been sick all day.

07/07/59. Sidi's little boy is looking better and eating *kaukau* (sweet potato) now. Praise the Lord for answering our prayers.

I've been spending a lot of time at the typewriter these days. We were having our prayer meeting this afternoon and after we had all prayed once, we were reading some more requests. In walked a young couple from *SIL* named Dick and Aretta Loving. We had some good Christian fellowship the rest of the afternoon. I can see that Julie will get along good with strangers. She went right up to Aretta and started talking to her. We had a sing tonight. Dick was telling us how the Lord had been teaching them how to trust Him for little things, like their health. Said he had hay-fever real bad, had had it for years. When they were trying to help others by talking to them, he felt that Satan was using this hay fever to make him sick so they couldn't speak for the Lord. They prayed together and he hasn't had hay fever since. They were a real blessing to my heart. We had a nice pork dinner, with *kaukau* and taro.

07/08/59. The *cargo boys* (carriers) went to get *cargo* (the supplies) this morning. Dick and wife went down to the meeting with me this morning. Raining this morning and it rained almost all day. We finished praying together today for the requests in *Brown Gold*.

Arvalee thinks that she just has morning sickness.

07/09/59. This morning went down for the meeting; we met in Morobe's house. Nu-u-da was trying to read. Helped Meniba some. I do wish he could read well. Morobe was able to tell most of the story about the Good Shepherd. Meniba asked what the good grass was like, no one knew, so he told them that it was God's Talk. The goats need good grass to eat to make them strong, we need God's Word to feed on (hear and read) so we will be strong.

The nails came yesterday so Etha-o wanted to get started. Meniba is helping them get started. Meniba told me that a young girl, about 10 or 12 years old died. All they know is that she went down to get water by herself and shortly after fell sick and died in a very short time. Meniba said that her mother was like a sister to him; she is from Meniba's clan and has married a man from Oaberu clan. Asked Meniba if we, Dave and I, should try to go down since we were not invited. He thought it best not to go. I told him that we wanted to help them when they were sad. We didn't just come here to have *lotu* (a church service). I let Meniba know that we were a bit hurt because we have not been asked to be in on these things.

Tonight Nu-u-da was taking some peanuts out of the big tin. Arvalee went out to see who was doing it and saw Nu-u-da run out the back door. After a bit he came back, so I went in to talk to him. Asked him if he was stealing peanuts. "Yes," he said real quickly, "and it's a bad fashion. I want to pray now." He said he was afraid and ran away first, but came back.

07/10/59. Meniba went down this morning before the meeting. He got back about 2:30. He said he talked to the mother and father. He told them that their daughter was in Heaven with Jesus. Said they didn't say anything when he told them.

Went down for the meeting and we sang together, then we prayed together.

The sun was out this morning, the first time for about 4 days, but cold and rainy all afternoon. Arvalee spent most all day in bed. We had prayer with Meniba today. He came in just as Dave and I were about to pray, so asked him to join us. I asked him about going out to Misapi and A-ibu to ask the fellows to come for the conference. He thought it would be all right if we sent some one. So we ask him to pray about it. Was so thankful that he prayed in Pidgin with us, we need to talk with him more. I do anyway.

07/12/59. Meniba said that his neck was sore and he didn't feel like going out today. I told him that I had planned on going over even if he didn't go. Went over the story of Jesus quieting the winds on the lake. I only tried half of it. Dave is going down to Misapi-biraisa or A-bo-pisa.

Arvalee not feeling too good today. Had a big rain last night.

Went over this morning for a meeting, all the men had gone wild pig hunting, said some of them went, after Esema called for them to go with him. These people just find it hard to keep their word. They do what they want to do when they want to do it. There were three women and some little kids there, so I had a meeting with them. It was good they helped me as I stumbled along. On my way back, I met some more women and kids and asked them if they would like a meeting. They said yes, so we met on the road.

07/13/59. We had a good day for washing, this morning, anyway. The rain came about 3:30. Dave is coming right along on the house. He sure is praising the Lord for the way it's been going up so good.

Started teaching again this morning, or I should say starting over again with a picture of a man carrying a big bag. We have named him *Manui* (darkness). I would like to teach on this for some time, trying to get across: Grace, Mercy, Trust and Believe.

Some fellows came up this noon from Imetai and some from U-he-zui-hu-tai. I went out to take a picture of them and then asked them if they would like to hear some of Jesus' Talk. They did, so I gave the story on Jesus stilling the storm, and then I went over each song with them.

Dave came out and said he would like to teach them some, so they stayed. Dave gave two stories in the language. Boy, I just praise the Lord the way He's helping Dave to speak.

We talked tonight about what our schedule would be during the conference. Our first meeting, will be from 9 to 10, and then an hour for games. Then our second meeting will be from 11 to 12, and then we will have one meeting at 2:00 p.m. then a night meeting. The 9 to 10 meeting will be on fellowship; the 11 to 12 meeting Dave will be telling and teaching about literacy. The afternoon meeting we hope to see Meniba take our booklet on the gospel presentation and teach it at this time. The night meeting we would like to be open to the believers.

07/14/59. It rained most all day today. We have been having good fellowship with Dave, when we meet for prayer each day. We have had good times of prayer together.

The kids have been trying these days, the little ones talk *kros* (speak angry words) at each other so much. Dave has been trying to help them in the morning devotions along this line. Meniba came in tonight and said that he was going to Tarabo tomorrow.

07/15/59. Aaron came to the meeting this morning. Meniba must have left about 7:00 for Tarabo. We had a good time singing together. Morobe is singing Otibe and Nu-u-da is singing Yesusu-Atho. Then Aizano and his wife are singing together Yesusu Amapi. We hope they can sing at the conference.

Dave is working on a new song. Aaron helped me with the story this morning. I was sure glad to see him. I feel the Lord is helping him. Dave said that last Sunday the 12th that he was getting some language from Aaron before he went to the village and asked Aaron if he would like to go with him. Aaron said "No." Dave came up to the house here and Aaron came up and said he would go with him to A-bo-pisa.

Arvalee was in bed all day. The cooking takes lots of my time. I'm baking bread today.

Esema came in this afternoon and had a stalk of good bananas (Cavendish) I gave him 1d. per pound. I showed him the gospel presentation booklet and then he went home, said he was coming to the conference. Little Nu-u-da is a lot of help.

07/16/59. Aaron came again to the morning meeting. Nu-u-da sang real good this morning, got a bit mixed up. Morobe did too, Aizano and his wife sang so well, the first time when they were sitting down, and then when I asked them to stand up they forgot everything.

Meniba got back from Tarabo about 10:00, I think.

07/17/59. After the meeting, well even in the meeting, we had some good talks about trusting. I think Meniba might be seeing a bit about what I'm getting at. A person may say with his mouth that he has become a "boy belong Jesus," (saved) but just knows it only in words. We must swing out on Jesus' Talk (trust God's Word); until we do that, we know not Him; and we have not been washed from our sins with His blood. If only Meniba can see this and understand what I'm trying to get at, then we can get away from this idea of saying, or asking, "have you asked for the blood of Jesus?" We need a Gimi word for trust.

> *Dale found it difficult to explain words like faith, trust, repent and saved; they were not concepts the Gimis knew. Some new believers were using other phrases like "asking for the blood of Jesus" which did not truly encompass repentance for the Gimis. He had taught: "When we hold these things and really believe them, it's like holding the kanda (rope) and isiosi (swinging) across the river." Arvalee*

07/18/59. Meniba left at noon, to go to Misapi to invite them to come to the conference. We talked this morning about the conference and some of the things we would be doing. Morobe said he would go down and ask Se-o and the *tultul* (assistant chief) from Hopunai. I said that I wanted to go down to Oraratu and Nu-u-da said he would go with me.

Arvalee yet sick spending most of the day in bed. The deaf woman has a swollen hand, where she got a stick in it from planting *ina* (taro). I cut it open, but nothing came out. She just about passed out on us. Sure looks bad.

07/19/59. Dave went down to U-he-zui-hu-tai this morning then over to Imetai, got back about 5:00 p.m. It's a long walk. He went to ask some of the fellows to come to the conference. I find that I get upset over little things, like the kids not coming when it's time to eat. This morning, I just saw that it was nothing but the Lord that could love one so full of self and He is so merciful to me.

07/20/59. Last night was up with the kids at 12:00 and 3:00 a.m. and never could get to sleep. I don't think I slept a bit.

I went down this morning, we sang and I gave the story the best I could. Morobe, Nu-u-da and Aizano were a help. Etha-o prayed this morning. I went over to help the fellows this morning to put the shingles on the new goat house. Two hours in the hot sun felt good, but tiring.

Fixed lunch, read till 1:30, studied the Word till 2:00 then we had prayer meeting. Told Dave how I wanted to teach, using sticks: 1 stick is not strong, but tie them together and they are strong: Christian fellowship. We are God's house, Jesus is the center post, and we must lean on Him.

Meniba got back today at 4:00 p.m. from Misapi. Four fellows came back with him. Said he saw Carroll and the *kiap* (patrol officer) is coming from Okapa today. These fellows said they would come up here with Meniba so they would be here.

Dave went down to Bebu's and Hu-a-ni-aba's place tonight to ask them to come up. Saw the fellow from Oraratu and asked him to come again and to tell the *tultul* (assistant chief), said he would.

The deaf woman's hand looks bad. Meniba came and talked to me about giving her a shot, so he sent word for her to come in the morning.

07/21/59. The men from Misapi came to the meeting this morning. I'm teaching on the story of *Manui* (darkness) and the rope and how it is like Jesus' Talk or Word and the things we did. We have got to trust in Jesus just the same way we trust the rope. Got word tonight that the patrol officer was at Negibi.

07/22/59. Dave went over this morning to see the *kiap* (patrol officer). To see if he would cooperate with us in our conference. He came back and had lunch with all of us. He told Dave at first, he would come on Thursday and Sunday, but after he got here he changed his mind. Said he was born a Christian in the RC church. I told him how that I had been a Christian with my mouth for some time, but now I'm a born again Christian and that is not just the mouth but also with the heart.

After Kevin Carter, the *kiap* (patrol officer), left to go back, Meniba asked me what we were going to do. I thought it would be good if Meniba would go over and talk to Kevin and see what he could do. Meniba got back about dark and said that he didn't have to go to the census this time.

The *boys* got here tonight from Olaguti, but no Fred Morris. James had to go to Lufa. Ibiabaribo came up tonight for the meetings tomorrow. Dave has been teaching the kids in the morning from Acts.

07/23/59. GIMI NATIONAL CONFERENCE STARTED TODAY

There were five of us in the morning prayer meeting. Arvalee is quite sick this morning and was sick in bed all today.

The first meeting was teaching on the sticks, how we are like sticks, and we are not strong. We need to be in a fellowship and this will make each of us strong. The rope is a picture of Jesus' Talk and it ties us together. We can break one stick, but when all the sticks are together they are strong. Then I asked who wanted a house of God in their village. They answered that they did; then I will teach you how to build one, I said. The center post is a type of Christ in the center, the cornerstone in 1 Peter 2:4-8.

Dave had a good literacy class this morning; he spoke in the Gimi tongue for over 20 minutes. It was a thrill to my heart to see so many men nodding in agreement as Dave spoke. At noon the *kiap* (patrol officer) called for the men from U-he-zui-hu-tai to come to Negibi for census.

Meniba had the afternoon meeting on the gospel presentation. Today Roland Boye and Fred Morris walked in from Olaguti. James and Ausoka came too.

07/24/59. James and Ausoka came to the prayer meeting this morning. Not too many came to the morning meeting this a.m. I spoke on Jesus as the Good Shepherd, how we need to have the Lord make our hearts ready for the day in the morning. We need to hear his voice first thing, then He will lead us out and when he calls we will hear and follow Him and not follow strangers, like Satan. Reviewed the story I gave yesterday.

Dave had a game of volley ball with the *boys* again from 10:00 to 11:00. Dave had his class again. I didn't go up this afternoon.

Arvalee is still sick and I have to spend most of my time in cooking. I'm also working on the booklet of *Manui* (darkness.) Sure having some good fellowship with Fred, he understands what is going on out here. He was a missionary in Japan.

Roland read his testimony in Pidgin and it was real good. Then he talked some time after; was a blessing to my heart.

James talked some tonight but not much help to me. Arvalee went to the meeting tonight.

07/25/59. Prayer meeting, not many came this morning. Yesterday I asked James to review the story this morning, so he did; after Dave gave the story of The Little Red Hen.

Arvalee felt like going up to Dave's house for the meeting this morning, too. I didn't get to the 11:00 o'clock meeting. Spoke tonight on the booklet I made on trust and the man named *Manui* (darkness).

07/26/59. We had prayer again this morning. Fred came to the meeting this morning. We didn't start the meeting till about 11:00 a.m. for not too many came until then. We met on the hill outside the house. At one time I counted about 200 but more came after that.

Dave reviewed The Little Red Hen. Then James reviewed the Good Shepherd then I reviewed the stick stories and the house of God.

The *kiap* (patrol officer) came when I was talking. We had lunch together and then started our afternoon meeting. Dave spoke first in Gimi and telling most of same things he had said before; that we are not going to each village but just to a few. Kevin came to this meeting and I tried to tell him a bit of what Dave was talking about. Then it was time for Meniba to speak. He talked for some time on Jesus dying on the cross and going back to Heaven. Just as Meniba was giving out the *kaukau* (sweet potato) for the

Lord's Supper, it started raining. Some were able to get under the eave of the house and the rest of us stood in the rain and finished.

We had tea and the *kiap* (patrol officer) went home in the rain. After the rain stopped we had an arrow shooting contest for three small 4 gallon drums. Two fellows from U-he-zui-hu-tai and a fellow from Oaberu won them.

THE CONFERENCE ENDED TODAY

07/27/59. This morning Meniba killed the goat. Not much sun today.

I spent most of the morning over talking to Fred in the little sleeping house. I was able to talk for about 2 hours. Trust it has helped him. I have sure enjoyed the fellowship with Fred; he is a real swell fellow in the Lord.

07/28/59. The fellows got off this morning about 7:30. Dave took Craig with him. Dave came back after a bit to get my shoes for Roland. He made himself a pair of boards with nails under them and tied them to his shoes. I tried to talk to him, but he felt he could walk in them. I told him to take my shoes even if they were big on him.

Arvalee got sick about noon and spent the rest of the day in bed. She lost all of her dinner.

It was cold and cloudy all day. Went down this morning and had prayer with the *boys*. Meniba went to help Morobe buy or get the rest of the pay for his wife. They came in tonight, said they had everything right now.

07/29/59. Meniba met with the fellows this morning for prayer. No sun today, not a good day for washing. Arvalee is still not feeling good. She was in bed all day.

07/30/59. Received a note from Kevin about Morobe this morning; so Morobe went to Mane this morning. Arvalee feeling much better today. Today has been beautiful all day.

This morning I spoke to the ones on God's plan for Husband and Wife to live together and be happy. I see more and more that we have got to help these young people in their married life, if we are going to have a strong leadership in the church of God.

07/31/59. Went down this morning to the meeting; it was cold so we met in Meniba's house. I read to them again from Ephesians 5:22 to 33. Husbands love your wives; God tells us to, and we must obey Him. Before, we didn't know what we should do, but now we have God's Word to help us. There are times when we are mad and upset and we don't want to hear what God tells us or we don't want to remember what we have heard. But we must remember God's talk and follow Him. I talked to the women the same way, Mu-u-nabi, Mubuone and Nimibeira were there; I asked them if this talk that I was giving them was true. Talked to A-a-mo-aba after about Wietho. When they left here they were having some trouble. He said he talked to her about it and they were working together now.

August, 1959

08/01/59. We talked to the men this morning. I tried to show them that we have got to love our wives even when they do the wrong thing. We have a big job as husbands for how can we love with a love like the Lord has for us? He must fill our hearts with love for our wives.

I talked to Morobe and Meniba about the kids who play around here with our kids. So many times they do things to our kids and run away and if our kids fight or do something wrong we have to whip them. Oni-namo and another kid have been out of hand for some time now. So I asked Morobe and Meniba if they would talk to them and whip them if it was needed. Meniba said that Peter told him the other day that Saubai had been playing much better since Meniba gave him a whipping. Meniba told the fellows that the *Master's* kids were bad too and they got a whipping for it, but we don't do anything to our kids. Paid Meniba off today.

08/02/59. Meniba said that he told the Christians over at Asu-mu-yaba's place that he was coming over today. He and Mu-u-nabi went over this morning and when they got back tonight he said that they had all gone pig hunting. He said that an old man was there so they sat and talked to him most of the day.

We all walked down to Nu-u-da's place and had a nice look around. His mother and father were there and we sat around with them for a time, and then came home.

08/03/59. Teaching about husband and wife. Mu-u-nabi came to the last part of the meeting. Esema and Meniba left to go to Ubai to see the *kiap* (patrol officer).

08/04/59. Went down this morning and we sang and prayed together. Started teaching on the life of Paul this morning.

08/05/59. We just prayed and sang again this morning. We reviewed the first story of Paul or Saul. Talked some about the Light. Who was the Light? Jesus. What did He say? Why are you persecuting me? I asked the kids if Saul was persecuting Jesus. No, he was persecuting Christians and it was the same as doing it to Himself. When we are kind to others, we are being kind to Jesus.

Yesterday Dave and Althea got here about 4:00 p.m. in the rain.

08/06/59. This morning I spoke on 1 Peter 3. The wife must be subject to her husband, he must live with his wife in knowledge. How Sara obeyed Abraham. We are to be together in our walk with the Lord, so we can always pray together. One mind, willing to help in little things, as well as big. Not doing evil back, but think how we did evil to Jesus and he loved us and made us new men, we need to try to help people who are evil to us.

God's eyes are on us and His ears are open to hear our prayers. Who will harm a follower of Jesus? If we have to suffer for Jesus we should be happy and not be afraid. When we speak back we should tell the person, *kiap* (patrol officer), fellowman or wife that God has made us new in our *liver* (heart). We should speak in meekness. We need not be ashamed of Jesus for look what he suffered for you and me. Praise His sweet name.

08/07/59. The Lawrences ate at their house this morning. Arvalee went down with me to the meeting this morning. I reviewed the 3rd chapter of 1 Peter. I trust the fellows will remember when they are under testing that Jesus is their Master and has suffered more than they could, ever.

Arvalee and I find it so easy to get upset over little things. I got a bit provoked at Pat this morning, because he wasn't helping set the table. I told him I was sorry for getting upset and speaking crossly. The Lord has many things to teach me to make me the Christian he wants.

08/08/59. Some of the people came over today. In the meeting this morning, I finished up on what I have been talking about for the past week. We went up to Dave's for supper tonight.

08/09/59. We had a good meeting this afternoon. The people were saying they were sorry we were going. I told them that they mustn't *[sic]* be sad, because we were going, but now they had met the Friend of all Friends. White men will come and go, but Jesus will always be with you. We have most everything packed.

We had some *kumu* (edible greens) and beans that the natives cooked tonight.

08/10/59. Things are coming along good with the packing. Meniba made a big *mumu* (steam cooking) this afternoon. We had two chickens.

08/11/59. We had a hard time getting off this morning. It was 9:00 a.m. and then we had to stop two or three times before we got to the river. Julie asked if we were at Grandma's, when we got down to Tabaribo's place. We were 4 hours getting to the horses. We stopped at Aniaru.

08/12/59. Got away at 8:45 this morning from Aniaru. After we stopped and had lunch, the *boys* carried Arvalee in the chair to Kosotaka. We got here, Olaguti, at 5:45 p.m. Sure good to meet all the folks.

08/13/59. Arvalee was quite sore all day today. Been talking a lot to Fred and all the rest. Jake doesn't say much.

08/15/59. Dean and Ken went up to a village for the week end, near Anuparu on the road.

08/17/59. Arvalee went to town today and Julie went too. The doctor said she is four months along, anyway. Fred left for the Watut.

08/18/59. George, Dean and I went to see Al Booth today. We have been praying about what to do if he moves the new couple into Frigano. So we thought it best to go see him and talk to him. God goes ahead. Praise His Name. Al said that after talking it over, that they all felt it would be best for Ken Johnson to go back towards Hegonofi, between Mason and Al. We had some good fellowship with them and were sure glad we went. Al really loves the Lord and wants to do God's best.

08/19/59. Arvalee was sick all day to day.

08/20/59. Harold came down from Lufa and he said that I told him we would be up today, but I thought I said Friday. We thought it best to go back with him. So we did.

08/21/59. Harold and Mary are very hungry for fellowship. We went up to see Ben and Talila this afternoon. They sure have a beautiful place.

08/22/59. We went down and saw Cleon and Aletha (Laughlin) for a bit.

08/23/59. Had a nice rest this Sunday. We got some more packing done.

08/24/59. Got to Goroka today about 8:15. We, Ken, Dean and I went into the District Office about 8:30 and got out at 10:00. We talked to Mr. Bill Driver. We talked about the land at Negibi first and told him that we wanted to abide by the law and do the right thing. I told him that Olaguti was our base and Negibi was an out station. He read the law about sitting down on land without a lease. We will have to apply for a small 5 year lease and we need a good long covering letter and tell why we want a short lease. Why we don't want anything but bush houses on these out stations. We are not planning to put improvements on these out stations, but we have and will improve our Olaguti base.

08/27/59. Left Olaguti this morning. Dean, Jack and I, to make a survey in the northwest part of the Eastern Highlands. We left Goroka about 10:25 a.m. and drove North over flat lands for about 45 minutes, then we swung to the West and started climbing up a well graded road. The mountains were steep, and there seems to be a group of people on every turn. These were the Upper Asaro people. The road is very winding and the bridges are very well built and they need to be. We climbed up to the Daulo Pass, which is 8,175 feet. Then we were in the Watabung people. We got to the Government Post about 12:10 and had lunch. The police boy said that the *kiap* (patrol officer) was in Chuave so we thought it good to come over here. We got to Chuave about 2:00 p.m. You can see Mt. Elimbari real good from here. Mr. John Young-Whitforde is the A.D.O. (Assistant District Officer) here. I met him for the first time over at Kainantu a year ago. We told him what we wanted to do; we asked him if anything was being done for any of the people around here to teach them to read. Yes, in English, he said. Nothing in the vernacular anywhere. We want to see the Word of God in the natives' hands. Will you just teach them to read and give them the Word of God? No, we will teach the Christian doctrine along with literacy. He (Mr. J. Young-Whitforde) said that Mr. Coate could tell us about the Gumi people, 37,000 population. Mr. Coate is the Medical Officer here and asked us over for a cup of tea. When we got there, he said that he was a born again believer and wanted to help us all he could. We talked for some time, and then went back over to the ADO's office. He got out all his maps and spent the afternoon with us. The Lord works in strange and marvelous ways. Coate asked us to spend the night with him. We had a nice chicken dinner. Praise His sweet name.

08/28/59. We left Chuave after going back up to see the ADO. He was friendly and helpful. After we climbed over the Daulo Pass, we walked down to a village called Korepa, it has a very large population and they have 3 Lutheran mission teachers there. They are very strong in the Watabung area. We drove up the road to the Upper Asaro, and we went up near the RC Mission. There is no one at Mirima but the RC, so we might get a work started up there in the Upper Asaro. The population there is 12,384. In the Lower Asaro around Goroka, 10,216 population. The natives tell us that the Upper Asaro and the Lower Asaro and Watabung languages are related some. This could give us maybe 29,000 people in one literacy group.

I see that the Chuave Patrol Post is 28,000 population. There are 3 sub-districts in the Eastern Highlands, the population of all three: 333,645 for 1958. We have the Kainantu sub-district. 80,278, then the Goroka sub-district. 99,426 and then the Chimbu sub-district of 153,941.

08/29/59. Ken went in to Goroka to get Ruth Parry, but she didn't come. Had a good talk to Dean this afternoon. Dean was thinking that Roland was feeling a bit bad because George keeps praying that the Lord will send him a partner, so he can go into the Keagana. I can see why George feels this way, for we felt during the conference that Roland would not be a partner for George. Right now, I look at it a bit differently. I don't feel that George has leadership abilities. And if George is going to work the Keagana area, we will have to have someone to work with him, either another single fellow with gifts of leadership or a couple with the same. The Keagana is a big work if we are going to do it right.

> *We flew from New Guinea to Australia a few days after the entries for August were written. After being at Plumpton, N. S. W. near Sydney, for about three weeks, we flew home towards the end of September 1959. Arvalee*

September, 1959
Plumpton, NSW, Australia

09/07/59. John Bull, one of the students in training, came over tonight and said he wanted to talk. He said, "Why is it that I have to waste my time here now, when all those poor heathen are up in New Guinea and all these false teachings are coming in. Looks like it would be best for me to go help out now! I have had training, been to Bible School, and been with Gospel Recordings."

I said, "Well, John, I know you had training, but did we ask what kind of training you had, before you came here?" "No," he said. "We have a fellowship and we want you to come into that fellowship here during training, then when you come to the field, you will be ready to join that fellowship. If you go now and do not know how to work in the fellowship, you won't fit in well"

I'm glad John was open with me. I have great hopes for a fellow like that. We talked for some time, and then we prayed together.

END OF THE DIARY

Epilogue # 1

God's Work Goes On
By Arvalee

These true stories were written about things that happened many years ago. The compiling of the book has been a labor of love on my part; now *God Plus Nothing* is finally going to print!

Wonderful and exciting things are happening today in Papua New Guinea, the country where we poured out our love so many years ago. New tribal areas continue to be opened where missionaries are faithfully learning the language and culture and preaching the gospel. Souls are being saved in tribes like the Yembi-Yembi, the Bagwido, and the Biem in the Sepik Region, but also in other regions of the country.

Remember, the Lord first burdened Dale to reach the people of New Guinea with the gospel, and then, after our arrival there, he was challenged with the needs of the Gimi people.

Today the Gimi people have the New Testament in their own language, translated by John White, a fellow New Tribes missionary. (God chose to call John to his heavenly home on June 23rd, 2011.)

After our departure from the field in 1993, the Lord gave us the privilege of returning for a visit to Papua New Guinea on two occasions. Dale was thrilled to meet face to face the present Gimi leaders and Bible teachers. He also met the two Gimi Christian men and their families who took on the task of translating the Chronological Bible Lessons into the Kora dialect of the Gimi language. In order to do this they had to move their families to this faraway location in West Gimi, a very difficult place to reach. The sacrifice of leaving friends and family for long periods of time was particularly difficult for the wives. Praise the Lord, their local church took up the challenge to support them, the first two Gimi missionaries, with their prayers and finances.

They were the first two Gimi missionary families, but today there are others. The many Bible Churches are faithfully teaching and reaching out to other villages who have never heard the good news.

We moved to Tucson in 2003 and bought a house with our oldest son, Pat. We both came to love the desert and Dale enjoyed the peace and tranquility immensely.

During the next few years, following our move to Arizona, Dale enjoyed going to several Christian schools where he loved to challenge young people to missions. He also spoke in churches from time to time. To the end, his fondest desire was to share the challenge of missions.

On June 13th, 2007, God suddenly called Dale to his heavenly reward. He was two weeks shy of his 78th birthday.

When he passed away, my children and I were almost overwhelmed with the many messages of condolences we received from friends all over the world. One of the faithful followers in the Gimi tribe, Siri-o, the son of Dale's devoted friend Ireso, wrote, "I am sorry that the man who loved us and prayed for us has died. They … left their families and brought us the Good News. I don't want the Good News to just end here in the Gimi. Let's keep taking the message out to others. Let's not waste our lives but use the little time we now have left."

One of our neighbors, Ivan, was talking to my son Peter a few weeks after Dale left us. He said, "I am sorry to hear of the death of your dad. But we know where he's at, don't we?"

Ivan's brother spoke up and said, "You mean they threw the pearly gates open for him?"

Ivan answered, "Oh, yes, they threw the pearly gates wide open for that man." What a wonderful testimony Dale left behind him.

I know without a doubt that Dale heard the words spoken by his Master, "Well done, thou good and faithful servant" (Matthew 25:21a).

Only God knows the lives that have been influenced by his vision of reaching the lost for Christ. Many are following in his footsteps, even the second and third generations of his immediate family, as well as many tribal believers. How rewarding to know that Dale's vision of reaching the lost for Christ did not die with him.

Epilogue # 2

Cleaning Out Leaves
By Peter and Joy Palmer

Once you've heard what a *Bird of Paradise* sounds like, you will frequently hear them early in the morning. But if you happen to catch a fleeting glimpse of this illusive bird, it's absolutely thrilling. One morning as I hiked Mt. Negibi, I was treated to just that. This was one of those unexpected side benefits of doing my job –cleaning leaves out of the water race.

So, did you read Dad's water race story? Dad's ingenuity + some rough old trees + a willing work force provided our jungle home with fresh spring water. Long before plastic pipe reached Mt. Negibi; Dad devised a system of hollowed out *pandanus* logs to bring water all the way down the mountain to our home.

Oh, yes, the leaves. Well, as Dad got more and more involved in discipleship, church planting, and Bible translation, those leaves still had to be cleaned out by somebody. Well, that 'somebody' was named Pat and Peter. When it was discovered that the water had stopped flowing, usually early in the morning, Mom would call one of our names and say, "we are out of water", so we would get up, get dressed, put on our hiking boots and head off up the slippery, wet trail. It was while fixing the leaf problem in the water race one misty morning, high on the mountain, that I got the thrill of seeing my first illusive Blue *Bird of Paradise*. Yes, it was beautiful and thrilling!

The point of this story though, is to say we were all part of the team for reaching the Gimi tribe for Christ. The whole family took part, and whether it was water race duty, gardening, fire wood hauling, house building, teaching literacy -- or whatever, we all got involved and we put our hand to anything that would make life easier for all of us and help the evangelistic effort of reaching the Gimi for the Lord.

I grew up watching Dad and his band of men making evangelistic trips to villages near and far; some of the Gimi villages were eight hours hike away in the mountains. Living and working alongside my parents, I was confronted with the spiritual neediness of the Gimi people. It was great firsthand training for my future work as a missionary, as Dad included me on some of the evangelistic trips he took his men on.

Joy and I now work out of Australia, doing pastoral care for our missionaries working in far off places like the Gimi tribe. This ministry is one of visiting, encouraging, teaching and helping our missionaries. They are the channels (water race) for the life-giving water of the Lord Jesus to flow through to the needy hearts around them.

It's now the year 2012 and I just returned from another field trip up to Papua New

Guinea. It's always exciting while in *PNG* to hear our missionaries tell of the many people getting saved, as the gospel is presented to an unreached people group for the first time. During this last visit I met with several of my Gimi friends; one young man named Meu told me that he and his team of church planters had just baptized thirty new believers at the village of Beha; thrilling news about the power of the gospel in a dark place. There are now eighteen churches planted in the Gimi, most were planted by the spiritual children or grandchildren of the original band of faithful men that travelled the trails with Dad, on evangelistic trips.

What a thrill to hear stories from these men, as they are now the missionaries reaching out to the far borders of their own needy tribe. So, Paul's instruction to Timothy about teaching faithful men, who will pass on that teaching to others, continues with the Gimi church even today, (II Timothy 2:2).

Funny, isn't it? But it's like my *Bird of Paradise* story. It's as we are hiking in the hard places doing our job, getting up early in the morning on the slippery mountain trails and scooping leaves out of the water race that we get to see the beauty, hear the full story, feel the heat of the battle and see the changed lives, and the hand of God at work.

What a thrill! What a privilege to see the church of God as it blossoms and grows!

Here are some statistics from NTM PNG:

NTM PNG has worked / is working in 72 people groups.
NTM PNG is still actively working in 46 of these groups.[1]
Missionaries of NTM PNG or disciples of NTM have planted more than 300 churches at last count.[1]

[1] David Pierce from NTM PNG communications.

Epilogue # 3

Recent Ponderings
By Julie Dale Melendes

I was listening the other day to Charles Stanley preaching on the radio from Hebrews 12:1 about the great cloud of witnesses that has gone before us and naming Abraham, Moses, Joshua, David, etc. and the lessons we learn from their recorded lives and how it encourages us today to persevere as it challenges us in the rest of verse one, to lay off every weight, and the sin that so easily entangles us, and run with patience the race that is set before us.

As I continued pondering, my thoughts turned to Dad and the many times he encouraged me with what he had been studying. I remember his thoughts on 'the yoke' and how he even drew a picture of what a yoke was like and that the animals had to be perfectly matched in order for the yoke to work properly. We have Jesus to be yoked with as He teaches us to be gentle and humble like Him. Matthew 11:29, 30.

Another period of time he studied Ezra's life and the spiritual leadership he gave to the remnant of Jews returning to outfit the temple. After that he studied Nehemiah's life and his dedication to rebuild the walls amidst much opposition and ridicule from the enemy.

My mind went further back to my childhood days and the deputation meetings Dad had and how I never tired of hearing Dad expounding on the 'water race' and how the little leaves that fell over a period of time would pile up at a turn, and, more often than not, were the cause of the water not making it all the way down the mountain to our house and how the little sins in our lives, if not confessed, can keep our river of living water from flowing too.

What a rich spiritual heritage Dad passed on to us and now, in a sense, Dad has joined the 'great cloud of witnesses' as we continue with our journey. Let us run with patience the race that is set before us!

Well, Mom, …you and Dad have been godly examples to many others besides your children, but I for one am very thankful for all you have passed on to me! It will be extra special to have a "book" about your lives and I thank you for the dedication and effort you have given to see this huge project completed. A very rich heritage indeed! With love and thanks, Julie Dale

Epilogue # 4

A Burden for the Lost
By Bob Kennell

I met Dale and Arvalee Palmer in July of 1971, in my junior year at Biola College. I was majoring in Social Science Missions, but I came to realize that I had no strong burden for the lost. That summer I attended a New Tribes Mission Conference in Northern California. Dale was one of the keynote speakers; as he showed slides of a people group living in a remote village in Papua New Guinea, with no gospel witness, God began speaking to my heart. Looking at the children with dirty faces and runny noses sitting on a hillside, I remember the question that Dale asked, "What if that were you? Wouldn't you want someone to come and share the gospel message with you? Wouldn't you want the opportunity to receive God's gift of eternal salvation?" I was challenged that evening, not only by the pictures I saw, but also by the passion for the lost seen in Dale's life. That evening, God gave me a burden and a passion for the lost and I determined in my heart to be involved in reaching tribal people with the gospel of Jesus Christ.

Dale's passion for the lost was part of his daily conversation. His passion and love for people was part of his daily life. Years later, as a missionary in Papua New Guinea, Jack Housley and I were making a supply run on the Sepik River. Our motor died shortly after we left that morning so we spent several hours poling our 40 foot canoe back upriver to the small town of Pagwi. From there, we hitchhiked for six hours on an uninhabited dirt road, arriving very tired and hungry at Dale and Arvalee's home at 11:00 at night. In spite of the late hour, they welcomed us warmly and after our showers, served us a meal of steak and potatoes. Jack and I were moved by their hospitality and love displayed that night. They had given their best.

It was my privilege and honor to work with and be mentored by Dale for many years in Papua New Guinea. As a leader, I watched him make and stand by difficult decisions, some of which were not always the most popular. Dale was a man who stood by his convictions and followed the course he believed God had for him. These actions included even being willing to ground a pilot on Christmas Eve, whose hours of flying had exceeded the limit. Dale was more concerned for the safety and longevity of the missionaries than just keeping everyone happy.

As a result of the pioneering work and vision of Dale Palmer, we now have tribal churches in 16 different tribes throughout the Sepik region of Papua New Guinea alone. I greatly respect Dale for being the man of God that he was. Throughout eternity, many tribal people will be praising the Lamb of God as a result of the ministry of R. Dale Palmer.

I thank God for men like Dale who have taken their passion and vision for the lost, mobilizing men and women to take the gospel message to unreached people groups throughout the world. The work of New Tribes Mission continues to move forward throughout Asia, Asia Pacific, Africa, South Africa, South America, Latin America and Europe. God continues to raise up men and women willing to go to the more remote and difficult locations on this earth to reach those who have never heard the Good News of the Gospel of Jesus Christ.

The face of missions has changed quite considerably over the last decade. We still have many countries, such as Papua New Guinea, where we can work freely as missionaries. But the majority of the world's population still remains unreached with the gospel in countries where that freedom has been restricted.

After the terrorist attacks of September 11, 2001, it has become more difficult to enter these countries, with more restrictions and denials of visas and work permits. However, that has only multiplied our efforts to go, especially where access is limited.

The work of the missionary for NTM has not changed. We still have men and women scattered all over the world in remote, difficult, isolated situations. Against very difficult odds and the onslaught of the enemy, the languages and cultures of people groups are being studied, literacy is being taught, the Word of God is being translated, systematic teaching of the Word is taking place and new believers are being discipled in their position in Christ.

We remain thankful for the privilege God has given us to be co-laborers together with Christ in seeing the world evangelized. We ask you to pray with us that the Lord of the Harvest would continue to send forth laborers to the fields, white unto harvest.

Contents Listing Individual Stories

Acknowledgements 5

Dedication..6

Foreword..8

Preface 10

Words, Phrases and Meanings 16

Introduction 17

PART ONE~Our Vision

    Chapter 1 How I First Heard of New Guinea, 1942 25

        Our Marriage

        Our Lives Continue

    Chapter 2 Entering Missionary Training, 1950.............................37

        A New Baby and Tragic News

        Extra Duty

        Daily Life

        Brothers

        Training Days are Over and…

        Our Third Baby

    Chapter 3 Sailing for Australia, 1953 49

        Our Time in Australia

PART TWO~New Beginnings

    Chapter 4 On to New Guinea, 1953 59

        Settling at Kami

        My First Gimi Patrol, 1954

        Our Departure

        "Will You Help My People?"

        The District Commissioner of Goroka

        Our Vision for the Gimi

        Our Trip to Gono, 1954

    Chapter 5 The Turning Point 81

        The Wrong Goat

        Horses, 1955

        Twenty-Seven Bee Stings, 1955

        Meniba and Our Dream of a Horse Road

    Chapter 6 A Choice Land Site 93

        Esema, the Leader of His People

        Our Bridge Washed Out

        The Gimi Horse Road

        (Excerpts from Dale's Diary, 1955)

        The End of the Road

PART THREE~Our Dream…A Reality
   Chapter 7 The Old Water Race 109
      The End of the Stockades, 1957
      New Co-Workers at Kami
      Julie Dale: A Special New Arrival, 1956
      Visitors
      An Angel to the Rescue, 1957
      Entertaining Angels Unawares, 1957
      Hepatitis, 1956
      Dale's Hepatitis
      Cargo Cult
      Making Bush Salt
      Gimi Initiations
   Chapter 8 Memories…Arvalee Remembers 133
      Memories So Clear Are Still Ringing in My Ear
      My First Trip to the Gimi, 1957
      Harold and Thelma Jackson's Visit
   Chapter 9 Family Moving to the Gimi, 1958 147
      A Near Death Experience
      Early Months in the Gimi
      The Lawrence Family
      Disturbing Thoughts
      Our Pet Cockatoo
      Ordering and Buying Supplies
      Life In The Gimi
      Excerpts from Dale's Diary
      January, 1959
      February, 1959
      March, 1959
      April, 1959
      May, 1959
      June, 1959
      July, 1959
      August, 1959
      Our First Furlough, 1959

PART FOUR~God's Faithfulness
   Chapter 10 Home in the USA, 1959 179
      Danny Boy
      Moving to Modesto and Traveling, 1960
      God's Promise to a Frightened Young Man
      More Travel Experiences
      Return Overseas, 1961
      New Guinea Bound, 1963
      Back to the Gimi, 1963

A New House, 1964-1965
Vacation Gimi Style, 1965
Chapter 11   Co-Workers Again 207
My Aussie Mates, Pat and Barbara Smith
Home Life in the Gimi and Home School
Dale Critically Ill
A Vehicle at Last
(Details provided by Pat)
Boarding School, 1966
Raro Village
Big Changes, 1967-1969
Our Second Furlough, 1969
Santa Paula, California
Chapter 12   Moving On; Another Surprise 231
The Story of Zato
God's Network

PART FIVE~Starting Over
Chapter 13   Our Third Term; First Days in the Sepik, 1972 275
Scared Stiff
Further Reflections
Settling in at Maprik Village
Life Goes on at Maprik
Palmer Family Events and First Wedding, 1973
Chapter 14   Exciting Days in the Sepik 289
Food and Fellowship at Maprik Base
Our Third Furlough, 1977
Wedding Bells Again, 1977
A 50th Wedding Celebration and Another Wedding, 1978
Our Fourth Term, 1979
Orientation Continues
Building a New House at Maprik
The Missionary Cat, 1981
A true story I like to tell to children's Sunday School classes.
Happy Arrivals, 1980, and Dan and Sandra's Wedding, 1981
Chapter 15   An Unexpected Turn of Events, 1982 305
Our Fourth Furlough at Lompoc, California, 1983
Our Fifth Term, 1984;
Computer Frustrations
Joy Amidst Sorrow;
Our Fifth Furlough, 1986
Julie and Dan's Wedding, 1986
Moving Grandpa and Granny to Eagle Point

PART SIX~A Rewarding Ministry
    Chapter 16 We Return to PNG, 1987, Via England and Ireland 315
        Our 6th Term, 1987
        The RI Class, 1990 and 1991
        A Frightening Encounter
        Angels Watching Over Us
        We Move to Rabaul, East New Britain, 1991
        The Gentle Island People
    Chapter 17 We Return to the USA, 1993 325
        Two Volcanoes Destroy Rabaul Town, 1994
        Shady Cove, Oregon
        Buying a House in Eagle Point
        A Sad Time
        Back Surgery
        More Sadness with Rejoicing
        Our Trip to PNG, 1997
        Back To the Highlands
        Our Gimi Visit
        Visiting Rabaul, 1997
        An Unforgettable Trip
        Our Trip to PNG, 2001
        Visiting the Gimi, 2001
        We Fly to the Gimi via Tarabo
        Leaving the Gimi
        Departing for Port Moresby
        Visiting Australia
    Chapter 18 A Major Decision, 2002 369
        Moving to Tucson, 2003
        A Near Tragedy
        Turn Down the Volume

APPENDIX (Dale's Complete Diary, 1955 and 1959) 379
        The Gimi Horse Road,
        August, 1955
        September, 1955
        October, 1955
        In the Gimi,
        January, 1959
        February, 1959
        March, 1959
        April, 1959
        May, 1959
        June, 1959
        July, 1959
        August, 1959

September, 1959
Plumpton, NSW, Australia

Epilogue # 1 453
Epilogue # 2 455
Epilogue # 3 457
Epilogue # 4 459
GLOSSARY 467
CONTACT INFORMATION 475

~GLOSSARY~

Abai	The Gimi name of the fruit of one species of the Pandanus tree family, it makes a sauce for eating, see abai grease, pandanus and marita. (Gimi)
Abai grease	A thick sauce made from the red or yellow fruit of the Pandanus tree, which was used as a sauce on food, or on the body as a lotion, see pandanus and marita. (Gimi)
A cuppa	A cup of tea, a tea break, usually with a sweet snack. (Australian)
All in	Australian term for tired or worn out. (Australian)
Anosa bana	Big man, as in chief or one in authority. (Gimi)
A-o-bana	The Gimi word for white-man; bana with adjective prefix A-o-, meaning red or pink in color, literally "pink man". (Gimi)
A-o-batha	The Gimi word for white-woman; batha with adjective prefix A-o-, meaning red or pink in color, literally "pink woman". (Gimi)
Aspro	Australian brand name for Aspirin. (Australian)
Atope	Potato or potatoes, not sweet potatoes. (Gimi)
Aussie	An Australian. (Australian)
Bagarap	Spoil, ruin or destroy, also hurt or damage. (Pidgin)
Bana	Man. (Gimi)
Batha	Woman. (Gimi)
Belo	Term for lunch time; literally, when the bell rings. (Pidgin)
Bilum	A net string bag, woven by the women, sometimes very colorful. (Pidgin)
Bird(s) of Paradise	Any of numerous brilliantly colored plumed birds (family Paradisaeidae) chiefly of New Guinea, neighboring islands and a few in eastern Australia. The Bird of Paradise is of cultural importance to the people of Papua New Guinea. The trade in plumes and/or feathers of the Birds of Paradise has been especially important in a bridal price, showing wealth and adorning dancers for singsings.
Bita	Good, or to mean it is nice or beautiful. (Gimi)
Bita ina	Good talk, often used as "I agree with you." (Gimi)
Blokes	Big strong fellows (Australian slang)
Boi	A native laborer or servant regardless of age; also used for the

	young men attending class or meetings but spelled boy. (Pidgin)
Boss boy	A foreman, mostly used during road construction. (Pidgin)
Boy or Boys	Early in the book: young child, one's own children. Later this is the English spelling for boi, a Pidgin word, see Boi. (English word but with several meanings)
BSA	British Small Arms 125cc street motor cycle.
Butoba	Early German tape recorder, had wind up motor and transistorized, battery powered amplifier.
Cargo	Supplies carried in from town or the main mission base, also baggage or load. (Pidgin)
Cargo boys	Carriers who carry supplies into the mission station. (Pidgin)
Cargo cult	The belief of some nationals that material possessions are sent from their ancestors and just fall from the sky. (Pidgin)
Cockatoo	Large parrot, white with yellow crest variety, makes a good pet, speaks and is very friendly, see Koki. (English)
Cook boy	A hired national who prepared the food, and did general clean up, washing dishes etc. (now an antiquated term.) see Kukboi. (Pidgin)
Court, court me	To ask for, or demand pay or compensation, take to trial through the local court system, see Kotim. (English slang)
Cuppa	See A cuppa. (Australian)
Dream man, driman	Witchdoctor, fortune teller or soothsayer. (Pidgin)
Dokta boi	A national medical orderly trained in first aid, usually ran the clinics. (Pidgin)
Erane	Hello, their most common greeting. (Gimi)
Em	Him or her, as in 'pulim em'. (Pidgin)
Furlough	Permission to be absent from duty, especially in the armed services. Now called leave or leave of absence. NTM prefers to call it "on home assignment."
Fuzzy Wuzzy Angels of Papua New Guinea	*(Compiled from the personal witness of Luther Briggs, testimonies and memories of many Australian and US soldiers from WWII and historical clips from various sites on the internet).* The Fuzzy Wuzzy Angels was the name given by Australian troops to the Papua New Guinean people who, during World War II, were a great help in transporting stores and equipment over the rough terrain. Most notably they would assist and escort injured Australian

troops out of the jungle and down the Kokoda trail. A close relationship and bond of friendship developed between these local men and the Australians, particularly from the sick and wounded who required transportation back to field aid stations. It is a well-accepted fact that many men would have died where they fell in Papua New Guinea had it not been for these men who became affectionately known as the 'Fuzzy Wuzzy Angels'. 1942 was a terrible time when an invasion of Australia by the Japanese Imperial Forces looked almost inevitable. Australian soldiers, nicknamed Diggers, were fighting and dying on lonely jungle tracks in almost impenetrable jungle in mountain ranges so high that it was very cold at night time. It was then that we found a new set of friends. The men of the tribes of New Guinea flocked to help the Aussies. Some fought independently because the Japanese mistreated them, something that the civilian Australian Patrol Officers had never done. Many were murdered by the Japanese. Naturally, this built up a huge degree of loathing for the invaders. Some fought in organized units and their story is told elsewhere in historic WWII writings. However, they acted as bearers, mostly. They carried food and ammo forward and the wounded back. By so doing they created a legend. They would move silently through the jungle and just appear to assist the soldiers. They were often praised as being as "gentle as a bush nurse." Australia owes them a Debt of Gratitude that is immense. (These Aussie soldiers fondly referred to the natives as the Fuzzy Wuzzy Angels.)

Girigiri	Very small sea shells used for beads or clothing decorations and as trade goods. (Pidgin)
GRH	Government rest house, small sleeping and cooking houses set up by the government, other travelers were free to use them as well.
Hanare	That's good. (Gimi)
Haus sik	House sick, a clinic or hospital. (Pidgin)
Hi-i	The tuberous root of a special bean, cooked and eaten in a bean root festival, very seasonal at harvest time. (Gimi)
He-re-	Vegetable, see pitpit. (Gimi)
Ina	Taro root, see taro. (Gimi)

Ire-	A Gimi word for a type of pitpit, an edible green. (Gimi)
Iremu	Edible greens, could include several varieties. (Gimi)
Iri-ara	Caregiver, as in "Jesus is our Meme Iri-ara," Good Shepherd. (Gimi)
Iron	Galvanized steel folded for a ridge cap or corrugated galvanized roofing, see kapa. (Pidgin, English spelling)
Isapa	Sweet potato, see kaukau. (Gimi)
Isiosi	To swing, like swing on a rope or vine. (Gimi)
Kalabus	The jail or prison. (Pidgin)
Kanda	Rattan, a jungle vine, very strong, used for furniture, bridges, rope and more. (Pidgin)
Kapa	Galvanized steel roofing, typically corrugated, see iron. (Pidgin, Pidgin spelling for English 'copper'. The word kapa was used for metal roofing regardless of the type of metal).
Karuka	The pandanus or screw pine. The leaves are used in some areas for thatch, while the red or yellow fruit is eaten as a delicacy. The Highland folk smear pandanus oil on their bodies. See Pandanus. (Pidgin)
Kaukau	Sweet potato, see Isapa. (Pidgin)
Kiap	A Government Patrol Officer, the official census taker. (Pidgin)
Koki	Cockatoo, see Cockatoo (Pidgin)
Kotim	To bring suit against, to take one to court. (Pidgin)
Kros or Krosim	Getting mad at, angry, doing wrong to someone. (Pidgin)
Kukboi	A cook boy, one who cooks food, cleans, etc. An antiquated term see Cook boy. (Pidgin)
Kumu	Edible greens, cultivated or wild varieties. (Pidgin)
Kunai	The term in Pidgin English for the tall, sharp sword grass of the grasslands; also grass in general. Kunai is also used for roofing a house. (Pidgin)
Laplap	A cloth used for a wraparound sarong, (Pidgin)
Liver	Used as the center of emotions instead of heart, see ru-a-au. (English word with a Gimi meaning)
Longlong	A crazy man or person. (Pidgin)
Longwe liklik	Not too far, literally "it is a long way but a little way". (Pidgin)
Lotu	A worship service, or a church building. (Fiji)
Luluai	Chief in a tribe or village. (Pidgin)
MAF	Mission Aviation Fellowship.

Manui	Darkness, as in a deep pit, the Gimi people feared these places. (Gimi)
Marita	The fruit of one species of the Pandanus tree family, see Pandanus and abai. (Pidgin)
Marked or makim	To survey, layout or stake out for making a road; also used for selecting a person, as in "choosing a bride." (Pidgin)
Marrow	Australian for squash. (Australian)
Master, Masta	A European man, left over from colonial rule. (Pidgin)
Masara, Matmat	A burial place, a graveyard. (Pidgin)
Meme	A goat, also used for sheep when illustrating an animal needing a shepherd as the Gimi did not have this concept, see iri-ara. Many Pidgin words like meme were assimilated into Gimi because there were now goats in the Gimi as well as neighboring tribes. (Pidgin)
Misis	A European woman, left over from colonial rule. (Pidgin)
Missisio	A European woman, misis with excitement or sometimes when calling out to the misis. (Gimi slang)
Mono iri bana	Story Telling Man. (Gimi)
Mumu	The traditional New Guinea way of cooking food in the ground over hot rocks, cooked by steam. (Pidgin)
Nanonebo	Oh, Mother! an exclamation like Oh Wow! (Gimi)
Nau- ru-a-au	My liver, see ru-a-au. (Gimi)
Nautene	Strong desire; I would really like to. (Gimi)
Obu	A star or stars. (Gimi)
Oure ami	Sins, bad works. (Gimi)
Pain or pained	As being in pain, hurt or hurting. See Pen. (English word but with Pidgin meaning)
Pandanus	Pandanus trees provide materials for housing, clothing and textiles, food (nuts and sauce), medication, decorations, fishing, and religious uses. These are a few that are known. See Karuka. (English)
Pangal	The sago palm leafstalk or stem, used for making walls etc. (Pidgin)
Papa	Father, as in starting a prayer, Father God, ... (Pidgin)
Pas	A letter or note. (Pidgin)
Patrol	To walk or go through or around an area for the purpose of guarding or inspecting, a group of government men on patrol. (Australian)

Patrol Officer	The patrol officers were appointed by the government and were in charge of keeping law and order in the interior tribal areas, as well as taking the census. (Australian)
Patrol Post	The patrol officers were stationed at the patrol posts, far interior and many miles away from civilization. (Australian)
Pekpek blut	Dysentery. (Pidgin)
Pen	As being in pain, hurt or hurting. See Pain. (Pidgin)
Pitpit	One of two kinds of an edible shoot cultivated in their gardens. He-re- was usually boiled or steamed. Yo-o, the other mealy kind was baked or cooked in a mumu. Stalks from the wild cane used for making woven mats. See He-re- and Yo-o. (Pidgin)
Pitsaw or pit sawn	Sawing lumber with a large handsaw worked by two men, one on top of the log and the other below the log, usually in a pit, lumber that is pit sawn.
Plaited floor, walls	Woven bamboo or cane used for building. (English)
Planim Pos	Literally: to plant a post, but really means making strong foundation posts as in building a house. (Pidgin)
PMV	A public motor vehicle, licensed to carry passengers, a taxi or bus license. We carried a PMV license on our vehicles because we carried passengers, it did not matter if they were paying or not, we could also buy and sell goods from the vehicle so we could help the people out by having a store of sorts way out in the bush.
PNG	Papua New Guinea, called New Guinea in the early years.
Poison or posin	To work sorcery on someone. (Pidgin)
Pound	Australian money, as in pounds, shillings and pence. There were 12 pence (pennies, written 1d) in a shilling and 20 shillings in a pound.
Pul or Pulim	To entice, influence or persuade. See Pulling. (Pidgin)
Pull or pulling	To influence, to withhold; English spelling for Pidgin, see pul or pulim. (Pidgin)
Pulpul or Purpur	A woman's grass skirt. (Pidgin)
Rattan	See kanda. (English)
Rausim	To get rid of it or throw something away. (Pidgin)
Ru-a-au	Liver, used for center of emotions, like we use heart in English. (Gimi)
Rucksack	A backpack. See Ruksak. (English)
Ruksak	A rucksack, a haversack, or knapsack, a backpack. (Pidgin)

Sak or sakim	To disobey, to contradict. (Pidgin)
[sic]	The usual purpose of this notation is to inform the reader that any errors or apparent errors in the transcribed material do not arise from transcription errors, and the errors have been repeated intentionally, i.e., that they are reproduced exactly as set down by the original writer or printer. Dale's stories are told in his own words, in his unique style.
SIL	The Summer Institute of Linguistics or Wycliffe.
Sing or sing out	Call out, calling across a canyon, sending a message. (Pidgin)
Singsing	Any festival implying singing, dancing and feasting. (Pidgin)
Sked	Slang; short for schedule, as in radio schedule.
Stone Age	People still living in a primitive life style, using stone tools. (English)
Tanim tok	To translate, see Turn Talk. (Pidgin, Pidgin spelling)
Taro	Edible root plant used to make poi in Hawaii, see ina. (English / Fiji)
Thabi	Sugar or sugar cane. (Gimi)
Thani (River)	The main river in the Gimi, see Zani. (English spelling of Zani)
Thobi	A seasoning or bush salt made in the Gimi. (Gimi)
Tiri	Bamboo, the large bamboo used for building. (Gimi)
Tins or tinned	Canned food. (Australian)
Tultul	The assistant village chief appointed by the government. (Pidgin)
Turn Talk	To translate or interpret the language into Pidgin English, or from Pidgin English into the language; the person doing the translating. (Pidgin, English spelling)
Uncontrolled	An area yet to be controlled by the government, no permanent government presence in the area, tribal warfare area. (Australian)
Work detail	The term used to describe the work projects assigned to the students in missionary training.
Yo-o	Vegetable, see pitpit. (Gimi)
Zani	The main river in the Gimi, see Thani. (Gimi spelling of Thani)
Zobi	A seasoning or bush salt made in the Gimi. (Gimi)

END OF THE GLOSSARY

~CONTACT INFORMATION~

To order God Plus Nothing or check for e-books that are available please visit the web site:

www.godplusnothing.com

To write to me please email to:

arvalee@godplusnothing.com

Or write to:

Arvalee Palmer
P.O. Box 90403
Tucson, AZ 85752-0403
USA